Pub. No. 9

AMERICAN PRACTICAL NAVIGATOR

AN EPITOME OF NAVIGATION

ORIGINALLY BY

NATHANIEL BOWDITCH, LL.D.

Volume I

1977 Edition

PUBLISHED BY THE

DEFENSE MAPPING AGENCY HYDROGRAPHIC CENTER

For sale by authorized Sales Agents of the Defense Mapping Agency Hydrographic Center

DMA STOCK NO. NVPUB9V1

Nath Bowditch

Last painting by Gilbert Stuart (1828). Considered by the family of Bowditch to be the best of various paintings made, although it was unfinished when the artist died.

NATHANIEL BOWDITCH

(1773–1838)

Nathaniel Bowditch was born on March 26, 1773, at Salem, Mass., fourth of the seven children of shipmaster Habakkuk Bowditch and his wife, Mary.

Since the migration of William Bowditch from England to the Colonies in the 17th century, the family had resided at Salem. Most of its sons, like those of other families in this New England seaport, had gone to sea, and many of them became shipmasters. Nathaniel Bowditch himself sailed as master on his last voyage, and two of his brothers met untimely deaths while pursuing careers at sea.

It is reported that Nathaniel Bowditch's father lost two ships at sea, and by late Revolutionary days he returned to the trade of cooper, which he had learned in his youth. This provided insufficient income to properly supply the needs of his growing family, and hunger and cold were often experienced. For many years the nearly destitute family received an annual grant of fifteen to twenty dollars from the Salem Marine Society. By the time Nathaniel had reached the age of ten, the family's poverty necessitated his leaving school and joining his father in the cooper's trade.

Nathaniel was unsuccessful as a cooper, and when he was about 12 years of age, he entered the first of two ship-chandlery firms by which he was employed. It was during the nearly ten years he was so employed that his great mind first attracted public attention. From the time he began school Bowditch had an all-consuming interest in learning, particularly mathematics. By his middle teens he was recognized in Salem as an authority on that subject. Salem being primarily a shipping town, most of the inhabitants sooner or later found their way to the ship chandler, and news of the brilliant young clerk spread until eventually it came to the attention of the learned men of his day. Impressed by his desire to educate himself, they supplied him with books that he might learn of the discoveries of other men. Since many of the best books were written by Europeans, Bowditch first taught himself their languages. French, Spanish, Latin, Greek, and German were among the two dozen or more languages and dialects he studied during his life. At the age of 16 he began the study of Newton's *Principia*, translating parts of it from the Latin. He even found an error in that classic, and though lacking the confidence to announce it at the time, he later published his findings and had them accepted.

During the Revolutionary War a privateer out of Beverly, a neighboring town to Salem, had taken as one of its prizes an English vessel which was carrying the philosophical library of a famed Irish scholar, Dr. Richard Kirwan. The books were brought to the Colonies and there bought by a group of educated Salem men who used them to found the Philosophical Library Company, reputed to have been the best library north of Philadelphia at the time. In 1791, when Bowditch was 18, two Harvard-educated ministers, Rev. John Prince and Rev. William Bentley, persuaded the Company to allow Bowditch the use of its library. Encouraged by these two men and a third—Nathan Read, an apothecary and also a Harvard man—Bowditch studied the works of the great men who had preceded him, especially the mathematicians and the astronomers. By the time he became of age, this knowledge, acquired before and after his long working hours and in his spare time, had made young Bowditch the outstanding mathematician in the Commonwealth, and perhaps in the country.

In the seafaring town of Salem, Bowditch was drawn to navigation early, learning the subject at the age of 13 from an old British sailor. A year later he began studying surveying, and in 1794 he assisted in a survey of the town. At 15 he devised an almanac reputed to have been of great accuracy. His other youthful accomplishments included the construction of a crude barometer and a sundial.

When Bowditch went to sea at the age of 21, it was as captain's writer and nominal second mate, the officer's berth being offered him because of his reputation as a scholar. Under Captain Henry Prince, the ship *Henry* sailed from Salem in the winter of 1795 on what was to be a year-long voyage to the Ile de Bourbon (now called Île de la Réunion) in the Indian Ocean.

Bowditch began his seagoing career when accurate time was not available to the average naval or merchant ship. A reliable marine chronometer had been invented some 60 years before, but the prohibitive cost, plus the long voyages without opportunity to check the error of the timepiece, made the large investment an impractical one. A system of determining longitude by "lunar distance," a method which did not require an accurate timepiece, was known, but this product of the minds of mathematicians and astronomers was so involved as to be beyond the capabilities of the uneducated seamen of that day. Consequently, ships navigated by a combination of dead reckoning and parallel sailing (a system of sailing north or south to the latitude of the destination and then east or west to the destination).

To Bowditch, the mathematical genius, computation of lunar distances was no mystery, of course, but he recognized the need for an easier method of working them in order to navigate ships more safely and efficiently. Through analysis and observation, he derived a new and simplified formula during his first trip, a formula which was to open the book of celestial navigation to all seamen.

John Hamilton Moore's *The Practical Navigator* was the leading navigational text when Bowditch first went to sea, and had been for many years. Early in his first voyage, however, the captain's writer-second mate began turning up errors in Moore's book, and before long he found it necessary to recompute some of the tables he most often used in working his sights. Bowditch recorded the errors he found, and by the end of his second voyage, made in the higher capacity of supercargo, the news of his findings in *The Practical Navigator* had reached Edmund Blunt, a publisher at Newburyport, Mass. At Blunt's request, Bowditch agreed to correct Moore's book. The first edition of *The New Practical Navigator* was published in 1799, with correction of the errors Bowditch had found to that time, and with some additional information. The following year a second edition was published with additional corrections. Bowditch eventually found more than 8,000 errors in the work, however, and it was finally decided to completely rewrite the book and to publish it under his own name. In 1802 the first edition of *The New American Practical Navigator* by Nathaniel Bowditch was published, and his vow to put nothing in the book he could not teach every member of his crew served to keep the work within the understanding of the average seaman. In addition to the improved method of determining longitude, Bowditch's book gave the ship's officer information on winds, currents, and tides; directions for surveying; statistics on marine insurance; a glossary of sea terms; instruction in mathematics; and numerous tables of navigational data. His simplified methods, easily grasped by the intelligent seaman willing to learn, paved the way for "Yankee" supremacy of the seas during the clipper ship era.

Two months before sailing for Cadiz on his third voyage, in 1798, Bowditch married Elizabeth Boardman, daughter of a shipmaster. While he was away, his wife died at the age of 18. Two years later, on October 28, 1800, he married his cousin, Mary Ingersoll, she, too, the daughter of a shipmaster. They had eight children.

Bowditch made a total of five trips to sea, over a period of about nine years, his last as master and part owner of the three-masted *Putnam*. Homeward bound from a 13-month voyage to Sumatra and the Ile de France (now called Mauritius) the *Putman* approached Salem harbor on December 25, 1803, during a thick fog without having had a celestial observation since noon on the 24th. Relying upon his dead reckoning, Bowditch conned his wooden-hulled ship to the entrance of the rocky harbor, where he had the good fortune to get a momentary glimpse of Eastern Point, Cape Ann, enough to confirm his position. The *Putnam* proceeded in, past such hazards as "Bowditch's Ledge" (named after a great-grandfather who had wrecked his ship on the rock more than a century before) and anchored safely at 1900 that evening. Word of the daring feat, performed when other masters were hove-to outside the harbor, spread along the coast and added greatly to Bowditch's reputation. He was, indeed, the "practical navigator."

His standing as a mathematician and successful shipmaster earned him a lucrative (for those times) position ashore within a matter of weeks after his last voyage. He was installed as president of a Salem fire and marine insurance company, at the age of 30, and during the 20 years he held that position the company prospered. In 1823 he left Salem to take a similar position with a Boston insurance firm, serving that company with equal success until his death.

From the time he finished the *"Navigator"* until 1814, Bowditch's mathematical and scientific pursuits consisted of studies and papers on the orbits of comets, applications of Napier's rules, magnetic variation, eclipses, calculations on tides, and the charting of Salem harbor. In that year, however, he turned to what he considered the greatest work of his life, the translation into English of *Mécanique Céleste*, by Pierre Laplace. *Mécanique Céleste* was a summary of all the then known facts about the workings of the heavens. Bowditch translated four of the five volumes before his death, and published them at his own expense. He gave many formula derivations which Laplace had not shown, and also included further discoveries following the time of publication. His work made this information available to American astronomers and enabled them to pursue their studies on the basis of that which was already known. Continuing his style of writing for the learner, Bowditch presented his English version of *Mécanique Céleste* in such a manner that the student of mathematics could easily trace the steps involved in reaching the most complicated conclusions.

Shortly after the publication of *The New American Practical Navigator*, Harvard College honored its author with the presentation of the honorary degree of Master of Arts, and in 1816 the college made him an honorary Doctor of Laws. From the time the Harvard graduates of Salem first assisted him in his studies, Bowditch had a great interest in that college, and in 1810 he was elected one of its Overseers, a position he held until 1826, when he was elected to the Corporation. During 1826–27 he was the leader of a small group of men who saved the school from financial disaster by forcing necessary economies on the college's reluctant president. At one time Bowditch was offered a Professorship in Mathematics at Harvard but this, as well as similar offers from West Point and the University of Virginia, he declined. In all his life he was never known to have made a public speech or to have addressed any large group of people.

Many other honors came to Bowditch in recognition of his astronomical, mathematical, and marine accomplishments. He became a member of the American Academy of Arts and Sciences, the East India Marine Society, the Royal Academy of Edinburgh, the Royal Society of London, the Royal Irish Academy, the American Philosophical Society, the Connecticut Academy of Arts and Sciences, the Boston Marine Society, the Royal Astronomical Society, the Palermo Academy of Science, and the Royal Academy of Berlin.

Nathaniel Bowditch outlived all of his brothers and sisters by nearly 30 years. Death came to him on March 16, 1838, in his sixty-fifth year. The following eulogy by the Salem Marine Society indicates the regard in which this distinguished American was held by his contemporaries:

"In his death a public, a national, a human benefactor has departed. Not this community, nor our country only, but the whole world, has reason to do honor to his memory. When the voice of Eulogy shall be still, when the tear of Sorrow shall cease to flow, no monument will be needed to keep alive his memory among men; but as long as ships shall sail, the needle point to the north, and the stars go through their wonted courses in the heavens, the name of Dr. Bowditch will be revered as of one who helped his fellow-men in a time of need, who was and is a guide to them over the pathless ocean, and of one who forwarded the great interests of mankind."

The New American Practical Navigator was revised by Nathaniel Bowditch several times after 1802 for subsequent editions of the book. After his death, Jonathan Ingersoll Bowditch, a son who made several voyages, took up the work and his name appeared on the title page from the eleventh edition through the thirty-fifth, in 1867. In 1868 the newly organized U.S. Navy Hydrographic Office bought the copyright. Revisions have been made from time to time to keep the work in step with navigational improvements. The name has been altered to the *American Practical Navigator*, but the book is still commonly known as "Bowditch." A total of more than 850,000 copies has been printed in about 70 editions during the more than a century and a half since the book was first published in 1802. It has lived because it has combined the best thoughts of each generation of navigators, who have looked to it as their final authority.

PREFACE

This epitome of navigation has been maintained continuously since it was first published in 1802. The U.S. Navy maintained "Bowditch" from 1868 until 1972, when the Defense Mapping Agency Hydrographic Center was assigned the responsibility for its publication.

The intent of the original author to provide a compendium of navigational material understandable to the mariner has been consistently followed. However, navigation is not presented as a mechanical process to be followed blindly. Rather, emphasis has been given to the fact that the aids provided by *science* can be used effectively to improve the *art* of navigation only if a well-informed person of mature judgment and experience is on hand to interpret information as it becomes available. Thus, the facts needed to perform the mechanics of navigation have been supplemented with additional material intended to help the navigator acquire perspective in meeting the various needs that arise.

Volume II of this extensively revised edition provides the tables, formulas, data, and instructions needed by the navigator to perform many of the computations associated with dead reckoning, piloting, and celestial navigation. All references to tables 1 through 37 in this volume are with respect to the tables in volume II.

Many institutions, organizations, groups, and individuals have assisted in the preparation of volume I, but all of the material has been edited by one individual to assure continuity and consistency. Particular acknowledgement is given the following: Dr. P. Kenneth Seidelmann, Director, Nautical Almanac Office, U. S. Naval Observatory, for assistance in matters pertaining to navigational astronomy and the almanacs; Dr. William J. Klepczynski, Time Service Division, U. S. Naval Observatory, for guidance in the treatment of the dissemination of time; Commander Guy P. Clark, U. S. Coast Guard, for assistance in matters pertaining to visual and audible aids to navigation, piloting, and navigational safety; Dr. William H. Guier and Mr. John W. Casey, Applied Physics Laboratory, The Johns Hopkins University, for the satellite navigation chapter; Lieutenant Commander Richard A. Smith, Royal Navy, when Chairman, Department of Navigation, U.S. Naval Academy, for assistance in practical areas; Commander Carl W. Fisher, National Oceanic and Atmospheric Administration, Chief, Oceanographic Division, National Ocean Survey, for assistance in matters pertaining to tides and tidal currents; Dr. Robert J. Renard, Professor of Meteorology, Naval Postgraduate School, Monterey, California, for assistance in matters pertaining to weather elements; Mr. Richard M. DeAngelis, Environmental Data Service, National Oceanic and Atmospheric Administration, for his contributions to the tropical cyclones chapter; Chief Aerographer's Mate Robert J. Kemple, U.S. Navy, Naval Postgraduate School, Monterey, California, for assistance in matters pertaining to weather observations; Mr. Max W. Mull, Chief, Marine Weather Services Branch, National Weather Service, National Oceanic and Atmospheric Administration, for guidance in matters pertaining to meteorology and ship weather routing; Commander William G. Schramm, U.S. Navy, Fleet Numerical Weather Central, Monterey, California, for assistance in matters pertaining to oceanography; Mr. Lyman W. Griswold, Head, Sensors Branch, Naval Ship Research and Development Center, Annapolis, Maryland, for assistance in matters pertaining to speed logs; Messrs. Donald R. Lesnick and Rosario Casamento of the Naval Ship Engineering Center, and Mr. Eric L.

Puckett, Navy Ships Parts Control Center, for their assistance in matters pertaining to navigation instruments; Lieutenant Commander Arthur J. Tuttle, U.S. Navy, when Executive Officer, USS *Kawishiwi* (AO–146), and Master Chief Quartermaster Byron E. Franklin (SS), U.S. Navy, for assistance in practical areas; Mrs. Irene Fischer, Chief, Geoid Branch, Defense Mapping Agency Topographic Center, for assistance in matters pertaining to geodesy; Mr. James E. Gearhart, staff cartographer, Marine Chart Division, National Ocean Survey and Mr. Anthony S. Basile of this Center for their contributions to the nautical chart chapter; Mr. Peter A. Mitchell, Naval Oceanographic Office, for contributions to the ice in the sea chapter; Mr. D. H. Luzius, Headquarters U. S. Coast Guard, for guidance in matters pertaining to position reporting systems; Lieutenants Wilson E. Fitch and Timothy L. Vaughan, U. S. Navy, Department of Navigation, U.S. Naval Academy, and Mr. Richard M. Plant, Maritime Institute of Technology and Graduate Studies, Linthicum Heights, Maryland, for their contributions to the appendix addressing the use of hand-held digital calculators for navigational calculations; Commander William M. Ross, U.S. Navy, when Chairman, Department of Navigation, U.S. Naval Academy, and Captain Wayne M. Waldo, Maritime Institute of Technology and Graduate Studies, for assistance in practical areas; Commander Cortland G. Pohle, U.S. Coast Guard (Ret.), U.S. Merchant Marine Academy, for constructive suggestions; Dr. Milton Y. J. Cha, when with the Omega Navigation System Operations Detail, U.S. Coast Guard, for his assistance in matters pertaining to the characteristics of propagation of very low frequency radio waves; Messrs. David C. Scull, Robert M. Willems, and Peter B. Morris, Omega Navigation System Operations Detail, U.S. Coast Guard, for their assistance in matters pertaining to the Omega Navigation System; Mr. David T. Haislip, Chief, Radionavigation Aids Branch, U.S. Coast Guard Headquarters, for his assistance in matters pertaining to radionavigation; Mr. Richard J. Sandifer, Associate Professor of Astronomy, Anne Arundel Community College, Arnold, Maryland, for his contribution to the chapter on tides and tidal currents; Lieutenant Commander Raymond A. Helbig, U.S. Navy, Physics Department, U.S. Naval Academy, for his contribution to the chapter on doppler sonar navigation; Messrs. William M. Clune and George L. Hammond, Fleet Numerical Weather Central, Monterey, California, for the ship weather routing chapter; Mr. William M. Clune for assistance in matters pertaining to weather observations, and material assistance to the editor in coordinating the contributions made at Monterey; Captain Joel H. Jacobs for assistance in matters pertaining to the sextant; Mr. Melvin E. Cruser, Naval Guided Missiles School, Dam Neck, Virginia Beach, Virginia, for his contribution to the inertial navigation chapter; and the U.S. Power Squadrons for suggestions relating to the graph of article 1206 for height of tide determination; and many individuals, especially the marine navigation instructors and experienced practicing navigators who have responded to our questionnaires and offered constructive suggestions or directed attention to errors in previous editions.

Users should refer corrections, additions, and comments for improving this product to DIRECTOR, DEFENSE MAPPING AGENCY HYDROGRAPHIC CENTER, Washington, D.C. 20390, ATTN: Code PR.

CONTENTS

CONTENTS

PART FOUR

THE PRACTICE OF NAVIGATION

PART FIVE

NAVIGATIONAL SAFETY

PART SIX

OCEANOGRAPHY

PART SEVEN

WEATHER

PART EIGHT

ELECTRONICS AND NAVIGATION

CONTENTS

APPENDICES

PART ONE
FUNDAMENTALS

PART ONE

FUNDAMENTALS

CHAPTER I

HISTORY OF NAVIGATION

Introduction

101. Background.—Navigation began with the first man. One of his first conscious acts probably was to home on some object that caught his eye, and thus **land navigation** was undoubtedly the earliest form. His first venture upon the waters may have come shortly after he observed that some objects float, and through curiosity or an attempt at self-preservation he learned that a larger object, perhaps a log, would support him. **Marine navigation** was born when he attempted to guide his craft.

The earliest marine navigation was a form of **piloting,** which came into being as man became familiar with landmarks and used them as guides. **Dead reckoning** probably came next as he sought to predict his future positions, or perhaps as he bravely ventured farther from landmarks. **Celestial navigation,** as it is known today, had to await acquisition of information regarding the motions of the heavenly bodies, although these bodies were used to steer by almost from the beginning.

102. From art to science.—Navigation is the process of directing the movements of a craft from one point to another. To do this safely is an *art*. In perhaps 6,000 years— some writers make it 8,000—man has transformed this art almost into a *science*, and navigation today is so nearly a science that the inclination is to forget that it was ever anything else. It is commonly thought that to navigate a ship one must have a chart to determine the course and distance, a compass to steer by, and a means of determining the positions of the ship during the passage. *Must* have? The word "must" betrays how dependent the modern navigator has become upon the tools now in his hands. Many of the great voyages of history—voyages that made known much of the world—were made without one or more of these "essentials."

103. Epic voyages.—History records a number of great voyages of varying navigational significance. Little or nothing is known of the navigational accomplishments of the ancient mariners, but the record of the knowledge and equipment used during later voyages serves to illustrate periodic developments in the field.

104. Pre-Christian navigation.—Down through the stream of time a number of voyages have occurred without navigational significance. Noah's experience in the ark is of little interest navigationally, except for his use of a dove to locate land. There is evidence to support the view that at least some American Indians reached these shores by sea, the earliest of several groups probably having come about 2200 BC, the approximate time that a general exodus seems to have occurred from a center in southwestern Asia. This is about the time the Tower of Babel is believed to have been built. It is noteworthy that almost every land reached by the great European explorers was already inhabited.

It is not difficult to understand how a people not accustomed to the sea might make a single great voyage without contributing anything of significance to the advancement of navigation. Not so clear, however, is the fact that the Norsemen and the Polynesians, great seafaring people, left nothing more than conflicting traditions of their methods. The reputed length of the voyages made by these people suggests more advanced navigational methods than their records indicate, although the explanation may be that they

1

left few written accounts of any kind. Or perhaps they developed their powers of perception to such an extent that navigation to them, was a highly advanced art. In this respect their navigation may not have differed greatly from that of some birds, insects, fishes, and animals.

One of the earliest well-recorded voyages is known today through the book of observations written by Pytheas of Massalia, a Greek astronomer and navigator. Sometime between the years 350 BC and 300 BC he sailed from a Mediterranean port and followed an established trade route to England. From there he ventured north to Scotland and Thule, the legendary land of the midnight sun. He went on to explore Norwegian fiords, and rivers in northwest Germany. He may have made his way into the Baltic.

Pytheas' voyage, and others of his time, were significant in that they were the work of men who had no compasses, no sextants, no chronometers, no electronic devices such as are commonplace today. The explanation of how they did it is not what some historians have said, that before seafaring men had adequate equipment, the compass especially, they hugged the shore and sailed only by daylight in fair weather. Many undoubtedly did use this practice. But the more intrepid did not creep along the coast, venturing nothing more daring than sailing from headland to headland. They were often out of sight of land, and yet knew sufficiently well where they were and how to get home again. They were able to use the sun, the stars, and the winds without the aid of mechanical devices.

Pytheas had none of the equipment considered essential by the modern navigator—none, at least, as it is thought of today. It would be incorrect, however, to say that he had no navigational aids whatever. He was not the first to venture upon the sea, and even in his time man was the inheritor of his predecessors' knowledge.

He must have known what the mariners of his time, Phoenician and Greek, knew about navigation. There was a fair store of knowledge about the movements of the stars, for example, which all seafaring men shared. They had a practical grasp of some part of what is now called celestial navigation, for the moving celestial bodies were their compasses. Pytheas may not have been acquainted with the *Periplus* of Scylax, the earliest known sailing directions, but it is reasonable to suppose that he had similar information.

If there were sailing directions, there may well have been charts of a sort, even though no record of them exists.

Even if Pytheas and his contemporaries had sailing directions and charts, these must have been far from comprehensive, and they undoubtedly did not cover the areas north of Britain. But these early seamen knew direction by day or night if the sky was clear, and they could judge it reasonably well when the sky was overcast, using the wind and the sea. They knew the hot Libyan wind from the desert—today called the **sirocco**—and the northern wind, the **mistral.**

They could estimate distance. Their ships must have carried some means of measuring time—the sand glass was known to the ancients—and they could estimate speed by counting the strokes of the oars, a common practice from galley to modern college racing shell. Mariners who spent their lives traveling the Mediterranean knew what their ships could do, even if today it is not known what they meant by "a day's sail"—whether 35 miles, or 50, or 100.

105. Sixteenth century navigation.—Progress in the art of navigation came slowly during the early centuries of the Christian era, all but stopped during the Dark Ages, and then spurted forward when Europe entered a golden age of discovery. The circumnavigation of the globe by the expedition organized by Ferdinand Magellan, a disgraced Portuguese nobleman who sailed under the flag of Spain, was a voyage which illustrates the advances made during the 1,800 years following Pytheas.

Magellan was able to find justification for his belief that a navigable pass to the Pacific Ocean existed in high southern latitudes, in Martin Behaim's globe or chart of the world, in the globe constructed by Johann Schoner of Nuremberg in 1515, and in Leonardo da Vinci's map of the world drawn in the same year. He obtained further information for his voyage from Ruy Faleiro, an astronomer and cartographer whose charts, sailing directions, nautical tables, and instructions for use of the astrolabe and cross-staff were considered to be among the best available. Faleiro was also an advocate of the fallacious methods of determining longitude by variation.

When Magellan sailed in 1519, his equipment included sea charts, parchment skins to be made into charts en route, a terrestrial globe, wooden and metal theodolites, wooden and wood-and-bronze quadrants, compasses, magnetic needles, hour glasses and "timepieces," and a log to be towed astern.

So the 16th century navigator had crude charts of the known world, a compass to steer by, instruments with which he could determine his latitude, a log to estimate speed, certain sailing directions, and solar and traverse tables. The huge obstacle yet to be overcome was an accurate method of determining longitude.

106. Eighteenth century navigation.—Little is known today of the "timepieces" carried by Magellan, but surely they were not used to determine longitude. Two hundred years later, however, the chronometer began to emerge. With it, the navigator, for the first time, was able to determine his longitude accurately and fix his position at sea.

The three voyages of discovery made by James Cook of the Royal Navy in the Pacific Ocean between 1768 and 1779 may be said to mark the dawn of modern navigation. Cook's expedition had the full backing of England's scientific organizations, and he was the first captain to undertake extended explorations at sea with navigational equipment, techniques, and knowledge that might be considered modern.

On his first voyage Cook was provided with an astronomical clock, a "journeyman" clock, and a watch lent by the Astronomer Royal. With these he could determine longitude, using the long and tedious lunar distance method. On his second voyage four chronometers were provided. These instruments, added to those already possessed by the mariner, enabled Cook to navigate his vessels with a precision undreamed of by Pytheas and Magellan.

By the time Cook began his explorations, astronomers had made great contributions to navigational advancement, and the acceptance of the heliocentric theory of the universe had led to the publication of the first official nautical almanac. Charts had progressed steadily, and adequate projections were available. With increased understanding of variation, the compass had become reliable. Good schools of navigation existed, and textbooks which reduced the mathematics of navigation to the essentials had been published. Speed through the water could be determined with reasonable accuracy by the logs then in use. Most important, the first chronometers were being produced.

107. Twentieth century navigation.—The maiden voyage of the SS *United States* in July 1952 served to illustrate the progress made in navigation during the 175 years since Cook's voyages. Outstanding because of its record trans-Atlantic passage, the vessel is of interest navigationally in that it carried the most modern equipment then available and exemplified the fact that navigation had become nearly a science.

Each of the deck officers owned a sextant with which he could make observations more accurately than did Cook. Reliable chronometers, the product of hundreds of years of experimental work, were available to determine the time of each observation. The gyrocompass indicated true north regardless of variation and deviation.

Modern, convenient almanacs were used to obtain the coordinates of various celestial bodies, to an accuracy greater than needed. Easily used altitude and azimuth tables gave the navigator data for determining his Sumner (celestial) line of position by the method of Marcq St.-Hilaire. Accurate charts were available for the waters plied, sailing directions for coasts and ports visited, light lists giving the characteristics of the various aids to navigation along these coasts, and pilot charts and navigational texts for reference purposes.

Electronics served the navigator in a number of ways. Radio time signals and weather reports enabled him to check his chronometers and avoid foul weather. A radio direction finder was available to obtain bearings, and a radio telephone was used to communicate with persons on land and sea. The electrically operated echo sounder indicated the depth of water under the keel, radar the distances and bearings of objects within range, even in the densest fog. Using Loran, the navigator could fix the position of his ship a thousand miles and more from transmitting stations.

Piloting and Dead Reckoning

108. Background.—The history of piloting and dead reckoning extends from man's earliest use of landmarks to the latest model of the gyrocompass. In the thousands of years between, navigation by these methods has progressed from short passages along known coastlines to transoceanic voyages during which celestial observations cannot be, or are not, made.

109. Charts.—A form of sailing directions was written several hundred years before Christ. Although charts cannot be traced back that far, they may have existed during the same time. From earliest times men have undoubtedly known that it is more difficult to explain how to get to a place than it is to draw a diagram, and since the first charts known are comparatively accurate and cover large areas, it seems logical that earlier charts served as guides for the cartographers.

Undoubtedly, the first charts were not made on any "projection" (ch. III) but were simple diagrams which took no notice of the shape of the earth. In fact, these "plane" charts were used for many centuries after chart projections were avilable.

The **gnomonic projection** (art. 317) is believed to have been developed by Thales of Miletus (640–546 BC), who was chief of the Seven Wise Men of ancient Greece; founder of Greek geometry, astronomy, and philosophy; and a navigator and cartographer.

The size of the earth was measured at least as early as the third century BC, by Eratosthenes. He observed that at noon on the day of the summer solstice, a certain well at Syene (Assuan) on the tropic of Cancer was lighted throughout its depth by the light of the sun as it crossed the meridian; but that at Alexandria, about 500 miles to the north, shadows were cast by the sun at high noon. He reasoned that this was due to curvature of the earth, which must be spherical. By double measurement of the arc of the meridian between the two places in degrees and stadia, Eratosthenes determined the circumference of the earth to be 252,000 stades (art. 113).

Eratosthenes is believed to have been the first person to measure latitude, using the degree for this purpose. He constructed a 16-point wind rose, prepared a table of winds, and recognized local and prevailing winds. From his own discoveries and from information gleaned from the manuscripts of mariners, explorers, land travelers, historians, and philosophers, he wrote an outstanding description of the known world, which helped elevate geography to the status of a science.

Stereographic (art. 318) and **orthographic** (art. 319) **projections** were originated by Hipparchus in the second century BC.

Ptolemy's World Map. The Egyptian Claudius Ptolemy was a second century AD astronomer, writer, geographer, and mathematician who had no equal in astronomy until the arrival of Copernicus in the 16th century. An outstanding cartographer, for his time, Ptolemy constructed many charts and listed the latitudes and longitudes, as determined by celestial observations, of the places shown. As a geographer, however, he made his most serious mistake. Though Eratosthenes' calculations on the circumference of the earth were available to him, he took the estimate of the Stoic philosopher, Posidonius (circa 130–51 BC), who calculated the earth to be 180,000 stadia in circumference. The result was that those who accepted his work—and for many hundreds of years few thought to question it—had to deal with a concept that was far too small. In 1409 the Greek original of Ptolemy's *Cosmographia*, a book in which he declared this doctrine, was discovered and translated into Latin. It served as the basis for future cartographic work, and so it was that Columbus died convinced that he had found a shorter route to the East Indies. Not until 1669, when Jean Picard computed the circumference of the earth to be 24,500 miles, was a more accurate figure generally used.

Ptolemy's map of the world (fig. 109a) was a great achievement, however. It was the original conic projection, and on it he located some 8,000 places by latitude and longitude. It was he who fixed the convention that the top of the map is north.

Asian Charts. Through the Dark Ages some progress was made. Moslem cartographers as well as astronomers took inspiration from Ptolemy. However, they knew that Ptolemy had overestimated the length of the Mediterranean by some 20°. Charts of the Indian Ocean, bearing horizontal lines indicating parallels of latitude, and vertical lines dividing the seas according to the direction of the wind, were drawn by Persian and Arabian navigators. The prime meridian separated a windward from

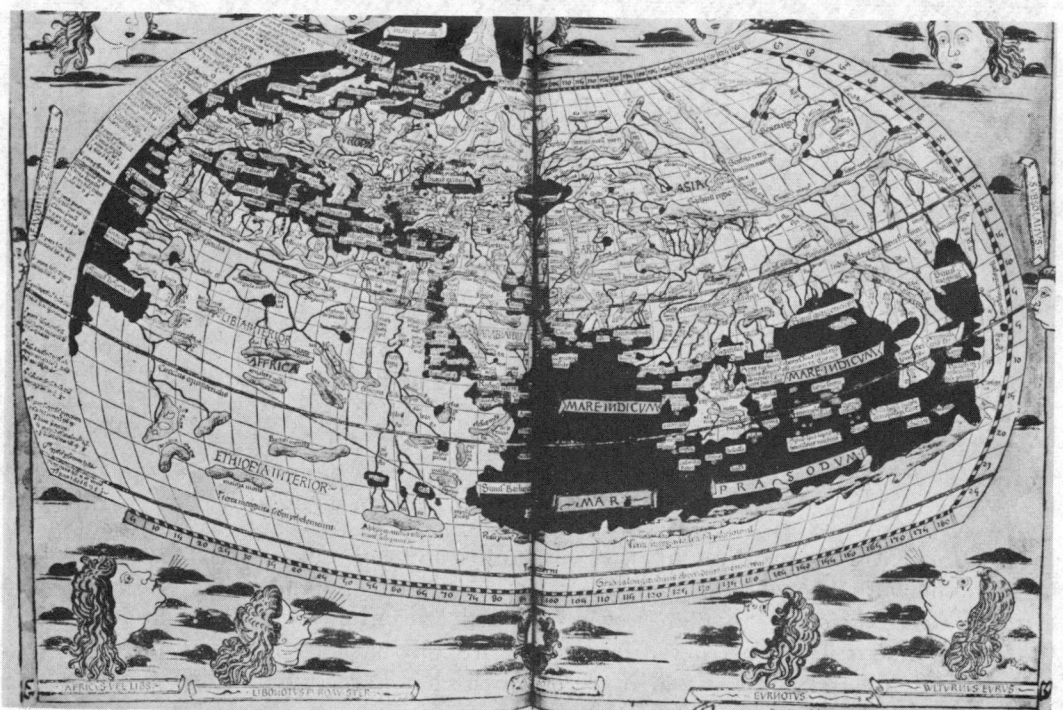

Courtesy of the Map Division of the Library of Congress.

FIGURE 109a.—The world, as envisioned by Ptolemy about AD 150. This chart was prepared in 1482 by Nicolaus Germanus for a translation of *Cosmographia*.

a leeward region and other meridians were drawn at intervals indicating "three hours sail." This information, though far from exact, was helpful to the sailing ship masters.

Portolan Charts. The mariners of Venezia (Venice), Livorno (Leghorn), and Genova (Genoa) must have had charts when they competed for Mediterranean trade before, during, and after the Crusades. Venice at one time had 300 ships, a navy of 45 galleys, and 11,000 men engaged in her maritime industry. But perhaps the rivalry was too keen for masters carelessly to leave charts lying about. At any rate, the earliest useful charts of the Middle Ages that are known today were drawn by seamen of Catalonia (now part of Spain).

The Portolan charts were constructed from the knowledge acquired by seamen during their voyages about the Mediterranean. The actual courses and dead reckoning distances between land points were used as a skeleton for the charts, and the coasts between were usually filled in from data obtained in land surveys. After the compass came into use, these charts became quite accurate. Some, for example, indicated the distance between Gibraltar and Bayrūt (Beirut) to be 3,000 Portolan miles, or 40°5 of longitude. The actual difference of longitude is 40°8.

These charts were distinguished by a group of long rhumb lines intersecting at a common point, surrounded by eight or 16 similar groups of shorter lines. Later *Portolanis* had a *rose dei venti* (rose of the winds), the forerunner of the compass rose, superimposed over the center (fig. 109b). They carried a scale of miles, located nearly all the known hazards to navigation, and had numerous notes of interest to the pilot. They were not marked with parallels of latitude or meridians of longitude, but present-day harbor and coastal charts trace their ancestry directly to them.

Courtesy of the Map Division of the Library of Congress.

FIGURE 109b.—A 14th-century Portolan chart.

Padrón Real. The growing habit of assembling information for charts took concrete form in the *Padrón Real.* This was the pattern, or master, map kept after 1508 by the *Casa de Contratación* at Seville. It was intended to contain everything known about the world, and it was constructed from facts brought back by mariners from voyages to newly discovered lands. From it were drawn the charts upon which the explorers of the Age of Discovery most depended.

World maps of the Middle Ages. In 1515 Leonardo da Vinci drew his famous map of the world. On it, America is represented as extending more to the east and west than to the north and south, with only a chain of islands, the largest named Florida, between it and South America. A wide stretch of ocean is shown between South America and *Terra Australis Nondum Cognita*, the mythical south-seas continent whose existence in the position shown was not disproved until 250 years later.

Ortelius' atlas *Theatrum Orbis Terra* was published at Antwerp in 1570. One of the most magnificent ever produced, it illustrates Europe, Africa, and Asia with comparative accuracy. North and South America are poorly depicted, but Magellan's Strait is shown. All land to the south of it, as well as Australia, is considered part of *Terra Australis Nondum Cognita* (fig. 109c).

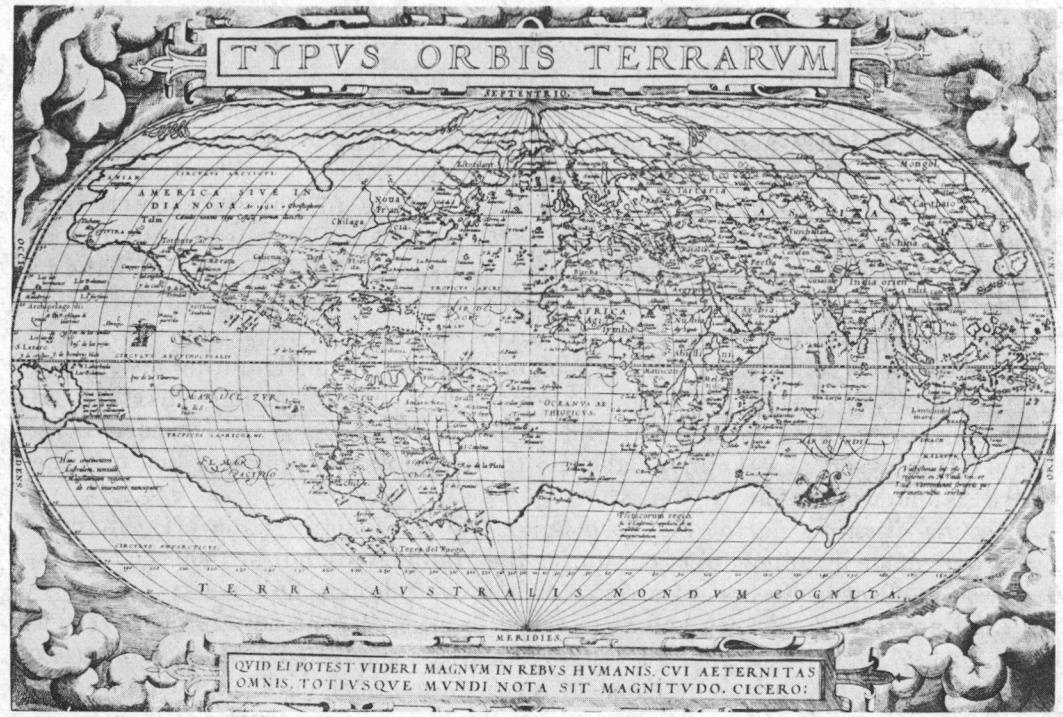

FIGURE 109c.—Ortelius' world map, from his atlas *Theatrum Orbis Terra*, published at Antwerp in 1570.

The Mercator projection (art. 305). For hundreds, perhaps thousands, of years cartographers drew their charts as "plane" projections, making no use of the discoveries of Ptolemy and Hipparchus. As the area of the known world increased, however, the attempt to depict that larger area on the flat surface of the plane chart brought map makers to the realization that allowance would have to be made for the curvature of the earth.

Gerardus Mercator (Latinized form of Gerhard Kremer) was a brilliant Flemish geographer who recognized the need for a better method of chart projection. In 1569 he published a world chart which he had constructed on the principle since known by his name. The theory of his work was correct, but Mercator made errors in his computation, and because he never published a complete description of the mathematics involved, mariners were deprived of the full advantages of the projection for another 30 years.

Then Edward Wright published the results of his own independent study in the matter, explaining the Mercator projection fully and providing the table of meridional parts which enabled all cartographers to make use of the principle.

Wright was a mathematician at Caius College who developed the method and table and gave them to certain navigators for testing. After these proved their usefulness, Wright decided upon publication, and in 1599 *Certaine Errors in Navigation Detected and Corrected* was printed.

The Lambert projections. Johann Heinrich Lambert, 1728–1777, self-educated son of an Alsace tailor, designed a number of map projections. Some of these are still widely used, the most renowned being the **Lambert conformal** (art. 314).

110. Sailing directions.—From earliest times there has been a demand for knowledge of what lay ahead, and this gave rise to the early development of sailing directions (art. 1301).

The *Periplus* of Scylax, written sometime between the sixth and fourth centuries BC, is the earliest known book of this type. Surprisingly similar to modern sailing directions, it provided the mariner with information on distances between ports, aids and dangers, port facilities, and other pertinent matters. The following excerpt is typical:

"Libya begins beyond the Canopic mouth of the Nile. . . . The first people in Libya are the Adrymachidae. From Thonis the voyage to Pharos, a desert island (good harbourage but no drinking water), is 150 stadia. In Pharos are many harbors. But ships water at the Marian Mere, for it is drinkable. . . . The mouth of the bay of Plinthine to Leuce Acte (the white beach) is a day and night's sail; but sailing round by the head of the bay of Plinthine is twice as long. . . ."

Parts Around the World, Pytheas' book of observations made during his epic voyage in the fourth century BC, was another early volume of sailing directions. His rough estimates of distances and descriptions of coastlines would be considered crude today, but they served as an invaluable aid to navigators who followed him into these otherwise unknown waters.

Sailing directions during the Renaissance. No particularly noteworthy improvements were made in sailing directions during the Middle Ages, but in 1490 the *Portolano Rizo* was published, the first of a series of improved design. Other early volumes of this kind appeared in France and were called "routiers"—the **rutters** of the English sailor. In 1557 the Italian pilot Battista Testa Rossa published *Brieve Compendio del Arte del Navigar*, which was designed to serve the mariner on soundings and off. It forecast the single, all-inclusive volume that was soon to come, the **Waggoner.**

About 1584 the Dutch pilot Lucas Janszoon Waghenaer published a volume of navigational principles, tables, charts, and sailing directions which served as a guide for such books for the next 200 years. In *Spieghel der Zeevaerdt* (The Mariner's Mirror), Waghenaer gave directions and charts for sailing the waters of the Low Countries and later a second volume was published covering waters of the North and Baltic seas.

These "Waggoners" met with great success and in 1588 an English translation of the original book was made by Anthony Ashley. During the next 30 years, 24 editions of the book were published in Dutch, German, Latin, and English. Other authors followed the profitable example set by Waghenaer, and American, British, and French navigators soon had "Waggoners" for most of the waters they sailed.

The success of these books and the resulting competition among authors were responsible for their eventual discontinuance. Each writer attempted to make his work more inclusive than any other (the 1780 *Atlantic Neptune* contained 257 charts of North America alone) and the result was a tremendous book difficult to handle. They were too bulky, the sailing directions were unnecessarily detailed, and the charts too large. In 1795 the British Hydrographic Department was established, and charts and sailing directions were issued separately. The latter, issued for specific waters, were returned to the form of the original *Periplus*.

Modern sailing directions. The publication of modern sailing directions by the Defense Mapping Agency Hydrographic Center is one of the achievements properly attributed to Matthew Fontaine Maury. During the two decades he headed the Depot of Charts and Instruments (renamed U. S. Naval Observatory and Hydrographical Office in 1854), Maury gathered data that led to the publication of eight volumes of sailing directions.

111. The compass.—Early in the history of navigation man noted that the pole star (it may have been *α Draconis* then) remained close to one point in the northern sky. This served as his compass. When it was not visible, he used other stars, the sun and moon, winds, clouds, and waves. The development of the magnetic compass, perhaps a thousand years ago, and the 20th century development of the gyrocompass, offer today's navigator a method of steering his course with an accuracy as great as he is capable of using.

The **magnetic compass** (art. 623) is one of the oldest of the navigator's instruments. Its origin is not known. In 203 BC, when Hannibal set sail from Italy, his pilot was said to be one *Pelorus.* Perhaps the compass was in use then; no one can say for certain that it was not. There is little to substantiate the story that the Chinese invented it, and the legend that Marco Polo introduced it into Italy in the 13th century is almost certainly false. It is sometimes stated that the Arabs brought it to Europe, but this, too, is unlikely. Probably it was known first in the west. The Norsemen of the 11th century were familiar with it, and about 1200 a compass used by mariners when the pole star was hidden was described by a French poet, Guyot de Provins.

A needle thrust through a straw and floated in water in a container comprised the earliest compass known. A 1248 writer, Hugo de Bercy, spoke of a new compass construction, the needle "now" being supported on two floats. Petrus Peregrinus de Maricourt, in his *Epistola de Magnete* of 1269, wrote of a pivoted floating compass with a lubber's line, and said that it was equipped with sights for taking bearings.

The reliability of the magnetic compass of today is a comparatively recent achievement. It was not until the 1870's that Sir William Thomson (Lord Kelvin) was able to successfully combine all of the requirements for a good dry-card compass, and mount it in a well-designed binnacle. The dry-card compass was the standard compass in the Royal Navy until 1906 when the Board of Admiralty adopted the liquid compass as the standard compass.

The **compass card,** according to tradition, originated about the beginning of the 14th century, when Flavio Gioja of Amalfi attached a sliver of lodestone or a magnetized needle to a card. But the rose on the compass card is probably older than the needle. It is the wind rose of the ancients. Primitive man naturally named directions by the winds. The prophet Jeremiah speaks of the winds from the four quarters of heaven (Jer. 49:36) and Homer named four winds—Boreas, Eurus, Notus, and Lephyrus. Aristotle is said to have suggested a circle of 12 winds, and Eratosthenes, who measured the world correctly, reduced the number to eight about 200 BC. The "Tower of Winds" at Athens, built about 100 BC, had eight sides. The Latin rose of 12 points was common on most compasses used in the Middle Ages.

Variation (art. 706) was well understood 200 years ago, and navigators made allowance for it, but earliest recognition of its existence is not known. Columbus and even the 11th century Chinese have been given credit for its discovery, but little proof can be offered for either claim.

The secular change in variation was determined by a series of magnetic observations made at Limehouse, England. In 1580 William Borough fixed the variation in that area at approximately 11°25' east. Thirty-two years later Edmund Gunter, professor of astronomy at Gresham College, determined it to be 6°13' east. At first it was believed that Borough had made an error in his work, but in 1633 a further decrease was found, and the earth's changing magnetic field was established.

A South Atlantic expedition was led by Edmond Halley at the close of the 17th century to gather data and to map, for the first time, lines of variation. In 1724 George Graham published his observations in proof of the diurnal change in variation. Canton determined that the change was considerably less in winter than in summer, and about 1785 the strength of the magnetic force was shown by Paul de Lamanon to vary in different places.

The existence of **deviation** (art. 709) was known to John Smith in 1627 when he wrote of the "bittacle" as being a "square box nailed together with wooden pinnes, because iron nails would attract the Compasse." But no one knew how to correct a compass for deviation until Captain Matthew Flinders, while on a voyage to Australia in HMS *Investigator* in 1801–02, discovered a method of doing so. Flinders did not understand deviation completely, but the vertical bar he erected to correct for it was part of the solution, and the **Flinders bar** (art. 720) used today is a memorial to its discoverer. Between 1839 and 1855 Sir George Airy, then Astronomer Royal, studied the matter further and developed combinations of permanent magnets and soft iron masses for adjusting the compass. The introduction, by Lord Kelvin, of short needles as compass magnets made adjustment more precise.

The gyrocompass (art. 631). The age of iron ships demanded a compass which could be relied upon to indicate true north at all times, free from disturbing forces of variation and deviation.

In 1851, at the Pantheon in Paris, Leon Foucault performed his famous pendulum experiment to demonstrate the rotation of the earth. Foucault's realization that the swinging pendulum would maintain the plane of its motion led him, the following year, to develop and name the first gyroscope, using the principle of a common toy called a "rotascope." Handicapped by the lack of a source of power to maintain the spin of his gyroscope, Foucault used a microscope to observe the indication of the earth's rotation during the short period in which his manually operated gyroscope remained in rotation. A gyrocompass was not practical until electric power became available, more than 50 years later, to maintain the spin of the gyroscope.

Elmer A. Sperry, an American, and Anschutz-Kampfe, a German, independently invented gyrocompasses during the first decade of the 20th century. Tested first in 1911 on a freighter operating off the East Coast of the United States and then on American warships, Sperry's compass was found adequate, and in the years following World War I gyrocompasses became standard equipment on all large naval and merchant ships.

Gyrocompass auxiliaries commonly used today were added later. These include gyro repeaters, to indicate the vessel's heading at various locations; gyro pilots, to steer vessels automatically; course recorders, to provide a graphic record of courses steered; gyro-magnetic compasses, to repeat headings of magnetic compasses so located as to be least affected by deviation; and others in the fields of fire control, aviation, and guided missiles.

112. The log.—Since virtually the beginning of navigation, the mariner has attempted to determine his speed in traveling from one point to another. The earliest method was probably by estimate.

The oldest speed measuring device known is the **Dutchman's log.** Originally, any object which would float was thrown overboard on the lee side, from a point well forward, and the time required for it to pass between two points on the deck was noted. The time, as determined by sand glass, was compared with the known distance along the deck between the two points to determine the speed.

Near the end of the 16th century a line was attached to the log, and as the line was paid out a sailor recited certain sentences. The length of line which was paid out during the recitation was used to determine the speed. There is record of this method having been used as recently as the early 17th century. In its final form this **chip log, ship log,** or **common log** consisted of the *log chip* (or *log ship*), *log line, log reel,* and *log glass.* The chip was a quadrant-shaped piece of wood weighted along its circumference to keep it upright in the water (fig. 112). The log line was made fast to the log chip by means

FIGURE 112.—The common or chip log, showing the log reel, the log line, the log chip, and the log glass.

of a bridle, in such manner that a sharp pull on the log line dislodged a wooden peg and permitted the log chip to be towed horizontally through the water, and hauled aboard. Sometimes a *stray line* was attached to the log to veer it clear of the ship's wake. In determining speed, the observer counted the knots in the log line which was paid out during a certain time. The length of line between knots and the number of seconds required for the sand to run out were changed from time to time as the accepted length of the mile was altered.

The chip log has been superseded by patent logs that register on dials. However, the common log has left its mark on modern navigation, as the use of the term **knot** to indicate a speed of one nautical mile per hour dates from this device. There is evidence to support the opinion that the expression "dead reckoning" had its origin in this same device, or perhaps in the earlier Dutchman's log. There is logic in attributing "dead" reckoning to a reckoning relative to an object "dead" in the water.

Mechanical logs first appeared about the middle of the 17th century. By the beginning of the 19th century, the forerunners of modern mechanical logs were used by some navigators, although many years were to pass before they became generally accepted.

In 1773 logs on which the distance run was recorded on dials secured to the taffrail were tested on board a British warship and found reasonably adequate, although the comparative delicateness of the mechanism led to speculation about their long-term worth. Another type in existence at the time consisted of a wheel arrangement made fast on the underside of the keel, which transmitted readings to a dial inside the vessel as the wheel rotated.

An improved log was introduced by Edward Massey in 1802. This log gave considerably greater accuracy by means of a more sensitive rotator attached by a short length of line to a geared recording instrument. The difficulty with this log was that it had to be hauled aboard to take each reading. Various improvements were made, notably by Alexander Bain in 1846 and Thomas Walker in 1861, but it was not until 1878 that a log was developed in which the rotator could be used in conjunction with a dial secured to the after rail of the ship, and although refinements and improvements have been made, the patent log used today is essentially the same as that developed in 1878.

Engine revolution counters (art. 616) had their origin with the observations of the captains of the first paddle steamers, who discovered that by counting the paddle revolutions, they could, with practice, estimate their runs in thick weather as accurately as they could by streaming the log. Later developments led to the modern revolution counter on screw-type vessels, which can be used with reasonable accuracy if the propeller is submerged and an accurate estimate of slip is made.

Pitot-static and **impeller logs** (arts. 613, 614) are mechanical developments in the field of speed measurement. Each utilizes a retractable "rodmeter" which projects through the hull of the ship into the water. In the Pitot-static log, static and dynamic pressures on the rodmeter transmit readings to the master speed indicator. In the impeller log an electrical means of transmitting speed indications is used.

113. Units of distance and depth.—The modern navigator is concerned principally with four units of linear measure: the **nautical mile,** the **fathom,** the **foot** and the **meter.** Primitive man, however, used such natural units as the width of a finger, the **span** of his hand, the length of his foot, the distance from his elbow to the tip of the middle finger (the **cubit** of biblical renown), or the **pace** (sometimes one but usually a double step) to measure short distances.

Although the **Roman mile** had a value of about 1,488 meters or about 0.9248 of our statute mile of 5,280 feet, several standards were in use among the cities of ancient Greece at the same time. The Greek stadia being variable, there is uncertainty as to the accuracy of the measurement of the earth by Eratosthenes.

The **nautical mile** bears little relation to these land measures, which were not associated with the size of the earth. With the emergence of the nautical chart, it became customary to show a scale of miles on the chart, and the accepted value of this unit varied over the centuries with the changing estimates of the size of the earth. These estimates varied widely, ranging from about 44.5 to 87.5 modern nautical miles per degree of latitude, although generally they were too small. Columbus and Magellan used the value 45.3. Actually, the earth is about 32 percent larger. The *Almagest* of Ptolemy considered 62 Roman miles equivalent to one degree, but a 1466 edition of this book contained a chart of southern Asia drawn by Nicolaus Germanus on which 60 miles were shown to a degree. Whether the change was considered a correction or an adaptation to provide a more convenient relationship between the mile and the degree is not clear, but this is the earliest known use of this ratio.

Later, when the size of the earth was determined by measurement, the relationship of 60 Roman miles of 4,858.60 U. S. feet to a degree of latitude was seen to be in error. Both possible solutions to the problem—changing the ratio of miles to a degree, or changing the length of the mile—had their supporters, and neither group was able to convince the other. As a result, the shorter mile remained as the **land** or **statute mile** (now established as 5,280 feet in the United States), and the longer **nautical mile** gradually became established at sea. The earliest known reference to it by this name occurred in 1730.

Finer instruments and new methods make increasingly more accurate determinations of the size of the earth an ever-present possibility. Hence, a unit of length defined in terms of the size of the earth is undesirable. Recognition of this led, in 1875, to a change in the definition of the **meter** from one ten-millionth of the distance from the pole to the equator of the earth to the distance between two marks (approximately 39.37 U. S. inches) on a standard platinum-iridium bar kept at the Pavillon de Breteuill at Sevres, near Paris, France, by the International Commission of Weights and Measures. In further recognition of this principle, the International Hydrographic Bureau in 1929 recommended adoption of a standard value for the nautical mile, and proposed 1,852 international meters. This International Nautical Mile of 1,852 meters exactly has been adopted by nearly all maritime nations. The U. S. Departments of Defense and Commerce adopted this value in July 1954. With the yard-meter relationship then in use, the International Nautical Mile was equivalent to 6,076.10333 feet, approximately. Using the yard-meter exact relationship of one yard equal to 0.9144 meter adopted by the United States on July 1, 1959, the International Nautical Mile is equivalent to 6,076.11549 feet, approximately. In October 1960, the Eleventh General (International) Conference on Weights and Measures redefined the meter as equal to 1,650,763.73 wavelengths of the orange-red radiation in vacuum of krypton 86.

The **meter** as a unit of depth and height on U. S. nautical charts is of recent origin. The current policy of the Defense Mapping Agency Hydrographic Center of converting new compilations of nautical and special purpose charts to the metric system was implemented on January 2, 1970.

The **fathom** as a unit of length or depth is of obscure origin, but primitive man considered it a measure of the outstretched arms, and the modern seaman still estimates the length of a line in this manner. That the unit was used in early times is indicated by reference to it in the detailed account given of the Apostle Paul's voyage to Rome, as recorded in the 27th chapter of the *Acts of the Apostles*. Posidonius reported a sounding of more than 1,000 fathoms in the second century BC. How old the unit was at that time is unknown.

114. Soundings.—Probably the most dangerous phase of navigation occurs when the vessel is "on soundings." Since man first began navigating the waters, the possibility of grounding his vessel has been a major concern, and frequent soundings have been the most highly valued safeguard against that experience. Undoubtedly used long before the Christian era, the lead line is perhaps the oldest instrument of navigation.

The lead line. The **hand lead** (art. 618), consisting of a lead weight attached to a line usually marked in fathoms, has been known since antiquity and, with the exception of the markings, is probably the same today as it was 2,000 or more years ago. The **deep sea lead,** a heavier weight with a longer line, was a natural outgrowth of the hand lead. A 1585 navigator speaks of soundings of 330 fathoms, and in 1773, in the Norwegian Sea, Captain Phipps had all the sounding lines on board spliced together to obtain a sounding of 683 fathoms. Matthew Fontaine Maury made his deep sea soundings by securing a cannon shot to a ball of strong twine. The heavy weight caused the twine to run out rapidly, and when bottom was reached, the twine was cut and the depth deduced from the amount remaining on the ball.

The sounding machine. The biggest disadvantage of the deep sea lead is that the vessel must be stopped if depths are to be measured accurately. This led to the development of the sounding machine.

Early in the 19th century a sounding machine similar to one of the earlier patent logs was invented. A wheel was secured just above the lead and the cast made in such a way that all the line required ran out freely and the lead sank directly to the bottom. The motion through the water during the descent set the wheel revolving, and this in turn caused the depth to be indicated on a dial. Ships sailing at perhaps 12 knots required 20 or 30 men to heave aboard the heavy line with its weight of 50 or more pounds after each cast. A somewhat similar device was the **buoy sounder.** The lead was passed through a buoy in which a spring catch was fitted and both were cast over the side. The lead ran freely until bottom was reached, when the catch locked, preventing further running out of the line. The whole assembly was then brought on board, the depth from the buoy to the lead being read.

The first use of the pressure principle to determine the depth of water occurred early in the 19th century when the "Self-acting Sounder" was introduced. A hollow glass tube open at its lower end contained an index which moved up in the tube as greater water pressure compressed the air inside. The index retained its highest position when hauled aboard the vessel, and its height was proportional to the depth of the water.

The British scientist, Sir William Thomson (Lord Kelvin) in 1878 perfected the sounding machine after repeated tests at sea. Prior to his invention, fibre line was used exclusively in soundings. His introduction of piano wire solved the problem of rapid descent of the lead and also that of hauling it back aboard quickly. The chemically coated glass tube which he used to determine depth was an improvement of earlier methods, and the worth of the entire machine is evidenced by the fact that it is still used in essentially the same form.

Echo sounding. Based upon the principle that sound travels through sea water at a nearly uniform rate, automatic depth-registering devices (art. 619) have been invented to indicate the depth of water under a vessel, regardless of its speed. In 1911 an account was published of an experiment performed by Alexander Behm of Kiel, who timed the echo of an underwater explosion, testing this theory. High frequency sounds in water were produced by Pierre Langevin, and in 1918 he used the principle for echo depth finding. The first practical echo sounder was developed by the United States Navy in 1922.

The actual time between emission of a sonic or ultrasonic signal and return of its echo from the bottom, the angle at which the signal is beamed downward in order that its echo will be received at another part of the vessel, and the phase difference between signal and echo have all been used in the development of the modern echo sounder.

115. Aids to navigation.—The Cushites and Libyans constructed towers along the Mediterranean coast of Egypt, and priests maintained beacon fires in them. These were the earliest known lighthouses. At Sigeum in the Troad (part of Troy) a lighthouse was built before 660 BC. One of the seven wonders of the ancient world was the lighthouse called the Pharos of Alexandria, which may have been more than 200 feet tall. It was built by Sostratus of Cnidus (Asia Minor) in the third century BC, during the reign of Ptolemy Philadelphus. The word "pharos" has since been a general term for lighthouses. Some time between 1584 and 1611 the light of Cordouan, the earliest wave-swept lighthouse, was erected at the entrance to the Gironde river in western France. An oak log fire illuminated this structure until the 18th century.

Wood or coal fires were used in the many lighthouses built along the European and British coasts in the 17th and 18th centuries. One of these, the oak pile structure erected by Henry Whiteside in 1776 to warn shipmasters of Small's Rocks, subsequently played a major role in navigational history, as it was this light which figured in the discovery of the celestial line of position by Captain Thomas Sumner some 60 years later (art. 131).

In England such structures were privately maintained by interested organizations. One of the most famous of these groups, popularly known as "Trinity House," was organized in the 16th century, perhaps earlier, when a "beaconage and buoyage" fee was levied on English vessels. This prompted the establishment of Trinity House "to make, erect, and set up beacons, marks, and signs for the sea" and to provide vessels with pilots. The organization is now in its fifth century of operation, and its chief duties are to serve as a general lighthouse and pilotage authority, and to supply pilots.

The first lightship was a small vessel with lanterns hung from its yardarms. It was stationed at the Nore in the Thames estuary, in 1732.

The pilot's profession is not much younger than that of the mariner. The Bible relates (1 Kings 9:27) that Hiram of Tyre provided pilots for King Solomon. The duties of these pilots are not specified. In the first century AD, fishermen of the

Gulf of Cambay, India, met seagoing vessels and guided them into port. It is probable that pilots were established in Delaware Bay earlier than 1756.

Seafaring people of the United States had erected lighthouses and buoys before the Revolutionary War, and in 1789 Congress passed legislation providing for federal expansion of the work. About 1767 the first buoys were placed in the Delaware River. These were logs or barrels, but about 1820 they were replaced with spar buoys. In that same year, the first lightship was established in Chesapeake Bay.

As the maritime interests of various countries grew, more and better aids to navigation were made available. In 1850 Congress prescribed the present system of coloring and numbering United States buoys (app. Y). Conformity as to shape resulted from the recommendations of the International Marine Conference of 1889. The second half of the 19th century saw the development of bell, whistle, and lighted buoys, and in 1910 the first lighted buoy in the United States utilizing high pressure acetylene apparatus was placed in service. Stationed at the entrance to Ambrose Channel in New York, it provided the basis for the high degree of perfection which has been achieved in the lighted buoy since that time. The complete buoyage system maintained by the U. S. Coast Guard today is chiefly a product of the 20th century. In 1900 there were approximately 5,000 buoys of all types in use in the United States, while today there are more than 20,000.

116. The sailings.—The various methods of mathematically determining course, distance, and position arrived at have a history almost as old as mathematics itself. Thales, Hipparchus, Napier, Wright, and others contributed the formulas that led to the tables permitting computation of course and distance by plane, traverse, parallel, middle-latitude, Mercator, and great-circle sailings.

Plane sailing (art. 810). Based upon the assumption that the surface of the earth is plane, or flat, this method was used by navigators for many centuries. The navigator solved problems by laying down his course relative to his meridian, and stepping off the distance run to the new position. This system is used with accuracy today in measuring short runs on a Mercator chart, which compensates for the convergence of the meridians, but on the plane chart, serious errors resulted. Early navigators might have obtained mathematical solutions to this problem, with no greater accuracy, but the graphical method was commonly used.

Traverse sailing (art. 810). Because sailing vessels were subject to the winds, navigators of old were seldom able to sail one course for great distances, and consequently a series of small triangles had to be solved. Equipment was designed to help seamen in maintaining their dead reckoning positions. The modern **rough log** evolved from the *log board*, hinged wooden boards that folded like a book and on which courses and distances were marked in chalk. Each day the position was determined from this data and entered in the ship's journal, today's **smooth log.**

The log board was succeeded by the **travas,** a board with lines radiating from the center in 32 compass directions. Regularly spaced along the lines were small holes into which pegs were fitted to indicate time run on the particular course. In 1627 John Smith described the travas as a "little round board full of holes upon lines like the compasse, upon which by the removing of a little sticke they (seamen) keepe an account, how many glasses (which are but halfe houres) they steare upon every point of the compasse."

These devices were of great value to the navigator in keeping a record of the courses and distances sailed, but still left him the long mathematical solutions necessary to determine the new position. In 1436 what appears to have been the first **traverse table** was prepared by Andrea Biancho. Using this table of solutions of right-angled plane triangles, the navigator was able to determine his course and distance made good after sailing a number of distances in different directions.

Parallel sailing (art. 810) was an outgrowth of the navigator's inability to determine his longitude. Not a mathematical solution in the sense that the other sailings are, it involved converting the distance sailed along a parallel (departure), as determined by dead reckoning, into longitude.

Middle-latitude sailing (art. 810). The inaccuracies involved in plane sailing led to the improved method of middle-latitude sailing early in the 17th century. A mathematician named Ralph Handson is believed to have been its inventor.

Middle-latitude sailing is based upon the assumption that the use of a parallel midway between those of departure and arrival will eliminate the errors inherent in plane sailing due to the convergence of the meridians. The assumption is reasonably accurate and although the use of Mercator sailing usually results in greater accuracy, middle-latitude sailing still serves a useful purpose.

Mercator sailing (art. 810). Included in Edward Wright's *Certaine Errors in Navigation Detected and Corrected*, of 1599, was the first published table of meridional parts which provided the basis for the most accurate of rhumb line sailings—Mercator sailing.

Great-circle sailing (art. 812). For many hundreds of years mathematicians have known that a great circle is the shortest distance between two points on the surface of a sphere, but it was not until the 19th century that navigators began to regularly make use of this information.

The first printed description of great-circle sailing appeared in Pedro Nunes' 1537 *Tratado da Sphera*. The method had previously been proposed by Sebastian Cabot in 1498, and in 1524 Verrazano sailed a great-circle course to America. But the sailing ships could not regularly expect the steady winds necessary to sail such a course, and their lack of knowledge concerning longitude, plus the necessity of stopping at islands along their routes to take supplies, made it impractical for most voyages at that time.

The gradual accumulation of knowledge concerning seasonal and prevailing winds, weather conditions, and ocean currents eventually made it possible for the navigator to plan his voyage with more assurance. Nineteenth century writers of navigational texts recommended the use of great-circle sailing, and toward the close of that century such sailing became increasingly popular, particularly in the Pacific.

117. Hydrographic offices.—The practice of recording hydrographic data was centuries old before the establishment of the first official hydrographic office, in 1720. In that year the **Depot des Cartes, Plans, Journaux et Memoirs Relatifs a la Navigation** was formed in France with the Chevalier de Luynes in charge. The Hydrographic Department of the British Admiralty, though not established until 1795, has played a major part in European hydrographic work.

The **National Ocean Survey** was originally founded when Congress, in 1807, passed a resolution authorizing a survey of the coast, harbors, outlying islands, and fishing banks of the United States. On the recommendation of the American Philosophical Society, President Jefferson appointed Ferdinand Hassler, a Swiss immigrant who had founded the Geodetic Survey of his native land, the first Director of the "Survey of the Coast." The survey was renamed "Coast Survey" in 1836.

The approaches to New York were the first sections of the coast charted, and from there the work spread northward and southward along the eastern seaboard. In 1844 the work was expanded and arrangements made to chart simultaneously the gulf and east coasts. Investigation of tidal conditions began, and in 1855 the first tables of tide predictions were published. The California gold rush gave impetus to the survey of the west coast, which began in 1850, the year California became a State. The survey ship *Washington* undertook investigations of the Gulf Stream. Coast pilots, or sailing directions, for the Atlantic coast of the United States were privately published in the first half of the 19th century, but about 1850 the Survey began accumulating data that led to federally produced coast pilots. The 1889 *Pacific Coast Pilot* was an outstanding contribution to the safety of west coast shipping.

In 1878 the survey was renamed "Coast and Geodetic Survey"; in 1970 the survey became the "National Ocean Survey."

Today the National Ocean Survey provides the mariner with the charts and coast pilots of all waters of the United States and its possessions, and tide and tidal current tables for much of the world.

Defense Mapping Agency Hydrographic Center. In 1830 the U. S. Navy established a "Depot of Charts and Instruments" in Washington, D.C. Primarily, it was to serve as a storehouse where such charts and sailing directions as were available, together with navigational instruments, could be assembled for issue to Navy ships which required them. Lieutenant L. M. Goldsborough and one assistant, Passed Midshipman R. B. Hitchcock, constituted the entire staff.

The first chart published by the Depot was produced from data obtained in a survey made by Lieutenant Charles Wilkes, who had succeeded Goldsborough in 1834, and who later earned fame as the leader of a United States exploring expedition to Antarctica.

From 1842 until 1861 Lieutenant Matthew Fontaine Maury served as Officer-in-Charge. Under his command the Depot rose to international prominence. Maury decided upon an ambitious plan to increase the mariner's knowledge of existing winds, weather, and currents. He began by making a detailed record of pertinent matter included in old log books stored at the Depot. He then inaugurated a hydrographic reporting program among shipmasters, and the thousands of answers received, along with the log book data, were first utilized to publish the *Wind and Current Chart of the North Atlantic* of 1847. The United States instigated an international conference in 1853 to interest other nations in a system of exchanging nautical information. The plan, which was Maury's, was enthusiastically adopted by other maritime nations, and is the basis upon which hydrographic offices operate today.

In 1854 the Depot was redesignated the "U. S. Naval Observatory and Hydrographical Office," and in 1866 Congress separated the two, broadly increasing the functions of the latter. The Office was authorized to carry out surveys, collect information, and print every kind of nautical chart and publication, all "for the benefit and use of navigators generally."

One of the first acts of the new Office was to purchase the copyright of *The New American Practical Navigator*. Several volumes of sailing directions had already been published. The first *Notice to Mariners* appeared in 1869. Daily broadcast of navigational warnings was inaugurated in 1907, and in 1912, following the sinking of the SS *Titanic*, Hydrographic Office action led to the establishment of the International Ice Patrol.

The development by the U. S. Navy of an improved depth finder in 1922 made possible the acquisition of additional information concerning bottom topography. During the same year aerial photography was first employed as an aid in chart making. The Hydrographic Office published the first chart for lighter-than-air craft in 1923.

In 1962 the U. S. Navy Hydrographic Office was redesignated the U. S. Naval Oceanographic Office. In 1972 certain hydrographic functions of the latter office were transferred to the Defense Mapping Agency Hydrographic Center.

The **International Hydrographic Organization** (IHO) was originally established in 1921 as the **International Hydrographic Bureau** (IHB). The present name was adopted in 1970 as a result of a revised international agreement among member nations. However, the former name, International Hydrographic Bureau, was retained for the IHO's administrative body of three Directors and a small Staff at the Organization's headquarters in Monaco.

The IHO (as did the former IHB) sets forth hydrographic standards as they are agreed upon by the member nations. All member States are urged and encouraged to follow these standards in their surveys, nautical charts, and publications. As these standards are uniformly adopted, the products of the world's hydrographic and oceanographic offices become more uniform. Much has been done in the field of standardization since the Bureau was founded.

The principal work undertaken by the IHO is:

1. to bring about a close and permanent association between national hydrographic offices;

2. to study matters relating to hydrography and allied sciences and techniques;

3. to further the exchange of nautical charts and documents between hydrographic offices of Member Governments;

4. to circulate the appropriate documents;

5. to tender guidance and advice upon request, in particular to countries engaged in setting up or expanding their hydrographic service;

6. to encourage coordination of hydrographic surveys with relevant oceanographic activities;

7. to extend and facilitate the application of oceanographic knowledge for the benefit of navigators;

8. to cooperate with international organizations and scientific institutions which have related objectives.

During the 19th century, many maritime nations established hydrographic offices to provide means for improving the navigation of naval and merchant vessels by providing nautical publications, nautical charts, and other navigational services. Non-uniformity of hydrographic procedures, charts, and publications was much in evidence. In 1889, an International Marine Conference was held at Washington, D.C., and it was proposed to establish a "permanent international commission." Similar proposals were made at the sessions of the International Congress of Navigation held at St. Petersburg in 1908 and again in 1912.

In 1919 the hydrographers of Great Britain and France cooperated in taking the necessary steps to convene an international conference of hydrographers. London was selected as the most suitable place for this conference, and on July 24, 1919, the First International Conference opened, attended by the hydrographers of 24 nations. The object of the conference was clearly stated in the invitation to attend. It read, "To consider the advisability of all maritime nations adopting similar methods in the preparation, construction, and production of their charts and all hydrographic publications; of rendering the results in the most convenient form to enable them to be readily used; of instituting a prompt system of mutual exchange of hydrographic information between all countries; and of providing an opportunity to consultations and discussions to be carried out on hydrographic subjects generally by the hydrographic experts of the world." In general, this is still the purpose of the International Hydrographic Organization. As a result of the conference, a permanent organization was formed and statutes for its operations were prepared. The International Hydrographic Bureau, now the International Hydrographic Organization, began its activities in 1921 with 18 nations as members. The Principality of Monaco was selected because of its easy communication with the rest of the world and also because of the generous offer of Prince Albert I of Monaco to provide suitable accommodations for the Bureau in the Principality. The IHO, including the three Directors and their staff, is housed in its own headquarters which were built and are maintained by the Government of Monaco.

The works of the IHO are published in both French and English and are distributed through various media. Many of the publications are available to the general public, and a discount of 30 percent is offered to naval and merchant marine officers of any of the member nations. Inquiries as to the availability of the publications should be made directly to the "International Hydrographic Bureau, Avenue President J. F. Kennedy, Monte-Carlo, Monaco."

118. Navigation manuals.—Although navigation is as old as man himself, navigation textbooks, as they are thought of today, are a product of the last several centuries. Until the end of the Dark Ages such books, or manuscripts, as were available were written by astronomers for other astronomers. The navigator was forced to make use of these, gleaning what little was directly applicable to his profession. After 1500, however, the need for books on navigation resulted in the publication of a series of manuals of increasing value to the mariner.

Sixteenth century manuals. Frequently a command of Latin was required to study navigation during the 16th century. *Regimento do estrolabio e do quadrante* (fig. 130a), which was published at Lisbon in 1509, or earlier, explained the method of finding latitude by meridian observations of the sun and the pole star, contained a traverse table for finding the longitude by dead reckoning, and listed the longitudes of a number of places. Unfortunately, the author made several errors in transcribing the declination tables published by Abraham Zacuto in 1474, and this resulted in errors being made for many years in determining latitude. Nevertheless, the nameless writer of the *Regimento* performed a great service for all mariners. His "Handbook for the Astrolabe and Quadrant"—to translate the title—had many editions and many emulators.

In 1519 Fernandez de Encisco published his *Suma de Geographia*, the first Spanish manual. The book was largely a translation of the *Regimento*, but new information was included, and revisions were printed in 1530 and 1546.

The Flemish mathematician and astronomer R. Gemma Frisius published a book on navigation in 1530. This manual, entitled *De Principiis Astronomiae*, gave an excellent description of the sphere, although the astronomy was that of Ptolemy, and discussed at length the use of the globe in navigation. Gemma gave courses in terms of the principal winds, proposed that longitude be reckoned from the Fortunate Islands (Canary Islands), and gave rules for finding the dead reckoning position by courses and distances sailed.

Tratado da Sphera, Pedro Nunes' great work, appeared in 1537. In addition to the first printed description of great-circle sailing, Nunes' book included a section on determining the latitude by two altitudes of the sun (taken when the azimuths differed by not less than 40°) and solving the problem on a globe. The method was first proposed by Gemma. *Tratado da Sphera* contained the conclusion of a study of the "plane chart" which Nunes had made. He exposed its errors, but was unable to develop a satisfactory substitute.

During the years that followed, an extensive navigational literature became available. The Spaniards Pedro de Medina and Martin Cortes published successful manuals in 1545 and 1551, respectively. Medina's *Arte de Navegar* passed through 13 editions in several languages and *Breve de la Spera y de la Arte de Navegar*, Cortes' book, was eventually translated into English and became the favorite of the British navigator. Cortes discussed the principle which Mercator used 18 years later in constructing his famous chart, and he also listed accurately the distance between meridians at all latitudes.

The first western hemisphere navigation manual was published by Diego Garcia de Palacio at Mexico City in 1587. His *Instrucion Nauthica* included a partial glossary of nautical terms and certain data on ship construction.

John Davis' *The Seaman's Secrets* of 1594 was the first of the "practical" books. Davis was a celebrated navigator who asserted that it was the purpose of his book to give "all that is necessary for sailors, not for scholars on shore." Davis' book discussed at length the navigator's instruments, and went into detail on the "sailings." He explained the method of dividing a great circle into a number of rhumb lines, and the work he had done with Edward Wright qualified him to report on the method and advantages of Mercator sailing. He endorsed the system of determining latitude by two observations of the sun and the intermediate bearing.

Although best known for the presentation of the theory of Mercator sailing, Edward Wright's *Certaine Errors in Navigation Detected and Corrected* (1599) was a sound navigation manual in its own right. Particularly, he advocated correcting sights for dip, refraction, and parallax (ch. XVI).

Later manuals. The next 200 years saw a succession of navigation manuals made available to the navigator; so many that only a few can be mentioned. Among those which enjoyed the greatest success were Blundeville's *Exercises*, John Napier's *Mirifici Logarithmorum Canonis Descriptio* (which introduced the use of logarithms at sea), the tables and rules of Edmund Gunter, *Arithmetical Navigation* by Thomas Addison, and Richard Norwood's *The Sea-mans Practice* (which gave the length of the nautical mile as 6,120 feet). Robert Dudley filled four volumes in writing the *Arcano del Mare* (1646–47) as did John Robertson with *Elements of Navigation*. Jonas and John Moore, William Jones, and several Samuel Dunns were others who contributed navigation books before Nathaniel Bowditch in America and J. W. Norie in England wrote the manuals which navigators found best suited to their needs.

Bowditch's *The New American Practical Navigator* was first published in 1802 (fig. 118), and Norie's *Epitome of Navigation* appeared the following year. Both were outstanding books which enabled the mariner of little formal education to grasp the essentials of his profession. The Englishman's book passed through 22 editions in that country before losing its popularity to Captain Lecky's famous *"Wrinkles"* in *Practical Navigation* of 1881. The *American Practical Navigator* is still read widely, more than a century-and-a-half after its original printing.

A number of worthy navigation manuals have appeared in recent years.

Celestial Navigation

119. Astronomy is sometimes called the oldest of sciences. The movements of the sun, moon, stars, and planets were used by the earliest men as guides in hunting, fishing, and farming. The first maps were probably of the heavens.

Babylonian priests studied celestial mechanics at a very early date, possibly as early as 3800 BC, more probably about 1500 years later. These ancient astronomers predicted lunar and solar eclipses, constructed tables of the moon's hour angle, and are believed to have invented the zodiac. The week and month as known today originated with their calendar. They grouped the stars by constellations. It is probable that they were arranged in essentially their present order as early as 2000 BC. The five planets easily identified by the unaided eye were known to the Babylonians, who were apparently the first to divide the sun's apparent motion about the earth into 24 equal parts. They published this and other astronomical data in ephemerides. There is evidence that the prophet Abraham had an excellent knowledge of astronomy.

THE NEW AMERICAN

PRACTICAL NAVIGATOR;

BEING AN

EPITOME OF NAVIGATION;

CONTAINING ALL THE TABLES NECESSARY TO BE USED WITH THE

NAUTICAL ALMANAC,

IN DETERMINING THE

LATITUDE;

AND THE

LONGITUDE BY LUNAR OBSERVATIONS;

AND

KEEPING A COMPLETE RECKONING AT SEA:

ILLUSTRATED BY

PROPER RULES AND EXAMPLES:

THE WHOLE EXEMPLIFIED IN A

JOURNAL,

KEPT FROM

BOSTON TO MADEIRA,

IN WHICH ALL THE RULES OF NAVIGATION ARE INTRODUCED:

ALSO

The Demonstration of the most useful Rules of TRIGONOMETRY: With many useful Problems in MENSURATION, SURVEYING, and GAUGING: And a Dictionary of SEA-TERMS; with the Manner of performing the most common Evolutions at Sea.

TO WHICH ARE ADDED,

Some GENERAL INSTRUCTIONS and INFORMATION to MERCHANTS, MASTERS of VESSELS, and others concerned in NAVIGATION, relative to MARITIME LAWS and MERCANTILE CUSTOMS.

FROM THE BEST AUTHORITIES.

ENRICHED WITH A NUMBER OF

NEW TABLES,

WITH ORIGINAL IMPROVEMENTS AND ADDITIONS, AND A LARGE VARIETY OF NEW AND IMPORTANT MATTER:

ALSO,

MANY THOUSAND ERRORS ARE CORRECTED,

WHICH HAVE APPEARED IN THE BEST SYSTEMS OF NAVIGATION YET PUBLISHED.

BY NATHANIEL BOWDITCH,

FELLOW OF THE AMERICAN ACADEMY OF ARTS AND SCIENCES.

ILLUSTRATED WITH COPPERPLATES.

First Edition.

PRINTED AT NEWBURYPORT, (MASS.) 1802,

BY

EDMUND M. BLUNT, (Proprietor)

FOR CUSHING & APPLETON, SALEM.

SOLD BY EVERY BOOK-SELLER, SHIP-CHANDLER, AND MATHEMATICAL-INSTRUMENT-MAKER, IN THE UNITED STATES AND WEST-INDIES

FIGURE 118.—Original title page of *The New American Practical Navigator*, written by Nathaniel Bowditch and published in 1802.

The Chinese, too, made outstanding contributions to the science of the heavens. They may have fixed the solstices and equinoxes before 2000 BC. They had quadrants and armillary spheres, used water clocks, and observed meridian transits. These ancient Chinese determined that the sun made its annual apparent revolution about the earth in 365¼ days, and divided circles into that many parts, rather than 360. About 1100 BC the astronomer Chou Kung determined the sun's maximum declination within about 15′.

Astronomy was used by the Egyptians in fixing the dates of their religious festivals almost as early as the Babylonian studies. By 2000 BC or earlier the new year began with the heliacal rising of Sirius; that is, the first reappearance of this star in the eastern sky during morning twilight after having last been seen just after sunset in the western sky. The heliacal rising of Sirius coincided approximately with the annual Nile flood. The famous Pyramid of Cheops, which was probably built in the 17th century BC, was so constructed that the light of Sirius shone down a southerly shaft when at upper transit, and the light of the Pole Star shone down a northerly shaft at lower transit, the axes of the two shafts intersecting in the royal burial chamber. When the pyramid was constructed, α *Draconis*, not Polaris, was the Pole Star.

The Greeks learned of navigational astronomy from the Phoenicians. The earliest Greek astronomer, Thales, was of Phoenician ancestry. He is given credit for dividing the year of the western world into 365 days, and he discovered that the sun does not move uniformly between solstices. Thales is most popularly known, however, for predicting the solar eclipse of 585 BC, which ended a battle between the Medes and the Lydians. He was the first of the great men whose work during the next 700 years was the controlling force in navigation, astronomy, and cartography until the Renaissance.

120. Shape of the earth.—Advanced as the Babylonians were, they apparently considered the earth to be flat. Land surveys of about 2300 BC show a "salt water river" encircling the country (fig. 120).

But seafarers knew that the last to be seen of a ship as it disappeared over the horizon was the masthead. They recognized the longer summer days in England when they sailed to the tin mines of Cornwall, as early as 900 BC. In that "northland" the Mediterranean sailors noticed that the Pole Star was higher in the sky and the lower southern constellations were no longer visible. When Thales invented the gnomonic projection

Courtesy of the Map Division of the Library of Congress.

FIGURE 120.—The original and reconstruction of a Babylonian map of about 500 BC. The Babylonians believed the earth to be a flat disk encircled by a salt water river.

about 600 BC, he must have believed the earth to be a sphere. Two centuries later Aristotle wrote that the earth's shadow on the moon during an eclipse was always circular. Archimedes (287–212 BC) used a glass celestial globe with a smaller terrestrial globe inside it. Although the average man has understood the spherical nature of the earth for only a comparatively short period, learned astronomers have accepted the fact for more than 25 centuries.

121. Celestial mechanics.—Among astronomers the principal question for 2,000 years was not the shape of the earth, but whether it or the sun was the center of the universe. A stationary earth seemed logical to the early Greeks, who calculated that daily rotation would produce a wind of several hundred miles per hour at the equator. Failing to realize that the earth's atmosphere turns with it, they considered the absence of such a wind proof that the earth was stationary.

The belief among the ancients was that all celestial bodies moved in circles about the earth. However, the planets—the "wanderers," as they were called—contradicted this theory by their irregular motion. In the fourth century BC Eudoxus of Cnidus attempted to account for this by suggesting that planets were attached to concentric spheres which rotated about the earth at varying speeds. The plan of **epicycles,** the theory of the universe which was commonly accepted for 2,000 years, was first proposed by Appolonius of Perga in the third century BC. Ptolemy accepted and amplified the plan, explaining it in his famous books, the *Almagest* and *Cosmographia.* According to Ptolemy, the planets moved at uniform speeds in small circles, the centers of which moved at uniform speeds in circles about the earth (fig. 121).

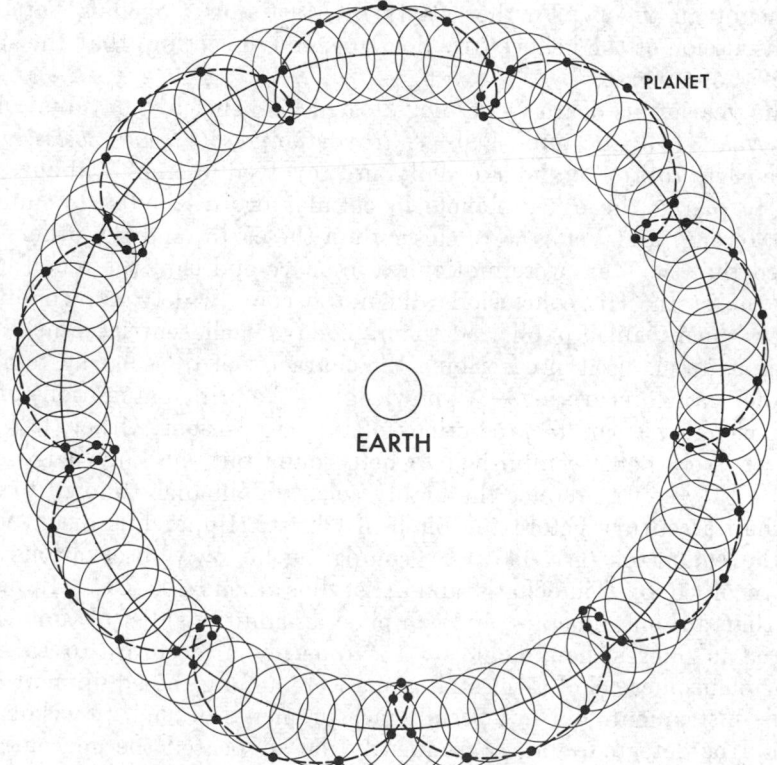

FIGURE 121.—The plan of epicycles, by which the ancients explained the retrograde motion of the planets. The planets were believed to rotate in small circles whose centers moved about the earth in a large circle.

At first the Ptolemaic theory was accepted without question, but as the years passed, forecasts based upon it proved to be inaccurate. By the time the *Alfonsine Tables* were published in the 13th century AD, a growing number of astronomers considered the Ptolemaic doctrine unacceptable. However, Purbach, Regiomontanus, Bernhard Walther of Nuremberg, and even Tycho Brahe in the latter part of the 16th century, were among those who tried to reconcile the earth-centered epicyclic plan to the observed phenomena of the heavens.

As early as the sixth century BC, a brotherhood founded by Pythagoras, a Greek philosopher, proposed that the earth was round and self-supported in space, and that it, the other planets, the sun, and the moon revolved about a central fire which they called *Hestia*, the hearth of the universe. The sun and the moon, they said, shone by reflected light from Hestia.

The central fire was never located, however, and a few hundred years later Aristarchus of Samos advanced a genuine heliocentric theory. He denied the existence of Hestia and placed the sun at the center of the universe, correctly considering it to be a star which shone by itself. The Hebrews apparently understood the correct relationship at least as early as Abraham (about 2000 BC), and the early inhabitants of the Western Hemisphere probably knew of it before the Europeans did.

The Ptolemaic theory was generally accepted until its inability to predict future positions of the planets could no longer be reconciled. Its replacement by the heliocentric theory is credited principally to Nicolaus Copernicus (or Koppernigk). After studying mathematics at the University of Cracow, Copernicus went to Bologna, where he attended the astronomical lectures of Domenicao Maria Novara, an advocate of the Pythagorean theory. Further study in Martianus Copella's *Satyricon*, which includes a discussion of the heliocentric doctrine, convinced him that the sun was truly the center of the universe.

Until the year of his death Copernicus tested his belief by continual observations, and in that year, 1543, he published *De Revolutionibus Orbium Coelestium*. In it he said that the earth rotated on its axis daily and revolved in a circle about the sun once each year. He placed the other planets in circular orbits about the sun also, recognizing that Mercury and Venus were closer than the earth, and the others farther out. He concluded that the stars were motionless in space and that the moon moved circularly about the earth. His conclusions did not become widely known until nearly a century later, when Galileo publicized them. Today, "heliocentric" and "Copernican" are synonymous terms used in describing the character of the solar system.

122. Other early discoveries.—A knowledge of the principal motions of the planets permitted reasonably accurate predictions of future positions. Other, less spectacular data, however, were being established to help round out the knowledge astronomers needed before they could produce the highly accurate almanacs known today.

More than a century before the birth of Christ, Hipparchus discovered the **precession of the equinoxes** (art. 1419) by comparing his own observations of the stars with those recorded by Timocharis and Aristyllus about 300 BC. Hipparchus cataloged more than a thousand stars, and compiled an additional list of time-keeping stars which differed in sidereal hour angle by 15° (one hour), accurate to 15'. A spherical star map, or planisphere, and a celestial globe were among the equipment he designed. However, his instruments did not permit measurements of such precision that stellar parallax could be detected, and, consequently, he advocated the geocentric theory of the universe.

Three centuries later Ptolemy examined and confirmed Hipparchus' discovery of precession. He published a catalog in which he arranged the stars by constellations and gave the magnitude, declination, and right ascension (art. 1426) of each. Following Hipparchus, Ptolemy determined longitudes by eclipses. In the *Almagest* he included the plane and spherical trigonometry tables which Hipparchus had developed, mathematical tables, and an explanation of the circumstances upon which the equation of time (art. 1809) depends.

The next thousand years saw little progress in the science of astronomy. Alexandria continued as a center of learning for several hundred years after Ptolemy, but succeeding astronomers at the observatory confined their work to comments on his great books. The long twilight of the Dark Ages had begun.

Alexandria was captured and destroyed by the Arabs in AD 640, and for the next 500 years Moslems exerted the primary influence in astronomy. Observatories were erected at Baghdād and Damascus during the ninth century. Ibn Yunis' observatory near Cairo gathered the data for the Hakimite tables in the 11th century. Earlier, the Spanish, under Moorish tutelage, set up schools of astronomy at Cordova and Toledo.

123. Modern astronomy may be said to date from Copernicus, although it was not until the invention of the telescope, about 1608, that precise measurement of the positions and motions of celestial bodies was possible.

Galileo Galilei, an Italian, made outstanding contributions to the cause of astronomy, and these served as a basis for the work of later men, particularly Isaac Newton. He discovered Jupiter's satellites, providing additional opportunities for determining longitude on land. He maintained that it is natural for motion to be uniform and in a straight line and that a force is required only when direction or speed is changing. Galileo's support of the heliocentric theory, his use and improvement of the telescope, and particularly the clarity and completeness of his records provided firm footing for succeeding astronomers.

Early in the 17th century, before the invention of the telescope, Tycho Brahe found that planet Mars to be in a position differing by as much as 8' from that required by the geocentric theory. When the telescope became available, astronomers learned that the apparent diameter of the sun varied during the year, indicating that the earth's distance from the sun varies, and that its orbit is not circular.

Johannes Kepler, a German who had succeeded Brahe and who was attempting to account for his 8' discrepancy, published in 1609 two of astronomy's most important doctrines, the **law of equal areas,** and the **law of elliptical orbits.** Nine years later he announced his third law, relating the periods of revolution of any two planets to their respective distances from the sun (art. 1407).

Kepler's discoveries provided a mathematical basis by which more accurate tables of astronomical data were computed for the maritime explorers of the age. His realization that the sun is the controlling power of the system and that the orbital planes of the planets pass through its center almost led him to the discovery of the law of gravitation.

Sir Isaac Newton reduced Kepler's conclusions to the **universal law of gravitation** (art. 1407) when he published his three laws of motions in 1687. Because the planets exert forces one upon the other, their orbits do not agree exactly with Kepler's laws. Newton's work compensated for this and, as a result, the astronomer was able to forecast with greater accuracy the positions of the celestial bodies. The navigator benefited through more exact tables of astronomical data.

Between the years 1764 and 1784, the Frenchmen Lagrange and Laplace conclusively proved the solar system's mechanical stability. Early in the 19th century, Nathaniel Bowditch translated and commented upon Laplace's *Mécanique Céleste*, bringing it up-to-date. Prior to their work this stability had been questioned due to apparent inconsistencies in the motions of some of the planets. After their demonstrations, men were convinced and could turn to other important work necessary to refine and improve the navigator's almanac.

But there were real, as well as apparent, irregularities of motion which could not be explained by the law of gravitation alone. By this law the planets describe ellipses about the sun, and these orbits are repeated indefinitely, except as the other planets influence the orbits of each by their own gravitational pull. Urbain Leverrier, one-time Director of the Paris Observatory, found that the line of apsides of Mercury was advancing 43″ per century faster than it should, according to the law of gravitation and the positions of other known planets. In an attempt to compensate for the resulting errors in the predicted positions of the planet, he suggested that there must be a mass of circulating matter between the sun and Mercury. No such circulating matter has been found, however, and Leverrier's discovery is attributed to a shortcoming of Newton's law, as explained by Albert Einstein.

In Einstein's hands, Leverrier's 43″ became a fact as powerful as Brahe's 8′ had been in the hands of Kepler. Early in the 20th century, Einstein announced the general theory of relativity. He stated that for the planets to revolve about the sun is natural, and gravitational force is unnecessary for this, and he asserted that there need be no circulating matter to account for the motion of the perihelion of Mercury as this, too, is in the natural order of things. Calculated from his theory, the correction to the previously computed motion of the perihelion in 100 years is 42″9.

Prior to Einstein's work, other discoveries had helped round out man's knowledge of the universe.

Aberration (art. 1417), discovered by James Bradley about 1726, accounted for the apparent shifting of the stars throughout the year, due to the combined orbital speed of the earth and the speed of light. Twenty years later Bradley described the periodic wobbling of the earth's axis, called **nutation** (art. 1417), and its effect upon precession of the equinoxes.

Meanwhile, in 1718 Edmond Halley, England's second Astronomer Royal, detected a motion of the stars, other than that caused by precession, that led him to conclude that they, too, were moving. By studying the works of the Alexandrian astronomers, he found that some of the most prominent stars had changed their positions by as much as 32′. Jacques Cassini gave Halley's discovery further support when he found, a few years later, that the declination of Arcturus had changed 5′ in the 100 years since Brahe made his observations. This **proper motion** (art. 1414) is motion in addition to that caused by precession, nutation, and aberration.

Sir William Herschel, the great astronomer who discovered the planet Uranus in 1781, proved that the solar system is moving toward the constellation *Hercules*. As early as 1828 Herschel advocated the establishment of a standard time system. Neptune was discovered in 1846 after its position had been predicted by the Frenchman Urbain Leverrier. Based upon the work of Percival Lowell, an American, Pluto was identified in 1930. Uranus, Neptune, and Pluto are of little concern to the navigator.

A more recent discovery may well have greater navigational significance. This is the existence of sources of electromagnetic energy in the sky in the form of **radio stars** (art. 1414). The sun has been found to transmit energy of radio frequency, and instruments have been built which are capable of tracking it across the sky regardless of weather conditions.

124. Sextant.—Prior to the development of the magnetic compass, the navigator used the heavenly bodies chiefly as guides by which to steer. The compass, however, led to more frequent long voyages on the open sea, and the need for a vertical-angle measuring device which could be used for determining altitude, so that latitude could be found.

Probably the first such device used at sea was the **common quadrant,** the simplest form of all such instruments. Made of wood, it was a fourth part of a circle, held vertical by means of a plumb bob. An observation made with this instrument at sea was a two- or three-man job. This device was probably used ashore for centuries before it went to sea, although its earliest use by the mariner is unknown.

Invented perhaps by Apollonius of Perga in the third century BC, the **astrolabe** (fig. 124a)—from the Greek for *star* and *to take*—had been made portable by the Arabs possibly as early as AD 700. It was in the hands of Christian pilots by the end of the 13th century, often as an elaborate and beautiful creation wrought of precious metals. Some astrolabes could be used as **star finders** (art. 2210) by fitting an engraved plate to one side. Large astrolabes were among the chief instruments of 15th and 16th century observatories, but the value of this instrument at sea was limited.

The principle of the astrolabe was similar to that of the common quadrant, but the astrolabe consisted of a metal disk, graduated in degrees, to which a movable sight vane was attached. In using the astrolabe, which may be likened to a pelorus held on its side, the navigator adjusted the sight vane until it was in line with the star, and

Courtesy of the John Carter Brown Library, Brown University.

FIGURE 124a.—An ancient astrolabe, one of the earliest kinds of altitude-measuring instruments.

then read the zenith distance from the scale. As with the common quadrant, the vertical was established by plumb bob.

Three men were needed to make an observation with the astrolabe (one held the instrument by a ring at its top, another aligned the sight vane with the body, a third made the reading) and even then the least rolling or pitching of a vessel caused large acceleration errors in observations. Therefore, navigators were forced to abandon the plumb bob and make the horizon their reference.

The **cross-staff** (fig. 124b) was the first instrument which utilized the visible horizon in making celestial observations. The instrument consisted of a long, wooden shaft upon which one of several cross-pieces was mounted perpendicularly. The cross-pieces were of various lengths, the one being used depending upon the angle to be measured. The navigator fitted the appropriate cross-piece on the shaft and, holding one end of the shaft beside his eye, adjusted the cross until its lower end was in line with the horizon and its upper end with the body. The shaft was calibrated to indicate the altitude of the body observed.

In using the cross-staff, the navigator was forced to look at the horizon and the celestial body at the same time. In 1590 John Davis, author of *The Seaman's Secrets*, invented the **backstaff** (fig. 124c) or **sea quadrant.** He was one of the few practical seamen (Davis Strait is named for him, in honor of his attempt to find the Northwest Passage) to invent a navigational device. The backstaff marked a long advance and was particularly popular among American colonial navigators.

In using this instrument, the navigator turned his back to the sun and aligned its shadow with the horizon. The backstaff had two arcs, and the sum of the values shown on each was the zenith distance of the sun. Later, this instrument was fitted with a mirror to permit observations of bodies other than the sun.

Another instrument developed about the same time was the **nocturnal** (fig. 124d). Its purpose was to provide the mariner with the appropriate correction to be made to the altitude of Polaris to determine latitude. By sighting on Polaris through the hole

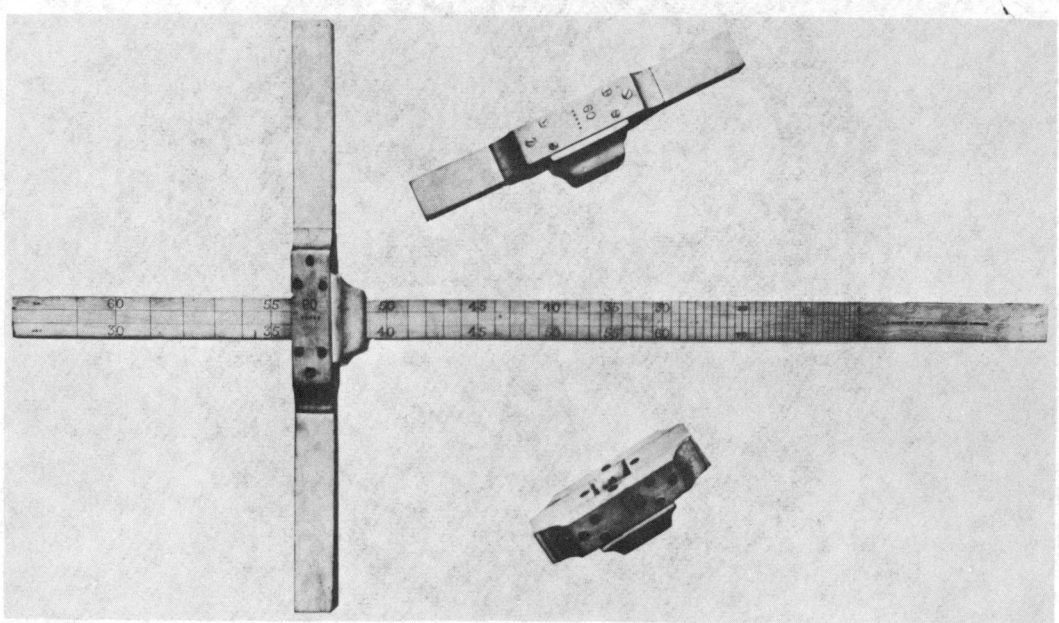

Courtesy of Peabody Museum of Salem.

FIGURE 124b.—The cross-staff, the first instrument to utilize the visible horizon in making celestial observations.

in the center of the instrument and adjusting the movable arm so that it pointed at Kochab, the navigator could read the correction from the instrument. Most nocturnals had an additional outer disk graduated for the months and days of the year and by adjusting this the navigator could also determine solar time.

Tycho Brahe designed several instruments with arcs of 60°, having one fixed sight and another movable one. He called the instruments **sextants** and the name is now commonly applied to all altitude-measuring devices used by the navigator (ch.

Courtesy of Peabody Museum of Salem.

FIGURE 124c.—The backstaff, or sea quadrant, a favorite instrument of American colonial navigators.

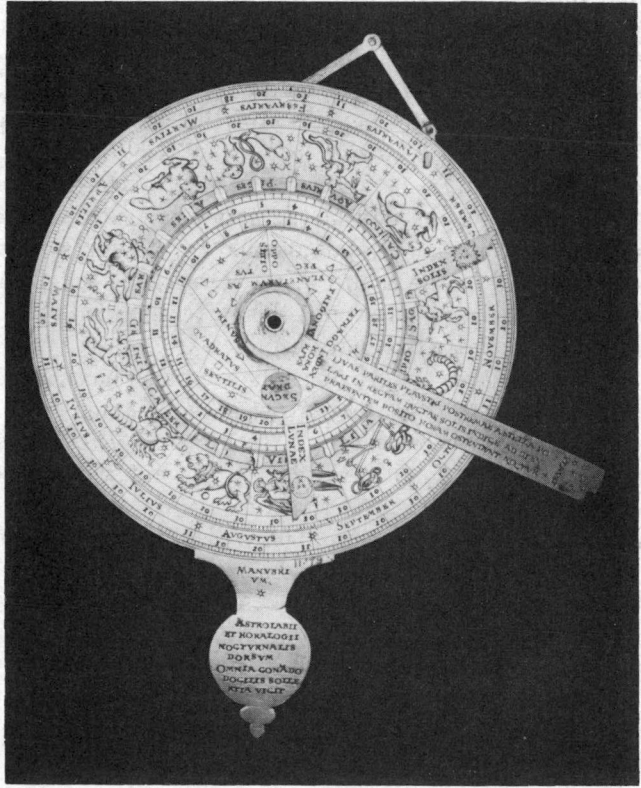

British Crown copyright. Science Museum, London, England.

FIGURE 124d.—The nocturnal, an instrument used to determine latitude by an observation of Polaris.

XV). In 1700 Sir Isaac Newton sent to Edmond Halley, the Astronomer Royal, a description of a device having double-reflecting mirrors, the principle of the modern marine sextant. However, this was not made public until after somewhat similar instruments had been made in 1730 by the Englishman John Hadley, and the American Thomas Godfrey.

The original instrument constructed by Hadley was, in fact, an *octant*, but due to the double-reflection principle it measured angles up to one-fourth of a circle, or 90°. Godfrey's instrument is reported to have been a *quadrant*, and so could measure angles through 180°. The two men received equal awards from England's Royal Society, as their work was considered to be a case of simultaneous independent invention, although Hadley probably preceded Godfrey by a few months in the actual construction of his sextant.

In the next few years both instruments were successfully tested at sea, but 20 years or more passed before the navigator gave up his backstaff or sea quadrant for the new device. In 1733 Hadley attached a spirit level to a quadrant, and with it was able to measure altitudes without reference to the horizon. Some years later the first bubble sextant (art. 1513) was developed.

Pierre Vernier, in 1631, had attached to the limb of a quadrant a second, smaller graduated arc, thereby permitting angles to be measured more accurately, and this device was incorporated in all later angle-measuring instruments.

The sextant has remained practically unchanged since its invention more than two centuries ago. The only notable improvements have been the addition of an endless tangent screw and a micrometer drum, both having been added during the 20th century.

125. Determining latitude.—The ability to determine longitude at sea is comparatively modern, but latitude has been available for thousands of years.

Meridian transit of the sun. Long before the Christian era, astronomers had determined the sun's declination for each day of the year, and prepared tables listing the data. This was a comparatively simple matter, for the zenith distance obtained by use of a shadow cast by the sun on the day of the winter solstice could be subtracted from that obtained on the day of the summer solstice to determine the range of the sun's declination, about 47°. Half of this is the sun's maximum declination, which could then be applied to the zenith distance recorded on either day to determine the latitude of the place. Daily observations thereafter enabled the ancient astronomers to construct reasonably accurate declination tables.

Such tables were available long before the average navigator was ready to use them, but certainly by the 15th century experienced seamen were determining their latitude at sea to within one or two degrees. In his 1594 *The Seaman's Secrets*, Davis made use of his experience in high latitudes to explain the method of determining latitude by lower transit observations of the sun.

Ex-meridian observation of the sun. The possibility of overcast skies at the one time each day when the navigator could get a reliable observation for latitude led to the development of the "ex-meridian" sight. Another method, involving two sights taken with a considerable time interval between, had previously been known, but the mathematics were so involved that it is doubtful that many seamen made use of it.

There are two methods by which ex-meridian observations can be solved. The direct process was the more accurate, although it required a trigonometrical solution. By the latter part of the 19th century, tables were introduced which made the method of reduction to the meridian more practical and, when occasion demands such an observation, this is the method generally used today. However, with the development of line of position methods and the modern inspection table, ex-meridian observations have lost much of their popularity.

Latitude by Polaris. First use of the Pole Star to determine latitude is not known, but many centuries ago seamen who used it as a guide by which to steer were known to comment upon its change of altitude as they sailed north or south.

By Columbus' time some navigators were using Polaris to determine latitude, and with the invention of the nocturnal late in the 16th century, providing corrections to the observed altitude, the method came into more general use. The development of the chronometer in the 18th century permitted exact corrections, and this made determination of latitude by Polaris a common practice. Even today, more than a century after discovery of the celestial line of position, the method is still in use. The modern inspection table has eliminated the need for meridian observations as a special method for determining latitude. Perhaps when the almanacs and sight reduction tables make the same provision for solution of Polaris sights as they do for any other navigational star, this last of the special methods will cease to be used for general navigation. But customs die slowly, and one as well established as that of position finding in terms of separate latitude and longitude observations—instead of lines of position—is not likely to disappear completely for many years to come.

126. The search for a method of "discovering" longitude at sea.—A statement once quite common was, "The navigator always knows his latitude." A more accurate statement would have been, "The navigator never knows his longitude." In 1594 Davis wrote: "Now there be some that are very inquisitive to have a way to get the longitude, but that is too tedious for seamen, since it requireth the deep knowledge of astronomy, wherefore I would not have any man think that the longitude is to be found at sea by any instrument, so let no seamen trouble themselves with any such rule, but let them keep a perfect account and reckoning of the way of their ship." In speaking of conditions of his day, he was correct, for it was not until the 19th century that the average navigator was able to determine his longitude with accuracy.

Parallel sailing. Without knowledge of his longitude, the navigator of old found it necessary on an ocean crossing to sail northward or southward to the latitude of his destination, and then to follow that parallel of latitude until the destination was reached, even though this might take him far out of his way. Because of this practice, parallel sailing was an important part of the navigator's store of knowledge. The method was a crude one, however, and the time of landfall was often in error by a matter of days, and, in extreme cases, even weeks.

Eclipses. Almost as early as the rotation of the earth was established, astronomers recognized that longitude could be determined by comparing local time with that at the reference meridian. The problem was the determination of time at the reference meridian.

One of the first methods proposed was that of observing the disappearance of Jupiter's satellites as they were eclipsed by their planet. This method, originally proposed by Galileo for use on land, required the ability to observe and identify the satellites by using a powerful telescope, knowledge of the times at which the eclipses would take place, and the skill to keep the instrument directed at the bodies while aboard a small vessel on the high seas. Although used in isolated cases for many years, the method was not satisfactory at sea, due largely to the difficulty of observation (some authorities recommended use of a telescope as long as 18 or 19 feet) and the lack of sufficiently accurate predictions.

Variation of the compass was seriously considered as a method of determining longitude for 200 years or more. Faleiro, Magellan's advisor, believed it could be so utilized, and, until development of the chronometer, work was carried on to perfect the theory. Although there is no simple relationship between variation and longitude, those who advocated the method felt certain that research and investigation would eventually provide the answer. Many others were convinced that such a solution did not exist. In 1676, Henry Bond published *The Longitude Found,* in which he stated that the latitude of a place and its variation could be referred to the prime meridian to determine longitude. Two years later Peter Blackborrow rebutted with *The Longitude Not Found.*

Variation was put to good use in determining the nearness to land by shipmasters familiar with the waters they plied, but as the solution to the longitude problem it was a failure, and with the improvement of lunar distance methods and the invention of the chronometer, interest in the method waned. If it had been possible to provide the mariner with an accurate chart of variation, and to keep it up-to-date, a means of establishing an approximate line of position in areas where the gradient is large would have resulted; in many cases this would have established longitude if latitude were known.

Lunar distances. The first method widely used at sea to determine longitude with some accuracy was that of lunar distances (art. 131), by which the navigator determined GMT by noting the position of the relatively fast-moving moon among the stars. Both Regiomontanus, in 1472, and John Werner, in 1514, have been credited with being the first to propose the use of the lunar distance method. At least one source states that Amerigo Vespucci, in 1497, determined longitude using the moon's position relative to that of another body. One of the principal reasons for establishing the Royal Observatory at Greenwich was to conduct the observations necessary to provide more accurate predictions of the future positions of the moon. Astronomers, including the Astronomers Royal, favored this method, and half a century after the invention of the chronometer it was still being perfected. In 1802 Nathaniel Bowditch simplified the method and its explanation, thus eliminating much of the mystery surrounding it and making it understandable to the average mariner. By using Bowditch's method, the navigator was able to head more or less directly toward his destination, rather than travel the many additional miles often required in "running down the latitude" and then using parallel sailing. An explanation of the lunar distance method, and tables for its use, were carried in the *American Practical Navigator* until 1914.

The Board of Longitude. The lunar distance method, using the data and equipment available early in the 18th century, was far from satisfactory. Ships, cargoes, and lives were lost because of inaccurately determined longitudes. During the Age of Discovery, Spain and Holland posted rewards for solution to the problem, but in vain. When 2,000 men were lost as a squadron of British men-of-war ran aground on a foggy night in 1707, officers of the Royal Navy and Merchant Navy petitioned Parliament for action. As a result, the Board of Longitude was established in 1714, empowered to reward the person who could solve the problem of "discovering" longitude at sea. A voyage to the West Indies and back was to be the test of proposed methods which were deemed worthy. The discoverer of a system which could determine the longitude within 1° by the end of the voyage was to receive £10,000; within 40', £15,000; and within 30', £20,000. These would be handsome sums today. In the 18th century they were fortunes.

127. Evolution of the chronometer.—Many and varied were the solutions proposed for finding longitude, and as the different methods were found unsatisfactory, it became increasingly apparent that the problem was one of keeping the time of the prime meridian. But the development of a device that would keep accurate time during a long voyage seemed to most men to be beyond the realm of possibility. Astronomers were flatly opposed to the idea and felt that the problem was properly theirs. There is even some evidence to indicate that the astronomers of the Board of Longitude made unfair tests of chronometers submitted to them.

Christian Huygens (1629–95), a Dutch scientist and mathematician, made a number of contributions of great value in the field of astronomy, but his most memorable work, to the navigator, was his attempt at constructing a prefect timepiece. It was probably Galileo who first suggested using a pendulum in keeping time. Huygens realized that an error would result from the use of a simple pendulum, however, and he devised one in which the bob hung from a double cord that passed between two plates in such a way that it traced a cycloidal path.

In 1660 Huygens built his first chronometer. The instrument utilized his cycloidal pendulum, actuated by a spring. To compensate for rolling and pitching, Huygens mounted the clock in gimbals. Two years later the instrument was tested at sea, with promising results. The loss of tension in the spring as it ran down was the major weakness in this clock. Huygens compensated for this by attaching oppositely tapered cones and a chain to the spring. A 1665 sea test of the new timepiece showed greater accuracy, but still not enough for determination of longitude. In 1674 he constructed a chronometer with a special balance and long balance-spring. Although it was the best marine timepiece then known, Huygens' last clock was also unsuited for use at sea due to the error caused by temperature changes.

John Harrison was a carpenter's son, born in Yorkshire in 1693. He followed his father's trade during his youth, but soon became interested in the repair and construction of clocks. At the age of 20 he completed his first timekeeper, a pendulum-type clock with wooden wheels and pinions. Harrison's gridiron pendulum, one which maintained its length despite temperature changes, was designed about 1720, and contained alternate iron and brass rods to eliminate distortion. Until the time that metal alloys having small coefficients of temperature expansion were developed, Harrison's invention was the type pendulum used by almost all clockmakers.

By 1728 Harrison felt ready to take his pendulum, an escapement he had invented, and plans for his own marine timepiece before the Board of Longitude. In London, however, George Graham, a famous clockmaker, advised him to first construct the timekeeper. Harrison did, and in 1735 he submitted his No. 1 chronometer (fig. 127). The Board authorized a sea trial aboard HMS *Centurion*. The following year, that vessel sailed for Lisbon with Harrison's clock on board, and upon her return, the error was found to be three minutes of longitude, a performance which astounded members of the Board. But the chronometer was awkward and heavy, being enclosed in glass and weighing some 65 pounds, and the Board voted to give Harrison only £500, to be used in producing a more practical timepiece.

During the next few years he constructed two other chronometers, which were stronger and less complicated, although there is no record of their being tested by the Board of Longitude. Harrison continued to devote his life to the construction of an accurate clock to be used in determining longitude, and finally, as he approached old age, he developed his No. 4. Again he went before the Board, and again a test was arranged. In November of 1761, HMS *Deptford* sailed for Jamaica with No. 4 aboard, in the custody of Harrison's son, William. On arrival, after a passage lasting two months, the watch was only nine seconds slow (2¼ minutes of longitude). In January of 1762 it was placed aboard HMS *Merlin* for the return voyage to England. When the *Merlin* anchored in English waters in April of that year, the total error shown by the chronometer was 1 minute, 54.5 seconds. This is equal to less than a half degree of longitude, or less than the minimum error prescribed by the Board for the largest prize. Harrison applied for the full £20,000, but the Board, led by the Astronomer Royal, allowed him only a fourth of that, and insisted on another test.

William Harrison sailed again with No. 4 for Barbados in March of 1764, and throughout the almost four-months-long voyage the chronometer showed an error of

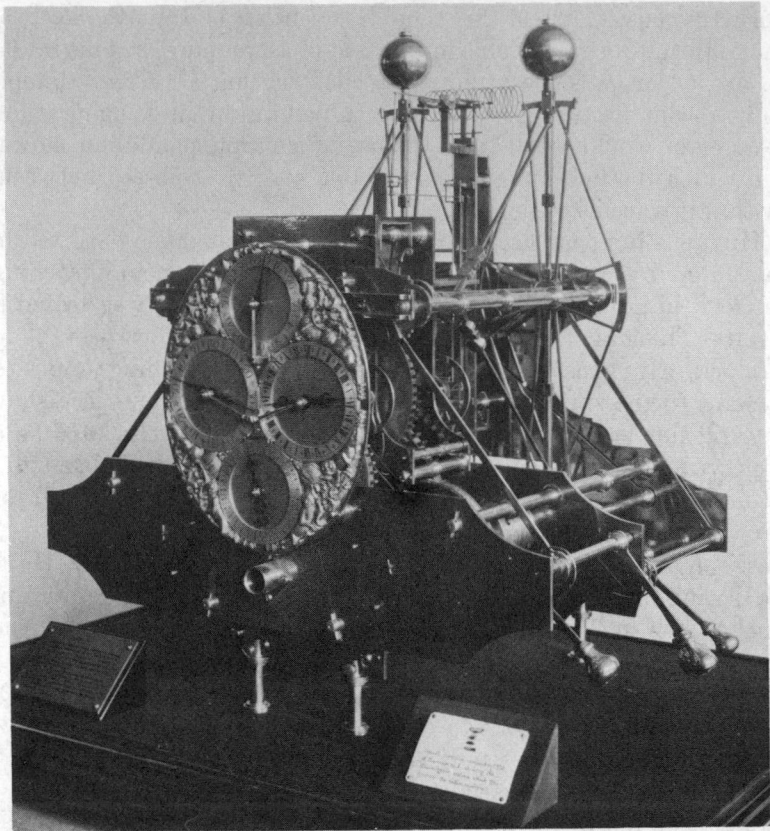

FIGURE 127.—Harrison's No. 1 chronometer. The first of four time-
keepers constructed by Harrison, this clock weighs 65 pounds.

only 54 seconds, or 13.5 minutes of longitude. The astronomers of the Board reluc-
tantly joined in a unanimous declaration that Harrison's timepiece had exceeded all
expectations, but they still would not pay him the full reward. An additional £5,000
were paid on the condition that plans be submitted for the construction of similar
chronometers. Even when this was done, the Board delayed payment further by
having one of its members construct a timepiece from the plans. Not until 1773,
Harrison's 80th year, was the rest of the reward paid, and only then because of inter-
vention by the king himself.

Pierre LeRoy, a great French clockmaker, constructed a chronometer in 1766
which has since been the basis for all such instruments. LeRoy's several inventions
made his chronometer a timepiece which has been described as a "masterpiece of
simplicity, combined with efficiency." Others to contribute to the art of watchmaking
included Ferdinand Berthoud of France and Thomas Mudge of England, each of
whom developed new escapements. The balance wheel was improved by John Arnold,
who invented the escapement acting in one direction only, substantially that used
today. Acting independently, Thomas Earnshaw invented a similar escapement. He
built the first reliable chronometer at a relatively low price. The chronometer the
Board of Longitude had made from Harrison's plans cost £450; Earnshaw's cost £45.

Timepieces designed to provide the navigator with information other than time
were popular a century or more ago. One showed the times of high and low water,

the state of the tide at any time, and the phases of the moon; another gave the equation of time and the apparent motions of the stars and planets; a third offered the position of the sun and both mean and sidereal times. But the chronometers produced by LeRoy and Earnshaw were the ones of greatest value to the navigator; they gave him a simple and reliable method of determining his longitude.

Time signals, which permit the mariner at sea to check the error in his chronometer, are essentially a 20th century development. Telegraphic time signals were inaugurated in the United States at the end of the Civil War, and enabled ships to check their chronometers in port by **time ball** signals. Previously, the Navy's "standard" chronometer had been carried from port to port to allow such comparison. In their most advanced form, time balls were dropped by telegraphic action. In 1904 the first official "wireless" transmission of time signals began from a naval station at Navesink, N. J. These were low-power signals which could be heard for a distance of about 50 miles. Five years later the range had been doubled, and, as other nations began sending time signals, the navigator was soon able to check his chronometer around the world.

The search for longitude was ended.

128. Establishment of the prime meridian.—Until the beginning of the 19th century, there was little uniformity among cartographers as to the meridian from which longitude was measured. The navigator was not particularly concerned, as he could not determine his longitude, anyway.

Ptolemy, in the second century AD, had measured longitude eastward from a reference meridian two degrees west of the Canary Islands. In 1493 Pope Alexander VI drew a line in the Atlantic west of the Azores to divide the territories of Spain and Portugal, and for many years this meridian was used by chart makers of the two countries. In 1570 the Dutch cartographer Ortelius used the easternmost of the Cape Verde Islands. John Davis, in his 1594 *The Seaman's Secrets*, said the Isle of Fez in the Canaries was used because there the variation was zero. Mariners paid little attention, however, and often reckoned their longitude from several different capes and ports during a voyage, depending upon their last reliable fix.

The meridian of London was used as early as 1676, and over the years its popularity grew as England's maritime interests increased. The system of measuring longitude both east and west through 180° may have first appeared in the middle of the 18th century. Toward the end of that century, as the Greenwich Observatory increased in prominence, English map makers began using the meridian of that observatory as a reference. The publication by the Observatory of the first British *Nautical Almanac* in 1767 further entrenched Greenwich as the prime meridian. A later and unsuccessful attempt was made in 1810 to establish Washington as the prime meridian for American navigators and cartographers. At an international conference held in Washington in 1884 the meridian of Greenwich was officially established, by the 25 nations in attendance, as the prime meridian. Today all maritime nations have designated the Greenwich meridian the prime meridian, except in a few cases where local references are used for certain harbor charts.

129. Astronomical observatories.—Thousands of years before the birth of Christ, crude observatories existed, and astronomers constructed primitive tables which were the forerunners of modern almanacs. The famous observatory at Alexandria, the first "true" observatory, was constructed in the third century BC, but the Egyptians, as well as the Babylonians and Chinese, had already studied the heavens for many centuries. The **armillary sphere** (fig. 129a) was the principal instrument used by the early astronomers. It consisted of a skeleton sphere with several movable rings which could be adjusted to indicate the orbits of the various celestial bodies. One source attributes the invention of the armillary sphere to Eratosthenes in the third century

BC; another says the Chinese knew it 2,000 years earlier, as well as the water clock and a form of astrolabe. The Alexandrian observatory was the seat of astronomical learning in the western world for several centuries, and there Hipparchus discovered the precession of the equinoxes, and Ptolemy did the work which led to his *Almagest*.

Astronomical study did not cease entirely during the Dark Ages. The Arabians erected observatories at Baghdād and Damascus in the ninth century AD, and observatories in Cairo and northwestern Persia followed. The Moors brought the astronomical knowledge of the Arabs into Spain, and the *Toledan Tables* of 1080 resulted from an awakening of scientific interest that brought about the establishment of schools of astronomy at Cordova and Toledo in the tenth century.

The great voyages of western discovery began early in the 15th century, and chief among those who recognized the need for greater precision in navigation was Prince Henry "The Navigator" of Portugal. About 1420 he had an observatory constructed at Sagres, on the southern tip of Portugal, so that more accurate information might be available to his captains. Henry's hydrographic expeditions added to the geographical knowledge of the mariner, and he was responsible for the simplification of many navigational instruments.

The Sagres observatory was rudimentary, however, and not until 1472 was the first complete observatory built in Europe. In that year Bernard Walther, a wealthy astronomer, constructed the Nuremberg Observatory, and placed Regiomontanus in charge. Regiomontanus, born Johann Müller, contributed a wealth of astronomical data of the greatest importance to the navigator.

The observatory at Cassel, built in 1561, had a revolving dome and an instrument capable of measuring altitude and azimuth at the same time. Tycho Brahe's Uraniburgum Observatory, located on the Danish island Hveen, was opened in 1576, and the results of his observations contributed greatly to the navigator's knowledge. Prior to the discovery of the telescope, the astronomer could increase the accuracy of his observations only by using larger instruments. Brahe used a quadrant with a radius of 19 feet, with which he could measure altitudes to 0.'6, an unprecedented degree of precision at that time. He also had an instrument with which he could determine altitude and azimuth simultaneously (fig. 129b). After Brahe, Kepler made use of the observatory and his predecessor's records in determining the laws which bear his name.

The **telescope,** the modern astronomer's most important tool, was invented by Hans Lippershey about 1608. Galileo heard of Lippershey's invention, and soon improved upon it. In 1610 he discovered the four great moons of Jupiter, which led to the "longitude by eclipse" method successfully used ashore for many years and experimented with at sea. With the 32-power telescope he eventually built, Galileo was able to observe clearly the motions of sun spots, by which he proved that the sun rotates on its axis. In Paris, in 1671, the French National Observatory was established.

Greenwich Royal Observatory. England had no early privately supported observatories such as those on the continent. The need for navigational advancement was ignored by Henry VIII and Elizabeth I, but in 1675 Charles II, at the urging of John Flamsteed, Jonas Moore, Le Sieur de Saint-Pierre, and Christopher Wren, established the Greenwich Royal Observatory. Charles limited construction costs to £500, and appointed Flamsteed the first Astronomer Royal, at an annual salary of £100. The equipment available in the early years of the observatory consisted of two clocks, a "sextant" of seven-foot radius, a quadrant of three-foot radius, two telescopes, and the star catalog published almost a century before by Tycho Brahe. Thirteen years passed before Flamsteed had an instrument with which he could determine his latitude accurately. In 1690 a transit instrument equipped with a telescope and vernier was invented by Romer, and he later added a vertical circle to the device. This enabled the astronomer to

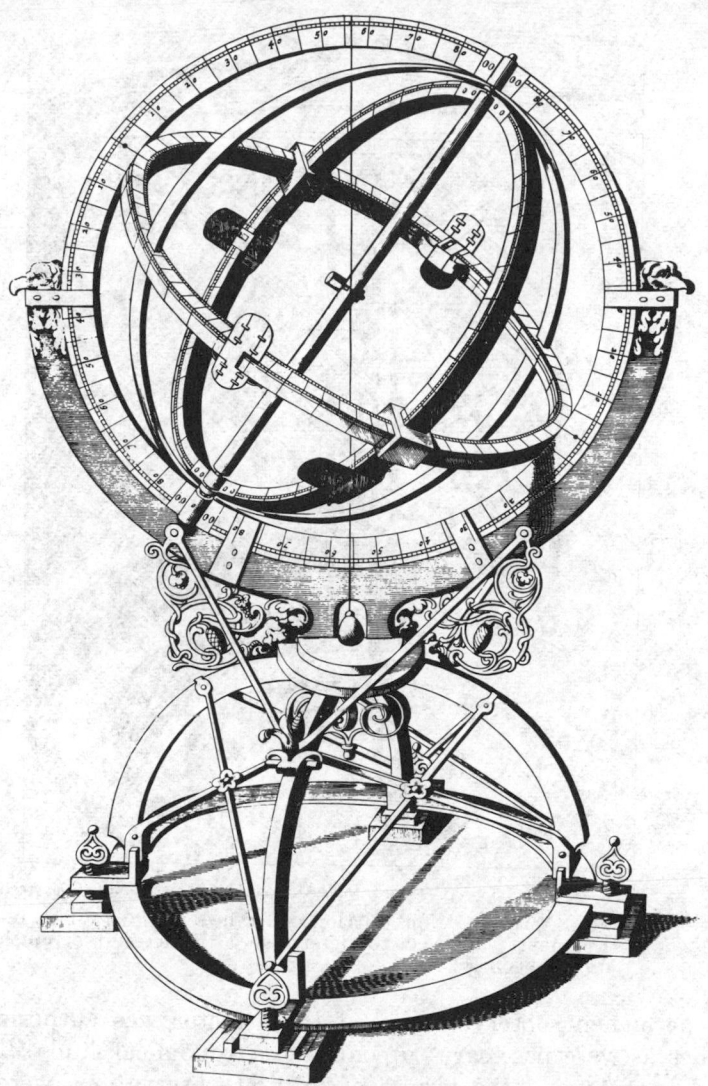

Courtesy of the Map Division of the Library of Congress.

FIGURE 129a.—An armillary sphere, one of the most important instruments
of the ancient astronomers.

determine declination and right ascension at the same time. One of these instruments was
added to the equipment at Greenwich in 1721, replacing the huge quadrant previously
used. The development and perfection of the chronometer in the next hundred years
added further to the accuracy of observations.

Other national observatories were constructed in the years that followed; at
Berlin in 1705, St. Petersburg in 1725, Palermo in 1790, Cape of Good Hope in 1820,
Parramatta in New South Wales in 1822, and Sydney in 1855.

U. S. Naval Observatory. The first observatory in the United States is said to
have been built in 1831–1832 at Chapel Hill, N.C. The Depot of Charts and Instruments, established in 1830, was the agency from which the U. S. Navy Hydrographic
Office and the Naval Observatory evolved 36 years later. Under Lieutenant Charles
Wilkes, the second Officer-in-Charge, the Depot about 1835 installed a small transit
instrument for rating chronometers. The Mallory Act of 1842 provided for the estab-

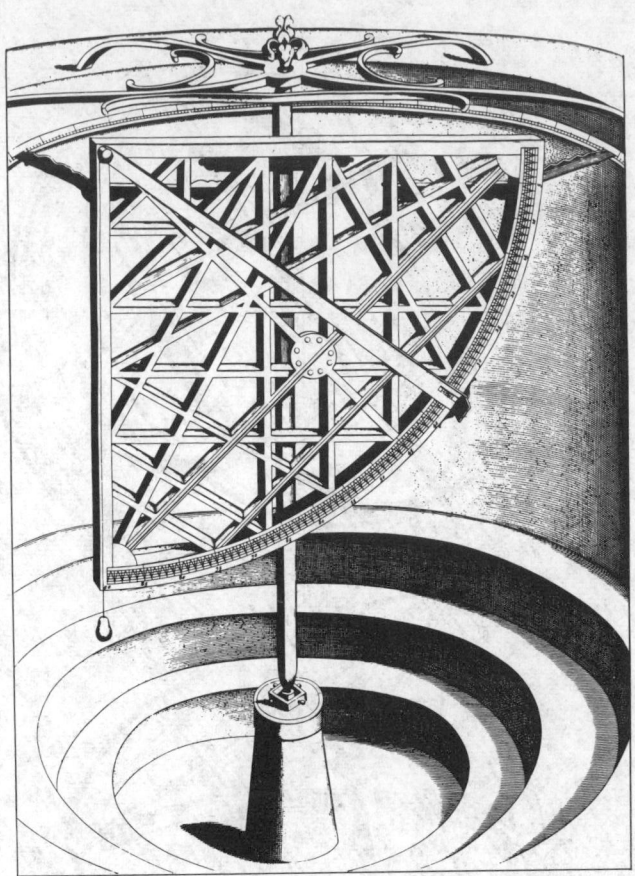

Courtesy of the Map Division of the Library of Congress.

FIGURE 129b.—A reproduction of Brahe's pelorus. This instrument was used to determine altitude and azimuth
simultaneously.

ishment of a permanent observatory, and the director was authorized to purchase
all such supplies as were necessary to continue astronomical study. The observatory
was completed in 1844 and the results of its first observations were published two
years later. Congress established the Naval Observatory as a separate agency in 1866.
In 1873 a refracting telescope with a 26-inch aperture, then the world's largest, was
installed. The observatory, located at Washington, D.C., has occupied its present
site since 1893.

The **Mount Wilson Observatory** of the Carnegie Institution of Washington was
built in 1904–05. The observatory's 100-inch reflector telescope opened wider the
view of the heavens, and enabled astronomers to study the movements of celestial
bodies with greater accuracy than ever before. But a still finer tool was needed, and
in 1934 the 200-inch reflector for the **Palomar Mountain Observatory** was cast. The
six-million-dollar observatory was built by the Rockefeller General Education Board
for the California Institute of Technology, which also operates the Mount Wilson Observatory. The 200-inch telescope makes it possible to see individual stars 20,000,000
light-years away and galaxies at least 1,600,000,000 light-years away.

As with earlier instruments, the telescope has about reached the limit of practical
size. Present efforts are being directed toward application of the electron microscope
to the telescope, to increase the range of present instruments.

130. Almanacs.—From the beginning, astronomers have undoubtedly recorded the results of their observations. Tables computed from such results have been known for centuries. The work of Hipparchus, in the second century BC, and Ptolemy, in his famous *Almagest*, are examples. Then the *Toledan Tables* appeared in AD 1080, and the *Alfonsine Tables* in 1252. Even with these later tables, however, few copies were made, for printing had not yet been invented, and those that were available were kept in the hands of astronomers. Not until the 15th century were the first almanacs printed and made available to the navigator. In Vienna, in 1457, George Purbach issued the first almanac. Fifteen years later the Nuremberg Observatory, under Regiomontanus, issued the first of the ephemerides it published until 1506. These tables gave the great maritime explorers of the age the most accurate information available. In 1474 Abraham Zacuto introduced his *Almanach Perpetuum* (fig. 130a) which contained tables of the sun's declination in the most useful form yet available to the mariner. *Tabulae Prutenicae*, the first tables to be calculated on Copernican principles, were published by Erasmus Reinhold in 1551 and gave the mariner a clearer picture of celestial movements than anything previously available. The work of Brahe and Kepler at the Uraniburgum Observatory provided the basis for the publication of the *Rudolphine Tables* in 1627.

Still, the information contained in these books was intended primarily for the use of the astronomer, and the navigator carried the various tables only that he might make use of the portions applicable to his work. The first official almanac, *Connaissance des Temps*, was issued by the French National Observatory in 1696. The French Observatory rose to its greatest prominence during the 20 years that Urbain Leverrier held the position of director.

In 1767 the British *Nautical Almanac* was first published. Nevil Maskelyne was then Astronomer Royal, and he provided the navigator with the best information available. The book contained tables of the sun's declination, and corrections to the observed altitude of Polaris. The moon's position relative to other celestial bodies was included at 12-hour intervals, and lunar distance tables gave the angular distance between the moon and certain other bodies at three-hour intervals.

For almost a hundred years the British *Nautical Almanac* was the one used by American navigators, but in 1852 the Depot of Charts and Instruments published the first *American Ephemeris and Nautical Almanac*, for the year 1855.

Early American almanacs were distinguished by their excessive detail in some cases and shortage of data of importance to the navigator in others. Declination was given to the nearest $0\overset{''}{.}1$ and the equation of time to the nearest $0\overset{s}{.}01$. Most figures were given only for noon at Greenwich, and a tedious interpolation was involved in converting the information to that at a given time at the longitude of the observer. Lunar distances were given at three-hour intervals. Few star data were listed (fig. 130b).

Since 1858 the *American Nautical Almanac* has been printed without the ephemeris section, that part of value chiefly to astronomers. Until 1908 the positions of the brighter stars were given only for January 1st, and in relation to the meridian of Washington. Beginning in that year, the apparent places of 55 major stars were given for the first of each month. In 1912, the tables of lunar distances were omitted. In 1919, sunrise and sunset tables were added.

One of the greatest inconveniences involved in using the old almanacs was the astronomical day, which began at noon of the civil day of the same date. This system was abolished in 1925, and the United States adopted the expression "civil time" to designate time by the new system. Greenwich hour angle was first published for the moon in the *Lunar Ephemeris for Aviators* for the last four months of 1929. This

Courtesy of the John Carter Brown Library, Brown University.

FIGURE 130a.—An excerpt from the Portuguese *Regimento do estrolabio e do quadrante* of about 1509, giving the sun's declination and other data based upon Zacuto's calculations for the month of March. The first day of spring, the 11th by the Julian calendar then in use, is marked by the symbol of Aries, the ram (Υ).

publication became a supplement to the *Nautical Almanac* in 1931, and for 1932 the two were merged.

The *Air Almanac*, designed by Captain P. V. H. Weems, USN (Ret.), was published for 1933, giving Greenwich hour angle for all bodies included. For 1934 this information was given in the *Nautical Almanac*, and the *Air Almanac* was discontinued. The first British air almanac was published for the last quarter of 1937, and modified for 1939 with features followed closely in the first *American Air Almanac*, for 1941. In 1950 a revised *Nautical Almanac* appeared, patterned after the popular *American Air Almanac*. Starting with the 1953 edition, the British and American air almanacs were combined in a single publication. In that year the United States reverted to the expression "mean time" in place of "civil time." In 1958, the British and American nautical almanacs were combined, and in 1960, the name was standardized.

131. The navigational triangle.—It is customary for modern navigators to reduce their celestial observations by solving the triangle whose points are the elevated pole, the celestial body, and the zenith of the observer. The sides of this triangle are the polar distance of the body (codeclination), its zenith distance (coaltitude), and the polar distance of the zenith (colatitude of the observer).

Lunar distances. A spherical triangle was first used at sea in solving lunar distance problems. Simultaneous or nearly simultaneous observations were made of the altitudes

FIXED STARS, 1855.

MEAN PLACES OF 100 PRINCIPAL FIXED STARS, FOR JANUARY 1, 1855.					
Star's Name.	Mag.	Right Ascension.	An. Variation.	Declination.	An. Variation.
		h. m. s.	s.	° ' "	"
α Andromedæ .	2	0 0 53.97	+ 3.067	+28 17 23.3	+19.93
γ Pegasi (Algenib)	3.2	0 5 46.37	3.065	+14 22 38.1	20.05
β Hydri . .	3	0 18 3.62	3.292	—78 4 23.1	20.23
α Cassiopeæ .	var.	0 32 18.36	3.356	+55 44 29.2	19.83
β Ceti . .	2	0 36 18.45	3.016	—18 47 0.1	19.86
α Urs. Min. (Polaris)	2	1 6 29.82	+18.117	+88 32 11.3	+19.23
θ' Ceti . .	3	1 16 46.57	3.000	— 8 55 58.6	18.74
α Eridani (Achernar)	1	1 32 18.42	2.238	—57 58 28.2	18.59
α Arietis . .	2	1 59 0.44	3.365	+22 46 28.4	17.29
γ Ceti . .	3.4	2 35 47.42	3.102	2 37 19.4	15.44
α Ceti . .	2.3	2 54 42.21	+ 3.129	+ 3 31 4.7	+14.40
α Persei . .	2	3 13 59.52	4.243	49 20 26.8	13.25
η Tauri . .	3	3 38 52.31	3.553	+23 39 11.0	11.54
γ' Eridani . .	3	3 51 15.91	2.796	—13 55 26.7	10.59
α Tauri (Aldebaran)	1	4 27 36.26	3.436	+16 12 49.4	7.72
α Aurigæ (Capella) .	1	5 5 59.03	+ 4.423	+45 50 41.8	+ 4.27
β Orionis (Rigel)	1	5 7 34.23	2.884	— 8 22 22.5	4.54
β Tauri . .	2	5 17 7.72	3.791	+28 28 48.3	3.55
δ Orionis . .	2	5 24 36.06	3.066	— 0 24 37.8	3.05
α Leporis . .	3	5 26 20.19	2.648	—17 55 46.0	2.94
ε Orionis . .	2	5 28 51.43	+ 3.044	— 1 17 54.6	+ 2.71
α Columbæ . .	2	5 34 24.05	2.177	—34 9 13.3	2.23
α Orionis . .	var.	5 47 19.35	3.249	+ 7 22 32.6	+ 1.11
μ Geminorum .	3	6 14 11.30	3.636	+22 34 59.9	— 1.37
α Argus (Canopus) .	1	6 20 44.13	1.330	—52 37 4.7	— 1.81
51 (Hev.) Cephei .	5	6 31 6.10	+30.650	+87 15 7.9	— 2.80
α Canis Maj. (Sirius)	1	6 38 45.60	2.646	—16 31 12.8	4.52
ε Canis Majoris .	2.1	6 52 55.69	2.360	—28 46 40.3	4.58
δ Geminorum .	3.4	7 11 27.65	3.597	+22 14 41.7	6.16
α² Geminor. (Castor)	2.1	7 25 20.49	3.841	32 12 6.2	7.37
α Can. Min. (Procyon)	1	7 31 42.52	+ 3.145	+ 5 35 35.7	— 8.79
β Geminor. (Pollux)	1.2	7 36 26.23	3.681	+28 22 19.9	8.26
15 Argus . .	3	8 1 22.22	2.557	—23 53 20.5	10.06
ε Hydræ . .	3.4	8 39 5.74	3.189	+ 6 56 52.2	12.86
ι Ursæ Majoris .	3	8 49 15.44	4.123	+48 36 26.7	13.78
ι Argus . .	2	9 13 12.52	+ 1.602	—58 40 3.3	—14.91
α Hydræ . .	2	9 20 27.65	2.951	— 8 1 56.8	15.36
θ Ursæ Majoris .	3	9 23 7.85	4.048	+52 20 6.3	16.13
ε Leonis . .	3	9 37 36.82	3.424	24 26 22.0	16.34
α Leonis (Regulus)	1.2	10 0 38.72	3.205	+12 40 26.4	17.40
η Argus . .	2	10 39 26.75	+ 2.306	—58 55 21.5	—18.74

FIGURE 130b.—Star data from the 1855 *Nautical Almanac.*
The annual corrections in declination and right ascension
can be used to obtain reasonably correct values today.

of the moon and the sun or a star near the ecliptic, and the angular distance between the moon and the other body. The zenith of the observer and the two celestial bodies formed the vertices of the triangle, whose sides were the two coaltitudes and the angular distance between the bodies. By means of a mathematical calculation the navigator "cleared" this distance of the effects of refraction and parallax applicable to each altitude, and other errors. The corrected value was then used as an argument for entering the almanac, which gave the true lunar distance from the sun and several stars at three-hour intervals.

Previously, the navigator had set his watch or checked its error and rate, which could be relied upon for short periods, with the local mean time determined by celestial observations. The local mean time of the watch, properly corrected, applied to the Greenwich mean time obtained from the lunar distance observation, gave the longitude.

The mathematics involved was tedious, and few mariners were capable of solving the triangle until Nathaniel Bowditch published his simplified method in 1802 in *The*

New American Practical Navigator. Chronometers were reliable by that time, but their high cost prevented their general use aboard the majority of naval and merchant ships. Using Bowditch's method, however, most navigators, for the first time, could determine their longitude, and so eliminate the need for parallel sailing and the lost time associated with it. The popularity of the lunar distance method is indicated by the fact that tables for its solution were carried in the *American Nautical Almanac* until the second decade of the 20th century.

The determination of latitude was considered a separate problem, usually solved by means of a meridian altitude or an observation of Polaris.

The time sight. The theory of the time sight (art. 2106) had been known to mathematicians since the dawn of spherical trigonometry, but not until the chronometer was developed could it be used by mariners.

The time sight made use of the modern navigational triangle. The codeclination, or polar distance, of the body could be determined from the almanac. The zenith distance (coaltitude) was determined by observation. If the colatitude were known, three sides of the triangle were available. From these the meridian angle was computed. The comparison of this with the Greenwich hour angle from the almanac yielded the longitude.

The time sight was mathematically sound, but the navigator was not always aware that the longitude determined was only as accurate as the latitude, and together they merely formed a point on what is known today as a line of position. If the observed body was on the prime vertical, the line of position ran north and south and a small error in latitude generally had little effect on the longitude. But when the body was close to the meridian, a small error in latitude produced a large error in longitude.

The line of position by celestial observation (art. 1703) was unknown until discovered in 1837 by 30-year-old Captain Thomas H. Sumner, a Harvard graduate and son of a United States Congressman from Massachusetts. The discovery of the "Sumner line," as it is sometimes called, was considered by Maury "the commencement of a new era in practical navigation." In Sumner's own words, the discovery took place in this manner:

"Having sailed from Charleston, S.C., 25th November, 1837, bound to Greenock, a series of heavy gales from the Westward promised a quick passage; after passing the Azores, the wind prevailed from the Southward, with thick weather; after passing Longitude 21° W., no observation was had until near the land; but soundings were had not far, as was supposed, from the edge of the Bank. The weather was now more boisterous, and very thick; and the wind still Southerly; arriving about midnight, 17th December, within 40 miles, by dead reckoning, of Tusker light; the wind hauled S.E., true, making the Irish coast a lee shore; the ship was then kept close to the wind, and several tacks made to preserve her position as nearly as possible until daylight; when nothing being in sight, she was kept on E.N.E. under short sail, with heavy gales; at about 10 A.M. an altitude of the sun was observed, and the Chronometer time noted; but, having run so far without any observation, it was plain the Latitude by dead reckoning was liable to error, and could not be entirely relied on.

"Using, however, this Latitude, in finding the Longitude by Chronometer, it was found to put the ship 15′ of Longitude, E. from her position by dead reckoning; which in Latitude 52° N. is 9 nautical miles; this seemed to agree tolerably well with the dead reckoning; but feeling doubtful of the Latitude, the observation was tried with a Latitude 10′ further N., finding this placed the ship E.N.E. 27 *nautical* miles, of the former position, it was tried again with a Latitude 20′ N. of the dead reckoning; this also placed the ship still further E.N.E., and still 27 *nautical miles* further; these three positions were then seen to lie in the direction of *Small's light*. It then at once appeared that the observed altitude must have happened at *all the three* points, and at *Small's light*, and at the ship, at the *same instant of time;* and it followed, that Small's light must bear E.N.E., if the Chronometer was right. Having been convinced of this truth, the ship was kept on her course, E.N.E., the wind being still S.E., and in less than an hour, Small's light was made bearing E.N.E. ½ E., and close aboard."

In 1843 Sumner published his book, *A New and Accurate Method of Finding a Ship's Position at Sea by Projection on Mercator's Chart,* which met with great acclaim. In it he proposed that a single time sight be solved twice, as he had done (fig. 131), using latitudes somewhat greater and somewhat less than that arrived at by dead reckoning, and joining the two positions obtained to form the line of position. It is significant that Sumner was able to introduce this revolutionary principle without seriously upsetting the method by which mariners had been navigating for years. Perhaps he realized that a better method could be derived, but almost certainly navigators would not have accepted the line of position so readily had he recommended that they abandon altogether the familiar time sight.

The Sumner method required the solution of two time sights to obtain each line of position. Many older navigators preferred not to draw the lines on their charts, but to fix their position mathematically by a method which Sumner had also devised and included in his book. This was a tedious procedure, but a popular one. Lecky recommended the method, and it was still in use early in the 20th century.

The alternative to working two time sights in the Sumner method was to determine the azimuth of the body and to draw a line perpendicular to it through the point obtained by working a single time sight. Several decades after the appearance of Sumner's book, this method was made available to navigators through the publication of accurate azimuth tables, and the system was widely used until comparatively recent times. The 1943 edition of the *American Practical Navigator* included examples of its use. The two-minute azimuth tables still found on many ships were designed principally for this purpose. The mathematical solution for azimuth was not at first a part of the time sight.

132. Modern methods of celestial navigation.—Sumner gave the mariner the line of position; St.-Hilaire the altitude difference or intercept method. Others who followed these men applied their principles to provide the navigator with rapid means for determining his position. The new navigational methods developed by these men, although based upon work done earlier, are largely a product of the 20th century.

Four hundred years ago Pedro Nunes used a globe to obtain a fix by two altitudes of the sun, and the azimuth angles. Fifty years later Robert Hues determined his latitude on a globe by using two observations and the time interval between them. G. W. Littlehales, of the U. S. Navy Hydrographic Office, advocated using a stereographic projection to obtain computed altitude and azimuth in his *Altitude, Azimuth, and Geographical Position,* published in 1906.

Various graphic and mechanical methods have also been proposed. Of these, only one, the *Star Altitude Curves* of Captain P. V. H. Weems, USN (Ret.), has had wide usage, almost entirely among aviators. During World War II, some aircraft were fitted with a device called an "astrograph," which projected star altitude curves from film upon a special plotting sheet. The curves could be moved to allow for the earth's rotation. When they were properly oriented, part of the line of position could be traced on the plotting sheet. More generally, however, the navigational triangle has been solved mathematically or by the use of tables.

Spherical trigonometry is the basis for solving every navigational triangle, and until about 80 years ago the navigator had no choice but to completely solve each triangle himself. The cosine formula is a fundamental spherical trigonometry formula

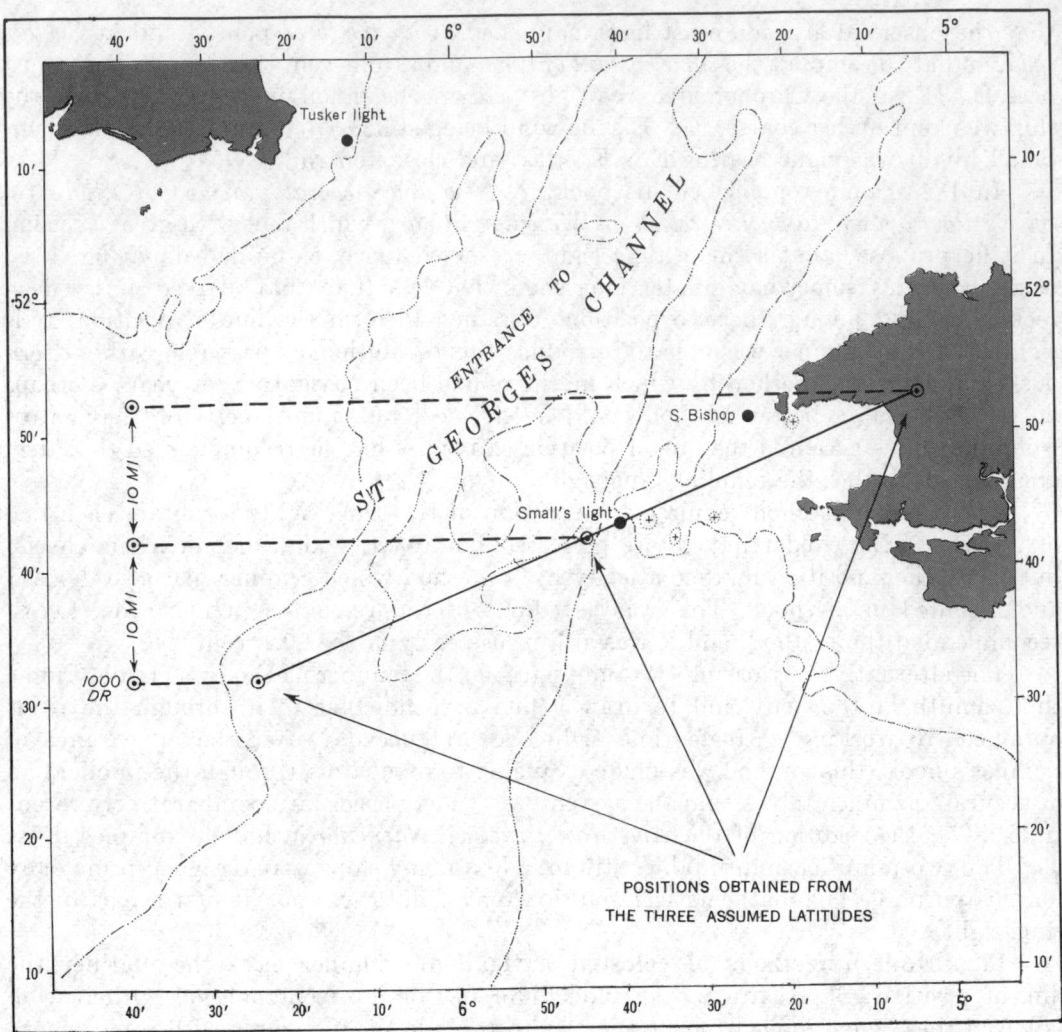

FIGURE 131.—The first celestial line of position, obtained by Captain Thomas Sumner in 1837.

by which the navigational triangle can be conveniently solved. This formula was commonly used in lunar distance solutions when they were first introduced, but, because ambiguous results are obtained when the azimuth is close to 90° or 270°, mathematicians turned to the haversine, which has the advantage of increasing numerically from 0° to 180°. The **cosine-haversine formula** (art. 2109) was used by navigators until recent years.

Toward the end of the 19th century the "short" methods began to appear. About 1875, A. C. Johnson of the British Royal Navy published his book *On Finding the Latitude and Longitude in Cloudy Weather*. No plotting was involved in Johnson's method, but he made use of the principle that a single time sight be worked, rather than the two that Sumner proposed, and the line of position drawn through the point thus determined.

In 1879 Percy L. H. Davis, of the British Nautical Almanac Office, and Captain J. E. Davis collaborated on a *Sun's True Bearing or Azimuth Table*, which enabled the navigator to lay down a line of position using a computed azimuth. *Chronometer Tables*, published by Percy Davis 20 years later, covered latitudes up to 50° and gave local hour angle values for selected altitudes to one minute of arc. In 1905 his *Requisite*

Tables were issued, enabling the mariner to "solve spherical triangles with three variable errors."

These were the first of a large number of "short" solutions which followed the work of Marcq St.-Hilaire. Generally, they consist of adaptations of the formulas of spherical trigonometry, and tables of logarithms in a convenient arrangement. It is customary for such methods to divide the navigational triangle into two right spherical triangles by dropping a perpendicular from one vertex to the side opposite. In some methods, partial solutions are made and the results tabulated. Aquino and Braga of Brazil; Ball, Comrie, Davis, and Smart of England; Bertin, Hugon, and Souillagouet of France; Fuss of Germany; Ogura and Yonemura of Japan; Blackburne of New Zealand; Pinto of Portugal; Garcia of Spain; and Ageton, Driesonstok, Gingrich, Rust, and Weems of the United States are but a few of those providing such solutions. Although "inspection tables" have largely superseded them, many of these "short" methods are still in use, kept alive largely by the compactness of their tables and the universality of their application. They are an intermediate step between the tedious earlier solutions and the fast tabulated ones, and they encouraged the navigator to work to a practical precision. The earlier custom of working to a precision not justified by the accuracy of the information used created a false sense of security in the mind of some navigators, especially those of little experience.

A book of tabulated solutions, from which an answer can be extracted by inspection, is not a new idea. Lord Kelvin, generally considered the father of modern navigational methods, expressed interest in such a method. However, solution of the many thousands of triangles involved would have made the project too costly if done by hand. Electronic computers have provided a practical means of preparing tables. In 1936 the first published volume of Pub. No. 214 was made available, and later Pub. No. 249 was provided for air navigators. British Admiralty editions of both these sets of tables have been published. Editions of Pub. No. 214 have also been published by the Instituto Hidrographico de la Marina, Cadiz, Spain, and by the Istituto Idrografico della Marina, Genova, Italy.

Electronics and Navigation

133. Electricity.—Twenty-five hundred years ago Thales of Miletus commented on basic electrical phenomena, but more than two millenniums passed before men first approached an understanding of electricity and the uses to which it could be put.

Until about 1682 the only known method of creating electricity was by rubbing glass with silk or amber with wool. Then Otto von Guericke of Magdeburg invented an "electric machine" and made possible the creation of electricity for experimental work. The Leyden jar, the electrical condenser (or machine) commonly used today, had its origin in 1745 when its principle was accidentally discovered independently by P. van Musschenbroek, of the University of Leyden, and von Kleist.

Stephen Gray, about 1729, demonstrated the difference between conductors and non-conductors, or insulators, and ten years later Hawkesbee and DuFay, working independently, each discovered the positive and negative qualities of electricity.

In the middle of the 18th century Sir William Watson of England, developer of the Leyden jar in essentially its present form, sent electricity more than two miles by wire. Whether Watson was aware of the tremendous possibilities his experiment demonstrated is not known. Twenty-five years later, about 1774, Lesage devised what is believed to have been the first method of electrical communication. He had a separate wire for each letter of the alphabet and momentarily charged the appropriate wire to send each letter.

A German scholar, Francis Aepinus (1728–1802), was the first to recognize the reciprocal relationship of electricity and magnetism. In 1837 Karl Gauss and Wilhelm Weber collaborated in inventing a reflecting galvanometer for use in telegraphic work, which was the forerunner of the galvanometer at one time employed in submarine signaling. Michael Faraday (1791–1867), in a lifetime of experimental work, contributed most of what is known today in the field of electromagnetic induction. In 1864 James Clerk Maxwell of Edinburgh made public his electromagnetic theory of light. Many consider it the greatest single advancement in man's knowledge of electricity.

134. Electronics.—In 1887 Heinrich Hertz provided the proof of Maxwell's theory by producing electromagnetic waves and showing that they could be reflected. A decade later Joseph J. Thomson discovered the electron and so provided the basis for the development of the vacuum tube by Fleming and DeForest. In 1899 R. A. Fessenden pointed out that directional reception of radio signals was possible if a single coil or frame aerial was used as the receiving antenna. In 1895 Guglielmo Marconi transmitted a "wireless" message a distance of about one mile. By 1901 he was able to communicate between stations more than 2,000 miles apart. The following year Arthur Edwin Kennelly and Oliver Heaviside introduced the theory of an ionized layer in the atmosphere and its ability to reflect radio waves. Pulse ranging had its origin in 1925 when Gregory Breit and Merle A. Tuve used this principle to measure the height of the ionosphere.

135. Application of electronics to navigation.—Perhaps the first application of electronics to navigation was the transmission of radio **time signals** (art. 1826) in 1904, thus permitting the mariner to check his chronometer at sea. Telegraphic time signals had been sent since 1865, providing a means of checking the chronometer in various ports.

Next, radio broadcasts providing navigational warnings, begun in 1907 by the U. S. Navy Hydrographic Office, helped increase the safety of navigation at sea.

By the latter part of World War I the directional properties of a loop antenna were successfully utilized in the **radio direction finder** (art. 4201). The first radiobeacon was installed in 1921.

Early 20th century experiments by Behm and Langevin led to the development, by the U. S. Navy, of the first practical **echo sounder** (art. 619) in 1922.

As early as 1904, Christian Hulsmeyer, a German engineer, obtained patents in several countries on a proposed method of utilizing the reflection of radio waves as an obstacle detector and a navigational aid to ships. Apparently, the device was never constructed. In 1922 Marconi said, "It seems to me that it should be possible to design apparatus by means of which a ship could radiate or project a divergent beam of these rays (electromagnetic waves) in any desired direction, which rays if coming across a metallic object, such as another ship, would be reflected back to a receiver screened from the local transmitter on the sending ship, and thereby immediately reveal the presence and bearing of the other ship in fog or thick weather."

In the same year of 1922 two scientists, Dr. A. Hoyt Taylor and Leo C. Young, testing a communication system at the Naval Aircraft Radio Laboratory at Anacostia, D.C., noted fluctuations in the signals when ships passed between stations on opposite sides of the Potomac River. Although the potential value of the discovery was recognized, work on its exploitation did not begin until March 1934, when Young suggested to Dr. Robert M. Page, an assistant, that this might bear further investigation. By December, Page had constructed a pulse-signal device that determined the positions of aircraft. This was the first **radar** (art. 4301). In the spring of 1935 the British, unaware of American efforts, began work in this field, and developed radar independently. In 1937 the USS *Leary* tested the first seagoing radar. In 1940 United States and British scientists combined their efforts, resulting in more rapid progress. The British revealed the principle of the multicavity magnetron developed by J. T. Randall and H. A. H. Boot at the University of Birmingham in 1939. This magnetron made microwave radar practical. Probably no scientific or industrial development in history expanded so rapidly in all phases—research, development, design, production, trials, and training—and on such a scale. In 1945, at the close of hostilities of World War II, radar was made available for commercial use.

136. Development of hyperbolic radio aids.—The work on television and cosmicray counting devices in the decade prior to World War II provided the electronic techniques needed for the practical development of radio aids to navigation based upon the time of transmission of radio signals. Because the frequency stability of oscillators used in those early days was very poor—about a million times less than is available in 1975—it was obvious that only the *difference* in transmission times of two or more signals from different places could be measured. But this quantity would become useful only if the various signals could be kept in close synchronism by some control mechanism. Using this method, with the assumption of a constant velocity of propagation, it was clear that two signals would define a family of hyperbolic lines of position having the transmitting antennas as foci, and signals from either three or four different stations would establish a position fix.

It was also obvious, since the velocity of light is about 300 meters or nearly 1000 feet per microsecond, that time-difference measurements would have to be made within a very few microseconds if positional accuracy comparable to other methods of navigation were to be achieved. This precision generally exceeded that attained in ionospheric pulse-sounding techniques available at the time, but not by a very substantial margin. The only potentially difficult problem was the irregular variations of transmission times of most radio signals. These variations could be reduced or practically eliminated only by operating at very high frequencies where line-of-sight transmission could be achieved without interference from waves reflected from the ionosphere. It was natural, therefore, that the first operational hyperbolic radio aid was arranged to use these principles in the very high frequency part of the radio spectrum.

This first aid to navigation of the new kind was the British **Gee** system, proposed by Robert J. Dippy in 1937 and brought into operation by a team headed by Dippy in early 1942. This system was designed in accordance with the principles given above. Gee operated with a pulse length of about 5 microseconds at frequencies from 30 to 80 megahertz with separations between transmitters of the order of 100 miles. For highflying aircraft the system could be used at distances up to 350 or 400 miles. Even though it was heavily jammed over western Europe, Gee was of the greatest importance to the night flying of the Bomber Command of the Royal Air Force, as it made return to bases in the British Isles relatively easy and accurate even under very poor flying conditions.

In 1940 the Microwave Committee of the U. S. National Defense Research Committee was assigned a project to develop a long-range, precision aircraft navigation system. Operational specifications for the system included an accuracy of about 1,000 feet at a range of 200 miles. To meet these requirements it was planned to use synchronized pairs of pulse-type transmitting stations separated by distances of several hundred miles. Transmitters radiating a peak power of about 1½ megawatts in the 30 to 40 megahertz band were contemplated. Except for instrumentation, the system would have been very similar to Gee.

The original system concepts used groundwave signals only. However during the course of system developments, measurements were made of the timing stability of pulsed radio waves having frequencies of from about 2 to 8 megahertz received via reflections from the ionosphere. Contrary to what was generally believed at the time, the stability of the signal reflected from the E-layer of the ionosphere was found to be quite good. Computations based on these measurements indicated that a long-range system using a combination of groundwaves and skywaves would provide a fixed accuracy of better than 5 miles at a range of 1,500 miles. The possibilities of a navigational system with this range and accuracy were so great that the original concept was abandoned and all efforts were concentrated toward this new goal. The revised project was assigned to the Radiation Laboratory of the Massachusetts Institute of Technology in the summer of 1941. Experimental transmitting stations were located at U. S. Coast Guard facilities near Montauk Point, New York, and Fenwick Island, Delaware.

In January 1942 the first skywave accuracy tests were made; a radio-frequency band was selected. Trials in moving vehicles were undertaken in June. By October 1942 a four-station chain was inaugurated for extended field trials by the U. S. Navy. About 40 receiver-indicators were installed in naval vessels during the next 4 or 5 months. Data were rapidly taken that defined the necessary skywave correction to reduce nighttime E-layer signals to the equivalent groundwave readings given on the charts.

On January 1, 1943, the administration of the new Loran program was assigned to the U. S. Navy. The U. S. Coast Guard and the Royal Canadian Navy were assigned responsibility for operation of the transmitting stations. The Loran system became fully operational in the spring of 1943 when charts for the four-station North Atlantic chain became available. The first chain comprised the two test stations at Montauk Point and Fenwick Island plus two new stations at Baccaro and Deming, Nova Scotia. The Fenwick station was first moved to Bodie Island, North Carolina, and later to Cape Hatteras, North Carolina. The Montauk Point station was moved to Nantucket Island. Installations in the Aleutians and the South Pacific soon followed.

This first version of Loran which operated on channels in the 1800 to 2000 kilohertz band was originally called **Standard Loran** to distinguish it from other experimental versions then being evaluated. Standard Loran later became known as **Loran-A.**

The most successful variation of Standard Loran during World War II was known as **Skywave Synchronized (SS) Loran.** This SS Loran operated at 2 megahertz, but, as its name implies, the stations maintained synchronization by using skywaves rather than the groundwave. This system was usable only during nighttime because of radio propagation conditions. SS Loran was first tested on the night of April 10, 1943, between Fenwick Island, Delaware, and Bonavista, Newfoundland, 1,100 miles away. Observations at the Radiation Laboratory, Cambridge, Massachusetts, revealed a line of position probable error of about 0.5 mile. This demonstrated the important fact that the errors of a few microseconds in the skywave transmission would not prevent position fixing to a useful accuracy when a sufficiency long baseline could be used. By the fall of 1943 two SS Loran pairs were in operation with transmitting stations at East Brewster, Massachusetts, Gooseberry Falls, Montana, Montauk Point, New York and Key West, Florida. Extensive evaluation flights by U. S. and Allied Forces revealed an average position-fixing error of 1 to 2 miles.

In the early spring of 1944, the four SS Loran stations in the U. S. were dismantled, and the equipment was installed in Europe and North Africa. Stations were located in Scotland, Tunisia, Algeria, and Libya. This system became operational in October 1944 and was used extensively for night bombing operations. The combination of very long baselines (approximately 950 miles) and favorable baseline orientation provided nighttime service over a large part of Europe with an accuracy of 1 to 2 miles. SS Loran systems were also operated successfully in Southeast Asia. Lack of daytime coverage was the major limitation of SS Loran.

Skywave Long Baseline Loran was tested by the U. S. Coast Guard shortly after World War II. This system was similar to SS Loran but operated at 10.585 megahertz during the day and at 2 megahertz during the night for synchronization purposes. In order to provide normal 2 megahertz service, transmitters were operated at 2 megahertz during the day as well as at night, being controlled by the synchronization on 10.585 megahertz in daytime.

Preliminary tests were conducted between Chatham, Massachusetts, and Fernandina, Florida, in May 1944. These tests were followed by additional tests between Hobe Sound, Florida, and Point Chinato, Puerto Rico, in December 1945 and January 1946. Results of these tests demonstrated the basic concepts to be sound, but the difficulty in obtaining a suitable frequency allocation ended development.

It was recognized early that a low frequency Loran system would provide improved accuracy and greatly extended navigational coverage during the day and night with fewer transmitting stations. The first experimental low frequency Loran system, operating at 180 kilohertz and called **LF Loran,** was placed in operation in 1945 with transmitting stations at Cape Cod, Massachusetts, Cape Fear, North Carolina, and Key Largo, Florida. Monitor stations for overwater observations were installed at Bermuda, the Azores, Puerto Rico, and Trinidad. Overland signals were observed at monitor stations in Ohio, Minnesota, and aboard specially equipped aircraft.

The LF Loran system was basically an extension of the techniques of 2 megahertz Loran to the lower frequency. However, the LF stations operated in synchronized triplets instead of pairs, and the individual radio-frequency cycles of the master and slave pulses were displayed on the user's receiver-indicator. The receivers were designed to provide for visual matching of pulse and cycles. A rough match was made first using the envelopes of the two pulses, as in standard Loran, and then a fine measurement was made by matching selected radio-frequency cycles within each pulse.

In 1946 all equipment installed in the experimental east coast LF Loran system was transferred to northwest Canada where it served the requirements of special Arctic maneuvers in the area. Upon completion of the maneuvers, a joint Canadian-United States project was initiated to evaluate the system. Nine fixed-monitor stations and a number of specially equipped aircraft were placed in operation and comprehensive tests were made over a period of months. These operational tests, together with results of the east coast tests, showed that the LF Loran system could operate with substantially longer baselines than was feasible with the 2 megahertz system and that a 24-hour service coverage over land would be of the order of two-thirds of that of sea water as opposed to the almost negligible overland coverage provided by 2 megahertz Loran. The accuracy achieved was equivalent to an average line of position error of 160 feet at 750 miles. Beyond 750 miles, accuracy deteriorated rapidly due to skywave interference.

However, operators found that they could not select the correct pair of cycles more than 75 percent of the time without prior knowledge of the correct pulse envelope delay. The resulting positional ambiguities were operationally unacceptable; the system was judged unsatisfactory for general purpose navigation. Work was begun in 1946 on the development of cycle-identification and phase-measuring techniques to correct these positional ambiguities. This work by government and industry culminated in the field tests of a low frequency, cycle matching Loran system called **Cyclan.** This name was derived from **Cycle** matching **Loran**.

Cyclan was the first fully automatic Loran system. The cyclic ambiguity problem was solved through the use of pulse transmissions on two frequencies 20 kilohertz apart. At first 180 and 200 kilohertz were used, followed by operation on 160 and 180 kilohertz. Slope matching on the first 50 microseconds of the pulse was followed by cycle matching within the pulse envelope for precise determination of arrival time-differences. Incorrect cycle matching at one frequency was readily apparent by an obvious mismatch at the second frequency utilized. Cyclan coverage was limited to the groundwave region and, depending on local noise, gave a range of about 1,000 to 1,500 miles. Operational tests with Cyclan were complicated by serious interference problems involving broadcast stations and aeronautical radiobeacons on adjacent frequencies. The tests did show, however, that the radio-frequency cycle identification problem could be solved. Significant progress was also made in instrumentation. It became necessary to seek another solution when the 1947 Atlantic City Radio Conference designated the 90 to 110 kilohertz band (20 kilohertz bandwidth) for the development of long range navigational systems; Cyclan required a total bandwidth of approximately 40 kilohertz.

Navaglobe was an early system investigated as a potential low frequency system operating within the 90 to 110 kilohertz band. Work on this system started in 1945. The directional characteristics were obtained from a configuration of three vertical antennas placed at the corners of an equilateral triangle. The antennas were excited alternately in pairs so that three overlapping figure-eight patterns were obtained. Measurement of the relative amplitudes of the received signals determined the navigator's bearing from the transmitting station. Cross bearings were required to establish position. To obtain range information, parallel development of a distance measuring system called **Facom** was carried out. This system also operated in the 90 to 110 kilohertz band. Coarse distance data were developed by comparing the phase of a low frequency modulating tone on a local oscillator with the phase of a similar tone on the continuous wave signal from the Facom ground station. Fine distance measurements were made on the radio frequency cycles in the carrier.

Navarho, the combined Navaglobe-Facom system, was extensively evaluated during 1957. The project was discontinued because the overall system performance was unsatisfactory.

Navarho was the first system to attempt the distance-difference measurement from observation of the change of phase of the received signal relative to a very stable, locally generated reference signal of the same frequency. To obtain useful navigational accuracy the frequencies of the transmitted signals and of the receiver's reference signals had to be synchronized with an accuracy of a part in a billion or better. One of the first commercial cesium beam frequency standards was used to control the frequency of the signals radiated from three towers at Camden, New York. Although the airborne crystal oscillators were awkward to operate, requiring close attention to attain the necessary stability, the results of numerous flights out to ranges of 2,000 miles demonstrated acceptable range and accuracy in the distance measurement; the bearing measurements at long range, however, were relatively poor.

In 1952 work began under government contract on a long range, automatic, ground-reference tactical bombing system known as **Cytac**. A pulsed, hyperbolic navigation system operating in the 90 to 110 kilohertz band was an integral part of the Cytac system. Equipment development was completed in 1955, and three transmitting stations were constructed at Forestport, New York; Carolina Beach, North Carolina; and Carrabelle, Florida. Tests with the navigational component of the system throughout 1956 showed that automotic instrumentation could solve the radio frequency cycle identification problem and could measure time-difference in a hyperbolic system with an average error of a few tenths of a microsecond. The coverage area extended from the Atlantic Ocean to the Mississippi River, and from the Great Lakes to the Gulf of Mexico. Monitor stations installed at widely separated locations collected data during a year of testing. The results of the tests demonstrated that the system was not only capable of a high degree of precision but also that the laws controlling its accuracy were sufficiently well known to permit sound predictions of accuracy prior to installation. For operational reasons, the Cytac concept was abandoned. Its use as a navigational aid was immediately apparent.

In 1957 an operational requirement for a highly accurate long range maritime radionavigation aid was developed. The stated accuracy and range requirements were considerably in excess of the capabilities of existing Loran-A equipment. On the basis of the results of the Cytac tests, it was believed that this requirement could be satisfied by implementing the Cytac concepts as well as some of the Cytac equipment. Consequently, equipment from stations at Forestport, New York, and Carrabelle, Florida, was transferred to Martha's Vineyard, Massachusetts, and Jupiter, Florida, respectively. These stations operating in conjunction with the existing station at Carolina Beach, North Carolina, were placed in operation in 1957. The U. S. Coast Guard in accordance with the U. S. Federal Laws assumed responsibility for operation of the stations in August 1958. Comprehensive tests by both ships and aircraft showed that the original concepts were sound. The new system, designated **Loran-C,** was at that time placed in operational status.

Following the closing of the Radiation Laboratory at the Massachusetts Institute of Technology, a small group of the scientists moved to the Cruft Laboratory of Harvard University, intending to apply some of the new techniques the war had brought forward to various investigations of radio wave propagation. A theoretical study was made of the stability of the phase of a modulated signal that might be expected under the conditions of interference between modes of propagation in long-distance ionospheric transmission. This study indicated that a relatively long-period modulation might be measureable with nearly the accuracy that had been achieved in the LF Loran trials. Refinement of this concept led to the proposal in 1947 of a system called **Radux.**

This new system was to be very similar to LF Loran, except that the arrival times would be measured in terms of the phase of 200 Hertz modulation instead of the time of a pulse having a duration of about 300 microseconds. Because a 200 Hertz modulation could be radiated from a good low frequency antenna at a frequency as low as 40 or 50 kilohertz, it was hoped that a 1,000-mile baseline could be used and that useful service could be provided as far as 3,000 miles. However, little was known about propagational characteristics in this frequency region.

After 2 to 3 years of study of the proposal, the U. S. Navy assigned the Navy Electronics Laboratory (NEL) the task of making the necessary tests to develop Radux as an aid to navigation. With the advice of an informal steering committee, representing several naval technical bureaus and laboratories and commercial contractors, NEL proceeded to build and install transmitters where suitable antennas could be found, initially in Hawaii and San Diego, and to procure and operate receivers. This work occupied nearly the entire decade of the 1950's. The results were very much like those of the work of the Radiation Laboratory on LF Loran; the range and accuracy were less than desired.

Going back to 1953, Dr. Louis Essen of the National Physical Laboratory (NPL) in Teddington, England, who had designed by far the best crystal oscillator then available (the Essen ring) and who was developing the first practical cesium frequency standard, visited Harvard University. He called attention to the fact that the British Post Office transmitter at Rugby had begun transmitting a standard frequency of 60 kilohertz. This transmission was made for only 1 hour per day, but it was derived from an Essen ring oscillator and the frequency was accurately monitored by both the Post Office and NPL. The group at Harvard University immediately began observing this transmission, and made the pleasing discovery that the frequency could be measured to a part in 10^{10} during the 1-hour transmission. This accuracy exceeded by a factor of 10^2 to 10^3 that available through high-frequency transmission of standard frequencies. This link from Rugby to Cambridge, Massachusetts became for a time the primary intercomparison mechanism between the British and American systems of standard time, which differed greatly in those days. The first international intercomparison of cesium-controlled clocks was made in the same way.

The Rugby (GBR) frequency was stabilized in 1954. This started an era in which the frequencies of most VLF transmissions have been stabilized so that they can be used for frequency intercomparisons and for new kinds of propagational research. It was soon found that daily measurement yielded an accuracy of about 2 parts in 10^{11} in frequency, even at distances of thousands of miles.

The Radux work was being done under conditions of military classification. These new VLF discoveries were therefore published only through their bearing on frequency comparison. In April, 1955, however, a letter report to the Office of Naval Research and verbal and other communications with the Naval Laboratories recommended extension of the navigational efforts to the very low frequencies; in particular to those below 14 kilohertz, where circuit bandwidths are so low that the frequencies are not of general interest for communication.

It had been found that the accuracy of Radux, while inadequate to resolve cyclic ambiguities at 40 kilohertz (periods of 25 microseconds), would resolve the four times larger phase ambiguities at a frequency of 10 kilohertz. A composite system was therefore proposed which could operate as Radux, probably at 40 kilohertz, while coherent bursts of 10 kilohertz carrier, radiated from the same antenna at different times, would permit measurements of much greater precision but with 8-mile ambiguities resolvable, at least in theory, by measurements of the 200 Hertz modulation of Radux. This composite system was called **Radux-Omega,** and was investigated for a few years. It rapidly became obvious that this marriage was an unfortunate one, because the useful range of the 10 kilohertz component greatly exceeded that of Radux, while the relatively short baselines of Radux spoiled the geometrical accuracy of the Omega (10 kilohertz) component at long distances, and kept the ultimate accuracy far less than it might otherwise be.

One of the primary reasons for the suggestion of such a low modulation frequency as 200 Hertz was to guard against the cyclic ambiguities that are a feature of any phase measuring system. When measuring at 200 Hertz in a hyperbolic system, any possible ambiguities would be separated by 400 miles or more and could be disregarded as an operational problem.

During the decade beginning in 1950, forces were at work that made the design of Radux less attractive than it had seemed in 1947. The most obvious change was a general increase in the desired accuracy of a navigational aid. When Loran was developed the only standard of excellence in the deep-water environment was celestial navigation, with perhaps 3 nautical miles as a typical error. Loran, especially Loran-C and a number of short-distance aids, gave navigators a desire for higher accuracy. Two other factors became important: (1) a general improvement in dead reckoning, including the inertial systems, and (2) a very great increase in the reliability of electronic devices. The first of these made the recovery of a lost cycle count much more probable, while the second made the loss of a count itself a relatively unlikely event.

The overall result of these external forces was to reduce by a large factor the fear of lane ambiguity. It therefore became possible to think of satisfying the need for accuracy beyond that of Radux by using a much more ambiguous system, with real hope that the possibility of ambiguities would not become a serious operational defect.

These considerations gradually led to the abandoning of Radux, leaving Omega to stand by itself. During the hybrid period, enough data had been taken to confirm the phenomenal range available at VLF, with timing errors that did not increase markedly with increasing distance. It was also realized that long baselines are especially effective on a spherical earth. For example, with a baseline subtending 60 degrees of arc the divergence of the hyperbolic lines of position is limited to a factor of two, instead of increasing infinitely as it does with a baseline negligibly long in comparison with the curvature of the earth. And, of course, if a pair can link the opposite ends of a diameter of the earth there is no divergence at all, and a measurement accuracy of 12 microseconds in time-difference corresponds to a positional accuracy of a nautical mile, anywhere on earth.

The Omega experiments began with the pair linking Hawaii and California, operating at first at 12.5 kilohertz, although experiments were rapidly extended throughout the 9 to 15 kilohertz region, and even higher at times. One of the earliest experiments gave an exciting and convincing demonstration of the merits of VLF cycle matching. Commander Lyle C. Read, USN, who was the Radux Program Officer at the Navy Electronics Laboratory, was traversing the baseline with an early Omega receiver on a naval vessel, essentially counting the number of wavelengths between Hawaii and California as a check on the then somewhat nebulous ideas about phase velocity at very low frequencies. Fortunately, the ship got a little ahead of schedule and Commander Read was able to induce the captain to make a standard 360° turn midway in the passage. Although only a single pair was being tracked, the double amplitude of the sinusoidal variation on the phase record gave the diameter of the ship's turning circle within 50 yards.

This and many other demonstrations of the sensitivity of the Omega technique accelerated the decision to concentrate on VLF because of its range and potential accuracy, and to accept the best that could be done to solve the ambiguity problem.

From this point, the work went rapidly for a time. A station in the Panama Canal Zone was borrowed from Naval Communications, and one in Wales from the British Post Office. With these, and San Diego and Hawaii, the network was large enough to permit monitoring from Alaska to South America and from Hawaii to Europe. Early ideas of the velocity of propagation and of its variation with time of day were refined (a process that is still being carried forward) and innumerable trials and demonstrations were conducted.

By 1966 Omega signals were being transmitted on a regular basis from stations located in New York, Hawaii, Trinidad, and Norway. But since these stations utilized existing facilities and developmental equipment, none of these stations was capable of transmitting the power required for an operational system. However, signals were being transmitted full time from a four station complex providing the vital ingredients necessary to further system development.

By 1976 seven of the eight stations of the fully implemented system were in normal operation. The developmental station at Trinidad remained in operation pending implementation of the South Pacific station.

Other developments include **Decca** (art. 4344), a short to medium range hyperbolic system, which was first used under the code name "QM" during the landings in Normandy in 1944. Another World War II development was the rotating electronic beam utilized in the German navigation system called **sonne,** later further perfected by the British under the name **Consol** (art. 4354).

In the late 1950's the Decca Navigator Company Ltd., developed an experimental VLF radionavigation system known as **Delrac,** a name derived from **Decca** long-range area coverage. In principle, this system was similar to Omega.

137. Development of satellite navigation.—The Navy Navigation Satellite System (**NAVSAT**) was developed within the Navy to fulfill a requirement established by the Chief of Naval Operations for an accurate worldwide navigation system for all naval surface vessels, aircraft, and submarines. The system was conceived and developed by the Applied Physics Laboratory of The Johns Hopkins University under Navy contract.

The underlying concept that led to development of the system dates back to 1957 and the first launch of an artificial satellite into orbit—Russia's **Sputnik I.** Dr. William H. Guier and Dr. George C. Wieffenbach at the Applied Physics Laboratory of the Johns Hopkins University were monitoring the famous "beeps" transmitted by the passing satellite. They plotted the received signals at precise intervals, and noticed that a characteristic doppler curve emerged. Since celestial bodies followed fixed orbits, they reasoned that this curve could be used to describe the satellite orbit. Later, they demonstrated that they could determine all of the orbital parameters for a passing satellite by doppler observation of a single pass from a single fixed station. The doppler shift apparent while receiving a transmission from a passing satellite was proven to be an effective measuring device for establishing the satellite orbit.

Dr. Frank T. McClure, also of the Applied Physics Laboratory concluded inversely that if the satellite-orbit were known, doppler shift measurement could be used to determine one's position on earth—thereby suggesting a new method for navigation—a more precise method than any yet known, available anywhere on earth without regard for weather conditions. His studies earned for him the first National Aeronautics and Space Administration award for important contributions to space study development.

In 1958, on the strength of Dr. McClure's studies, the Applied Physics Laboratory proposed to the Bureau of Naval Weapons that possibilities be explored for establishing a satellite doppler navigation system. The Chief of Naval Operations set forth requirements for such a system to provide accurate all-weather worldwide navigation, recommending to the Advanced Research Projects Agency that funds be made available for the purpose. Although this was only one of a number of proposals to utilize satellites for navigation, it was accepted, and, until 1960, all work on the system was performed by the Navy with that Agency's backing. An experimental satellite that failed to achieve orbit in September 1959 indicated the feasibility of tracking by doppler; the first successful launching of a prototype system satellite in April 1960 demonstrated its operational usefulness for navigation.

138. Development of inertial navigation.—The first inertial navigation system was developed in 1942 for use in the V–2 missile by the Peenmunde group under the leadership of Dr. Wernher von Braun. This system used two 2-degree-of-freedom gyroscopes and an integrating accelerometer to determine the missile velocity. By the end of World War II, the Peenmunde group had developed a stable platform with three single-degree-of-freedom gyroscopes and an integrating accelerometer.

Following World War II inertial navigation development in the United States was conducted by four groups, one sponsored by the Army and three by the Air Force. The Army group included the Peenmunde group under Dr. Wernher von Braun. This group later became the inertial group for the National Aeronautics and Space Administration. The Air Force-sponsored groups were Northrup Aircraft, Autonetics Division of North American Aviation, and the Massachusetts Institute of Technology Instrumentation Laboratory, which was later to become The Charles Stark Draper Laboratory.

At first the systems developed for the Air Force were combinations of stellar and inertial systems. As the state-of-the-art improved, purely inertial systems were designed.

During this development the principal proponent of purely inertial systems was Dr. Charles Stark Draper of the Massachusetts Institute of Technology.

The Autonetics Division of North American Aviation ingeniously adapted one of its systems for shipboard use. In 1958 this system was used to navigate the USS *Nautilus* under the ice to the North Pole.

The development of purely inertial systems for air and marine applications proceeded along parallel lines. Missile and space applications followed.

The development of the **Ship Inertial Navigation System** (SINS) began in 1951 and was completed in 1954. The initial system test on the highway provided realistic operating conditions under close monitoring and control. The results of the shipboard test of SINS in 1955 indicated that it provided what was needed for the fleet ballistic missile submarine.

Conclusion

139. Navigation has come a long way, but there is no evidence that it is nearing the end of its development. Progress will continue as long as man remains unsatisfied with the means at his disposal.

References

Collinder, Per. *A History of Marine Navigation*. Tr. Maurice Michael. New York, St. Martin's, 1955.

Hewson, J. B. *A History of the Practice of Navigation*. Glasgow, Brown, 1951.

May, W. E. *A History of Marine Navigation*. Oxfordshire, G. T. Foulis and Company Limited, 1973.

Petze, C. L., Jr. *The Evolution of Celestial Navigation*. Vol. 26, Ideal Series. New York, Motor Boating, 1948.

Pierce, J. A., and R. H. Woodward. "The Development of Long-Range Hyperbolic Navigation in the United States." Harvard University, Cambridge, Massachusetts, Office of Naval Research Technical Report No. 620, February 1971.

Stewart, J. Q., and N. L. Pierce. "The History of Navigation." *Marine and Air Navigation* (Boston, Ginn, 1944). Chap. 29.

Taylor, E. G. R. *The Mathematical Practitioners of Tudor and Stuart England*. London, Cambridge University Press, 1955.

Taylor, E. G. R. *The Haven-Finding Art*. London, Hollis and Carter, 1956.

Taylor, E. G. R. *The Geometrical Seaman*. London, Hollis and Carter, 1962.

Waters, D. W. *The Art of Navigation in England in Elizabethan and Early Stuart Times*. New Haven, Yale University Press, 1958.

Wroth, L. C. *Some American Contributions to the Art of Navigation*, 1519–1802. Providence, John Carter Brown Library, 1947.

In addition, articles pertaining to the history of navigation are frequently carried in certain periodicals, including:

The American Neptune. (Salem)

The Journal of Navigation. (London)

The Nautical Magazine. (Glasgow)

NAVIGATION: *Journal of the Institute of Navigation*.

NAVIGATION: *Revue Technique de Navigation Maritime*, Aerienne *et Spatiale*. (Paris)

United States Naval Institute Proceedings. (Annapolis)

CHAPTER II

BASIC DEFINITIONS

201. Navigation is the process of directing the movements of a craft, expeditiously and safely, from one point to another. The word *navigate* is from the Latin *navigatus*, the past participle of the verb *navigere*, which is derived from the words *navis*, meaning "ship," and *agere*, meaning "to move" or "to direct." Navigation of water craft is called **marine navigation** to distinguish it from navigation of aircraft, called **air navigation.** Navigation of a vessel on the surface is sometimes called **surface navigation** to distinguish it from **underwater navigation** of a submerged vessel. Navigation of vehicles across land or ice is called **land navigation.** The expression **lifeboat navigation** is used to refer to navigation of lifeboats or life rafts, generally involving rather crude methods. The expression **polar navigation** refers to navigation in the regions near the geographical poles of the earth, where special techniques are employed.

The principal divisions of navigation are as follows:

Dead reckoning is the determination of position by advancing a known position for courses and distances. A position so determined is called a **dead reckoning position.** It is generally accepted that the course *steered* and the speed *through the water* should be used, but the expression is also used to refer to the determination of position by use of the course and speed expected to be made good over the ground, thus making an estimated allowance for disturbing elements such as current and wind. A position so determined is better called an **estimated position.** The expression "dead reckoning" probably originated from use of the Dutchman's log a buoyant object thrown overboard, to determine the speed of the vessel relative to the object, which was assumed to be *dead* in the water. Apparently, the expression **deduced reckoning** was used when allowance was made for current and wind. It was often shortened to *ded reckoning* and the similarity of this expression to *dead reckoning* was undoubtedly the source of the confusion that is still associated with these expressions.

Piloting (or **pilotage**) is navigation involving frequent or continuous determination of position or a line of position relative to geographic points, and usually requiring need for close attention to the vessel's draft with respect to the depth of water. It is practiced in the vicinity of land, dangers, etc., and requires good judgment and almost constant attention and alertness on the part of the navigator. **Celestial navigation** is navigation using information obtained from celestial bodies.

Radionavigation is navigation using radio waves for determination of position or of a line of position. Radar navigation and satellite navigation are parts of the radionavigation division. **Radar navigation** involves the use of radio waves, usually in the centimeter band, to determine the distance and direction of an object reflecting the waves to the sender. **Satellite navigation** involves the use of artificial earth satellites for determination of position.

The term **electronic navigation** is used to refer to navigation involving the use of electronics in any way. Thus, the term includes the use of the gyrocompass for steering and the echo sounder when piloting. Because of the wide use of electronics in navigation equipment, the term electronic navigation has limited value as a term for a division of navigation.

Electronics is the science and technology relating to the emission, flow, and effects of electrons in a vacuum or through a semiconductor, and to systems using devices in which this action takes place.

202. The earth is approximately an **oblate spheroid** (a sphere flattened at the poles). Approximations of its dimensions and the amount of flattening are given in appendix X. However, for many navigational purposes, the earth is assumed to be a sphere, without intolerable error.

The **axis of rotation** or **polar axis** of the earth is the line connecting the North Pole and the South Pole.

203. Circles of the earth.—A **great circle** is the line of intersection of a sphere and a plane through the center of the sphere (fig. 203a). This is the largest circle that can be drawn on a sphere. The shortest line on the surface of a sphere between two points on that surface is part of a great circle. On the spheroidal earth the shortest line is called a **geodesic.** A great circle is a near enough approximation to a geodesic for most problems of navigation.

A **small circle** is the line of intersection of a sphere and a plane which does not pass through the center of the sphere (fig. 203a).

A **meridian** is a great circle through the geographical poles of the earth. Hence, all meridians meet at the poles, and their planes intersect each other in a line, the **polar axis** (fig. 203b). The term **meridian** is usually applied to the **upper branch** only, that half from pole to pole which passes through a given point. The other half is called the **lower branch.**

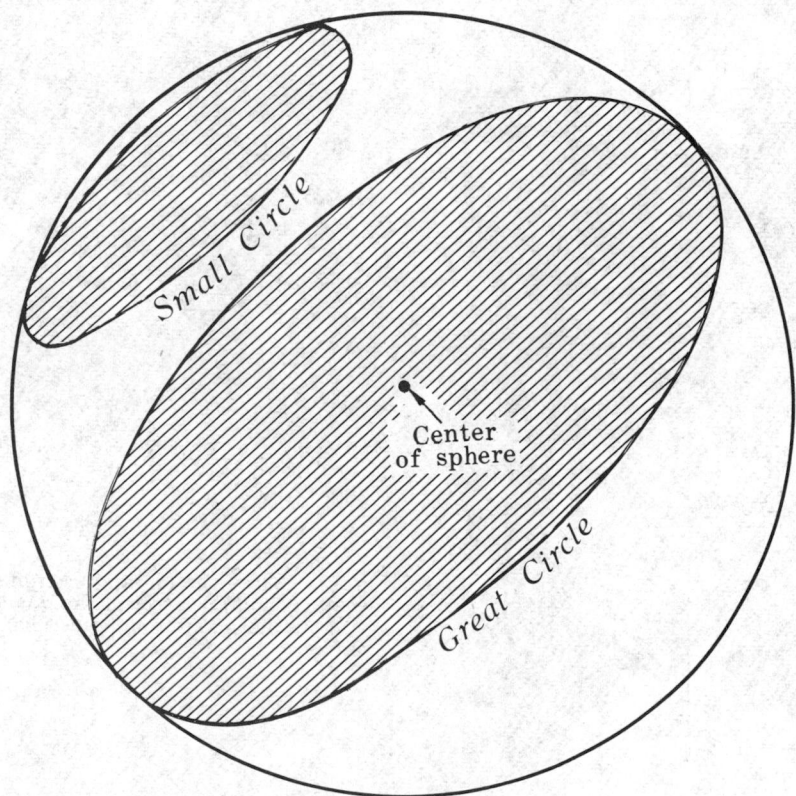

FIGURE 203a.—Great and small circles.

The **prime meridian** is that meridian used as the origin for measurement of longitude (fig. 203c). The prime meridian used almost universally is that through the original position of the British Royal Observatory at Greenwich, near London.

The **equator** is the terrestrial great circle whose plane is perpendicular to the polar axis (fig. 203d). It is midway between the poles.

A **parallel** or **parallel of latitude** is a circle on the surface of the earth, parallel to the plane of the equator (fig. 203e). It connects all points of equal latitude. The equator, a great circle, is a limiting case connecting points of 0° latitude. The poles, single points at latitude 90°, are the other limiting case. All other parallels are small circles.

204. Position on the earth.—A position on the surface of the earth (except at either of the poles) may be defined by two magnitudes called **coordinates.** Those customarily used are *latitude* and *longitude*. A position may also be expressed in relation to known geographical positions.

Latitude (L, lat.) is angular distance from the equator, measured northward or southward along a meridian from 0° at the equator to 90° at the poles (fig. 203c). It is designated *north* (N) or *south* (S) to indicate the direction of measurement.

The **difference of latitude** (*l*, D. Lat.) between two places is the angular length of arc of any meridian between their parallels (fig. 203c). It is the numerical difference of the latitudes if the places are on the same side of the equator, and the sum if they are on opposite sides. It may be designated *north* (N) or *south* (S) when appropriate.

The **middle** or **mid latitude (Lm)** between two places on the same side of the equator is half the sum of their latitudes. Mid latitude is labeled N or S to indicate whether it is north or south of the equator. The expression is occasionally used with

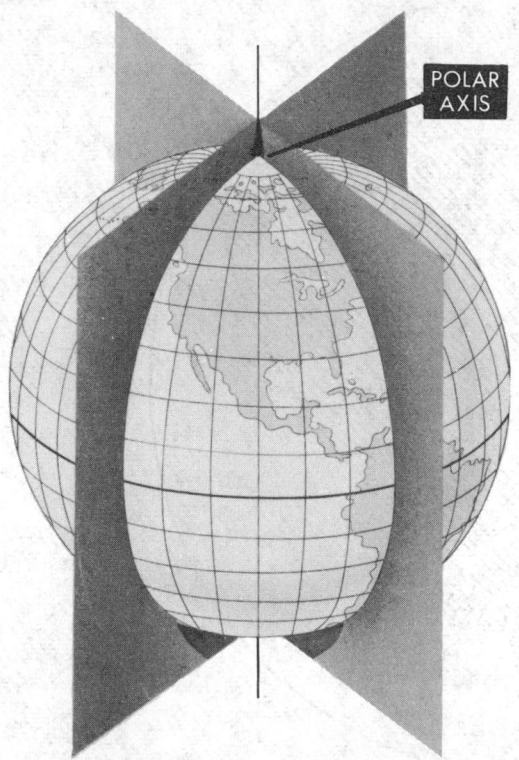

FIGURE 203b.—The planes of the meridians meet at the polar axis.

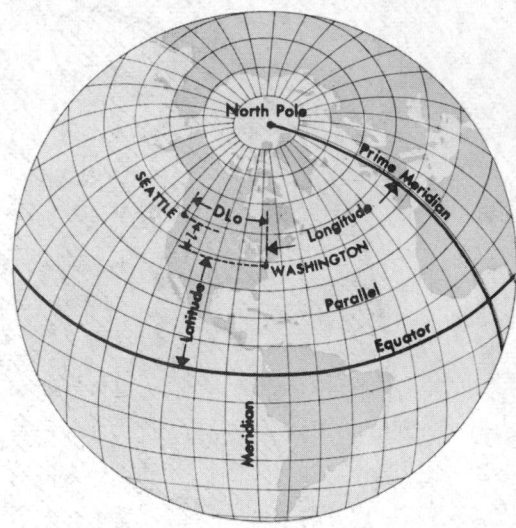

FIGURE 203c.—Circles and coordinates of the earth. All parallels except the equator are small circles; the equator and meridians are great circles.

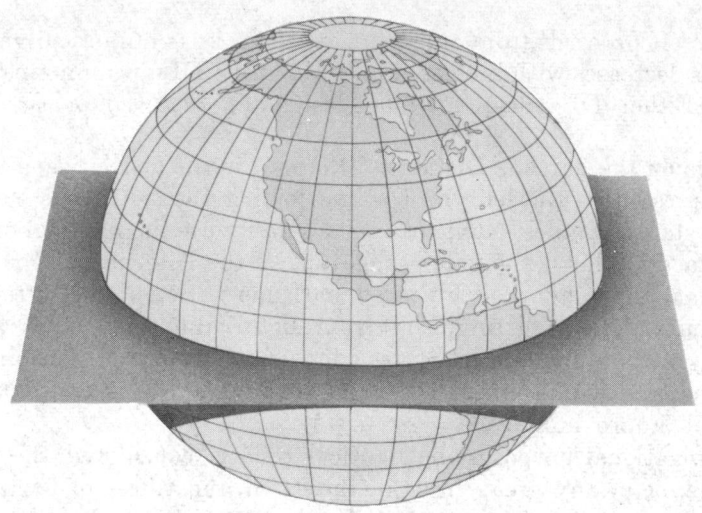

FIGURE 203d.—The equator is a great circle midway between the poles.

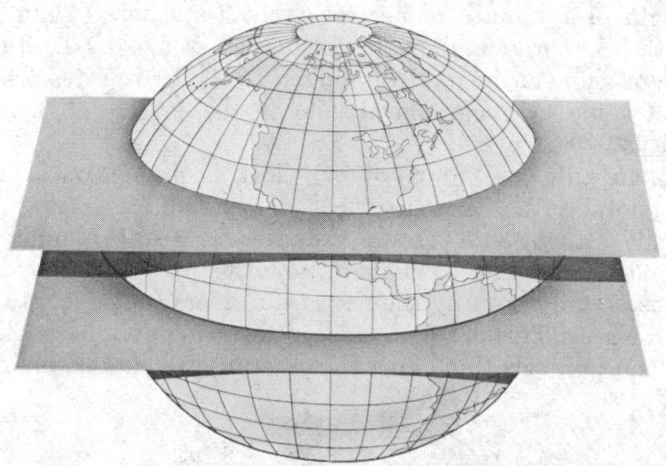

FIGURE 203e.—A parallel of latitude is parallel to the equator.

reference to two places on opposite sides of the equator, when it is equal to half the *difference* between the two latitudes, and takes the name of the place farthest from the equator. However, this usage is misleading, as it lacks the significance usually associated with the expression. When the places are on opposite sides of the equator, two mid latitudes are generally used, the average of each latitude and 0°.

Longitude (λ, long.) is the arc of a parallel or the angle at the pole between the prime meridian and the meridian of a point on the earth, measured eastward or westward from the prime meridian through 180° (fig. 203c). It is designated *east* (E) or *west* (W) to indicate the direction of measurement.

The **difference of longitude (DLo)** between two places is the shorter arc of the parallel or the smaller angle at the pole between the meridians of the two places (fig. 203c). If both places are on the same side (east or west) of Greenwich, DLo is the numerical difference of the longitudes of the two places; if on opposite sides, DLo is the numerical sum unless this exceeds 180°, when it is 360° minus the sum. The distance between two meridians at any parallel of latitude, expressed in distance units, usually nautical miles, is called **departure (p, Dep.)**. It represents distance made good to the east or west as a craft proceeds from one point to another. Its numerical value between any two meridians decreases with increased latitude, while DLo is numerically the same at any latitude. Either DLo or p may be designated *east* (E) or *west* (W) when appropriate.

205. Distance on the earth.—Distance (**D, Dist.**) is the spatial separation of two points, and is expressed as the length of a line joining them. On the surface of the earth it is usually stated in miles. Navigators customarily use the **nautical mile** (**mi., M**) of 1852 meters exactly. This is the value suggested by the International Hydrographic Bureau in 1929, and since adopted by most maritime nations. It is often called the **International Nautical Mile** to distinguish it from slightly different values used by some countries. On July 1, 1959, the United States adopted the exact relationship of 1 yard = 0.9144 meter. The length of the International Nautical Mile is consequently equal to 6,076.11549 feet (approximately).

For most navigational purposes the nautical mile is considered the length of 1 minute of latitude, or of any great circle of the earth, regardless of location. On the Clarke spheroid of 1866, used for mapping North America, the length of 1 minute of latitude varies from about 6,046 feet at the equator to approximately 6,108 feet at the poles. The length of 1 minute of a great circle of a sphere having an area equal to that of the earth, as represented by this spheroid, is 6,080.2 United States feet. This was the standard value of the nautical mile in the United States prior to adoption of the international value. A **geographical mile** is the length of 1 minute of the equator, or about 6,087 feet.

The **land** or **statute mile** (**mi., St M**) of 5,280 feet is commonly used for navigation on rivers and lakes, notably the Great Lakes of North America.

The nautical mile is about 38/33 or approximately 1.15 statute miles. A conversion table for nautical and statute miles is given in table 20.

Distance, as customarily used by the navigator, refers to the length of the **rhumb line** connecting two places. This is a line making the same oblique angle with all meridians. Meridians and parallels (including the equator) which also maintain constant

FIGURE 205.—A rhumb line or loxodrome.

true directions, may be considered special cases of the rhumb line. Any other rhumb line spirals toward the pole, forming a **loxodromic curve** or **loxodrome** (fig. 205). Distance along the great circle connecting two points is customarily designated **great-circle distance.**

206. Speed (S) is rate of motion, or distance per unit of time.

A **knot (kn.)**, the unit of speed commonly used in navigation, is a rate of one nautical mile per hour. The expression "knots per hour" refers to acceleration, not speed.

The expression **speed of advance (SOA)** is used to indicate the speed intended to be made along the track (art. 207), and **speed over ground (SOG)** the speed along the path actually followed. **Speed made good (SMG)** is the speed along the course made good.

207. Direction on the earth.—Direction is the position of one point relative to another, without reference to the distance between them. In navigation, direction is customarily expressed as the angular difference in degrees from a reference direction, usually north or the ship's head. Compass directions (east, south by west, etc.) or points (of $11\frac{1}{4}°$ or $\frac{1}{32}$ of a circle) are seldom used by modern navigators for precise directions.

Course (C, Cn) is the horizontal direction in which a vessel is steered or intended to be steered, expressed as angular distance from north, usually from 000° at north, clockwise through 360°. Strictly, the term applies to direction *through the water*, not the direction intended to be made good *over the ground*. The course is often designated as **true, magnetic, compass,** or **grid** as the reference direction is true, magnetic, compass, or grid north, respectively. **Course made good (CMG)** is the single resultant direction from the point of departure to point of arrival at any given time. Sometimes the expression **course of advance (COA)** is used to indicate the direction intended to be made good over the ground, and **course over ground (COG)** the direction of the path actually followed, usually a somewhat irregular line. **Course line** is a line extending in the direction of a course.

In making computations it is sometimes convenient to express a course as an angle from *either* north or south, through 90° or 180°. In this case it is designated **course angle (C)** and should be properly labeled to indicate the origin (prefix) and direction of measurement (suffix). Thus, C N35°E=Cn 035° (000°+35°), C N155°W =Cn 205° (360°−155°), C S47°E=Cn 133° (180°−47°). But Cn 260° may be either C N100°W or C S80°W, depending upon the conditions of the problem.

The symbol C is always used for *course angle*, and is usually used for *course* where there is little or no possibility of confusion.

Track (TR) is the intended or desired horizontal direction of travel with respect to the earth and also the path of intended travel. The terms **intended track** and **track-line** are also used to indicate the path of intended travel (fig. 207a). The path actually followed is usually a somewhat irregular line. The track consists of one or a series of course lines from the point of departure to the destination, along which it is intended the vessel will proceed. A great circle which a vessel intends to follow approximately is called a **great-circle track.**

Heading (Hdg., SH) is the direction in which a vessel is pointed, expressed as angular distance from north, usually from 000° at north, clockwise through 360°. *Heading* should not be confused with *course. Heading* is a constantly changing value as a vessel oscillates or yaws back and forth across the course due to the effects of sea, wind, and steering error.

Bearing (B, Brg.) is the direction of one terrestrial point from another, expressed as angular distance from a reference direction, usually from 000° at the reference direction, clockwise through 360°. When measured through 90° or 180° from *either* north or south, it is called **bearing angle (B),** which bears the same relationship to

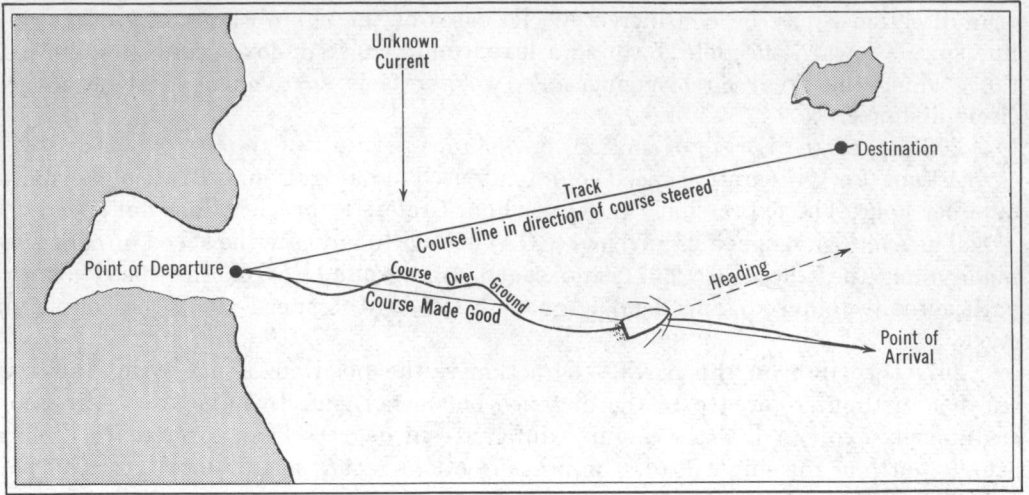

FIGURE 207a.—Course line, track, course over ground, course made good, and heading.

bearing as *course angle* does to *course*. *Bearing* and *azimuth* are sometimes used inter-changeably, but the latter is better reserved exclusively for reference to horizontal direction of a point on the celestial sphere from a point on the earth.

A relative bearing is one relative to the heading, or to the vessel itself. It is usually measured from 000° at the heading, clockwise through 360°. However, it is some-times conveniently measured right or left from 0° at the ship's head through 180°. This is particularly true when using table 7. Older methods, such as indicating the number of degrees or points from some part of the vessel (10° forward of the starboard beam, two points on the port quarter, etc.) are seldom used by modern navigators to indicate precise directions, except for bearings dead ahead or astern, or broad on the bow, beam, or quarter.

To convert a relative bearing to a bearing from north (fig. 207b), express the rela-tive bearing in terms of the 0°–360° system and add the heading:

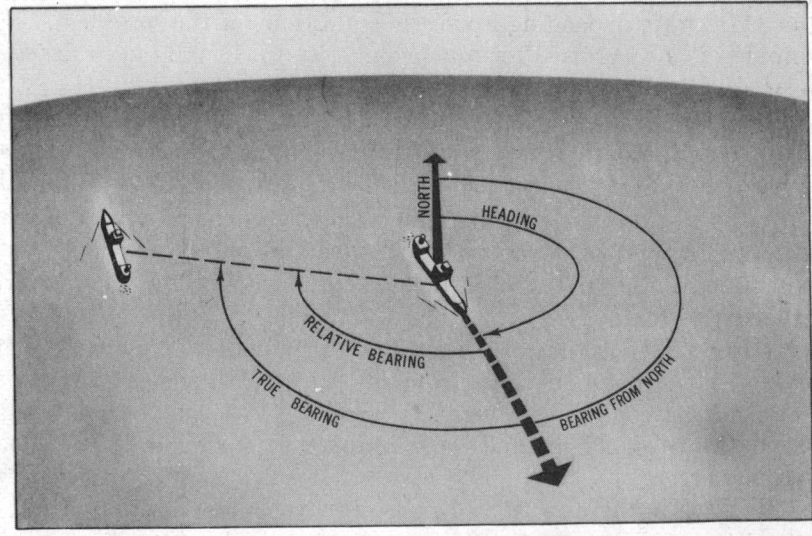

FIGURE 207b.—Relative bearing.

True Bearing=Relative Bearing+True Heading.

Thus, if another vessel bears 127° relative from a ship whose heading is 150°, the bearing from north is 127°+150°=277°. If the total exceeds 360°, subtract this amount. To convert a bearing from north to a relative bearing, subtract the heading:

Relative Bearing=True Bearing−True Heading.

Thus, a lightship which bears 241° from north bears 241°−137°=104° relative from a ship whose heading is 137°. If the heading is larger than the true bearing, add 360° to the true bearing before subtracting.

CHAPTER III

CHART PROJECTIONS

General

301. The navigator's chart.—A **map** is a conventional representation, usually on a plane surface, of all or part of the physical features of the earth's surface or any part of it. A **chart** is such a representation intended primarily for navigation. A **nautical** or **marine chart** is one intended primarily for marine navigation. It generally shows depths of water (by soundings and sometimes also by depth curves), aids to navigation, dangers, and the outline of adjacent land and such land features as are useful to the navigator.

Chart making presents the problem of representing the surface of a spheroid upon a plane surface. The surface of a sphere or spheroid is said to be **undevelopable** because no part of it can be flattened without distortion. A **map projection** or **chart projection** is a method of representing all or part of the surface of a sphere or spheroid upon a plane surface. The process is one of transferring points on the surface of the sphere or spheroid onto a plane, or onto a **developable** surface (one that can be flattened to form a plane) such as a cylinder or cone. If points on the surface of the sphere or spheroid are projected from a single point (including infinity), the projection is said to be **perspective** or **geometric**. Most map projections are not perspective.

302. Selecting a projection.—Each projection has distinctive features which make it preferable for certain uses, no one projection being best for all conditions. These distinctive features are most apparent on charts of large areas. As the area becomes smaller, the differences between various projections become less noticeable until on the largest scale chart, such as of a harbor, all projections become practically identical. Some of the desirable properties are:

1. *True shape* of physical features.
2. *Correct angular relationship*. A projection with this characteristic is said to be **conformal** or **orthomorphic**.
3. *Equal area*, or the representation of areas in their correct relative proportions.
4. *Constant scale* values for measuring distances.
5. *Great circles* represented as straight lines.
6. *Rhumb lines* represented as straight lines.

It is possible to preserve any one and sometimes more than one property in any one projection, but it is impossible to preserve all of them. For instance, a projection cannot be both conformal and equal area, nor can both great circles and rhumb lines be represented as straight lines.

303. Types of projection.—Projections are usually classified primarily as to the type of developable surface to which the spherical or spheroidal surface is transferred. They are sometimes further classified as to whether the projection (but not necessarily the charts made by it) is centered on the equator (**equatorial**), a pole (**polar**), or some point or line between (**oblique**). The name of a projection often indicates its type and sometimes, in addition, its principal feature.

The projection used most frequently by mariners is commonly called **Mercator**, after its inventor (art. 109). Classified according to type this is an **equatorial cylindri-**

64

cal orthomorphic projection, the cylinder conceived as being tangent along the equator. A similar projection based upon a cylinder tangent along a meridian is called **transverse Mercator** or **transverse cylindrical orthomorphic.** It is sometimes called **inverse Mercator** or **inverse cylindrical orthomorphic.** If the cylinder is tangent along a great circle other than the equator or a meridian, the projection is called **oblique Mercator** or **oblique cylindrical orthomorphic.**

In a **simple conic** projection points on the surface of the earth are conceived as transferred to a tangent cone. In a **Lambert conformal** projection the cone intersects the earth (a **secant** cone) at two small circles. In a **polyconic** projection, a series of tangent cones is used.

An **azimuthal** or **zenithal** projection is one in which points on the earth are transferred directly to a plane. If the origin of the projecting rays is the center of the earth, a **gnomonic** projection results; if it is the point opposite the plane's point of tangency, a **stereographic** projection; and if at infinity (the projecting lines being parallel to each other), an **orthographic** projection (fig. 303). The gnomonic, stereographic, and orthographic are perspective projections. In an **azimuthal equidistant** projection, which is not perspective, the scale of distances is constant along any radial line from the point of tangency.

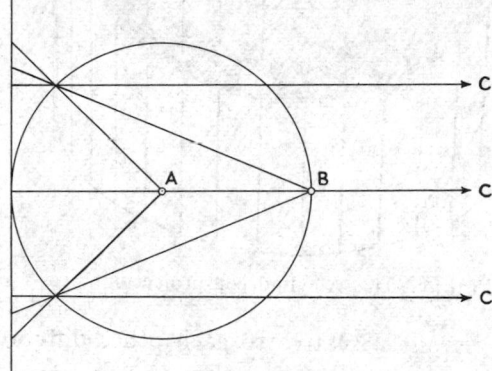

FIGURE 303.—Azimuthal projections: *A*, gnomonic; *B*, stereographic; *C* (at infinity), orthographic.

Cylindrical and plane projections can be considered special cases of conical projections with the heights infinity and zero, respectively.

A **graticule** is the network of latitude and longitude lines laid out in accordance with the principles of any projection.

Cylindrical Projections

304. Features.—If a cylinder is placed around the earth, tangent along the equator, and the planes of the meridians are extended, they intersect the cylinder in a number of vertical lines (fig. 304). These lines, all being vertical, are parallel, or everywhere equidistant from each other, unlike the terrestrial meridians, which become closer together as the latitude increases. On the earth the parallels of latitude are perpendicular to the meridians, forming circles of progressively smaller diameter as the latitude increases. On the cylinder they are shown perpendicular to the projected meridians, but because a cylinder is everywhere of the same diameter, the projected parallels are all the same size.

If the cylinder is cut along a vertical line (a meridian) and spread out flat, the meridians appear as equally spaced, vertical lines, and the parallels as horizontal

FIGURE 304.—A cylindrical projection.

lines. The spacing of the parallels relative to each other differs in the various types of cylindrical projections.

The cylinder may be tangent along some great circle other than the equator, forming an oblique or transverse cylindrical projection, on which the pattern of latitude and longitude lines appears quite different, since the line of tangency and the equator no longer coincide.

305. Mercator projection.—The only cylindrical projection widely used for navigation is the **Mercator** or **equatorial cylindrical orthomorphic,** named for its inventor Gerhard Kremer (Mercator), a Flemish geographer. It is not perspective and the parallels cannot be located by geometrical projection, the spacing being derived mathematically. The use of a tangent cylinder to explain the development of the projection has been used, but the relationship of the terrestrial latitude and longitude lines to those on the cylinder is often carried beyond justification, resulting in misleading statements and illustrations.

The distinguishing feature of the Mercator projection (fig. 305) among cylindrical projections is that both the meridians and parallels are expanded at the same ratio with increased latitude. The expansion is equal to the secant of the latitude, with a small correction for the ellipticity of the earth. Since the secant of 90° is infinity, the projection cannot include the poles. Expansion is the same in all directions and angles are correctly shown, the projection being conformal. Rhumb lines appear as straight lines, the directions of which can be measured directly on the chart. Distances can also be measured directly, to practical accuracy, but not by a single distance scale over the entire chart, unless the spread of latitude is small. The latitude scale is customarily used for measuring distances, the expansion of the scale being the same as that of distances at the same latitude. Great circles, except meridians and the equator, appear as curved lines concave to the equator (fig. 310a). Small areas appear in their correct shape but of increased size unless they are near the equator. Plotting of positions by latitude and longitude is done by means of rectangular coordinates, as on any cylindrical projection.

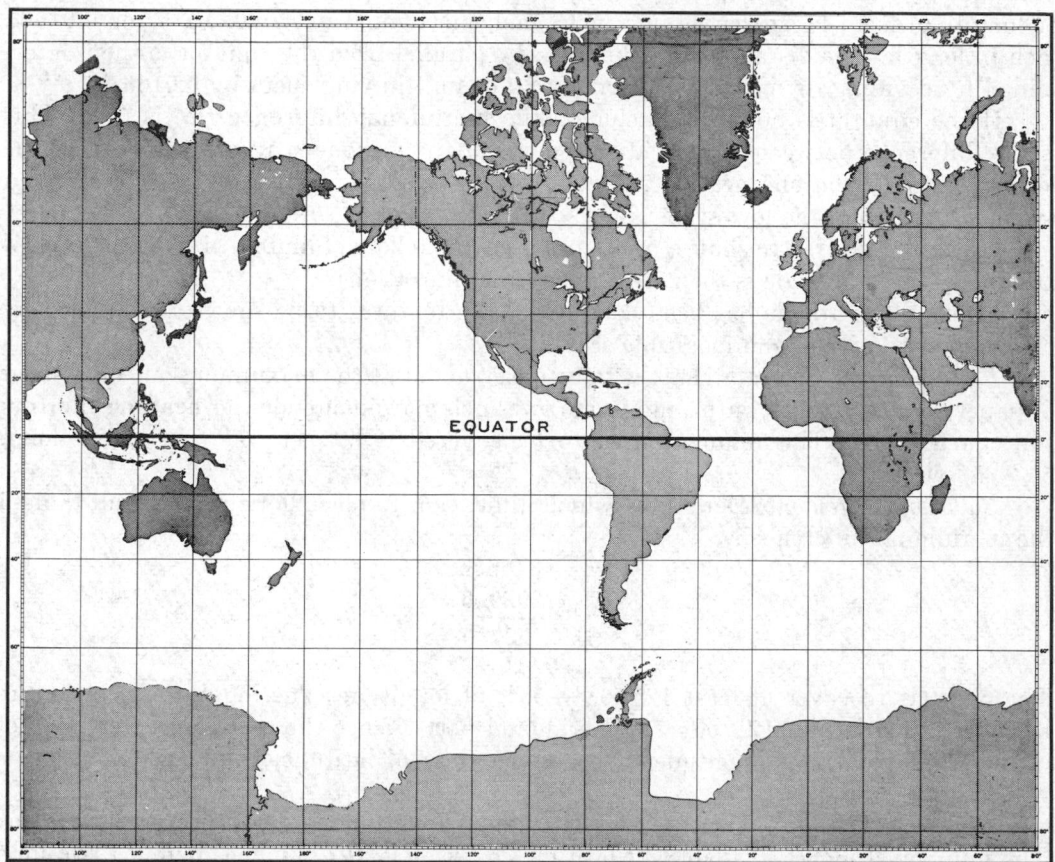

FIGURE 305.—A Mercator map of the world.

306. Meridional parts.—At the equator a degree of longitude is approximately equal in length to a degree of latitude. As the distance from the equator increases, degrees of latitude remain approximately the same (not exactly because the earth is not quite a sphere), while degrees of longitude become progressively shorter. Since degrees of longitude appear everywhere the same length in the Mercator projection, it is necessary to increase the length of the meridians if the expansion is to be equal in all directions. Thus, to maintain the correct proportions between degrees of latitude and degrees of longitude, the former are shown progressively longer as the distance from the equator increases (fig. 305).

The length of the meridian, as thus increased between the equator and any given latitude, expressed in minutes of the equator as a unit, constitutes the number of **meridional parts** (**M**) corresponding to that latitude. Meridional parts, given in table 5 for every minute of latitude from the equator to the pole, afford facilities for constructing a Mercator chart and for solving problems in Mercator sailing. These values are for the Clarke spheroid of 1866. The formula for meridional parts, given in the explanation to table 5, is derived from an integral representing the exact relationship.

307. Mercator chart construction.—To construct a Mercator chart, first select the scale and then proceed as follows:

Draw a series of vertical lines to represent the meridians, spacing them in accordance with the scale selected. If the chart is to include the equator, the distances of the various parallels from the equator are given directly in table 5, although it may be desirable to convert the tabulated values to more convenient units. Thus, if $1°(60')$ of longitude is to be shown as one inch, each meridional part will be $\frac{1}{60}$ or 0.01667 inch in length. The distance, in inches, of any parallel from the equator is then determined by dividing its meridional parts by 60 or multiplying them by 0.01667.

If the equator is not to be included, the **meridional difference** (**m**) is used. This is the difference between the meridional parts of the various latitudes and that of the lowest parallel (the one nearest the equator) to be shown. Distances so determined are measured from the lowest parallel.

It is often desired to show a minimum area on a chart of limited size, to the largest possible scale. The scale is then dictated by the limitations.

When the graticule has been completed, the features to be shown are located by means of the latitude and longitude scales.

Example.—A Mercator chart is to be constructed at the maximum scale on a sheet of paper 35×46 inches, with a minimum two-inch margin outside the **neatline** limiting the charted area. The minimum area to be covered is lat. $44°–50°$ north and long. $56°–68°$ west.

Solution.—*Step one:* Determine which dimension to place horizontal. From table 5 the meridional difference is:

$$M_{50°} \quad 3456.6$$
$$M_{44°} \quad 2929.6$$
$$m \qquad \overline{527.0}$$

The chart is to cover at least $12°$ $(68°-56°)$ of longitude. The longitude is therefore to cover a distance of $12 \times 60 = 720$ meridional parts. Since there are a greater number of meridional parts of longitude to be shown than of latitude, the long dimension is placed horizontal.

Step two: Determine whether the latitude or longitude is the limiting scale factor. The number of inches available for latitude coverage is 31 (35 inches minus a two-inch margin top and bottom). If 527 meridional parts are to be shown in 31 inches, each meridional part will be $\frac{31}{527} = 0.05882$ inch. There are $46-4=42$ inches available for longitude, and therefore the length of each meridional part will be $\frac{42}{720} = 0.05833$ inch. Thus, the longitude is the limiting scale factor, for all of the desired area could not be shown in the available space if the larger scale were to be used. Using the smaller scale, it is found that 30.74 inches (0.05833×527) will be needed to show the desired latitude coverage. The top and bottom margins can be increased slightly, or additional latitude coverage can be shown. If it is desired to include the additional coverage, the amount can be determined by dividing the available space, 31 inches, by the scale, 0.05833. This is 531.5 meridional parts, or 4.5 more than the minimum. By inspection of table 5, it is seen that the latitude can be extended either 3.3 below 44° or 2.9 above 50°. Suppose it is decided that the margin will be increased slightly and only the desired minimum coverage shown.

Step three: Determine the spacing of the meridians and parallels. Meridians 1° or 60′ apart will be placed 60×0.05833=3.50 inches apart. Next, determine each degree of latitude separately. First, compute the meridional difference between the lowest parallel and the various parallels to be shown:

$M_{45°}$	3013.5	$M_{46°}$	3098.8	$M_{47°}$	3185.7	$M_{48°}$	3274.2	$M_{49°}$	3364.5	$M_{50°}$	3456.6
$M_{44°}$	2929.6	$M_{44°}$	2929.6	$M_{44°}$	2929.6	$M_{44°}$	2929.6	$M_{44°}$	2929.6	$M_{44°}$	2929.6
m	83.9	m	169.2	m	256.1	m	344.6	m	434.9	m	527.0

Next, determine the distance of each parallel from that of L 44°N by multiplying its meridional difference by the scale, 0.05833:

$$\text{L } 44° \text{ to L } 45° = 0.05833 \times\ 83.9 =\ 4.89 \text{ in.}$$
$$\text{L } 44° \text{ to L } 46° = 0.05833 \times 169.2 =\ 9.87 \text{ in.}$$
$$\text{L } 44° \text{ to L } 47° = 0.05833 \times 256.1 = 14.94 \text{ in.}$$
$$\text{L } 44° \text{ to L } 48° = 0.05833 \times 344.6 = 20.10 \text{ in.}$$
$$\text{L } 44° \text{ to L } 49° = 0.05833 \times 434.9 = 25.37 \text{ in.}$$
$$\text{L } 44° \text{ to L } 50° = 0.05833 \times 527.0 = 30.74 \text{ in.}$$

Step four: Draw the graticule. Draw a horizontal line 2.13 inches $\left(\dfrac{35-30.74}{2}\right)$ from the bottom. This is the lower neatline. Label it "44°N." Draw the right-hand neatline two inches from the edge. Label it "56°W." Along the lower parallel measure off distances in units of 3.50 inches from λ 56°W at the right to λ 68°W at the left. Through the points thus located draw vertical lines to represent the meridians. Along any meridian measure upward from the horizontal line a series of distances as

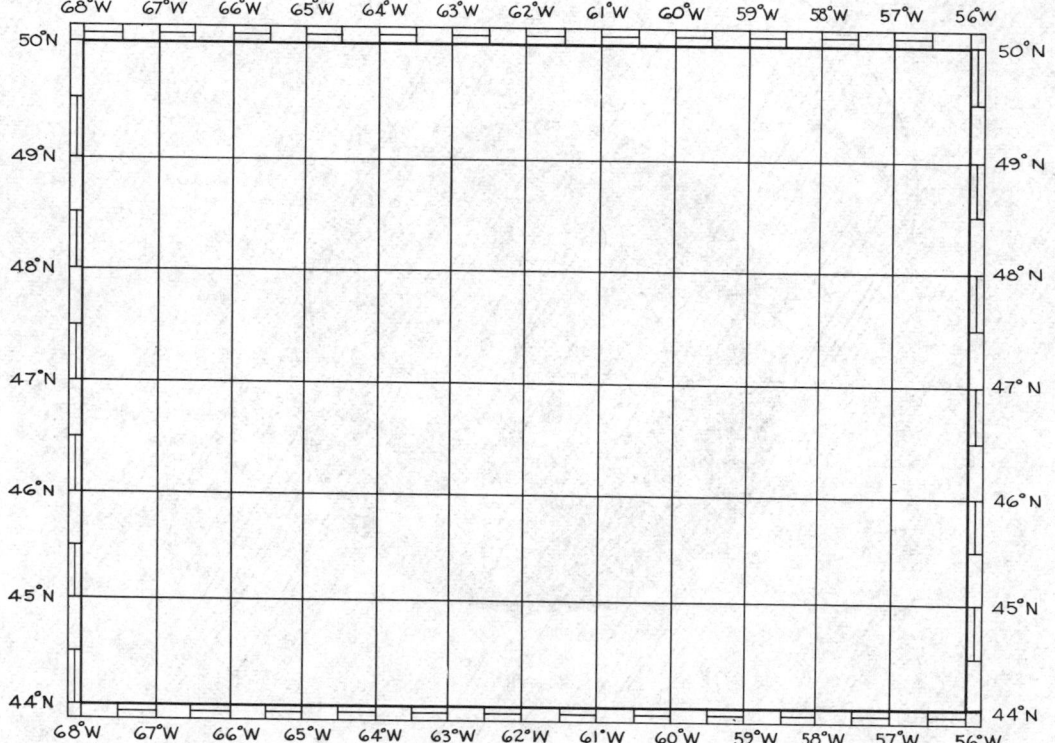

FIGURE 307.—The graticule of a Mercator chart from L 44° N to L 50° N and from λ 56° W to λ 68° W.

determined by the calculations above. Through these points draw horizontal lines to represent the parallels. Label the meridians and parallels as shown in figure 307.

Step five: Mark off the latitude and longitude scales around the neatline. The scales can be graduated in units as small as desired. Determine the longitude scale by dividing the degrees into equal parts. Establish the latitude scale by computing each subdivision of a degree in the same manner as described above for whole degrees. In low latitudes degrees of latitude can be divided into equal parts without serious loss of accuracy.

Step six: Fill in the desired detail.

In *south* latitude the distance between consecutive parallels increases toward the *south*. The top parallel is drawn first and distances measured downward from it. Latitude labels increase toward the *south* (down).

In *east* longitude the longitude labels increase toward the *east* (right).

308. Transverse and oblique Mercator projections.—If Mercator principles are used to construct a chart, but with the cylinder tangent along a meridian, a **transverse Mercator** or **transverse cylindrical orthomorphic** projection results. The word "inverse" is sometimes used in place of "transverse" with the same meaning. If the cylinder is tangent at some great circle other than the equator or a meridian (fig. 308a), the projection is called **oblique Mercator** or **oblique cylindrical orthomorphic.** These projections utilize a **fictitious graticule** similar to but offset from the familiar network of meridians and parallels (fig. 308b). The tangent great circle is the **fictitious equator.**

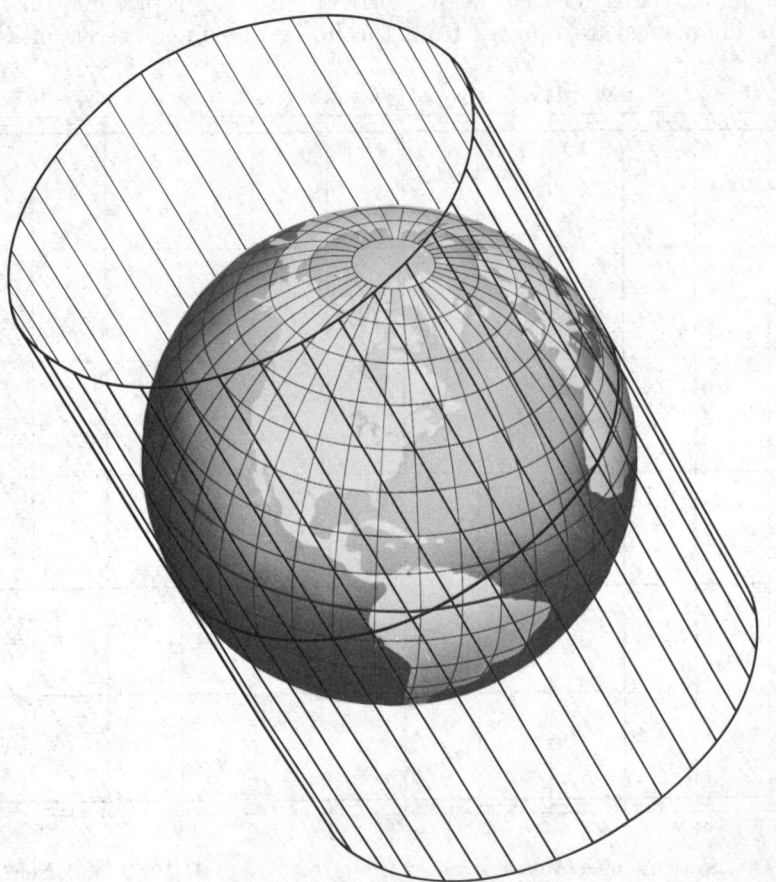

FIGURE 308a.—An oblique Mercator projection.

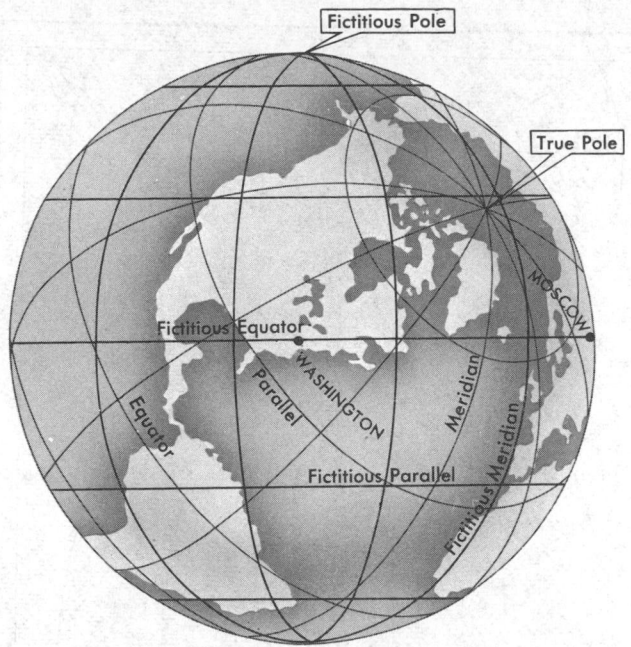

FIGURE 308b.—The fictitious graticule of an oblique Mercator projection.

Ninety degrees from it are two **fictitious poles.** A group of great circles through these poles and perpendicular to the tangent great circle are the **fictitious meridians,** while a series of circles parallel to the plane of the tangent great circle form the **fictitious parallels.**

The actual meridians and parallels appear as curved lines (figs. 309, 310b, and 322).

A straight line on the transverse or oblique Mercator projection makes the same angle with all fictitious meridians, but not with the terrestrial meridians. It is therefore a **fictitious rhumb line.** Near the tangent great circle a straight line closely approximates a great circle. It is in this area that the chart is most useful.

The **Universal Transverse Mercator (UTM) grid** is a military grid superimposed upon a transverse Mercator graticule, or the representation of these grid lines upon any graticule.

This grid system and these projections are often used for large-scale (harbor) nautical charts and military charts.

309. Transverse Mercator projection.—A special case of the Mercator projection in which the cylinder is tangent along a meridian is called a **transverse (inverse) Mercator** or **transverse (inverse) cylindrical orthomorphic** projection. Since the area of minimum distortion is near a meridian, this projection is useful for charts covering a large band of latitude and extending a relatively short distance on each side of the tangent meridian (fig. 309) or for charts of the polar regions (fig. 322). It is sometimes used for star charts showing the evening sky at various seasons of the year (figs. 2205–2208).

310. Oblique Mercator projection.—The Mercator projection in which the cylinder is tangent along a great circle other than the equator or a meridian is called an **oblique Mercator** or **oblique cylindrical orthomorphic** projection. This projection is used principally where it is desired to depict an area in the near vicinity of an oblique great circle, as, for instance, along the great-circle route between two important, widely

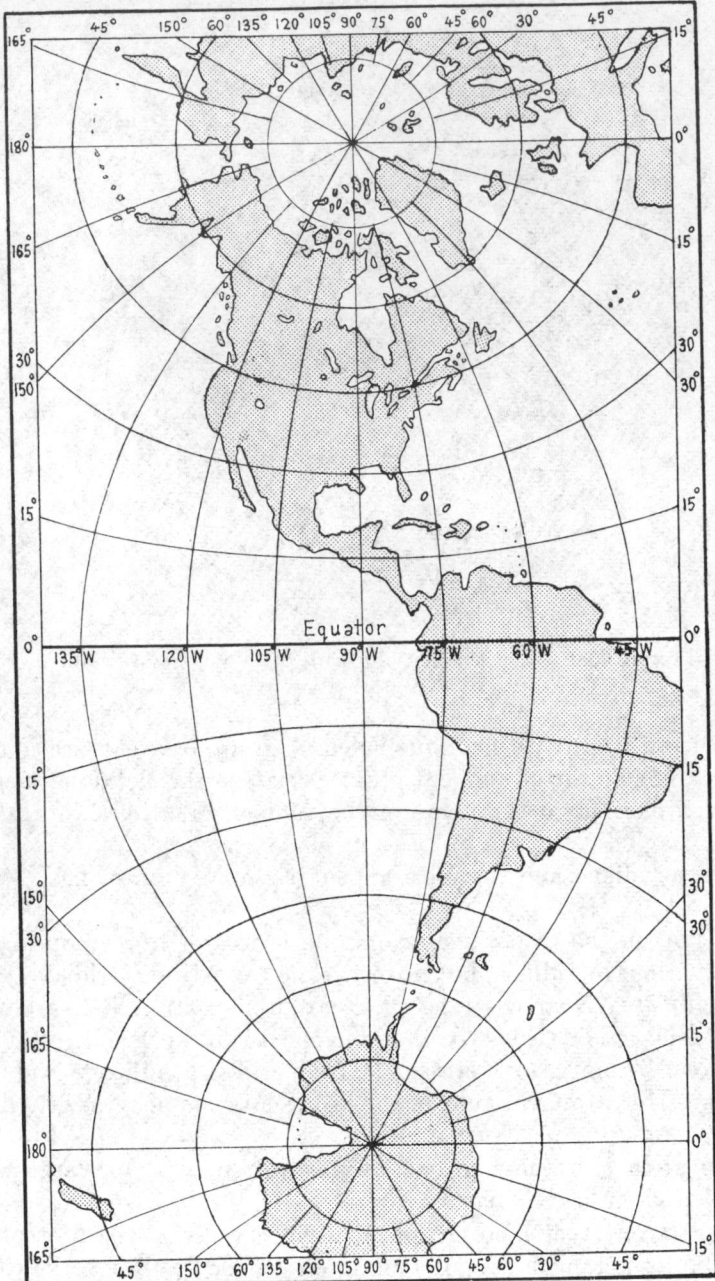

FIGURE 309.—A transverse Mercator map of the western hemisphere.

separated centers. Figure 310a is a Mercator map showing Washington and Moscow and the great circle joining them. Figure 310b is an oblique Mercator map with the great circle between these two centers as the tangent great circle or fictitious equator (as in fig. 308b). The limits of the chart of figure 310b are indicated in figure 310a. Note the large variation in scale as the latitude changes.

311. Rectangular projection.—A cylindrical projection similar to the Mercator but with uniform spacing of the parallels is called a **rectangular** projection (fig. 311). It is convenient for graphically depicting information where distortion is not important. The principal navigational use of this projection is for the star chart of the *Air Almanac*

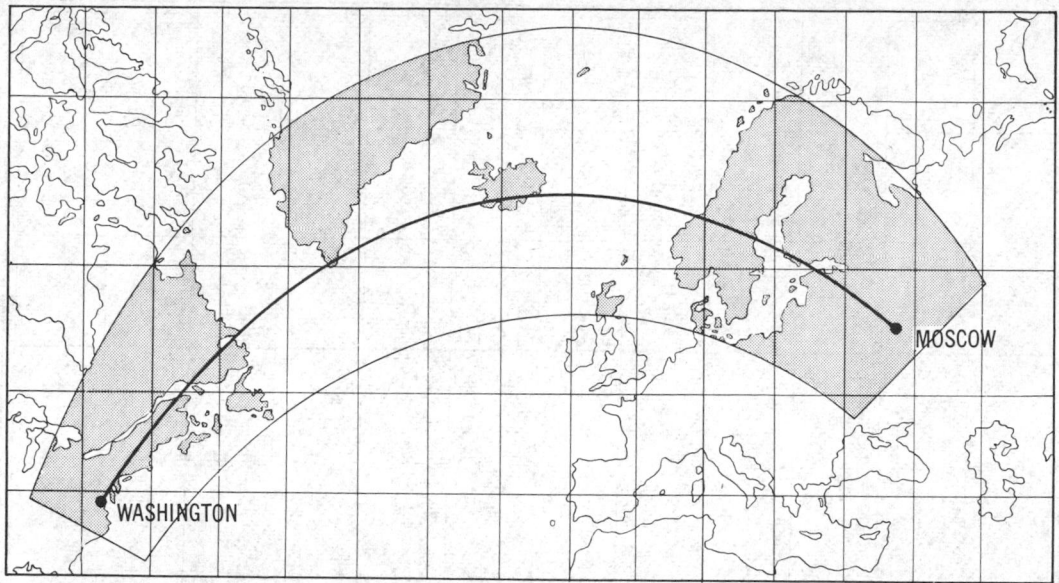

FIGURE 310a.—The great circle between Washington and Moscow as it appears on a Mercator map. See figures 308b and 310b.

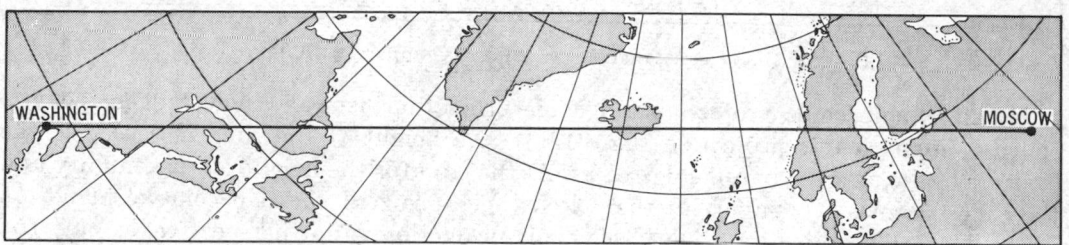

FIGURE 310b.—An oblique Mercator map based upon a cylinder tangent along the great circle through Washington and Moscow. The map includes an area 500 miles on each side of the great circle. The limits of this map are indicated on the Mercator map of figure 310a.

(art. 2204), where positions of stars are plotted by rectangular coordinates representing declination (ordinate) and sidereal hour angle (abscissa). Since the meridians are parallel, the parallels of latitude (including the equator and the poles) are all represented by lines of equal length.

Conic Projections

312. Features.—A conic projection is produced by transferring points from the surface of the earth to a cone or series of cones which are then cut along an element and spread out flat to form the chart. If the axis of the cone coincides with the axis of the earth, the usual situation, the parallels appear as arcs of circles and the meridians as either straight or curved lines converging toward the nearer pole. Excessive distortion is usually avoided by limiting the area covered to that part of the cone near the surface of the earth. A parallel along which there is no distortion is called a **standard parallel.** Neither the **transverse conic** projection, in which the axis of the cone is in the equatorial plane, nor the **oblique conic** projection, in which the axis of the cone is oblique to the plane of the equator, are ordinarily used for navigation, their chief use being for illustrative maps.

The appearance and features of conic projections are varied by using cones tangent at various parallels, using a secant (intersecting) cone, or by using a series of cones.

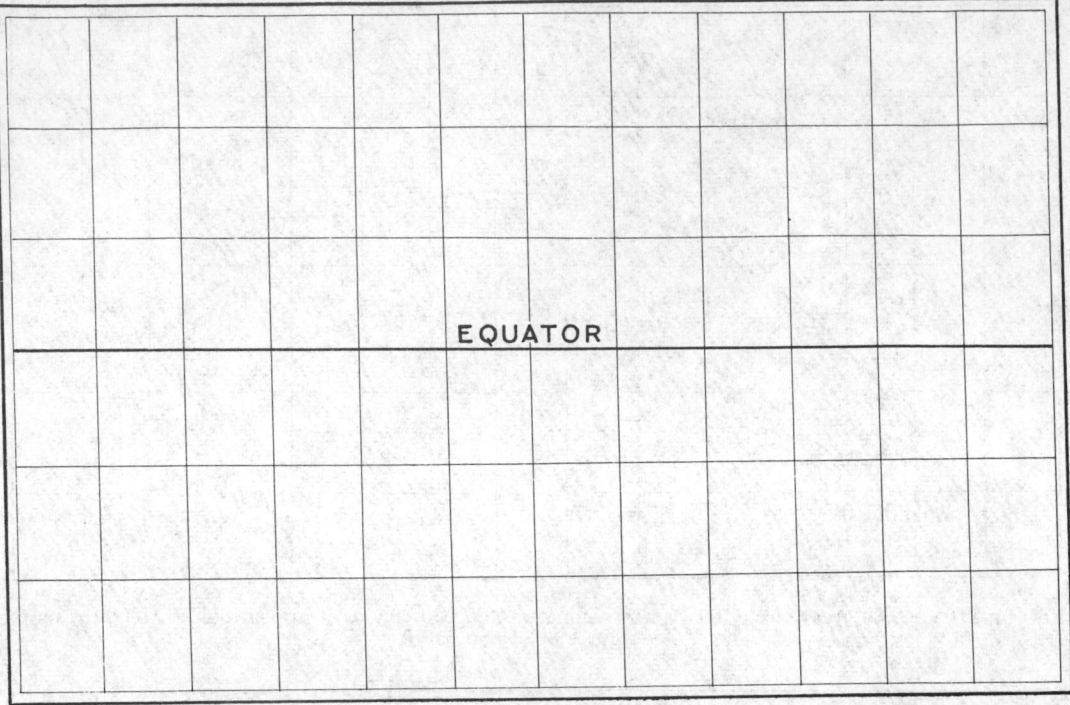

FIGURE 311.—A rectangular graticule.   Compare with figure 305.

313. Simple conic projection.—A conic projection using a single tangent cone is called a **simple conic** projection (fig. 313a). The height of the cone increases as the latitude of the tangent parallel decreases. At the equator the height reaches infinity and the cone becomes a cylinder. At the pole its height is zero and it becomes a plane. As in the Mercator projection, the simple conic projection is not perspective, as only the meridians are projected geometrically, each becoming an element of the cone. When this is spread out flat to form a map, the meridians appear as straight lines converging at the apex of the cone. The standard parallel, or that at which the cone is tangent to the earth, appears as the arc of a circle with its center at the apex of the cone, or the

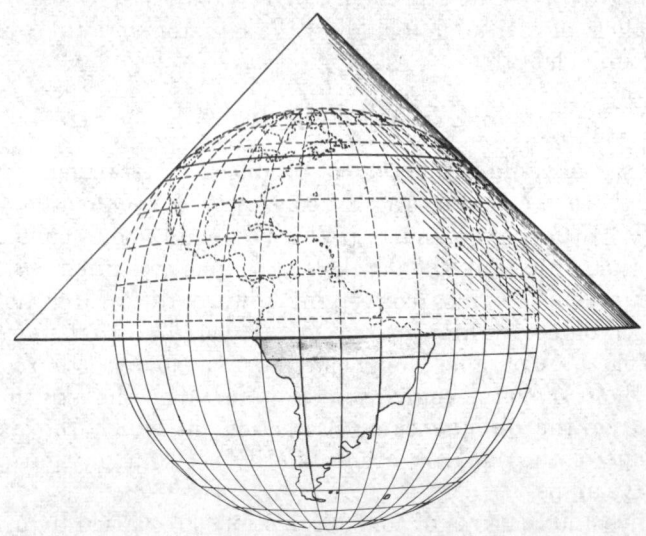

FIGURE 313a.—A simple conic projection.

common point of intersection of all the meridians. The other parallels are concentric circles, the distance along any meridian between consecutive parallels being in correct relation to the distance on the earth, and hence derived mathematically. The pole is represented by a circle (fig. 313b). The scale is correct along any meridian and along the standard parallel. All other parallels are too great in length, the error increasing with increased distance from the standard parallel. Since the scale is not the same in all directions about every point, the projection is not conformal, its principal disadvantage for navigation. Neither is it an equal-area projection.

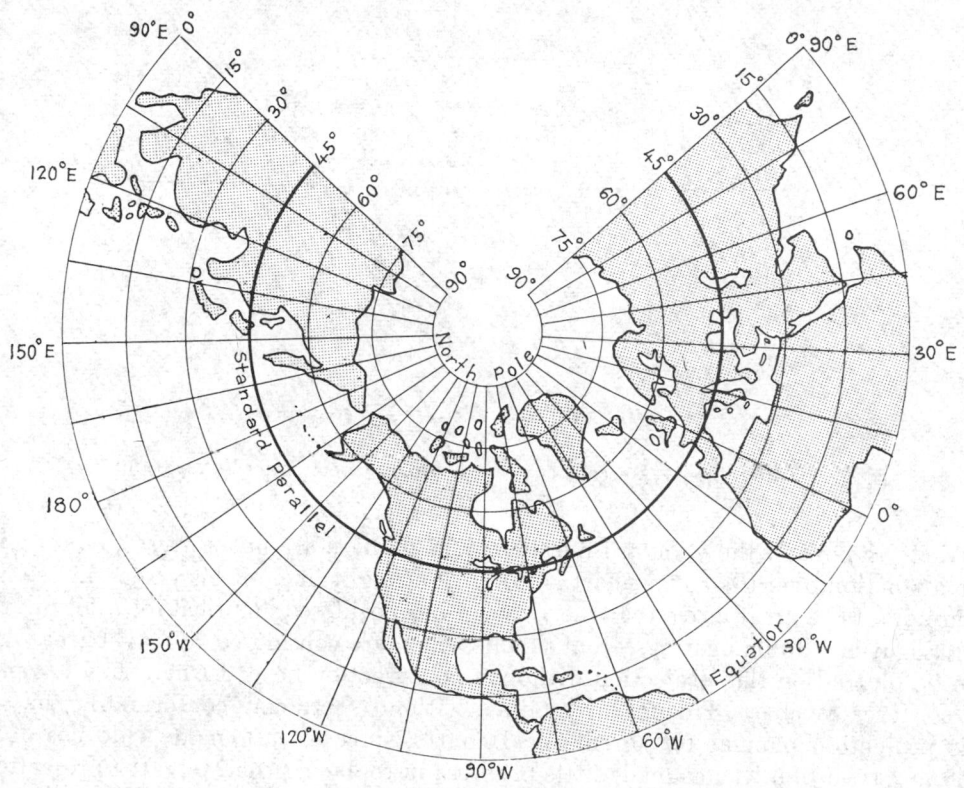

FIGURE 313b.—A simple conic map of the northern hemisphere.

Since the scale is correct along the standard parallel and varies uniformly on each side, with comparatively little distortion near the standard parallel, this projection is useful for mapping an area covering a large spread of longitude and a comparatively narrow band of latitude. It was developed by Claudius Ptolemy in the second century after Christ to map just such an area, the Mediterranean.

314. Lambert conformal projection.—The useful latitude range of the simple conic projection can be increased by using a secant cone intersecting the earth at two standard parallels (fig. 314). The area between the two standard parallels is compressed, and that beyond is expanded. Such a projection is called a **secant conic** or **conic projection with two standard parallels.**

If, in such a projection, the spacing of the parallels is altered so that the distortion is the same along them as along the meridians, the projection becomes conformal. This is known as the **Lambert conformal** projection, after its eighteenth century Alsatian inventor, Johann Heinrich Lambert. It is the most widely used conic projection for navigation, though its use is more common among aviators than mariners. Its appearance is very much the same as that of the simple conic projection. If the chart is not

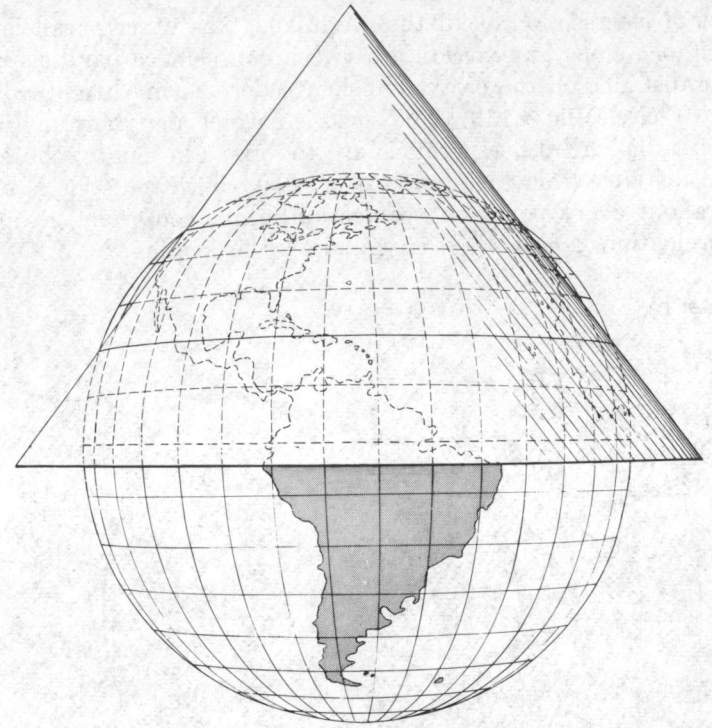

FIGURE 314.—A secant cone for a conic projection with two standard parallels.

carried far beyond the standard parallels, and if these are not a great distance apart,
the distortion over the entire chart is small. A straight line on this projection so nearly
approximates a great circle that the two can be considered identical for many purposes
of navigation. Radio bearings, from signals which are considered to travel great circles,
can be plotted on this projection without the correction needed when they are plotted
on a Mercator chart. This feature, gained without sacrificing conformality, has made
this projection popular for aeronautical charts, since aircaft make wide use of radio
aids to navigation. It has made little progress in replacing the Mercator projection for
marine navigation, except in high latitudes. In a slightly modified form this projection
has been used for polar charts (art. 321).

315. **Polyconic projection.**—The latitude limitations of the secant conic projection
can be essentially eliminated by the use of a series of cones, resulting in a **polyconic**
projection. In this projection each parallel is the base of a tangent cone (fig. 315a).
At the edges of the chart the area between parallels is expanded to eliminate gaps. The
scale is correct along any parallel and along the central meridian of the projection.
Along other meridians the scale increases with increased difference of longitude from
the central meridian. Parallels appear as nonconcentric circles and meridians as curved
lines converging toward the pole and concave to the central meridian.

The polyconic projection is widely used in atlases, particularly for areas of large
range in latitude and reasonably large range in longitude, as for a continent such as
North America (fig. 315b). However, since it is not conformal, this projection is not
customarily used in navigation, except for **boat sheets** used in hydrographic surveying.

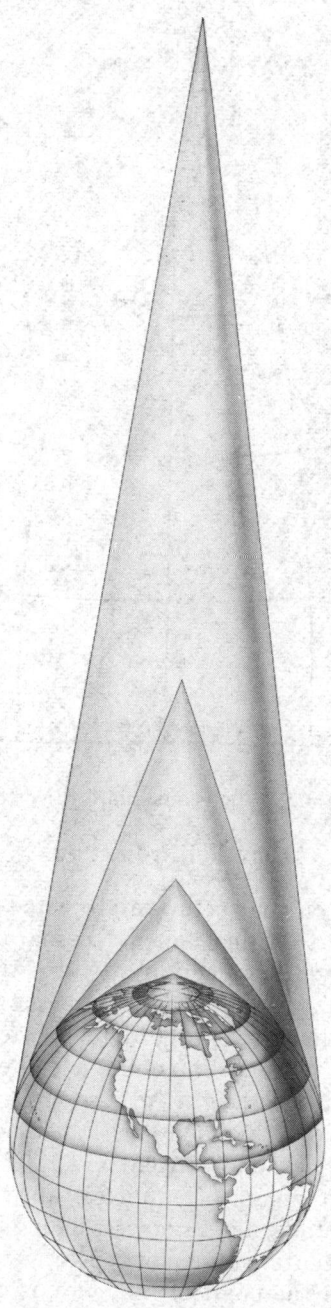

FIGURE 315a.—A polyconic projection.

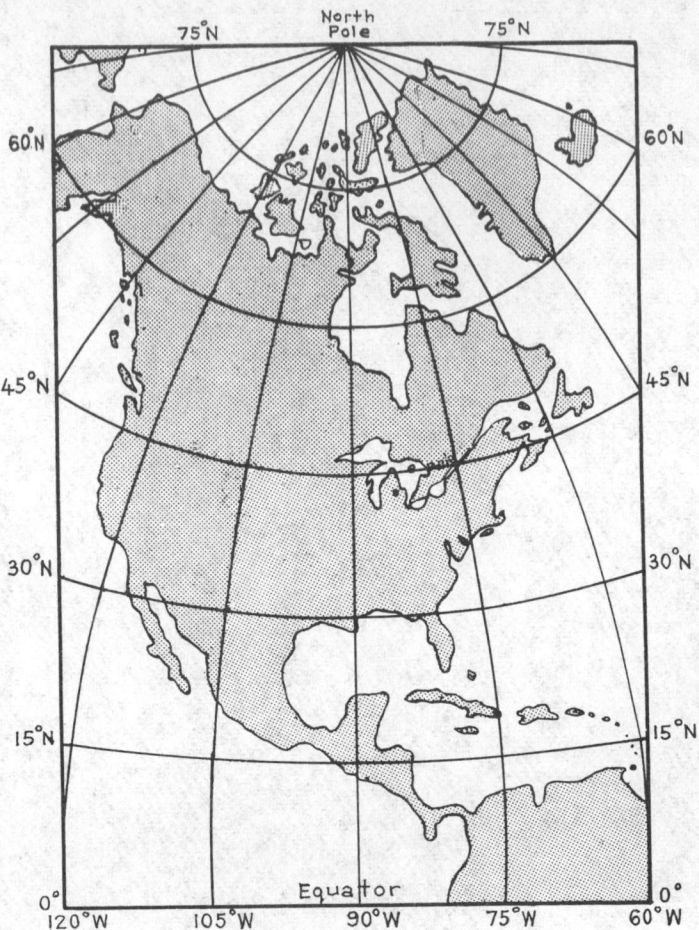

FIGURE 315b.—A polyconic map of North America.

Azimuthal Projections

316. Features.—If points on the earth are projected directly to a plane surface, a map is formed at once, without cutting and flattening, or "developing." This can be considered a special case of a conic projection in which the cone has zero height.

The simplest case of the azimuthal projection is one in which the plane is tangent at one of the poles. The meridians are straight lines intersecting at the pole, and the parallels are concentric circles with their common center at the pole. Their spacing depends upon the method of transferring points from the earth to the plane.

If the plane is tangent at some point other than a pole, straight lines through the point of tangency are great circles, and concentric circles with their common center at the point of tangency connect points of equal distance from that point. Distortion, which is zero at the point of tangency, increases along any great circle through this point. Along any circle whose center is the point of tangency, the distortion is constant. The bearing of any point from the point of tangency is correctly represented. It is for this reason that these projections are called **azimuthal.** They are also called **zenithal.** Several of the common azimuthal projections are prespective.

317. Gnomonic projection.—If a plane is tangent to the earth, and points are projected geometrically from the center of the earth, the result is a **gnomonic** projection (fig. 317a). This is probably the oldest of the projections, believed to have been devel-

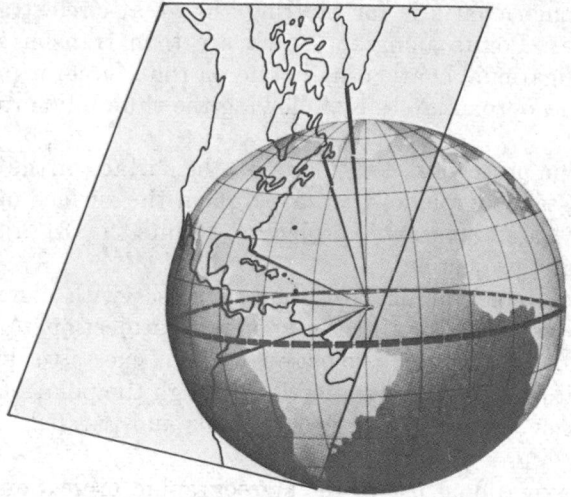

FIGURE 317a.—An oblique gnomonic projection.

oped by Thales about 600 BC. Since the projection is perspective, it can be demonstrated by placing a light at the center of a transparent terrestrial globe and holding a flat surface tangent to the sphere.

For the oblique case the meridians appear as straight lines converging toward the nearer pole. The parallels, except the equator, appear as curves (fig. 317b). As in all azimuthal projections, bearings from the point of tangency are correctly represented. The distance scale, however, changes rapidly. The projection is neither conformal nor equal area. Distortion is so great that shapes, as well as distances and areas, are very poorly represented, except near the point of tangency.

The usefulness of the projection rests upon the one feature that *any* great circle appears on the map as a straight line. This is apparent when it is realized that a great circle is the line of intersection of a sphere and a plane through the center of the sphere, this center being the origin of the projecting rays for the map. This plane intersects any other nonparallel plane, including the tangent plane, in a straight line. It is this one useful feature that gives charts made on this projection the common name **great-circle charts.**

Gnomonic charts published by the Defense Mapping Agency Hydrographic Center bear instructions for determining direction and distance on the charts. The principal

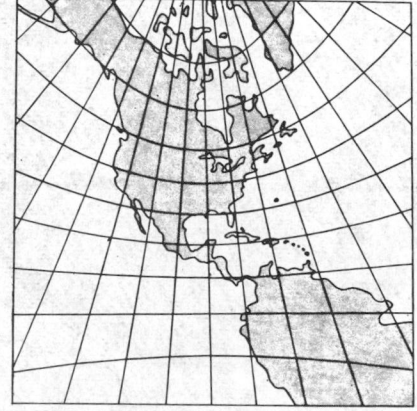

FIGURE 317b.—A gnomonic map with point of tangency at latitude 30° N, longitude 90° W.

navigational use of such charts is for plotting the great-circle track between points, for planning purposes. Points along the track are then transferred, by latitude and longitude, to the navigational chart, usually one on the Mercator projection. The great circle is then followed approximately by following the rhumb line from one point to the next (art. 813).

318. Stereographic projection.—If points on the surface of the earth are projected geometrically onto a tangent plane, from a point on the surface of the earth opposite the point of tangency, a **stereographic** projection results (fig. 318a). It is also called an **azimuthal orthomorphic** projection.

The scale of the stereographic projection increases with distance from the point of tangency, but more slowly than in the gnomonic projection. An entire hemisphere can be shown on the stereographic projection without excessive distortion (fig. 318b). As in other azimuthal projections, great circles through the point of tangency appear as straight lines. All other circles, including meridians and parallels, appear as circles or arcs of circles.

The principal navigational use of the stereographic projection is for charts of the polar regions and devices for mechanical or graphical solution of the navigational triangle (art. 2122).

319. Orthographic projection.—If terrestrial points are projected geometrically from infinity (projecting lines parallel) to a tangent plane, an **orthographic** projection results (fig. 319a). This projection is neither conformal nor equal area and has no advantages as a map projection. Its principal navigational use is in the field of navigational astronomy, where it is useful for illustrating or graphically solving the navigational triangle and for illustrating celestial coordinates. If the plane is tangent at a point on the equator, the usual case, the parallels (including the equator) appear as straight lines and the meridians as ellipses, except that the meridian through the point of tangency appears as a straight line and the one 90° away as a circle (fig. 319b).

320. Azimuthal equidistant projection.—An azimuthal projection in which the distance scale along any great circle through the point of tangency is constant is called an **azimuthal equidistant** projection. If a pole is the point of tangency, the meridians appear as straight radial lines and the parallels as concentric circles, equally spaced.

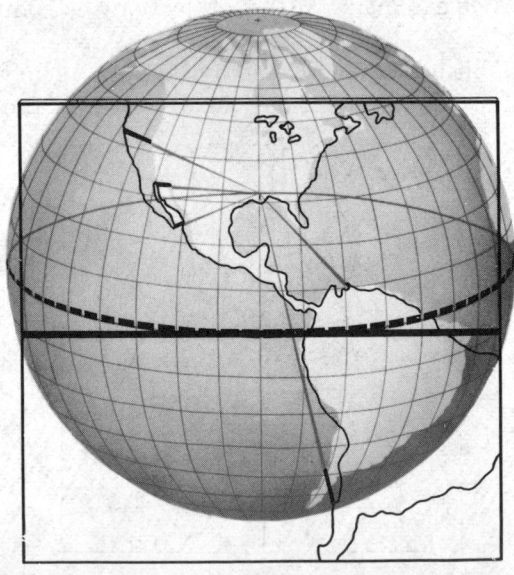

FIGURE 318a.—An equatorial stereographic projection.

FIGURE 318b.—A stereographic map of the western hemisphere.

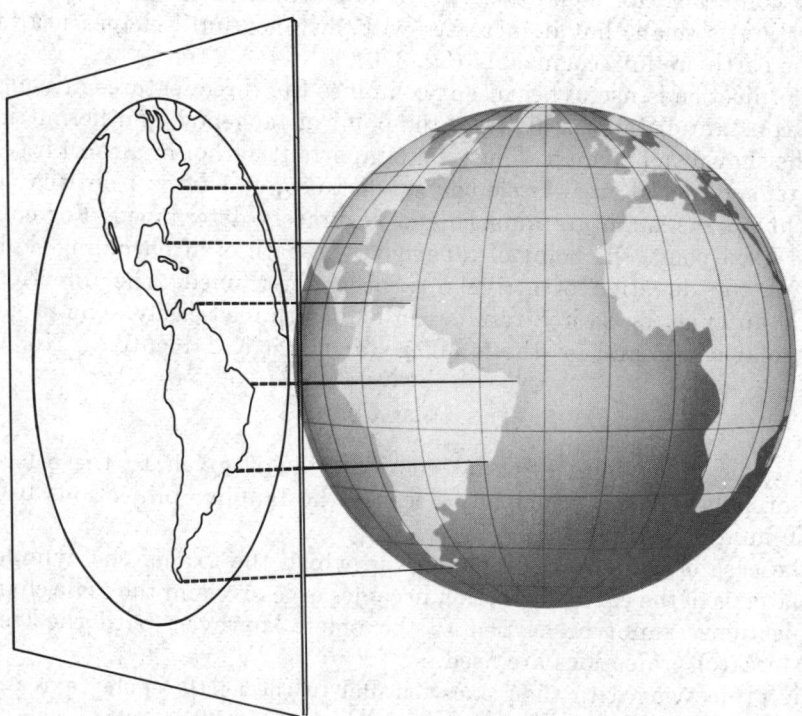

FIGURE 319a.—An equatorial orthographic projection.

FIGURE 319b.—An orthographic map of the western hemisphere.

If the plane is tangent at some point other than a pole, the concentric circles represent distance from the point of tangency. In this case meridians and parallels appear as curves. The projection can be used to portray the entire earth, the point 180° from the point of tangency appearing as the largest of the concentric circles. The projection is neither conformal nor equal area, nor is it perspective. Near the point of tangency the distortion is small, but it increases with distance until shapes near the opposite side of the earth are unrecognizable (fig. 320).

The projection is useful because it combines the three features of being azimuthal, having a constant distance scale from the point of tangency, and permitting the entire earth to be shown on one map. Thus, if an important harbor or airport is selected as the point of tangency, the great-circle course, distance, and track from that point to any other point on the earth are quickly and accurately determined. For communication work at a fixed point, the point of tangency, the path of an incoming signal is at once apparent if the direction of arrival has been determined. The direction to train a directional antenna for desired results can be determined easily. The projection is also used for polar charts and for the familiar star finder and identifier, No. 2102-D (art. 2210).

Polar Charts

321. Polar projections.—Special consideration is given to the selection of projections for polar charts, principally because the familiar projections become special cases with unique features.

In the case of cylindrical projections in which the axis of the cylinder is parallel to the polar axis of the earth, distortion becomes excessive and the scale changes rapidly. Such projections cannot be carried to the poles. However, both the transverse and oblique Mercator projections are used.

Conic projections with their axes parallel to the earth's polar axis are limited in their usefulness for polar charts because parallels of latitude extending through a full 360° of longitude appear as arcs of circles rather than full circles. This is because a

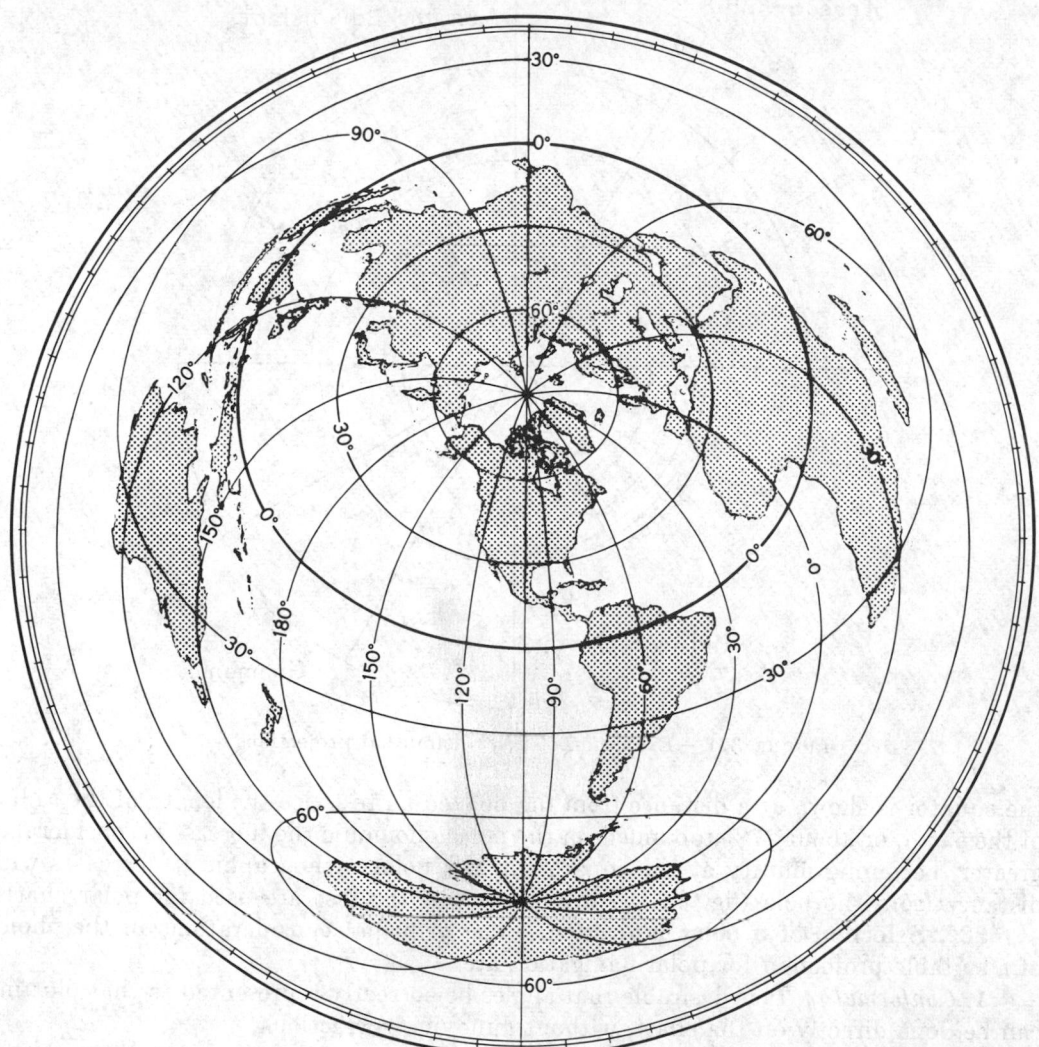

FIGURE 320.—An azimuthal equidistant map of the world with the point of tangency at latitude 40° N, longitude 100° W.

cone, when cut along an element and flattened, does not extend through a full 360° without stretching or resuming its former conical shape. The usefulness of such projections is also limited by the fact that the pole appears as an arc of a circle instead of a point. However, by using a parallel very near the pole as the higher standard parallel, a conic projection with two standard parallels can be made which requires little stretching to complete the circles of the parallels and eliminate that of the pole. Such a projection, called the **modified Lambert conformal** or **Ney's** projection, is useful for polar charts. It is particularly acceptable to those accustomed to using the ordinary Lambert conformal charts in lower latitudes.

Azimuthal projections are in their simplest form when tangent at a pole, since the meridians are straight lines intersecting at the pole, and parallels are concentric circles with their common center at the pole. Within a few degrees of latitude of the pole they all look essentially alike, but as the distance becomes greater, the spacing of the parallels becomes distinctive in each projection. In the polar azimuthal equidistant it is uniform; in the polar stereographic it increases with distance from the pole until

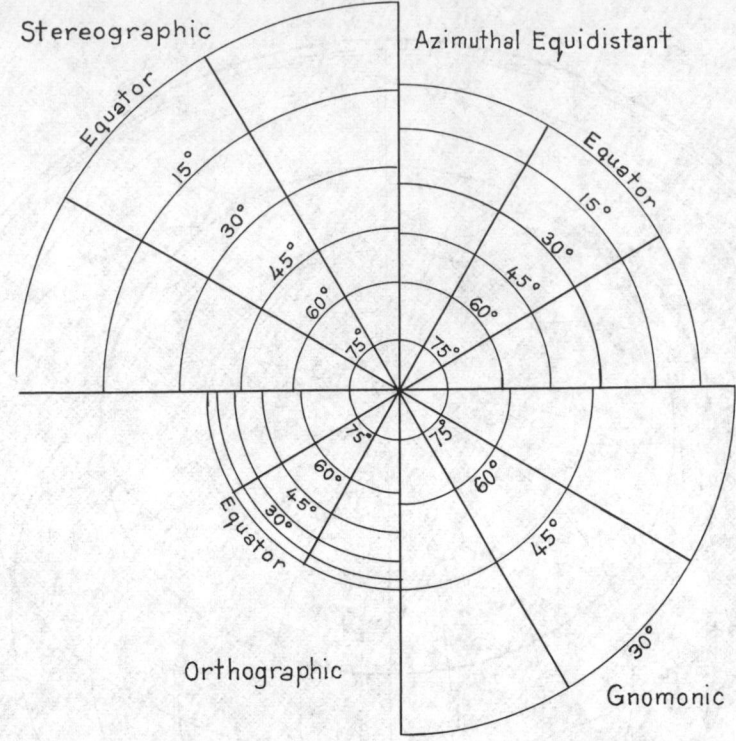

FIGURE 321.—Expansion of polar azimuthal projections.

the equator is shown at a distance from the pole equal to twice the length of the radius of the earth, or about 27% too much; in the polar gnomonic the increase is considerably greater, becoming infinity at the equator; in the polar orthographic it decreases with distance from the pole (fig. 321). All of these but the last are used for polar charts.

322. Selection of a polar projection.—The principal considerations in the choice of a suitable projection for polar navigation are:

1. *Conformality.* It is desirable that angles be correctly represented so that plotting can be done directly on the chart, without annoying corrections.

2. *Great-circle representation.* Since great circles are more useful than rhumb lines in high latitudes, it is desirable that great circles be represented by straight lines.

3. *Scale variation.* Constant scale over an entire chart is desirable.

4. *Meridian representation.* Straight meridians are desirable for convenience and accuracy of plotting, and for grid navigation (art. 2510).

5. *Limits of utility.* Wide limits are desirable to reduce to a minimum the number of projections needed. The ideal would be a single projection for world coverage.

The projections commonly used for polar charts are the transverse Mercator, modified Lambert conformal, gnomonic, stereographic, and azimuthal equidistant. Near the pole there is little to choose between them. Within the limits of practical navigation all are essentially conformal and on all a great circle is nearly a straight line.

As the distance from the pole increases, however, the distinctive features of each projection become a consideration. The transverse Mercator is conformal and its type of distortion is familiar to one accustomed to using a Mercator chart. Distances can be measured in the same manner as on any Mercator chart. The tangent meridian and all straight lines perpendicular to it are great circles. All other great circles, including the meridians, are curves. The departure of a great circle from a straight line becomes a maximum at the outer edges parallel to the tangent meridian, where the straight lines are nearer the pole than the arcs of great circles between the same points. A slight inconvenience in measurement of angles may result from the curvature of the meridians (fig. 322). The projection is excellent for a narrow band along the tangent meridian and for use with automatic navigation equipment generating transverse latitude and transverse longitude.

The modified Lambert conformal projection is virtually conformal over its entire extent, and the amount of its scale distortion is comparatively little if it is carried only to about 25° or 30° from the pole. Beyond this, the distortion increases rapidly. A great circle is very nearly a straight line anywhere on the chart. Distances and directions can be measured directly on the chart in the same manner as on a Lambert conformal chart. However, for highly accurate work this projection is not suitable, for it is not strictly conformal, and great circles are not exactly straight lines.

The polar gnomonic projection is the one polar projection on which great circles are exactly straight lines. The excessive distortion and lack of conformality of this projection make it unsuitable for ordinary navigation.

The polar stereographic projection is conformal over its entire extent, and a great circle differs but little from a straight line. The scale distortion is not excessive for a considerable distance from the pole, but is greater than that of the modified Lambert conformal projection.

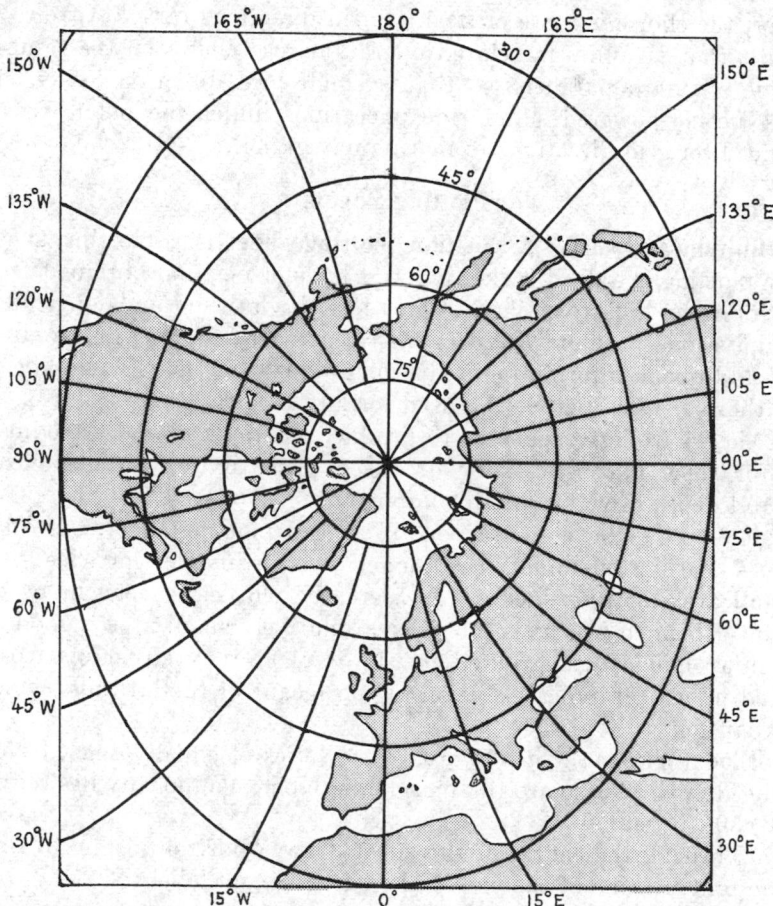

FIGURE 322.—A polar transverse Mercator map with the cylinder tangent at the 90° E-90° W meridian.

The polar azimuthal equidistant projection is useful for showing a large area such as a hemisphere, because there is no expansion along the meridians. However, the projection is not conformal, and distances cannot be measured accurately in any but a north-south direction. Great circles other than the meridians differ somewhat from straight lines. The equator is a circle centered at the pole.

The three projections most commonly used for charts for ordinary navigation near the poles are the transverse Mercator, modified Lambert conformal, and the polar stereographic. When a directional gyro is used as a directional reference, the track of the craft is approximately a great circle. A desirable chart is one on which a great circle is represented as a straight line with a constant scale and with angles correctly represented. These requirements are not met entirely by any single projection, but they are approximated by both the modified Lambert conformal and the polar stereographic. The scale is more nearly constant on the former, but the projection is not strictly conformal. The polar stereographic is conformal, and its maximum scale variation can be reduced by using a plane which intersects the earth at some parallel intermediate between the pole and the lowest parallel, so that that portion within this standard parallel is compressed, and that portion outside is expanded.

The selection of a suitable projection for use in polar regions, as in other areas, depends upon the requirements, which establish relative importance of the various features. For a relatively small area, any of several projections is suitable. For a large area, however, the choice is more critical. If grid directions (art. 2510) are to be used, it is important that all units in related operations use charts on the same projection, with the same standard parallels, so that a single grid direction exists between any two points. Nuclear powered submarine operations under the polar icecap have increased the need for grid directions in marine navigation.

Plotting Sheets

323. Definition and use.—A position plotting sheet is a plotting sheet designed primarily for plotting the dead reckoning and lines of position obtained from celestial observations or radio aids to navigation. It has the latitude and longitude graticule, and it may have one or more *compass roses* (art. 516) for measuring direction, but little or no additional information. The meridians are usually unlabeled by the publisher so the plotting sheet can be used for any longitude.

Plotting sheets are less expensive to produce than charts and are equally suitable or superior for some purposes. They are used primarily when land, visual aids to navigation, and depth of water are not important.

Any projection can be used for constructing a plotting sheet, but that used for the navigator's charts is customarily employed also for his plotting sheets.

324. Small area plotting sheets.—A Mercator plotting sheet can be constructed by the method explained in article 307. For a relatively small area a good approximation can be more quickly constructed by the navigator by either of two alternative methods based upon a graphical solution of the secant of the latitude, which approximates the expansion.

First method (fig. 324a). *Step one.* Draw a series of equally spaced, vertical lines at any spacing desired. These are the meridians; label them at any desired interval, as 1′, 2′, 5′, 10′, 30′, 1°, etc.

Step two. Through the center of the sheet draw a horizontal line to represent the parallel of the mid latitude of the area to be covered, and label it.

Step three. Through any convenient point, such as the intersection of the central meridian and the parallel of the mid latitude, draw a line making an angle with the *horizontal* equal to the mid latitude. In figure 324a this angle is 35°.

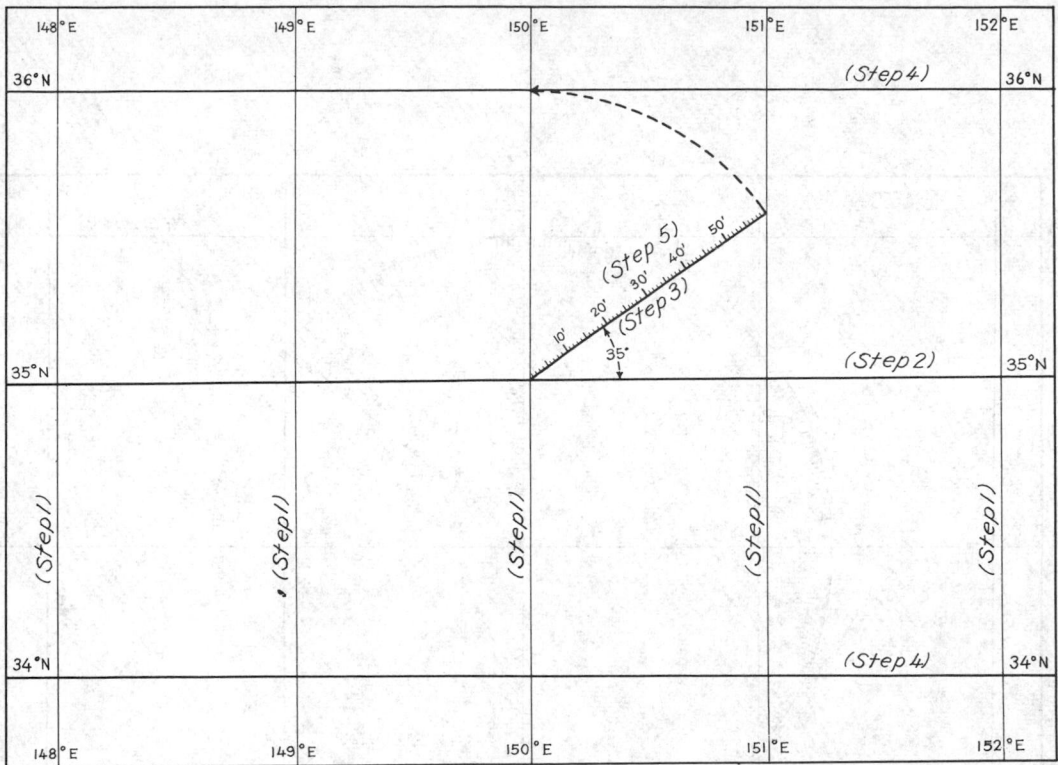

FIGURE 324a.—Small area plotting sheet with selected longitude scale.

Step four. Draw in and label additional parallels. The length of the oblique line between consecutive meridians is the perpendicular distance between consecutive parallels, as shown by the broken arc. The number of minutes of arc between consecutive parallels thus drawn is the same as that between the meridians shown.

Step five. Graduate the oblique line into convenient units. If 1′ is selected, this scale serves as both a latitude and mile scale. It can also be used as a longitude scale by measuring horizontally from a meridian instead of obliquely along the line.

Second method (fig. 324b). *Step one.* At the center of the sheet draw a circle with a radius equal to 1° (or any other convenient unit) of latitude at the desired scale. If a sheet with a compass rose is available, as in figure 324b, the compass rose can be used as the circle and will prove useful for measuring directions. It need not limit the scale of the chart, as an additional concentric circle can be drawn and desired graduations extended to it.

Step two. Draw horizontal lines through the center of the circle and tangent at the top and bottom. These are parallels of latitude; label them accordingly, at the selected interval (as every 1°, 30′, etc.).

Step three. Through the center of the circle draw a line making an angle with the *horizontal* equal to the mid latitude. In figure 324b this angle is 40°.

Step four. Draw in and label the meridians. The first is a vertical line through the center of the circle. The second is a vertical line through the intersection of the oblique line and the circle. Additional meridians are drawn the same distance apart as the first two.

Step five. Graduate the oblique line into convenient units. If 1′ is selected, this scale serves as a latitude and mile scale. It can also be used as a longitude scale by measuring horizontally from a meridian instead of obliquely along the line.

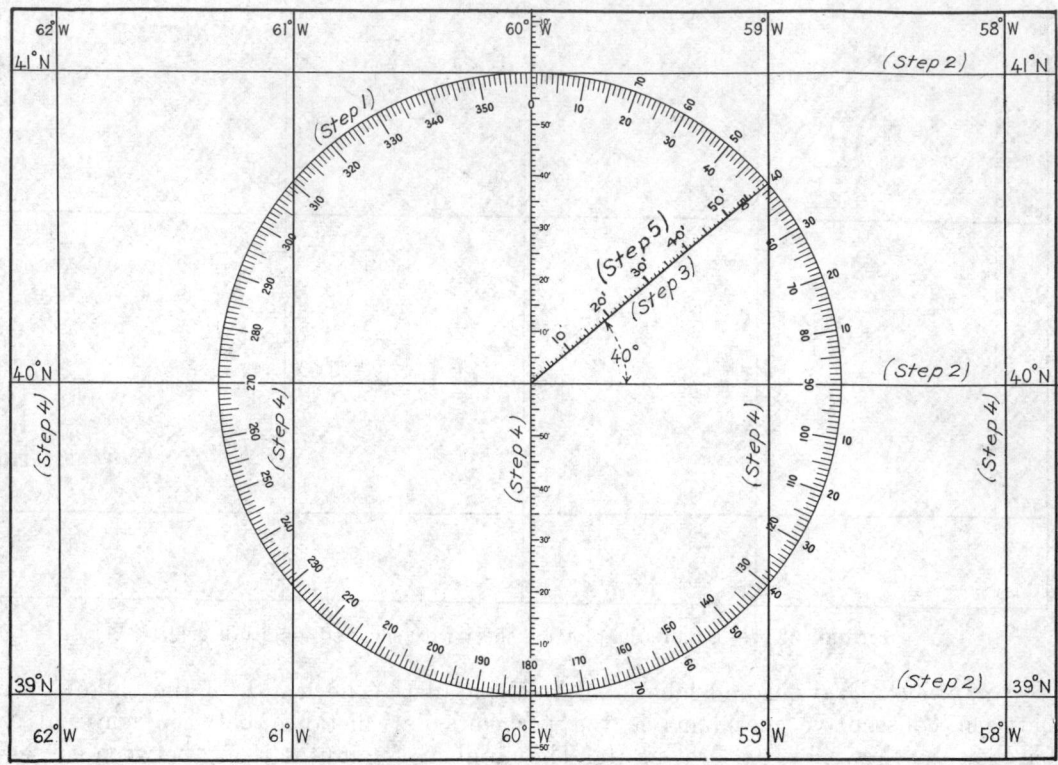

FIGURE 324b.—Small area plotting sheet with selected latitude scale.

The same end result is produced by either method. The first method, starting with the selection of the longitude scale, is particularly useful when the longitude limits of the plotting sheet determine the scale. When the latitude coverage is more important, the second method may be preferable. If a standard size is desired, part of the sheet can be printed in advance, forming what is called a **universal plotting sheet.** This is done by the Defense Mapping Agency Hydrographic Center. In either method a central compass rose might be printed. In the first method the meridians may be shown at the desired interval and the mid parallel may be printed and graduated in units of longitude. In using the sheet it is necessary only to label the meridians and draw the oblique line and from it determine the interval and draw in and label additional parallels. If the central meridian is graduated, the oblique line need not be. In the second method the parallels may be shown at the desired interval, and the central meridian may be printed and graduated in units of latitude. In using the sheet it is necessary only to label the parallels, draw the oblique line and from it determine the interval and draw in and label additional meridians. If the central meridian is graduated, as shown in figure 324b, the oblique line need not be.

Both methods use a constant relationship of latitude to longitude over the entire sheet and both fail to allow for the ellipticity of the earth. For practical navigation these are not important considerations for a small area. If a larger area is to be shown or if more precise results are desired, the method of article 307 should be used.

Grids

325. Purpose and definition of grid.—No system has been devised for showing the surface of the earth *on a flat surface,* without distortion. Moreover, the appearance of any portion of the surface varies with the projection and, in many cases, with the location of the portion with respect to the point or line of tangency. For some purposes (particularly military) it is desirable to be able to identify a location or area by rectangular coordinates, using numbers or letters, or a combination of numbers and letters, without the necessity of indicating the units used or assigning a name (north, south, east, or west), thus reducing the possibility of a mistake. This is accomplished by means of a **grid.** In its usual form this consists of two series of lines which are mutually perpendicular *on the chart,* with suitable designators.

326. Types of grids.—A grid may use the rectangular graticule of the Mercator projection, or a set of arbitrary lines on a particular projection. The most widely used system of the first is called the **World Geographic Referencing System (Georef).** It is merely a method of designating latitude and longitude by a system of letters and numbers instead of by angular measure, and therefore is not strictly a grid, except on a Mercator projection. It is particularly useful for operations extending over a wide area. Examples of the second type of grid are the **Universal Transverse Merctor (UTM) grid,** the **Universal Polar Stereographic (UPS) grid,** and the **Temporary Geographic Grid (TGG).** Since these systems are used primarily by military forces, they are sometimes called **military grids.**

References

Chamberlin, Wellman. *The Round Earth on Flat Paper.* Washington, National Geographic Society, 1947.

Deetz, C. H., and O. S. Adams. *Elements of Map Projection.* 5th ed. U. S. Coast and Geodetic Survey Special Publication No. 68. Washington, U. S. Govt. Print. Off., 1945.

Greenhood, David. *Down to Earth: Mapping for Everybody.* New York, Holiday House, 1944.

Hinks, A. R. *Map Projections.* 2nd ed. London, Cambridge University Press, 1921.

Jameson, A. H., and M. T. M. Ormsby. *Mathematical Geography.* Vol. I, *Elementary Surveying and Map Projection.* London, Pitman, [1942?].

Jervis, W. W. *The World in Maps.* New York, Oxford, 1937.

Mainwaring, James. *An Introduction to the Study of Map Projection.* London, Macmillan, 1942.

Raisz, Erwin. *General Cartography.* New York, McGraw-Hill, 1938.

Steers, J. A. *An Introduction to the Study of Map Projections.* Rev. ed. London, U. of London Press, 1929.

CHAPTER IV

VISUAL AND AUDIBLE AIDS TO NAVIGATION

401. Introduction.—The term **aid to navigation**, as used herein, means any device external to a vessel intended to be of assistance to a navigator in his determination of position or safe course, or to provide him with a warning to dangers or obstructions to navigation. This term includes lighthouses, beacons, lightships, sound signals, buoys, marine radiobeacons, racons, and the medium and long range radionavigation systems. The discussion of the various aids to navigation in this chapter is limited to the visual and audible aids established in the navigable waters of the United States and its possessions.

Aids to navigation are placed at various points along the coast and navigable waterways as markers and guides to mark safe water and to provide navigators with means to determine their position with relation to the land and to hidden dangers. Within the bounds of actual necessity, each aid is designed to be seen or heard so that it provides the necessary system coverage to enable safe transit of a waterway.

As all aids to navigation serve the same general purpose, structural differences, such as those between an unlighted buoy and a lightship, are solely for the purpose of meeting the conditions and requirements of the particular location at which the aid is established.

The maintenance of marine aids to navigation is a function of the United States Coast Guard. This responsibility includes the maintenance of lighthouses, lightships, radiobeacons, racons, Loran, sound signals, buoys, and beacons upon all navigable waters of the United States and its possessions, including the Atlantic and Pacific coasts of the continental United States, the Great Lakes, the Mississippi River and its tributaries, Puerto Rico, the U.S. Virgin Islands, the Hawaiian Islands, Alaska, Trust Territory of the Pacific Islands, and such other places where aids to navigation are required to serve the needs of the armed forces.

Lights on Fixed Structures

402. Lights on fixed structures vary from the tallest lighthouse on the coast, flashing with an intensity of millions of candlepower, to a simple battery-powered lantern on a wooden pile in a small creek. Being in fixed positions enabling accurate charting, lights provide navigators with reliable means to determine their positions with relation to land and hidden dangers during daylight and darkness. The structures are often distinctively colored to facilitate their observation during daylight.

A **major light** is a light of high intensity and reliability exhibited from a fixed structure or on a marine site (except range lights). Major lights include primary seacoast lights and secondary lights. **Primary seacoast lights** are those major lights established for the purpose of making landfalls and coastwise passages from headland to headland. **Secondary lights** are those major lights, other than primary seacoast lights, established at harbor entrances and other locations where high intensity and reliability are required. Major lights are usually located at manned or monitored automated stations.

A **minor light** is an automatic unmanned (unwatched) light on a fixed structure showing usually low to moderate intensity. Minor lights are established in harbors, along channels, rivers, and isolated locations. They usually have the same numbering, **coloring,** and light and sound characteristics as the lateral system of buoyage (art. 411).

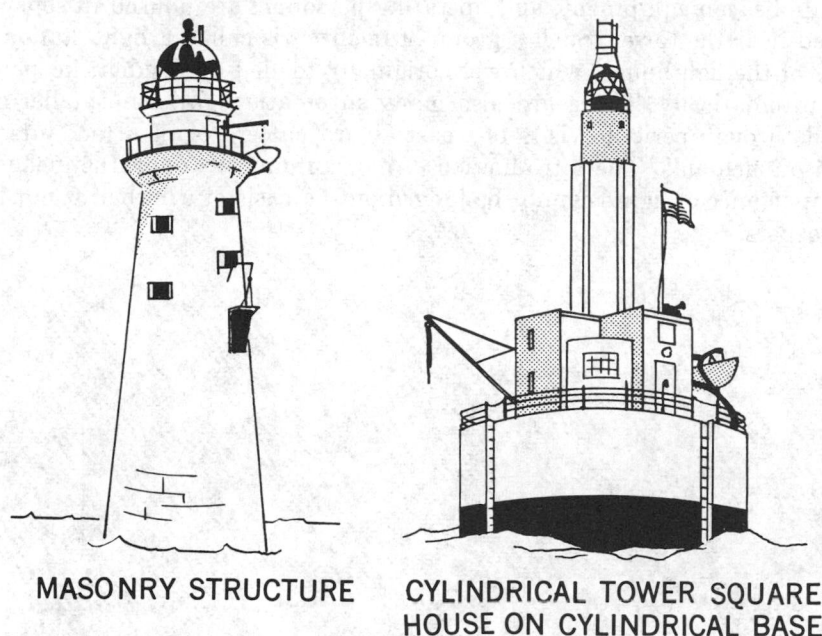

MASONRY STRUCTURE   CYLINDRICAL TOWER SQUARE
HOUSE ON CYLINDRICAL BASE

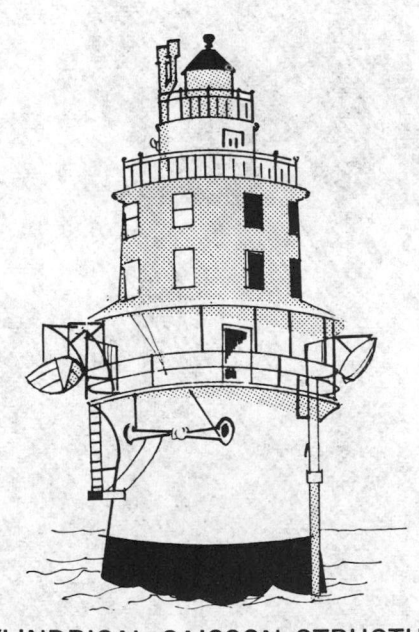

CYLINDRICAL CAISSON STRUCTURE   SKELETON IRON STRUCTURE

FIGURE 402a.—Typical light structures.

Lighthouses (fig. 402a), all of which exhibit major lights, are placed where they will be of most use: on prominent headlands, at entrances, on isolated dangers, or at other points where it is necessary that mariners be warned or guided. Their principal purpose is to support a light at a considerable height above the water. In many instances, sound signals, radiobeacon equipment, and operating personnel are housed in separate buildings located near the tower. Such a group of facilities is called a **light station.**

Many of the lighthouses which were originally tended by resident keepers are now operated automatically. There are also many automatic lights on smaller structures maintained through periodic visits of Coast Guard cutters or of attendants in charge of a group of such aids. The introduction of new automatic apparatus means that the relative importance of lights cannot be judged on the basis of whether or not they have resident keepers.

FIGURE 402b.—Typical offshore light station.

Offshore light stations and large navigational buoys (art. 408) are replacing lightships (art. 407) where practicable. The offshore light stations in U. S. waters, such as the one shown in figure 402b have helicopter landing surfaces. In the 1975 *Light List*, the CHESAPEAKE LIGHT station is described as a blue tower on a white square superstructure on four black piles. "CHESAPEAKE" is on sides; the piles are floodlighted sunset to sunrise.

Range lights (fig. 402c) are pairs of lights so located as to form a range in line with the center of channels or entrance to a harbor. The rear light is higher than the front light and a considerable distance in back of it, thus enabling the mariner to use the range by keeping the lights in line as he progresses up the channel. Range lights are sometimes used during daylight hours through the use of high intensity lights. Otherwise, the range light structures are equipped with daymarks (art. 412) for ordinary daytime use.

Range lights are usually white, red, or green, and display various characteristics to differentiate them from surrounding lights.

FIGURE 402c.—Range lights.

A **directional light** is a single light which projects a beam of high intensity, separate color, or special characteristic in a given direction. It has limited use for those cases where a two-light range may not be practicable or necessary, and for special applications. The directional light is essentially a narrow sector light with or without adjacent sectors which give information as to the direction of and relative displacement from the narrow sector.

Aeronautical lights, which are lights of high intensity, may be the first lights observed at night from vessels approaching the coast. Those situated near the coast are accordingly listed in the *List of Lights* (art. 1301) in order that the navigator may be able to obtain more complete information concerning their description. These lights are not listed in the U. S. Coast Guard *Light List*.

Aeronautical lights are placed in geographic sequence in the body of the text of the *List of Lights* along with lights for marine navigation. It should be borne in mind, however, that these lights are not designed or maintained for marine navigation, and that they are *subject to changes of which neither lighthouse authorities nor the marine navigator may receive prompt notification*.

Bridges across navigable waters of the United States are generally marked with red, green, and white lights for nighttime navigation. Red lights mark piers and other parts of the bridge. Red lights are also used on drawbridges to show when they are in the closed position. Green lights are used to mark the centerline of navigable channels through fixed bridges. The preferred channel, if there are two or more channels through the bridge, is marked by three white lights in a vertical line above the green light.

Green lights are also used on drawbridges to show when they are in the open position. Because of the variety of drawbridges, the position of the green lights on the bridge will vary according to the type of structure. Navigational lights on bridges are prescribed by regulation.

Bridges infrequently used may be unlighted. In unusual cases the type and method of lighting may be different than normally found.

Drawbridges required to be operated for passage of vessels operate upon sound and light signals given by the vessel and acknowledged by the bridge. These signals are prescribed by regulation.

In addition to lighting, certain bridges may be equipped with sound signals and radar reflectors where unusual geographic or weather conditions require them.

Light Characteristics

403. Characteristics.—Lights are given distinctive characteristics so that one light may be distinguished from another navigational light or from the general background of shore lights or as a means of conveying certain definite information. This distinctiveness may be obtained by giving each light a distinctive sequence of light and dark intervals, having lights that burn steadily and others that flash or occult, or by giving each light a distinctive color, or color sequence. In the light lists, the dark intervals are referred to as **eclipses.** An **occulting light** is a light totally eclipsed at regular intervals, the duration of light always being greater than the duration of darkness. A **flashing light** is a light which flashes at regular intervals, the duration of light always being less than the duration of darkness. An **equal interval light** is a light which flashes at regular intervals, the duration of light always being equal to the duration of darkness. This light is also called an **isophase light.**

404. Light phase characteristics (fig. 404) are the distinctive sequences of light and dark intervals or distinctive sequences in the variations of the luminous intensity of a light. The light phase characteristics of lights which change color do not differ from those of lights which do not change color. A continuous steady light which shows periodic color change is described as an **alternating light.** The alternating characteristic is also used with other light phase characteristics as shown in figure 404.

A *Light List* entry for an **alternating fixed and flashing light** may be given as:

> Alt. F.W., F.R. and Fl. R.
> 90ˢ (F.W., 59ˢ, F.R., 14ˢ,
> Fl. R. 3ˢ (high intensity),
> F.R. 14ˢ).

With each 90ˢ period the light is first fixed white for 59ˢ, then fixed red for 14ˢ, then there is a flash of brilliant red for 3ˢ, and finally the light is fixed red for 14ˢ.

A *Light List* entry for a **group flashing light** may be given as:

> Gp. Fl. W., 15ˢ
> 0.2ˢ fl., 3.0ˢ ec.
> 0.2ˢ fl., 11.6ˢ ec.
> 2 flashes.

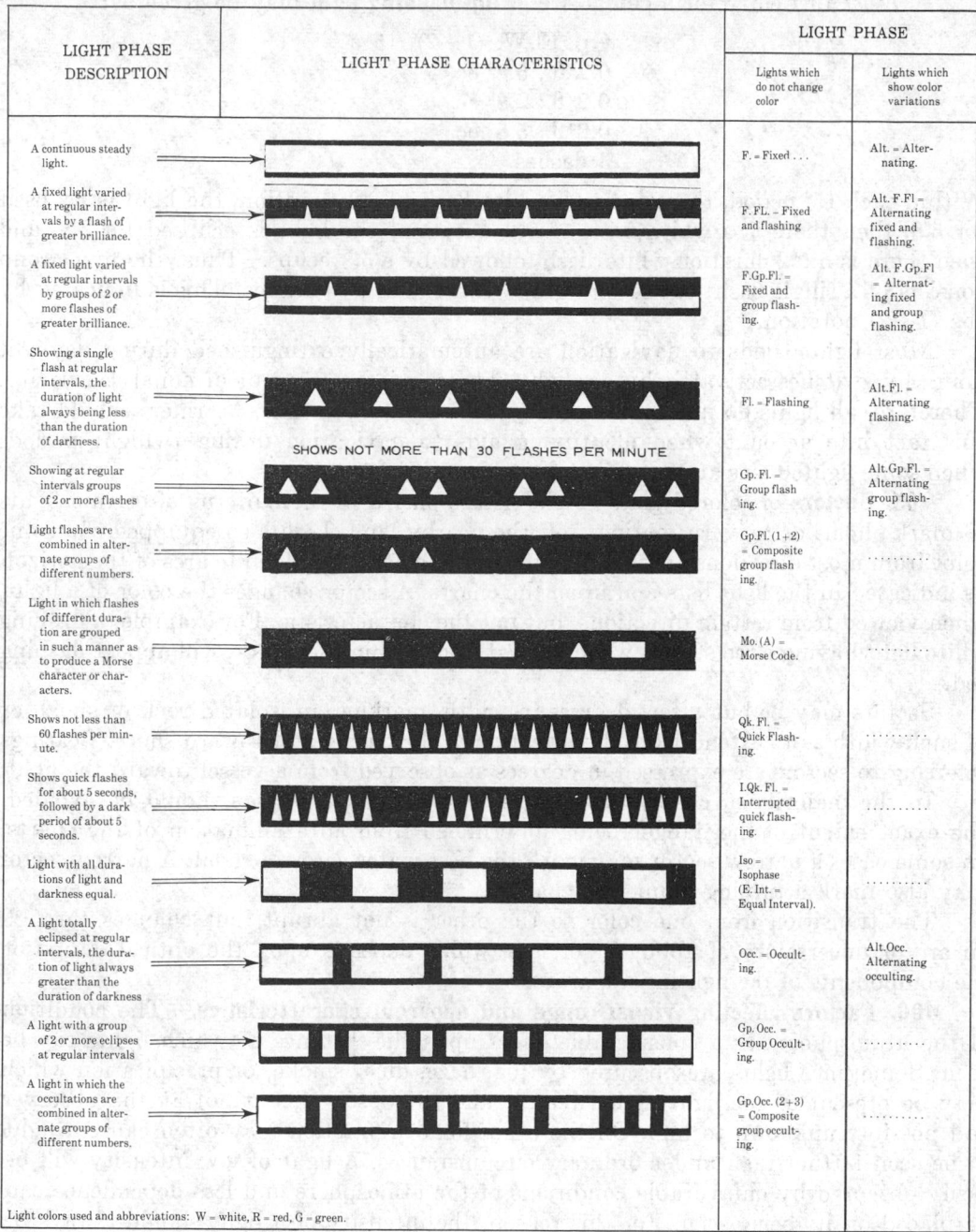

FIGURE 404.—Light phase characteristics.

Within each 15ˢ period, there is first a white flash of 0ˢ2 duration, the light is eclipsed (extinguished) for 3ˢ, then there is a white flash of 0ˢ2 duration, and then the light is eclipsed for 11ˢ6 before the sequence begins again.

A *Light List* entry for a **composite group flashing light** may be given as:

$$\text{Gp. Fl.W. } (1+2), 15^s$$
$$0.2^s \text{fl., } 5.8^s \text{ ec.}$$
$$0.2^s \text{fl., } 2.8^s \text{ ec.}$$
$$0.2^s \text{fl., } 5.8^s \text{ ec.}$$
$$3 \text{ flashes.}$$

Within each 15^s period, there is first a white flash of 0.2^s duration, the light is eclipsed for 5.8^s, then there is a white flash of 0.2^s duration, the light is eclipsed for 2.8^s, and then there is a 0.2^s duration white flash followed by a 5.8^s eclipse. Thus, the first group consists of a single flash; the second group consists of two flashes. This is indicated by the $(1+2)$ notation.

Most lighted aids to navigation are automatically extinguished during daylight hours by switches activated by daylight. These switches are not of equal sensitivity. Therefore, all lights do not come on or go off at the same time. Mariners should take this fact into account when identifying aids to navigation during twilight periods when some lighted aids are on while others are not.

405. Sectors of colored glass or plastic are placed in the lanterns of certain lights to mark shoals or to warn mariners off the nearby land. Lights so equipped show one color from most directions and a different color or colors over definite arcs of the horizon as indicated in the light lists and upon the charts. A sector changes the color of a light, when viewed from certain directions, but not the characteristic. For example, a flashing white light having a red sector, when viewed from within the sector, will appear flashing red.

Sectors may be but a few degrees in width, marking an isolated rock or shoal, or of such width as to extend from the direction of the deep water toward shore. Bearings referring to sectors are expressed in degrees as observed from a vessel toward the light.

In the majority of cases, water areas covered by red sectors should be avoided, the exact extent of the danger being determined from an examination of the charts. In some cases a narrow sector may mark the best water across a shoal. A narrow sector may also mark a turning point in a channel.

The transition from one color to the other is not abrupt, but changes through an arc of uncertainty of about $2°$ or less, which depends upon the optical design of the components of the lighting apparatus.

406. Factors affecting visual range and apparent characteristics.—The condition of the atmosphere has a considerable effect upon the distance at which lights can be seen. Sometimes lights are obscured by fog, haze, dust, smoke, or precipitation which may be present at the light or between it and the observer, but not at the observer and possibly unknown to him. On the other hand, refraction may often cause a light to be seen farther than under ordinary circumstances. A light of low intensity will be easily obscured by unfavorable conditions of the atmosphere and less dependence can be placed on its being seen. For this reason, the intensity of a light should always be considered when expecting to sight it in thick weather. Haze and distance may reduce the apparent duration of the flash of a flashing light. In some conditions of the atmosphere white lights may have a reddish hue. In clear weather green lights may have a whitish hue.

It should be remembered that lights placed at great elevations are more frequently obscured by clouds, mist, and fog than those near sea level.

In regions where ice conditions prevail in the winter, the lantern panes of unattended lights may become covered with ice or snow, which will greatly reduce the luminous ranges of the lights and may also cause lights to appear of different color.

The increasing use of brilliant shore lights for advertising, illuminating bridges, and other purposes, may cause navigational lights, particularly those in densely inhabited areas, to be outshone and difficult to distinguish from the background lighting. Mariners are requested by the U. S. Coast Guard to report such cases as outlined above in order that steps may be taken to attempt to improve the conditions.

The "loom" of a powerful light is often seen beyond the geographic range of the light. The loom may sometimes appear sufficiently sharp to obtain a bearing.

At short distances, some *of the brighter* flashing lights may show a faint continuous light between flashes.

It should be borne in mind that, when attempting to sight a light at night, the geographic range is considerably increased from aloft. By noting a star immediately over the light an accurate compass bearing may be indirectly obtained on the light from the navigating bridge although the light is not yet visible from that level.

The distance of an observer from a light cannot be estimated by its apparent intensity. *Always check the characteristics of lights* in order that powerful lights visible in the distance shall not be mistaken for nearby lights showing similar characteristics at lower intensity (such as those on lighted buoys).

If lights are not sighted within a reasonable time after prediction, a dangerous situation may exist requiring prompt resolution or action to insure the safety of the vessel.

The apparent characteristic of a complex light may change with the distance of the observer. For example, a light which actually displays a characteristic of fixed white varied by flashes of alternating white and red (the phases having a decreasing range of detection in the order: flashing white, flashing red, fixed white) may, when first sighted in clear weather, show as a simple flashing white light. As the vessel draws nearer, the red flash will become visible and the characteristic will apparently be alternating flashing white and red. Later, the fixed white light will be seen between the flashes and the true characteristic of the light finally recognized—fixed white, alternating flashing white and red (F.W.Alt.Fl. W. and R.).

There is always the possibility of a light being extinguished. In the case of unattended lights, this condition might not be immediately detected and corrected. The mariner should immediately report this condition. During periods of armed conflict, certain lights may be deliberately extinguished without notice if the situation warrants such action.

Lightships and Large Navigational Buoys

407. Lightships serve the same purposes as lighthouses, being equipped with lights, sound signals, and radiobeacons. They take the form of ships only because they are placed at points where it has been impracticable to build lighthouses. Lightships mark the entrances to important harbors or estuaries and dangerous shoals lying in much frequented waters. They also serve as leading marks for both transocean and coastwise traffic. The two lightships in United States waters are painted red with the name of the station in white on both sides. Superstructures are white; masts, lantern galleries, ventilators, and stacks are painted buff. Relief lightships are painted the same as the regular station ships, with the word "RELIEF" in white letters on the sides.

By night a lightship displays a characteristic masthead light and a less brilliant light on the forestay. The forestay indicates the direction in which the vessel is headed, and hence the direction of the current (or wind), since lightships head into the wind or current. By day a lightship displays the International Code signal of the station when requested, or if an approaching vessel does not seem to recognize it.

It should be borne in mind that most lightships are anchored to a very long scope of chain and, as a result, the radius of their swinging circle is considerable. The chart symbol represents the approximate location of the anchor. Furthermore, under certain conditions of wind and current, they are subject to sudden and unexpected sheers which are certain to hazard a vessel attempting to pass close aboard.

During extremely heavy weather and due to their exposed locations, lightships may be carried off station without the knowledge and despite the best efforts of their crews. The mariner should, therefore, not implicitly rely on a lightship maintaining its precisely charted position during and immediately following severe storms. A lightship known to be off station will secure her light, sound signal, and radiobeacon and fly the International Code signal "LO" signifying "I am not in my correct position."

Station buoys, often called **watch buoys,** are sometimes moored near lightships to mark the approximate station should the lightship be carried away or temporarily

FIGURE 408.—Large navigational buoy.

removed and to give the crew an indication of dragging. Since these buoys are always unlighted and, in some cases, moored as much as a mile from the lightship, the danger of a closely passing vessel colliding with them is always present—particularly so during darkness or periods of reduced visibility.

Experience shows that lightships and offshore light stations cannot be safely used as leading marks to be passed close aboard, but should always be left broad off the course, whenever searoom permits.

408. Large navigational buoys and offshore light stations are replacing lightships where practicable. These 40-foot diameter buoys (fig. 408) may show secondary lights (art. 402) from heights of about 36 feet above the water. In addition to the light, these buoys may mount a radiobeacon and provide sound signals. A station buoy (art. 407) may be moored nearby.

Buoyage and Beaconage

409. Buoys are used to delineate channels, indicate shoals, mark obstructions, and warn the mariner of dangers where the use of fixed aids for such purposes would be uneconomical or impracticable. By their color, shape, number, and light or sound characteristics, buoys provide indications to the mariner as to how he may avoid navigational hazards.

There are many different sizes and types of buoys to meet the wide range of environmental conditions and user requirements. The principle types of buoys used by the United States are lighted, lighted sound, unlighted sound, and unlighted. Some examples of these types are illustrated in figure 409a.

A **lighted buoy** consists of a floating hull with a tower on which a lantern is mounted. Batteries to power the light are contained in special pockets in the buoy hull. To keep the buoy in an upright stable position a large counterweight (fig. 409b) sometimes is extended from a tube attached to the base of the hull below the water surface. The radar reflector (art. 4301), on those buoys so equipped, forms a part of the buoy tower.

Lighted sound buoys have the same general configuration as lighted buoys but are equipped with either a gong, bell, whistle, or electronic horn. Bells and gongs on buoys are sounded by tappers that hang from the tower and swing as the buoys roll in the sea. Bell buoys produce sound of only one tone; gong buoys produce several tones.

Whistle buoys make a loud moaning sound caused by the rising and falling motions of the buoy in the sea. A sound buoy equipped with an electronic horn will produce a pure tone at regular intervals and will operate continually regardless of the sea state.

Unlighted sound buoys have the same general appearance as lighted buoys (except for old whistle buoys) but are not equipped with any light apparatus.

Unlighted buoys have either a can or nun shape. **Can buoys** have a cylindrical shape whereas **nun buoys** have a conical shape usually located on top of a cylindrical shape. Since these buoys are unlighted there is no requirement for battery pockets, and the hull of the buoy forms part of the shape.

Buoys are *floating aids* and therefore require moorings to hold them in position. Typically the mooring consists of chain and a large concrete sinker (fig. 409c). Because buoys are subjected to waves, wind, tides, and other conditions, the moorings must be deployed in lengths greater than the water depth. The scope of chain can be as much as 5 times the depth of water or more but normally will be about 3 times the water depth. For this reason the buoy can be expected to swing in a circle as the current, wind, and wave conditions change.

410. Fallibility of buoys.—It is *imprudent* for a navigator to rely on floating aids to navigation to always maintain their charted positions and to constantly and unerringly display their advertised characteristics.

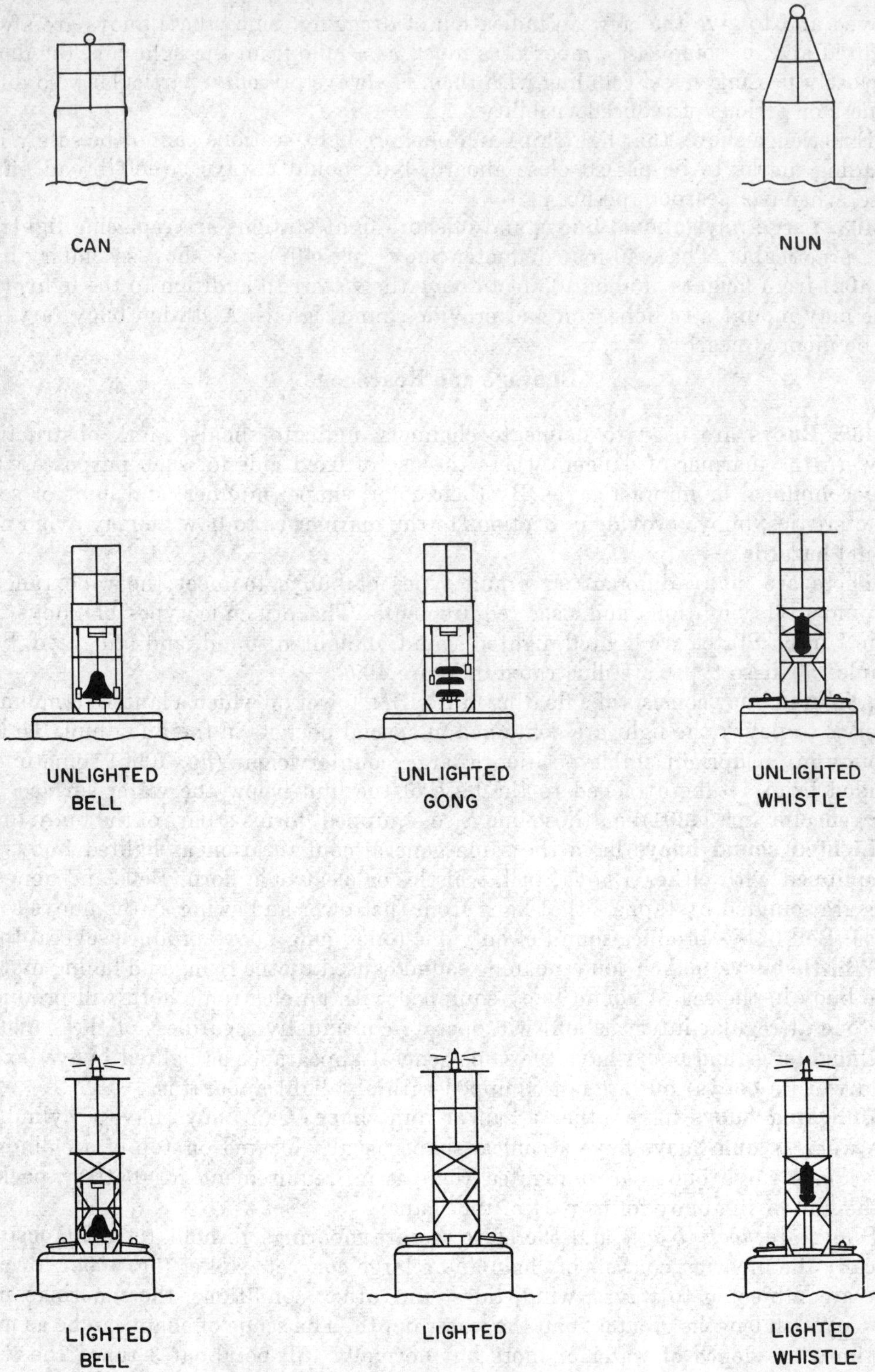

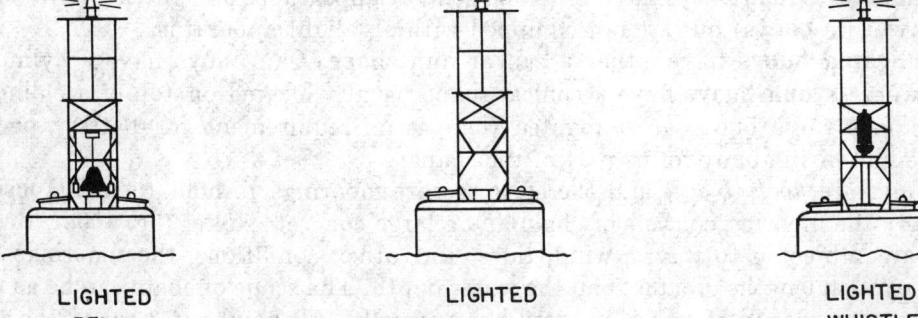

FIGURE 409a.—Principal types of buoys in U. S. waters.

FIGURE 409b.—Buoy showing counterweight.   FIGURE 409c.—Sinkers used to anchor bouys.

The buoy symbol shown on charts indicates the approximate position of the buoy body and the sinker which secures the buoy to the seabed. The approximate position is used because of practical limitations in placing and keeping buoys and their sinkers in exact geographical locations. These limitations include, but are not limited to, inherent inaccuracies in position fixing methods, prevailing atmospheric and sea conditions, the slope of and the material making up the seabed, the fact that buoys are moored to sinkers with more chain than the water depth, and the fact that the positions of the buoys and the sinkers are not under continuous surveillance but are normally checked only during periodic maintenance visits which often occur more than a year apart. The position of the buoy can be expected to shift inside and outside the area shown by the the chart symbol due to the forces of nature. The mariner is also cautioned that buoys are liable to be missing, shifted, overturned, etc. Lighted buoys may be extinguished or sound signals may not function because of ice, running ice, natural causes, collisions, or other accidents.

For these reasons, a prudent mariner must not rely completely upon the position or operation of buoys, but will also navigate using bearings of charted features, structures, and aids to navigation on shore. Further a vessel attempting to pass too close always risks a collision with a yawing buoy or with the obstruction which the buoy marks.

The concept that a wreck buoy always occupies a position directly over the wreck it is intended to mark is erroneous. Buoys must be placed in position by a vessel. It is usually physically impossible for these vessels to maneuver directly over a wreck to place the sinker without incurring serious underwater damage. For this reason, a wreck buoy is usually placed on the seaward or channelward side of a wreck, the proximity thereto being governed by existing conditions. To avoid confusion in some situations, two buoys may be used to mark the wreck. Both may not be located on the seaward or channelward side of the wreck, but the wreck will lie between them. Obviously, the mariner should not attempt to pass between buoys so placed.

Sunken wrecks are not always static. They are sometimes moved away from their buoys by severe sea conditions or other causes. Just as shoals may shift away from the buoys placed to mark them, wrecks may shift away from wreck buoys.

All buoys should, therefore, be regarded as warnings, guides, or aids but not as infallible navigation marks, especially those located in exposed positions. Whenever possible, a mariner should navigate by bearings or angles of reliable and identifiable fixed charted features or landmarks and by soundings rather than by sole reliance on buoys.

411. Buoyage systems.—Most maritime countries use either a **lateral system** of buoyage or the **cardinal system,** or both. In the lateral system, used on all navigable waters of the United States, the coloring, shape, numbering, and lighting of buoys indicate the direction to a danger relative to the course which should be followed. In the cardinal system the coloring, shape, and lighting of buoys indicate the cardinal direction to a danger relative to the buoy itself. The color, shape, lights, and numbers of buoys in the lateral system as used by the United States are determined relative to a direction *from* seaward. Along the *coasts* of the United States, the *clockwise* direction around the country is arbitrarily considered to be the direction "from seaward." Proceeding in a westerly and northerly direction on the Great Lakes (except Lake Michigan), and in a southerly direction on Lake Michigan, is proceeding "from seaward." On the Intracoastal Waterway proceeding in a general southerly direction along the Atlantic coast, and in a general westerly direction along the gulf coast, is considered as proceeding "from seaward." On the Mississippi and Ohio Rivers and their tributaries the aids to navigation characteristics are determined as proceeding from sea toward the head of navigation although local terminology describes "left bank" and "right bank" as proceeding with the flow of the river. Some countries using the lateral system have methods of coloring their buoys and lights opposite to that of the United States. Appendix Y treats this subject in greater detail.

In United States waters the following distinctive system of identification is used:

Red nun buoys mark the *right* side of channels for an inbound vessel and obstructions which should be kept to starboard. They have *even* numbers which increase from seaward.

Black can buoys mark the *left* side of channels for an inbound vessel and obstructions which should be kept to port. They have *odd* numbers which increase from seaward.

Red and black horizontally banded buoys mark junctions and bifurcations of channels or wrecks or obstructions that can be passed on either side. The color (red or black) of the top band and the shape (nun or can) indicate the side on which the buoy should be passed by a vessel proceeding along the primary channel. If the topmost band is black, the primary channel will be followed by keeping the buoy on the port hand of an *inbound* vessel. If the topmost band is red, the primary channel will be followed by keeping the buoy on the starboard hand of an *inbound* vessel. It may not be possible for an *outbound* vessel to pass on either side of these buoys; the navigational chart should always be consulted to determine how these buoys should be passed by an outbound vessel.

Black and white vertically striped buoys mark the fairway or midchannel and should be passed close aboard. These mid-channel or fairway buoys can have any shape.

Lighted buoys, *spar* buoys, and *sound* buoys are not differentiated by shape to indicate the side on which they should be passed. No special significance is attached to the shapes of these buoys, their purpose being indicated only by the coloring, numbering, or light characteristics.

All *solid red* and *solid black* buoys are numbered, the red buoys bearing even numbers and the black buoys bearing odd numbers, the numbers for each increasing from seaward. The numbers are kept in approximate sequence on both sides of the channel by omitting numbers where required. Buoys of other colors are not numbered; however, a buoy of any other color may be lettered for the purpose of identification.

Lights. Red lights are used only on red buoys and buoys with a red band at the top, green lights are used only on black buoys and buoys with a black band at the top. White lights are used without any color significance. Lights on red or black buoys are always regularly flashing or regularly occulting. Quick flashing lights are used when a light of distinct cautionary significance is desired, as at a sharp turn or constriction in the channel. Interrupted quick flashing lights are used on red and black horizontally banded buoys. White Morse A flashing lights are used on midchannel buoys.

Special purpose buoys. White buoys mark anchorages. Yellow buoys mark quarantine anchorages. White buoys with green tops are used in dredging and survey operations. Black and white horizontally banded buoys mark fish net areas. Yellow and black vertically striped buoys mark seadromes. White and international orange banded, either horizontally or vertically, are used for special purposes to which neither the lateral system colors nor the other special purpose colors apply. The shape of special purpose buoys has no significance. They are not numbered but may be lettered. They may display any color light except red or green. Only fixed, occulting, or Slow-Flash A characteristics are used.

Wreck buoys are generally placed on the seaward or channel side, as near the wreck as conditions permit. To avoid confusion in some situations, two buoys may be used to mark the wreck. The possibility of the wreck having shifted position due to sea action since the buoy was placed should not be overlooked.

Station buoys are placed close to some lightships and important buoys to mark the approximate position of the station. Such buoys are colored and numbered the same as the regular aid, lightship station buoys having the letters "LS" above the initials of the station. If a station is marked with an additional station buoy, and the two buoys are not found close together, it is an indication that at least one of the buoys has moved. However, it is not an indication as to which buoy has moved.

Minor lights and daybeacons (art. 412) used to mark the sides of channels are given numbers and characteristics in accordance with the lateral system of buoyage.

Certain aids to navigation are fitted with light reflecting material (reflectors) to assist in their location in darkness. The colors of such reflectors have the same lateral significance as the color of lights.

Certain aids to navigation may be fitted with, or have incorporated in their design, radar reflectors designed to enhance their ability to reflect radar energy. In general, these reflectors will materially improve the aids for use by vessels equipped with radar.

412. Beacons are fixed aids to navigation placed on shore or on marine sites. If unlighted, the beacon is referred to as a **daybeacon.** A daybeacon is identified by its color and the color, shape, and number of its daymark. The simplest form of daybeacon consists of a single pile with a daymark affixed at or near its top (fig. 412).

Daybeacons may be used instead of range lights (art. 402) to form a **range** (art. 1005).

Daymarks serve to make aids to navigation readily visible and easily identifiable against daylight viewing backgrounds. For example, the distinctive color pattern and shape of a lighthouse aid identification during the daytime as does the color and shape of a buoy. The size of the daymark that is required to make the aid conspicuous depends upon how far the aid must be seen. On those structures which do not by themselves present an adequate viewing area to be seen at the required distance, the

FIGURE 412.—Daybeacon.

aid is made more visible by affixing a daymark to the structure. These daymarks have a distinctive shape and color depending upon the purpose of the aid. Most daymarks also display numbers or letters so that the daymark can be more readily identified as a particular aid. The numbers and letters, as well as portions of most daymarks (and portions of unlighted buoys) are made to be retro-reflective to enhance their illumination by the mariner.

Increasing amounts of information are conveyed by a daymark as the mariner approaches. At the detection distance, the daymark will convey only the information of its existence; it will be just detectable from its background. At the recognition distance, the daymark can be recognized as an aid to navigation. At this distance the distinctive shape or color pattern is recognizable. At the identification distance, when the number or letter can be read, the daymark can be identified as a particular aid.

The detection, recognition, and identification distances vary widely for any particular daymark depending upon the viewing conditions. This is an inherent limitation of any visual signal but is especially true for passive visual signals which utilize the sun as the source for their signal energy. The reflectivity of the daymark surface varies with the angle of the sun relative to the daymark. This causes the luminance of the daymark to vary. The detection, recognition, and identification distances depend upon the relative difference between the luminance of the daymark and that of the background, the position of the sun relative to the observer, and the meteorological visibility.

Beginning in 1975, a revised system of daymarks is gradually being implemented in the United States. The significant changes include the following:

1. On port side daymarks, green is used in lieu of the colors black or white; green numbers and letters are used.

2. On starboard side daymarks, red numbers and letters are used in lieu of white numbers and letters.

3. On ICW daymarks (art. 415), a yellow horizontal reflective strip is used in lieu of a yellow reflective border as the marking.

4. On junction daymarks, green is used in lieu of black in the color pattern.

Sound Signals

413. Sound signals.—Most lighthouses, light platforms, and lightships and some minor light structures and buoys are equipped with sound-producing instruments to aid the mariner in periods of low visibility.

Charts and light lists of the particular area should be consulted for positive identification. Caution: buoys fitted with a bell, gong, or whistle and actuated by wave motion may produce no sound when the sea is calm. Their positive identification is not always possible.

Any sound-producing instrument operated in time of fog from a definite point shown on the charts, such as a lighthouse, lightship, or buoy, serves as a useful fog signal. To be effective as an aid to navigation, a mariner must be able to identify it and to know from what point it is sounded.

At all lighthouses and lightships equipped with sound signals, these signals are operated by mechanical or electrical means and are sounded during periods of low visibility, providing the desirable feature of positive identification.

The characteristics of mechanized signals are varied blasts and silent periods. A definite time is required for each signal to perform a complete cycle of changes. Where the number of blasts and the total time for a signal to complete a cycle is not sufficient for positive identification, reference may be made to details in the *Light List* regarding the exact length of each blast and silent interval. The various types of sound signals also differ in tone, and this facilitates recognition of the respective stations.

Diaphones produce sound by means of a slotted piston moved back and forth by compressed air. Blasts may consist of two tones of different pitch, in which case the first part of the blast is high and the last of a low pitch. These alternate-pitch signals are called "two-tone."

Diaphragm horns produce sound by means of a disc diaphragm vibrated by compressed air or electricity. Duplex or triplex horn units of differing pitch produce a chime signal.

Sirens produce sound by means of either a disc or a cup-shaped rotor actuated by compressed air, steam, or electricity.

Whistles produce sound by compressed air emitted through a circumferential slot into a cylindrical bell chamber.

Bells are sounded by means of a hammer actuated by a descending weight, compressed gas or electricity.

414. Limitations of sound signals.—Sound signals depend upon the transmission of sound through air. As aids to navigation, they have limitations that should be considered. Sound travels through the air in a variable and frequently unpredictable manner.

It has been clearly established that:

1. Sound signals are heard at greatly varying distances and that the distance at which a sound signal can be heard may vary with the bearing of the signal and may be different on occasion.

2. Under certain conditions of the atmosphere, when a sound signal has a combination high and low tone, it is not unusual for one of the tones to be inaudible. In the case of sirens, which produce a varying tone, portions of the blast may not be heard.

3. There are occasionally areas close to the signal in which it is wholly inaudible. This is particularly true when the sound signal is screened by intervening land or other obstruction, or the signal is on a high cliff.

4. A fog may exist a short distance from a station and not be observable from it, so that the signal may not be in operation.

5. Some sound signals cannot be started at a moment's notice.

6. Even though a sound signal may not be heard from the deck or bridge of a ship when the engines are in motion, it may be heard when the ship is stopped, or from a quiet position. Sometimes it may be heard from aloft though not on deck.

7. The loudness of the sound emitted by a sound signal may be greater at a distance than in the immediate proximity.

All these considerations point to the necessity for the utmost caution when navigating near land in a fog. Mariners are therefore warned that sound signals can never be implicitly relied upon, and that the practice of taking soundings of the depth of water should never be neglected. Particular attention should be given to placing lookouts in positions in which the noises in the ship are least likely to interfere with hearing a sound signal. Sound signals are valuable as warnings but the mariner should not place implicit reliance upon them in navigating his vessel. They should be considered solely as warning devices.

Emergency sound signals are sounded at some of the light and fog signal stations when the main and stand-by sound signal is inoperative. Some of these emergency sound signals are of a different type and characteristic than the main sound signal. The characteristics of the emergency sound signals are listed in the *Light List*.

The mariner must not assume:

1. That he is out of ordinary hearing distance because he fails to hear the sound signal.

2. That, because he hears a sound signal faintly, he is at a great distance from it.

3. That he is near to it because he hears the sound plainly.

4. That the distance from and the intensity of a sound on any one occasion is a guide to him for any future occasion.

5. That the sound signal is not sounding because he does not hear it, even when in close proximity.

6. That the sound signal is in the direction the sound appears to come from.

415. Intracoastal Waterway aids to navigation.—The Intracoastal Waterway (ICW) runs parallel to the Atlantic and gulf coasts from Manasquan Inlet on the New Jersey shore to the Mexican border. Aids marking these waters have some portion of them marked with yellow as shown in Chart No. 1. Otherwise, the coloring and numbering of buoys and beacons follow the same system as that in other U. S. waterways.

In order that vessels may readily follow the Intracoastal Waterway route where it coincides with another marked waterway such as an important river, special markings are employed. These special markings are applied to the buoys or other aids which already mark the river or waterway for other traffic. These aids are then referred to as "Dual Purpose" aids. The marks consist of a yellow square or a yellow triangle, placed on a conspicuous part of the dual purpose aid. The yellow square, in outline similar to a can buoy, indicates that the aid on which it is placed should be kept on the left hand when following the Intracoastal Waterway down the coast. The yellow triangle has the same meaning as a nun; it should be kept on the right side. Where such dual purpose marking is employed, the mariner following the Intracoastal Waterway disregards the color and shape of the aid on which the mark is placed, being guided solely by the shape of the yellow mark.

416. Mississippi River system.—Aids to navigation on the Mississippi River and its tributaries in the Second Coast Guard District and parts of the Eighth Coast Guard District generally conform to the lateral system of buoyage. The following differences are significant:

1. Buoys are not numbered.

2. The numbers on lights and daybeacons do not have lateral significance; they indicate the mileage from a designated point downstream, normally the river mouth.

3. Flashing lights on the left side proceeding upstream show single green or white flashes while those on the right side show double (group flashing) red or white flashes.

4. "Crossing daymarks" are used to indicate where the channel crosses from one side of the river to the other.

417. The Uniform State Waterway Marking System (USWMS) was developed jointly by the U. S. Coast Guard and state boating administrators to assist the small craft operator in those state waters marked by participating states. The USWMS consists of two categories of aids to navigation. One is a system of aids to navigation, generally compatible with the Federal lateral system of buoyage, to supplement the federal system in state waters. The other is a system of regulatory markers to warn the small craft operator of dangers or to provide general information and directions.

On a well-defined channel, including a river or other relatively narrow, natural or improved waterway, solid colored red and black buoys are established in pairs (called "gates"), one on each side of the navigable channel which they mark, and opposite to each other to inform the user that the channel lies between the buoys and that he should pass between the buoys. The buoy which marks the left side of the channel viewed looking upstream or toward the head of navigation is colored all black; the buoy which marks the right side of the channel is colored all red.

On an irregularly-defined channel, solid colored buoys may be staggered on alternate sides of the channel but spaced at sufficiently close intervals to inform the user that the channel lies between the buoys and that he should pass between the buoys.

When there is no well-defined channel or when a body of water is obstructed by objects whose nature or location is such that the obstruction can be approached by a vessel from more than one direction, aids to navigation having cardinal meaning may be used. The aids conforming to the cardinal system consist of three distinctly colored buoys:

1. A white buoy with a red top is used to indicate to a vessel operator that he must pass to the south or west of the buoy.

2. A white buoy with a black top is used to indicate to a vessel operator that he must pass to the north or east of the buoy.

3. A buoy showing alternate vertical red and white stripes is used to indicate to a vessel operator that an obstruction to navigation extends from the nearest shore to the buoy and that he must not pass between the buoy and the nearest shore.

The shape of buoys has no significance in the USWMS.

Regulatory buoys are colored white with international orange horizontal bands completely around the buoy circumference. One band is at the top of the buoy with a second band just above the waterline of the buoy so that both orange bands are clearly visible from approaching vessels.

Geometric shapes are placed on the white portion of the buoy body and are colored international orange. The authorized geometric shapes and meanings associated with them are as follows:

1. A vertical open faced diamond shape means danger.

2. A vertical open faced diamond shape having a cross centered in the diamond means that vessels are excluded from the marked area.

3. A circular shape means that vessels in the marked area are subject to certain operating restrictions.

4. A square or rectangular shape indicates that directions or information is contained inside.

Regulatory markers consist of square and rectangular shaped signs displayed from a fixed structure. Each sign is white with an international orange border. Geometric shapes with the same meanings as those displayed on buoys are centered on the sign boards. The geometric shape displayed on a regulatory marker is intended to convey specific meaning to a vessel operator—whether or not he should stay well clear of the marker or may safely approach the marker in order to read any wording on the marker.

418. Private aids to navigation are those aids not established and maintained by the U. S. Coast Guard. Private aids include those established by other federal agencies with prior U. S. Coast Guard approval, those aids to navigation on marine structures or other works which the owners are legally obligated to establish, maintain, and operate as prescribed by the U. S. Coast Guard, and those aids which are merely desired, for one reason or another, by the individual, corporation, state or local government, or other body that has established the aid with U. S. Coast Guard approval.

Before any private aid to navigation consisting of a fixed structure is placed in the navigable waters of the United States, authorization to erect such structure shall first be obtained from the District Engineer, U. S. Army Corps of Engineers, in whose district the aid will be located.

Private aids to navigation are similar to the aids established and maintained by the U. S. Coast Guard, but are specially designated on the chart and *Light List*.

Although private aids to navigation are inspected periodically by the U. S. Coast Guard, the mariner should exercise special caution when using them for general navigation.

419. Protection by law.—All aids to navigation, including private aids, are protected by law (14 USC 83). The *Code of Federal Regulations* (33 CFR 70) refers.

It is unlawful to take possession of or make use of for any purpose, or build upon, alter, deface, destroy, move, injure, obstruct by fastening vessels thereto or otherwise, or in any manner whatever impair the usefulness of any aid to navigation established and maintained by the United States or with approval of the U. S. Coast Guard.

Whenever any vessel collides with an aid to navigation established and maintained by the United States or any private aid established or maintained in accordance with 33 CFR 64, 67, or 68, or is connected with any such collision, it shall be the duty of the person in charge of such vessel to report the accident to the nearest Officer in Charge, Office of Marine Inspection, U. S. Coast Guard.

CHAPTER V
THE NAUTICAL CHART

General Information

501. Introduction.—A nautical chart is a conventional graphic representation, on a plane surface, of a navigable portion of the surface of the earth. It shows the depth of water by numerous soundings, and sometimes by soundings and depth contours, the shoreline of adjacent land, topographic features that may serve as landmarks, aids to navigation, dangers, and other information of interest to navigators. It is designed as a work sheet on which courses may be plotted, and positions ascertained. It assists the navigator in avoiding dangers and arriving safely at his destination. The nautical chart is one of the most essential and reliable aids available to the navigator.

502. Projections.—Nearly all nautical charts used for ordinary purposes of navigation are constructed on the Mercator projection (art. 305). Large-scale harbor charts are sometimes constructed on the transverse Mercator projection. Charts for special purposes, such as great-circle sailing or polar navigation, are on appropriate projections; great-circle sailing charts are usually on the gnomonic projection (art. 317); polar charts are often on the polar stereographic projection (art. 318). The principal projections, with their navigational uses, are discussed in chapter III.

503. Scale.—The *scale* of a chart is the ratio of a given distance on the chart to the actual distance which it represents on the earth. It may be expressed in various ways. The most common are:

A simple ratio or fraction known as the **representative fraction.** For example, 1:80,000 or $\frac{1}{80,000}$ means that one unit (such as an inch) on the chart represents 80,000 of the same unit on the surface of the earth. This scale is sometimes called the **natural** or **fractional scale.**

A statement of that distance on the earth shown in one unit (usually an inch) on the chart, or vice versa. For example, "30 miles to the inch" means that 1 inch on the chart represents 30 miles of the earth's surface. Similarly, "2 inches to a mile" indicates that 2 inches on the chart represent 1 mile on the earth. This is sometimes called the **numerical scale.**

Graphic scale. A line or bar may be drawn at a convenient place on the chart and subdivided into nautical miles, yards, etc. All charts vary somewhat in scale from point to point, and in some projections the scale is not the same in all directions about a single point. A single subdivided line or bar for use over an entire chart is shown only when the chart is of such scale and projection that the scale varies a negligible amount over the chart, usually one of about 1:75,000 or larger. Since 1 minute of latitude is very nearly equal to 1 nautical mile, the latitude scale serves as an approximate graphical scale. On most nautical charts the east and west borders are subdivided to facilitate distance measurements.

On a Mercator chart the scale varies with the latitude. This is noticeable on a chart covering a relatively large distance in a north-south direction. On such a chart the scale at the latitude in question should be used for measuring distances.

Of the various methods of indicating scale, the graphical method is normally available in some form on the chart. In addition, the scale is customarily stated on charts on which the scale does not change appreciably over the chart.

The ways of expressing the scale of a chart are readily interchangeable. For instance, in a nautical mile there are about 6,076.11549 feet or 6,076.11549×12=72,913.39 inches. If the natural scale of a chart is 1:80,000, one inch of the chart represents 80,000 inches of the earth, or a little more than a mile. To find the exact amount, divide the scale by the number of inches in a mile, or $\frac{80,000}{72,913.39}$=1.097. Thus, a scale of 1:80,000 is the same as a scale of 1.097 (or approximately 1.1) miles to an inch. Stated another way, there are $\frac{72,913.39}{80,000}$=0.911 (approximately 0.9) inch to a mile. Similarly, if the scale is 60 nautical miles to an inch, the representative fraction is 1:(60×72,913.39)=1:4,374,803. Table 37 provides the scale equivalents.

A chart covering a relatively large area is called a *small-scale* chart and one covering a relatively small area is called a *large-scale* chart. Since the terms are relative, there is no sharp division between the two. Thus, a chart of scale 1:100,000 is large scale when compared with a chart of 1:1,000,000 but small scale when compared with one of 1:25,000.

504. Chart classification by scale.—Charts are constructed on many different scales, ranging from about 1:2,500 to 1:14,000,000 (and even smaller for some world charts). Small-scale charts covering large areas are used for planning and for offshore navigation. Charts of larger scale, covering smaller areas, should be used as the vessel approaches pilot waters. Several methods of classifying charts according to scale are in use in various nations. The following classifications of nautical charts are those used by the National Ocean Survey:

Sailing charts are the smallest scale charts used for planning, fixing position at sea, and for plotting the dead reckoning while proceeding on a long voyage. The scale is generally smaller than 1:600,000. The shoreline and topography are generalized and only offshore soundings, the principal navigational lights, outer buoys, and landmarks visible at considerable distances are shown.

General charts are intended for coastwise navigation outside of outlying reefs and shoals. The scales range from about 1:150,000 to 1:600,000.

Coast charts are intended for inshore coastwise navigation where the course may lie inside outlying reefs and shoals, for entering or leaving bays and harbors of considerable width, and for navigating large inland waterways. The scales range from about 1:50,000 to 1:150,000.

Harbor charts are intended for navigation and anchorage in harbors and small waterways. The scale is generally larger than 1:50,000.

In the classification system used by the Defense Mapping Agency Hydrographic Center, the sailing charts are incorporated in the general charts classification (smaller than about 1:150,000); those coast charts especially useful for approaching more confined waters (bays, harbors) are classified as **approach charts.**

505. Accuracy.—The accuracy of a chart depends upon:

1. *Thoroughness and up-to-dateness of the survey and other navigational information.* Some estimate of the accuracy of the survey can be formed by an examination of the source notes given in the title of the chart. If the chart is based upon very old surveys, it should be used with caution. Many of the earlier surveys were made under conditions

that were not conducive to great accuracy. It is safest to question every chart based upon surveys of doubtful accuracy.

The number of soundings and their spacing is some indication of the completeness of the survey. Only a small fraction of the soundings taken in a thorough survey are shown on the chart, but sparse or unevenly distributed soundings indicate that the survey was probably not made in detail. Large or irregular blank areas, or absence of depth contours (commonly called **depth curves**), generally indicate lack of soundings in the area. If the water surrounding such a blank area is deep, there is generally considerable depth in the blank; conversely, shallow water surrounding such an area indicates the strong possibility of shoal water. If neighboring areas abound in rocks or are particularly uneven, the blank area should be regarded with additional suspicion. However, it should be kept in mind that relatively few soundings are shown when there is a large number of depth contours or where the bottom is flat or gently and evenly sloping. Additional soundings are shown when they are helpful in indicating the uneven character of a rough bottom (figs. 505a and 505b).

Even a detailed survey may fail to locate every rock or pinnacle, and in waters where their existence is suspected, the best methods for determining their presence are wire drag surveys. Areas that have been dragged may be indicated on the chart and a note added to show the effective depth at which the drag was operated.

Changes in the contour of the bottom are relatively rapid in areas where there are strong currents or heavy surf, particularly when the bottom is composed principally of soft mud or sand. The entrances to bar harbors are especially to be regarded with suspicion. Similarly, there is sometimes a strong tendency for dredged channels to shoal, especially if they are surrounded by sand or mud, and cross currents exist. Notes are sometimes shown on the chart when the bottom contours are known to change rapidly. However, the absence of such a note should not be regarded as evidence that rapid change does not occur.

Changes in aids to navigation, structures, etc., are more easily determined, and charts are generally corrected in this regard to the date of printing. However, there is always the possibility of a change having occurred since the chart was printed. All issues of *Notice to Mariners* printed after that date (art. 506) should be checked to insure accuracy in this respect.

2. *Suitability of the scale for the design and intended navigational use.* The same detail cannot be shown on a small-scale chart as on one of a larger scale. On small-scale charts detailed information, including minor aids to navigation, is omitted or generalized in the areas covered by larger scale charts. Therefore, it is good practice to use the largest scale chart available when in the vicinity of shoals or other dangers.

3. *Presentation and adequacy of data.* The amount and kind of detail to be shown, and the method of presentation, are continually under study by charting agencies. Development of a new navigational aid may render many previous charts inadequate. An example is radar. Many of the charts produced before radar became available lack the detail needed for reliable identification of targets.

Part of the responsibility for the continuing accuracy of charts lies with the user. If charts are to remain reliable, they must be corrected as indicated by the *Notice to Mariners*. In addition, the user's reports of errors and changes and his suggestions often are useful to the publishing agencies in correcting and improving their charts. Navigators and maritime activities have contributed much to the reliability and usefulness of the modern nautical chart. If a chart becomes wet, the expansion and subsequent shrinkage when the chart dries are likely to cause distortion.

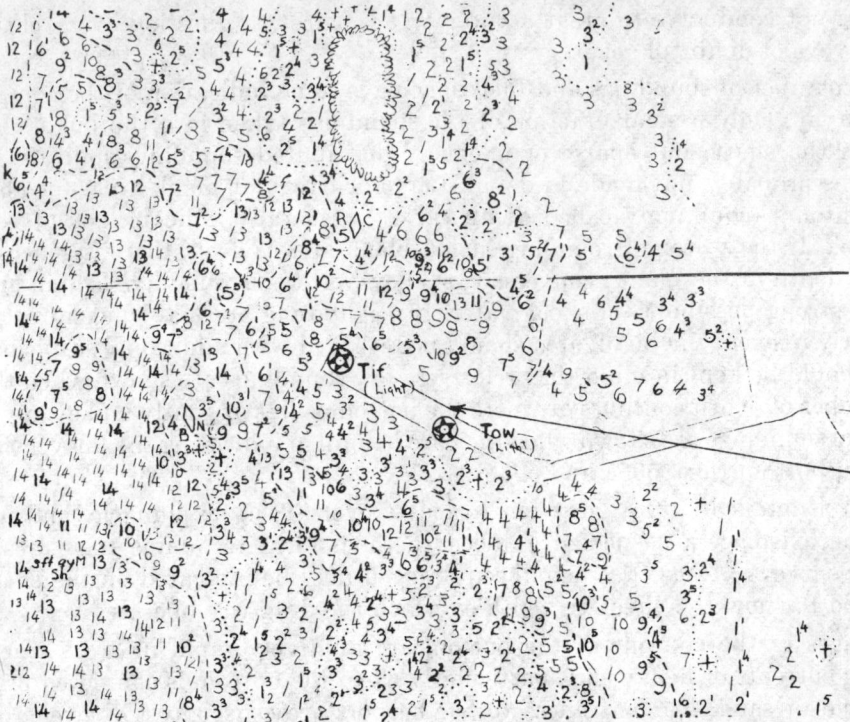

FIGURE 505a.—Part of a boat sheet, showing the soundings obtained in a survey.

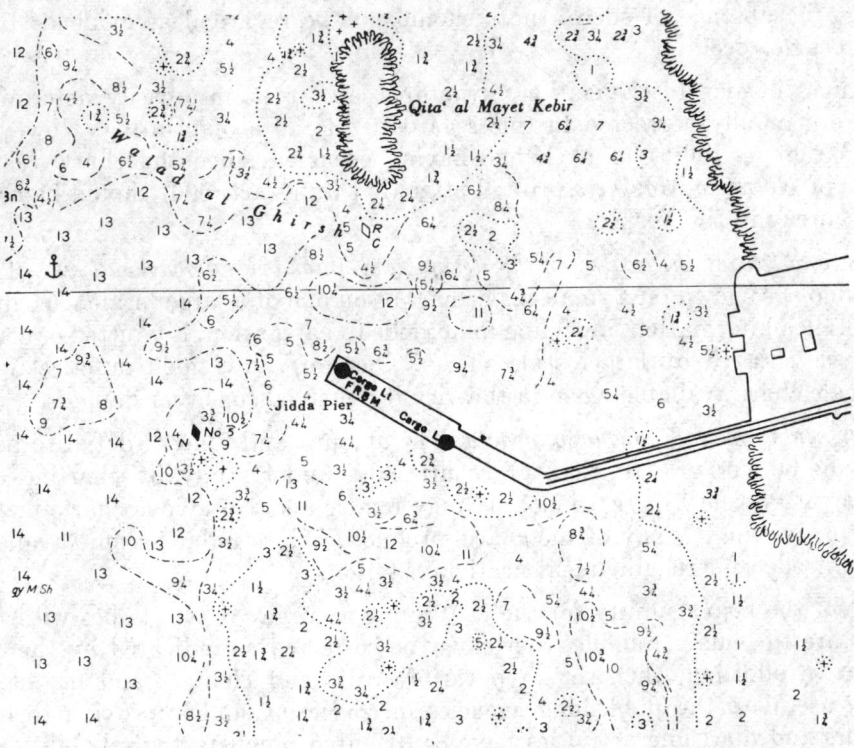

FIGURE 505b.—Part of a nautical chart made from the boat sheet of figure 505a. Compare the number of soundings in the two figures.

1st Ed., July 1956

KILOMETERS NAUTICAL MILE

CATALOG: REGION 9

QUARANTINE ANCHORAGE

59'   155°   54" 01'   30"   02'

43°01'25"N
155°02'36"E

NORTH PACIFIC

SUITLAND ISLAND

PORT MAURY

From U.S. Navy surveys to 1960
with additions and corrections to 1976

SOUNDINGS IN FATHOMS
(Under 11 in fathoms and feet)
reduced to Lowest Low Water

HEIGHTS IN FEET
Contour Interval 100 feet

For Symbols and Abbreviations, See Chart No. 1

MERCATOR PROJECTION
WORLD GEODETIC SYSTEM—1972 DATUM

SCALE 1:20,000

TŌKYŌ DATUM ADJUSTMENT

This chart is on World Geodetic System—72
Datum. To place this chart on the Tōkyō
Datum, shift all parallels 3.6 seconds north,
and all meridians 10.4 seconds west.

NOTE

The area tinted green has been swept in 1975
to various depths indicated in feet—for example, 40.

MAGNETIC

VAR 23°00' W (1975)
ANNUAL CHANGE 2'W

Gillis Sta.

Mast

Tanks

Lt

CHY
(conspic)

Chy

MAURY

Tanks

Piles
Chys

Fl G 4sec
Dredged to 25 feet (1975)
Fl R 4sec
FS
Weir Pt.
Tanks
FG
FG
Occ G 6sec 46ft 12M
R Bn
Lights in line 087°
Flinders
Shipyard
TR
AERO
Alt Fl WR
RDF
Goldsborough
Park
Chauvenet
University
Occ R 6sec 46ft 12M
SIREN
185

Submerged jetty
crs S Sh
Cranes
Tk
Luce Hall
Weems Airport
Cem
Tank

Harbor Limit

Int Qk Fl
R Bn
Obstr

Lecky Shoal
Rust Pt.
WHIS

43°
54"

Dutton Rks

BELL

Beito I
(25)

R Bn
"Maury"
Gp Fl (2) 10sec 55ft 14M
DIA
302
Uncov 5 ft
hrd S Co
G Sh
40

Ageton Reef
Uncov 1 ft
Uncov 3 ft

MT BOWDITCH
882
800
700
600
500
400
300
200
100
Bn

Point Sumner
Occ R 5sec 140ft 18M
Obstr
Wk

Neatlines 7.58" N.S., 11.38" E.W.

154°58'10"E
42°59'15"N
154°58'10"E

54" 59'   30"   155°   01'   02'

LOGARITHMIC SPEED SCALE

YARDS (IN THOUSANDS)

DEPTH
CONVERSION
SCALE

FEET   METERS   FATHOMS

Left margin labels:
Anchorage
Coarse sand
Compass rose
...and feet
Wire drag
Fathoms
...depth is ...clearance
...signal
...water
...datum
...dies
...wire
Chart with soundings

Right margin labels:
Chimney, conspicuous
Dangerous wreck with only mast visible
Logarithmic Speed Scale usually shown here
(1:40,000 and larger)
Heights of land and conspicuous objects are given
in feet above Mean High Water, unless otherwise
stated in the title of the chart.
Aeronautical light and radio direction finding station
Mooring buoy
Marsh area
Submarine cable
Rock which covers and uncovers with height
above chart sounding datum
Topographic contours
Obstruction
Dangerous wreck over which depth is known
High obstruction above swept depth

4th Ed., July 3, 1976

Users should refer corrections, addi-
tions, and comments for improving
this product to: DIRECTOR, DEFENSE
MAPPING AGENCY HYDROGRAPHIC
CENTER, Washington, D.C. 20390.
ATTN: Code PR

Prepared and published by the
DEFENSE MAPPING AGENCY HYDROGRAPHIC CENTER
Washington, D.C. 20390

WARNING

The prudent mariner will not rely solely on any single
aid to navigation, particularly on floating aids. See
paragraph No. 1 of Notice to Mariners No. 1 or Sailing
Directions Planning Guides for DMAHC Charts.

Port Maury
SOUNDINGS IN FATHOMS—SCALE 1:20,000

00000

DMA STOCK NO.
97AHA00000

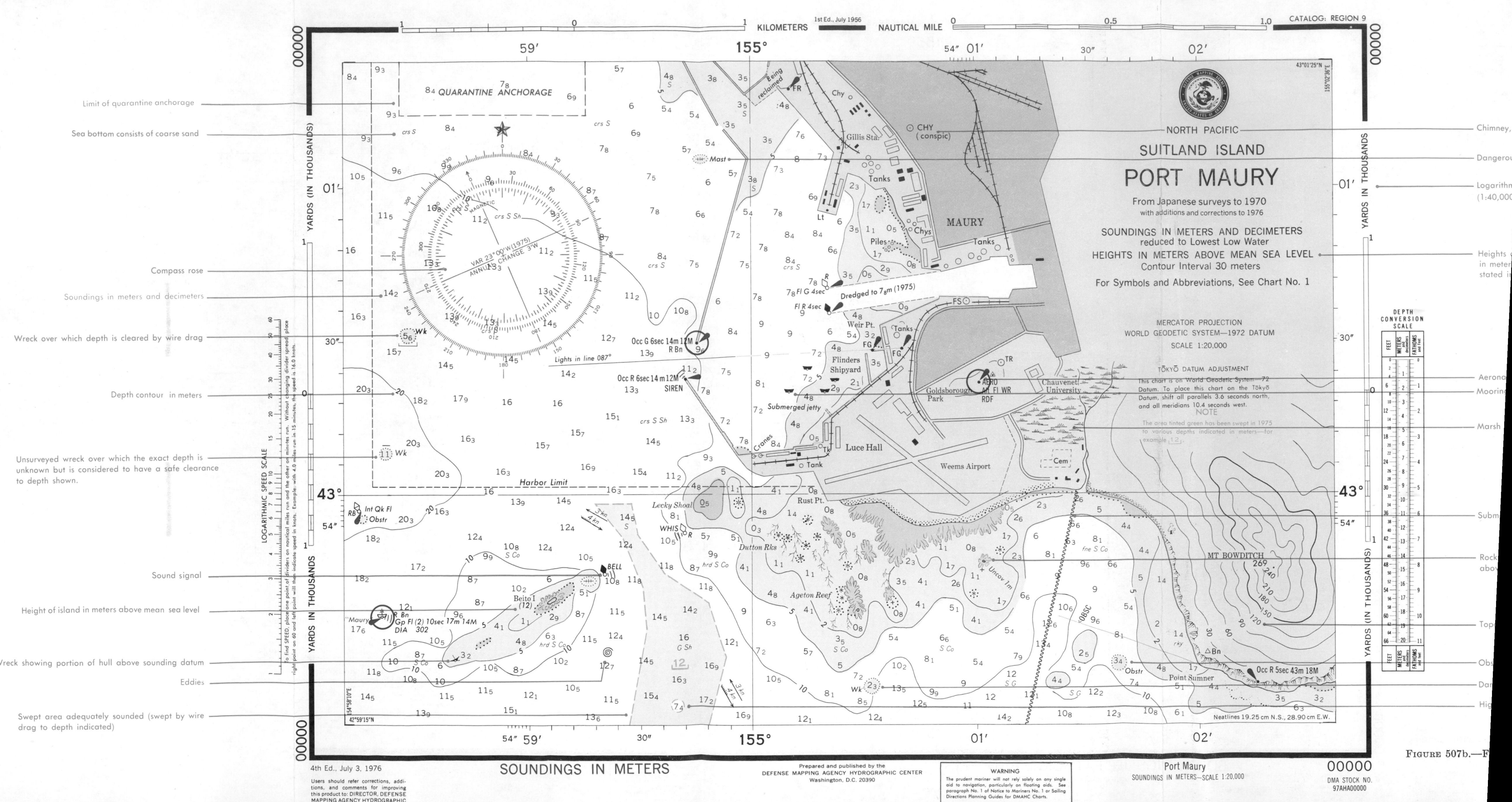

SOUNDINGS IN METERS

1st Ed., July 1956

KILOMETERS   NAUTICAL MILE

CATALOG: REGION 9

NORTH PACIFIC

SUITLAND ISLAND

PORT MAURY

From Japanese surveys to 1970
with additions and corrections to 1976

SOUNDINGS IN METERS AND DECIMETERS
reduced to Lowest Low Water

HEIGHTS IN METERS ABOVE MEAN SEA LEVEL
Contour Interval 30 meters

For Symbols and Abbreviations, See Chart No. 1

MERCATOR PROJECTION
WORLD GEODETIC SYSTEM—1972 DATUM

SCALE 1:20,000

TŌKYŌ DATUM ADJUSTMENT

This chart is on World Geodetic System—72
Datum. To place this chart on the Tōkyō
Datum, shift all parallels 3.6 seconds north,
and all meridians 10.4 seconds west.
NOTE

The area tinted green has been swept in 1975
to various depths indicated in meters—for
example (12).

Limit of quarantine anchorage

Sea bottom consists of coarse sand

Compass rose

Soundings in meters and decimeters

Wreck over which depth is cleared by wire drag

Depth contour in meters

Unsurveyed wreck over which the exact depth is
unknown but is considered to have a safe clearance
to depth shown.

Sound signal

Height of island in meters above mean sea level

Wreck showing portion of hull above sounding datum

Eddies

Swept area adequately sounded (swept by wire
drag to depth indicated)

QUARANTINE ANCHORAGE

VAR 23°00'W(1975)
ANNUAL CHANGE 3'W

Lights in line 087°

Occ G 6sec 14m 12M
R Bn

Occ R 6sec 14m 12M
SIREN

Harbor Limit

Int Qk Fl
Obstr

Lecky Shoal

WHIS

Dutton Rks

BELL

Beito I (12)

"Maury"
Bn
Gp Fl (2) 10sec 17m 14M
DIA 302

Being
reclaimed
FR

Chy

CHY
(conspic)

Gillis Star

Mast

Tanks

Lt

Piles

MAURY

Tanks

Fl G 4sec
Dredged to 7₈m (1975)

Fl R 4sec

Weir Pt.

FG

Flinders
Shipyard

FG

Submerged jetty

Cranes

Tank

AERO
Al Fl WR
RDF

TR

Goldsborough
Park

Chauvenet
University

Luce Hall

Weems Airport

Cem

Rust Pt.

Ageton Reef

Uncov 1m

OBSC

MT BOWDITCH
269
240
210
180
150
120
90

Point Sumner

Occ R 5sec 43m 18M

Neatlines 19.25 cm N.S., 28.90 cm E.W.

DEPTH
CONVERSION
SCALE

Chimney,

Dangerous

Logarithmic
(1:40,000

Heights
in meters
stated in

Aeronautical

Mooring

Marsh

Rock

Topo

Obstr

Danger

High

4th Ed., July 3, 1976

Users should refer corrections, addi-
tions, and comments for improving
this product to: DIRECTOR, DEFENSE
MAPPING AGENCY HYDROGRAPHIC
CENTER, Washington, D.C. 20390.
ATTN: Code PR

Prepared and published by the
DEFENSE MAPPING AGENCY HYDROGRAPHIC CENTER
Washington, D.C. 20390

SOUNDINGS IN METERS

WARNING
The prudent mariner will not rely solely on any single
aid to navigation, particularly on floating aids. See
paragraph No. 1 of Notice to Mariners No. 1 or Sailing
Directions Planning Guides for DMAHC Charts.

Port Maury
SOUNDINGS IN METERS—SCALE 1:20,000

00000

DMA STOCK NO.
97AHA00000

FIGURE 507b.—F

506. Dates on charts.—The system of dates now used on charts published by the Defense Mapping Agency Hydrographic Center and the National Ocean Survey is as follows:

First edition. The original date of issue of a new chart is shown at the top center margin, thus:

1st Ed., Sept. 1950

New edition. A new edition is made when, at the time of printing, the corrections are too numerous or too extensive to be reported in *Notice to Mariners*, making previous printings obsolete. The date of the first edition is retained at the top margin. At the lower left-hand corner it is replaced by the number and date of the new edition. The latter date is the same as that of the latest *Notice to Mariners* to which the chart has been corrected, thus:

5th Ed., July 11, 1970

Revised print. A revised print published by the National Ocean Survey may contain corrections which have been published in *Notice to Mariners* but does not supersede a current edition. The date of the revision is shown to the right of the edition date, thus:

5th Ed., July 11, 1970; Revised 4/12/75.

Reprint. A reprint is initiated by a low stock situation and is a reprint of the chart with a limited number of corrections from *Notice to Mariners*. The magnetic variation data on a reprint published by the Defense Mapping Agency Hydrographic Center is updated to the latest epoch at the time of printing.

Chart Reading

507. Chart symbols.—Much of the information contained on charts is shown by conventional symbols which make no attempt at accuracy in scale or detail, but are shown at the correct location and make possible the showing of a large amount of information without congestion or confusion. The standard symbols and abbreviations which have been approved for use on regular nautical charts published by the United States of America are shown in Chart No. 1, *Nautical Chart Symbols and Abbreviations* (app. Z). A knowledge of the meanings of these symbols is essential to a full understanding of charts. Fictitious sample charts (figs. 507a and 507b) show some of these symbols.

Most of the symbols and abbreviations shown in Chart No. 1 are in agreement with those recommended by the International Hydrographic Organization (IHO). Symbol and abbreviation status is indicated by alphanumeric style differences in the first column of Chart No. 1. The status is explained in the general remarks section of Chart No. 1.

The symbols and abbreviations on any given chart may differ somewhat from those shown in Chart No. 1 because of a change in the standards since printing of the chart or because the chart was published by an agency having a different set of standards.

508. Lettering.—Certain standards regarding lettering have been adopted, except on charts made from reproducibles furnished by foreign nations.

Vertical type is used for features which are dry at high water and not affected by movement of the water, except for heights above water.

Slanting type is used for water, underwater, and floating features, except soundings.

The type of lettering used may be the only means of determining whether a feature may be visible at high tide. For instance, a rock might bear the title "‗‗‗‗‗‗Rock" whether or not it extends above the surface. If the name is given in vertical letters, the rock constitutes a small islet; if in slanting type, the rock constitutes a reef.

509. The shoreline shown on nautical charts represents the line of contact between the land and a selected water elevation. In areas affected by tidal fluctuations, this line of contact is usually the mean high-water line. In confined coastal waters of diminished tidal influence, a mean water level line may be used. The shoreline of interior waters (rivers, lakes) is usually a line representing a specified elevation above a selected datum. A shoreline is symbolized by a heavy line. A broken line indicates that the charted position is approximate only. The nature of the shore may be indicated, as shown by the symbols in part A of Chart No. 1.

Where the low-water line differs considerably from the high-water line, the low-water line may be indicated by dots in the case of mud, sand, gravel, or stones, with the kind of material indicated, and by a characteristic symbol in the case of rock or coral. The area alternately covered and uncovered may be shown by a tint which is usually a combination of the land tint and a blue water tint as shown in figures 507a and 507b.

The apparent shoreline is used on charts to show the outer edge of marine vegetation where that limit would reasonably appear as the shoreline to the mariner, or where it prevents the shoreline from being clearly defined. The apparent shoreline is symbolized by a light line. The inner edge is marked by a broken line when no other symbol (such as a cliff, levee, etc.) furnishes such a limit. The area between inner and outer limits may be given the combined land-water tint or the land tint.

510. Water areas.—Soundings or depths of water are shown in several ways. Individual soundings are shown by numbers. These do not follow the general rule for lettering. They may be either vertical or slanting, or both may be used on the same chart to distinguish between the data based upon different surveys, different datums, smaller scale charts, or furnished by different authorities.

The unit of measurement used for soundings on each chart is shown in large block letters at the top and bottom of the chart. When the unit of measurement is meters or meters and decimeters, SOUNDINGS IN METERS is shown. When soundings in fathoms or fathoms and fractions are used, SOUNDINGS IN FATHOMS is shown, and when the soundings are in fathoms and feet, SOUNDINGS IN FATHOMS AND FEET is shown.

A depth conversion scale is placed outside the neatline on the chart for use in converting charted depths to feet, meters, or fathoms.

"No bottom" soundings are indicated by a number with a line over the top and a dot over the line, thus: $\dot{\overline{45}}$. This indicates that the spot was sounded to the depth indicated without reaching the bottom. Areas which have been wire dragged (fig. 510a) are shown by a broken limiting line, and the clear effective depth is indicated, with a characteristic symbol under the numbers.

On charts of the Defense Mapping Agency Hydrographic Center, a purple tint is shown within the limits of the swept area unless such tinting would result in excessive use of purple, in which case a green tint is shown within the limits of the swept area.

The soundings are supplemented by a series of *depth contours* (fig. 510b) connecting points of equal depth. These lines present a graphic indication of the configuration of the bottom. The types of lines used for various depths are shown in part R of Chart No. 1. On some charts depth contours are shown in solid lines, the depth represented by each being shown by numbers placed in breaks in the lines, as with land contours. Solid line depth contours are derived from intensively developed hydrographic surveys.

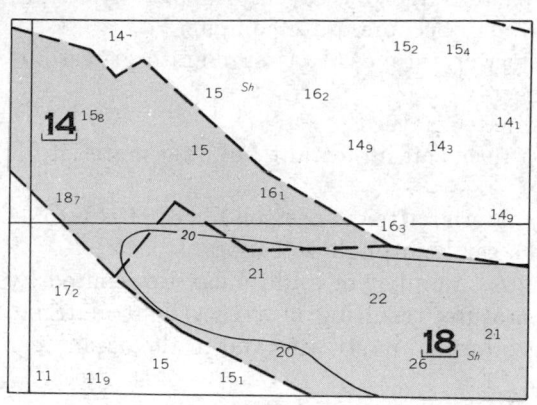

FIGURE 510a.—Swept area.

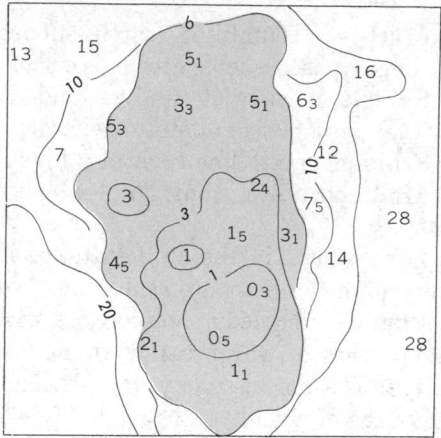

FIGURE 510b.—Depth contours.

A broken or indefinite contour is substituted for a solid depth contour whenever the reliability of the contour is questionable. Depth contours are labeled with numerals in the unit of measurement of the soundings. This type chart, presenting a more detailed indication of the bottom configuration with fewer numerical soundings, is particularly useful to the vessel equipped with an echo sounder permitting continuous determination of a profile of the bottom. Such a chart, to be reliable, can be made only for areas which have been surveyed in great detail.

Areas which uncover at low tide are tinted as indicated in article 509. Those areas out to a given depth often are given a blue tint, and occasionally a lighter blue is carried to some greater depth. On older charts the one-, two-, and three-fathom curves have stippled edges. Charts designed to give maximum emphasis to the configuration of the bottom show depths, beyond the 100-fathom curve, over the entire chart by depth contours similar to the contours shown on land areas to indicate graduations in height. These are called *bottom contour* or *bathymetric* charts.

The side limits of dredged channels are indicated by broken lines. The *project depth* (art. 2715) and the date of dredging, if known, are shown by a statement in or along the channel. The possibility of silting should be considered. Local authorities should be consulted for the *controlling depth* (art. 2715).

The chart scale is generally too small to permit all soundings to be shown. In the selection of soundings to be shown, *least* depths are generally chosen first and a sounding pattern worked out to provide safety, a practical presentation of the bottom configuration, and a neat appearance. Depths greater than those indicated may be found close to charted depths, but steep changes in depth are given every consideration in sounding selection. Also, the state of the tide affects the depth at any given moment. An isolated shoal sounding should be approached with caution, or avoided, unless it is known that the area has been wire dragged, for there is always the possibility that a depth less than the least shown may have escaped detection. Also, the shoal area near a coast little frequented by vessels is sometimes not surveyed with the same thoroughness as other areas. Such areas and those where rocks, coral, etc., are known to exist should be entered with caution, or avoided.

The substance forming the bottom is shown by abbreviations, as listed in part S of Chart No. 1. The meaning of some of the less-well-known terms is given below:

Ooze is a soft, slimy, organic sediment composed principally of shells or other hard parts of minute organisms.

Marl is a crumbling, earthy deposit, particularly one of clay mixed with sand, lime, decomposed shells, etc. A layer of marl may become quite compact.

Shingle consists of small, rounded, waterworn stones. It is similar to gravel but with the average size of stone generally larger.

Schist is crystalline rock of a finely laminated nature.

Madrepore is a stony coral which often forms an important building material for reefs.

Lava is rock in the fluid state, or such material after it has solidified. It is formed at very high temperature and issues from the earth through volcanoes.

Pumice is cooled volcanic glass with a great number of minute cavities caused by the expulsion of water vapor at high temperature, resulting in a very light material.

Tufa is a porous rocky deposit sometimes formed in streams and in the ocean near the mouths of rivers.

Scoria (plural *scoriae*) is rough, cinderlike lava.

Sea tangle is any of several species of seaweed, especially those of large size.

Spicules are the small skeletons of various marine animals such as sponges.

Foraminifera (plural) are small marine animals with hard shells of from one to many chambers.

Globigerina is a very small marine animal of the foraminifera order, with a chambered shell, or the shell of such an animal. In large areas of the ocean the calcareous shells of these animals are very numerous, being the principal constituent of a soft mud or **globigerina ooze,** forming part of the ocean bed.

Diatom is a microscopic animal with external skeletons of silica, often found in both fresh and salt water. Part of the ocean bed is composed of a sedimentary ooze consisting principally of large collections of the skeletal remains of diatoms.

Radiolaria (plural) are minute sea animals with a siliceous outer shell. The skeletons of these animals are very numerous, especially in the tropics.

Pteropod is a small marine animal with or without a shell and having two thin, winglike feet. These animals are often so numerous they cover the surface of the sea for miles. In some areas their shells cover the bottom.

Polyzoa (plural) are very small marine animals which reproduce by budding, many generations often being permanently connected by branchlike structures.

Cirripeda (plural) are barnacles and certain other parasitic marine animals.

Fucus is a coarse seaweed growing attached to rocks.

Matte is a dense, twisted growth of a sea plant such as grass.

"Calcareous" is an adjective meaning "containing or composed of calcium or one of its compounds."

511. Chart sounding datum.—*Depths.* All depths indicated on charts are reckoned from some selected level of the water, called the *chart sounding datum*. The various chart datums are explained in chapter XXXI. On charts made from surveys conducted by the United States the chart datum is selected with regard to the tides of the region, so that depths might be shown in their least favorable aspect. On charts based upon those of other nations the datum is that of the original authority. When it is known, the datum used is stated on the chart. In some cases where the chart is based upon old surveys, particularly in areas where the range of tide is not great, the actual chart datum may not be known.

For National Ocean Survey charts of the Atlantic and gulf coasts of the United States and Puerto Rico the chart datum is *mean low water*. For charts of the Pacific coast of the United States, including Alaska, it is *mean lower low water*. Most Defense Mapping Agency Hydrographic Center charts are based upon *mean low water, mean lower low water*, or *mean low water springs*. The chart datum for charts published by other countries varies greatly, but is usually lower than mean low water. On charts of the Baltic Sea, Black Sea, the Great Lakes, and other areas where tidal effects are small or without significance, the datum adopted is an arbitrary height approximating the mean water level.

The chart datum of the largest-scale charts of an area is generally the same as the reference level from which height of tide is tabulated in the tide tables.

The height of a chart datum is usually only an approximation of the actual mean value specified, for determination of the actual mean height usually requires a longer series of tidal observations than is available to the cartographer, and the height changes somewhat over a period of time.

Since the chart datum is generally a computed mean or average height at some state of the tide, the depth of water at any particular moment may be less than shown on the chart. For example, if the chart datum is *mean lower low water*, the depth of water at *lower low water* will be less than the charted depth about as often as it is greater. A lower depth is indicated in the tide tables by a minus sign (−).

Heights. The shoreline shown on charts is the high-water line, generally the level of mean high water. The heights of lights, rocks, islets, etc., are generally reckoned from this level. However, heights of islands, especially those at some distance from the coast, are often taken from sources other than hydrographic surveys, and may be reckoned from some other level, often mean sea level. The plane of reference for topographic detail is frequently not stated on the chart.

Since heights are usually reckoned from high water and depths from some form of low water, the reference levels are seldom the same. This is generally of little practical significance, but it might be of interest under some conditions, particularly where the range of tide is large.

512. Dangers are shown by appropriate symbols, as indicated in part O of Chart No. 1.

A rock that uncovers at mean high water may be shown as an islet. If an isolated, offlying rock is known to uncover at the chart datum but to be covered at high water, the appropriate symbol is shown and the height above the chart datum, if known, is usually given, either by statement such as *"Uncov 2 ft"* or by the figure indicating the number of feet above the chart datum underlined and usually enclosed in parentheses, thus: (2). This is illustrated in figure 512a. A rock which does not uncover is shown by the appropriate symbol. If it is considered a danger to surface vessels, the symbol is enclosed by a dotted curve for emphasis.

A distinctive symbol is used to show a detached coral reef which uncovers at the chart datum. For a coral or rocky reef which is submerged at chart datum, the sunken rock symbol or an appropriate statement is used, enclosed by a dotted or broken line if the limits have been determined.

Several different symbols are used for wrecks, depending upon the nature of the wreck or scale of the chart. The usual symbol for a visible wreck is shown in figure 512b. A sunken wreck with less than 11 fathoms of water over it is considered dangerous and its symbol is surrounded by a dotted curve. The safe clearance depth found over a wreck is indicated by a standard sounding number placed at the wreck, (fig. 512c). If this depth is determined by a wire drag, the sounding is underscored by the wire drag symbol (art. 510). An unsurveyed wreck over which the exact depth is unknown, but is considered to have a safe clearance to the depth shown is depicted as shown in figure 512c.

Tide rips, eddies, and kelp are shown by symbol or lettering.

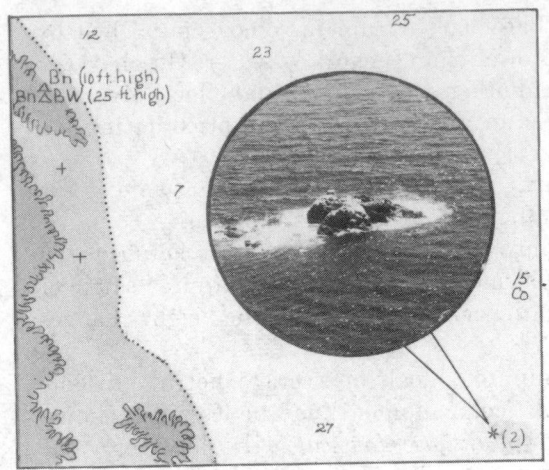

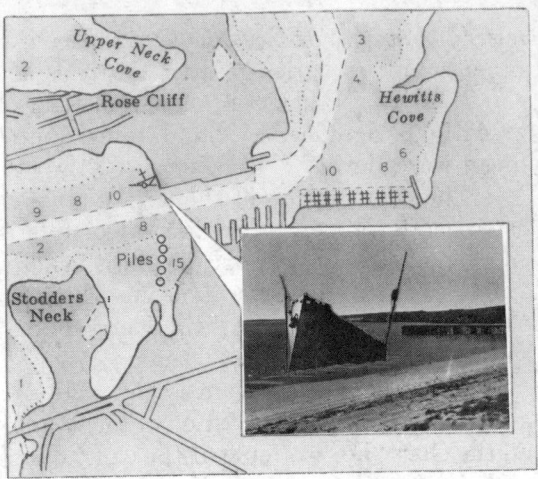

FIGURE 512a.—A rock awash.   FIGURE 512b.—A visible wreck.

Piles, dolphins (clusters of piles), snags, stumps, etc., are shown by small circles and a label identifying the type of obstruction. If such dangers are submerged, the letters "Subm" precede the label.

Fish stakes and traps are shown when known to be permanent or hazardous to navigation.

The importance of knowing the chart symbols for dangers to navigation cannot be emphasized strongly enough. Most dangers are emphasized with a blue tint and dotted line surrounding the danger. Some of the danger symbols are shown in figure 512c.

513. Aids to navigation are shown by symbol, as given in Chart. No 1, usually supplemented by abbreviations and sometimes by additional descriptive text. In order to render the symbols conspicuous it is necessary to show them in greatly exaggerated size relative to the scale of the chart. It is therefore important that the navigator know which part of the symbol represents the actual position of the aid. For floating aids (lightships and buoys), the position part of the symbol marks the approximate location of the anchor or sinker, the aid swinging in an orbit around this approximate position.

The principal charted aids to navigation are lighthouses, other lights on fixed structures, beacons, lightships, radiobeacons, and buoys. The number of aids shown and the amount of information concerning them varies with the scale of the chart. Unless otherwise indicated, lights which do not alternate in color are white, and alternating lights are red and white. Light lists give complete navigational information concerning them.

Lighthouses and *other lights on fixed structures* are shown as black dots surrounded by nautical purple disks or as black dots with purple flare symbols. The center of the black dot is the position of the light.

On large-scale charts the characteristics of lights are shown in the following order:

Characteristic	Example	Meaning
1. Character	Gp Fl	group flashing
2. Color	R	red
3. Period	(2) 10 sec	two flashes every 10 seconds
4. Height	160 ft	160 feet
5. Range	19M	19 nautical miles (See article 1307)
6. Number	"6"	light number 6

The legend for this light would appear on the chart:

Gp Fl R (2) 10 sec 160 ft 19 M "6"

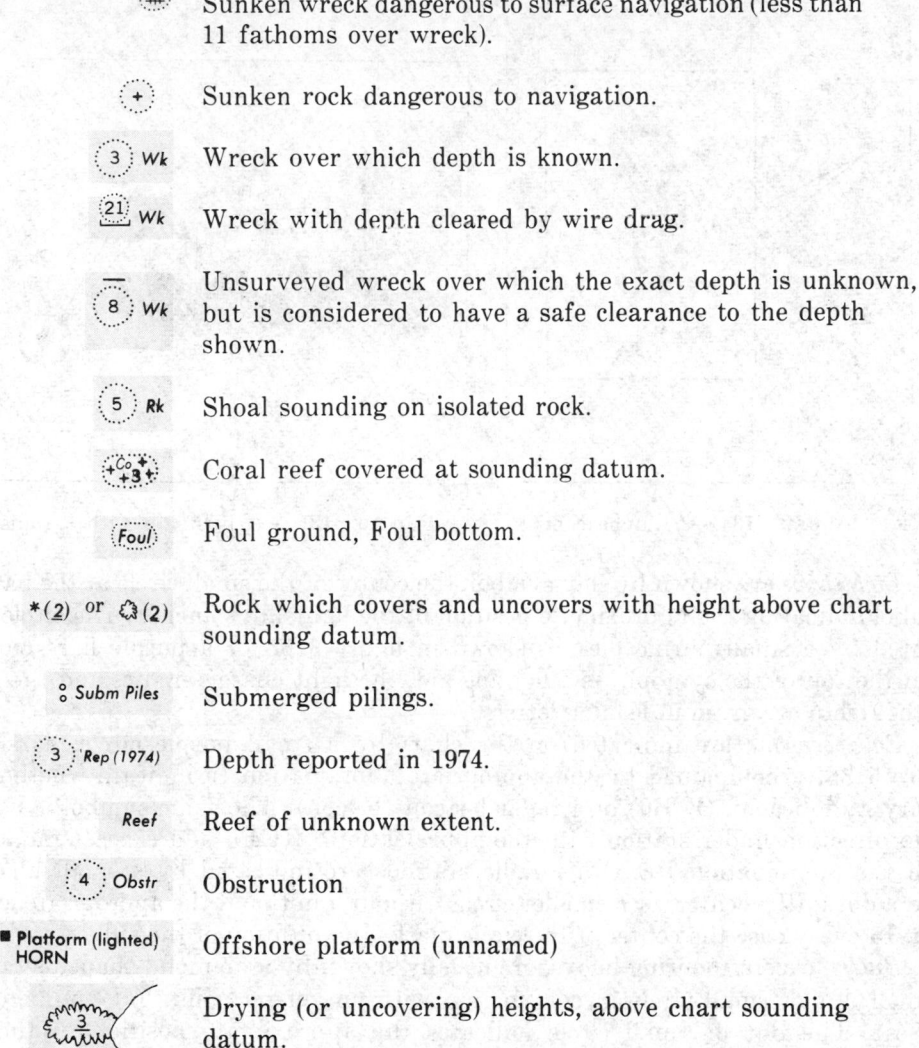

	Sunken wreck dangerous to surface navigation (less than 11 fathoms over wreck).
	Sunken rock dangerous to navigation.
3 Wk	Wreck over which depth is known.
21 Wk	Wreck with depth cleared by wire drag.
8 Wk	Unsurveved wreck over which the exact depth is unknown, but is considered to have a safe clearance to the depth shown.
5 Rk	Shoal sounding on isolated rock.
+Co +3+	Coral reef covered at sounding datum.
Foul	Foul ground, Foul bottom.
*(2) or (2)	Rock which covers and uncovers with height above chart sounding datum.
° Subm Piles	Submerged pilings.
3 Rep (1974)	Depth reported in 1974.
Reef	Reef of unknown extent.
4 Obstr	Obstruction
□ ■ Platform (lighted) HORN	Offshore platform (unnamed)
3	Drying (or uncovering) heights, above chart sounding datum.

FIGURE 512c.—Danger symbols.

On older charts this form is varied slightly. As the chart scale becomes smaller the six items listed above are omitted in the following order: first, height; second, period (seconds); third, number (of flashes, etc.) in group; fourth, light number; fifth, visibility. Names of unnumbered lights are shown when space permits.

Daybeacons (unlighted beacons) are shown as depicted in Chart No. 1. When daybeacons are shown by small triangles, the center of the triangle marks the position of the aid. Except on Intracoastal Waterway charts and charts of state waterways the abbreviation Bn is shown beside the symbol, with the appropriate abbreviation for color if known. For black beacons the triangle is solid black and there is no color abbreviation. All beacon abbreviations are in vertical lettering, as appropriate for fixed aids (fig. 513a).

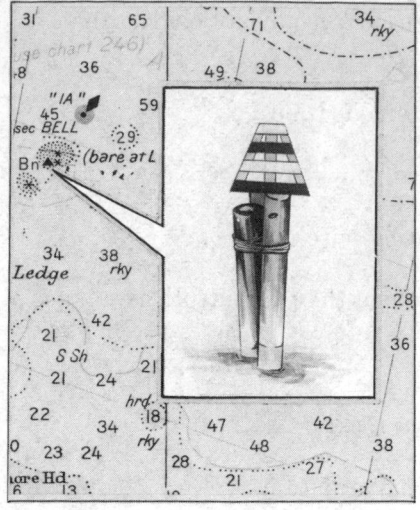

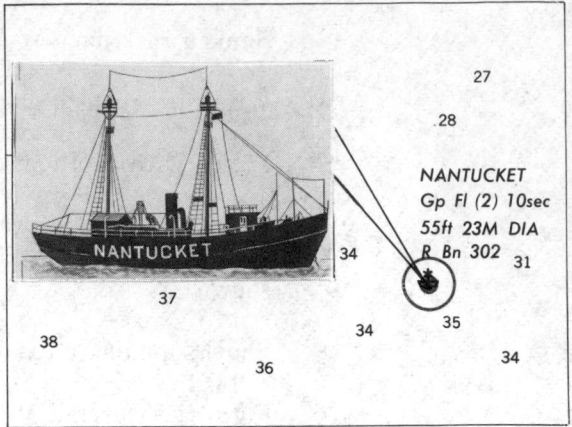

FIGURE 513a.—A daybeacon.   FIGURE 513b.—A lightship with a radiobeacon.

Lightships are shown by ship symbol, the center of the small circle at the base of the symbol indicating the approximate position of the lightship's anchor. The circle is overprinted by a small purple disk as shown in figure 513b or a purple flare emanating from the top of the symbol. As a floating aid, the light characteristics and the name of the lightship are given in leaning letters.

Radiobeacons are indicated on the chart by a small purple circle, as shown in figure 513b, accompanied by the appropriate abbreviation to indicate whether an ordinary radiobeacon (R Bn) or a radar beacon (Racon). The same symbol is used for a radio direction finder station with the abbreviation "RDF" and a coast radar station with the abbreviation Ra. Other radio stations are indicated by a small black circle with a dot in the center, or a smaller circle without a dot, and the appropriate abbreviation. In every case the center of the circle marks the position of the aid.

Buoys, except mooring buoys, are usually shown by a diamond-shaped symbol and a small dot or small circle in conjunction with one of its points (at one of its acute angles). The dot or small circle indicates the approximate position of the buoy's sinker. A mooring buoy is shown by a distinctive symbol as indicated in part L of Chart No. 1. The small circle interrupting the symbol's base line indicates the approximate position of the sinker.

A black buoy is shown by a solid black diamond symbol, without abbreviation. For all other buoys, color is indicated by an abbreviation, or in full by a note on the chart. In addition, the diamond-shaped symbols of red buoys often are colored purple. A buoy symbol with a line connecting the side points (shorter axis), half of the symbol being purple or open and the other half black, indicates horizontal bands. A line connecting the upper and lower points (longer axis) represents vertical stripes. Two lines connecting the opposite *sides* of the symbol indicate a checkered buoy.

There is no significance to the angle at which the diamond-shape appears on the chart. The symbol is placed so as to avoid interference with other features of the chart.

Lighted buoys are indicated by a purple flare emanating from the buoy symbol or by a small purple disk centered on the dot or small circle indicating the approximate position of the buoy's sinker, as shown in figure 513c.

Abbreviations for light characteristics, type and color of buoy, number of the buoy, and any other pertinent information given near the symbol are in slanting letters. The

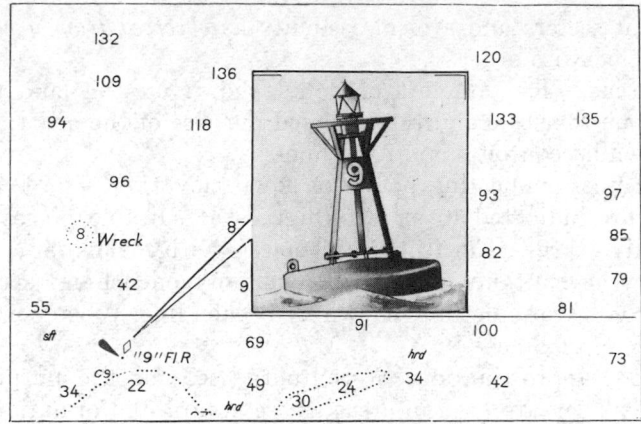

FIGURE 513c.—A lighted buoy.

letter *C*, *N*, or *S*, indicates a can, nun. or spar, respectively (art. 409). The words "bell," "gong," and "whistle," are shown as *BELL*, *GONG*, and *WHIS*, respectively. The number or letter designation of the buoy is given in quotation marks on National Ocean Survey charts. On other charts they may be given without quotation marks or punctuation, thus: No 1, No 2, etc.

Station buoys are not shown on small-scale charts, but are given on some large-scale charts.

Aeronautical lights included in the light lists are shown by the lighthouse symbol, accompanied by the abbreviation "AERO." The completeness to which the characteristics are shown depends principally upon the effective range of other navigational lights in the vicinity, and the usefulness of the light for marine navigation.

Ranges are indicated by a broken or solid line. The solid line, which indicates that part of the range intended for navigation, may be broken at irregular intervals to avoid being drawn through soundings. That part of the range line drawn only to guide the eye to the objects to be kept in range is broken at regular intervals. If the direction is given, it is expressed in degrees clockwise from true north.

Sound signal apparatus is indicated by the appropriate word in capital letters (*HORN, BELL, GONG*, etc.) or an abbreviation indicating the type of sound. Sound signals of all types other than submarine sound signals are represented by three arcs of concentric circles within an angle of 45°, orientated and placed as necessary for clarity. The letters "DFS" indicate a **distance finding station** having synchronized sound and radio signals. The location of a sound signal which does not accompany a visual aid, either lighted or unlighted, is shown by a small circle and the appropriate word in vertical block letters.

Private aids, when shown, are marked "Priv maintd." Some privately maintained unlighted aids are indicated by a small circle accompanied by the word "Marker," or a larger circle with a dot in the center and the word "MARKER." The center of the circle indicates the position of the aid. A privately maintained lighted aid has the light symbol and is accompanied by the characteristics and the usual indication of its private nature. Private aids should be used with caution.

A *light sector* is the sector or area bounded by two radii and the arc of a circle in which a light is visible or in which it has a distinctive color different from that of adjoining sectors. The limiting radii are indicated on the chart by dotted lines.

Colors of the sectors are indicated by words spelled out if space permits, or by abbreviation (W, R, etc.) if it does not.

Limits of light sectors and arcs of visibility *as observed from a vessel* are given in the light lists, in clockwise order.

514. Land areas.—The amount of detail shown on the land areas of nautical charts depends upon the scale and the intended purpose of the chart.

Relief is shown by contours and form lines.

Contours are lines connecting points of equal elevation. The heights represented by the contours are indicated in slanting figures at suitable places along the lines. Heights are usually expressed in feet (or in meters with means for conversion to feet). The interval between contours is uniform over any one chart, except that certain intermediate contours are sometimes shown by broken line. When contours are broken, their locations are approximate.

Form lines are approximations of contours used for the purpose of indicating relative elevations. They are used in areas where accurate information is not available in sufficient detail to permit exact location of contours. Elevations of individual form lines are not indicated on the chart.

Spot elevations are generally given only for summits or for tops of conspicuous landmarks. The heights of spot elevations and contours are given with reference to mean high water when this information is available.

When there is insufficient space to show the heights of islets or rocks, they are indicated by slanting figures enclosed in parentheses in the water area nearby.

Cities and roads. Cities are shown in a generalized pattern that approximates their extent and shape. Street names are generally not charted except those along the waterfront on the largest scale charts. In general, only the main arteries and thoroughfares or major coastal highways are shown on smaller scale charts. Occasionally, highway numbers are given. When shown, trails are indicated by a light broken line. Buildings along the waterfront or individual ones back from the waterfront but of special interest to the mariner are shown on large-scale charts. Special symbols are used for certain kinds of buildings, as indicated in part I of Chart No. 1. Both single and double track railroads are indicated by a single line with cross marks. In general, city electric railways are not charted. A fence or sewer extending into the water is shown by a broken line, usually labeled. Airports are shown on small-scale charts by symbol and on large-scale charts by shape and extent of runways. Breakwaters and jetties are shown by single or double lines depending upon the scale of the chart. A submerged portion and the limits of the submerged base are shown by broken lines.

515. Landmarks are shown by symbols, as given in Chart No. 1.

A large circle with a dot at its center is used for selected landmarks that have been accurately located. Capital letters are used to identify the landmark: HOUSE, FLAGPOLE, STACK, sometimes followed by "(conspic)."

A small circle without a dot is used for landmarks not accurately located. Capital and lower case letters are used to identify the landmark: Mon, Cup, Dome. The abbreviation "PA," for position approximate, is used when necessary as a safety feature.

When only one object of a group is charted, its name is followed by a descriptive legend in parenthesis, including the number of objects in the group, for example (TALLEST OF FOUR) or (NORTHEAST OF THREE).

Some of the accompanying labels on a chart are interpreted as follows:

Building or **house.** One of these terms, as appropriate, is used when the entire structure is the landmark, rather than an individual feature of it.

A **spire** is a slender pointed structure extending above a building. It is seldom less than two-thirds of the entire height of the structure, and its lines are rarely broken by stages or other features. The term is not applied to a short pyramid-shaped structure rising from a tower or belfry.

A **cupola** (kū′pō·là) is a small dome-shaped tower or turret rising from a building (fig. 515).

A **dome** is a large, rounded, hemispherical structure rising above a building, or a roof of the same shape. A prominent example is that of the Capitol of the United States, in Washington, D.C.

A **chimney** is a relatively small, upright structure projecting above a building for the conveyance of smoke.

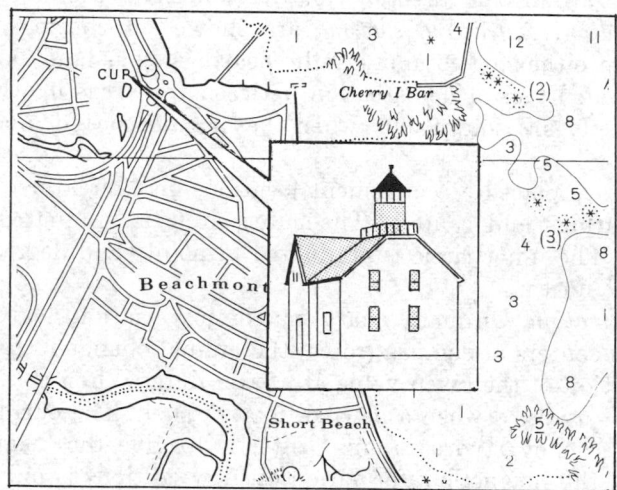

FIGURE 515.—A cupola.

A **stack** is a tall smokestack or chimney. The term is used when the stack is more prominent as a landmark than accompanying buildings.

A **flagpole** is a single staff from which flags are displayed. The term is used when the pole is not attached to a building.

The term **flagstaff** is used for a flagpole rising from a building.

A **flag tower** is a scaffold-like tower from which flags are displayed.

A **radio tower** is a tall pole or structure for elevating radio antennas.

A **radio mast** is a relatively short pole or slender structure for elevating radio antennas, usually found in groups.

A **tower** is any structure with its base on the ground and high in proportion to its base, or that part of a structure higher than the rest, but having essentially vertical sides for the greater part of its height.

A **lookout station** or **watch tower** is a tower surmounted by a small house from which a watch is kept regularly.

A **water tower** is a structure enclosing a tank or standpipe so that the presence of the tank or standpipe may not be apparent.

A **standpipe** is a tall cylindrical structure, in a waterworks system, the height of which is several times the diameter.

The term **tank** is used for a water tank elevated high above the ground by a tall skeleton framework.

The expression **gas tank** or **oil tank** is used for the distinctive structures described by these words.

516. Miscellaneous.—*Measured mile.* A measured nautical mile indicated on a chart is accurate to within six feet of the correct length. Most measurements in the United States were made before 1959, when the United States adopted the International Nautical Mile. The new value is within six feet of the previous standard length of 6,080.20 feet, adjustments not having been made. If the measured distance differs from the standard value by more than six feet, the actual measured distance is stated and the words "measured mile" are omitted.

Periods after abbreviations in water areas are omitted, as these might be mistaken for rocks. However, a lower case *i* or *j* is dotted.

Courses shown on charts are given in true directions, to the nearset minute of arc.

Bearings shown are in true directions *toward* (not from) the objects.

Commercial radio broadcasting stations are shown on charts when they are of value to the mariner either for obtaining radio bearings or as landmarks.

Rules of the road. Lines of demarcation between the areas in which international and inland rules apply are shown only when they cannot be adequately described in notes on the chart.

Compass roses are placed at convenient locations on Mercator charts to facilitate the plotting of bearings and courses. The outer circle is graduated in degrees with zero at true north. The inner circle is graduated in points and degrees with the arrow indicating magnetic north.

Magnetic information. On many charts magnetic variation is given to the nearest 15′ by notes in the centers of compass roses; the annual change is given to the nearest 1′ to permit correction of the given value at a later date. When this is done, the magnetic information is updated when a new edition is issued. The current practice of the Defense Mapping Agency Hydrographic Center is to give the magnetic variation to the nearest 1′, but the magnetic information on new editions is only updated to conform with the latest epoch (1975.0, 1980.0, etc.). Whenever a chart is reprinted, the magnetic information is updated to the latest epoch. On other charts the variation is given by a series of **isogonic lines** connecting points of equal variation, usually a separate line being given for each degree of variation. The line of zero variation is called the **agonic line.** Many plans and insets show neither compass roses nor isogonic lines, but indicate magnetic information by note. A local magnetic disturbance of sufficient force to cause noticeable deflection of the magnetic compass, called **local attraction,** is indicated by a note on the chart.

Currents are sometimes shown on charts by means of arrows giving the directions, and figures giving the speeds. The information thus given refers to the usual or average conditions, sometimes based upon very few observations. It is not safe to assume that conditions at any given time will not differ considerably from those shown.

Longitudes are reckoned eastward and westward from the meridian of Greenwich, England, unless otherwise stated.

Notes on charts should be read with care, as they may give important information not graphically presented. Several types of notes are used. Those in the margin give such information as the chart number and (sometimes) publication and edition notes, identification of adjoining charts, etc. Notes in connection with the chart title include such information as scale, sources of charted data, tidal information, the unit in which soundings are given, cautions, etc. Another class of notes is that given in proximity to the detail to which it refers. Examples of this type of note are those referring to local magnetic disturbance, controlling depths of channels, measured miles, dangers, dumping grounds, anchorages, etc.

Overlapping charts constructed on different horizontal geodetic datums (app. X) may carry the following note:

> ## CAUTION
>
> **Differences in latitude and longitude may exist between this and other charts of the area; therefore, the transfer of positions from one chart to another should be done by bearings and distances from common features.**

Horizontal geodetic datum shifts may be given to provide the corrections necessary to shift to a different datum (app. X). It is the practice of the Defense Mapping Agency Hydrographic Center to provide, if plottable, the corrections to new charts and new editions of charts that are necessary to shift the geodetic datum to the World Geodetic System.

Anchorage areas are shown within purple broken lines and labeled as such. Anchorage berths are shown as purple circles with the number or letter assigned to the berth inscribed within the circle. Caution notes are sometimes shown when there are specific anchoring regulations.

Spoil areas are shown within short broken black lines. The area is tinted blue (National Ocean Survey charts only) and labeled SPOIL AREA.

Firing and bombing practice areas in the United States territorial and adjacent waters are shown on National Ocean Survey charts and Defense Mapping Agency Hydrographic Center charts of the same area and comparable scale. Danger areas established for short periods of time are not charted, but are announced locally. Danger areas in effect for longer periods are published in the *Notice to Mariners*. Any aid to navigation established to mark a danger area or a fixed or floating target is shown on charts.

Traffic separation schemes show routes to increase safety of navigation, particularly in areas of high density shipping. Traffic separation schemes are shown on standard nautical charts of scale 1:600,000 and larger and are printed in purple. The arrows printed on charts to indicate tracks are intended to give the general direction of traffic only, ships need not set their courses strictly by the arrows. At points where several recommended routes meet, circular or triangular separation zones with traffic direction arrows are shown.

Recommended tracklines, portrayed in black, are used to indicate suggested courses through particular passages and are selected according to their value for oceangoing ships.

A *logarithmic time-speed-distance nomogram* with an explanation of its application is shown on harbor charts at scales of 1:40,000 and larger.

Tidal boxes (fig. 516a) are shown on charts of scales 1:75,000 and larger.

TIDAL INFORMATION						
Place	Position		Height above datum of soundings			
			Mean High Water		Mean Low Water	
	N. Lat.	E. Long.	Higher	Lower	Lower	Higher
Olongapo.......	14°49′	120°17′	meters ...0.9...	meters .... 0.4...	meters ...0.0...	meters .... 0.3....

FIGURE 516a.—Tidal box.

Tabulations of controlling depths (fig. 516b) are shown on National Ocean Survey harbor charts.

NANTUCKET HARBOR							
Tabulated from surveys by the Corps of Engineers - report of June 1972 and surveys of Nov. 1971							
Controlling depths in channels entering from seaward in feet at Mean Low Water					Project Dimensions		
Name of Channel	Left outside quarter	Middle half of channel	Right outside quarter	Date of Survey	Width (feet)	Length (naut. miles)	Depth M.L.W. (feet)
Entrance Channel	11.1	15.0	15.0	11-71	300	1.2	15
Note.-The Corps of Engineers should be consulted for changing conditions subsequent to the above.							

FIGURE 516b.—Tabulations of controlling depths.

Title. The chart title may be at any convenient location, usually in some area not important to navigation. It is composed of several distinctive parts as shown in figure 516c.

Reproductions of Foreign Charts

517. Modified facsimile charts are modified reproductions of foreign charts produced in accordance with bilateral agreements. Such agreements serve to provide the mariner with more up-to-date charts.

Modified facsimile charts published by the Defense Mapping Agency Hydrographic Center are, in general, reproduced with minimal changes. Such changes may include all or part of the following:

1. The original name of the chart is removed and replaced by an anglicized version.

2. English language equivalents of names and terms on the original chart are printed in a suitable glossary on the reproduction, as appropriate.

3. All hydrographic information, except bottom characteristics, is shown as depicted on the original chart.

4. Bottom characteristics are shown as depicted in Chart No. 1.

5. The unit of measurement used for soundings is shown in block letters outside the upper and lower neatlines.

6. A scale for converting charted depth to feet, meters, or fathoms is added.

7. A blue tint is shown from a significant depth curve to the shoreline.

8. A blue tint is added to all dangers enclosed by a dotted danger curve.

9. A blue tint is added to dangerous wrecks, foul areas, obstructions, rocks awash, sunken rocks, and swept wrecks.

10. Aids to navigation, landmarks, and special area symbols and abbreviations on the original chart are changed to conform with Chart No. 1.

11. Caution notes are shown in purple and enclosed in a box.

12. Restricted, danger, and prohibited areas are usually outlined in purple and labeled "RESTRICTED AREA," "DANGER AREA," etc.

13. Traffic separation schemes are shown in purple.

14. A note on traffic separation schemes, printed in purple, is added to the chart.

15. Wire dragged (swept) areas are shown in purple or green.

16. If plottable, suitable corrections are provided to shift the horizontal datum to the World Geodetic System (1972).

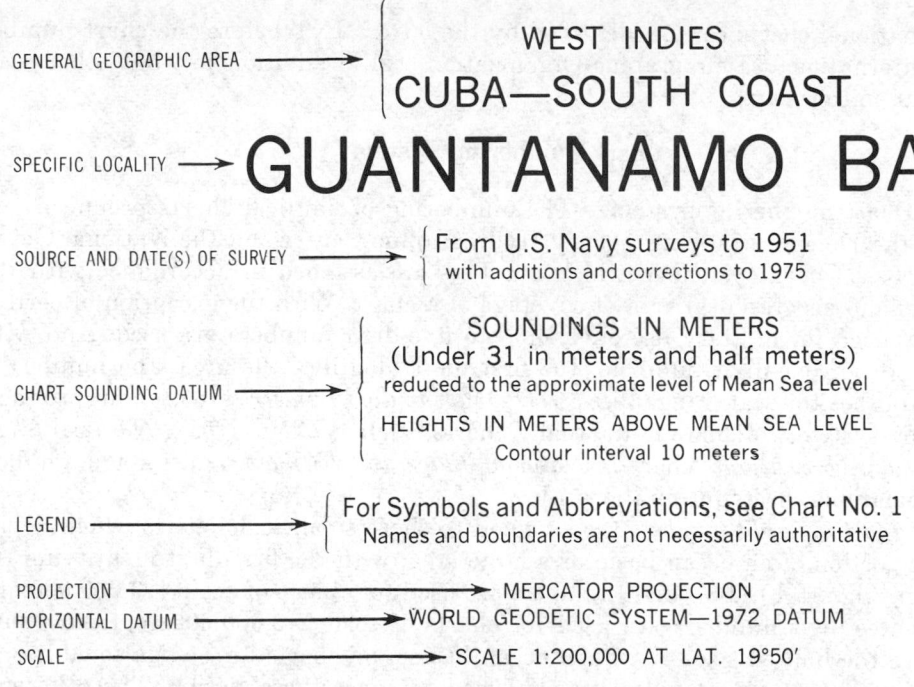

GENERAL GEOGRAPHIC AREA ⟶

WEST INDIES
CUBA—SOUTH COAST

SPECIFIC LOCALITY ⟶ GUANTANAMO BAY

SOURCE AND DATE(S) OF SURVEY ⟶ From U.S. Navy surveys to 1951
with additions and corrections to 1975

CHART SOUNDING DATUM ⟶
SOUNDINGS IN METERS
(Under 31 in meters and half meters)
reduced to the approximate level of Mean Sea Level
HEIGHTS IN METERS ABOVE MEAN SEA LEVEL
Contour interval 10 meters

LEGEND ⟶ For Symbols and Abbreviations, see Chart No. 1
Names and boundaries are not necessarily authoritative

PROJECTION ⟶ MERCATOR PROJECTION
HORIZONTAL DATUM ⟶ WORLD GEODETIC SYSTEM—1972 DATUM
SCALE ⟶ SCALE 1:200,000 AT LAT. 19°50′

FIGURE 516c.—A chart title.

518. International charts.—The need for mariners and chartmakers to understand and use nautical charts of different nations became increasingly apparent during the late 19th and 20th centuries as the maritime nations of the world developed their own establishments for the compilation and publication of nautical charts from hydrographic surveys. There followed a growing awareness that international standardization of symbols and presentation was desirable, which led to twenty-two maritime nations sending their representatives to a Hydrographic Conference in London in 1919. That conference resulted in the establishment of the International Hydrographic Bureau (IHB) in Monaco in 1921, where the seat of the International Hydrographic Organization (IHO), with a membership of over forty States remains today.

Recognizing that there was considerable duplication of effort by various Member States when each was charting the same parts of the ocean, and being conscious of the significant level of standardization in chart symbolization which had been reached, a move was made by the IHO in 1967 to introduce the first international chart. A Committee of representatives from six Member States was organized which reported in 1970. The Committee drew up plans and specifications for two series of international charts of the oceans on scales 1:10,000,000 and 1:3,500,000, respectively. The limits of each of some 83 of these charts, giving worldwide small scale navigational cover, were agreed, and responsibility for compiling each of these has subsequently been accepted by Member States' Hydrographic Offices.

Once a Member State publishes an international chart, reproduction material is made available to any other Member State which may wish to print the chart for its own purposes.

By 1974 twenty-one of these international charts had been published by 12 Member States, while four Member States had availed themselves of the right to reprint. This encouraging beginning to a new era of international hydrographic cooperation has led to the establishment of a committee to study the problems involved in extending the concept to larger scale charts.

International charts can be identified by the letters INT before the chart number and the International Hydrographic Organization seal in addition to what other seals may appear on the chart.

Chart Numbering System

519. Chart numbering system.—The numbering of nautical charts produced and issued by the Defense Mapping Agency Hydrographic Center and the National Ocean Survey is based on a system in which numbers are assigned in accordance with the scale range and geographical area of coverage of a chart. With the exception of certain charts produced for military use only, one- to five-digit numbers are used. And with the exception of one-digit numbers, the first digit identifies the area; the number of digits establishes the scale range (fig. 519a). The *one-digit numbers* are used for products in the chart system which are not actually charts, such as Chart No. 1, *Nautical Chart Symbols and Abbreviations*, chart 5, *National Flags and Ensigns*, and foreign symbols and abbreviations sheets for military use.

Two- and three-digit numbers are assigned to those small-scale charts which depict the major portion of an ocean basin or a large area, with the first digit identifying the ocean basin (fig. 519b). Two-digit numbers are used for charts of scale 1:9,000,000 and smaller. Three-digit numbers are used for charts of scale 1:2,000,000 to 1:9,000,000.

Due to the limited sizes of certain ocean basins, no charts for navigational use at scales of 1:9,000,000 and smaller are published to cover these basins. The otherwise unused two-digit numbers (30 to 49 and 70 to 79) are assigned to special world charts, such as chart 33, *Horizontal Intensity of the Earth's Magnetic Field*, chart 42, *Magnetic Variation*, and chart 76, *Standard Time Zone Chart of the World*.

One exception to the scale range criteria for three-digit numbers is the use of three-digit numbers for a series of position plotting sheets which are of larger scale than 1:2,000,000 because they have application in ocean basins and can be used in all longitudes.

Number of Digits	Scale
1	No Scale
2	1:9,000,000 and smaller.
3	1:2,000,000 to 1:9,000,000.
4	Nonnavigational and special purpose.
5	1:2,000,000 and larger.

FIGURE 519a.—Scales ranges for number of digits in chart number.

Four-digit numbers are used for nonnavigational and special purpose charts, such as chart 5090, *Maneuvering Board*, chart 5101, *Gnomonic Plotting Chart North Atlantic*, and chart 7707, *Omega Plotting Chart*.

Five-digit numbers are assigned to those charts of scale 1:2,000,000 and larger that cover portions of the coastline rather than significant portions of ocean basins. These charts are based on the regions of the nautical chart index (fig. 519c).

The first of the five digits indicates the region; the second digit indicates the subregion; the last three digits indicate the geographical sequence of the chart within

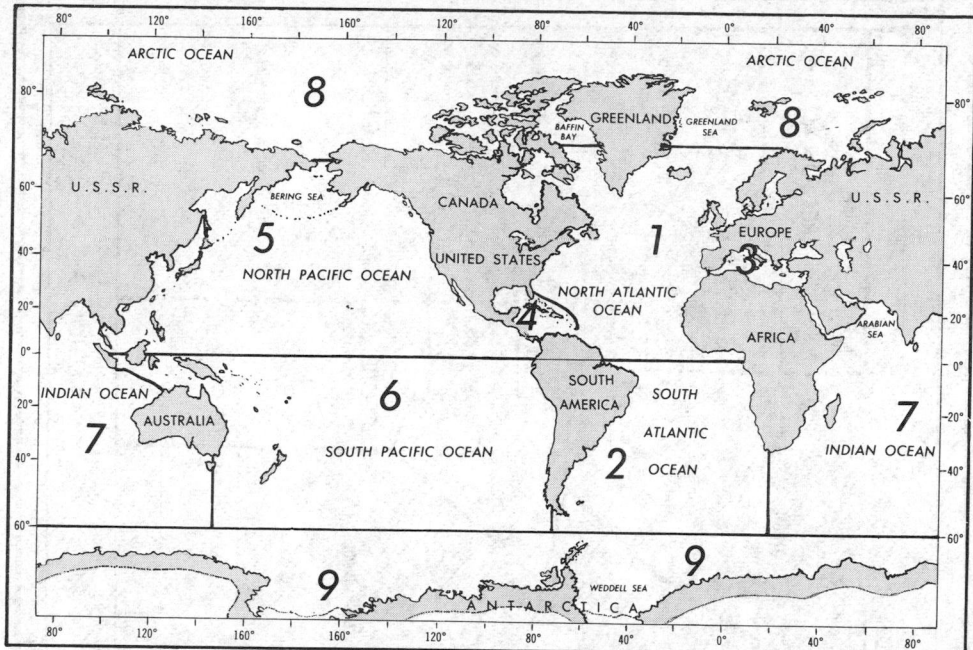

FIGURE 519b.—Ocean basins.

the subregion. Many numbers have been left unused in order that future charts may be placed in their proper geographical sequence as they are produced.

In order to establish a logical numbering system within the geographical subregions (for the 1:2,000,000 and larger-scale charts), a worldwide skeleton framework of coastal charts was laid out at a scale 1:250,000. This skeleton series was used as basic coverage for the numbering except in areas where a coordinated series at about this scale already existed. An example of an exception is the coast of Norway were a coordinated series of 1:200,000 coast charts is in existence. Within each region, the geographical subregions are numbered counterclockwise around the continents, and within each subregion the basic (1:250,000 skeleton) series also is numbered counterclockwise around the continents. The skeleton coverage is assigned generally every 20th digit, except that the first 40 numbers in each subregion are reserved for smaller-scale coverage. Charts with scales larger than the skeleton coverage are assigned one of the 19 numbers following the number assigned to the skeleton sheet within which it falls. Thus, charts on the west coast of the Iberian Peninsula and the northwest coast of Africa are numbered as shown in figure 519d.

As shown in figure 519d, five-digit numbers are assigned to the charts produced by other hydrographic offices. This numbering system is applied to foreign charts so that they can be filed in logical sequence with the charts produced by the Defense Mapping Agency Hydrographic Center and the National Ocean Survey.

Exceptions to the numbering system to satisfy military needs are as follows:

1. Bottom contour and non-submarine contact charts at a scale larger than 1:2,000,000 do not portray portions of a coastline but chart parts of the ocean basins. In view of the characteristics of these charts, they are identified with an alphabetical character plus four digits. The letter B denotes bottom contour charts with or without Loran-A. The letter C denotes bottom contour charts with Loran-C information.

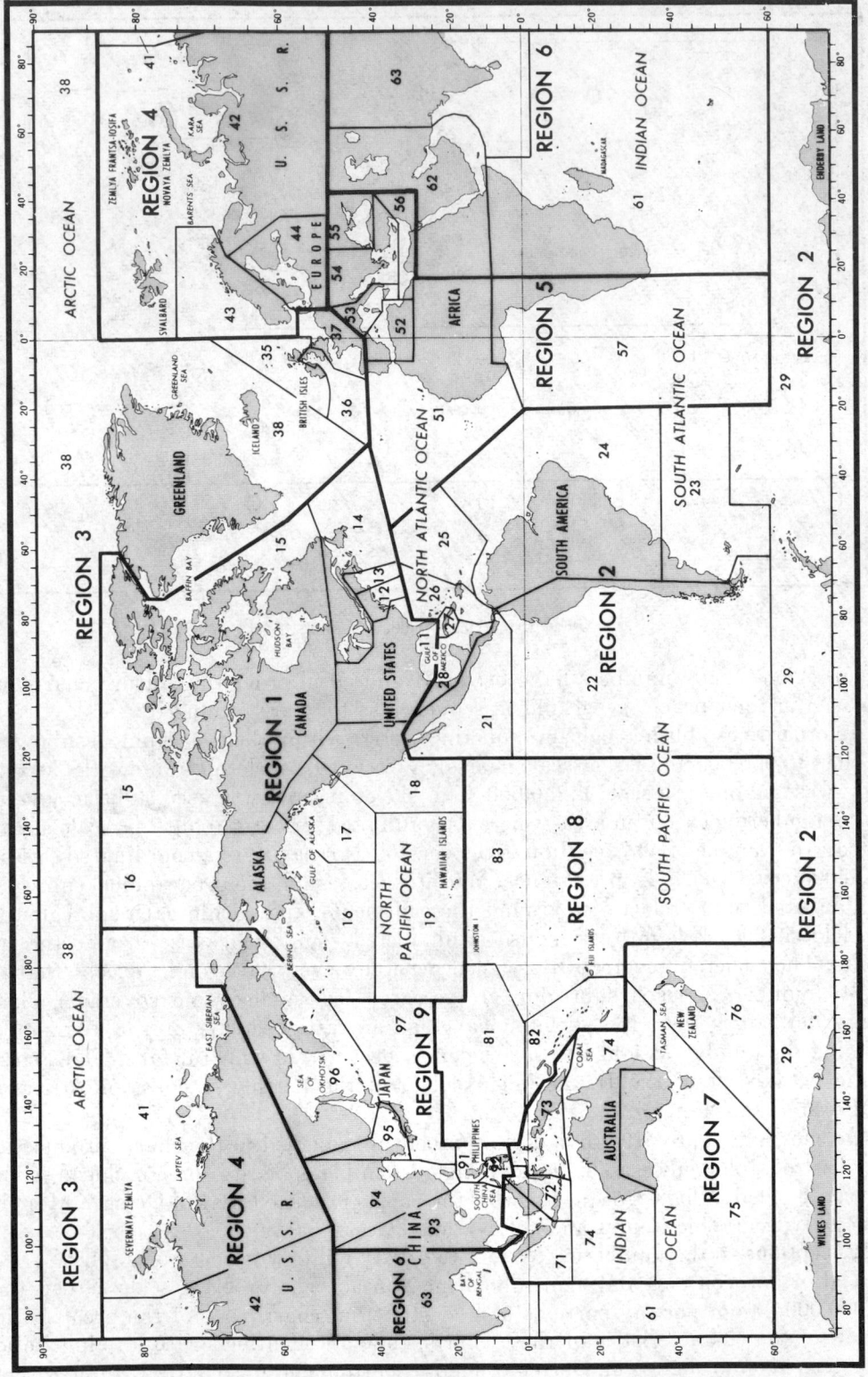

Figure 519c.—Regions and subregions of the nautical chart index.

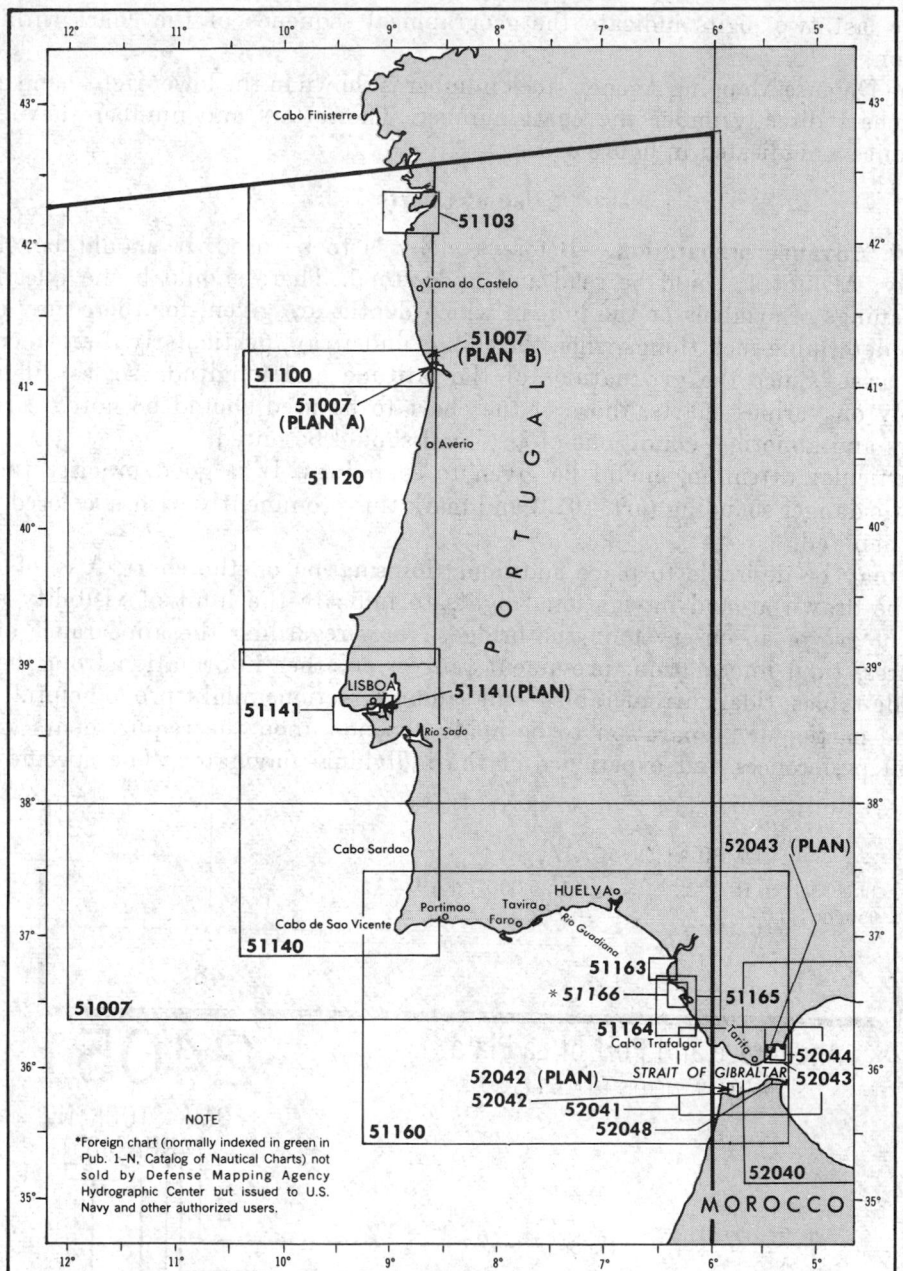

FIGURE 519d.—Area of subregion 51 illustrating the numerical sequence of larger-scale charts along a coast.

The letter N denotes non-submarine contact charts containing Loran-C, and the letter D denotes bottom contour charts with Omega information. The first two digits of these charts describe the longitude band and the last two digits the latitude band, which in itself is a logical system.

2. Combat charts at a scale of 1:50,000, which would otherwise be assigned five-digit numbers, are assigned four digits separated by a letter of the alphabet. The first two digits indicate the region and subregion; the third character is a letter of the alpha-

bet; the last two digits indicate the geographical sequence of the chart within the subregion.

The Defense Mapping Agency stock number is shown in the lower right-hand corner of the chart directly under the chart number. The letters and numbers have chart significance as indicated in figure 519e.

Use of Charts

520. Advance preparation.—Before a chart is to be used, it should be studied carefully. All notes should be read and understood. There should be no question of the meanings of symbols or the unit in which depths are given, for there may not be time to determine such things when the ship is underway, particularly if an emergency should arise. Since the graduations of the latitude and longitude scales differ considerably on various charts, those of the chart to be used should be noted carefully. Dangers and abnormal conditions of any kind should be noted.

Particular attention should be given to soundings. It is good practice to select a realistic danger sounding (art. 1013) and mark this prominently with a colored pencil other than red.

It may be desirable to place additional information on the chart. Arcs of circles might be drawn around navigational lights to indicate the limit of visibility at the height of eye of an observer on the bridge. Notes regarding the appearance of light structures, tidal information, prominent ranges, or other information from the light lists, tide tables, tidal current tables, and sailing directions might prove helpful.

The particular preparation to be made depends upon the requirements and the personal preferences and experience of the individual navigator. The specific infor-

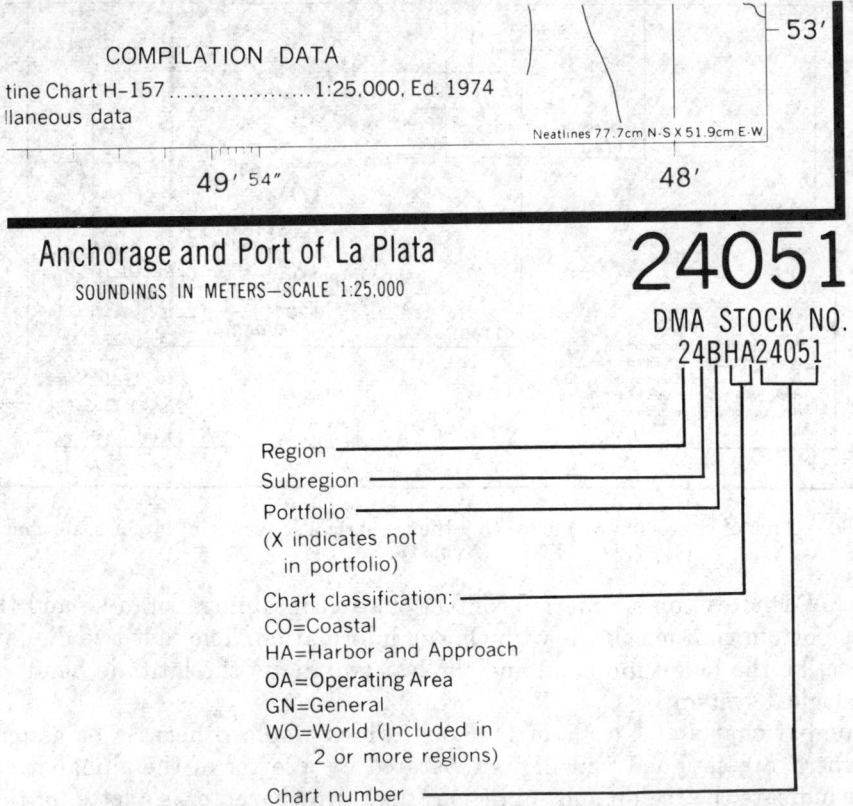

FIGURE 519e.—Defense Mapping Agency stock number.

mation selected is not important. But it *is* important that the navigator familiarize himself with his chart so that in an emergency the information needed will be available and there will be no question of its meaning.

521. Maintaining charts.—The print date in the lower left-hand corner of the chart is the date of the latest *Notice to Mariners* used to update the chart. Responsibility for maintaining it after this date lies with the user. *An uncorrected chart is a menace.* The various issues of *Notice to Mariners* subsequent to the print date contain all the information needed for maintaining charts. The more urgent items are also given in advance in the *Daily Memorandum* or by radio broadcast. A convenient way of keeping a record of the *Notice to Mariners* corrections made to each chart on hand is by means of the 5x8–inch *Chart/Publication Correction Record Card* (DMAHC 8660/9).

Periodically the Defense Mapping Agency Hydrographic Center publishes a *Summary of Corrections* containing previously published *Notice to Mariners* corrections.

When a new edition of a chart is published, it should be obtained and the old one retired from use. The very fact that a new edition has been prepared generally indicates that there have been changes that cannot adequately be shown by hand correction.

522. Use and stowage of charts.—Charts are among the most important aids of the navigator, and should be treated as such. When in use they should be spread out flat on a suitable chart table or desk, and properly secured to prevent loss or damage. Every effort should be made to keep charts dry, for a wet chart stretches and may not return to the original dimensions after drying. The distortion thus introduced may cause inaccurate results when measurements are made on the chart.

Permanent corrections to charts should be made in ink so that they will not be inadvertently erased. All other lines should be drawn lightly in pencil so that they can be easily erased without removing permanent information or otherwise damaging the chart. To avoid possible confusion, lines should be drawn no longer than necessary, and adequately labeled. When a voyage is completed, the charts should be carefully and thoroughly erased unless there has been an unusual incident such as a grounding or collision, when they should be preserved without change, as they will undoubtedly be requested by the investigating authority. After a chart has been erased, it should be inspected carefully for possible damage and for incompletely erased or overlooked marks that might prove confusing when the chart is next used.

When not in use charts should be stowed flat in their proper drawers or portfolios, with a minimum of folding. The stowed charts should be properly indexed so that any desired one can be found when needed. In removing or replacing a chart, care should be exercised to avoid damage to it or other charts.

A chart that is given proper care in use and stowage can have a long and useful life.

523. Chart lighting.—In the use of charts it is important that adequate lighting be provided. However, the light on the bridge of a ship underway at night should be such as to cause the least interference with the darkness-adaptation of the eyes of bridge personnel who watch for navigational lights, running lights, dangers, etc. Experiments by the Department of the Navy have indicated that red light is least disturbing to eyes which have been adapted to maximum vision during darkness. In some instances red lights, filters, or goggles have been provided on the bridges or in chartrooms of vessels. However, the use of such light seriously affects the appearance of a chart. Red, orange, and buff disappear. Other colors may appear changed. This has led to the substitution of nautical purple for red and orange, and gray for buff on some charts. However, before a chart is used in any light except white, a preliminary test should be made and the effect noted carefully. If a glass or plastic top is provided for the chart table or desk, a dim white light *below* the chart may provide sufficient illumination to permit chart reading, without objectionable disturbance of night vision.

524. Use of small-craft charts.—Although the small-craft charts published by the National Ocean Survey are designed primarily for boatmen, these charts at scales of 1:80,000 and larger are in some cases the only charts available of inland waters transited by large vessels. In other cases the small-craft charts may provide a better presentation of navigational hazards than the standard nautical chart because of scale and detail. *Therefore, it behooves navigators of large vessels transiting inland waters not to ignore the small-craft charts.*

PART TWO

PILOTING AND DEAD RECKONING

PART TWO

PILOTING AND DEAD RECKONING

CHAPTER VI

INSTRUMENTS FOR PILOTING AND DEAD RECKONING

Introduction

601. Kinds of instruments.—The word "instrument" has several meanings, at least two of which apply to navigation: (1) an implement or tool, and (2) a device by which the present value of a quantity is measured. Thus, a straightedge and a mechanical log are both instruments, the first serving as a tool, and the second as a measuring device. This chapter is concerned with the navigational instruments used for plotting, and those for measuring distance or speed, depth, and direction. Instruments for measuring time are discussed in chapter XV. These quantities are the basic data in dead reckoning (ch. VIII) and piloting (ch. X). Other instruments are discussed in chapters XV and XXXVII.

In addition to the instruments discussed, several others are important to the navigator. Binoculars are helpful in observing landmarks. A flashlight has many uses, the principal one being to illuminate the scales of instruments when they are to be read at night. Erasers should be soft, and pencils should not be so hard that they damage the surface of the chart. The navigator's chart is discussed in chapter V.

Plotting Instruments

602. Dividers and compasses.—**Dividers,** or "pair of dividers," is an instrument originally used for dividing a line into equal segments. The instrument consists essentially of two hinged legs with pointed ends which can be separated to any distance from zero to the maximum imposed by physical limitations. The setting is retained either by friction at the hinge, as in the usual navigational dividers, or by means of a screw acting against a spring.

If one of the legs carries a pencil or ruling pen, the instrument is called **compasses.** The two legs may be attached to a bar of metal or wood instead of being hinged, thus permitting greater separation of the points. Such an instrument is called **beam compasses** or **beam dividers.**

The principal use of dividers in navigation is to measure or transfer distances on a chart, as described in article 804. Compasses are used for drawing distance circles or any plotting requiring an arc of a circle.

The friction at the hinge of most dividers and compasses can be varied, and should be adjusted so that the instrument can be manipulated easily with one hand, but will retain the separation of the points in normal handling. A drop of oil on the hinge may be required occasionally. The points should be sharp, and should have equal length, permitting them to be brought close together for the measurement of very short distances.

For navigation, it is desirable to have dividers and compasses with comparatively long legs, to provide adequate range for most requirements. It is desirable to learn to manipulate dividers or compasses with one hand.

603. Parallel rulers are an instrument for transferring a line parallel to itself. In its most common form it consists of two parallel bars or rulers, connected in such a

137

manner that when one is held in place on a flat surface, the other can be moved, remaining parallel to its original direction. Firm pressure is required on one ruler while the other is being moved, to prevent slippage. The principal use of parallel rulers in navigation is to transfer the direction of a charted line to a compass rose, and vice versa.

The edges of the rulers should be truly straight; and in the case of double-edged rulers, should be parallel to each other in order that either edge can be used. Parallelism can be tested by comparison of all edges with the same straight line, as a meridian or parallel of a Mercator chart. The linkage can be tested for looseness and lack of parallelism by "walking" the rulers between parallel lines on opposite sides of the chart and back again.

Some metal parallel rulers have a protractor engraved on the upper surface to permit orientation of the ruler at any convenient meridian.

In one type of instrument, parallelism during transfer is obtained by supporting a single ruler on two knurled rollers. Both rollers have the same diameter, and the motion of one is transmitted to the other by an axle having a cover which provides a convenient handle. This type of ruler is convenient and accurate, and is less likely to slip than the linked double-ruler type. However, care is necessary to prevent its rolling off the chart table when the vessel is rolling or pitching.

Directions can also be transferred by means of two triangles such as are used in drafting, or by one triangle and a straightedge. One edge of a triangle is aligned in the desired direction and the triangle is then moved along a straightedge held firmly against one of its other edges until the first edge is at the desired place on the chart. Some triangles have protractors (art. 604) engraved on them to assist in transferring lines. Such a triangle becomes a form of plotter (art. 605).

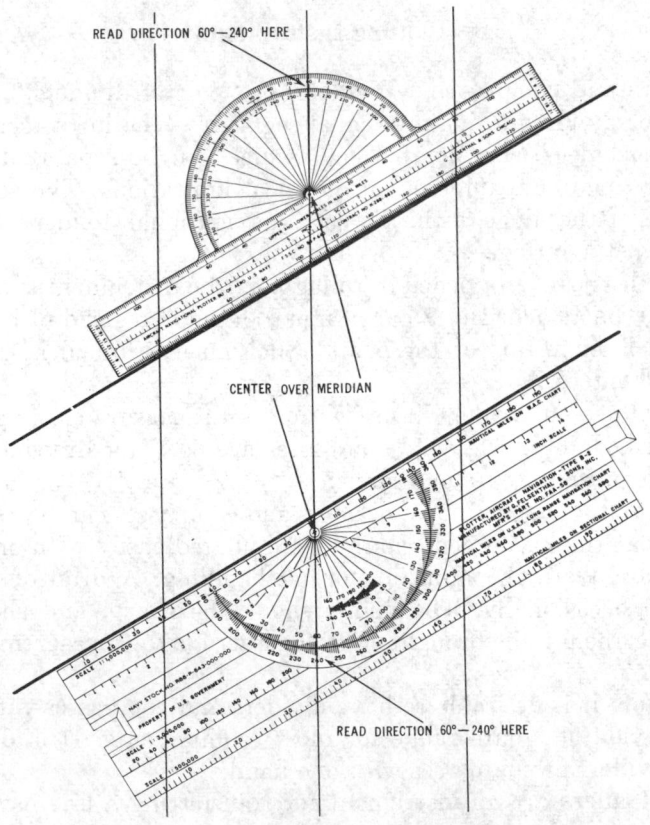

FIGURE 605.—Two plotters having no movable parts.

604. Protractor.—A **protractor** is a device for measuring angles on a chart or other surface. It consists essentially of a graduated arc, usually of 180°, on suitable material such as metal or plastic.

A **three-arm protractor** consists essentially of a circular protractor with three radial arms attached. This instrument is discussed in greater detail in article 1102.

605. Plotters.—The increased popularity of graphical methods in practical navigation during recent decades has resulted in the development of a wide variety of devices to facilitate plotting. In its most common form, such a device consists essentially of a protractor combined with a straightedge. There are two general types, one having no movable parts, and the other having a pivot at the center of the arc of the protractor, to permit rotation of the straightedge around the protractor. Examples of the fixed type are illustrated in figure 605. Those shown were designed for air navigation, but are applicable to many processes of marine navigation. The direction of the straightedge is controlled by placing the center of the protractor arc and the desired scale graduation on the same reference line. If the reference line is a meridian, the directions shown by the straightedge are true geographic directions. If, as in some processes of celestial navigation, it is desired to plot a line perpendicular to another line, the direction may be measured from a parallel of latitude or its equivalent, instead of adding or subtracting 90° from the value and measuring from a meridian. Some fixed-type plotters have auxiliary scales labeled to indicate true direction if a parallel is used as the reference.

Most plotters also provide linear distance scales, as shown in figure 605. In the movable-arm type of plotter, a protractor is aligned with a meridian, and the movable arm is rotated until it is in the desired direction.

606. Drafting machine.—If a chart table of sufficient size is available, a **drafting machine** (fig. 606) is probably the most desirable plotting instrument. The straightedge of this instrument can be clamped so as to retain its direction during movement over the entire plotting area. Straightedges of various lengths and linear scales are interchangeable. Some models make provision for mounting two straightedges perpendicular to each other. However, for most purposes of navigation, the perpendicular is more conveniently obtained by the use of a triangle with a single straightedge. The movable protractor also retains its orientation, and can be adjusted to conform to the compass rose of a chart secured in any position on the chart table. Directions of the straightedge can then be read or set on the protractor without reference to charted compass roses. Use of the clamped protractor requires that charted meridians be straight and parallel, as on a Mercator chart (art. 305). Its use is restricted with projections such as the Lambert conformal (art. 314), on which meridians converge.

When a drafting machine is used, the chart or plotting sheet is first secured to the chart table. The straightedge is aligned with a meridian (or parallel) and clamped in position. The protractor is then adjusted so that 000° and 180° (090° and 270° if a parallel is used) are at the ruler indices, and clamped. With this setting, any subsequent position of the ruler is indicated as a true direction. If the protractor is offset by the amount of the compass error (ch. VII), true directions can be plotted by setting the straightedge at the compass direction on the protractor, without need for applying compass error arithmetically. However, it is generally preferable to keep it set to true directions.

If accurate results are to be obtained, the anchor base must be rigidly fastened to the chart table. This should be checked from time to time, as the base may be loosened by vibration or normal use. The pivots in the anchor base should be firm without binding. The endless belts of the parallel motion mechanism should be taut if rigidity of the ruler is to be preserved. Provision is usually made for adjusting each of the

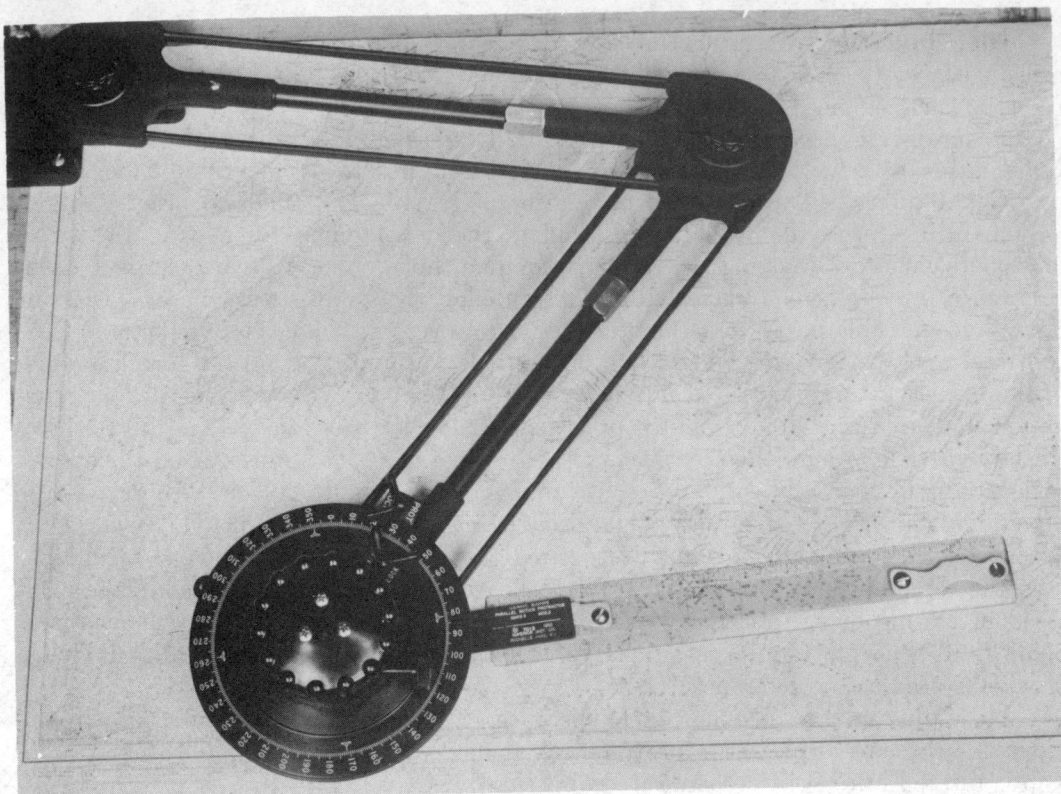

FIGURE 606.—Drafting machine.

various rulers to uniformity of alignment so that any other ruler can be substituted without changing the setting. As with parallel rulers, the device can be checked for parallelism by means of meridians or parallels on opposite sides of a Mercator chart.

Distance and Speed Measurement

607. Units of measurement.—Mariners generally measure horizontal distances in nautical miles (art. 205), but occasionally in yards or feet. Feet, meters, and fathoms are used for measuring depth of water, and feet or meters for measuring height above water. Nations which have adopted the metric system use meters in place of yards, feet, and fathoms, and for some purposes they use kilometers in place of nautical miles. Conversion factors for these and other units are given in appendix D. Nautical miles of 6,076.11549 feet (approximately) and land or statute miles of 5,280 feet can be interconverted by means of table 20. Meters, feet, and fathoms can be interconverted by means of table 21.

Speed is customarily expressed in knots (art. 206), or for some purposes, in kilometers per hour, or yards or feet per minute. For short distances, a nautical mile can be considered equal to 2,000 yards or 6,000 feet. This is a useful relationship because $\frac{6,000 \text{ feet}}{60 \text{ minutes}} = 100$ feet per minute. Thus, speed in knots is equal approximately to hundreds of feet per minute or, hundreds of yards per 3-minute interval.

608. Distance, speed, and time are related by the formula

$$distance = speed \times time.$$

Therefore, if any two of the three quantities are known, the third can be found. The units, of course, must be consistent. Thus, if speed is measured in knots, and time in hours, the answer is in nautical miles. Similarly, if distance is measured in yards, and time in minutes, the answer is in yards per minute.

Table 19 is a speed, time, and distance table which supplies one of the three values if the other two are known. It is intended primarily for use in finding the distance steamed in a given time at a known speed. Table 18 is for use in determining speed by measuring the time needed to steam exactly one mile.

The solution of problems involving distance, speed, and time can easily be accomplished by means of a slide rule (art. 115 vol. II). If the index of scale C is set opposite speed in knots on scale D, the distance in nautical miles appears on scale D opposite time in hours on scale C. If 60 of scale C is set opposite speed in knots on scale D, the distance covered in any number of *minutes* is shown on scale D opposite the minutes on scale C. Several circular slide rules particularly adapted for solution of distance, speed, and time problems have been devised. One of these, called the "Nautical Slide Rule," is shown in figure 608.

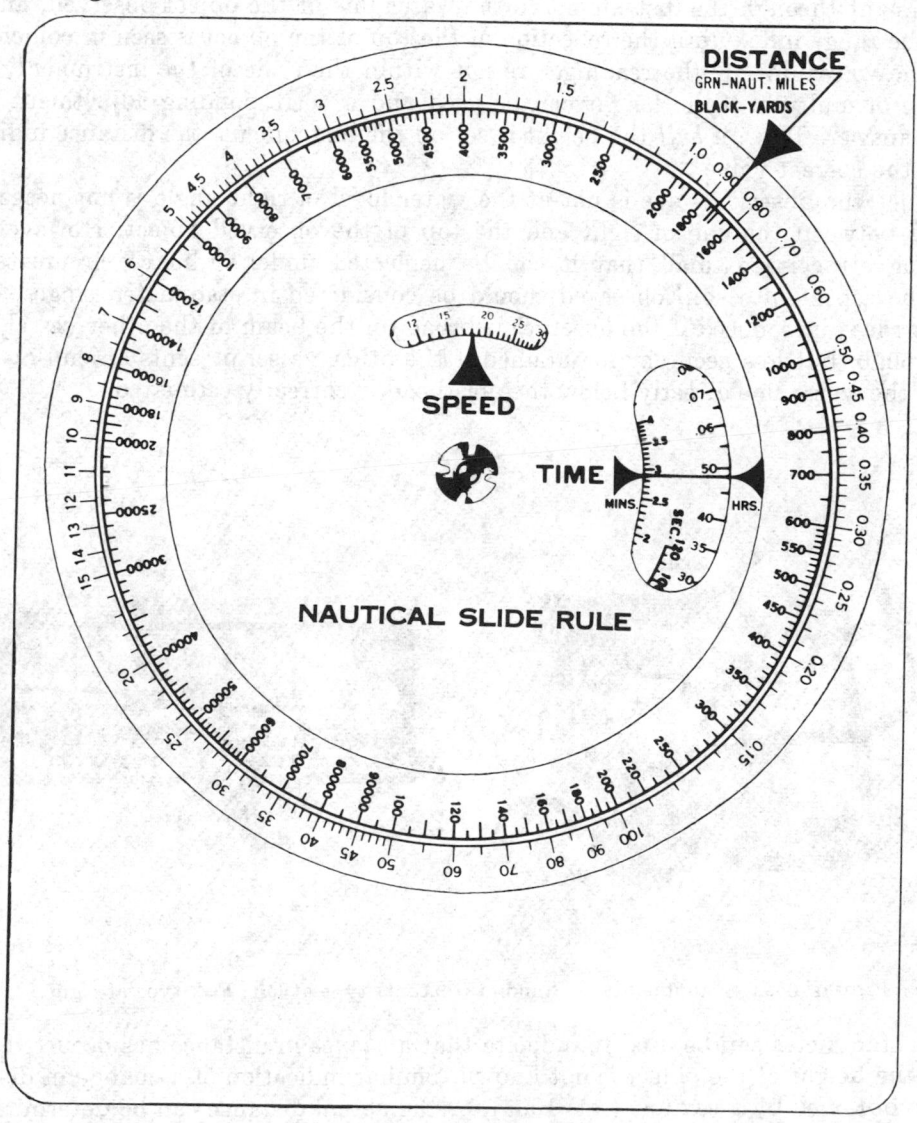

FIGURE 608.—The Nautical Slide Rule.

609. Measurement of distance to an object can be made in a variety of ways, as by radar (art. 4301) sextant angle (table 9), range finder, or by several indirect methods. Another method used principally for measuring distance between ships in formation, but useful in measuring other distances, is by means of a small, hand-held instrument called a **stadimeter.**

Two types of stadimeters are illustrated in figure 609a. Both the Brandon or sextant type and the Fisk type operate on the principle used in table 9:

In a plane right triangle, ABC, having opposite sides a, b, and c,

$$\tan A = \frac{a}{b}, \text{ and } b = a \cot A.$$

This is applied to the stadimeter as shown in figure 609b. The height of the object is set on the height scale of the instrument, and the measured subtended angle is expressed in yards on the distance (range) scale. To measure the angle, one directs the line of sight through the instrument to the water line of the object observed, and adjusts the range index until the reflection of the top of the object is seen in coincidence with the water line. If the readings are not within the scale of the instrument, some fraction or multiple of the height can be used and a corresponding adjustment made to the answer. Thus, if *half* the height is set on the instrument, the distance indicated is *half* the correct value.

Since the observer's eye is not at the water level, a right angle is not necessarily formed between the line of sight and the top of the observed object. However, the resulting error is so small that it can be neglected under ordinary circumstances.

The aspect of a ship observed should be considered in stadimeter ranges. Thus, little error is introduced if the observer is broad on the beam of the other vessel, as in figure 609b, but less accuracy is obtained if the other vessel presents an end-on view, unless the water line directly below the masthead is correctly estimated.

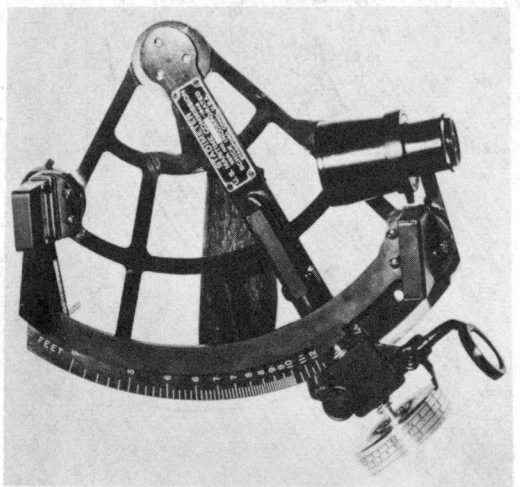 

FIGURE 609a.—Stadimeters.   Brandon (sextant) type at left; Fisk type at right.

A stadimeter can be used to indicate that a *change* in distance has occurred, even when the height of the object is not known. Similar indication of a change in distance can be obtained by a sextant (art. 1005), or the actual distance can be determined by the measured angle and table 9 if the height is known.

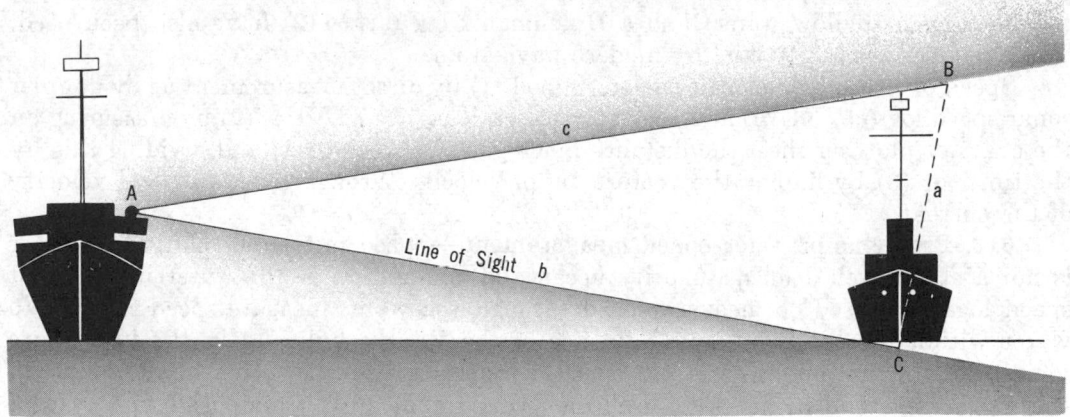

FIGURE 609b.—Geometry of a stadimeter measurement.   The distance $b = a \cot A$.

610. Measurement of distance traveled may be made directly, or the distance can be determined indirectly by means of the speed and time, using the relationship given in article 608.

One of the simplest mechanical distance-measuring devices is the **taffrail log,** consisting of (1) a *rotator* which turns like a screw propeller when it is towed through the water; (2) a braided *log line*, up to 100 fathoms in length, which tows the rotator and transmits its rotation to an indicator on the vessel; and (3) a dial and pointer mechanism which registers the distance traveled through the water. In some installations, the readings of the register are transferred electrically to a dial on or near the bridge.

The taffrail log is usually streamed from the ship's quarter, although it may be carried at the end of a short boom extending outboard from the vessel. The log line should be sufficiently long, and attached in such position, that the rotator is clear of the disturbed water of the wake of the vessel; otherwise an error is introduced. Errors may also be introduced by a head or following sea; by mechanical wear or damage, such as a bent fin; or by fouling of the rotator, as by seaweed or refuse.

An accurately calibrated taffrail log in good working order provides information of sufficient reliability for most purposes of navigation. Its readings should be checked at various speeds by towing it over a known distance in an area free from currents. Usually, the average of several runs, preferably in opposite directions, is more accurate than a single one. If an error is found, it is expressed as a percentage and applied to later readings. The calibration should be checked from time to time.

Although a taffrail log is included in the equipment carried by many oceangoing vessels, the convenience and reliability of other methods of determining distance or speed have reduced the dependence formerly placed upon this instrument.

611. Measurement of speed.—Speed can be determined indirectly by means of distance and time, or it can be measured directly. All instruments now in common use for measuring speed determine rate of motion *through the water*. This is done (1) by electromagnetic induction, (2) by differential pressure or measurement of the water pressure due solely to the forward motion of the vessel, (3) by measuring the resistance to the motion of the vessel, (4) by means of a small screw propeller having a speed of rotation proportional to the speed of the vessel, and (5) by determining the relationship between vessel speed and speed of rotation of its screw or screws. Instruments for measuring speed, like those for measuring distance, are called **logs.**

Before the development of modern logs, speed was determined in a number of ways. Perhaps the most common primitive device is the **chip log** (art. 112), although a

ground log (a weight, with line attached, which was thrown overboard and rested on the bottom in shallow water) and a **Dutchman's log** (art. 112) have also been used. These devices are rarely used by modern navigators.

Speed over the bottom can be determined (1) by direct measurement as by doppler sonar speed log (ch. XLVI) and sensing accelerations (ch. XLVII); (2) by measuring on the chart or plotting sheet the distance made good between fixes, and dividing this by the time; or (3) by finding the vector sum of velocity through the water and velocity of the current.

612. Problems of water-speed measurement.—Speed measured relative to water is not a stable well-defined quantity because of the motion of the water itself. Most speed logs now used to measure speed through the water measure speed relative to water within the hydrodynamic influence of the vessel's hull and in the immediate vicinity of the motion sensor itself. Speed measured with respect to a small volume of the water disturbed by a vessel's hull may vary significantly from speed with respect to a nearby volume of water. In addition, the motions of a vessel, such as yaw and pitch, introduce variations in the speed over ground. These speed variations combined with sensor response characteristics can generate appreciable errors in the speed measurement. Many of the uncertainties and errors in the measurement of a vessel's speed are functions of the ocean environment and of the characteristics of the vessel carrying the speed sensor. These causes of measurement uncertainty limit the ultimate accuracy of a speed log installation irrespective of the accuracy of the instrumentation itself.

The **potential flow field** represents the changes in the water velocity and pressure distributions caused by the shape, size, and orientation to the flow of the vessel carrying the speed sensor. As water changes its flow direction to pass around the underwater body of a vessel of a given configuration, the resulting accelerations and decelerations generate water velocities near the hull that are significantly different from the velocity of water relative to the vessel far from the influence of the vessel's hull.

Since each hull configuration experiences different local velocities, each system (hull and sensor) must be calibrated to remove the *system errors* inherent in the combination of hull and sensor. The usefulness of measured-mile calibrations in calibrating out system errors is limited by the water depth. Many of the available measured-mile courses are too shallow for accurate calibration. The viscosity of the water results in a friction **boundary layer** or layer of water carried along with the hull. The thickness of this boundary layer varies from fractions of inches at the bow to the order of feet near the stern. In this layer, the water velocity changes from zero at the hull to a value within several percent of free-stream velocity at the outer edge of the boundary layer. As a consequence, sensing elements usually have to extend beyond the boundary layer.

Appendages, such as sonar domes, create wakes that cause error in speed sensors located downstream. For optimum operation, speed sensors should not be mounted near wakes of appendages. However, it is not always possible to place a sensor entirely out of the wake of an appendage and the resulting error must be accepted.

Shallow water effect is a particular aspect of the potential-flow problem that occurs when a vessel is in shallow water. The closeness of the bottom changes the potential-flow velocity distribution by restricting the region in which the water can flow around the hull, causing an increase in the speed reading of a bottom-mounted sensor. The speed problem is compounded because shallow water increases the drag of a vessel causing a decrease of actual speed. It is possible that the speed-reading error coupled with the actual speed decrease may result in no change in indicated speed, while, in fact, the vessel has actually slowed. The precise effects of shallow water on the speed reading are difficult to determine for any specific vessel, and there is no rule of thumb that is applicable to all types and sizes of hulls.

The speed sensor is usually rigidly attached to and undergoes the motions of the vessel carrying it. The vessel may be considered a rigid body with six degrees of freedom, three translation degrees of the vessel's center of gravity and three rotational degrees about the center of gravity. The speed sensor or sensing region is seldom located at the vessel's center of gravity; therefore, the sensor undergoes additional linear displacements proportional to the distance from the center of gravity and the rotation rate.

Average motion errors result from static or dynamic orientation difference from the designed sensor orientation. Speed sensors are usually orientated to measure the water velocity component parallel to the longitudinal axis of the vessel. Neglecting the effects of vessel trim on the water flow near the hull, a change in the static trim from the design trim could reduce the sensed velocity by the cosine of the trim angle through the geometric effects alone. Also, the vessel is normally pitching, yawing, and rolling. The instantaneous pitch and yaw angles cause similar cosine function reductions because the vessel's actual velocity vector is not parallel to the longitudinal axis, and the sensor signal is always reduced by these effects. A more significant error results when the vessel has a drift component due to wind. The speed sensor will not measure this leeway. Most of the average motion errors are quite small (less than a few tenths of 1 percent) and can be neglected. Leeway due to wind may be several knots and cannot be neglected if accurate velocity sensing is required.

Oscillatory errors are the differences between the instantaneous speed reading and the vessel's speed caused by its motion. The oscillatory errors tend to average out over a period of several minutes but may cause appreciable errors in applications requiring a continuous speed input. While almost all of the vessel's motions affect the instantaneous speed reading, the primary cause of the oscillatory error is the pitching motion. For example, for a vessel pitching with an amplitude of only $2\frac{1}{2}$ degrees and a period of 5 seconds with the sensor mounted 10 feet below the center of gravity, the oscillatory error is $\pm 1/3$ knot.

Maneuvering errors are those speed-sensing errors caused by controlled motions of the vessel. For example, when a vessel turns, a drift angle is developed between the heading and the actual water velocity vector at the sensor. The speed sensor only measures the longitudinal velocity component, and the speed is reduced by the cosine of the drift angle at the sensor.

Variability is one of the primary characteristics of water movement in the ocean. This allows prediction of only average values, with the possibility that at any particular time the actual current may be quite different in both direction and magnitude. For example, in the Gulf Stream off Florida, there is 72 percent probability that the current will be toward the northeast with a strength greater than 2 knots. However, there is a 4 percent probability of no current, and a 7 percent probability that the current will be toward the southwest with a strength of 2/3 to 1 knot. In the Sargasso Sea there is almost equal probability of any current direction with magnitudes of 1/3 to 2/3 knot. Thus, it becomes obvious that in correcting for current, average values can be predicted, but large errors are possible unless currents can be accurately measured.

Problems of water-speed measurement by doppler sonar speed logs are discussed in chapter XLV.

613. The electromagnetic underwater log, commonly called the **EM log,** consists essentially of a rodmeter, sea valve, indicator-transmitter, and remote control unit (fig. 613a). The rodmeter is a strut of streamlined cross section. A sensing device near its tip develops a signal voltage proportional to the speed of the water past it. Of the two general types of rodmeters, one is fixed hull mounted and the other is retractable through a sea valve. The sea valve is mounted in the hull of the vessel and provides a watertight support through which the retractable rodmeter protrudes. It also seals

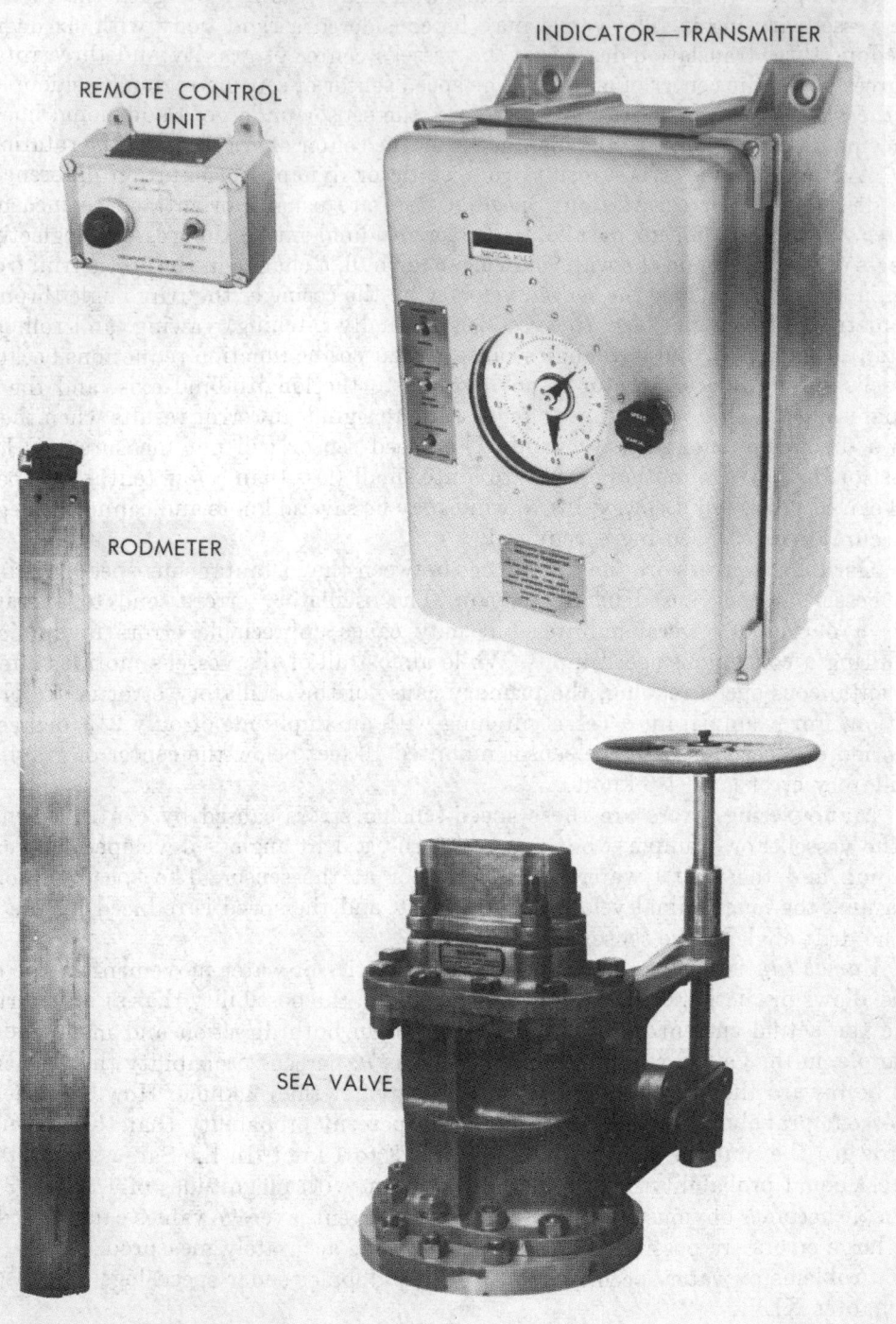

INDICATOR—TRANSMITTER

REMOTE CONTROL
UNIT

RODMETER

SEA VALVE

FIGURE 613a.—Components of electromagnetic underwater log.

the vessel's hull when the rodmeter is removed. The indicator-transmitter houses all moving parts of the equipment and performs the following functions: (1) It indicates the vessel's speed in knots on a dial, (2) it operates synchro transmitters to generate corresponding synchro signals for transmission of speed signals to receivers, (3) it registers on a counter the distance in nautical miles that the vessel has traveled through the water, and (4) it develops a synchro signal representing distance for transmission to receivers. The remote control unit may be used to set speed into the indicator-transmitter. In this mode the underwater log is being used as a **dummy log.**

The fixed rodmeter is designed for submarines, mounts on the exterior of the hull, and does not require a sea valve. The hull penetration is small since only the connector end of the rodmeter passes into the hull. There may be two or three rods installed, depending on the submarine. One is usually mounted topside. A fixed rodmeter has also been developed for use on surface vessels.

The principle of the electromagnetic log is that any conductor will produce a voltage when it is moved across a magnetic field or when a magnetic field is moved with respect to the conductor. Figure 613b illustrates this in elementary form. Note that the direction of the field, the direction of motion, and the direction of the induced voltage are all at right angles to each other. If the magnetic field remains constant, the magnitude of the voltage will be proportional to the speed of movement in the direction indicated.

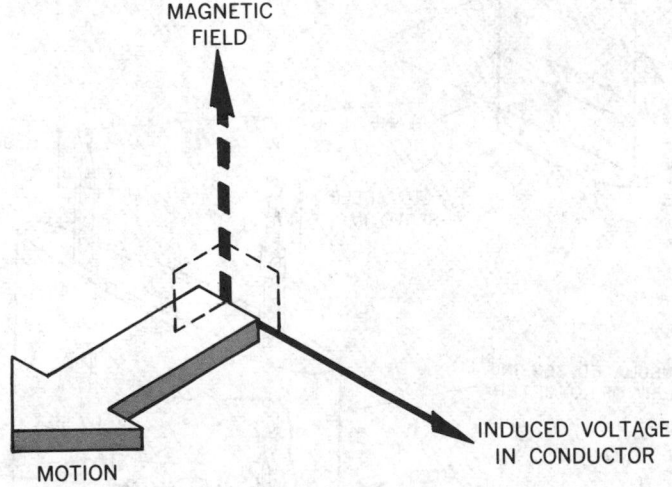

FIGURE 613b.—Voltage induced by relative movement between magnetic field and conductor.

In the electromagnetic log system, a magnetic field produced by a coil in the sensing unit at the outer end of the rodmeter is set up in the water in which the vessel is floating. The sensing unit's outer surface is an insulating layer or boot, except for two Monel (nickel-copper alloy) buttons, one on each side of the rodmeter. As shown in the inset at the upper left of figure 613c, the horizontal plane in which the buttons are located is in the water. The axis of the coil in the sensing unit is perpendicular to this plane, and so are its magnetic flux lines where they cut the plane. If the vessel is moving in the direction indicated by the white arrow, the flux lines cut the water in this plane and induce a voltage in it. Since the plane is cut by the insulating boot of the rodmeter, the induced voltage, sometimes called electromotive force (emf), appears at the buttons in the boot.

A better understanding of this effect can be obtained by comparing the inset of figure 613c with the main part of the figure. The main part shows the coil, its flux field, and one possible symmetrical "water circuit" (the broken white line from button to button) in which the voltage is induced. The inset shows the plane in which the "water circuit" (one of the many that are possible) exists.

The voltage induced by the vessel's motion is in general proportional to the rodmeter's speed with respect to the water. The induced voltage is affected by the flow characteristics of the water past the rodmeter (whether laminar (smooth) or turbulent). The sensor and electronics are designed so that no significant current is drawn from the induced voltage and normal variations of water conductivity do not affect the sensor accuracy.

The vessel's motion other than forward speed, such as pitch and roll, will also produce output signals from the rodmeter.

In order to accurately measure the precise speed signal generated by the sensing unit, most electromagnetic log systems employ a "null-balance" type of electronic voltmeter. For systems currently in naval service, this voltmeter employs an electromechanical servo and dial indicator system such as the one illustrated in figure 613d. Newer systems use all electronic instrumentation and have digital displays. Typical system characteristics include: (1) sensor output signal of 325 microvolts per knot;

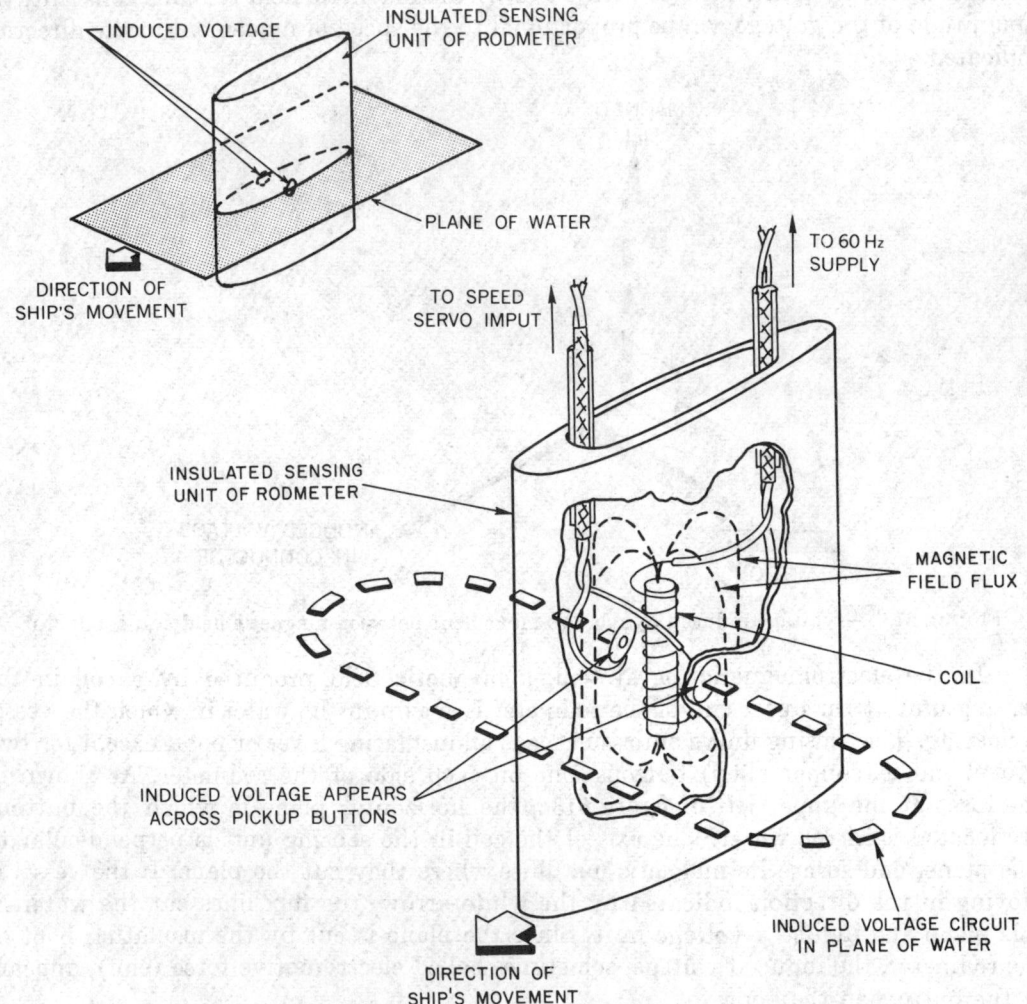

FIGURE 613c.—Sensing principle of electromagnetic log.

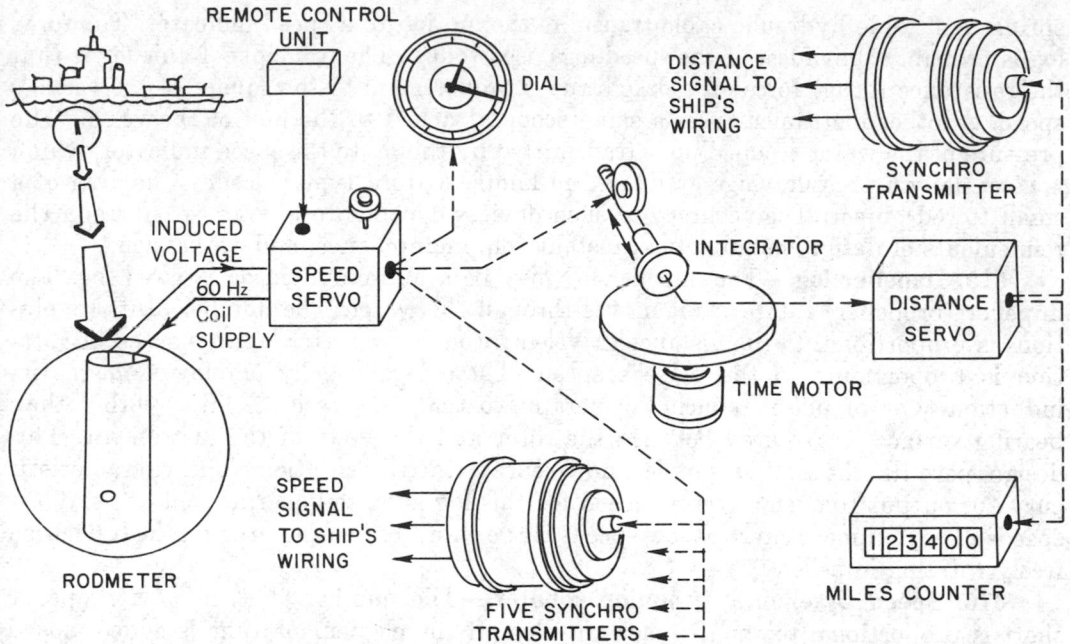

FIGURE 613d.—Electromagnetic log speed measuring system.

(2) instrument speed accuracy of 0.05 knot; (3) sensitivity to speed changes of 0.01 knot; (4) instrument distance accuracy of better than 1 percent of water distance traveled; and (5) capability to compensate for different hull flow characteristics. Several commercial electromagnetic logs provide slightly less precision.

614. Speed measurement by dynamic water pressure.—When an object is moving through a fluid such as water or air, its forward side is exposed to a *dynamic* pressure which is proportional to the speed at which the object is moving, in addition to the *static* pressure due to depth and density of the fluid above the object. Therefore, if dynamic pressure can be measured, this principle can be used for determining speed.

One of the most widely used means of measuring dynamic pressure is by a **Pitot tube.** This device consists of a tube having an opening on its forward side or end. If the tube is stationary in the water, this opening is subject to static pressure only. But when the tube is in motion, the pressure at the opening is the sum of static and dynamic pressures. This is called **Pitot pressure** or **total pressure.** The Pitot tube is surrounded by an outer tube which has openings along its athwartship sides. Whether the tube is stationary or in motion, these openings are subject to static pressure only.

In the **Pitot-static log** the Pitot tube is in the form of a vertical "rodmeter" which extends through and is supported by a sea valve in the the vessel's bottom. The tube extends 24 to 30 inches below the bottom of the vessel, into water relatively undisturbed by motion of the hull. The two pressures, Pitot and static, are led to separate bellows attached to opposite ends of a centrally pivoted lever. This lever is electrically connected to a mechanism which controls the speed of a pump. When the vessel is dead in the water, the pressures are equal, and the pump is stopped. When the ship is moving, the pump speed is regulated so that the pressures in the two bellows are equalized. Thus, the pump speed is proportional to the ship speed.

Various less accurate instruments have been devised for determining speed by measuring water pressure due to forward motion of the vessel. These are relatively simple, inexpensive instruments intended primarily for use by small craft. One instrument, the **force log,** has a strut which the water pressure forces aft against a calibrated spring. A flexible hydraulic cable transmits the motion to a speed indicator. The force log is probably the oldest of the speed logs used today. The principle of this log is that the resistance (drag) force on a drag strut is proportional to the square of the vessel's speed. Another instrument uses a small scoop attached to the hull of the vessel. The pressure of the water scooped up is transmitted by tubing to the speed indicator, which is essentially a pressure gage graduated in knots. A third type measures the drag of a small towed object. The accuracy of such devices depends to a large extent upon the refinements of design, manufacture, installation, maintenance, and calibration.

615. Impeller log.—The impeller log may be a hull-mounted or a towed log. The impeller (propeller) rotates as it moves through the water. The number of its revolutions is proportional to the distance traveled through the water, and its speed of rotation is proportional to the vessel's speed. These logs usually employ a magnetic-induction type of pulse frequency generator so that no physical contact, other than bearing surface, is required between the rotor and the body of the instrument. This design permits the use of simple and accurate instrumentation. The characteristic curve of output frequency versus speed for this log is quite linear, except at very low speeds. The nonlinear curve at low speeds is the result of bearing drag on the otherwise freely rotating impeller.

616. Speed by engine revolution counter.—The number of turns of a propeller shaft is proportional to the distance traveled. If the element of time is added, speed can be determined. If the screw were advancing through a solid substance, the distance it would advance in one revolution would be the **pitch** of the screw. Thus, if a propeller having a pitch of ten feet turns at 200 revolutions per minute, it advances 2,000 feet in one minute, equivalent to a speed of 19.75 knots. It does not do so in water because of **slip,** the difference between the distance it would advance in a solid substance and actual distance traveled, expressed as a percentage of the former. For example, if slip is 18 percent, both the ship's speed and distance covered are reduced by this percentage. Thus, instead of 19.75 knots, the speed is only $19.75 \times 0.82 = 16.2$ knots.

Slip depends upon the type and speed of rotation of the propeller, the type of ship, the condition of loading and ship's bottom, the state of the sea and the ship's course relative to it, and the apparent wind. Despite the many variables, slip can be determined with sufficient accuracy for practical navigation. This is usually accomplished by steaming a known distance and noting the time of passage. The speed corresponding to the number of revolutions being used can then be determined by means of the formula of article 608, in the form

$$\text{speed} = \frac{\text{distance}}{\text{time}}$$

or by reference to table 18 (if the distance is exactly one mile). Thus, speed can be determined directly, without computing slip, and a table or curve of ship speed for various engine revolution speeds can be made. Appendix U provides guidelines for determining speed in this manner. Any suitable distance can be used, but a distance of one nautical mile has been measured at various convenient locations. Each such **measured mile** is suitably marked on the beach, and shown on the chart, with the course to steer.

This method of determining speed is widely used in the merchant marine. By means of an **engine revolution counter** the number of revolutions during any suitable time interval can be measured. If a **tachometer** is available, the *rate* of shaft revolution is determined, usually in revolutions per minute. For best results, allowance should be made for condition of the bottom, draft and trim of the vessel, and the state of the sea.

Depth Measurement

617. Importance.—Accurate knowledge of the depth of water under a vessel is of such navigational importance that there is a legal requirement that American merchant vessels of 500 gross tons or more engaged in ocean and coastwise service "shall be fitted with an efficient mechanical deep-sea sounding apparatus in addition to the deep-sea hand leads."

618. The lead (lĕd) is a device consisting of a suitably marked line having a weight attached to one of its ends. It is used for measuring depth of water. Although the lead is probably the oldest of all navigational aids, it is still a highly useful device, particularly in periods of reduced visibility. Although its greatest service is generally in the shoal water near the shore, it sometimes can provide valuable information when the vessel is out of sight of land.

Two types of lead are in common use, the **hand lead,** weighing from 7 to 14 pounds and having a line marked to about 25 fathoms; and the **deep-sea (dipsey) lead,** weighing from 30 to 100 pounds and having a line marked to 100 fathoms or more in length. The markings commonly used on lead lines are as follows:

Distance from lead in fathoms	Marking	Distance from lead in fathoms	Marking
2	two strips of leather	20	short line with two knots
3	three strips of leather	25	short line with one knot
5	white rag (usually cotton)	30	short line with three knots
7	red rag (usually wool)	35	short line with one knot
10	leather with hole	40	short line with four knots
13	same as three fathoms	45	short line with one knot
15	same as five fathoms	50	short line with five knots
17	same as seven fathoms		etc.

Fathoms marked on the lead line are called **marks.** The intermediate whole fathoms are called **deeps.** In reporting depths it is customary to use these terms, as "by the mark five," "deep six," etc. The only fractions of a fathom usually reported are halves and quarters, the customary expressions being "and a half, eight," "less a quarter, four," etc. A practice sometimes followed is to place distinctive markings on the hand lead line at each foot near the critical depths of the vessel with which it is to be used. The markings should be placed on the lead line when it is wet, and the accuracy of the marking should be checked from time to time to detect any changes in the length of the line. The distance from the hand of the leadsman to the surface of the water under various conditions of loading should be determined so that correct allowance can be made when the marking nearest the surface cannot be observed.

The lead itself has a recess in its bottom. If this recess is filled with tallow or other suitable substance, a sample of the bottom can sometimes be obtained. This information can prove helpful in establishing the position of the vessel. If tallow is not available, some other substance can be used. Soap is suitable if it is replaced from time to time. When the recess is filled for obtaining a sample, the lead is said to be **armed** with the substance used.

619. Echo sounder.—Most soundings are made by means of an **echo sounder.** In this instrument a pulse of electrical energy is converted periodically to sound energy and transmitted downward by a transducer. When the energy strikes the bottom (or any other object having acoustic properties different from those of water), a portion is reflected back to the transducer as an echo. This energy is reconverted to electrical energy for presentation. Because the speed of sound in water is nearly constant, the amount of time which elapses between the transmission of a pulse and the reception of its echo is a measure of the distance traveled, or in this case, depth.

Depth information is presented in either of two ways; namely, an indicator consisting of a cathode-ray tube or a recorder which records depth on calibrated paper.

There are many forms of echo sounder. A typical installation (fig. 619a) consists essentially of a receiver-transmitter, transducer, and interconnecting cables. The receiver-transmitter includes all components and subassemblies of the system, except the transducer and interconnecting cables. The recorder performs the function of recording depth versus time on a paper roll visible through a window in the cabinet's front door. When the recorder is used, it keys the transmitter at a predetermined rate. The cathode-ray tube indicator, mounted below the recorder, indicates depth on a cathode-ray tube; a calibrated circular dial overlays the cathode-ray tube providing a means for reading the depth through an opening in the cabinet's front door. When the indicator is used, it keys the transmitter at a predetermined rate. The transducer converts the electrical energy to sound energy, transmits the sound into the water, receives returned echoes, and converts the returned energy to electrical energy.

When the recorder of the typical installation (fig. 619a) is energized by placing the depth range switch in one of the three recorder positions (600 feet, 600 fathoms, 6000 fathoms), a specially treated recording paper, held between two rollers, is moved at a uniform speed horizontally in front of a grounded plate. At the same time a stylus assembly is moved at a uniform speed vertically across the face of the paper. The rate of movement depends on the range selected, and is so fixed that one of the two stylii appears at the top of the recording paper (0 depth) when the transmitter is keyed and reaches the bottom of the paper at the same time as an echo would be received from the maximum depth of the selected depth range.

The recording paper is marked by the application of a voltage between the stylus and the grounded plate when the echo is received.

In the same installation, depth indication on the 100 feet and 100 fathom scales is given on the face of a cathode-ray tube by radial modulation of a circular sweep. The illuminated trace follows a circular course at a constant angular velocity. The time to complete one revolution is the time required for an echo to return from 100 feet or 100 fathoms at the assumed speed of sound in water. The transmitted pulse and the returned echoes cause radial modulations. Beams of light thus appear behind a calibrated screen covering the indicator tube face, one at position zero (transmitted pulse) and the others at positions corresponding to the echoes (fig. 619b).

The transmitter is keyed mechanically by the recorder or electronically by the cathode-ray tube indicator circuit, depending on the depth range scale in use. Keying may be automatic or manual.

The operator must observe certain precautions in his use of this typical installation. He must change depth range scales when conditions warrant. For example, a depth of 300 feet can be recorded on the 6000-fathom scale, better on the 600-fathom scale, but best on the 600-foot scale. If a range is selected which is less than the water depth, the echo will return either after the stylus that keyed the transmitter has left the paper (resulting in no indication) or after the other stylus has reached the paper (resulting in a false indication). Similarly, if an indicator range is selected which is less than the water depth, the result will be no indication or a false indication.

Examples of how false echoes can be produced follow. Suppose the water depth beneath the vessel is 1,300 feet and the 600-foot recorder scale is in use. Refer to figure 619c. Stylus A marks the paper at zero and travels downward while stylus B travels upward. Stylus B must travel a distance corresponding to 1,200 feet before it appears

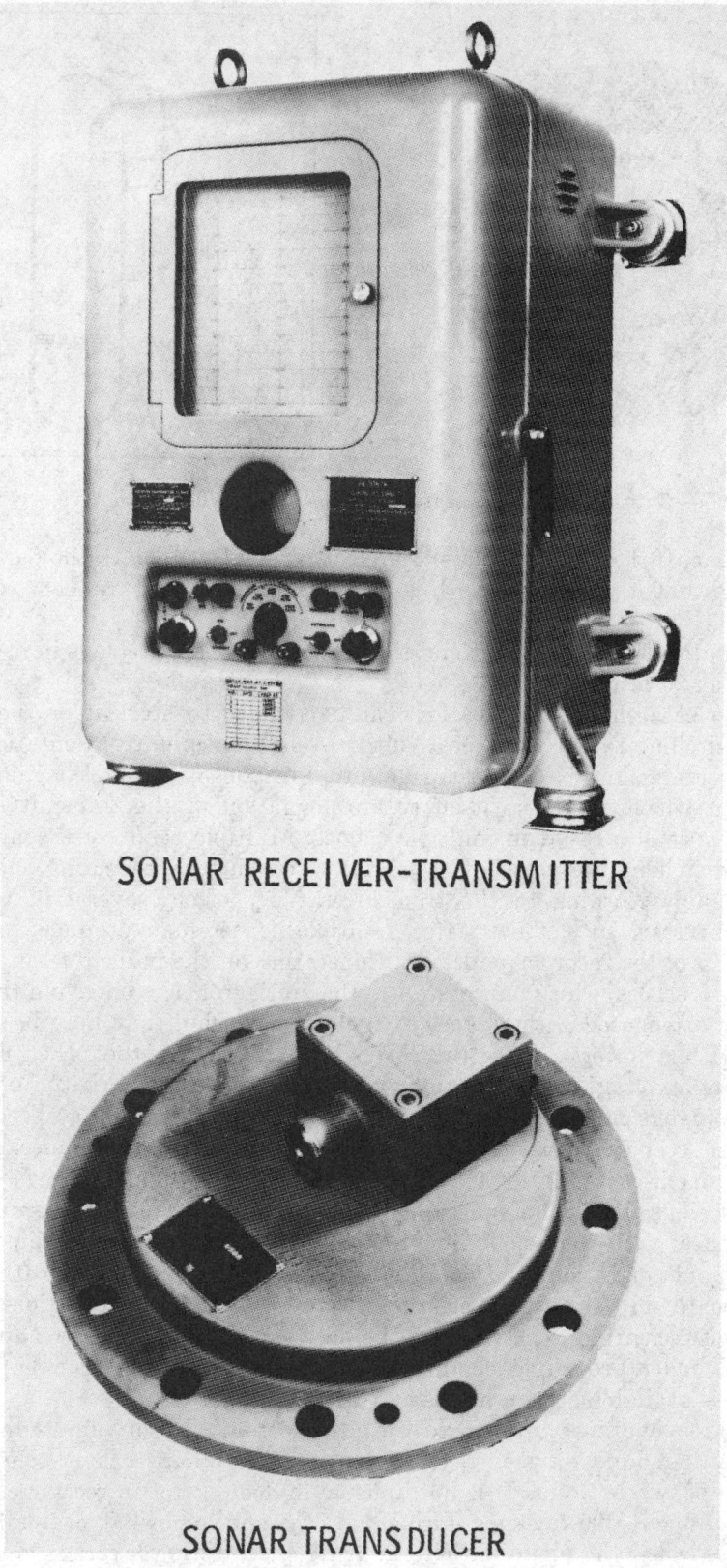

SONAR RECEIVER-TRANSMITTER

SONAR TRANSDUCER

FIGURE 619a.—Echo sounder.

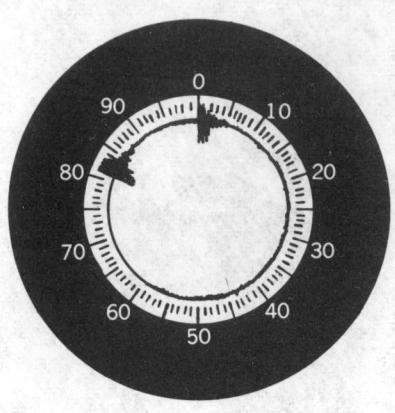

FIGURE 619b.—Cathode-ray tube indicator.   FIGURE 619c.—Side view of stylus belt.

at the zero line. If the water depth is 1,300 feet, stylus B will mark the paper at 100 feet. It is obvious that if the water depth is from 600 to 1,200 feet, no echo will appear on the paper.

If the water depth is 120 feet and the 100-foot indicator scale is in use, a false echo will appear at 20 feet.

In either case, the false indications can be avoided by starting on the highest scale and then switching to the scale best suited to give optimum presentation.

The receiver gain must be set for optimum response. Too high a gain will result in reverberation which manifests itself as an elongation of the transmitted pulse. Too high a gain may also result in multiple echoes. Multiple echoes are caused by the returning echo striking the vessel's keel or the water surface, reflecting back to the bottom, and again returning to the transducer. Very often, several of these multiple echoes can be seen. In shallow water, multiple echoes may produce a straight line the full length of the recorder paper or, if operating on the indicator ranges, produce a solid mass of echoes which merges with the initial pulse. Since multiple echoes are considerably attenuated with respect to the original echo, they may be eliminated by operating with a lower gain setting. Too low a gain, on the other hand, will not develop enough voltage from an otherwise suitable echo to mark the paper.

Echo sounders of American manufacture are calibrated for a speed of sound of 4,800 feet per second. The actual speed varies primarily with the temperature, pressure, and salinity, as discussed in article 3503, but in the ocean is nearly always faster than the speed of calibration. The error thus introduced is on the side of safety unless the water is fresh or very cold. Soundings shown on charts are those obtained by an echo sounder without correction, and can therefore be compared directly with the readings obtained aboard ship since the variation in speed from mean conditions is not great. Only in precise scientific work should it be necessary to correct the readings for actual sound speed under prevailing conditions. Accurate adjustment can be made only if information is available on conditions at various depths.

Errors are sometimes introduced by false bottoms. If soft mud covers the ocean floor, some of the sound-wave energy may penetrate to a harder layer beneath, resulting in indication of two bottoms. It is not unusual in deep water to receive a strong return at a depth of about 200 fathoms during the day, and somewhat nearer the surface at night. This is called the **phantom bottom** or **deep scattering layer.** It is believed to be due to large numbers of tiny marine animals. Schools of fish return an echo sufficiently strong to make the echo sounder a valuable aid to commercial fishermen.

In modern equipment the sound waves, whether sonic or ultrasonic, are produced electrically by means of a **transducer,** a device for converting electrical energy to sound waves, or vice versa. The transducer utilizes either the piezo-electric properties of quartz or the magnetostriction properties of nickel and its alloys.

Early models produced sound signals by striking the ship's hull with a mechanical hammer in the forward part of the vessel. The echo was received by a microphone in the after part of the vessel, depth being determined by the angle at which the signal returned.

Direction Measurement

620. Reference directions.—A horizontal direction is generally expressed as an angle between a line extending in some **reference direction** and a line extending in the given direction. The angle is numerically equal to the difference between the two directions, called the **angular distance** from the reference direction. Unless the reference direction is stated or otherwise understood, the intended direction is in doubt. Thus, to a navigator, direction 135° is southeast. To an astronomer or surveyor, it may be northwest.

A number of reference directions are used in navigation. If a direction is stated in three figures, without designation of reference direction, it is generally understood that the direction is related to true (geographical) north. When grid navigation (art. 2510) is being used, particularly in high latitudes, grid north is generally used as the reference direction. The reference direction for magnetic directions is magnetic north, and that for compass directions is compass north. For relative bearings it is the heading of the ship. For amplitudes, the reference direction is east or west, usually 090° or 270° true, but magnetic, compass, or even grid east or west may be used. In maneuvering situations, the heading of another vessel might be used as the reference direction.

The primary function of an instrument used for measuring direction is to determine the reference direction. This having been done, other directions can be indicated by a compass rose oriented in the reference direction. North is established by some form of compass. A compass rose is attached to the north-seeking element so that other directions can be determined directly. However, if one always keeps in mind that the primary function of the instrument is to indicate a reference direction, he should be able to avoid some of the mistakes commonly made in the application of compass errors.

621. Desirable characteristics of a navigational compass.—To adequately serve its purpose, a navigational compass needs to have certain characteristics to permit it to meet requirements of accuracy, reliability, and convenience.

The most important characteristic is accuracy. No other quality, however important or to whatever extent it may be possessed, compensates for the lack of accuracy. This does not mean that the compass need be without error, but that such errors as it may possess can be readily determined. Provisions should be made for removing deviation or reducing it to a minimum (ch. VII). If accurate horizontal directions are to be determined, the compass needs to be provided with some type of compass rose maintained in a horizontal position (art. 303, vol. II). Adequate sighting equipment is needed if bearings are to be observed, and an index is needed to mark the forward direction parallel to the keel if heading is to be measured. Accurate readings cannot be expected from a compass that **hunts** (oscillates) excessively. A characteristic closely related to accuracy is precision (art. 103, vol. II). The amount of precision required varies somewhat with the use and depends as much upon the steadiness of the compass and its design as upon its inherent qualities.

A compass is reliable when its operation is not often interrupted; when its indications are relatively free from unknown or unsuspected disturbances; when it is little affected by extremes of temperature, moisture, vibration, or the shock of gunfire; and when it is not so sensitive that large errors are introduced by ordinary changes in conditions or equipment near the compass.

The value of a compass is dependent somewhat upon the convenience with which it can be used. Accuracy, too, may be involved. Thus, a compass should not be installed in such a position that one must be in an unnatural or uncomfortable position to use it. A compass intended for use in obtaining bearings is of reduced value if it is installed at a location that does not permit an unobstructed view in most directions. The compass graduations and index should be clean, adequately lighted if the instrument is to be used at night, and clearly marked.

622. Kinds of compasses.—The compasses commonly used by the mariner are (1) *magnetic* and (2) *gyroscopic.* The magnetic compass tends to align itself with the magnetic lines of force of the earth, while the gyrocompass seeks the true (geographic) meridian. The word "compass" is also applied to instruments which do not continuously indicate some form of north. Thus, the free gyro (art. 630) tends to remain approximately aligned with any great circle to which it is set.

A compass may be designated to indicate its principal use, as a **standard, steering, or boat compass.** The compass designated as standard is usually a magnetic compass installed in an exposed position having an unobstructed view in most directions, permitting accurate determination of error. Preferably, it is located at a magnetically favorable position near the bridge. Before the development of a reliable gyrocompass, the standard compass was used for navigation of the vessel and for determining the error of the steering compass.

Although the modern, reliable gyrocompass has largely superseded the magnetic compass for most purposes, directional information is so important to a vessel that the availability of a second method is considered justified. It is wise to understand both types, keep a record of errors and the performance of all compasses, and to compare the indications of magnetic and gyrocompasses at frequent intervals, as every half hour when underway.

623. Magnetic compasses.—If a small magnet is pivoted at its center of gravity in such manner that it is free to turn and dip, it will tend to align itself with the magnetic field of the earth (art. 706). It thus provides a directional reference and becomes a simple compass. However, such a compass would not be adequate for use aboard ship. For this purpose a compass should have a stronger directive element than that provided by a single, pivoted magnet, should have provision for measuring various directions, should have some means of damping the oscillations of the directive element, should be approximately horizontal, and should have some means of neutralizing local magnetic influences.

In a mariner's compass, several magnets are mounted parallel to each other. To them is attached a **compass card** having a compass rose to indicate various directions (art. 624). Both magnets and compass card are enclosed in a bowl having a glass top through which the card can be seen. The bowl is weighted at the bottom and is suspended in gimbals in such manner that it remains nearly horizontal as the vessel rolls and pitches. In nearly all modern compasses the bowl is filled with a liquid that supplies a buoyant force almost equal to the force of gravity acting upon the directive element and card. This reduces the friction on the pivot (a metal point in a jeweled bearing), and provides a means of damping the oscillations of the compass card. The card is mounted in such manner as to remain in an essentially horizontal position. A mark called a **lubber's line** is placed on the inner surface of the bowl, adjacent to the compass card, to indicate the forward direction parallel to the keel when the bowl is correctly installed. The gimbals used for mounting the compass bowl are attached to a stand called a **binnacle,** which in most installations is permanently and rigidly attached to the deck of the vessel, usually on its longitudinal center line. Most binnacles provide means for neutralization of local magnetic influences due to magnetism within the vessel. A cover or "hood" is provided to protect the compass from the elements, dust, etc.

Directional information is of such importance that selection and installation of a suitable compass should be made carefully, seeking such guidance as may be needed. In the U. S. Navy this is covered by systems command directives. For merchant vessels and yachts, one would do well to consult a dependable compass adjustor before selecting and installing a compass or making any alteration in the vicinity of the compass. Common errors are the use of a compass designed for a different type craft (as an aircraft compass in a boat), permitting chrome plating of a binnacle by someone who does not know how to do this without creating a magnetic field, authorizing electric welding of steel near the compass, improper installation of magnetic equipment or electric appliances near the compass, allowing short circuits to occur in the vicinity of the compass, etc.

After the compass has been selected and installed, proper adjustment and compensation (ch. VII) are important, and future care of the instrument should not be neglected. It should be checked and overhauled at regular intervals, and any indication of malfunctioning or deterioration, however slight, should not be overlooked. Discoloration of the liquid or the presence of a bubble, for instance, indicates a condition that should be investigated and corrected at once. If it becomes necessary to add liquid, one should be certain that he has the correct substance, and should attempt to determine the source of the leak. Except as a temporary expedient, this is best done by a professional. Some compasses should be protected from prolonged exposure to sunlight, to prevent discoloration of the card and liquid.

624. The compass card is composed of light, nonmagnetic material. In nearly all modern compasses the card is graduated in 360°, increasing clockwise from north through east, south, and west. An older system still used somewhat is to graduate the card through 90° in each quadrant, increasing from both north and south. Some compass cards are graduated in "points," usually in addition to the degree graduations. There are 32 **points of the compass,** 11¼° apart. The four **cardinal points** are north, east, south, and west. Midway between these are four **intercardinal points** at northeast, southeast, southwest, and northwest. These eight points are the only ones appearing on the cards of compasses used by the U. S. Navy. The eight points between cardinal and intercardinal points are named for the two directions between which they lie, the cardinal name being given first, as north northeast, east northeast, east southeast, etc. The remaining 16 points are named for the nearest cardinal or intercardinal point "by" the next cardinal point in the direction of measurement, as north by east, northeast by north, etc. Smaller graduations are provided by dividing each point into four "quarter points," thus producing 128 graduations altogether. There are several systems of naming the quarter points. That used in the U. S. Navy when quarter points were used is given in table. 2.

The naming of the various graduations of the compass card in order is called **boxing the compass,** an important attainment by the student mariner of earlier generations. The point system of indicating relative bearings (art. 1004) survived long after degrees became almost universally used for compass and true directions. Except for the cardinal and intercardinal points, and occasionally the two-point graduations, all of which are used to indicate directions generally (as "northwest winds," meaning winds from a general northwesterly direction), the point system has become largely historical.

625. The U. S. Navy 7½-inch compass has a liquid-filled bowl in which a 7½-inch aluminum card is pivoted. There is provision for either one or two pairs of magnets, symmetrically placed. The card and magnet assembly is provided with a central float or air chamber to reduce the weight on the pivot to between 60 and 90 grains (0.14 and 0.21 oz.) at 60°F when the correct compass fluid is used. Older compasses use a fluid consisting of 45 percent ethyl alcohol and 55 percent distilled water. Newer compasses use a highly refined petroleum distillate similar to varsol. Use of this oil increases the stability and efficiency of the compass. A hollow cone extends into the underside of the float. The bottom of this cone is open. The pointed top has a jewel bearing of synthetic sapphire. The card-float-magnet assembly rests on an osmium-iridium tipped pivot at the jewel center. This pivot extends upward from the bottom of the bowl. This compass is illustrated in figure 625.

The compass bowl is made of cast bronze, and has a tightly gasketed glass top cover to prevent leakage of the liquid. A bellows-type expansion chamber is provided to allow for changes in volume of the liquid as the temperature changes. The top rim or bezel of the bowl is accurately machined so that an azimuth or bearing circle can be placed over it. The compass is equipped with a gimbal ring for keeping the compass level when mounted in a binnacle. In addition to providing support for the compass, the binnacle has provision for housing the correctors used to partially neutralize local magnetic effects within the vessel.

626. The U. S. Navy 5-inch compass is lighter in weight and requires less space than the 7½-inch compass. This U. S. Navy No. 3 compass has a brass compass card with photo-etched perforations which permit underlighting with red light to meet darkness adaptation requirements. When such a card is used with both transmitted and reflected light in all combinations, there is a "twilight zone" in which the intensity of the

FIGURE 625.—U. S. Navy 7½-inch compass.

FIGURE 626a.—Binnacle for U. S. Navy 5-inch magnetic compass.

light transmitted through the perforations is equal to that of the reflected light from the surrounding area. In the U. S. Navy No. 3 compass this problem is overcome by the installation of a shaded lamp inside the binnacle hood. The light from this lamp is directed at the lubber's line and adjacent compass card area. This light enables daylight viewing of the compass card. The red illumination is required only when practically complete darkness prevails.

In addition to providing support for the compass, the binnacle illustrated in figure 626a has provision for housing the correctors used to partially neutralize local magnetic effects within the vessel. The correctors consist of a tube assembly with heeling magnet, quadrantal correctors, fixed fore-and-aft and athwartship permanent magnetic correctors, and permanent magnet correctors rotatable about fore-and-aft and athwartship axes.

The fixed permanent magnets are in the form of wire magnet bundles of up to seven magnets each and are contained in three magnet tubes as shown in figure 626a. The athwartship tube is fixed to the after side of the binnacle. One fore-and-aft tube is on the port side of the binnacle; the other is on the starboard side.

The fixed fore-and-aft and athwartship magnets are used to obtain a "coarse" correction; the rotatable correctors are used to obtain a "fine" correction. Normally the coarse correction reduces the deviation from its original value to about 5°, the fine correction reduces the deviation to its residual value.

Except for the heeling magnet the various correctors are shown in schematic form in figure 626b. When the rotatable magnets on either axis lie in a plane parallel to the plane of the compass card, the associated magnetic field has no effect on the compass card magnets. This magnetic field is shown schematically in figure 626c for

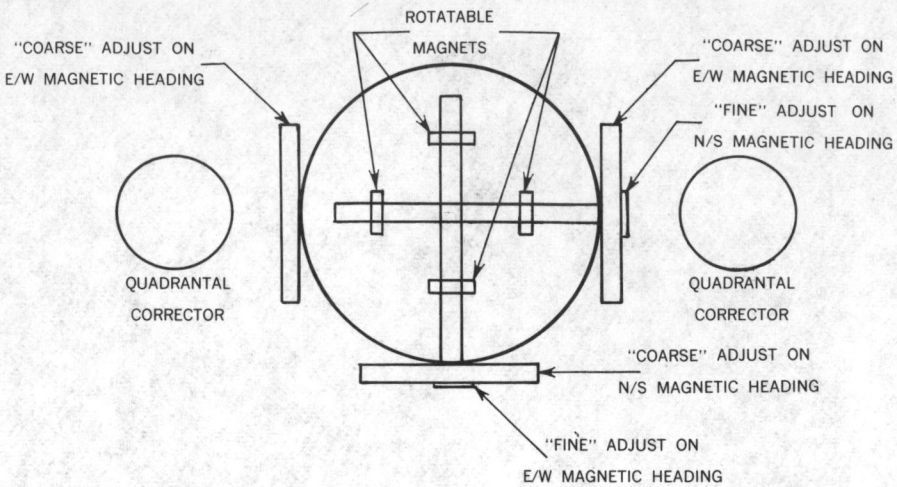

FIGURE 626b.—Correcting system of U. S. Navy 5-inch magnetic compass.

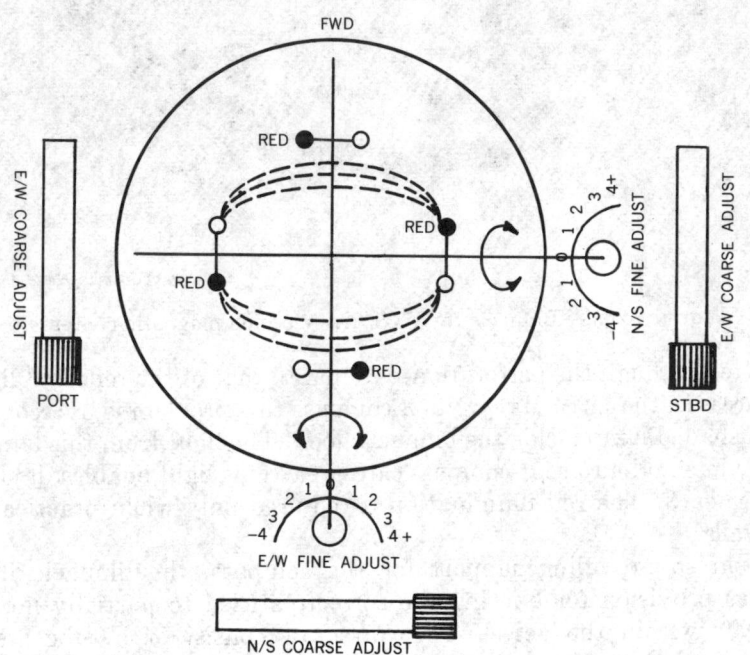

FIGURE 626c.—Coarse and fine adjustments of U. S. Navy 5-inch magnetic compass.

the magnets rotatable about the athwartship axis. When the rotatable magnets are inclined to the plane of the compass card, the effect on the compass card magnets varies with the sine function of the angle of inclination, the maximum effect being when the plane of the rotatable magnets is inclined 90° to the plane of the compass card.

Figure 626d illustrates the fine adjustment control used to rotate the magnets. The fine adjustment should be limited to approximately the last 5° of deviation correction or to the range in which the sine function is more nearly linear.

627. Other magnetic compasses.—The U. S. Navy No. 5 magnetic boat compass (fig. 627a) is a top reading, flat glass topped unit. The 3-inch compass card is made of sheet aluminum and incorporates an annular float to obtain a degree of buoyancy

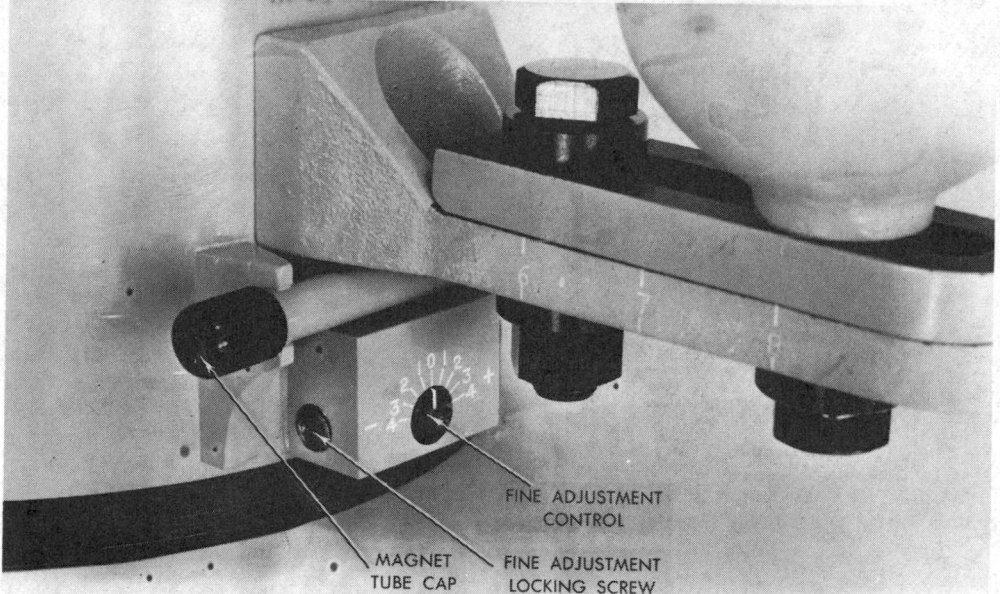

FINE ADJUSTMENT
CONTROL

MAGNET   FINE ADJUSTMENT
TUBE CAP   LOCKING SCREW

Courtesy of John E. Hand & Sons Company.

FIGURE 626d.—Fine adjustment control.

in the Varsol compass fluid. The card is supported on a jewel post without the use of gimbals. The compass bowl employs a bellows expansion chamber which permits volumetric changes of the compass fluid without bubble formation.

The correctors consist of quadrantal correctors, fore-and-aft and athwartship permanent magnet correctors.

A wide variety of magnetic compasses are used in merchant ships and yachts. The basic principles of operation of all magnetic compasses are the same, the various types differing only in details of construction. A feature which is widely used in commercial compasses is a hemispherical top (fig. 627b) which provides magnification of the graduations.

Reflection binnacles providing a periscopic readout in the wheelhouse enable mounting of the compass where it is usually less subject to the vessel's magnetic field and the installed electrical and electronic equipment than a wheelhouse installation. Location on the flying bridge also serves to facilitate compass adjustment and bearing observations.

628. Magnetic compass limitations.—Because of its essential simplicity, a magnetic compass does not easily become totally inoperative. Being independent of any power supply or other service, a magnetic compass may survive major damage to its ship without losing its utility. Small boat compasses often remain serviceable under the most rigorous conditions.

Despite its great reliability, however, a magnetic compass is subject to some limitations. Since it responds to *any* magnetic field, it is affected by any change in the local magnetic situation. Hence, the undetected presence or change of position of magnetic material near the compass may introduce an unknown error. Thus, an error might be introduced by a steel wrench or paint can left near the compass, or by a change in position of a steel boom or gun in the vicinity of the compass. Even such small amounts of magnetic material as might be included in a pocketknife or steel keys are sufficient to affect the compass if brought as close as they are when on the person of an individual standing by a compass. Nylon clothing may also introduce error in a magnetic compass. As distance from the compass increases, the strength of the mag-

FIGURE 627a.—U. S. Navy No. 5 magnetic boat compass.

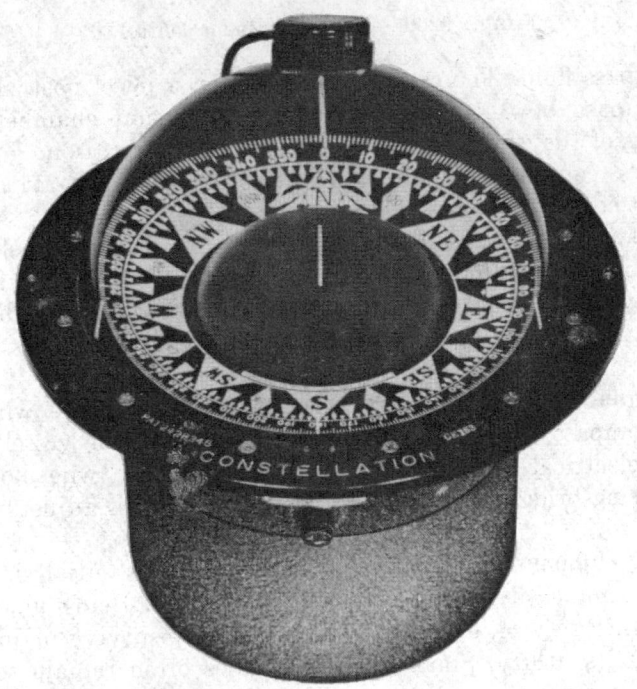

Courtesy of Danforth Division of The Eastern Company, a Connecticut Corporation.

FIGURE 627b.—A compass with a hemispherical top.

netic field needed to introduce an error increases. A cargo of large amounts of iron or steel may be sufficient to affect the compass. The compass may a'so be affected by changes of the magnetic characteristics of the vessel itself. Such changes may occur during a protracted docking period, during a long sea voyage on substantially the same course, when repairs or changes of equipment are made, if the ship sustains heavy shock as by gunfire or riding out a heavy sea, if the vessel is struck by lightning, or if a short circuit occurs near the compass.

The directive force acting upon a magnetic compass is the horizontal component of the earth's magnetic field. This component is strongest at or near the magnetic equator, decreasing to zero at the magnetic poles (ch. VII). Near the magnetic poles, therefore, the magnetic compass is useless (art. 2513), and in a wider area its indications are of questionable reliability. The magnetic field of the earth has a number of local anomalies due to the presence of magnetic material within the earth. During magnetic storms (art. 2526) it may be altered considerably. Changes in the magnetic field surrounding a vessel, due either to changes of the field itself or to change of position of the vessel within the field, affect the magnetism of the vessel and the correctors used to neutralize this effect, with a possible disturbance of the balance set up between them.

For these and other reasons, frequent determination of compass error is necessary for safe navigation. Methods of determining and correcting compass error are discussed in chapter VII.

629. Magnetic compass accessories.—Compass heading is indicated by the lubber's line. Compass bearings may be measured by sighting across the compass, bringing the object and the vertical axis of the compass in line. Accuracy in making this alignment is increased by the use of a device to direct the line of sight across the center of the compass. Perhaps the simplest device of this kind is a **bearing bar,** consisting of two vertical **sighting vanes** mounted at opposite ends of a horizontal bar having a small pivot which fits into a hole drilled part way through the glass cover of the compass, at its center. The "near" vane (nearer the eye of the observer) has a very thin, open, vertical slot through which the line of sight is directed; the "far" vane has a thin, vertical wire or thread mounted on a suitable frame. The bar is rotated until the object is in line with the two vanes. The bearing is the reading of the compass in line with the vanes, on the far side from the observer. If a reflecting surface is pivoted to the far vane to permit observation of the azimuth (art. 1428) of a celestial body, the device is called an **azimuth instrument.** Bearing bars and azimuth instruments are usually used only with smaller compasses, and never with an after-reading compass (art. 627).

Larger compasses or repeaters (art. 643) are usually provided with a **bearing circle** or **azimuth circle** (fig. 629). These devices take a variety of forms, but consist essentially of two parts: (1) a pair of sighting vanes attached to a ring which fits snugly over the compass, and (2) a mirror to reflect the compass graduation into the line of sight. The use of these devices is similar to that of the bearing bar and azimuth instrument. The azimuth circle has a pivoted reflecting surface attached to the far vane, to permit observation of celestial bodies. In most cases it also has a reflecting mirror and prism mounted on opposite sides of the ring, midway between the vanes. The prism is covered with opaque material except for a thin, vertical slot at its center. The surface of the mirror is curved so that reflection of sunlight falling upon it is in the form of a slender vertical line (at the distance of the prism) of about the same width as the slot. When the azimuth circle is adjusted so that this line of light falls upon the slot, a thin, bright line appears on the compass card graduations at the bearing of the sun. Most bearing and azimuth circles are provided with reverse compass rose graduations to permit reading of relative bearings or azimuths (by the vanes) at a mark on top of the compass bowl, in line with the lubber's line; bubbles for indicating the level position during observation; means for adjusting the snugness of the fit over the compass bowl; and handles for turning the device.

If a bearing or azimuth circle does not fit snugly over the compass bowl, an error might be introduced. Inaccuracy may also result from tilting of the reflecting surface

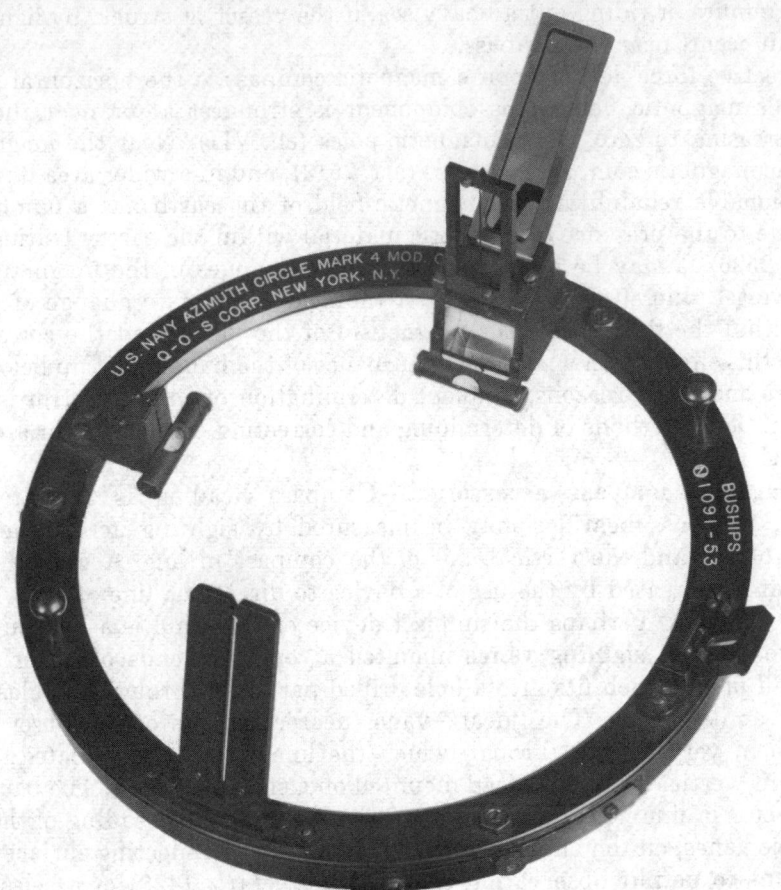

FIGURE 629.—An azimuth circle.

of an **azimuth** circle with respect to the vertical plane through the line of sight. This can be checked by comparing an azimuth of the sun observed by means of the prism with one observed with the sighting vanes (with suitable protection being provided for the eyes). If the prism attachment is not available, a check can be made by comparing observed (compass) azimuths at different altitudes with computed (true) values at the time of observation. If both observed and computed azimuths are correct, the difference between them will be constant (if the compass error remains constant throughout the observation).

None of the bearing or azimuth instruments described above can be used with a compass not designed for it, as one having a hemispherical top, or an after-reading compass.

Some modern magnetic compasses are provided with electrical pick-offs of sufficient sensitivity that the instrument can be used to control such devices as remote indicators, automatic steering equipment, course recorders, and dead reckoning equipment without disturbing the reliability of the compass. However, these devices are more commonly controlled by a gyrocompass and hence are considered later in the chapter, after a discussion of this type compass.

630. The gyroscope.—Leon Foucault, a French physicist, first demonstrated the rotation of the earth by means of a pendulum. However, the pendulum was not entirely acceptable as proof of rotation because it required the earth's gravity for operation. In 1852, he gave the name **gyroscope** to a toy top which had been known for a quarter of a century as a "rotascope." By means of the gyroscope, Foucault illustrated the earth's rotation without the use of gravity.

A conventional gyroscope consists of a comparatively massive, wheel-like rotor balanced in gimbals which permit rotation in any direction about three mutually perpendicular axes through the center of gravity. The three axes are called the **spin axis,** the **horizontal axis,** and the **vertical axis,** as shown in figure 630a.

Since the rapidly spinning rotor is balanced at its center of gravity, it is in a state of neutral rotational equilibrium. If the gimbal bearings were completely frictionless, the spin axis would retain its direction in space despite any motion applied to the system as a whole, as by the rotation of the earth. This property is called **gyroscopic inertia.** Thus, if the spin axis were directed toward a star, the axis would continue to point toward the star during its apparent motion across the sky. To an observer on the earth, the spin axis would appear to change direction as the earth rotated eastward.

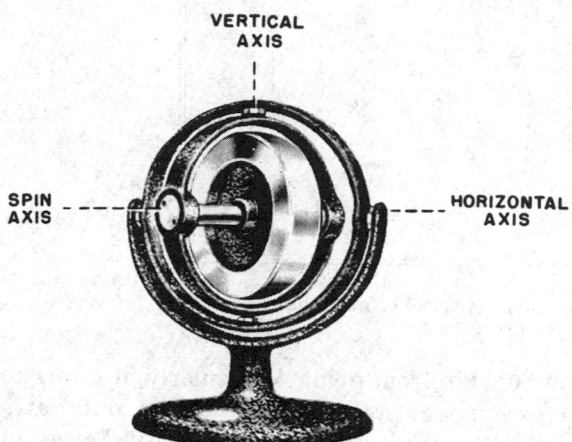

FIGURE 630a.—Gyroscope.

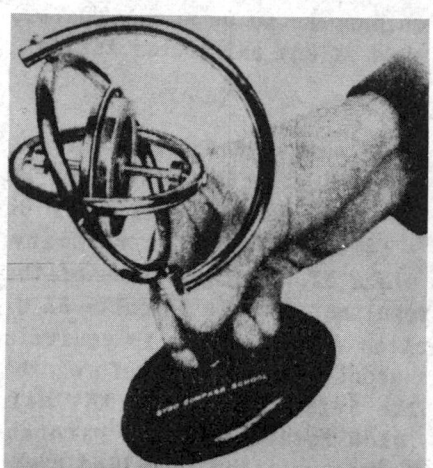

FIGURE 630b.—Demonstration of gyroscopic inertia.

This phenomenon, also known as **rigidity in space,** can be demonstrated by slowly tilting the base of the gyroscope as shown in figure 630b. If the gyroscope rotor is stationary, bearing friction will cause the rotor to tilt as the base is tilted. If the rotor is spinning, the rotor maintains the original plane of rotation as the gyroscope is tilted. It will continue to maintain the original plane of rotation no matter how much the gyroscope is tilted, as long as it continues to spin with sufficient velocity. Although bearing friction still affects the gyroscope, it affects it to a lesser degree than when the rotor was stationary.

Gyroscopic inertia depends upon angular velocity, mass, and the radius at which the mass is concentrated. For a given mass, maximum effect is obtained, therefore, from a mass rotating at high speed with the principal part of the mass concentrated near the periphery of the wheel.

Gyroscopic precession is that property of a gyroscope exhibited when a force is applied which tends to change the *direction* in space of the spin axis. The motion resulting from such a force is not in line with the force, as might be expected, but *perpendicular* to it. Precession can be demonstrated by applying a torque to the spinning gyroscope about its horizontal axis. This is done by applying a force at point A as illustrated in figure 630c. The gyroscope instead of turning about the horizontal axis as it would if it were not spinning, turns or precesses about its vertical axis. The direction of precession is such that it appears as though a force applied to the rotor at A is, instead,

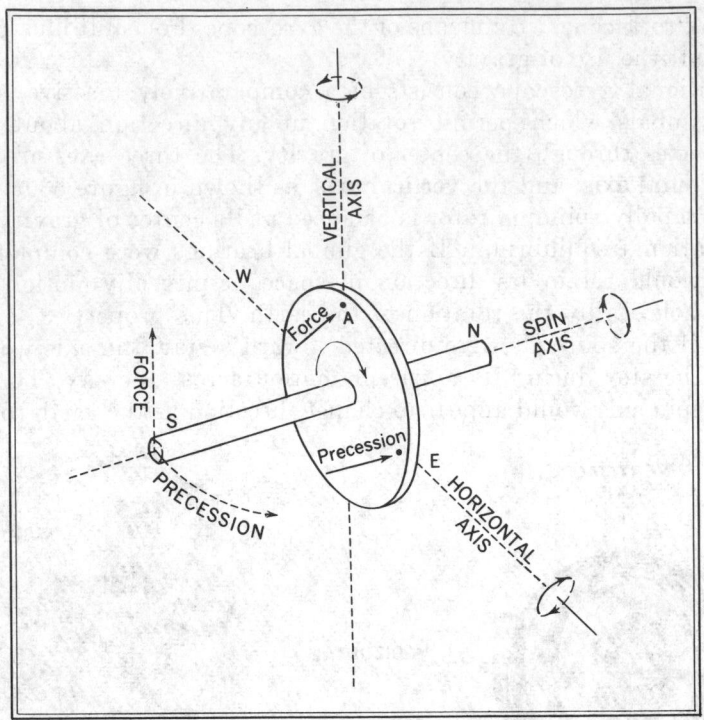

FIGURE 630c.—Axes of a gyroscope, and the direction of precession.

applied at a point 90° away in the direction of spin from point A. Similarly, if a torque is applied about the vertical axis, the gyroscope will precess about its horizontal axis in a direction such that it appears as though the force is applied at a point 90° away in the direction of spin from the point where the force is applied on the rotor.

A **torque** is defined as that which effects or tends to effect rotation or torsion and which is measured by the product of the applied force and the perpendicular distance from the line of action of the force to the axis of rotation. It is obvious that a force acting through or parallel to an axis cannot produce any turning effect about that axis. In a gyroscope the three axes about which rotation is possible all intersect at the center of gravity of the entire system (excluding the supporting frame). A force, therefore, acting through the center of gravity acts through all the axes and cannot exert torque about any axis. But a force acting at any other point will produce a torque about one or more axes.

Precession can be caused only by a force attempting to tilt or turn the spin axis about one of the other axes. So, a force through the center of gravity of a gyroscope (or force of translation) cannot cause the gyroscope to precess, but can only cause it to move as a whole in the direction of the force, with its axle always pointing in the same direction and the plane in which the rotor is spinning always parallel to its original plane of spin.

A torque about the spin axis of a gyroscope does not attempt to change the plane in which the rotor is spinning, so it cannot cause precession. The only effect such a torque can have on the rotor is to increase or decrease its speed.

Any torque about either the horizontal or vertical axis of a gyroscope will cause it to precess about an axis at right angles to that about which the torque acts. This precession will continue as long as the torque acts, but will cease when the torque is removed. If the plane in which the torque is acting remains unchanged, the gyroscope will precess until the plane of the spin of the rotor is in the plane of the torque. When this position is reached, the torque will be about the spin axis and can cause no further precession. If, however, the plane in which the torque acts moves at the same rate and in the same direction as the precession it causes, the precession will be continuous.

The rotor of the conventional gyroscope previously described has three degrees of freedom: (1) freedom to spin on its axle, (2) freedom to tilt about its horizontal axis, and (3) freedom to turn about its vertical axis. These three degrees of freedom permit the rotor to assume any position with respect to the supporting frame. This gyroscope is called a **free gyroscope**.

The term **degree-of-freedom** refers to the number of orthogonal axes about which the spin axis is free to rotate, the spin axis not being counted in one convention.

The reason for gyroscopic precession may be explained simply by considering what happens to a single particle on the rim of the gyroscope wheel as shown in figure 630d. Assume that the wheel is spinning in the direction of arrow R. Also assume that a force F is applied against the wheel at point B on the particular particle P, which happens to be at the position shown at any particular instant.

Force F exerts a force upon this small particle along the vector BL and therefore accelerates it in that direction. During a short interval of time, the acceleration will give the particle a component of velocity BL. This velocity vector and the velocity of the particle along the vector BJ, due to rotation of the wheel, have as a resultant the vector BK, different in direction from BJ. This is equivalent to a rotation about axis, YY. Therefore, the effect of a torque acting about the XX axis is to cause a rotation of the gyroscope wheel about the YY axis. This rotation about the YY axis is gyroscopic precession.

If the gyroscope, or **gyro** as it is commonly called, is mounted at the equator with its spin axis pointing east and west, figure 630e illustrates how it would appear from a point in space beyond the South Pole. From the observation point in space, the earth is seen turning from west to east at a rate of 15° per hour carrying the gyro with it. However, the spin axis of the gyro, because of gyroscopic inertia, remains in rigid space just as it did when the base was tilted in figure 630b. To an observer on earth the same gyro appears to rotate about its horizontal axis with an angular velocity equal but opposite in direction to the rate of rotation of the earth. This effect, commonly referred to as **horizontal earth rate,** is equal to the rate of rotation of the earth (**earth rate**) times the cosine function of the latitude. It is therefore zero at the poles and increases to earth rate at the equator.

Similarly, if the gyro is mounted at the North or South Pole with its spin axis horizontal, as shown in figure 630f, the gyro will appear to rotate about its vertical axis. This effect is commonly referred to as **vertical earth rate.** At points between the poles and the equator, the gyro appears to turn partly about the horizontal axis and partly about the vertical axis as shown in figure 630g, because it is affected by both horizontal and vertical earth rates.

In general, horizontal earth rate causes the spin axis of the gyro to appear to tilt about its horizontal axis; vertical earth rate causes the gyro to appear to rotate about its vertical axis. The apparent motion of stars (art. 1416) can be used as a convenient reminder of the effect of the earth's rotation on a **free gyro.** Being rigid in space, the spin axis remains pointing at the same fixed star as the earth rotates. Thus, the spin axis describes a circle about Polaris in a counterclockwise direction as the earth rotates.

With reference to space the direction of the spin axis of the free gyro remains the same as the earth rotates. With respect to the earth, however, the spin axis rotates as just described. It is this rotation with respect to the earth which makes it possible to apply the force of gravity so as to convert the free gyro into a north-seeking gyrocompass.

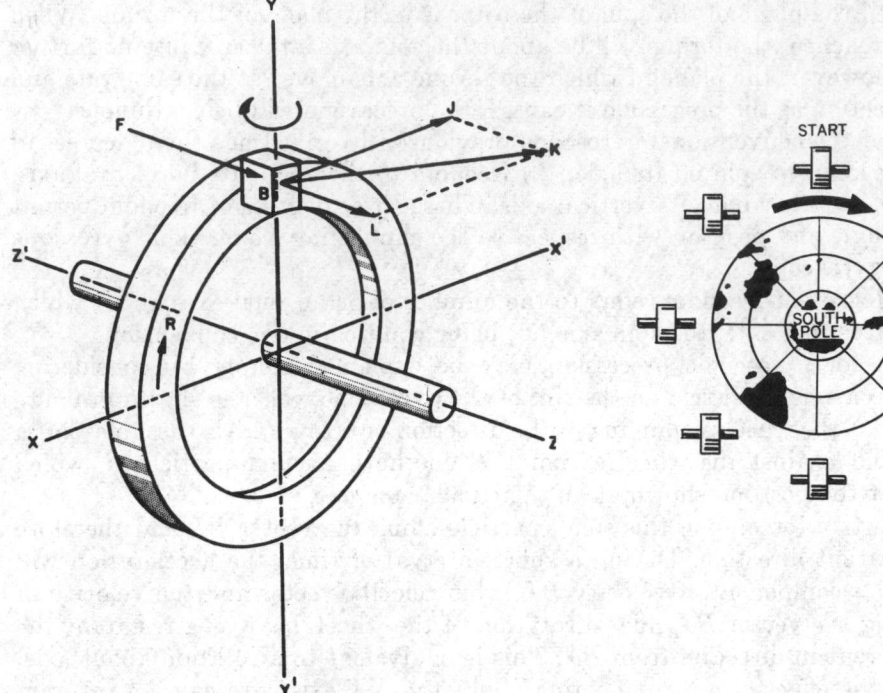

FIGURE 630d.—Forces causing precession of gyroscope rotor.

FIGURE 630e.—Demonstration of horizontal earth rate of gyro.

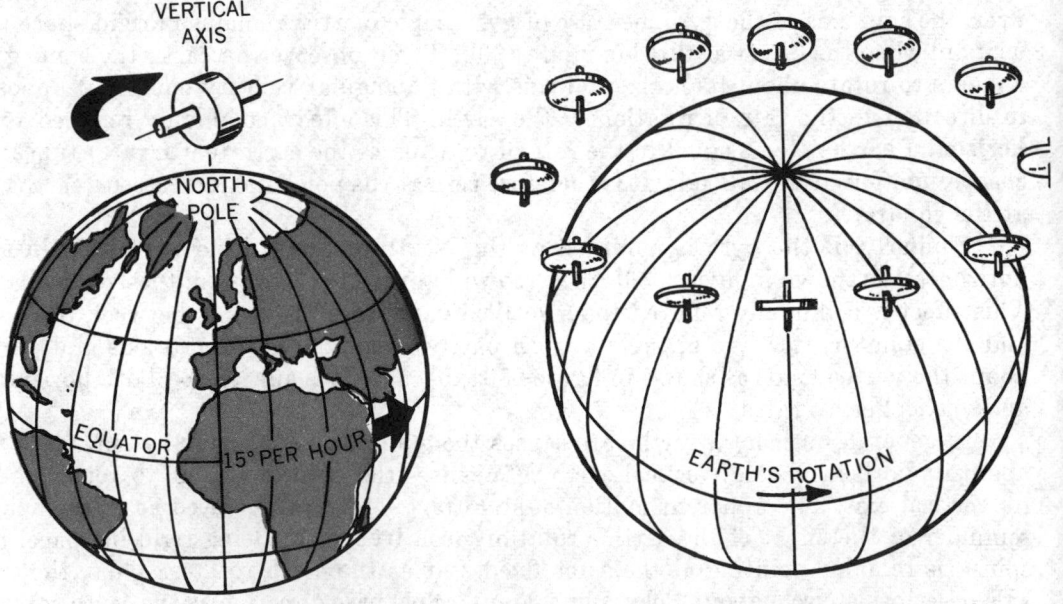

FIGURE 630f.—Demonstration of vertical earth rate of gyro.

FIGURE 630g.—Combined effects of horizontal and vertical earth rates.

631. The gyrocompass depends upon four natural phenomena for its operation. It is only the methods whereby these phenomena are utilized that distinguish one type of gyrocompass from another. Of the four natural phenomena, two are inherent properties of the gyroscope, namely gyroscopic inertia and gyroscopic precession; the other two are the earth's rotation and gravity.

Before a free gyro can be converted into a gyrocompass, the mounting structure must be changed slightly. As shown in figure 631a, the rotor is mounted in a sphere (**gyrosphere**) and the sphere is supported in what is called the **vertical ring.** The sphere and vertical ring are, in turn, mounted in a base called the **phantom.** Means are provided for the vertical ring and phantom to follow the gyro as it turns about its vertical axis.

With no further additions, the gyro shown in figure 631a will, neglecting friction, maintain its direction in space so long as no outside forces are exerted on it. To make the gyro into a gyrocompass, the gyro has to be made *to seek and maintain true north*. Since north is the direction represented by a horizontal line in the plane of the meridian, some means have to be provided to: (1) make the gyro spin axis seek the meridian plane, (2) make the spin axis horizontal, and (3) make it maintain its position once reached.

The first step in making a gyro a gyrocompass is to make the gyro seek the meridian. To do this, a weight W is added to the bottom of the vertical ring, as shown in figure 631b. This causes the vertical ring to be pendulous about the horizontal axis.

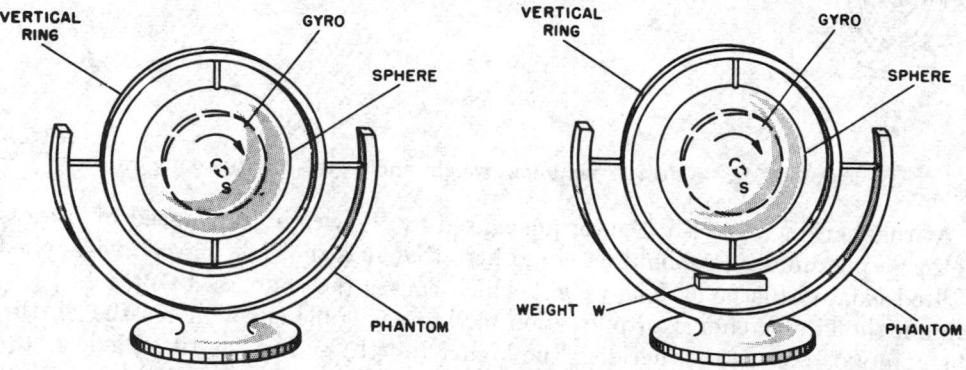

FIGURE 631a.—Modified model gyroscope.   FIGURE 631b.—Making the free gyro seek north by the addition of a weight to the vertical ring.

If as at A of figure 631c the gyro is at the *equator*, the spin axis is horizontal pointing east-west, and the rotor is spinning clockwise as viewed from the west, the rotor and vertical ring are vertical and no torque is created by the added weight. At this point both properties of the gyroscope, gyroscopic inertia and precession, are brought into play. As the earth rotates, the spin axis and, therefore, the vertical ring become inclined to the horizontal as shown at B. The weight W is raised against the pull of gravity and consequently causes a torque about the horizontal axis of the gyro. This torque causes precession about the vertical axis in the direction indicated at C. The spin axis then has moved out of its original east-west direction.

As the end of the spin axis which was first pointing east (which will now be referred to as the north end) continues to rise, the torque on the gyro caused by the weight becomes greater since the moment arm through which the weight acts gets longer due to the greater tilt. Since the speed of precession is closely proportional to the tilt, the gyro turns about its vertical axis as shown at D at an increasing speed until the axis is on the meridian.

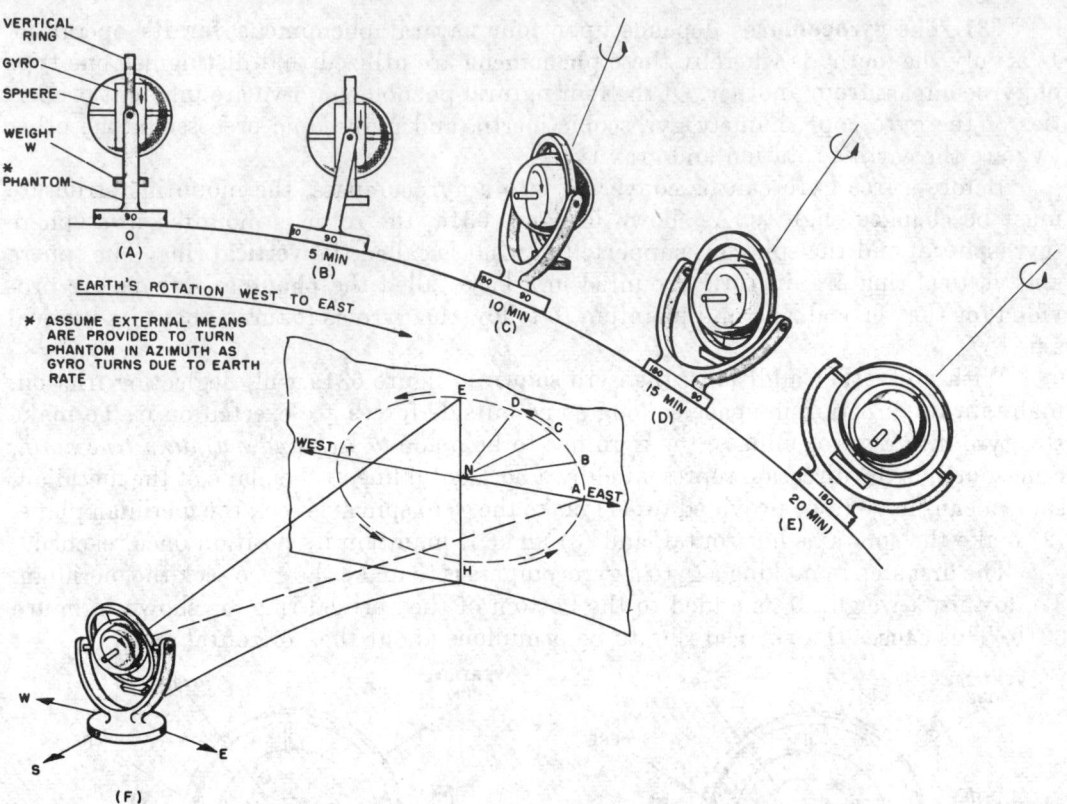

FIGURE 631c.—Effect of pendulous weight and earth's rotation on gyro.

At the meridian, the tilt, the torque caused by the weight, and speed of precession are all at a maximum. It should be noted here that it is the righting couple applied to the tilted axis by the pendulous weight which causes the compass to precess past the meridian, the kinetic energy of precession having negligible effect. After the north end of the spin axis crosses the meridian the higher (north) end of the tilted axle is to the west of the meridian. As a result, referring back to figure 630e, the earth's rotation reduces the tilt. As the tilt becomes less, the speed of precession in azimuth decreases. Finally the spin axis becomes horizontal and precession to the west stops; the weight on the vertical ring causes no torque about the horizontal axis since its force acts in the same plane as the gyro rotor and vertical ring. At this point, the axle has precessed as far west of the meridian as it was to the east originally.

As the earth continues to rotate, the north end of the spin axis starts to dip. The weight W is raised on the opposite side of the horizontal axis in the opposite direction carrying the spin axis back across the meridian to its original position. At this point, the cycle is repeated and will go on indefinitely. The oscillation about the meridian may be clearly understood by referring to F in figure 631c which shows the movement of the end of the spin axis projected on a vertical plane. The ellipse is the result of a displacement of the spin axis only a few degrees from the meridian. If the spin axis were pointing east-west at the beginning of the cycle as shown at A in figure 631c, precession would take place through 180 degrees in each direction, and at one extreme the axle would point east, at the other, west, In any case, the gyro never comes to rest since there is no force tending to restore the spin axis to the horizontal position until it has passed the meridian.

The ratio of the movement about the horizontal axis (caused by apparent rotation) to the precessional movement about the vertical axis caused by the swing of the weight determines the shape of the ellipse. If the weight is increased, the speed of precession will increase and the ellipse will be flatter. If the weight is decreased, the speed of precession will decrease and the ellipse would, theoretically, be almost circular. The time, in minutes, required for one complete oscillation, is called the period of oscillation. For any given wheel and speed at a certain point on the earth, the period will be nearly the same regardless of the angle through which the wheel oscillates. The period can be changed by changing the amount of weight on the bottom of the vertical ring.

With such a gyroscope modified by hanging a weight on the vertical ring, the first requirement to make a gyroscope into a gyrocompass, that of making the spin axis seek the meridian, has been fulfilled. However, some means must be provided for damping these oscillations so the gyro wheel will quickly come to rest with its spin axis level in the north-south position.

To damp the oscillations of the spin axis about the meridian a small weight W_1 is added to the sphere in which the rotor is housed. This weight is placed on the east side of the sphere in a position shown in figure 631d. With the spin axis level, the torque produced by gravity acting upon the weight W_1 is restrained by the vertical axis bearings. When the spin axis tilts due to earth rate, the vertical axis is no longer vertical; the force of gravity, however, still pulls straight down on the weight. This allows the torque to act about the vertical axis.

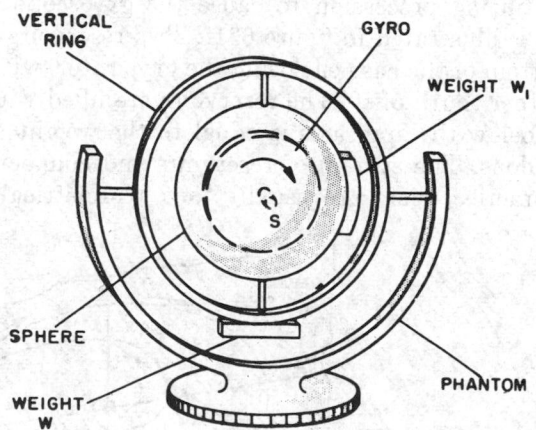

FIGURE 631d.—Modified model gyroscope with weights on the vertical ring and sphere.

Now, with both weights, the spin axis will begin to tilt due to earth rate and as soon as it tilts, the spin axis precesses toward the meridian and downward toward the level position. As a result of the leveling action of weight W_1, the spin axis is not tilted up as much when it reaches the meridian as it was with only weight W. Since the spin axis is not tilted as much, the torque produced by weight W is not as great. Therefore, the spin axis will not precess as far to the west of the meridian as it was east of the meridian when it was started.

After reaching a point where the spin axis is level and as far west of the meridian as it is going due to the action of weight W, earth rate is still causing the spin axis to tilt downward. As a result, the forces due to the weights are reversed and torques are created which precess the gyro to the east and up. The same action takes place in the reverse direction. The gyro is not precessed as far to the east as it was to the west. Thus, the added weight W_1 causes the ellipse to be reduced each successive oscillation;

the north end of the gyro axle will follow a spiral path as shown in figure 631e instead of an elliptical path as previously.

A careful consideration of the action of the two weights will make it apparent that the only position of rest that the gyro can find will be with the spin axis horizontal and on the meridian. The period of the compass can be changed by varying the weight W. With a given period the speed with which it settles to a level position can be changed by varying the weight W_1.

With the second modification to the model gyroscope (adding a weight to the sphere in which the gyro is housed), the second requirement to make a gyroscope into a gyrocompass, that of making the spin axis horizontal, has been fulfilled. However, when this modified gyroscope is moved, accelerations on the weights, because they are pendulous, will cause torques on the gyroscope. Also any change in latitude from the equator will result in false indications. The model gyroscope, as so far modified, does not fulfill the third requirement, that of *maintaining* the level position in the plane of the meridian once reached. Therefore, some means must be provided to eliminate the effect of unbalanced weights hanging on the modified gyroscope; means must be provided to compensate for false indications resulting from change in latitude from the equator.

Practical gyrocompasses employ both pendulous and nonpendulous gyroscopes. In addition these compasses have means of compensating for influences that might introduce errors into their indications.

One method of utilizing precession to cause the gyroscope of a practical gyro-compass to seek north is illustrated in figure 631f. Two reservoirs connected by a tube are attached to the bottom of the case enclosing the gryo rotor, with one reservoir north of the rotor and the other south of it. The reservoirs are filled with mercury to such a level that the weight below the spin axis is equal to the weight above it, so that the gyroscope is nonpendulous. The system of reservoirs and connecting tubes is called a **mercury ballistic.** In practice, there are usually four symmetrically placed reservoirs.

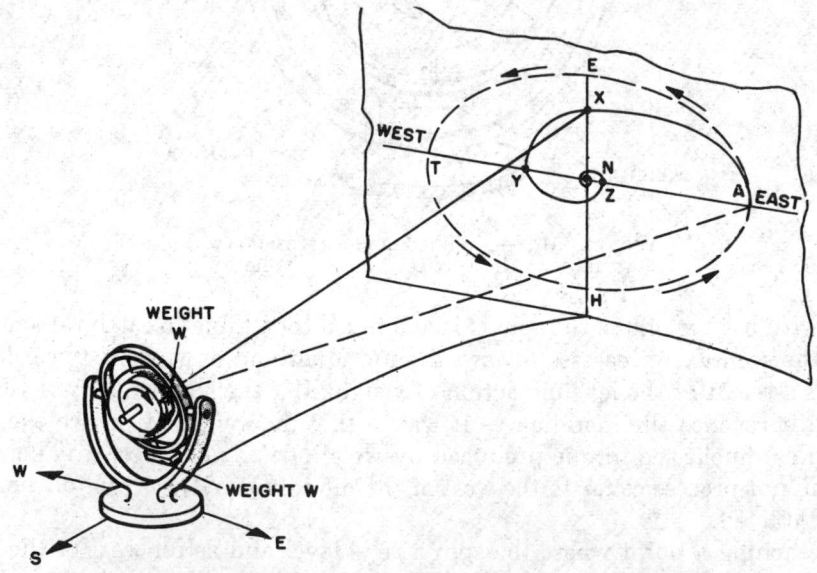

FIGURE 631e.—Settling on the meridian.

Suppose that the spin axis is horizontal but is directed to the eastward of north. As the earth rotates eastward on its axis, the spin axis tends to maintain its direction in space; that is, it appears to follow a point, such as a star rising in the northeastern sky.

With respect to the earth, the north reservoir rises and some of the mercury flows under the force of gravity into the south reservoir. The south side becomes heavier than the north side, and a force is applied to the bottom of the rotor case at point A. If the gyro rotor is spinning in the direction shown, the north end of the spin axis precesses slowly to the westward, following an elliptical path. When it reaches the meridian, upward tilt reaches a maximum. Precession continues, so that the axis is carried past the meridian and commences to sink as the earth continues to rotate. When the sinking has continued to the point where the axis is horizontal again, the excess mercury has returned to the north reservoir and precession stops. As sinking continues, due to continued rotation of the earth, an excess of mercury accumulates in the north reservoir, thus reversing the direction of precession and causing the spin axis to return slowly to its original position with respect to the earth, following the path shown at the right of figure 631f. One circuit of the ellipse requires about 84 minutes.

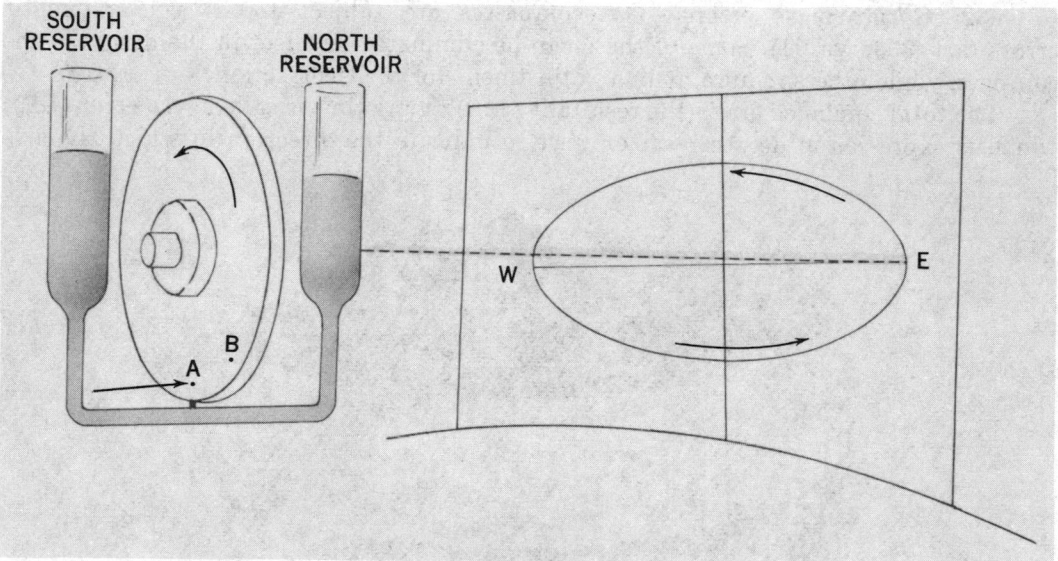

FIGURE 631f.—The mercury ballistic (left) and the elliptical path (right) of the axis of spin without damping.

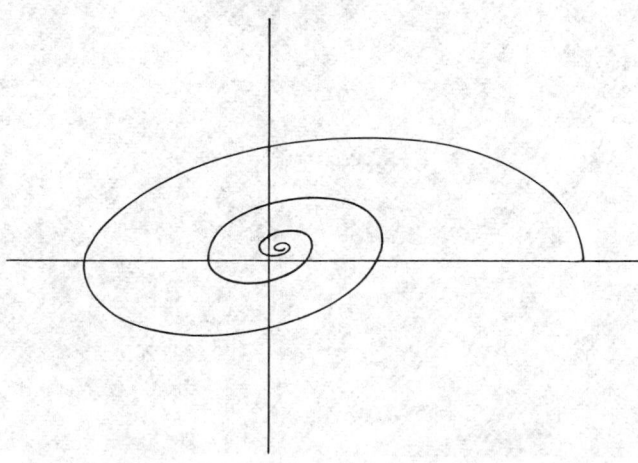

FIGURE 631g.—Spiral path of the axis of spin with damping.

The elliptical path is symmetrical with respect to the meridian, and, neglecting friction, would be retraced indefinitely, unless some method of damping the oscillation were found. One method is by offsetting the point of application of the force from the mercury ballistic. Thus, if the force is applied not in the vertical plane, but at a point to the eastward of it, as at B in figure 631f, the resulting precession causes the spin axis to trace a spiral path as shown in figure 631g, and eventually to settle near the meridian. The gyroscope is now north-seeking. The gyrocompass shown in figure 631h uses this method to seek north.

Another method of damping the oscillations caused by the rotation of the earth is to reduce the precessing force of a pendulous gyro as the spin axis approaches the meridian. One way of accomplishing this is to cause oil to flow from one damping tank to another in such a manner as to counteract some of the tendency of an offset pendulous weight to cause precession. Oscillations are completely damped out in approximately one and one-half swings.

632. Gyrocompass errors.—Gyrocompasses are subject to several systematic errors (art. 303, vol. II). Some of these can be eliminated or offset in the design of the compass, while others require manual adjustment for their correction.

The total combined error (the resultant error) at any time is called **gyro error (GE)**, which is expressed in degrees east or west to indicate the direction in which the axis

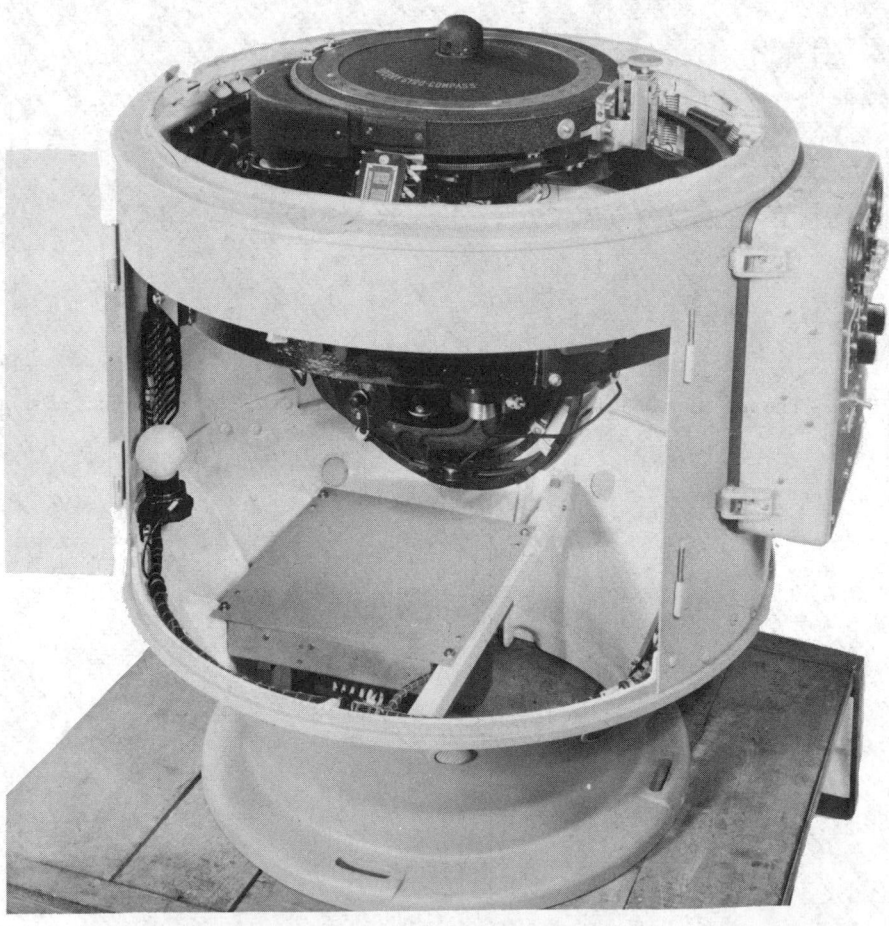

Courtesy of Sperry Marine Systems.

FIGURE 631h.—The Mark 14 Mod 2 Gyrocompass.

of the compass is offset from true north. If the gyro error is east, the readings are too low; and if it is west, they are too high. Thus, if GE is 1° W, 1° is subtracted from all readings of the compass, either headings or bearings, to determine the equivalent true directions. One degree is added to all true directions to determine the equivalent gyro directions. The gyro error of modern compasses is generally small. However, significant errors can be introduced in several ways, and it is good practice to compare the gyro heading with the magnetic heading at frequent intervals (as every half hour and after each change of course) and to check the accuracy of the gyrocompass by celestial observation or landmarks from time to time (as every morning and afternoon when means are available).

The errors generally associated with the gyrocompass are speed error, tangent latitude error, ballistic deflection error, ballistic damping error, quadrantal error, and gimballing error. In addition, gyrocompasses are subject to the errors common to directional instruments, such as those introduced by inaccurate graduation of the compass rose or incorrectly located lubber's line. Error may also be introduced, of course, by malfunctioning of the compass.

633. Speed error.—The north-seeking tendency of a gyrocompass depends upon the fact that north is at right angles to the west-to-east direction in which the earth's rotation carries the compass. If the gyrocompass is carried over the earth in some direction other than west to east, it will seek a settling position at right angles to that direction, whatever it may be.

A gyrocompass on the earth's surface is carried from west to east only when it is stationary with respect to the earth's surface, or when it is moving east or west. If the vessel in which the compass is installed is moving in other than an east or west direction the compass is, in effect, being carried in a direction which is a little to the north or south of exactly east. It will then seek a settling position which is at right angles to this direction, and will settle on a line at a small angle off true north.

This error, known as **speed error** and sometimes called **speed-course-latitude error,** is westerly if any component of the vessel's course is north, and easterly if south. Its magnitude depends upon the speed, course, and latitude of the vessel. Refer to figure 633a. If a vessel is at anchor at any point A, it is being carried eastward by rotation of the earth at the rate of 902.46 minutes of longitude per hour (with respect to the stars). In terms of knots, this is equal to 902.46 times the cosine of the latitude, approximately. Because of the ellipticity of the earth, the actual value is a little more than this in low latitudes, and a little less in high latitudes. The actual value at any latitude can be found by multiplying the length of a degree of longitude at that latitude (from table 6) by $\frac{902.46}{60} = 15.041$.

This eastward motion due to rotation of the earth is shown in figure 633a by the vector AB. The north-south axis of the gyrocompass settles in a direction 90° from the direction of motion. Therefore, if the vessel is stationary with respect to the earth, 0° on the compass card coincides with a true meridian, and no error is introduced. This is also true if the vessel is moving due east or due west. In this case the speed of the ship over the surface of the earth is added to or subtracted from the motion due to rotation of the earth, but the direction of motion is unchanged (unless the speed of the vessel is greater than the rotational speed of the earth, and in the opposite direction). The only effect, therefore, is to strengthen or weaken the directive force, usually by a small amount.

If the vessel is on course north or south, as shown by the vector AC in figure 633a, the motion in space is tilted toward the north or south of due east. In this case, it is the

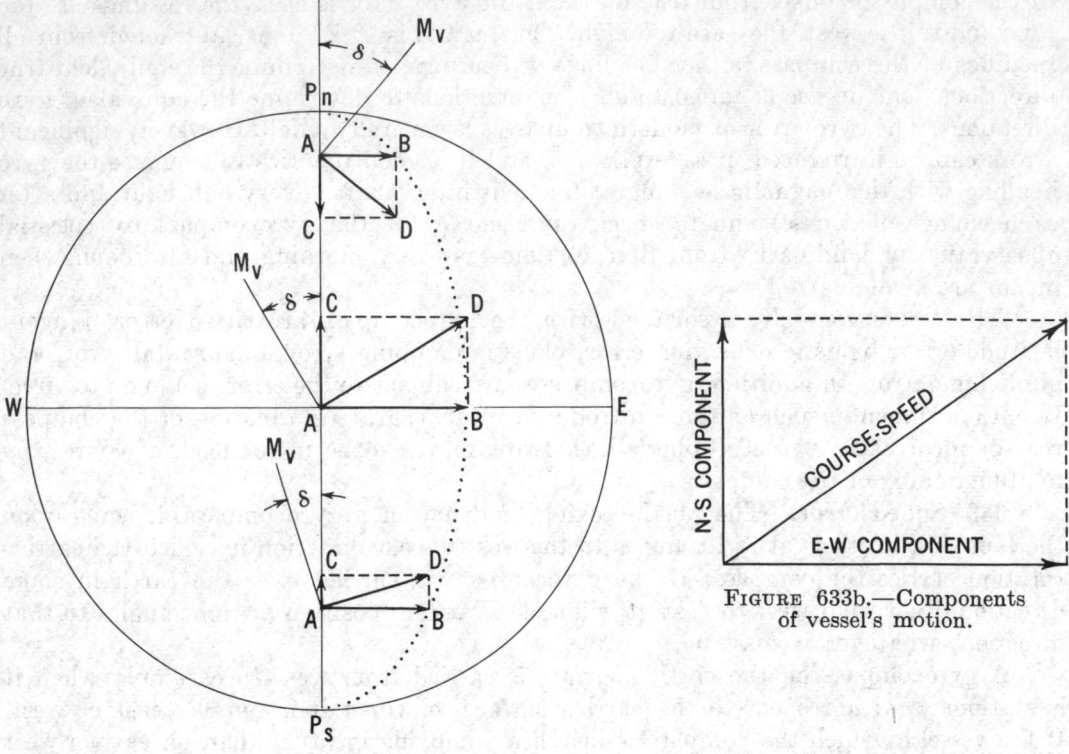

FIGURE 633a.—Speed error.

FIGURE 633b.—Components
of vessel's motion.

vector sum (art. 118, vol. II) of the motion due to rotation of the earth and the velocity of the vessel over the surface of the earth, or AD in figure 633a. Since AD is not due east, the perpendicular to it does not lie in the true meridian, but at some angle δ to it, along AM_v. Since the axis of the gyro lies along AM_v, the "virtual meridian," the angle is the error introduced by the motion of the vessel along its track. Since AD is perpendicular to AM_v, and AB is perpendicular to AC, angle BAD is equal to angle δ. Therefore, the angle δ can be found by the formula

$$\tan \delta = \frac{AC}{AB}.$$

Since AC is the speed of the vessel and AB is 902.46 cos L, approximately, the formula can be written

$$\tan \delta = \frac{S}{902.46 \cos L}$$

where S is the speed and L the latitude of the vessel.

If the course of the vessel is not a cardinal direction, the resultant is still the vector sum of two speed vectors, and can be found graphically or by computation. One method is to resolve the vessel's speed vector into two components, as shown in figure 633b, obtaining the N–S component along the true meridian, and the E–W component in the direction of rotation of the earth. The N–S component is equal to S cos C, and the E–W component to S sin C, where C is the true course angle. The total N–S motion is then S cos C. The total easterly motion is that due to rotation of the earth plus or minus the E–W component of the ship's speed across the surface of the earth, or 902.46 cos L±S sin C, approximately. The term S sin C is positive

(+) for easterly courses and negative (−) for westerly courses. The formula for finding δ now becomes

$$\tan \delta = \frac{S \cos C}{902.46 \cos L \pm S \sin C} \text{(approximately)}.$$

At ship speeds in latitudes less than 70°, the term S sin C is much smaller than 902.46 cos L and has so little effect upon the answer that it can be ignored. The angle δ is small enough that its tangent can be considered the angle itself (expressed in radians). That is, a tangent to a circle can be considered of the same length as an arc of the circle over a short distance from the point of tangency. Therefore, the formula for δ can be written

$$\delta = \frac{57.3 \; S \cos C}{902.46 \cos L}$$

or

$$\delta = 0.0635 \; S \cos C \sec L.$$

As shown in this formula, the speed error δ is affected by the three variables, speed, course, and latitude. If the course has a northerly component, the error is westerly; and if it has a southerly component, the error is easterly.

Example.—A ship at latitude 30°N is steaming on true course 045°, at a speed of 20 knots.

Required.—Speed error.

Solution.—

0.0635	log	8. 80277
S 20 kn.	log	1. 30103
C N45°E	*l* cos	9. 84949
L 30°N	*l* sec	10. 06247
δ 1°04W	log	10. 01576

Answer.—δ 1°04W.

In some gyrocompasses this error is corrected mechanically. Speed and latitude are set in by hand, and the cosine of the course is introduced automatically by means of a "cosine cam" running in an eccentric groove on the underside of the azimuth gear. In some compasses these corrections combine to offset the lubber's line by the correct amount. Small changes in speed or latitude have relatively little effect upon the result. Therefore, in normal operations, infrequent changes are sufficient for satisfactory results. If no provision is made for mechanically applying this correction, a table or curves can be used to indicate the correction to be applied mathematically to readings of the compass. These are made up from the formula given above, and are entered with the speed, course, and latitude (art. 639).

634. Tangent latitude error applies only to those gyrocompasses in which damping is accomplished by offsetting the point of application of the force from a mercury ballistic (art. 631). It can be found from the equation

$$\alpha = r \tan L$$

in which α is the damping error, r is the angle between the vertical through the spin axis of the gyro rotor and a line through this axis and the point of application of the force from the mercury ballistic (1°7 for Sperry compasses), and L is the latitude. The error is easterly in north latitude and westerly in south latitude.

Example.—A gyrocompass having a value of r of 1°7 is at latitude 50°N.

Required.—The tangent latitude error.

Solution.—

$$\alpha = r \tan L$$
$$= 1\overset{\circ}{.}7 \times 1.1918$$
$$= 2\overset{\circ}{.}03\text{E}$$

Answer.—$\alpha = 2\overset{\circ}{.}03\text{E}$.

As in the case of speed error, provision is made in most compasses (to which it applies) for correcting this error. An auxiliary latitude-correction scale is provided for this purpose. In some compasses this offsets the lubber's line. In others, it alters the position of a small weight attached to the casing near one end of the axle. The first method is preferable because it is unaffected by changes of gyro speed of rotation.

If this error is not corrected mechanically, it can be combined algebraically with speed error and a single set of tables or graphs made up. This is a method sometimes used in polar regions, beyond the scale of the latitude corrections (arts. 639, 2514).

635. Ballistic deflection error.—When the north-south component of the speed changes, an accelerating force acts upon the compass, causing a surge of mercury from one part of the system to another, or a deflection (along the meridian) of the mass of a pendulous compass. In either case, this is called **ballistic deflection.** It results in a precessing force which introduces a temporary **ballistic deflection error** in the readings of the compass unless it is corrected.

A change of course or speed also results in a change in the speed error, and unless the correcting mechanism responds promptly to this change, a temporary error from this source is also introduced. The sign of this error is opposite that of the ballistic deflection, and so the two tend to cancel each other. If they are of equal magnitude and equal duration, the cancellation is complete and the compass responds immediately and automatically to changes of speed error. This can be accomplished by designing the compass so that

$$\frac{B}{H} = 0.0211 \sec L.$$

in which B is the pendulous moment of a pendulous compass and the couple per unit angle applied by a mercury ballistic, H is the angular momentum of the gyro rotor, and L is the latitude.

Gyrocompasses using the fluid ballistic are often designed so that the ratio $\frac{B}{H}$ is correct for some particular latitude (as 41° or 45°) and accept the small residual error that is temporarily present at other latitudes. This is satisfactory for vessels which remain within relatively narrow limits of latitude, or which are seldom subjected to large accelerating forces. However, where these conditions are not met, provision is made for varying the ratio with latitude. In a compass having a mercury ballistic, this is customarily accomplished by moving the mercury reservoirs radially toward or away from the center of the compass, thus altering the value of B. In a pendulous gyro, the value of H is changed by altering the rotational speed of the gyro.

When the ratio $\frac{B}{H}$ is as given in the equation above, the period of oscillation about the vertical axis is given by the equation

$$T = \frac{\pi}{30} \sqrt{\frac{R}{g}}$$

in which T is the period in minutes, R is the radius of the earth in feet (approximately 20,900,000) and g is the acceleration due to gravity (approximately 32.2 feet per second). Substituting in the formula,

$$T = 0.1047 \sqrt{\frac{20,900,000}{32.2}}$$

=84 minutes (approximately).

This is sometimes stated as the period of a pendulum having a radius equal to the radius of the earth, since the equation for a short pendulum is the same as that given above with l (length) being substituted for R. More accurately, it is the period of a pendulum of infinite length with its bottom at the surface of the earth, or the largest period that a simple pendulum can have when acting under the gravitational force of the earth. When a device is adjusted so as to have this period it is said to be "Schuler tuned," after Max Schuler, a German scientist who discovered the relationship. It is because of this tuning of the gyrocompass that one oscillation occurs in about 84 minutes, and that the maximum effect of certain disturbing forces occurs about 21 minutes (one-fourth cycle) after application of the force.

636. Ballistic damping error is a temporary oscillatory error of a gyrocompass introduced during changes of course or speed as a result of the means used to damp the oscillations of the spin axis.

During a change of course or speed the fluid in the ballistic of the nonpendulous compass or in the damping tanks of the pendulous compass (art. 631) is accelerated. As shown in figure 636, during the turn from the westerly to the northerly direction the centrifugal force acting on the mercury causes an excess of mercury to accumulate in the south tanks of the ballistic at A. Because of the offset connection of the mercury ballistic, the excess mercury in the south tanks exerts a torque about the vertical axis in addition to the one being exerted about the horizontal axis during the turn. This torque about the vertical axis produces a downward tilt of the north end of the gyro axle at B as a result of precession. This tilt of the gyro axle causes an oscillation of the spin axis to start as the centrifugal force diminishes to zero at C. This oscillation on a compass with a damped period of about 84 minutes becomes a maximum at D, 21 minutes after the change of course is completed, and ends in about 2 hours.

The liquid in the damping tanks of the pendulous compass is subjected to the same centrifugal force on change of course. An excess of liquid collects in one tank. This action causes a torque and consequent movement of the spin axis from the meridian.

The ballistic damping error is eliminated in the nonpendulous compass by automatically moving the point of application of the mercury ballistic from the offset position to the true vertical axis of the gyro whenever rates of change of course or speed exceed certain limits. Moving the point of application of the mercury ballistic to the true vertical axis eliminates the torque about this axis caused by the centrifugal force and prevents the compass from going through a damped oscillation.

In the pendulous gyrocompass, the ballistic damping error is eliminated by automatically closing a valve in the pipe line between the damping tanks whenever rates of change of course or speed exceed certain limits.

637. Quadrantal error.—If a body mounted in gimbals is not suitably balanced, a disturbing force causes it to swing from side to side. A swinging body tends to rotate so that its long axis of weight is in the plane of the swing. The rolling of a vessel introduces the force needed to start a gyrocompass swinging. The effect reaches a maximum on intercardinal headings, midway between the two horizontal axes of the compass,

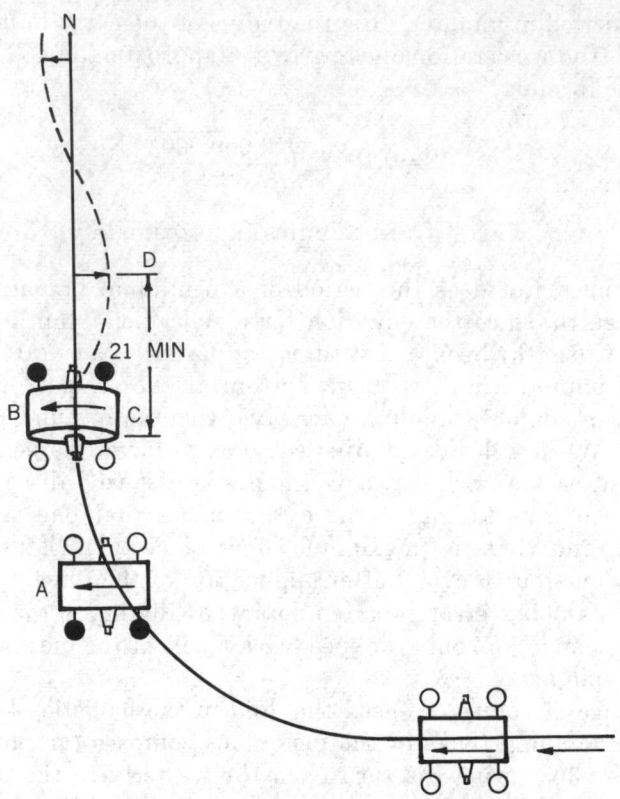

FIGURE 636.—Ballistic damping error.

and changes direction of error in consecutive quadrants. This is called **quadrantal error,** or sometimes **intercardinal rolling error.** It is corrected by the addition of weights to balance the compass so that the weight is the same in all directions from the center. Without a long axis of weight, there is no tendency to rotate during a swing.

A second cause of quadrantal error is more difficult to eliminate. As a vessel rolls, the apparent vertical is displaced first to one side and then to the other, due to the accelerations involved. The vertical axis of the gyrocompass tends to align itself with the apparent vertical. If the vessel is on a northerly or southerly course, the pivot of the compass is displaced from the vertical, resulting in a precession first to one side, then to the other. The effect is negligible and would be exactly balanced if successive rolls on opposite sides were equal. On an easterly or westerly heading, the pivot remains under the gyro axle, but the dynamic effect of the roll, acting upon the damping mechanism, introduces a precessing force which causes an error. However, the period is short and the error is in opposite directions on opposite rolls, so the effect is negligible. On noncardinal headings, both effects are present, and the relationship is such that the error is in the same direction regardless of the direction of roll. Thus, a persistent error is introduced, which changes direction in successive quadrants. This error is generally eliminated by the use of a second gyroscope. In some compasses, this is in the form of a small gyroscope called a **floating ballistic** which stabilizes the point of application of the mercury ballistic with respect to the true vertical as the vessel rolls. In others, two gyroscopes are used for the directive element and these are so installed that they tend to precess in opposite directions. Thus, they neutralize each other.

Another way of eliminating this error is to design the mercury ballistic system so that the surge of liquid due to north-south component of the roll is diminished in amount and delayed so that it is about a quarter of a cycle out of phase with the roll.

638. Gimballing error is that due to tilt of the compass rose. Directions are measured in the horizontal plane. If the compass card is tilted, the projection of its outer rim into the horizontal is an ellipse, and the graduations are not equally spaced with respect to a circle. This error, which applies to all instruments making use of a compass rose that can be tilted, is discussed in article (art. 303, vol. 11). For normal angles of tilt, this error is small and can be neglected. For accurate results, readings should be made when the card is horizontal. This error applies to the reading of the compass *or its repeaters* (art. 643), rather than to the compass itself. If the compass and its repeaters are installed so that the outer gimbals are in the longitudinal axis of the vessel, this error is minimized.

639. Use of the gyrocompass in polar regions is discussed in article 2514. If means are not available for determining an equivalent setting or correction, a correction graph can be constructed. Ballistic deflection error, quadrantal error, and gimballing error are temporary or corrected in the design of the compass, and so can be ignored. Speed error and tangent latitude error (if it applies to the particular compass involved) can be combined into a single table or curve of corrections, using the formulas of articles 633 and 634. In high latitudes the east-west component of the vessel's speed is significant, and the error may be too large to consider its tangent equal to the angle itself expressed in radians. Therefore, the applicable formulas are:

$$\tan \delta = \frac{S \cos C}{902.46 \cos L \pm S \sin C} \qquad (1)$$

$$\alpha = r \tan L. \qquad (2)$$

The only approximation remaining is the use of 902.46, which varies slightly with latitude. The error thus introduced is not significant. The U. S. Navy gyrocompass error curves for latitude 80° are shown in figure 639. From the intersection of the appropriate speed curve and the radial line representing the *true* course (interpolating if necessary) a horizontal line is drawn to the vertical line through the origin, where the correction is indicated. To construct the curve for speed 35 knots, proceed as follows:

1. Compute the speed error, δ, for true courses at intervals of perhaps 30°. As an example, the error for course 210° (C S30°W) is:

$$\tan \delta = \frac{35 \times 0.86603}{902.46 \times 0.17365 - 35 \times 0.50000}$$

$$= 0.21773.$$

$$\delta = 12°3E.$$

The error is easterly because the course has a southerly component (art. 633).

2. Compute the tangent latitude error. The curves of figure 639 are for a value of r of 1°7:

$$\alpha = 1°7 \times 5.6713 = 9°6E.$$

In northern latitudes tangent latitude error is easterly.

3. Combine δ and α algebraically to obtain gyro error (GE):

TC°	δ°	α°	GE°
000	12.6W	9.6E	3.0W
030	9.9W	9.6E	0.3W
060	5.3W	9.6E	4.3E
090	0.0	9.6E	9.6E
120	5.3E	9.6E	14.9E
150	9.9E	9.6E	19.5E
180	12.6E	9.6E	22.2E
210	12.3E	9.6E	21.9E
240	7.9E	9.6E	17.5E
270	0.0	9.6E	9.6E
300	7.9W	9.6E	1.7E
330	12.3W	9.6E	2.7W

4. To draw the curve, select a convenient origin and label this with the value of α. Draw a vertical line through the origin and mark off a convenient scale such that all values of δ can be shown both above and below the origin. The zero on this scale is at point α units above the origin (below in the Southern Hemisphere). Label the scale according to GE. Through the origin draw various radial lines at any convenient interval to represent true courses. For each computed course draw a horizontal construction line from the GE on the central scale to the appropriate radial line. The intersection of each pair of lines is one point on the curve. Connect all such points with a smooth curve, and erase the construction lines. If a straightedge or graph paper is used, the construction lines need not be drawn.

It is good practice to draw the curve for the highest speed first, to be sure that succeeding curves will fit on the paper. From such curves the gyro courses corresponding to various true courses can be determined and the radial lines labeled with these values for converting gyro directions to true directions.

The curves described in this article are for use *when all correctors are set on zero*, or if no provision is made for mechanically correcting for speed and damping errors. If the compass does not have a mercury ballistic, the tangent latitude error is omitted from the calculations and curves.

640. Desirable characteristics of the gyrocompass.—Since a gyrocompass is not affected by a magnetic field, it is not subject to magnetic compass errors (ch. VII), nor is it useless near the earth's magnetic poles. If an error is present, it is the same on all headings, and no table of corrections is needed. The directive force is sufficiently strong to permit directional pick-off for use in remote-indicating repeaters, automatic steering, dead reckoning and fire-control equipment, course recorders, etc.

641. Undesirable characteristics of the gyrocompass.—A gyrocompass is dependent upon a source of suitable electric power.

If operation of the compass is interrupted long enough to permit uncertainty in its indications, a considerable period (as much as four hours for some gyrocompasses) may be needed for it to settle on the meridian after it reaches operating speed. This period can be reduced by orienting the compass in the proper direction before it is started. If this is not practicable, the settling period can be hastened by leveling the compass when it reaches the meridian (one-fourth of a cycle or 21 minutes after starting at maximum deflection) or by leveling *and* precessing the gyro to the approximate meridian after its direction and rate of precession are observed for several minutes. Either process may need to be repeated several times and followed by a settling period.

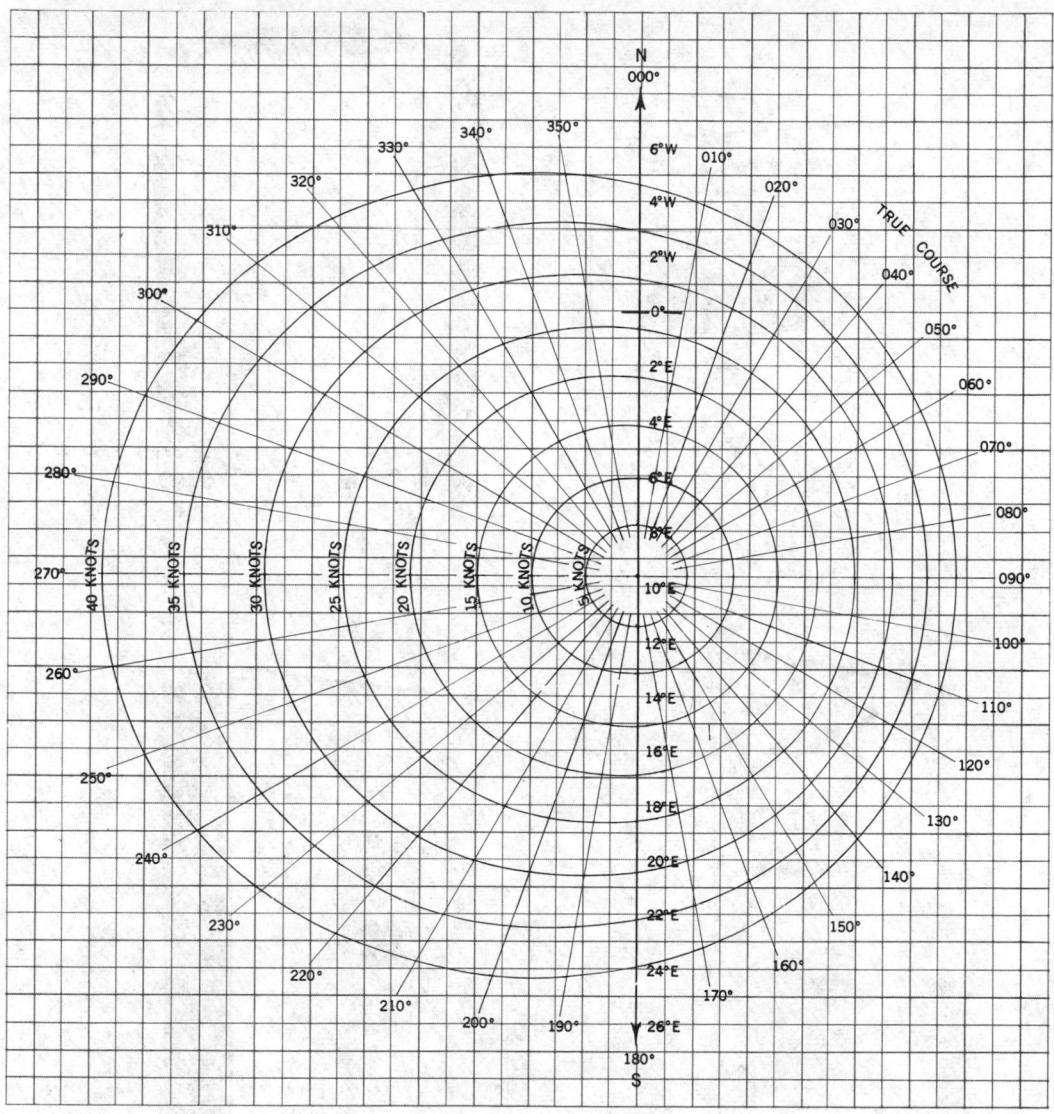

FIGURE 639.—Gyrocompass error curves for latitude 80°.

The gyrocompass is subject to certain errors requiring applications of corrections, either manually or automatically (art. 632).

The compass is an intricate mechanism of many parts. Thus, it requires some maintenance. In heavy seas a gyrocompass may become unreliable unless certain features are included in the design—features which are generally omitted from the small, simpler compasses.

The directive force of a gyrocompass decreases with latitude, being maximum at the equator and zero at the geographical poles.

642. Gyrocompass models.—The Mark 19 Gyrocompass System (fig. 642a) consists of four components: the master compass, the control cabinet, the compass failure annunciator, and the solid state power supply.

The two main elements of the master compass (fig. 642b) are the compass element and the supporting element. The compass element includes the sensitive element (meridian and slave gyros), the phantom or follower element, and the gimbal. The supporting

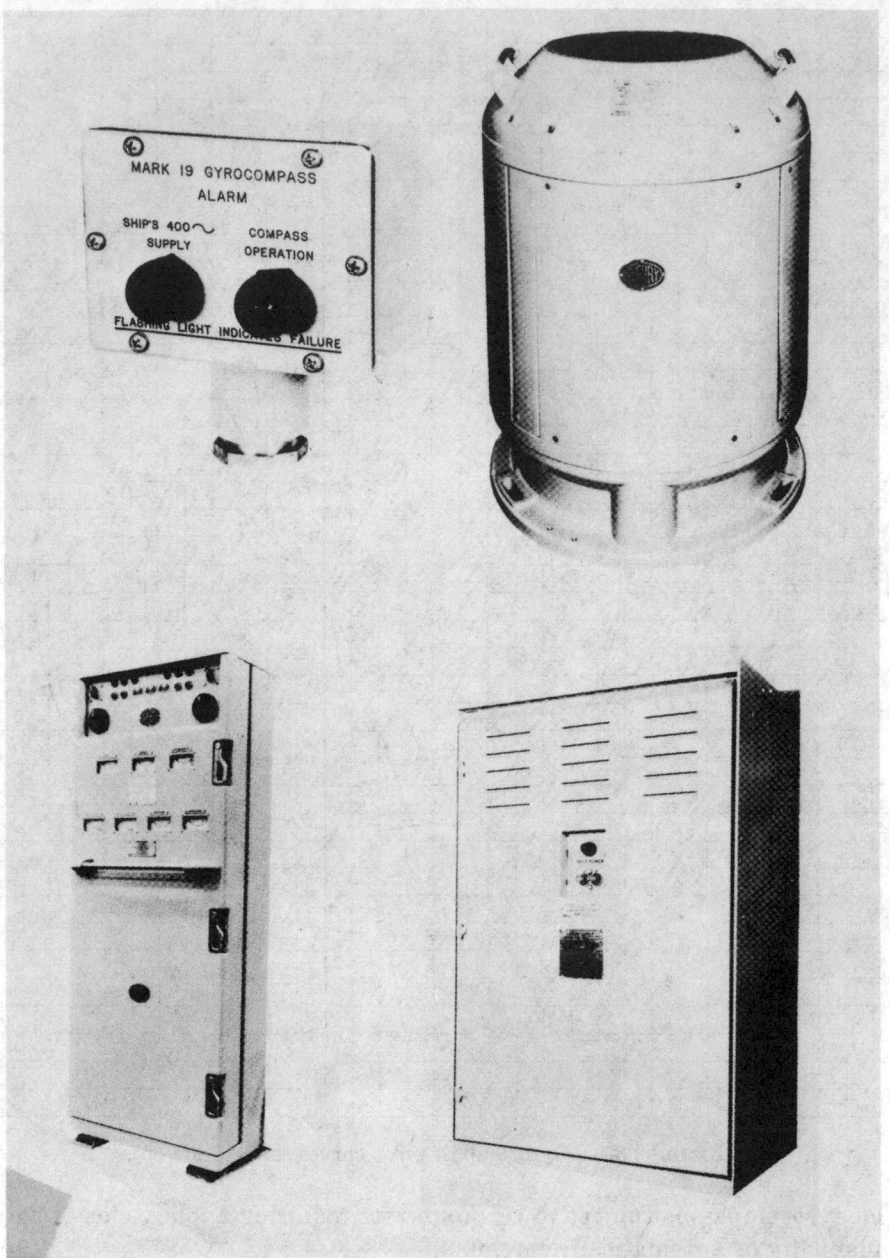

FIGURE 642a.—Mark 19 Gyrocompass System.

element includes the frame and binnacle which provide a shock-mount support for the compass element.

The control cabinet contains all controls and indicators necessary for the operation of the equipment.

The compass failure annunciator contains two indicator lights to indicate a malfunction of the compass system or failure of the vessel's 400 Hertz power supply.

The solid state power supply provides the power necessary for operation of the master compass, control cabinet, compass failure annunciator, and charging batteries used as emergency power. All other gyrocompass system components must be energized from ship power. In the event of loss of ship power, the solid state supply will continue

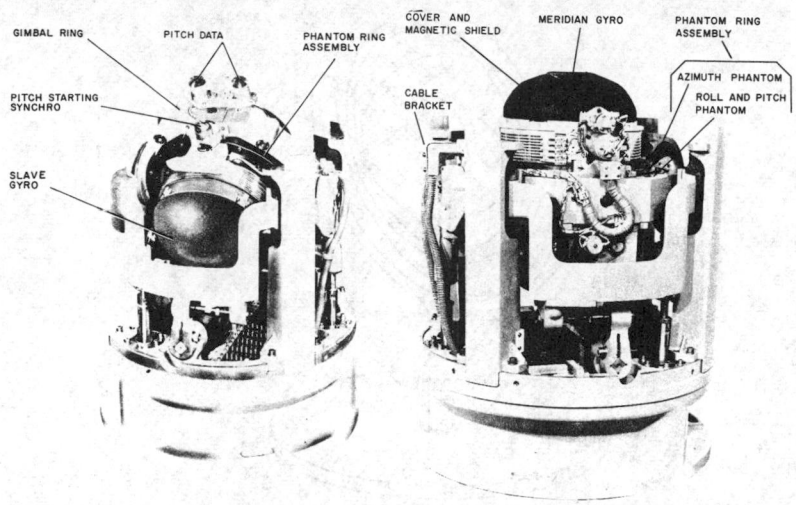

FIGURE 642b.—Mark 19 master compass.

to operate from the batteries until the ship's line is restored or the batteries are discharged.

Fluid suspension of the sensitive element provides high shock tolerance and greatly reduces the effect of accelerations. At running temperature, the specific gravity of the gyrosphere is the same as that of the oil in which it is immersed. Since the gyrosphere is in neutral buoyancy, it exerts no load on the vertical bearings which, therefore, serve only as guides for the sphere.

The Mark 19 Gyrocompass has four modes of operation. The normal mode provides optimum performance up to latitude 75°. The fast settle mode provides accelerated settling of the compass upon starting. The high latitude mode provides optimum performance from latitude 75° to about latitude 86°. The directional gyro mode enables operation of the compass as a free gyro with the spin axis oriented to grid north (art. 2510).

The Mark 19 Gyrocompass consists basically of two gyros (fig. 642c) placed with their spin axes mutually perpendicular in the horizontal plane. The spin axis of one gyro is directed along a north-south line, and the spin axis of the second is slaved to the first along an approximate east-west line. The north-seeking or meridian gyro and the slave gyro are mounted one above the other in a supporting ring. This ring is made to follow the gyros in heading and tilt by azimuth, roll, and pitch servos. These servos also drive the synchro transmitters which serve to supply output data.

The meridian gyro is essentially a gyrocompass. It furnishes indications of heading as well as tilt about the east-west axis. The slave gyro is essentially a free gyro and furnishes only an indication of tilt about the north-south axis. Thus, the Mark 19 Gyrocompass provides heading, roll, and pitch data.

In the meridian gyro of the Mark 19 Gyrocompass, the tilt is detected by a gravity reference attached to the vertical ring in such a way that it is parallel to the gyro axle. This device (electrolytic level) is a special level which transmits an electrical signal with magnitude and sense according to tilt. Since the gravity reference and axle are parallel and rigidly fixed with respect to one another, the signal emitted by the gravity reference is a measure of the gyro axle tilt about the east-west axis. In the more recent modifications of the gyrocompass, higher accuracy is obtained through the use of linear accelerometers instead of electrolytic levels to sense the direction of gravity.

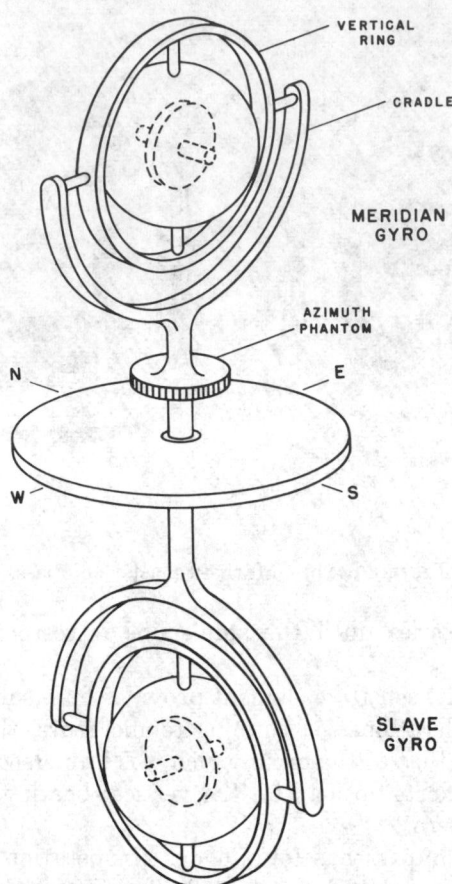

FIGURE 642c.—Simplified diagram of the Mark 19 compass element.

The tilt signal, after amplification, is applied to the control fields of electrical torquers, as shown in figure 642d, which cause torques about the vertical and horizontal axes. The torquers located about the horizontal axis are known as the azimuth torquers. They apply a torque about the horizontal axis proportional to the amount of tilt of the spin axis and cause the gyro to precess in azimuth. The effect of this torque is the same as making the gyro pendulous by attaching a heavy weight to the bottom of the vertical ring. When one end of the axis is tilted up, the resulting torque about the horizontal axis precesses the gyro in azimuth, i.e., about its vertical axis.

The leveling torquer, located about the vertical axis of the gyro, applies a torque about the vertical axis proportional to tilt and causes the gyro to precess about the horizontal axis to reduce the tilt to zero. The effect of this torque is the same as attaching a weight to the east side of the sphere (art. 631). When one end of the gyro axle is tilted up, the resulting torque about the vertical axis precesses the high end down. Thus, the effect of these two torques is to continually precess the axis to the meridian and make it level.

The Technical Manual for the Mark 19 Gyrocompass should be referred to for an explanation of the means used to control the compass.

The **Mark 27 Gyrocompass** (fig. 642e) consisting of two major components—the master compass unit and the compass electronics unit—is designed for both military and commercial, small to medium class vessels. The equipment is powered by an internal 400 Hz solid state supply (inverter) operating from a 24 volt DC battery source or

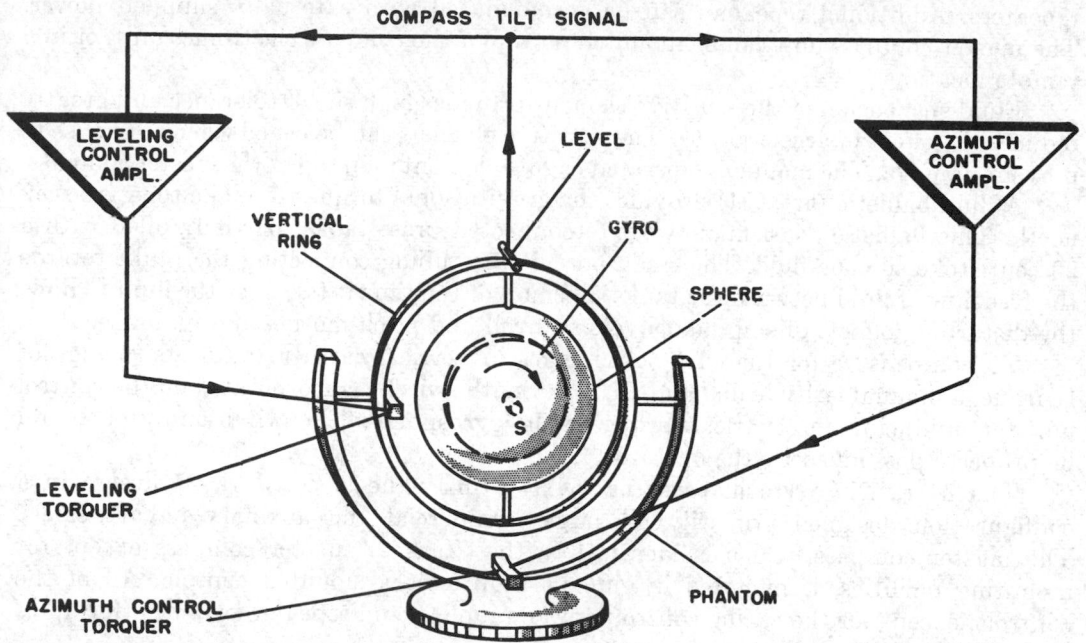

FIGURE 642d.—Simplified diagram of electrical azimuth and leveling controls for meridian gyro.

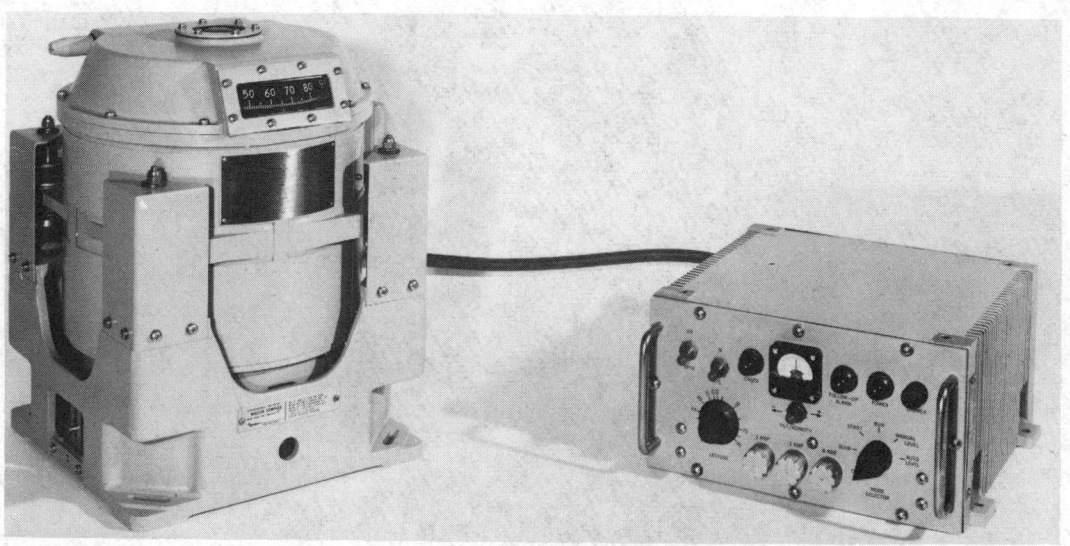

Courtesy of Sperry Marine Systems.

FIGURE 642e.—Mark 27 Gyrocompass System.

from an external 115 volt 60 to 400 Hz converter (rectifier) unit. The master compass unit is an oil-filled sealed unit containing the sensitive element, fluid ballistic, and the supporting gimbals and servo drive. The compass electronics unit contains the compass controls, supporting solid state electronics, and a solid state power supply. A direct-reading heading indication dial on the master compass has red illumination for night viewing. The master compass can be provided with various types of electrical transducers for transmission of the heading data to remote repeaters. The internal static power supply has the capability to power either two step repeaters or two servo synchro repeaters. Additional repeaters can be accomodated with externally supplied power. The master compass unit can be mounted on top of the compass electronics unit, or in a remote location.

Fluid suspension of the sensitive element provides high shock tolerance and greatly reduces the effect of accelerations. The sensitive element can be caged when not in use to prevent damage. The manually operated caging element is on top of the master compass.

A fluid ballistic (art. 631) provides the gravitational torques to make the gyro seek north. This ballistic consists of two interconnected brass tanks, partially filled with a 20 centistoke silicone fluid. The small bore of the tubing connecting the tanks retards the free flow of fluid between the tanks. Because of the time it takes for the fluid to flow, the disturbing effects of ship maneuvers and roll and pitch motion are minimized.

To compensate for the effect of changes in vertical earth rate due to change of latitude, a manual latitude dial and a North/South switch is incorporated on the control unit for producing an electrical torque on the gyrosphere. The switch and dial should be properly positioned by the operator.

The **Mark 227 Gyrocompass** (fig. 642f) utilizes the basic Mark 27 design in a configuration designed primarily for large commercial and auxiliary naval vessels. The master compass, which is identical to the Mark 27 master compass except for mounting facilities, is mounted in gimbals atop a deck-mounted console. All of the controls, except for the caging control, power supplies, and repeater switches (for up to

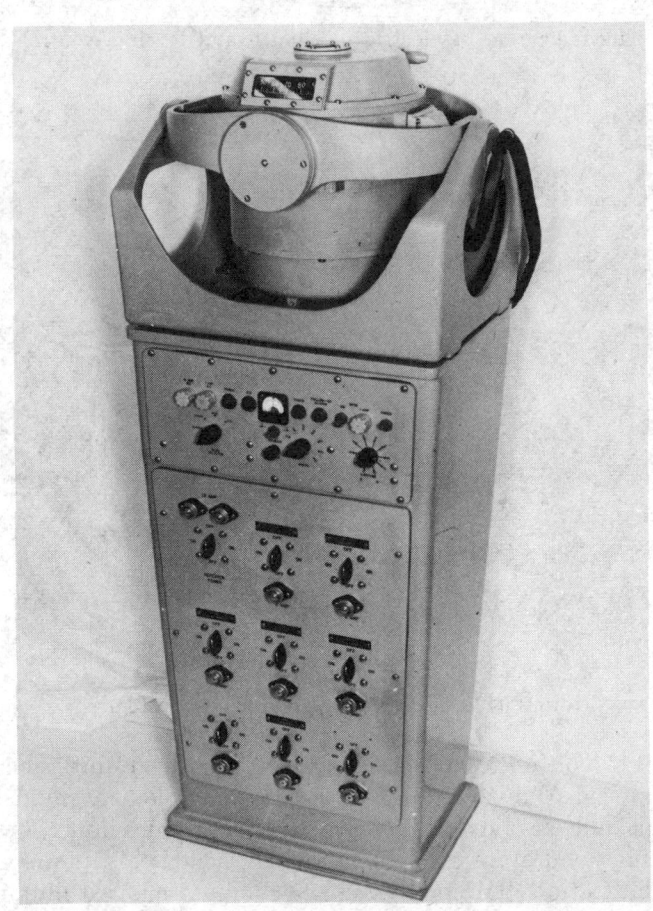

Courtesy of Sperry Marine Systems.

FIGURE 642f.—Mark 227 Gyrocompass System.

8 repeaters) are contained in the console. Standard units are equipped with a step transmitter and auxiliary equipment to power 8 step repeaters. Synchros, either 60 or 400 Hz, can be added to supply single or single and 36-speed data. Input power to this unit is 115 volt 60 to 400 Hz. Speed correction has been added and is set with a front panel knob. The additional gimbals enable transmission of azimuth data free of error due to deck tilt.

643. Gyrocompass repeaters.—A gyrocompass is customarily located at a favorable position below decks, and its indications transmitted electrically to various positions throughout the vessel. Each repeater consists of a compass rose on a suitable card so mounted that the direction of the ship's head is indicated at a lubber's line. Although the repeater may be mounted in any position, including vertically on a bulkhead, it is generally placed in gimbals in a bowl, similar to the mounting of a compass, which it resembles (fig. 643). This is true particularly of repeaters used for obtaining bearings. A gyro repeater used primarily to indicate the gyro heading is sometimes called a **ship's course indicator.**

Gyrocompass indications are also used in automatic steering devices, direction-stabilized radarscopes, wind indicators, fire control equipment, etc.

A compass used to control other equipment, particularly repeaters, is sometimes called a **master compass.** In the case of a gyrocompass, it is usually called a **master**

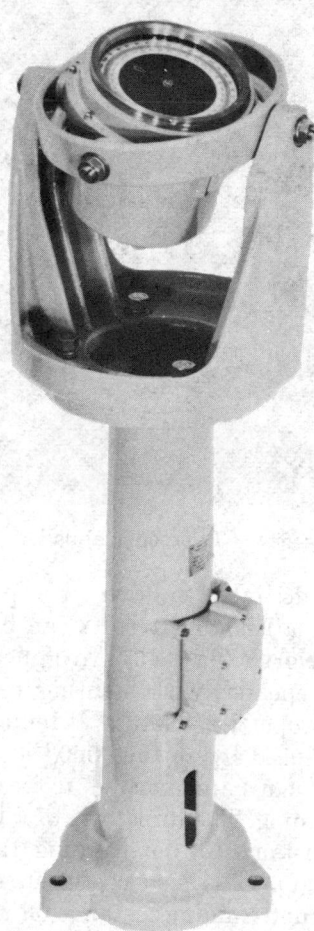

Courtesy of Ahrendt Instrument Co.

FIGURE 643.—A gyro repeater used as a ship's course indicator (Mark 2 Mod 5).

gyrocompass. It is good practice to check all repeaters periodically with the master compass to insure continued synchronization.

644. Gyro repeater accessories.—The bearing circle and azimuth circle (art. 629) are also used with the gyro repeater for bearing and azimuth observations. A **telescopic alidade** (fig. 644) may also be provided for bearing observations from repeaters. The telescopic alidade is basically similar to the bearing circle, except that it is fitted with a telescope instead of sighting vanes. The telescope of the telescopic alidade shown in figure 644 is mounted on a ring that fits on the gyro repeater. The erecting telescope is fitted with crosshair, level vial, polarizing light filter, and internal focusing. The optical system projects the image of approximately 25° of the compass card together with a view of the level vial onto the optical axis of the telescope. By this means, both the observed object and its bearing can be viewed at the same time through the eyepiece.

FIGURE 644.—Telescopic alidade.

645. Pelorus.—Although it is desirable to have a compass, a compass repeater, or an alidade for obtaining bearings, satisfactory results can be obtained by means of an inexpensive device known as a **pelorus** (fig. 645). In appearance and use this device resembles a compass or compass repeater, with sighting vanes or a sighting telescope attached, but it has no directive properties. That is, it remains at any *relative* direction to which it is set. It is generally used by setting 000° at the lubber's line. Relative bearings are then observed. They can be converted to bearings true, magnetic, grid, etc., by *adding* the appropriate heading. The direct use of relative bearings is sometimes of value. A pelorus is useful, for instance, in determining the moment at which an aid to navigation is broad on the beam. It is also useful in measuring pairs of relative bearings for use with table 7 or for determining distance off and distance abeam without a table.

If the true heading is set at the lubber's line, true bearings are observed directly. Similarly, compass bearings can be observed if the compass heading is set at the lub-

FIGURE 645.—A pelorus.

ber's line, etc. However, the vessel must be on the heading to which the pelorus is set if accurate results are to be obtained, or else a correction must be applied to the observed results. Perhaps the easiest way of avoiding error is to have the steersman indicate when the vessel is on course. This is usually done by calling out "mark, mark, mark" as long as the vessel is within a specified fraction of a degree of the desired heading. The observer, who is watching a distant object across the pelorus, selects an instant when the vessel is steady and is on course. An alternative method is to have the observer call out "mark" when the relative bearing is steady, and the steersman note the heading. If the compass is swinging at the moment of observation, the observation should be rejected. The number of degrees between the desired and actual headings is *added* if the vessel is to the *right* of the course, and *subtracted* if to the *left*. Thus, if the course is 060° and the heading is 062° at the moment of observation, a correction of 2° is added to the bearing.

Each observer should determine for himself the technique that produces the most reliable results.

646. Course recorder.—A continuous graphical record of the headings of a vessel can be obtained by means of a **course recorder** (fig. 646). In its usual form, paper with both heading and time graduations is slowly wound from one drum to another, its speed being controlled by a spring-powered clockwork mechanism. A pen is in contact with the paper, tracing a line to indicate the heading at each moment. The pen is attached to an arm controlled by indications from a compass, usually the master gyrocompass.

647. Dead reckoning equipment.—The primary navigational functions of **dead reckoning equipment** (DRE) are to (1) provide continuous indications of the vessel's present latitude and longitude, and (2) provide a graphical record of the vessel's dead reckoning track. In addition, most types of dead reckoning equipment provide means for tracking one or more other craft, to obtain a graphical record of the other craft's course and speed. This equipment is generally installed only on warships.

Dead reckoning equipment consists in general of four components: (1) an analyzer; (2) latitude and longitude indicator dials; (3) a desk-size unit called a **dead reckoning tracer** (DRT); and (4) a glass plotting surface over the dead reckoning tracer.

The analyzer receives directional signals from the vessel's gyrocompass, and distance signals from the underwater log. The course and distance data are transformed

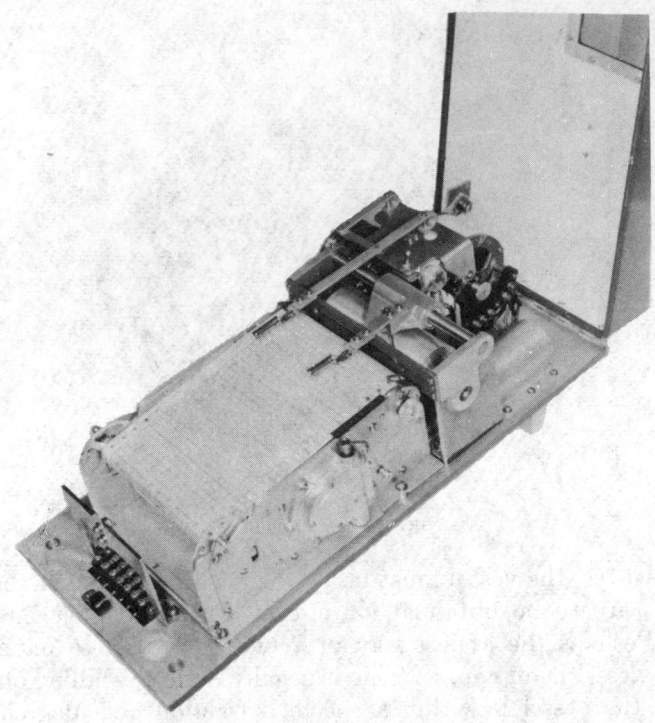

Courtesy of Sperry Marine Systems.

FIGURE 646.—A course recorder.

automatically to electrical signals proportional to the north-south and east-west components of the vessel's movement. These distance signals are transmitted to the latitude and longitude indicators, changing their readings by the correct amount to indicate the new latitude and the new longitude in degrees and minutes. Since the number of miles in the north-south component of distance traveled is nearly equal to the change in latitude expressed in minutes, the latitude indicator is fed directly. Departure (art. 204) is automatically tranformed to difference of longitude before being registered on the longitude indicator dials. If the indicator dials are correctly set to latitude and longitude, they continuously show subsequent dead reckoning positions of the vessel.

The north-south and east-west component signals from the analyzer are also transmitted to the DRT (fig. 647), where they control the motion of a pencil which moves across a chart or plotting sheet attached to the DRT base. The pencil draws a line which conforms to the maneuvers of the vessel. The mechanism can be set to plot the track at any scale from ¼ mile per inch (¹⁄₁₀ mile on some) to 16 miles per inch. A clock-controlled contact lifts the pencil from the paper for 15 seconds of each minute and for a longer period each 10 minutes, thus providing automatic time measurement. The pencil carriage can be moved manually to any part of the chart for initial setting and the direction of travel can be adjusted so that the chart can be placed with any cardinal direction "up."

The cover of the DRT is a sheet of glass to which a plotting sheet or blank paper can be fastened. An electric lamp on the top of the pencil carriage throws a spot of light through the paper directly over the carriage, thus providing a moving reference scaled to the course and speed of the vessel. If the position of the spot of light is marked periodically on the paper, a second record of the vessel's track is obtained. However,

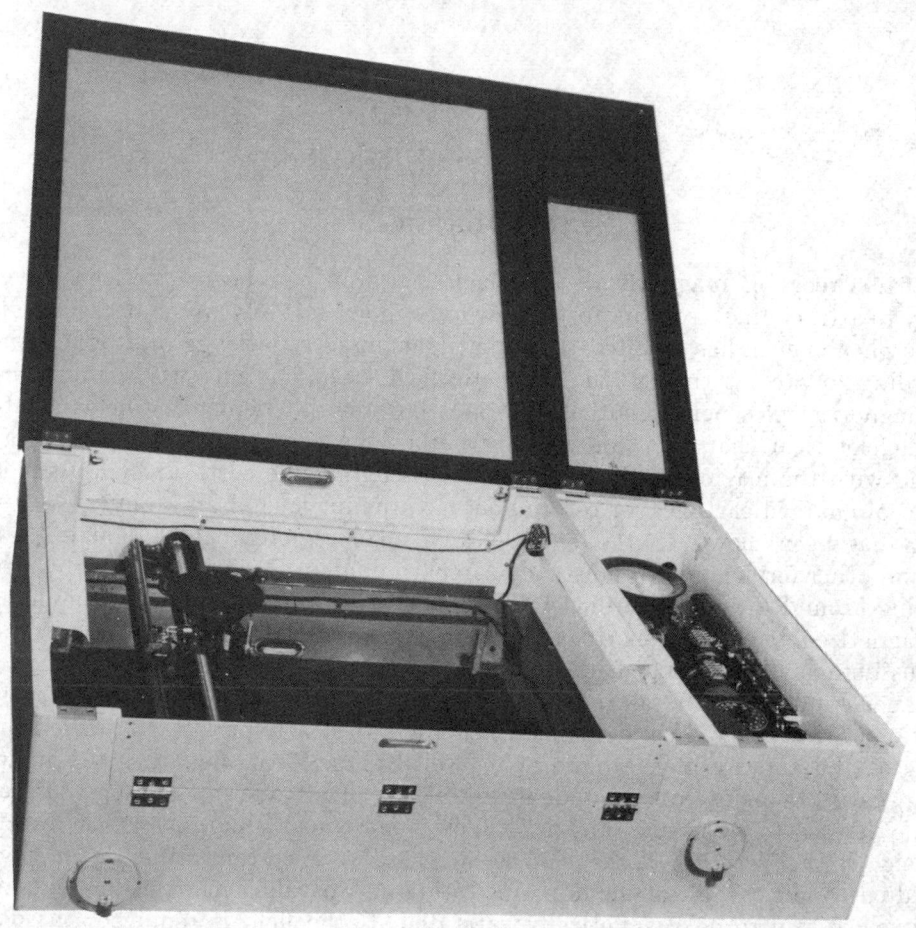

FIGURE 647.—A dead reckoning tracer.   *Courtesy of Ahrendt Instrument Co.*

the principal use of this sheet is for plotting successive positions of another craft, using the spot of light as the origin. A polar grid centered on the light may be projected onto the paper to facilitate measurement. The course of the other vessel can be measured directly from the plot, and its speed can be determined by means of the time needed to travel any distance measured on the plot. This process is called **tracking.** If the ranges and bearings are plotted from a fixed point, *relative* movement is determined, a practice commonly followed in connection with radar.

While dead reckoning equipment is a great convenience, particularly when changes of course or speed are numerous, its indications should be checked by graphical plot on the chart or plotting sheet. Reliable dead reckoning is too important to be left entirely to mechanical equipment without an independent check.

CHAPTER VII

COMPASS ERROR

Magnetism

701. Theory of magnetism.—The fact that iron can be magnetized (given the ability to attract other iron) has been known for thousands of years, but the explanation of this phenomenon has awaited the recently acquired knowledge of atomic structure. According to present theory, the magnetic field around a current-carrying wire and the magnetism of a permanent **magnet** are the same phenomenon—fields created by moving electrical charges. This occurs whether the charge is moving along a wire, flowing with the magma of the earth's core, encircling the earth at high altitude as a stream of charged particles, or rotating around the nucleus of an atom.

It has been shown that microscopically small regions, called **domains,** exist in iron and other ferromagnetic substances. In each domain the fields created by electrons spinning around their atomic nuclei are parallel to each other, causing the domain to be magnetized to saturation. In a piece of unmagnetized iron, the directions of the various domains are arranged in a random manner with respect to each other. If the substance is placed in a weak magnetic field, the domains rotate somewhat toward the direction of that field. Those domains which are more nearly parallel to the field increase in size at the expense of the more non parallel ones. If the field is made sufficiently strong, entire domains rotate suddenly by angles of as much as 90° or 180° so as to become parallel to that "crystal axis" which is most nearly parallel to the direction of the field. If the strength of the field is increased to a certain value depending upon individual conditions, all of the domains rotate into parallelism with the field, and the iron itself is said to be magnetically **saturated.** If the field is removed, the domains have a tendency to rotate more or less rapidly to a more natural direction parallel to some crystal axis, and more slowly to random directions under the influence of thermal agitation.

Magnetism which is present only when the material is under the influence of an external field is called **induced magnetism.** That which remains after the magnetizing force is removed is called **residual magnetism.** That which is retained for long periods without appreciable reduction, unless the material is subjected to a demagnetizing force, is called **permanent magnetism.**

Certain substances respond readily to a magnetic field. These **magnetic materials** are principally those composed largely of iron, although nickel and cobalt also exhibit magnetic properties. The best magnets are made of an alloy composed mostly of iron, nickel, and cobalt. Aluminum and some copper may be added. Platinum and silver, properly alloyed with other material, make excellent magnets, but for ordinary purposes the increased expense is not justified by the improvement in performance. Permanent magnets occur in nature in the form of **lodestone,** a form of magnetite (an oxide of iron) possessing magnetic properties. A piece of this material constitutes a **natural magnet.**

702. Hard and soft iron.—In some alloys of iron, the crystals can be so arranged and internally stressed that the domains remain parallel to each other indefinitely, and the metal thus becomes a **permanent magnet.** Such alloys are used for the magnets of a compass. In other kinds of iron, the domains reorient themselves rapidly to conform

194

to the direction of a changing external field, and soon take random directions if the field is removed. A ferromagnetic substance which retains much of its magnetism in the absence of an external field, is said to have high **remanence** or **retentivity.** The strength of a reverse field (one of opposite polarity) required to reduce the magnetism of a magnet to zero is called the **coercivity** or **coercive force** of the magnet. Hence, a compass magnet should have high remanence in order to be strong, and high coercivity so that stray fields will not materially affect it. For convenience, iron is called "hard" if it has high rema-nence, and "soft" if it has low remanence. **Permeability** (μ) is the ratio of the strength of the magnetic field inside the metal (B) to the strength of the external field (H), or $\mu = \dfrac{B}{H}$.

703. Lines of force.—The direction of a magnetic field is usually represented by lines, called **lines of force.** Relative intensity in different parts of a magnetic field is indicated by the spacing of the lines of force, a strong field having the lines close together. If a piece of unmagnetized iron is placed in a magnetic field, the lines of force tend to crowd into the iron, following its long axis, and the field is stronger in the vicinity of the iron, somewhat as shown in figure 703a. If the iron becomes permanently magnetized and is removed from this field, the lines of force around the iron follow paths about as shown in figure 703b.

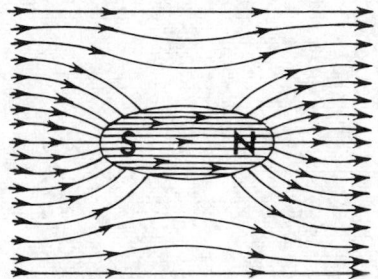

FIGURE 703a.—Lines of force crowd into ferromagnetic material placed in a magnetic field.

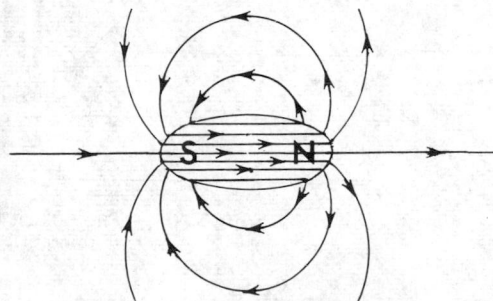

FIGURE 703b.—Field of a permanent magnet.

704. Magnetic poles.—The region in which the lines of force enter the iron is called the **south pole,** and the region in which they leave the iron is called the **north pole.** Thus, the lines of force are directed from south to north within the magnet, and from north to south in the external field. Every magnet has a north pole and a south pole. If a magnet is cut into two pieces, each becomes a magnet with a north pole and south pole. A single pole cannot exist independently. If two magnets are brought close to-gether, *unlike poles attract each other and like poles repel.* Thus, a north pole attracts a south pole but repels another north pole.

The earth itself has a magnetic field (art. 706), with its magnetic poles being some distance from the geographical poles. If a permanent bar magnet is supported so that it can turn freely, both horizontally and vertically, it aligns itself with the magnetic field of the earth, which at most places is in a general north-south direction and inclined to the horizontal. Since the north pole of the magnet points in a northerly direction, the earth's magnetic pole in the Northern Hemisphere has *south* magnetism. Nevertheless, it is called the **north magnetic pole** because of its geographical location. For a similar reason, the pole in the Southern Hemisphere, although it has north magnetism, is called the **south magnetic pole.** To avoid confusion, north magnetism is usually called "red," and south magnetism, "blue." The red (north) pole of a magnet is usually painted red, and in some cases the south (blue) pole is painted blue. The north magnetic pole of the earth is a blue pole, and the south magnetic pole is a red pole.

705. The magnetism of soft iron, in which remanence is low, depends upon the position of the iron with respect to an external field. It is strongest if the long axis is parallel to the lines of force, and decreases to a minimum if the material is rotated so that the long axis is perpendicular to the lines of force. Figure 705 shows three positions of a bar magnet with respect to a magnetic field. At position X the pole at the upper end of the bar is red and relatively strong. As the bar is rotated toward position Y, the upper end remains red, but its strength decreases. At position Y, no pole is apparent at either end, but a red pole extends along the entire left side of the bar, and a blue pole along the right side. Poles are strongest when concentrated into a small area. Hence, when spread over an entire side, as at position Y, they are relatively weak. At position Z, the upper end is blue.

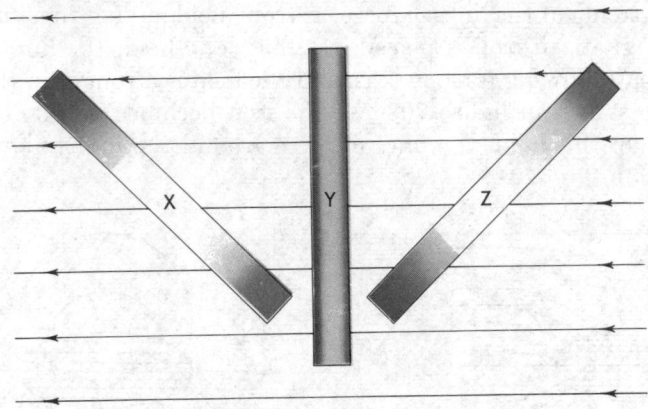

FIGURE 705.—The polarity of a soft iron bar in a
magnetic field.

The change in polarity as a bar of soft iron is rotated in a magnetic field can easily be demonstrated. If a bar of soft iron is placed vertical in northern magnetic latitudes (as in any part of the United States), the north (red) end of a compass magnet brought near it will be attracted by the upper end of the bar, and repelled by the lower end. If the bar is inverted, so that its ends are interchanged, the upper end (which as the lower end previously repelled the compass needle) will attract the north end of the needle, and the lower end will repel it. Thus, the polarity of the rod is reversed, *either* end having blue magnetism if it is at the top. This changing polarity of soft iron in the earth's field is a major factor affecting the magnetic compasses of a steel vessel.

706. Terrestrial magnetism.—The earth itself can be considered to be a gigantic magnet. Although man has known for many centuries that the earth has a magnetic field, the origin of the magnetism is not completely understood. Nevertheless, the horizontal component of this field is a valuable reference in navigation, for it provides the directive force for the magnetic compass, which indicates the ship's heading *in relation to the horizontal component of this field.*

The world-wide pattern of the earth's magnetism is roughly like that which would result from a short, powerful, bar magnet near the earth's center, as shown in figure 706. The geographical poles are at the top and bottom, and the magnetic poles are offset somewhat from them. This representation, however, is greatly simplified. The actual field is more complex, and requires measurement of its strength and direction at many places (art. 707) before it can be defined accurately enough to be of practical use to the navigator. Not only are the magnetic poles offset from the geographical poles, but the magnetic poles themselves are not 180° apart and, in general, a magnetic compass aligned with the lines of force does not point toward either magnetic pole. In 1975, the north magnetic pole was located at latitude 76°.1N, longitude 100°.0W, approximately, to the northward of Prince of Wales Island; and the south magnetic pole was at latitude 65°.8S, longitude 139°.4E, approximately, off the coast of the northeastern part of Wilkes Land. However, the magnetic poles are not stationary. The entire magnetic field of the earth, including the magnetic poles, undergoes a small daily or **diurnal change,** and a very slow, progressive **secular change.** In addition, temporary sporadic changes occur from time to time during magnetic storms (art. 2526). During a severe storm, variation may change as much as 5°, or more. However, such disturbances are never so rapid as to cause noticeable deflection of the compass card, and in most navigable waters the change is so little that it is not significant in practical navigation. Even when there is no temporary disturbance, the earth's field is considerably more intricate than indicated by an isomagnetic chart (art. 708). Natural magnetic irregularities occurring over relatively small areas are called **magnetic anomalies** by the magneticians, but the navigator generally refers to these phenomena as **local disturbances.** Notes warning of such disturbances are shown on charts. In addition, artificial disturbances may be quite severe when a vessel is in close proximity to other vessels, piers, machinery, electric currents, etc.

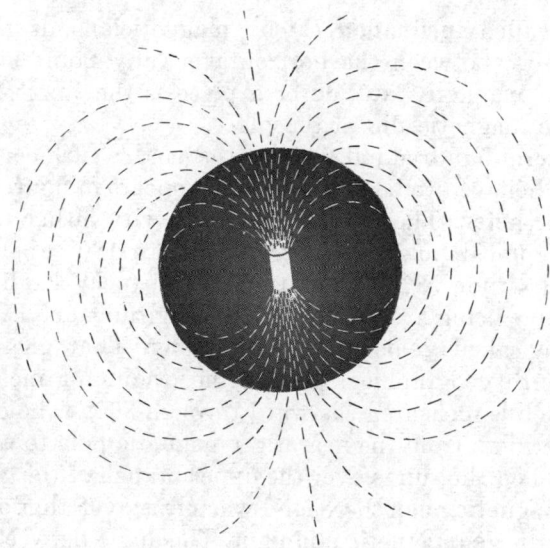

FIGURE 706.—The magnetic field of the earth.

The elements of the earth's field are as follows:

Total intensity (F) is the strength of the field at any point, measured in a direction parallel to the field. Intensity is sometimes measured in **oersteds,** one oersted being equal to a force of one dyne acting on a unit pole. The range of intensity of the earth's field is about 0.25 to 0.70 oersted. For convenience in geomagnetic surveying, a small unit is used, called the **gamma.** One oersted equals 100,000 gammas, so that the range of intensity of the earth's field is about 25,000 to 70,000 gammas.

Horizontal intensity (H) is the horizontal component of the total intensity. At the **magnetic equator,** which corresponds roughly with the geographic equator, the field is parallel to the surface of the earth, and the horizontal intensity is the same as total intensity. At the magnetic poles of the earth, the field is vertical and there is no horizontal component. The direction of the horizontal component at any place defines the **magnetic meridian** at that place. This component provides the desired directive force of a magnetic compass.

North component (X) is the horizontal intensity's component along a geographic (true) meridian.

East component (Y) is the horizontal intensity's component perpendicular to the north component.

Vertical intensity (Z) is the vertical component of the total intensity. It is zero at the magnetic equator. At the magnetic poles it is the same as the total intensity. While the vertical intensity has no direct effect upon the direction indicated by a magnetic compass, it does induce magnetic fields in vertical soft iron, and these may affect the compass.

Variation (V, Var.), called **declination (D)** by magneticians, is the angle between the geographic and magnetic meridians at any place. The expression **magnetic variation** is used when it is necessary to distinguish this from other forms of variation. This element is measured in angular units and named east or west to indicate the side of true north on which the (magnetic) northerly part of the magnetic meridian lies. For computational purposes, easterly variation is sometimes designated positive (+), and westerly variation negative (−). **Grid variation (GV)** or **grivation** is the angle between the grid and magnetic meridians at any place, measured and named in a manner similar to variation.

Magnetic dip (I), called **inclination (I)** by magneticians, is the vertical angle, expressed in angular units, between the horizontal at any point and a line of force through that point. The **magnetic latitude** of a place is the angle having a tangent equal to half that of the magnetic dip of the place.

At a distance of several hundred miles above the earth's surface, the magnetic field surrounding the earth is believed to be uniform, as it appears in figure 706, and centered around two **geomagnetic poles.** These do not coincide with either the magnetic poles (art. 704) or the geographical poles. However, they are 180° apart, the north geomagnetic pole being at latitude 78°.5N, longitude 69°W (near Etah, Greenland) and the south geomagnetic pole being at latitude 78°.5S, longitude 111°E. The great circles through these poles are called **geomagnetic meridians.** That geomagnetic meridian passing through the south geographical pole is the origin for measurement of **geomagnetic longitude,** which is measured eastward through 360°. The complement of the arc of a geomagnetic meridian from the nearer geomagnetic pole to a place is called the **geomagnetic latitude.** When the sun is over the upper branch of the geomagnetic meridian of a place, it is **geomagnetic noon** there, and when it is over the lower branch of the geomagnetic meridian, it is **geomagnetic midnight.** The angle between the lower branch of the geomagnetic meridian of a place and the geomagnetic meridian over which the sun is located is called **geomagnetic time.** The diurnal change is related to geomagnetic time. The auroral zones (art. 2526) are centered on the geomagnetic poles.

707. Measurement of the earth's magnetic field is made continuously at about 70 permanent **magnetic observatories** throughout the world. In addition, large numbers of temporary stations are occupied for short periods to add to man's knowledge of the earth's field. In the past, measurements at sea have been made by means of nonmagnetic ships constructed especially for this purpose. However, this is a slow and expensive method, and quite inadequate to survey properly the 71 percent of the earth's surface covered with water. Since World War II, a satisfactory **airborne magnetometer** has been developed by the U. S. Navy. By means of this instrument, continuous readings can be recorded automatically during long overwater flights.

708. Isomagnetic charts showing lines of equality of some magnetic element are published by the Defense Mapping Agency Hydrographic Center. The magnetic data are compiled by the United States Geological Survey with the assistance of the National Oceanic and Atmospheric Administration and in collaboration with the U. S. Naval Oceanographic Office. The three charts of each element consist of one on the Mercator projection (art. 305) covering most of the world, and one on a polar projection (azimuthal equidistant (art. 320) or stereographic) for each of the two polar areas. All charts now included in the series are published at intervals of 10 years, showing the values for the beginning of each year ending in five. Charts showing variation are also published for the years ending in zero (1950, 1960, etc.).

The isomagnetic chart of most concern to a navigator is chart 42, *Magnetic Variation*, a simplified version of which is shown in figure 708a. The lines connecting points of equal magnetic variation are called **isogonic lines.** *These are not magnetic meridians (lines of force).* The line connecting points of zero variation is called the **agonic line.** Variation is also shown on nautical charts. Those of relatively small scale generally show isogonic lines. Those of scale larger than 1:100,000 generally give the information in the form of statements inside compass roses placed at various places on the chart, and sometimes, also, by a **magnetic compass rose** within the true compass rose and offset from it by the amount of the variation. By means of this arrangement, true directions can be plotted without arithmetically applying variation to magnetic directions, or magnetic directions can be read directly from the chart. The magnetic compass rose is generally graduated in both degrees and points. Variation is given to the nearest 15′, and the annual change to the nearest 1′. However, since the rate of change is not constant, a very old chart should not be used, even though it has been corrected for all changes shown in *Notices to Mariners*.

Another isomagnetic chart of value to the mariners is chart 30, *Magnetic Inclination or Dip*, figure 708b. Lines connecting points of equal magnetic dip are called **isoclinal lines.** The line connecting points of zero dip is called the **magnetic equator.**

Other isomagnetic charts are chart 33, showing horizontal intensity in gammas (art. 706); chart 36, showing vertical intensity in gammas; and chart 39, showing total intensity in gammas. Lines connecting points of equal intensity on any of these charts are called **isodynamic lines.**

Other isomagnetic charts show (1) magnetic inclination in north and south polar areas; (2) horizontal intensity, including horizontal intensity in north and south polar areas; (3) vertical intensity, including vertical intensity in north and south polar areas; (4) total intensity, including total intensity in north and south polar areas; (5) magnetic variation in north and south polar areas; and (6) magnetic grid variation.

All of the isomagnetic charts also show **isopors,** in a distinctive color, connecting points of equal **annual change** of the element at the epoch of the chart.

The charts are as accurate as can be made with available information, except that the lines are smoothed somewhat, rather than depicting every small irregularity. The larger irregularities are reflected in the information shown on nautical charts, but local disturbance is indicated by warning notes at appropriate places. In areas where measurements of the magnetic field have not been made for a long period, the previous information is altered in accordance with the best information available on secular change, with some adjustment to provide continuous smooth curves. When information is thus carried forward for many years, errors may be introduced, particularly in areas where the rate of change is large and variable. Magneticians have not detected a recognizable worldwide pattern in secular change, such as would occur if it were due only to shifting of the positions of the magnetic poles. Rather, these shifts are part of the general complex, little-understood secular change.

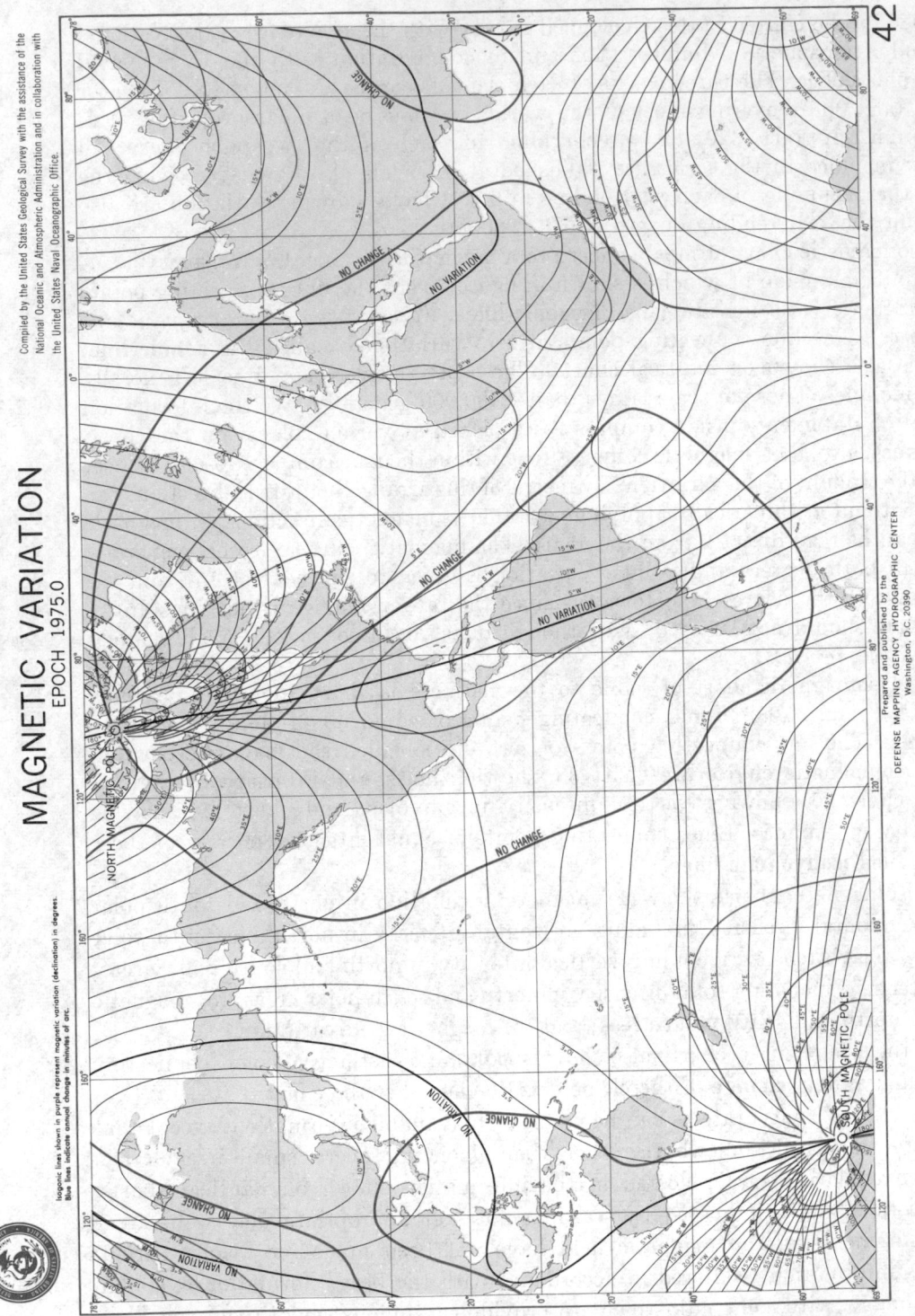

FIGURE 708a.—Variation. A simplification of chart 42.

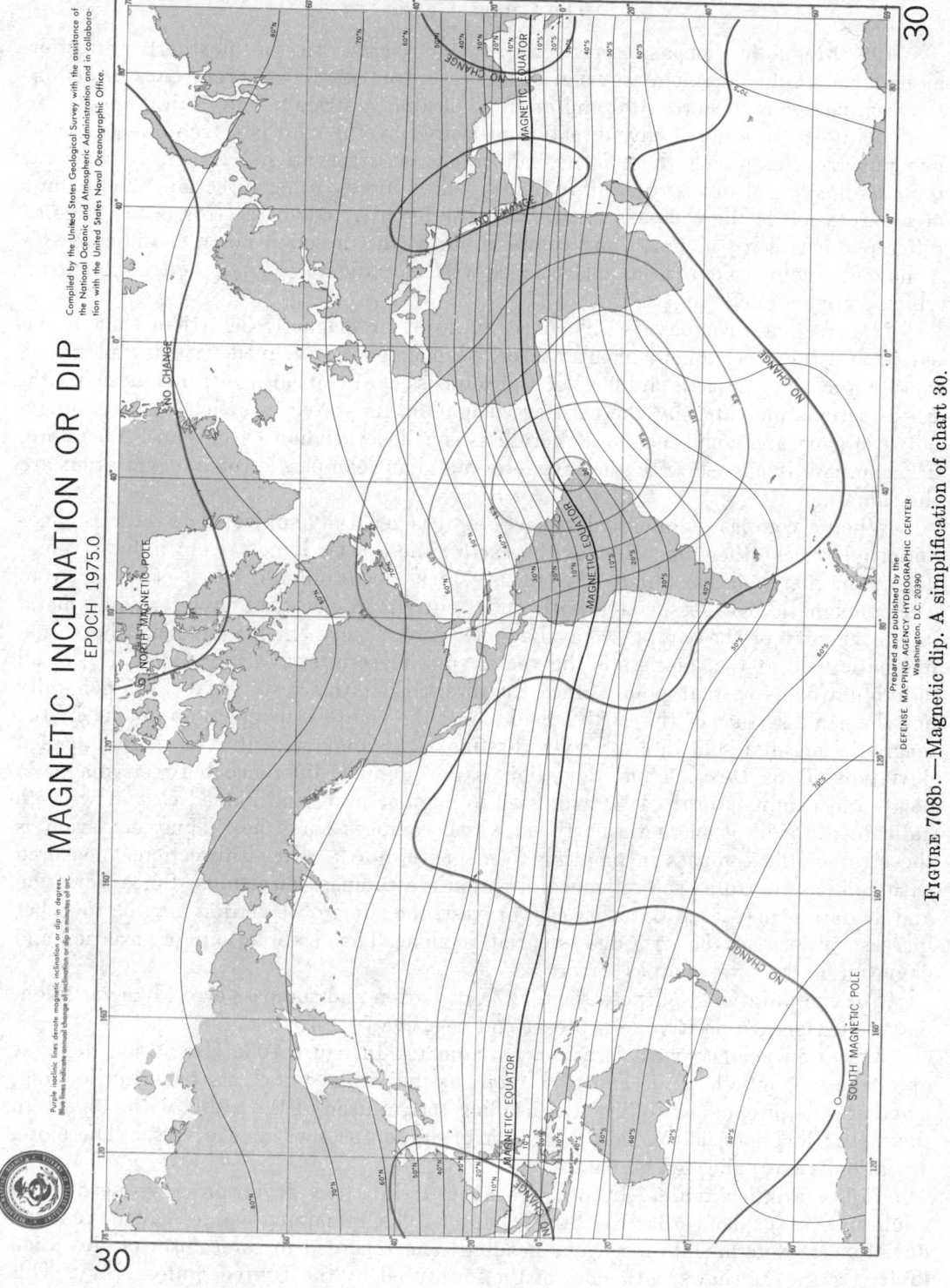

MAGNETIC INCLINATION OR DIP
EPOCH 1975.0

Compiled by the United States Geological Survey with the assistance of
the National Oceanic and Atmospheric Administration and in collaboration with the United States Naval Oceanographic Office.

Purple isoclinic lines denote magnetic inclination or dip in degrees.
Blue lines indicate annual change of inclination or dip in minutes of arc.

Prepared and published by the
DEFENSE MAPPING AGENCY HYDROGRAPHIC CENTER
Washington, D.C. 20390

FIGURE 708b.—Magnetic dip. A simplification of chart 30.

The Compass Error

709. Magnetic compass error.—Directions relative to the northerly direction along a geographic meridian are **true.** In this case, true north is the **reference direction.** If a compass card is horizontal and oriented so that a straight line from its center to 000° points to true north, any direction measured by the card is a true direction and has no error (assuming there is no calibration or observational error). If the card remains horizontal but is rotated so that it points in any other direction, the amount of the rotation is the **compass error.** Stated differently, compass error is the angular difference between true north and **compass north** (the direction north as indicated by a magnetic compass). It is named east or west to indicate the side of true north on which compass north lies.

If a magnetic compass is influenced by no other magnetic field than that of the earth, and there is no instrumental error, its magnets are aligned with the magnetic meridian at the compass, and 000° of the compass card coincides with **magnetic north.** All directions indicated by the card are **magnetic.** As stated in article 706, the angle between geographic and magnetic meridians is called **variation** (**V** or **Var.**). Therefore, if a compass is aligned with the magnetic meridian, compass error and variation are the same.

When a compass is mounted in a vessel, it is generally subjected to various magnetic influences other than that of the earth. These arise largely from induced magnetism in metal decks, bulkheads, masts, stacks, boat davits, guns, etc., and from electromagnetic fields associated with direct current in electrical circuits. Some metal in the vicinity of the compass may have acquired permanent magnetism. The actual magnetic field at the compass is the vector sum, or resultant (art. 118, vol. II), of all individual fields at that point. Since the direction of this resultant field is generally not the same as that of the earth's field alone, the compass magnets do not lie in the magnetic meridian, but in a direction that makes an angle with it. This angle is called **deviation** (**D** or **Dev.**). Thus, deviation is the angular difference between magnetic north and compass north. It is expressed in angular units and named east or west to indicate the side of magnetic north on which compass north lies. Thus, deviation is the error of the compass in pointing to magnetic north, and all directions measured with compass north as the reference direction are **compass directions.** Since variation and deviation may each be either east or west, the effect of deviation may be to either increase or decrease the error due to variation alone. The algebraic sum of variation and deviation is the total compass error.

For computational purposes (art. 727), deviation and compass error, like variation, may be designated positive (+) if east and negative (−) if west.

Variation changes with location, as indicated in figure 708a. Deviation depends upon the magnetic latitude and also upon the individual vessel, its trim and loading, whether it is pitching or rolling, the heading (orientation of the vessel with respect to the earth's magnetic field), and the location of the compass within the vessel. Therefore, deviation is not published on charts.

710. Deviation table.—In practice aboard ship, the deviation is reduced to a minimum, as explained later in this chapter. The remaining value, called **residual deviation,** is determined on various headings and recorded in some form of **deviation table.** Figure 710 shows both sides of the form used by the United States Navy. This table is entered with the magnetic heading, and the deviation on that heading is determined from the tabulation, separate columns being given for degaussing (DG) off and on (art. 740). If the deviation is not more than about 2° on any heading, satisfactory results may be obtained by entering the values at intervals of 45° only.

MAGNETIC COMPASS TABLE

NAVSEA RPT. 3530-2

NAVSEA 3120/4 (REV. 6-72) (FRONT) *(Formerly NAVSHIPS 1104)*
S/N 0105-601-9521

U.S.S. _____ NO. _____ *(BB, CL, DD, etc.)*

[X] PILOT HOUSE [ ] SECONDARY CONNING STATION [ ] OTHER _____

BINNACLE TYPE: [X] NAVY ST'D [ ] OTHER _____

COMPASS 7-1/2 MAKE C.G. Conn SERIAL NO. 8560

TYPE CC COILS "K" DATE 9 September 1975

READ INSTRUCTIONS ON BACK BEFORE STARTING ADJUSTMENT

SHIPS HEAD MAGNETIC	DEVIATIONS DG OFF	DEVIATIONS DG ON	SHIPS HEAD MAGNETIC	DEVIATIONS DG OFF	DEVIATIONS DG ON
0	0.5E	0.5E	180	0.5W	0.0
15	1.0E	1.0E	195	1.0W	0.5W
30	1.5E	1.5E	210	1.0W	1.0W
45	2.0E	1.5E	225	1.5W	1.5W
60	2.0E	2.0E	240	2.0W	2.0W
75	2.5E	2.5E	255	2.0W	2.5W
90	2.5E	3.0E	270	1.5W	2.0W
105	2.0E	2.5E	285	1.0W	1.5W
120	1.5E	2.0E	300	1.0W	1.0W
135	1.5E	1.5E	315	0.5W	0.5W
150	1.0E	1.0E	330	0.5W	0.5W
165	0.0	0.5E	345	0.0	0.0

DEVIATIONS DETERMINED BY: [ ] SUN'S AZIMUTH [X] GYRO [ ] SHORE BEARINGS

B 6 MAGNETS RED [ ] FORE [X] AFT AT 12" FROM COMPASS CARD

C 4 MAGNETS RED [ ] PORT [X] STBD AT 6" FROM COMPASS CARD

D 2-7" [X] SPHERES [ ] CYLS AT 12" [X] ATHWART-SHIP [ ] SLEWED - ° [ ] CLOCKWISE [ ] CTR. CLOCKWISE

HEELING MAGNET: [ ] RED UP [X] BLUE UP 6" FROM COMPASS CARD FLINDERS BAR: [X] FORE [ ] AFT 12"

[X] LAT 18°00'N [X] LONG 120°00'E
[ ] H 0.385 [ ] Z 0.151

SIGNED *(Adjuster or Navigator)* _____ APPROVED *(Commanding)* _____

VERTICAL INDUCTION DATA
(Fill out completely before adjusting)

RECORD DEVIATION ON AT LEAST TWO ADJACENT CARDINAL HEADINGS

BEFORE STATING ADJUSTMENT: N 8 W E 0 S 4 E W 9 E.

RECORD BELOW INFORMATION FROM LAST NAVSHIPS 3120/4 DEVIATION TABLE:

DATE 5 December 1974 [ ] LAT 32 53N [ ] LONG 117 18W
[ ] H .260 [ ] Z .420

12" FLINDERS BAR [X] FORWARD [ ] AFT DEVIATIONS N 2.5W E 7E S 6.5E W 5W.

RECORD HERE DATA ON RECENT OVERHAULS, GUNFIRE, STRUCTURAL CHANGES, FLASHING, DEPERMING, WITH DATES AND EFFECT ON MAGNETIC COMPASSES:

Shipyard overhaul:
3 Oct - 2 Dec 1974
Depermed at Norfolk, Va.:
3 Dec 1974

PERFORMANCE DATA

COMPASS AT SEA:	[ ] UNSTEADY	[X] STEADY	
COMPASS ACTION:	[ ] SLOW	[X] SATISFACTORY	
NORMAL DEVIATIONS:	[X] CHANGE	[ ] REMAIN RELIABLE	
DEGAUSSED DEVIATIONS:	[X] VARY	[ ] DO NOT VARY	

REMARKS

INSTRUCTIONS

1. This form shall be filled out by the Navigator for each magnetic compass as set forth in Chapter 9240 of NAVAL SHIPS TECHNICAL MANUAL.

2. When a swing for deviations is made, the deviations should be recorded both with degaussing coils off and with degaussing coils energized at the proper currents for heading and magnetic zone.

3. Each time this form is filled out after a swing for deviations, a copy shall be submitted to: Naval Ship Engineering Center Hyattsville, Maryland 20782. A letter of transmittal is not required.

4. When choice of box is given, check applicable box.

5. Before adjusting, fill in section on "Vertical Induction Data" above.

NAVSEA 3120/4 (REV. 6-72) (REVERSE) C-24855

FIGURE 710.—Deviation table.

If the deviation is small, no appreciable error is introduced by entering the table with either magnetic or compass heading. If the deviation on some headings is large, the desirable action is to reduce it, but if this is not practicable, a separate deviation table for compass heading entry may be useful. This may be made by applying the tabulated deviation to each entry value of magnetic heading, to find the corresponding compass heading, and then interpolating between these to find the value of deviation at each 15° compass heading. Another method is to plot the values on cross-section paper and select the desired values graphically.

A nomogram especially designed for interconversion of magnetic and compass headings is called a **Napier diagram,** having been devised by James Robert Napier (1821–79). It consists of a dotted, vertical centerline graduated from 000° to 360° (usually in two parallel parts of 180° each), with two series of crosslines making angles of 60° with the dotted vertical line and with each other. If magnetic headings are used, deviation is measured along a solid crossline; and if compass headings are used, deviation is measured along a dotted crossline. A deviation curve is drawn through the various points. To convert a magnetic heading to a compass heading, one finds the magnetic heading on the vertical centerline, moves parallel to a solid crossline until the curve is reached, and returns to the centerline by moving parallel to a dotted line. The compass heading is the value at the point of return. The reverse process is used for converting a compass heading to a magnetic heading. This nomogram is of particular value where the deviation is large and changing rapidly. It is now possible, however, to reduce deviation to such small values that the Napier diagram has lost much of its appeal and is seldom used.

Another solution is to make a deviation table with one column for magnetic heading, a second column for deviation, and a third for compass heading. Still another solution, most popular among yachtsmen, is to center a compass rose inside a larger one so that an open space is between them, and a radial line would connect points of the same graduation on both roses. Each magnetic heading for which deviation has been determined is located on the outer rose, and a straight line is drawn from this point to the corresponding compass heading on the inner rose.

A variation of this method is to draw two parallel lines a short distance apart, and graduate each from 0 to 360 so that a perpendicular between the two lines connects points of the same graduation. Straight lines are drawn from magnetic directions on one line to the corresponding compass directions on the other. If the lines are horizontal and the upper one represents magnetic directions, the slope of the line indicates the direction of the deviation. That is, for westerly deviation the upper part of the connecting line is left (west) of the bottom part, and for easterly deviation it is right.

An important point to remember regarding deviation is that it varies with the *heading*. Therefore, a deviation table is *never* entered with a bearing (art. 1004). If the deviation table converts directly from one type heading to another, deviation is found by taking the difference between the two values. On the compass rose or straight-line type, the deviation can be written alongside the connecting line, and the intermediate values determined by estimate. If one has trouble determining whether to add or subtract deviation when bearings are involved, he has only to note which heading, magnetic or compass, is larger. The same relationship holds between the two values of bearing.

The deviation table should be protected from damage due to handling or weather, and placed in a position where it will always be available when needed. A method commonly used is to mount it on a board, cover it with shellac or varnish, and attach it to the binnacle. Another method is to post it under glass near the compass. It is good practice for the navigator to keep a second copy available at a convenient place for his use.

711. Applying variation and deviation.—As indicated in article 709, a single direction may have any of several numerical values depending upon the reference direction used. One should keep clearly in mind the relationship between the various expressions of a direction. Thus, true and magnetic directions differ by the variation, magnetic and compass directions differ by the deviation, and true and compass directions differ by the compass error. Other relationships are also useful. Thus, grid (art. 2510) and magnetic directions differ by the grid variation or grivation, and true and relative directions differ by the true heading. The use of variation and deviation is considered here. Other relationships are discussed elsewhere in this volume.

If variation or deviation is easterly, the compass card is rotated in a clockwise direction. This brings smaller numbers opposite the lubber's line. Conversely, if either error is westerly, the rotation is counterclockwise and larger numbers are brought opposite the lubber's line. Thus, if the heading is 090° true (fig. 711, A) and variation is 6°E, the magnetic heading is 090°−6°=084° (fig. 711, B). If the deviation on this heading is 2°W, the compass heading is 084°+2°=086° (fig. 711, C). Also, compass error is $6°E-2°W=4°E$, and compass heading is $090°-4°=086°$. If compass error is easterly, the compass reads too low (in comparison with true directions), and if it is westerly, the reading is too high. Many rules-of-thumb have been devised as an aid to the memory, and any which assist in applying compass errors in the right direction are of value. However, one may forget the rule or its method of application, or may wish to have an independent check. If he understands the explanation given above, he can determine the correct sign without further information. The same rules apply to the use of gyro error. Since variation and deviation are compass errors, the process of removing either from an indication of a direction (converting compass to magnetic or magnetic to true) is often called **correcting.** Conversion in the opposite direction (inserting errors) is then called **uncorrecting.**

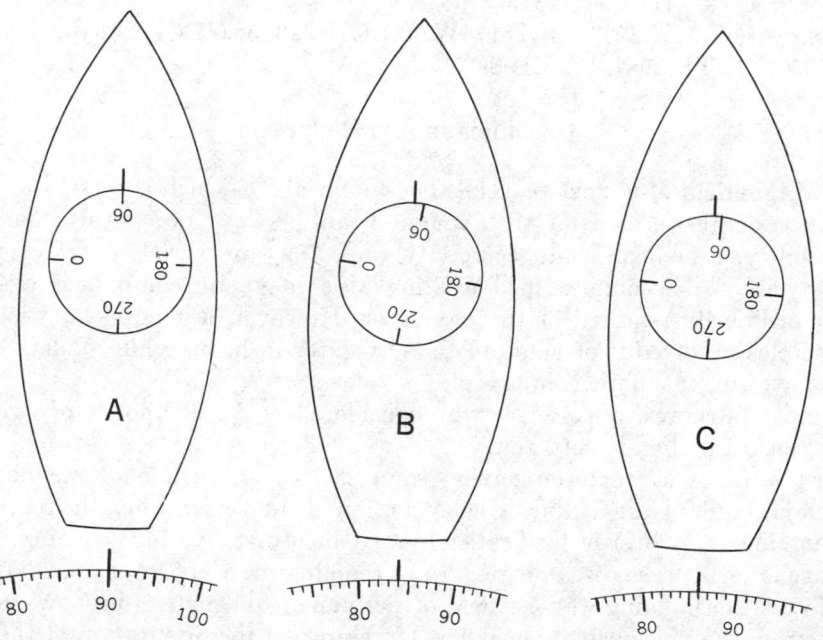

FIGURE 711.—Effect of variation and deviation on the compass card.

Example.—A vessel is on course 215° true in an area where the variation is 7°W. The deviation is as shown in figure 710. Degaussing is off. The gyro error (GE) is 1°E. A lighthouse bears 306°5 by magnetic compass.

Required.—(1) Magnetic heading (MH).
(2) Deviation.
(3) Compass heading (CH).
(4) Compass error.
(5) Gyro heading.
(6) Magnetic bearing of the lighthouse.
(7) True bearing of the lighthouse.
(8) Relative bearing (art. 904) of the lighthouse.
Solution.—

$$
\begin{array}{lll}
 & \text{TH} & 215° \\
 & \text{V} & \underline{7°W} \\
(1) & \text{MH} & 222° \\
(2) & \text{D} & \underline{1°5W} \\
(3) & \text{CH} & 223°5 \\
\end{array}
$$

The deviation is taken from the deviation table (fig. 710), to the nearest half degree.
(4) Compass error is $7°W+1°5W=8°5W$.

$$
\begin{array}{rl}
\text{TH} & 215° \\
\text{GE} & 1°E \\
(5)\ \text{H}_{pgc} & \overline{214°} \\
\text{CB} & 306°5 \\
\text{D} & 1°5W \\
(6)\ \text{MB} & \overline{305°} \\
\text{V} & 7°W \\
(7)\ \text{TB} & \overline{298°}
\end{array}
$$

(8) $RB=TB-TH=298°-215°=083°$.

Answers.—(1) MH 222°, (2) D 1°5W, (3) CH 223°5, (4) CE 8°5W, (5) H_{pgc} 214°, (6) MB 305°, (7) TB 298°, (8) RB 083°.

Deviation and its Reduction

712. Magnetism of a steel vessel.—The materials of which a vessel is constructed are not, in general, selected for their magnetic properties. As a result, many degrees of permeability, remanence, and coercivity (art. 702) exist within its structure. Detailed analysis of the complex field existing at a magnetic compass is a specialized study not ordinarily required of the navigator. However, a general knowledge of the basic principles involved is of value to the navigator in helping him understand better the behavior of his magnetic compasses.

For most purposes, a vessel can be considered to be composed of two types of material: "hard iron" and "soft iron."

"Hard iron" is all material having some degree of permanent magnetism. This magnetism is acquired largely during construction of the vessel, when the rearrangement of the domains (art. 701) is facilitated by the bending, riveting, welding, and other violent mechanical processes. Since a vessel remains on a constant magnetic heading while it is on the building ways, a field of permanent magnetism becomes established, the positions of the poles being dependent largely upon the orientation of the hull with respect to the magnetic field of the earth. If a vessel is constructed on a heading of magnetic north, at a place where the magnetic dip is 70°N (the approximate value at the midpoint of the east coast of the United States), its field of permanent magnetism is about as shown at the left of figure 712. The upper and stern portions are magnetically blue, while the lower and forward portions are magnetically red. If the vessel is built on a heading of magnetic east, the starboard and upper portions are blue, and the port and lower portions are red, as shown by the stern view at the right of figure 712. If the heading is magnetic northeast, the upper, starboard, and stern portions are blue, and the lower, port, and forward portions red. The red and blue portions for any given vessel can be visualized by drawing a sketch similar to that of figure 712, with the correct orientation.

The "permanent" magnetism thus acquired during construction is less permanent than that of a permanent magnet such as one of those used in a compass, and is modified somewhat after launching, particularly if the vessel remains on another heading for a considerable time during fitting out. The change is especially rapid during the first few days after launching, when the domains of the softer iron become reoriented. At this stage, deviation due to permanent magnetism may change several degrees. Further changes in the vessel's permanent magnetism may occur during long periods of being

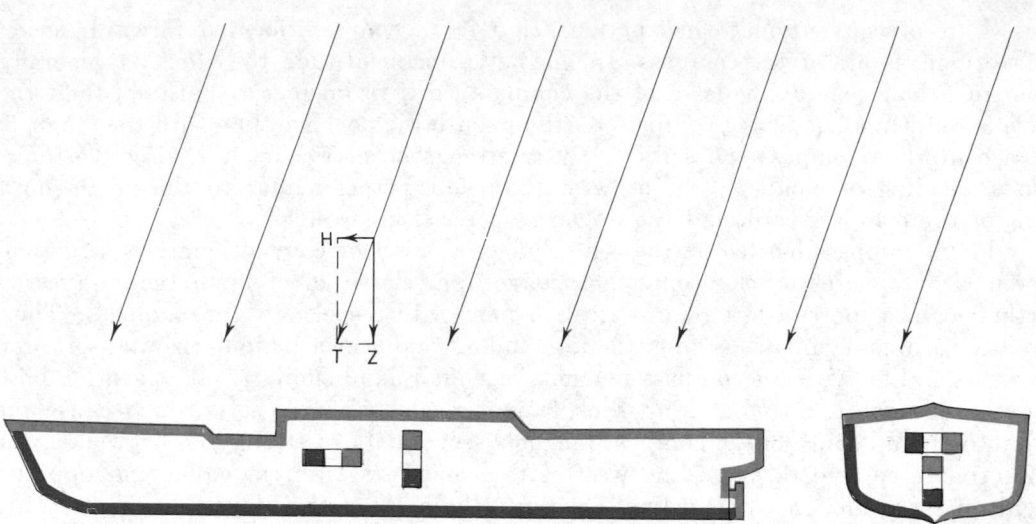

FIGURE 712.—Permanent magnetism of a vessel built on heading magnetic north (left) and magnetic east (right) at a place where the magnetic dip is 70°N.

moored on a constant heading, or during a run of several days on nearly the same heading. This change is gradual and affects the strength, but usually not the polarity, of the magnetic field. The permanent field may be changed quickly, in polarity as well as in strength, if the vessel grounds, collides with another vessel, is struck by lightning, undergoes magnetic treatment (art. 742), fires its guns, or is struck by shells or bombs, etc.

The effect that the permanent magnetism of hard iron has upon a compass depends upon the position and strength of the poles relative to the compass. When the poles are in line with the north-south axis of the compass card, the only effect is to strengthen or weaken the directive force of the compass. When the compass heading is approximately 90° away, so that the poles are east and west of the compass, the deviating effect is maximum. The direction of the deviation is the same as that of the blue pole with respect to the compass.

"Soft iron" is all that material in which induced magnetism (art. 701) is present. With respect to its effect upon the magnetic compass, it is classed as either vertical or horizontal. Unlike hard iron, its magnetic field changes quickly as its orientation with respect to the earth's field changes. It also changes as the strength of the earth's field changes. For some purposes induced magnetism can be treated as if it were concentrated in two bars of soft iron, one vertical and the other horizontal. The polarity depends upon the position of the vessel relative to the earth's magnetic field, and the strength depends upon the strength of the vertical and horizontal components of the earth's field. This is illustrated in figure 712. In north magnetic latitude the bottom of the vertical rod has red magnetism and the top has blue magnetism. In south magnetic latitude these are reversed. In both north and south magnetic latitudes the magnetic north end of the horizontal bar has red magnetism, and the magnetic south end has blue magnetism. Thus, whatever the position of the rod, that part in the direction of magnetic north has red magnetism, and that part in the direction of magnetic south has blue magnetism. That is, each end has magnetism opposite to that of the magnetic pole indicated by the direction in which it is pointed.

The effect upon a magnetic compass of the induced magnetism in soft iron depends upon the strength and direction of the field relative to the compass. The cumulative effect of the induced magnetism in vertical soft iron is generally on the centerline of the vessel (if of conventional construction), and for a compass located forward, as on the bridge, is aft of the compass. In magnetic north latitude the effect is generally that of a blue pole at the level of the compass card. In magnetic south latitude the pole is red. On a heading of compass north or south the pole is in line with the magnets of a centerline compass and serves only to strengthen or weaken the directive force. On a heading of compass east or west the pole is perpendicular to the north-south axis of the compass card, and the deviating force is greatest.

For a compass located on the centerline of a vessel of conventional construction, the horizontal soft iron close enough to have appreciable effect upon the compass is arranged in a more-or-less symmetrical manner with respect to the compass. Thus, on any cardinal compass heading, the fore-and-aft and athwartship horizontal soft iron is either in line with the compass magnets or equally and similarly arranged on both sides. No error is introduced by such symmetrical horizontal soft iron because the iron north and south of the compass magnets serves only to strengthen or weaken the directive force, and that east and west of the compass sets up an equal and opposite field on each side. On intercardinal headings, the poles of the induced magnetism are offset and a maximum deviating force occurs. That part of horizontal soft iron which is not symmetrically arranged with respect to the compass—the asymmetrical soft iron—produces deviation which is maximum on the cardinal headings and zero on the intercardinal headings (by compass). This type of deviation is particularly great in a compass not mounted on the centerline of the vessel. It may also produce deviation which is constant on all headings.

In wooden-hulled vessels such as certain yachts and small fishing vessels, one or more of these types of magnetism may be weak or entirely missing, but this does not justify the omission of any part of the correction procedure.

As far as its effect upon the compass is concerned, the magnetic field at a centerline compass located forward on a vessel of conventional construction, and on an even keel, is essentially the same as that which would result from four sources: (1) the earth's magnetism; (2) a single blue pole the location and strength of which depends upon the magnetic history of the vessel; (3) a single pole which is blue in north magnetic latitude and red in south magnetic latitude, is on the centerline aft of the compass, and increases in strength with higher magnetic latitude; and (4) a single blue pole on the starboard side for easterly headings and on the port side for westerly headings, being of zero strength on a heading of north or south and decreasing in strength with increased magnetic latitudes. The single pole concept assumes that the effect of one pole predominates. The locations of the poles depend partly upon the position of the compass to which they apply. The actual field surrounding any magnetic compass may be considerably more complex than indicated.

713. Compass adjustment.—There are at least two possible solutions to the problem of compass error. The error can be permitted to remain, and the various directions interconverted by means of variation and deviation, or compass error, as explained in article 711; or the error can be removed. In practice, a combination of both of these methods is used.

Variation depends upon location of the vessel, and the navigator has no control over it. Provision could be made for offsetting the lubber's line, but this would not be effective in correcting magnetic compass bearings, and this practice is not generally followed. Variation does not affect the operation of the compass itself, and so is not objectionable from this standpoint.

Deviation is undesirable because it is more troublesome to apply, and the magnetic field which causes it partly neutralizes the directive force acting upon the compass, causing it to be unsteady and sluggish. As the vessel rolls and pitches, or as it changes magnetic latitude, the magnetic field changes, producing a corresponding change in the deviation of an unadjusted compass.

Deviation is eliminated, as nearly as practicable, by introducing at the compass a magnetic field that is equal in magnitude and opposite in polarity to that of the vessel. This process is called **compass adjustment,** or sometimes **compass compensation,** although the latter designation is now more generally applied to the process of neutralizing the effect due to degaussing of the vessel (art. 745).

In general, the introduced field is of the same kind of magnetism as well as of the same intensity as those of the field causing deviation. That is, permanent magnets are used to neutralize permanent magnetism, and soft iron to neutralize induced magnetism, so that the adjustment remains effective with changes of heading and magnetic latitude. A relatively small mass of iron near the compass introduces a field equal to that of a much larger mass at a distance.

When a compass is properly adjusted, its remaining or **residual deviation** is small and practically constant at various magnetic latitudes, the directive force is as strong as is obtainable on all headings, and the compass returns quickly from deflections and is comparatively steady as the vessel rolls and pitches.

714. Effect of latitude.—As indicated in article 706, the magnetic field of the earth is horizontal at the magnetic equator, and vertical at the magnetic poles, the change occurring gradually as a vessel proceeds away from the magnetic equator. At any place the relative strength of the horizontal and vertical components depends upon the magnetic dip. The directive force of a magnetic compass, provided by the horizontal component of the earth's magnetic field, is maximum on or near the magnetic equator and gradually decreases to zero at the magnetic poles. Within a certain area surrounding each magnetic pole the directive force is so weak that the compass is unreliable (art. 2513).

Deviation changes with a change of the relative strength of either the deviating force or the directive force. Thus, with *either* an increase in deviating force or a decrease in directive force, the deviation increases. However, if both the deviating and directive forces change by the same proportion, and with the same sign, there is no change in deviation. Also, if a deviating force is neutralized by an equal and opposite force *of the same kind*, there is no change of deviation with a change of magnetic latitude.

Permanent magnetism is the same at any latitude. If the permanent magnetism of the vessel is neutralized by properly placed permanent magnets of the correct strength, a change of magnetic latitude can be made without introduction of deviation. But if residual deviation due to permanent magnetism is present, it increases with a change to higher latitude. The deviating force remains unchanged while the directive force decreases, resulting in an increase in the relative strength of the deviating force.

As magnetic latitude increases, the vertical component of the earth's magnetic field becomes stronger, increasing the amount of induced magnetism in vertical soft iron. At the same time the directive force of the compass decreases. Both effects result in increased deviation unless the deviating force is neutralized by induced magnetism in vertical soft iron.

As magnetic latitude increases, the induced magnetism in the horizontal soft iron decreases in the same proportion as the decrease in the directive force of the compass, since both are produced by the horizontal component of the earth's magnetic field. Therefore, any deviation due to this cause is the same at any latitude.

715. Parameters.—Compass adjustment might be accomplished by locating the pole of each magnetic field, and establishing another pole of opposite polarity and equal intensity at the same place, or of less intensity and nearer to the compass; or a pole of opposite polarity and suitable intensity might be established at the correct distance on the opposite side of the compass. Thus, a blue pole east of a compass attracts the red northern ends of the compass magnets and repels the blue southern ends. Both effects cause rotation of the compass magnets and the attached compass card in a clockwise direction, producing easterly deviation. Either a red pole east of a compass, or a blue pole west of it, causes westerly deviation. If there are two fields of opposite polarity, one will tend to neutralize the other. If the intensities of the two fields are equal at the compass, one will cancel the other, and no deviation occurs.

Because of the complexities of the magnetic field of a vessel, and the fact that each individual field making up the total is present continuously, the process of isolating individual poles would be a difficult and time-consuming one. Fortunately, this is unnecessary. The vessel's field is resolved into certain specified components. Each of these components, regardless of its origin or the number of individual fields contributing to it, can be neutralized separately. Each component is called a **parameter,** and the various parameters are designated by letter, as follows:

Permanent magnetism. **Parameter P** is the fore-and-aft component. It is positive $(+)$ if it is the equivalent of a blue pole forward of the compass, and negative $(-)$ if red.

Parameter Q is the athwartship component. It is positive if it is the equivalent of a blue pole to starboard.

Parameter R is the vertical component. It is positive if it is the equivalent of a blue pole below the compass.

Induced magnetism has nine parameters, each the equivalent of that produced by a slender rod of soft iron. Each *end* of a rod is positive if it is forward, to starboard, or below the compass. Each rod is positive if both ends are positive or if both ends are negative, and negative if the two ends are of opposite sign. The rods are as follows:

a, b, c—one end level with the compass and in its fore-and-aft axis, either forward or aft. It is an a rod if it extends fore-and-aft, a b rod if athwartships, and a c rod if vertical.

d, e, f—one end level with the compass and in its athwartships axis, either to starboard or to port. It is a d rod if it extends fore-and-aft, an e rod if athwartships, and an f rod if vertical.

g, h, k—one end in the vertical axis of the compass, either above it or below it. It is a g rod if it extends fore-and-aft, an h rod if athwartships, and a k rod if vertical.

716. Coefficients.—Deviation which is easterly throughout approximately 180° of heading and westerly throughout the remainder is called **semicircular deviation,** indicating that its sign remains unchanged throughout a semicircle. Deviation caused by permanent magnetism and that caused by induced magnetism in vertical soft iron are semicircular. Deviation which changes sign in each quadrant, being easterly in two opposite quadrants and westerly in the other two, is called **quadrantal deviation.** It is caused by induced magnetism in horizontal soft iron. The types of deviation resulting from the various parameters are called coefficients. There are six, as follows:

Coefficient A is constant on all headings. If its cause is magnetic, as from an asymmetrical combination of parameters, it is a "true" constant. If its cause is mechanical, as from an incorrectly placed lubber's line, or mathematical, as from an error in computation of magnetic azimuth, it is an "apparent" constant.

Coefficient B is semicircular deviation which is proportional to the sine of the compass heading. It is maximum on compass headings east or west, and zero on compass headings north or south. Coefficient B is caused by permanent magnetism, and also by induced magnetism in asymmetrical vertical soft iron.

Coefficient C is semicircular deviation which is proportional to the cosine of the compass heading. It is maximum on compass headings north or south, and zero on compass headings east or west. Coefficient C is caused by permanent magnetism or by induced magnetism in asymmetrical vertical soft iron athwartship of the compass.

Coefficient D is quadrantal deviation which is proportional to the sine of twice the compass heading. It is maximum on intercardinal compass headings, and zero on cardinal compass headings. Coefficient D is caused by induced magnetism in horizontal soft iron which is symmetrical with respect to the compass.

Coefficient E is quadrantal deviation which is proportional to the cosine of twice the compass heading. It is maximum on cardinal compass headings, and zero on intercardinal compass headings. Coefficient E is caused by induced magnetism in horizontal soft iron which is asymmetrical with respect to the compass.

Coefficient J is the change of deviation for a heel of 1° while the vessel is on compass heading 000°

The determination and use of the approximate coefficients in the analysis of compass deviation are discussed in article 727. The force components producing these coefficients are called **exact coefficients.** They are designated by the corresponding upper case German letters. The exact coefficients are now little used in practical navigation. They are fully discussed in various books on compass adjustment.

717. Effect of compass location.—The location of a magnetic compass greatly influences the amount and type of deviation, as well as the adjustment. Thus, if a compass is on the centerline, forward, the effective pole of vertical soft iron is aft of it; but if the compass is on the afterpart of the vessel, the effective pole is forward. If the compass is not on the centerline, as the steering compass of an aircraft carrier, the magnetic field of the vessel is not symmetrical with respect to the compass. If a compass is located in a steel pilot house, the surrounding metal acts as a shield and reduces the strength of the magnetic field of the earth. This is of particular significance in high magnetic latitudes, where the directive force is weak.

Many factors influence the selection of a position for the compass. The most important consideration is the use to be made of it. A steering compass is of little use unless it is located so that it can be seen by the steersman. A compass to be used for emergency steering should be at the emergency steering station. A compass to be used for observing bearings or azimuths, or a standard compass to be used for checking other compasses, should be located so as to have a clear view in most directions.

However, some choice is possible. A compass should not be placed off the centerline if it can be placed on the centerline and still serve its purpose. It should not be placed near iron or steel equipment that will frequently be moved, if this can be avoided. Thus, a location near a gun, boat davit, or boat crane is not desirable. The immediate vicinity should be kept free from sources of deviation—particularly those of a changing nature—if this can be done. That is, no source of magnetism, other than the structure of the vessel, should be permitted within a radius of several feet of the magnetic compass. Some sources which might be overlooked are electric wires carrying direct current; magnetic instruments, searchlights, windshield wipers, electronic equipment, or motors; steel control rods, gears, or supports associated with the steering apparatus; fire extinguishers, gas detectors, etc.; and metal coat hangers, flashlights, keys, pocketknives, metal cap devices, or nylon clothing. The effect of some items such as an ammeter or electric windshield wiper varies considerably at different times. If direct current is used to light the compass, the wires should be twisted.

A magnetic compass cannot be expected to give reliable service unless it is properly installed and protected from disturbing magnetic influences.

718. The binnacle.—The compass is housed in a **binnacle.** This may vary from a simple wooden box to an elaborate device of bronze or other nonmagnetic material. Most binnacles provide means for housing or supporting the various objects used for compass adjustment, as well as the equipment for compensating for deviation caused by degaussing. The standard binnacle for the U. S. Navy 7½-inch compass is shown in

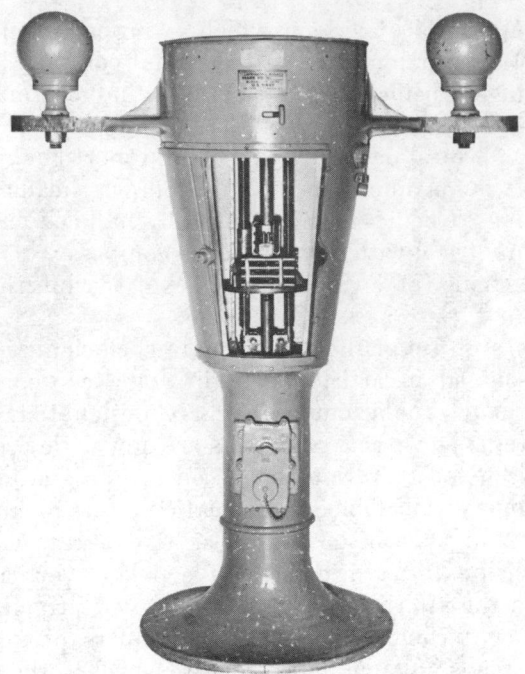

FIGURE 718.—The standard binnacle for a U. S.
Navy 7½-inch compass.

figure 718. The trays for holding the fore-and-aft and athwartship magnets (art. 719), and the tube for the heeling magnet (art. 724), can be seen through the open door.

719. Adjustment for deviation due to permanent magnetism.—Permanent magnetism can be considered concentrated in a single pole, the position of which depends upon the magnetic heading upon which the vessel was constructed, and the subsequent magnetic history of the vessel. Figure 719a indicates the condition if the permanent magnetism can be considered concentrated in a single blue pole which is directly south of the compass when the vessel is headed magnetic northeast. The only effect on this heading is to weaken the directive force. No deviation is produced because the pole is in line with the compass magnets. On heading magnetic southwest, the pole is also in line with the compass magnets and there is no deviation, but the directive force is strengthened. On any other heading, the pole is not in line with the compass magnets, and deviation occurs, being in the same direction as that of the blue pole from the compass, since the blue pole attracts the red northerly ends of the compass magnets and repels the blue southerly ends. The maximum effect occurs when the *compass* heading is approximately 90° from that of zero deviation. In figure 719a the headings shown on the compass card are the magnetic headings of the vessel. Their offset from the lubber's line shows the direction and relative magnitude of deviation.

If there were no other magnetism in the vessel, the poles might easily be located and neutralized by placing a magnet in such a position that a field of permanent magnetism but opposite polarity would occur at the compass. Although this method of adjustment has been used, it has not proven entirely satisfactory.

The usual method is to adjust for the fore-and-aft (parameter P) and athwartship (parameter Q) components separately. These are shown in figure 719b. The vertical parameter R does not produce deviation while the vessel is on an even keel. Its effect when the vessel heels is discussed in article 724. Thus, the effect of a single blue pole at the position shown in figure 719a is the same as that which would be produced by two

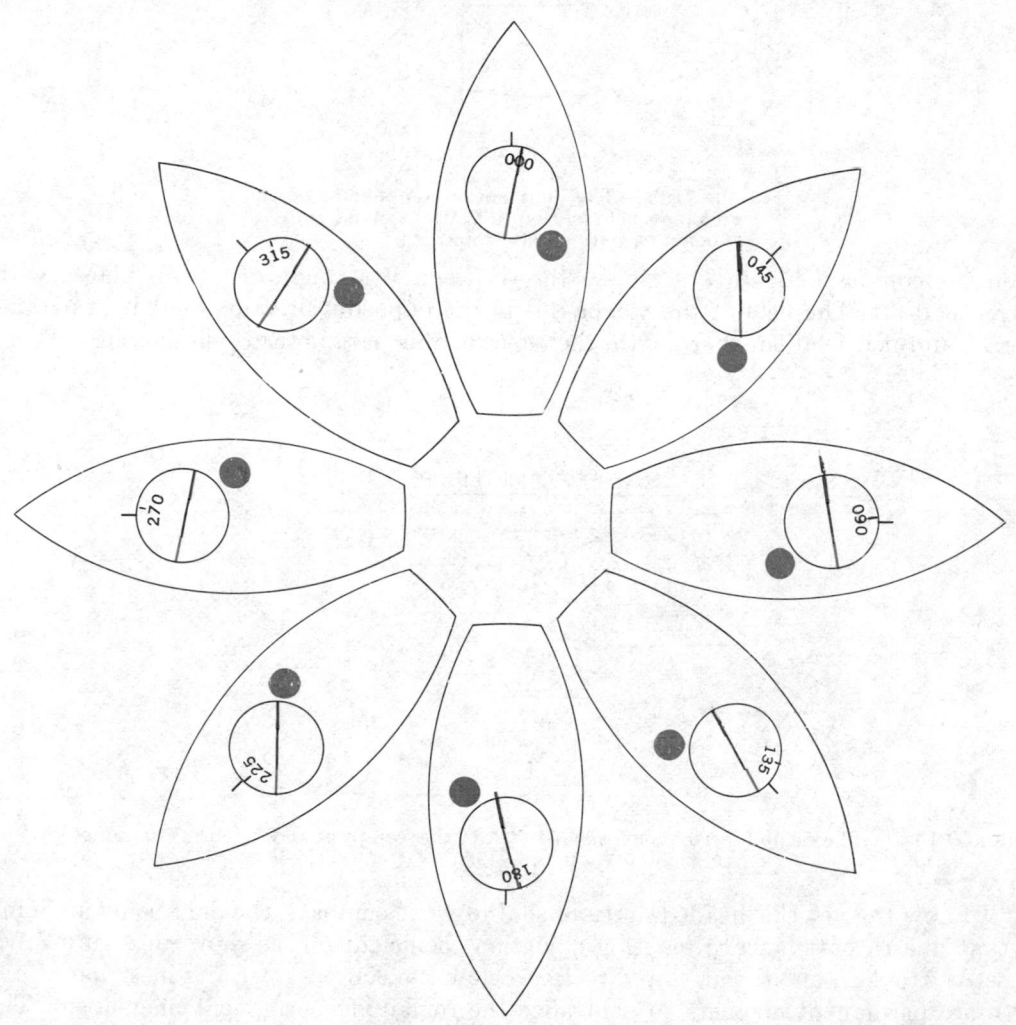

FIGURE 719a.—Deviation due to permanent magnetism if the resultant field is that of a blue pole on the starboard quarter of the vessel.

weaker poles as shown in figure 719b. On heading east or west by the compass, parameter Q does not produce deviation directly. However, on easterly headings it does weaken the directive force due to the earth's magnetic field and therefore the deviating force of parameter P (causing deviation coefficient B) is relatively stronger and has a greater deviating effect. On a westerly heading the directive force would be strengthened, with a corresponding decrease in the B coefficient of deviation. By weakening the directive force on easterly headings, parameter Q also makes the compass sluggish on these headings. In high latitudes, where the horizontal component of the earth's magnetic field is weak, the compass may lose its directivity at a greater distance from the magnetic pole. Nearer the pole, it might point in the opposite direction.

Many binnacles provide a group of several small tubes or "trays" extending in a fore-and-aft direction below the compass. One or more permanent magnets can be inserted in these trays, and the whole assembly moved up or down to vary the effect

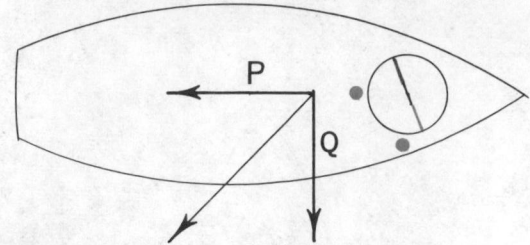

FIGURE 719b.—The horizontal component of the
permanent field of figure 719a resolved into its
components, parameters *P* and *Q*.

upon the compass. Figure 719c shows the situation if a single magnet is placed with
its red end aft. The field at the compass is in the opposite direction of that of parameter *P*, and if it is of equal strength, the effect of this parameter is eliminated.

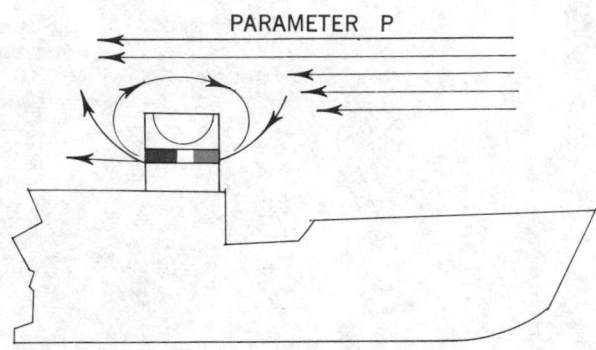

FIGURE 719c.— The field of permanent magnet below the compass and opposing parameter *P* of
figure 719b.

If now the vessel is headed north or south by the compass, the only pole remaining
is that due to parameter *Q* (causing deviation coefficient *C*), as shown in figure 719d.
A set of trays in an athwartship direction below the compass permits insertion of one
or more permanent magnets to neutralize the remaining permanent magnetism. The
effect of inserting a single magnet with red end to starboard is shown in figure 719e.
With both components removed, the field at the compass is completely neutralized.

Both the fore-and-aft (*B*) and athwartship (*C*) trays are in pairs with an equal
number of trays on each side of the vertical axis of the compass. In each set of trays
it is generally desirable to use an *even* number of magnets equally distributed on each
side, to produce a symmetrical field at the compass. However, under some conditions,
maximum reduction of deviation occurs with an *odd* number of magnets, particularly
when two magnets at maximum distance from the compass overcorrect. If there is
a choice, a greater number of magnets at a distance is preferable to a lesser number
close to the compass.

With each parameter, the trays to use are those which are approximately perpendicular to the compass magnets. The magnets are placed so that the red ends will
be on that side of the compass corresponding to the deviation. Thus, if deviation is
easterly, the magnets should be placed so that the red ends will be east of the compass
(forward if the heading is east, and to starboard if the heading is north). However,
if the wrong end is inserted in the trays, the fact will be immediately apparent because the compass card will rotate in the wrong direction. If the binnacle is not constructed to receive appropriate corrector magnets, these might be secured to some
supporting surface near the compass.

During adjustment, the unused magnets should be kept far enough from the compass so that they will not affect it.

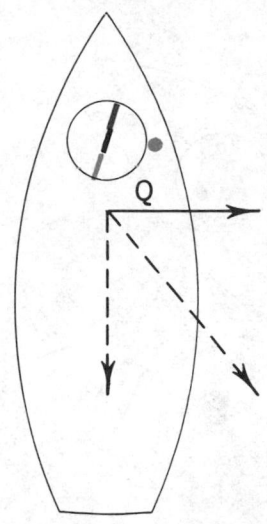

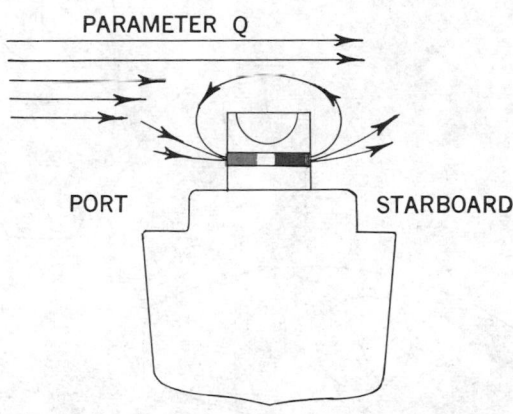

FIGURE 719e.—The field of a permanent magnet below the compass and opposing parameter *Q* of figure 719b.

FIGURE 719d.—The permanent field of figure 719a after neutralization of parameter *P*.

720. Adjustment for deviation due to induced magnetism in vertical soft iron.— Figure 720 shows the effect upon the compass of a single blue pole on the centerline of the vessel, aft of the compass. This is a typical situation for induced magnetism in vertical soft iron, for a centerline compass located in the forward part of a vessel in magnetic north latitude. On heading north by compass there is no deviating force, but the directive force is weakened. In high northern latitudes, where this pole becomes strong and the directive force becomes weak, magnetism of this type, if not neutralized, can cause the compass to be unreliable in a much larger area than if the force is neutralized. On a heading of south by compass there is no deviation, but the directive force is strengthened. On headings with an easterly component the deviation is westerly, and on headings with a westerly component the deviation is easterly. In each case the maximum occurs when the vessel is on compass heading approximately east or west. Thus, the deviation due to induced magnetism in vertical soft iron is semicircular, coefficient *B*. In figure 720 the headings shown on the compass card are the magnetic headings of the vessel. Their offset from the lubber's line shows the direction and relative magnitude of deviation.

The deviating force due to induced magnetism in vertical soft iron is neutralized by placing a bar of soft iron in a vertical position on the opposite side of the compass from the effective pole due to the field of the vessel. This piece of metal is called a **Flinders bar,** after Captain Matthew Flinders, RN (1774–1814), an English navigator and explorer who is generally given credit for discovering both the effect and method of adjustment (art. 111). Today, most binnacles for large ships provide a tube for insertion of a Flinders bar. The bar consists of various lengths of soft iron placed end to end; with the remainder of the tube being filled with spacers of nonmagnetic material, usually wood, brass, or aluminum. The standard Flinders bar is two inches in diameter and is divided into six sections, one each of 12, 6, 3, and 1½ inches, and two of ¾ inch. This permits use of any multiple of ¾ inch to 24 inches. All the iron pieces should be above the spacers in the tube, without a gap between pieces, the largest piece

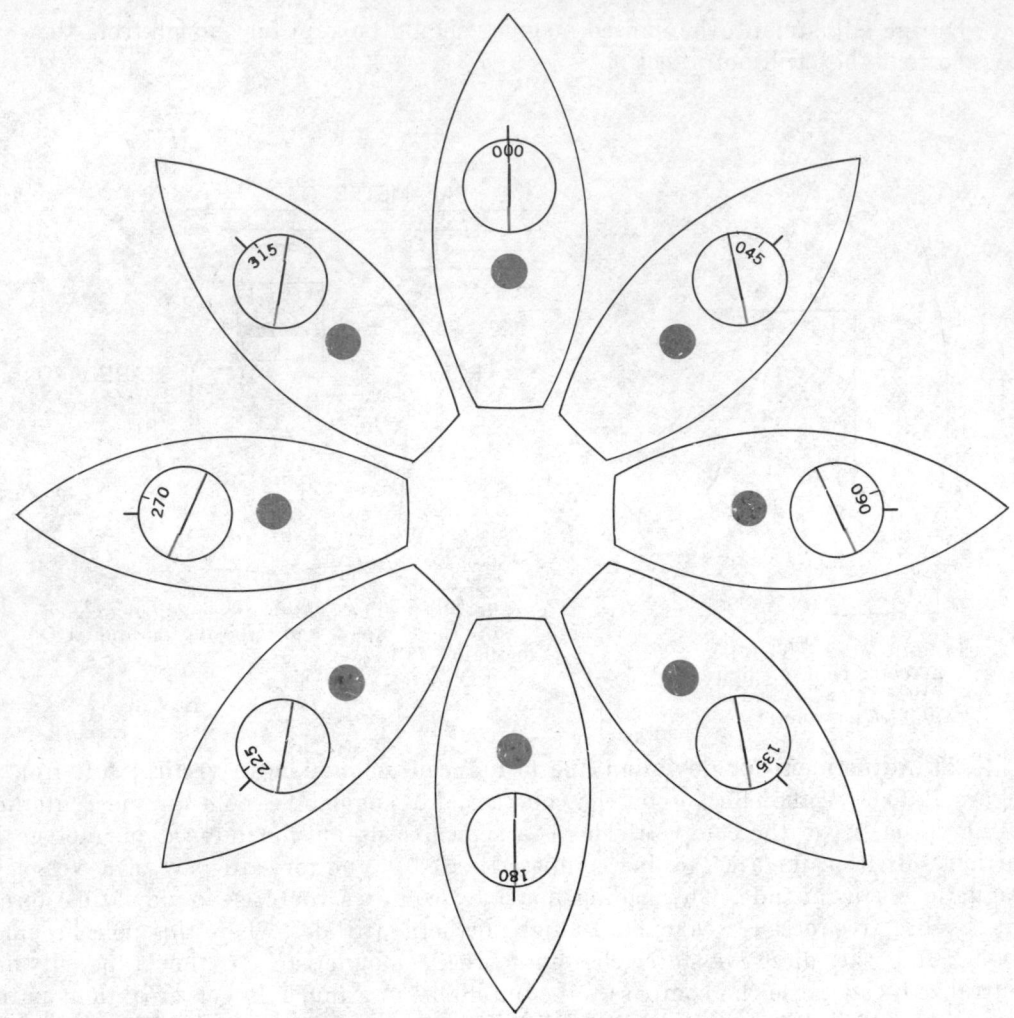

FIGURE 720.—Deviation due to induced magnetism in vertical soft iron if the resultant field is that of a blue pole on the center line aft of the compass.

being on top. The upper end is then about two inches above the level of the compass card. For short lengths, one or more spacers should be omitted so that about $\frac{1}{12}$ of the length of the bar is above the level of the compass card.

The various pieces should be inserted in the tube carefully. If they are dropped, they may acquire some permanent magnetism. This reduces their effectiveness for the purpose intended. Each piece should be tested from time to time to determine whether or not it has acquired permanent magnetism. This can be done by holding it vertical with one end east or west of the compass and very near the compass magnets, noting the reading of the compass, and then inverting the piece so that the ends are interchanged. If the reading differs, permanent magnetism has been acquired by the iron rod. The temporary change of reading while the rod is being inverted should be ignored. In making the test, one should be careful to place the rod in the same position relative to the compass before and after inversion. On an easterly or westerly heading the Flinders bar holder can be used. A small amount of permanent magnetism can be removed by holding the rod approximately parallel to the lines of force of the earth's field, with the blue pole of the rod toward the north, and tapping one end of the rod gently with a hammer. Several alternate tests and treatments may be needed to make the rod magnetically neutral. If this process is not effective in removing the permanent magnetism, the rod should be heated to a dull red and allowed to cool slowly.

An older type Flinders bar, rarely encountered with modern compasses, consists of a number of slender rods of equal length, the *number* of rods being varied rather than the length of a single rod. Another old system consists of using a single rod of fixed length, and varying its distance from the compass.

721. Determination of Flinders bar length.—As indicated in articles 719 and 720, coefficient B magnetism may be introduced both by permanent magnetism of the vessel and by induced magnetism in asymmetrical vertical soft iron. A problem thus arises as to what part of the deviation on headings magnetic east and west is due to each cause. If the vessel remains on an even keel at about the same magnetic latitude, adjustment can be made without this knowledge. However, satisfactory performance under all conditions requires separate adjustment for each cause.

There are several possible solutions to this problem. The two sources can be separated by use of the fact that a change of magnetic latitude affects them differently. On the magnetic equator there is no vertical component of the earth's magnetic field, and consequently no induced magnetism in vertical soft iron. Therefore, if the compass is adjusted on the magnetic equator, all coefficient B deviation is due to permanent magnetism, and is removed by the fore-and-aft magnets. After a considerable change of magnetic latitude, the deviation on a heading of magnetic east or west is again measured. By means of the curves of figure 721, A, the required amount of standard two-inch Flinders bar is determined. Accurate results will be obtained only if the vessel is magnetically the same at both latitudes. That is, a structural change, an alteration in the number or position of magnets or other devices used in the adjustment, magnetic treatment, etc., invalidates the measurement. After the required amount of Flinders bar has been inserted, some deviation may be present due to mutual induction among the various devices used for adjustment. This should be removed by means of the permanent magnets. Once the correct amount of Flinders bar has been installed, no change should be needed unless there is a substantial change in the amount or location of vertical soft iron, or unless the compass is relocated.

This method is not always practical. If the correct length and location of Flinders bar for another vessel of similar construction and compass location have been determined previously, the same length can be used for the compass being adjusted. If a large change in magnetic latitude can be made without appreciable change of deviation on headings east and west, the amount of Flinders bar is correct. If the deviation changes, readjustment is needed. By studying the structure of the vessel, an experienced compass adjuster may be able to make a reasonably accurate estimate of the length to use.

In the absence of enough reliable information to permit a reasonably accurate determination of the correct length, the Flinders bar may be omitted entirely, and the deviation on east and west headings removed by means of the fore-and-aft permanent magnets. This is common practice for yachts, fishing vessels, and even for some coastal vessels which do not change magnetic latitude more than a few degrees.

The correct length of Flinders bar can be determined by figure 721, B, if reliable data are available on the deviation occurring on magnetic east or west headings at two widely separated magnetic latitudes. The constant K is determined by computation, using the formula

$$K = \lambda \, \frac{H_2 \tan d_2 - H_1 \tan d_1}{Z_2 - Z_1}$$

in which

K=a constant proportional to the required length of Flinders bar.

λ=shielding factor, or the proportion of the earth's field effective at the compass. Generally, it varies from about 0.7 to 1.0, averaging about 0.9 for compasses in exposed positions, and 0.8 for those surrounded by metal deck houses.

H_1=horizontal intensity of earth's magnetic field at place of first deviation reading.

H_2=horizontal intensity of earth's magnetic field at place of second deviation reading.

d_1=total deviation on heading magnetic east or west at place of first deviation reading.

d_2=total deviation on heading magnetic east or west at place of second deviation reading.

Z_1=vertical intensity of earth's magnetic field at place of first deviation reading.

Z_2=vertical intensity of earth's magnetic field at place of second deviation reading.

The unit of intensity is the oerstead.

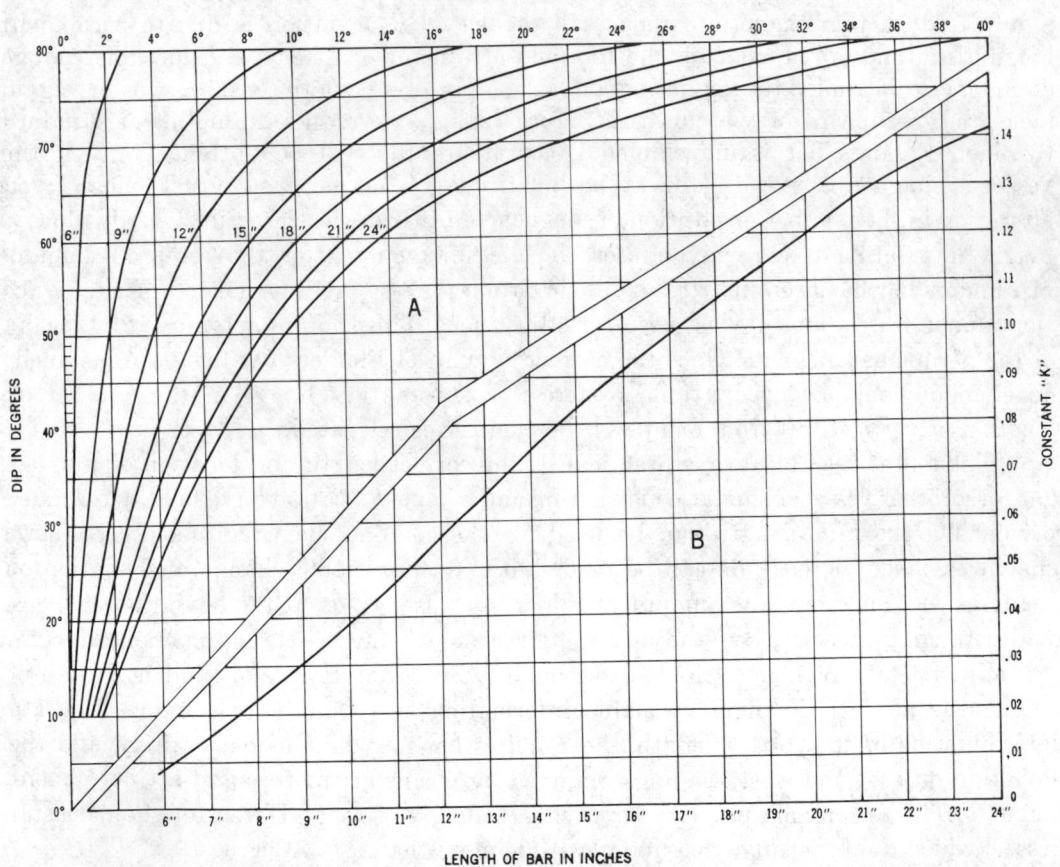

FIGURE 721.—Flinders bar curves: A, if deviation due to induced magnetism in vertical soft iron is known; B, if coefficient K is known.

The values of horizontal and vertical intensity (H and Z) can be obtained from charts 33 and 36, respectively, by dividing the values in gammas (art. 706) as shown on the charts by 100,000.

The constant K represents a mass of vertical soft iron (the c rod) causing deviation. From the intersection of the curve of figure 721, B, and a horizontal line through the value of constant K, draw a vertical line to the bottom scale, which shows the required length of Flinders bar.

If some length of Flinders bar was in place when the two deviation readings were made, enter the graph of figure 721, B, with this length and determine the corresponding value of K. Call this K_2 and that obtained by computation K_1. Algebraically add K_1 and K_2 to determine the value of K to use for finding the total length of Flinders bar required. If the Flinders bar is forward of the compass, K_2 is negative ($-$), and if aft of the compass, K_2 is positive ($+$). In the computation of K_2, both Z_1 and Z_2 are positive in north magnetic latitude and negative in south magnetic latitude. Also, d_1 and d_2 are positive if deviation is east on magnetic heading east in north latitude or magnetic heading west in south latitude. If *either* the heading or direction of the deviation is reversed, the sign of d_1 or d_2 is negative. If both are reversed, the sign is positive. If the value of K is negative, the Flinders bar should be installed forward of the compass, and if positive, it should be installed aft.

Example.—The deviation of a magnetic compass of a ship on heading magnetic east is 1°E in an area where H is 0.170 and Z is 0.539. It is 9°E in an area where H is 0.311 and Z is 0.260. The shielding factor is 0.8.

Required.—The correct length of Flinders bar if (1) no Flinders bar is in place during observations, (2) six inches of Flinders bar is in place forward of the compass during observations.

Solution.—

$$(1) \quad K_1 = 0.8 \left(\frac{0.311 \times 0.15838 - 0.170 \times 0.01746}{0.260 - 0.539} \right)$$

$$= (-)\, 0.133$$

$$K_2 = 0$$

$$K = K_1 + K_2 = (-)\, 0.133$$

From figure 721, B, the correct amount of Flinders bar is 22 inches. Since the amount used must be a multiple of ¾ inch, the amount to use is 21¾ inches. Since K is negative, the bar should be installed forward of the compass.

(2) From figure 721, B, the value of K_2 corresponding to six inches of Flinders bar is 0.009. The value is negative because the bar is forward of the compass. Therefore, $K_1 + K_2 = (-)0.133 + (-)0.009 = (-)0.142$. From figure 721, B, the *total* amount of Flinders bar required is 24 inches, which should be installed forward of the compass.

Answers.—(1) 21¾ inches of Flinders bar installed forward of the compass, (2) 24 inches of Flinders bar installed forward of the compass.

When the length of Flinders bar is determined in this way, accurate results can be expected only if the vessel is magnetically unchanged between deviation readings.

Lord Kelvin suggested the following rule for improving the adjustment for coefficient B if no better method is available:

Remove the deviation observed on magnetic east or west headings by means of fore-and-aft B magnets when the vessel has arrived at places of weaker vertical magnetic field, and by means of Flinders bar when it has arrived at places of stronger vertical magnetic field, whether in the Northern or Southern Hemisphere.

After a number of applications of this rule following alternate passage from weaker to stronger fields and then stronger to weaker fields, the amount of Flinders bar should be very nearly correct.

722. Adjustment for deviation due to induced magnetism in symmetrical horizontal soft iron.—That part of horizontal soft iron which is symmetrically arranged with respect to the compass can be considered equivalent to two rods extending through the compass, one in a fore-and-aft direction ($-a$ rod) and the other in an athwartship direction ($-e$ rod). The deviation caused by both of these rods is quadrantal, but of opposite sign. If both rods were equally effective in causing deviation, they would cancel each other and no deviation would result on any heading. In most vessels, however, the athwartships iron dominates, and deviation due to all horizontal soft iron can generally be considered to be that which would result from a single $(-)$ e rod. In figure 722a the deviation resulting from such a rod is shown for various magnetic

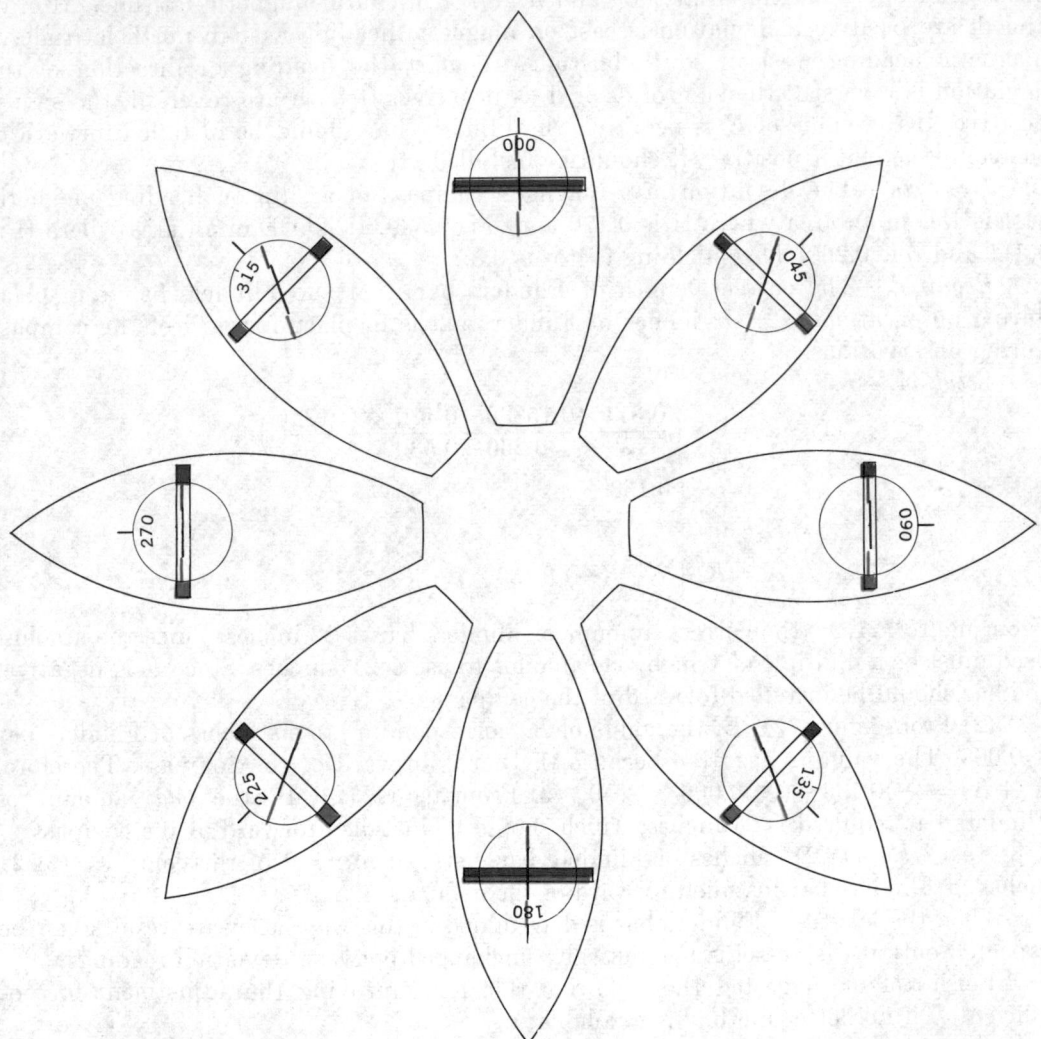

FIGURE 722a.—Deviation caused by induced magnetism in symmetrical horizontal soft iron.

headings in any latitude. There is no deviation on any cardinal heading, but the directive force is weakened on heading magnetic east or west. The maximum deviation occurs on intercardinal headings by compass, being easterly in the northeast and southwest quadrants, and westerly in the other two quadrants. This is coefficient D deviation. In figure 722a the headings shown on the compass card are the magnetic headings of the vessel. Their offset from the lubber's line shows the direction and relative magnitude of deviation.

The field causing this deviation is neutralized by installing two masses of soft iron abeam of the compass, on opposite sides and equidistant from its center. Such iron is usually in the form of hollow spheres or cylinders, called **quadrantal correctors.** These can be moved in or out in an athwartship direction along brackets on the sides of the binnacle.

Quadrantal correctors act as $(+)$ e parameters which neutralize the $(-)$ e parameter of the athwartships iron. As shown in figure 722b, the portion of the corrector adjacent

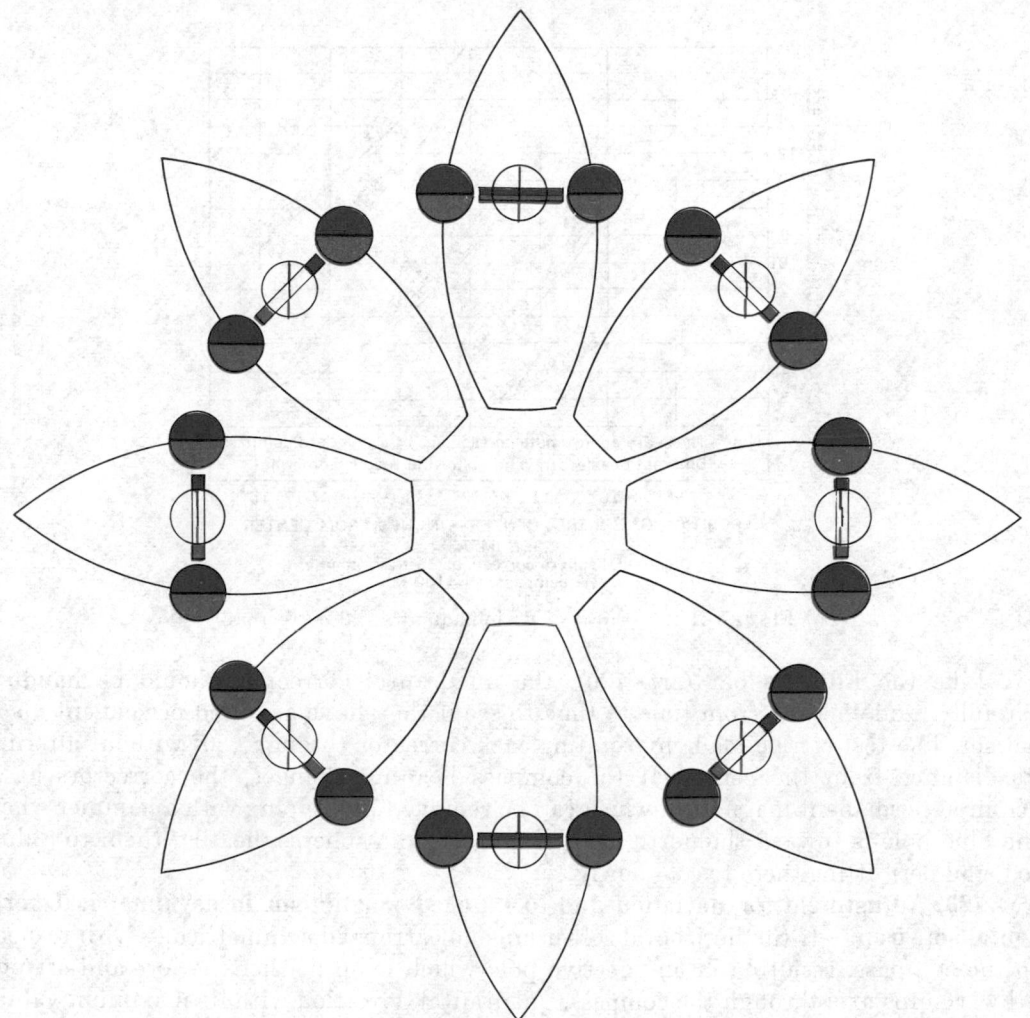

FIGURE 722b.—Adjustment for symmetrical horizontal soft iron.

to the compass is always of opposite polarity to the deflecting force. The amount of the correction can be adjusted by moving the correctors toward or away from the compass card. If the inboard limit of travel is reached without fully removing the deviation, larger correctors are needed. If overcorrection occurs at the outboard limit, smaller correctors are needed. A single corrector can be used, but this produces an unbalanced field which is less desirable than a balanced one. In general, large correctors at a greater distance are preferable to small correctors close up because there is less mutual induction between the correctors if they are widely separated. In the rare case when quadrantal deviation is *westerly* on heading northeast (coefficient D is negative, the fore-and-aft horizontal soft iron predominating), the quadrantal correctors should be mounted fore-and-aft on the binnacle.

Figure 722c shows the approximate amount of deviation correction to be expected from correctors of various sizes, shapes and distance from the center of a standard U. S. Navy 7½-inch compass. The data apply to either the athwartships or fore-and-aft position.

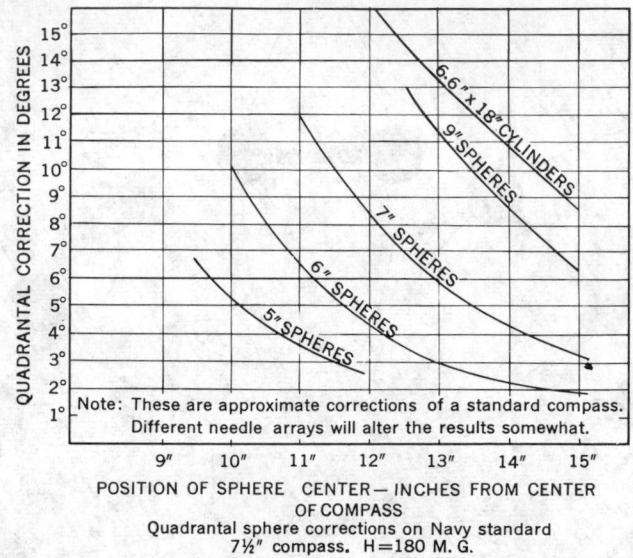

FIGURE 722c.—Effect of various quadrantal correctors.

Like the Flinders bar (art. 720), the quadrantal correctors should be handled carefully, and checked from time to time to see if they have acquired permanent magnetism. The test can be made by rotating each corrector through 180° without altering its distance from the center. If the compass heading changes, the correctors have acquired permanent magnetism which can be removed by tapping with a hammer when the blue pole is toward the north, or by removing the spheres, heating them to a dull red, and permitting them to cool slowly.

723. Adjustment for deviation due to induced magnetism in asymmetrical horizontal soft iron.—If the horizontal soft iron is not arranged symmetrically with respect to the compass, resulting in an effective pole which is on neither the fore-and-aft nor athwartships axis through the compass, quadrantal deviation with its maximum values on cardinal headings (coefficient E) results. Constant deviation (coefficient A) may also be used by this arrangement. Either coefficient E or A is due to a combination of parameters.

For a centerline compass on a ship of conventional construction, any deviation due to induced magnetism in asymmetrical horizontal soft iron is small, and many installations make no provision for neutralizing the effect. However, some binnacles are provided with a pair of **E-links,** which are bars that can be attached to the side brackets to permit the quadrantal correctors to be slewed somewhat with respect to the compass. When this has been done, the horizontal axis through the correctors and the compass makes an angle with the athwartship axis of the compass.

After a compass has been adjusted, any remaining constant deviation due to magnetic coefficient A is likely to be very small. If such deviation exists, its cause is likely to be chiefly mechanical. If a compass is used primarily for determining the heading (as a steering compass), all constant deviation can be removed by realignment of the binnacle so as to rotate the lubber's line by the required amount. However, if a compass is to be used for observing bearings or azimuths, only the mechanical A-error should be removed in this manner. This is because such readings are taken on the face of the card itself, and are therefore not affected by misalignment of the lubber's line. The two components of constant deviation can be separated in the following manner: Measure the deviation on various headings by means of bearings or azimuths (art. 1430). This includes only magnetic coefficient A. Then measure the deviation on various headings by means of the lubber's line, comparing the heading by compass with the magnetic heading determined by pelorus or gyrocompass. This includes the combined effect of magnetic and mechanical coefficient A deviation. The difference between the two values is the mechanical coefficient A. For a properly adjusted compass the magnetic coefficient A deviation is so small that provision is not made for its removal.

724. Heeling error.—All of the effects discussed previously refer to a vessel on an even keel. When the vessel heels, conditions are altered. Deviation which now appears or the *change* of deviation from that when the vessel was on an even keel, is called **heeling error.** For a constant angle of heel and a steady heading, this error remains essentially unchanged. However, it tends to increase as the heel becomes greater, and to reverse sign as the heel changes from one side to another. Therefore, if a vessel is rolling or pitching, the compass tends to oscillate. This increases the difficulty of reading the compass.

The cause of heeling error is the displacement of the permanent and induced magnetic fields with respect to the compass. Figure 724 shows a vessel heeled to star-

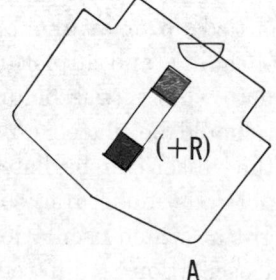 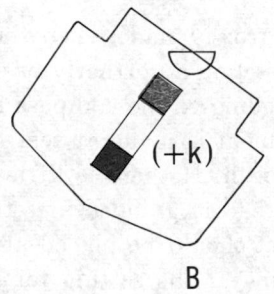 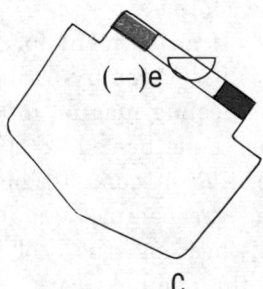

A B C

FIGURE 724.—Effect of heel.

board on heading magnetic north or south, in north magnetic latitude. The vessel was constructed in north magnetic latitude. On an even keel the vertical parameter R of permanent magnetism for a centrally located compass is directly below the compass, with the blue pole nearer the compass. When the vessel is heeled as shown at A, the blue pole is to port of the compass, causing deviation toward that side. A vertical rod of soft iron below the compass (parameter k) exerts a similar influence, as shown at B. An athwartship horizontal rod through the compass has no deviating effect while the vessel is on an even keel, but when it heels as shown in figure 724, the vertical component of the earth's field causes the port end to acquire a blue pole and the starboard end a red pole (parameter e), as shown at C. Each of the three causes shown in figure 724 results in a blue pole being established on the port or high side of the vessel. This causes the red north ends of the compass magnets to be attracted to this side. If the heading is magnetic north, the deviation is westerly, and if magnetic south, it is easterly. This effect is offset somewhat by the changed magnetic field surrounding the quadrantal correctors. On heading magnetic east or west, these components have no deviating effect, but the directive force of the compass is strengthened or weakened. When the vessel pitches, the effects described for north-south and east-west headings are reversed. On a heading other than a cardinal direction (magnetic) the effect is some combination of the two. The magnetic situation varies not only with the heading, but also with the magnetic latitude and the magnetic history of the vessel.

Although heeling error is due in part to permanent magnetism and in part to induced magnetism, the induced magnetism generally exerts the greater influence. The most effective method of neutralizing this effect would be to attack each parameter separately. This would require the placement of soft iron *above* the compass. Since this would not be a convenient arrangement, the condition is improved by placing a vertical permanent magnet, called a **heeling magnet,** centrally *below* the compass, and adjusting its height until the error is minimized. In north magnetic latitude, the red end is placed uppermost in most installations. As the vessel proceeds to lower magnetic latitudes, parameter R becomes less effective in producing deviation because of the stronger directive force due to the horizontal component of the earth's magnetic field. Parameters k and e become weaker because of decreased intensity of the vertical component of the earth's field, and the strengthening of the horizontal component also reduces their effect. Therefore, the heeling magnet requires readjustment as the magnetic latitude changes. As the vessel approaches the magnetic equator, the heeling magnet should be lowered. After the vessel crosses the magnetic equator, it may be necessary to invert the heeling magnets, so that the opposite end is uppermost. A change in the setting of the heeling magnet may introduce deviation on headings of compass east or west because of altered induction between the heeling magnet and the Flinders bar. This should be removed by means of the fore-and-aft (B) magnets in the trays below the compass.

If adjustment for heeling error is made when the vessel is tied up or at anchor, it is best done by listing the vessel on a northerly or southerly heading, and adjusting the heeling magnet until the reading of the compass is restored to what it was before the vessel heeled. If the adjustment is made at sea, the vessel should be placed on a heading of compass north or south. If there is little rolling, the vessel can be listed and the compass reading restored, as at dockside. If the vessel rolls moderately on this heading, the heeling magnet should be placed at that height at which oscillation of the compass card is minimum. If the setting for minimum oscillation is different on north and south headings, the mean position should be used. Any yawing of the vessel should be considered when reading the compass under rolling conditions.

The approximate position of the heeling magnet can be determined by means of an instrument known as a **heeling adjuster** or a **vertical force instrument,** a form of **dip needle.** This consists of a small magnet balanced about a horizontal axis by means of a small adjustable weight. A scale indicates the distance of the weight from the axis. The instrument is taken ashore and balanced at a place where the earth's field is undisturbed, the magnet being in a magnetic north-south direction, approximately. The instrument is then taken aboard ship, the compass removed from its binnacle, and the heeling adjuster installed in its place. The weight is set to a distance equal to the distance determined ashore, multiplied by λ, the shielding factor (art. 721). The heeling magnet is then moved up or down until the magnet of the instrument is level. This should be approximately the correct setting. This method is used principally when the listing of a vessel is difficult or impractical.

725. Soft iron correctors and nearby magnets.—The soft iron correctors used in compass adjustment are near enough to the compass magnets and the magnets used in compass adjustment to be influenced by them.

The Flinders bar acquires a certain amount of induced magnetism from the fields of the heeling magnet and the fore-and-aft (B) corrector magnets. The approximate amount of deviation caused by induced magnetism from the heeling magnet of a 7½-inch compass when H=0.165 is shown in figure 725. Because of such induced mag-

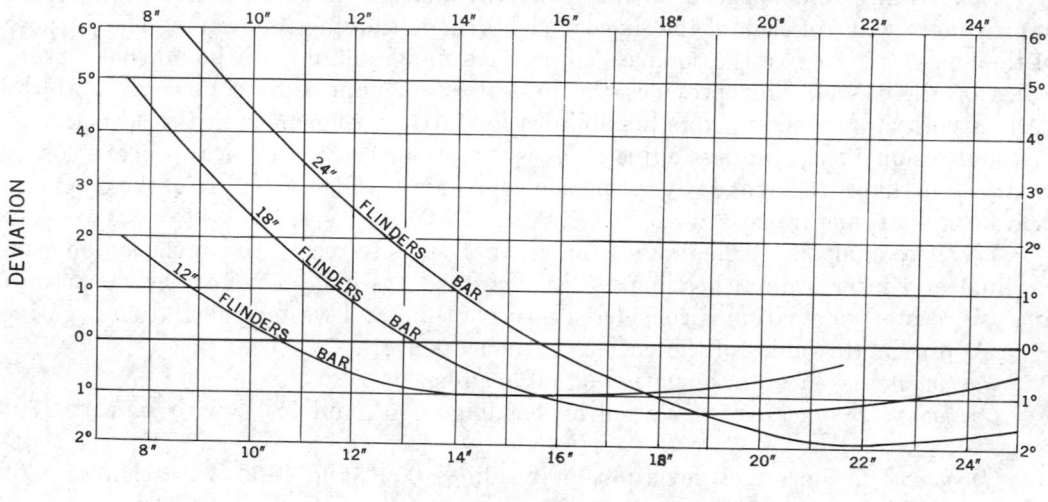

POSITION OF HEELING MAGNET

FIGURE 725.—Deviation due to inductive effect of heeling magnet on Flinders bar.

netism, the "drop-in" method of determining the amount of Flinders bar is not accurate˙ By this method, Flinders bar lengths are added until the compass reading changes by the required amount. Better adjustment is achieved by using the required amount of Flinders bar and removing any remaining deviation on east-west headings by means of the fore-and-aft magnets. The principal reason that it is preferable to use a larger number of magnets at a distance from the compass than a smaller number near it, is that the former arrangement produces less induced magnetism in the Flinders bar and quadrantal correctors. If the Flinders bar length is changed, the deviation on headings of magnetic east and west should be checked, and any needed adjustment made by means of fore-and-aft magnets. When all correctors have been put in place, their positions relative to each other are constant. Therefore, the Flinders bar acts as a permanent magnet, and the resulting deviation is semicircular (coefficient B). The Flinders bar may also introduce a small amount of quadrantal deviation (coefficient D), its action being somewhat like that of a quadrantal corrector placed in the fore-and-aft axis of the compass.

The quadrantal correctors acquire induced magnetism from the fields of the fore-and-aft (B) magnets, the athwartship (C) magnets, and the compass magnets. The magnetism acquired from the B and C magnets is semicircular (coefficient B from the B magnets, and coefficient C from the C magnets), and that acquired from the field of the compass magnets is quadrantal (coefficient D). The semicircular deviation is minimized by keeping the B and C magnets as far away from the quadrantal correctors as practicable, and any deviation that does exist is removed by means of these magnets. The quadrantal deviation is removed by means of the quadrantal correctors themselves. The compass magnets of most modern compasses have little effect upon the quadrantal correctors.

Because of the interaction between the various correctors, it is good practice to insert the required amount of Flinders bar, and to install the quadrantal correctors and heeling magnet at their approximate positions before adjusting the compass. If a radical change is subsequently made in any of these adjustments, the settings of the B and C magnets should be checked and altered if necessary.

Analysis of Deviation

726. Nature and purpose of analysis.—An analysis consists of determining the approximate value of each of the six coefficients, and studying the results. The purpose of the analysis is to give the compass adjuster an understanding of the magnetic properties of the vessel. This provides the basis for the approximate placement of the various correctors, and suggests possibilities for further refinement in the adjustment. Without an analysis, compass adjustment is a more-or-less mechanical process. Fewer mistakes are likely to be made by the person who understands the nature of the magnetic field he seeks to neutralize.

727. The analysis.—The first step in an analysis is to record the deviation on each cardinal and intercardinal heading *by the compass to be analyzed*. For the purpose of analysis, easterly deviation is considered positive (+), and westerly deviation negative (−). Approximate values of the various coefficients are:

Coefficient A—mean of deviation on all headings.

Coefficient B—mean of deviation on headings 090° and 270°, with sign at 270° reversed.

Coefficient C—mean of deviation on headings 000° and 180°, with sign at 180° reversed.

Coefficient D—mean of deviation on intercardinal headings, with signs at headings 135° and 315° reversed.

Coefficient E—mean of deviation on cardinal headings, with signs at 090° and 270° reversed.

Coefficient J—change of deviation for a heel of 1° while the vessel heads 000° by compass. It is considered *positive* if the north end of the compass card is drawn toward the *low* side, and *negative* if toward the *high* side.

Example.—A magnetic compass which has not been adjusted has deviation on cardinal and intercardinal compass headings as follows:

Compass heading	Deviation	Compass heading	Deviation
000°	1°5W	180°	8°0E
045°	34°0E	225°	1°5W
090°	31°0E	270°	29°0W
135°	13°5E	315°	36°0W

On heading compass north the deviation is 13°5W when the vessel heels 10° to starboard.

Required.—The approximate value of each coefficient.

Solution.—

$$A = \frac{-1°5 + 34°0 + 31°0 + 13°5 + 8°0 - 1°5 - 29°0 - 36°0}{8} = (+)2°3$$

$$B = \frac{31°0 + 29°0}{2} = (+)30°0$$

$$C = \frac{-1°5 - 8°0}{2} = (-)4°8$$

$$D=\frac{34\overset{\circ}{.}0-13\overset{\circ}{.}5-1\overset{\circ}{.}5+36\overset{\circ}{.}0}{4}=(+)13\overset{\circ}{.}8$$

$$E=\frac{-1\overset{\circ}{.}5-31\overset{\circ}{.}0+8\overset{\circ}{.}0+29\overset{\circ}{.}0}{4}=(+)1\overset{\circ}{.}1$$

$$J=\frac{-13\overset{\circ}{.}5+1\overset{\circ}{.}5}{10}=(-)1\overset{\circ}{.}2$$

Answers.—A (+) $2\overset{\circ}{.}3$, B (+) $30\overset{\circ}{.}0$, C (−) $4\overset{\circ}{.}8$, D (+) $13\overset{\circ}{.}8$, E (+) $1\overset{\circ}{.}1$, J (−) $1\overset{\circ}{.}2$.

On any compass heading (CH) the deviation (d) from each coefficient acting alone is:

Coefficient A: $d_A=A$
Coefficient B: $d_B=B \sin CH$
Coefficient C: $d_C=C \cos CH$
Coefficient D: $d_D=D \sin 2CH$
Coefficient E: $d_E=E \cos 2CH$
Coefficient J: $d_J=J \cos CH$.

For a vessel on an even keel, the total deviation on any compass heading is the algebraic sum of the deviation due to each of the first five coefficients:

$$d=d_A+d_B+d_C+d_D+d_E=A+B \sin CH+C \cos CH+D \sin 2CH+E \cos 2CH.$$

For the compass of the example given above, the deviation due to each component, and the total, on various headings is:

CH	A	B	C	D	E	d
°	°	°	°	°	°	°
000	+2. 3	0. 0	−4. 8	0. 0	+1. 1	−1. 4
015	+2. 3	+7. 8	−4. 6	+6. 9	+1. 0	+13. 4
030	+2. 3	+15. 0	−4. 2	+12. 0	+0. 6	+25. 7
045	+2. 3	+21. 2	−3. 4	+13. 8	0. 0	+33. 9
060	+2. 3	+26. 0	−2. 4	+12. 0	−0. 6	+37. 3
075	+2. 3	+29. 0	−1. 2	+6. 9	−1. 0	+36. 0
090	+2. 3	+30. 0	0. 0	0. 0	−1. 1	+31. 2
105	+2. 3	+29. 0	+1. 2	−6. 9	−1. 0	+24. 6
120	+2. 3	+26. 0	+2. 4	−12. 0	−0. 6	+18. 1
135	+2. 3	+21. 2	+3. 4	−13. 8	0. 0	+13. 1
150	+2. 3	+15. 0	+4. 2	−12. 0	+0. 6	+10. 1
165	+2. 3	+7. 8	+4. 6	−6. 9	+1. 0	+8. 8
180	+2. 3	0. 0	+4. 8	0. 0	+1. 1	+8. 2
195	+2. 3	−7. 8	+4. 6	+6. 9	+1. 0	+7. 0
210	+2. 3	−15. 0	+4. 2	+12. 0	+0. 6	+4. 1
225	+2. 3	−21. 2	+3. 4	+13. 8	0. 0	−1. 7
240	+2. 3	−26. 0	+2. 4	+12. 0	−0. 6	−9. 9
255	+2. 3	−29. 0	+1. 2	+6. 9	−1. 0	−19. 6
270	+2. 3	−30. 0	0. 0	0. 0	−1. 1	−28. 8
285	+2. 3	−29. 0	−1. 2	−6. 9	−1. 0	−35. 8
300	+2. 3	−26. 0	−2. 4	−12. 0	−0. 6	−38. 7
315	+2. 3	−21. 2	−3. 4	−13. 8	0. 0	−36. 1
330	+2. 3	−15. 0	−4. 2	−12. 0	+0. 6	−28. 3
345	+2. 3	−7. 8	−4. 6	−6. 9	+1. 0	−16. 0

The various components and the total deviation are shown in graphical form in figure 727. Since the various coefficients are only approximated by the method given above, the curve of total deviation found in this way should not be expected to coincide exactly with a curve drawn from values found by measurement on the various headings.

The *shapes* of the curves of figure 727 are typical of those of an unadjusted compass of a large steel ship. However, an analysis of the results indicates the following:

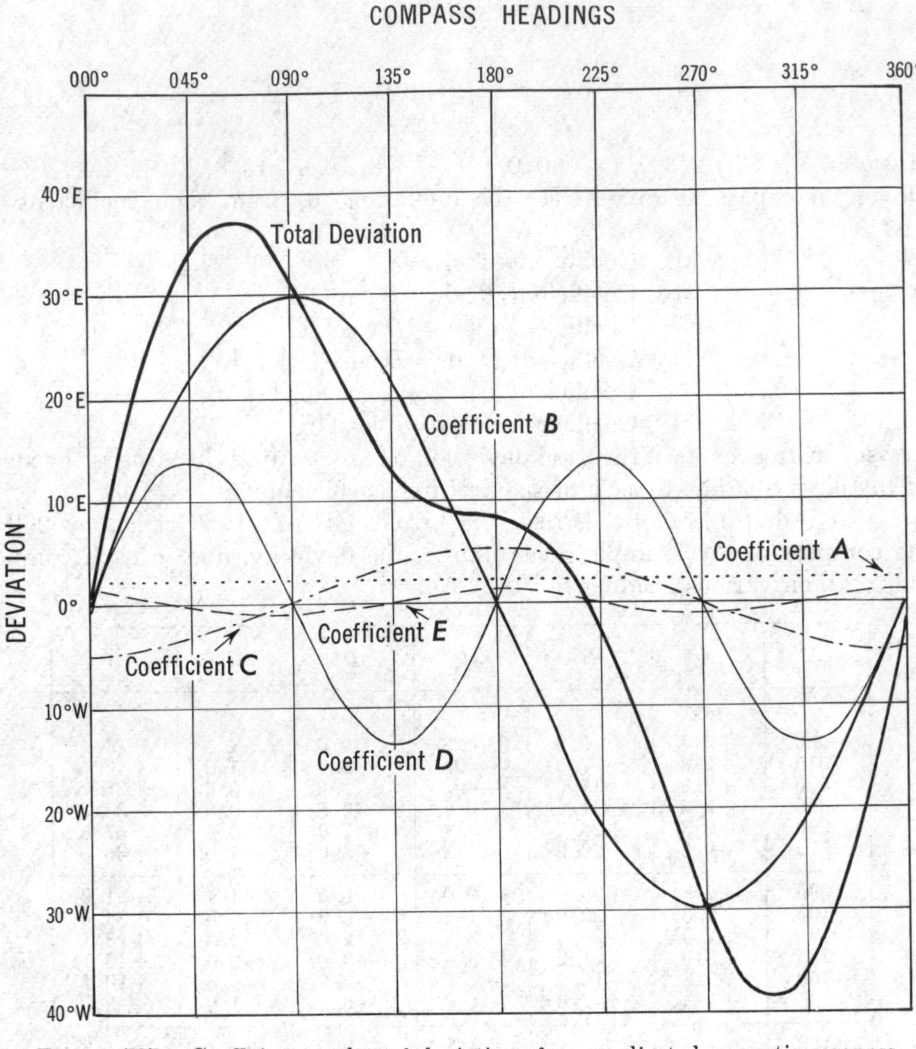

COMPASS HEADINGS

FIGURE 727.—Coefficients and total deviation of an unadjusted magnetic compass.

Coefficient A is normally negligible. The presence of more than 2° of constant error indicates an abnormal condition which should be discovered and corrected. If the vessel has been in service for some time without major structural change, and no misalignment of the lubber's line of the compass or the pelorus or gyrocompass used for measuring deviation has been noted previously, it is probable that a mistake has been made in determining the azimuth or bearing used for establishing deviation.

Coefficient E is normally negligible for a compass located on the centerline of the vessel. This vessel has an excessive amount, which should be corrected by slewing the quadrantal correctors, using an E-link.

Since deviation is east on heading 090° and west on 000°, it is probable that the blue pole of the vessel's permanent field is on the port bow.

The compass being unadjusted, no Flinders bar is in place, and the large B deviation on heading 090° is a combination of deviation from induced magnetism in vertical soft iron and that due to the permanent magnetism of the vessel. Since the deviation on heading 270° is nearly the same as that on 090°, but of opposite sign, adjustment on one of these headings should result in nearly correct adjustment on the other. Since some B and C deviation occurs on intercardinal headings, while no D deviation occurs on cardinal headings, adjustment for B and C should be made before that for final D adjustment.

A second analysis made after adjustment may reveal possibilities for further refinement in the adjustment.

If heeling error is measured on any heading other than compass north or south, the value of coefficient J can be found by means of the formula:

$$d = J \cos CH$$

converted to

$$J = \frac{d}{\cos CH}$$

or

$$J = d \sec CH.$$

If HE is the total observed change of deviation (heeling error), and i is the angle of heel in degrees (for relatively small angles), the formula becomes

$$J = \frac{HE \sec CH}{i}.$$

If heeling error is sought, the formula becomes

$$HE = Ji \cos CH.$$

Adjustment Procedure

728. Preliminary steps.—Efficient and accurate adjustment is preceded by certain preliminary steps best made while a vessel is moored or at anchor.

The magnetic environment of the compass should be carefully inspected. Stray magnetic influences such as those caused by tools, direct current electric appliances, personal equipment (such as keys, pocketknives, or steel belt buckles), nylon clothing etc., should be eliminated. Permanently installed equipment of magnetic material (such as cargo booms, boat davits, cranes, or guns) should be placed in the positions they normally occupy at sea. The degaussing coils should be secured by the reversing process (art. 743) if this has not already been done.

The compass itself should be checked carefully for bubbles, and to be sure it is centered on the vertical axis of the binnacle. If it is, and the vessel is on an even keel, there is no change of reading as the heeling magnet is raised and lowered in its tube. An adjustment should be made to the gimbal rings if the compass is off center. There should be no play in the position of the compass once it is centered.

The lubber's line, too, should be checked to be sure it is in line with the longitudinal axis of the vessel. This can be done by sighting on the jackstaff if the compass is on the centerline. If it is not, a batten might be erected at a distance from the centerline equal to the distance from the center of the compass to the centerline. Another way is to determine the distance from the compass to the centerline and from this point to the jackstaff. The first distance divided by the second is the natural tangent of the angle at the compass between the line of sight to the jackstaff and the line of sight through the lubber's line. If the compass is in an exposed position where bearings can be taken, and the true heading is known, the observed relative bearing of a distant object can be compared with that obtained by careful measurement on the chart. If the vessel is at anchor or underway, the method explained in article 723 can be used.

If a pelorus or gyrocompass or repeater is to be used in determining deviation of the compass, its lubber's line should be checked in the same manner, or by comparing a relative bearing of a distant object taken by two instruments, the lubber's line of one having previously been checked. If a gyrocompass is to be used, it is checked to see that it is synchronized with a repeater. With accurate synchronization, any error in one will also be present in the other. The speed and latitude adjustments of the gyrocompass should be checked carefully.

All devices to be used in the adjustment should be checked to see that they are on hand and in good condition. The trays for B and C permanent magnets, the quadrantal correctors, and heeling magnet should be checked for freedom of motion. The Flinders bar and quadrantal correctors should be checked for permanent magnetism. The correct amount of Flinders bar should be placed in its tube. The quadrantal correctors should be placed in their approximate positions, being centered if no better information is available. The heeling magnet is generally placed with the red end uppermost in north magnetic latitude, and the blue end uppermost in south magnetic latitude. If no better information is available, the heeling magnet should be placed near the bottom of the tube.

Plans for the actual adjustment should be made carefully. A suitable time and location should be selected. If landmarks are to be used, suitable ones should be selected to provide the information desired. Areas of heavy traffic should be avoided. If azimuths of the sun are to be used, a time should be selected when the sun will not be too high in the sky for suitable observation. A curve of magnetic azimuths (art. 731) should be made, and just before adjustment begins a comparing watch should be checked and set, if possible, to correct time. Local variation should be checked carefully, and corrected for date, if necessary. Any necessary recording and work forms should be made up. Each person to participate in the adjustment should be instructed regarding the general plan and his specific duties.

729. Underway procedure.—When everything is in order and the vessel has arrived at its adjusting area, final adjustment can begin. Trim should be normal, and the vessel free from list, so that no heeling error is present.

All adjustment headings should be *magnetic*. Compass headings can be used, but this results in a slight turn being required every time an adjustment is altered. Also, the coefficients are not completely separated unless the vessel is on magnetic headings.

Turns to each new heading should be made slowly, swinging slightly beyond the desired heading before steadying on it. If steering is by gyro, the gyro error should be checked on each heading if time and facilities permit. The vessel should remain on each heading for at least two minutes before the deviation is determined or an adjustment made, to permit the compass card to come to rest and the magnetic condition of the vessel to become settled. If observations are made before the vessel's magnetism becomes settled, the reading will be incorrect by an amount called the **Gaussin error.**

Adjustments should be carried out in the correct order, as follows:

1. Steady on magnetic heading 090° (or 270°) and adjust the fore-and-aft permanent magnets until the compass heading coincides with the magnetic heading, thus removing all coefficient B on this heading. Use magnets in pairs, from the bottom up, with the trays at the lowest point of travel. When overcorrection occurs, remove the two highest magnets and raise the trays until all deviation has been removed. If two magnets overcorrect, use a single magnet. It is not necessary to determine in ad-

vance which direction the red ends should occupy, for a mistake will be immediately apparent by an *increase* in the deviation.

2. Steady on magnetic heading 180° (or 000°) and adjust the athwartship permanent magnets until the compass heading coincides with the magnetic heading, thus removing all coefficient C on this heading. Use the same technique as in step 1.

3. Steady on magnetic heading 270° (090° if 270° was used in step 1) and remove *half* the deviation with the fore-and-aft magnets.

4. Steady on magnetic heading 000° (180° if 000° was used in step 2) and remove *half* the deviation with the athwartship magnets.

5. Steady on any intercardinal magnetic heading and adjust the position of the quadrantal correctors until the compass heading coincides with the magnetic heading, thus removing all coefficient D on this heading. Leave the quadrantal correctors at equal distances from the compass.

6. Steady on either intercardinal magnetic heading 90° from that used in step 5 and remove *half* the deviation by adjusting the positions of the quadrantal correctors, leaving them at equal distances from the compass.

7. Secure all correctors in their final positions and record their number, size, positions, and orientation, as appropriate, on the bottom of the deviation table form (if a standard form such as that shown in fig. 710 is used).

8. **Swing ship** for residual deviation. That is, determine the remaining deviation on a number of headings at approximately equal intervals. Every 15° is preferable, but if the maximum deviation is small, every 45° (cardinal and intercardinal headings) may suffice.

9. If the vessel has degaussing, energize the degaussing coils and repeat the swing.

10. Make a deviation table (art. 710) for each condition (degaussing off and on), giving values for headings at 15° intervals if the maximum deviation is large (more than about 2°), or at 45° intervals if the maximum deviation is small. Record values to the nearest half degree.

If preferred, the adjustment may be started on a north or south heading, thus reversing steps 1 and 2 and also 3 and 4.

With patience and skill, the readings can be made at exact headings. However, if some of the headings are off slightly during the swing, this need not invalidate the results. The exact headings should be recorded, and the deviation determined for these values. The results can then be plotted on cross-section paper with the deviation being one coordinate and the heading the other. The deviation at each heading to be recorded can then be read from the curve. This is good practice even when readings are made at exact headings, for if any large errors have been made, the fact will be immediately apparent. Also, such a curve may be of assistance in making an analysis. If a reason cannot be found for any marked irregularity in the curve, readings might be made again at the headings involved.

The deviation of all compasses aboard the vessel can be determined from a single swing if the heading by each compass is recorded at the moment the magnetic direction is noted. If deviation of one compass is determined by means of a magnetic bearing or azimuth (arts. 733–735), the readings of this compass can then be used to establish the magnetic headings for determining the deviation of each other compass (art. 732).

Compass adjustment is best made when the sea is relatively smooth, so that steady headings can be steered, and heeling error is absent. The setting of the heeling magnet can be checked later, preferably at the next time that the vessel is on a north or south heading and rolling moderately.

An analysis of deviation can be made either before or after adjustment. If this reveals an excessive amount of A (constant) deviation, the source of the error should be found and corrected (art. 723), if mechanical or mathematical. If an appreciable amount of E deviation is present, E-links should be used and the spheres slewed. This is particularly to be anticipated for compasses which are not on the centerline.

The procedure outlined above is for initial adjustment aboard a new or radically modified vessel. Deviation on the heading being used for navigation should be checked from time to time and any important differences from the values shown on the deviation table should be investigated. At sea, it is good practice to compare the magnetic and gyrocompasses at intervals not exceeding half an hour. The error of one or both of these compasses should be checked twice a day when means are available. In pilot waters deviation checks should be made as convenient opportunities present themselves.

Whenever there is reason to question the accuracy of the deviation table, the ship should be swung at the first opportunity and a new table made up if there are significant changes in the old one. Suitable occasions for swinging ship would be after a deviation check indicates a significant error or after any event that might result in changes in the magnetic field of the vessel (art. 712). Intervals of swing should not exceed three months even when there is no reason to question the accuracy of the deviation table.

If a swing indicates the presence of large maximum deviation, the compass should be readjusted. Unless there is reason to change it, the Flinders bar length should remain the same. Other adjustments are altered as needed, none of the correctors being removed at the beginning of adjustment. Whenever the vessel crosses the magnetic equator, the opportunity should be used to check the deviation on magnetic headings east and west. Any adjustment needed should be made by means of the fore-and-aft (B) magnets. Upon crossing the magnetic equator, the heeling magnet should be inverted.

The Flinders bar and quadrantal correctors should be checked for permanent magnetism at intervals of about a year, or more often if such magnetism is suspected.

Finding the Deviation

730. Placing a vessel on a desired magnetic heading.—As indicated in article 729 compass adjustment is best made with the vessel on *magnetic* headings. The compass being adjusted cannot be used for placing the vessel on a desired magnetic heading because its deviation is unknown, and is subject to change during the process of adjustment. A number of methods are available, including use of (1) another magnetic compass of known deviation, (2) a gyrocompass, (3) bearing of a distant object, and (4) azimuth (art. 1430) of a celestial body.

Magnetic compass. The deviation at the desired magnetic heading is determined from the deviation table for that compass, and applied to the magnetic heading to determine the equivalent compass heading.

Example 1.—It is desired to place a vessel on magnetic heading east, using the standard compass. The deviation table for this compass is shown in figure 710. Degaussing is off.

Required.—Heading per standard compass (psc).

Solution.—From figure 710 the deviation on heading 090° magnetic with degaussing off is found to be 2°.5E. Therefore, the equivalent compass heading is 090°−2°.5= 087°.5.

Answer.—H_{psc} 087°.5.

Gyrocompass. The variation is applied to the desired magnetic heading, to determine the equivalent true heading. Any gyro error is then applied to determine the equivalent gyro heading. This is the method commonly used by vessels equipped with a reliable gyrocompass.

Example 2.—It is desired to place a vessel on magnetic heading north, using the gyrocompass. The variation in this area is 6°W, and the gyro error is 1°E.

Required.—Heading per gyrocompass (pgc).

Solution.—The equivalent true heading is $000° - 6° = 354°$. The gyro heading is $354° - 1° = 353°$.

Answer.—H_{pgc} 353°.

Bearing of distant object. If a vessel remains within a small area during compass adjustment, the bearing of a distant object is essentially constant. The required distance of the object in miles is found by multiplying the cotangent of the maximum tolerable error by the *radius* in miles of the maneuvering circle. Thus, if the maximum error that can be tolerated is 0°5 (cotangent 114.6), and the vessel can be maneuvered within 200 yards (0.1 mile) of a fixed position such as a buoy, the object selected should be at least $114.6 \times 0.1 = 11.5$ miles away. The 200-yard limit is within radial lines centered at the distant object and tangent to a circle having a radius of 200 yards and its center at the center of the maneuvering area. Thus, a vessel has considerable maneuvering space along the line of sight, but very limited room across this line. However, it is not necessary that the vessel *stay* within the required area, but only that it be there when readings are made. Thus, if the center of the area is marked by a buoy, the vessel might steady on each heading while still some distance away, and note the required readings as the buoy is passed. In this way, a small radius may be practical even for a large vessel.

The object selected should be conspicuous and should have a clearly defined feature of small visible width upon which to observe bearings. The object having been selected, its true bearing from the center of the maneuvering area should be measured on the chart. To this, the variation *at the center of the maneuvering area* should be applied to determine the equivalent magnetic bearing. The desired magnetic heading should be set at the lubber's line of the pelorus, and the far vane set at the magnetic bearing of the distant object. The vessel should then be maneuvered until the object is in line with the vanes.

Example 3.—It is desired to place a vessel on magnetic heading northeast in an area where the variation is 4°E. The true bearing of a distant object is 219°.

Required.—The setting of the pelorus.

Solution.—Set 045° at the lubber's line, and set the far vane at $219° - 4° = 215°$.

If preferred, 000° can be set at the lubber's line, and the far vane at the relative bearing, 170° (magnetic bearing minus desired magnetic heading). If a gyro repeater or a magnetic compass is used instead of a pelorus, the true (or magnetic) bearing should be converted to the equivalent gyro (or compass) bearing.

If the distant object selected is not charted, or the position of the vessel is not known accurately, the approximate magnetic bearing of the object can be determined by measuring its *compass* bearing on each cardinal and intercardinal compass heading, and finding the mean of these readings. The value so determined will be incorrect by the amount of any constant deviation (coefficient A).

Example 4.—The compass bearings of a distant object are as shown below.

Required.—The magnetic bearing of the object, assuming no constant deviation (coefficient A).

Solution.—

CH	CB
°	°
000	324. 8
045	320. 7
090	312. 6
135	306. 8
180	304. 9
225	310. 8
270	316. 2
315	320. 0
sum	2516. 8
mean	314. 6

*Answer.—*MB 314°.6.

Azimuth of celestial body. The true azimuth of the celestial body selected should be computed (art. 719, vol. II) for the time of observation. The magnetic variation should then be applied to determine the equivalent magnetic azimuth. The desired magnetic heading should then be set at the lubber's line of the pelorus, and the far vane set at the magnetic azimuth of the celestial body. The vessel should then be maneuvered until the body is in line with the vanes.

Example 5.—It is desired to place a vessel on magnetic heading west in an area where the variation is 17°W, and at a time when the computed true azimuth of the sun is 098°.

*Required.—*The setting of the pelorus.

*Solution.—*Set 270° at the lubber's line, and set the far vane at 098°+17°=115°.

If preferred, 000° can be set at the lubber's line, and the far vane at the relative azimuth (magnetic azimuth minus desired magnetic heading). If a gyro repeater or a magnetic compass is used instead of a pelorus, the true (or magnetic) azimuth should be converted to the equivalent gyro (or compass) azimuth.

731. Curve of magnetic azimuths.—During the course of compass adjustment and swinging ship, a magnetic direction is needed many times, either to place the vessel on desired magnetic headings or to determine the deviation of the compass being adjusted. If a celestial body is used to provide the magnetic reference, the azimuth is continually changing as the earth rotates on its axis. Frequent and numerous computations can be avoided by preparing, in advance, a table or **curve of magnetic azimuths.** True azimuths at frequent intervals are computed. The variation at the center of the maneuvering area is then applied to determine the equivalent magnetic azimuths. These are plotted on cross-section paper, with time as the other argument, using any convenient scale. A curve is then faired through the points.

Points at intervals of half an hour (with a minimum of three) are usually sufficient unless the body is near the celestial meridian and relatively high in the sky, when additional points are needed. If the body *crosses* the celestial meridian, the direction of curvature of the line reverses.

Unless extreme accuracy is required, the Greenwich hour angle and declination can be determined for the approximate midtime, the same value of declination used for all computations, and the Greenwich hour angle considered to increase 15° per hour.

An illustration of a curve of magnetic azimuths of the sun is shown in figure 731. This curve is for the period 0700–0900 zone time on May 31, 1975, at latitude 23°09'.5N, longitude 82°24'.1W. The variation in this area is 2°47'E. At the midtime, the meridian

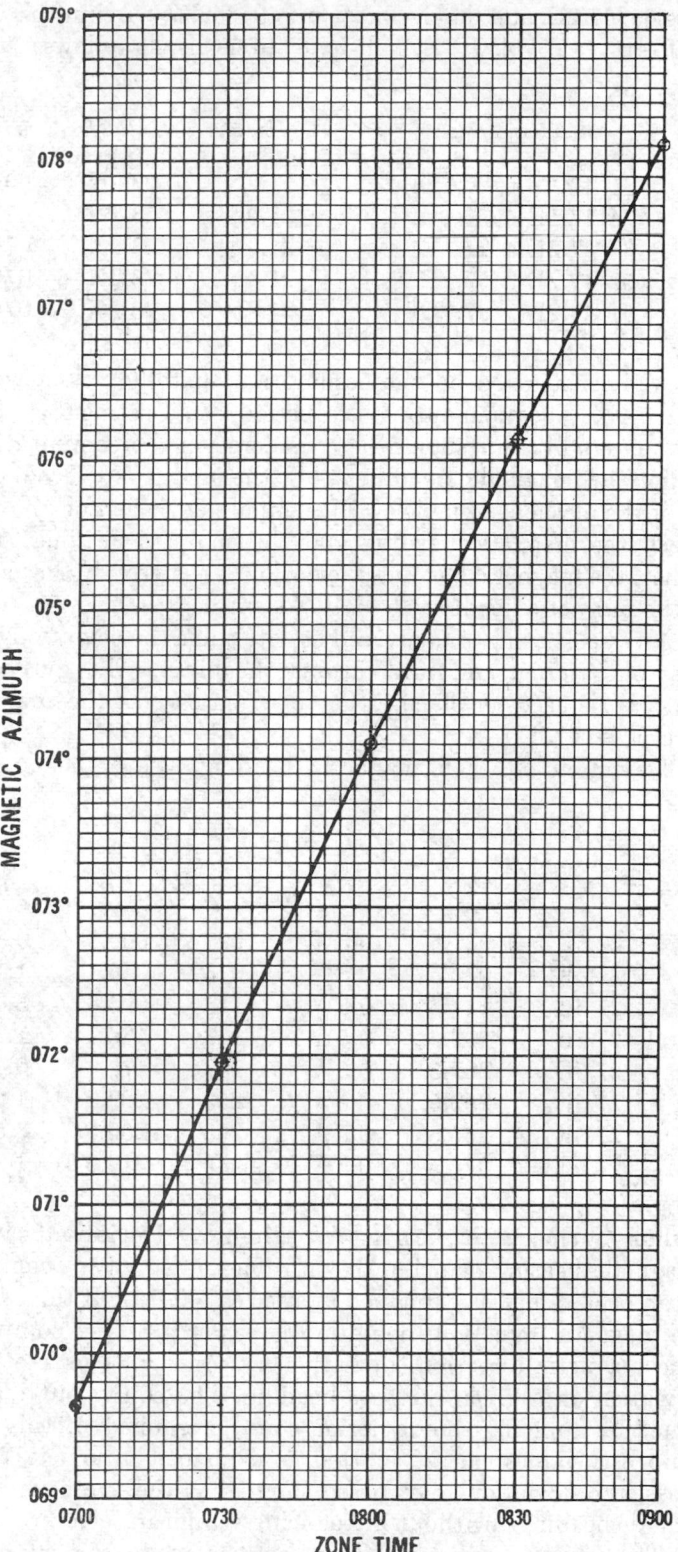

FIGURE 731.—Curve of magnetic azimuths.

angle of the sun is 66°47.'2E, and the declination is 21°52.'3N. Azimuths were computed by Pub. No. 260 (art. 719, vol. II) at half-hour intervals, as follows:

Zone time	Meridian angle			Declination	Latitude	Magnetic azimuth
	°	′	h m	°	°	° ′
0700	81	47.1E	(5 27.1E)	21.9N	23.2N	069 39
0730	74	17.1E	(4 57.1E)	21.9N	23.2N	071 57
0800	66	47.2E	(4 27.1E)	21.9N	23.2N	074 06
0830	59	17.2E	(3 57.1E)	21.9N	23.2N	076 08
0900	51	47.2E	(3 27.1E)	21.9N	23.2N	078 07

This curve was constructed on the assumption that the vessel would remain in approximately the same location during the period of adjustment and swing. If the position changes materially, this should be considered in the computation.

732. Deviation by magnetic headings.—If the vessel is placed on a magnetic heading by any of the methods of article 730, compass deviation on that heading is the difference between the magnetic heading and the compass heading. If the compass heading is less than the magnetic heading, deviation is easterly, if the compass heading is greater than the magnetic heading, deviation is westerly.

Example.—A vessel is being maneuvered to determine the deviation of the magnetic steering compass on cardinal and intercardinal headings. The gyrocompass, which has an error of 0°5W, is used for placing the vessel on each of the magnetic headings. Variation in the area is 27°5E.

Required.—Deviation on each magnetic heading, using the compass headings given below:

Solution.—

MH	V	TH	GE	Hpgc	CH	Dev.
°	°	°	°	°	°	°
000	27.5E	027.5	0.5W	028	000.3	0.3W
045	27.5E	072.5	0.5W	073	046.1	1.1W
090	27.5E	117.5	0.5W	118	093.6	3.6W
135	27.5E	162.5	0.5W	163	136.7	1.7W
180	27.5E	207.5	0.5W	208	179.6	0.4E
225	27.5E	252.5	0.5W	253	223.8	1.2E
270	27.5E	297.5	0.5W	298	266.5	3.5E
315	27.5E	342.5	0.5W	343	313.2	1.8E

733. Deviation by magnetic bearing or azimuth.—Deviation can be found by comparing a magnetic bearing or azimuth with one measured by compass. The magnetic direction can be obtained as explained in articles 730–731. If the compass direction is less than the magnetic direction, deviation is easterly; if the compass direction is greater than the magnetic direction, deviation is westerly. This method is used for determining deviation on a given *compass* heading. The equivalent magnetic heading can be determined by applying the deviation thus determined. If this method is used for swinging ship, the values can be plotted as explained in article 729. For a well-adjusted compass, the deviation may be so small that the compass headings can be considered magnetic headings, without introducing significant errors.

Example.—The standard compass of a vessel has been adjusted, and the vessel is to be swung for residual deviation during the period and for the place for which the curve of magnetic azimuths of figure 731 has been constructed.

Required.—Find the deviation on each heading given below, at the times indicated.

Solution.—

CH °	Time h m s	CZn °	MZn °	Deviation °
000	7 35 20	073.2	072.4	0.8W
045	7 41 12	074.0	072.8	1.2W
090	7 50 15	074.2	073.4	0.8W
135	7 57 36	074.0	073.9	0.1W
180	8 04 44	073.7	074.4	0.7E
225	8 10 10	073.5	074.8	1.3E
270	8 16 33	074.3	075.2	0.9E
315	8 24 51	075.8	075.7	0.1W

The magnetic azimuth (MZn) is determined from figure 731, and the deviation from compass azimuth (CZn) and magnetic azimuth.

734. Deviation by a range is a special case of deviation by magnetic bearing. Two objects appearing in line, one behind the other, constitute a **range.** Range markers are established in many places to mark important channels, the extremities of measured miles, etc. In addition, numerous good ranges occur naturally, as when a lighthouse is in line with a tank, or a tower with a chimney. The true direction of such a range can be determined by measurement on the chart, and variation applied to determine the equivalent magnetic direction. In the case of a natural range, the objects should preferably be at least an inch apart as they appear on the chart, to minimize any plotting errors.

A range is superior to the bearing of a single object because it provides a critical indication of when the vessel is in the correct position to take a reading. The vessel crosses the range on various compass headings. At each crossing, the compass bearing of the range is observed, and also the compass heading. It is well to use two ranges nearly 90° apart, if available, because of the difficulty of crossing at small angles.

Example.—A vessel maneuvering to adjust its compass in the Lower Bay of New York Harbor finds the true direction of the range between West Bank Light and Coney Island Light to be 032°. The variation in this area is 11°.2 W. The vessel steams across the range on various compass headings, noting the compass direction of the range at the times of crossing, as shown below.

Required.—The deviation on each compass heading indicated.

Solution.—The magnetic bearing on the range is 032°+11°.2=043°.2.

CH °	MB Range °	CB Range °	Deviation °
000	043.2	032.9	10.3E
045	043.2	023.7	19.5E
090	043.2	031.9	11.3E
135	043.2	044.2	1.0W
180	043.2	048.5	5.3W
225	043.2	051.0	7.8W
270	043.2	055.6	12.4W
315	043.2	049.8	6.6W

The analysis of these results (art. 727) indicates a constant error of 1°.0E. The mean compass bearing is 042°.2, differing from the correct magnetic bearing by the amount of constant error.

Ranges are widely used to check the deviation on the heading in use as a vessel proceeds through pilot waters. In this manner several checks can be made without advance preparation as a vessel enters or leaves port.

735. Deviation by reciprocal bearings.—Another method of using magnetic bearings is by means of a compass on the beach. This method is particularly useful when no suitable distant object or range is available, or where it may not be practical to remain close to a given bearing line.

A reliable compass is taken ashore to a location which is free from magnetic disturbance. If the location is not marked by a conspicuous object, such as a beacon, flagpole, prominent tree, etc., a temporary marker should be erected. A staff with a flag or bunting should be adequate. The marker should be of sufficient size and nature to be conspicuous at the vessel. At suitable visual or radio signals from the vessel, bearings are observed simultaneously aboard the vessel and ashore. The bearings of the vessel observed by the shore compass are magnetic. The reciprocals of these can be considered magnetic bearings of the shore station from the vessel. The bearings measured aboard the vessel are compass bearings. The difference is deviation. To avoid confusion in the sequence of bearings, the time of each bearing is recorded. Timepieces should be synchronized before the start of observations.

Example.—Simultaneous bearings are observed by a shore compass and the standard compass aboard a vessel, as shown below.

Required.—The deviation of the standard compass on each heading.

Solution.—

CH	Time	MB of vessel	MB of shore position	CB of shore position	Deviation
°		°	°	°	°
000	1112	307	127	137	10W
045	1120	309	129	131	2W
090	1126	312	132	130	2E
135	1018	296	116	113	3E
180	1029	295	115	109	6E
225	1039	288	108	096	12E
270	1052	288	108	113	5W
315	1104	289	109	115	6W
			mean 118	118	

The analysis of these results indicates no constant deviation. This is further indicated by the fact that the means of the bearings aboard and ashore are equal.

Adjustment by Deflector

736. Principles involved.—As indicated in article 713, the magnetic field of a vessel causes deviation of a magnetic compass, and also alters its directive force, strengthening it on some headings and weakening it on others. *The purpose of compass adjustment is to neutralize the effect of the vessel's magnetic field on the compass. If this is done completely, all deviation is removed, and the directive force is the same on all headings.* The usual procedure, described earlier in this chapter, is to adjust by reducing or eliminating the deviation. By the deflector method, the various correctors are adjusted until the directive force is the same on all cardinal headings. Deviation is then a minimum.

The *relative* directive force on various headings is determined by means of an instrument called a **deflector.** Actual measurement is of the setting of the instrument when the compass card has been rotated or "deflected" through 90° under certain standard conditions. The units are arbitrary "deflector units" which are used only for comparison with readings on other headings.

The deflector method provides a quick adjustment with only four headings being needed, without need for bearings, azimuths, or comparison with other compasses. It is easy to use. However, it is not as thorough as the method described in article 729, and should not be used when the usual method is available. The deflector method makes no provision for determination of coefficient A (art. 716), the amount of Flinders bar needed, the setting of the heeling magnet, or the residual deviation. Coefficient E can be determined, but is usually ignored. The method has never been popular in the United States. It offers little or no advantage for a vessel equipped with a reliable gyrocompass.

737. Adjustment by deflector.—The preliminary steps of adjustment are the same as indicated in article 728, omitting those relating to peloruses and other compasses. Preparations having been completed, the adjustment should be carried out as follows:

1. Steady on heading 000° (or 180°) *by the compass being adjusted*. Note the heading by another compass and keep the vessel on this heading, steering by means of the second compass. Put the deflector in place over the first compass, and deflect the compass card 90°. Record the reading on the deflector scale, and remove the deflector.

2. Steady on heading 090° (or 270°) by the compass being adjusted, and follow the procedure of step 1.

3. Steady on heading 180° (000° if 180° was used in step 1) by the compass being adjusted, and determine the deflector reading by the procedure of step 1. Leave the deflector in place and set it to the mean of the readings on headings 000° and 180°. Adjust the fore-and-aft permanent magnets until the deflection is 90°. This corrects for coefficient B, and the deflector readings on compass headings 000° and 180° should now be the same. Remove the deflector.

4. Steady on heading 270° (090° if 270° was used in step 2)by the compass being adjusted, and determine the deflector reading by the procedure of step 1. Leave the deflector in place and set it to the mean of the readings on headings 090° and 270°. Adjust the athwartship permanent magnets until the deflection is 90°. This corrects for coefficient C, and the deflector readings on compass headings 090° and 180° should now be the same.

5. Without changing the heading, set the deflector to the mean of the N–S and E–W means. Adjust the quadrantal correctors until the deflection is 90°. This corrects for coefficient D, and the deflector readings on all cardinal headings should be the same. Remove the deflector.

Adjustment is now complete. It can be checked by repeating the five steps, a procedure which is particularly recommended if the difference between deflector readings on opposite headings is more than ten units. If means are available, and time permits, the vessel should be swung for residual deviation. If preferred, a heading of east or west can be used, reversing steps 1 and 2 and also steps 3 and 4.

This method is particularly useful when a quick adjustment is needed following some change that affects the magnetic environment of the compass.

738. The Kelvin deflector was developed in Great Britain by Sir William Thomson (Lord Kelvin). It consists essentially of two permanent magnets hinged like a pair of dividers, with opposite poles at the hinge. The magnets are mounted vertically over the center of the compass, with the hinged end on top. The separation of the lower ends can be varied by means of a screw. The amount of separation, indicated by a scale and vernier drums, is the reading used in the adjustment.

The deflecting force increases as the separation becomes greater. When the deflector is in place over the compass, the blue pole is in line with the north (red) end of the compass magnets, as indicated by a pointer. As the deflecting magnets are rotated around the vertical axis of the instrument, the compass card rotates in the same direction, but at a slower rate. The separation is adjusted until the rotation of the instrument is 170° when the deflection of the compass card is 90°. These are the standard conditions under which readings are made.

The Kelvin type deflector provides adjustment to an accuracy of 2° to 3°.

739. The De Colong deflector was developed in Russia and provides an accuracy of $0°5$ to $1°0$. Essentially, this instrument consists of two horizontal magnets which are perpendicular to each other. The small magnet is held in a fixed position close to the compass card. The large magnet is mounted in a small tray which can be moved up and down along a vertical spindle mounted over the center of the compass. The red end of this magnet is placed toward the north. When it is positioned so that the directive force is exactly neutralized, the small magnet causes the compass card to be deflected 90°. The height of the large magnet is the deflector reading, the scale being on the vertical spindle, and the index on the movable tray.

Provision is made for mounting the large magnet vertically, to measure the vertical force of the magnetic field at the compass. A separate scale is provided for this purpose. Additional magnets are generally provided for use near the magnetic equator, where the vertical intensity is very small.

In practice, a separate deflector is provided for each compass, and they are not interchangeable. By the addition of an auxiliary scale, the instrument could be made usable for any compass.

Degaussing Compensation

740. Degaussing.—As indicated in article 712, a steel vessel has a certain amount of permanent magnetism in its "hard" iron, and induced magnetism in its "soft" iron. Whenever two or more magnetic fields occupy the same space, the total field is the vector sum (art. 118, vol. II) of the individual fields. Thus, within the effective region of the field of a vessel, the total field is the combined total of the earth's field and that due to the vessel. Consequently, the field due to earth's magnetism alone is altered or distorted due to the field of the vessel. This is indicated by a tendency of the lines of force to crowd into the metal of the vessel (art. 703), as shown in figure 741a.

Certain mines and other explosive devices are designed to be triggered by the magnetic influence of a vessel passing near them. It is therefore desirable to reduce to a practical minimum the magnetic field of a vessel. One method of doing this is to neutralize each component by means of an electromagnetic field produced by direct current of electricity in electric cables installed so as to form coils around the vessel. A unit sometimes used for measuring the strength of a magnetic field is the **gauss.** The reduction of the strength of a magnetic field decreases the number of gauss in that field. Hence, the process is one of **degaussing** the vessel.

When a vessel's degaussing coils are energized, the magnetic field of the vessel is completely altered. This introduces large deviation in the magnetic compasses. This is removed, as nearly as practicable, by introducing at each compass an equal and opposite force of the same type—one caused by direct current in a coil—for each component of the field due to the degaussing currents. This is called **compass compensation.** When there is a possibility of confusion with compass adjustment to neutralize the effects of the natural magnetism of the vessel, the expression **degaussing compensation** is used. Since the neutralization may not be perfect, a small amount of deviation due to degaussing may remain on certain headings. This is the reason for swinging ship twice—once with degaussing off and once with it on—and having two separate columns in the deviation table (fig. 710).

741. A vessel's magnetic signature.—A simplified diagram of the distortion of the earth's magnetic field in the vicinity of a steel vessel is shown in figure 741a. The strength of the field is indicated by the spacing of the lines, being stronger as the lines are closer together. If a vessel passes over a device for detecting and recording the strength of the magnetic field, a certain pattern is traced, as shown in figure 741b. Since the magnetic field of each vessel is different, each has a distinctive trace, known as its **magnetic signature.** The simplified signature shown in figure 741b is one that might result from an uncomplicated field such as that shown in figure 741a.

Several degaussing stations have been established to determine magnetic signatures and recommend the currents needed in the various degaussing coils. Since a vessel's induced magnetism varies with heading and magnetic latitude, the current settings of the coils which neutralize induced magnetism need to be changed to suit the conditions. A "degaussing folder" is provided each vessel to indicate the changes, and to give other pertinent information.

A vessel's permanent magnetism changes somewhat with time and the magnetic history of the vessel. Therefore, the information given in the degaussing folder should be checked from time to time by a return to the magnetic station.

742. Degaussing coils.—For degaussing purposes, the total field of the vessel is divided into three components: (1) vertical, (2) horizontal fore-and-aft, and (3) horizontal athwartships. The positive directions are considered downward, forward, and to port, respectively. These are the normal directions for a vessel headed north or east in north latitude. Each component is opposed by a separate degaussing field just strong enough to neutralize it. Ideally, when this has been done, the earth's field passes through the vessel smoothly and without distortion. The opposing degaussing fields are produced by direct current flowing in coils of wire. Each of the degaussing coils is placed so that the field it produces is directed to oppose one component of the ship's field.

The number of coils installed depends upon the magnetic characteristics of the vessel, and the degree of safety desired. The ship's permanent and induced magnetism may be neutralized separately so that control of induced magnetism can be varied as heading and latitude change, without disturbing the fields opposing the vessel's permanent field. The principal coils employed are the following:

Main (M) coil. The M-coil is placed horizontal, and completely encircles the vessel, usually at or near the waterline. Its function is to oppose the vertical component of the vessel's permanent and induced fields combined. Generally the induced field predominates. Current in the M-coil is varied or reversed according to the change of the *induced* component of the vertical field with latitude.

Forecastle (F) and quarterdeck (Q) coils. The F- and Q-coils are placed horizontal just below the forward and after thirds (or quarters), respectively, of the weather deck. The designation "Q" for quarterdeck is reminiscent of the days before World War II when the "quarterdeck" of naval vessels was aft along the ship's quarter. These coils, in which current can be individually adjusted, remove much of the fore-and-aft component of the ship's permanent and induced fields. More commonly, the combined F- and Q-coils consist of two parts; one part the FP- and QP-coils, to take care of the permanent fore-and-aft field, and the other part, the FI- and QI-coils, to neutralize the induced fore-and-aft field. Generally, the forward and after coils of each type are connected in series, forming a split-coil installation and designated FP-PQ coils and FI-QI coils. Current in the FP-QP coils is generally constant, but in the FI-QI coils is varied according to the heading and magnetic latitude of the vessel. In split-coil installations, the coil designations are often contracted to *P*-coil and *I*-coil.

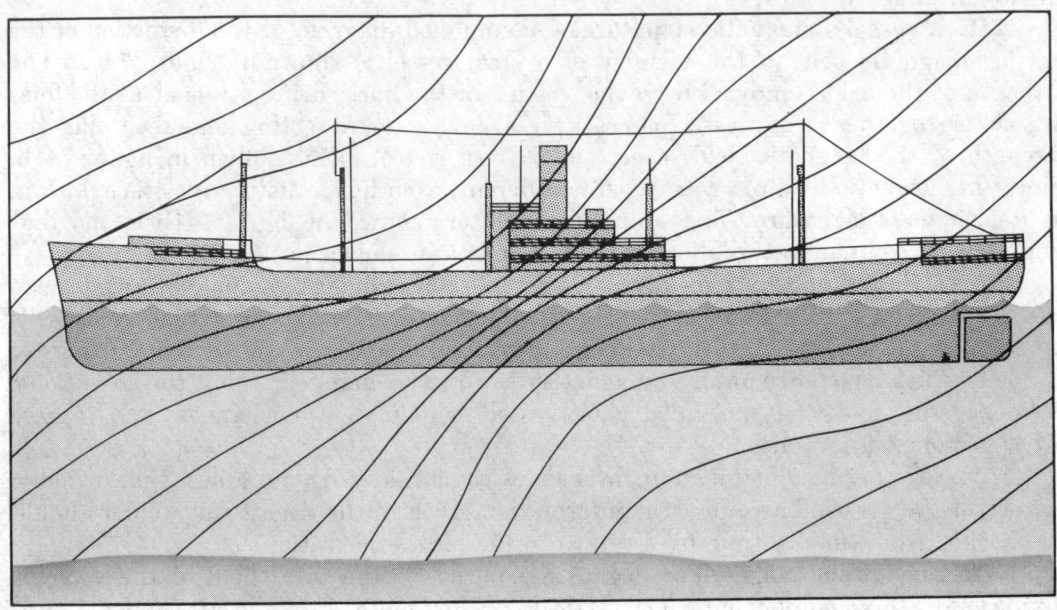

FIGURE 741a.—Simplified diagram of distortion of earth's magnetic field in the vicinity of a steel vessel.

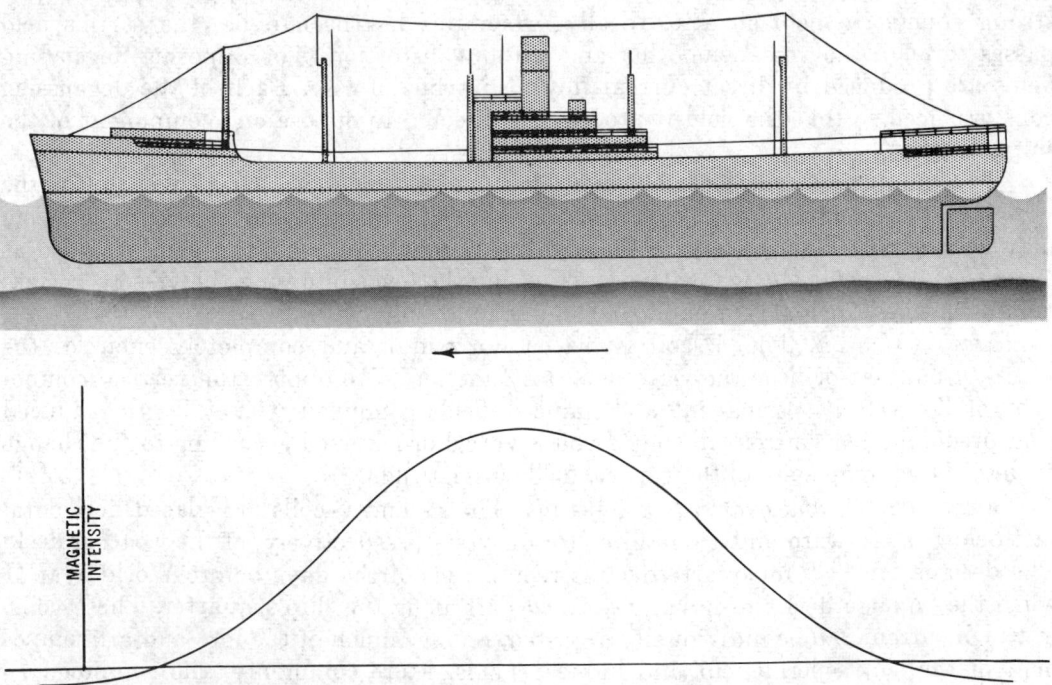

FIGURE 741b.—Simplified signature of vessel of figure 741a.

Longitudinal (L) coil. Better control of the fore-and-aft components, but at greater installation expense, is provided by placing a series of vertical, athwartships coils along the length of the ship. It is the *field*, not the coils, which is longitudinal. Current in an *L*-coil is varied as with the *FI-QI* coils. It is maximum on north and south headings, and zero on east and west headings.

Athwartship (A) coil. The *A*-coil is in a vertical fore-and-aft plane, thus producing a horizontal athwartship field which neutralizes the athwartship component of the vessel's field. In most vessels, this component of the permanent field is small and can be ignored. Since the *A*-coil neutralizes the induced field, primarily, the current is changed with magnetic latitude and with heading, being maximum on east or west headings, and zero on north or south headings.

The strength and direction of the current in each coil is indicated and adjusted at a control panel which is normally accessible to the navigator. Current may be controlled directly by rheostats at the control panel or remotely by push buttons which operate rheostats in the engine room.

Since degaussing fields oppose the vessel's fields, the positive directions of the degaussing fields are upward, aft, and to starboard. For positive fields in *M*, *F*, *FI*, *FP*, *Q*, *QI*, and *QP* coils, current flows forward on the starboard side of the vessel; and the north end of a small compass placed *above* any of these coils is deflected outboard. For a positive field in the *L*-coil, current flows upward on the starboard side, and the north end of a compass is deflected aft when placed *below* an upper, athwartship portion of the coil. For a positive field in the *A*-coil, current in the upper, fore-and-aft portion flows aft, and the north end of a compass is deflected to starboard when placed *below* this portion of the coil. The *FI-QI* coils are generally connected so that the field in the *FI*-coil is negative when that in the *QI*-coil is positive.

Appropriate values of the current in each coil are determined at a degaussing station, the various currents being adjusted until the vessel's signature is made as flat as possible. Recommended current values and directions for all headings and magnetic latitudes are set forth in the vessel's degaussing folder. This document is normally retained by the navigator, whose responsibility it is to see that the recommended settings are maintained whenever the degaussing system is energized.

743. Securing the degaussing system.—Unless the degaussing system is properly secured, residual magnetism may remain in the metal of the vessel. During degaussing compensation and at other times, as recommended in the degaussing folder, the "reversal" method is used. The steps in the reversal process are as follows:

1. Start with maximum degaussing current used since the system was last energized.

2. Decrease current to zero and increase it in the opposite direction to the same value as in step 1.

3. Decrease the current to zero and increase it to three-fourths maximum value in the original direction.

4. Decrease the current to zero and increase it to one-half maximum value in the opposite direction.

5. Decrease the current to zero and increase it to one-fourth maximum value in the original direction.

6. Decrease the current to zero and increase it to one-eighth maximum value in the opposite direction.

7. Decrease the current to zero and open switch.

744. Magnetic treatment of vessels.—In some instances, the degaussing can be made more effective by changing the magnetic characteristics of the vessel by a process known as **deperming.** Heavy cables are wound around the vessel in an athwartship direction, forming vertical loops around the longitudinal axis of the vessel. The loops are run beneath the keel, up the sides, and over the top of the weather deck at closely spaced equal intervals along the entire length of the vessel. Predetermined values of direct current are then passed through the coils. When the desired magnetic characteristics have been acquired, the cables are removed.

A vessel which does not have degaussing coils, or which has a degaussing system which is inoperative, can be given some temporary protection by a process known as **flashing.** A horizontal coil is placed around the outside of the vessel and energized with large predetermined values of direct current. When the vessel has acquired a vertical field of permanent magnetism of the correct magnitude and polarity to reduce to a minimum the resultant field below the vessel for the particular magnetic latitude involved, the cable is removed. This type protection is not as satisfactory as that provided by degaussing coils because it is not adjustable for various headings and magnetic latitudes, and also because the vessel's magnetism slowly readjusts itself following treatment.

During magnetic treatment it is a wise precaution to remove all magnetic compasses and Flinders bars from the vessel. Permanent adjusting magnets and quadrantal correctors are not materially affected, and need not be removed. If for any reason it is impractical to remove a compass, the cables used for magnetic treatment should be kept as far as practical from it.

745. Degaussing compensation.—The magnetic fields created by the degaussing coils would render the vessel's magnetic compasses useless unless compensated. This is accomplished by subjecting the compass to compensating fields along three mutually perpendicular axes. These fields are provided by small compensating coils adjacent to the compass. In nearly all installations, one of these coils, the heeling coil, is horizontal and on the same plane as the compass card. Current in the heeling coil is adjusted until the vertical component of the total degaussing field is neutralized. The other compensating coils provide horizontal fields perpendicular to each other. Current is varied in these coils until their resultant field is equal and opposite to the horizontal component of the degaussing field. In early installations, these horizontal fields were directed fore-and-aft and athwartships by placing the coils around the Flinders bar and the quadrantal spheres. Compactness and other advantages are gained by placing the coils on perpendicular axes extending 045°–225° and 315°–135° relative to the heading. A frequently used compensating installation, called the type "K," is shown in figure 745. It consists of a heeling coil extending completely around the top of the binnacle, four "intercardinal" coils, and three control boxes. The intercardinal coils are named for their positions relative to the compass when the vessel is on a heading of north, and also for the compass headings on which the current in the coils is adjusted to the correct amount for compensation. The NE–SW coils operate together as one set, and the NW–SE coils operate as another. One control box is provided for each set, and one for the heeling coil.

The compass compensating coils are connected to the power supply of the degaussing coils, and the currents passing through the compensating coils are adjusted by series resistances so that the compensating field is equal to the degaussing field. Thus, a change in the degaussing currents is accompanied by a proportional change in the compensating currents. Each coil has a separate winding for each degaussing circuit it compensates.

Degaussing compensation is carried out while the vessel is moored at the shipyard where the degaussing coils are installed. This is usually done by personnel of the yard, using the following procedure:

1. The compass is removed from its binnacle and a dip needle is installed in its place. The M-coil and heeling coil are then energized, and the current in the heeling coil is adjusted until the dip needle indicates the correct value for the magnetic latitude of the vessel. The system is then secured by the reversing process.

FIGURE 745.—Type "K" degaussing compensation installation.

2. The compass is restored to its usual position in the binnacle. By means of auxiliary magnets, the compass card is deflected until the compass magnets are parallel to one of the compensating coils or set of coils used to produce a horizontal field. The compass magnets are then perpendicular to the field produced by that coil. One of the degaussing circuits producing a horizontal field, and its compensating winding, are then energized, and the current in the compensating winding is adjusted until the compass reading returns to the value it had before the degaussing circuit was energized. The system is then secured by the reversing process. The process is repeated with each additional circuit used to create a horizontal field. The auxiliary magnets are then removed.

3. The auxiliary magnets are placed so that the compass magnets are parallel to the other compensating coils or set of coils used to produce a horizontal field. The procedure of step 2 is then repeated for each circuit producing a horizontal field.

When the vessel gets under way, it proceeds to a suitable maneuvering area. The vessel is then headed so that the compass magnets are parallel first to one compensating coil or set of coils and then the other, and any needed adjustment is made in the compensating circuits to reduce the error to a minimum. The vessel is then swung for residual deviation, first with degaussing off and then with degaussing on, and the correct current settings for each heading at the magnetic latitude of the vessel. From the values thus obtained, the "DG OFF" and "DG ON" columns of the deviation table (fig. 710) are filled in. If the results indicate satisfactory compensation, a record is made of the degaussing coil settings and the resistances, voltages, and currents in the compensating coil circuits. The control boxes are then secured.

Under normal operating conditions, the settings need not be changed unless changes are made in the degaussing system, or unless an alteration is made in the amount of Flinders bar or the setting of the quadrantal correctors. However, it is possible for a ground to occur in the coils or control box if the circuits are not adequately protected from sea water or other moisture. If this occurs, it should be reflected by a change in deviation with degaussing on, or by a decreased installation resistance. Under these conditions, compensation should be carried out again. If the compass is to be needed with degaussing on before the ship can be returned to a shipyard where the compensation can be made by experienced personnel, the compensation should be made at sea on the actual headings needed, rather than by deflection of the compass needles by magnets. More complete information related to this process is given in the degaussing folder.

If a vessel has been given magnetic treatment, its magnetic properties have been changed. This necessitates readjustment of each magnetic compass. This is best delayed for several days to permit stabilization of the magnetic characteristics of the vessel. If this cannot be delayed, the vessel should be swung again for residual deviation after a few days. Degaussing compensation should not be made until after compass adjustment has been completed.

Problems

711a. Fill in the blanks in the following:

	TC°	V°	MC°	D°	CC°	CE°
(1)	105	15E	—	5W	—	—
(2)	—	—	—	4E	215	14E
(3)	—	12W	—	—	067	7W
(5)	156	—	166	—	160	—
(5)	222	—	216	3W	—	—
(6)	009	—	357	—	—	10E
(7)	—	2W	—	6E	015	—
(8)	—	—	210	—	214	1W

Answers.—(1) MC 090°, CC 095°, CE 10°E; (2) TC 229°, V 10°E, MC 219°; (3) TC 060°, MC 072°, D 5°E; (4) V 10°W, D 6°E, CE 4°W; (5) V 6°E, CC 219°, CE 3°E; (6) V 12°E, D 2°W, CC 359°; (7) TC 019°, MC 021°, CE 4°E; (8) TC 213°, V 3°E, D 4°W.

711b. A vessel is on course 150° by compass in an area where the variation is 19°E. The deviation is as shown in figure 710. Degaussing is on.

Required.—(1) Deviation.

(2) Compass error.

(3) Magnetic heading.

(4) True heading.

Answers.—(1) D 1°E, (2) CE 20°E, (3)MH 151°, (4) TH 170°.

711c. A vessel is on course 055° by gyro and 041° by magnetic compass. The gyro error is 1°W. The variation is 15°E.

Required.—The deviation on this heading.

Answer.—D 2°W.

711d. A vessel is on course 177° by gyro. The gyro error is 0°.5E. A beacon bears 088° by magnetic compass in an area where variation is 11°W. The deviation is as shown in figure 710, degaussing off.

Required.—The true bearing of the beacon.

Answer.—TB 076°.

721a. A magnetic compass is adjusted on the magnetic equator, without any Flinders bar being used. The residual deviation on heading 090° magnetic is 1°E. Some days later, at latitude 37°N, dip 70°, the deviation on heading 090° is 12°W.

Required.—The length and location of Flinders bar required to restore a residual deviation of 1°E (using fig. 721, A) if the magnetic properties of the vessel are unchanged.

Answer.—Fifteen inches of Flinders bar forward of the compass.

721b. The deviation of a magnetic compass of a vessel on heading 270° magnetic is 2°E near Sydney, Australia (south magnetic latitude) and 12°W near Seattle, Wash. (north magnetic latitude). Near Sydney, H=0.258 and Z=0.51. Near Seattle, H=0.188 and Z=0.53. The shielding factor is 0.9.

Required.—The length of Flinders bar to use if (1) no Flinders bar is in place during observations, (2) 12 inches of Flinders bar is in place forward of the compass during observations.

Answers.—(1) 8¼ inches (8.5 inches by computation) of Flinders bar aft of the compass, (2) nine inches (8.8 inches by computation) of Flinders bar forward of the compass.

727. A magnetic compass which has not been adjusted has deviation on cardinal and intercardinal compass headings as follows:

Compass heading °	Deviation °	Compass heading °	Deviation °
000	2.0E	180	6.0E
045	20.5E	225	5.5W
090	18.5E	270	22.0W
135	8.0E	315	23.5W

On heading compass north the deviation is 6°.0W when the vessel heels 7° to starboard.

Required.—(1) The approximate value of each coefficient.

(2) The total deviation to be expected on compass heading 300°, with the vessel on an even keel.

(3) Heeling error on compass heading 060°, with a heel of 10°.

Answers.—(1) A (+)0°.5, B (+)20°.2, C (−)2°.0, D (+)7°.6, E (+)2°.9, J (−)1°.1; (2) d 26°.0W; (3) HE 5°.5.

730a. It is desired to place a vessel on magnetic heading west, using the magnetic steering compass. The deviation table for this compass is shown in figure 710. Degaussing is on.

Required.—Heading per steering compass (p stg c).

Answer.—H$_{p\,stg\,c}$ 272°.

730b. It is desired to place a vessel on magnetic heading south, using the gyrocompass. The variation in this area is 12°E, and the gyro error is 0°.5E.

Required.—Heading per gyrocompass.

Answer.—H$_{pgc}$ 191°.5.

730c. It is desired to place a vessel on magnetic heading southeast in an area where the variation is 6°W. The true bearing for a distant object is 047°.

Required.—(1) The magnetic bearing of the object.

(2) The relative bearing of the object when the vessel is on the desired magnetic heading.

Answers.—(1) MB 053°, (2) RB 278°.

730d. The compass bearings of a distant object are as follows:

CH °	CB °	CH °	CB °
000	358	180	002
045	357	225	006
090	351	270	012
135	353	315	009

Required.—The magnetic bearing of the object, assuming no constant deviation (coefficient *A*).

Answer.—MB 001°.

730e. It is desired to place a vessel on magnetic heading east in an area where the variation is 13°E, and at a time when the computed true azimuth of the sun is 218°.

Required.—(1) The magnetic azimuth of the sun.

(2) The relative azimuth when the vessel is on the desired magnetic heading.

(3) The azimuth by a magnetic compass having deviation as shown in figure 710 (DG on).

(4) The azimuth by a gyrocompass having a gyro error of 1°W.

Answers.—(1) MZn 205°, (2) RZn 115°, (3) CZn 202°, (4) Zn_{pgc} 219°.

732. A vessel is being maneuvered to determine the residual deviation of a magnetic compass. The gyrocompass, which has an error of 1°E, is used for placing the vessel on the magnetic headings indicated below. Variation in the area is 7°.8W. The following readings are obtained:

MH °	CH °	MH °	CH °
000	000.0	180	180.1
045	044.1	225	225.8
090	088.5	270	271.4
135	134.2	315	315.9

Required.—Gyro heading and deviation on each magnetic heading.

Answers.—

MH °	H_{pgc}	Dev. °	MH °	H_{pgc}	Dev. °
000	351.2	0.0	180	171.2	0.1W
045	036.2	0.9E	225	216.2	0.8W
090	081.2	1.5E	270	261.2	1.4W
135	126.2	0.8E	315	306.2	0.9W

733. A vessel is being swung for residual deviation during the period and at the place for which the curve of magnetic azimuths of figure 731 has been constructed. The following readings are obtained:

CH °	Time h m s	CZn °	CH °	Time h m s	CZn °
000	7 56 13	73.7	180	8 16 36	75.2
045	8 01 22	72.9	225	8 22 19	76.8
090	8 04 55	71.9	270	8 27 12	78.7
135	8 11 01	74.0	315	8 33 27	77.2

Required.—Deviation on each compass heading.

Answers.—

CH°	Deviation°	CH°	Deviation°
000	0.1E	180	0.0
045	1.3E	225	1.2W
090	2.6E	270	2.8W
135	0.9E	315	0.8W

734. A vessel being swung for residual deviation crosses a range on various compass headings as indicated below, the compass bearing of the range being observed at each crossing. The true direction of the range is 255°. The variation in the vicinity is 24.°5E.

CH°	CB°	CH°	CB°
000	230.3	180	230.6
045	228.7	225	232.4
090	227.4	270	233.8
135	228.0	315	232.3

Required.—Deviation on each compass heading.

Answers.—

CH°	Deviation°	CH°	Deviation°
000	0.2E	180	0.1W
045	1.8E	225	1.9W
090	3.1E	270	3.3W
135	2.5E	315	1.8W

735. Bearings of a vessel are taken by means of a compass ashore, and simultaneous bearings of the shore position are taken from the vessel, as follows:

CH°	CB of shore position°	MB of vessel°	CH°	CB of shore position°	MB of vessel°
000	020	198	180	003	184
045	013	189	225	009	194
090	004	174	270	013	204
135	001	172	315	017	205

Required.—(1) Deviation on each heading.

(2) The value of coefficient *A*.

Answers.—

(1)

CH°	Deviation°	CH°	Deviation°
000	2W	180	1E
045	4W	225	5E
090	10W	270	11E
135	9W	315	8E

(2) Coefficient *A* is zero.

CHAPTER VIII

DEAD RECKONING

801. Introduction.—Dead reckoning (DR) is the determination of position by advancing a known position for courses and distances. It is reckoning relative to something stationary or "dead" in the water, and hence applies to courses and speeds *through the water*. Because of leeway due to wind, inaccurate allowance for compass error, imperfect steering, or error in measuring speed, the actual motion through the water is seldom determined with complete accuracy. In addition, if the water itself is in motion, the course and speed over the bottom differ from those through the water. It is good practice to use the true course *steered* and the best determination of *measured* speed, which is normally speed *through the water*, for dead reckoning. Hence, geographically, a **dead reckoning position** is an approximate one which is corrected from time to time as the opportunity presents itself. Although of less than the desired accuracy, dead reckoning is the only method by which a position can be determined at *any* time and therefore might be considered *basic* navigation, with all other methods only appendages to provide means for correcting the dead reckoning. The prudent navigator keeps his direction- and speed- or distance-measuring instruments in top condition and accurately calibrated, for his dead reckoning is no more accurate than his measurement of these elements.

If a navigator can accurately assess the disturbing elements introducing geographical errors into his dead reckoning, he can determine a better position than that established by dead reckoning alone. This is properly called an **estimated position (EP)**. It may be established either by applying an estimated correction to a dead reckoning position, or by estimating the course and speed being made good over the bottom. The expression "dead reckoning" is sometimes applied loosely to such reckoning, but it is better practice to keep this "estimated reckoning" distinct from dead reckoning, if for no other reason than to provide a basis for evaluating the accuracy of one's estimates. When good information regarding current, wind, etc., is available, it should be used, but the practice of applying corrections based upon information of uncertain accuracy is, at best, questionable, and may introduce an error. Estimates should be based upon judgment and experience. Positional information which is incomplete or of uncertain accuracy may be available to assist in making the estimate. However, before adequate experience is gained, one should be cautious in applying corrections, for the estimates of the inexperienced are often quite inaccurate.

Dead reckoning not only provides means for continuously establishing an approximate position, but also is of assistance in determining times of sunrise and sunset, the celestial bodies available for observation, the predicted availability of electronic aids to navigation, the suitability and interpretation of soundings for checking position, the predicted times of making landfalls or sighting lights, estimates of arrival times, and in evaluating the reliability and accuracy of position-determining information. Because of the importance of accurate dead reckoning, a careful log is kept of all courses and speeds, times of all changes, and compass errors. These may be recorded directly in the log or first in a **navigator's notebook** for later recording in the log, but whatever the form, a careful record is important.

Modern navigators almost invariably keep their dead reckoning by plotting directly on the chart or plotting sheet, drawing lines to represent the direction and distance of travel and indicating dead reckoning and estimated positions from time to time. This method is simple and direct. Large errors are often apparent as inconsistencies in an otherwise regular plot. Before the advent of power vessels, when frequent course and speed changes were common, and when charts were sometimes of questionable accuracy, it was common practice to keep the dead reckoning mathematically by one, or a combination, of the "sailings" (chapter IX). Except for great-circle sailing, and occasionally composite and Mercator sailings, these are of little more than historical interest to modern navigators, other than those of small boats.

In determining distance run in a given time, one may find table 19 useful.

802. Plotting position on the chart.—A position is usually expressed in units of latitude and longitude, generally to the nearest 0.1, but it may be expressed as bearing and distance from a known position, such as a landmark or aid to navigation.

To plot a position on a Mercator chart, or to determine the coordinates of a point on such a chart, proceed as follows:

To plot a position when its latitude and longitude are known: Mark the given latitude on a convenient latitude scale along a meridian, being careful to note the unit of the smallest division on the scale. Place a straightedge at this point and parallel to a parallel of latitude (perpendicular to a meridian). Holding the straightedge in place, set one point of a pair of dividers at the given longitude on the longitude scale at the top or bottom of the chart (or along any parallel) and the other at a convenient printed meridian. Without changing the spread of the dividers, place one point on the same printed meridian at the edge of the straightedge, and the second point at the edge of the straightedge in the direction of the given longitude. This second point is at the given position. *Lightly* prick the chart. Remove first the straightedge and then the dividers, watching the point to be sure of identifying it. Make a dot at the point, enclose it with a small circle or square as appropriate (art. 805), and label it. If the dividers are set to the correct spread for longitude *before* the latitude is marked, one point of the dividers can be used to locate the latitude and place the straightedge, if one is careful not to disturb the setting of the dividers.

To determine the coordinates of a point on the chart: Place a straightedge at the given point and parallel to a parallel of latitude. Read the latitude where the straightedge crosses a latitude scale. Keeping the straightedge in place, set one leg of a pair of dividers at the given point and the other at the intersection of the straightedge and a convenient printed meridian. Without changing the spread of the dividers, place one end on a longitude scale, at the same printed meridian, and the other point on the scale, in the direction of the given point. Read the longitude at this second point.

Several variations of these procedures may suggest themselves. That method which seems most natural and is least likely to result in error should be used.

803. Measuring direction on the chart.—Since the Mercator chart, commonly used by the marine navigator, is *conformal* (art. 302), directions and angles are correctly represented. It is customary to orient the chart with 000° (north) at the top; other directions are in their correct relations to north and each other.

As an aid in measuring direction, **compass roses** are placed at convenient places on the chart or plotting sheet. A desired direction can be measured by placing a straightedge along the line from the center of a compass rose to the circular graduation representing the desired direction. The straightedge is then in the desired direction, which may be transferred to any other part of the chart by parallel motion, as by parallel rulers or two triangles (art. 603). The direction between two points is determined by transferring that direction to a compass rose. If a drafting machine (art. 606) or some form of plotter (art. 605) or protractor (art. 604) is used, measurement can be made directly at the desired point, without using the compass rose.

Measurement of direction, whether or not by compass rose, can be made at any convenient place on a Mercator chart, since meridians are parallel to each other and a line making a desired angle with any one makes the same angle with all others. Such a line is a **rhumb line,** the kind commonly used for course lines, except in polar regions. For direction on a chart having nonparallel meridians, measurement can be made at the meridian involved if the chart is conformal, or by special technique if it is not conformal. Explanation of the former is given in article 2511. The only nonconformal chart commonly used by navigators is the gnomonic, and instructions for measuring direction on this chart are usually given on the chart itself.

Compass roses for both true and magnetic directions may be given. A drafting machine can be oriented to any reference direction—true, magnetic, compass, or grid. When a plotter or protractor is used for measuring an angle with respect to a meridian, the resulting direction is true unless other than true meridians are used. For most purposes of navigation it is good practice to plot true directions only, and to label them in true coordinates.

804. Measuring distance on the chart.—The length of a line on a chart is usually measured in nautical miles, to the nearest 0.1 mile. For this purpose it is customary to use the latitude scale, considering one minute of latitude equal to one nautical mile. The error introduced by this assumption is not great over distances normally measured. It is maximum near the equator or geographical poles. Near the equator a ship traveling 180 miles by measurement on the chart would cover only 179 miles over the earth. Near the poles a run of 220 miles by chart measurement would equal 221 miles over the earth.

Since the latitude scale on a Mercator chart expands with increased latitude, measurement should be made at approximately the mid latitude. For a chart covering a relatively small area, such as a harbor chart, this precaution is not important because of the slight difference in scale over the chart. On such charts a separate mile scale may be given, and it may safely be used over the entire chart. However, habit is strong, and mistakes can probably be avoided by *always* using the mid latitude.

For long distances the line should be broken into a number of parts or *legs*, each one being measured at its mid latitude. The length of a line that should be measured in a single step varies with latitude, decreasing in higher latitudes. No realistic numerical value can be given, since there are too many considerations. With experience a navigator determines this for himself. On the larger scale charts this is not a problem because the usual dividers used for this purpose will not span an excessively long distance.

In measuring distance, the navigator spans with his dividers the length of the line to be measured and then, without altering the setting, transfers this length to the latitude scale, carefully noting the graduations so as to avoid an error in reading. This precaution is needed because of the difference from chart to chart. In measuring a desired length along a line, the navigator spans this length on the latitude scale opposite the line and then transfers his dividers to the line, without changing the setting. For a long line the navigator sets his dividers to some convenient distance and steps off the line, counting the number of steps, multiplying this by the length of the step, and adding any remainder. If the line extends over a sufficient spread of latitude to make scale difference a factor, he resets his dividers to the scale for the approximate mid latitude of each leg. The distance so measured is the length of the rhumb line.

For measuring distance on a nearly-constant-scale chart, such as the Lambert conformal, the mid-latitude precaution is usually unnecessary. Such charts generally have a mile scale independent of the latitude scale. On a gnomonic chart a special procedure is needed, and this is usually explained on the chart.

805. Plotting and labeling the course line and positions.—**Course** is the intended horizontal direction of travel through the water. A **course line** is a line extending in the direction of the course. From a known position of the ship the course line is drawn in the direction indicated by the course. It is good practice to label all lines and points of significance as they are drawn, for an unlabeled line or point can easily be misinterpreted later. Any simple, clear, logical, unambiguous system of labels is suitable. The following is widely used and might well be considered standard.

Label a course line with direction and speed. *Above* the course line place a capital C followed by three figures to indicate the course steered. It is customary to label and steer courses to the nearest whole degree, although they are generally computed to the nearest 0°.1. The course label should indicate *true* direction, starting with 000° at true north and increasing clockwise through 360°. *Below* the course line, and under the direction label, place a capital S followed by figures representing the speed in knots. Since the course is *always* given in degrees true and the speed in knots, it is not necessary to indicate the units or the reference direction (fig. 805).

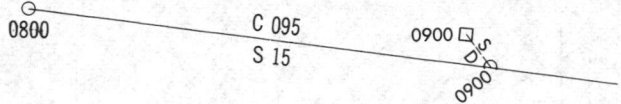

FIGURE 805.—A course line with labels.

A point to be labeled is enclosed by a small circle in the case of a **fix** (an accurate position determined without reference to any former position), a semicircle in the case of a dead reckoning position, and by a small square in the case of an estimated position. It is labeled with the time, usually to the nearest minute; the nature of the position is indicated by the symbol used. Time is usually expressed in four figures without punctuation, on a 24-hour basis (art. 1803). Zone time (art. 1807) is usually used, but Greenwich mean time (art. 1807) may be employed. A course line is a succession of an infinite number of dead reckoning positions. Only selected points are labeled.

The times of fixes and estimated positions are placed horizontally; the times of dead reckoning positions are placed at an angle to the course line.

806. Dead reckoning by plot.—As a vessel clears a harbor and proceeds out to sea, the navigator obtains one last good fix while identifiable landmarks are still available. This is called **taking departure,** and the position determined is called the **departure.** Piloting (ch. X) comes to an end and the course is set for the open sea. The course line is drawn and labeled, and some future position is indicated as a DR position. The number of points selected for labeling depends primarily upon the judgment and individual preference of the navigator. It is good practice to label each point where a change of course or speed occurs. If such changes are frequent, no additional points need be labeled. With infrequent changes, it is good practice to label points at some regular interval, as every hour. From departure, the dead reckoning plot continues unbroken until a new well-established position is obtained, when both DR and fix are shown. The fix serves as the start of a new dead reckoning plot. Although estimated positions are shown, it is generally not good practice to begin a new DR at these points.

A typical dead reckoning plot is shown in figure 806, indicating procedures both when there are numerous changes of course and speed and when there is a long continuous course. It is assumed that no fix is obtained after the initial one at 0800 on September 8. Note that course lines are not extended beyond their limits of usefulness, One should keep a neat plot and leave no doubt as to the meaning of each line and

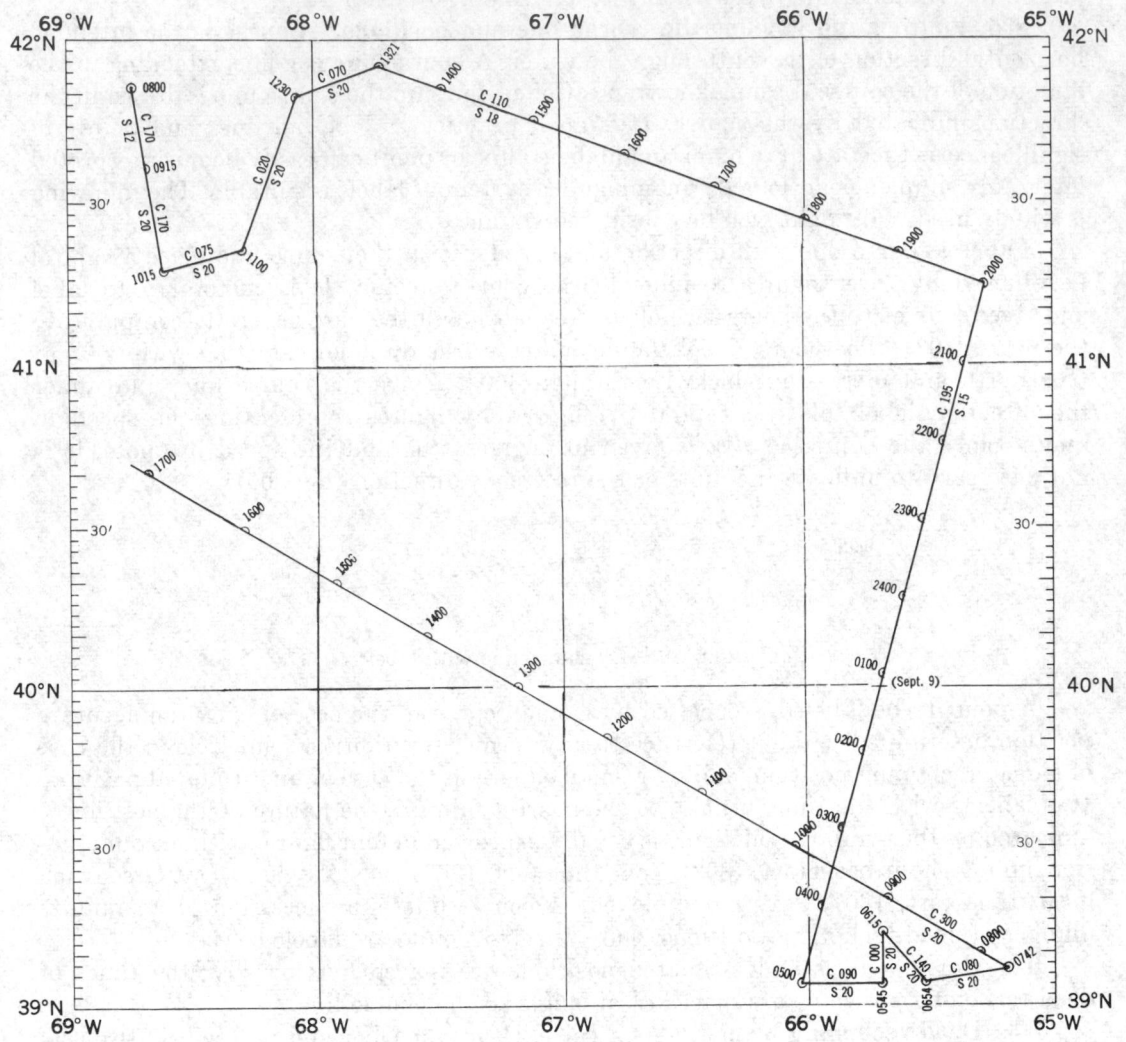

FIGURE 806.—A typical dead reckoning plot.

marked point. *A neat, accurate plot is the mark of a good navigator.* The plot of the **intended track** (art. 207) should be kept extended to some future time. A good navigator is always ahead of his ship. In shoal water or when near the shore, aids to navigation, dangers, etc., it is customary to keep the dead reckoning plot on a chart. A chart overprinted with a lattice of a radionavigation system may be used. But on the open sea, with only dead reckoning and celestial navigation available, it is good practice to use a plotting sheet (art. 323).

807. Current.—Water in essentially horizontal motion over the surface of the earth is called **current.** The direction in which the water is moving is called the **set,** and the speed is called the **drift.** In navigation it is customary to use the term "current" to include all factors introducing geographical error in the dead reckoning, whether their immediate effects are on the vessel or the water. When a fix is obtained, one assumes that the current has set *from* the DR position at the same time *to* the fix, and that the drift is equal to the distance in miles between these positions, divided by the number of hours since the last fix. This is true regardless of the number of changes of course or speed since the last fix.

If set and drift since the last fix are known, or can be estimated, a better position can be obtained by applying a correction to that obtained by dead reckoning. This is conveniently done by drawing a straight line in the direction of the set for a distance equal to the drift multiplied by the number of hours since the last fix, as shown in figure 805. The direction of a straight line from the last fix to the EP is the estimated **course made good,** and the length of this line divided by the time is the estimated **speed made good.** The course and speed actually made good over the ground are called the **course over the ground** (COG) and **speed over the ground** (SOG), respectively.

As shown in figure 805, the straight line drawn from the 0900 DR in the direction of the set is constructed as a broken line. The capital S above the line represents the set; the capital D below the line represents the drift.

If a current is setting in the same direction as the course, or its reciprocal, the course over the ground is the same as that through the water. The effect on the speed can be found by simple arithmetic. If the course and set are in the same direction, the speeds are added; if in opposite directions, the smaller is subtracted from the larger. This situation is not unusual when a ship encounters a tidal current while entering or leaving port. If a ship is *crossing* a current, solution can be made graphically by vector diagram (art. 118, vol. II) since velocity over the ground is the vector sum of velocity *through* the water and velocity *of* the water. Although *distances* can be used, it is generally easier to use *speeds*.

Example 1.—A ship on course 080°, speed ten knots, is steaming through a current having an estimated set of 140° and drift of two knots.

Required.—Estimated course and speed made good.

Solution (fig. 807a).—(1) From *A*, any convenient point, draw *AB*, the course and speed of the ship, in direction 080°, for a distance of ten miles.

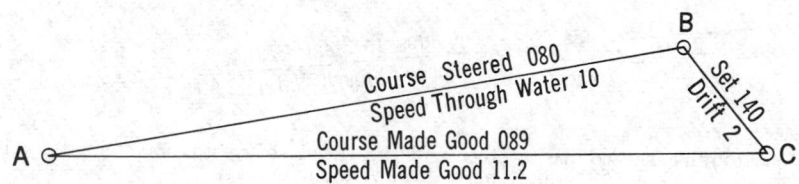

FIGURE 807a.—Finding course and speed made good through a current.

(2) From *B* draw *BC*, the set and drift of the current, in direction 140°, for a distance of two miles.

(3) The direction and length of *AC* are the estimated course and speed made good. Determine these by measurement.

Answers.—Estimated course made good 089°, estimated speed made good 11.2 kn.

If it is required to find the course to steer at a given speed to make good a desired course, plot the current vector from the origin, *A*, instead of from *B*.

Example 2.—The captain desires to make good a course of 095° through a current having a set of 170° and a drift of 2.5 knots, using a speed of 12 knots.

Required.—The course to steer and the speed made good.

Solution (fig. 807b).—(1) From *A*, any convenient point, draw line *AB* extending in the direction of the course to be made good, 095°.

(2) From *A* draw *AC*, the set and drift of the current.

(3) Using C as a center, swing an arc of radius CD, the speed through the water (12 knots), intersecting line AB at D.

(4) Measure the direction of line CD, 083°.5. This is the course to steer.

(5) Measure the length AD, 12.4 knots. This is the speed made good.

Answers.—Course to steer 083°.5, speed made good 12.4 kn.

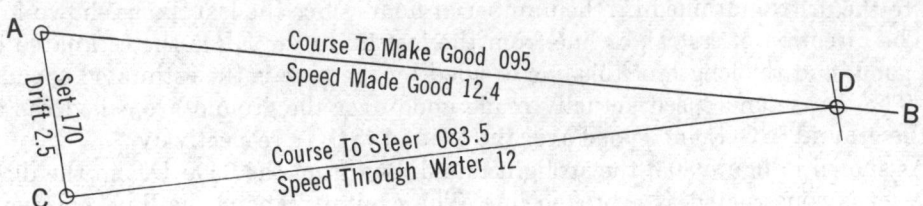

FIGURE 807b.—Finding the course to steer at a given speed to make good a given course through a current.

If it is required to find the course to steer and the speed to use to make good a desired course and speed, proceed as follows:

Example 3.—The captain desires to make good a course of 265° and a speed of 15 knots through a current having a set of 185° and a drift of three knots.

Required.—The course to steer and the speed to use.

Solution (fig. 807c).—(1) From A, any convenient point, draw AB in the direction of the course to be made good, 265°, and for a length equal to the speed to be made good, 15 knots.

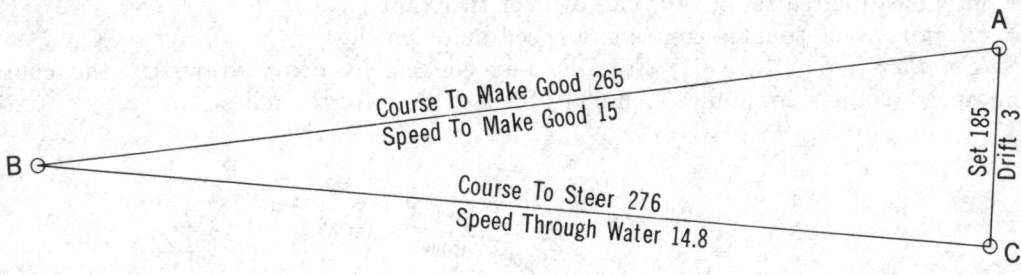

FIGURE 807c.—Finding the course to steer and the speed to use to make good a given course and speed through a current.

(2) From A draw AC, the set and drift of the current.

(3) Draw a straight line from C to B. The direction of this line, 276°, is the required course to steer; and the length, 14.8 knots, is the required speed.

Answers.—Course to steer 276°, speed to use 14.8 kn.

Such vector solutions can be made to any convenient scale and at any convenient place, such as the center of a compass rose, an unused corner of the plotting sheet, a separate sheet, or directly on the plot.

808. Leeway is the leeward motion of a vessel due to wind. It may be expressed as distance, speed, or angular difference between course steered and course through the water. However expressed, its amount varies with the speed and relative direction of the wind, type of vessel, amount of freeboard, trim, speed of the vessel, state of the sea, and depth of water. If information on the amount of leeway to be expected under various conditions is not available for the type vessel involved, it should be determined by observation. When sufficient data have been collected, suitable tables or graphs can be made for quick and convenient estimate. The accuracy of the information should be checked whenever convenient, and corrections made when sufficient evidence indicates the need.

Leeway is most conveniently applied by adding its effect to that of current and other elements introducing geographical error in the dead reckoning. It is customary to consider the combined effect of all such elements as current, and to make allowance for this as explained in article 807. In sailing ship days it was common practice to consider leeway in terms of its effect upon the course only, and to apply it as a correction in the same manner that variation and deviation are applied. While this method has merit even with power vessels, it is generally considered inferior to that of considering leeway as part of current.

809. Automatic dead reckoning.—Several types of devices are in use for performing automatically all or part of the dead reckoning. Perhaps the simplest is the automatic **course recorder,** which provides a graphical record of the various courses steered. In its usual form this device is controlled by the gyrocompass, and so indicates gyro courses.

Dead reckoning equipment receives inputs from the compass, usually the gyrocompass, and a mechanical log or engine revolution counter. It determines *change* in latitude and longitude, the latter by first determining departure and then mechanically multiplying this by the secant of the latitude. The device is provided with counters on which latitude and longitude can be set. As the vessel proceeds, the changes are then mechanically added to or subtracted from these readings to provide a continuous, instantaneous indication of the dead reckoning position. The navigator or an assistant reads these dials at intervals, usually each hour, and records the values in a notebook. Most models of dead reckoning equipment are provided, also, with a tracer for keeping a graphical record of dead reckoning in the form of a plot by moving a pencil or pen across a chart or plotting sheet. This part of the device is called a **dead reckoning tracer.** Whatever the form, dead reckoning equipment is a great convenience, particularly when a ship is maneuvering. However, such mechanical equipment is subject to possible failure. The prudent navigator keeps a hand plot and uses the dead reckoning equipment as a check. In navigation it is never wise to rely upon a single method if a second method is available as a check.

If it were possible to measure, with high accuracy, the direction and distance traveled *with respect to the earth*, an accurate geographical position could be known at all times. The two methods most commonly used are (1) doppler and (2) inertial. By the **doppler** method one or more beams of acoustic energy are directed downward at an angle. The return echo from the bottom is of a slightly different frequency due to the motion of the craft. The amount of the change, or doppler, is proportional to the speed. By proper selection of beams, it is possible to measure speed in a lateral direction as well as in a forward direction. Distance can be determined by mechanical or electronic integration of these measurements, and this can be converted into position. By the **inertial** method, accelerometers measure the acceleration in various directions, and by double integration this is converted to distance, from which position can be determined. Either of these methods can provide considerable accuracy over a period of several hours, but the error increases with time.

Problems

806a. Draw a small area plotting sheet by either method explained in article 324, covering the area between latitude 32°-34°N and longitude 118°-122°W. Plot the following points:

A L   33°49ʹ1N C L   33°38ʹ0N
      λ   120°52ʹ0W   λ   118°38ʹ6W
B L   32°17ʹ4N D L   32°30ʹ6N
      λ   121°28ʹ0W   λ   118°36ʹ2W

Required.—(1) The bearings of B, C, and D from A.

(2) The course and distance of A, B, and C from D.

Answers.—(1) B_{AB} 198°5, B_{AC} 095°5, B_{AD} 124°; (2) C_{DA} 304°, D_{DA} 138.8 mi., C_{DB} 264°5, D_{DB} 145.7 mi., C_{DC} 358°5, D_{DC} 67.2 mi.

806b. Use the plot of problem 806a. A ship starts from A at 1200, and steams as follows:

Time	Course	Speed
1200	120°	15 kn.
1330	240°	15 kn.
1500	240°	17 kn.
1800	125°	20 kn.
2000	090°	20 kn.
2300	015°	10 kn.
0500		

Plot and label the dead reckoning course line and DR positions.

Required.—(1) The dead reckoning position of the ship at 0500.

(2) The bearing and distance of D from the 2300 DR position.

(3) The course and distance from the 0500 DR position to C.

(4) Estimated time of arrival (ETA), to the nearest minute, at C if the ship proceeds directly from the 0500 DR position at 20 knots.

Answers.—(1) 0500 DR: L 33°35ʹ1N, λ 119°35ʹ8W; (2) B 096°, D 66.0 mi.; (3) C 086°, D 48.1 mi.; (4) ETA 0724.

807a. A ship on course 120°, speed 12 knots, is steaming through a current having a set of 350° and a drift of 1.5 knots.

Required.—Course and speed made good.

Answers.—Course made good 114°, speed made good 11.1 kn.

807b. The captain desires to make good a course of 180° through a current having a set of 090° and a drift of two knots, using a speed of 11 knots.

Required.—The course to steer and the speed made good.

Answers.—Course to steer 190°5, speed made good 10.8 kn.

807c. The captain desires to make good a course of 325° and a speed of 20 knots through a current having a set of 270° and a drift of one knot.

Required.—The course to steer and the speed to use.

Answers.—Course to steer 327°, speed to use 19.4 kn.

CHAPTER IX

THE SAILINGS

901. Introduction.—Dead reckoning involves the determination of position by means of course and distance from a known position. A closely related problem is that of finding the course and distance from one point to another. Although both of these problems are customarily solved by plotting directly on the chart, it occasionally becomes desirable to solve by computation, frequently by logarithms or traverse table (art. 1002, vol. II). The various methods of solution are collectively called the **sailings.**

The various kinds of sailings are:

1. **Plane sailing** is a method of solving the various problems involving a single course and distance, difference of latitude, and departure, in which the earth, or that part traversed, is regarded as a plane surface. Hence, the method provides solution for latitude of the point of arrival, but not for longitude of this point, one of the spherical sailings being needed for this problem. Because of the basic assumption that the earth is flat, this method should not be used for distances of more than a few hundred miles.

2. **Traverse sailing** combines the plane sailing solutions when there are two or more courses. This sailing is a method of determining the equivalent course and distance made good by a vessel steaming along a series of rhumb lines.

3. **Parallel sailing** is the interconversion of departure and difference of longitude when a vessel is proceeding due east or due west. This was a common occurrence when the sailings were first employed several hundred years ago, but only an incidental situation now.

4. **Middle-** (or **mid-**) **latitude sailing** involves the use of the mid or mean latitude for converting departure to difference of longitude when the course is not due east or due west and it is assumed such course is steered at the mid latitude.

5. **Mercator sailing** provides a mathematical solution of the plot as made on a Mercator chart. It is similar to plane sailing, but uses meridional difference and difference of longitude in place of difference of latitude and departure, respectively.

6. **Great-circle sailing** involves the solution of courses, distances, and points along a great circle between two points, the earth being regarded as a sphere.

7. **Composite sailing** is a modification of great-circle sailing to limit the maximum latitude.

The solutions of the sailings by computations are discussed in more detail in chapter X of volume II.

902. Rhumb lines and great circles.—The principal advantage of a **rhumb line** is that it maintains constant true direction. A ship following the rhumb line between two places does not change true course. A rhumb line makes the same angle with all meridians it crosses and appears as a straight line on a Mercator chart. It is adequate for most purposes of navigation, bearing lines (except long ones, as those obtained by radio) and course lines both being plotted on a Mercator chart as rhumb lines, except in high latitudes. The equator and the meridians are great circles, but may be considered special cases of the rhumb line. For any other case, the difference between the rhumb line and the great circle connecting two points increases (1) as the latitude increases, (2) as the difference of latitude between the two points decreases, and (3) as the difference

259

of longitude increases. It becomes very great for two places widely separated on the same parallel of latitude far from the equator.

A **great circle** is the intersection of the surface of a sphere and a plane through the center of the sphere. It is the largest circle that can be drawn on the surface of the sphere, and is the shortest distance, along the surface, between any two points on the sphere. Any two points are connected by only one great circle unless the points are antipodal (180° apart on the earth), and then an infinite number of great circles passes through them. Thus, two points on the same meridian are not joined by any great circle other than the meridian, unless the two points are antipodal. If they are the poles, *all* meridians pass through them. Every great circle bisects every other great circle. Thus, except for the equator, every great circle lies half in the Northern Hemisphere and half in the Southern Hemisphere. Any two points 180° apart on a great circle have the same latitude numerically, but contrary names, and are 180° apart in longitude. The point of greatest latitude is called the **vertex.** For each great circle there is one of these in each hemisphere, 180° apart. At these points the great circle is tangent to a parallel of latitude, and hence its direction is due east-west. On each side of these vertices the direction changes progressively until the intersection with the equator is reached, 90° away, where the great circle crosses the equator at an angle equal to the latitude of the vertex. As the great circle crosses the equator, its change in direction reverses, again approaching east-west, which it reaches at the next vertex.

On a Mercator chart a great circle appears as a sine curve extending equal distances each side of the equator. The rhumb line connecting any two points of the great circle on the same side of the equator is a chord of the curve, being a straight line nearer the equator than the great circle. Along any intersecting meridian the great circle crosses at a higher latitude than the rhumb line. If the two points are on opposite sides of the equator, the direction of curvature of the great circle relative to the rhumb line changes at the equator. The rhumb line and great circle may intersect each other, and if the points are equal distances on each side of the equator, the intersection takes place at the equator.

903. Great-circle sailing is used when it is desired to take advantage of the shorter distance along the great circle between two points, rather than to follow the longer rhumb line. The arc of the great circle between the points is called the **great-circle track.** If it could be followed exactly, the destination would be dead ahead throughout the voyage (assuming course and heading were the same). The rhumb line *appears* the more direct route on a Mercator chart because of chart distortion. The great circle crosses meridians at higher latitudes, where the distance between them is less.

The decision as to whether or not to use great-circle sailing depends upon the conditions. The saving in distance should be worth the additional effort, and of course the great circle should not cross land, or carry the vessel into dangerous waters or excessively high latitudes. A slight departure from the great circle or a modification called composite sailing (art. 901) may effect a considerable saving over the rhumb line track without leading the vessel into danger. If a fix indicates the vessel is a considerable distance to one side of the great circle, the more desirable practice often is to determine a new great-circle track, rather than to return to the original one.

Since a great circle is continuously changing direction as one proceeds along it, no attempt is customarily made to follow it exactly, except in polar regions (ch. XXV). Rather, a number of points are selected along the great circle, and rhumb lines are followed from point to point, taking advantage of the fact that for short distances a great circle and a rhumb line almost coincide.

The number of points to use is a matter of personal preference, a large number of points providing closer approximation to the great circle but requiring more frequent change of course. As a general rule, each 5° of longitude is a convenient length. Legs of equal length are not provided in this way, but this is not objectionable under normal conditions.

If a magnetic compass is used, the variation for the middle of the leg is usually used for the entire leg.

The problems of great-circle sailing can be solved by (1) chart (art. 904), (2) computation (art. 1010, vol. II), (3) table (art. 905), (4) graphically, or (5) mechanically. Of these, (4) and (5) are but graphical or mechanical solutions of (2). They usually provide solution only for initial course and the distance, and are not in common use.

904. Great-circle sailing by chart.—Problems of great-circle sailing, like those of rhumb line sailing, are most easily solved by plotting directly on a chart. For this purpose the Defense Mapping Agency Hydrographic Center publishes a number of charts on the gnomonic projection (art. 317), covering the principal navigable waters of the world. On this projection any straight line is a great circle, but since the chart is not conformal (art. 302), directions and distances cannot be measured directly, as on a Mercator chart. An indirect method is explained on each chart.

The usual method of using a gnomonic chart is to plot the great circle and, if it provides a satisfactory track, to determine a number of points along the track, using the latitude and longitude scales in the immediate vicinity of each point. These points are then transferred to a Mercator chart or plotting sheet and used as a succession of destinations to be reached by rhumb lines. The course and distance for each leg is determined by measurement on the Mercator chart or plotting sheet. This method is illustrated in figure 904, which shows a great circle plotted as a straight line on a gnomonic chart and a series of points transferred to a Mercator chart. The arrows represent corresponding points on the two charts. The points can be plotted directly

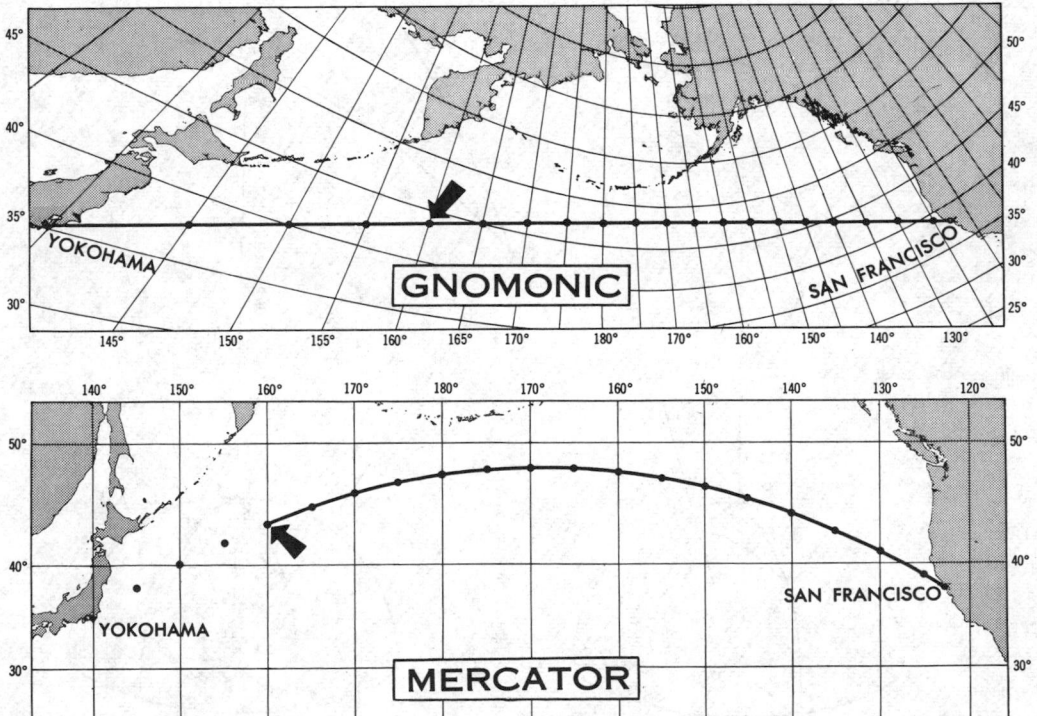

FIGURE 904.—Transferring great-circle points from a gnomonic chart to a Mercator chart.

on plotting sheets without the use of a small-scale chart, but the use of the chart provides a visual check to avoid large errors, and a visual indication of the suitability of the track.

Since gnomonic charts are normally used only because of their great-circle properties, they are often popularly called **great-circle charts.**

A projection on which a straight line is *approximately* a great circle can be used in place of a gnomonic chart with negligible error. If such a projection is conformal, as in the case of the Lambert conformal (art. 314), measurement of course and distance of each leg can be made directly on the chart, as explained in article 2511.

Some great circles are shown on pilot charts and certain other charts, together with the great-circle distances. Where tracks are recommended on charts or in sailing directions, it is good practice to follow such recommendations.

905. Great-circle sailing by table.—Any method of solving the astronomical triangle of celestial navigation can be used for solving great-circle sailing problems. When such an adaptation is made, the point of departure replaces the assumed position of the observer, the destination replaces the geographical position of the body, difference of longitude replaces meridian angle or local hour angle, initial course angle replaces azimuth angle, and great-circle distance replaces zenith distance (90°−altitude), as shown in figure 905. Therefore, any table of azimuths (if the entering values are meridian angle, declination, and latitude) can be used for determining initial great-circle course.

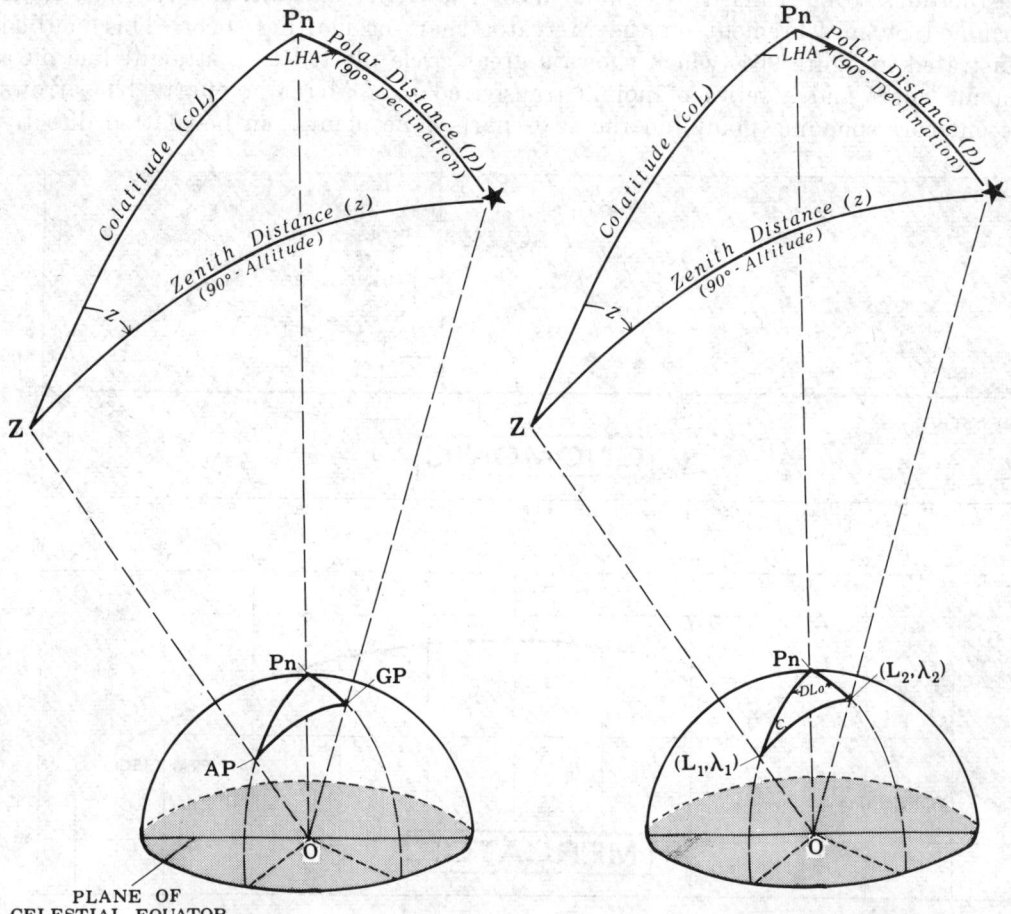

FIGURE 905.—Adapting the astronomical triangle to the navigational triangle of great-circle sailing.

Pubs. Nos. 214, 229, 249, 260, and 261 are examples of tables that can be used for this purpose. Tables which provide solution for altitude, such as Pubs. Nos. 214, 229, and 249, can be used for determining great-circle distance. The required distance is 90° — altitude (90° + negative altitudes).

In inspection tables such as Pubs. Nos. 214, 229, 249, 260, and 261, the given combination of L_1, L_2, and DLo may not be tabulated. In this case reverse the name of L_2 and use 180° — DLo for entering the table. The required course angle is then 180° minus the tabulated azimuth, and distance is 90° plus the altitude. If neither combination can be found, solution cannot be made by that method. By interchanging L_1 and L_2, one can find the supplement of the final course angle.

Solution by table often provides a rapid approximate check, but accurate results usually require triple interpolation (art. 204, vol. II). Except for Pub. No. 229, inspection tables do not provide a solution for points along the great circle. Pub. No. 229 provides solutions for these points only if interpolation is not required.

906. Great-circle sailing by Pub. No. 229.—By entering Pub. No. 229 with the latitude of the point of departure as latitude, latitude of destination as declination, and difference of longitude as LHA, the tabular altitude and azimuth angle may be extracted and converted to great-circle distance and course. As in sight reduction, the tables are entered in accordance to whether the name of the latitude of the point of departure is the same as or contrary to the name of the latitude of the destination (declination). If after so entering the tables, the respondent values correspond to those of a celestial body *above* the celestial horizon, 90° minus the arc of the tabular altitude becomes the distance; the tabular azimuth angle becomes the initial great-circle course angle. If the respondents correspond to those of a celestial body *below* the celestial horizon, the arc of the tabular altitude plus 90° becomes the distance; the supplement of the tabular azimuth angle becomes the initial great-circle course angle.

When the C–S Line is crossed in either direction, the altitude becomes negative; the body lies below the celestial horizon. For example: If the tables are entered with the LHA (DLo) at the bottom of a right-hand page and declination (L_2) such that the respondents lie above the C–S Line, the C–S Line has been crossed. Then the distance is 90° plus the tabular altitude; the initial course angle is the supplement of the tabular azimuth angle. Similarly, if the tables are entered with the LHA (DLo) at the top of a right-hand page and the respondents are found below the C–S Line, the distance is 90° plus the tabular altitude; the initial course angle is the supplement of the tabular azimuth angle. If the tables are entered with the LHA (DLo) at the bottom of a right-hand page and the name of L_2 is contrary to L_1, the respondents are found in the column for L_1 on the facing page. In which case, the C–S Line has been crossed; the distance is 90° plus the tabular altitude; the initial course angle is the supplement of the tabular azimuth angle.

Inspection of figures 2007a and 2007b reveals that the data in a latitude column are continuous with the data in the column for the same latitude on the facing page.

The tabular azimuth angle, or its supplement, is prefixed N or S for the latitude of the point of departure and suffixed E or W depending upon the destination being east or west of the point of departure.

If all entering arguments are integral degrees, the distance and course angle are obtained directly from the tables without interpolation. If the latitude of the destination is nonintegral, interpolation for the additional minutes of latitude is done as in correcting altitude for any declination increment; if the latitude of departure or difference of longitude is nonintegral, the additional interpolation is done graphically.

Since the latitude of destination becomes the declination entry, and all declinations appear on every page, the great-circle solution can always be extracted from the volume which covers the latitude of the point of departure.

Example 1.—By Pub. No. 229 (app. O) find the distance and initial great-circle course from lat. 32°S, long. 116°E to lat. 30°S, long 31°E.

Solution.—(1) Refer to figure 905. The point of departure (lat. 32°S, long. 116°E) replaces the AP of the observer; the destination (lat. 30°S, long. 31°E) replaces the GP of the celestial body; the difference of longitude (DLo 85°) replaces local hour angle (LHA) of the body.

(2) The solution by Pub. No. 229 is effected by entering volume 3 with lat. 32° (Same Name), LHA 85°, and declination 30°. The respondents as so found correspond to those of a celestial body *above* the celestial horizon. Therefore, 90° minus the tabular altitude (90°−19°12ʹ4=70°47ʹ6) becomes the distance; the tabular azimuth angle (S66°0W) becomes the initial great-circle course angle, prefixed S for the latitude of the point of departure and suffixed W due to the destination being west of the point of departure.

Answers.—(1) D 4248 nautical miles
　　　　　　　C S66°0W
　　　　　　(2) Cn 246°0.

Example 2.—By Pub. No. 229 (app. O) find the distance and initial great-circle course from lat. 38°N, long. 122°W to lat. 24°S, long. 151°E.

Solution.—(1) Refer to figure 905. The point of departure (lat. 38°N, long. 122°W) replaces the AP of the observer; the destination (lat. 24°S, long. 151°E) replaces the GP of the celestial body; the difference of longitude (DLo 87°) replaces local hour angle (LHA) of the body.

(2) The solution by Pub. No. 229 is effected by entering volume 3 with lat. 38° (Contrary Name), LHA 87°, and declination 24°. The respondents as so found correspond to those of a celestial body *below* the celestial horizon. Therefore, the tabular altitude plus 90° (12°17ʹ0+90°=102°17ʹ0) becomes the distance; the *supplement* of tabular azimuth angle (180°−69°0=111°0) becomes the initial great-circle course angle, prefixed N for the latitude of the point of departure and suffixed W due to the destination being west of the point of departure.

That the tabular data corresponds to a celestial body below the celestial horizon is indicated by the fact that the data is extracted from those tabulations across the C–S Line from the entering argument (LHA 85°).

Answers.—(1) D 6137 nautical miles
　　　　　　　C N111°0W
　　　　　　(2) Cn 249°.

Example 3.—By Pub. No. 229 (app. O) find the distance and initial great-circle course from Fremantle (32°03ʹS, 115°45ʹE) to Durban (29°52ʹS, 31°04ʹE).

Solution.—(1) Refer to figure 905. Since the latitude of the point of departure, the latitude of the destination, and the difference of longitude (DLo) between the point of departure and destination are not integral degrees, the solution is effected from an adjusted point of departure or assumed position of departure chosen as follows: the latitude of the assumed position (AP) is the integral degrees of latitude nearest to the point of departure; the longitude of the AP is chosen to provide integral degrees of DLo. This AP, which should be within 30ʹ of the longitude of the point of departure, is at latitude 32°S, longitude 116°04ʹE. The DLo is 85°.

(2) Enter the tables with 32° as the latitude argument (Same Name), 85° as the LHA argument, and 29° as the declination argument.

(3) From the tables extract the tabular altitude, altitude difference, and azimuth angle; interpolate altitude and azimuth angle for declination increment. The Dec. Inc. is the minutes that the latitude of the destination is in excess of the integral degrees used as the declination argument.

	ht (Tab. Hc)	d	Z
LHA 85°, Lat. 32° (Same), Dec. 29°	18°45′.4	(+)27′.0	66°.9
Dec. Inc. 52′, d(+)27′0 Tens	(+)17′.3		
Units	(+) 6′.1		
Interpolated for Dec. Inc.	19°08′.8		C S66°.1W
Initial great-circle course from AP			Cn 246°.1
Great-circle distance from AP(90°−19°08′.8)			4251.2 n.mi.

(4) Using the graphical method for interpolating altitude for latitude and LHA increments, the course line is drawn from the AP in the direction of the initial great-circle course from the AP (246°.1). As shown in figure 906a, a line is drawn from the point of departure perpendicular to the initial great-circle course line or its extension.

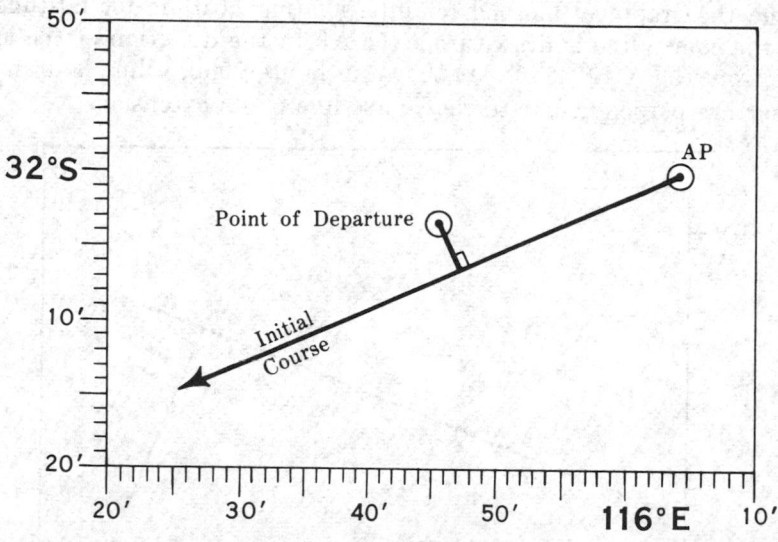

FIGURE 906a.—Graphical interpolation.

(5) The required correction, in units of minutes of latitude, for the latitude and DLo increments is the length along the course line between the foot of the perpendicular and the AP. The correction as applied to the distance from the AP is −15′.8; the great-circle distance is 4235 nautical miles.

(6) The azimuth angle interpolated for declination, LHA, and latitude increments is S66°.3W; the initial great-circle course from the point of departure is 246°.3.

Example 4.—By Pub. No. 229 (app. O) find the distance and initial great-circle course from San Francisco (37°49′N, 122°25′W) to Gladstone (23°51′S, 151°15′E).

Solution.—(1) Refer to figure 905. Since the latitude of the point of departure, the latitude of the destination, and the difference of longitude (DLo) between the point of departure and destination are not integral degrees, the solution is effected from an adjusted point of departure or assumed position of departure chosen as follows: the latitude of the assumed position (AP) is the integral degrees of latitude nearest to the point of departure; the longitude of the AP is chosen to provide integral degrees of

DLo. This AP, which should be within 30′ of the longitude of the point of departure, is at latitude 38°N, longitude 122°45′W. The DLo is 86°.

(2) Enter the tables with 38° as the latitude argument (Contrary Name), 86° as the LHA argument, and 23° as the declination argument.

(3) From the tables extract the tabular altitude, altitude difference, and azimuth angle; interpolate altitude for Dec. Inc. as if the altitude were positive, adhering strictly to the sign given d. After interpolation regard the results as negative. Subtract tabular azimuth angle from 180°; interpolate for Dec. Inc.

	ht(Tab. Hc)	d	Z
LHA 86°, Lat. 38° (Contrary), Dec. 23°	10°57′.0	(+)35′.9	69°.3
Dec. Inc. 51′, d(+)35′.9	Tens (+)25′.5		180°−Z=110°.7
	Units (+)5′.1		
Interpolated for Dec. Inc.	(−)11°27′.6		C N111°.4W
Initial great-circle course from AP			Cn 248°.6
Great-circle distance from AP (90°+11°27′.6)			6087.6 n.mi.

(4) Using the graphical method for interpolating altitude for latitude and LHA increments, the course line is drawn from the AP in the direction of the initial great-circle course from the AP (248°.6). As shown in figure 906b, a line is drawn from the point of departure perpendicular to the course line or its extension.

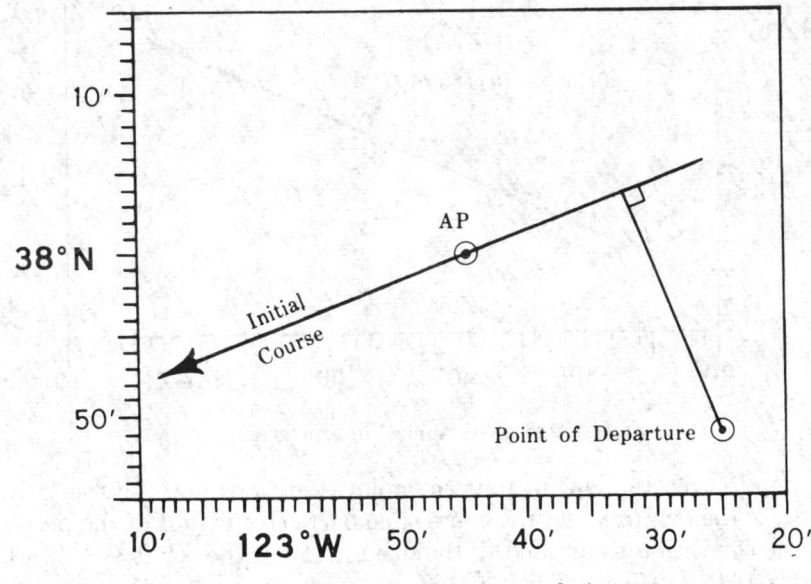

FIGURE 906b.—Graphical interpolation.

(5) The required additional correction, in units of minutes of latitude, for the latitude and DLo increments is the length along the course line between the foot of the perpendicular and the AP. The correction as applied to the distance from the AP is +10′.7; the great-circle distance is 6098 nautical miles.

(6) The azimuth angle interpolated for declination, LHA, and latitude increments is 111°.2; the initial great-circle course from the point of departure is 248°.8.

Example 5.—By Pub. No. 229 (app. O) find the distance and initial great-circle course from Cabo Pilar (52°43′S, 74°41′W) to Wake Island (19°17′N, 166°39′E).

Solution.—(1) Refer to figure 905. Since the latitude of the point of departure, the latitude of the destination, and the difference of longitude (DLo) between the point of departure and destination are not integral degrees, the solution is effected from an adjusted point of departure or assumed position of departure chosen as follows: the latitude of the assumed position (AP) is the integral degrees of latitude nearest to the point of departure; the longitude of the AP is chosen to provide integral degrees of DLo. This AP, which should be within 30′ of the longitude of the point of departure, is at latitude 53°S, longitude 74°21′W; the DLo is 119°.

(2) Enter the tables with 53° as the latitude argument (Contrary Name), 119° as the LHA argument, and 19° as the declination argument. Since the tables are entered with the LHA (DLo) at the bottom of a right-hand page and the name of L_2 is contrary to the name L_1, the respondents are found in the column for L_1 on the facing page. In which case the C–S Line has been crossed, and the respondents correspond to those of a celestial body below the celestial horizon.

(3) From the table, extract the tabular latitude, altitude difference, and azimuth angle; interpolate altitude for Dec. Inc. as if the altitude were positive, adhering strictly to the sign given d. After interpolation regard the results as negative. Subtract tabular azimuth angle from 180°; interpolate for Dec. Inc.

	ht (Tab. Hc)	d	Z
LHA 119°, Lat. 53° (Contrary), Dec. 19°	32°24′.2	(+)46′.8	101°.6
Dec. Inc. 17′, d(+)47′.1	Tens (+)11′.3		180°−Z=S78°.6W
	Units (+) 2′.0		
Interpolated for Dec. Inc.	(−)32°37′.5		C S78°.6W
Initial great-circle course from AP			Cn 258°.6
Great-circle distance from AP (90°+32°37′.5)			7357.5 n.mi.

(4) Using the graphical method for interpolating altitude for latitude and LHA increments, the course line is drawn from the AP in the direction of the initial great-circle course from the AP (258°.6). As shown in figure 906c a line is drawn from the point of departure perpendicular to the course line or its extension.

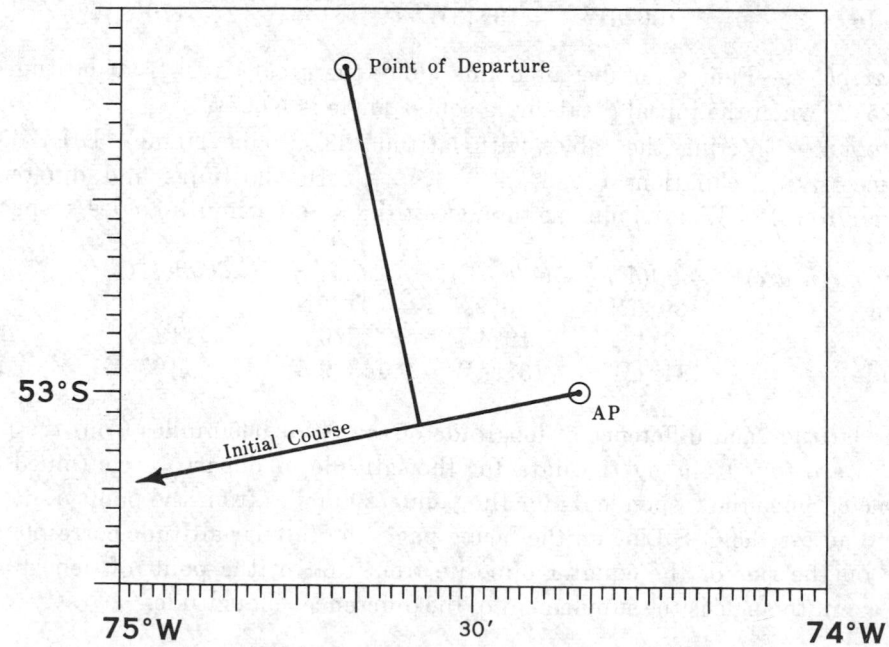

FIGURE 906c.—Graphical interpolation.

(5) The required additional correction, in units of minutes of latitude, for the latitude and DLo increments is the length along the course line between the foot of the perpendicular and the AP. The correction as applied to the distance from the AP is −8ʹ5; the great-circle distance is 7349 nautical miles.

(6) The azimuth angle interpolated for declination, LHA, and latitude increments is 79°1; the initial great-circle course from the point of departure is 259°1.

Points Along Great Circle

If, as in examples 1 and 2, the latitude of the point of departure and the initial great-circle course angle are integral degrees, points along the great circle are found by entering the tables with the latitude of departure as the latitude argument (always Same Name), the initial great-circle course angle as the LHA argument, and 90° minus distance to a point on the great circle as the declination argument. The latitude of the point on the great circle and the difference of longitude between that point and the point of departure are the tabular altitude and azimuth angle respondents, respectively. If, however, the respondents are extracted from across the C–S Line, the tabular altitude corresponds to a latitude on the side of the equator opposite from that of the point of departure; the tabular azimuth angle is the supplement of the difference of longitude.

Example 6.—Find a number of points along the great-circle from latitude 38°N, longitude 125°W when the initial great-circle course angle is N111°W.

Solution.—(1) Entering the tables with latitude 38° (Same Name), LHA 111°, and with successive declinations of 85°, 80°, 75° . . . the latitudes and differences in longitude, from 125°W, are found as tabular altitudes and azimuth angles respectively:

Distance n.mi. (arc)	300(5°)	600(10°)	900(15°)	3600(60°)	4800(80°)
Latitude	36°1N	33°9N	31°4N	3°6N	3°1S
DLo	5°8	11°3	16°5	54°1	61°5
Longitude	130°8W	136°3W	141°5W	179°1W	173°5E

Example 7.—Find a number of points along the great-circle from latitude 38°N, long. 125°W when the initial great-circle course angle is N69°W.

Solution.—Entering the tables with latitude 38° (Same Name), LHA 69°, and with successive declinations of 85°, 80°, 75° . . . the latitudes and differences of longitude, from 125°W, are found as tabular altitudes and azimuth angles, respectively:

Distance n.mi.(arc)	300(5°)	600(10°)	900(15°)	6600(110°)	7200(120°)
Latitude	39°6N	40°9N	41°9N	3°1N	3°6S
DLo	6°1	12°4	18°9	118°5	125°9
Longitude	131°1W	137°4W	143°9W	116°5E	109°1E

The latitude and difference of longitude of the point 6600 miles from the point of departure are found among the data for the latitude of departure continued on the facing page. Since the respondents for the point 7200 miles from the point of departure are found across the C–S Line on the facing page, the tabular altitude corresponds to a latitude on the side of the equator opposite from that of the point of departure; the tabular azimuth angle is the supplement of the difference of longitude.

Finding The Vertex

The use of Pub. No. 229 to find the approximate position of the vertex of a great-circle track provides a rapid check on the solution by computation. This approximate solution is also useful for voyage planning purposes.

Using the procedures for finding points along the great circle, the column of data for the latitude of the point of departure is inspected to find the maximum value of tabular altitude. This maximum tabular altitude and the tabular azimuth angle correspond to the latitude of the vertex and the difference of longitude of the vertex and the point of departure.

Example 7.—Find the vertex of the great-circle track from lat. 38°N, long. 125°W when the initial great-circle course angle is N69°W.

Solution.—(1) Enter Pub. No. 229 with lat. 38° (Same Name), LHA 69°, and inspect the column for lat. 38° to find the maximum tabular altitude.

(2) The maximum tabular altitude is found to be 42°38ʹ1 at a distance of 1500 nautical miles (90°−65°=25°) from the point of departure. The corresponding tabular azimuth angle is 32°4. Therefore, the difference of longitude of vertex and point of departure is 32°4.

Answers.—(1) Latitude of vertex 42°38ʹ1N.

(2) Longitude of vertex 157°4W.

907. Altering a great-circle track to avoid obstructions.—Great-circle sailing cannot be used unless the great-circle track is free from obstructions. It does not start until one clears the harbor and takes his departure (art. 806), and often ends near the entrance to the destination. However, islands, points of land, or other obstructions may prevent the use of great-circle sailing over the entire distance. One of the principal advantages of solution by great-circle chart is that the presence of any obstructions is immediately apparent.

Often a relatively short run by rhumb line is sufficient to reach a point from which the great-circle track can be followed. Where a choice is possible, the rhumb line selected should conform as nearly as practicable to the direct great circle.

If the great circle crosses a small island, one or more legs may be altered slightly, or perhaps the drift of the vessel will be sufficient to make any planned alteration unnecessary. The possible use of the island in obtaining an en route fix should not be overlooked. If a larger obstruction is encountered, as in the case of the Aleutian Islands on a great circle from Seattle to Yokohama, some judgment may be needed in selecting the track. It may be satisfactory to follow a great circle to the vicinity of the obstruction, one or more rhumb lines along the edge of the obstruction, and another great circle to the destination. Another possible solution is the use of composite sailing (art. 908), and still another the use of two great circles, one from the point of departure to a point near the maximum latitude of unobstructed water, and the second from this point to the destination.

It is sometimes desirable to alter a great-circle track to avoid unfavorable winds or currents. The shortest route is not always the quickest.

Whatever the problem, a great-circle chart can be helpful in its solution.

908. Composite sailing.—When the great circle would carry a vessel to a higher latitude than desired, a modification of great-circle sailing, called **composite sailing,** may be used to good advantage. The composite track consists of a great circle from the point of departure and tangent to the limiting parallel, a course line along the parallel, and a great circle tangent to the limiting parallel and through the destination.

Solution of composite sailing problems is most easily made by means of a great-circle chart. Lines from the point of departure and the destination are drawn tangent to the limiting parallel. The coordinates of various selected points along the composite track are then measured and transferred to a Mercator chart, as in great-circle sailing (art. 904).

Composite sailing problems can also be solved by computation (art. 1011, vol. II).

CHAPTER X

PILOTING

General

1001. Introduction.—On the high seas, where there is no immediate danger of grounding, navigation is a comparatively leisurely process. Courses and speeds are maintained over relatively long periods, and fixes are obtained at convenient intervals. Under favorable conditions a vessel might continue for several days with no positions other than those obtained by dead reckoning, or by estimate, and with no anxiety on the part of the captain or navigator. Errors in position can usually be detected and corrected before danger threatens.

In the vicinity of shoal water the situation is different. Frequent or continuous positional information is usually essential to the safety of the vessel. An error, which on the high seas may be considered small, may in what are called **pilot waters** be intolerably large. Frequent changes of course and speed are common. The proximity of other vessels increases the possibility of collisions and restricts movements.

In some waters the services of a specially qualified navigator having local knowledge may be necessary to insure safe navigation. **Local knowledge** extends beyond that publicly available in charts and publications, being more detailed, intimate, and current. The pilot's knowledge of his waters is gained not only through his own experience and familiarity, but by his availing himself of all local information resources, public and private, recent and longstanding, particularly concerning underwater hazards and obstructions, uncharted above-water landmarks and topographical configurations, local tides and currents, recent shoaling, temporary changes or deficiencies in aids to navigation, and similar matters of local concern. This local knowledge should enable a pilot to traverse his waters safely without reliance on man-made aids to navigation and to detect any unusual conditions or departure from a safe course. This service does not substitute for the ship's own safe navigation, but complements it. Prudence may also dictate the use of this specially qualified navigator to better insure safe navigation in situations where local knowledge is not essential. This navigator specially qualified for specific waters is called a **pilot**; his services are referred to as **pilotage** or **piloting.**

In its more general sense, the term **piloting** is used to mean the art of safely conducting a vessel on waters the hazards of which make necessary frequent or continuous positioning with respect to *charted* features and close attention to the vessel's draft with respect to the depth of water. Except for special circumstances, such as proceeding along a **range** (art. 1004), this positioning normally must be effected by constructing a plot on the chart based upon accurate navigational observations of charted features.

No other form of navigation requires the continuous alertness needed in piloting. At no other time is navigational experience and judgment so valuable. The ability to work rapidly and to correctly interpret all available information, always keeping "ahead of the vessel," may mean the difference between safety and disaster.

1002. Preparation for piloting.—Because the time element is often of vital importance in piloting, adequate preparation is important. Long-range preparation includes the organization and training of those who will assist in any way. This includes

271

the steersman, who will be granted less tolerance in straying from the prescribed course than when farther offshore.

The more immediate preparation includes a study of the charts and publications of the area to familiarize oneself with the channels, shoals, tides, currents, aids to navigation, etc. One seldom has time to seek such information once he is proceeding in pilot waters. This preparation also includes the development of a definite plan for transiting the hazardous waters. Since the services provided by pilots having local knowledge are usually *advisory*, prudence dictates that the regularly assigned navigational personnel be advised of the pilot's plan. Otherwise, their ability to counteract any imprudent action on the part of the pilot may be severely limited. Also, knowledge of the pilot's plan enables the regularly assigned navigational personnel to act more effectively in verifying that the pilot is making a safe passage. The more detailed preparation required for leaving or entering port is given in chapter XXIII.

Position

1003. Lines of position.—As in celestial and radionavigation, piloting makes extensive use of **lines or position.** Such a line is one on some point of which the vessel may be presumed to be located, as a result of observation or measurement. It may be highly reliable, or of questionable accuracy. Lines of position are of great value, but one should always keep in mind that *they can be in error* because of imperfections in instruments used for obtaining them and human limitations in those who use the instruments and utilize the results. The extent to which one can have confidence in various lines of position is a matter of judgment acquired from experience.

A line of position might be a straight line (actually a part of a great circle), an arc of a circle, or part of some other curve such as a hyperbola (art. 134, vol. II). An appropriate label should be placed on the plot of a line of position *at the time it is drawn*, to avoid possible error or confusion. A label should include all information essential for identification, but no extraneous information. *The labels shown in this volume are recommended.*

1004. Bearings.—A **bearing** is the horizontal direction of one terrestrial point from another. It is usually expressed as the angular difference between a reference direction and the given direction. In navigation, north is generally used as the reference direction, and angles are measured clockwise through 360°. It is customary to express all bearings in three digits, using preliminary zeros where needed. Thus, north is 000° or 360°, a direction 7° to the right of north is 007°, east is 090°, southwest is 225°, etc.

For plotting, *true* north is used as the reference direction. A bearing measured from this reference is called a **true bearing. A magnetic, compass,** or **grid bearing** results from using magnetic, compass, or grid north, respectively, as the reference direction. This is similar to the designation of courses. In the case of bearings, however, one additional reference direction is often convenient. This is the heading of the ship. A bearing expressed as angular distance from the heading is called a **relative bearing.** It is usually measured clockwise through 360°. A relative bearing may be expressed in still another way, as indicated in figure 1004. Except for dead ahead and points at 45° intervals from it, this method is used principally for indicating directions obtained visually, without precise measurement. An even more general indication of relative bearing may be given by such directions as "ahead," "on the starboard bow," "on the port quarter," "astern." The term *abeam* may be used as the equivalent of either the general "on the beam" or, sometimes, the more precise "broad on the beam." Degrees are sometimes used instead of points to express relative bearings by the system illustrated in figure 1004. However, if degrees are used, a better practice is to use the 360°

system. Thus, a relative bearing of "20° forward of the port beam" is better expressed as "290°."

True, magnetic, and compass bearings are interconverted by the use of variation and deviation, or compass error, in the same manner as courses. Interconversion of relative and other bearings is accomplished by means of the heading. If true heading is added to relative bearing, true bearing results. If magnetic, compass, or grid heading is added to relative bearing, the corresponding magnetic, compass, or grid bearing is obtained.

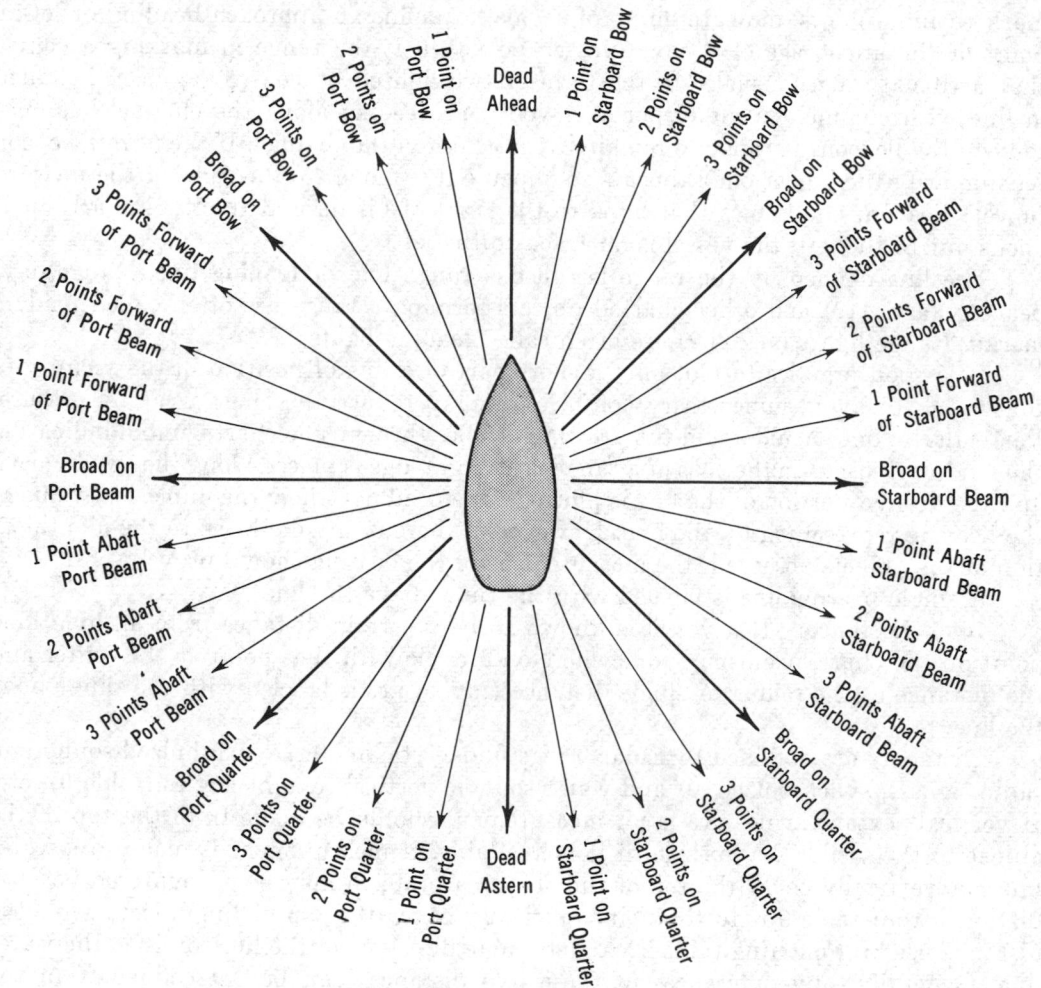

FIGURE 1004.—One method of expressing relative bearings.

A **bearing line** extending in the direction of an observed bearing of a charted object is one of the most widely used lines of position. If one knows that an identified landmark has a certain bearing from his vessel, the vessel can only be on the line at which such a bearing might be observed, for at any other point the bearing would be different. This line extends outward from the landmark, along the *reciprocal* of the observed bearing. Thus, if a lighthouse is *east* of a ship, that ship is *west* of the lighthouse. If a beacon bears 156°, the observer must be on a line extending 156°+180°=336° from the beacon. Since observed bearing lines are great circles, this relationship is not strictly accurate, but the error is significant only where the great circle departs materially from the rhumb line, as in high latitudes (ch. XXV).

Bearings are obtained by compass, gyro repeater, pelorus, alidade, radar, etc. One type of bearing can be obtained by eye without measurement. When two objects appear directly in line, one behind the other, they are said to be "in range," and together they constitute a **range**. For accurately charted objects, a range may provide the most accurate line of position obtainable, and one of the easiest to observe. Tanks, steeples, towers, cupolas, etc., sometimes form **natural ranges.** A navigator should be familiar with prominent ranges in his operating area, particularly those which can be used to mark turning points, indicate limits of shoals, or define an approach heading or let-go point of the anchorage of a naval vessel. So useful is the range in marking a course that artificial ranges, usually in the form of two lighted beacons, have been installed in line with channels in many ports. A vessel proceeding along the channel has only to keep the beacons in range to remain in the center of the channel. If the *farther* beacon (customarily the higher one) appears to "open out" (move) to the right of the forward (lower) beacon, one knows that he is to the right of his desired track. Similarly, if it opens out to the left, the vessel is off track to the left.

The line defined by the range is called a **range line** or **leading line**. Range day-beacons (art. 412) and other charted objects forming a range are often called **leading marks**. Range lights (art. 402) are often called **leading lights**.

It is good practice to plot only a short part of a line of position in the vicinity of the vessel, to avoid unnecessary confusion and to reduce the chart wear by erasure. Particularly, one should avoid the drawing of lines through the chart symbol indicating the landmark used. In the case of a range, a straightedge is placed along the two objects, and the desired portion of the line is plotted. One need not know the numerical value of the bearing represented by the line. However, if there is any doubt as to the identification of the objects observed, the measurement of the bearing should prove useful.

A single bearing line is labeled with the time above the line.

1005. Distance.—If a vessel is known to be a certain distance from an identified point on the chart, it must be somewhere on a circle with that point as the center and the distance as the radius. A single distance (range) arc is labeled with the time above the line.

Distances are obtained by radar, range finder, stadimeter, synchronized sound and radio signals, synchronized air and water sounds, vertical sextant angles (table 9), etc. If vertical sextant angles are used, measurement should be made from the top of the object to the visible sea horizon, if it is available. If measurement is made to a water line not vertically below the top of the object, a problem may be encountered because distance from table 9 is to the point vertically below the top of the object, while the distance used for entering table 22 to determine dip short of the horizon is to the water line. Generally, any differences in these two distances can be determined from the chart. This problem may, in some cases, be avoided by decreasing the height of eye sufficiently to bring the horizon between the observer and the object.

1006. The fix.—A line of position, however obtained, represents a series of possible positions, but not a single position. However, if *two simultaneous, nonparallel* lines of position are available, the only position that satisfies the requirements of being on both lines at the same time is the intersection of the two lines. This point is one form of **fix.** Examples of several types of fix are given in the illustrations. In figure 1006a a fix is obtained from two bearing lines. The fix of figure 1006b is obtained by two distance circles. Figure 1006c illustrates a fix from a range and a distance. In figure 1006d a bearing and distance of a single object are used. A small circle is used to indicate the fix at the intersection of the lines of position. The time of the fix is the time at which the lines of position were established.

Some consideration should be given to the selection of objects to provide a fix. It is essential, for instance, that the objects be identified. The angle between lines of position is important. The ideal is 90°. If the angle is small, a slight error in measuring or plotting either line results in a relatively large error in the indicated position. In the case of a bearing line, nearby objects are preferable to those at a considerable distance, because the linear (distance) error resulting from an angular error increases with distance.

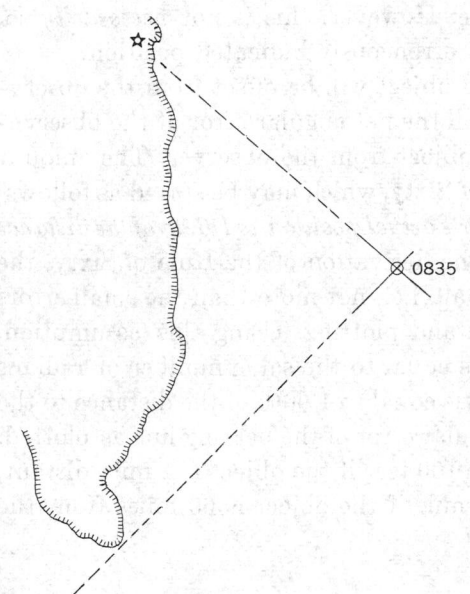

FIGURE 1006a.—A fix by two bearing lines.

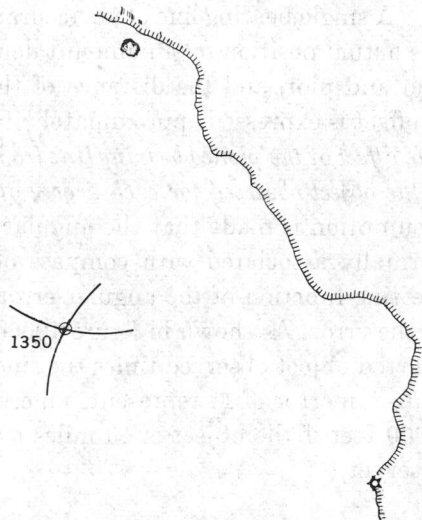

FIGURE 1006b.—A fix by two distances.

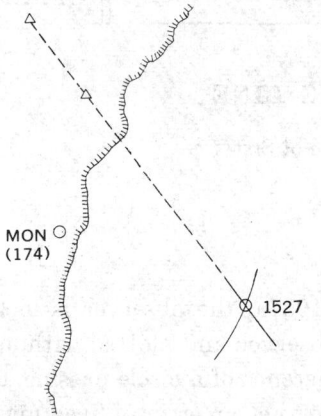

FIGURE 1006c.—A fix by a range and distance.

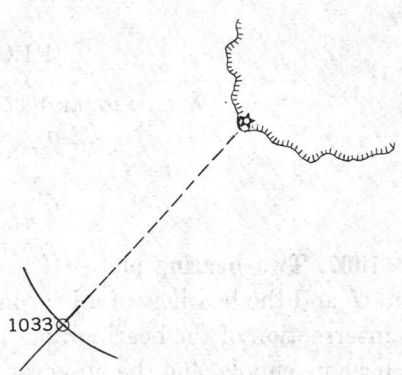

FIGURE 1006d.—A fix by distance and bearing of single object.

Another consideration is the type of object. Lighthouses, spires, flagpoles, etc., are good objects because the point of observation is well defined. A large building, most nearby mountains, a point of land, etc., may leave some reasonable doubt as to the exact point used for observation. If a tangent is used (fig. 1006a), there is a possibility that a low spit may extend seaward from the part observed. A number of towers, chimneys, etc., close together require careful identification. A buoy or a lightship may drag anchor and be out of position. Most buoys are secured by a single anchor and so have a certain radius of swing as the tide, current, and wind change.

Although two accurate nonparallel lines of position completely define a position, if they are taken at the same time, an element of doubt always exists as to the accuracy of the lines. Additional lines of position can serve as a check on those already obtained, and, usually, to reduce any existing error. If three lines of position cross at a common point, or form a small triangle, it is usually a reasonable assumption that the position is reliable, and defined by the center of the figure. However, this is not *necessarily* so, and one should be aware of the possibility of an erroneously indicated position.

A single bearing line of an accurately charted object will be offset from the observer's actual position by an amount dependent upon the net angular error of the observation and plot, and the distance of the charted object from the observer. The amount of offset is expressed approximately in the **Rule of Sixty,** which may be stated as follows: *The offset of the plotted bearing line from the observer's actual position is 1/60th of the distance to the object observed for each degree of error.* In the derivation of the Rule of Sixty, the assumption is made that the angular error is small, i.e., not more than the small errors normally associated with compass observations and plotting. Using this assumption, the sine function of the angular error is taken as equal to the same number of radians as the error. As shown in figure 1006e, the offset is equal to 1/60th of the distance to the charted object observed times the sine of the angular error of the bearing line as plotted. Thus, an error of 1° represents an error of about 100 feet if the object is 1 mile distant, 1,000 feet if the object is 10 miles away, and 1 mile if the object is 60 miles from the observer.

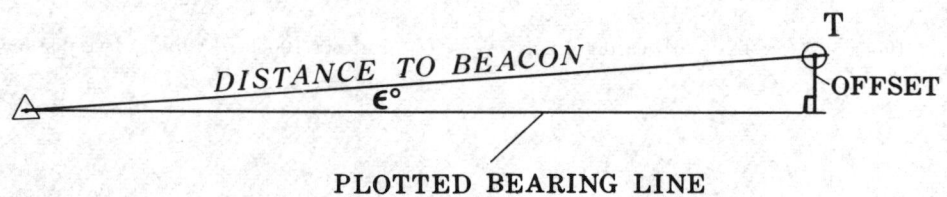

FIGURE 1006e.—Basis of the Rule of Sixty.

1007. Two-bearing plot.—If as shown in figure 1007a, the observer is located at point T and the bearings of a beacon and cupola are observed and plotted without error, the intersection of the bearing lines lies on the circumference of a circle passing through the beacon, cupola, and the observer. With *constant error*, i.e., an error of fixed magnitude and sign (or direction) for a given set of observations, the angular difference of the bearings of the beacon and the cupola is not affected. Thus, the angle formed at point F by the bearing lines plotted with constant error is equal to the angle formed at point T by the bearing lines plotted without error. From geometry it is known that angles having their apexes on the circumference of a circle and that are subtended by the same chord are equal. Since the angles at points T and F are equal and the angles are subtended by the same chord, the intersection at point F lies on the circumference of a circle passing through the beacon, cupola, and the observer.

Assuming only constant error in the plot, the direction of displacement of the two-bearing fix from the position of the observer is in accordance with the sign (or direction) of the constant error. However, a third bearing is required to determine the direction of the constant error.

Assuming only constant error in the plot, the two-bearing fix lies on the circumference of the circle passing through the two charted objects observed and the observer. The fix error, i.e., the length of the chord FT in figure 1007b, is dependent upon the magnitude of the constant error ϵ, the distance between the charted objects, and the cosecant of the angle of cut, angle θ. In figure 1007b,

$$\text{fix error} = FT = \frac{\epsilon \; BC \csc \theta}{2} \qquad \text{(where } \epsilon \text{ is a small angle).}$$

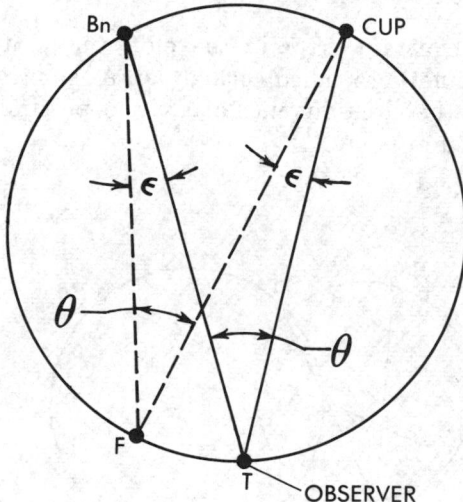

FIGURE 1007a.—Two-bearing plot.

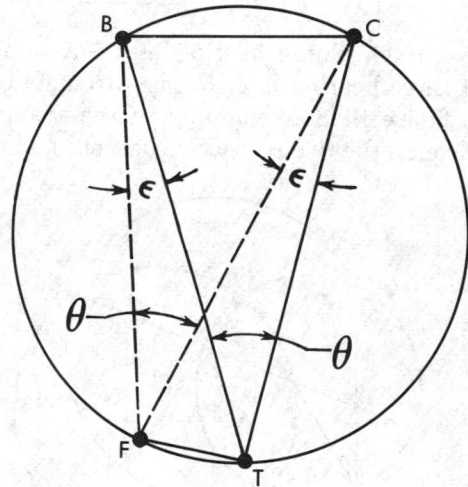

FIGURE 1007b.—Two-bearing plot with constant error.

Thus, the fix error is least when the angle of cut is 90°. As illustrated in figure 1007c, the error increases in accordance with the cosecant function as the angle of cut decreases. The increase in the error becomes quite rapid after the angle of cut has decreased to below about 30°. With an angle of cut of 30°, the fix error is about twice that at 90°.

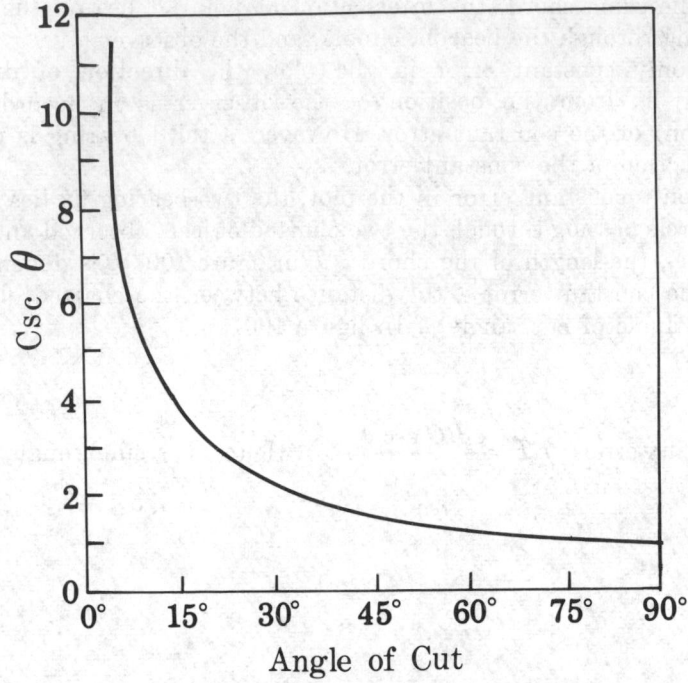

FIGURE 1007c.—Error of two-bearing plot.

1008. Three-bearing plot.—Assuming only constant error in the plot, the plot of three bearing lines forms a **triangle of error,** sometimes called **cocked hat.** As shown in figure 1008a, each apex of the triangle lies on the circumference of a circle passing through the two respective beacons and the observer at point T.

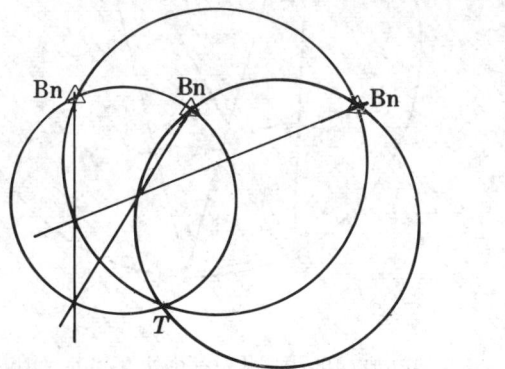

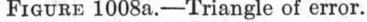

FIGURE 1008a.—Triangle of error.

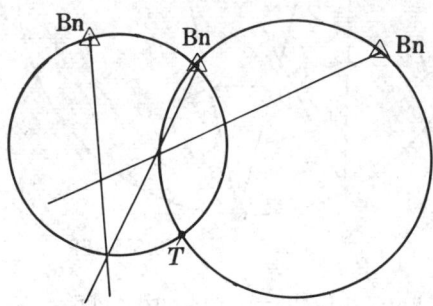

FIGURE 1008b.—Three-bearing plot.

The same situation is shown in figure 1008b, but only two of the circles are drawn through their respective beacons. For the set of angular differences established by the differences of the bearing observations, the observer can be located only at the intersection of the two circles at point T. Note that point T is not inside the triangle in this instance. If all error is due to constant error and the bearing spread, i.e., the angular difference between the extreme left and right beacons, is less than 180°, point T is *always* outside the triangle. If all error is due to constant error, and the bearing spread is greater than 180°, point T is always inside the triangle as shown in figure 1008c.

With a bearing spread greater than 180°, and assuming only constant error, the fix position in a three-bearing plot forming a triangle of error is the geometric center of the triangle as shown in figure 1008c. The geometric center is located at the intersection of the bisectors of the three interior angles as illustrated in figure 1008d.

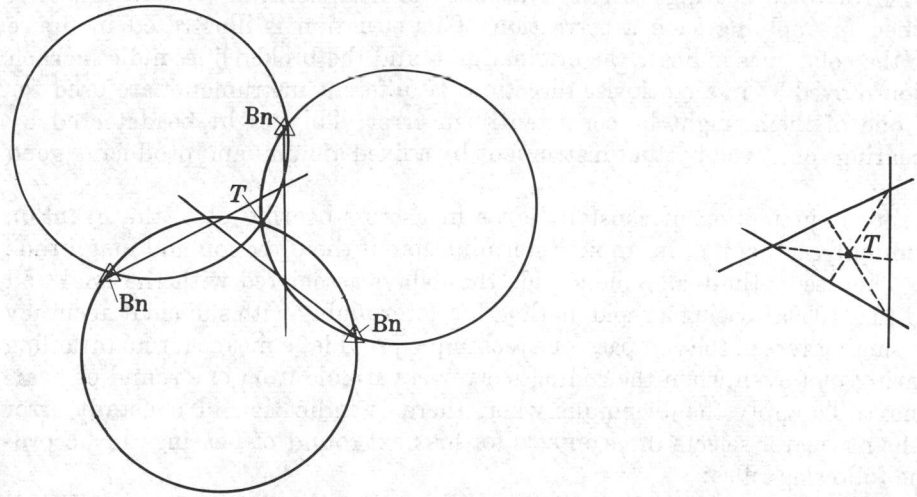

FIGURE 1008c.—Three-bearing plot.

FIGURE 1008d.—Bisecting the interior angles of a triangle of error.

With a bearing spread less than 180°, and assuming only constant error, the fix position in a three-bearing plot forming a triangle of error lies outside the triangle at the point of common intersection obtained by rotating each bearing line an equal amount in the same direction. This common intersection lies at the intersection of the bisectors of the appropriate two adjacent exterior angles and the opposite interior angle. Examination of figure 1008e, and similar constructions for bearing spreads of less than 180°, reveals that the common intersection cannot lie within the area bounded by the bearing lines extending from the triangle toward their respective objects. Further examination reveals that of the two remaining sets of adjacent exterior angles being investigated to determine that set which, with its opposite interior angle, should be bisected to determine the common intersection, only one set is immediately adjacent to the area bounded by the bearing lines extending from the triangle toward their respective objects. The set adjacent to the latter area is the set to be bisected.

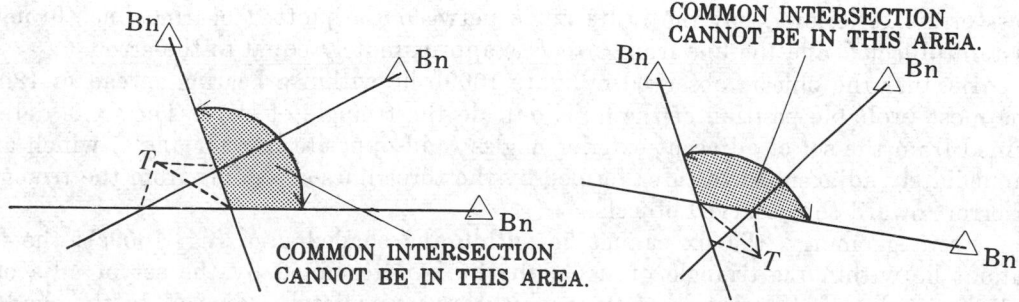

FIGURE 1008e.—Bisecting the exterior angles of a triangle of error.

1009. Adjusting a fix for constant error.—If several fixes obtained by bearings on three objects produce triangles of error of about the same size, one might reasonably suspect a constant error in the observation of the bearings, particularly if the same instrument is used for all observations, or in the plotting of the lines. If the application of a constant error to all bearings results in a point, or near-point fix, the navigator is usually justified in applying such a correction. This situation is illustrated in figure 1009a, where the solid lines indicate the original plot, and the broken lines indicate each line of position moved 3° in a clockwise direction. If different instruments are used for observation, one of them might be consistently in error. This might be detected by altering all bearings observed by that instrument by a fixed amount and producing good fixes.

When there is indication of constant error in a cross-bearing plot, the **Franklin Piloting Technique** can be used for rapid determination of the direction and magnitude of the error. The use of the technique avoids the delays associated with the trial and error method (fig. 1009a). Being a rapid method for determining with sufficient accuracy the normally small errors of the compass, the technique provides a means for maintaining the cross-bearing plot even when the compass error is variable from one round of bearings to the next. To apply the technique when there is indication of constant error in the plot, the navigator selects three objects for his next round of bearings in accordance with the following rules:

1. Two of the three objects should be nearby so that the displacements of their plotted bearings lines from the observer's actual position, as a result of a small constant error, will be small.

2. The third object should be at least two and one-half times the distance of the farther of the two nearby objects so that the displacement of its plotted bearing line from the observer's actual position, as a result of a small constant error, will be relatively large.

3. Preferably, the third object should lie in a direction from the observer approximately parallel to a line between the two nearby objects.

With selection as in (3) above, the line drawn from the third object to the intersection of the bearing lines of the two nearby objects is nearly tangent to the circle through these nearby objects and the observer's actual position (fig. 1009b). Being nearly tangent to this circle, the line drawn from the most distant object passes close to the observer's actual position, which is close to the point of tangency for small constant errors.

As shown in figure 1009b, the bearing lines through nearby objects A and B intersect at F on the circle through A, B, and the observer's actual position at point T. The acute angle between the plotted bearing line through distant object C and a line from C to T is exactly equal to the error, assuming that all error is due to a constant compass error. It follows that the acute angle between the plotted bearing line through distant object C and the line from C to F is approximately equal to the error.

Because the objects observed in figure 1009b lie within a bearing spread of 180°, the most probable position of the fix is outside the triangle of error. The fix is determined from the set of adjacent exterior angles (and opposite interior angle) which are immediately adjacent to the area formed by the three lines extending from the triangle of error toward the observed objects.

From geometry, the fix cannot lie within the shaded area (fig. 1009c); the fix cannot lie within the triangle of error; the fix is determined by the set of adjacent exterior angles of the triangle of error which are immediately adjacent to the shaded area. The adjacent set establishes the fix at T.

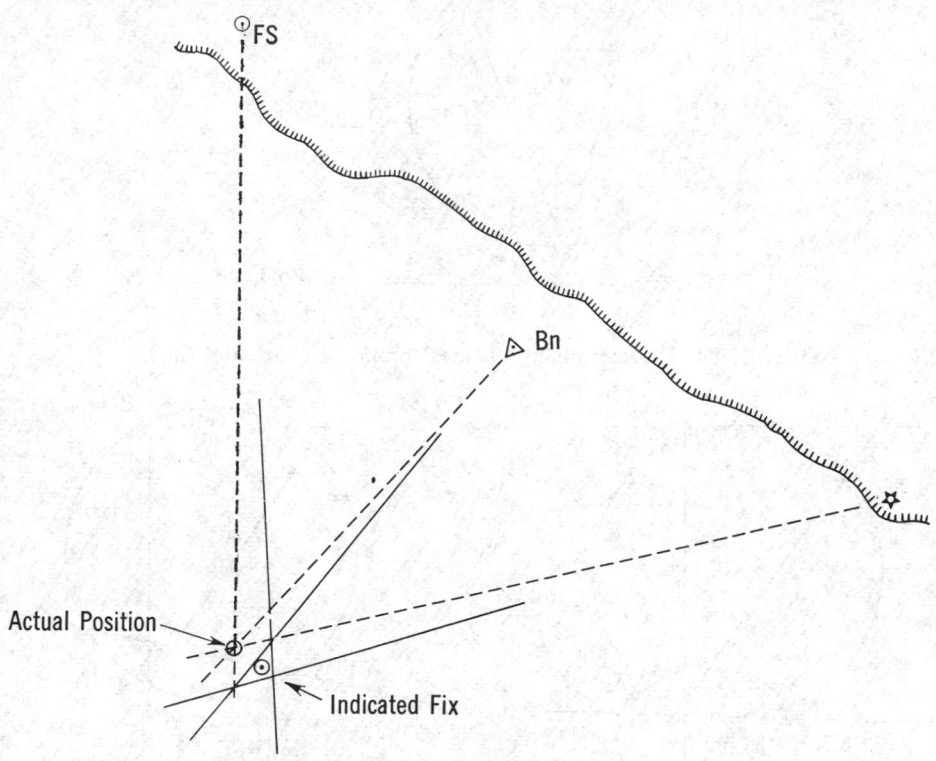

FIGURE 1009a.—Adjusting a fix for constant error.

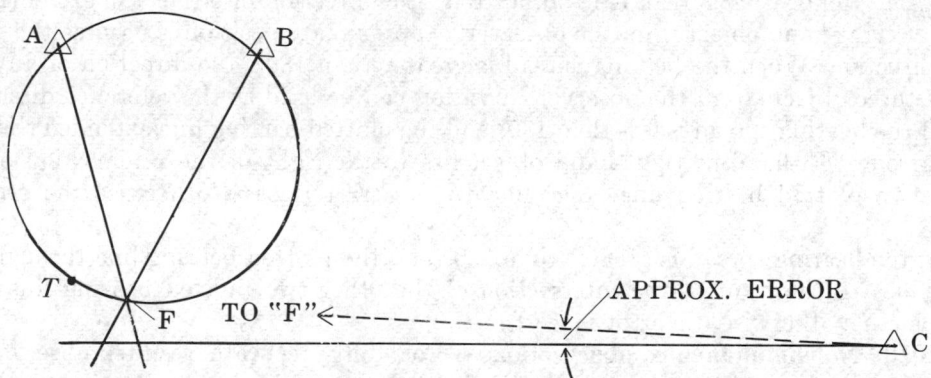

FIGURE 1009b.—Selection of charted objects for observation.

Although the foregoing use of the geometry of the cross-bearing plot could be used to find the direction of the constant error, the Franklin technique provides a simpler means. However, a reference direction must first be established. This reference direction is used to determine whether the plotted bearing line of one of the three objects lies to the left or right of the intersection of the bearing lines of the other two. For example, in the left-hand plot of figure 1009d the intersection at F is taken as being to the right of the plotted bearing line of object C.

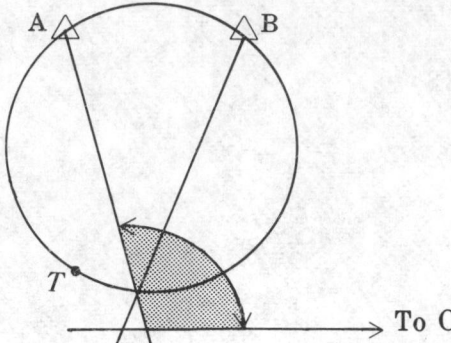

FIGURE 1009c.—Determining the most probable position of the fix.

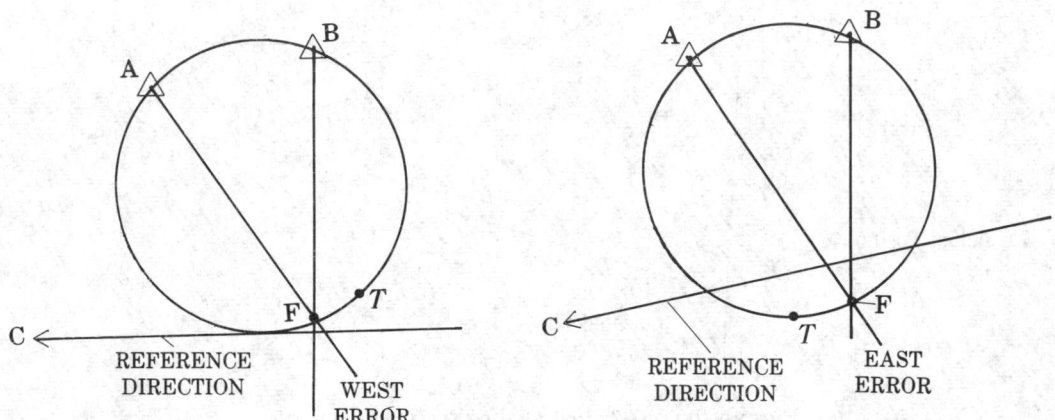

FIGURE 1009d.—Determining constant error when bearing spread is less than 180°.

When the bearing spread is less than 180°, the direction of either the extreme left-hand or right-hand object from the observer's approximate position is used as the reference direction. When the bearing spread is greater than 180°, the direction of any one of the three objects from the observer's position can be used as the reference direction.

If the bearing spread is less than 180° and the plotted bearing line extended through the extreme left-hand or right-hand object lies to the right of the intersection of the other two plotted bearing lines (fig. 1009d), the error is east; otherwise the error is west.

If the bearing spread is greater than 180° and the plotted bearing line through one object lies to the right of the intersection of the other two plotted bearing lines, the error is east; otherwise the error is west.

1010. Nonsimultaneous observations.—For fully accurate results, observations made to fix the position of a moving vessel should be made simultaneously, or nearly so. On a slow-moving vessel, relatively little error is introduced by making several observations in quick succession. A wise precaution is to observe the objects more nearly ahead or astern first, since these are least affected by the motion of the observer. However, when it is desired to obtain a good estimate of the speed being made good, it may be desirable to observe the most rapidly changing bearing first, assuming that such observation can be better coordinated with the time "mark."

Sometimes it is not possible or desirable to make simultaneous or nearly simultaneous observations. Such a situation may arise, for instance, when a single object is available for observation, or when all available objects are on nearly the same or reciprocal bearings, and there is no means of determining distance. Under such conditions, a period of several minutes or more may be permitted to elapse between observations to provide lines of position crossing at suitable angles. When this occurs, the lines can be adjusted to a common time to obtain a **running fix.** Refer to figure 1010a. A ship is proceeding along a coast on course 020°, speed 15 knots. At 1505 lighthouse L bears 310°. If the line of position is accurate, the ship is somewhere on it at the time of observation. Ten minutes later the ship will have traveled 2.5 miles in direction 020°. If the ship was at A at 1505, it will be at A' at 1515. However, if the position at 1505 was B, the position at 1515 will be B'. A similar relationship exists between C and C', D and D', E and E', etc. Thus, if *any* point on the original line of position is moved a distance equal to the distance run, and in the direction of the motion, a line through this point, parallel to the original line of position, represents all possible positions of the ship at the later time. This process is called **advancing** a line of position. The moving of a line *back* to an *earlier* time is called **retiring** a line of position.

The accuracy of an adjusted line of position depends not only upon the accuracy of the original line, but also upon the reliability of the information used in moving the line. A small error in the course made good has little effect upon the accuracy of a bearing line of an object near the beam, but maximum effect upon the bearing line of an object nearly ahead or astern. Conversely, the effect of an error in speed is maximum upon the bearing line of an object abeam. The opposite is true of circles of position. The best estimate of course and speed made good should be used in advancing or retiring a line of position.

If there are any changes of course or speed, these should be considered, for the motion of the line of position should reflect as accurately as possible the motion of the observer between the time of observation and the time to which the line is adjusted.

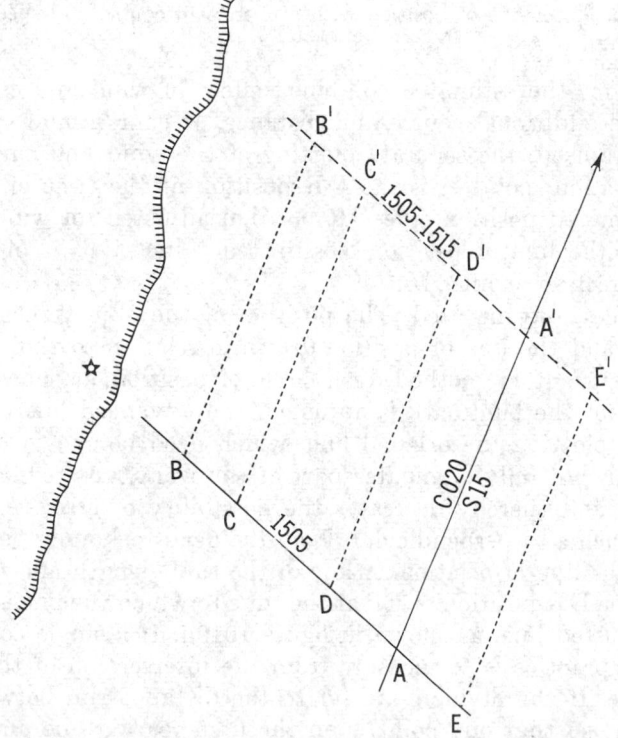

Figure 1010a.—Advancing a line of position.

Perhaps the easiest way to do this is to measure the direction and distance between dead reckoning or estimated positions at the two times, and use these to adjust some point on the line of position. This method is shown in figure 1010b. In this illustration

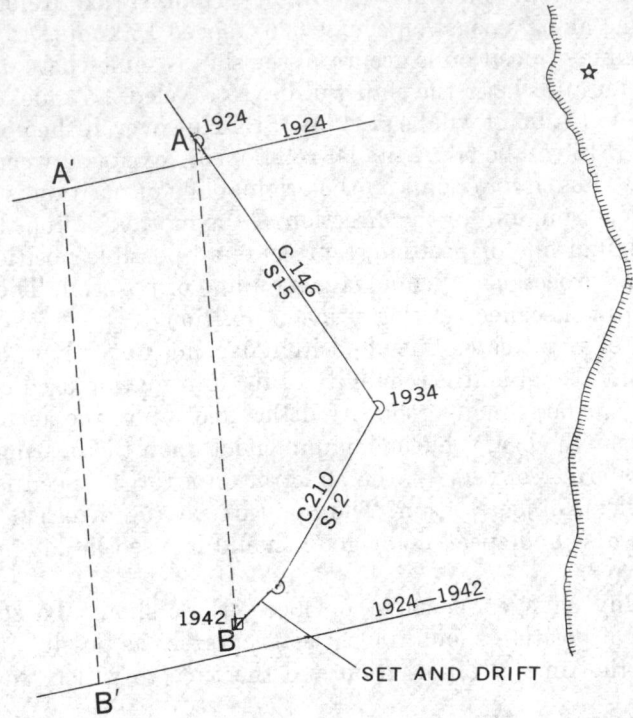

FIGURE 1010b.—Advancing a line of position with a change in course and speed, and allowing for current.

allowance is made for the estimated combined effect of wind and current, this effect being plotted as an additional course and distance. If courses and speeds made good over the ground are used, the separate plotting of the wind and current effect is not used. In the illustration, point A is the DR position at the time of observation, and point B is the estimated position (the DR position adjusted for wind and current) at the time to which the line of position is adjusted. Line $A'B'$ is of the same length and in the same direction as line AB.

Other techniques may be used. The position of the object observed may be advanced or retired, and the line of position drawn in relation to the adjusted position. This is the most satisfactory method for a circle of position, as shown in figure 1010c. When the position of the landmark is adjusted, the advanced line of position can be laid down without plotting the original line, which need be shown only if it serves a useful purpose. This not only eliminates part of the work, but reduces the number of lines on the chart, and thereby decreases the possibility of error. Another method is to draw any line, such as a perpendicular, from the dead reckoning position at the time of observation to the line of position. A line of the same length and in the same direction, drawn from the DR position or EP at the time to which the line is adjusted, locates a point on the adjusted line, as shown in figure 1010d. If a single course and speed is involved, common practice is to measure from the intersection of the line of position and the course line. If the dividers are set to the distance run between bearings and placed on the chart so that one point is on the first bearing line and the other point

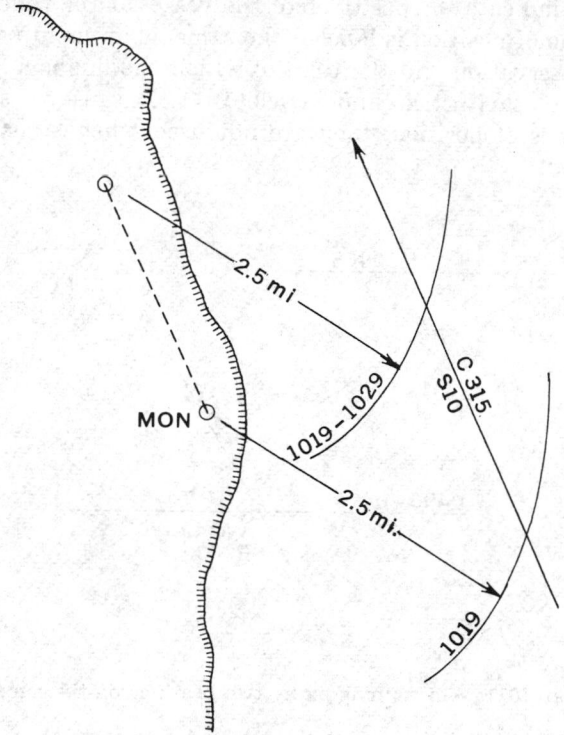

FIGURE 1010c.—Advancing a circle of position.

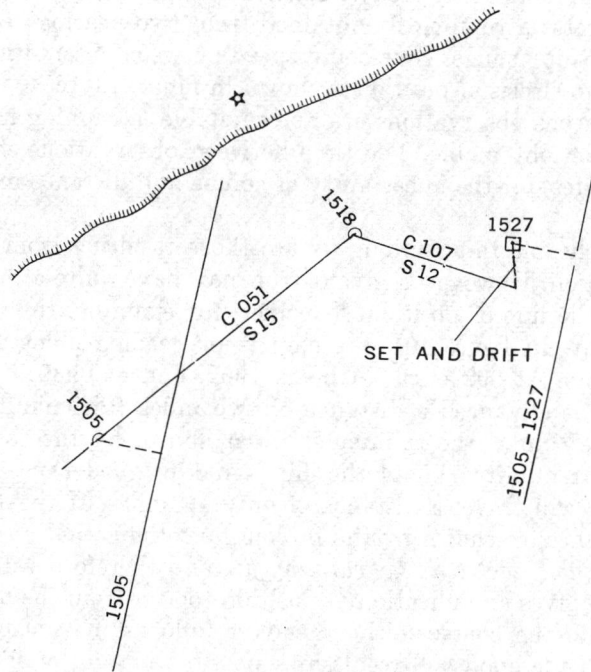

FIGURE 1010d.—Advancing a line of position by its relation to the dead reckoning.

is on the second bearing line, and the line connecting the points is parallel to the course line, the points will indicate the positions of the vessel at the times of the bearings.

An adjusted line of position is labeled the same as an unadjusted one, except that both the time of observation and the time to which the line is adjusted are shown, as in the illustrations of this article and article 1011. Because of additional sources of error in adjusted lines of position, they are not used when satisfactory simultaneous lines can be obtained.

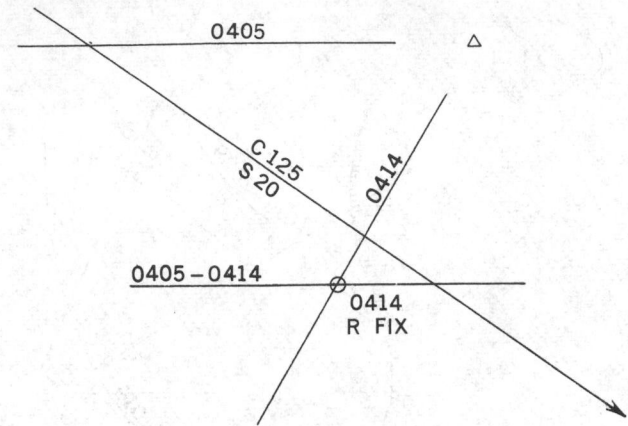

FIGURE 1011a.—A running fix by two bearings on the same object.

1011. The running fix.—As stated in article 1010, a fix obtained by means of lines of position taken at different times and adjusted to a common time is called a **running fix.** In piloting, common practice is to *advance* earlier lines to the time of the last observation. Figure 1011a illustrates a running fix obtained from two bearings of the same object. In figure 1011b the ship changes course and speed between observations of two objects. A running fix by two circles of position is shown in figure 1011c.

When simultaneous observations are not available, a running fix may provide the most reliable position obtainable. The time between observations should be no longer than about 30 minutes, for the uncertainty of course and distance made good increases with time.

The errors applicable to a running fix are those resulting from errors of the individual lines of position. However, a given error may have quite a different effect upon the fix than upon the line of position. Consider, for example, the situation of an unknown head current. In figure 1011d a ship is proceeding along a coast, on course 250°, speed 12 knots. At 0920 light A bears 190°, and at 0930 it bears 143°. If the earlier bearing line is advanced a distance of two miles (ten minutes at 12 knots) in the direction of the course, the running fix is as shown by the solid lines. However, if there is a head current of two knots, the ship is making good a speed of only ten knots, and in ten minutes will travel a distance of only 1⅔ miles. If the first bearing line is advanced this distance, as shown by the broken line, the actual position of the ship is at B. *This is nearer the beach than the running fix,* and therefore a dangerous situation. A following current gives an indication of position too far from the object. Therefore, if a current *parallel* to the course (either head or following) is suspected, a *minimum* estimate of speed made good will result in a possible margin of safety. If the second bearing is of a different object, a *maximum* estimate of speed should be made if the second object is on the same side and farther forward, or on the opposite side and farther aft, than the first object was when observed. All of these situations assume that danger

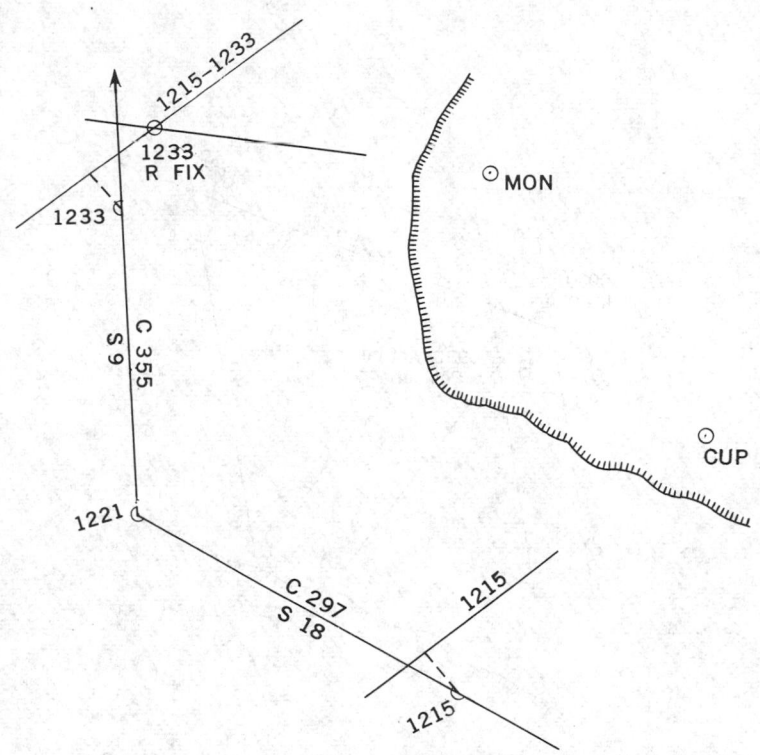

FIGURE 1011b.—A running fix with a change of course and speed between observations on separate landmarks.

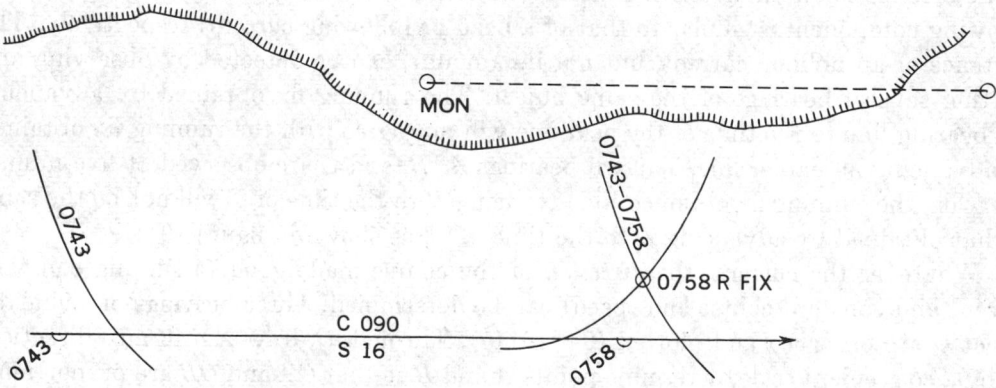

FIGURE 1011c.—A running fix by two circles of position.

is on the same side as the object observed first. If there is either a head or following current, a series of running fixes based upon a number of bearings of the same object will plot in a straight line parallel to the course line, as shown in figure 1011e. The plotted line will be too close to the object observed if there is a following current, and too far out if there is a head current. The existence of the current will not be apparent unless the actual speed over the ground is known. The position of the plotted line relative to the dead reckoning course line is not a reliable guide.

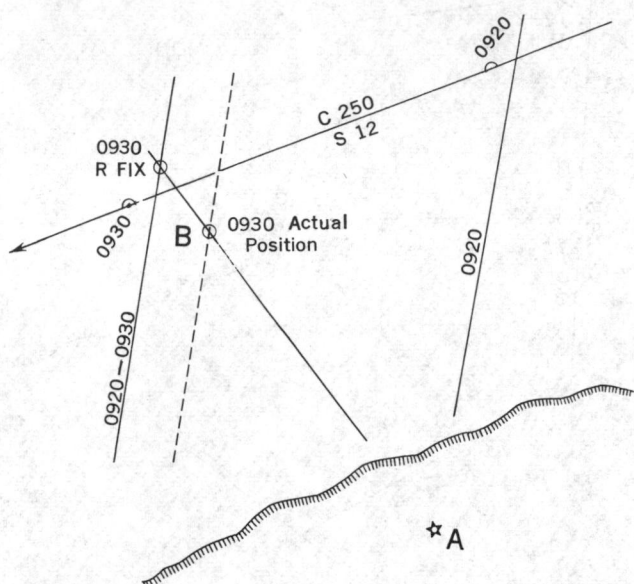

FIGURE 1011d.—Effect of a head current on a running fix.

A current oblique to the course will result in an incorrect position, but the direction of the error is indeterminate. In general, the effect of a current with a strong head or following component is similar to that of a head or following current, respectively. The existence of an oblique current, but not its amount, can be detected by observing and plotting several bearings of the same object. The running fix obtained by advancing one bearing line to the time of the next one will not agree with the running fix obtained by advancing an earlier line. Thus, if bearings A, B, and C are observed at five-minute intervals, the running fix obtained by advancing B to the time of C will not be the same as that obtained by advancing A to the time of C, as shown in figure 1011f.

Whatever the current, the *direction* of the course made good (assuming constant current and constant course and speed) can be determined. Three bearings of a charted object O are observed and plotted (fig. 1011g). Through O draw XY in any direction. Using a convenient scale, determine points A and B so that OA and OB are proportional to the time intervals between the first and second bearings and the second and third bearings, respectively. From A and B draw lines parallel to the second bearing line, intersecting the first and third bearing lines at C and D, respectively. The direction of the line from C and D is the course being made good.

The principle of the method shown in figure 1011g is based on the property of similar triangles. A frequently desirable variation of the method is to use the first bearing line as the side of the triangle that is divided in proportion to the time intervals between bearings (fig. 1011h). This method of solution of the **three-bearing problem** is presented in *The Complete Coastal Navigator* by Charles H. Cotter.

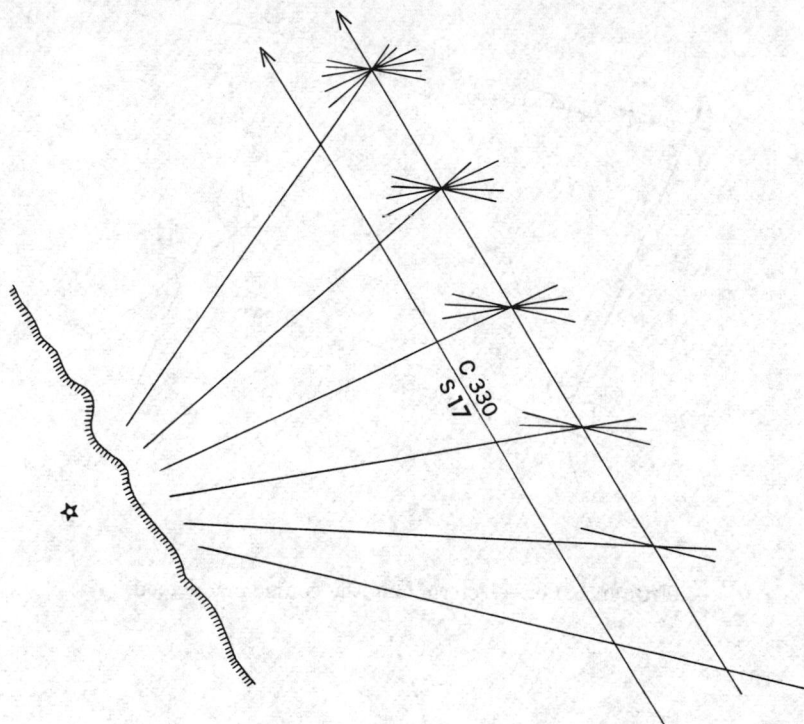

FIGURE 1011e.—A number of running fixes with a following current.

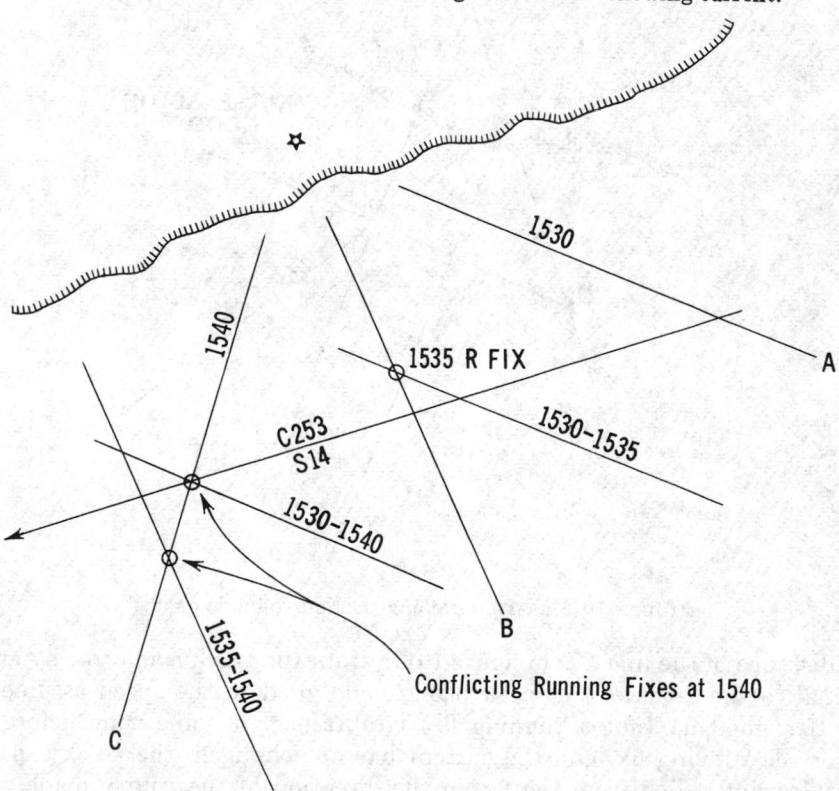

FIGURE 1011f.—Detecting the existence of an oblique current, by a series of running fixes.

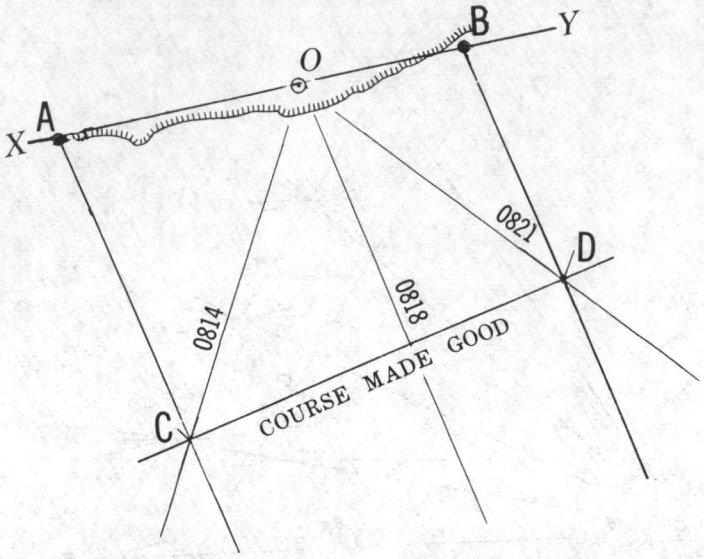

FIGURE 1011g.—Determining the course made good.

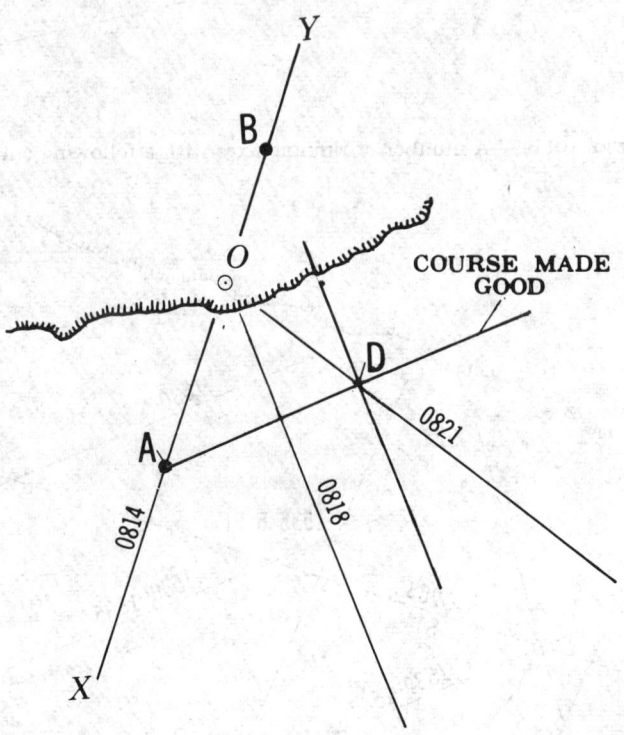

FIGURE 1011h.—Determining the course made good.

The distance of the line *CD* in figure 1011g from the track is in error by an amount proportional to the ratio of the speed being made good to the speed assumed for the solution. If a good fix (not a running fix) is obtained at some time before the first bearing for the running fix, and the current has not changed, the track can be determined by drawing a line from the fix, in the direction of the course made good. The intersection of the track with any of the bearing lines is an actual position.

The current can be determined whenever a dead reckoning position and fix are available for the same time. The direction *from* the dead reckoning position *to* the fix is the set of the current. The distance between these two positions, divided by the time (expressed in hours and tenths) since the last fix, is the drift of the current in knots. For accurate results, the dead reckoning position must be run up from the previous fix without any allowance for current. Any error in either the dead reckoning position (such as poor steering, unknown compass error, inaccurate log, wind, etc.) or the fix will be reflected in the determination of current. *When the dead reckoning position and fix are close together, a relatively small error in either may introduce a large error in the apparent set of the current.*

1012. Distance of an object by two bearings.—A running fix can be obtained by utilizing the mathematical relationships involved. A ship steams past landmark D (fig. 1012). At any point A a bearing of D is observed and expressed as degrees right or left of the course (*a relative bearing if the ship is on course*). At some later time, at B, a second bearing of D is observed and expressed as before. At C the landmark is broad on the beam. The angles at A, B, and C are known, and also the distance run between points. The various triangles could be solved by trigonometry to find the distance from D at any bearing. Distance and bearing provide a fix. Table 7 provides a quick and easy solution.

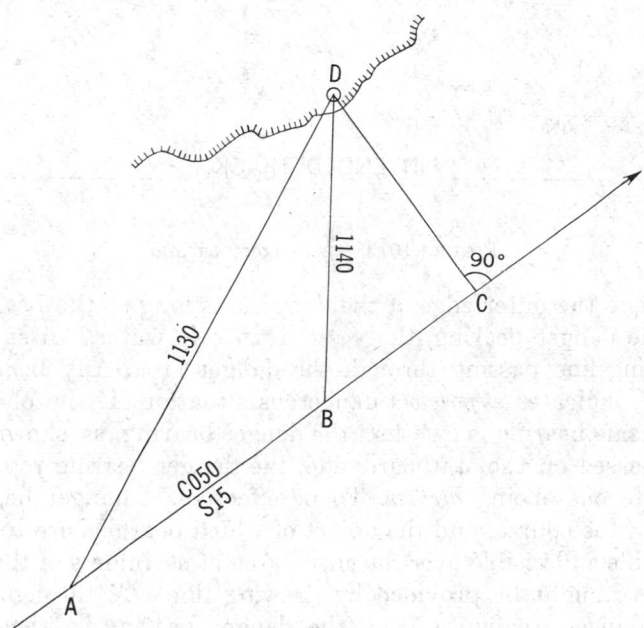

FIGURE 1012.—Triangles involved in a running fix.

Solution by table 7 or one of the special cases is accurate only *if a steady course has been steered, the vessel is unaffected by current, and the speed used is the speed over ground.*

There are certain *special cases* arising under the method of obtaining a running fix from two bearings and the intervening run which do not require the use of tables. Two of these cases arise when the multiplier is equal to unity, and the distance run is therefore equal to the distance from the object.

If the second difference (angle CBD of figure 1012) is double the first difference (angle BAD), triangle BAD is isosceles (art. 128, vol. II) with equal angles at A and

D. Therefore, side *AB* (the run) is equal to side *BD* (the distance off at the time of the second bearing). This is called **doubling the angle on the bow.** If the first angle is 45° and the second 90°, the distance run equals the distance when broad on the beam. These are called **bow and beam bearings.** Solutions by special cases are discussed in more detail in article 1205 of volume II.

1013. Safe piloting without a fix.—A fix or running fix is not always necessary to insure safety of the vessel. If a ship is proceeding up a dredged channel, for instance, the only knowledge needed to prevent grounding is that the ship is within the limits of the dredged area. This information might be provided by a range in line with the channel. A fix is not needed except to mark the point at which the range can no longer be followed with safety.

Under favorable conditions a **danger bearing** might be used to insure safe passage past a shoal or other danger. Refer to figure 1013. A vessel is proceeding along a coast, on intended track *AB*. A shoal is to be avoided. A line *HX* is drawn from light-

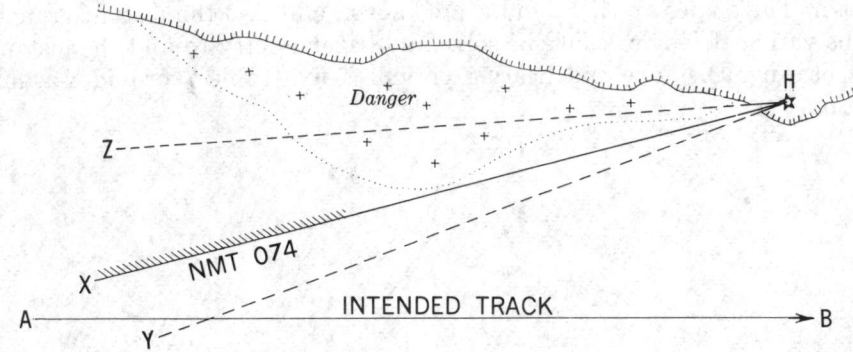

FIGURE 1013.—A danger bearing.

house *H*, tangent to the outer edge of the danger. As long as the bearing of light *H* is *less* than *XH*, the danger bearing, the vessel is in safe water. An example is *YH*, no part of the bearing line passing through the danger area. Any bearing *greater* than *XH*, such as *ZH*, indicates a *possible* dangerous situation. If the object is passed on the port side, the safe bearing is *less* than the danger bearing, as shown in figure 1013. If the object is passed on the starboard side, the danger bearing represents the minimum bearing, safe ones being *greater*. To be effective, a danger bearing should not differ greatly from the course, and the object of which bearings are to be taken should be easily identifiable and visible over the entire area of usefulness of the danger bearing. A margin of safety might be provided by drawing line *HX* through a point a short distance off the danger. In figure 1013, the danger bearing is labeled NMT 074 to indicate that the bearing of the light should not be more than 074°. The hazardous side of the bearing line is hatched. If a natural or artifical range is available as a danger bearing, it should be used.

A vessel proceeding along a coast may be in safe water as long as it remains a minimum distance off the beach. This information may be provided by any means available. One method useful in avoiding particular dangers is the use of a **danger angle** (art. 1109).

A vessel may sometimes be kept in safe water by means of a **danger sounding.** The value selected depends upon the draft of the vessel and the slope of the bottom. It should be sufficiently deep to provide adequate maneuvering room for the vessel to reach deeper water before grounding, once the minimum depth is obtained. In an area where the shoaling is gradual, a smaller margin of depth can be considered than in an area of rapid shoaling. Where the shoaling is very abrupt, as off Point Conception, California, no danger sounding is practical. It is good practice to prominently mark the danger sounding line on the chart. A colored pencil is useful for this purpose.

If it is desired to round a point marked by a prominent landmark, without approaching closer than a given minimum distance, this can be done by steaming until the minimum distance is reached and then immediately changing course so as to bring the landmark broad on the beam. Frequent small changes of course are then used to keep the landmark near, *but not forward of*, the beam. This method is not reliable if the vessel is being moved laterally by wind or current.

An approximation of the distance off can be found by noting the rate at which the bearing changes. If the landmark is kept abeam, the change is indicated by a change of heading. During a change of $57°5$, the distance off is about the same as the distance run. For a change of $28°5$, the distance is about twice the run; for $19°$ it is about three times the run; for $14°5$ it is about four times the run; and for $11°5$ it is about five times the run. Another variation is to measure the number of seconds required for a change of $16°$. The distance off is equal to this interval multiplied by the speed in knots and divided by 1,000. That is, $D = \dfrac{St}{1,000}$, where D is the distance in nautical miles, S is the speed in knots, and t is the time interval in seconds. This method can also be used for straight courses (with bearings $8°$ forward and abaft the beam), but with somewhat reduced accuracy.

1014. Soundings.—The most important use of soundings is to determine whether the depth is sufficient to provide a reasonable margin of safety for the vessel. For this reason, soundings should be taken continuously in pilot waters. A study of the chart and the establishment of a danger sounding (art. 1013) should indicate the degree of safety of the vessel at any time.

Under favorable conditions, soundings can be a valuable aid in establishing the position of the vessel. Their value in this regard depends upon the configuration of the bottom, the amount and accuracy of information given on the chart, the type and accuracy of the sounding equipment available aboard ship, and the knowledge and skill of the navigator. In an area having a flat bottom devoid of distinctive features, or in an area where detailed information is not given on the chart, little positional information can be gained from soundings. However, in an area where depth curves run roughly parallel to the shore, a sounding might indicate distance from the beach. In any area where a given depth curve is sharply defined and relatively straight, it serves as a line of position which can be used with other lines, such as those obtained by bearings of landmarks, to obtain a fix. The 100-fathom curve at the outer edge of the continental shelf might be crossed with a line of position from celestial observation or Loran. The crossing of a sharply defined trench, ridge, shoal, or flat-topped seamount (a **guyot**) might provide valuable positional information.

In any such use, identification of the feature observed is important. In an area of rugged underwater terrain, identification might be difficult unless an almost continuous determination of position is maintained, for it is not unusual for a number of features within a normal radius of uncertainty to be similar. If the echo sounder produces a continuous recording of the depth, called a **bottom profile**, this can be matched to the chart in the vicinity of the course line. If no profile is available, a rough approximation of one can be constructed as follows: Record a series of soundings at short intervals, the length being dictated by the scale of the chart and the existing situation. For most purposes the interval might be each minute, or perhaps each half-mile or mile. Draw a straight line on transparent material and, at the scale of the chart, place marks along the line at the distance intervals at which soundings were made. For this purpose the line might be superimposed over the latitude scale or a distance scale of the chart. At each mark record the corresponding sounding. Then place the transparency over the chart and, by trial and error, match the recorded soundings to those indicated on the chart. Keep the line on the transparency parallel or nearly parallel to the course line plotted on the chart. A current may cause some difference between the plotted course line and the course made good. Also, speed over the bottom might be somewhat different from that used for the plot. This should be reflected in the match. This method should be used with caution, because it may be possible to fit the **line of soundings** to several places on the chart.

Exact agreement with the charted bottom should not be expected at all times. Inaccuracies in the soundings, tide, or incomplete data on the chart may affect the match, but general agreement should be sought. Any marked discrepancy should be investigated, particularly if it indicates less depth than anticipated. If such a discrepancy cannot be reconciled, the wisest decision might well be to haul off into deeper water or anchor and wait for more favorable conditions or additional information.

1015. Most probable position (MPP).—Since information sufficient to establish an *exact* position is seldom available, the navigator is frequently faced with the problem of establishing the most probable position of the vessel. If three reliable bearing lines cross at a point, there is usually little doubt as to the position, and little or no judgment is needed. But when conflicting information or information of questionable reliability is received, a decision is required to establish the MPP. At such a time the experience of the navigator can be of great value. Judgment can be improved if the navigator will continually try to account for all apparent discrepancies, even under favorable conditions. If a navigator habitually analyzes the situation whenever positional information is received, he will develop judgment as to the reliability of various types of information, and will learn something of the conditions under which certain types should be treated with caution.

When complete positional information is lacking, or when the available information is considered of questionable reliability, the most probable position might well be considered an **estimated position** (EP). Such a position might be determined from a single line of position, from a line of soundings, from lines of position which are somewhat inconsistent, from a dead reckoning position with a correction for current or wind, etc.

Whether the most probable position is a fix, running fix, estimated position, or dead reckoning position, it should be kept continually in mind, together with some estimate of its reliability. The practice of continuing a dead reckoning plot from one good fix to another is advisable, whether or not information is available to indicate a most probable position differing from the dead reckoning position, for the DR plot provides an indication of current and leeway. A series of estimated positions may not be consistent because of the continual revision of the estimate as additional information is received. However, it is good practice to plot all MPP's, and sometimes to maintain a separate EP plot based upon the best estimate of course and speed being made good over the ground, for this should furnish valuable information to indicate whether the present course is a safe one.

1016. Allowing for turning characteristics of vessel.—When precise piloting is necessary (as in an area where maneuvering space is limited, when a specified anchorage is approached, or when steaming in formation with other ships), the turning characteristics of the vessel should be considered. That is, a ship does not complete a turn instantaneously, but follows a curve the characteristics of which depend upon the vessel's length, beam, underwater contour, draft, trim, rudder angle, speed, effects of wind and sea, etc. At the moment the rudder is put over, the vessel begins to follow a

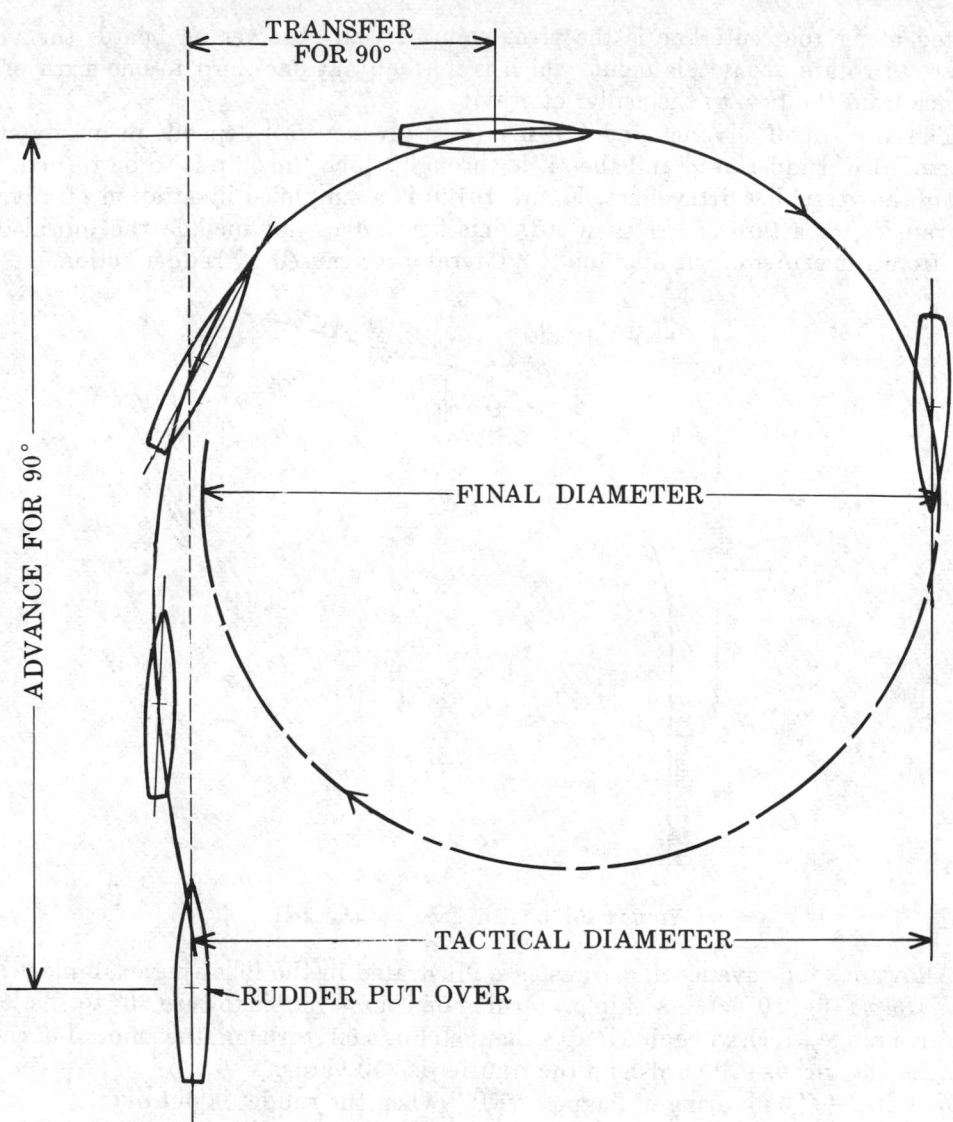

FIGURE 1016a.—Turning circle.

spiral path (fig. 1016a). This path becomes circular when the vessel has turned about 90°. The distance the vessel moves in the direction of the original course until the new course is reached is called **advance.** The distance the vessel moves perpendicular to the original course during the turn is called **transfer.** The **tactical diameter** is the distance gained to the right or left of the original course after a turn of 180° with a constant rudder angle. The **final diameter** is the diameter of a circle traversed by a vessel after turning through 360° and maintaining the same speed and rudder angle. This diameter is always less than the tactical diameter. It is measured perpendicular to the original course and between the tangents at the points where 180° and 360° of the turn have been completed. The vessel turns with its bow inside and its stern outside the tangent to the path of its center of gravity. The angle between the tangent to this path, the **turning circle,** and the centerline of the vessel is the **drift angle.** After the vessel has assumed its drift angle in a turn, the point on the centerline between the bow and the center of gravity at which the resultant of the velocities of rotation and translation is directed along the centerline is the **pivot point.** To an observer on board, the vessel appears to rotate about this point, which is normally at one-third to one-sixth of the distance from the bow to the center of gravity.

The amount of advance and transfer for a given vessel depends primarily upon the amount of rudder used and the angle through which the ship is to be turned. The speed of the vessel has little effect. Figure 1016b is a simplified illustration of advance and transfer for a turn of less than 90°. This figure does not include the initial drift away from the center of turning due to a lateral force caused by rudder action.

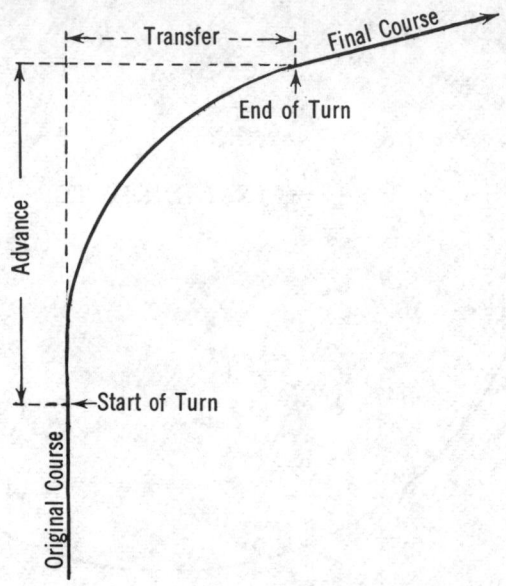

FIGURE 1016b.—Advance and transfer.

Allowance for advance and transfer is illustrated in the following example.

Example (fig. 1016c).—A ship proceeding on course 100° is to turn 60° to the left to come on a range which will guide it up a channel. For a 60° turn and the amount of rudder used, the advance is 920 yards and the transfer is 350 yards.

Required.—The bearing of flagpole "FP." when the rudder is put over.

Solution.—(1) Extend the original course line, *AB.*

(2) At a perpendicular distance of 350 yards, the transfer, draw a line *A'B'* parallel to the original course line *AB.* The point of intersection, *C,* of *A'B'* with the new course line (located by the range) is the place at which the turn is to be completed.

(3) From *C* draw a perpendicular, *CD,* to the original course line, intersecting it at *D.*

(4) From *D* measure the advance, 920 yards, *back* along the original course line. This locates *E,* the point at which the turn should be started.

(5) The direction of "FP." from *E,* 058°, is the bearing when the turn should be started.

Answer.—B 058°.

A frequently useful alternative procedure is the **distance to new course method.** From the vessel's tactical characteristics, a table is constructed to indicate, for various course alterations, speeds, and rudder angles, the distance from the point where the rudder is put over to the intersection (fig. 1016d) of the original course line and the extension of the intended new course line.

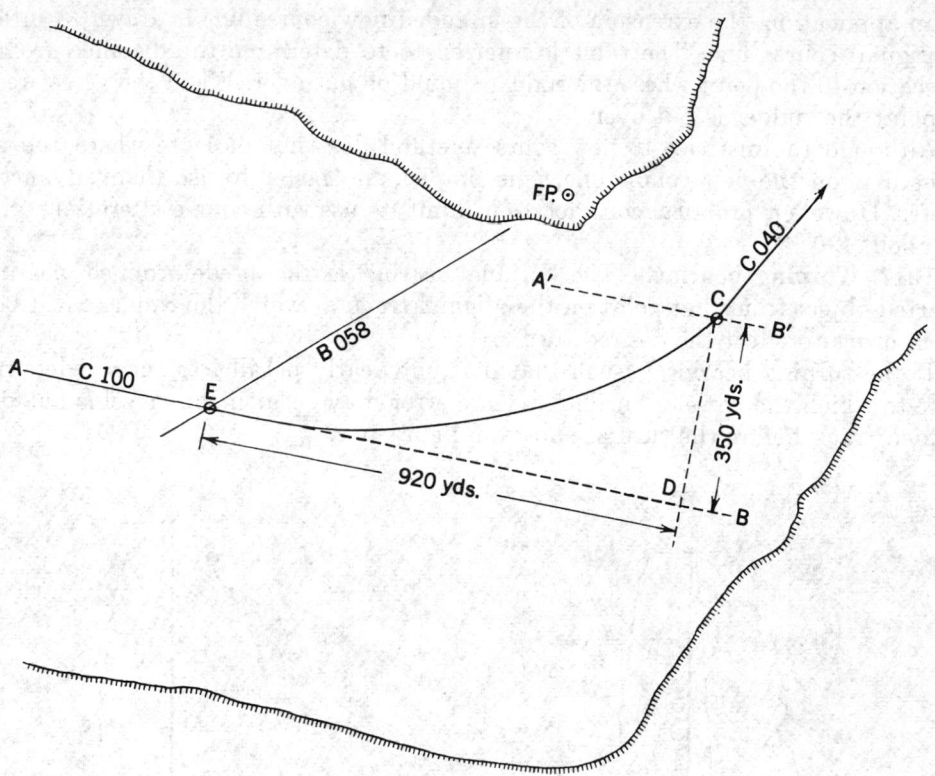

FIGURE 1016c.—Allowing for advance and transfer.

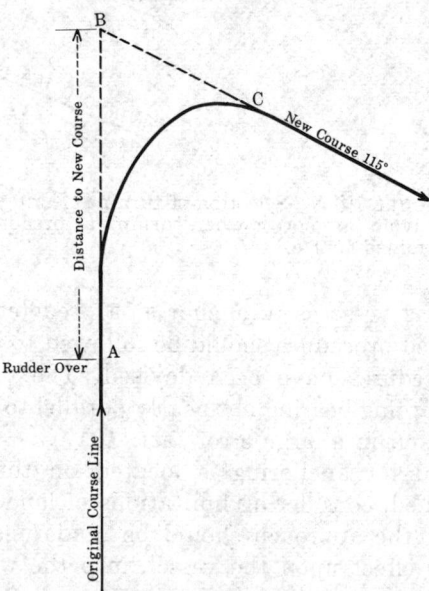

FIGURE 1016d.—Distance to new course
method.

In application, the extension of the intended new course line is drawn to intersect the original course line. The table is referred to to determine the distance from this intersection to the point where the rudder should be put over. When the vessel reaches this point the rudder is put over.

Although the distance to new course method does not indicate where the vessel will be first on the new course line, it is simpler and faster to use than advance and transfer. However, practical considerations limit its use with course alterations greater than about 120°.

1017. Turning bearing.—The turning bearing is the predetermined bearing to a charted object from that point on the original track at which the rudder must be put over in order to effect the desired turn.

If the turning bearing is such that it is not nearly parallel to the predetermined course to which the vessel is turning, a large error may occur if the vessel is not on the intended track before the turn as shown in figure 1017.

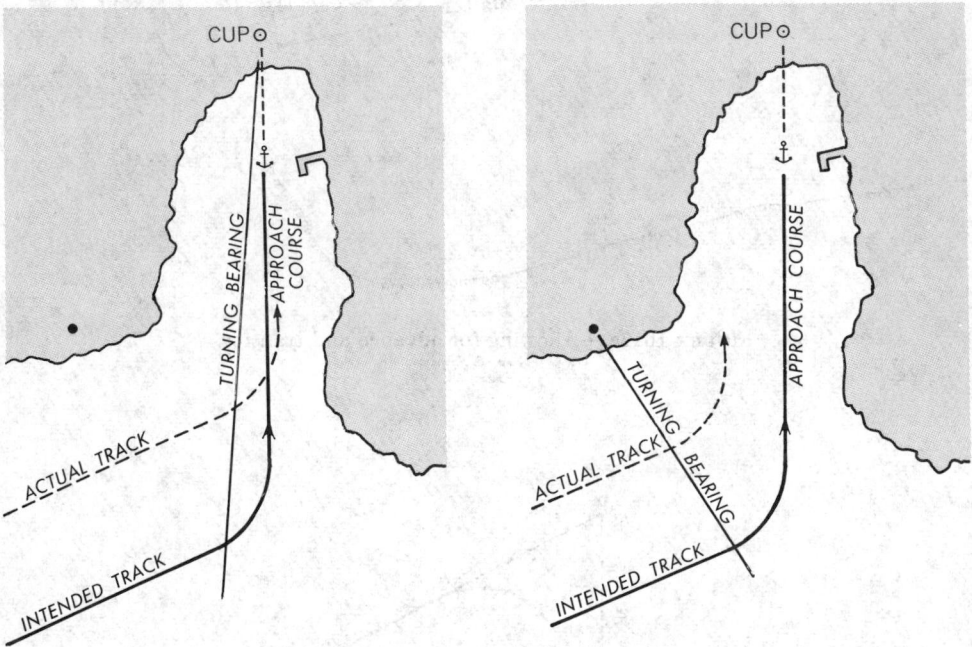

FIGURE 1017.—Selection of turning bearing to avoid large error when turning to predetermined course.

1018. Anchoring.—If a vessel is to anchor at a predetermined point, as in an assigned berth, an established procedure should be followed to insure accuracy of placing the anchor. Several procedures have been devised. The following is representative (fig. 1018). The use of a turning bearing not nearly parallel to the predetermined course, as in figure 1018, may result in a large error (art. 1017).

The position selected for anchoring is located on the chart. The direction of approach is then determined, considering limitations of land, shoals, other vessels, etc. Where conditions permit, the approach should be made heading into the current or, if the wind has a greater effect upon the vessel, into the wind. It is desirable to approach from such direction that a prominent object, or preferably a range, is available dead ahead to serve as a steering guide. It is also desirable to have a range or prominent object near the beam at the point of letting go the anchor. If practicable a straight

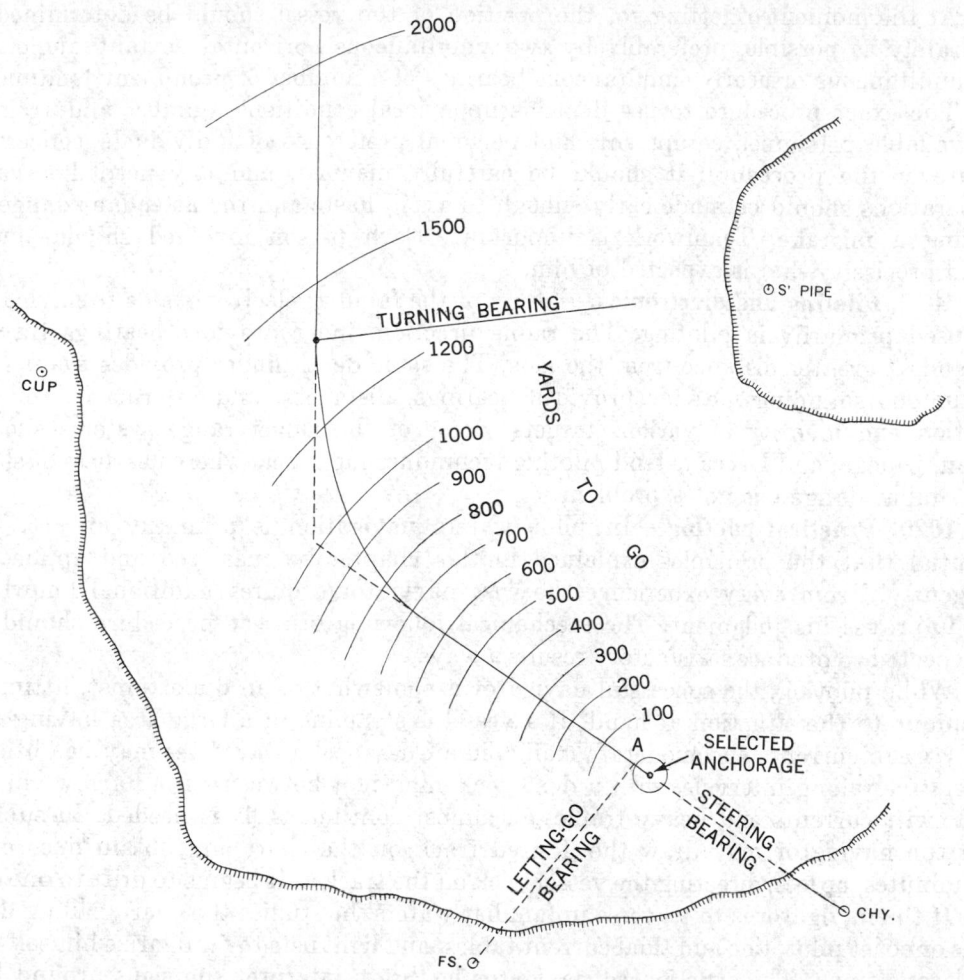

FIGURE 1018.—Anchoring.

approach of at least 500 yards should be provided to permit the vessel to steady on the required course. The track is then drawn in, allowing for advance and transfer during any turns.

Next, a circle is drawn with the selected position of the anchor as the center, and with a radius equal to the distance between the hawsepipe and pelorus, alidade, etc., used for measuring bearings. The intersection of this circle and the approach track, point A, is the position of the vessel (bearing-measuring instrument) at the moment of letting go. A number of arcs of circles are then drawn and labeled as shown in figure 1018. The desired position of the anchor is the common center of these arcs. The selected radii may be chosen at will. Those shown in figure 1018 have been found to be generally suitable. In each case the distance indicated is from the small circle. Turning bearings may also be indicated.

During the approach to the anchorage, fixes are plotted at frequent intervals, the measurement and plotting of bearings going on continuously, usually to the nearest half or quarter degree. The navigator advises the captain of any tendency of the vessel to drift from the desired track, so that adjustments can be made. The navigator also keeps the captain informed of the distance to go, to permit adjustment of the speed so that the vessel will be nearly dead in the water when the anchor is let go.

At the moment of letting go, the position of the vessel should be determined as accurately as possible, preferably by two simultaneous horizontal sextant angles, or by simultaneous or nearly simultaneous bearings of a number of prominent landmarks.

The exact procedure to use depends upon local conditions, number and training of available personnel, equipment, and personal preference of individuals concerned. Whatever the procedure, it should be carefully planned, and any needed advance preparations should be made early enough to avoid haste and the attendant danger of making a mistake. Teamwork is important. Each person involved should understand precisely what is expected of him.

1019. Piloting and electronics.—Many of the familiar electronic aids to navigation are used primarily in piloting. The radio direction finder provides bearings through fog and at greater distance from the aids. The sonic depth finder provides frequent or continuous soundings. Radar provides bearings, distances, and information on the location and identity of various targets. Some of the longer range systems such as Loran, Omega, and Decca extend piloting techniques far to sea, where nearness of shoals and similar dangers is not a problem.

1020. Practical piloting.—In pilot waters navigation is primarily an art. It is essential that the principles explained in this chapter be mastered and applied intelligently. From every experience the wise navigator acquires additional knowledge and improves his judgment. The mechanical following of a set procedure should not be expected to produce satisfactory results always.

While piloting, the successful navigator is somewhat of an opportunist, fitting his technique to the situation at hand. If a vessel is steaming in a large area having relatively weak currents and moderate traffic, like Chesapeake Bay, fixes may be obtained at relatively long intervals, with a dead reckoning plot between. In a narrow channel with swift currents and heavy traffic, an almost continuous fix is needed. In such an area the navigator may draw the desired track on the chart and obtain fixes every few minutes, or less, directing the vessel back on the track as it begins to drift to one side.

If the navigator is to traverse unfamiliar waters, he studies the chart, sailing directions or coast pilot, tide and tidal current tables, and light lists to familiarize himself with local conditions. The experienced navigator learns to interpret the signs around him. The ripple of water around buoys and other obstructions, the direction and angle of tilt of buoys, the direction at which vessels ride at anchor, provide meaningful information regarding currents. The wise navigator learns to interpret such signs when the position of his vessel is not in doubt. When visibility is poor, or available information is inconsistent, the ability developed at favorable times can be of great value.

With experience, a navigator learns when a danger angle or danger bearing is useful, and what ranges are reliable and how they should be used. However familiar one is with an area, he should not permit himself to become careless in the matter of timing lights for identification, plotting his progress on a chart, or keeping a good recent position. Fog sometimes creeps in unnoticed, obscuring landmarks before one realizes its presence. A series of frequent fixes obtained while various aids are visible provides valuable information on position and current.

Practical piloting requires a thorough familiarity with principles involved and local conditions, constant alertness, and judgment. A study of avoidable groundings reveals that in most cases the problem is not lack of knowledge, but failure to use or interpret available information. Among the more common errors are:

1. Failure to obtain or evaluate soundings.
2. Failure to identify aids to navigation.
3. Failure to use available navigational aids effectively.
4. Failure to correct charts.

5. Failure to adjust a magnetic compass or maintain an accurate table of corrections.

6. Failure to apply deviation, or error in its application.

7. Failure to apply variation, or to allow for change in variation.

8. Failure to check gyro and magnetic compass readings at frequent and regular intervals.

9. Failure to keep a dead reckoning plot.

10. Failure to plot information received.

11. Failure to properly evaluate information received.

12. Poor judgment.

13. Failure to do own navigating (following another vessel).

14. Failure to obtain and use information available on charts and in various publications.

15. Poor ship organization.

16. Failure to "keep ahead of the vessel."

Further discussion on practical piloting is given in chapter XXIII.

CHAPTER XI

USE OF SEXTANT IN PILOTING

1101. Introduction.—The marine sextant provides the most accurate means generally available to the mariner for fixing his position in confined waters. But following the widespread use of the highly reliable gyrocompass, the mariner's use of the sextant for piloting has declined to such an extent that it is seldom if ever used by many. This is unfortunate because the sextant can be used to advantage in situations where other methods or tools, including the gyrocompass, are inadequate.

The applications of the sextant during daylight in coastal waters, harbor approaches, and more confined waters may be summarized as follows:

1. fixing to make a safe transit of hazardous waters;
2. fixing to take a specific geographic position;
3. fixing to establish accurately the position of the anchor on anchoring;
4. fixing to determine whether or not the ship is dragging anchor;
5. using horizontal and vertical danger angles;
6. using vertical angles to determine distance off;
7. fixing to determine the positions of uncharted objects, or to verify the positions of charted features;
8. using the sextant to evaluate the accuracy of navigation by other means.

Because the use of the sextant has declined, many navigators, unfortunately, do not have the proficiency necessary to use it to advantage in those situations where other methods are inadequate. Proficiency in the use of the sextant can be invaluable in situations where even a small error in either observing or plotting cross bearings can result in a grounding.

1102. Three-point problem.—Normally, three charted objects are selected for measuring horizontal sextant angles to determine the observer's position, one of the objects being common to each angular measurement. With simultaneous or nearly simultaneous measurements of the horizontal angles between each pair of charted

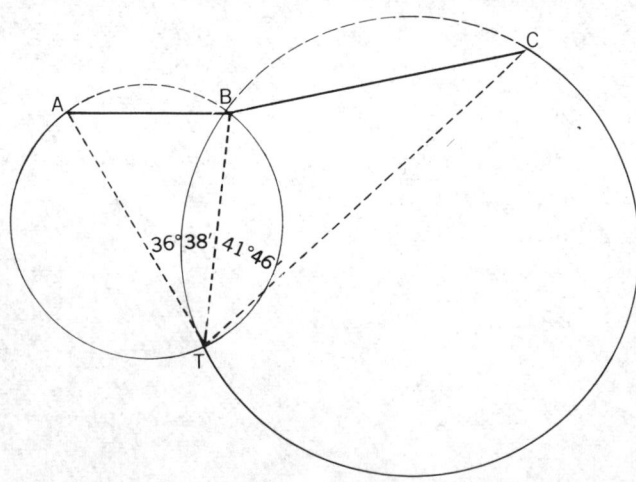

FIGURE 1102a.—Solving the three-point problem.

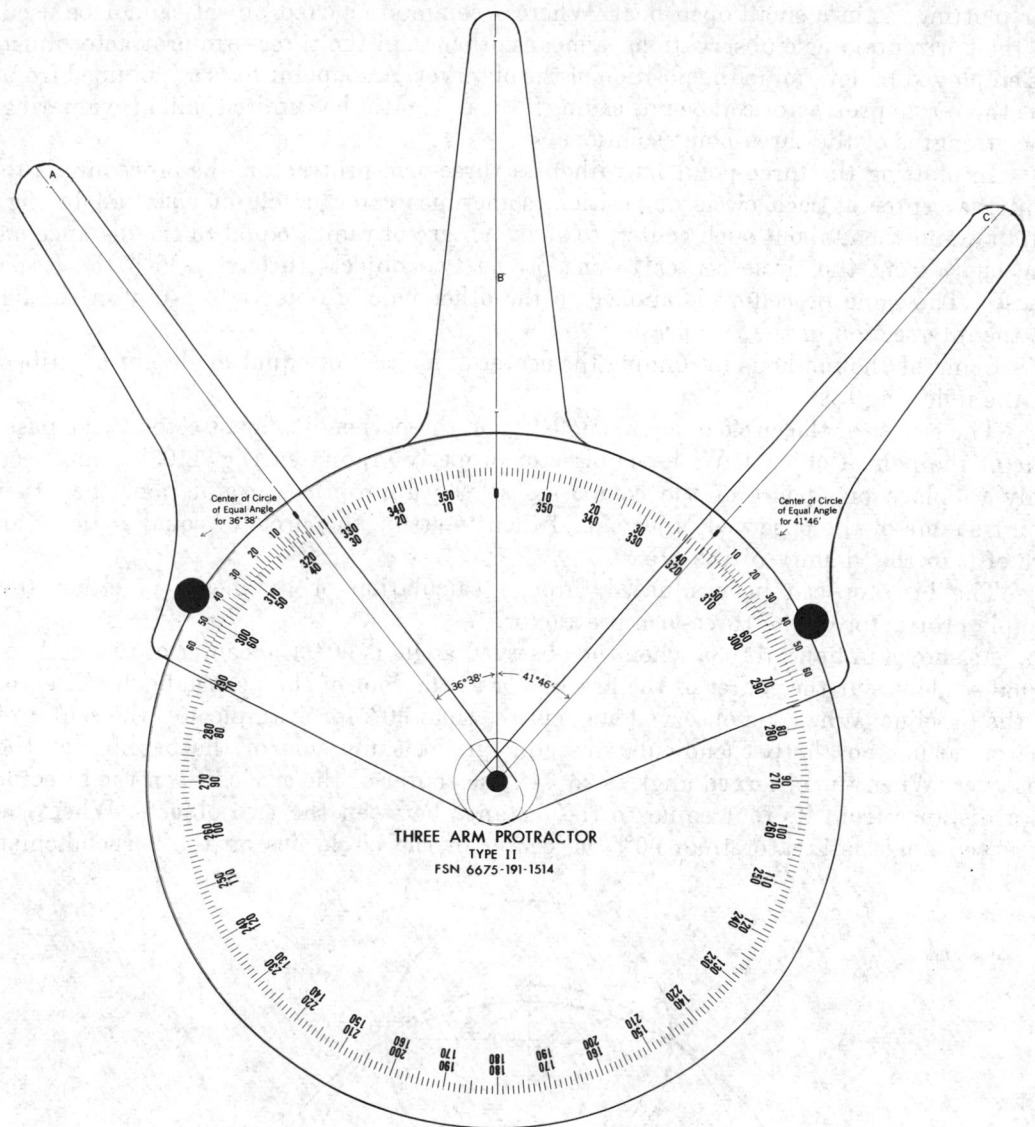

FIGURE 1102b.—Use of three-arm protractor.

objects, the observer establishes two circles of position. For each pair of objects, there is only one circle which passes through the two objects and the observer's position. Thus, there are two circles, intersecting at two points as shown in figure 1102a, which pass through the observer's position at T.

Since the observer knows that he is not at the intersection at B, he must be at T.

The solution of what is known as the **three-point problem** is effected by placing the hairlines of the arms of a plastic three-arm protractor over the three observed objects on the chart as shown in figure 1102b. With the arms so placed, the center of the protractor disk is over the observer's position on the chart at the time of the measurements.

1103. Solution without three-arm protractor.—Although the conventional solution of the three-point problem is obtained by placing the arms of a three-arm protractor over the three observed objects on the chart, the use of the protractor is not necessary. The use of the protractor may not be practicable because of limited room and facilities for plotting, as in a small open boat. Where a common charted object cannot be used in the horizontal angle observations, a means other than the three-arm protractor must be employed to determine the position of the observer. Also, point fixes as obtained from the three-arm protractor can be misleading if the navigator has limited skill in evaluating the strengths of the three-point solutions.

In plotting the three-point fix without a three-arm protractor, the procedure is to find the center of each circle of position, sometimes called **circle of equal angle** (fig. 1103a), and then, about such center, to strike an arc of radius equal to the distance on the chart from the circle center to one of the two objects through which the circle passes. The same procedure is applied to the other pair of objects to establish the fix at the intersection of the two arcs.

Some of the methods for finding the center of a circle of equal angle are described in the following text.

The center of the circle of equal angle lies on the perpendicular bisector of the baseline of the pair of objects. With the bisector properly graduated (fig. 1103b), one need only to place one point of the compasses at the appropriate graduation, the other point at one of the observed objects, and then to strike the circle of equal angle or an arc of it in the vicinity of the DR.

The bisector can be graduated through calculation or by means of either the simple protractor or the three-arm protractor.

As shown in figure 1103a when the observed angle is 90°, the center of the circle of equal angle lies at the center of the baseline or at the foot of the perpendicular bisector of the baseline. When the observed angle is less than 90°, for example 40°, the center of the circle lies on the perpendicular bisector on the same side of the baseline as the observer. When the observed angle is 26°34′, the center of the circle lies on the bisector at a distance from its foot equal to the distance between the two objects. When the observed angle is greater than 90°, the center of the circle lies on the perpendicular

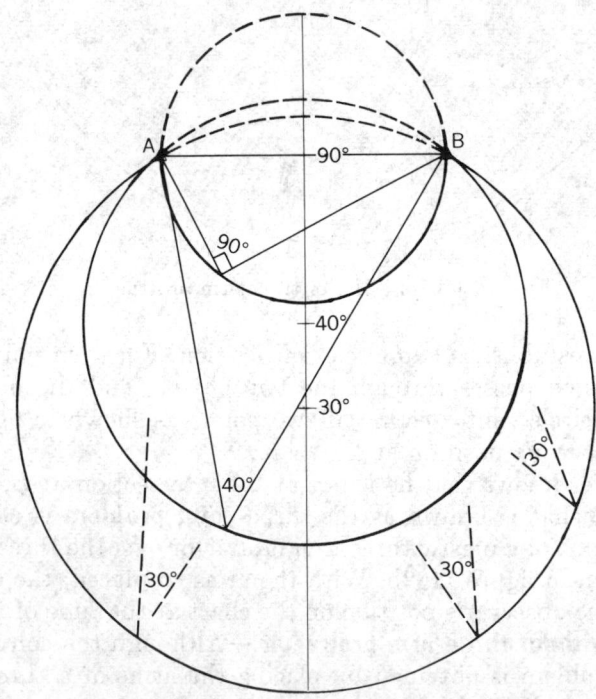

FIGURE 1103a.—Circles of equal angle.

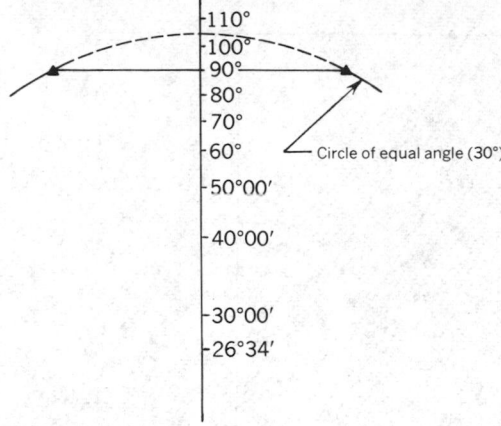

FIGURE 1103b.—Graduated perpendicular bisector.

bisector on the side of the baseline opposite from the observer. The center for 100° is the same distance from the baseline as the center for 80°; the center for 110° is the same distance as the center for 70°, etc. These facts can be used to construct a nomogram for finding the distances of circles of equal angle from the foot of the perpendicular for various angles.

From geometry the central angle subtended by a chord is twice the angle with its vertex on the circle and subtended by the same chord. Therefore, when the observed horizontal angle is 30°, the central angle subtended by the baseline is 60°. Or, the angle at the center of the circle between the perpendicular bisector and the line in the direction of one of the observed objects is equal to the observed angle, or 30° as shown in figure 1103c. The angle at the object between the baseline and the center of the circle on the bisector is 90° minus observed angle, or 60°.

The 30° graduation can be located quickly using a suitable protractor as shown in figure 1103d. The placement of the protractor as shown in the upper part of the figure requires moving its center along the bisector until the straightedge passes through the object. The method shown in the lower part enables more rapid location of the 30° graduation because there is no need to slide the protractor after its center is placed over the object and the angle is set.

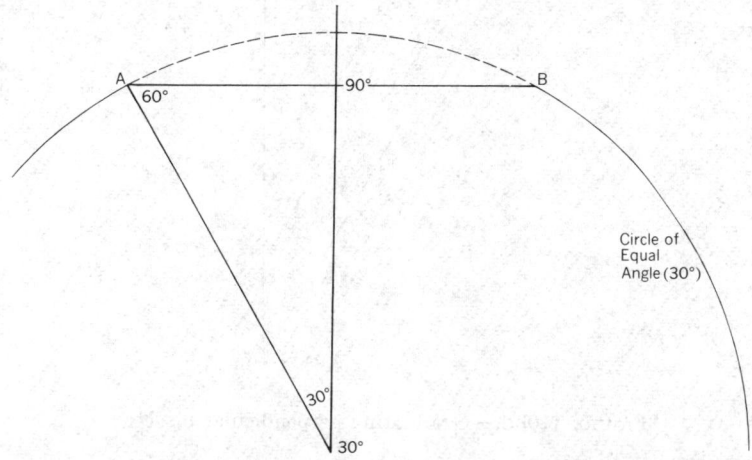

FIGURE 1103c.—Circle of equal angle (30°).

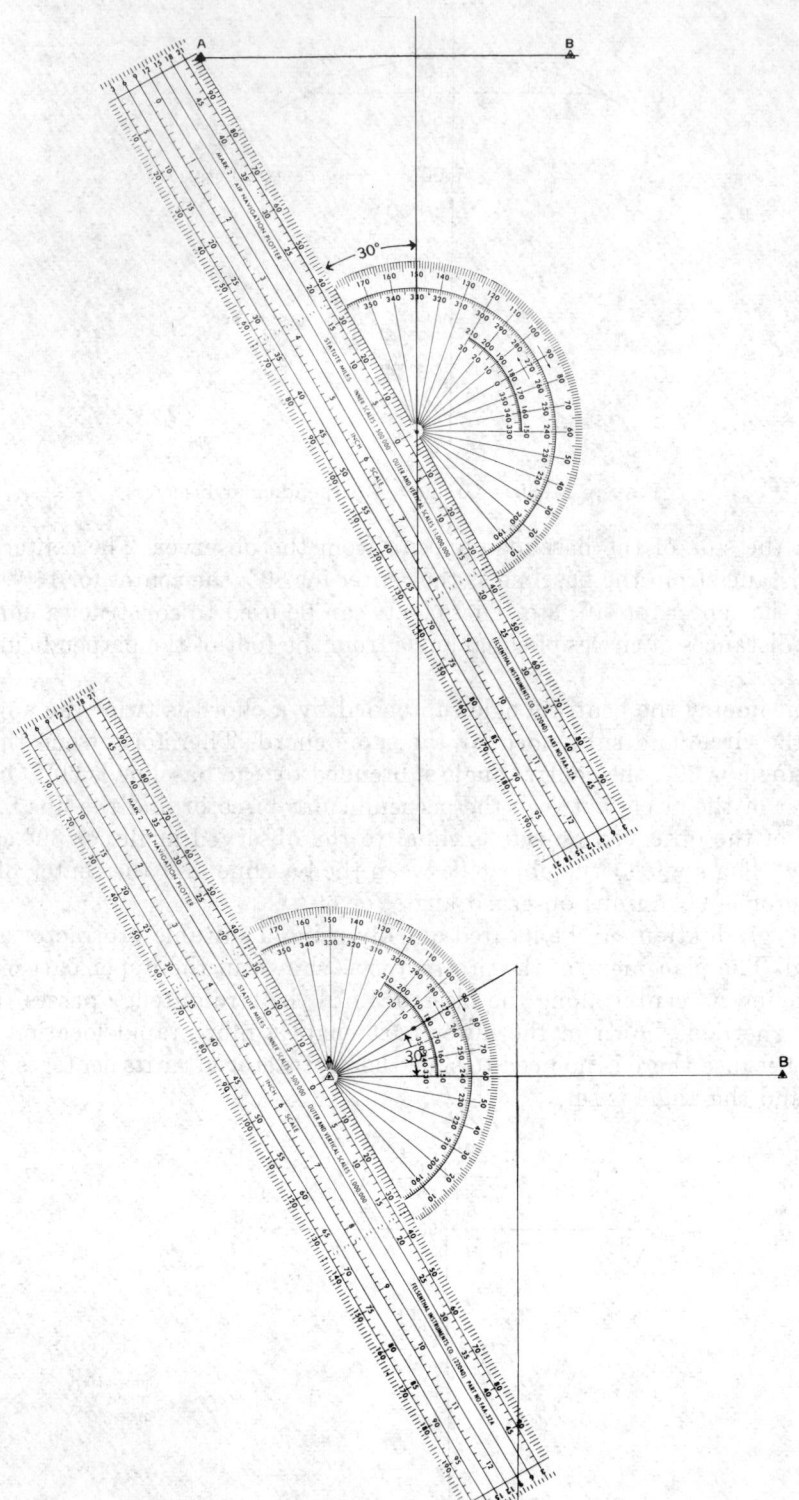

FIGURE 1103d.—Graduating perpendicular bisector.

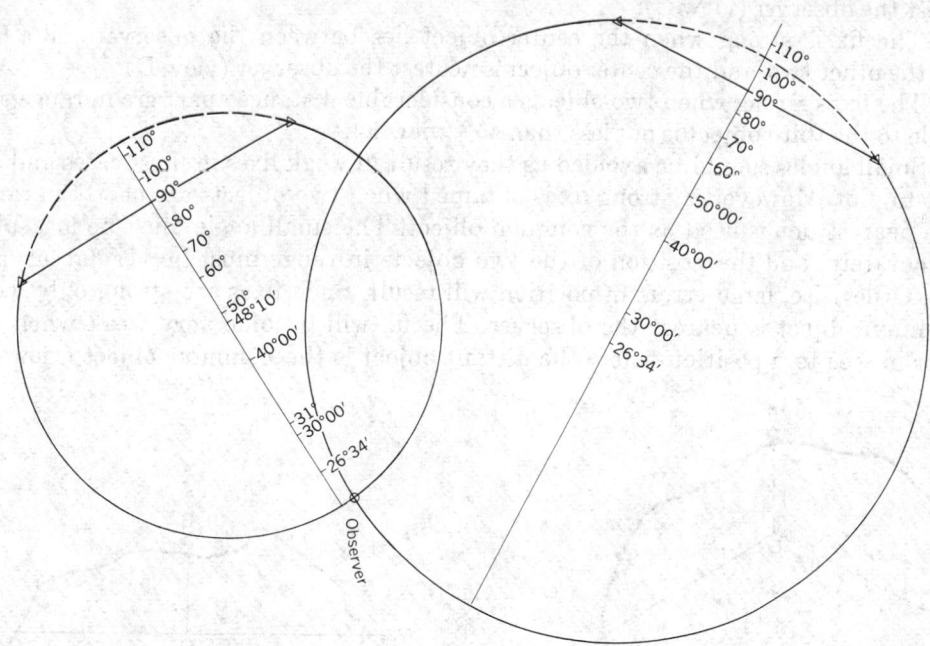

FIGURE 1104.—Split fix.

1104. Split fix.—Occasions when a common charted object cannot be used in horizontal angle observations are not infrequent. On these occasions the mariner must obtain what is called a **split fix** through observation of two pairs of charted objects, with no object being common. As with the three-point fix, the mariner will obtain two circles of equal angle, intersecting at two points. As shown in figure 1104, one of these two intersections will fix the observer's position.

1105. Conning aid.—Preconstructed circles of equal angle can be helpful in conning the vessel to a specific geographic position when fixing by horizontal angles. In one application, the vessel is conned to keep one angle constant, or nearly constant, in order to follow the circumference of the associated circle of equal angle to the desired position; the other angle is changing rapidly and is approaching the value for the second circle of equal angle passing through the desired position.

1106. Strength of three-point fix.—Although an experienced hydrographer can readily estimate the strength of a three-point fix, and is able to select the objects providing the strongest fix available quickly, others often have difficulty in visualizing the problem and may select a weak fix when strong ones are available. The following generally useful but not infallible rules apply to selection ·of charted objects to be observed:

1. The strongest fix is obtained when the observer is inside the triangle formed by the three objects. And in such case the fix is strongest where the three objects form an equilateral triangle (fig. 1106, view A), the observer is at the center, and the objects are close to the observer.

2. The fix is strong when the sum of the two angles is equal to or greater than 180° and neither angle is less than 30°. The nearer the angles are equal to each other, the stronger is the fix (view B).

3. The fix is strong when the three objects lie in a straight line and the center object is nearest the observer (view C).

4. The fix is strong when the center object lies between the observer and a line joining the other two, and the center object is nearest the observer (view D).

5. The fix is strong when two objects a considerable distance apart are in range and the angle to the third object is not less than 45° (view E).

6. Small angles should be avoided as they result in weak fixes in most cases and are difficult to plot. However, a strong fix is obtained when two objects are nearly in range and the nearest one is used as the common object. The small angle must be measured very accurately, and the position of the two objects in range must be very accurately plotted. Otherwise, large errors in position will result. Such fixes are strong only when the common object is nearest the observer. The fix will become very weak when the observer moves to a position where the distant object is the common object (view F).

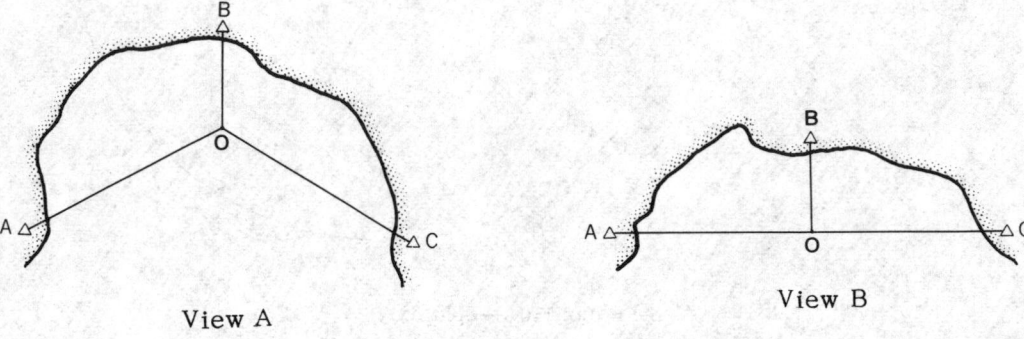

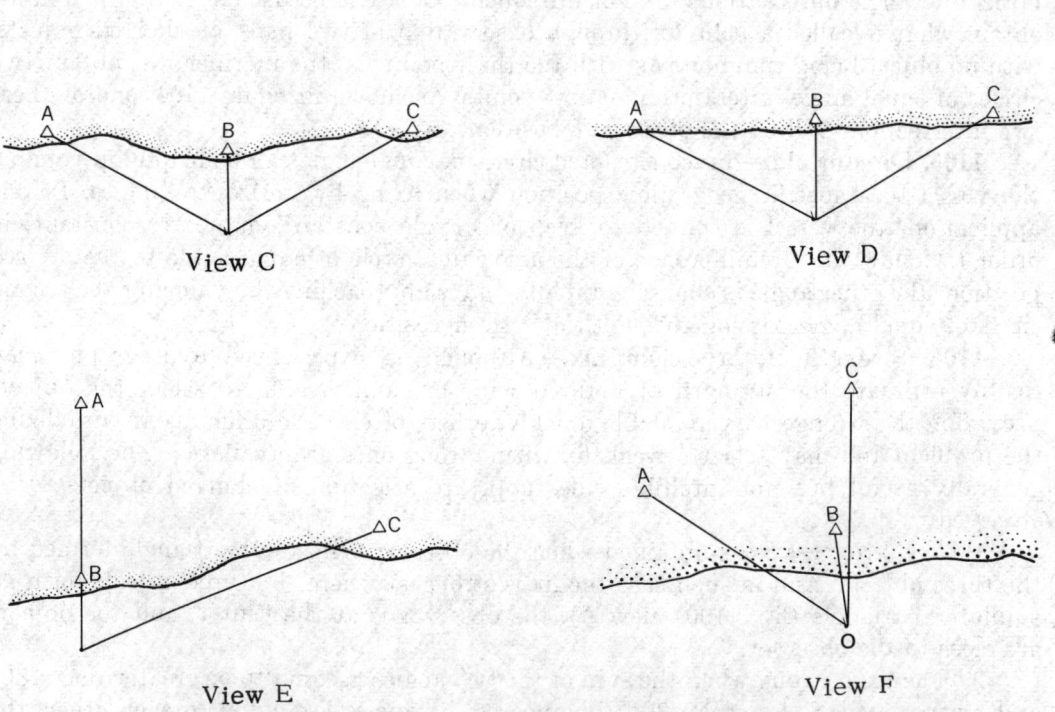

FIGURE 1106.—Strengths of three-point fixes.

7. A fix is strong when at least one of the angles changes rapidly as the vessel moves from one location to another.

8. The sum of the two angles should not be less than 50°; better results are obtained when neither angle is less than 30°.

9. Do not observe an angle between objects of considerably different elevation. Indefinite objects such as tangents, hill-tops, and other poorly defined or located points should not be used. Take care to select prominent objects such as major lights, church spires, towers or buildings which are charted and are readily distinguished from surrounding objects.

Beginners should demonstrate the validity of the above rules by plotting examples of each and their opposites. It should be noted that a fix is strong if, in plotting, a slight movement of the center of the protractor moves the arms away from one or more of the stations, and is weak if such movement does not appreciably change the relation of the arms to the three points. An appreciation of the accuracy required in measuring angles can be obtained by changing one angle about five minutes in arc in each example and noting the resulting shift in the plotted positions.

The **error of the three-point fix** will be due to:

1. error in measurement of the horizontal angles;

2. error resulting from observer and observed objects not lying in a horizontal plane;

3. instrument error; and

4. plotting error.

The magnitude of the error varies directly as the error in measurement, the distance of the common object from the observer, (D) and inversely as the sine function of the angle of cut (θ). The magnitude of the error also depends upon the following ratios:

1. The distance to the object to the left of the observer divided by the distance from this object to the center object (r_1).

2. The distance to the object to the right of the observer divided by the distance from this object to the center object (r_2).

Assuming that each horizontal angle has the same error (α), the magnitude of the error (E) is expressed in the formula

$$E = \frac{\alpha D}{\sin \theta} \sqrt{r^2_1 + r^2_2 + 2r_1 r_2 \cos \theta},$$

where error in measurement (α) is expressed in radians.

The magnitude of the error (E) is expressed in the formula

$$E = \frac{.00029 \alpha D}{\sin \theta} \sqrt{r^2_1 + r^2_2 + 2r_1 r_2 \cos \theta},$$

where error in measurement (α) is expressed in minutes of arc.

To avoid mistakes in the identification of charted objects observed, either a check bearing or a check angle should be used to insure that the objects used in observation and plotting are the same.

1107. Avoiding the swinger.—Avoid a selection of objects which will result in a **"revolver"** or **"swinger"**; that is, when the three objects observed on shore and the ship are all on, or near, the circumference of a circle (fig. 1107). In such a case the ship's position is indeterminate by three-point fix.

If *bearings* as plotted are affected by unknown and uncorrected compass error, the bearing lines may intersect at a point when the objects observed ashore and the ship are all on, or near, the circumference of a circle.

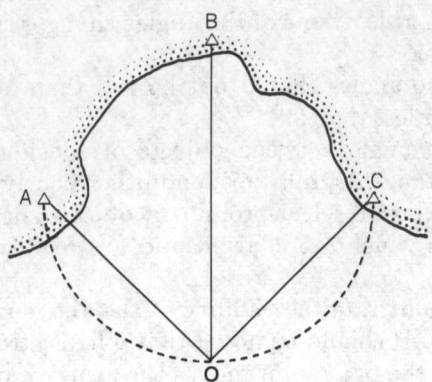

FIGURE 1107.—Revolver or swinger.

1108. Cutting in uncharted objects.—To cut in or locate on the chart uncharted objects, such as newly discovered offshore wrecks or objects ashore which may be useful for future observations, proceed as follows:

1. Fix successive positions of the ship or ship's boat by three-point fixes, i.e., by horizontal sextant angles. At each fix, simultaneously measure the sextant angle between one of the objects used in the fix and the object to be charted (fig. 1108a). For more accurate results, the craft from which the observations are made should be either lying to or proceeding slowly.

2. For best results, the angles should be measured simultaneously. If verification is undertaken, the angles observed should be interchanged among observers.

3. The fix positions should be selected carefully to give strong fixes, and so that the cuts to the object will provide a good intersection at the next station taken for observations. A minimum of three cuts should be taken.

An alternative procedure is to select observing positions so that the object to be charted will be in range with one of the charted objects used to obtain the three-point fix (fig. 1108b). The charted objects should be selected to provide the best possible intersections at the position of the uncharted object.

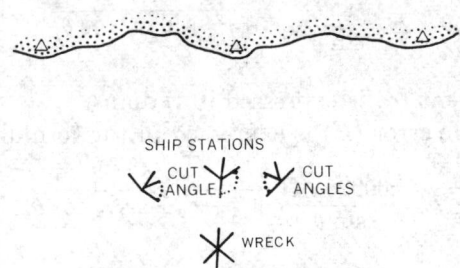

FIGURE 1108a.—Cutting in uncharted objects.

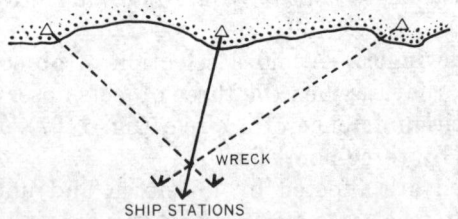

FIGURE 1108b.—On range method.

1109. Horizontal and vertical danger angles.—A vessel proceeding along a coast may be in safe water as long as it remains a minimum distance off the beach. This information may be provided by any means available. One method useful in avoiding particular dangers is the use of a **danger angle.** Refer to figure 1109. A ship is proceeding along a coast on course line AB, and the captain wishes to remain outside a danger D. Prominent landmarks are located at M and N. A circle is drawn through M and N and tangent to the outer edge of the danger. If X is a point on this circle, angle MXN is the same as at any other point on the circle (except that part between M and N). Anywhere within the circle the angle is *larger* and anywhere outside the circle it is *smaller*. Therefore, any angle smaller than MXN indicates a safe position and any angle larger than MXN indicates possible danger. Angle MXN is therefore a maximum **horizontal danger angle.** A minimum horizontal danger angle is used when a vessel is to pass *inside* an offlying danger, as at D' in figure 1109. In this case the circle is drawn through M and N and tangent to the *inner* edge of the danger area. The angle is kept larger than MYN. If a vessel is to pass *between* two danger areas, as in figure 1109, the horizontal angle should be kept smaller than MXN but larger than MYN. The minimum danger angle is effective only while the vessel is inside the larger circle through M and N. Bearings on either landmark might be used to indicate the entering and leaving of the larger circle. A margin of safety can be provided by drawing the circles through points a short distance off the dangers. Any method of measuring the angles, or difference of bearing of M and N, can be used. Perhaps the most accurate is by horizontal sextant angle. If a single landmark of known height is available, similar procedure can be used with a **vertical danger angle** between top and bottom of the object. In this case the charted position of the object is used as the center of the circles.

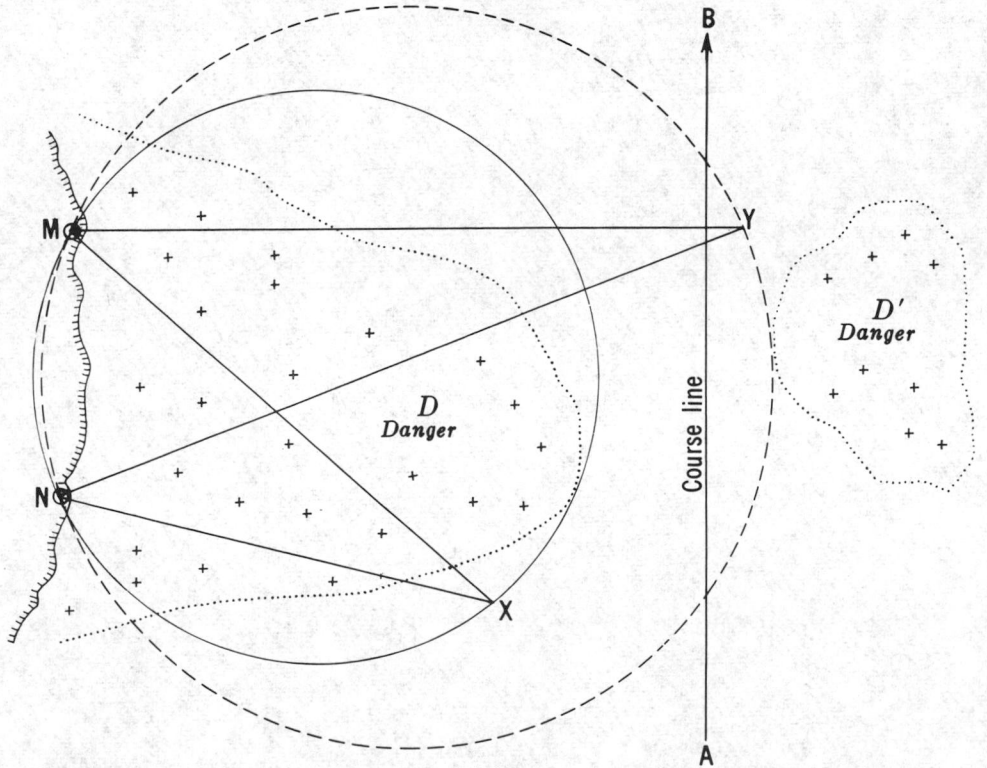

FIGURE 1109.—Horizontal danger angles.

1110. Distance by vertical angle.—Table 9 provides means for determining the distance of an object of known height above sea level. The vertical angle between the top of the object and the visible (sea) horizon (the sextant altitude) is measured and corrected for index error and dip only. If the visible horizon is not available as a reference, the angle should be measured to the bottom of the object, and dip short of the horizon (tab. 22) used in place of the usual dip correction. This may require several approximations of distance by alternate entries of tables 9 and 22 until the same value is obtained twice. The table is entered with the difference in the height of the object and the height of eye of the observer, in feet, and the corrected vertical angle; and the distance in nautical miles is taken directly from the table. An error may be introduced if refraction differs from the standard value used in the computation of the table. Use of the table is explained in article 1203 of volume II.

1111. Evaluation.—As time and conditions permit, it behooves the navigator to use the sextant to evaluate the accuracy of navigation by other means in pilot waters. Such accuracy comparisons tend to provide navigators with better appreciation of the limitations of fixing by various methods in a given piloting situation.

CHAPTER XII

TIDE AND CURRENT PREDICTIONS

1201. Tidal effects.—The daily rise and fall of the **tide,** with its attendant flood and ebb of **tidal current,** is familiar to every mariner. He is aware, also, that at **high water** and **low water** the depth of water is momentarily constant, a condition called **stand.** Similarly, there is a moment of **slack water** as a tidal current reverses direction. As a general rule, the *change* in height or the current speed is at first very slow, increasing to a maximum about midway between the two extremes, and then decreasing again. If plotted against time, the height of tide or speed of a tidal current takes the general form of a sine curve. Sample curves, and more complete information about causes, types, and features of tides and tidal currents, are given in chapter XXXI. The present chapter is concerned primarily with the application of tides and currents to piloting, and predicting the tidal conditions that might be encountered at any given time.

Although tides and tidal currents are caused by the same phenomena, the time relationship between them varies considerably from place to place. For instance, if an estuary has a wide entrance and does not extend far inland, the time of maximum speed of current occurs at about the mid time between high water and low water. However, if an extensive tidal basin is connected to the sea by a small opening, the maximum current may occur at about the time of high water or low water outside the basin, when the difference in height is maximum.

The *height of tide* should not be confused with *depth of water*. For reckoning tides a reference level is selected. Soundings shown on the largest scale charts are the vertical distances from this level to the bottom. At any time the actual depth is this charted depth *plus* the height of tide. In most places the reference level is some form of low water. But all low waters at a place are not the same height, and the selected reference level is seldom the *lowest* tide that occurs at the place. When lower tides occur, these are indicated by a negative sign. Thus, at a spot where the charted depth is 15 feet, the actual depth is 15 feet plus height of tide. When the tide is three feet, the depth is 15+3=18 feet. When it is (—) 1 foot, the depth is 15—1=14 feet. It is well to remember that *the actual depth can be less than the charted depth*. In an area where there is a considerable **range of tide** (the difference between high water and low water), the height of tide might be an important consideration in using soundings to assist in determining position, or whether the vessel is in safe water.

One should remember that heights given in the tide tables are *predictions*, and that when conditions vary considerably from those used in making the predictions, the heights shown may be considerably in error. Heights lower than predicted are particularly to be anticipated when the atmospheric pressure is higher than normal, or when there is a persistent strong offshore wind. Along coasts where there is a large inequality between the two high or two low tides during a tidal day the height predictions are less reliable than elsewhere.

The current encountered in pilot waters is due primarily to tidal action, but other causes are sometimes present. The tidal current tables give the best prediction of total current, regardless of cause. The predictions for a river may be considerably in error following heavy rains or a drought. The effect of current is to alter the course and speed made good over the bottom. Due to the configuration of land (or shoal areas) and water, the set and drift may vary considerably over different parts of a harbor. Since this is generally an area in which small errors in position of a vessel are of considerable importance to its safety, a knowledge of predicted currents can be critical, particularly if the visibility is reduced by fog, snow, etc. If the vessel is proceeding at reduced speed, the effect of current with respect to distance traveled is greater than normal. Strong currents are particularly to be anticipated in narrow passages connecting larger bodies of water. Currents of more than five knots are encountered from time to time in the Golden Gate at San Francisco. Currents of more than 13 knots sometimes occur at Seymour Narrows, British Columbia.

In straight portions of rivers and channels the strongest currents usually occur in the middle, but in curved portions the swiftest currents (and deepest water) usually occur near the outer edge of the curve. Countercurrents and eddies may occur on either side of the main current of a river or narrow passage, especially near obstructions and in bights.

In general, the range of tide and the speed of tidal current are at a minimum upon the open ocean or along straight coasts. The greatest tidal effects are usually encountered in rivers, bays, harbors, inlets, bights, etc. A vessel proceeding along a coast can be expected to encounter stronger sets toward or away from the shore while passing an indentation than when the coast is straight.

1202. Predictions of tides and currents to be expected at various places are published annually by the National Ocean Survey. These are supplemented by eleven sets of tidal current charts (art. 1211), each set consisting of charts for each hour of the tidal cycle. On these charts the set of the current at various places in the area is shown by arrows, and the drift by numbers. Since these are *average* conditions, they indicate in a general way the tidal conditions on any day and during *any* year. They are designed to be used with tidal current diagrams (art. 1211) or the tidal current tables (except those for New York Harbor, and Narragansett Bay, which are used with the tide tables). These charts are available for Boston Harbor, Narragansett Bay to Nantucket Sound, Narragansett Bay, Long Island Sound and Block Island Sound, New York Harbor, Delaware Bay and River, upper Chesapeake Bay, Charleston Harbor, San Francisco Bay, Puget Sound (northern part), and Puget Sound (southern part). Current arrows are sometimes shown on nautical charts. These represent average conditions and should not be considered reliable predictions of the conditions to be encountered at any given time. When a strong current sets over an irregular bottom, or meets an opposing current, ripples may occur on the surface. These are called **tide rips.** Areas where they occur frequently are shown on charts.

Usually, the mariner obtains tidal information from tide and tidal current tables. However, if these are not available, or if they do not include information at a desired place, the mariner may be able to obtain locally the **mean high water lunitidal interval** or the **high water full and change.** The approximate *time* of high water can be found by adding either interval to the time of transit (either upper or lower) of the moon (art. 2020). Low water occurs approximately ¼ tidal day (about 6^h12^m) before and after the time of high water. The actual interval varies somewhat from day to day, but approximate results can be obtained in this manner. Similar information for tidal currents (**lunicurrent interval**) is seldom available.

1203. Tide tables for various parts of the world are published in four volumes by the National Ocean Survey. Each volume is arranged as follows:

Table 1 contains a complete list of the predicted times and heights of the tide for each day of the year at a number of places designated as **reference stations.**

Table 2 gives differences and ratios which can be used to modify the tidal information for the reference stations to make it applicable to a relatively large number of **subordinate stations.**

Table 3 provides information for use in finding the approximate height of the tide at any time between high water and low water.

Table 4 is a sunrise-sunset table at five-day intervals for various latitudes from 76°N to 60°S (40°S in one volume).

Table 5 provides an adjustment to convert the local mean time of table 4 to zone or standard time.

Table 6 (two volumes only) gives the zone time of moonrise and moonset for each day of the year at certain selected places.

Certain astonomical data are contained on the inside back cover of each volume.

Extracts from tables 1, 2, and 3 for the East Coast of North and South America are given in appendix L.

1204. Tide predictions for reference stations.—The first page of appendix L is the table 1 daily predictions for New York (The Battery) for the first quarter of 1975. As indicated at the bottom of the page, times are for Eastern Standard Time (+5 zone, time meridian 75°W). Daylight saving time is not used. Times are given on the 24-hour basis. The tidal reference level for this station is mean low water.

For each day, the date and day of week are given, and the time and height of each high and low water are given in chronological order. Although high and low waters are not labeled as such, they can be distinguished by the relative heights given immediately to the right of the times. Since *two* high tides and *two* low tides occur each tidal day, the type of tide at this place is *semidiurnal*. The *tidal* day being longer than the *civil* day (because of the revolution of the moon eastward around the earth), any given tide occurs *later* from day to day. Thus, on Saturday, March 29, 1975, the first tide that occurs is the lower low water (−1.2 feet at 0334). The following high water (lower high water) is 4.9 feet above the reference level (a 6.1 foot rise from the preceding low water), and occurs at 0942. This is followed by the higher low water (−0.9 feet) at 1547, and then the higher high water of 5.5 feet at 2206. The cycle is repeated on the following day with variations in height, and later times.

Because of later times of corresponding tides from day to day, certain days have only one high water or only one low water. Thus, on January 17 high tides occur at 1120 and 2357. The next following high tides are at 1154 on January 18 and 0029 on January 19. Thus, only one high tide occurs on January 18, the previous one being shortly before midnight on the seventeenth, and the next one occurring early in the morning of the nineteenth, as shown.

1205. Tide predictions for subordinate stations.—The second page of appendix L is a page of table 2 of the tide tables. For each subordinate station listed, the following information is given:

Number. The stations are listed in geographical order and given consecutive numbers. At the end of each volume an alphabetical listing is given, and for each entry the consecutive number is shown, to assist in finding the entry in table 2.

Place. The list of places includes both subordinate and reference stations, the latter being given in bold type.

Position. The approximate latitude and longitude are given to assist in locating the station. The latitude is north or south, and the longitude east or west, depending upon the letters (N, S, E, W) next *above* the entry. These may not be the same as those at the *top* of the column.

Differences. The differences are to be applied to the predictions for the reference station shown in bold capitals next *above* the entry on the page. Time and height differences are given separately for high and low waters. Where differences are omitted, they are either unreliable or unknown.

The time difference is the number of hours and minutes to be applied to the time at the reference station to find the time of the corresponding tide at the subordinate station. This interval is added if preceded by a plus sign (+), and subtracted if preceded by a minus sign (−). The results obtained by the application of the time differences will be in the zone time of the time meridian shown directly above the difference for the subordinate station. Special conditions occurring at a few stations are indicated by footnotes on the applicable pages. In some instances, the corresponding tide falls on a different date at reference and subordinate stations.

Height differences are shown in a variety of ways. For most entries separate height differences in feet are given for high water and low water. These are applied to the height given for the reference station. In many cases a *ratio* is given for either high water or low water, or both. The height at the reference station is multiplied by this ratio to find the height at the subordinate station. For a few stations, *both* a ratio and difference are given. In this case the height at the reference station is first multiplied by the ratio, and the difference is then applied. An example is given in each volume of tide tables. Special conditions are indicated in the table or by footnote. Thus, a footnote on the second page of appendix L indicates that "Values for the Hudson River above George Washington Bridge are based upon averages for the six months May to October, when the fresh-water discharge is a minimum."

Ranges. Various ranges are given, as indicated in the tables. In each case this is the difference in height between high water and low water for the tides indicated.

Example.—List chronologically the times and heights of all tides at Yonkers. (No. 1531) on January 2, 1975.

Solution.—

Date	January 2, 1975
Subordinate station	Yonkers
Reference station	New York
High water time difference	(+) 1^{h}09^m
Low water time difference	(+) 1^{h}10^m
High water height difference	(−) 0.8 ft.
Low water height difference	0.0 ft.

	New York			Yonkers	
HW	2321 (1st)	4.6 ft.		0030	3.8 ft.
LW	0516	(−) 0.6 ft.		0626	(−) 0.6 ft.
HW	1138	4.9 ft.		1247	4.1 ft.
LW	1749	(−) 0.9 ft.		1859	(−) 0.9 ft.

1206. Finding height of tide at any time.—Table 3 of the tide tables provides means for determining the approximate height of tide at any time. It is based upon the assumption that a plot of height versus time is a sine curve (art. 140, vol. II). Instructions for use of the table are given in a footnote below the table, which is reproduced in appendix L.

Example 1.—Find the height of tide at Yonkers (No. 1531) at 1000 on January 2, 1975.

Solution.—The given time is between the low water at 0626 and the high water at 1247 (example of art. 1205). Therefore, the tide is rising. The duration of rise is 1247−0626=6^{h}21^m. The range of tide is 4.1−(−0.6)=4.7 feet. The given time is 2^{h}47^m *before* high water, the nearest tide. Enter the upper part of the table with duration of rise 6^{h}20^m (the nearest tabulated value to 6^{h}21^m), and follow the line horizontally to 2^{h}45^m (the nearest tabulated value to 2^{h}47^m). Follow this column vertically downward to the entry 1.8 feet in the line for a range of tide of 4.5 feet (the nearest tabulated value to 4.7 feet). This is the correction to be applied to the nearest tide. Since the nearest tide is high water, subtract 1.8 from 4.1 feet. The answer, 2.3 feet, is the height of tide at the given time.

Answer.—Ht. of tide at 1000, 2.3 ft. A suitable form (fig. 1206a) is used to facilitate the solution.

Interpolation in this table is not considered justified.

TIDE AND CURRENT TABLES
SRNC-USNA-NC&M-3161/31(1-71)

NAVIGATION DEPARTMENT   DIVISION OF NAVAL COMMAND AND MANAGEMENT

COMPLETE TIDE TABLE

Date: Jan. 2, 1975

Substation	Yonkers
Reference Station	New York
HW Time Difference	(+) 1h 09m
LW Time Difference	(+) 1h 10m
Difference in height of HW	(−) 0.8ft.
Difference in height of LW	0.0ft.

Reference Station		Substation	
HW 2231	4.6ft.	0030	3.8ft.
LW 0516	(−) 0.6ft.	0626	(−) 0.6ft.
HW 1138	4.9ft.	1247	4.1ft.
LW 1749	(−) 0.9ft.	1859	(−) 0.9ft.
HW ___	___	___	___
LW ___	___	___	___

HEIGHT OF TIDE AT ANY TIME

Locality: Yonkers   Time: 1000   Date: Jan. 2, 1975

Duration of Rise or Fall:	6h 21m
Time from Nearest Tide:	2h 47m
Range of Tide:	4.7ft.
Height of Nearest Tide:	4.1ft.
Corr. from Table 3:	1.8ft.
Height of Tide at: 1000	2.3ft.

FIGURE 1206a.—U.S. Naval Academy tide form.

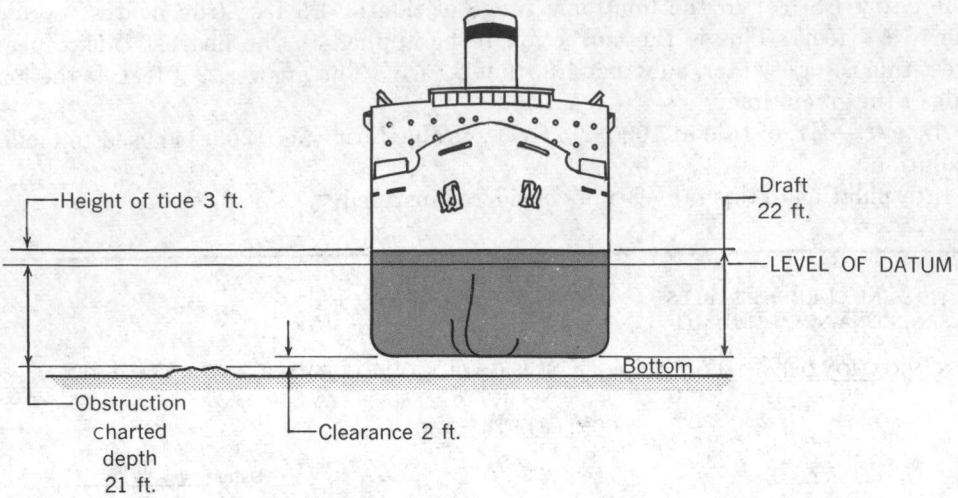

FIGURE 1206b.—Height of tide required to pass clear of charted obstruction.

It may be desired to know at what time a given depth of water will occur. In this case, the problem is solved in reverse.

Example 2.—The captain of a vessel drawing 22 feet wishes to pass over a temporary obstruction near Days Point, Weehawken (No. 1521), having a charted depth of 21 feet, passage to be made during the morning of January 31, 1975. Refer to figure 1206b.

Required.—The earliest time after 0800 that this passage can be made, allowing a safety margin of two feet.

Solution.—The least acceptable depth of water is 24 feet, which is three feet more than the charted depth. Therefore, the height of tide must be three feet or more. At the New York reference station a low tide of (−)0.9 foot occurs at 0459, followed by a high tide of 4.9 feet at 1120. At Days Point the corresponding low tide is (−)0.9 foot at 0522, and the high tide is 4.6 feet at 1144. The duration of rise is 6^h22^m, and the range of tide is 5.5 feet. The least acceptable tide is 3.0 feet, or 1.6 feet less than high tide. Enter the *lower* part of table 3 with range 5.5 feet and follow the horizontal line until 1.6 feet is reached. Follow this column vertically *upward* until the value of 2^h19^m is reached on the line for a duration of 6^h20^m (the nearest tabulated value to 6^h22^m). The minimum depth will occur about 2^h19^m *before* high water or at about 0925.

Answer.—A depth of 24 feet occurs at 0925.

If the range of tide is more than 20 feet, *half* the range (*one third* if the range is greater than 40 feet) is used to enter table 3, and the correction to height is *doubled* (*trebled* if one third is used).

A diagram for a graphical solution is given in figure 1206c. Eye interpolation can be used if desired. The steps in this solution are as follows:

1. Enter the upper graph with the duration of rise or fall. This is represented by a horizontal line.

2. Find the intersection of this line and the curve representing the interval from the nearest *low* water (point *A*).

3. From *A*, follow a vertical line to the sine curve of the lower diagram (point *B*).

4. From *B*, follow horizontally to the vertical line representing the range of tide (point *C*).

5. Using *C*, read the correction from the series of curves.

6. Add (algebraically) the correction of step 5 to the *low* water height, to find the height at the given time.

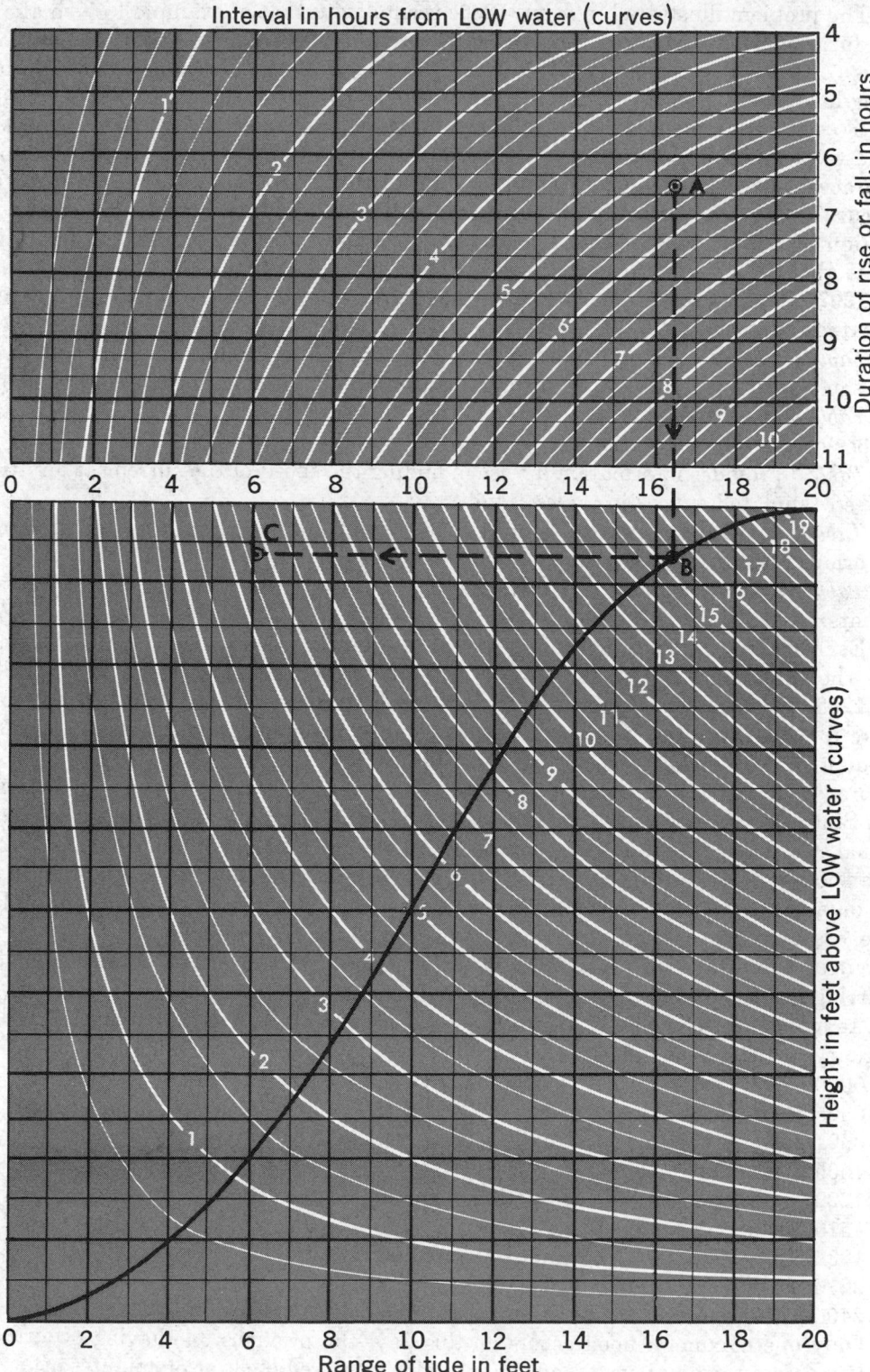

Interval in hours from LOW water (curves)

Duration of rise or fall, in hours

Range of tide in feet

Height in feet above LOW water (curves)

FIGURE 1206c.—Graphical solution for height of tide at any time.

The problem illustrated in figure 1206c is similar to that of example 1 given above. The duration of rise is 6^h25^m, and the interval from *low* water is 5^h23^m. The range of tide is 6.1 feet. The correction (by interpolation) is 5.7 feet. If the height of the preceding low tide is $(-)0.2$ foot, the height of tide at the given time is $(-)0.2+5.7=5.5$ feet. To solve example 2 by the graph, enter the lower graph and find the intersection of the vertical line representing 5.5 feet and the curve representing 3.9 feet (the minimum acceptable height above low water). From this point follow horizontally to the sine curve, and then vertically to the horizontal line in the upper figure representing the duration of rise of 6^h22^m. From the curve, determine the interval 4^h00^m. The earliest time is about 4^h00^m *after* low water, or at about 0922.

1207. Tidal current tables are somewhat similar to tide tables, but the coverage is less extensive, being given in two volumes. Each volume is arranged as follows:

Table 1 contains a complete list of predicted times of maximum currents and slack, with the velocity (speed) of the maximum currents, for a number of reference stations.

Table 2 gives differences, ratios, and other information related to a relatively large number of subordinate stations.

Table 3 provides information for use in finding the speed of the current at any time between tabulated entries in tables 1 and 2.

Table 4 gives the number of minutes the current does not exceed stated amounts, for various maximum speeds.

Table 5 (Atlantic Coast of North America only) gives information on rotary tidal currents.

Each volume contains additional useful information related to currents. Extracts from the tables for the Atlantic Coast of North America are given in appendix M.

1208. Tidal current predictions for reference stations.—The extracts of appendix M are for The Narrows, New York Harbor. Times are given on the 24-hour basis, for meridian 75°W. *Daylight saving time is not used.*

For each day, the date and day of week are given, with complete current information. Since the cycle is repeated twice each tidal day, currents at this place are semidiurnal. On most days there are four slack waters and four maximum currents, two of them floods (F) and two of them ebbs (E). However, since the tidal day is longer than the civil day, the corresponding condition occurs later from day to day, and on certain days there are only three slack waters or three maximum currents. At some places, the current on some days runs maximum flood twice, but ebb only once, a minimum flood occurring in place of the second ebb. The tables show this information.

As indicated by appendix M, the sequence of currents at The Narrows on Monday, February 3, 1975, is as follows:

0000 Flood current, 5^m after maximum velocity (speed).
0305 Slack, ebb begins.
0621 Maximum ebb of 2.0 knots, setting 160°.
1005 Slack, flood begins.
1222 Maximum flood of 1.5 knots, setting 340°.
1516 Slack, ebb begins.
1839 Maximum ebb of 1.9 knots, setting 160°.
2216 Slack, flood begins.
2400 Flood current, 56^m before maximum velocity (speed).

Only one maximum flood occurs on this day, the previous one having occurred 5 minutes before the day began, and the following one predicted for 56 minutes after the day ends.

1209. Tidal current predictions for subordinate stations.—For each subordinate station listed in table 2 of the tidal current tables, the following information is given:

Number. The stations are listed in geographical order and given consecutive numbers, as in the tide tables (art. 1205). At the end of each volume an alphabetical listing is given, and for each entry the consecutive number is shown, to assist in finding the entry in table 2.

Place. The list of places includes both subordinate and reference stations, the latter being given in bold type.

Position. The approximate latitude and longitude are given to assist in locating the station. The latitude is north or south and the longitude east or west as indicated by the letters (N, S, E, W) next *above* the entry. The current given is for the center of the channel unless another location is indicated by the station name.

Time difference. Two time differences are tabulated. One is the number of hours and minutes to be applied to the tabulated times of slack water at the reference station to find the times of slack waters at the subordinate station. The other time difference is applied to the times of maximum current at the reference station to find the times of the corresponding maximum current at the subordinate station. The intervals, which are added or subtracted in accordance with their signs, include any difference in time between the two stations, so that the answer is correct for the standard time of the subordinate station. Limited application and special conditions are indicated by footnotes.

Velocity (speed) ratios. Speed of the current at the subordinate station is found by multiplying the speed at the reference station by the tabulated ratio. Separate ratios may be given for flood and ebb currents. Special conditions are indicated by footnotes.

As indicated in appendix M, the currents at The Battery (No. 2375) can be found by *adding* 1^h30^m for slack water and 1^h35^m for maximum current to the times for The Narrows, and multiplying flood currents by 0.9 and ebb currents by 1.2. Applying these to the values for Monday, February 3, 1975, the sequence is as follows:

0000 Flood current, 1^h30^m before maximum velocity (speed).

0130 Maximum flood of 1.8 knots, setting 015°.

0435 Slack, ebb begins.

0756 Maximum ebb of 2.4 knots, setting 195°.

1135 Slack, flood begins.

1357 Maximum flood of 1.4 knots, setting 015°.

1646 Slack, ebb begins.

2014 Maximum ebb of 2.3 knots setting 195°.

2346 Slack, flood begins.

2400 Flood current, 14^m after slack.

1210. Finding speed of tidal current at any time.—Table 3 of the tidal current table provides means for determining the approximate velocity (speed) at any time. Instructions for its use are given below the table, which is reproduced in appendix M.

Example 1.—Find the speed of the current at The Battery at 1500 on February 3, 1975.

Solution.—The given time is between the maximum flood of 1.4 knots at 1357 and the slack at 1646 (art. 1209). The interval between slack and maximum current (1646 −1357) is 2^h49^m. The interval between slack and the desired time (1646−1500) is 1^h46^m. Enter the table (A) with 2^h40^m at the top, and 1^h40^m at the left side (the nearest tabulated values to 2^h49^m and 1^h46^m, respectively), and find the factor 0.8 in the body of the table. The approximate speed at 1500 is $0.8 \times 1.4 = 1.1$ knots, and it is flooding.

Answer.—Speed 1.1 kn. A suitable form (fig. 1210) is used to facilitate the solution.

It may be desired to determine the period during which the current is less (or greater) than a given amount. Table 4 of the tidal current tables can be used to determine the period during which the speed does not exceed 0.5 knot. For greater

NAVIGATION DEPARTMENT   DIVISION OF NAVAL COMMAND AND MANAGEMENT

COMPLETE CURRENT TABLE

Locality: The Battery   Date: Feb. 3, 1975

Reference Station: The Narrows

Time Difference: Slack Water: (+) 1ʰ 30ᵐ
                   Maximum Current: (+) 1ʰ 35ᵐ
Velocity Ratio: Maximum Flood: 0.9
                   Maximum Ebb: 1.2

Flood Direction: 015°
Ebb Direction: 195°

Reference Station: The Narrows   Locality: The Battery

				0000	F
2355	2.0F			0130	1.8F
0305	0			0435	0
0621	2.0E			0756	2.4E
1005	0			1135	0
1222	1.5F			1357	1.4F
1516	0			1646	0
1839	1.9E			2014	2.3E
2216	0			2346	0
2400	F			2400	F

VELOCITY OF CURRENT AT ANY TIME

Int. between slack and desired time:	1ʰ 46ᵐ	
Int. between slack and maximum current:	2ʰ 49ᵐ	(Ebb) (Flood)
Maximum current:	1.4 kn	
Factor, Table 3:	0.8	
Velocity:	1.1 kn	
Direction:	015°	

DURATION OF SLACK

Times of maximum current:	0756	1357
Maximum current:	2.4 kn	1.4 kn
Desired maximum:	0.3	0.3
Period — Table 4:	35ᵐ	46ᵐ
Sum of periods:		81ᵐ
Average period:		40ᵐ
Time of slack:		1135
Duration of slack: From: ___1115___ To: ___1155___		

FIGURE 1210.—U.S. Naval Academy tidal current form.

speeds, and for more accurate results under some conditions, table 3 of the tidal current tables can be used, solving by reversing the process used in example 1.

Example 2.—During what period on the evening of February 3, 1975, does the ebb current equal or exceed 1.0 knot at The Battery?

Solution.—The maximum ebb of 2.3 knots occurs at 2014. This is preceded by a slack at 1646, and followed by the next slack at 2346. The interval between the earlier slack and the maximum ebb is 3ʰ28ᵐ, and the interval between the ebb and following slack is 3ʰ32ᵐ. The desired factor is $\dfrac{1.0}{2.3}=0.4$. Enter table A with 3ʰ20ᵐ (the nearest tabulated value to 3^{h}28^m) at the top, and follow down the column to 0.4 (midway between 0.3 and 0.5). At the left margin the interval between slack and the desired time is found to be 0^{h}50^m (midway between 0^{h}40^m and 1^{h}00^m). Therefore, the current becomes 1.0 knot at 1646+0^{h}50^m=1736. Next, enter table A with 3^{h}40^m (the nearest tabulated value to 3^{h}32^m) at the top, and follow down the column to 0.4. Follow this line to the left margin, where the interval between slack and desired time is found to be 1^{h}00^m. Therefore, the current is 1.0 knot or greater until 2346−1^{h}00^m=2246. If the two intervals between maximum current and slack were nearest the same 20^m interval, table A would have to be entered only once.

   Answer.—The speed equals or exceeds 1.0 knot between 1736 and 2246.

   The predicted times of slack water given in the tidal current tables indicate the instant of zero velocity. There is a period each side of slack water, however, during which the current is so weak that for practical purposes it may be considered as negligible. Table 4 of the tidal current tables gives, for various maximum currents, the approximate period of time during which weak currents not exceeding 0.1 to 0.5 knot will be encountered. This duration includes the last of the flood or ebb and the beginning of the following flood or ebb, that is, half of the duration will be before and half after the time of slack water.

   When there is a difference between the velocities of the maximum flood and ebb preceding and following the slack for which the duration is desired, it will be sufficiently accurate for practical purposes to find a separate duration for each maximum velocity and take the average of the two as the duration of the weak current.

   Of the two subtables of table 4, table A should be used for all places *except* those listed for table B; table B should be used for all places listed, and all stations in table 2 which are referred to them.

   Example 3.—Find the period from just before until just after the slack at The Battery at 1135 on February 3, 1975, that the current does not exceed 0.3 kn.

   Solution.—Refer to table 4. Table A of table 4 of the tidal current tables is entered with the maximum current before the slack to find the period during which the current does not exceed 0.3 kn. Since there is a difference between the velocities of the maximum ebb and flood preceding and following the slack for which the duration is desired, table A is re-entered with the maximum current after the slack to find the period during which the current does not exceed 0.3 kn. The average of the two values so found is taken as the duration of the weak current. The form shown in figure 1210 is used to facilitate the solution.

   Answer.—Duration 40 min. (from 1115 to 1155).

   1211. Tidal current charts present a comprehensive view of the hourly speed and direction of the current in 11 bodies of water (art. 1202). They also provide a means for determining the speed and direction of the current at various localities throughout these bodies of water. The arrows show the direction of the current; the figures give the speed in knots at the time of spring tides, that is, during the time of new or full moon when the currents are stronger than average. When the current is given as weak, the speed is less than 0.1 knot. The decimal point locates the position of the station.

   The charts depict the flow of the tidal current under normal weather conditions. Strong winds and freshets, however, bring about nontidal currents which may modify considerably the speed and direction shown on the charts.

   The speed of the tidal current varies from day to day principally in accordance with the phase, distance, and declination of the moon. Therefore, to obtain the speed for any particular day and hour, the *spring speeds* shown on the charts must be modified by correction factors. A correction table given in the charts can be used for this purpose.

The **tidal current diagrams** are a series of 12 monthly diagrams to be used with the tidal current charts. There is one diagram for each month of the year. A new set of diagrams must be used each year. The diagrams are computer constructed lines that locate each chart throughout all hours of every month. The diagrams indicate directly the chart and the speed correction factor to use at any desired time.

1212. Current diagrams.—A current diagram is a graph showing the speed of the current along a channel at different stages of the tidal current cycle. The current tables include such diagrams for Vineyard and Nantucket Sounds (one diagram); East River, New York; New York Harbor; Delaware Bay and River (one diagram); and Chesapeake Bay. The diagram for New York Harbor is reproduced in appendix M.

On this diagram each vertical line represents a given instant identified in terms of the number of hours before or after slack at The Narrows. Each horizontal line represents a distance from Ambrose Channel Entrance, measured along the usually traveled route. The names along the left margin are placed at the correct distances from Ambrose Channel Entrance. The current is for the center of the channel opposite these points. The intersection of any vertical line with any horizontal line represents a given moment in the current cycle at a given place in the channel. If this intersection is in a shaded area, the current is flooding; if in an unshaded area, it is ebbing. The speed in knots can be found by interpolation (if necessary) between the numbers given in the body of the diagram. The given values are *averages*. To find the value at any given time, multiply the speed found from the diagram by the ratio of *maximum speed of the current involved* to the *maximum shown on the diagram*, both values being taken for The Narrows. If the diurnal inequality is large, the accuracy can be improved by altering the width of the shaded area to fit conditions. The diagram covers 1½ current cycles, so that the right-hand third is a duplication of the left-hand third.

If the current for a single station is desired, table 1 or 2 should be used. The current diagrams are intended for use in either of two ways: First, to determine a favorable time for passage through the channel. Second, to find the average current to be expected during any passage through the channel. For both of these uses a number of "speed lines" are provided. When the appropriate line is transferred to the correct part of the diagram, the current to be encountered during passage is indicated along the line.

Example.—During the morning of January 3, 1975, a ship is to leave Pier 83 at W. 42nd St., and proceed down the bay at ten knots.

Required.—(1) Time to get underway to take maximum advantage of a favorable current, allowing 15 minutes to reach mid channel.

(2) Average speed over the bottom during passage down the bay.

Solution.—(1) Transfer the line (slope) for ten knots southbound to the diagram, locating it so that it is centered on the unshaded ebb current section between W. 42nd St. and Ambrose Channel Entrance. This line crosses a horizontal line through W. 42nd St. about one-half of the distance between the vertical lines representing three and two hours, respectively, after ebb begins at The Narrows. The setting is not critical. Any time within about half an hour of the correct time will result in about the same current. Between the points involved, the entire speed line is in the ebb current area.

(2) Table 1 indicates that on the morning of January 3 ebb begins at The Narrows at 0132. Two hours twenty-eight minutes after ebb begins, the time is 0400. Therefore, the ship should reach mid channel at 0400. It should get underway 15 minutes earlier, at 0345.

(3) To find the average current, determine the current at intervals (as every two miles), add, and divide by the number of entries.

Distance	Current
18	1.2
16	1.4
14	1.9
12	1.5
10	2.0
8	1.9
6	1.3
4	1.2
2	1.4
0	1.2
sum	15.0

The sum of 15.0 is for ten entries. The average is therefore $15.0 \div 10 = 1.5$ knots.

(4) This value of current is correct only if the ebb current is an average one. From table 1 the maximum ebb involved is 2.2 knots. From the diagram the maximum value at The Narrows is 2.0 knots. Therefore, the average current found in step (3) should be increased by the ratio $2.2 \div 2.0 = 1.1$. The average for the run is therefore $1.5 \times 1.1 = 1.6$ knots. Speed over the botton is $10 + 1.6 = 11.6$ knots.

Answers.—(1) T 0345, (2) S 11.6 kn.

In the example, an ebb current is carried throughout the run. If the transferred speed line had been partly in a flood current area, all ebb currents (those increasing the ship's speed) should be given a positive sign (+), and all flood currents a negative sign (−). A separate ratio should be determined for each current (flood or ebb), and applied to the entries for that current. In Chesapeake Bay it is not unusual for an outbound vessel to encounter three or even four separate currents during passage down the bay. Under the latter condition, it is good practice to multiply *each* current taken from the diagram by the ratio for the current involved.

If the time of starting the passage is fixed, and the current during passage is desired, the starting time is identified in terms of the reference tidal cycle. The speed line is then drawn through the intersection of this vertical time line and the horizontal line through the place. The average current is then determined in the same manner as when the speed line is located as described above.

Problems

1202. The mean high water lunitidal interval at a certain port is 2^h17^m.

Required.—The approximate times of each high and low water on a day when the moon transits the local meridian at 1146.

Answers.—HW at 0139 and 1403, LW at 0751 and 2015.

1204. List chronologically the times and heights of all tides at New York (The Battery) on February 11, 1975.

Answer.—

Time	Tide	Height
0222	LW	(−) 0.4 ft.
0829	HW	4.6 ft.
1449	LW	(−) 0.6 ft.
2053	HW	4.2 ft.

1205. List chronologically the times and heights of all tides at Castle Point, Hoboken, N.J. (No. 1519) on March 18, 1975.

Answer.—

Time	Tide	Height
0533	LW	0.2 ft.
1141	HW	3.5 ft.
1724	LW	0.3 ft.
0003	HW	4.1 ft.

1206a. Find the height of tide at Union Stock Yards, New York (No. 1523) at 0600 on February 6, 1975.

*Answer.—*Ht. of tide at 0600, 3.8 ft.

1206b. The captain of a vessel drawing 24 feet wishes to pass over a temporary obstruction near Bayonne, N.J. (No. 1505) having a charted depth of 23 feet, passage to be made during the afternoon of March 5, 1975.

*Required.—*The earliest and latest times that the passage can be made, allowing a safety margin of two feet.

*Answers.—*Earliest time 1316, latest time 1531.

1208. Determine the sequence of currents at The Narrows on January 15, 1975.

Answer.—

    0000 Ebb current, 42^m after slack.
    0231 Maximum ebb of 1.9 knots.
    0557 Slack, flood begins.
    0822 Maximum flood of 1.7 knots.
    1137 Slack, ebb begins.
    1455 Maximum ebb of 2.1 knots.
    1836 Slack, flood begins.
    2051 Maximum flood of 1.5 knots.
    2400 Flood current, 2^m before slack.

1209. Determine the sequence of currents at Ambrose Channel Entrance (No. 2310) on January 12, 1975.

Answer.—

    0000 Ebb current, 42^m after maximum velocity (speed).
    0241 Slack, flood begins.
    0533 Maximum flood of 2.0 knots, setting 310°.
    0828 Slack, ebb begins.
    1155 Maximum ebb of 2.5 knots.
    1527 Slack, flood begins.
    1801 Maximum flood of 1.5 knots, setting 310°.
    2040 Slack, ebb begins.
    2400 Ebb current, 3^m before maximum velocity (speed).

1210a. Find the speed of the current at Bear Mountain Bridge (No. 2445) at 0900 on February 19, 1975.

*Answer.—*Speed 0.8 kn.

1210b. At about what time during the afternoon of February 3, 1975, does the flood current northwest of The Battery (No. 2375) reach a speed of 1.0 knot?

*Answer.—*T 1245.

1212. A vessel arrives at Ambrose Channel Entrance two hours after flood begins at The Narrows on the morning of February 16, 1975.

Required.—(1) The speed through the water required to take fullest advantage of the flood tide in steaming to Chelsea Docks.

(2) The average current to be expected.

(3) Estimated time of arrival off Chelsea Docks.

Answers.—(1) S 9 kn., (2) S 1.4 kn., (3) ETA 1035.

CHAPTER XIII

SAILING DIRECTIONS AND LIGHT LISTS

1301. Introduction.—Sailing directions (pilots) and light lists provide the information that cannot be shown graphically on the nautical chart and that is not readily available elsewhere. In pilot waters, the prudent navigator makes effective use of all three tools: the nautical chart, sailing directions, and light lists. He does not use one to the exclusion of the others.

Sailing Directions

1302. Format.—The format of the 70 volumes of the sailing directions produced by the Defense Mapping Agency Hydrographic Center prior to 1971 was such that each volume, as it related to specific foreign areas, provided detailed descriptions of coasts, channels, dangers, aids, winds, currents, tides, port facilities, signal systems, pilotage, instructions for approaching and entering harbors, as well as a variety of other material required by mariners. This format differed little from sailing directions of centuries past. There were the same geographic divisions and lengthy descriptions of approaches or harbors even though improved charts had obviated the necessity for such detail.

In the earlier format the limited geographic coverage of a given volume precluded inclusion of important information pertaining to transoceanic passages.

Using a new format, the Defense Mapping Agency Hydrographic Center is replacing the previous 70 volumes with 43 volumes: 35 *Sailing Directions (Enroute)* and 8 *Sailing Directions (Planning Guide)*. Port facilities data is contained in Pub. No. 150, *World Port Index*.

The old sailing directions described and located features by bearing and distance from previously described landmarks and formed a maze of descriptive hydrography covering the coasts of the world. Sometimes, the description amounted to a mass of verbosity, especially when it pertained to an archipelago. The new Index-Gazetteer, listing each feature by its coordinates, eliminates the need for lengthy, unwieldy descriptive text. Another innovation is the fact that the features described are referred to in the text by page numbers rather than by the chapter-paragraph method used in the old sailing directions.

1303. *Sailing Directions (Planning Guide)*.—Each of the 8 *Sailing Directions (Planning Guide)* contains five chapters, the titles of which are shown in figure 1303a.

The Planning Guides are relatively permanent because of the nature of the material they contain. The *Sailing Directions (Enroute)* must be updated by relatively frequent changes, and so must the *World Port Index*.

The new sailing directions are designed to assist the navigator in planning a voyage of any extent, particularly if it involves an ocean passage. Each of the *Sailing Directions (Planning Guide)* covers one of the world's great land-sea areas based on an arbitrary division of the world's seaways into eight "ocean basins" as shown in figure 1303b.

Chapter 1 of the Planning Guide, COUNTRIES, contains useful information about all of the countries adjacent to the particular ocean basin being covered by one of the eight publications. This is the chapter concerned with pratique, pilotage, signals, and

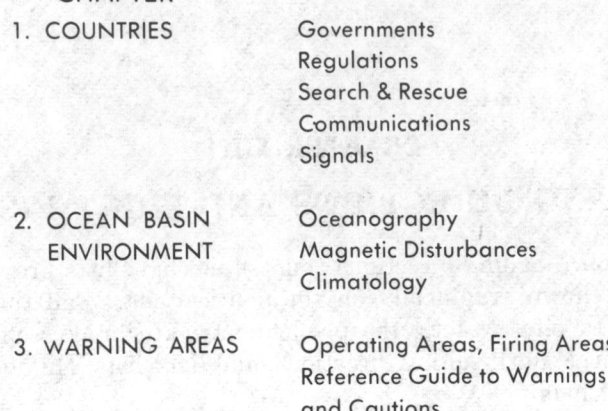

CHAPTER

1. COUNTRIES   Governments
                              Regulations
                              Search & Rescue
                              Communications
                              Signals

2. OCEAN BASIN   Oceanography
   ENVIRONMENT   Magnetic Disturbances
                              Climatology

3. WARNING AREAS   Operating Areas, Firing Areas
                              Reference Guide to Warnings
                              and Cautions

4. OCEAN ROUTES   Route Chart & Text
                              Traffic Separation Schemes

5. NAVAID SYSTEMS   Electronic Navigation Systems
                              Systems of Lights & Buoyage

FIGURE 1303a.—Table of contents of *Sailing Directions* (*Planning Guide*).

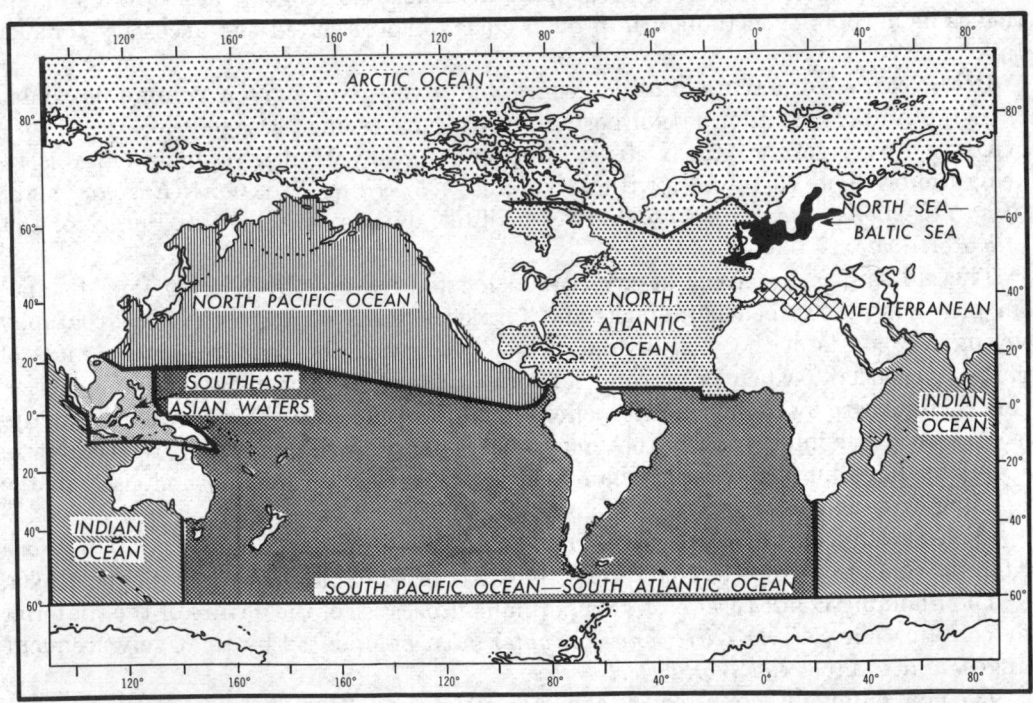

FIGURE 1303b.—Division of world's great land-sea areas into eight ocean basins.

pertinent regulations for shipping. A treatment of Search and Rescue includes graphics showing all lifesaving stations and radio stations open to public correspondence.

Chapter 2 of the Planning Guide, OCEAN BASIN ENVIRONMENT, contains important information relative to the physical environment of an ocean basin. It consists of Ocean

Summaries and local coastal phenomena not found in referenced atlases, and provides the mariner with general, concise information concerning the physical forces he must consider in planning a route.

Chapter 3 of the Planning Guide, WARNING AREAS, includes firing danger areas published in foreign sailing directions and not already shown on nautical charts or in other Defense Mapping Agency Hydrographic Center publications. A graphic key identifies Submarine Operating Areas. References are made to publications and periodicals which list danger areas, for example *Notice to Mariners No. 1* which gives an annual listing of Atlantic and Pacific danger areas. General cautions pertinent to navigation are given.

In Chapter 4 of the Planning Guide, ROUTES, the recommended steamship routes are described and shown graphically. To facilitate planning, the new publication shows entire routes as they originate from all major U. S. ports and naval bases and terminate at foreign ports in the Planning Guide area. The new concept is in sharp contrast to the localized method used in the old sailing directions. Chapter 4 also includes all applicable Traffic Separation Schemes.

The Planning Guide concludes with Chapter 5, NAVAID SYSTEMS. In keeping with the principles of the new concept, all radionavigation systems pertaining to the ocean area are described. The national and international systems of lights, beaconage, and buoyage are also described and illustrated.

1304. Sailing Directions (Enroute).—Each volume of the 35 *Sailing Directions (Enroute)* is divided into numbered sectors. Figure 1304a shows a portion of the sectors covered by one of the two *Sailing Directions (Enroute)* covering the English Channel. Figure 1304b illustrates a typical table of contents for a sector.

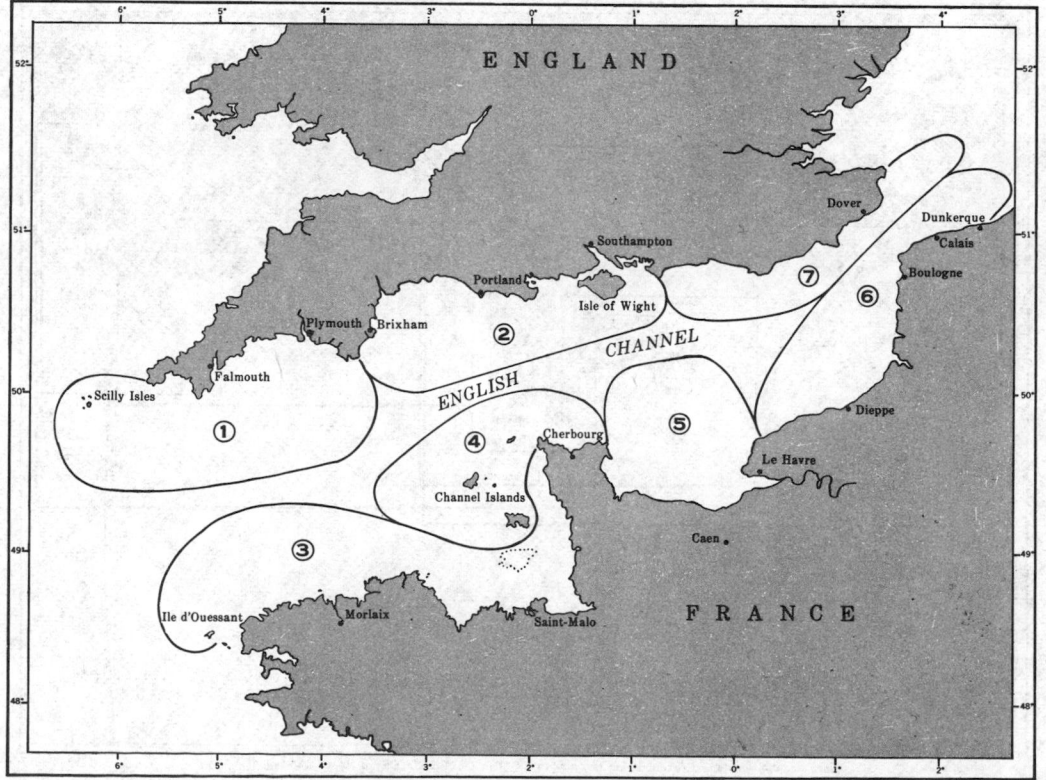

FIGURE 1304a.—Typical diagram of sector limits.

SECTOR 1
   CHART INFORMATION GRAPHIC
   COASTAL WINDS & CURRENTS GRAPHIC
   OUTER DANGERS
   COASTAL FEATURES
   ANCHORAGES (COASTAL)
   MAJOR PORTS
      —Directions; Landmarks; Navaids; Depths;
        Limitations; Restrictions; Pilotage; Regulations;
        Winds; Tides; Currents; Anchorages

FIGURE 1304b.—Typical table of contents of *Sailing Directions (Enroute)*.

Chart Information, the first subtitle in the sample table of contents, refers to a graphic key to charts pertaining to a sector. Figure 1304c is an actual sample of the graphic key for Sector 1, "English Channel—Scilly Isles to Start Point." The graduation of the border scale of the chartlet in five-minute increments enables navigators to quickly identify the largest scale chart for a location and to find a feature listed in the publications Index-Gazetteer.

The Index-Gazetteer is simply an alphabetical listing, including both described features and charted features. Each feature is listed with its geographic coordinates and sector number for use with the graphic key. Only features mentioned in the text are given a page number.

Coastal Winds and Currents, the second subtitle in the table of contents, refers to a graphic depicting coastal winds, weather, tides, and currents. Figure 1304d is a

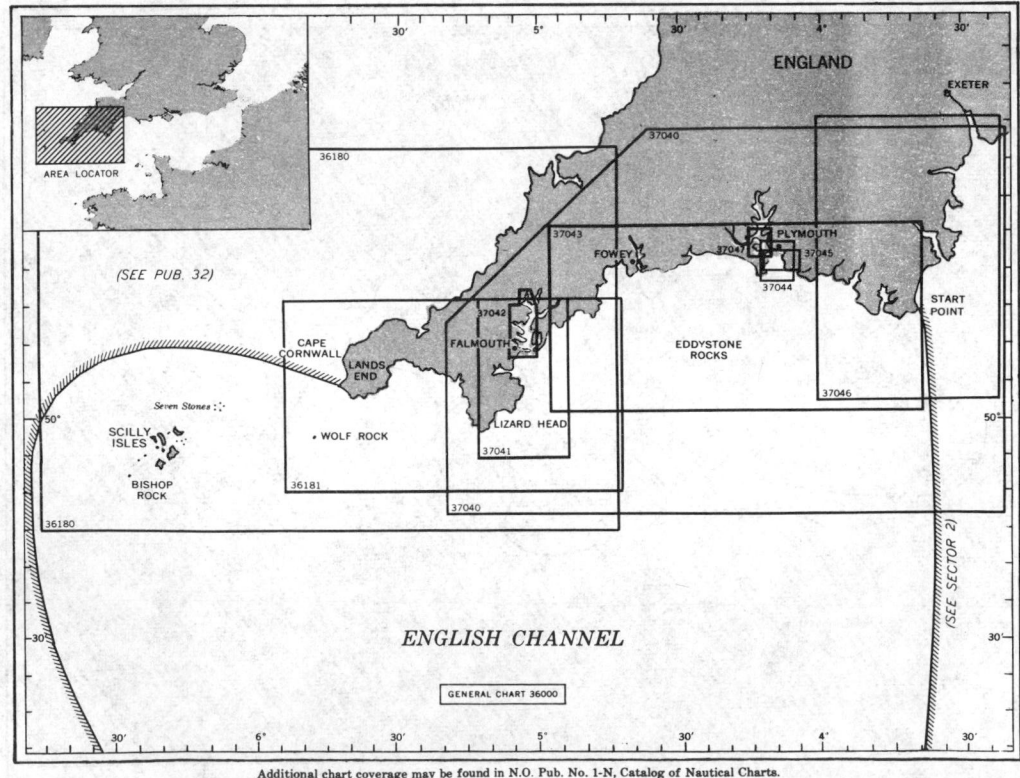

Additional chart coverage may be found in N.O. Pub. No. 1-N, Catalog of Nautical Charts.

FIGURE 1304c.—Graphic key to charts within a sector.

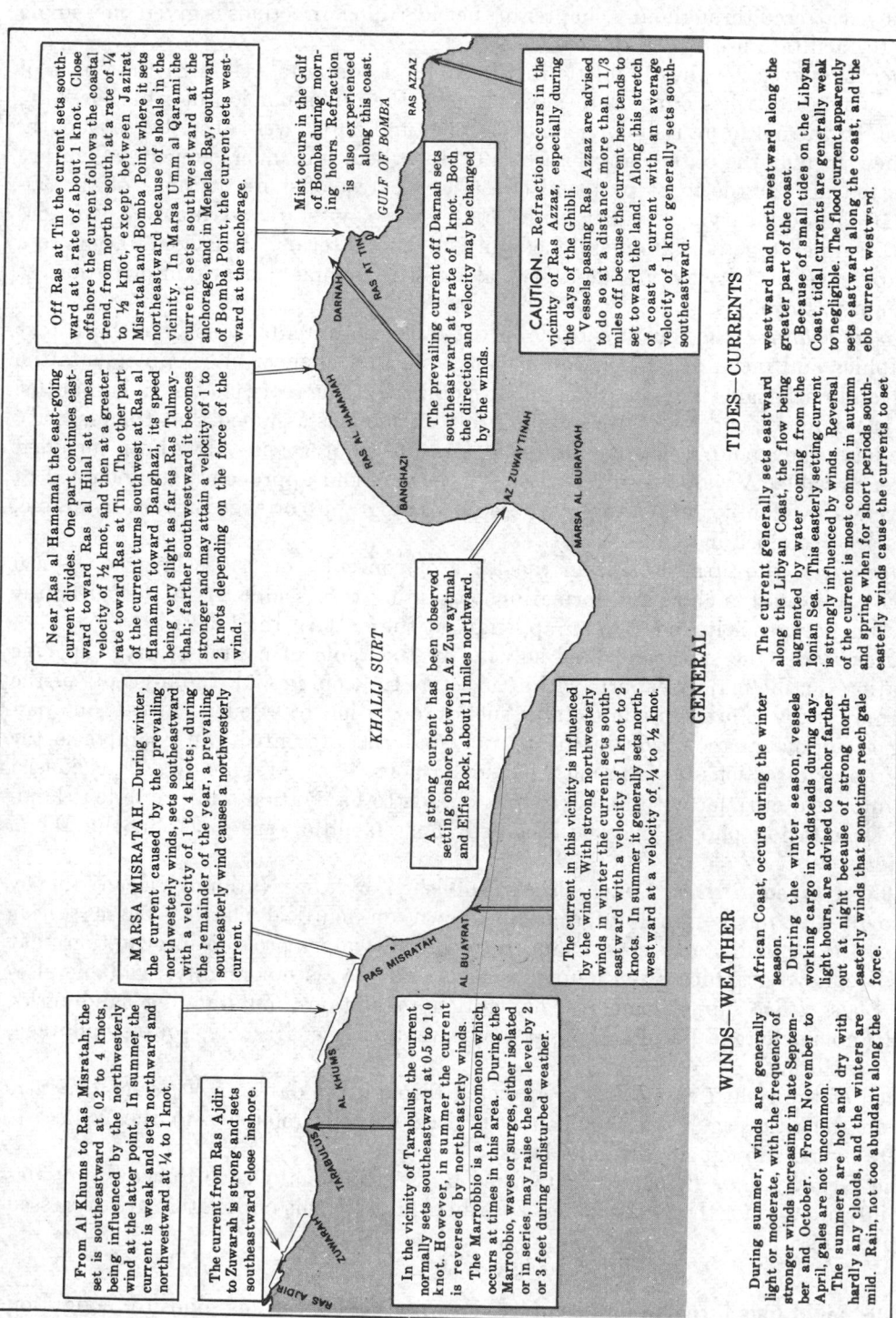

Off Ras at Tin the current sets southward at a rate of about 1 knot. Close offshore the current follows the coastal trend, from north to south, at a rate of ¼ to ½ knot, except between Jazirat Misratah and Bomba Point where it sets northeastward because of shoals in the vicinity. In Marsa Umm al Qarami the current sets southwestward at the anchorage, and in Menelao Bay, southward of Bomba Point, the current sets westward at the anchorage.

Mist occurs in the Gulf of Bomba during morning hours. Refraction is also experienced along this coast.

The prevailing current off Darnah sets southeastward at a rate of 1 knot. Both the direction and velocity may be changed by the winds.

CAUTION.—Refraction occurs in the vicinity of Ras Azzaz, especially during the days of the Ghibli.

Vessels passing Ras Azzaz are advised to do so at a distance more than 1⅓ miles off because the current here tends to set toward the land. Along this stretch of coast a current with an average velocity of 1 knot generally sets southeastward.

Near Ras al Hamamah the east-going current divides. One part continues eastward toward Ras al Hilal at a mean velocity of ½ knot, and then at a greater rate toward Ras at Tin. The other part of the current turns southwest at Ras al Hamamah toward Banghazi, its speed being very slight as far as Ras Tulmaythah; farther southwestward it becomes stronger and may attain a velocity of 1 to 2 knots depending on the force of the wind.

MARSA MISRATAH.—During winter, the current caused by the prevailing northwesterly winds, sets southeastward with a velocity of 1 to 4 knots; during the remainder of the year, a prevailing southeasterly wind causes a northwesterly current.

A strong current has been observed setting onshore between Az Zuwaytinah and Elfie Rock, about 11 miles northward.

From Al Khums to Ras Misratah, the set is southeastward at 0.2 to 4 knots, being influenced by the northwesterly wind at the latter point. In summer the current is weak and sets northward and northwestward at ¼ to 1 knot.

The current from Ras Ajdir to Zuwarah is strong and sets southeastward close inshore.

The current in this vicinity is influenced by the wind. With strong northwesterly winds in winter the current sets southeastward with a velocity of 1 knot to 2 knots. In summer it generally sets northwestward at a velocity of ¼ to ½ knot.

In the vicinity of Tarabulus, the current normally sets southeastward at 0.5 to 1.0 knot. However, in summer the current is reversed by northeasterly winds.

The Marrobbio is a phenomenon which occurs at times in this area. During the Marrobbio, waves or surges, either isolated or in series, may raise the sea level by 2 or 3 feet during undisturbed weather.

GENERAL

WINDS—WEATHER

During summer, winds are generally light or moderate, with the frequency of stronger winds increasing in late September and October. From November to April, gales are not uncommon.

The summers are hot and dry with hardly any clouds, and the winters are mild. Rain, not too abundant along the African Coast, occurs during the winter season.

During the winter season, vessels working cargo in roadsteads during daylight hours, are advised to anchor farther out at night because of strong northeasterly winds that sometimes reach gale force.

TIDES—CURRENTS

The current generally sets eastward along the Libyan Coast, the flow being augmented by water coming from the Ionian Sea. This easterly setting current is strongly influenced by winds. Reversal of the current is most common in autumn and spring when for short periods southeasterly winds cause the currents to set westward and northwestward along the greater part of the coast.

Because of small tides on the Libyan Coast, tidal currents are generally weak to negligible. The flood current apparently sets eastward along the coast, and the ebb current westward.

RAS AZZAZ

GULF OF BOMBA

RAS AT TIN

DARNAH

RAS AL HAMAMAH

BANGHAZI

AZ ZUWAYTINAH

MARSA AL BURAYQAH

KHALIJ SURT

RAS MISRATAH

AL BUAYRAT

AL KHUMS

TARABULUS

ZUWARAH

RAS AJDIR

FIGURE 1304d.—Graphic depicting coastal winds, weather, tides and currents.

reproduction of the graphic for a sector covering the coast of Libya and which appears in one of the new *Sailing Directions* (*Enroute*). In the new format all of the information previously scattered throughout a chapter of the old sailing directions is given on a single graphic to facilitate use by navigators.

Outer Dangers, the third subtitle in the table of contents, refers to that part of Sector 1 which describes dangers to navigation in the outer portion of a harbor, bay, river, etc. In the old format all dangers, both inner and outer, were described at length. In the new format the outer dangers are fully described, but inner dangers which are well-charted are for the most part omitted. The greatest offshore distance of the 20-meter (10-fathom) curve, or other appropriate curve, is stated. Numerous offshore dangers, grouped together, are mentioned only in general terms. Dangers adjacent to a coastal passage or fairway are described along with supplementary information to ensure safe passage.

Coastal Features, the fourth subtitle in the table of contents, consists of both text and graphics and includes information in geographical sequence that supplements the charted landmarks, aids to navigation, salient points, fringing reefs, shoals, river mouths, coastal islets, inlets, and bays. In compiling this section it is assumed that the majority of ships have radar and, hence, annotated radarscope photographs have been included whenever possible. Aerial and surface views of harbors and approaches are included to aid mariners in identifying features. Where no photographs or sketches are available, features are described in the text.

Anchorages, the fifth subtitle in the table of contents, describes in geographical sequence all coastal anchoring information pertaining to a sector. A tabulated listing of these anchorages is included in an appendix at the back of the book.

Major Ports, the sixth and final subtitle in the table of contents, gives specific information for the major seaports within a sector. In keeping with the precepts of the new format every effort is made to limit such information to essential facts, thus permitting a significant reduction in the textual material presented. An example is the use of graphic directions for entering a particular port. These graphic directions consist of an annotated chartlet with line drawings of aids to navigation and prominent landmarks. Orientation photos may be included. Port facilities are given in the *World Port Index*.

1305. United States Coast Pilots published by the National Ocean Survey supplement the navigational information shown on nautical charts. These *sailing directions* for United States coastal and intracoastal waters provide information that cannot be shown graphically on nautical charts and that is not readily available elsewhere. *Coast Pilot* subjects include navigation regulations, outstanding landmarks, channel and anchorage peculiarities, dangers, weather, ice, freshets, routes, pilotage, and port facilities.

Each of the eight *Coast Pilots* is corrected through the dates of *Notice to Mariners* shown on the title page, and should not be used without reference to the *Notices to Mariners* issued subsequent to those dates.

The **Great Lakes Pilot,** also published by the National Ocean Survey, provides similar information for the Great Lakes. Distances given in this publication are expressed in statute miles.

Light Lists

1306. Light lists furnish more complete information concerning aides to navigation than can be conveniently shown on charts. They are not intended to be used for navigation in place of charts and sailing directions (pilots), and should not be so used. The charts should be consulted for the location of all aids to navigation. It may be dangerous to use aids to navigation without reference to charts. Likewise, the charts should not be used without reference to the more detailed information given in the light list, even during daylight. For example: Only the light list may reveal that certain channel buoys are actually located some 50 yards beyond the charted channel limits. Or, only the light list may reveal that a certain charted lighted buoy with a radar reflector is replaced by a nun buoy when endangered by ice. Since this replacement is indicated in the light list, it would not normally be included in *Notice to Mariners*.

Light lists give detailed information regarding navigational lights and sound signals. The U. S. Coast Guard *Light List* for the United States and its possessions, including the Intracoastal Waterway, the Great Lakes (both United States and certain aids on Canadian shores), and the Mississippi River and its navigable tributaries also gives information on unlighted buoys, radiobeacons, radio direction finder calibration stations, daybeacons, racons, and Loran stations. The *Light List* does not include aeronautical lights.

In addition to information on lighted aids to navigation and sound signals, the Defense Mapping Agency Hydrographic Center *List of Lights* for coasts other than the United States and its possessions provides information on storm signals, signal stations, racons, radiobeacons, and radio direction finder calibration stations located at or near lights. However, for detailed information on radio aids the navigator should refer to Pubs. Nos. 117A and 117B, *Radio Navigational Aids*. The *List of Lights* does not include information on lighted buoys in harbors. Those aeronautical lights situated near the coast are listed in the *List of Lights* in order that the marine navigator may be able to obtain more complete information concerning their description. However, it should be borne in mind that these lights are not designed or maintained for marine navigation, and they are subject to changes of which the marine navigator may not receive prompt notification.

Within each volume of the *Light List* aids to navigation are listed in geographic order from north to south along the Atlantic coast, from east to west along the gulf coast, and from south to north along the Pacific coast. Seacoast aids are listed first, followed by entrance and harbor aids listed from seaward to the head of navigation. In volumes I and II, Intracoastal Waterway aids are listed last and in geographic order from north to south along the Atlantic coast and south to north and east to west along the gulf coast.

The introductions to the light lists contain useful information pertaining to the contents which should be carefully studied by the user. In addition to the notes in the remarks columns of the lists, *the user should be sure to refer to all other notes, such as those which may be given near the head of the location column.*

The U. S. Coast Guard *Light List* is published in five volumes; the Defense Mapping Agency Hydrographic Center *List of Lights* is published in seven volumes. The data in both lists are corrected through the *Notice to Mariners* specified in the preface of each volume. For example, the 1975 *Light List, Volume I, Atlantic Coast*, is corrected through *Local Notice to Mariners* issued by the 1st, 3rd, and 5th U. S. Coast Guard District Commanders through October 5, 1974, and *Notice to Mariners* No. 45 of November 9, 1974, published by the Defense Mapping Agency Hydrographic Center. Corrections which have accumulated since the latter date are included in section IV weekly. All of these corrections should be applied in the appropriate places and their insertion noted in the "Record of Corrections."

1307. Visual range of lights.—Usually a navigator wants to know not only the identity of a light, but also the area in which he might reasonably expect to observe it. His track is planned to take him within range of lights which can prove useful during periods of darkness. If lights are not sighted within a reasonable time after prediction, a dangerous situation may exist, requiring resolution or action to insure safety of the vessel.

The area in which a light can be observed is normally a circle with the light as the center, and the visual range as the radius. However, on some bearings the range may be reduced by obstructions. In this case the obstructed arc might differ with height of eye and distance. Also, lights of different colors may be seen at different distances. This fact should be considered not only in predicting the distance at which a light can be seen, but also in identifying it. The condition of the atmosphere has a considerable effect upon the distance at which lights can be seen. Sometimes lights are obscured by fog, haze, dust, smoke, or precipitation which may be present at the light, or between it and the observer, but not at the observer, and possibly unknown to him. There is always the possibility of a light being extinguished. In the case of unwatched lights, this condition might not be detected and corrected at once. During periods of armed conflict, certain lights might be deliberately extinguished if they are considered of greater value to the enemy than to one's own vessels.

On a dark, clear night the visual range is limited primarily by one of two ways: (1) luminous intensity and (2) curvature of the earth. A weak light cannot normally be expected to be seen beyond a certain range, regardless of the height of eye. This distance is called luminous range. Light travels in almost straight lines, so that an observer below the visible horizon of the light should not expect to see the light, although the loom extending upward from the light can sometimes be seen at greater distances. Table 8 gives the distance to the horizon at various heights. A condensed version of table 8 is given in the light lists. The tabulated distances assume normal refraction. Abnormal conditions might extend this range somewhat (or in some cases reduce it). Hence, the geographic range, as the luminous range, is not subject to exact prediction at any given time.

The **luminous range** is the maximum distance at which a light can be seen under existing visibility conditions. This luminous range takes no account of the elevation of the light, the observer's height of eye, the curvature of the earth, or interference from background lighting. The luminous range is determined from the known nominal luminous range, called the nominal range, and the existing visibility conditions. The **nominal range** is the maximum distance at which a light can be seen in clear weather as defined by the International Visibility Code (meteorological visibility of 10 nautical miles). The **geographic range** is the maximum distance at which the curvature of the earth permits a light to be seen from a particular height of eye *without* regard to the luminous intensity of the light. The geographic range *sometimes* printed on charts or tabulated in light lists is the maximum distance at which the curvature of the earth permits a light to be seen from a height of eye of 15 feet above the water when the elevation of the light is taken above the height datum of the largest scale chart of the locality.

The geographic range depends upon the height of both the light and the observer, as shown in figure 1307a. In this illustration a light 150 feet above the water is shown. At this height, the distance to the horizon, by table 8, is 14.0 miles. Within this range the light, *if powerful enough and atmospheric conditions permit*, is visible regardless of the height of eye of the observer (if there is no obstruction). Beyond this range, the visual range depends upon the height of eye. Thus, by table 8 an observer with height of eye of five feet can see the light on his horizon if he is 2.6 miles beyond the horizon of the light, or a total of 16.6 miles. For a height of 30 feet the distance is 14.0+6.3=20.3 miles. If the height of eye is 70 feet, the geographic range is 14.0+9.6=23.6 miles.

Except for range and some directional lights, the nominal range is listed in the U. S. Coast Guard *Light List*. The **Luminous Range Diagram** shown in the *Light List* and figure 1307b is used to convert the nominal range to the luminous range. When using this diagram, it must be remembered that the ranges obtained are approximate, the transmissivity of the atmosphere may vary between the observer and the light, and *glare from background lighting will reduce considerably the range at which lights are sighted.* After estimating the meteorological visibility with the aid of the Meteorological Optical Range Table shown in table 1307, the Luminous Range Diagram is entered with the nominal range on the horizontal nominal range scale; a vertical line is followed until it intersects the curve or reaches the region on the diagram representing the meteorological visibility; from this point or region a horizontal line is followed until it intersects the vertical luminous range scale.

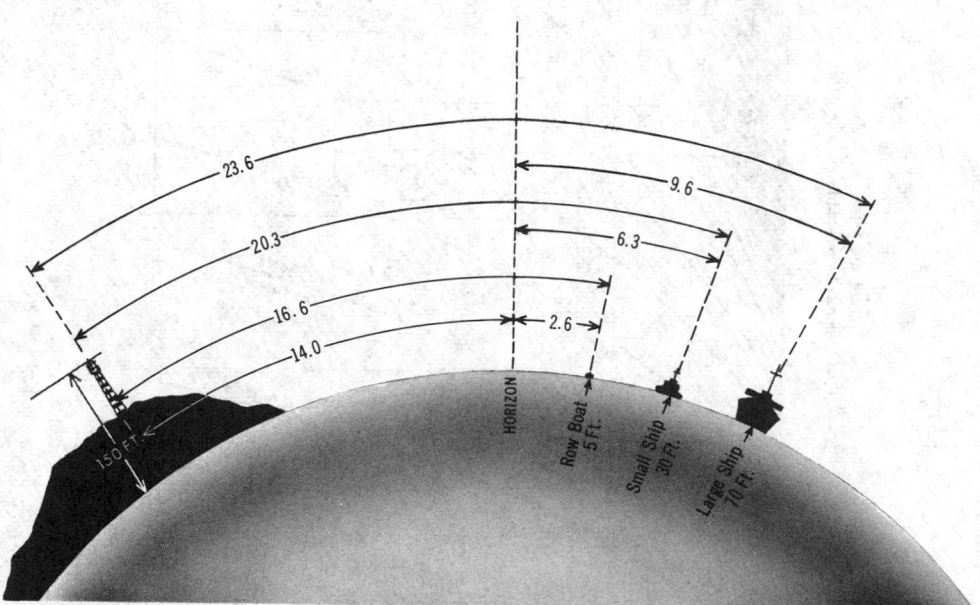

FIGURE 1307a.—Geographic range of a light.

Example 1.—The nominal range of a light as extracted from the *Light List* is 15 nautical miles.

Required.—The luminous range when the meteorological visibility is (1) 11 nautical miles and (2) 1 nautical mile.

Solution.—To find the luminous range when the meteorological visibility is 11 nautical miles, the Luminous Range Diagram is entered with nominal range 15 nautical miles on the horizontal nominal range scale; a vertical line is followed until it intersects the curve on the diagram representing a meteorological visibility of 11 nautical miles; from this point a horizontal line is followed until it intersects the vertical luminous range scale at 16 nautical miles. A similar procedure is followed to find the luminous range when the meteorological visibility is 1 nautical mile.

Answers.—(1) 16 nautical miles; (2) 3 nautical miles.

In predicting the range at which a light can be seen, one should first determine the geographic range to compare this range with the luminous range, if known. If the geographic range is less than the luminous range, the geographic range must be taken as the limiting range. If the luminous range is less than the geographic range, the luminous range must be taken as the limiting range.

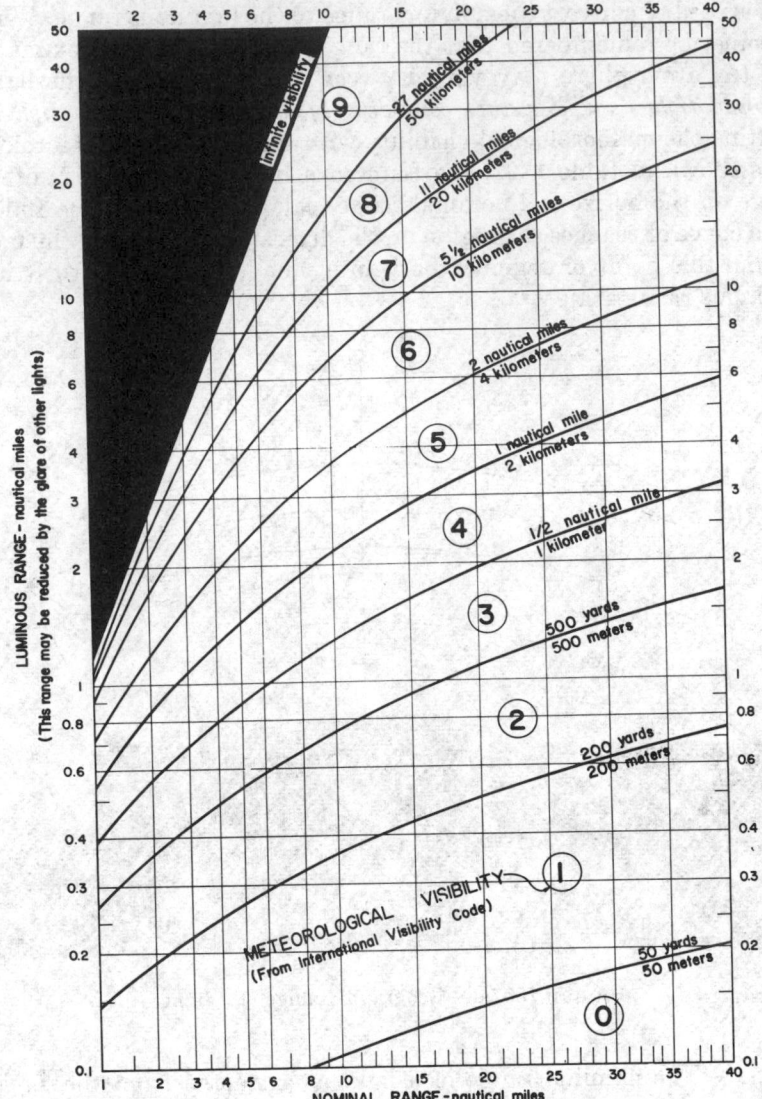

FIGURE 1307b.—Luminous Range Diagram.

These predictions are simple when using the U. S. Coast Guard *Light List* because only nominal ranges are tabulated. Also the current practice of the National Ocean Survey is to follow the *Light List* when printing the range of a light on a chart.

Example 2.—The nominal range of a navigational light 120 feet above the chart datum is 20 nautical miles. The meteorological visibility is 27 nautical miles.

Required.—The distance at which an observer at a height of eye of 60 feet can expect to see the light.

Solution.—The maximum range at which the light may be seen is the lesser of the luminous and geographic ranges.

At 120 feet the distance to the horizon, by table 8, is 12.5 miles. Adding 8.9 miles, the distance to the horizon at a height of eye of 60 feet, the geographic range (12.5 mi.+ 8.9 mi.=21.4 mi.) is found to be less than the luminous range, which is 40 nautical miles.

Answer.—21 nautical miles. Because of various uncertainties, the range is given only to the nearest whole mile.

If the range of a light as printed on a chart, particularly a foreign chart or a reproduction of a foreign chart, or tabulated in a light list other than the U. S. Coast Guard *Light List*, approximates the geographic range for a 15-foot height of eye of the observer, one is generally safe in assuming that this range is the geographic range. With lesser certainty, one may also assume that the lesser of the geographic and nominal ranges is printed on the chart or tabulated in the light list. Using these assumptions, the predicted range is then found by adding the distance to the horizon for both the light and the observer, or approximately, by the *difference* between 4.4 miles (the distance to the horizon at a height of 15 feet) and the distance for the height of eye of the observer (a constant for any given height) and *adding* this value to the tabulated or charted geographic range (subtracting if the height of eye is less than 15 feet). In making a prediction, one should keep in mind the possibility of the luminous range being *between* the tabulated or charted geographic range and the predicted range. The intensity of the light, if known, should be of assistance in identifying this condition.

Code No.	Weather	Yards
0	Dense fog	Less than 50
1	Thick fog....................	50–200
2	Moderate fog.................	200–500
3	Light fog....................	500–1000
		Nautical Miles
4	Thin fog....................	½–1
5	Haze	1–2
6	Light haze.................	2–5½
7	Clear......................	5½–11
8	Very clear.................	11.0–27.0
9	Exceptionally clear..........	Over 27.0

From the International Visibility Code.

TABLE 1307.—Meteorological Optical Range Table.

Example 3.—The range of a light as printed on a foreign chart is 17 miles. The light is 120 feet above chart datum. The meteorological visibility is 10 nautical miles.

Required.—The distance at which an observer at a height of eye of 60 feet can expect to see the light.

Solution.—At 120 feet the distance to the horizon, by table 8, is 12.5 miles. Adding 4.4 miles (the distance to the horizon at a height of 15 feet), the geographic range is found to approximate the range printed on the chart. Then assuming that the latter range is the geographic range for a 15-foot height of eye of the observer and that the nominal range is the greater value, the predicted range is found by adding the distance to the horizon for both the light and the observer (predicted range =12.5 mi. + 8.9 mi. = 21.4 mi.). The additional distance, i.e., the distance in excess of the assumed charted geographic range, is dependent upon the luminous intensity of the light and the meteorological visibility.

If one is approaching a light, and wishes to predict the *time* at which it should be sighted, he first predicts the range. It is then good practice to draw an arc indicating the visual range. The point at which the course line crosses the arc of visual range is the predicted position of the vessel at the time of sighting the light. The predicted time of arrival at this point is the predicted time of sighting the light. The direction of the light from this point is the predicted bearing at which the light should be sighted. Conversion of the true bearing to a relative bearing is usually helpful in sighting the light. The accuracy of the predictions depends upon the accuracy of the predicted range, and the accuracy of the predicted time and place of crossing the visual range arc. If the course line crosses the visual range arc at a small angle, a small lateral error in track may result in a large error of prediction, both of bearing and time. This is particularly apparent if the vessel is *farther* from the light than predicted, in which case the light might be passed without being sighted. Thus, if a light is not sighted at the predicted time, the error *may* be on the side of safety. However, such an interpretation should not be given unless confirmed by other information, for there is always the possibility of reduced meteorological visibility, or of the light being extinguished.

When a light is first sighted, one might determine whether it is on the horizon by immediately reducing the height of eye by several feet, as by squatting or changing position to a lower height. If the light disappears, and reappears when the original height is resumed, it is on the horizon. This process is called **bobbing a light.** If a vessel has considerable vertical motion due to the condition of the sea, a light sighted on the horizon may alternately appear and disappear. This may lead the unwary to assign faulty characteristics and hence to err in its identification. The true characteristics should be observed after the distance has decreased, or by increasing the height of eye of the observer.

PART THREE

CELESTIAL NAVIGATION

PART THREE

CELESTIAL NAVIGATION

CHAPTER XIV

NAVIGATIONAL ASTRONOMY

Preliminary Considerations

1401. Introduction.—**Astronomy** is that science which deals with the size, constitution, motions, relative positions, etc., of celestial bodies. **Navigational astronomy** is that part of astronomy of direct use to a navigator, comprising principally celestial coordinates, time, and the apparent motions of celestial bodies with respect to the earth. Sometimes it is called **nautical astronomy.**

1402. Apparent and absolute motions.—All celestial bodies of which man has knowledge are in motion. Since the earth itself is one of these moving bodies, the motion of other bodies, as seen by an observer on the earth, is **apparent motion.** If the earth were stationary in space, any change in the position of another body, relative to the earth, would be due only to the motion of that body. This would be **absolute motion,** or motion relative to a fixed point. But since it has been impossible to identify a fixed point in space, all motion of which man is aware is apparent, made up of a combination of the movement of the other body and the motions of the observer. A person without suitable instruments is not aware of motion in the line of sight, and therefore only motions across the line of sight are observed.

Since all motion is relative, one should be cognizant of the position of the observer when motions are discussed. When one speaks of planets following their orbits around the sun, he is placing the observer at some distant point in space, usually one of the poles of the ecliptic (art. 1419). When he speaks of a body rising or setting, the observer is on the earth. If he refers to a particular rising or setting, he must locate the observer at a particular point on the earth, since the setting sun for one observer may be the rising sun for another. At the same time it may be crossing the meridian of a third observer.

1403. The celestial sphere.—As one looks at the sky on a dark night, he is not aware of the differences in the distances to the various celestial bodies. They might easily be imagined as being equally distant from the earth, all located on the inner surface of a vast hollow sphere of infinite radius, with the earth at its center. This is the **celestial sphere** (fig. 1403). For most purposes of navigation it can be considered an actuality. Since the navigator is concerned primarily with apparent motion for an observer on the earth, this geocentric universe of Ptolemy (art. 121) is a useful concept. While the motions of various bodies relative to each other are important to the astronomer who predicts future positions of celestial bodies, and perhaps to the navigational scientist who designs navigation tables, the navigator speaks of bodies rising, crossing the celestial meridian, and setting, as though these were absolute motions.

1404. Units of astronomical distance.—The distances between celestial bodies, even those within a single family such as the solar system, are so great that terrestrial units are unsatisfactory to express them. The units commonly used for astronomical distances are:

Astronomical unit (AU), the mean distance between the earth and the sun, approximately 92,960,000 statute miles. The astronomical unit is often used as a unit of measurement for distances within the solar system.

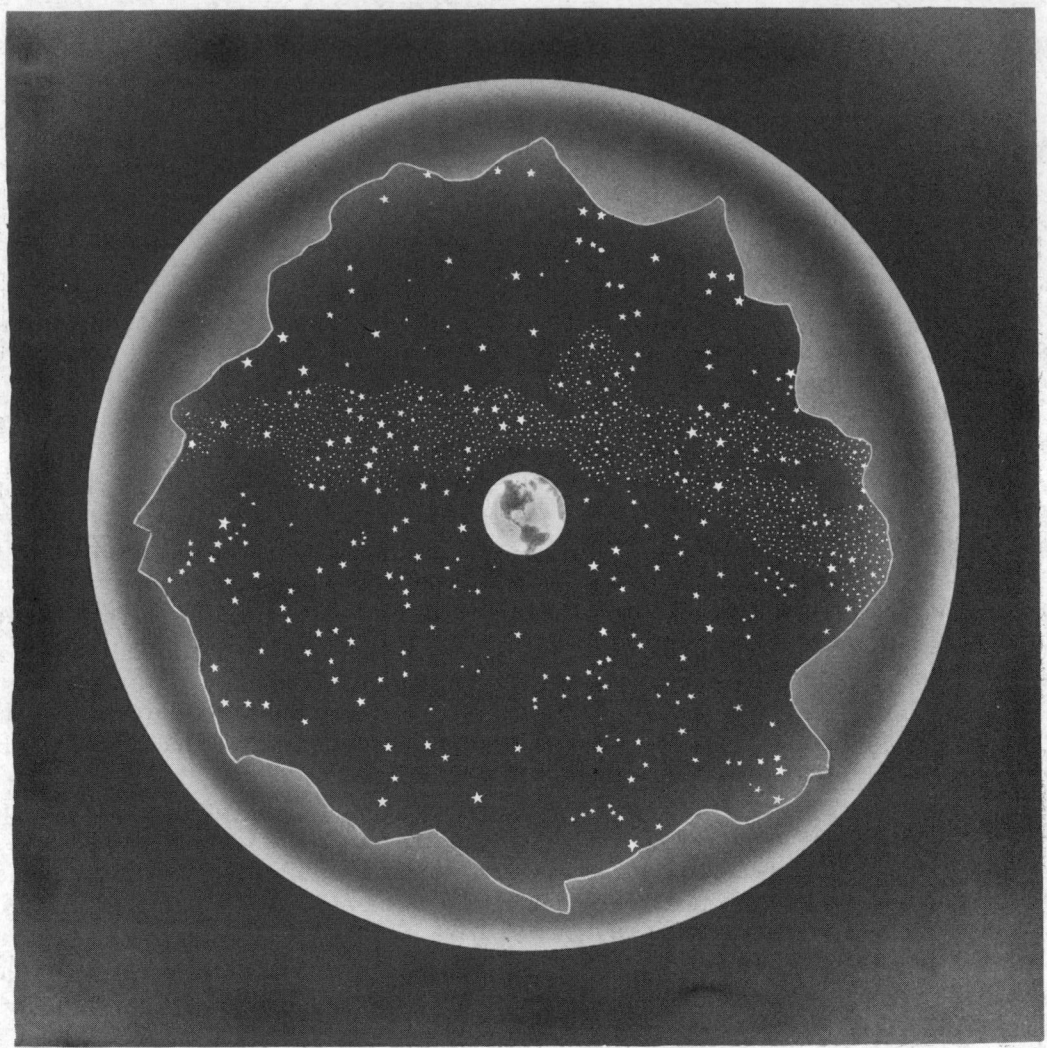

FIGURE 1403.—The celestial sphere.

Light-year, the distance light travels in one year. Since the speed of light is about 186,000 statute miles per *second* and there are about 31,600,000 seconds per year, the length of one light-year is about 5,880,000,000,000 (5.88×10^{12}) statute miles, or 63,280 astronomical units. The light-year is commonly used for expressing distances to the stars and galaxies. Alpha Centauri and its neighbor Proxima, generally considered the nearest stars, are 4.3 light-years away. Relatively few stars are less than 100 light-years away, and the most distant galaxies are in excess of one billion light-years away. However, most navigational stars are relatively close. Light travels from the sun to the earth in about 8⅓ *minutes,* and from the moon to the earth in about 1¼ *seconds.*

Parsec, the distance at which the **heliocentric parallax** (difference in apparent position as viewed from the earth and the sun) is 1″. At this distance a star would appear to change its position 2″ among the distant stars, if observed from points 180° apart on the earth's orbit. The name is derived from the first letters of the words **par**allax and **sec**ond. One parsec is equal to about 3.26 light-years. Hence, even the nearest star is more than one parsec away. This unit is used to express distances to stars and galaxies.

The difficulty of illustrating astronomical distances and sizes is indicated by the fact that if the earth were represented by a circle one inch in diameter, the moon would be a circle one-fourth inch in diameter at a distance of 30 inches, the sun would be a circle nine feet in diameter at a distance of nearly a fifth of a mile, and Pluto would be a circle half an inch in diameter at a distance of about seven miles. The nearest star would be one-fifth the actual distance to the moon.

1405. Magnitude.—The relative brightness of celestial bodies is indicated by a scale of stellar magnitudes. In the *Almagest* (art. 121) Ptolemy divided the stars into six groups according to brightness, the 20 brightest being classified as of the first magnitude, and the dimmest being of the sixth magnitude. In modern times, when it became desirable to define more precisely the limits of magnitude, a first magnitude star was considered 100 times brighter than one of the sixth magnitude, the approximate value of Ptolemy's ratio. Since the fifth root (art. 109, vol. II) of 100 is 2.512, this number is considered the **magnitude ratio.** A first magnitude star is 2.512 times as bright as a second magnitude star, which is 2.512 times as bright as a third magnitude star, etc. A second magnitude is $2.512 \times 2.512 = 6.310$ times as bright as a fourth magnitude star. A first magnitude star is $2.512^{20} \times 100^4 = 100,000,000$ times as bright as a star of the twenty-first magnitude, the dimmest that can be seen through the 200-inch telescope.

Brightness is normally tabulated to the nearest 0.1 magnitude, about the smallest change that can be detected by the unaided eye of a trained observer. All stars of magnitude 1.50 or brighter are popularly called "first magnitude" stars. Those between 1.51 and 2.50 are called "second magnitude" stars, those between 2.51 and 3.50 are called "third magnitude" stars, etc. Sirius, the brightest star, has a magnitude of $(-)1.6$. The only other star with a negative magnitude is Canopus, $(-)0.9$. At greatest brilliance Venus has a magnitude of about $(-)4.4$. Mars, Jupiter, and Saturn are sometimes of negative magnitude. The full moon has a magnitude of about $(-)12.6$, but varies somewhat. The magnitude of the sun is about $(-)26.7$.

The Universe

1406. The solar system.—The **sun,** the most conspicuous celestial object in the sky, is the central body of the solar system. Associated with it are at least nine principal **planets,** of which the earth is one; a number of **satellites** accompanying some of the planets; thousands of **minor planets** or **asteroids;** multitudes of **comets;** and vast numbers of **meteors.**

1407. Motions of bodies of the solar system.—Astronomers distinguish between the two principal motions of celestial bodies, as follows: **rotation** is a spinning motion about an axis within the body, while **revolution** is the motion of a body in its elliptical **orbit** around another body, called its **primary.** For the satellites, the primary is a planet. For the planets and other bodies of the solar system, the primary is the sun. The entire solar system is held together by the gravitational force of the sun. The whole system revolves around the center of its galaxy (art. 1415) as a unit, and the galaxy is probably in motion relative to its neighboring galaxies. The motion of bodies of the solar system relative to surrounding stars is called **space motion.**

Rotation and revolution may be further classified as **synodic** or **sidereal.** During one synodic *rotation* the body makes one complete turn relative to the sun. On the earth it is called an **apparent solar day.** During one sidereal rotation the body makes one complete turn relative to the stars. Because of motion of the body in its orbit, a sidereal rotation is either longer or shorter, by a small amount, than a synodic rotation. If both rotation and revolution are in the same direction (in the solar system they are both *east* for most bodies, that is, counter clockwise as seen from above the North Pole)

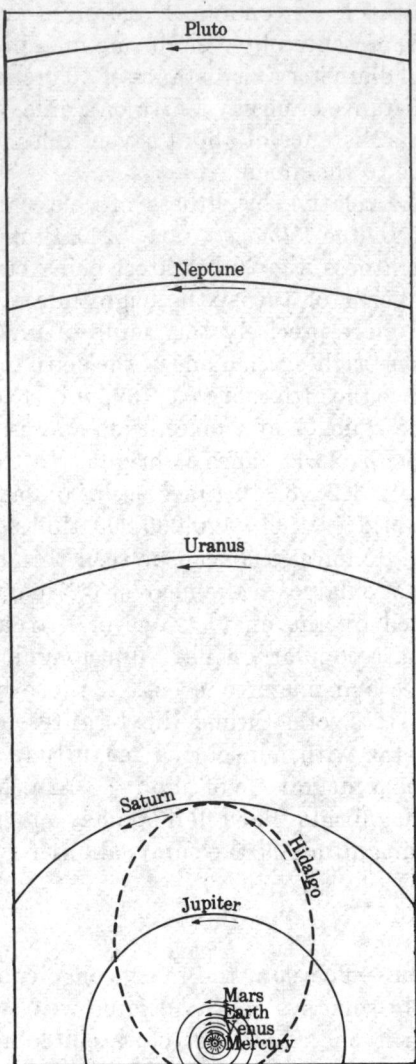

FIGURE 1407a.—Relative size of planetary orbits.

the sidereal rotation is shorter. During a synodic *revolution* a celestial body makes one trip around the sun, *as viewed from the earth*. Hence, the earth cannot have a synodic revolution. During a sidereal revolution, a celestial body makes one trip around its orbit with respect to the stars; to an observer on the celestial body, the sun would appear to make one trip around the celestial sphere, with respect to the stars. On the earth this is one year.

All of the planets revolve around the sun in nearly circular orbits. The flattening or **eccentricity** of the earth's orbit is only 0.017 (zero would be a circle). Some of the minor planets have orbits more eccentric than that of any principal planet (note the orbit of Hidalgo in fig. 1407a). The orbits of comets are highly eccentric. The orbits of all known planets except Pluto are in nearly the same plane, that of the ecliptic (art. 1419). The orbit of Pluto is inclined more than 17° to the ecliptic.

The laws governing the motions of planets in their orbits were discovered by Johannes Kepler, and are now known as **Kepler's laws:**

1. *The orbits of the planets are ellipses, with the sun at a common focus.*

2. *The straight line joining the sun and a planet (the* **radius vector**) *sweeps over equal areas in equal intervals of time.*

3. *The squares of the sidereal periods of any two planets are proportional to the cubes of their mean distances from the sun.*

In 1687 Isaac Newton stated three "laws of motion," which he believed were applicable to the planets. **Newton's laws of motion** are:

1. *Every body continues in a state of rest or of uniform motion in a straight line unless acted upon by an external force.*

2. *When a body is acted upon by an external force, its acceleration is directly proportional to that force, and inversely proportional to the mass of the body, and acceleration takes place in the direction in which the force acts.*

3. *To every action there is an equal and opposite reaction.*

Newton also stated a single **universal law of gravitation,** which he believed applied to all bodies, although it was based upon observation within the solar system only:

Every particle of matter attracts every other particle with a force that varies directly as the product of their masses and inversely as the square of the distance between them.

From these fundamental laws of motion and gravitation, Newton derived Kepler's empirical laws. He proved rigorously that the gravitational interaction between any two bodies results in an orbital motion of each body about the barycenter of the two masses that is some form of conic section, that is a circle, ellipse, parabola, or hyperbola.

Circular and parabolic orbits are unlikely to occur in nature because of the precise speeds required. Hyperbolic orbits are open, that is one body, due to its speed, recedes into space. Therefore, a planet's orbit must be elliptical as found by Kepler.

Both the sun and each body revolve about their common center of mass. Because of the preponderance of the mass of the sun over that of the individual planets, the common center of the sun and each planet except Jupiter lies within the sun. The common center of the combined mass of the solar system moves in and out of the sun.

The various laws governing the orbits of planets apply equally well to the orbit of any body with respect to its primary.

In each planet's orbit that point nearest the sun is called the **perihelion.** That point farthest from the sun is called the **aphelion** (ă·fē′lē·ŏn). The line joining periphelion and aphelion is called the **line of apsides** (ăp′sĭ·dēz). In the orbit of the moon, that point nearest the earth is called the **perigee,** and that point farthest from the earth is called the **apogee.** Figure 1407b shows the orbit of the earth (with exaggerated eccentricity), and the orbit of the moon around the earth.

1408. The sun is the dominant member of the solar system because its mass is nearly a thousand times that of all other bodies of the solar system combined. It supplies heat and light to the entire system.

The diameter of the sun is about 866,000 miles. At the distance of the earth, varying between 91,300,000 and 94,500,000 miles, the visible diameter is about 32′. At the closest approach early in January the sun appears largest, being 32′.6 in diameter. Six months later the apparent diameter is 31′.5, the minimum.

Of the various physical features of the sun, one of particular interest is the appearance from time to time of **sun spots** on the surface (fig. 1408). These spots are apparently areas of cooler gas which have risen to the surface and appear dark in contrast to the hotter gases around them. In size they vary from perhaps 50,000 miles in diameter to the smallest spots that can be detected (a few hundred miles in diameter), and perhaps smaller. They generally appear in groups. At the start of each cycle of about 11 years the spots appear at a maximum distance of about 40° on each side of the solar equator. Succeeding spots of the cycle appear progressively closer to the solar equator, until a minimum solar latitude of 5° may be reached. The maximum number

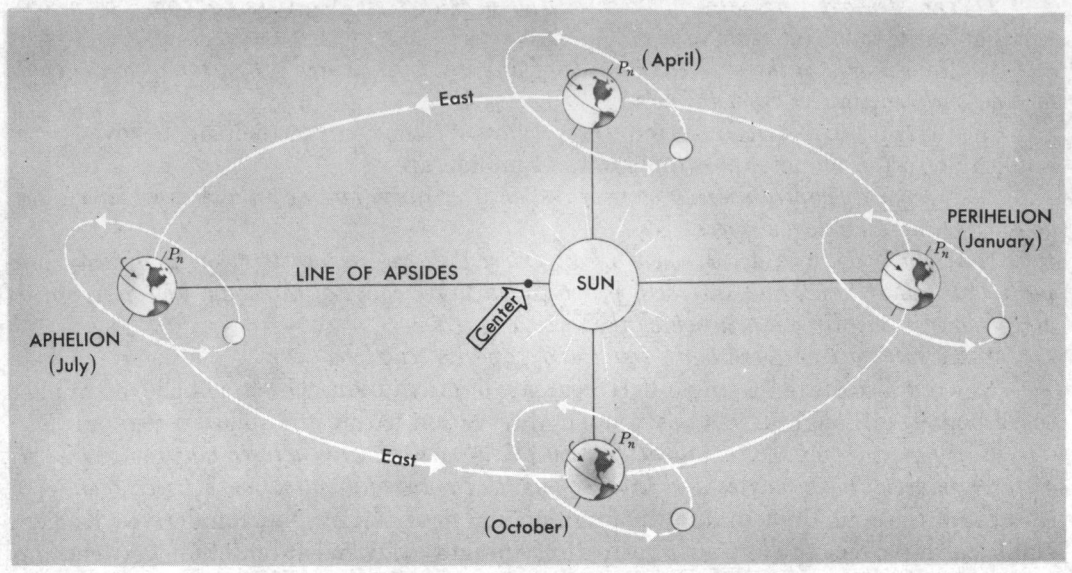

FIGURE 1407b.—Orbits of the earth and moon.

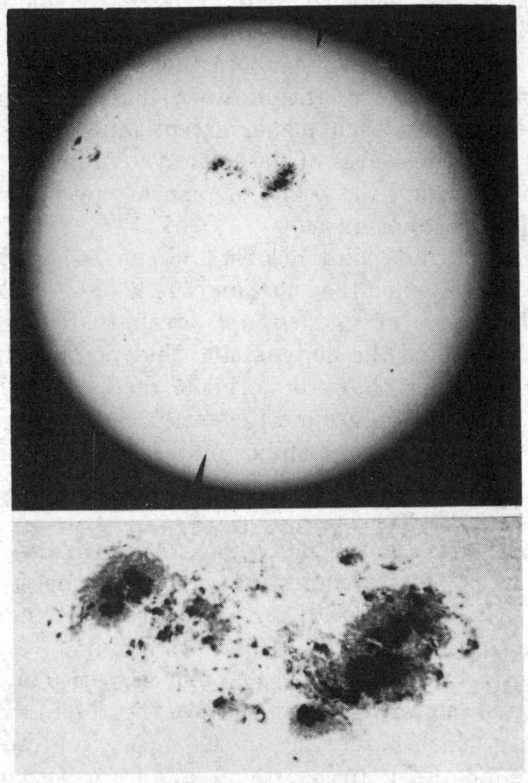

Courtesy of Mt. Wilson and Palomar Observatories.

FIGURE 1408.—Whole solar disk and an enlargement of the great spot group of April 7, 1947.

of sun spots occurs about midway in the cycle, when the spots are about 16° from the solar equator. Large sun spots can be seen without a telescope if the eyes are protected, as by the shade glasses of a sextant. The shade glasses of inexpensive "training" sextants may not have the optical quality required for protection. Sun spots have magnetic properties. For one cycle all spots north of the solar equator are of positive polarity, and all those to the south are of negative polarity. During the next cycle, which may begin before the last spots of the old cycle have disappeared, the polarity is reversed. Sun spots are related to magnetic storms which adversely affect radio, including radio aids to navigation, on the earth. At such times the **auroras** (art. 2526) are particularly brilliant and widespread.

The sun rotates on its axis, the period of rotation varying from about 25 days at the solar equator to 34 days at the poles, but this fact has little or no navigational significance beyond its effect upon the changing positions of sun spots relative to the earth. The sun is moving approximately toward Vega at about 12 miles per second, or about two-thirds as fast as the earth moves in its orbit around the sun. The path of the sun toward Vega is called the **sun's way.** This is in addition to the motion of the sun around the center of its galaxy (art. 1415).

1409. Planets.—The principal bodies having nearly circular orbits around the sun are called **planets,** from a Greek word meaning "wandering." They were so named because they were observed to change position or "wander" among the "fixed stars" which remained in about the same positions relative to each other. Because the sun and moon had a similar wandering motion, the ancients considered them planets, also.

Nine principal planets are known. In order of increasing distance from the sun, these are Mercury, Venus, Earth, Mars, Jupiter, Saturn, Uranus, Neptune, and Pluto. Of these, only four are commonly used for celestial navigation. These are Venus, Mars, Jupiter, and Saturn, sometimes called the **navigational planets.** The two planets with orbits smaller than that of the earth are called **inferior planets,** and those with orbits larger than that of the earth are called **superior planets.** The four planets nearest the sun are sometimes called the **inner planets,** and the others the **outer planets.** Jupiter, Saturn, Uranus, and Neptune are so much larger than the others that they are sometimes classed as **major planets.** Neptune and Pluto are not visible to the unaided eye, and Uranus is barely so, being of the sixth magnitude.

The orbits of the many thousand tiny **minor planets** lie chiefly between the orbits of Mars and Jupiter.

Six of the planets are known to have satellites, a total of 33 having been discovered Mercury, Venus, and Pluto have no known satellites.

1410. The earth as a planet.—In common with other planets, the earth rotates on its axis and revolves in its orbit around the sun. These actual motions (discussed in articles 1416 and 1417) are the principal source of the apparent motions of other celestial bodies. Also, the rotation of the earth results in a deflection of water and air currents to the right in the Northern Hemisphere and to the left in the Southern Hemisphere. Because of the earth's rotation, the high tides on the open sea lag behind the meridian transit of the moon.

For most navigational purposes, the earth can be considered a sphere, but, like the other planets, the earth is approximately an **oblate spheroid,** or **ellipsoid of revolution,** being flattened at the poles and bulged at the equator. Therefore, the polar diameter is less than the equatorial diameter, and the meridians are slightly elliptical, rather than circular. The dimensions of the earth are recomputed from time to time, as additional and more precise measurements become available. Since the earth is not *exactly* an ellipsoid, results differ slightly when equally precise and extensive measurements are made on different parts of the surface. Hence, different "spheroids" are used for mapping various parts of the earth. That used for charts of North America was computed by the English geodesist A. R. Clarke in 1866. However, since Clarke did not clearly define his units, the U. S. Coast and Geodetic Survey in 1880 considered

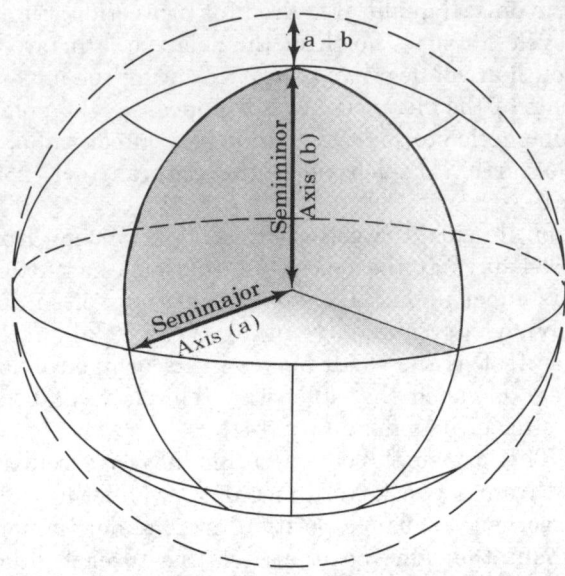

FIGURE 1410.—Oblate spheroid or ellipsoid of revolution.

it desirable to adopt standard values which probably added about 170 feet to the diameter computed by Clarke. In 1880, also, Clarke himself made a new estimate of the size and shape of the earth but this has not been adopted by the United States. Although the Clarke spheroid of 1866 is still used for charting North America, the International Astronomical Union System of Astronomical Constants provides a slightly better approximation of the size and shape of the earth. According to these constants, the dimensions of the earth are (fig. 1410):

Equatorial radius (a)=3,963.205 statute miles=3,443.931 nautical miles
Polar radius (b) =3,949.917 statute miles=3,432.384 nautical miles
Mean radius   =3,958.775 statute miles=3,440.082 nautical miles

$$\text{Flattening or ellipticity}\ \left(f=\frac{a-b}{a}\right)=\frac{1}{298.25}$$

The mean radius is the average of the polar radius and two equatorial radii perpendicular to each other (the three dimensions of the solid), or $\dfrac{(2a+b)}{3}$.

1411. Other planets and the minor planets.—**Mercury** in some ways resembles the moon more than it does other planets. Its diameter is only about 50 percent larger than that of the moon and about the same as those of Jupiter's two largest satellites. Like the moon it has little or no atmosphere, and is believed to keep the same side turned toward its primary. Mercury's mass is only about five percent that of the earth, and its orbit is so small that the planet is never seen more than about 28° from the sun. It is for this reason that Mercury is not commonly used for navigation. Near greatest elongation (art. 1422) it appears near the western horizon after sunset or the eastern horizon before sunrise. At these times it resembles a first magnitude star, and is sometimes reported as a new or strange object in the sky. As seen from the earth, Mercury goes through all the phases similar to those of the moon, and occasionally **transits** (crosses) the face of the sun, appearing as a tiny, dark, inconspicuous dot on the surface. Mercury has no known satellite. Mercury rotates with a period of about 59 days.

Venus, like Mercury, has no known satellite, goes through the various phases similar to those of the moon, and may transit the sun. In size of orbit, sidereal period of revolution, diameter, volume, mass, density, and surface gravity it resembles the earth more than any other planet. Its orbit is more nearly circular than that of any other planet (eccentricity 0.007). At maximum brilliance, about five weeks before and after inferior conjunction (art. 1422), it has a magnitude of about (—)4.4 and is brighter than any other object in the sky except the sun and moon. At these times it can be seen during the day, and is sometimes observed for a celestial line of position.

Mars (fig. 1411) has a diameter only a little more than half that of the earth, and a mass of 11 percent as much, although its density is nearly 72 percent that of the earth. It has a thin atmosphere, but few clouds. Its day is only slightly longer than that on the earth, but its year is nearly twice as long. Being a superior planet (art. 1409), it is seen only in the full or gibbous phase (art. 1423). When nearest the earth, its apparent diameter is about eight times that at conjunction (art. 1422). Mars has two satellites. **Phobos** is about 10 miles in diameter and has an orbit the diameter of which is only about three times the diameter of Mars. To an observer on Mars it would appear to have a diameter about one-third the diameter of the moon as seen from the earth, and would appear to rise in the west and set in the east, going through three-fourths of its cycle of phases while above the horizon. It would do this three times each day, since its sidereal period of revolution is only about one-third the period of rotation of Mars. No other natural satellite is known to *revolve* faster than its primary *rotates*. **Deimos** is only about 5 miles in diameter, and at greatest brilliance would appear as a very bright star. About 66 hours would elapse between rising and setting, during which it would go through the various phases twice.

Jupiter (fig. 1411), largest of the known planets, has more than twice the mass of all other known planets combined. Its density is low and its rotation fast (9^h50^m), resulting in a pronounced equatorial bulge. It is believed to have a dense, solid core, surrounded by lighter material, and a deep atmosphere of ammonia, methane, helium, and hydrogen. Two of Jupiter's 13 known satellites are about the same size as Mercury, and may have atmospheres. The four outermost satellites revolve from east to west, opposite to the general direction of revolution within the solar system.

Saturn (fig. 1411) is the only planet having a density less than that of water, yet it has a mass of nearly one-third that of Jupiter, and nearly three times that of all other known planets combined. Its composition is believed to be similar to that of Jupiter. It is more oblate than any other known planet. Perhaps the most interesting feature of this planet is its rings, composed of a great number of small solid particles spread out in three thin, flat rings more than 170,000 miles in diameter. The particles nearest the planet revolve more rapidly than those farther out, the innermost ones completing a revolution in less time than the planet completes a rotation. During half the 29.5-year sidereal period of revolution of the planet one side of the rings is visible to observers on the earth, and during the second half of the period the opposite side is visible. Saturn has ten known satellites, the outermost one of which revolves from east to west.

Uranus is barely visible to the unaided eye, being of the sixth magnitude. It is a comparatively large planet, and probably is similar in composition to Jupiter and Saturn. The inclination of the equator of Uranus to the plane of the ecliptic is 98°, or 82° if the revolution is considered from east to west. Its five known satellites, all small, revolve in the equatorial plane, in the same direction as that of rotation of the planet.

Neptune is slightly smaller than Uranus, but has greater mass, and a longer period of rotation. Relatively little is known of this remote planet of the eighth magnitude. However, it is known to have two satellites, the larger (probably bigger than the moon) revolving from east to west.

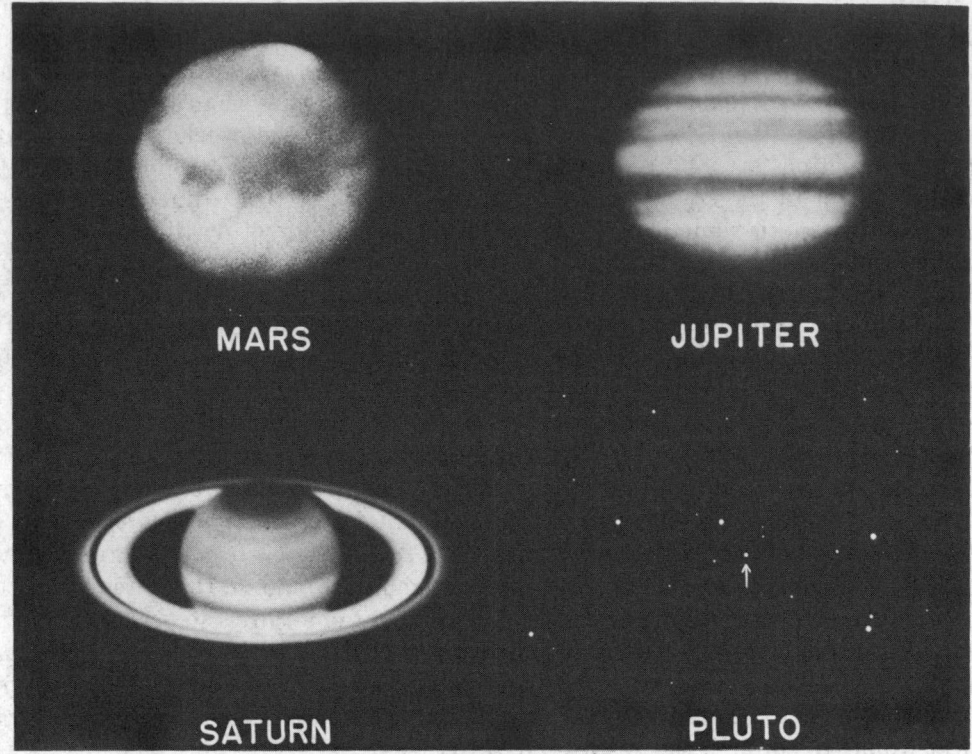

Courtesy of Mt. Wilson and Palomar Observatories.

FIGURE 1411.—Mars, Jupiter, Saturn, and Pluto.   First three photographed with 100-inch
telescope, Pluto with 200-inch telescope.

Pluto (fig. 1411) was identified in 1930. It is of the 15th magnitude, and cannot
be seen in small telescopes. In all but the 200-inch telescope it appears as a point of light.
Its diameter is less than half that of the earth. Its orbit is the most eccentric and has
the greatest inclination to the ecliptic of any of the known planets. At perihelion it
is closer to the sun than Neptune, and there is some evidence to support the view that
it was at one time a satellite of the larger planet.

Minor planets. About 1,800 of these tiny planets have been discovered, but it is
estimated that there may be as many as 50,000 bright enough to be seen by the largest
telescopes, when they are nearest the earth. The largest, **Ceres,** has a diameter of
about 480 miles. All but a few are less than 100 miles in diameter. Since there is no
known lower limit, there may be no distinction between minor planets and meteors.
The combined mass of all minor planets probably does not exceed 0.1 percent that of the
earth. The orbits, of various degrees of eccentricity and inclination to the ecliptic, lie
mostly between those of Mars and Jupiter. However, at perihelion some of the minor
planets are inside the earth's orbit. The orbit of **Hidalgo** is shown in figure 1407a.

1412. The moon is the only satellite of direct navigational interest, although the
satellites of Jupiter were at one time used to determine Greenwich mean time, so that
longitude could be found (art. 126). The rotation and revolution of the moon are both
west to east, and both are of the same duration, $27^d07^h43^m11^s.5$ with respect to the
stars (the **sidereal month**) and $29^d12^h44^m02^s.8$ with respect to the sun (the **synodical
month**). Because there is no difference in the periods of rotation and revolution, the
same side of the moon is always turned toward the earth. However, about 59 percent
of the moon's surface has been seen from earth, due to **libration. Libration in latitude**

occurs because the axis of rotation is tilted about 6°.5 with respect to the axis of revolution. **Libration in longitude** occurs because the speed of revolution varies in accordance with Kepler's second law (art. 1407), while the rotational speed is essentially constant. **Diurnal libration** occurs because of the changing position of the observer relative to the moon, due to rotation of the earth. **Physical libration** is a small pendulum-like rotational oscillation of the moon with respect to its radius vector.

At **perigee** the moon is about 221,000 statute miles from the earth's center, and at **apogee** it is about 253,000 miles distant. The average distance is about 238,862 miles. Because of the relative nearness of the moon, its **geocentric parallax** (difference in position relative to the background of stars, as observed from the surface and center of the earth) is comparatively large. It is a maximum when the moon is on the horizon, when it is called **horizontal parallax.** The **equatorial horizontal parallax** for an observer at the equator, where the maximum radius of the earth is involved, is tabulated in the *Nautical Almanac* and the *American Ephemeris and Nautical Almanac,* and used in sextant altitude corrections given in the nautical and air almanacs. The **parallax** varies from a maximum at the horizon to zero at the zenith. The parallax at any altitude is sometimes called **parallax in altitude.** The apparent diameter of the moon is approximately the same as that of the sun, but varies through wider limits. Because the moon is so near, the radius of the earth is an appreciable percentage of the distance between earth and moon, and the apparent diameter of the moon increases a measurable amount as its altitude increases (decreasing the distance from the observer). This apparent increase is called **augmentation** (fig. 1412). A similar effect for the sun is very small.

As with the planets and sun, the moon and earth both revolve around their common center of mass, which is about 2,900 miles from the center of the earth. It is this center of mass that describes the orbit of the earth (and moon) around the sun.

Because of its relative nearness and size, the moon is the principal source of the gravitational attraction that causes tides, although the sun has an appreciable effect, also. The action of these bodies in causing tides is described in article 3103. Because of the frictional action of tides, the rotation of the earth is slowing, the length of the day increasing about 0°.001 per century.

On the moon, the day is equal in length to the synodical month (about 29½ days). The earth would remain almost stationary in the sky for an observer on the 41 percent of the moon's surface always visible from the earth, would rise and set at about the same point on the horizon for one on the 18 percent which is sometimes visible, and would never appear for one on the 41 percent not seen from the earth.

1413. Comets and meteors.—**Comets** are swarms of relatively small, widely separated, solid bodies held together by mutual attraction. Around this **nucleus,** a more spectacular, gaseous head or **coma** and **tail** may form as the comet approaches the sun. The tail is directed *away* from the sun, so that it follows the head while the comet is approaching the sun, and precedes the head while the comet is receding. The total mass of a comet is very small, and the tail is so thin that stars can easily be seen through it. In 1910 the earth passed through the tail of Halley's comet (fig. 1413) without noticeable effect.

Comets are erratic and inconsistent. Some travel east to west and some west to east, in highly eccentric orbits inclined at any angle to the ecliptic. The shortest period of revolution is about 3.3 years. Some periods are so long that astronomers speculate as to whether some comets may not come in from outside the solar system for a single trip around the sun, and then leave the solar system, never to return. In such a case the orbit would be approximately a **parabola** (art. 134, vol. II).

Without their tails, which exist only when near the sun, comets are not spectacular. Because of the small size of their nuclei, which shine by reflected light from the sun,

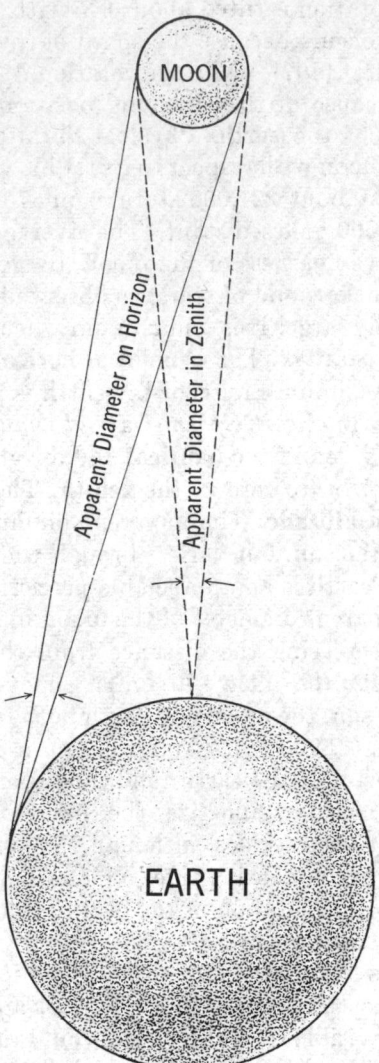

FIGURE 1412.—Augmentation.

comets are visible for only a small part of their period of revolution, and this is the part of most rapid motion, in accordance with Kepler's second law (art. 1407). An average of about five comets is observed each year, and about two-thirds of these are identified as previously observed comets. Very few comets are ever visible without a telescope. The spectacular Halley's comet reached aphelion in 1948 and started back toward the sun. It is expected to reach perihelion about February, 1986.

Meteors, popularly called **shooting stars,** are tiny, solid bodies too small to be seen until heated to incandescence by air friction while passing through the earth's atmosphere. A particularly bright meteor is called a **fireball.** One that explodes is called a **bolide.** A meteor that is not consumed during its fall through the atmosphere, but lands as a solid particle, is called a **meteorite.** These are composed principally of iron, with some nickel, and smaller quantities of other material.

Vast numbers of meteors exist. It has been estimated that an average of about 1,000,000 bright enough to be seen enter the earth's atmosphere each hour, and many times this number undoubtedly enter, but are too small to attract attention. A faint

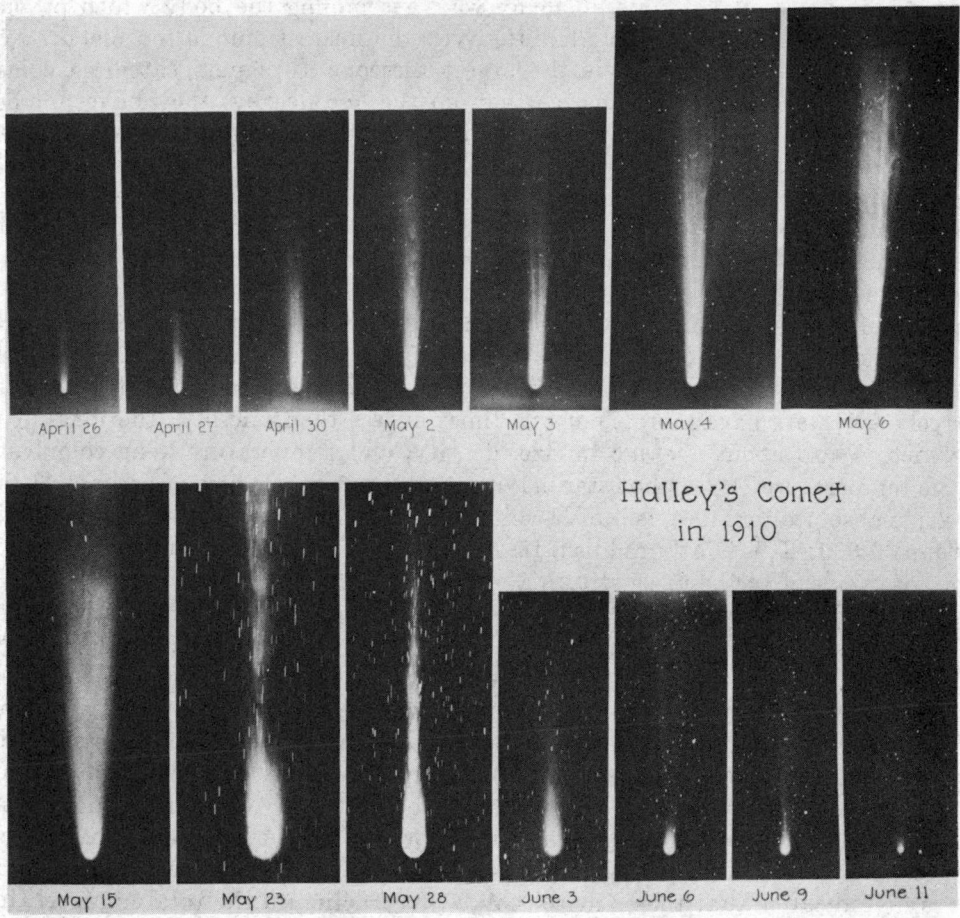

Halley's Comet in 1910

Courtesy of Mt. Wilson and Palomar Observatories.

FIGURE 1413.—Halley's Comet; fourteen views, made between April 26 and June 11, 1910.

glow sometimes observed extending upward approximately along the ecliptic before sunrise and after sunset has been attributed to the reflection of sunlight from quantities of such material. This glow is called **zodiacal light.** A faint glow at that point of the ecliptic 180° from the sun is called the **gegenschein** or **counterglow.** Comets may be an assemblage of a large number of meteors traveling together, and minor planets (art. 1411) may be larger meteors. **Meteor showers** occur at certain times of the year when the earth is believed to be passing through **meteor swarms,** the scattered remains of comets that have broken up. At these times the number of meteors observed is many times the usual number.

Since such large amounts of this material are in existence, much of it in an orbit near the ecliptic, and since the orbits of most minor planets lie between those of Mars and Jupiter, where astronomers compute the orbit of another planet should be located, it is possible that another planet may have existed there at one time and been disrupted, perhaps by an atomic explosion of hydrogen or other material. The estimated total mass of all meteors, comets, and minor planets would make a small planet, but if the material which has fallen on other planets and satellites, and perhaps some or all of the satellites themselves, are added, a sizeable planet might be accounted for.

1414. Stars are distant suns, in many ways resembling the body which provides the earth with most of its light and heat. Even the nearest star is too distant to be seen as more than a point of light in the largest telescope. If planets, satellites, comets, etc., accompany those distant suns, as they do the one nearby, they have not been detected. However, comparatively dark companions of planetary size are known to accompany some stars. Nonluminous stars may exist, since most of the **radio stars** (points from which radio energy emanates) are not marked by a body visible to observers on the earth. The distance of the stars is so great that none is known to have a **heliocentric parallax** (difference in apparent position as observed from the earth and the sun) of as much as 1″.

Stars differ in size from gaseous giants having diameters greater than that of the *orbit* of the earth, to dense dwarfs which may be no larger than the major planets. Although the size and density cover wide ranges, the mass does not differ greatly. Relatively few stars have more than five times or less than one-fifth the mass of the sun, which is also about average in size, density, and temperature. The color varies with the temperature. A very hot star, having a surface temperature of perhaps 20,000° K (Celsius absolute) or more, is bluish-white; while a cooler star, having a temperature of perhaps 2,000° K, is faintly reddish. In *Orion*, blue Rigel and red Betelgeuse, located on opposite sides of the belt, constitute a noticeable contrast.

Under ideal viewing conditions, the dimmest star that can be seen with the unaided eye is of the sixth magnitude. In the entire sky there are about 6,000 stars of this magnitude or brighter. Half of these are below the horizon at any time. Because of the greater absorption of light near the horizon, where the path of a ray travels for a greater distance through the atmosphere, not more than perhaps 2,500 stars are visible to the unaided eye at any time. The 200-inch telescope on Palomar Mountain permits stars as dim as the twenty-first magnitude to be seen. It has been estimated that there are about 1,000,000,000 of this magnitude or brighter. A long-term photographic exposure with the 200-inch telescope permits observation of about twice this number. There is no indication that this is more than a tiny fraction of the total number. However, the average navigator seldom uses more than perhaps 20 or 30 of the brighter stars. Stars which exhibit a noticeable change of magnitude are called **variable stars.** A star which suddenly becomes several magnitudes brighter and then gradually fades is called a **nova.** A particularly bright one is called a **supernova.**

Two stars which appear to be very close together are called a **double star.** If more than two stars are included in the group, it is called a **multiple star;** and if a large number appear in approximately spherical shape, it is called a **globular cluster.** A group of stars moving through space together, but not exhibiting the intimate relationship of a globular cluster, is called an **open cluster.** The Pleiades and some stars of the Big Dipper (with certain other stars) are examples of open clusters. A group of stars which *appear* close together, regardless of actual distances, is popularly called a **constellation,** particularly if the group forms a striking configuration. Among astronomers a constellation is now considered a region of the sky having precise boundaries so arranged that all of the sky is covered, without overlap. The ancient Greeks recognized 48 constellations covering only certain groups of stars. Modern astronomers recognize 88 constellations. The constellation names and meanings are given in appendix K.

A cloudy patch of matter in the heavens is called a **nebula** (plural *nebulae*). If it is within the galaxy of which the sun is a part, it is called a **galactic nebula;** if outside, it is called an **extragalactic nebula.**

Stars rotate on their axes, and revolve around the center of their galaxy, in addition to influencing and being influenced by surrounding stars. Motion of a star through space, like that of any celestial body, is called **space motion.** That component in the line of sight is called **radial motion;** while that component across the line of sight, causing a star to change its apparent position relative to the background of more distant stars, is called **proper motion.**

1415. Galaxies.—A great number of the nebulae have been identified as extra-galactic, and as telescopes became more powerful, it was discovered that these small cloudy patches are groups of stars, in many ways resembling the group of stars of which the sun is a part. Each such vast assemblage of stars constitutes an island universe as widely separated from others, comparatively, as individual stars in one group. Such a group is called a **galaxy.** It was not until well within the twentieth century that the sun was recognized as a part of such a galaxy, the **Milky Way.** In a galaxy the stars tend to congregate in groups called **star clouds** arranged in long spiral arms. The spiral nature is believed due to revolution of the stars about the center of the galaxy, the inner stars revolving more rapidly than the outer ones (fig. 1415). At the position of the sun, about two-thirds of the way out from the center, and nearly midway between "top" and "bottom," the period of revolution is about 200,000,000 years at the present speed of about 175 miles per second. This is nearly ten times the speed of the earth in its orbit. An average estimate of the size of a galaxy is that it is about 100,000 light years in diameter, 15,000 light years thick at the center, and 5,000 light years thick near the outer edge, and that it contains perhaps 100,000,000,000 stars. This is about 100 times the number of stars that can be seen through the 200-inch telescope. Within the radius of 1,600,000,000 light years that man is able to penetrate there are perhaps 100,000,000 galaxies, although only a small fraction of this number has been actually observed.

The galaxies which have been discovered are observed to congregate in groups, somewhat similar to stars in a galaxy. Whether the part seen is but a small portion of a larger unit too vast to be seen with present instruments has not been established. Through his progress in astronomy man hopes to see much more of what surrounds him in space, and perhaps to answer some of the questions which confront him.

Courtesy of Mt. Wilson and Palomar Observatories.

FIGURE 1415.—Spiral nebula Messier 51, in *Canes Venetici.*
Satellite nebula is NGC 5195.

Apparent Motion

1416. Apparent motion due to rotation of the earth is much greater than any other observed motion of celestial bodies. It is this motion that causes celestial bodies to appear to rise somewhere along the eastern half of the horizon, climb to maximum altitude as they cross the meridian, and set along the western horizon, at about the same point relative to due west as the rising point was to due east. This apparent motion along the daily path, or **diurnal circle,** of the body is approximately parallel to the plane of the equator. It would be exactly so if rotation of the earth were the only motion, and the axis of rotation of the earth were stationary in space (arts. 1417 and 1419).

The apparent effect due to rotation of the earth varies with the latitude of the observer. At the equator, where the equatorial plane is vertical (since the axis of rotation of the earth is parallel to the plane of the horizon), bodies appear to rise and set vertically. Every celestial body is above the horizon approximately half the time. The celestial sphere as seen by an observer at the equator is called the **right sphere,** shown in figure 1416a. Several unique relationships of the right sphere are discussed in article 1433.

For an observer at one of the poles, bodies having constant declination neither rise nor set (neglecting precession of the equinoxes and changes in refraction), but circle the sky, always at the same altitude, making one complete trip around the horizon each day. At the North Pole the motion is clockwise, and at the South Pole it is counter-clockwise. Approximately half the stars are always above the horizon and the other half never are. This is modified somewhat by actual conditions, a description of which is given in chapter XXV. The **parallel sphere** at the poles is illustrated in figure 1416b.

Between these two extremes, the apparent motion is a combination of the two. On this **oblique sphere,** illustrated in figure 1416c, **circumpolar** celestial bodies remain above the horizon during the entire 24 hours, circling the elevated celestial pole (art. 1426) each day. The stars of the Big Dipper and *Cassiopeia* are circumpolar for many observers in the United States. An approximately equal part of the celestial sphere remains below the horizon during the entire day. The Southern Cross is not visible to most observers in the United States. Other bodies rise obliquely along the eastern horizon, climb to maximum altitude at the celestial meridian, and set along the western horizon. The length of time above the horizon, and the altitude at meridian transit, vary with both the latitude of the observer and the declination of the body. Several

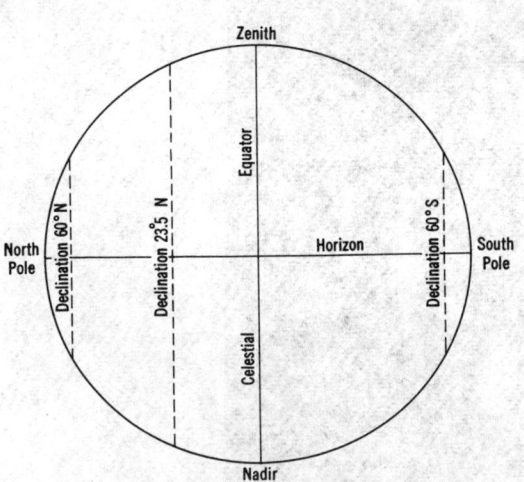

FIGURE 1416a.—The right sphere.

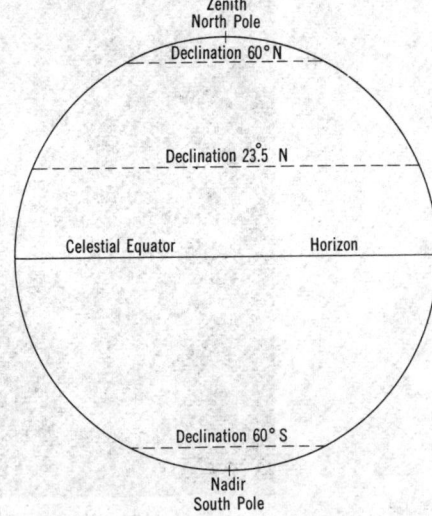

FIGURE 1416b.—The parallel sphere.

useful relationships of the oblique sphere are indicated in article 1432. At the polar circles (art. 1419) of the earth and beyond, even the sun becomes circumpolar. This is the land of the **midnight sun,** where the sun does not set during part of the summer, and does not rise during part of the winter.

The increased obliquity at higher latitudes explains why days and nights are always about the same length in the tropics, and the change of length of the day becomes greater as the latitude increases. It also explains why twilight lasts longer in higher latitudes. **Twilight** is that period of incomplete darkness following sunset and preceding sunrise. **Evening twilight** starts at sunset, and **morning twilight** ends at sunrise. The darker limit of twilight occurs when the center of the sun is a stated number of degrees below the celestial horizon. Three kinds of twilight are defined, depending upon the darker limit. These are:

Twilight	Lighter limit	Darker limit	At darker limit
civil	$-0°50'$	$-6°$	Horizon clear and bright stars visible
nautical	$-0°50'$	$-12°$	Horizon not visible
astronomical	$-0°50'$	$-18°$	Full night

The conditions at the darker limit are relative and vary considerably under different atmospheric conditions.

In figure 1416d the twilight band is shown, with the darker limits of the various kinds indicated. The nearly vertical celestial equator line is for an observer at latitude 20°N. The nearly horizontal celestial equator line is for an observer at latitude 60°N. The broken line in each case is the diurnal circle of the sun when its declination is 15°N. The relative duration of any kind of twilight at the two latitudes is indicated by that portion of the diurnal circle between the horizon and the darker limit, although it is not directly proportional to the relative length of line shown, since the projection is orthographic (art. 319). The duration of twilight at the higher latitude is longer, proportionally, than shown. Note that complete darkness does not occur at latitude 60°N when the declination of the sun is 15°N.

1417. Apparent motion due to revolution of the earth.—If it were possible to stop the *rotation* of the earth so that the celestial sphere would appear stationary, the effects of the *revolution* of the earth would become more noticeable. In one year the sun would appear to make one complete trip around the earth, from west to east.

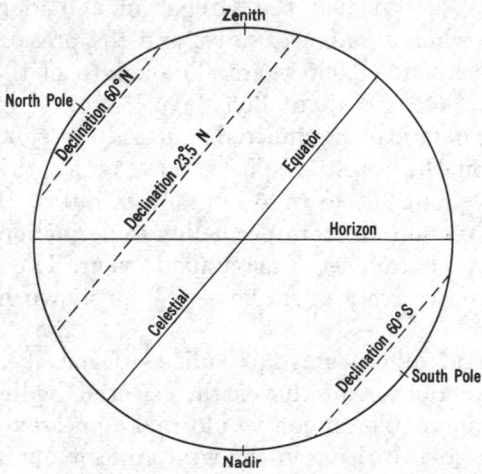

FIGURE 1416c.—The oblique sphere at lat. 40° N.

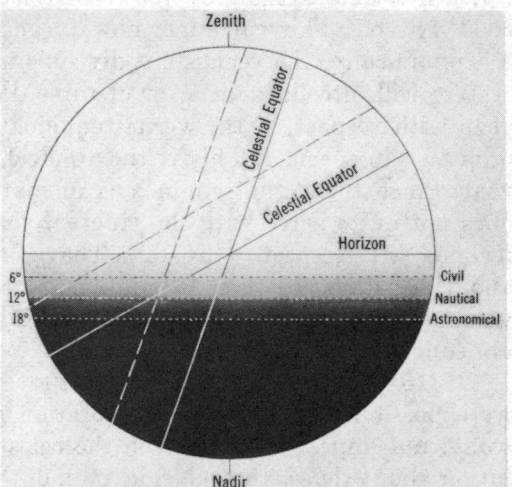

FIGURE 1416d.—The various twilights at lat. 20° N and lat. 60° N.

Hence, it would seem to move eastward a little less than 1° per day. This motion can be observed by watching the changing position of the sun among the stars. But since both sun and stars generally are not visible at the same time, a better way is to observe the constellations at the same time each night. On any night a star rises nearly four minutes earlier than on the previous night. Thus, the celestial sphere appears to shift westward nearly 1° each night, so that different constellations are associated with different seasons of the year.

Apparent motions of planets and the moon are due to a combination of their motions and those of the earth. If the rotation of the earth were stopped, the combined apparent motion due to the revolutions of the earth and other bodies would be similar to that occurring if both rotation and revolution of the earth were stopped, as discussed in article 1418, but with different timing. Stars would appear nearly stationary in the sky, but would undergo a small annual cycle of change due to **aberration.** The motion of the earth in its orbit is sufficiently fast to cause the light from stars to appear to shift slightly in the direction of the earth's motion. This is similar to the illusion one has when walking in rain that is falling vertically, but appearing to come from ahead due to his own motion. The apparent direction of the light ray from the star is the vector difference (art. 118, vol. II) of the motion of light and the motion of the earth, similar to that of apparent wind on a moving vessel. This effect is most apparent for a body perpendicular to the line of travel of the earth in its orbit, for which it reaches a maximum value of 20".5. The effect of aberration can be noted by comparing the co-ordinates (declination and sidereal hour angle) of various stars throughout the year. A change is observed in some bodies as the year progresses, but at the end of the year the values have returned almost to what they were at the beginning. That they do not return exactly is due to proper motion (art. 1418), precession of the equinoxes (art. 1419), and **nutation,** which is an irregularity in the motion of the earth due to the disturbing effect of other celestial bodies, principally the moon. **Eulerian motion** is a slight wobbling of the earth about its axis of rotation, often called **polar motion,** and sometimes **wandering of the poles.** This motion, which does not exceed 40 feet from the mean position, produces slight **variation of latitude and longitude** of places on the earth.

By the **calendar,** one year is of 365 days duration for **common years** and 366 days for **leap years.** A leap year is any year divisible by four, unless it is a century year, which must be divisible by 400 to be a leap year. Thus, 1900 was not a leap year, but 2000 will be. This calendar, now in general use, is called the **Gregorian calendar.** Astronomically, the year is not divisible into a whole number of days, and the present system will introduce an error of three days in about 10,000 years. The length of the year with respect to the vernal equinox (art. 1419) is about 365 days, 5 hours, 48 minutes, 46 seconds. This is the **tropical, astronomical, equinoctial, natural,** or **solar year.** Since the vernal equinox is in motion on the celestial sphere (art. 1419), this does not quite agree with the **sidereal year** of about 365 days, 6 hours, 9 minutes, 10 seconds, with respect to the stars. The period of revolution from perihelion to perihelion, about 365 days, 6 hours, 13 minutes, 53 seconds, is called the **anomalistic year.** These values vary slightly from year to year, and progressively over the years, as shown in appendix D.

1418. Apparent motion due to movement of other celestial bodies.—Even if it were possible to stop both the rotation and revolution of the earth, celestial bodies would not appear stationary on the celestial sphere. The moon would make one revolution about the earth each sidereal month (art. 1412), rising in the west and setting in the east. The inferior planets would appear to move eastward and westward relative to the sun, as explained in article 1422, staying within the zodiac. Superior planets would appear to make one revolution around the earth, from west to east, each sidereal period.

Since the sun (and the earth with it) and all other stars, as far as is known, are in motion relative to each other, slow apparent motions would result in slight changes in the positions of the stars relative to each other. This **space motion** (art. 1414) is, in fact, observed by telescope. That component of such motion across the line of sight, called **proper motion,** produces a change in the apparent position of the star. The maximum which has been observed is that of "Barnard's Star," which is moving at the rate of 10″.3 per year. This is a tenth-magnitude star, and hence not visible to the unaided eye. Of the 57 stars listed on the daily pages of the almanacs, Rigil Kentaurus has the greatest proper motion, about 3″.7. Arcturus, with 2″.3, has the greatest proper motion of the navigational stars in the Northern Hemisphere. In a few thousand years proper motion will be sufficient to materially alter some familiar configurations of stars, notably the Big Dipper.

1419. The ecliptic is the path the sun appears to take among the stars due to the annual revolution of the earth in its orbit. It is considered a great circle of the celestial sphere, inclined at an angle of about 23°27′ to the celestial equator, but undergoing a continuous slight change. This angle is called the **obliquity of the ecliptic.** This inclination is due to the fact that the axis of rotation of the earth is not perpendicular to its orbit. It is this inclination which causes the sun to appear to move north and south during the year, giving the earth its **seasons,** and changing lengths of periods of daylight. This seasonal variation is one of the factors making the earth a desirable place on which to live.

Refer to figure 1407b. The earth is at perihelion early in January and at aphelion six months later. On or about June 21, about ten or eleven days before reaching aphelion, the northern part of the earth's axis is tilted toward the sun. The north polar regions are having continuous sunlight; the Northern Hemisphere is having its **summer** with long, warm days and short nights; the Southern Hemisphere is having winter with short days and long, cold nights; and the south polar region is in continuous darkness. This is the **summer solstice.** Three months later, about September 23, the earth has moved a quarter of the way around the sun, but its axis of rotation still points in about *the same direction in space.* The sun shines equally on both hemispheres, and days and nights are the same length over the entire world. The sun is setting at the North Pole, and rising at the South Pole. The Northern Hemisphere is having its **autumn,** and the Southern Hemisphere its spring. This is the **autumnal equinox.** In another three months, on or about December 22, the Southern Hemisphere is tilted toward the sun and conditions are the reverse of those six months earlier, the Northern Hemisphere having its **winter,** and the Southern Hemisphere its summer. This is the **winter solstice.** Three months later, when both hemispheres again receive equal amounts of sunshine, the Northern Hemisphere is having **spring** and the Southern Hemisphere autumn, the reverse of conditions six months before. This is the **vernal equinox.**

The word "equinox," meaning "equal nights," is applied because it occurs at the time when days and nights are of approximately equal length all over the earth. The word "solstice," meaning "sun stands still," is applied because the sun stops its apparent northward or southward motion and momentarily "stands still" before it starts in the opposite direction. This action, somewhat analogous to the "stand" of the tide (art. 3104), refers to the motion in a north-south direction only, and not to the daily apparent revolution around the earth. Note that it does not occur when the earth is at perihelion and aphelion (fig. 1407b). Refer to figure 1419a. At the time of the vernal equinox, the sun is directly over the equator, crossing from the Southern Hemisphere to

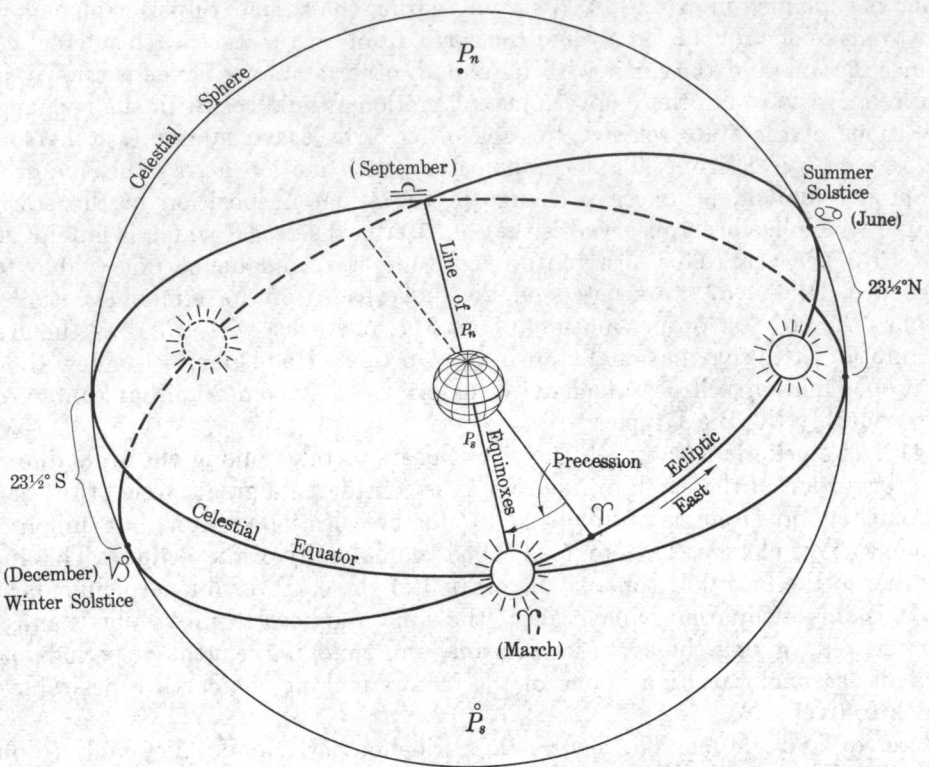

FIGURE 1419a.—Apparent motion of the sun in the ecliptic.

the Northern Hemisphere. It rises due east and sets due west, remaining above the horizon about 12 hours. It is not exactly 12 hours because of refraction, semidiameter, and the height of the eye of the observer. These cause it to be above the horizon a little longer than below the horizon. Following the vernal equinox, the northerly declination increases, and the sun climbs higher in the sky each day (at the latitudes of the United States), until the summer solstice, when a declination of about 23°27′ north of the celestial equator is reached. The sun then gradually retreats southward until it is again over the equator at the autumnal equinox, at about 23°27′ south of the celestial equator at the winter solstice, and back over the celestial equator again at the next vernal equinox.

The sun is nearest the earth during the northern hemisphere winter. Hence, it is not the distance that is responsible for the difference in temperature during the different seasons. The reason is to be found in the altitude of the sun in the sky and the length of time it remains above the horizon. During the summer the rays are more nearly vertical, and hence more concentrated, as shown in figure 1419b. Since the sun is above the horizon more than half the time, heat is being added by absorption during a longer period than it is being lost by radiation. This explains the lag of the seasons. Following the longest day, the earth continues to receive more heat than it dissipates, but at a decreasing proportion. Gradually the proportion decreases until a balance is reached, after which the earth cools, losing more heat than it gains. This is analogous to the day, when the highest temperatures normally occur several hours after the sun reaches maximum altitude at meridian transit, and for the same reason. A similar lag occurs at other seasons of the year. *Astronomically*, the seasons *begin* at the equinoxes and solstices. *Meteorologically*, they differ from place to place.

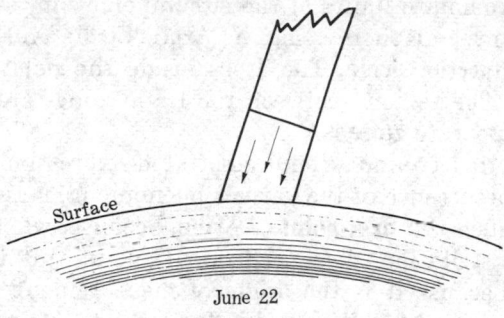

June 22

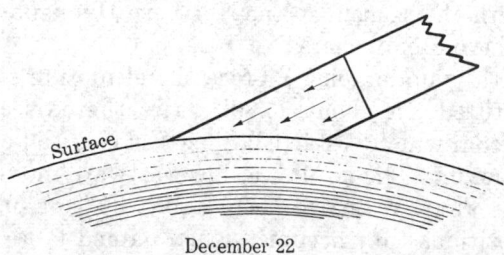

December 22

FIGURE 1419b.—Sunlight in summer and winter. Compare the surface covered by the same amount of sunlight on the two dates.

By Kepler's second law, the earth travels faster when nearest the sun, as shown in figure 1419c. Hence, the northern hemisphere (astronomical) winter is shorter than its summer, the difference being about seven days.

Everywhere between the parallels of about 23°27′N and about 23°27′S the sun is directly overhead at some time during the year. Except at the extremes, this occurs twice, once as the sun appears to move northward, and the second time as it moves southward. This is the **torrid zone.** The northern limit is the **Tropic of Cancer,** and the southern limit the **Tropic of Capricorn.** These names come from the constellations which the sun entered at the solstices when the names were first applied, more than 2,000 years ago. Today, the sun is in the next constellation toward the west, because of precession of the equinoxes, described below. The parallels about 23°27′ from the

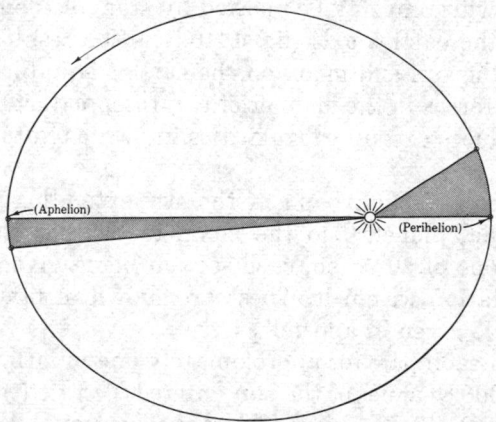

FIGURE 1419c.—Kepler's second law. Since the shaded areas are equal, speed at perihelion is greater than at aphelion.

poles, marking the approximate limits of the circumpolar sun, are called **polar circles,** the one in the Northern Hemisphere being the **Arctic Circle** and the one in the Southern Hemisphere the **Antarctic Circle.** The areas inside the polar circles are the north and south **frigid zones.** The regions between the frigid zones and the torrid zones are the north and south **temperate zones.**

The expression "vernal equinox," and associated expressions, are applied both to the *times* and *points* of occurrence of the various phenomena. Navigationally, the vernal equinox is sometimes called the **first point of Aries,** because, when the name was given, the sun entered the constellation *Aries,* the ram (♈), at this time. This point is of interest to navigators because it is the origin of measurement of sidereal hour angle (art. 1426). The expressions **March equinox, June solstice, September equinox,** and **December solstice** are occasionally applied as appropriate, because the more common names are associated with the seasons in the Northern Hemisphere, and are six months out of step for the Southern Hemisphere.

The axis of the earth is undergoing a precessional motion similar to that of a top spinning with its axis tilted. In about 25,800 years the axis completes a cycle and returns to the position from which it started. Since the celestial equator is 90° from the celestial poles, it too is moving. The result is a slow westward movement of the equinoxes and solstices, which has already carried them about 30°, or one constellation, along the ecliptic from the positions they occupied when named more than 2,000 years ago. Since sidereal hour angle (art. 1426) is measured from the vernal equinox, and declination (art. 1426) from the celestial equator, the coordinates of celestial bodies would be changing even if the bodies themselves were stationary. This westward motion of the equinoxes along the ecliptic is called **precession of the equinoxes** (fig. 1419a). The total amount, called **general precession,** is about 50".27 per year (in 1975). It may be considered divided into two components, **precession in right ascension** (about 46".10 per year) measured along the celestial equator, and **precession in declination** (about 20".04 per year) measured perpendicular to the celestial equator. The annual change in the coordinates of any given star, due to precession alone, depends upon its position on the celestial sphere, since these coordinates are measured relative to the polar axis while the precessional motion is relative to the ecliptic axis (art. 1431).

Due to precession of the equinoxes, the celestial poles are describing circles in the sky. The north celestial pole is moving closer to Polaris, which it will pass at a distance of approximately 28' about the year 2102. Following this, the polar distance will increase, and eventually other stars, in their turn, will become the Pole Star. Similarly, the south celestial pole will some day be marked by stars of the false Southern Cross.

The precession of the earth's axis (fig. 1419d) is the result of gravitational forces exerted principally by the sun and moon on the earth's equatorial bulge. The spinning earth responds to these forces in the manner of a gyroscope (art. 630). Regression of the nodes (art. 1423) introduces certain irregularities known as nutation in the precessional motion.

1420. The zodiac is a circular band of the sky extending 8° on each side of the ecliptic. The navigational planets and the moon are within these limits. The zodiac is divided into 12 sections of 30° each, each section being given the name and symbol ("sign") of the constellation within it. These are shown in figure 1420. The complete list of signs and names is given in appendix C.

The sun remains in each part for approximately one month. When the names were assigned, more than 2,000 years ago, the sun entered *Aries* (♈) at the vernal equinox, *Cancer* (♋) at the summer solstice, *Libra* (♎) at the autumnal equinox, and *Capricornus* (♑) at the winter solstice. Even though this is no longer true because of precession of the equinoxes, these constellations are still used for the position of the sun at the

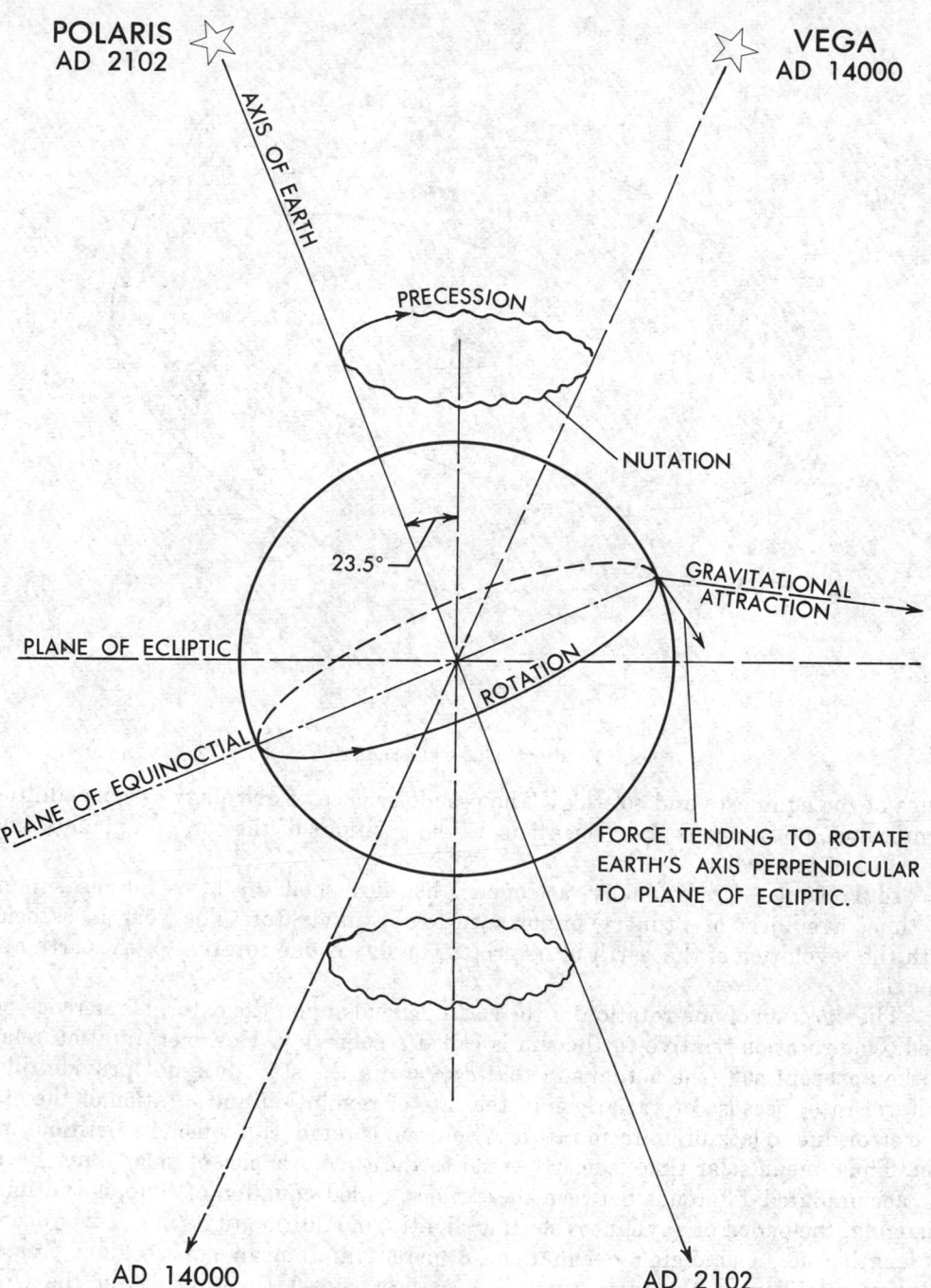

FIGURE 1419d.—Precession and nutation.

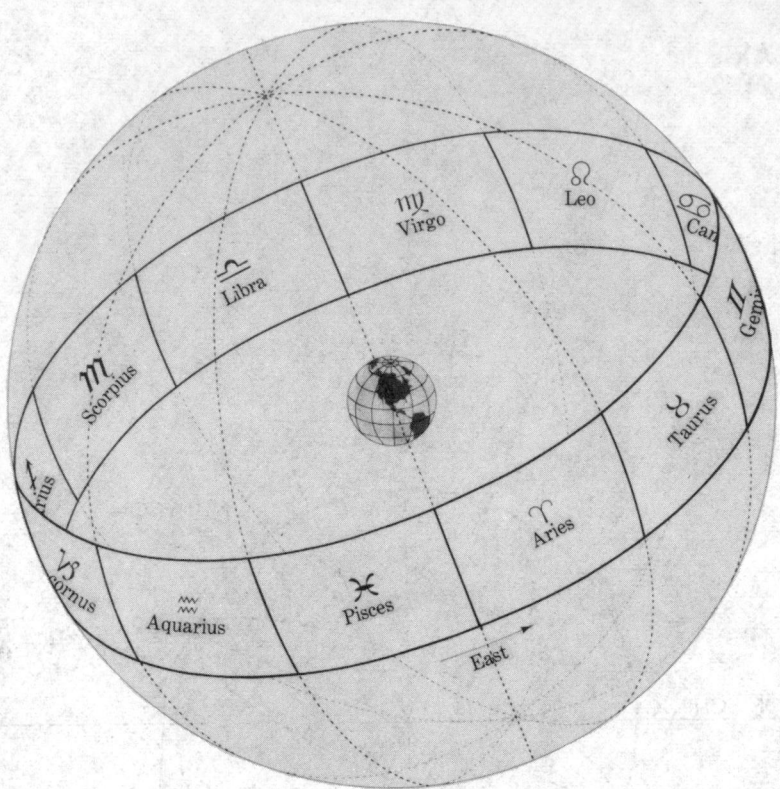

FIGURE 1420.—The zodiac.

times of the equinoxes and solstices. The pseudo science of **astrology** assigns additional significance, not recognized by scientists, to the positions of the sun and planets among the signs of the zodiac.

1421. Time.—Traditionally, astronomy has furnished the basis for measurement of time, a subject of primary importance to the navigator. The **year** is associated with the revolution of the earth in its orbit. The **day** is one rotation of the earth about its axis.

The *duration* of one rotation of the earth depends upon the external reference point used. One rotation relative to the sun is called a **solar day.** However, rotation relative to the **apparent sun** (the actual sun that *appears* in the sky) does not provide time of uniform rate, because of variations in the rate of revolution and rotation of the earth. The error due to lack of uniform rate of revolution is removed by using a fictitious **mean sun.** Thus, **mean solar time** is nearly equal to the *average* **apparent solar time.** Because the accumulated difference between these times, called **equation of time,** is continually changing, the period of daylight is shifting slightly, in addition to its increase or decrease in length due to changing declination. Apparent and mean suns seldom cross the celestial meridian at the same time. The earliest sunset (in latitudes of the United States) occurs about two weeks *before* the winter solstice, and the latest sunrise about two weeks *after* winter solstice. A similar but smaller apparent discrepancy occurs at the summer solstice.

Universal Time is a particular case of the measure known in general as mean solar time. Universal Time is the mean solar time on the Greenwich meridian, reckoned in days of 24 mean solar hours beginning with 0^h at midnight. Universal Time and sidereal time are rigorously related by a formula so that if one is known the other can be found.

Universal Time, in principle, is determined by the *average* rate of the apparent daily motion of the sun relative to the meridian of Greenwich; but in practice the numerical measure of Universal Time at any instant is computed from sideral time.

Universal Time is the standard in the application of astronomy to navigation. Observations of Universal Times are made by observing the times of transit of stars.

If the vernal equinox is used as the reference, a **sidereal day** is obtained, and from it, **sidereal time.** This indicates the approximate positions of the stars, and for this reason is the basis of star charts (art. 2204) and star finders (art. 2210). Because of the revolution of the earth around the sun, a sidereal day is about 3ᵐ56ˢ *shorter* than a solar day, and there is one more sidereal than solar days in a year. One mean solar day equals 1.00273791 mean sidereal days. Because of precession of the equinoxes, one rotation of the earth with respect to the stars is not quite the same as one rotation with respect to the vernal equinox. One mean solar day averages 1.0027378118868 rotations of the earth with respect to the stars.

In tide analysis, the moon is sometimes used as the reference, producing a **lunar day** averaging 24^h50^m (mean solar units) in length, and **lunar time.**

Since each kind of day is divided arbitrarily into 24 hours, each hour having 60 minutes of 60 seconds, the length of each of these units differs somewhat in the various kinds of time.

Time is also classified according to the terrestrial meridian used as a reference. **Local time** results if one's own meridian is used, **zone time** if a nearby reference meridian is used over a spread of longitudes, and **Greenwich** or **Universal Time** if the Greenwich meridian is used.

The subject of time is discussed in more detail in XVIII.

1422. Planetary configurations.—Since the orbit of an inferior planet lies within that of the earth, the planet and sun are nearly in line twice each synodic period of revolution of the inferior planet. When the sun is between the earth and the other planet, that planet is at **superior conjunction.** When the planet is between the earth and sun, it is at **inferior conjunction.** If the orbit of the planet had no inclination to the ecliptic, the planet would cross or **transit** the face of the sun at inferior conjunction and be eclipsed or **occulted** by the sun at superior conjunction. Occasionally this does occur.

Refer to figure 1422, showing orbits of the earth, Venus (an inferior planet,) and Mars (a superior planet). As shown, the relative sizes of the orbits are correct, and the relative sizes of the planets are correct, but the planets are too large for their orbits and the sun, and the sun is too large for the orbits of the planets. The earth is considered stationary in its orbit. The positions of Venus are shown at superior and inferior conjunctions. In moving eastward from one to the other. Venus appears to move to the left of the sun. As observed from the earth, the angle between lines to the sun and a planet, particularly an inferior planet, is called the planet's **elongation,** which may be designated east or west to indicate the apparent position of the planet relative to the sun. As Venus continues along its orbit, its elongation increases slowly until the planet arrives at the point where a straight line from the earth is tangent to its orbit, when the elongation becomes maximum. Here it is called **greatest elongation east.** As Venus continues along its orbit, its elongation decreases rapidly, becoming zero at inferior conjunction. Through the second half of its synodic period its elongation increases rapidly to **greatest elongation west,** and then decreases slowly to zero at the next superior conjunction. The greatest elongation of Venus is about 46°, but varies because its orbit and that of the earth are elliptical, and the phenomenon occurs at different points on the orbits.

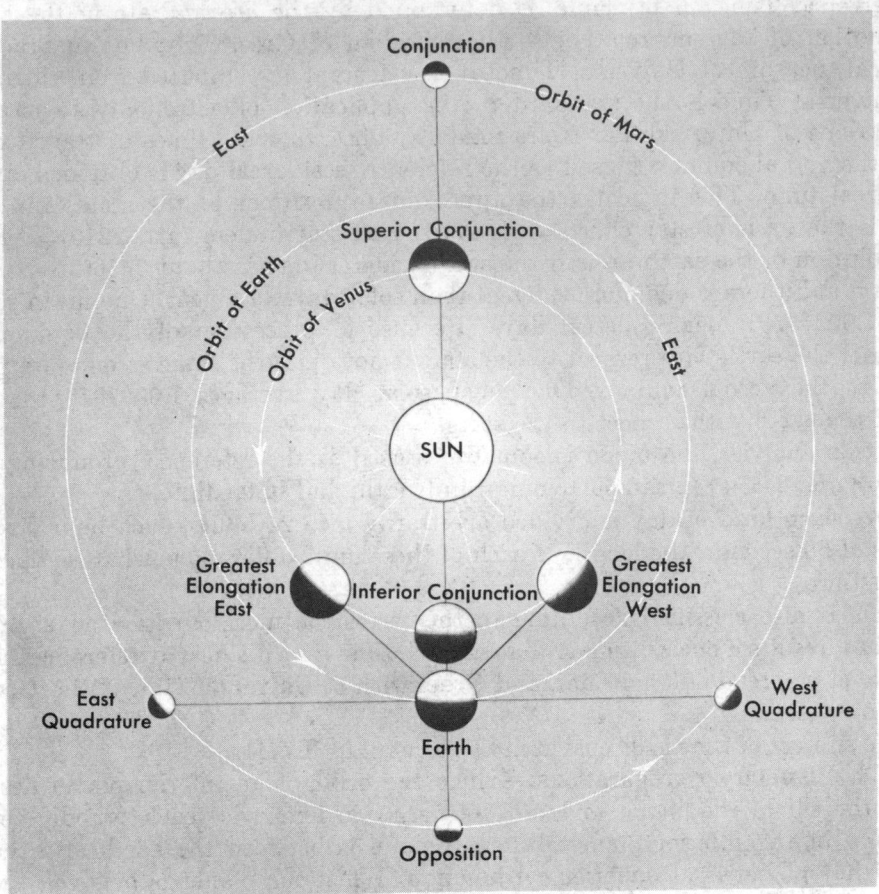

FIGURE 1422.—Planetary configurations.

The orbit of the planet Mercury lies inside that of Venus, and hence the greatest elongation is not as great, being about 28°. It is because the apparent position of Mercury is never far from the sun that this planet is not considered navigationally important. Since its synodic period of revolution is only 115.9 days, it is at conjunction a little oftener than once every two months. By comparison, Venus is at conjunction a little oftener than once every ten months, having a synodic period of revolution of 583.9 days.

As shown in figure 1422, an inferior planet goes through all phases similar to those of the moon (art. 1423), being "full" at superior conjunction, "new" at inferior conjunction, and at "quarter" when it reaches greatest elongation. A telescope is needed to see the phases.

For a superior planet the situation is different. Refer again to figure 1422. When the sun is between the earth and the planet, that planet (Mars in the illustration) is at **conjunction** (σ). The adjective "superior" is not needed because a superior planet, when on the opposite side is *away* from the sun, or at **opposition** ($\mathcal{8}$) and can never be at inferior conjunction. When its elongation is 90°, a superior planet is at east or west **quadrature** ($\square$), depending upon its apparent position relative to the sun. Since a superior planet has a longer period of revolution than the earth, it *appears* to move westward around the sun, being at conjunction, east quadrature, opposition, west quadrature, and back to conjunction. It is at "full" phase at conjunction and opposition, and gibbous between.

Unless a planet is in the ecliptic, it is not directly in line with the earth and sun at conjunction and opposition. These points are defined as those at which either the sidereal hour angles (art. 1426) or the celestial longitudes (art. 1431) are the same (in the case of conjunction) or 180° apart (at opposition).

The apparent positions of the planets in relation to other members of the solar system, particularly the relationships shown in figure 1422, are called **planetary configurations.** The motions of planets with respect to the sun would be true, generally with respect to the stars, also, if the earth were stationary in its orbit, as shown. However, because of the earth's motion around the sun, the sun appears to move eastward among the stars. This is usually the direction of apparent motion of the planets, too, and is called **direct motion.** When a planet is near opposition or inferior conjunction, its apparent *westerly* motion relative to the sun is greater than the apparent *easterly* motion of the sun relative to the stars, and the planet appears to move in a *westerly* direction relative to the stars. This is called **retrograde motion.**

The brightest planet in the western sky following sunset is popularly called the **evening star,** and the brightest planet in the eastern sky preceding sunrise is popularly called the **morning star.**

1423. Phases of the moon.—Relative to the sun, the moon makes one complete trip around the celestial sphere each synodical month (about 29½ days). As it does so, it goes through a cycle of aspects or **phases** to an observer on the earth, because the moon, like the planets, shines chiefly by reflected light from the sun. The orbit of the moon is inclined about 5° to the ecliptic, and undergoes a precessional motion called **regression of the nodes.** It is similar to precession of the equinoxes of the earth (art. 1419), and is chiefly responsible for nutation (art. 1417). However, the cycle is completed in a little more than 18 years, as compared with about 25,800 years for the earth.

Because of the small inclination of its orbit, the moon is never far from the ecliptic. At conjunction, when the moon passes nearly between the earth and sun, its illuminated portion is *away* from the earth (*toward* the sun), as shown in figure 1423. (In this illustration, the outer figures show various positions of the moon relative to the earth and sunlight. The inner circle of moons shows the appearance from the earth.) It is then a **new moon,** and may be barely visible because of **earthshine,** which is sunlight reflected from the illuminated side of the earth. To an observer on the moon, the "full earth" would be visible at this time, three and one-half times as great in diameter and nearly 40 times as bright as the full moon appears to an observer on the earth. Since it is at conjunction, the new moon rises, transits the celestial meridian, and sets at approximately the same time as the sun.

A day later the moon has moved about 12°2 eastward of the sun and a thin **crescent** appears on the side toward the sun, with the horns or **cusps** pointing away from the sun. The moon is low in the western sky after sunset. Because of glow from this illuminated portion, and the fact that the side of the earth toward the moon is not quite "full," that part of the moon illuminated by earthshine is not quite as bright. Each day the moon moves approximately 12°2 east, relative to the sun. As it does so, the crescent grows fatter, and the earthshine less conspicuous.

When the moon reaches quadrature, about a week after new moon, it is at **first quarter.** That half of the moon toward the sun is illuminated. The moon is now about 90° or six hours *behind* the sun. It rises about noon, is on the celestial meridian about 6 PM, and sets about midnight.

As the moon continues eastward on successive days, the line separating the illuminated and dark portions, called the **terminator,** moves on across the moon. The moon is now in the **gibbous** phase, which continues until the moon is at opposition,

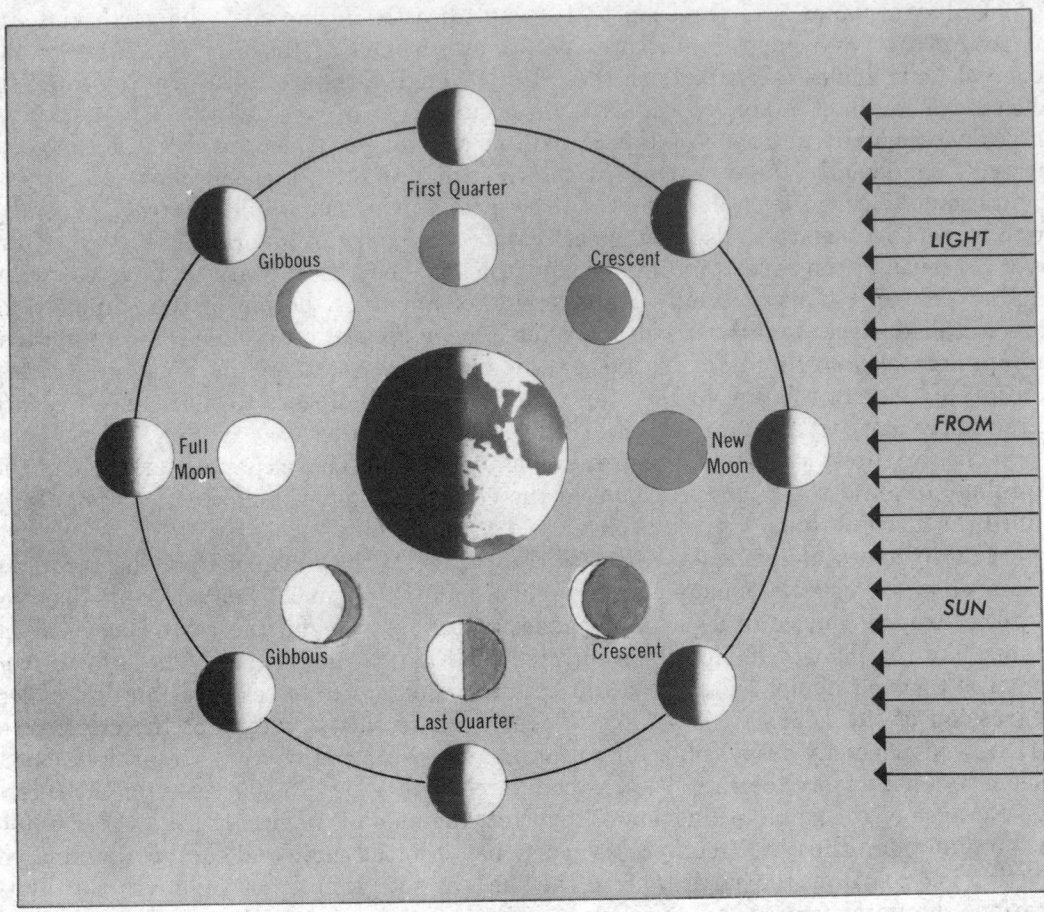

FIGURE 1423.—Phases of the moon. The inner figures of the moon represent its appearance from the earth.

or **full moon.** It now rises about the time of sunset, reaches the celestial meridian about midnight, and sets about the time of sunrise.

On succeeding days the moon again becomes gibbous, and at quadrature it is at **last quarter,** rising about midnight, crossing the celestial meridian about 6 AM, and setting about noon. During the remainder of its cycle the moon again goes through the cresent phase and returns to new moon to start another cycle.

During the first half of the cycle, the moon is **waxing,** and during the second half it is **waning.** The elapsed time since new moon, usually expressed as days and tenths of a day is called **age of the moon.** Since the moon appears to move *eastward* relative to the sun, crossing the meridian *later* each day, one day each synodical month is without a moonrise, and another is without a moonset.

The times of moonrise and moonset indicated above are approximate only. When the difference between the declination of the sun and moon is considerable, the times given may be in error by as much as several hours, particularly in high latitudes. The times of crossing the celestial meridian vary through smaller limits.

At full moon, the sun and moon are on opposite sides of the ecliptic. Therefore, in the winter the full moon rises early, crosses the celestial meridian high in the sky, and sets late; as the sun does in the summer. In the summer the full moon rises in the southeastern part of the sky (Northern Hemisphere), remains relatively low in the sky, and sets along the southwestern horizon after a short time above the horizon.

At the time of the autumnal equinox, that part of the ecliptic opposite the sun is most nearly parallel to the horizon. Since the eastward motion of the moon is approximately along the ecliptic, the delay in the time of rising of the full moon from night to night is less than at other times of the year. The full moon nearest the autumnal equinox is called the **harvest moon.** The full moon occurring about a month later is called the **hunter's moon.**

1424. Eclipses.—Because of the inclination of the moon's orbit with respect to the ecliptic, the sun, earth, and moon are usually not so nearly in line at conjunction and opposition of the moon that either the earth or moon passes through the shadow of the other. However, when this does occur, an **eclipse** takes place. Since the sun and moon are of nearly the same apparent size to an observer on the earth, an eclipse is a much more spectacular occurrence than the transit of an inferior planet across the face of the sun, or the occultation of a star or planet by the sun or moon (art. 1422).

When conditions are suitable, the moon passes between the sun and earth, as shown in figure 1424a. If the moon's apparent diameter is larger than that of the sun, the moon being near perigee, its shadow reaches the earth as a nearly round dot only a few miles in diameter. The dot moves rapidly across the earth, from west to east, as the moon continues in its orbit. Within the dot, the sun is completely hidden from view, and a **total eclipse** of the sun occurs. For a considerable distance around the shadow, part of the surface of the sun is obscured, and a **partial eclipse** occurs. In the line of travel of the shadow a partial eclipse occurs as the round disk of the moon appears to move slowly across the surface of the sun, hiding an ever-increasing part of it, until the total eclipse occurs. Because of the uneven edge of the mountainous moon, the light is not cut off evenly, but several last illuminated portions appear through the valleys or passes between the mountain peaks. These are called **Baily's Beads.** A total eclipse is a spectacular phenomenon. As the last light from the sun is cut off, the solar **corona,** or envelope of thin, illuminated gas around the sun, becomes visible. Wisps of more dense gas may appear as **solar prominences** (fig. 1424b). The only light reaching the observer is that diffused by the atmosphere surrounding the shadow. As the moon appears to continue on across the face of the sun, the sun finally emerges from the other side, first as Baily's Beads, and then as an ever widening crescent until no part of its surface is obscured by the moon.

The duration of a total eclipse depends upon how nearly the moon crosses the center of the sun, the location of the shadow on the earth, the relative orbital speeds of the moon and earth, and (principally) the relative apparent diameters of the sun and moon. The maximum length that can occur is a little more than seven minutes.

If the apparent diameter of the moon is less than that of the sun, its shadow does not quite reach the earth. Over a small area of the earth directly in line with the moon and sun, the moon appears as a black disk almost covering the surface of the sun,

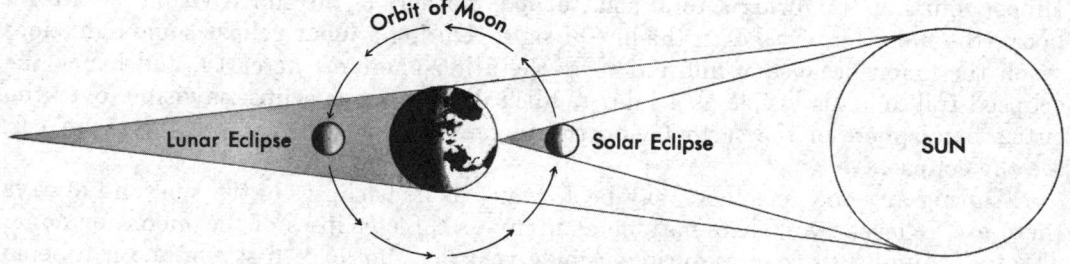

FIGURE 1424a.—Eclipses of the sun and moon.

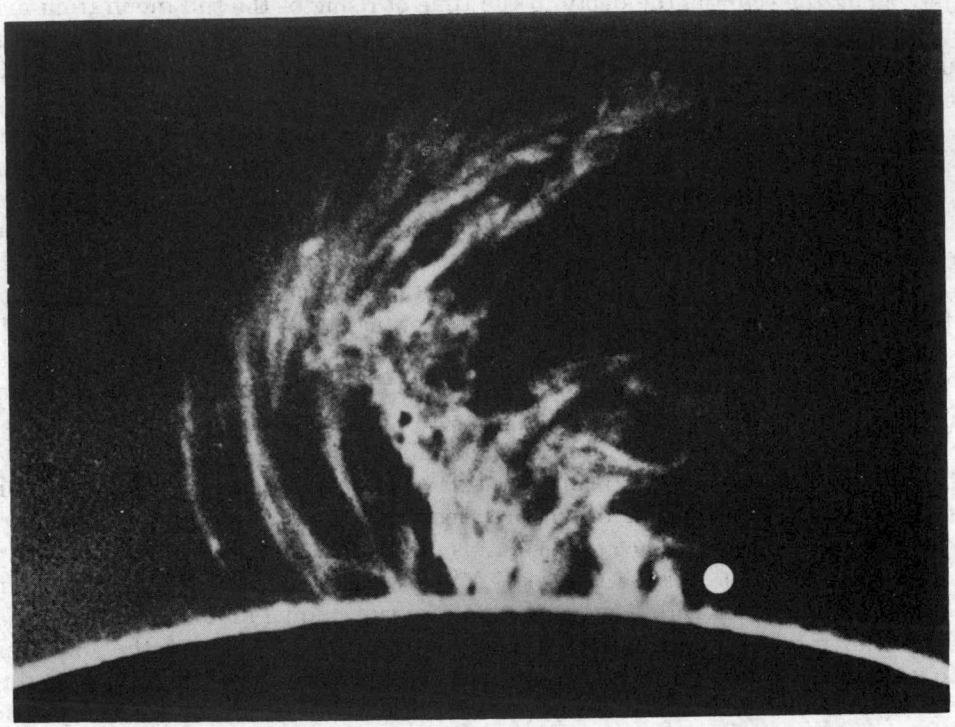

Courtesy of Mt. Wilson and Palomar Observatories.

FIGURE 1424b.—Solar prominence, 140,000 miles high, photographed in light of calcium. July 9, 1917. Small white disk shows relative size of earth.

but with a thin ring of the sun around its edge. This is an **annular eclipse,** and occurs a little oftener than a total eclipse.

If the shadow of the moon passes close to the earth, but not directly in line with it, a partial eclipse may occur without a total or annular eclipse.

An eclipse of the moon occurs when the moon passes through the shadow of the earth, as shown in figure 1424a. Since the diameter of the earth is about three and one-half times that of the moon, the earth's shadow at the distance of the moon is much larger than that of the moon. A total eclipse of the moon can last nearly one and three-quarters hours, and some part of the moon may be in the earth's shadow for almost four hours. During a total **solar eclipse** no part of the sun is visible because a body (the moon) intervenes in the line of sight. During a **lunar eclipse** some light does reach the moon because of diffraction by the atmosphere of the earth, and hence the eclipsed full moon is visible as a faint reddish disk. A lunar eclipse is visible over the entire hemisphere of the earth facing the moon. Anyone who can see the moon can see the eclipse.

During any one year there may be as many as five eclipses of the sun, and always there are at least two. There may be as many as three eclipses of the moon, or none. The total number of eclipses during a single year does not exceed seven, and can be as few as two. There are more solar than lunar eclipses, but the latter are more numerous at any one place because of the restricted areas over which solar eclipses are visible.

The two points of intersection of the moon's orbit and the ecliptic are called **nodes,** and the line connecting them, the **line of nodes.** Eclipses occur when the sun, earth, and moon are nearly on this line, twice each **eclipse year** of 346.6 days. This is less than a calendar year because of regression of the nodes (art. 1423). In a little more than 18 years the line of nodes returns to approximately the same position with respect to the sun, earth, and moon. During an almost equal period, called the **saros,** a cycle of eclipses occurs. During the following saros the cycle is repeated with only minor differences.

Eclipses have considerable value in establishing additional facts about the sun and moon, and in determining distances between two widely separated points on the earth, at which accurate timing of the eclipse is made.

Coordinates

1425. Latitude and longitude are coordinates used for locating positions on the earth. Several types, differing slightly from each other, are defined. Three of these are discussed here.

Astronomic latitude is the angle (ABQ, fig. 1425) between a line in the direction of gravity (AB) at a station and the plane of the equator (QQ'). **Astronomic longitude** is the angle between the plane of the celestial meridian at a station and the plane of the celestial meridian at Greenwich. These coordinates are customarily found by means of celestial observations. If the earth were perfectly homogeneous and level, these positions would be consistent and satisfactory. However, because of **deflection of the vertical** (app. X) due to uneven distribution of the mass of the earth, lines of equal astronomic latitude and longitude are not circles, although the irregularities are small. In the United States the prime-vertical component (affecting longitude) may be a little more than 18″, and the meridional component (affecting latitude) as much as 25″.

Geodetic latitude is the angle (ACQ, fig. 1425) between a normal to the spheroid (AC) at a station and the plane of the geodetic equator (QQ'). **Geodetic longitude** is the angle between the plane defined by the normal to the spheroid and the axis of the earth, and the plane of the geodetic meridian at Greenwich. These values are obtained when astronomical latitude and longitude are corrected for deflection of the vertical. These coordinates are the ones used for charting, and are frequently referred to as **geographic latitude** and **geographic longitude,** although these expressions are sometimes used to refer to astronomical latitude and longitude.

Geocentric latitude is the angle (ADQ, fig. 1425) at the center of the ellipsoid between the plane of its equator (QQ') and a straight line (AD) to a point on the surface

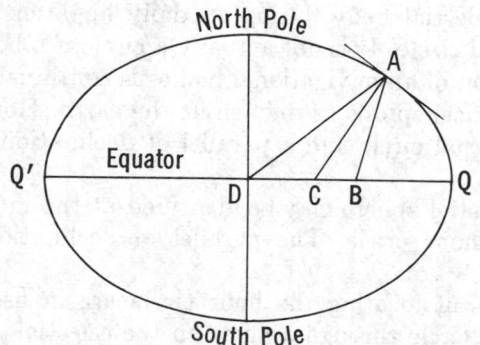

FIGURE 1425.—Three kinds of latitude at point A.

of the earth. This differs from geodetic latitude because the earth is a spheroid, rather than a sphere, and the meridians are ellipses. Since the parallels of latitude are considered to be circles, geodetic longitude is geocentric, and a separate expression is not used. The difference between geocentric and geodetic latitudes is a maximum of about 11.́6 at latitude 45°.

Because of the oblate shape of the ellipsoid, the length of a degree of geodetic latitude is not everywhere the same, increasing from about 59.7 nautical miles at the equator to about 60.3 nautical miles at the poles, as shown by table 6. The value of 60 nautical miles customarily used everywhere by the navigator is correct at about latitude 45°.

Measurement on the Celestial Sphere

1426. Elements of the celestial sphere.—The celestial sphere (art. 1403) is an imaginary sphere of infinite radius with the earth at its center (fig. 1426a). The north and south **celestial poles** of this sphere are located by extension of the earth's axis. The **celestial equator** (sometimes called **equinoctial**) is formed by projecting the plane of the earth's equator to the celestial sphere. A **celestial meridian** is formed by the intersection of the plane of a terrestrial meridian, extended, and the celestial sphere. It is the arc of a great circle through the poles of the celestial sphere.

The point on the celestial sphere vertically overhead of an observer is the **zenith** and the point on the opposite side of the sphere, vertically below him, is the **nadir.** The zenith and nadir are the extremities of a diameter of the celestial sphere through the observer and the common center of the earth and the celestial sphere. The arc of a celestial meridian between the poles is called the **upper branch** if it contains the zenith and the **lower branch** if it contains the nadir. The upper branch is frequently used in navigation and references to a celestial meridian are understood to mean only its upper branch unless otherwise stated. Celestial meridians take the names, as 65° west, of their terrestrial counterparts.

An **hour circle** is a great circle through the celestial poles and a point or body on the celestial sphere. It is similar to a celestial meridian, but moves with the celestial sphere as it rotates about the earth, while a celestial meridian remains fixed with respect to the earth.

The location of a body along its hour circle is defined by the body's angular distance from the celestial equator. This distance, called **declination,** is measured north or south of the celestial equator in degrees, from 0° through 90°, similar to latitude on the earth.

A circle parallel to the celestial equator is called a **parallel of declination,** since it connects all points of equal declination. It is similar to a parallel of latitude on the earth. The path of a celestial body during its daily apparent revolution around the earth is called its **diurnal circle.** It is not actually a circle if a body changes its declination. Since the declination of all navigational bodies is continually changing, the bodies are describing flat, spherical spirals as they circle the earth. However, since the change is relatively slow, a diurnal circle and a parallel of declination are usually considered identical.

A point on the celestial sphere may be identified at the intersection of its parallel of declination and its hour circle. The parallel of declination is identified by the declination.

Two basic methods of locating the hour circle are in use. Its angular distance west of a reference hour circle through a point on the celestial sphere called the **vernal equinox** or **first point of Aries** is called **sidereal hour angle** (SHA) (fig. 1426b). This

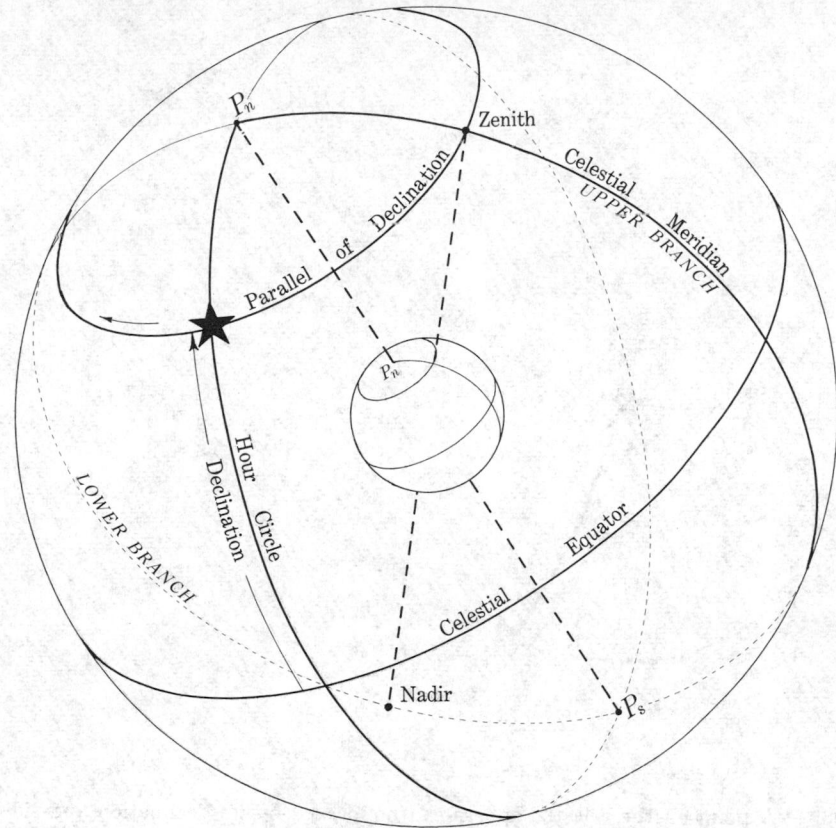

FIGURE 1426a.—Elements of the celestial sphere. The celestial equator is the primary great circle.

angle measured eastward from the vernal equinox is called **right ascension,** and is usually expressed in time units.

The second method of locating the hour circle is to indicate its angular distance *west* of a celestial meridian (fig. 1426c). If the Greenwich celestial meridian is used as the reference, the angular distance is called **Greenwich hour angle (GHA),** and if the meridian of the observer, it is called **local hour angle (LHA).** It is sometimes more convenient to measure hour angle either eastward or westward, as longitude is measured on the earth, in which case it is called **meridian angle (t).** These coordinates are discussed further in article 1428.

A point on the celestial sphere may also be located by means of **altitude** and **azimuth,** coordinates based upon the horizon as the primary great circle, instead of the celestial equator. This system is discussed in article 1430.

Two additional systems used by astronomers are based upon the ecliptic (art. 1419) and the galactic equator (the approximate mid great circle of the galaxy). The coordinates of the ecliptic system are **celestial latitude** and **celestial longitude** and those of the galactic system are **galactic latitude** and **galactic longitude.**

1427. Coordinate systems.—Various systems of coordinates on the celestial sphere, all of them similar to the familiar latitude and longitude on the earth, were discussed briefly in article 1426. Of these, the navigator is rarely concerned with any but the celestial equator system and the horizon system. The former is but an extension to the celestial sphere of the geographical system of the earth. The latter is a similar system in which the horizon replaces the celestial equator as the primary great circle, and the

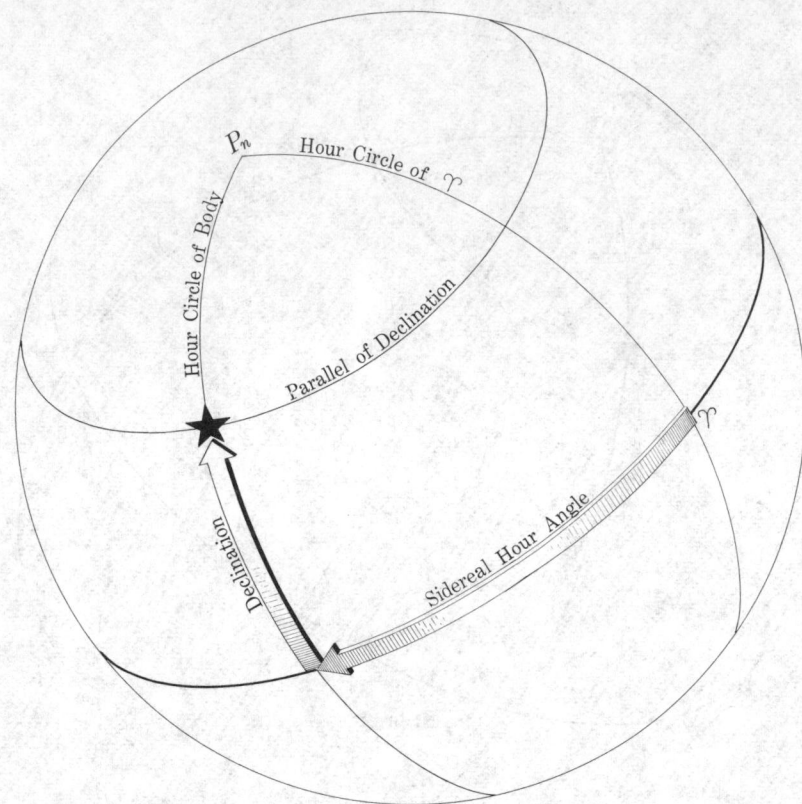

FIGURE 1426b.—A point on the celestial sphere can be located by its declination and sidereal hour angle.

zenith and nadir are the poles. These two systems are the almost constant companions of the celestial navigator.

1428. The celestial equator system of coordinates.—If the familiar graticule of latitude and longitude lines is expanded until it reaches the celestial sphere of infinite radius, it forms the basis of the celestial equator system of coordinates, as explained in article 1426. On the celestial sphere the familiar *latitude* becomes **declination** (**Dec.** or **d**), and *longitude*, measured always toward the west, through 360°, becomes **sidereal hour angle** (**SHA**) if measured from the vernal equinox.

Declination (**Dec.** or **d**) is angular distance north or south of the celestial equator (d in fig. 1428a). It is measured along an hour circle, from 0° at the celestial equator through 90° at the celestial poles, and is labeled N or S to indicate the direction of measurement. All points having the same declination lie along a **parallel of declination.**

Polar distance (**p**) is angular distance from a celestial pole, or the arc of an hour circle between the celestial pole and a point on the celestial sphere. It is measured along an hour circle and may vary from 0° to 180°, since either pole may be used as the origin of measurement. It is usually considered the complement of declination, though it may be either 90°−d or 90°+d, depending upon the pole used.

Local hour angle (**LHA**) is angular distance west of the local celestial meridian, or the arc of the celestial equator between the upper branch of the local celestial meridian and the hour circle through a point on the celestial sphere, measured westward from the local celestial meridian, through 360°. It is also the similar arc of the parallel of declination and the angle at the celestial pole, similarly measured. If the Greenwich (0°) meridian is used as the reference, instead of the local meridian, the expression **Green-**

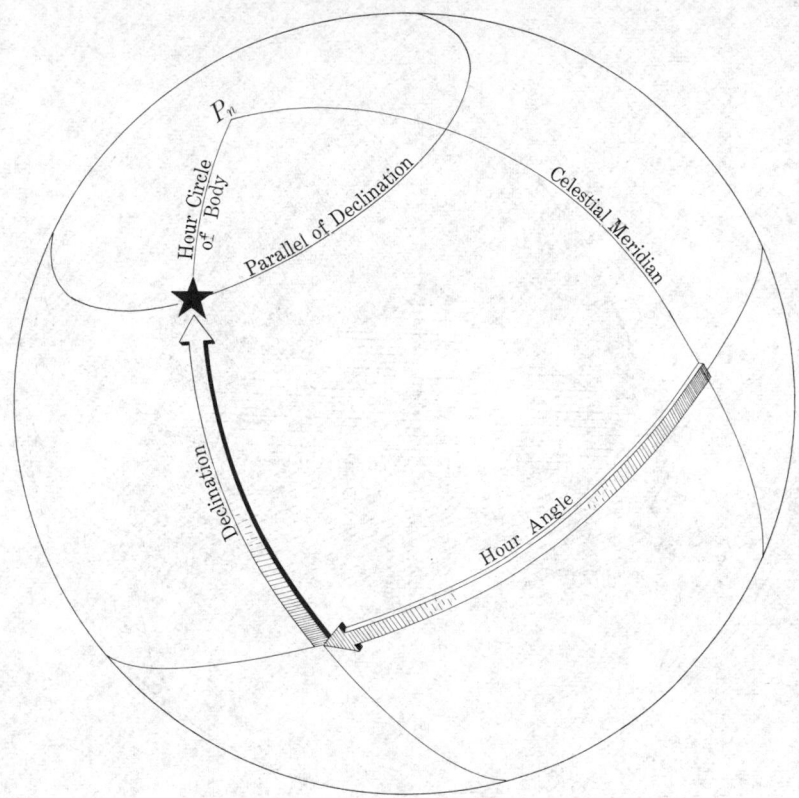

FIGURE 1426c.—A point on the celestial sphere can be located by its declination and hour angle.

wich hour angle (**GHA**) is applied. It is sometimes convenient to measure the arc or angle in *either* an easterly or westerly direction from the local meridian, through 180°, when it is called **meridian angle** (**t**) and labeled E or W to indicate the direction of measurement. All bodies or other points having the same hour angle lie along the same **hour circle.**

Because of the apparent daily rotation of the celestial sphere, hour angle continually increases, but meridian angle increases from 0° at the celestial meridian to 180°W, which is also 180°E, and then decreases to 0° again. The rate of change for the mean sun (art. 1421) is 15° per hour. The rate of all other bodies except the moon is within 3′ of this value. The average rate of the moon is about 14°.5.

As the celestial sphere rotates, each body crosses each branch of the celestial meridian approximately once a day. This crossing is called **meridian transit** (sometimes called **culmination**). It may be called **upper transit** to indicate crossing of the upper branch of the celestial meridian, and **lower transit** to indicate crossing of the lower branch.

The time diagram shown in figure 1428b illustrates the relationship between the various hour angles and meridian angle. The circle is the celestial equator as seen from above the *South Pole*, with the upper branch of the observer's meridian (P_sM) at the top. The radius P_sG is the Greenwich meridian, $P_s\Upsilon$ the hour circle of the vernal equinox, and P_sS and P_sS' the hour circles of celestial bodies to the *west* and *east*, respectively, of the observer's celestial meridian. Note that when LHA is less than 180°, t is numerically the same and is labeled W, but that when LHA is greater than 180°, t=360°−LHA and is labeled E. In figure 1428b arc *GM* is the longitude, which in

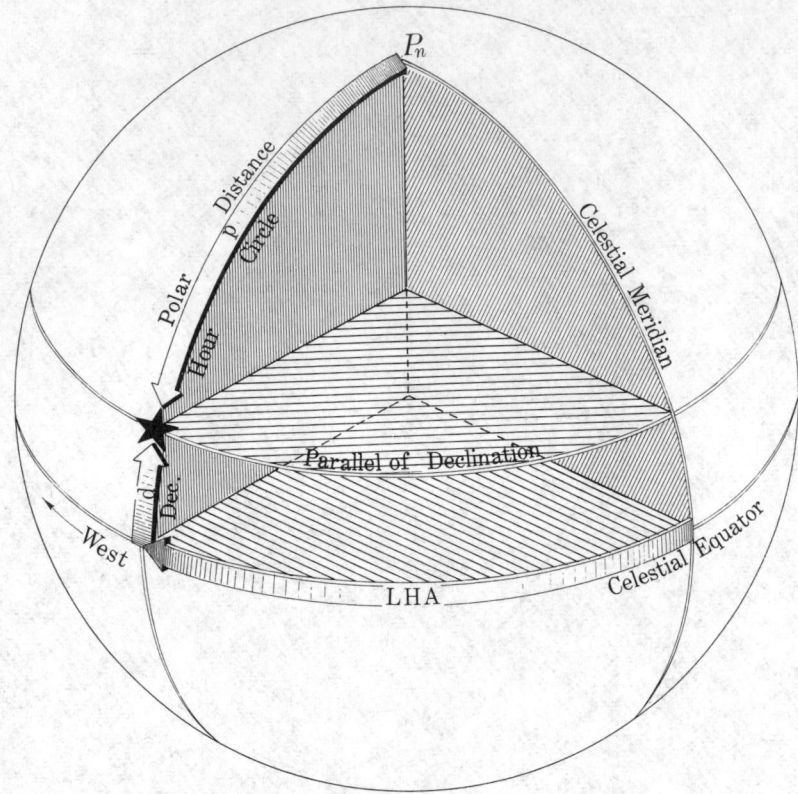

FIGURE 1428a.—The celestial equator system of coordinates, showing measurement of declination, polar distance, and local hour angle.

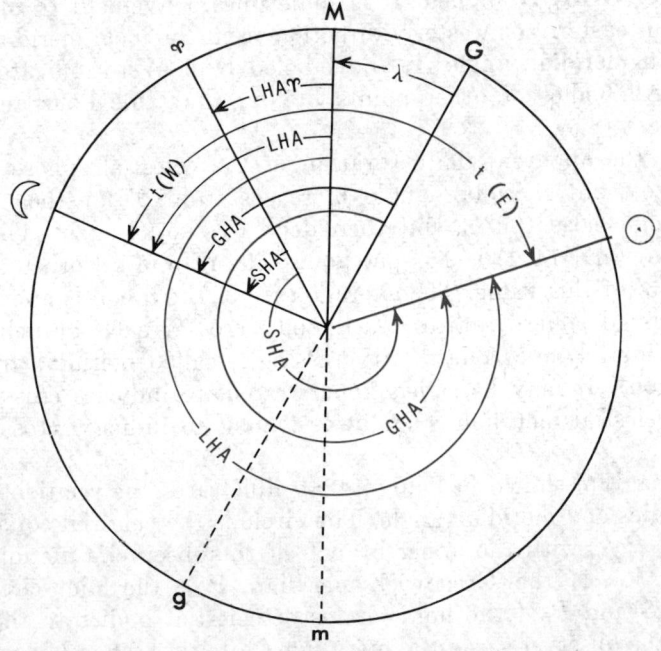

FIGURE 1428b.—Time diagram. Local hour angle, Greenwich hour angle, and sidereal hour angle are measured westward through 360°. Meridian angle is measured eastward or westward through 180° and labeled E or W to indicate the direction of measurement.

this case is west. The relationships shown apply equally to other arrangements of radii, except for relative magnitudes of the quantities involved.

1429. The horizons.—The second set of celestial coordinates with which the navigator is directly concerned is based upon the **horizon** as the primary great circle. However, since several different horizons are defined, these should be thoroughly understood before proceeding with a consideration of the horizon system of coordinates.

The line where earth and sky appear to meet is called the **visible** or **apparent horizon.** On land this is usually an irregular line unless the terrain is level. At sea the visible horizon appears very regular and often very sharp. However, its *position relative to the celestial sphere* depends primarily upon (1) the refractive index of the air, and (2) the height of the observer's eye above the surface.

Figure 1429 shows a cross section of the earth and celestial sphere through the position of an observer at *A* above the surface of the earth. A straight line through *A* and the center of the earth *O* is the vertical of the observer, and contains his zenith (*Z*) and nadir (*Na*). A plane perpendicular to the true vertical is a horizontal plane, and its intersection with the celestial sphere is a horizon. It is the **celestial horizon** if the plane passes through the center of the earth, the **geoidal horizon** if it is tangent to the earth, and the **sensible horizon** if it passes through the eye of the observer at *A*. Since the radius of the earth is considered negligible with respect to that of the celestial sphere, these horizons become superimposed, and most measurements are referred only to the celestial horizon. This is sometimes called the **rational horizon** from the latin word "ratio," reckoning.

If the eye of the observer is at the surface of the earth, his visible horizon coincides with the plane of the geoidal horizon; but when elevated above the surface, as at *A*, his eye becomes the vertex of a cone which, neglecting refraction, is tangent to the earth at the small circle *BB*, and which intersects the celestial sphere in *B'B'*, the **geometrical horizon.** This expression is sometimes—but less appropriately—applied to the celestial horizon.

Because of refraction (art. 1605), the visible horizon *C'C'* appears above but is actually slightly below the geometrical horizon as shown in figure 1429.

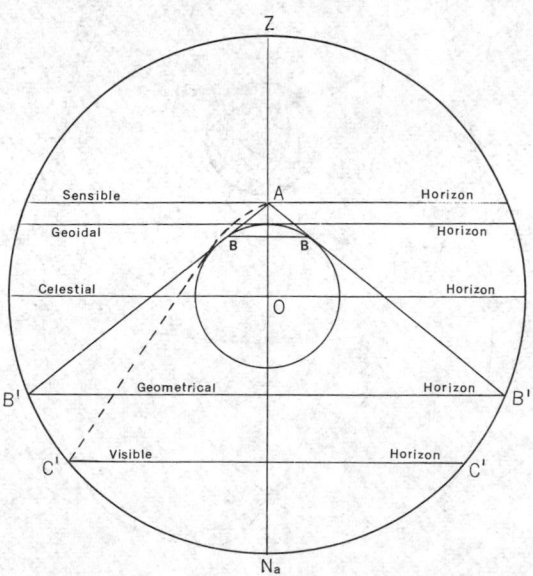

FIGURE 1429.—The horizons used in navigation.

For any elevation above the surface, the celestial horizon is usually *above* the geometrical and visible horizons, the difference increasing as elevation increases. It is thus possible to observe a body which is above the visible horizon but below the celestial horizon. That is, the body's altitude is negative and its zenith distance is greater than 90° (art. 1430).

1430. The horizon system of coordinates is based upon the celestial horizon as the primary great circle, and a series of secondary **vertical circles,** which are great circles through the zenith and nadir of the observer and hence perpendicular to his horizon (fig. 1430a). Thus, the celestial horizon is similar to the equator, and the vertical circles are similar to meridians, but with one important difference. The celestial horizon and vertical circles are dependent upon the position of the observer and hence move with him as he changes position, while the primary and secondary great circles of both the geographical and celestial equator systems are independent of the observer. The horizon and celestial equator systems coincide for an observer at the geographical pole of the earth, and are mutually perpendicular for an observer on the equator. At all other places the two are oblique.

The vertical circle through the north and south points of the horizon passes through the poles of the celestial equator system of coordinates. One of these poles (having the same name as the latitude) is above the horizon and is called the **elevated pole.** The other, called the **depressed pole,** is below the horizon. Since this vertical circle is a great circle through the celestial poles, and includes the zenith of the observer, it is also a celestial meridan. In the horizon system it is called the **principal vertical circle.**

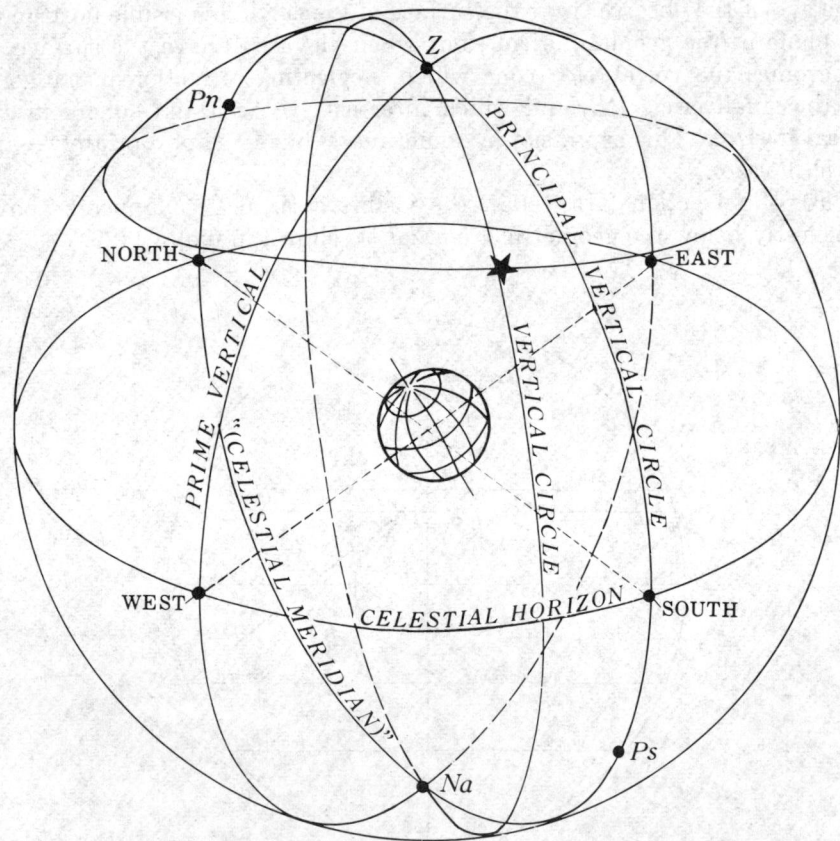

FIGURE 1430a.—Elements of the celestial sphere. The celestial horizon is the primary great circle.

The vertical circle through the east and west points of the horizon, and hence perpendicular to the principal vertical circle, is called the **prime vertical circle,** or simply the **prime vertical.**

As shown in figure 1430b, **altitude** is angular distance above the horizon. It is measured along a vertical circle, from 0° at the horizon through 90° at the zenith. Altitude measured from the visible horizon may exceed 90° because of the dip of the horizon, as shown in figure 1429. Angular distance below the horizon, called **negative altitude,** is provided for by including certain negative altitudes in some tables for use in celestial navigation, such as Pub. No. 249. All points having the same altitude lie along a **parallel of altitude** or **almucantar.**

Zenith distance (z) is angular distance from the zenith, or the arc of a vertical circle between the zenith and a point on the celestial sphere. It is measured along a vertical circle from 0° through 180°. It is usually considered the complement of altitude. For a body above the celestial horizon it is equal to 90°—h and for a body below the celestial horizon it is equal to 90°−(−h) or 90°+h; or 90°+a negative altitude.

The horizontal direction of a point on the celestial sphere, or the bearing of the geographical position is called **azimuth** or **azimuth angle** depending upon the method of measurement. In both methods it is an arc of the horizon (or parallel of altitude) or an angle at the zenith. It is **azimuth (Zn)** if measured clockwise through 360°, starting at the north point on the horizon; and **azimuth angle (Z)** if measured *either* clockwise or counterclockwise through 180°, starting at the north point of the horizon in north latitude and the south point of the horizon in south latitude.

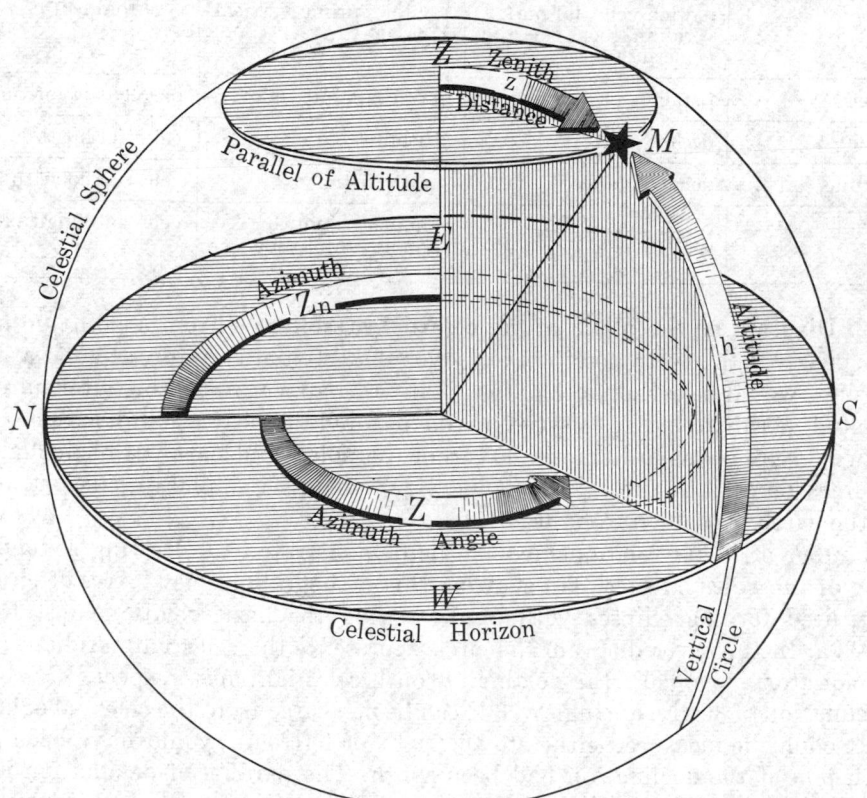

FIGURE 1430b.—The horizon system of coordinates, showing measurement of altitude, zenith distance, azimuth, and azimuth angle.

The **ecliptic system** is based upon the **ecliptic** as the primary great circle, analogous to the equator. The points 90° from the ecliptic are the north and south **ecliptic poles.** The series of great circles through these poles, analogous to meridians, are **circles of latitude.** The circles parallel to the plane of the ecliptic, analogous to parallels on the earth, are **parallels of latitude** or **circles of longitude.** Angular distance north or south of the ecliptic, analogous to latitude, is **celestial latitude. Celestial longitude** is measured *eastward* along the ecliptic through 360°, starting at the vernal equinox. This system of coordinates is of interest chiefly to astronomers. Another system of interest primarily to astronomers is known as the **galactic system.**

1431. Summary of coordinate systems.—The four systems of celestial coordinates are analogous to each other and to the terrestrial system, although each has distinctions such as differences in directions, units, and limits of measurement. The following table indicates the analogous term or terms under each system. For differences, see the description of each system, given earlier in the chapter, or appendix E.

Earth	Celestial Equator	Horizon	Ecliptic
equator	celestial equator	horizon	ecliptic
poles	celestial poles	zenith, nadir	ecliptic poles
meridians	hour circles, celestial meridians	vertical circles	circles of latitude
prime meridian	hour circle ♈, Greenwich celestial meridian, local celestial meridian	principal vertical circle, prime vertical circle	circle of latitude through ♈
parallels	parallels of declination	parallels of altitude	parallels of latitude
latitude	declination	altitude	celestial latitude
colatitude	polar distance	zenith distance	celestial colatitude
longitude	SHA, RA, GHA, LHA, t	azimuth, azimuth angle, amplitude	celestial longitude

1432. Diagram on the plane of the celestial meridian.—From a point outside the celestial sphere (if this were possible) and over the celestial equator, at such a distance that the view would be orthographic, the great circle appearing as the outer limit would be a celestial meridian. Other celestial meridians would appear as ellipses. The celestial equator would appear as a diameter 90° from the poles, and parallels of declination as straight lines parallel to the equator. The view would be similar to the orthographic view of the earth, as shown in figure 319b.

A number of useful relationships can be demonstrated by drawing a **diagram on the plane of the celestial meridian** showing this orthographic view. Arcs of circles can be substituted for the ellipses without destroying the basic relationships. Refer to figure 1432a. In the lower diagram the circle represents the celestial meridian, QQ' the celestial equator, Pn and Ps the north and south celestial poles, respectively. If a star has a declination of 30° N, an angle of 30° can be measured from the celestial equator, as shown. It could be measured either to the right or left, and would have been toward the south pole if the declination had been south. The parallel of declination is a line through this point and parallel to the celestial equator. The star is somewhere on this line (actually a circle viewed on edge).

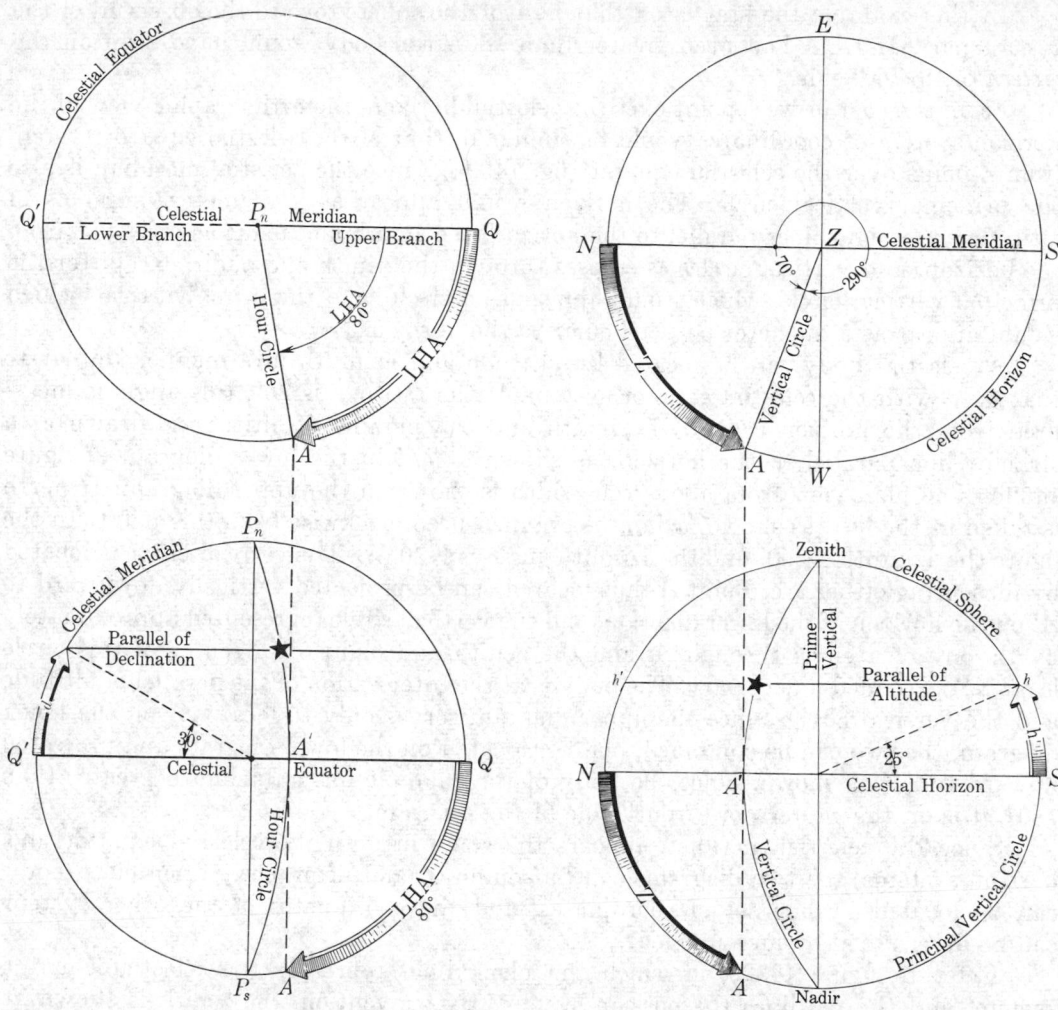

FIGURE 1432a.—Measurement of celestial
equator system of coordinates.

FIGURE 1432b.—Measurement of horizon
system of coordinates.

To locate the hour circle, draw the upper diagram so that Pn is directly above
Pn of the lower figure (in line with the polar axis Pn Ps), and the circle is of the same diameter as that of the lower figure. This is the plan view, looking down on the celestial
sphere from the top. The circle is the celestial equator. Since the view is from above
the *north* celestial pole, west is clockwise. The diameter QQ' is the celestial meridian
shown as a circle in the lower diagram. If the *right* half is considered the upper branch,
local hour angle is measured clockwise from this line to the hour circle, as shown. In
this case the LHA is 80°. The intersection of the hour circle and celestial equator,
point A, can be projected down to the lower diagram (point A') by a straight line parallel
to the polar axis. The elliptical hour circle can be represented approximately by an
arc of a circle through A', Pn, Ps. The center of this circle is somewhere along the
celestial equator line QQ', extended if necessary. It is usually found by trial and error.
The intersection of the hour circle and parallel of declination locates the star.

Since the upper diagram serves only to locate point A' in the lower diagram, the
two can be combined. That is, the LHA arc can be drawn in the lower diagram, as
shown, and point A projected *upward* to A'. In practice, the upper diagram is not
drawn, being shown here for illustrative purposes only.

In this example the star is on that half of the sphere toward the observer, or the *western* part. If LHA had been greater than 180°, the body would have been on the *eastern* or "back" side.

From the east or west point over the celestial horizon, the orthographic view of the horizon system of coordinates would be similar to that of the celestial equator system from a point over the celestial equator (fig. 1432a), since the celestial meridian is also the principal vertical circle. The horizon would appear as a diameter, parallels of altitude as straight lines parallel to the horizon, the zenith and nadir as poles 90° from the horizon, and vertical circles as ellipses through the zenith and nadir, except for the principal vertical circle, which would appear as a circle, and the prime vertical, which would appear as a diameter perpendicular to the horizon.

A celestial body can be located by altitude and azimuth in a manner similar to that used with the celestial equator system. If the altitude is 25°, this angle is measured from the horizon toward the zenith and the parallel of altitude is drawn as a straight line parallel to the horizon, as shown at *hh'* in the lower diagram of figure 1432b. The plan view from above the zenith is shown in the upper diagram. If north is taken at the left, as shown, azimuths are measured clockwise from this point. In the figure the azimuth is 290° and the azimuth angle is N70°W. The vertical circle is located by measuring either arc. Point *A* thus located can be projected vertically downward to *A'* on the horizon of the lower diagram, and the vertical circle represented approximately by the arc of a circle through *A'* and the zenith and nadir. The center of this circle is on *NS*, extended if necessary. The body is at the intersection of the parallel of altitude and the vertical circle. Since the upper diagram serves only to locate *A'* on the lower diagram, the two can be combined, point *A* located on the lower diagram and projected upward to *A'*, as shown. Since the body of the example has an azimuth greater than 180°, it is on the western or "front" side of the diagram.

Since the celestial meridian appears the same in both the celestial equator and horizon systems, the two diagrams can be combined and, if properly oriented, a body can be located by one set of coordinates, and the coordinates of the other system can be determined by measurement.

Refer to figure 1432c, in which the black lines represent the celestial equator system, and the red lines the horizon system. By convention, the zenith is shown at the top and the north point of the horizon at the left. The west point on the horizon is at the center, and the east point directly behind it. In the figure the latitude is 37°N. Therefore, the zenith is 37° north of the celestial equator. Since the zenith is established at the top of the diagram, the equator can be found by measuring an arc of 37° toward the south, along the celestial meridian. If the declination is 30°N and the LHA is 80°, the body can be located as shown by the black lines, and described above.

The altitude and azimuth can be determined by the reverse process to that described above. Draw a line *hh'* through the body and parallel to the horizon, *NS*. The altitude, 25°, is found by measurement, as shown. Draw the arc of a circle through the body and the zenith and nadir. From *A'*, the intersection of this arc with the horizon, draw a vertical line intersecting the circle at *A*. The azimuth, N70°W, is found by measurement, as shown. The prefix N is applied to agree with the latitude. The body is left (*north*) of *ZNa*, the prime vertical circle. The suffix W applies because the LHA, 80°, shows that the body is west of the meridian.

If altitude and azimuth are given, the body is located by means of the red lines. The parallel of declination is then drawn parallel to *QQ'*, the celestial equator, and the declination determined by measurement. Point *L'* is located by drawing the arc of a circle through *Pn*, the star, and *Ps*. From *L'* a line is drawn perpendicular to *QQ'*,

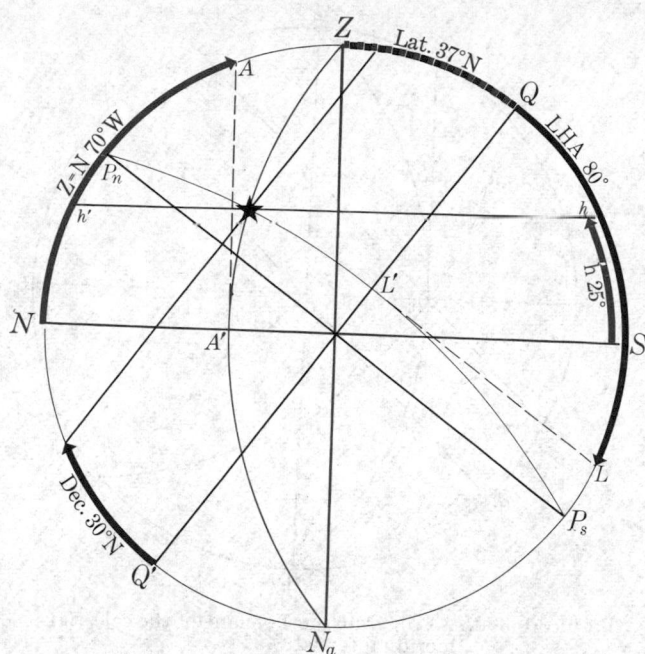

FIGURE 1432c.—Diagram on the plane of the celestial meridian.

locating L. The meridian angle is then found by measurement. The declination is known to be north because the body is between the celestial equator and the north celestial pole. The meridian angle is west to agree with the azimuth, and hence LHA is numerically the same.

Since QQ' and $PnPs$ are perpendicular, and ZNa and NS are also perpendicular, arc NPn is equal to arc ZQ. That is, *the altitude of the elevated pole is equal to the declination of the zenith, which is equal to the latitude.* This relationship is the basis of the method of determining latitude by an observation of Polaris (art. 2105).

The diagram on the plane of the celestial meridian is useful in approximating a number of relationships. Consider figure 1432d. The latitude of the observer (NPn or ZQ) is 45°N. The declination of the sun ($Q4$) is 20°N. Neglecting the change in declination for one day, note the following: At sunrise, position 1, the sun is on the horizon (NS), at the "back" of the diagram. Its altitude, h, is 0°. Its azimuth angle, Z, is the arc NA, N63°E. This is prefixed N to agree with the latitude and suffixed E to agree with the meridian angle of the sun at sunrise. Hence, Zn=0°+63°=063°. The amplitude, A, is the arc ZA, E27°N. The meridian angle, t, is the arc QL, 110°E. The suffix E is applied because the sun is east of the meridian at rising. The LHA is 360°−110°=250°.

As the sun moves upward along its parallel of declination, its altitude increases. It reaches position 2 at about 0600, when t=90°E. At position 3 it is on the prime vertical, ZNa. Its azimuth angle, Z, is N90°E, and Zn=090°. The altitude is Nh' or Sh, 27°.

Moving on up its parallel of declination, it arrives at position 4 on the celestial meridian about noon—when t and LHA are both 0°, by definition. On the celestial meridian a body's azimuth is 000° or 180°. In this case it is 180° because the body is south of the zenith. The maximum altitude occurs at meridian transit, in this case the arc $S4$, 65°. The zenith distance, z, is the arc $Z4$, 25°. A body is not in the zenith

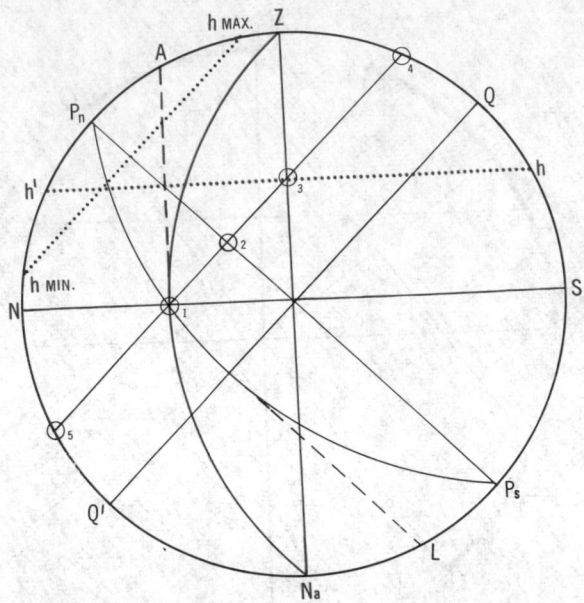

FIGURE 1432d.—A diagram on the plane of the celestial
meridian for lat. 45° N.

at meridian transit unless its declination is numerically, and by name, the same as the latitude.

Continuing on, the sun moves downward along the "front" or western side of the diagram. At position 3 it is again on the prime vertical. The altitude is the same as when previously on the prime vertical, and the azimuth angle is numerically the same, but now measured toward the west. The azimuth is 270°. The sun reaches position 2 six hours after meridian transit, and sets at position 1, when the azimuth angle is numerically the same as at sunrise, but westerly, and Zn=360°−63°=297°. The amplitude is W27°N.

After sunset the sun continues on downward along its parallel of declination until it reaches position 5, on the lower branch of the celestial meridian, about midnight. Its negative altitude, arc N5, is now greatest, 25°, and its azimuth is 000°. At this point it starts back up along the "back" of the diagram, arriving at position 1 at the next sunrise, to start another cycle.

Half the cycle is from the crossing of the 90° hour circle (the $PnPs$ line, position 2) to the upper branch of the celestial meridian (position 4) and back to the $PnPs$ line (position 2). When the declination and latitude have the **same name** (both north or both south), more than half the parallel of declination (position 1 to 4 to 1) is above the horizon, and the body is above the horizon more than half the time, crossing the 90° hour circle above the horizon. It rises and sets on the same side of the prime vertical as the elevated pole. If the declination is of the same name but numerically smaller than the latitude, the body crosses the prime vertical above the horizon. If the declination and latitude have the same name and are numerically equal, the body is in the zenith at upper transit. If the declination is of the same name but numerically *greater* than the latitude, the body crosses the upper branch of the celestial meridian between the zenith and elevated pole, and does not cross the prime vertical. If the declination is of the same name as the latitude and complementary to it (d+L=90°), the body is on the horizon at lower transit, and does not set. If the declination is of the same name as the latitude and numerically *greater* than the colatitude, the body is above the horizon during its entire daily cycle, and has maximum and minimum altitudes, as shown by the black dotted line in figure 1432d.

If the declination is 0° at any latitude, the body is above the horizon half the time, following the celestial equator QQ', and rising and setting on the prime vertical. If the declination is of **contrary name** (one north and the other south), the body is above the horizon less than half the time, and crosses the 90° hour circle below the horizon. It rises and sets on the opposite side of the prime vertical from the elevated pole. If the declination is of contrary name and numerically smaller than the latitude, the body crosses the prime vertical below the horizon. This is the situation with the sun in winter, when days are short. If the declination is of contrary name and numerically equal to the latitude, the body is in the nadir at lower transit. If the declination is of contrary name and complementary to the latitude, the body is on the horizon at upper transit. If the declination is of contrary name and numerically greater than the co-latitude, the body does not rise.

All of these relationships, and those that follow, can be derived by means of a diagram on the plane of the celestial meridian. They are modified slightly by atmospheric refraction, height of eye, semidiameter, parallax, changes in declination, and apparent speed of the body along its diurnal circle.

It is customary to keep the same orientation in south latitude, as shown in figure 1432e. In this illustration the latitude is 45°S, and the declination of the body is 15°N. Since Ps is the elevated pole, it is shown above the southern horizon, with both SPs and ZQ equal to the latitude, 45°. The body rises at position 1, on the opposite side of the prime vertical from the elevated pole; moves upward along its parallel of declination to position 2, on the upper branch of the celestial meridian, bearing north; and then downward along the "front" of the diagram to position 1, where it sets; remaining above the horizon for less than half the time because declination and latitude are of contrary name. The azimuth at rising is arc NA, the amplitude ZA, and the azimuth angle SA. The altitude circle at meridian transit is shown at hh'.

A diagram on the plane of the celestial meridian can be used to demonstrate the effect of a change in latitude. As the latitude increases, the celestial equator becomes more nearly parallel to the horizon. The colatitude becomes smaller, increasing the number of circumpolar bodies and those which neither rise nor set, and also increasing the difference in the length of the days between summer and winter. At the poles (fig. 1416b), celestial bodies circle the sky, parallel to the horizon. At the equator (fig. 1416a) the 90° hour circle coincides with the horizon. Bodies rise and set vertically; and are above the horizon half the time. At rising and setting the amplitude is equal to the declination. At meridian transit the altitude is equal to the codeclination. As the latitude changes name, the same-contrary name relationship with declination reverses. This accounts for the fact that one hemisphere has winter while the other is having summer.

The error arising from showing the hour circles and vertical circles as arcs of circles instead of ellipses increases with increased declination or altitude. More accurate results can be obtained by measurement of azimuth on the parallel of altitude instead of the horizon, and of hour angle on the parallel of declination instead of the celestial equator. Refer to figure 1432f. The vertical circle shown is for a body having an azimuth angle of S60°W. The arc of a circle is shown in black, and the ellipse in red. The black arc is obtained by measurement around the horizon, locating A' by means of A, as previously described. The intersection of this arc with the altitude circle at 60° places the body at M. If a semicircle is drawn with the altitude circle as a diameter, and the azimuth angle measured around this, to B, a perpendicular to the hour circle locates the body at M', on the ellipse. By this method the altitude circle, rather than the hori-

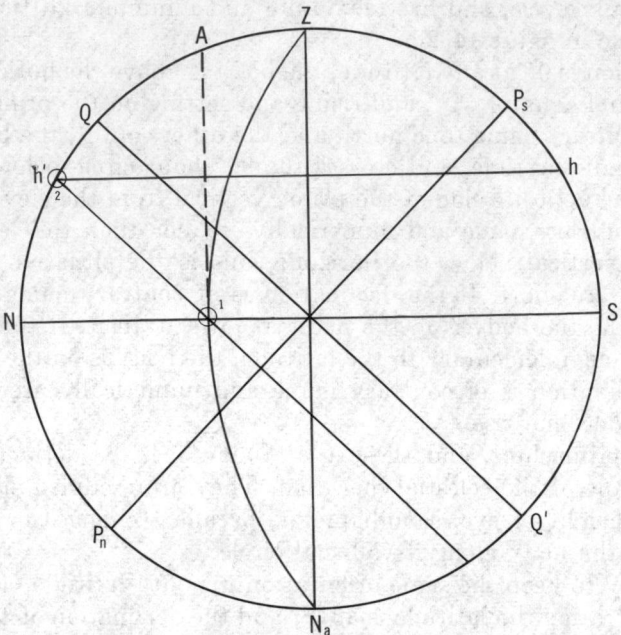

FIGURE 1432e.—A diagram on the plane of the celestial
meridian for lat. 45° S.

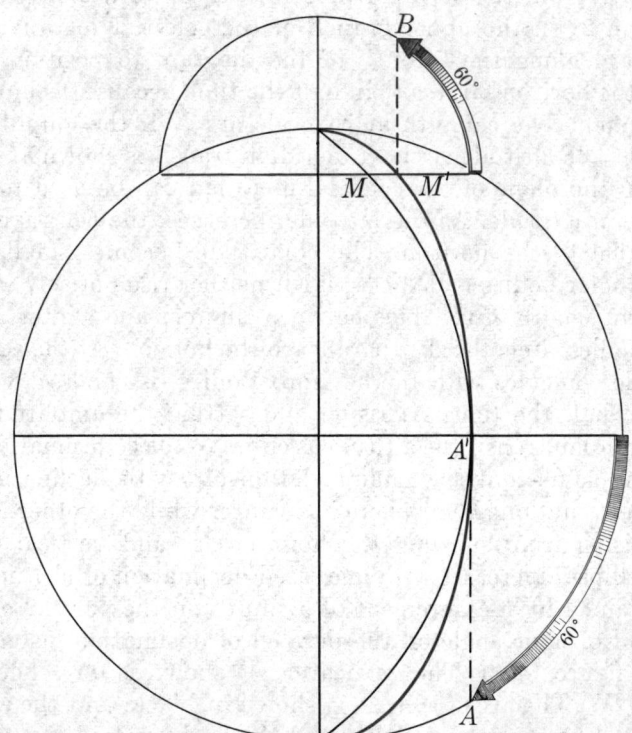

FIGURE 1432f.—Locating a point on an ellipse of a diagram
on the plane of the celestial meridian.

zon, is, in effect, rotated through 90° for the measurement. This refinement is seldom used because actual values are usually found mathematically, the diagram on the plane of the meridian being used primarily to indicate relationships.

With experience, one may mentally visualize the diagram on the plane of the celestial meridian without making an actual drawing. Devices with two sets of spherical coordinates, on either the orthographic (art. 319) or stereographic (art. 318) projection, pivoted at the center, have been produced commercially to provide a mechanical diagram on the plane of the celestial meridian. However, since the diagram's principal use is to illustrate certain relationships, such a device is not a necessary part of the navigator's equipment.

1433. The navigational triangle.—A triangle formed by arcs of great circles of a sphere is called a **spherical triangle.** A spherical triangle on the celestial sphere is called a **celestial triangle.** The spherical triangle of particular significance to navigators is called the **navigational triangle.** It is formed by arcs of a celestial meridian, an hour circle, and a vertical circle. Its vertices are the elevated pole, the zenith, and a point on the celestial sphere (usually a celestial body). The terrestrial counterpart is also called a navigational triangle, being formed by arcs of two meridians and the great circle connecting two places on the earth, one on each meridian. The vertices are the two places and a pole. In great-circle sailing these places are the point of departure and the destination. In celestial navigation they are the **assumed position** (**AP**) of the observer and the **geographical position** (**GP**) of the body (the place having the body in its zenith). The GP of the sun is sometimes called the **subsolar point,** that of the moon the **sublunar point,** that of a satellite (either natural or artificial) the **subsatellite point,** and that of a star its **substellar** or **subastral point.** When used to solve a celestial observation, either the celestial or terrestrial triangle may be called the **astronomical triangle.**

The navigational triangle is shown in figure 1433a on a diagram on the plane of the celestial meridian, labeled as in article 1432, but with the hour circle and vertical circle properly shown as ellipses. The earth is at the center, O. The star is at M, dd' is its parallel of declination, and hh' its altitude circle.

In the figure, arc QZ of the celestial meridian is the latitude of the observer, and PnZ, one side of the triangle, is the **colatitude.** Arc AM of the vertical circle is the altitude of the body, and side ZM of the triangle is the zenith distance, or **coaltitude.** Arc LM of the hour circle is the declination of the body, and side PnM of the triangle is the polar distance, or **codeclination.**

The angle at the elevated pole, $ZPnM$, having the hour circle and the celestial meridian as sides, is the meridian angle, t. The angle at the zenith, $PnZM$, having the vertical circle and that arc of the celestial meridian which includes the elevated pole as sides, is the azimuth angle. The angle at the celestial body, $ZMPn$, having the hour circle and the vertical circle as sides, is the **parallactic angle** (**X**) (sometimes called the **position angle**), which is not generally used by the navigator.

A number of problems involving the navigational triangle are encountered by the navigator, either directly or indirectly. Of these, the most common are:

1. Given latitude, declination, and meridian angle, to find altitude and azimuth angle. This is used in the reduction of a celestial observation, to establish a line of position (ch. XX).

2. Given latitude, altitude, and azimuth angle, to find declination and meridian angle. This is used to identify an unknown celestial body (ch. XXII).

3. Given meridian angle, declination, and altitude, to find azimuth angle. This may be used to find azimuth when the altitude is known (ch. XX).

4. Given the latitude of two places on the earth and the difference of longitude between them, to find the initial great-circle course and the great-circle distance (ch.

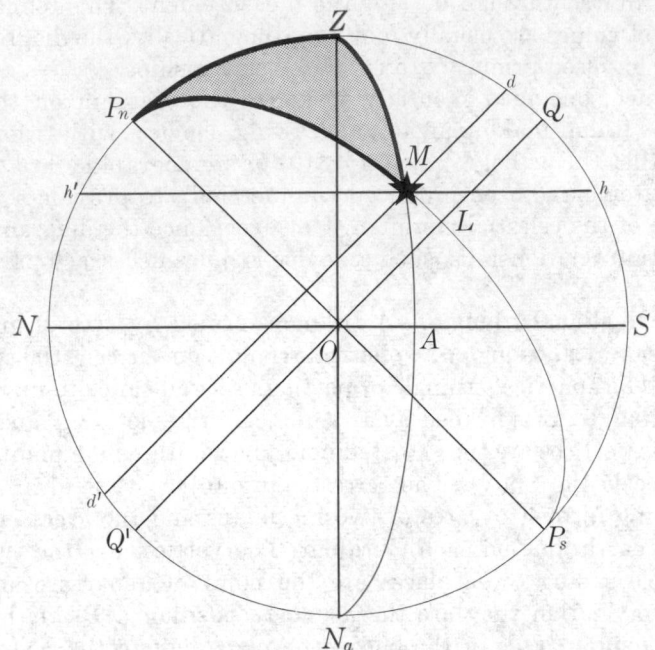

FIGURE 1433a.—The navigational triangle.

IX). This involves the same parts of the triangle as in 1, above, but in the terrestrial triangle, and hence defined differently.

Both celestial and terrestrial navigational triangles are shown in perspective in figure 1433b.

Problems

1428. *Given.*—An observer is at longitude 77°E. The sun is 60° east of the meridian. GHA ♈ is 37°.

Required.—(1) LHA of the sun.

(2) GHA of the sun.

(3) SHA of the sun.

(4) Approximate time at the local meridian.

Answers.—(1) LHA 300°, (2) 223°, (3) SHA 186°, (4) T 0800.

1430a. *Required.*—Convert Z to Zn in the following:

(1) N174°E	(4) S39°E
(2) S1°E	(5) N106°W
(3) S90°W	(6) N90°W

Answers.—(1) Zn 174°, (2) Zn 179°, (3) Zn 270°, (4) Zn 141°, (5) Zn 254°, (6) Zn 270°.

1430b. *Required.*—Convert Zn to Z in the following, using the 180° system:

Zn	Lat.		Zn	Lat.
(1) 214°	N		(4) 333°	S
(2) 163°	S		(5) 206°	N
(3) 007°	N		(6) 206°	S

Answers.—(1) Z N146°W, (2) Z S17°E, (3) Z N7°E, (4) Z S153°W, (5) Z N154°W, (6) Z S26°W.

1430c. *Required.*—Convert Zn to Z in the following, using the 90° system:

(1) 051°	(3) 251°
(2) 151°	(4) 351°

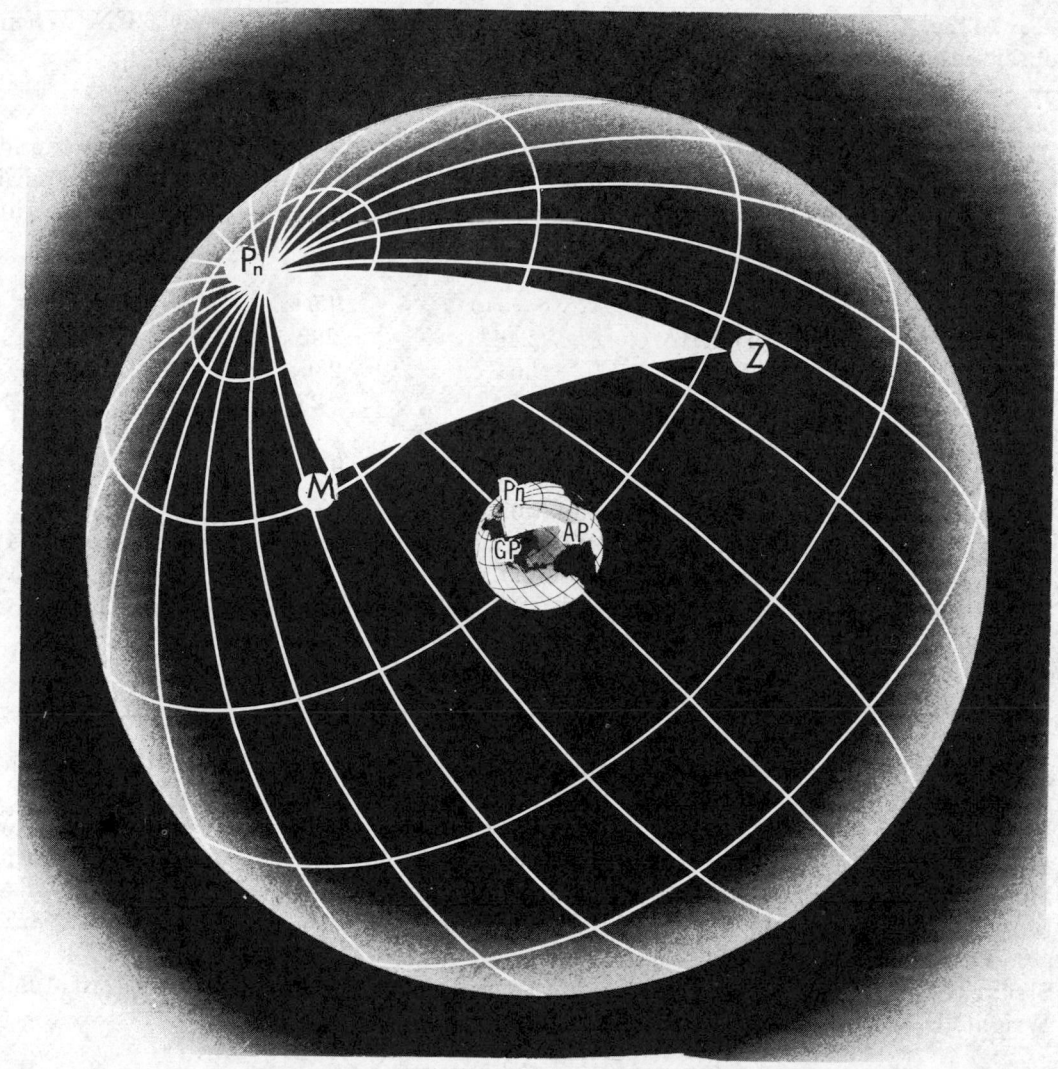

FIGURE 1433b.—The navigational triangle in perspective.

Answers.—(1) Z N51°E, (2) Z S29°E, (3) Z S71°W, (4) Z N9°W.

Solve the following problems by diagrams on the plane of the celestial meridian:

1432a. *Given.*—L 32°N, t 71°W, d 27°N.

Required.—Altitude and azimuth.

Answers.—h 28°, Zn 288°.

1432b. *Given.*—L 17°S, t 64°E, d 28°S.

Required.—Altitude and azimuth.

Answers.—h 28°, Zn 115°.

1432c. *Given.*—L 59°N, h 27°, Zn 052°.

Required.—Declination and meridian angle.

Answers.—d 41°N, t 111°E.

1432d. *Given.*—L 31°N, declination of sun 18°S.

Required.—(1) Azimuth at sunrise, (2) maximum altitude, (3) altitude when the azimuth is 234°, (4) azimuth angle when the altitude in the afternoon is 10°, (5) amplitude at sunset.

Answers.—(1) Zn 111°, (2) h 41°, (3) h 18°, (4) Z N118°W, (5) A W21°S.

1432e. *Given.*—The declination of the star Dubhe is approximately 62°N. When observed at lower transit, its altitude is 43°.

Required.—(1) Latitude of the observer, (2) azimuth at upper transit.

Answers.—(1) L 71°N, (2) Zn 180°.

1432f. *Required.*—For an observer at latitude 39°N, find for the sun at summer and winter solstices, respectively: (1) LHA at sunrise, (2) LHA when on the prime vertical during the morning, (3) maximum altitude, (4) LHA at sunset, (5) length of daylight if the sun moves 15° per hour.

Answers.—

		Summer	*Winter*
(1)	LHA	248°	292°
(2)	LHA	304°	236° (below horizon)
(3)	h	74°	28°
(4)	LHA	112°	68°
(5)	T	14^h56^m	9^h04^m

1432g. *Given.*—L 83°N, sun's declination 4°S.

Required.—(1) LHA at sunrise, (2) maximum altitude, (3) LHA at sunset, (4) length of daylight (sun moving 15° per hour).

Answers.—(1) LHA 305°, (2) max h 3°, (3) LHA 55°, (4) T 7^h20^m.

References

ELEMENTARY

Abell, G. O. *Exploration of the Universe.* 3rd ed. New York, Holt, Rinehart and Winston, 1975.

Alter, D., and C. H. Cleminshaw. *Pictorial Astronomy.* New York, Crowell, 1952.

Baker, R. H. *An Introduction to Astronomy.* 6th ed. Princeton, Van Nostrand, 1961.

Hood, P. *Observing the Heavens.* New York, Oxford, 1951.

Mayall, R. N., and M. W. Mayall. *A Beginner's Guide to the Skies.* New York, Putnam, 1960.

Struve, O., B. Lynds, and H. Pillans. *Elementary Astronomy.* New York, Oxford, 1959.

Wright, H. *Palomar.* New York, Macmillan, 1952.

ADVANCED

Baker, R. H. *Astronomy.* 8th ed. Princeton, Van Nostrand, 1964.

Brouwer, D., and G. M. Clemence. *Methods of Celestial Mechanics.* New York, Academic, 1961.

Jones, Sir Harold Spencer. *General Astronomy.* 4th ed. New York, Longmans, 1961.

Krogdahl, W. S. *The Astronomical Universe.* New York, Macmillan, 1952.

Rudaux, L., and G. De Vaucouleurs. *Larousse Encyclopedia of Astronomy.* New York. Prometheus, 1959.

Russell, H. N., R. S. Dugan, and J. Q. Stewart. *Astronomy.* Vol. I, *The Solar System.* Rev. ed. 1945. Vol. II, *Astrophysics and Stellar Astronomy.* Boston, Ginn, 1938.

CHAPTER XV

INSTRUMENTS FOR CELESTIAL NAVIGATION

1501. The marine sextant is a hand-held instrument for measuring the angle between the lines of sight to two points by bringing into coincidence at the eye of the observer the direct ray from one point, and a double-reflected ray from the other, the measured angle being twice the angle between the reflecting surfaces. Its principal use is to measure the altitudes of celestial bodies above the visible sea horizon. Sometimes it is turned on its side and used for measuring the *difference* in bearing of two terrestrial objects. Because of its great value for determining position at sea, the sextant has been a symbol of navigation for more than 200 years. The quality of his instrument, the care he gives it, and the skill with which he makes observations are to the navigator matters of professional pride.

The name "sextant" is from the Latin *sextans*, "the sixth part." The arc of early marine sextants is approximately the sixth part of a circle, but because of the optical principle involved (art. 1502), the instrument measures angles of 120°. Most modern instruments measure something more than this.

1502. Optical principles.—When a ray of light is reflected from a plane surface, the **angle of reflection** is equal to the **angle of incidence** (fig. 1502a). From optics the angle between the first and final directions of a ray of light that has undergone double reflection in the same plane is twice the angle that the two reflecting surfaces make with each other (fig. 1502b).

In figure 1502b, *AB* is a ray of light from a celestial body. The index mirror of the sextant is at *B*, the horizon glass at *C*, and the eye of the observer at *D*. Construction lines *EF* and *CF* are perpendicular to the index mirror and horizon glass, respectively, and lines *BG* and *CG* are parallel to these mirrors. Therefore, angles *BFC* and *BGC* are equal because their sides are mutually perpendicular (art. 127, vol. II). Angle *BGC* is, the inclination of the two reflecting surfaces. The ray of light *AB* is reflected at mirror *B*,

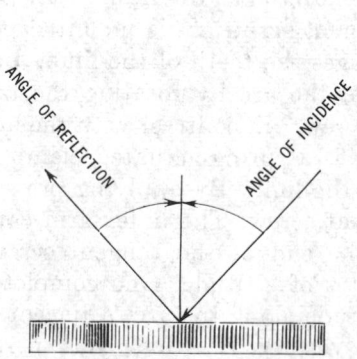

FIGURE 1502a.—Angle of reflection equals angle of incidence.

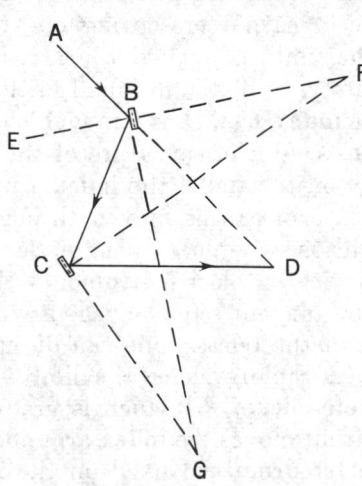

FIGURE 1502b.—Optical principle of the marine sextant.

391

proceeds to mirror C, where it is again reflected, and then continues on to the eye of the observer at D. Since the angle of reflection is equal to the angle of incidence,

$$ABE = EBC, \text{ and } ABC = 2EBC$$
$$BCF = FCD, \text{ and } BCD = 2BCF.$$

Since an exterior angle of a triangle equals the sum of the two nonadjacent interior angles (art. 128, vol. II),

$$ABC = BDC + BCD, \text{ and } EBC = BFC + BCF.$$

Transposing,

$$BDC = ABC - BCD, \text{ and } BFC = EBC - BCF.$$

Substituting $2EBC$ for ABC, and $2BCF$ for BCD in the first of these equations,

$$BDC = 2EBC - 2BCF, \text{ or } BDC = 2(EBC - BCF).$$

Since

$$BFC = EBC - BCF, \text{ and } BFC = BGC,$$

therefore

$$BDC = 2BFC = 2BGC.$$

That is, BDC, the angle between the first and last directions of the ray of light, is equal to $2BGC$, twice the angle of inclination of the reflecting surfaces. Angle BDC is the altitude of the celestial body.

If the two mirrors are parallel, the incident ray from any observed body must be parallel to the observer's line of sight through the horizon glass; i.e., the altitude of the body is zero. Accordingly, the 0° graduation on the arc coincides with that position of the index arm when the index mirror is parallel to the horizon glass. Since the angle that these two reflecting surfaces make with each other is one-half the angle actually observed, the arc is so graduated that 10° of arc on the limb is labelled 20°, 20° of arc is labelled 40°, etc.

1503. Micrometer drum sextant.—A modern marine sextant, called a **micrometer drum sextant,** is shown in figure 1503a. In most marine sextants, the **frame,** A, is made of brass or aluminum. There are several variations of the design of the frame, nearly all conforming generally to that shown. The **limb,** B, is cut on its outer edge with teeth, each representing one degree of celestial altitude. The altitude graduations, C, along the limb, are called the **arc.** Some sextants have an arc marked in a strip of brass, silver, or platinum inlaid in the limb.

The **index arm,** D, is a movable bar of the same material as the frame. It is pivoted about the center of curvature of the limb. The **tangent screw,** E, is mounted perpendicularly on the end of the index arm, where it engages the teeth of the limb. Because the index arm can be moved through the length of the arc by rotating the tangent screw, this is sometimes called an "endless tangent screw," in contrast with the limited-range device on older instruments. The **release,** F, is a spring-actuated clamp which keeps the tangent screw engaged with the teeth of the limb. By applying pressure on the legs of the release, one can disengage the tangent screw. The index arm can then be moved rapidly along the limb. Mounted on the end of the tangent screw is a **micrometer drum,** G, which is graduated in minutes of altitude. One complete turn of the drum moves the index arm one degree of altitude along the arc. Adjacent to the micrometer drum and fixed on the index arm is a **vernier,** H, which aids in reading fractions of a minute. The vernier shown is graduated into ten parts, permitting readings to six seconds. Other sextants (generally of European manufacture) have verniers

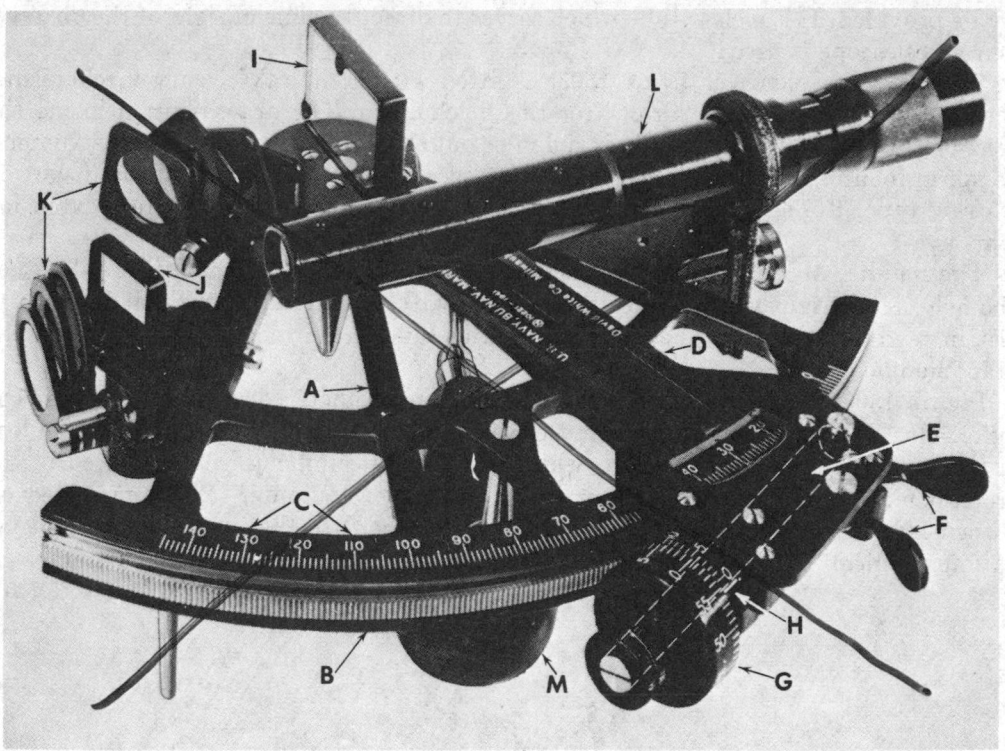

FIGURE 1503a.—U. S. Navy Mark 2 micrometer drum sextant.

graduated into only five parts, permitting readings to 12 seconds.

The **index mirror,** *I,* is a piece of silvered plate glass mounted on the index arm, perpendicular to the plane of the instrument, with the center of the reflecting surface directly over the pivot of the index arm. The **horizon glass,** *J,* is a piece of optical glass silvered on its half nearer the frame. It is mounted on the frame, perpendicular to the plane of the sextant. The index mirror and horizon glass are mounted so that their surfaces are parallel when the micrometer drum is set at 0°, if the instrument is in perfect adjustment. **Shade glasses,** *K,* of varying or variable darkness, are mounted on the frame of the sextant in front of the index mirror and horizon glass. They can be moved into the line of sight at will, to reduce the intensity of light reaching the eye of the observer. Some sextants have two sets of shade glasses, as shown in figure 1504.

The **telescope,** *L,* screws into an adjustable collar in line with the horizon glass, and should then be parallel to the plane of the instrument. Most modern sextants are provided with only one telescope, but some are equipped with two or more. When only one telescope is provided, it is of the "erect image type," either such as shown or one with a wider "object glass" (far end of telescope), which generally is shorter in length and gives a greater field of view. The second telescope, if provided, may be the "inverting type." The inverting telescope, having one lens less than the erect type, absorbs less light, but at the expense of producing an inverted image. A small colored glass cap is sometimes provided, to be placed over the "eyepiece" (near end of telescope) to reduce the glare. With this in place, shade glasses are generally not needed. A "peep sight" may be provided. It is a clear tube which serves to direct the line of sight of the observer when no telescope is used.

The telescope shown in figure 1503a is fitted with a "spiral focusing mechanism." Other sextants substitute a "draw" for this mechanism. The draw is fitted inside the telescope tube without threads and is slid in or out as necessary to focus the instrument. The spiral focusing mechanism is easily adjusted each time the sextant is used, but on the draw type, the navigator should mark the draw to indicate the correct extension for his eyes.

The **handle,** *M*, of most sextants is made of wood or plastic. Sextants are designed to be held in the right hand. Some are equipped with a small light on the index arm to assist in reading altitudes. The batteries for this light are fitted inside a recess in the sextant handle.

Figure 1503b shows the U. S. Navy Mark 3 micrometer drum sextant from the handle side. This figure shows parts not clearly shown in figure 1503a, such as the legs and the tangent screw. This sextant, which is generally similar to sextants used in the merchant marine, is fitted with a four power telescope. A diopter scale is provided on the focusing mechanism of the telescope for adjustment to the individual user's eye. The "anatomical" handle is designed for decreased arm fatigue and hand tremor. A

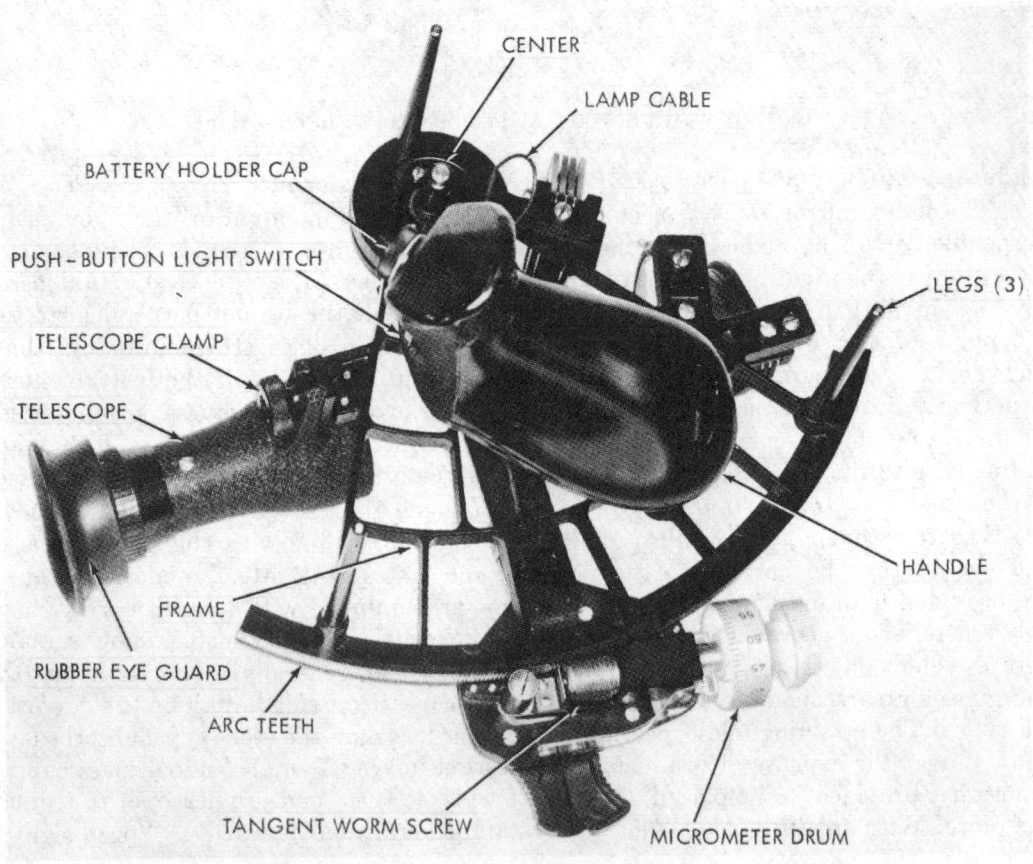

FIGURE 1503b.—U. S. Navy Mark 3 micrometer drum sextant.

light switch and batteries are conveniently located in the handle. Large coated optics are provided for more light transmission and improved field of view, resolution, and magnification.

There are two basic designs commonly used for mounting and adjusting mirrors on marine sextants. On the U. S. Navy Mark 3 and other sextants, the mirror is mounted so that it can be moved against retaining or mounting springs within its frame. Only one perpendicular adjustment screw is required. On the U. S. Navy Mark 2 and other sextants the mirror is fixed within its frame. Two perpendicular adjustment screws are required. *One screw must be loosened before the other screw bearing on the same surface is tightened.*

Figure 1503c shows a sextant with a silver arc inserted in the limb, a micrometer drum graduated oppositely to the one in figure 1503a, a vernier graduated into six parts, a shorter telescope with a wider object glass than that in figure 1503a, a telescope draw substituted for a spiral focusing mechanism, and a light fitted on the index arm.

FIGURE 1503c.—A micrometer drum sextant used in the merchant marine.

1504. Vernier sextant.—Nearly all marine sextants of recent manufacture are of the type described in article 1503. At least two older-type sextants are still in use. These differ from the micrometer drum sextant principally in the manner in which the final reading is made. They are called **vernier sextants**.

The **clamp screw vernier sextant** is the older of the two. In place of the modern "release," a **clamp screw** is fitted on the underside of the index arm. To move the index arm, one loosens the clamp screw, releasing the arm. When the arm is placed at the approximate altitude of the body being observed, the clamp screw is tightened. Fixed to the clamp screw and engaged with the index arm is a long tangent screw. When this screw is turned, the index arm moves slowly, permitting accurate setting. Movement of the index arm (by the tangent screw) is limited to the length of the screw (several degrees of arc). Before an altitude is measured, this screw should be set to the approximate mid-point of its range. The final reading is made on a vernier set in the index arm below the arc. A small microscope or magnifying glass fitted to the index arm is used in making the final reading. Figure 1504 shows a clamp screw vernier sextant.

The **endless tangent screw vernier sextant** is identical with the micrometer drum sextant, except that it has no drum, and the fine reading is made by a vernier along the arc, as with the clamp screw vernier sextant. The release is the same as on the micrometer drum sextant and teeth are cut into the underside of the limb which engage with the endless tangent screw. The vernier itself is explained in article 1506.

FIGURE 1504.—A clamp screw vernier sextant.

1505. Use of the sextant.—When the *sun* is observed, the sextant is held vertically in the right hand, and the line of sight is directed at the point on the horizon directly below the body. Suitable shade glasses are moved into the line of sight, and the index arm is moved outward from near the 0° point until the reflected image of the sun appears in the horizon glass, near the direct view of the horizon. The sextant is then tilted slightly to the right and left to check its perpendicularity. As the sextant is tilted, the image of the sun appears to move in an arc, and the observer may have to change slightly the direction in which he is facing, to prevent the image from moving out of the horizon glass. When the sun appears at the *bottom* of its apparent arc resulting from this **swinging the arc,** or **rocking the sextant,** the sextant is vertical, and in the correct position for making the observation. If the sextant is tilted, too *great* an angle will be measured. When the sextant is vertical, and the observer is facing directly toward the sun, its reflected image appears at the center of the horizon glass, half on the silvered part, and half on the clear part. The index arm is then moved slowly until the sun appears to be resting exactly on the horizon, which is tangent to the **lower limb.** Occasionally, the sun image is brought *below* the horizon, and the **upper limb** observed. It is good practice to make several observations, moving the limb away from the horizon, alternately above and below it, between readings. Practice is needed to determine the appearance at tangency, which occurs at only one point, to avoid the common error of beginners of bringing the image down too far (too little for an upper-limb observation). Some navigators get more accurate observations by letting the body contact the horizon by its own apparent motion, bringing it slightly below the horizon if rising, and above if setting. At the instant the horizon is tangent to the disk, the time is noted. The **sextant altitude** is the uncorrected reading of the sextant. Figure 1505a illustrates the major steps in making an observation of the sun. At the left, the index arm has been moved a short distance from 0°. In the center, it has been clamped with the sun in the approximate position for a reading, and the sextant is being rocked. At the right, the sun is in the correct position for a reading.

When the *moon* is observed, the procedure is the same as for the sun, except that shade glasses are usually not required. The upper limb of the moon is observed more often than that of the sun, because of the phases of the moon. When the terminator (art. 1423) is nearly vertical, care should be exercised in selecting the limb that is illuminated, if an inaccurate reading is to be avoided. Sights of the moon are best made during daylight hours, or during that part of twilight in which the moon is least luminous. During the night, false horizons nearly always appear below the moon, due to illumination of the water by moonlight.

When a *star* or *planet* is observed, three methods of making the initial approximation of the altitude are in common use. In a common method, the index arm and micrometer drum are set on zero and the line of sight is directed at the body to be observed. Then, while keeping the reflected image of the body in the mirrored half of the horizon glass, the index arm is slowly swung *out* and the frame of the sextant is rotated *down*. The reflected image of the body is kept in the mirror until the horizon appears in the clear part of the horizon glass.

When there is little contrast between brightness of the sky and the body, this procedure is difficult, for if the body is "lost" while it is being brought down, it may not be recovered without starting again at the beginning of the procedure. An alternative method frequently used consists of holding the sextant upside down in the left

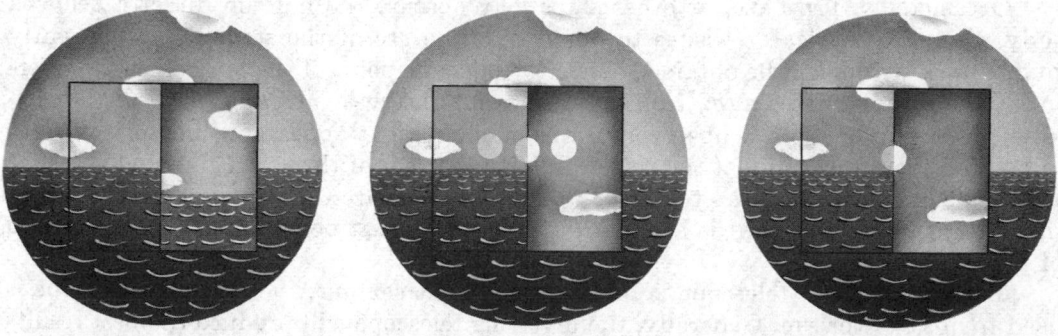

FIGURE 1505a.—*Left*, view through telescope with index arm set near zero. *Center*, "swinging the arc" after the sun has been brought close to the horizon. *Right*, sun at the instant of tangency.

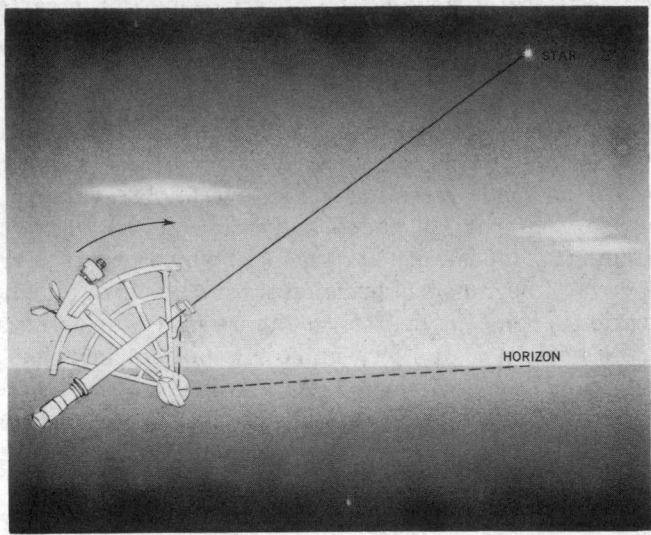

FIGURE 1505b.—Method of bringing horizon "up" to body.

hand, directing the line of sight at the body, and slowly moving the index arm out until the horizon appears in the horizon glass. This is illustrated in figure 1505b. After contact is made, the sextant is inverted and the sight taken in the usual manner.

A third method consists of determining in advance the approximate altitude and azimuth of the body by a **star finder** such as No. 2102–D (art. 2210). The sextant is set at the indicated altitude, and the observer faces in the direction indicated by the azimuth. After a short search, during which the index arm is moved backward and forward a few degrees, and the azimuth in which the observer faces is changed a little to each side, the image of the body should appear in the horizon glass. The best method to use for any observation is that which produces the desired result with the least effort. It is largely a matter of personal preference.

Measurement of the altitude of a star or planet differs from that of the sun or moon in that the *center* of a star or planet, rather than a limb, is brought into coincidence with the horizon. Figure 1505c shows the reflected image of a star as it should appear at the time of observation. Because of this difference, and the limited time usually available for observation during twilight, the method of letting a star or planet intersect the horizon by its own motion is little used. As with the sun and moon, however, the navigator should not forget to swing the arc to establish perpendicularity of the sextant.

Occasionally, fog, haze, or other ships may obscure the horizon directly below a body which the navigator wishes to observe. If the arc of the sextant is sufficiently long, a **back sight** might be obtained, using the opposite point of the horizon as the reference. The observer faces *away* from the body and observes the *supplement* of the altitude. If the sun or moon is observed in this manner, what appears in the horizon glass to be the lower limb is in fact the upper limb. In the case of the sun, it is usually preferable to observe what appears to be the upper limb. The arc that appears when rocking the sextant for a back sight is inverted; that is, the *highest* point indicates the position of perpendicularity.

If more than one telescope is furnished with the sextant, the erecting telescope is used to observe the sun. Generally, the inverting telescope will produce the best results for daylight observations, although some navigators prefer not to use any telescope, thus obtaining a wider field of view. The collar into which the sextant telescope fits

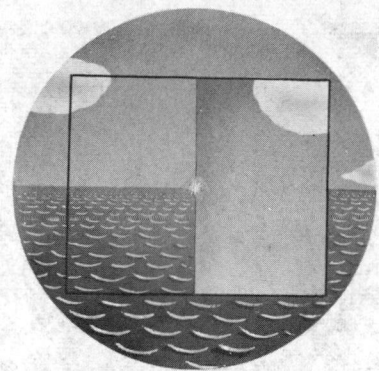

FIGURE 1505c.—Correct position of planet or star at moment of observation.

may be adjusted in or out in relation to the frame. When moved in, more of the mirrored half of the horizon glass is visible to the navigator, and a star or planet is more easily observed when the sky is relatively bright. Near the darker limit of twilight, the telescope can be moved out, giving a broader view of the clear half of the glass, and making the less distinct horizon more easily discernible. If both eyes are kept open until the last moments of an observation, eye strain will be lessened. But in making the final measurement, the nonsighting eye should be closed to permit full ocular concentration. Practice will permit observations to be made quickly, reducing inaccuracy due to eye fatigue. If several observations are made in succession, with a short rest between them, the best results should be obtained. With experience, the observer should be able to "call his shots," identifying the better ones.

When an altitude is being measured, it is desirable to have an assistant note the time, so that simultaneous values of time and altitude will be available. He should be given a warning "stand-by" when the measurement is nearly completed, and a "mark" at the moment a reading is made. He should be instructed to read the three hands in order of their rapidity of motion; the second hand first, then the minute hand, and finally the hour hand. If it is sufficiently dark that a light is needed to make the reading, the assistant should read both the time, and then the altitude, *behind* the observer and facing away from him, to avoid impairment of the observer's eye adaption to sky and horizon lighting conditions.

If an assistant is not available to time the observations, the observer holds the watch in the palm of his left hand, leaving his fingers free to manipulate the tangent screw of the sextant. After making the observation, he quickly shifts his view to the watch, and notes the positions of the second, minute, and hour hands, respectively. The delay between completing the altitude observation and noting the time should not be more than one or two seconds. The average time should be determined by having someone measure it for several observations, or by counting the half seconds (learning to count with the half-second beats of a chronometer). This interval can then be subtracted from the observed time of each sight.

1506. Reading the sextant.—The reading of a micrometer drum sextant is made in three steps. The degrees are read by noting the position of the arrow on the index arm in relation to the arc. The minutes are read by noting the position of the zero on the vernier with relation to the graduations on the micrometer drum. The fraction of a minute is read by noting which mark on the vernier most nearly coincides with one of the graduations on the micrometer drum. This is similar to reading the time by means of the hour, minute, and second hands of a watch. In both, the relationship of one part of the reading to the others should be kept in mind. Thus, if the hour

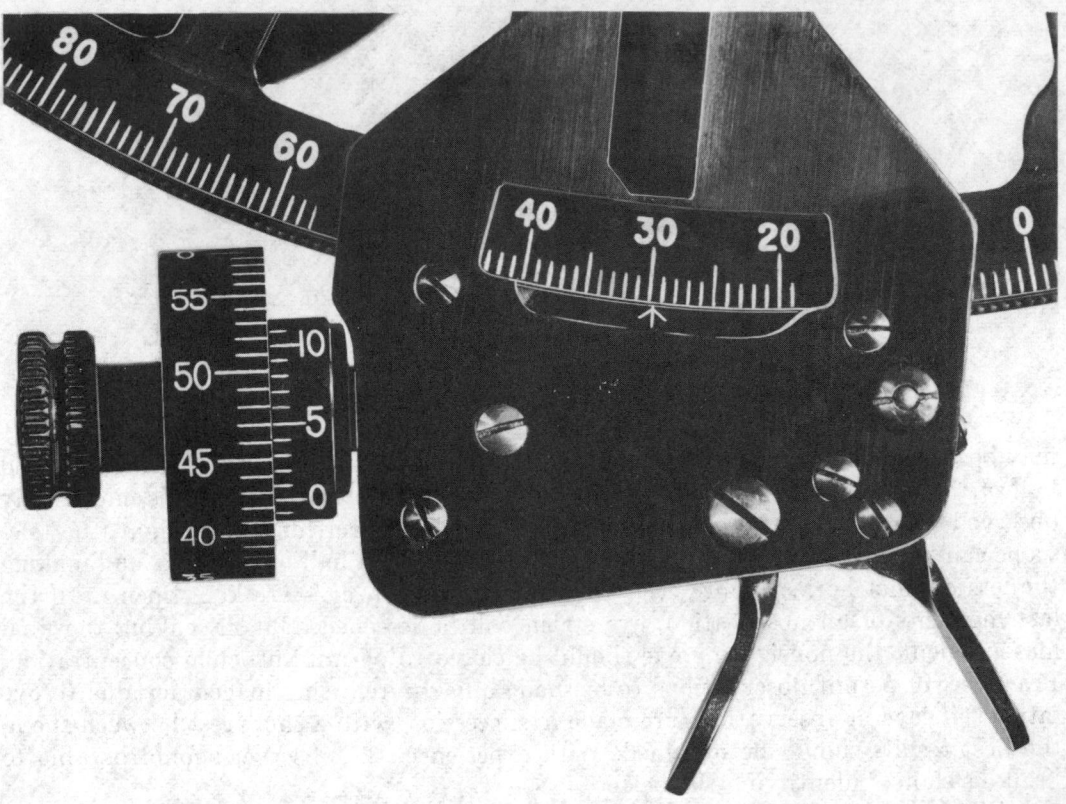

FIGURE 1506a.—Micrometer drum sextant set at 29°42ʹ.5.

hand of a watch were *about* on "4," one would know that the time was about four o'clock. But if the minute hand were on "58," one would know that the time was 0358 (or 1558), not 0458 (or 1658). Similarly, if the arc indicated a reading of about 40°, and 58ʹ on the micrometer drum were opposite zero on the vernier, one would know that the reading was 39°58ʹ, not 40°58ʹ. Similarly, any doubt as to the correct minute can be removed by noting the fraction of a minute from the position of the vernier. In figure 1506a the reading is 29°42ʹ.5. The arrow on the index mark is between 29° and 30°, the zero on the vernier is between 42ʹ and 43ʹ, and the "0ʹ.5" graduation on the vernier coincides with one of the graduations on the micrometer drum.

The principle of reading a vernier type sextant is the same, but the reading is made in two steps. Figure 1506b shows a typical altitude setting on this type sextant. Each degree on the arc of this sextant is graduated into three parts, permitting an initial reading by the reference mark on the index arm to the nearest full 20 minutes of arc. In this illustration the reference mark lies between 29°40ʹ and 30°00ʹ, indicating a reading between these values. The reading for the fraction of 20ʹ is made by means of the vernier, which is engraved on the index arm and has the small reference mark as its zero graduation. On this vernier, 40 graduations coincide with 39 graduations on the arc. Each graduation on the vernier is equivalent to $\frac{1}{40}$ of one graduation (20ʹ) on the arc, or 0ʹ.5 (30ʺ). In the illustration, the vernier graduation representing 2½ minutes (2ʹ30ʺ) most nearly coincides with one of the graduations on the arc. Therefore, the reading is 29°42ʹ30ʺ, or 29°42ʹ.5, as before. When a vernier of this type is used, any doubt as to which mark on the vernier coincides with a graduation on the arc can usually be resolved by noting the position of the vernier mark on each side of the one that seems to be in coincidence.

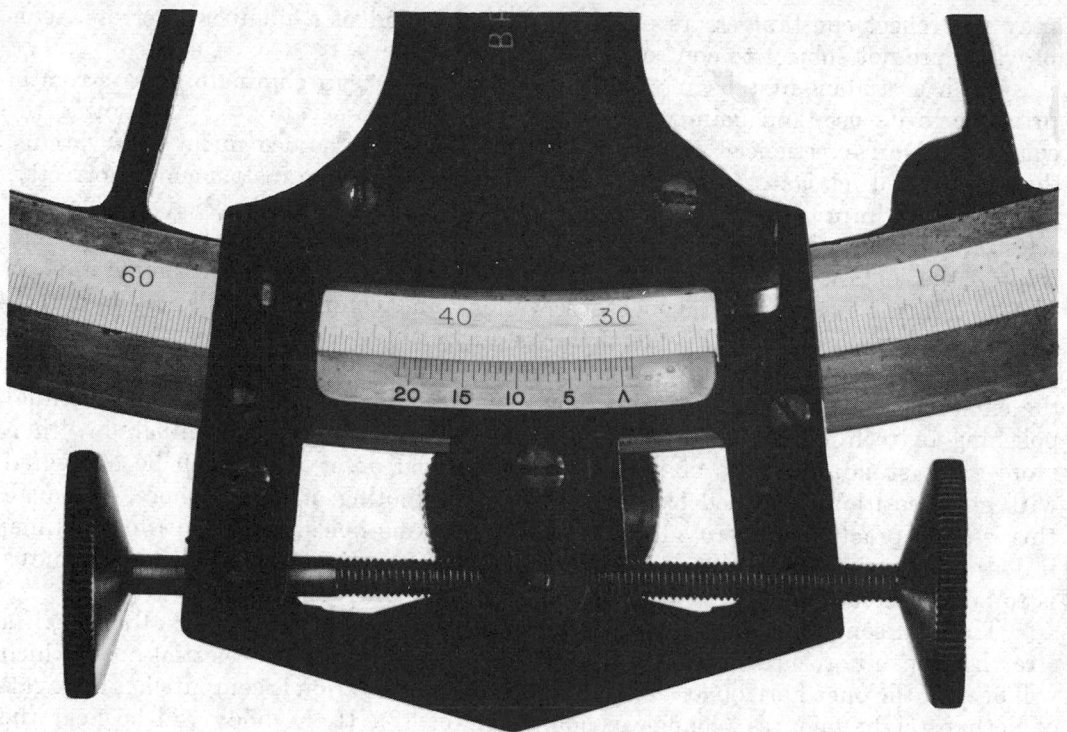

FIGURE 1506b.—Vernier sextant set at **29°42′30″**.

Negative readings (as in determining index correction, art. 1603) are made in the same manner as positive readings, the various parts being added algebraically (art. 106, vol. II). Thus, if the three parts of a micrometer drum reading are $(-)1°$, $56'$, and $0'.3$, the total reading is $(-)1°+56'+0'.3=(-)3'.7$.

1507. Developing observational skill.—A well-constructed marine sextant is capable of measuring angles with an instrument error not exceeding $0'.1$. Lines of position from altitudes of this accuracy would not be in error by more than about 200 yards. However, there are various sources of error, other than instrumental, in altitudes measured by sextant. One of the principal sources is the observer himself. There is probably no single part of his work that the navigator regards with the same degree of professional pride as his ability to make good celestial observations. Probably none of his other tasks requires the same degree of skill.

The first fix a student navigator obtains by his observation of celestial bodies is likely to be disappointing. Most navigators require a great amount of practice to develop the skill needed to make good observations. But practice alone is not sufficient, for if a mistake is repeated many times, it will be difficult to eradicate. Early in his career a navigator would do well to establish good observational technique—and continue to develop it during the remainder of his days as navigator. Many good pointers can be obtained from experienced navigators, but it should be remembered that each develops his own technique, and a practice that proves highly successful for one observer may not help another. Also, an experienced navigator is not necessarily a good observer, although he may consider himself such. Navigators have a natural tendency to judge the accuracy of their observations by the size of the figure formed when the lines of position are plotted. Although this is some indication, it is an imperfect one, because it does not indicate the errors of individual observations, and may not reflect constant errors. Also, it is a compound of a number of errors, some of which are not subject to control by the navigator.

When a student first begins to use the sextant, he can eliminate gross errors of principle in its use, and gain some ability in making observations, by accepting the coaching of an experienced navigator. By watching the novice make observations, the experienced navigator can observe a tendency to hold the instrument incorrectly, swing the arc improperly, or make other mistakes. When a celestial body is near the celestial meridian, the experienced navigator might make an observation and quickly transfer the sextant to the inexperienced one, who can see how the sight should appear. The two might make simultaneous observations and compare results. At first it is well to select bodies of low altitude, if they are available.

This procedure is helpful in detecting gross mistakes, but since the observations of the experienced navigator are not without error, this method is not suitable for final polishing of technique. For this purpose, observations should be compared with a more exact standard. Lines of position from celestial observations can be compared with good positions obtained by electronics or by piloting, if near a shore. Although this is good practice and provides a means of checking one's skill from time to time, it does not provide the large number of comparisons in a short time needed if technique is to be perfected.

This can sometimes be accomplished when a vessel is at anchor, or at a pier, if a stretch of open horizon is available. In advance, the altitude of a celestial body which will be over the open horizon at a time favorable for observation is computed at intervals of perhaps eight minutes (change in hour angle of 2°). If the body will be near the meridian, a smaller interval should be used. The altitude is determined for the position of the vessel, and all sextant altitude corrections (ch. XVI) are applied with reversed sign. These altitudes are then plotted versus time on cross-section paper, to a large scale, and a curve drawn through the points. At the selected time, a large number of observations are made at short intervals, allowing only enough time between observations for resting the eyes and arms. These observations are then plotted on the cross-section paper and compared with the curve.

An analysis of the results should be instructive. Erratic results indicate poor observational conditions or the need for practice and more care in making observations. If the measured altitudes are consistently too great, the sextant may not be rocked properly, the condition of tangency of the lower limb of the sun or moon may not be judged accurately, a false horizon in the water may have been used, subnormal refraction (dip) might be present, the eye might be higher above water than estimated, time might be in error, the index correction may have been determined incorrectly, the sextant might be out of adjustment, an error may have been made in the computation, the horizontal (vertical) may be tilted slightly by nearby mountains, etc. If the measured altitudes are consistently too low, the condition of tangency of the upper limb of the sun or moon may not be judged accurately, a low cloud may have been used as the horizon, abnormal refraction (dip) might be present, height of eye might be lower than estimated, time might be in error, the index error may have been determined incorrectly, the sextant might be out of adjustment, an error may have been made in the computation, the waves or swell at the horizon might be higher than at the ship, the horizontal (vertical) may be tilted slightly, a planet or bright star may have been placed "tangent" to the horizon rather than centered on the horizon, etc.

A single test of this type, while instructive, may not be conclusive. Several tests should be made with different celestial bodies, at various altitudes, under various conditions of weather and sea, and at different places. Generally, it is possible and desirable to correct any errors being made in the technique of observation, but occasionally a

personal error (sometimes called **personal equation**) will persist. This might be different for the sun and moon than for planets and stars, and might vary with degree of
fatigue of the observer, and other factors. For this reason, a personal error should be
applied with caution. However, if a relatively constant personal error persists, and
experience indicates that observations are improved by applying a correction to remove
its effect, better results might be obtained by this procedure than by attempting to
eliminate it from one's observations.

When lines of position of great reliability are desired, even an experienced navigator
can usually improve his results by averaging to reduce random error (art. 304, vol. II). A
number of observations, preferably not less than ten, are made in quick succession.
These can then be plotted versus time, on cross-section paper, and a curve faired through
the points. Unless the body is near the celestial meridian, this curve should be very
nearly a straight line. *Any* point on the curve can be used as the observation, using
the time and altitude indicated by the point. It is best to use a point near the middle
of the line, to avoid possible errors in its slope.

The slope can be determined by means of Pub. No. 214, using Δt, which is the
change of altitude relative to change in meridian angle (time). Meridian angle changes
at the rate of $1'$ in 4^s. Therefore, the change in altitude, in minutes of arc per second
of time, is equal to Δt (expressed as minutes of arc) divided by 4^s, or $\dfrac{\Delta t'}{4^s}$. Thus, if
Δt is 0.66, the altitude changes $\dfrac{0.66}{4^s}=0.165$ per second, or $15' \times 0.66 = 9.9$ per minute of
time, increasing if the body is rising, and decreasing if it is setting. This rate may be
altered by motion of the ship, the amount being the distance traveled in one minute,
multiplied by the natural cosine of the relative azimuth of the body. Thus, if the speed
is 15 knots, the ship moves 0.25 mile per minute. If the body is 30° on the bow, the altitude changes $0.25 \times 0.86603 = 0.2$ per minute due to motion of the ship, in addition to
its own apparent motion due to rotation of the earth. If the body is forward of the beam,
the effect of the ship's motion is to *increase* the altitude; if abaft the beam, to decrease
it. The total effect is the algebraic sum of the separate effects due to rotation of the
earth and motion of the vessel, since rate *at the vessel* is desired. Rapid change of Δt
indicates a curved rate line. If a large number of observations is made, the slope of the
line should be apparent from the plotted points.

A somewhat simpler variation is generally available if observations are made at
equal intervals, unless the body is near the meridian. It is based upon the assumption
that the change in altitude should be equal for equal intervals of time. A number of
observations might be made by having an assistant give a warning "stand-by" and
then a "mark" at equal intervals of time, as every ten or 20 seconds. Perhaps a better
procedure is to make the observations at equal altitude increments. After the first
observation, the altitude is changed by a set amount according to its rate of change,
as $5'$. The setting is *increased* if the body is rising, and *decreased* if it is setting. The
body is then permitted to cross the horizon by its own motion, and at the instant of
doing so, the time is noted. If time intervals are constant, the *mid time* and the *average
altitude* are used as the observation. If altitude increments are constant, the *average
time* and *mid altitude* are used. An uneven number of observations simplifies the finding
of the mid value, but with ten observations the finding of the average value is easier.

If only a small number of observations is available, as three, it is usually preferable
to solve all observations and plot the resulting lines of position, adjusting them to a
common time. The *average* position of the line might be used, but it is generally better
practice to use the middle line (or a line midway between the two middle ones if there
are an even number).

In this discussion of averaging, it has been assumed that all observations are considered of nearly equal value. Any observation considered unreliable, either in the judgment of the observer or as a result of a plot, should be rejected in finding an average.

1508. Care of the sextant.—The modern marine sextant is a well-built, precision instrument capable of rendering many years of reliable service, with minimum attention. However, its usefulness can easily be impaired by careless handling or neglect. If it is ever dropped, it may never again provide reliable information. If this occurs, the instrument should be taken to an expert for careful testing and inspection.

When not in use, a sextant should invariably be kept in its case and properly stowed. The sextant case should be a well-constructed hardwood box fitted on its exterior with a lock, a handle, and two hooks, preferably the type having safety catches. The interior of the case should be fitted with blocks in which the handle or legs, or both, are placed when the sextant is stowed. Some sextant cases are fitted with catches which clamp over the handle when the sextant is stowed, and some are fitted with felt-lined blocks on the inside of the cover, to clamp down on the extreme ends of the arc when the case is closed. The case should be so constructed that it can be closed with the shade glasses and index arm in nearly any normal position, and preferably with the telescope in place. The last is particularly valuable to the navigator on an overcast day when only one opportunity to observe the sun may present itself, and the sight may have to be taken quickly. A case such as the plastic case (fig. 1508) for the U. S. Navy Mark 3 sextant is an adequate alternative. In this case, the sextant is stowed snugly within a polyurethane cushion. A keeper prevents movement of the sextant. However, the index arm must be placed at 20° before the sextant can be placed in the recesses of the cushion.

The case itself should be securely stowed in a convenient place away from excessive heat, dampness, and vibration. A shelf with built-up sides into which the case fits snugly is a good stowage place. The practice of leaving the sextant in its case on a chart room settee is a bad one, and the instrument should *never* be left unattended on the chart table.

To remove the sextant from its case, grasp the frame firmly with the left hand, making sure that no pressure is applied to the index arm, and lift the instrument from the box. Then take the sextant in the right hand, by its handle, leaving the left hand free to make any adjustments necessary before taking a sight. The instrument should never be held by its limb, index arm, or telescope.

Next to careless handling, the greatest enemy of the sextant is moisture. The mirrors, especially, and the arc should be wiped dry after each use. A new sheet of plain lens paper is best to use for this purpose, and linen second best. Over a period of time, however, linen collects dust, which may contain abrasives that will scratch the surface of the mirrors. For this reason, linen, if it is used, should be kept in a small bag to protect it from dust in the air. Chamois leather and silk are particularly likely to collect abrasive dusts from the air and they should not be used to clean the mirrors or telescope lenses. Should the mirrors become particularly dirty, they can be cleaned with a small amount of alcohol, applied with a clean piece of lens paper. The arc can be cleaned, when necessary, with ammonia, but never with a polishing compound. In cleaning or drying the mirrors and arc, care should be taken that excessive pressure is not applied to any part of the instrument.

A small bag of silica gel kept in the sextant case will help in keeping the air in the case free from moisture, and will help to preserve the mirrors. Occasionally, the silica gel should be heated in an oven to remove the absorbed moisture.

It may be necessary to wash the sextant with fresh water if it is subjected to sea spray. After washing, the sextant should be wiped gently, using a soft cotton cloth. Then, the optics should be gently polished using lens paper.

Glass optics do not transmit the whole of the light received. This is due to the tendency of air-to-glass surfaces to reflect a portion of the light received with resultant

FIGURE 1508.—Case for Mark 3 sextant showing sextant stowed in polyurethane cushion.

decrease in the light transmitted. This loss of light reduces the brightness of the image of the object viewed through such a glass optic. If the object is viewed through several glass optics, as is the case with the sextant telescope assembly, then the brightness of the image seen will be seriously affected and the image will be indistinct. The reflection also causes a glare which obscures the image of the object being viewed.

To reduce to a minimum the effect of this reflection from air-to-glass surfaces, and thus, to improve light transmission, the glass optics are treated with an anti-reflection coating. The coatings are extremely thin and can be easily damaged. Therefore, only light pressure should be applied when polishing the coated optics with lens paper. It is good practice to blow loose dust off the lens before attempting to clean. This will insure that there will be no grit under the lens paper.

The tangent screw and the teeth on the side of the limb should be kept clean and lightly oiled, using the oil provided with the sextant. It is good practice to set occasionally the index arm of an endless tangent screw at one extremity of the limb and then to rotate the tangent screw over the length of the arc. This will clean the teeth and spread the oil through them. At any time that the sextant is to be stowed for a long period, the arc should be protected with a thin coat of petroleum jelly.

If the mirrors need resilvering, they are best taken to an instrument shop where a professional job can be done. However, on rare occasions it may be necessary to re-silver the mirrors of a sextant at sea. In anticipation of this possibility, the navigator should obtain the necessary materials in advance, as makeshift substitutes cannot be relied upon to do the job adequately. The required materials are xylene (available in most pharmacies), dilute nitric acid (optional), alcohol, cotton, tin foil about 0.005 inch thick, a small amount of mercury, a clean blotter, and some tissue paper. Do not substitute aluminum foil commonly used in packaging candy and cigarettes.

First, remove the protective coating with alcohol (or better, acetone) from the back of the mirror to be resilvered, and clean the glass with xylene or acid. If the old silvering is difficult to remove, soak it in water. Place the blotter on a flat surface and turn up and seal the edges to form a tray. This will serve to contain the mercury if the vessel should roll during the operation. Using cotton, clean and smooth out both sides of a piece of tin foil slightly larger than the glass to be silvered, first with alcohol and then with xylene (do not use acid). Make certain that no lint adheres to the foil, and place it on the blotter. Clean the mercury by squeezing it through cheese cloth, and apply a drop to the foil. Carefully spread it over the surface with a finger, making sure that none of the mercury gets under the foil. Add a few more drops of mercury until the entire surface of the foil is covered and tacky. The mercury combines with some of the tin to form an amalgam. Place the chemically cleaned glass on a piece of clean tissue paper with the side to be silvered face down. Then place the glass and the paper on the amalgam. Apply slight pressure to the glass and withdraw the tissue paper. Following this, grasp the edge of the tin foil and lift it and the mirror from the blotter. Invert the glass and the tin foil and place in an inclined position, silvered side up. Any mercury remaining on the blotter is no longer pure and should be disposed of. Five or six hours later any loose foil may be scraped from the sides of the mirror, and the following day a coat of commercial varnish or lacquer should be applied to the silvered surface. Should the mirrored half of the horizon glass require silvering, the clear half may be protected by a strip of cellulose or adhesive tape.

1509. Sextant adjustments.—There are at least seven sources of error in the marine sextant, three nonadjustable by the navigator, and four adjustable.

The **nonadjustable errors** are: "prismatic error," "graduation error," and "centering error."

The **prismatic error** is present if the two faces of the shade glasses and mirrors are not parallel. Error due to lack of parallelism in the shade glasses may be called **shade error.** Shade error in the shade glasses near the index mirror can be determined by comparison of an angle measured when a shade glass is in the line of sight with the same angle measured when the glass is not in the line of sight. In this manner, the error for each shade glass can be determined and recorded. If shade glasses are used in combination, their combined error should be determined separately. If additional shading is needed for the observations, use the colored telescope eyepiece cover. This does not introduce an error because direct and reflected rays are traveling together when they reach it, and are therefore affected equally by any lack of parallelism of its two sides.

Lack of parallelism of the two faces of the index mirror can be detected by carefully measuring a series of angles; then removing the index mirror, inverting it, and replacing it; and then measuring the same angles again. Half the difference is the prismatic error. After the index mirror has been inverted, it should be checked carefully for perpendicularity to the frame of the sextant, as explained below.

Lack of parallelism of the two faces of the horizon glass will appear as part of the index error, and so need not have separate attention. The same is true of prismatic error in the shade glasses located near the horizon glass, but unless index error is determined with the shade glasses in place, the measured index error will not be the correct value for the combined error.

Graduation errors occur in the arc, micrometer drum, and vernier of a sextant which is improperly cut or incorrectly calibrated. Normally, the navigator cannot determine whether the arc of a sextant is improperly cut, but the principle of the vernier makes it possible to determine the existence of graduation errors in the micrometer drum or vernier and is a useful guide in detecting a poorly made instrument. The first and last markings on any vernier should align perfectly with one less graduation on the adjacent micrometer drum. In figure 1503a, the vernier is graduated in ten units. When the zero point is aligned with any graduation on the micrometer drum, the "ten" graduation should be in perfect alignment with a micrometer graduation nine units greater than the one in line with zero on the vernier. In figure 1503c, the vernier is graduated in six units and should align perfectly with any two graduations five units apart on the micrometer.

Centering error results if the index arm is not pivoted at the exact center of curvature of the arc. It can be determined by measuring known angles, after the adjustable errors have been removed. Horizontal angles can be used by determining the accurate value by careful measurement with a theodolite. Several readings by both theodolite and sextant should minimize errors. An alternative method is to measure angles between the lines of sight to stars, comparing the measured angles with computed values. To minimize refraction errors, one should select stars at about the same altitude, and avoid stars near the horizon.

The same shade glasses, if any, used for determining or eliminating index error should be used for measuring centering error. The errors determined in this manner include any error due to faulty graduation, and prismatic error of the index mirror, unless corrections are applied for these errors. However, since all vary with the angle measured, they need not be separated. Usually, it is preferable to make a single correction table for all three errors, called **instrument error.** Customarily, such a table is determined by the manufacturer and attached to the inside cover of the sextant case.

The sign of the error is reversed, so that the values given are for **instrument correction (I).**

The **adjustable errors** in the sextant are those related to *perpendicularity* of (1) the frame and the index mirror, and (2) the frame and the horizon glass, and *parallelism* of (3) the index mirror and horizon glass to each other at zero setting, and of (4) the telescope to the frame. Each of these errors, if it exists, can be removed from the sextant by careful adjustment. In making these adjustments, *never tighten one adjusting screw without first loosening the other screw which bears on the same surface.* The adjustments should be made in the order indicated.

The first adjustment is for *perpendicularity of the index mirror* to the frame of the sextant. To test for perpendicularity, place the index arm at about 35° on the arc, and hold the sextant on its side, with the index mirror "up" and toward the eye. Observe the direct and reflected views of the sextant arc, as illustrated in figure 1509a. If the two views do not appear to be joined in a straight line, the index mirror is not perpendicular. If the reflected image is above the direct view, the mirror is inclined forward. If the reflected image is below the direct view, the mirror is inclined backward. An alternative and sometimes more satisfactory method of determining perpendicularity involves the use of two small vanes, or similar objects, of exactly the same height. Figure 1509b illustrates this method. Again the index arm is set at about 35°. The vanes are placed upright on the extremities of the limb, in such a way that the observer can, by placing his eye near the index mirror, see the direct view of one vane and the reflected image of the other. The tops of the objects are then observed for alignment. The use of vanes permits observation in the plane of adjustment, rather than at an angle. Adjustment is made by means of two screws at the back of the index mirror.

The second adjustment is for *perpendicularity of the horizon glass* to the frame of the sextant. An error resulting from the horizon glass not being perpendicular is called **side error.** To test for perpendicularity, set the index arm at zero and direct the line of sight at a star. Then rotate the tangent screw back and forth so that the reflected image passes alternately above and below the direct view. If, in changing from one position to the other, the reflected image passes directly over the star as seen without reflection, no side error exists, but if it passes to one side, the horizon glass is not perpendicular to the frame of the sextant. Figure 1509c illustrates observations without

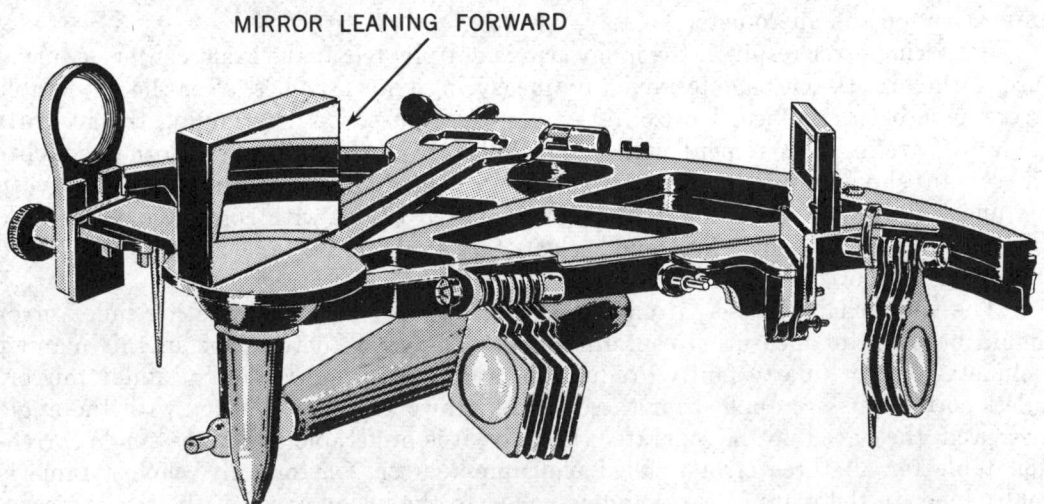

MIRROR LEANING FORWARD

FIGURE 1509a.—Testing the perpendicularity of the index mirror. Here the mirror is not perpendicular.

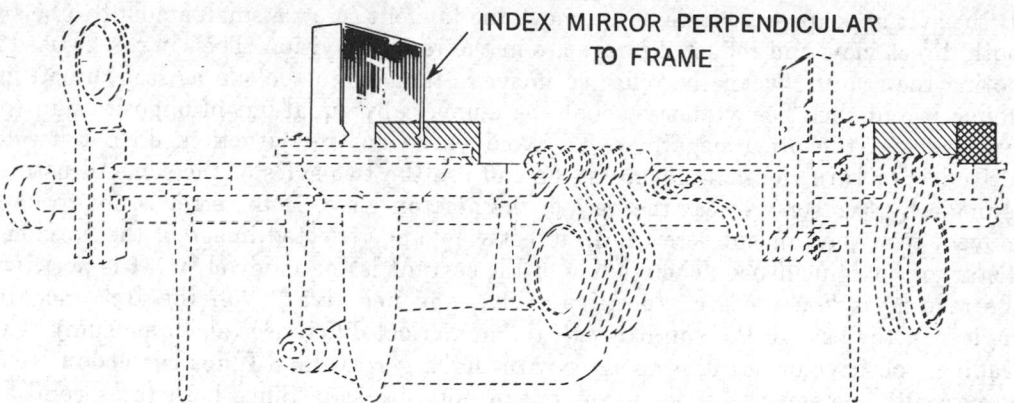

INDEX MIRROR PERPENDICULAR
TO FRAME

FIGURE 1509b.—Alternative method of testing the perpendicularity of the index mirror. Here the mirror is perpendicular.

side error (left) and with side error (right). Whether the sextant reads zero when the true and reflected images are in coincidence is immaterial in this test. An alternative method is to observe a vertical line, such as one edge of the mast of another vessel (or the sextant can be held on its side and the horizon used). If the direct and reflected portions do not form a continuous line, the horizon glass is not perpendicular to the frame of the sextant. A third method is to hold the sextant vertical, as in observing the altitude of a celestial body, and bring the reflected image of the horizon into coincidence with the direct view, so that it appears as a continuous line across the horizon glass. Then tilt the sextant right or left. If the horizon still appears continuous, the horizon glass is perpendicular to the frame, but if the reflected portion appears above or below that part seen direct, the glass is not perpendicular. Adjustment is made by means of two screws near the base of the horizon glass.

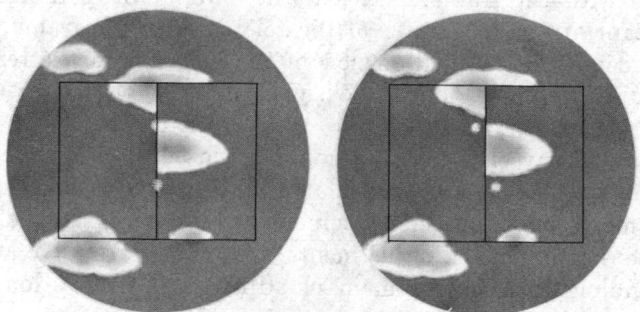

FIGURE 1509c.—Testing the perpendicularity of the horizon glass. *Left*, side error does not exist. *Right*, side error does exist.

The third adjustment is to make the *index mirror and horizon glass parallel* when the index arm is set exactly at zero. The error which results when the two are not parallel is the principal cause of **index error,** the total error remaining after the four adjustments have been made. Index error should be determined each time the sextant is used and need not be removed if its value is known accurately. To make the test for parallelism of the mirrors, set the instrument at zero, and direct the line of sight at the horizon or a star. Side error having been eliminated, the direct view and reflected image of the horizon appear as a continuous line, or the star as a single point, if the two mirrors are parallel. If the mirrors are not parallel, the horizon appears broken at the edge of the mirrored part of the horizon glass, one part being higher than the other. The reflected image of a star appears above or below the star seen without reflection.

If the star appears as a single point, move the tangent screw a small amount to be sure both direct view and reflected image are in the range of vision. The sun can be used by noting the reading when the reflected image is tangent to the sun as seen direct, first above it and then below. These should be numerically equal but of opposite sign (one positive and the other negative). To avoid variations in refraction, do not use low altitudes; or turn the sextant on its side and use the two sides of the sun. Adjustment is made by two screws near the base of the horizon glass. If the error is not to be removed, turn the tangent screw until direct view and reflected image of the horizon or a star are in coincidence. The reading of the sextant is the index error. It is positive if the reading is "on the arc" (positive angle), and negative if "off the arc" (negative angle). In the case of the sun it is *half* the numerical difference (algebraic sum) of the readings, positive or negative to agree with the larger reading. **Index correction** (**IC**) is numerically the same as index error, but of opposite sign. Since both the second and third adjustments involve the position of the horizon glass, it is good practice to recheck for side error after index error has been eliminated. Index error should always be checked after adjustment for side error.

The fourth adjustment is to make the *telescope parallel* to the frame of the sextant. If the line of sight through the telescope is not parallel to the plane of the instrument, an **error of collimation** will result, and altitudes will be measured as greater than their actual values. To check for parallelism of the telescope, insert it in its collar, and observe two stars 90° or more part, bringing the reflected image of one into coincidence with the direct view of the other, near either the right or left edge of the field of view (the upper or lower edge if the sextant is horizontal). Then tilt the sextant so that the stars appear near the opposite edge. If they remain in coincidence, the telescope is parallel to the frame, but if they separate, it is not. An alternative method is to place the telescope in its collar and then lay the sextant on a flat table. Sight along the frame of the sextant and have an assistant place a mark on the opposite bulkhead, in line with the frame. Place another mark above the first at a distance equal to the distance from the center of the telescope to the frame. This second line should be in the center of the field of view of the telescope if the telescope is parallel to the frame. Adjustment for nonparallelism is made to the collar, by means of the two screws provided for this purpose.

Determination of any of the errors should be based upon a series of observations, rather than a single one. This is particularly true in the case of index error, which should be determined by approaching coincidence from opposite directions (up and down) on alternate readings. If adjustments are made carefully, and the sextant is given proper handling, it should remain in adjustment over a long period of time. Unless the navigator has reason to question the accuracy of the adjustments, they need not be checked at intervals of less than several months, except in the case of index error, which has the greatest effect on accuracy of readings, and should be checked each time the sextant is used. If the horizon is used for determining index error, this check should be made *before* evening twilight observations, and *after* morning twilight observations, while the horizon is sharp and distinct. If a star is used, the index error should be determined *after* evening observations and *before* morning sights are taken. During the day, it should be checked both before and after observations.

Frequent manipulation of the adjusting screws should be avoided, as it may cause excessive wear. Except in the case of index error, slight lack of adjustment has little effect on the results, and should be ignored. If adjustments are needed at frequent intervals, the sextant is not receiving proper care, or has worn parts which should be replaced at a navigation instrument shop. If index error is not constant, it should not be removed, but index correction should be determined before or after every observation and applied to the readings, until the sextant can be repaired. A small variable error might well be accepted, but should be watched to see that it does not become unduly large.

1510. Selection of a sextant.—For satisfactory results a sextant should be selected carefully. For accurate work the radius of the arc should be about 6½ inches or more. The instrument should be light, but strongly built. The various moving parts should fit snugly, but move freely without binding or gritting. If the index arm is either too loose or too tight at either end of the arc, the pivot may not be perpendicular to the frame of the sextant. The telescope should be easy to insert or remove from its holder, and to focus.

The use to be made of a sextant should be considered in its selection. For ordinary use in measuring altitudes of celestial bodies, an arc of 90° or slightly more is sufficient. A longer arc is desirable if back sights are to be made, or if horizontal angles are to be measured. If use of the sextant is to be limited to horizontal angles, less accuracy is required. The arc can be of smaller radius, and small nonadjustable errors are unimportant.

If practicable, a sextant should be examined by an expert, and tested for non-adjustable errors before acceptance.

1511. Octants, quintants, and quadrants.—Originally, the term "sextant" was applied to the navigator's double-reflecting, altitude-measuring instrument only if its arc was 60° in length—a sixth of a circle—permitting measurement of angles from 0° to 120°. In modern usage the term is applied to all navigational altitude-measuring instruments, regardless of angular range or principles of operation, although some are octants (angular range 90°), some quintants (144°), some quadrants (180°), and many have an intermediate range.

1512. The artificial horizon.—Measurement of altitude requires a horizontal reference. In the case of the marine sextant this is commonly provided by the visible sea horizon. If this is not clearly visible, reliable altitudes cannot be measured unless a different horizontal reference is available. Such a reference is commonly called an **artificial horizon.** If it is attached to, or part of, the sextant, altitudes can be measured at sea, on land, or in the air, whenever celestial bodies are available for observations. On land, where the visible horizon is not a reliable indication of the horizontal, an external artificial horizon can be devised.

Any horizontal reflecting surface will serve the purpose. A pan of mercury, heavy oil, molasses, or other viscous liquid sheltered from the wind is perhaps simplest. A piece of plate glass fitting snugly across the top of the container is usually the best shelter. If there is any reasonable doubt as to the parallelism of the two sides of the glass, two readings should be made with the glass turned 180° in azimuth between readings, and the average value taken. The pan and liquid should be clean, as foreign material on the surface of the liquid is likely to distort the image and introduce an error in the reading.

To use an external artificial horizon, the observer stands or sits in such a position that the celestial body to be observed is reflected in the liquid, and is also visible by direct view. By means of the sextant, the double-reflected image is brought into co-incidence with the image appearing in the liquid. In the case of the sun or moon the *bottom* of the double-reflected image is brought into coincidence with the *top* of the image in the liquid, if a lower-limb observation is desired. For an upper-limb obser-vation, the opposite sides are brought into coincidence. If one image is made to cover the other, the observation is of the *center* of the body.

When the observation has been made, apply the index correction and any other instrumental correction, as well as any correction for personal error. Then take *half* the remaining angle and apply all other corrections except dip (height of eye) correction, since this is not applicable. If the *center* of the sun or moon is observed, omit, also, the correction for semidiameter. Chapter XVI explains the various corrections and their applications.

A commercial artificial horizon consisting of a metal tray, mercury, cover of two sloping glass sides held in a metal frame, metal bottle to hold the mercury when not in use, and a funnel for pouring, was at one time a familiar part of a navigator's equipment, but the modern navigator might experience difficulty in locating such a device.

1513. Artificial-horizon sextants.—Shortly after the marine sextant was invented (art. 124), an attempt was made to extend its use to periods of darkness. This was done by providing a spirit level attachment. The observer brought the double-reflected image of the celestial body being observed into coincidence with the bubble of the spirit level. Such devices have been made available from time to time, and are still being manufactured. However, they have never come into general use, and are of questionable value.

Charles A. Lindbergh's historic solo flight across the North Atlantic in 1927 demonstrated the practicability of long over-water flights. The development of a suitable instrument for observing altitudes of celestial bodies during darkness and when the horizon was obscured by clouds or haze became a virtual requirement. Various forms of artificial horizon have been used, including a bubble, gyroscope, and pendulum. Of these, the bubble has been most widely used. Figure 1513a illustrates a modern periscopic sextant permitting observation with only a small tube protruding through the top of the aircraft. Figure 1513b shows the optical principle of a different type aircraft sextant.

With an artificial horizon of the bubble or pendulum type, considerable skill is needed to make an observation. The image of the horizontal reference (a circle or horizontal line) and the celestial body both appear in the field of view, and both may seem unsteady. An observation is made by matching the two near the center of the field of view. The appearance at coincidence depends upon the instrument. Some bubbles appear dark and are placed on a level with the body. Others have a clear center and are placed over the body. One pendulum type has a horizontal line that is customarily placed directly across the body, although a limb observation can be made if desired. Bubbles can be regulated in size, and the instructions provided with the instrument should be followed. In general, the bubble diameter should be about one-sixth to one-fourth the size of the field of view. This is about three to four times the size of the sun or full moon as seen through the eyepiece. A very small bubble should be avoided because it tends to lag sextant movements so much that it is unreliable as a horizontal reference.

A considerable amount of practice is needed to develop skill in making reliable observations with an artificial-horizon sextant, even on land or other steady platform. At sea or in the air the motions of the craft greatly increase the difficulty of observation. In addition to compounding the difficulty of making coincidence, the craft motion introduces a sometimes large and rapidly varying **acceleration error.** That is, motions of the craft produce an acceleration on the pendulum or the liquid of the bubble chamber, causing false indication of the horizontal. In smooth air the accelerations tend to follow a cycle of about one to two minutes in length. They are largely eliminated by use of an averaging device. In making an observation, the observer attempts to maintain coincidence continuously over a period, usually two minutes. The *average* altitude, generally indicated on a dial or drum, is used with the *mid* time of observation. Thus, perhaps 60 individual observations, or a continuously integrated altitude, are available to smooth out errors of individual observations.

FIGURE 1513a.—Aircraft periscopic sextant.

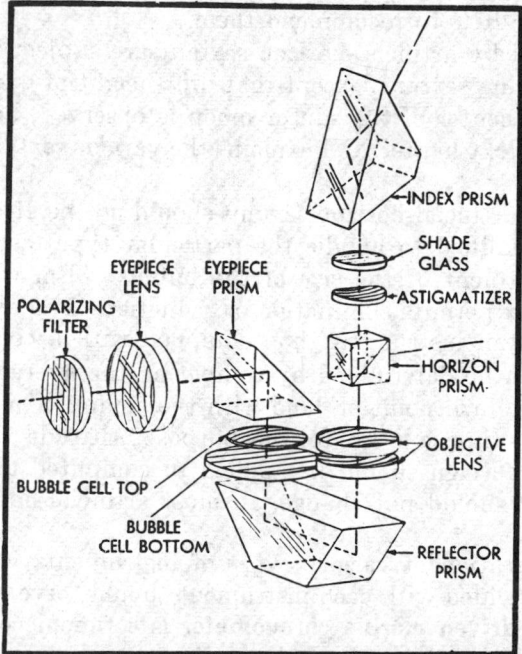

FIGURE 1513b.—Optical principle of a typical
bubble sextant.

On land or other steady platform a skillful observer using a two-minute averaging bubble or pendulum sextant can measure altitudes to an accuracy of perhaps 2′ (two miles). This, of course, refers to the accuracy of measurement only, and does not include additional errors such as abnormal refraction, deflection of the vertical, computational and plotting errors, etc. In steady flight through smooth air the error of a two-minute observation is increased to perhaps five to ten miles. At sea, conditions are different. In a glassy sea with virtually no roll or pitch, results should approach those on land. However, with even a slight, gentle roll the accelerations to which a vessel is subjected are quite complex, as indicated by the difficulty one not accustomed to the sea has in getting his "sea legs" during the early part of a voyage. If the vessel is yawing, a large Coriolis error (art. 815, vol. II) may be introduced. Under these conditions observational errors of 10–15 miles are not unreasonable. With a moderate sea, errors of 30 miles or more are common. In a heavy sea, any useful observations are virtually impossible to obtain. Single altitude observations in a moderate sea can be in error by a matter of *degrees*.

Because of the difficulty of observing, and the large acceleration errors encountered aboard a vessel, bubble and pendulum type sextants have very limited use at sea. A submarine on war patrol, surfacing only during darkness, may have use for such an instrument. A large number of observations on a reasonably calm night can produce results of some value. However, even under these conditions some navigators report better results with a marine sextant and dark-adapted eyes. In pack ice a ship generally provides a reasonably steady platform. When the horizon is obscured by ice or haze, polar navigators can sometimes obtain better results with an artificial-horizon sextant than with a marine sextant. Some artificial-horizon sextants have provision for making observations with the natural horizon as a reference, but since this is a secondary usage, results are not generally as satisfactory as by marine sextant. Because of their more complicated optical systems, and the need for providing a horizontal reference, artificial-horizon sextants are generally much more costly to manufacture than marine sextants. Designed for use in the air, they serve a useful purpose there, but for ordinary use aboard ship they have little to recommend them.

Altitudes observed by artificial-horizon sextant are subject to the same errors as those observed by marine sextant, except that dip (height of eye) correction does not apply. Also, when the center of the sun or moon is observed, no correction for semidiameter should be made. Chapter XVI explains the various sextant altitude corrections and their applications.

Adjustment of an artificial-horizon sextant should not be attempted by other than an instrument man qualified to handle the particular type instrument involved. An exception is the adjustment of the size of the bubble. Also, with some instruments an easily movable index permits elimination or reduction of index error. This error can best be determined in an instrument shop equipped with a collimator. If one is not available, the error can be determined by comparing the average of a number of observations made at a known point on land with the computed values. A precomputed curve of altitude versus time is useful for this purpose. Altitude corrections equal to the errors but with reversed sign should be applied to computed altitudes. With normal usage, the index error should not change. In most artificial-horizon sextants there is no index error.

The care and operation of various types of instruments vary considerably. The instruction booklet provided with each instrument should serve as the guide.

1514. The spring-driven marine chronometer is a timepiece having a nearly constant rate. It is used aboard ship to provide accurate time, primarily for timing celestial observations for lines of position, and secondarily for setting the ship's other timepieces.

It differs from a watch principally in that it contains a variable lever device to maintain even pressure on the mainspring, and a special balance designed to compensate for temperature variations. A ship in which celestial navigation is used carries one or more chronometers.

A spring-driven chronometer is set approximately to Greenwich mean time (GMT) and is not reset until the instrument is overhauled and cleaned, usually at three-year intervals. Resetting might disturb the rate. Instead, the difference between GMT and **chronometer time** (C) is carefully determined, and applied as a correction to all chronometer readings. This difference, called **chronometer error** (CE), is "fast" (F) if chronometer time is later than GMT, and "slow" (S) if earlier. The amount by which chronometer error changes in one day is called **chronometer rate,** or sometimes **daily rate,** considered "gaining" or "losing" as the chronometer is running faster or slower than the correct rate. An erratic rate indicates a defective instrument, or need for overhaul. The methods of determining and applying chronometer error and chronometer rate are explained in chapter XVIII.

A spring-driven chronometer is mounted in gimbals in a box, which should be carefully stowed to protect the instrument from damage due to heavy rolling and pitching, vibration, temperature variations, and electrical and magnetic influences. Usually this is done by fitting the box snugly into a heavily padded case suitably located in the chart room of merchant ships, and below decks, near the center of motion, in U. S. Navy ships.

The principal maintenance requirement aboard ship is regular winding at about the same time each day. Aboard United States naval vessels this is customarily done at about 1130 each morning, and reported to the commanding officer at 1200. Aboard merchant ships it is usually wound at about 0800. Although a spring-driven chronometer is designed to run for more than two days, daily winding helps insure a uniform rate, and constitutes a daily routine that decreases the possibility of letting the instrument run down. On the face of each chronometer is a small dial that indicates the number of hours before the chronometer will be run down. To wind the chronometer, gently turn the instrument on its side, and slide back the guard covering the keyhole. Insert the key and carefully wind in a counterclockwise direction. Seven half-turns should suffice. If a chronometer should run down, wait until GMT is nearly the same as the time indicated before winding. If the chronometer does not start after winding, move the case back and forth gently. Check the error and rate carefully.

At maximum intervals of about three years, a spring-driven chronometer should be sent to a good chronometer repair shop for cleaning and overhaul. When transported by hand, a chronometer should be clamped in its gimbals and stowed in the large case provided. When shipped, it should be allowed to run down, and the balance secured by a cork before the chronometer is stored in the large case.

1515. Quartz crystal marine chronometers are being used as replacements for the spring-driven chronometers aboard ships of the U. S. Navy. The accuracy of these instruments is such that the time can be read without resort to chronometer rate. Should the second hand be in error by a readable amount, it can be reset electrically.

The quartz crystal chronometer designed for U. S. Navy use (fig. 1515a) displays time using a 24-hour dial. It indicates the day of the week. The chronometer is furnished in a case suitable for direct installation in shipboard chronometer lockers or modular type chart tables without gimbaling or other special mounting or restraining features.

The basic element for time generation is a quartz crystal oscillator. The quartz crystal is temperature compensated and is hermetically sealed in an evacuated envelope. A calibrated adjustment capability is provided to adjust for the aging of the crystal. The performance requirements for this chronometer are shown in figure 1515b.

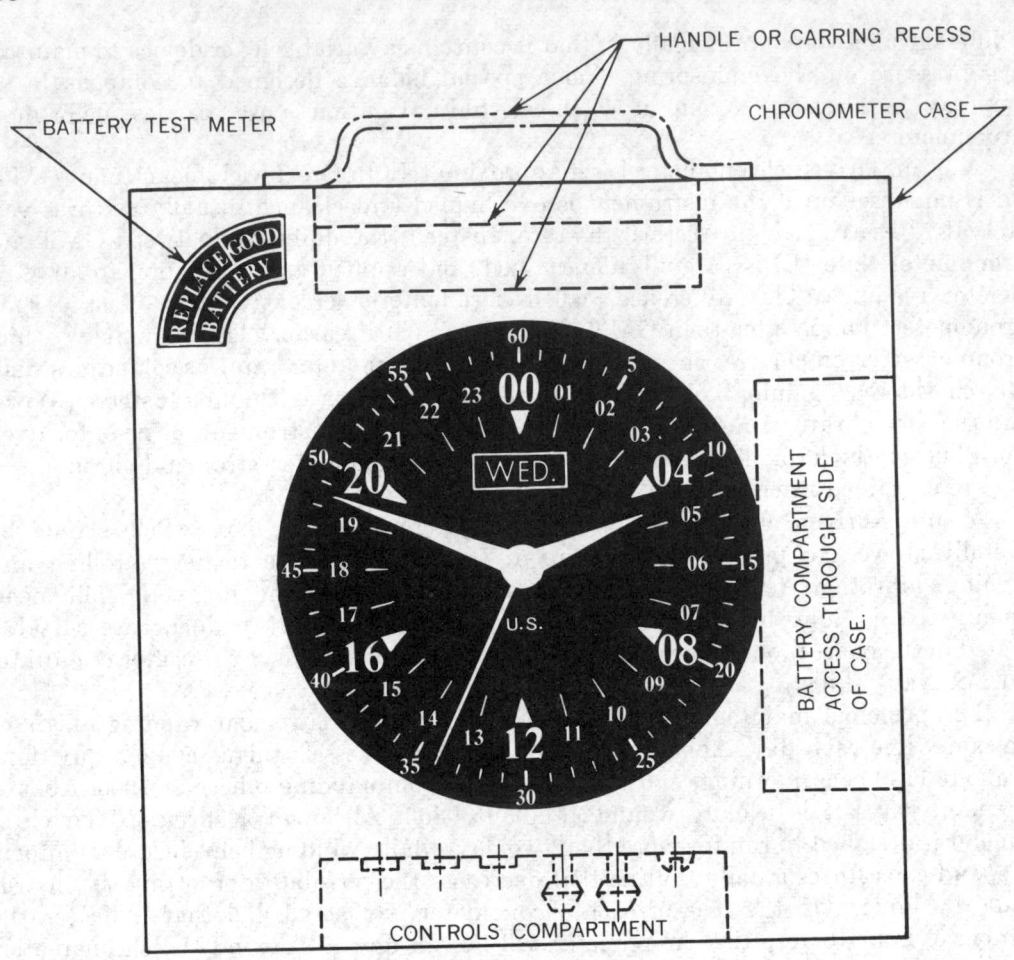

FIGURE 1515a.—Quartz crystal chronometer.

The chronometer is designed to operate a minimum of 1 year on a single set of batteries. A built-in battery test meter is operated by means of a push button. The meter indicates the relative strength of the battery. The dial is marked to indicate the point at which the battery should be replaced. The chronometer continues to operate and keep the correct time for at least 5 minutes while the batteries are being changed. The chronometer is designed to accommodate the gradual voltage drop during the life of the batteries by which it is powered while maintaining accuracy requirements.

A two-position setting mechanism is provided to set the three hands. One position of the mechanism permits the minutes and hours to be set without any movement of the second hand. Return of the mechanism to the other (normal) position results in resumption of the measurement of time.

Two electrical push buttons are provided for making small corrections in time by electrical means. Depression of one button stops the chronometer movement and depression of the other speeds up the movement. Operation of the push buttons does not upset the synchronization of the minute and second hands.

1516. Watches.—In the interest of accuracy, a spring driven chronometer is not disturbed more than necessary. Celestial observations are timed and ship's clocks set by means of a **comparing watch.** This is a high-grade pocket watch which is set by compari-

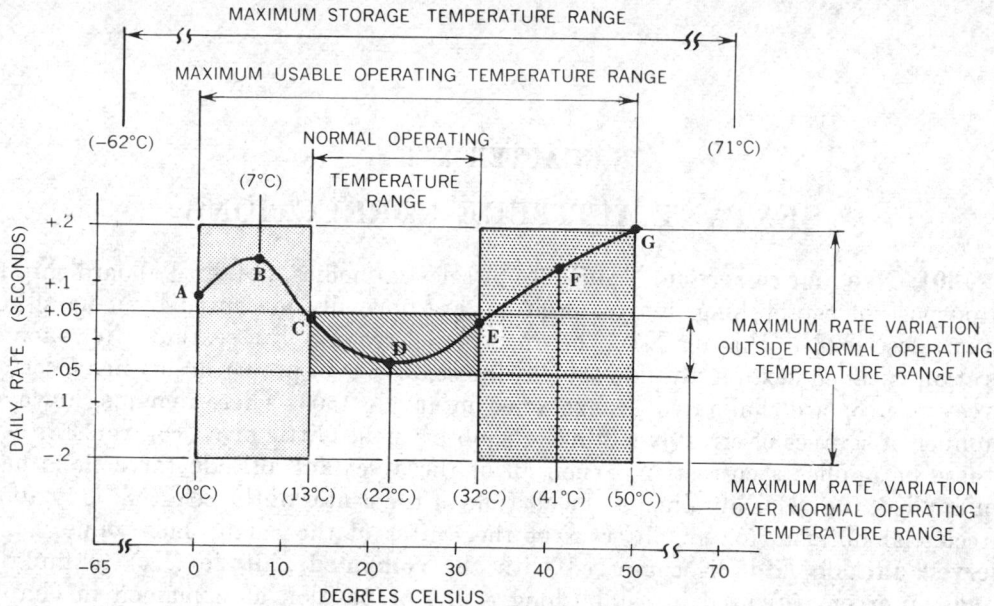

FIGURE 1515b.—Performance requirements.

son with a chronometer, and then carried to the place where accurate time is needed. For celestial navigation, a comparing watch should have a large sweep-second hand which can be set. A comparing watch used for timing celestial observations should preferably be set to Greenwich mean time, to avoid the necessity of applying a correction for each observation.

If the second hand cannot be set, the watch should be set to the nearest whole minute, being sure that the second hand is in synchronism with the minute hand, and the **watch error** (**WE**) determined. If a watch is to be used for other purposes than timing of celestial observations, it might preferably be set to zone time. A comparing watch should be set, or watch error determined, immediately before or after celestial observations are made, to avoid the necessity for determining and applying a correction for **watch rate,** and to eliminate a possible error due to an inaccurate or variable rate. If a watch set to GMT is used for timing celestial observations, care should be taken to avoid a possible error of 12 hours or 24 hours. The mental application of zone description of ship's time indicates the approximate GMT and the Greenwich date. The subject of time is discussed more fully in chapter XVIII. A stop watch may also be used for celestial observations.

1517. Other instruments.—The sextant, chronometer, and comparing watch (or stop watch) are the principal instruments of celestial navigation. The azimuth circle for observing azimuths of celestial bodies is discussed in article 629. Plotting equipment is the same as that for dead reckoning (arts. 602–606). A flashlight might be needed for reading the sextant and the comparing watch. A pocket notebook is desirable or recording predicted positions of celestial bodies if a star finder is used, and for recording the observations. A workbook is desirable for solving celestial observations so that a permanent record is available. Work forms are desirable, but should form part of the work book, and not be kept separately. These might be provided by rubber stamp, or by printing. In the latter case a looseleaf work book may be desirable to permit arrangement of the various papers in chronological order.

CHAPTER XVI

SEXTANT ALTITUDE CORRECTIONS

1601. Need for correction.—Altitudes of celestial bodies, obtained aboard ship for the purpose of establishing lines of position, are normally measured by a hand-held **sextant,** described in chapter XV. The uncorrected reading of a sextant after such an operation is called **sextant altitude (hs).** If the sextant is in proper adjustment, certain sources of error are eliminated, as explained in article 1509. There remains, however, a number of sources of error over which the observer has little or no control. For each of these he applies a correction. When all of these **sextant altitude corrections** have been applied, the value obtained is the altitude of the center of the celestial body above the celestial horizon, for an observer at the center of the earth. This value, called **observed altitude (Ho),** is compared with the **computed altitude (Hc)** to find the **altitude intercept** (*a*) used in establishing a line of position as explained in chapter XVII.

Articles 1602–1614 describe the various corrections. For highly accurate results, all of these are needed to the greatest accuracy obtainable. The needs of ordinary practical navigation, however, make no such exacting requirements, and in the course of his usual day's work at sea, the navigator has relatively few corrections to apply, from conveniently-arranged tables readily accessible to him. The more detailed information in chapter VIII of volume II is given to (1) provide the basis for a better understanding of the problem, (2) furnish the information needed for evaluation of results, and (3) provide a source of reference material beyond that given in the usual navigation text.

1602. Instrument correction (**I**) is the combined correction for nonadjustable errors (prismatic error, graduation error, and centering error) of the sextant, as explained in article 1509. Usually, this correction is determined by the manufacturer, and recorded on a card attached to the inside of the top of the sextant box. It varies with the angle, may be either positive or negative, and is applied to all angles measured by that instrument. For a well-made instrument, the maximum value is so small that this correction can be ignored for all except the most accurate work. Normally, instrument error of artificial-horizon sextants is so small, considering the precision to which angles can be measured by such instruments, that no correction is provided.

1603. Index correction (**IC**), due primarily to lack of parallelism of the horizon glass and index mirror at zero reading, is discussed in article 1509. Until the adjustment is disturbed, the index correction remains constant for all angles, and is applicable to all angles measured by the instrument. It may be either positive or negative. Normally, artificial-horizon sextants do not have index corrections.

1604. Personal correction (**PC**) is numerically the same as personal error (art 1507), but of opposite sign, either positive or negative. If experience indicates the need for such a correction, it should be made to altitudes of the bodies to which it applies. However, the observer should be sensitive to changes in its value. Unless the observer has sufficient evidence to be sure of the existence and relative constancy of a personal error, no correction should be applied.

1605. Dip (**D**) of the horizon is the angle by which the visible horizon (art. 1429) differs from the horizontal at the eye of the observer (the sensible horizon, art. 1429).

418

Thus, it applies only when the visible horizon is used as a reference, and not when an artificial horizon, either internal or external to the sextant, is used. It applies to all celestial bodies. If the eye of the observer were at the surface of the earth, visible and sensible horizons would coincide, and there would be no dip. This is never the situation aboard ship, however, and at any height *above* the surface, the visible horizon is normally *below* the sensible horizon, as shown in figure 1605a. Normally, then, an altitude measured from the visible horizon is too *great*, and the correction is *negative*. It increases with greater height of the observer's eye. Because of this, it is sometimes called **height of eye correction.**

If there were no atmospheric refraction (art. 1606), dip would be the angle between the horizontal at the eye of the observer, and a straight line from this point tangent to the surface of the earth. With refraction, dip is the angle (∠ HAC′ of figure 1605b) between the horizontal at the eye of the observer and a straight line tangent at the eye of the observer to the curved ray of light from the visible horizon.

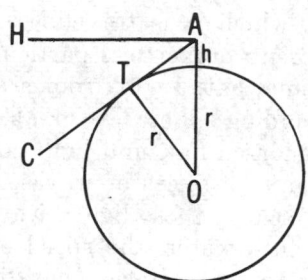

Figure 1605a.—Dip without refraction.

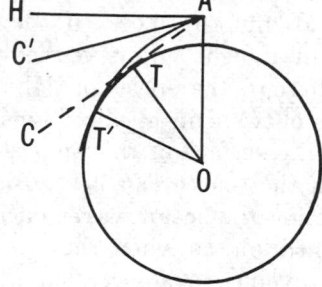

Figure 1605b.—Dip with refraction.

The amount by which refraction alters dip varies with changing atmospheric conditions. Even the *average* value has not been established with certainty, and several methods of computing dip have been proposed. The values given in the critical table on the inside front cover of the *Nautical Almanac* were computed by the equation

$$D = 0.97\sqrt{h}$$

where D is the dip, in minutes of arc; and h is the height of eye of the observer, in feet. Part of this table is repeated on the page facing the inside back cover. The *Air Almanac* table was computed independently by a different method, to a precision of whole minutes. The minor discrepancies thus introduced are not important in practical navigation.

The values given in the table are satisfactory for practical navigation under most conditions. An investigation by the Carnegie Institution of Washington showed that of 5,000 measurements of dip at sea, no value differed from the tabulated value by more than 2ʹ5, except for one difference of 10ʹ6. Extreme values of more than 30ʹ have been reported, and even values of several *degrees* have been encountered in polar regions. Greatest variations from tabulated values can be expected in calm weather, with large differences between sea and air temperatures, particularly if mirage effects are present. Irregularities in the shape of the rising or setting sun may indicate abnormal conditions. Large variations may also be present shortly after passage of a squall line, when errors of as much as 15ʹ have been reported. When a temperature inversion is known to exist, the tabulated dip may be too small, numerically. The effect of sea-air temperature difference is discussed in greater detail in chapter VIII of volume II.

In the determination of height of eye, position on the ship should be considered, and also the condition of loading and trim. If an observation is made from a position differing from the usual place, the altered height of eye should not be overlooked. Momentary changes due to rolling and pitching can be neutralized, to a large extent, by making observations from a point on the centerline of the vessel, at the axis of pitch.

Since variations from normal dip may be one of the principal sources of error in celestial observations, the observer should be alert to conditions affecting terrestrial refraction. Any observation taken within half an hour after passage of a squall line should be regarded as unreliable.

If dip cannot be measured, the effects of abnormal conditions can be minimized by observing three bodies differing in azimuth by about 120° (or four bodies by 90°, five bodies by 72°, etc.). If the error is constant in all directions, its effect is to increase (or possibly to decrease) the size of the closed figure formed by the lines of position without altering the position of its center. Hence, the size of the figure is not necessarily an indication of the accuracy of the fix.

1606. Refraction (R).—Light, or other radiant energy, is assumed to travel in a straight line at uniform speed, if the medium in which it is traveling has uniform properties. But if light enters a medium of different properties, particularly if the density is different, the speed of light changes somewhat. Light from a single point source travels outward in all directions, in an expanding sphere. At great distances, a small part of the surface of this sphere can be considered flat, and light continuing to emanate from the source can be considered similar to a series of waves, in some respects resembling the ocean waves encountered at sea. If these light "waves" enter a more dense medium, as when they pass from air into water, the speed decreases. If the light is traveling in a direction perpendicular to the surface separating the two media (in this case vertically downward), all parts of each wave front enter the new medium at the same time, and so all parts change speed together, as shown in figure 1606a. But if the light enters the more dense medium at an oblique angle, as shown in figure 1606b, the change in speed occurs progressively along the wave front as the different parts enter the more dense medium. This results in a change in the direction of travel, as shown. This change in direction of motion is called **refraction.** If light enters a more dense medium, it is refracted *toward* the normal (*NN'*), as in figure 1606b. If it enters a less dense medium, it is refracted *away* from the normal, as light traveling in the opposite direction to that shown in figure 1606b.

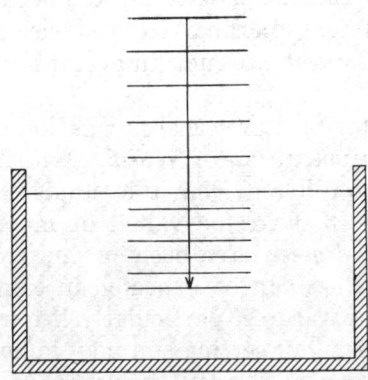

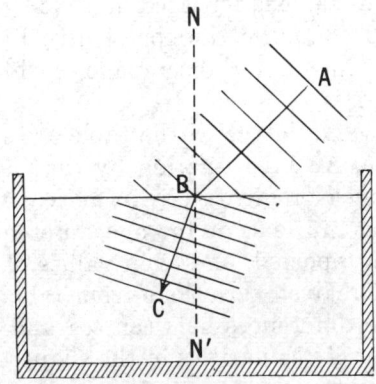

FIGURE 1606a.—No refraction occurs when light enters denser medium normal to the surface.

FIGURE 1606b.—A ray entering a denser medium at an oblique angle is bent toward the normal.

The *amount* of the change in direction is directly proportional to the angle between the direction of travel and the normal (angle *ABN* in figure 1606b). The ratio of this angle to the similar angle after refraction takes place (angle *CBN'* in figure 1606b) is constant, so that as one increases, the other increases at the same *rate*. Hence, the *difference* between them (the change in direction) also increases at the same rate. Therefore, if the *incident* ray (*AB*) is nearly parallel to the surface at which refraction takes place, relatively large amounts of refraction occur.

The amount of refraction is also directly proportional to the relative speed of travel in the two media. Various substances are compared by means of a number called the **index of refraction** (μ), which depends primarily upon the density of the substance. In figure 1606b, angle *ABN* is called the **angle of incidence** (ϕ) and angle *CBN'* the **angle of refraction** (θ). These are related by Snell's law, which states that *the sines of the angle of incidence and angle of refraction are inversely proportional to the indices of refraction of the substances in which they occur*. Thus, if μ_1 is the index of refraction of the substance in which ϕ occurs, and μ_2 is the index of refraction of the substance in which θ occurs

$$\frac{\sin\phi}{\sin\theta} = \frac{\mu_2}{\mu_1}.$$

If the index of refraction changes suddenly, as along the surface separating water and air (as shown in fig. 1606b), the change in direction is equally sudden. However, if a ray of light travels through a medium of gradually changing index of refraction, its path is curved, undergoing increased refraction as the index of refraction continues to change. This is the situation in the earth's atmosphere, which generally decreases in density with increased height. The gradual change of direction occurring there is called **atmospheric refraction.** The bending of a ray of light traveling from a point on or near the surface of the earth, to the eye of the observer, is called **terrestrial refraction.** This affects dip of the horizon, as discussed in article 1605. A ray of light entering the atmosphere from outside, as from a star, undergoes a similar bending called **astronomical refraction.**

The effect of astronomical refraction is to make a celestial body appear *higher* in the sky than it otherwise would, as shown in figure 1606c. If a body is in the zenith, its light is not refracted, except for a very slight amount when the various layers of the atmosphere are not exactly horizontal. As the zenith distance increases, the refraction becomes greater. At an altitude of 20° it is about 2ʹ6; at 10°, 5ʹ3; at 5°, 9ʹ9; and at the horizon, 34ʹ5. A table of refraction is given on the inside front cover and facing page of the *Nautical Almanac*, in the columns headed "Stars and Planets."

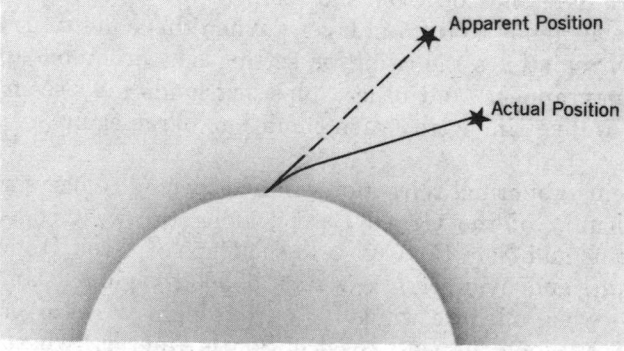

FIGURE 1606c.—Astronomical refraction.

As height above the surface of the earth increases, light from an outside source travels through less of the atmosphere, and refraction decreases. At shipboard heights the difference is negligible, but at aircraft heights the change is a consideration. Therefore, the refraction table given near the back of the *Air Almanac* is a double-entry table.

The values given in the tables are for average conditions. This is called **mean refraction.** A considerable amount of research has been conducted to determine the mean values, the conditions under which values differ from the mean, and the amount of such differences. A number of different mean refraction tables have been produced. Values in the various tables differ slightly because of different assumptions, different methods of observation, and different observed results under apparently similar conditions. This last source of difference is due primarily to the fact that conditons could be determined at the position of the observer, but not at various points along the line traveled by the ray of light in passing through the atmosphere. Nevertheless, the various tables agree very well down to a minimum altitude of 2°. Below this, the refraction is erratic, and differences between values in the various tables are not as important as differences between mean and instantaneous values. The values given in the almanac tables are in excellent agreement with those actually measured.

Because of their variability, refraction and dip (also affected by refraction) are the principal uncertainties in the accuracy of celestial observations of a careful observer. As a result of this uncertainty, navigators formerly avoided all observations below some arbitrary altitude, usually 15°. While this is still good practice if higher bodies are available, the growing knowledge of atmospheric refraction has increased the confidence with which navigators can use low-altitude sights. There is little reason for lack of confidence in sights as low as 5°. Below this, other available corrections should be applied (art. 1626). If altitudes below 2° are used, larger probable errors should be anticipated, even with the use of additional corrections. Generally, the error in tabulated refraction should not exceed two or three minutes, even at the horizon. However, a knowledge of conditions affecting refraction is helpful in determining the confidence to be placed in such observations. Since refraction elevates both the celestial body and the visible horizon, the error due to abnormal refraction is minimized if the visible horizon is used as a reference.

The atmosphere contains many irregularities which are erratic in their influence upon refraction. Normally, the navigator has not the information needed to correct for such conditions, but only to recognize their existence. He must recognize that those observations made within half an hour after passage of a squall line might be considerably in error. The passage of any front might have a similar effect. A temperature inversion (art. 3815) may upset normal refraction. Abnormal values may be expected when there is a large difference between the temperature of the sea and air. With an absence of wind, the air tends to form in layers. When this condition becomes extreme, mirage effects occur. Sometimes the rising or setting sun or moon appears distorted. Multiple horizons may appear, and other ships or islands may seem to float a short distance above the water. Under any such conditions large errors in refraction might be encountered.

Conditions causing abnormal refraction can be expected to occur with considerable frequency in the vicinity of the Grand Banks, along the west coast of Africa from Mogador to Cap Blanc and from the Congo to the Cape of Good Hope, in the Red Sea and the Persian Gulf, and over ice-free water in polar regions. Abnormal refraction may be encountered when offshore winds blow from high, snow-covered mountains to nearby tropical seas, as along the west coast of South America; where cold water from large rivers such as the Mississippi flows into warm sea water; when a strong current flows past a bay or coast, causing colder water to be drawn to the surface, as in the Bay of Rio de Janeiro and Santos, and along the Atlantic coast of Africa between Cape Palmas and Cape Three Points during the time of the southwest monsoon; and along the east coast of Africa in the vicinity of Capo Guardafui during the summer. In the temperate zones abnormal refraction is most common during the spring and summer.

Of the more systematic errors which affect refraction, two can be evaluated, and corrections applied. These are for air temperature (art. 1607) and atmospheric pressure (art. 1608). However, these corrections are based upon assumed standard *gradients* (changes) with height.

Since refraction causes celestial bodies to appear elevated in the sky, they are above the horizon longer than they otherwise would be. The mean diameter of the sun and moon are each about 32′, and horizontal refraction is 34′.5. Therefore, the entire sun or moon is actually below the visible horizon when the lower limb appears tangent to the horizon. The effect of dip is to further increase the time above the horizon. Near the horizon the sun and moon appear flattened because of the rapid change of refraction with altitude, the lower limb being raised by refraction to a greater extent than the upper limb.

As a correction to sextant altitudes, refraction is negative because it causes the measured altitude to be too *great*. It *decreases* with increased altitude, and applies to all celestial bodies, regardless of sextant or horizon used.

1607. Air temperature correction (T).—The *Nautical Almanac* refraction table is based upon an air temperature of 50°F (10°C) at the surface of the earth. At other temperatures the refraction differs somewhat, becoming greater at lower temperatures, and less at higher temperatures. Table 23 provides the correction to be applied to the altitude to correct for this condition. If preferred, this correction can be applied with *reversed sign* to the refraction from the almanac, and a single refraction applied to the altitude. A combined correction for nonstandard air temperature and nonstandard atmospheric pressure (art. 1608) is given on page A4 of the *Nautical Almanac*. The correction for air temperature varies with the temperature of the air and the altitude of the celestial body, and applies to all celestial bodies, regardless of the method of observation. However, except for extreme temperatures or low altitudes, this correction is not usually applied unless results of unusual accuracy are desired.

1608. Atmospheric pressure correction (B).—The *Nautical Almanac* refraction table is based upon an atmospheric pressure of 29.83 inches of mercury (1010 millibars) at sea level. At other pressures the refraction differs, becoming greater as pressure increases, and smaller as it decreases. Table 24 provides the correction to be applied to the altitude for this condition. A combined correction for nonstandard air temperature (art. 1607) and nonstandard atmospheric pressure is given on page A4 of the *Nautical Almanac*. If the correction is to be applied to the refraction, reverse the sign. This correction varies with atmospheric pressure and altitude of the celestial body, and is applicable to all celestial bodies, regardless of the method of observation. However, except for extreme pressures or low altitudes, this correction is not usually applied unless results of unusual accuracy are desired.

1609. Irradiation correction (J).—When a bright surface is observed adjacent to a darker one, a physiological effect in the eye causes the brighter area to appear to be larger than is actually the case; conversely, the darker area appears smaller. This is called **irradiation.** Thus, since the sun is considerably brighter than the sky background, the sun appears larger than it really is; and when the sky is considerably brighter than the water, the horizon appears slightly depressed. The effects on the horizon and lower limb of the sun are in the same direction and tend to cancel each other while the effect on the upper limb of the sun is in the opposite direction to that on the horizon and tends to magnify the effect.

From 1958–1970 a correction of 1ʹ2 was included in the *Nautical Almanac* data for the upper limb of the sun as an average correction for the effect of irradiation. Recent investigations have not supported that average value and have revealed that the magnitude of the effect depends on the individual observer, the size of the ocular, the altitude of the sun, and other variables. In summary, the accuracy of observations of the limb of the sun at low altitudes may be affected systematically by irradiation, but the size of the correction is so dependent upon the variables enumerated above that it is not feasible to include an average correction in the tables.

1610. Semidiameter (SD) of a celestial body is half the angle, at the observer's eye, subtended by the visible disk of the body. The position of the lower or upper limb of the sun or moon with respect to the visible horizon can be judged with greater precision than that of the center of the body. For this reason it is customary, when using a marine sextant and the visible horizon, to observe one of the limbs of these two bodies, and apply a correction for semidiameter. Normally, the lower limb is used if it is visible. In the case of a gibbous or crescent moon, however, only the upper limb may be available. Semidiameter is shown in figure 1612.

The semidiameter of the sun varies from a little less than 15ʹ8 early in July, when the earth is at its greatest distance from the sun, to nearly 16ʹ3 early in January, when the earth is nearest the sun. In the *Nautical Almanac* the semidiameter of the sun at GMT 12^h on the middle day of each page opening of the daily page section is given to the nearest 0ʹ1 at the bottom of the sun's GHA column. The altitude correction tables of the sun, given on the inside front cover and facing page, are divided into two parts, to be used during different periods of the year. The mean semidiameter of each period is included in the tables of both upper and lower limb corrections. The semidiameter each day is listed to the nearest 0ʺ01 in the *American Ephemeris and Nautical Almanac*. In the *Air Almanac* the semidiameter to the nearest 0ʹ1 is given near the lower right-hand corner of each daily page.

The moon undergoes a similar change in semidiameter as its distance from the earth varies. However, because of the greater eccentricity of the moon's orbit than that of earth, the variation in semidiameter is also greater, varying between about 14ʹ7 and 16ʹ8. The variation is more rapid, partly because of the greater spread of values, but principally because the moon completes its revolution in approximately one month, while the earth makes one revolution per year. In the *Nautical Almanac*, semidiameter of the moon at 12^h each day is given to the nearest 0ʹ1 at the bottom of the moon data columns. The correction for semidiameter of the moon is included in the corrections given on the inside back cover and facing page. In the *Air Almanac*, semidiameter is given to the nearest whole minute, being shown on the daily pages, immediately below the value for the sun. The semidiameter at intervals of half a day is given to the nearest 0ʺ01 in the *American Ephemeris and Nautical Almanac*.

The navigational planets have small semidiameters. For Venus it varies between about 5ʺ and 32ʺ; for Mars, 2ʺ7 to 12ʺ6; for Jupiter, 16ʺ to 25ʺ; and for Saturn, 7ʺ to 10ʺ. The value for any date is given in the *American Ephemeris and Nautical Almanac*, but not in the *Nautical Almanac* or *Air Almanac* because the apparent *centers* of these bodies are customarily observed.

Stars have no measurable semidiameter.

The computed altitude of a body refers to the *center* of that body, since the coordinates listed in the almanacs are for the center. If the *lower* limb is observed, the sextant altitude is *less* than the altitude of the center of the body, and hence the correction is *positive*. If the *upper* limb is observed, the correction is *negative*. The correction does not apply when the center of the body is observed, which is usually the case when an artificial-horizon sextant is used. With a marine sextant and either the natural or an artificial horizon, semidiameter is customarily applied to observations of the sun and moon, but not other celestial bodies.

1611. Phase correction (F).—Because of phase (fig. 1612), the actual centers of planets and the moon may differ somewhat from the apparent centers. Average corrections for this difference are included in the additional corrections for Venus and Mars given on the inside front cover of the *Nautical Almanac*. They should be applied only when these bodies are observed during twilight. At other times the magnitude and even the sign of the correction might differ from those tabulated, because of a different relationship between the body and the horizon. The phase correction for navigational planets other than Venus and Mars is too small to be significant.

A phase correction may apply to observations of the moon if the apparent center of the body is observed, as with an artificial-horizon sextant. However, no provision is made for a correction in this case; the need for it can be avoided by observing one of the limbs of the body.

Phase correction does not apply to observations of the sun or stars.

1612. Augmentation (A).—As indicated in article 1610, semidiameter changes with distance of the celestial body from the observer, becoming greater as the distance decreases. The semidiameter given in the ephemeris and used in the almanacs is for a fictitious observer at the center of the earth. If the celestial body is on the actual observer's horizon, its distance is approximately the same as from the center of the earth; but if the body is in the zenith, its distance is less by about the radius of the earth (fig. 1612). Therefore, the semidiameter *increases* as the altitude becomes greater. This increase is called **augmentation.** For the moon, the augmentation from horizon to zenith is about 0.'3 at the mean distance of the moon. At perigee it is about 2" greater, and at apogee about 2" less. Augmentation of the sun from horizon to zenith is about 1/24 of one second of arc. For planets it is correspondingly small, varying with the positions of the planets and the earth in their orbits. At any altitude the augmentation is equal to the sine of the altitude times the value at the zenith.

Augmentation increases the size of the semidiameter correction, whether positive or negative. It is included in the moon correction tables on the inside back cover and facing page of the *Nautical Almanac*. It is not included in the correction tables of other bodies or in the *Air Almanac* tables.

1613. Parallax (P) is the difference in apparent position of a point as viewed from two different places. If a finger is held upright at arm's length and the right and left eyes closed alternately, the finger appears to move right and left a short distance. Similarly, if one of the nearer stars were observed from the earth and from the sun, it would appear to change slightly with respect to the background of more distant stars. This is called **heliocentric parallax** or **stellar parallax.** The nearest star has a parallax of less than 1". Even if the value were greater, no correction to sextant altitudes would be needed, for the difference would be reflected in the tabulated position of the body.

However, positions of celestial bodies are given relative to the *center* of the earth, while observations are made from its surface. The difference in apparent position from these two points is called **geocentric parallax.** If a body is in the zenith, at Z in figure 1613, there is virtually no parallax, for the line from the body to the center of the earth passes approximately through the observer at A. Suppose, however, the moon is at M. From A it appears to be along the line AM, while at the center of the earth it would appear to be along OM. The altitude at A would be the angle SAM, and that at O the angle COM. Angle COM is equal to angle SBM, which is exterior to the triangle ABM, and hence equal to the sum of angles SAM and AMO.

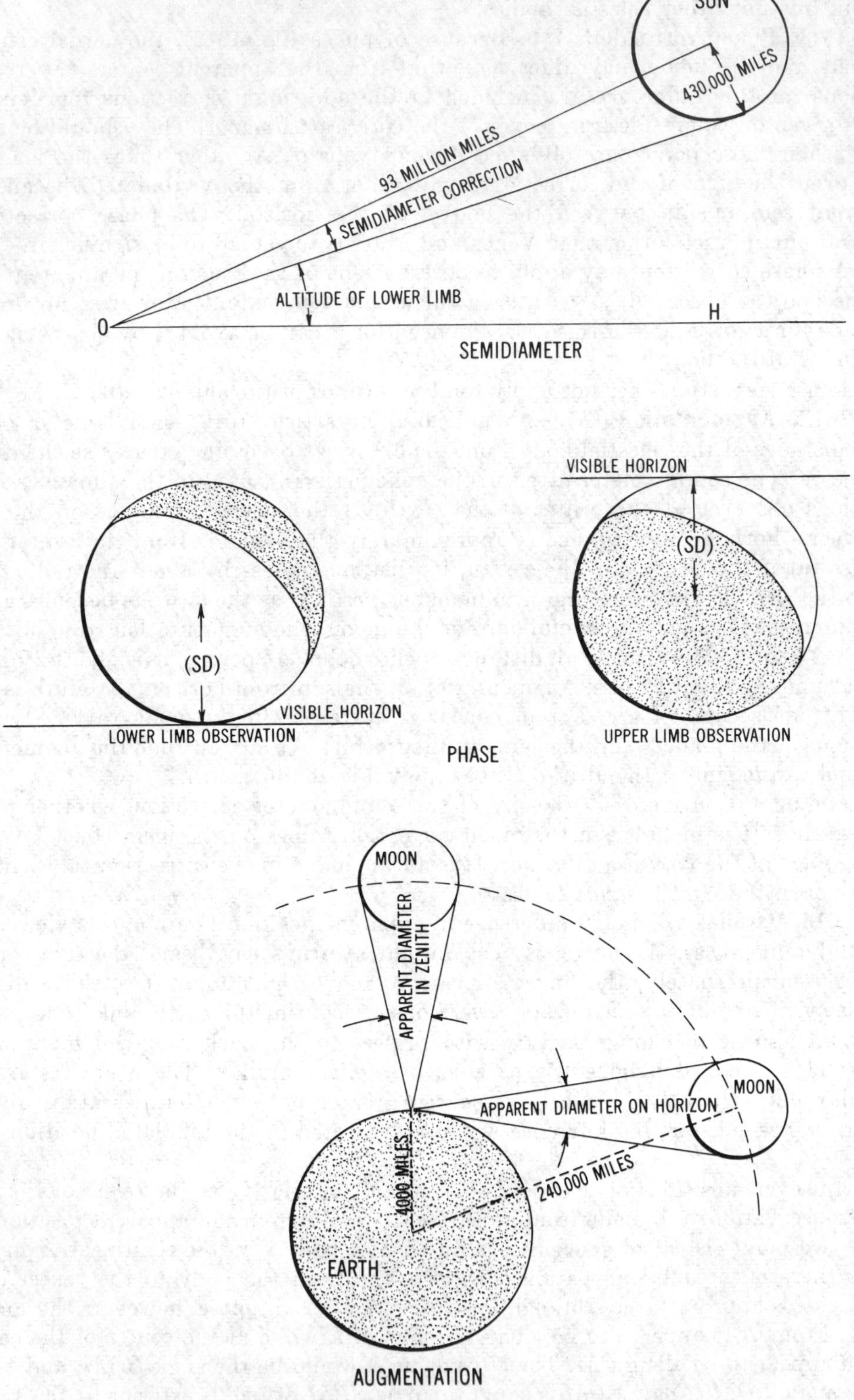

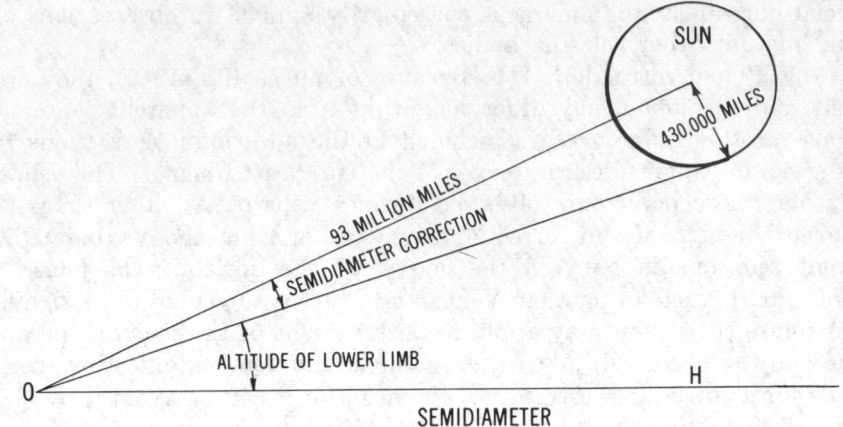

FIGURE 1612.—Semidiameter, phase, and augmentation.

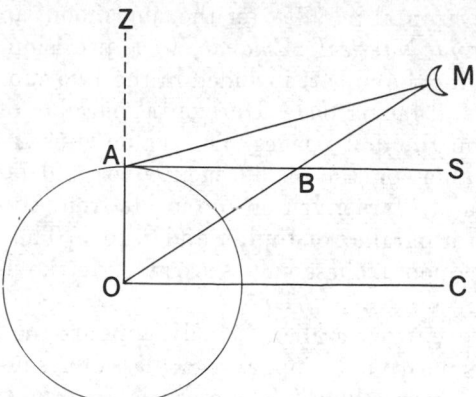

FIGURE 1613.—Geocentric parallax.

Since

$$\angle COM = \angle SBM = \angle SAM + \angle AMO,$$

then

$$\angle AMO = \angle COM - \angle SAM.$$

That is, the angle at the body between lines to the observer and the center of the earth is equal to the difference in altitude at the two places. Angle AMO is the geocentric parallax. Since it varies with altitude, it is sometimes called **parallax in altitude** (**P in A**). The maximum value for a visible body occurs when that body is on the horizon, at S. At this position the value is called **horizontal parallax** (**HP**).

The sine of horizontal parallax is equal to $\frac{r}{D}$, where r is the radius of the earth, and D the distance of the body from the center of the earth. Thus, the sine of the horizontal parallax is directly proportional to the radius of the earth, and inversely proportional to the distance of the body. Since the earth is an oblate spheriod, and not a sphere, the parallax varies slightly over different parts of the earth. The value at the equator, called **equatorial horizontal parallax,** is greatest, and the value at the poles, called **polar horizontal parallax,** is least. The difference is not enough to be of practical navigational significance. The parallax in altitude is equal almost exactly to the horizontal parallax times the cosine of the altitude (h). That is,

P in A=HP cos h.

The moon, being nearest the earth, has the greatest parallax of any celestial body used for navigation. The equatorial horizontal parallax at mean distance is 57′02″.70. As the distance of the moon varies, so does the parallax, becoming greater as the moon approaches closer to the earth, and less as it recedes, horizontal parallax varying several minutes each side of the value at mean distance. For the sun, mean equatorial horizontal parallax, called **solar parallax,** is 8″.794. Differences in position on the earth, and distance from the sun, have small effect, the maximum variation due to the latter being about 0″.15. Horizontal parallax of the planets varies considerably because of the large differences in their distances from the earth. For Venus the value varies between 5″ and 32″; for Mars, 3″ and 24″; for Jupiter, 1″ and 2″; and for Saturn, 0″.8 and 1″.0. The geocentric parallax of stars is too small to be measured, even by the most precise telescopes, since the value for the nearest star is only 0″.00003.

Daily values of horizontal parallax for the sun, moon, and planets are given in the *American Ephemeris and Nautical Almanac*, to a precision of 0″.01. In the *Nautical Almanac*, mean values for the sun are included in the two sun correction tables given on the inside front cover and facing page. Horizontal parallax of the moon is tabulated at intervals of one hour on the daily pages. This value is used to enter the lower part of the moon correction tables on the inside back cover and facing page. The additional corrections for Venus and Mars given on the inside front cover are partly for parallax. No correction is given for parallax of Jupiter and Saturn. The *Air Almanac* gives parallax corrections only for the moon. These values are given in the "Moon's P in A" column on each daily page.

Because of the geocentric parallax, a body appears too *low* in the sky. Therefore, the correction is always positive. It applies regardless of the method of observation.

1614. Summary of corrections.—The essential information regarding the application of the various corrections may be tabulated as shown below. In the "Bodies" column, the symbols are: ⊙, sun; ☾, moon; P, planets; ☆, stars. In the "Sextants" column, M refers to a marine sextant with visible horizon, A refers to a marine sextant with artificial horizon, and B refers to an artificial-horizon sextant. The tabulation assumes that completely accurate results are desired and that corrections are to be made in the usual manner, where they are available. Some of the entries need qualification or explanation which may be found in the preceding articles or chapter VIII of volume II.

Correction	Symbol	Sign	Increases with	Bodies	Sextants	Source
Instrument	I	±	changing altitude	⊙, ☾, P, ☆	M, A, B	sextant box
Index	IC	±	constant	⊙, ☾, P, ☆	M, A, B	measurement
Personal	PC	±	constant	⊙, ☾, P, ☆	M, A, B	measurement
Dip	D	−	higher height of eye	⊙, ☾, P, ☆	M	almanacs
Sea-air temp. diff.	S	±	greater temp. diff.	⊙, ☾, P, ☆	M	computation
Refraction	R	−	lower altitude	⊙, ☾, P, ☆	M, A, B	almanacs
Air temp.	T	±	greater diff. from 50° F	⊙, ☾, P, ☆	M, A, B	almanacs, table 23
Atmospheric pressure	B	±	greater diff. from 29.83 inches of mercury	⊙, ☾, P, ☆	M, A, B	*Nautical Almanac*, table 24
Irradiation	J	−		⊙	M, A	
Semidiameter	SD	±	lesser dist. from earth	⊙, ☾	M, A	almanacs
Phase	F	±	phase	P	M, A, B	*Nautical Almanac*
Augmentation	A	±	higher altitude	☾	M, A	*Nautical Almanac*
Parallax	P	+	lower altitude	⊙, ☾, P	M, A, B	almanacs

These corrections can be considered to fall into five groups:

1. *Corrections for inaccuracies in reading*. Instrument correction, index correction*, and personal correction.

2. *Corrections for inaccuracies in reference level*. Dip* and sea-air temperature difference.

3. *Corrections for bending of ray of light from body*. Refraction*, air temperature, atmospheric pressure.

4. *Adjustment to equivalent reading at center of body*. Irradiation, semidiameter*, phase, augmentation.

5. *Adjustment to equivalent reading at center of earth*. Parallax*.

In the ordinary practice of seamen, extreme accuracy is not required, and only the principal correction of each group is applied (except that augmentation is applied for the moon). These principal corrections are indicated by asterisks. For low altitudes, additional corrections are applied, as indicated in chapter VIII of volume II.

1615. Order of applying corrections.—For purposes of ordinary navigation, sextant altitudes can be applied in any order desired, using sextant altitude for the entering argument whenever altitude is required. This practice is not strictly accurate, but for altitudes usually observed, the error thus introduced is too small to be of practical significance. When extreme accuracy is desired, however, or at low altitudes, where small changes in altitude result in significant changes in correction, the order of applying corrections is important. Corrections from the first two groups of article 1614 are applied to sextant altitude (hs) to obtain **apparent (rectified) altitude (ha),** which is then used as an entering argument for obtaining corrections of the third group. For strictest accuracy, all corrections of the first three groups and, in addition, irradiation and semidiameter, should be applied before augmentation, and all other corrections before parallax.

1616. Marine sextant corrections.—Under normal conditions and when the highest accuracy is not required, it is necessary to apply only a few corrections. Several of these corrections may be combined within a single altitude correction table. In addition to corrections for index error, dip, and mean refraction, the normal altitude corrections when using the *Nautical Almanac* are: phase and parallax for Venus and Mars; semidiameter and parallax for the sun; and semidiameter, augmentation, and parallax for the moon.

1617. Artificial-horizon corrections.—When an artificial horizon is used, index correction (and any others of the first group of article 1614) is first applied. The result is then divided by two. Other corrections are then applied to the result, as applicable, in the same manner as for observations using the visible horizon. The sun and full moon are normally observed by bringing the lower limb of one image tangent to the upper limb of the other image. The lower limb is observed if the image seen in the horizon mirror is *above* the image seen in the artificial horizon, unless an inverting telescope is used, when the opposite relationship holds. With a gibbous or crescent moon, judgment may be needed to establish the positions of the limbs. In some cases better results may be obtained by superimposing one image over the other, as with a planet or star. When this is done, the *center* of the body has been observed, and no correction is applied for semidiameter (or irradiation, phase, or augmentation). There is no correction for dip (or sea-air temperature) when an artificial horizon is used.

1618. Artificial-horizon sextant corrections are the same as those for observations made by the use of the visible horizon, with two notable exceptions. First, there is no correction for dip (or sea-air temperature difference or wave height), none for semidiameter (or irradiation, phase, or augmentation), and usually none for index correction (or instrument correction). Second, because of the lower accuracy normally obtainable by artificial-horizon sextant, corrections are normally made only to the nearest whole minute of arc. As a result of these differences, refraction is the only correction normally applied, except in the case of the moon, where parallax is also applied.

1619. Corrections by *Nautical Almanac*.—In the *Nautical Almanac*, certain corrections or parts of corrections are combined. Index correction, of course, is not included because this depends upon adjustment of the sextant. The various correction tables are as follows:

"*Sun*," on the inside front cover and facing page, gives mean refraction, mean semidiameter for each of two periods during the year, and mean solar parallax. The table on the inside front cover, and repeated on the loose bookmark, is of the critical type, with altitude as the entering value. Thus, a tabulated correction applies to any value of altitude between that given half a line above it and that half a line below it. If an exact tabulated altitude is used to enter the table, the correction half a line *above* it should be used. In ordinary navigation, index correction, dip, and the correction from this table are needed for correcting marine sextant observations of the sun. For low altitudes or extremes of temperature or atmospheric pressure, a correction from the table on almanac page A4 (or tables 23 and 24 of volume II) should be applied.

"Stars and planets," on the inside front cover and repeated on the loose bookmark, gives mean refraction only, for the main tabulation. This is a critical type table, with altitude as the entering argument. The correction is always negative. In ordinary navigation, index correction, dip, and the correction from this table are the only ones needed for stars and the planets Jupiter and Saturn. For Venus and Mars, an additional correction for parallax and phase is given to the right of the main tabulation. The entering altitudes are limited to those occuring during twilight. If observations are made at other times, this additional correction should not be applied even though the altitude may fall within the tabulated range.

"Dip," on the inside front cover and repeated on the loose bookmark, is for dip of the horizon. An abbreviated dip table is also given on the page facing the inside back cover. The tables are of the critical type, and the entering argument is the height of the observer's eye, in feet and meters, above the surface of the sea. The correction, always negative, applies to all observations made with the visible sea horizon as a reference.

"Additional Correction Tables" for *nonstandard conditions,* given on almanac page A4, provides an additional correction for nonstandard temperature and atmospheric pressure. The sign of each correction is indicated. Equivalent information is given, with increased range of entering values, in tables 23 and 24 of volume II.

"Altitude Correction Tables—Moon," on the inside back cover and facing page, gives mean refraction, semidiameter, augmentation, and parallax. The entering argument is altitude for the upper portion of the table, and altitude and horizontal parallax for the lower portion. The combined correction is always positive, but 30' is to be subtracted from the altitude of the upper limb. In ordinary navigation, index correction, dip, and the correction from this table are needed in correcting marine sextant observations of the moon.

The various separate corrections available from the *Nautical Almanac* can be found as follows:

Dip. Dip table on inside front cover and repeated on loose bookmark, and on the page facing the inside back cover.

Refraction. Mean refraction from "Stars and Planets" table on inside front cover and repeated on loose bookmark, and on the facing page.

Semidiameter. For the sun, the semidiameter for the middle day of each page opening of this daily page section is given at the bottom of the sun GHA column. For the moon, semidiameter for each day is given at the bottom of the moon data columns. The values given are for GMT 1200 on the dates indicated.

Parallax. For the sun, parallax in altitude can be considered $0'.1$ for altitudes $0°$ to $70°07'$, and $0'.0$ for higher altitudes, with negligible error. This is based upon the mean value of $8''.794$. For the moon, horizontal parallax each hour is tabulated on the daily pages. Parallax in altitude is this value multiplied by the cosine of the altitude.

If artificial-horizon sextant altitudes of the sun or moon are corrected by *Nautical Almanac,* the upper and lower limb corrections can be found and the average computed.

1620. Corrections by *Air Almanac.*—In the *Air Almanac,* various corrections as applicable to hand-held marine sextant obseavations are given separately in critical type tables, to the nearest whole minute (nearest two or five minutes of refraction for low altitudes), as follows:

Dip. Inside back cover.

Refraction. Near the back. Aboard ship use the values for zero height.

Air temperature. Near the back. This is shown, not as a separate correction, but as an adjustment to mean refraction. Instructions for use of the table are given within the table.

Semidiameter. For the sun and moon, on the A.M. and P.M. pages, below the moon's P in A. Values given are for GMT 1200.

Parallax. For the moon, in the P in A table on the A.M. and P.M. pages. Horizontal parallax is the value for 0° altitude.

1621. Correcting altitudes of the sun.—In the normal practice of navigation, sun observations obtained by marine sextant with the visible horizon as reference are corrected as shown in the following examples:

Example 1.—On June 2, 1975, the lower limb of the sun is observed with a marine sextant having an IC of (−)2′.0, from a height of eye of 38 feet. The hs is 51°28′.4.

Required.—Ho using (1) *Nautical Almanac,* and (2) *Air Almanac.*

Solution.—

(1)	+ ☉ −		(2)	+ ☉ −	
IC		2′.0	IC		2′
D		6′.0	D		6′
☉	15′.2		R		1′
sum	15′.2	8′.0	SD	16′	
corr.		(+)7′.2	sum	16′	9′
hs		51°28′.4	corr.		(+)7′
Ho		51°35′.6	hs		51°28′
			Ho		51°35′

Example 2.—On June 2, 1975, the upper limb of the sun is observed with a marine sextant having an IC of (+)1′.0, from a height of eye of 45 feet. The hs is 32°47′.9.

Required.—Ho using (1) *Nautical Almanac,* and (2) *Air Almanac.*

Solution.—

(1)	+ ☉̄ −		(2)	+ ☉̄ −	
IC	1′.0		IC	1′	
D		6′.5	D		7′
☉̄		17′.3	R		2′
sum	1′.0	23′.8	SD		16′
corr.		(−)22′.8	sum	1′	25′
hs		32°47′.9	corr.		(−)24′
Ho		32°25′.1	hs		32°48′
			Ho		32°24′

A convenient work form is helpful in the solution. Once the form is prepared, the corrections can be entered in any order desired. The symbols ☉ and ☉̄ are used for the corrections from the sun table on the inside front cover of the *Nautical Almanac.* If additional corrections are used, they are included in the same manner as those shown. Observations by artificial horizon and by artificial-horizon sextant, and low-altitude observations and back sights, are discussed elsewhere in this chapter.

1622. Correcting altitudes of the moon.—Moon observations by marine sextant with the visible horizon as reference are normally corrected as shown in the following examples:

Example 1.—At about GMT 1100 on June 2, 1975, the lower limb of the moon is observed with a marine sextant having an IC of (+) 3′.2, from a height of eye of 32 feet. The hs is 18°04′.6.

Required.—Ho using (1) *Nautical Almanac*, and (2) *Air Almanac*.
Solution.—

(1)	+ ☾ −		(2)	+ ☾ −	
IC	3′.2		IC	3′	
D		5′.5	D		6′
☾	62′.5		R		3′
L	0′.8		SD	15′	
sum	66′.5	5′.5	P	51′	
corr.	(+)1°01′.0		sum	69′	9′
hs	18°04′.6		corr.	(+)60′	
Ho	19°05′.6		hs	18°05′	
			Ho	19°05′	

Example 2.—At about GMT 0900 on June 2, 1975, the upper limb of the moon is observed with a marine sextant having an IC of (−)1′.6, from a height of eye of 70 feet. The hs is 66°47′.3.

Required.—Ho using (1) *Nautical Almanac*, and (2) *Air Almanac*.
Solution.—

(1)	+ ☾ −		(2)	+ ☾ −	
IC		1′.6	IC		2′
D		8′.1	D		8′
☾	33′.1		R		−
U	3′.2		SD		15′
add'l	30′.0		P	21′	
sum	36′.3	39′.7	sum	21′	25′
corr.	(−)3′.4		corr.	(−)4′	
hs	66°47′.3		hs	66°47′	
Ho	66°43′.9		Ho	66°43′	

The typical work forms shown are useful in problems of this type. The symbol ☾ is used for the correction from the upper part of the moon correction table on the inside back cover, and facing page, of the *Nautical Almanac*. The letters L and U are used for the corrections from the lower part of this table. Observations by artificial horizon, and by artificial-horizon sextant, and low-altitude observations and back sights, are discussed elsewhere in this chapter, as are additional corrections for use when unusual accuracy is desired.

1623. Correcting altitudes of planets.—When Venus and Mars are observed by marine sextant using the visible horizon as reference, sextant altitudes are normally corrected as shown in the following example:

Example.—On June 19, 1975, Venus is observed with a marine sextant having no IC, from a height of eye of 28 feet. The hs is 44°21′.3.

Required.—Ho using (1) *Nautical Almanac*, and (2) *Air Almanac*.
Solution.—

(1)	+ V −		(2)	+ V −	
IC	−	−	IC	−	−
D		5′.1	D		5′
☆-P		1′.0	R		1′
add'l	0′.3		sum	−	6′
sum	0′.3	6′.1	corr.	(−)6′	
corr.	(−)5′.8		hs	44°21′	
hs	44°21′.3		Ho	44°15′	
Ho	44°15′.5				

For Jupiter and Saturn, no additional correction is given. Correction of observations of these bodies is the same as corrections of star observations (art. 1624). Work forms are useful. The symbol ☆-P is used for the correction taken from the "Star-Planet" table on the inside front cover of the *Nautical Almanac*. If additional corrections are to be used, for results of unusual accuracy or low altitudes, they are included in the form in the same manner as those shown. Observations by artificial horizon and by artificial-horizon sextant, and low-altitude observations and back sights are discussed elsewhere in this chapter.

1624. Correcting altitudes of stars.—Star observations by marine sextant, using the visible horizon as reference, are normally corrected as shown in the following example:

Example.—Miaplacidus is observed with a marine sextant having an IC of (+)1ʹ.0, from a height of eye of 50 feet. The hs is 27°54ʹ.0.

Required.—Ho using (1) *Nautical Almanac*, and (2) *Air Almanac*.

Solution.—

(1)	+ ☆ −			(2)	+ ☆ −	
IC	1ʹ.0			IC	1ʹ	
D		6ʹ.9		D		7ʹ
☆-P		1ʹ.8		R		2ʹ
sum	1ʹ.0	8ʹ.7		sum	1ʹ	9ʹ
corr.		(−)7ʹ.7		corr.		(−)8ʹ
hs		27°54ʹ.0		hs		27°54ʹ
Ho		27°46ʹ.3		Ho		27°46ʹ

Work forms for such problems are helpful. Additional corrections, used when unusual accuracy is desired, are included in the same manner as those shown. Observations by artificial horizon and by artificial-horizon sextant, and low-altitude observations and back sights, are discussed elsewhere in this chapter.

1625. Low altitudes are normally avoided because of large and variable refraction. But sometimes these are the only observations available. This is particularly true in polar regions, where the sun may be the only celestial body available, and may not reach an altitude of more than a few degrees over a considerable period. In lower latitudes the sun may appear briefly just before sunset or just after sunrise. Low-altitude observations can supply useful information if additional corrections are applied. Reliable lines of position can generally be obtained from low-altitude observations, but when conditions are abnormal, the errors introduced are generally larger than for higher altitudes, and the precautions of article 806 of volume II should be particularly observed.

In correcting low-altitude observations, which for normal conditions can be defined as those less than 5°, first apply corrections from the first two groups of article 1614 to obtain apparent altitude (ha). Normally, this includes only index correction and dip. Then apply the remaining corrections, using apparent altitude when an altitude is needed for entering correction tables. The corrections normally applied are mean refraction, air temperature, atmospheric pressure, semidiameter (as applicable), and parallax (for the sun and moon).

In practice, sextant altitudes are corrected in the usual manner, except that additional corrections are applied, and the process is divided into two parts. The use of apparent altitude for finding parallax introduces an error but this is too small (less than 0ʹ.1) for practical consideration. If the *Nautical Almanac* is used, corrections for altitudes between the horizon and 10° are given in a noncritical type table on almanac page A3. The correction for a negative altitude can be obtained by extrapolation without introducing a significant error for values obtained at ship heights of eye. A combined temperature-atmospheric pressure correction can be obtained from the table on almanac page A4. This table is intended for use without interpolation between columns. Separate corrections can be obtained from tables 23 and 24 of volume II, which provide interpolated values for greater accuracy. They also provide greater range of temperature and atmospheric pressure.

To correct a low altitude of the sun, then, apply index correction and dip to sextant altitude to find apparent altitude. Using this altitude as an entering value, find the following corrections and apply them to apparent altitude:

sun correction (☽ or ☉), from page A3 of the *Nautical Almanac;*

combined temperature-atmospheric pressure correction (TB), from page A4 of the *Nautical Almanac* (separate corrections for temperature (T) and atmospheric pressure (B) from tables 23 and 24, respectively, can be used *in place of* the combined correction).

If the *Air Almanac* is used, the mean refraction and air temperature corrections can be combined by using the factor in the refraction table. A semidiameter correction of 16′ is added if the lower limb is observed, and subtracted if the upper limb is observed. Since corrections are to whole minutes only, parallax is not used for the sun. In summary, apply index correction and dip to sextant altitude to find apparent altitude. Using this altitude as an entering value, where needed, apply the following corrections to apparent altitude:

refraction (adjusted for air temperature) (R), from table near back of *Air Almanac;*
atmospheric pressure (B), from table 24;
semidiameter (SD), 16′ (add if lower limb, and subtract if upper limb).

Example 1.—On June 2, 1975, the lower limb of the sun is observed with a marine sextant having an IC of (+)1′8 from a height of eye of 45 feet. The hs is 1°24′4, air temperature 88°F, and atmospheric pressure 29.78 inches.

Required.—Ho using (1) *Nautical Almanac,* (2) tables 23 and 24, and (3) *Air Almanac.*

Solution.—

(1)

	+	☉ −
IC	1′8	
D		6′5
sum	1′8	6′5
corr.		(−)4′7
hs		1°24′4
ha		1°19′7

	☉	6′0
TB	2′5	
sum	2′5	6′0
corr.		(−)3′5
ha		1°19′7
Ho		1°16′2

(2)

	+	☉ −
IC	1′8	
D		6′5
sum	1′8	6′5
corr.		(−)4′7
hs		1°24′4
ha		1°19′7

	☉	6′0
T	1′5	
B	−	
sum	1′5	6′0
corr.		(−)4′5
ha		1°19′7
Ho		1°15′2

(3)

	+	☉ −
IC	2′	
D		7′
sum	2′	7′
corr.		(−)5′
hs		1°24′
ha		1°19′

R		18′
B	−	
SD	16′	
sum	16′	18′
corr.		(−)2′
ha		1°19′
Ho		1°17′

The larger intervals given in the *Air Almanac* refraction table may introduce additional error. In this example, the temperature is changed to Celsius (centigrade), giving a value of 31°. The factor at a height of 0 feet corresponding to this temperature is 0.9. With this and the apparent altitude, the combined refraction and air temperature correction is found to be as shown. Approximately the same result would have been obtained by correcting for mean refraction (without the factor) and temperature (from table 23) separately.

If the moment at which either limb is tangent to the horizon is noted, an observation of 0° altitude has been made without a sextant.

Example 2.—On June 2, 1975, the sun is observed at sunset as the upper limb drops below the horizon, from a height of eye of 38 feet. The air temperature is (−)10° F, and atmospheric pressure 30.06 inches. Double extrapolation would be needed to solve this problem by the *Nautical Almanac*. A better solution is provided by means of tables 23 and 24.

Required.—Ho using (1) tables 23 and 24, and (2) *Air Almanac.*

Solution.—

(1)	+ ☉ −		(2)	+ ☉ −	
IC	−	−	IC	−	−
D		6ʹ0	D		6ʹ
sum	−	6ʹ0	sum		6ʹ
corr.		(−)6ʹ0	corr.		(−)6ʹ
hs		0°00ʹ0	hs		0°00ʹ
ha		(−)0°06ʹ0	ha		(−)0°06ʹ
☉		51ʹ5	R		42ʹ
T		4ʹ8	B		−
B		0ʹ3	SD		16ʹ
sum	−	56ʹ6	sum	−	58ʹ
corr.		(−)56ʹ6	corr.		(−)58ʹ
ha		(−)0°06ʹ0	ha		(−)0°06ʹ
Ho		(−)1°02ʹ6	Ho		(−)1°04ʹ

Corrections are applied algebraically. Therefore, for negative altitudes a negative correction is *numerically* added, and a positive correction is *numerically* subtracted.

To correct low altitudes of the moon, apply index correction and dip to sextant altitude to find apparent altitude. Using this altitude as an entering value, find the following corrections and apply them to apparent altitudes:

moon correction (☾), from inside back cover, and facing page, of *Nautical Almanac;*

lower or upper limb correction (L or U), from inside back cover, and facing page, of *Nautical Almanac;*

additional correction (add'l, (−)30ʹ, for upper limb observation only);

combined temperature-atmospheric pressure correction (TB), from page A4 of the *Nautical Almanac* (separate corrections for temperature (T) and atmospheric pressure (B) from tables 23 and 24, respectively, can be used in place of the combined correction).

If the *Air Almanac* is used, correct the apparent altitude by applying the following corrections:

refraction (adjusted for air temperature) (R), from table near back of *Air Almanac;*

atmospheric pressure (B), from table 24;

semidiameter, from daily page;

parallax, from daily page.

Example 3.—At GMT 17ʰ14ᵐ27ˢ on June 2, 1975, the upper limb of the moon is observed with a marine sextant having no IC, from a height of eye of 33 feet. The hs is 2°35ʹ4, air temperature 63° F, and atmospheric pressure 29.81 inches.

Required.—Ho using (1) *Nautical Almanac,* (2) tables 23 and 24, and (3) *Air Almanac.*

Solution.—

(1)	+ ☽ −		(2)	+ ☽ −		(3)	+ ☽ −	
IC	−	−	IC	−	−	IC	−	−
D		5ʹ6	D		5ʹ6	D		6ʹ
sum	−	5ʹ6	sum	−	5ʹ6	sum	−	6ʹ
corr.		(−)5ʹ6	corr.		(−)5ʹ6	corr.		(−)6ʹ
hs		2°35ʹ4	hs		2°35ʹ4	hs		2°35ʹ
ha		2°29ʹ8	ha		2°29ʹ8	ha		2°29ʹ

(1)			(2)			(3)		
☽ 52ʹ1			☽ 52ʹ1			R		16ʹ
U 1ʹ1			U 1ʹ1			B −		
add'l		30ʹ0	add'l		30ʹ0	SD		15ʹ
TB 0ʹ4			T 0ʹ4			P	54ʹ	
sum 53ʹ6		30ʹ0	B −			sum	54ʹ	31ʹ
corr.		(+)23ʹ6	sum 53ʹ6		30ʹ0	corr.		(+)23ʹ
ha		2°29ʹ8	corr.		(+)23ʹ6	ha		2°29ʹ
Ho		2°53ʹ4	ha		2°29ʹ8	Ho		2°52ʹ
			Ho		2°53ʹ4			

A lower limb solution would be the same, except that an L correction would have been used from the *Nautical Almanac* and there would be no "add'l" correction, and in the *Air Almanac* solution the sign of the semidiameter correction would be reversed. The moon correction table on the inside back cover, and facing page, of the *Nautical Almanac* extends to a minimum altitude of 0°. The corrections for negative altitudes can be found by extrapolation.

To correct low altitudes of the planets Venus and Mars, apply index correction and dip to sextant altitude to find apparent altitude. Using this altitude as an entering value, find the following corrections and apply them to apparent altitude:

    star-planet correction (☆-P), from page A3 of the *Nautical Almanac;*

    additional correction (add'l), from page A2 of the *Nautical Almanac;*

    combined temperature-atmospheric pressure correction (TB), from page A4 of the *Nautical Almanac* (separate corrections for temperature (T) and atmospheric pressure (B) from tables 23 and 24, respectively, can be used *in place of* the combined correction).

If the *Air Almanac* is used, correct the apparent altitude by applying the following corrections:

    refraction (adjusted for air temperature) (R), from table near back of *Air Almanac;*

    atmospheric pressure (B), from table 24.

Example 4.—On November 28, 1975, Mars is observed with a marine sextant having an IC of (+)3ʹ5, from a height of eye of 17 feet. The hs is 4°02ʹ6, air temperature 2°F, and atmospheric pressure 29.67 inches.

Required.—Ho using (1) *Nautical Almanac,* (2) tables 23 and 24, and (3) *Air Almanac.*

Solution.—

(1)	+ M −		(2)	+ M −		(3)	+ M −

(1)
	+ M −
IC	3′.5
D	4′.0
sum	3′.5 4′.0
corr.	(−)0′.5
hs	4°02′.6
ha	4°02′.1

(2)
	+ M −
IC	3′.5
D	4′.0
sum	3′.5 4′.0
corr.	(−)0′.5
hs	4°02′.6
ha	4°02′.1

(3)
	+ M −
IC	4′
D	4′
sum	4′ 4′
corr.	—
hs	4°03′
ha	4°03′

(1)
☆-P	11′.7
add'l	0′.3
TB	1′.5
sum	0′.3 13′.2
corr.	(−)12′.9
ha	4°02′.1
Ho	3°49′.2

(2)
☆-P	11′.7
add'l	0′.3
T	1′.2
B	0′.1
sum	0′.4 12′.9
corr.	(−)12′.5
ha	4°02′.1
Ho	3°49′.9

(3)
R	14′
B	—
sum	14′
corr.	(−)14′
ha	4°03′
Ho	3°49′

The solution for Jupiter and Saturn, and for stars, is identical with that of example 4, except that the additional correction (phase and parallax) is omitted.

1626. Back sights.—An altitude measured by facing *away* from the celestial body being observed is called a **back sight.** It may be used when an obstruction, such as another vessel, obscures the horizon under the body; when that horizon is indistinct; or when observations are made in both directions, either to determine dip or to avoid error due to suspected abnormal dip. Such an observation is possible only when the arc of the sextant is sufficiently long to permit measurement of the angle, which is the supplement of the altitude. For such an observation of the sun or moon, the lower limb is observed when the image is brought below the horizon, appearing as a normal upper limb observation, and vice versa. To correct such an altitude, subtract it from 180° and reverse the sign of corrections of the first two groups of article 1614 (normally only index correction and dip).

Example.—On June 2, 1975, a back sight is taken of the lower limb of the sun, with a marine sextant having an IC of (−)2′.0, from a height of eye of 24 feet. The measured sextant altitude is 118°41′.4.

Required.—Ho using (1) *Nautical Almanac,* and (2) *Air Almanac.*

Solution.—

(1)
	+ ☉ −
IC	2′.0
D	4′.8
☉	15′.4
sum	22′.2 —
corr.	(+)22′.2
180°−hs	61°18′.6
Ho	61°40′.8

(2)
	+ ☉ −
IC	2′
D	5′
R	1′
SD	16′
sum	23′ 1′
corr.	(+)22′
180°−hs	61°19′
Ho	61°41′

1627. Correcting horizontal angles.—When a marine sextant is used to measure the horizontal angle between two objects, the result is not usually desired to a precision that makes correction necessary, unless the sextant has an unusually large index error. However, if precise results are desired, corrections of the first group only of article 1614 are applied. If a personal error exists, it is not likely to be the same as for altitudes. For measuring angles between two objects differing widely in altitude, as between two stars, it is not likely that results will be required to such precision that additional correction for the third, fourth, and fifth groups of article 1614 will be needed. If they are, the method of application can be determined from the principles of spherical trigonometry. In this case, the altitudes of both bodies will also be needed. Corrections for the second group of article 1614 are not applicable.

Problems

1617a. At about GMT 0800 on June 2, 1975, the following bodies are observed with marine sextants having an IC of (+)2ʹ.2, using an artificial horizon: sun (lower limb) hs 134°33ʹ.9, moon (upper limb) hs 77°23ʹ.4, Venus hs 98°04ʹ.6, Schedar hs 43°24ʹ.4.

Required.—Ho of each observation using (1) *Nautical Almanac*, and (2) *Air Almanac.*

Answers.—(1) Sun Ho 67°33ʹ.6, moon Ho 39°09ʹ.1, Venus Ho 49°02ʹ.6, Schedar Ho 21°40ʹ.9; (2) sun Ho 67°34ʹ, moon Ho 39°09ʹ, Venus Ho 49°03ʹ, Schedar Ho 21°41ʹ.

1617b. At about GMT 0300 on June 2, 1975, the following bodies are observed with bubble sextants having no IC: sun hs 23°51ʹ, moon hs 52°20ʹ, Jupiter hs 63°18ʹ, Eltanin hs 24°45ʹ.

Required.—Ho of each observation using (1) *Nautical Almanac*, and (2) *Air Almanac.*

Answers.—(1) and (2) Sun Ho 23°49ʹ, moon Ho 52°52ʹ, Jupiter Ho 63°18ʹ, Eltanin Ho 24°43ʹ.

1621a. On June 2, 1975, the lower limb of the sun is observed with a marine sextant having an IC of (+)1ʹ.8, from a height of eye of 34 feet. The hs is 41°34ʹ.8.

Required.—Ho using (1) *Nautical Almanac*, and (2) *Air Almanac.*

Answers.—(1) Ho 41°45ʹ.8; (2) Ho 41°46ʹ.

1621b. On June 2, 1975, the upper limb of the sun is observed with a marine sextant having no IC, from a height of eye of 30 feet. The hs is 15°21ʹ.7.

Required.—Ho using (1) *Nautical Almanac*, and (2) *Air Almanac.*

Answers.—(1) Ho 14°57ʹ.1; (2) Ho 14°57ʹ.

1621c. On June 2, 1975, the lower limb of the sun is observed with a marine sextant having an IC of (−)1ʹ.3, from a height of eye of 43 feet. Another ship is between the observer and the horizon, at a distance of 1.4 miles from the observer. The water line of this ship is used as the horizontal reference. The hs is 25°18ʹ.2.

Required.—Ho using table 22 and (1) *Nautical Almanac*, and (2) *Air Almanac.*

Answers.—(1) Ho 25°12ʹ.9; (2) Ho 25°13ʹ.

1622a. At about GMT 2100 on June 2, 1975, the lower limb of the moon is observed with a marine sextant having an IC of (−)2ʹ.5, from a height of eye of 55 feet. The hs is 47°35ʹ.5.

Required.—Ho using (1) *Nautical Almanac*, and (2) *Air Almanac.*

Answers.—(1) Ho 48°16ʹ.3; (2) Ho 48°16ʹ.

1622b. At about GMT 2300 on June 2, 1975, the upper limb of the moon is observed with a marine sextant having an IC of (+)4ʹ.0, from a height of eye of 12 feet. The hs is 22°58ʹ.3.

Required.—Ho using (1) *Nautical Almanac*, and (2) *Air Almanac*.

Answers.—(1) Ho 23°31.8; (2) Ho 23°32′.

1623a. On June 18, 1975, Mars is observed with a marine sextant having an IC of (+)2.2, from a height of eye of 60 feet. The hs is 34°11.7.

Required.—Ho using (1) *Nautical Almanac*, and (2) *Air Almanac*.

Answers.—(1) Ho 34°05.1; (2) Ho 34°05′.

1623b. Jupiter is observed with a marine sextant having an IC of ( )1.0, from a height of eye of 27 feet. The hs is 11°23.9.

Required.—Ho using (1) *Nautical Almanac*, and (2) *Air Almanac*.

Answers.—(1) Ho 11°13.2; (2) Ho 11°13′.

1624. Alpheratz is observed with a marine sextant having no IC, from a height of eye of 42 feet. The hs is 38°20.3.

Required.—Ho using (1) *Nautical Almanac*, and (2) *Air Almanac*.

Answers.—(1) Ho 38°12.8; (2) Ho 38°13′.

1625a. On June 2, 1975, the lower limb of the sun is observed with a marine sextant having an IC of (−)2.3, from a height of eye of 24 feet. The hs is 2°04.6, air temperature 65°F, and atmospheric pressure 30.81 inches.

Required.—Ho using (1) *Nautical Almanac*, (2) tables 23 and 24, and (3) *Air Almanac*.

Answers.—(1) Ho 1°55.1; (2) Ho 1°55.1; (3) Ho 1°55′.

1625b. On July 2, 1975, the sun is observed as the upper limb drops below the horizon at sunset, from a height of eye of 19 feet. The air temperature is 16°F, and atmospheric pressure 29.90 inches.

Required.—Ho using (1) *Nautical Almanac*, (2) tables 23 and 24, and (3) *Air Almanac*.

Answers.—(1) Ho (−)0°59.9; (2) Ho (−)0°57.8; (3) Ho (−)0°58′.

1625c. At GMT 6^{h}03^{m}29^s on June 2, 1975, the upper limb of the moon is observed with a marine sextant having an IC of (+)2.6, from a height of eye of 35 feet. The hs is 1°12.6, air temperature (−)23°F, and atmospheric pressure 29.04 inches.

Required.—Ho using (1) tables 23 and 24, and (2) *Air Almanac*.

Answers.—(1) Ho 1°22.3; (2) Ho 1°20′.

1625d. At GMT 12^{h}44^{m}01^s on June 2, 1975, the lower limb of the moon is observed with a marine sextant having an IC of (+)3.2, from a height of eye of 22 feet. The hs is 0°24.4, air temperature 40°F, and atmospheric pressure 29.94 inches.

Required.—Ho using (1) *Nautical Almanac*, (2) tables 23 and 24, and (3) *Air Almanac*.

Answers.—(1) Ho 1°01.2; (2) Ho 1°01.5; (3) Ho 0°58′.

1625e. On January 19, 1975, Venus is observed with a marine sextant having an IC of (−)0.5, from a height of eye of 31 feet. The hs is 3°29.8, air temperature 55°F, and atmospheric pressure 30.15 inches.

Required.—Ho using (1) *Nautical Almanac*, (2) tables 23 and 24, and (3) *Air Almanac*.

Answers.—(1) Ho 3°10.7; (2) Ho 3°10.7; (3) Ho 3°10′.

1625f. Saturn is observed with a marine sextant having an IC of (−)2.3, from a height of eye of 37 feet. The hs is 4°39.2, air temperature 76°F, and atmospheric pressure 28.89 inches.

Required.—Ho using (1) *Nautical Almanac*, (2) tables 23 and 24, and (3) *Air Almanac*.

Answers.—(1) Ho 4°21.1; (2) Ho 4°21.1; (3) Ho 4°21′.

1625g. Gienah is observed with a marine sextant having no IC, from a height of eye of 44 feet. The hs is 2°46′.1, air temperature 35°F, and atmospheric pressure 29.92 inches.

Required.—Ho using (1) *Nautical Almanac*, (2) tables 23 and 24, and (3) *Air Almanac*.

Answers.—(1) Ho 2°23′.4; (2) Ho 2°36′.6; (3) Ho 2°21′.

1626. On June 2, 1975, a back sight is taken of the lower limb of the sun, with a marine sextant having an IC of (+)1′.7, from a height of eye of 49 feet. The measured sextant altitude is 141°04′.9.

Required.—Ho using (1) *Nautical Almanac*, and (2) *Air Almanac*.

Answers.—(1) Ho 39°15′.0; (2) Ho 39°15′.

1627. The horizontal angle between two objects is measured with a marine sextant having an IC of (+)4′.0. The measured angle is 85°14′.6.

Required.—Corrected angle.

Answer.—Corrected angle 85°18′.6.

CHAPTER XVII

LINES OF POSITION FROM CELESTIAL OBSERVATIONS

1701. Circles of equal altitude.—For every point on the earth there is a zenith (art. 1426) vertically overhead on the celestial sphere (art. 1403). Likewise, every point on the celestial sphere is vertically over *some* terrestrial point, called its **geographical position** (**GP**). However, since the earth rotates on its axis, causing *apparent* rotation of the celestial sphere, the GP of any point on the celestial sphere is continually moving to the westward, at the rate of about 15° per hour. If a celestial body is changing its apparent position on the celestial sphere, this motion is added to that caused by rotation, so that the rates of motion of the GP's of various bodies differ slightly. Further, this motion may not be exactly westward, having a small northerly or southerly component

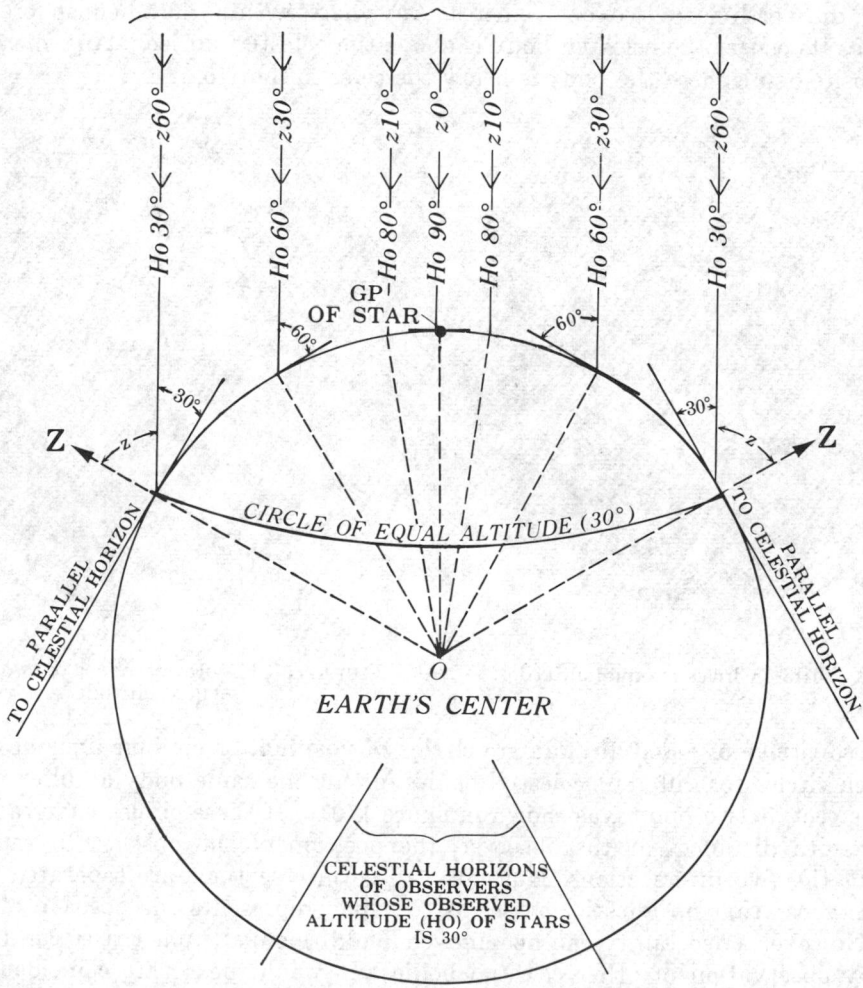

FIGURE 1701a.—Circles of equal altitude.

as the body changes declination, due either to its own proper motion or precession of the equinoxes (art. 1419), or a combination of the two.

At any moment the declination of a celestial body is equal to the latitude of its GP. The Greenwich hour angle (GHA) of the body, if not greater than 180°, is equal to the longitude (west) of the GP. If the GHA is greater than 180°, its explement (360°−GHA) is equal to the longitude (east). Thus, if it is established that a body of known coordinates is in the zenith of an observer, the position of the observer is known. However, for the celestial bodies used in navigation, this condition rarely occurs for any individual observer, and is difficult to determine when it does occur.

More commonly, the altitude (art. 1430) is measured, and from this the zenith distance (art. 1430) can be determined. This value defines a circle on the earth, as shown in figures 1701a and 1701b. Thus, if the observer is one mile from the GP, in *any* direction, he is 1′ from it, and his zenith is 1′ from the celestial body. Anywhere on a circle of one mile (1′) radius, with the GP as the center, the zenith distance is 1′. Similarly, if the zenith distance is 10°, the observer may be anywhere on a circle (assuming a spherical earth) of radius 10×60=600 miles, with the GP as the center. If the zenith distance is 30°, the radius is 1,800 miles; if 60°, the radius is 3,600 miles; and if 90° (body on the celestial horizon), the radius is 5,400 miles. This is a great circle dividing the earth into two hemispheres. Anywhere within that hemisphere having the GP as its center the celestial body is above the celestial horizon. Anywhere within the opposite hemisphere the body is below the celestial horizon.

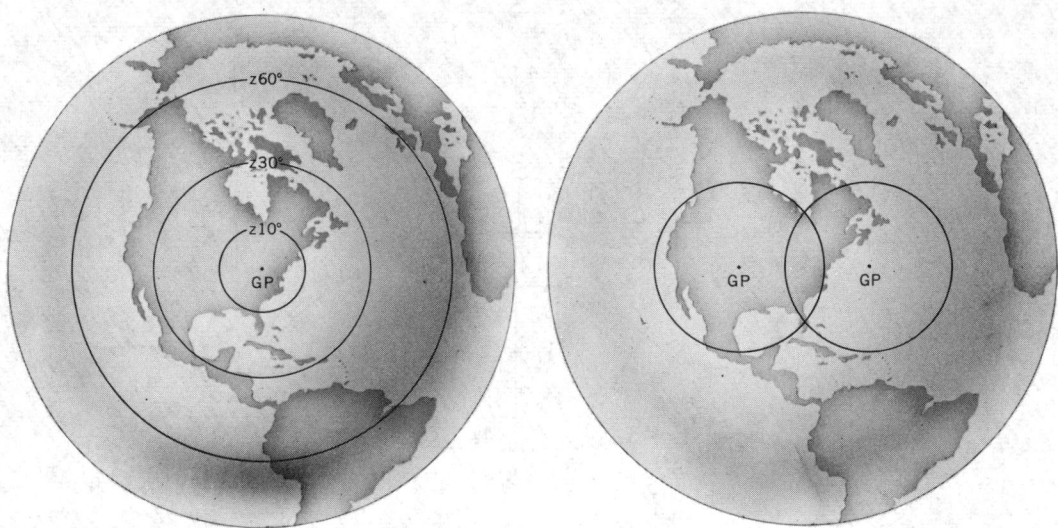

FIGURE 1701b.—Circles of equal altitude.   FIGURE 1701c.—Intersections of two circles of equal altitude.

These **circles of equal altitude** are **circles of position,** or circular **lines of position.** Two such circles for different celestial bodies, or for the same body at different times, may intersect at two points, as shown in figure 1701c. If these circles have radii equal to the zenith distances at the observer, the position of the observer is established at one of the two intersections. Normally, these intersections are separated by such great distances that no question arises as to which represents the position of the observer. However, uncertainty can be removed if additional altitude circles can be established by observation of other celestial bodies. It would be a rare coincidence for a third such circle to pass through both intersections of the first two. The third observation also serves as a check on the accuracy of the first two. The ambiguity might also be resolved by noting the azimuth of either or both of the bodies, for the azimuth should be in the same direction as the radius of the circle of position, measured at the intersection.

1702. Utilizing circles of equal altitude.—For most altitudes conveniently observed, the plotting of circles of equal altitude involves certain difficulties. Because of the long radii of such circles, a chart of very small scale would be needed, and virtually any chart distortion would introduce some error, unless an azimuthal projection (art. 316) centered upon the GP were used, an impractical procedure with a moving GP for each body. The appearance of two circles of equal altitude plotted on a Mercator chart is shown in figure 1702.

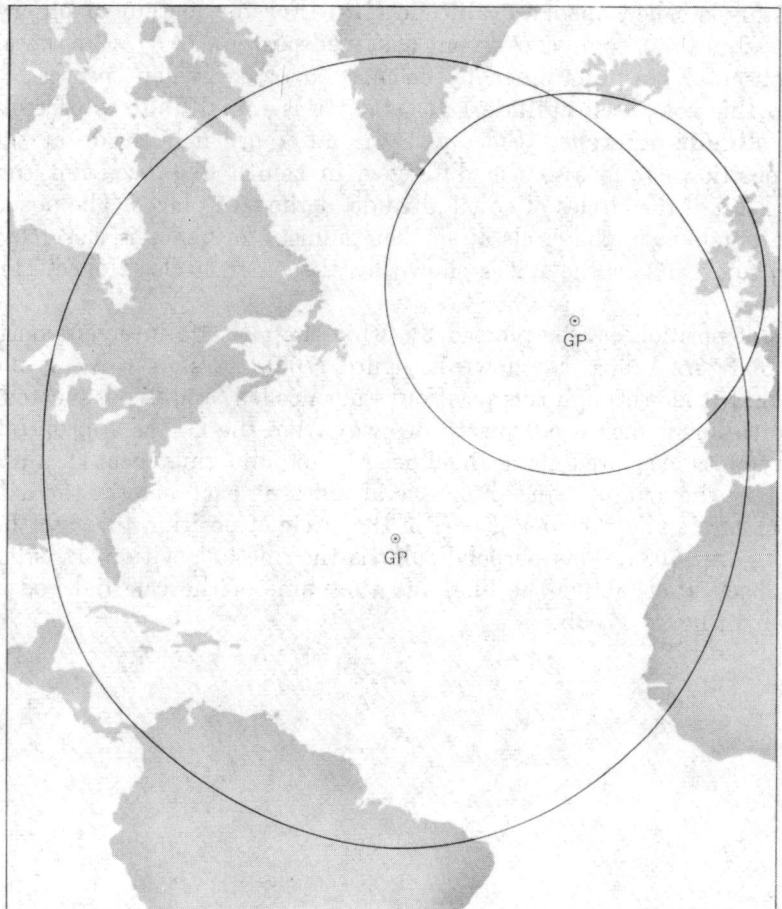

FIGURE 1702.—Circles of equal altitude on a Mercator chart.

It has been suggested that the second difficulty, that of distortion, might be overcome by plotting directly on a sphere, using equipment designed for this purpose. While theoretically sound, this procedure does not overcome the first difficulty, that of scale, and has not proved practical. A variation of this has been the use of movable arcs, by which a small-scale model of one or more navigational triangles (art. 1433) is mechanically produced. The coordinates are carefully measured by means of sliding indices controlled by verniers or micrometers. Another variation has been a graphical solution based upon the drawing of a diagram according to any of various principles. Although a number of mechanical and graphical solutions have been devised, and some have proved practical (ch. XXI), none has been generally accepted as superior to the commonly used tabular methods of solution.

However, as the altitude of a body increases, reducing the zenith distance, both distortion and scale difficulties decrease. Also, on a Mercator chart, they decrease as the GP approaches the equator. The observation of a celestial body near the zenith is difficult, but in the case of the sun no alternative may be available near noon in the Tropics. Such a situation does provide an easy solution and may permit obtaining of a fix from two observations of the same body, with only a few minutes between observations. This solution is discussed further in article 2011.

1703. The line of position.—For zenith distances too great to plot conveniently, a line of position can be laid down in another manner.

The altitude of a celestial body may be measured. After appropriate corrections are applied, this is called **observed altitude (Ho).** For the instant of observation, the altitude and azimuth at some convenient **assumed position (AP)** near the actual position of the observer are determined by calculation or equivalent process. The difference between this **computed altitude (Hc)** and Ho is the **altitude intercept (a),** sometimes called **altitude difference.** Since a is the difference in altitude at the assumed and actual positions, it is also the difference in zenith distance, and therefore the difference in radii of the circles of equal altitude at the two places. The position having the greater altitude is on the circle of smaller radius, and hence is closer to the GP of the body. In figure 1703a the AP is shown on the inner circle. Hence, Hc is greater than Ho.

The line of position can be plotted by using the altitude intercept portion of the information of figure 1703a, as shown in figure 1703b. First, the AP is plotted. The circle of equal altitude through this position is not needed, and is not plotted. From the AP the azimuth line is measured toward or away from the GP as appropriate, and the altitude intercept is measured along this line. At the point thus located, a line is drawn perpendicular to the azimuth line. For several miles on each side of the azimuth line, this perpendicular can be considered part of the circle of position through the observer, as shown in figure 1703a. This perpendicular is the line of position. It is labeled with the time of observation above the line, and the name of the celestial body below the line, as shown in figure 1703b.

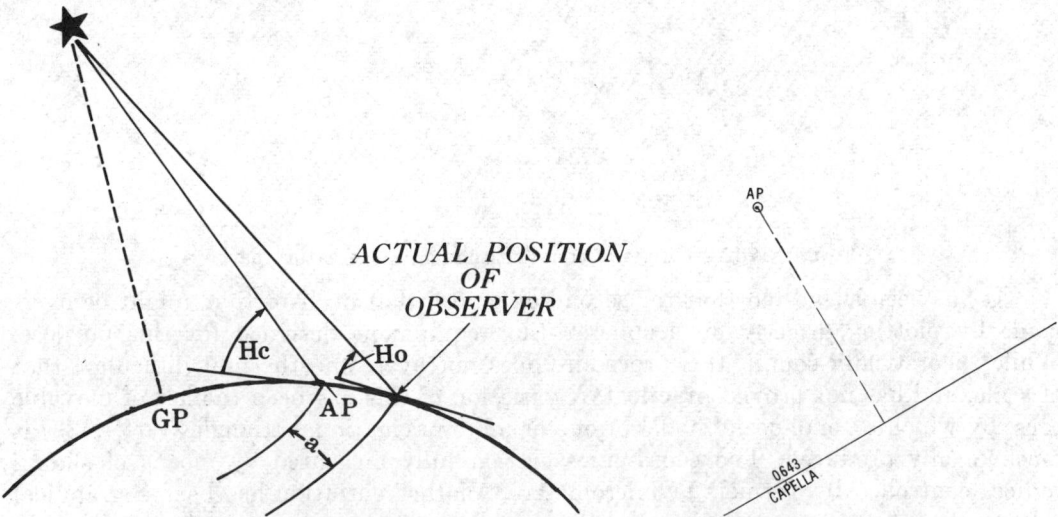

FIGURE 1703a.—The basis for the line of position from a celestial observation.

FIGURE 1703b.—A line of position from observation of the star Capella at 0643.

For neatness of plot the azimuth line should not be extended beyond the line of position for the AP, unless it is extended a short distance in the direction of the body, and the symbol of the body observed is shown to indicate whether a "toward" or "away" observation. This method is used in the examples of Pub. No. 229. Some navigators may omit the azimuth line, showing only the AP and line of position, and using a straightedge as a guide for the dividers in measuring the altitude difference. This is good practice, for it reduces the number of lines on the plotting sheet, and therefore minimizes the possibility of making an error. However, until one gains confidence in plotting lines of position, it is desirable to show the azimuth line.

For plotting a line of position from a celestial observation, then, only the assumed position, altitude intercept (with an indication of which altitude is greater), and azimuth are needed.

The assumed position is chosen somewhat arbitrarily. It may be the dead reckoning position, an estimated position, or any arbitrarily chosen position nearby. Most commonly, however, the **assumed latitude** (aL) is taken as the *nearest* whole degree of latitude to the DR or EP; and the **assumed longitude** ($a\lambda$) is selected so that the local hour angle is a whole degree. The location of the line of position is independent of the location of the AP (within reasonable limits), assuming only that the altitude intercept is measured from the AP used for determining Hc. That is, each AP has its own altitude intercept, depending upon its distance from the line of position.

The altitude intercept, the numerical difference between Hc and Ho, is customarily expressed in nautical miles (minutes of arc), and labeled **T** or **A** to indicate whether the line of position is **toward** or **away** from the GP, as measured from the AP:

$$
\begin{array}{ll}
\text{Hc } 37°51\!.6 & \text{Hc } 61°57\!.3 \\
\text{Ho } \underline{37°43\!.9} & \text{Ho } \underline{62°12\!.7} \\
a \quad\quad 7.7\text{A} & a \quad\quad 15.4\text{T}
\end{array}
$$

The azimuth is customarily determined by computation or table at the time of determining Hc.

This method of plotting a line of position from a celestial observation was suggested by Marcq St.-Hilaire (art. 2108), and generally bears his name. It is used almost universally by modern navigators. The method is based upon knowledge of one point on the line, and the direction of the line. Another method of utilizing the same principle is to assume the latitude and compute the longitude at which the line of position crosses that parallel (the time sight method, art. 2106), or vice versa. When this method is used, the azimuth is customarily found separately, from a table or graph. A third method is to compute two points on the line of position and draw a straight line through them. This line is a chord, rather than a tangent, of the circle of position, but in most cases the difference is negligible. This third method was that originally proposed by Captain Thomas H. Sumner (art. 131), and for this reason the resulting line of position is sometimes called a **Sumner line,** although the expression may be applied to any line of position resulting from celestial observation.

When celestial navigation is used, plotting is generally done on plotting sheets (art. 323) published by the Defense Mapping Agency Hydrographic Center. These are less expensive than charts, and the absence of detail eliminates a possible source of confusion and error.

1704. Using lines of position from celestial observations.—Like any other line of position, one resulting from a celestial observation does not pinpoint the position of the craft, but may provide all the information needed to insure safety of the vessel. The selection of a celestial body and the time of observation to provide the desired information is based upon the fact that the line of position is perpendicular to the azimuth line. If the celestial body is on or near the celestial meridian, the line of position is a **latitude line,** indicating the latitude at the time of observation, sometimes called the **observed latitude.** Similarly, a body on or near the prime vertical provides a **longitude line,** indicating the **observed longitude.** One ahead or astern provides a **speed line,** since the line of position is perpendicular to the course, and hence is an indication of the speed made good since the last speed line or fix. Similarly, a body on the beam provides a **course line** which indicates to what extent the course is being made good. If the azimuth line is perpendicular to a coastline, shoal, or other hazard, the line of position indicates the distance of the vessel from the danger. Passage parallel to such a danger, or between two of them, might be made safely by means of a series of observations of a body on the beam during passage, without fixing the position of the vessel. This problem might be simplified by precomputing the sextant altitude at intervals during passage, and plotting this versus time on cross-section paper, so that sextant altitudes can be compared immediately with the values taken from the curve to determine any deviation from the desired track. In a perpendicular approach to a coast, the point at which landfall will be made can be predicted with considerable accuracy if a body having an azimuth parallel to the beach is observed.

During twilight, with clear skies, the selection of a celestial body to provide desired information is simply a matter of choosing the body with azimuth nearest that desired, remembering that bodies having azimuths differing by 180° should provide the same line of position. Observation of bodies in opposite directions provides a check, and a better one than two observations of the same body, or observations of two bodies having nearly the same azimuth, for any constant error in the observations, such as might be caused by abnormal dip, can be eliminated by observing bodies on opposite azimuths and using a line midway between the two plotted lines of position.

When a limited number of bodies is available for a considerable period, as during daylight, the best time to make an observation to obtain a line of position in a desired direction can be determined by means of an azimuth table or diagram, or an inspection table such as Pub. No. 229. The azimuth is located, and the corresponding local hour angle is recorded. The local hour angle can then be converted to GHA, and the time at which this GHA occurs can be determined from the almanac (art. 2104).

Lines of position can be used for determining an estimated position (art. 1705), or they can be advanced or retired (art. 1706) to obtain a fix (art. 1707) or running fix (art. 1708). If a single body is available for observation, increased accuracy can usually be obtained by making three or more observations, adjusting all lines to a common time (art. 1706), and using either the middle line, or the average position of all lines.

1705. Estimated position.—As indicated in chapter VIII, a **dead reckoning (DR) position** is determined by advancing a known position for courses and distances. In the absence of additional information, the DR position is the best estimate of the position of the vessel. However, the expression **estimated position (EP)** is generally applied to one determined by using additional but inconclusive information. If the effects of wind and current can be estimated, and these effects have not been considered in establishing the DR position, they can be applied separately to establish an EP. As each additional item of information is received, an improved estimate might be made.

A single line of position can be useful in establishing an estimated position. If an accurate line is obtained, the actual position is somewhere on this line. In the absence of better information, a perpendicular from the previous DR position or EP to the line of position establishes the new EP, as shown in figure 1705a. The foot of the perpendicular from the AP has no significance in this regard, since it is used only to locate the line of position.

The establishment of a good EP is dependent upon accurate interpretation of all information available. Generally, such ability can be acquired only by experience. If, in the judgment of the navigator or captain, the course has been made good, but the speed has been uncertain, the best estimate of the position might be at the intersection of the course line and the line of position, as shown in figure 1705b. If the speed since the last fix is considered accurate, but the course is considered uncertain, the EP might be at the intersection of the line of position and an arc centered on the previous fix and of radius equal to distance traveled, as shown in figure 1705c.

More often, neither course nor speed is known to be entirely accurate, but if one is considered more accurate than the other, the EP may be located accordingly. Even the line of position might properly be considered of questionable accuracy, and some estimate of its reliability established. Figure 1705d shows an EP that might be established by considering the line of position of greatest but incomplete accuracy, the speed of secondary accuracy, and the course as least accurate.

The expression **most probable position** (**MPP**) is sometimes used as the equivalent of *estimated position*. However, the former is of somewhat broader application, since it may apply equally well to establishment of the fix when more than two lines of position are available.

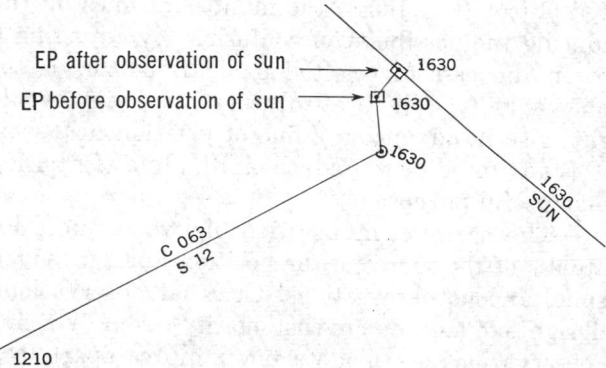

FIGURE 1705a.—Estimated positions before and after observation of the sun for a line of position, allowing for current.

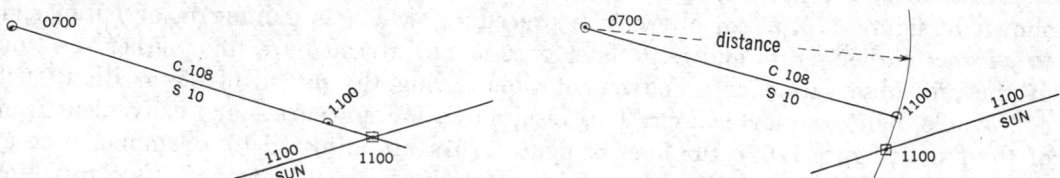

FIGURE 1705b.—An estimated position when the course and a line of position are considered accurate.

FIGURE 1705c.—An estimated position when the speed and a line of position are considered accurate.

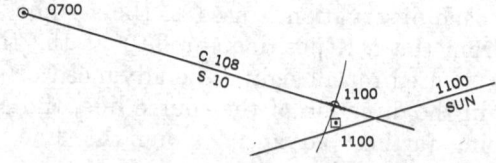

FIGURE 1705d.—An estimated position when a line of position is considered of first accuracy, speed of second accuracy, and course of third accuracy.

Further discussion of navigational accuracy is included in chapter III of volume II.

1706. Advancing and retiring lines of position.—For a stationary observer, lines of position resulting from observations made at different times are equally applicable without adjustment. However, for a moving observer, as one aboard a vessel underway at sea, any line of position (except a course line) applies only to the position at the time of observation. If lines resulting from observations made at different times are to be utilized for determining position, they should be adjusted for the motion of the observer between observations.

A line of position resulting from observation of a celestial body can be advanced or retired in the same manner as other lines of position (art. 1010), by selecting any point associated with the line of position and running it forward or backward by dead reckoning, or by estimate. For most accurate results, the best estimate of course and speed made good (over the bottom) between the time of observation and the time to which the line is to be adjusted should be used. Any error in determining these values is reflected in the adjusted line of position. However, error in speed does not affect the accuracy of an adjusted course line, nor does error in course introduce an appreciable error in the accuracy of an adjusted speed line. The time label of an adjusted line of position includes both the time of observation and the time to which the line is adjusted.

As in the case of a line of position resulting from observation of the bearing of an identifiable, charted object (art. 1004), the number of lines on the chart can be kept to a minimum, reducing the possibility of confusion, by adjusting the point from which the line is drawn. In the case of celestial navigation, this is the assumed position. This method applies equally well to all observations, and avoids some possible difficulty which might arise in advancing a line of position nearly parallel to the course line. When the AP is advanced or retired, the initial line of position need not be drawn unless it serves some useful purpose.

1707. The fix.—The common intersection of two or more lines of position constitutes a fix, regardless of the source of the position lines, provided only that the lines are based upon simultaneous observations. Celestial observations are seldom simultaneous because all sights of a group are customarily taken by a single observer, usually the navigator. If observations are made a few minutes apart (a **round of sights**), as during a twilight period, all lines are adjusted to a common time, and the position is considered a fix, rather than a running fix. Many navigators advance earlier lines to the time of the last observation, and consider the fix applicable at this time, as shown in figure 1707a. An alternative procedure, which is gaining in acceptance, is to *advance* earlier sights and *retire* later ones to an intermediate time, either the time of the mid observation or a convenient time during the period of observation, such as a whole, half, or quarter hour. This results in a more accurate and convenient time of the fix. In figure 1707b the lines of figure 1707a are adjusted to a common time at a whole hour. With any procedure, the time of the fix is the common time to which the lines of position are adjusted.

In figures 1707a and 1707b the assumed positions are typical of those which might be used with a modern method of sight reduction such as Pub. No. 229 (ch. **XX**). *Any* position in the vicinity might be used. If the dead reckoning (or estimated) position at the time of each observation is used as the assumed position for that sight, all sights are plotted from the DR position (or EP) at the time for which the fix is desired. If the same AP is used for all sights, the advanced or retired AP's are along a straight line extending in the direction of the course line, the AP corresponding to the earliest observation being farthest advanced along this line, and others progressing along it in a direction *opposite* to that of the course. If there is any change of course or speed between observations, this should be considered in advancing or retiring a line

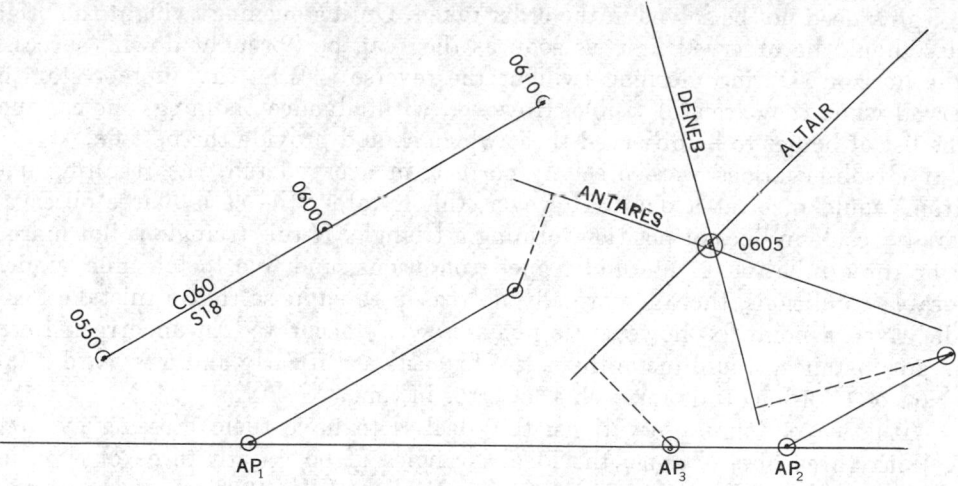

FIGURE 1707a.—A fix obtained by advancing earlier lines of position to the time of the last observation.

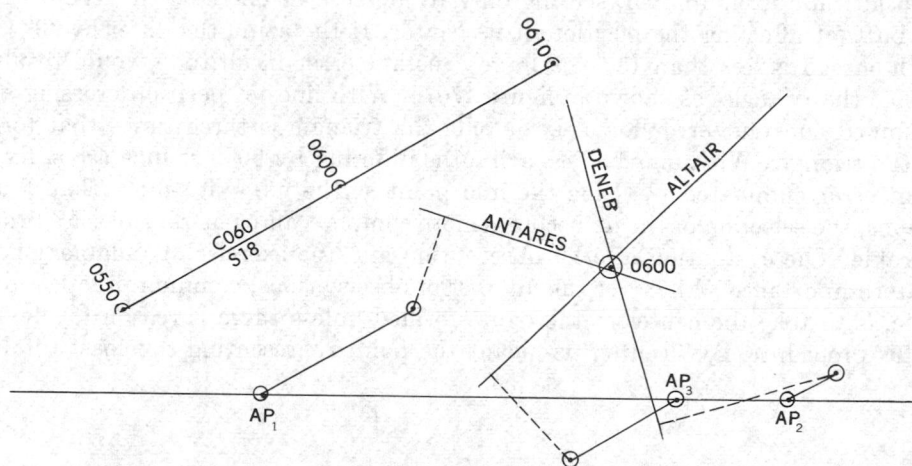

FIGURE 1707b.—A fix obtained by adjusting the lines of position of figure 1707a to a convenient time during the period of observation.

of position, as it would in running forward the dead reckoning. Under normal conditions, lines of position adjusted for a short interval to obtain a fix are moved by dead reckoning, without separate allowance for current.

Two lines of position provide a fix, but when additional celestial bodies are available, it is good practice to observe them. Additional lines serve as a check on the accuracy of the first two, and should decrease the error of the fix. However, the increased accuracy of a fix resulting from a number of lines of position, over that resulting from only two, is not great under normal conditions, and the principal reason for the additional observations is the increased confidence the navigator has in the reliability of his fix.

In selecting bodies for observation, one should generally consider azimuth primarily, and such factors as brightness, altitude, etc., secondarily. Individual circumstances, however, may dictate departures from this procedure. During twilight, when skies are clear and the entire horizon is good, one generally has ample choice of bodies to observe. It is good practice to make several more observations than the minimum considered acceptable, so that additional lines of position will be available, if needed, to resolve possible ambiguities or confirm doubtful results.

Sights need not be solved in the order taken. During evening twilight the brightest bodies should be observed first, as soon as they can be "brought down" successfully to the horizon. During morning twilight the reverse is true, the dimmer stars being observed while they are still visible. However, with advance planning, one can include in the list of bodies to be observed those which should provide the best fix.

If all observations were precisely correct, in every detail, the resulting lines of position would meet at a point. However, this is rarely the case. Three observations generally result in lines of position forming a triangle. If this triangle is not more than two or three miles on a side under good conditions, and five to ten miles under unfavorable conditions, there is normally no reason to suppose that a mistake has been made. Even a point fix, however, is not *necessarily* accurate. An uncorrected error in time, for instance, would move the entire fix eastward if early and westward if late, at the rate of 1' of longitude for each 4^s of error in time.

With two or four observations, the ideal is to have them crossing at angles of 90°. With three observations, the ideal is angles of 60°. With three observations it is good practice to observe bodies differing in azimuth by 120°, as nearly as possible. This provides lines of position crossing at angles of 60°, and, in addition, any constant error in altitude is eliminated, serving only to increase or decrease the size of the triangle, but not affecting the position of its center. If the azimuths differ by 60° (or the azimuth spread is less than 180°), a large constant error in altitude would result in a fix *outside* the triangle, as shown in figure 1707c. With lines of position crossing at 60°, the assumed constant error for a fix outside the triangle is three times that for a fix inside the triangle. With four bodies, azimuths differing by 90° produce a box fix, with constant error eliminated by using the mid point as the fix. With more than four observations, the selection of the fix becomes more complex, and general rules are probably undesirable. The evaluation of each observation and the exercise of judgment become of greater importance. Whatever the number of observations, common practice, backed by logic, is to take the center of the figure formed unless there is reason for deviating from this procedure. By "center" is meant the point representing the least total error

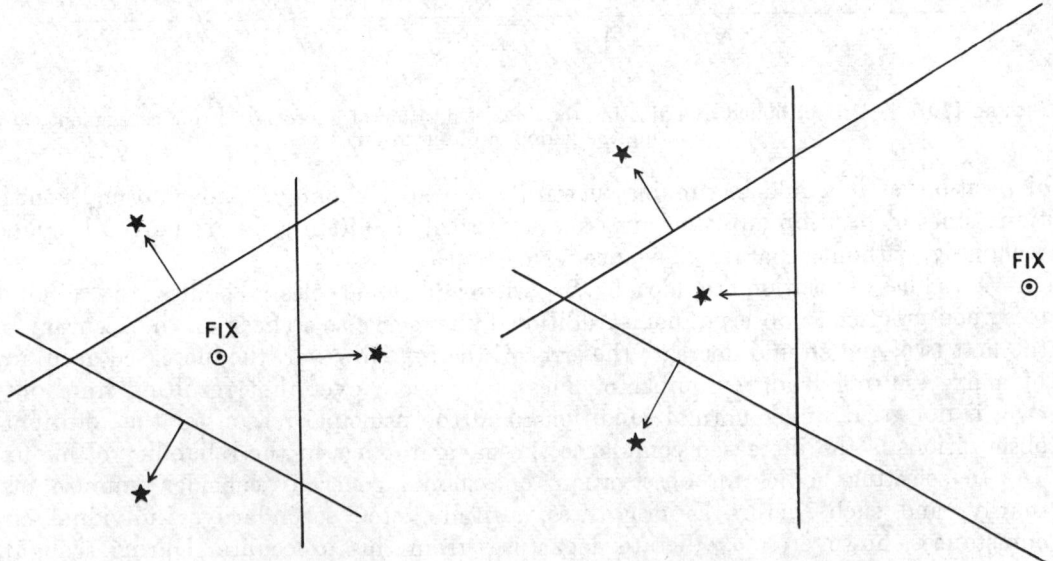

FIGURE 1707c.—A fix from three lines of position, assuming a constant error in altitude. If all lines are moved away (in this case) from the bodies observed, they would meet in a point which might be either inside (left) or outside (right) the triangle.

of all lines considered reliable. With three lines of position, the center is considered that point, within the triangle, which is equidistant from the three sides. It may be found by bisecting the angles, but more commonly it is located by eye. If a fix outside the triangle is to be used, and eye interpolation is not considered sufficiently reliable, the point can be found by bisecting two external angles and the internal angle at the third intersection. If a constant error is assumed, the most probable position of the fix can always be found, whether within or outside the triangle, by bisecting the angle formed by azimuth lines originating at each intersection.

The matter of navigational errors as applied to this problem is further discussed in chapter III of volume II.

1708. A running fix (R FIX), in celestial navigation, is a position obtained by observations separated by a considerable time interval, usually several hours. The usual occasion for a running fix is the availability of a single celestial body for observation, generally the sun. The delay between observations is usually to permit the azimuth to change sufficiently to provide a good angle of cut between lines of position. Thus, the sun may be observed about 0900, and again about noon.

Generally, a longer wait results in a more nearly perpendicular intersection of the two lines of position, but it may also increase the error of the advanced line. The earlier line is advanced for the course and distance made good. The ability with which these can be predicted determines the accuracy of the running fix, assuming accurate observation, sight reduction, and plotting. For this reason it is impractical to set a specific time limit upon the advancement of a line of position. This should be determined by the conditions of each situation, in the best judgment of the navigator. Experience is valuable in acquiring such judgment.

When an observation of a single body is made, with the intent of later advancing it to obtain a running fix with a second observation, the line of position should be plotted for the time of observation, regardless of the method used for advancing it, for the single line usually provides some useful information, as indicated in article 1704.

Allowance for current, when advancing a line of position, can be made by solving a vector diagram, as indicated in article 807, to determine the course and speed made good. An alternative method is to advance the AP or line without allowance for current, and then to advance it a second time in the direction of set of the current, for a distance equal to the drift multiplied by the number of hours between the time of observation and the time to which the line is advanced. This method is illustrated in figure 1708a. The distance AB is equal to the distance between the 0800 and 1152 DR positions. The direction BC is the estimated set of the current, and the length BC is the distance through which the current is assumed to act.

A third method provides accurate results even when a reliable estimate of the current is not available, provided (1) a good fix was obtained several hours before the time of observation, and (2) the average current between the time of the previous fix and the time of observation can be assumed to continue until the time to which the line is to be advanced. This method is illustrated in figure 1708b. The 0510 fix is shown at the left, and the DR positions at 0830 and 1215, the ship being on course 074°, speed 12 knots. The sun is observed at 0830 and again at 1215, and it is desired to advance the earlier line to obtain a running fix at 1215. The lines of position at 0830 and 1215 are plotted. To advance the 0830 line of position, the distance AB is assumed to increase uniformly with time interval from 0510. The interval to 0830 is 3^h20^m, and that to 1215 is 7^h05^m. Therefore, $A'B' = AB \times \dfrac{7^h05^m}{3^h20^m} = AB \times 2.1$. The advanced line of position is drawn through B', parallel to the original line through B. The running fix is at the intersection of the 1215 line and the advanced 0830 line.

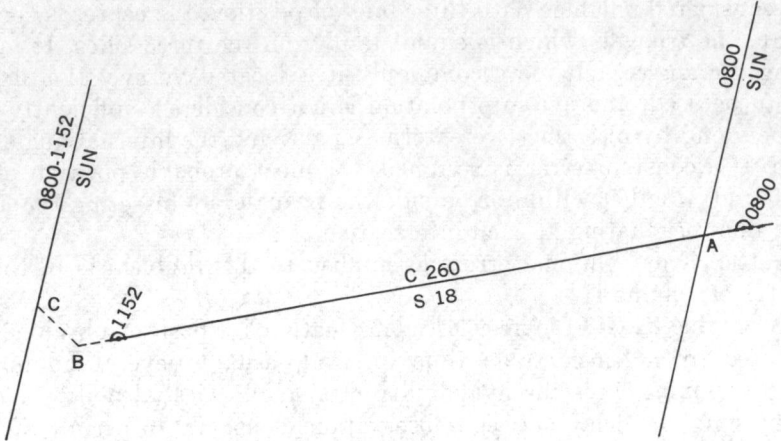

FIGURE 1708a.—Advancing a line of position with allowance for current, without determining course and speed made good.

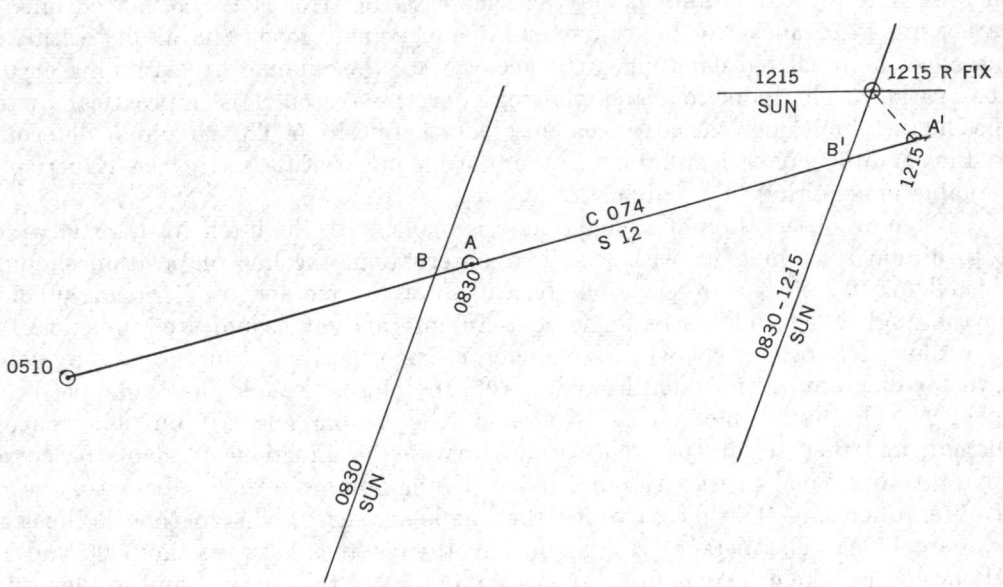

FIGURE 1708b.—Advancing a line of position without previous knowledge of the current.

The set of the average current *between 0510 and 0830* is the direction from A' to the 1215 running fix, and the drift is equal to this distance divided by 7^h05^m. The direction of a straight line (not shown) from the 0510 fix to the 1215 running fix is the course made good between 0510 and 0830, and the length of this line divided by the time (7^h05^m) is the speed made good to 0830.

The points B and B' need not be at the intersection of the lines of position and the course line. *Any* point on the line of position can be used, and the line $A'B'$ drawn parallel to AB. Changes of course and speed do not affect the accuracy of the solution as long as $A'B'$ is parallel to AB.

Several other variations are possible. A convenient one is to measure the distance from the earlier fix to point B, and divide this by the time to determine an "assumed" speed (based upon the assumption that point B represents the position of the vessel at the time of observation), and then to use this speed to advance the line of position.

This variation should not be used without adjustment if a change of course or speed is involved between the earlier fix and the time to which the line is to be advanced.

This method should be used with caution. Any error in either the earlier fix or the first line of position is *increased* in proportion to the elapsed time. Thus, in figure 1708b, if *AB* is in error by one mile, *A′B′* is in error by 2.1 miles. It should not be used when there is reason to suspect a change in current between fixes.

1709. Celestial navigation and dead reckoning.—As indicated in chapter VIII, dead reckoning consists of advancing a known position for courses and speeds. Some difference in technique arises from a difference of opinion among navigators on the definition of (1) "known position" and (2) courses and speeds.

Regarding the first, no position determined by celestial navigation as commonly practiced at sea is known with perfect accuracy. An average error of two miles is realistic. Because of the varying conditions encountered, it is difficult to establish limits of a "known" position. In general, however, a reasonably reliable fix or running fix is considered sufficiently accurate to justify a new start in the dead reckoning. An estimated position or a fix or running fix of doubtful accuracy is considered an indication, but an inconclusive one, of the error in the dead reckoning. Therefore, it is considered good practice to avoid starting a new dead reckoning track from such a position unless there is a compelling reason for doing so. After long experience and the development of sound judgment, a navigator might acquire great skill in establishing a most probable position of sufficient reliability to justify more frequent breaks in the continuity of the dead reckoning, but even under these conditions any reasonable element of doubt should be given great respect.

What has been said regarding "known position" applies, also, in large measure to course and speed. The course steered and the speed at which a ship is being driven forward by its engines can be determined with relatively little error. Allowance for wind and current is a matter largely of judgment based upon experience. If the dead reckoning is to be meaningful, considerable caution should be exercised in allowing for wind and current when determining the course and speed to use for plotting. In the absence of information of a high degree of reliability, it is considered prudent to determine dead reckoning without allowing for estimated effects of wind and current.

In the absence of better information, then, it is considered good practice to start a new dead reckoning track only from a reliable fix or running fix, and to use courses and speeds without allowance for wind and current. This does not mean, however, that the navigator should not continually be aware of the possibility of error in his position as determined by dead reckoning, nor should he fail to make an estimate of the size and direction of the error. In this ability, and that of accurately interpreting all navigational information received, lies the test of a good navigator. This is largely the *art* of navigation, as distinguished from the somewhat mechanical process of making observations and computing and plotting the results, and also from the *science* of devising the aids that are used in modern navigation.

When it is desired to determine "average current," this expression being used to mean the resultant of all dead reckoning errors, the dead reckoning should be run forward from a fix (not a running fix) to the time of the next fix (or running fix if the method of art. 1708 is used). A dead reckoning position determined in any other way is not usable, unless it is adjusted to provide a "no-current" position. A straight line connecting such a dead reckoning position and the fix at the same time indicates the current. The direction of the line *from* the DR position *to* the fix is the **set** of the current, and the length of this line divided by the number of hours since the last fix is the **drift,** as in piloting.

Problems

A Position Plotting Sheet such as chart 969, covering latitudes 27° to 30° north and south is needed for most of the problems of this chapter. If this is not available, one can be constructed by means of table 5, as explained in article 307; or small area plotting sheets can be constructed as explained in article 324.

1703a. In each of the following, determine the altitude intercept, a, and label it T or A, as appropriate:

	Hc	Ho
(1)	18°21′4	18°25′9
(2)	53°02′7	52°35′5
(3)	(−)0°05′2	(−)0°12′7
(4)	(−)0°11′1	0°01′1

Answers.—(1) a 4.5 T, (2) a 27.2 A, (3) a 7.5 A, (4) a 12.2 T.

1703b. The 0930 DR position of a ship is lat. 29°20′4N, long. 130°25′2W. At this time the navigator observes the sun, and computes Hc and Zn for the 0930 DR position, as follows: Hc 45°42′9, Ho 45°50′2, Zn 157°3. As a check, he also solves the same sight for an assumed position of lat. 29°00′0N, long. 130°30′0W, with the following results: Hc 46°00′0, Zn 157°0.

Required.—Plot the two lines of position, and account for the result.

Answer.—The two lines of position plot as approximately the same line, which is not dependent upon the assumed position, but only upon the observed altitude and the time of observation.

1705a. The 0500 fix of a ship is lat. 27°10′0N, long. 142°55′5W. The ship is on course 068°, speed 9 knots. At 0800 the navigator observes the sun, with the following results:

$$a \quad 6.6 \text{ T} \qquad aL \quad 27°00′0N$$
$$Zn \quad 105°0 \qquad a\lambda \quad 142°39′1W$$

The current since the morning fix is estimated to set 130°, at a drift of 1.4 knots.

Required.—(1) The 0800 DR position.

(2) The 0800 EP if there were no observation, and no current was anticipated.

(3) The 0800 EP using the current, if there were no observation.

(4) The 0800 EP using the line of position, but not the current.

(5) The 0800 EP using all available information.

Answers.—(1) 0800 DR: L 27°20′0N, λ 142°27′2W; (2) 0800 EP without current and line of position: L 27°20′0N, λ 142°27′2W; (3) 0800 EP with current but no line of position: L 27°17′4N, λ 142°23′5W; (4) 0800 EP with line of position but no current: L 27°19′5N, λ 142°25′3W; (5) 0800 EP with current and line of position: L 27°18′7N, λ 142°25′8W.

1705b. The 0530 fix of a ship is lat. 28°55′8N, long. 161°51′7E. The ship is on course 060°, speed 10 knots. At 0830 the navigator observes the sun, with the following results:

$$a \quad 6.7 \text{ A} \qquad aL \quad 29°00′0N$$
$$Zn \quad 110°0 \qquad a\lambda \quad 162°28′9E$$

Required.—(1) The 0830 EP if the course is believed to have been made good, and the line of position is considered accurate.

(2) The 0830 EP if the speed is believed to be correct, and the line of position is considered accurate.

(3) The 0830 EP if the course and speed are considered of equal reliability, and the line of position is considered accurate.

(4) The 0830 EP if the course is of questionable accuracy, but considered more reliable than the speed, and the line of position is considered accurate.

(5) The 0830 EP if the speed is of questionable accuracy, but considered more reliable than the course, and the line of position is considered accurate.

(6) The 0830 EP if the course is believed to have been made good, and the error contributed by the uncertainty of the line of position is believed to be twice that contributed by the uncertainty of the speed.

Answers.—(1) 0830 EP: L 29°13′.5N, λ 162°26′.3E; (2) 0830 EP: L 29°06′.5N, λ 162°23′.6E; (3) 0830 EP: L 29°09′.8N, λ 162°25′.0E; (4) 0830 EP: any place between (1) and (3); (5) 0830 EP: any place between (2) and (3); (6) 0830 EP: L 29°11′.4N, λ 162°22′.8E.

1707a. At 1740 the navigator and two assistants observe simultaneously three stars, with the following results:

	Fomalhaut	Deneb	Aldebaran
Hc	28°10′.3	34°59′.6	39°52′.8
Ho	28°05′.3	35°05′.6	39°46′.8
Zn	210°.0	308°.7	089°.3
aL	28°00′.0N	28°00′.0N	28°00′.0N
aλ	42°31′.7W	42°29′.0W	42°23′.2W

Required.—The 1740 fix.

Answer.—1740 fix: L 28°06′.6N, λ 42°30′.5W.

1707b. The 1800 DR position of a ship is lat. 27°02′.2N, long. 170°17′.0W. The ship is on course 045°, speed 14 knots. During evening twilight the navigator observes three stars, with the following results:

	Dubhe	Altair	Spica
Time	1815	1821	1830
Hc	34°45′.2	22°11′.8	47°24′.8
Ho	34°51′.3	22°15′.7	47°20′.4
Zn	331°.5	090°.3	219°.9
aL	27°00′.0N	27°00′.0N	27°00′.0N
aλ	170°10′.2W	170°05′.0W	169°54′.8W

Required.—The 1830 fix.

Answer.—1830 fix: L 27°11′.5N, λ 170°00′.5W.

1707c. The 1930 DR position of a ship is lat. 29°10′.5S, long. 122°35′.4W. The ship is on course 320°, speed 16 knots. During evening twilight the navigator observes a planet and two stars, with the following results:

	Saturn	Regulus	Rigil Kent.
Time	1931	1942	1951
Hc	46°58′.5	53°04′.0	24°19′.5
Ho	46°55′.5	53°09′.3	24°30′.0
Zn	023°.5	170°.2	297°.6
aL	29°00′.0S	29°00′.0S	29°00′.0S
aλ	122°55′.0W	122°45′.1W	122°35′.2W

Required.—The 1942 fix.

Answer.—1942 fix: L 29°05.3S, λ 122°47.4W.

1707d. The 0500 DR position of a ship is lat. 29°53.9N, long. 69°32.1W. The ship is on course 130°, speed 13 knots. During morning twilight the navigator observes a planet and two stars, with the following results:

	Mars	Kochab	Spica
Time	0451	0502	0511
Hc	17°14.1	38°26.2	33°35.2
Ho	17°24.5	38°19.2	33°47.8
Zn	130.1	353.2	237.9
aL	30°00.0N	30°00.0N	30°00.0N
aλ	69°41.7W	69°30.0W	69°18.3W

Required.—The 0500 fix.

Answer.—0500 fix: L 29°54.0N, λ 69°30.5W.

1707e. The 0930 DR position of a ship is lat. 28°40.4N, long. 125°30.4E. The ship is on course 220°, speed 25 knots. The navigator observes the sun and moon, and solves each sight from the DR position at the time of sight, with the following results:

	Sun	Moon
Time	0936	0943
Hc	54°24.3	37°07.9
Ho	54°26.3	37°14.7
Zn	200.2	142.6

Required.—The 0943 fix.

Answer.—0943 fix: L 28°32.1N, λ 125°32.3E.

1707f. A ship is on course 314°, speed 24 knots. During evening twilight the navigator observes two stars and the moon, and solves all three sights using assumed latitude 28°00.0S, assumed longitude 41°19.5W as the AP, with the following results:

	Peacock	Moon	Alpheratz
Time	1855	1900	1905
Hc	57°12.6	66°58.2	23°00.5
Ho	57°17.9	67°01.2	22°53.7
Zn	194.7	300.5	038.2

Required.—The 1900 fix.

Answer.—1900 fix: L 28°03.5S, λ 41°26.5W.

1707g. The 0400 DR position of a ship is lat. 27°01.8N, long. 51°36.0E. The ship is on course 037°, speed 20 knots. At 0545 the course is changed to 309°. During morning twilight the navigator observes two stars, with the following results:

	Vega	Alpheratz
Time	0537	0602
a	4.5 T	7.8 T
Zn	300.5	075.7
aL	27°00.0N	27°00.0N
aλ	51°45.2E	51°50.1E

Required.—The 0602 fix.

Answer.—0602 fix: L 27°28.1N, λ 51°51.1E.

1707h. The 0600 DR position of a ship is lat. 27°50′.3N, long. 20°58′.2W. The ship is on course 000°, speed 20 knots. During morning twilight the navigator observes four stars, with the following results:

	Dubhe	Kaus Aust.	Spica	Vega
Time	0551	0554	0558	0604
Hc	29°01′.1	21°57′.8	37°59′.4	54°33′.1
Ho	28°53′.4	22°11′.7	38°03′.5	54°28′.5
Zn	330°.0	149°.7	233°.3	057°.3
aL	28°00′.0N	28°00′.0N	28°00′.0N	28°00′.0N
aλ	20°54′.6W	21°08′.4W	20°56′.7W	20°51′.3W

Required.—The 0600 fix.

Answer.—0600 fix: L 27°53′.5N, λ 20°55′.0W.

1707i. The 1815 DR position of a ship is lat. 29°41′.5S, long. 163°52′.3W. The ship is on course 295°, speed 18 knots. During evening twilight the navigator observes three stars, with the following results:

	Regulus	Pollux	Aldebaran
Time	1810	1815	1821
Hc	45°18′.6	35°50′.7	22°50′.8
Ho	45°26′.2	36°03′.4	22°57′.7
Zn	040°.2	350°.7	300°.5
aL	30°00′.0S	30°00′.0S	30°00′.0S
aλ	163°45′.0W	163°49′.8W	163°54′.0W

Required.—(1) The 1815 fix, assuming random errors.

(2) The 1815 fix, assuming a constant error.

Answers.—(1) 1815 fix: L 29°47′.2S, λ 163°51′.2W; (2) 1815 fix: L 29°51′.4S, λ 163°50′.6W.

1708a. The 0830 DR position of a ship is lat. 29°25′.4S, long. 9°34′.7E. The ship is on course 326°, speed 22 knots. The sun is observed during the morning, and again at 1200, with the following results:

	Sun	Sun
Time	0830	1200
a	15.2 A	28.4 A
Zn	062°.3	169°.5
aL	29°00′.0S	29°00′.0S
aλ	9°37′.0E	8°52′.1E

Required.—The 1200 running fix.

Answer.—1200 R fix: L 28°31′.6S, λ 8°50′.0E.

1708b. The 0900 DR position of a ship is lat. 28°05′.6N, long. 93°44′.0W. The ship is on course 220°, speed 20 knots, and is believed to be in a current with set of 110° and a drift of 1.5 knots. The sun is observed during the morning, and again at 1200, with the following results:

	Sun	Sun
Time	0900	1200
a	11.2T	17.0 A
Zn	103°.2	172°.0
aL	28°00′.0N	27°00′.0N
aλ	93°54′.0W	94°38′.9W

Required.—The 1200 running fix.

Answer.—1200 R fix: L 27°19ʹ8N, λ 94°17ʹ5W.

1708c. The 0715 fix of a ship is lat. 28°28ʹ9S, long. 81°14ʹ8W. The ship is on course 120°, speed 15 knots. During the morning the sun is observed twice, with the following results:

	Sun	Sun
Time	0945	1200
a	9.4A	0
Zn	095°0	005°0
aL	29°00ʹ0S	29°00ʹ0S
aλ	80°26ʹ1W	80°11ʹ2W

Required.—(1) The 1200 running fix, allowing for current.

(2) Set and drift of the current.

(3) Course made good between 0715 and 0945.

Answers.—(1) 1200 R fix: L 29°01ʹ0S, λ 80°00ʹ2W; (2) set 049°, drift 1.1 kn.; (3) course made good 116°0.

1708d. The 0500 fix of a ship is lat. 28°36ʹ5N, long 143°22ʹ0E. The courses and speeds during the morning are as follows:

Time	Course	Speed
0500	047°	24 kn.
0600	102°	20 kn.
0715	038°	16 kn.
0845	075°	19 kn.
1000	030°	23 kn.
1045	085°	25 kn.

During the morning the sun is observed twice, with the following results:

	Sun	Sun
Time	0915	1200
a	8.8A	20.0A
Zn	125°0	191°7
aL	29°00ʹ0N	29°00ʹ0N
aλ	144°44ʹ8E	145°29ʹ8E

Required.—(1) The 1200 running fix, allowing for current.

(2) Set and drift of the current.

(3) Course and speed made good between fixes, assuming no change in current.

Answers.—(1) 1200 R fix: L 29°20ʹ0N, λ 145°33ʹ0E; (2) set 200°, drift 1.7 kn.; (3) course made good 070°, speed made good 17.7 kn.

1709a. The 0400 DR position of a ship is lat. 27°41ʹ8S, long. 64°54ʹ0E. This position has been run forward from a fix at 1715 the previous evening. The ship is on course 215°, speed 19 knots, but at 0600 the course is changed to 125°. At 0715 a fix locates the ship at lat. 28°23ʹ0S, long. 65°04ʹ3E.

Required.—Set and drift of the current between fixes.

Answers.—Set 073°, drift 1.0 kn.

1709b. The 0500 fix of a ship is lat. 27°09ʹ0N, long. 158°09ʹ5W. The ship is on course 310°, speed 14 knots. At 1155 a running fix locates the ship at lat. 28°01ʹ2N, long. 159°33ʹ2W. A new dead reckoning plot is started from this position. At 1900 a star fix is obtained, locating the ship at lat. 28°57ʹ8N, long. 160°54ʹ9W.

Required.—Set and drift of the average current between morning and evening fixes.

Answers.—Set 167°, drift 1.2 kn.

CHAPTER XVIII

TIME

1801. Introduction.—Time serves to regulate affairs aboard ship, as it does ashore. But to the navigator, it has additional significance. It is not enough to know *where* the ship is, was, or might be located in the future. The navigator wants to know *when* the various positions were or can reasonably be expected to be occupied. Time serves as a measure of progress. By considering the time at which a ship occupied various positions in the past, and by comparing the speed and various conditions it has encountered with those anticipated for the future, the skillful navigator can predict with reasonable accuracy the time of arrival at various future positions. Time can serve as a measure of safety, for it indicates when a light or other aid to navigation might be sighted, and if it is not seen by a certain time, the navigator knows he has cause for concern.

To the celestial navigator, time is of added significance, for it serves as a measure of the *phase* of the earth's rotation. That is, it indicates the position of the celestial bodies relative to meridians on the earth. Until an accurate *measure* of time became available at sea, longitude could not be found.

Very small *intervals* of time are used in certain electronic navigational aids, such as radar and Loran.

Whatever the type of navigation, a thorough mastery of the subject of time is important to the navigator.

The four independent base units of measurement currently used in science are length, mass, time, and temperature. It is true that, except for fields of science such as cosmology, geology, and astronomy, time interval is the more important time concept, and date (astronomical) is of much less importance to the rest of science. This is true because the "basic laws" of physics are differential in nature and only involve small time intervals. In essence, physical "laws" do not depend upon when (i.e., the date) they are applied.

Based on these laws and extensive experimentation, scientists have been able to demonstrate that frequency can be controlled and measured with the smallest percentage error of any physical quantity. The frequency of a periodic phenomenon is the number of cycles of this phenomenon per unit of time (i.e., per second). The name of the unit of frequency is the **hertz** (**Hz**) and is identical to a cycle per second (cps). Since most clocks depend upon some periodic phenomenon (e.g., a pendulum) in order to "keep time," and since one can make reliable electronic counters to count the "swings" of the periodic phenomenon, we can construct clocks with timekeeping accuracy (rate accuracy) equal to the accuracy of the frequency standard. Today's most precise and accurate clocks incorporate a cesium atomic beam as the "pendulum" of the clock.

1802. Clocks and timekeeping.—In early times, the location of the sun in the sky was the only reliable indication of the time of day. Of course, when the sun was not visible, one was unable to know the time with much precision. People developed devices (called clocks) to interpolate between checks with the sun. The sun was sort of a "master clock" that could be read with the aid of a sundial. An ordinary clock, then, was a device used to interpolate between checks with the sun. The gain in accuracy of the different clock devices over a period of years is shown in figure 1802. (Timekeeping has shown nearly 10 orders of magnitude improvement within the last 6 centuries with about 6 orders occurring within 70 years of the 20th century.) Thus, a clock could be a "primary clock" like the position of the sun in the sky, or it could be a secondary clock and only interpolate between checks with the primary clock or time standard. Historically, some people have used the word "clock" with the connotation of a secondary time reference, but today this usage would be too restrictive.

When one thinks of a clock, it is customary to think of some kind of pendulum or balance wheel, a group of gears, and a clock face. Each time the pendulum completes a swing, the hands of the clock are moved a precise amount. In effect, the gears and hands of the clock "count" the number of swings of the pendulum. The face of the clock, of course, is not marked off in the number of swings of the pendulum but rather in hours, minutes, and seconds.

One undesirable characteristic of pendulum-type clocks is that no two clocks ever keep exactly the same time. This is one reason for looking for a more stable "pendulum" for clocks. In the past, the most stable "pendulums" were found in astronomy. Here one obtains a significant advantage because only one universe exists—at least for observation purposes, and time defined by this means is available to anyone—at least in principle. Thus, one can obtain a very reliable time scale which has the property of universal accessibility. In this chapter, time scale (art. 1804) is used to refer to a conceptually distinct method of assigning dates to events.

In a very real sense, the pendulum of ordinary, present-day electric clocks is the electric current supplied by the power company. In the United States the power utilities generally synchronize their generators to the National Bureau of Standards (NBS) low frequency broadcast, WWVB. Thus, the right number of pendulum swings occur each day. Since all electric clocks which are powered by the same source have, in

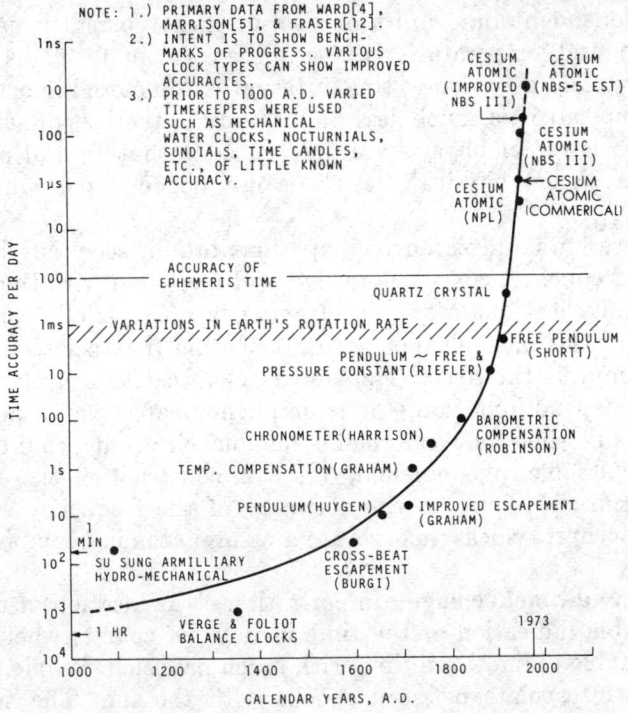

FIGURE 1802.—Progress in timekeeping accuracy.

effect, the same pendulum, these clocks do not gain or lose time relative to each other; i.e., they run at the same rate. Indeed, they will remain fairly close to the time as broadcast by WWVB ($\pm$ 5 seconds) and will maintain the same time difference with respect to each other ($\pm$ 1 millisecond) over long periods of time.

It has been known for some time that atoms have characteristic resonances or, in a loose sense, "characteristic vibrations." The possibility therefore exists of using the "vibrations of atoms" as pendulums for clocks. Presently, microwave resonances (vibrations) of atoms are the most precisely determined and reproducible physical phenomena that man has encountered. A clock which uses "vibrating atoms" as a pendulum will generate a time scale more uniform than even its astronomical counterparts.

But due to intrinsic errors in any actual clock system, atomic clocks drift relative to other similar clocks. Of course, the rate of drift is much smaller for atomic clocks than the old pendulum clocks, but nonetheless real and important. The attribute of universal accessibility for atomic time is accomplished by coordination between laboratories generating atomic time.

1803. Basic concepts of time.—One can use the word "time" in the sense of date. (By "date" we mean a designated mark or point on a time scale.) One can also consider the concept of time interval or "length" of time between two events. The difference between these concepts of date and time interval is important and has often been confused in the single word "time."

The *date* of an event on an earth-based time scale is obtained from the number of cycles (and fractions of cycles) of the apparent sun counted from some agreed-upon origin. Similarly, atomic time scales are obtained by counting the cycles of a signal in resonance with certain kinds of atoms.

The word "epoch" is sometimes used in a similar manner to the word "date." However, dictionary definitions of epoch show gradations of meanings such as time duration, time instant, or a particular time reference point, as well as a geological period of time. Thus, epoch often simultaneously embodies concepts of both date and duration. Because of such considerable ambiguity in the word "epoch," its use in this volume will be restricted to a time instant.

Another aspect of time is that of *simultaneity*; i.e., coincidence in time of two events. For example, we might synchronize clocks upon the arrival of portable clocks at a laboratory. Here we introduce an additional term, *synchronization*, which implies that the two clocks are made to have the same reading in some frame of reference. Note that the clocks need not be synchronized to an absolute time scale. As an example, two people who wish to communicate with each other might not be critically interested in the date, they just want to be *synchronized* as to when they use their communications equipment.

1804. Time scales.—A system of assigning dates to events is called a **time scale.** The apparent motion of the sun in the sky constitutes one of the most familiar time scales but is certainly not the only time scale. Note that to completely specify a date using the motion of the sun as a time scale, one must count days (i.e., make a calendar) from some initially agreed-upon beginning. In addition (depending on accuracy needs) one measures the fractions of a day (i.e., "time of day") in hours, minutes, seconds, and maybe even fractions of seconds. That is, one counts cycles (and even fractions of cycles) of the sun's daily apparent motion around the earth.

1805. Fundamental kinds of time.—There are three fundamentally different kinds of time. These are time based on the rotation of the earth on its axis; time based on long term observations of the annual revolution of the earth around the sun; and time based on transitions in the atom.

Time based on the rotation of the earth on its axis has several forms, all of which are related to each other by rigorous formulae or by appropriate tables. These forms are the various sidereal times, mean and apparent, and solar times, mean and apparent.

Time defined by the daily rotation of the earth with respect to the equinox or first point of Aries is known as **sidereal time.** The sidereal time is numerically measured by the hour angle of the equinox, which represents the position of the equinox in the daily rotation. The period of one rotation of the equinox in hour angle, between two consecutive upper meridian transits, is a **sidereal day;** it is divided into 24 sidereal hours, reckoned from 0^h at upper transit which is known as **sidereal noon.** The true equinox is at the intersection of the true celestial equator of date with the ecliptic of date; the time measured by its daily rotation is **apparent sidereal time.** The position of the true equinox is affected by the nutation of the axis of rotation of the earth; and the nutation consequently introduces irregular periodic inequalities into the apparent sidereal time and the length of the sidereal day. The time measured by the daily motion of the mean equinox of date, which is affected only by the secular inequalities due to the precession of the axis, is **mean sidereal time.** The maximum difference between apparent and mean sidereal times is only a little over a second, and its greatest daily change is a little more than a hundredth of a second. Because of its variable rate, apparent sidereal time is used by astronomers only as a measure of epoch; it is not used for time interval. Mean sidereal time is deduced from apparent sidereal time by applying the equation of equinoxes.

Universal Time (UT) is a particular case of the measure known in general as **mean solar time** (art. 1808). Universal Time is the mean solar time on the Greenwich meridian, reckoned in days of 24 mean solar hours beginning with 0^h at midnight. Universal Time and sidereal time are rigorously related by a formula so that if one is known the other can be found. The ratio of the mean solar day to the mean sidereal day is 1.0027379093, and the equivalent measures of the length of the day are:

Mean sidereal day _____ $23^h56^m04^s09054$ of mean solar time
Mean solar day _____ $24^h03^m56^s55536$ of mean sidereal time.

Universal Time, in principle, is determined by the *average* rate of the apparent daily motion of the sun relative to the meridian of Greenwich; but in practice the numerical measure of Universal Time at any instant is computed from sidereal time.

Universal Time is the standard in the application of astronomy to navigation. Observations of Universal Times are made by observing the times of transit of stars.

The Universal Time determined directly from astronomical observations is denoted **UT0.** Since the earth's rotation is non-uniform, corrections must be applied to UT0 to obtain a more uniform time. This more uniform time is obtained by correcting for two known periodic motions.

One motion, the **polar motion** (the motion of the geographic poles) is the result of the axis of rotation continuously moving with respect to the earth's crust. The corrections for this motion are quite small (± 15 milliseconds for Washington, D.C.). On applying the correction to UT0, the result is **UT1,** which is the same as **Greenwich mean time (GMT)** used in celestial navigation.

The second known periodic motion is the variation in the earth's speed of rotation due to winds, tides, and other phenomena. As a consequence, the earth suffers an annual variation in its speed of rotation of about ± 30 milliseconds. When UT1 is corrected for the mean seasonal variations in the earth's rate of rotation, the result is **UT2.**

Although UT2 was at one time believed to be a uniform time system, it was later determined that there are secular variations in the earth's rate of rotation, possibly caused by random accumulations of matter in the convection core of the earth. Such accumulations would change the earth's moment of inertia and thus its rate of rotation.

The second fundamental kind of time, **Ephemeris Time (ET),** is, by definition, a uniform time system. Ephemeris Time is the uniform measure of time defined by the law of dynamics and determined in principle from the orbital motions of the planets, specifically the orbital motion of the earth as represented by Newcomb's *Tables of the Sun.* Ephemeris Time is the measure of time in which Newcomb's *Tables of the Sun* agree with observation. Ephemeris Time is time based on the **ephemeris second** defined as $1/31556925.9747$ of the tropical year for 1900 January 0^d12^h ET. The ephemeris day is 86,400 ephemeris seconds. The ephemeris second is a fundamental invariable unit of time.

The Ephemeris Time at any instant is obtained from observation by directly comparing observed positions of the sun, moon, and planets with gravitational ephemerides of their coordinates; observations of the moon are most effective and expeditious for this purpose. Ephemeris Time is used by astronomers in the fundamental ephemerides of the sun, moon, and planets, but is not used by navigators.

The third fundamental kind of time, **Atomic Time (AT),** is based on transitions in the atom.

The basic principle of the **atomic clock** is that electromagnetic waves of a particular frequency are emitted when an atomic transition occurs. The frequency of the **cesium beam atomic clock** was found to be 9,192,631,770 cycles per second of Ephemeris Time in an experiment conducted jointly by the National Physical Laboratory, Teddington, England, and the U. S. Naval Observatory during 1955–1958.

In 1967 the **atomic second** was defined by the Thirteenth General Conference on Weights and Measures as the duration of 9,192,631,770 periods of the radiation corresponding to the transition between two hyperfine levels of the ground state of the cesium atom 133. This value was established to agree as closely as possible with the ephemeris second. Thus, the atomic second became the unit of time in the **International System of Units (SI).**

UT2 and A1, the atomic time scale established by the U. S. Naval Observatory in 1958, were identical on January 1, 1958. To the accuracy currently available, A1 and ET differ only by a constant such that $ET - A1 = 32^s.15$.

The advent of atomic clocks, which have accuracies better than 1 part in 10^{10}, led in 1961 to the coordination of time and frequency emissions of the U. S. Naval Observatory and the Royal Greenwich Observatory. The master oscillators controlling the signals were calibrated in terms of the cesium standard (A1) and corrections determined at the U. S. Naval Observatory and the Royal Greenwich Observatory were made simultaneously at all transmitting stations. Because of the divergence of the astronomical and atomic time scales due to the unpredictable variations in the earth's rotation, the time emissions were adjusted by applying a frequency offset to the oscillator so that the rate defined by the timing pulses was in general agreement with UT2. If, in spite of this, the departure of the time signals from UT2 became unacceptable, the epoch of the signals was adjusted by 100 millisecond steps. These adjustments kept the transmitted time synchronized with the rotation of the earth within a tolerance of $0^s.1$. This system became known as **Coordinated Universal Time (UTC)** and was accepted by many authorities following its formal recommendation in 1961 by the International Astronomical Union (IAU) and in 1963 by the International Radio Consultative Committee (CCIR), a committee of the International Telecommunications Union (ITU) which controls international coordination of time signal transmission.

In February 1970 at the Plenary Assembly of the ITU, it was agreed that commencing January 1, 1972, the use of frequency offsets would be discontinued and that all time signal transmissions would be based strictly on the internationally adopted definition of the second. The ITU also agreed that the coordinated time transmission based on the atomic second be maintained in approximate agreement with UT1 by stepping the transmitted time one whole second whenever necessary.

In accordance with the implementation resolutions of the IAU, the new system was inaugurated January 1, 1972, using the second defined in terms of an **International Atomic Time** (**TAI**) scale (art. 1806) as the unit of time and UT1 as the astronomical reference. Beginning at this time, UTC was then maintained in approximate agreement with UT1 by step adjustments (**leap seconds**) as directed by the Bureau Internationale de l'Heure (BIH).

At the end of 1971, before the new system was inaugurated, there was a difference of almost 10 seconds between TAI and UTC. In order that this difference be an integral number of whole seconds (in this case 10^s) a special negative adjustment of approximately 0.108^s was made in accordance with BIH directive so that the reading on the UTC scale was 1 January 1972, $00^h00^m00^s$ at the instant the TAI scale was 1 January 1972, $00^h00^m10^s$.

1806. International Atomic Time (**TAI**) **scale.**—In October 1971, the General Conference on Weights and Measures endorsed the Bureau Internationale de l'Heure (BIH) atomic time scale as the International Atomic Time (TAI) scale defined as follows:

"International Atomic Time is the time reference coordinate established by the Bureau Internationale de l'Heure on the basis of the readings of atomic clocks functioning in various establishments in accordance with the definition of the second, the SI Unit (International System of Units) of time."

The Atomic Time (AT) scales maintained in the United States by the National Bureau of Standards and the U. S. Naval Observatory constitute approximately 37½ percent of the stable reference information used in maintaining a stable TAI scale by the BIH.

1807. Time interval and time scales.—One should note sources of confusion which can exist in the measurement of time and in the use of the word "second." Suppose that two events occurred at two different dates. For example the dates of these two events were 15 December 1970, $15^h30^m00^s000000$ UTC and 15 December 1970, $16^h30^m00^s000000$ UTC. At first thought one would say that the time interval between these two events was exactly 1 hour$=3600.000000$ seconds, but this is *not* true. (The actual interval was longer by about 0.000108 seconds [3600 seconds $\times300\times10^{-10}$]. Refer to table 1807.) Recall that the UTC time scale (like all the UT scales and the ET scale) was not defined in accordance with the definition of the interval of time, the second. Thus, one cannot simply subtract the dates of two events as assigned by the UTC scale (or any UT scale or the ET scale) in order to obtain the precise time interval between these events. Historically, the reason behind this state of affairs is that navigators need to know the earth's position (i.e., UT1)—not the duration of the second. Yet, many scientists need to know an exact and reproducible time interval. Note that this might also be true of the new UTC system if the particular time interval included one or more leap seconds.

It is also confusing that the dates assigned by the UT, ET, and UTC scales involve the same word as the unit of time interval, the second. For accurate and precise measurements, this distinction can be extremely important.

Year	Offset rate of UTC in parts per 10^{10}
1960	-150
1961	-150
1962	-130
1963	-130
1964	-150
1965	-150
1966	-300
1967	-300
1968	-300
1969	-300
1970	-300
1971	-300
1972 → future	0

TABLE 1807.—Frequency offsets of UTC from 1960 to 1972.

1808. Solar time.—The basis of time measurement in celestial navigation is the period of rotation of the earth. This period is not quite constant; it is subject to variations which may reach a few milliseconds per day. These variations will be disregarded initially; the earth will be conceived as rotating at a constant rate.

The earth's rotation causes the sun and other celestial bodies to appear to cross the sky from east to west each day. If a person located on the earth's equator measured the time interval between two successive transits overhead of a very distant star, he would thereby measure the period of the earth's rotation. If he then made similar measurements on the sun instead of a star, he would obtain a result about 4 minutes longer than before. This difference is due to the earth's motion around the sun, which continuously changes the apparent place of the sun among the stars. Thus, during the course of a day the sun appears to move a little to the east among the stars so that the earth must rotate on its axis through more than 360° in order to bring the sun overhead again. Of course this apparent eastward movement of the sun cannot be observed directly.

If the sun is on the observer's meridian when the earth is at point A (fig. 1808) in its orbit around the sun, it will not be on the observer's meridian after the earth has rotated through 360° because the earth will have moved along its orbit to point B. Before the sun is again on the observer's meridian, the earth must turn still more on its axis. The sun will be on the observer's meridian again when the earth has moved to point C in its orbit. Thus, during the course of a day the sun appears to move eastward with respect to the stars.

Even if the earth did not rotate on its own axis, the sun would rise and set once during the year because of the earth's orbit around it. The stars, however, are not within the earth's orbit. Since they are generally more than a million times as distant as the sun, their apparent positions are only very slightly affected by the earth's orbital motion. The apparent positions of the stars are commonly reckoned with reference to an imaginary point called the **vernal equinox,** which is the intersection of the celestial equator and the ecliptic. The sun is at the vernal equinox at the beginning of spring, when it passes over the equator on its apparent journey northward. The period of the

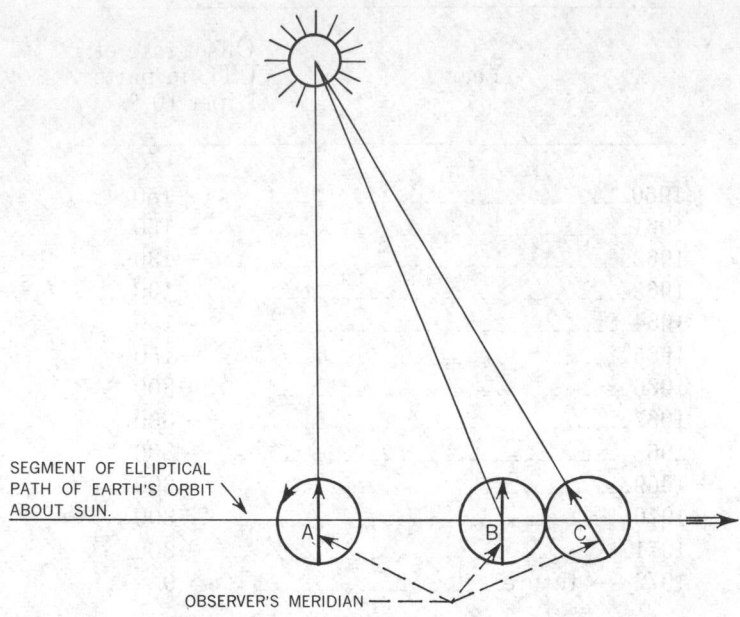

FIGURE 1808.—Apparent eastward movement of the sun with respect to the stars.

earth's rotation measured with respect to the vernal equinox is called a **sidereal day.**
The period with respect to the sun is called an **apparent solar day.**

With the sun moving eastward among the stars so that the difference between the
apparent solar and sidereal day is about 4 minutes of time, on any night a star will rise
about 4 minutes earlier than on the previous night. Thus, the celestial sphere appears
to shift westward about 1° each night. The complete shift through 360° is associated
with the **year,** the period of one revolution of the earth around the sun. By the calendar,
one year is 365 days duration for a **common year** and 366 days for a **leap year.** A leap
year is any given year divisible by 4, unless it is a century year, which must be divisible
by 400 to be a leap year. Thus, 1900 was not a leap year, but 2000 will be. This calendar,
now in general use, is called the **Gregorian calendar.**

When measuring time by the rotation of the earth, the time is **apparent solar time**
if the apparent (real) sun is used as the celestial reference.

Use of the apparent sun as a celestial reference for time results in time of nonconstant rate for at least three reasons. First, revolution of the earth in its orbit is not
constant. Second, motion of the apparent sun is along the ecliptic, which is tilted with
respect to the celestial equator, along which time is measured. Third, rotation of the
earth on its axis is not constant. The effect due to this third cause is extremely small.

For the various forms of mean solar time, the apparent sun is replaced by a fictitious
mean sun, conceived as moving eastward along the celestial equator at a uniform speed
equal to the average speed of the apparent sun along the ecliptic, thus providing a
nearly uniform measure of time equal to the approximate average apparent time. The
speed of the mean sun along the celestial equator is taken as 15° per hour of mean
solar time.

1809. Equation of time.—Mean solar time, or **mean time** as it is commonly called,
is sometimes ahead of and sometimes behind apparent solar time (**sundial time**). The
difference, which never exceeds about 16^m4, is called the **equation of time (Eq. T.).**

By one convention, the equation of time is the time interval which must be added
algebraically to the mean time to obtain apparent time. This convention is used here.

In accordance with Kepler's second law (art. 1407), the speed of the earth in its elliptical orbit around the sun varies with the changing distance between the two bodies. The earth moves faster at perihelion than it does at aphelion. Consequently, as seen from the earth the sun appears to move faster in January than it does in July. Even if the earth's orbital speed were uniform, the hour angle of the sun would still change at a variable rate because the sun as observed from the earth appears to move in the plane of the ecliptic, which is inclined at an angle of about 23°27′ to the plane of the celestial equator.

In deriving the value of the equation of time it is simpler to consider the contributions of the ellipticity and obliquity of the apparent orbit of the sun about the earth separately. In considering the ellipticity and obliquity contributions separately, it is convenient to introduce a second fictitious sun. This second sun, known as the **dynamical mean sun,** is conceived to move eastward along the ecliptic at the average rate of the apparent (true) sun. The dynamical mean sun and the apparent sun occupy the same position when the earth is at perihelion (or the sun is at perigee when using the concept that the sun orbits the earth). The dynamical mean sun and the mean sun, or **astronomical mean sun** as it is sometimes called, occupy the same position at the time of the vernal equinox.

That part of the equation of time due to the ellipticity of the orbit and known as the **eccentricity component** is the difference, in mean solar time units, between the hour angles of the apparent (true) sun and the dynamical mean sun. It is also the difference in the right ascensions of these two suns. That part of the equation of time due to the obliquity of the orbit is the difference in units of mean solar time, between the hour angles of the dynamical mean sun and the astronomical mean sun. It is also the difference in the right ascensions of these two suns.

Figure 1809a illustrates the apparent orbit of the sun about the earth. In accordance with Kepler's second law the radius vector sweeps through equal areas in equal time intervals. Therefore, the angular velocity of the true sun is greatest at perigee. With the true sun T and the dynamical mean sun D occupying the same position at perigee P around 1 January, following perigee the true sun moves ahead of the dynamical mean sun which is moving eastward along the ecliptic at the average rate of the true sun. The maximum separation of about 2° (8 minutes) occurs about 1 April. Because of Kepler's

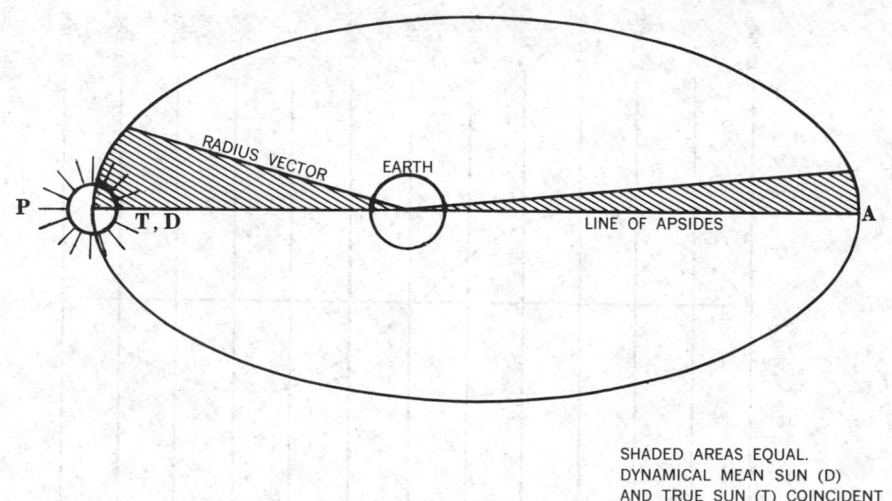

SHADED AREAS EQUAL.
DYNAMICAL MEAN SUN (D)
AND TRUE SUN (T) COINCIDENT
AT APOGEE (A) AND PERIGEE (P).

FIGURE 1809a.—Apparent orbit of the sun about the earth.

second law, the dynamical mean sun and the true sun must be in coincidence again at apogee *A* about 1 July. The time for the true sun to move from perigee to apogee is equal to the time for the true sun to move from apogee to perigee. Since the dynamical mean sun moves at the average rate of the true sun, the time to complete the orbit of the ecliptic is equal to the time required for the true sun to complete the same orbit. Since the line of apsides bisects the sun's apparent orbit, it follows that the time required for the dynamical mean sun to complete half the orbit is the same as that required for the true sun to complete half the orbit. Therefore, the dynamical mean sun and the true sun occupy the same position at apogee.

With the true sun and the dynamical mean sun occupying the same position at apogee and with the angular velocity of the true sun being least at apogee, following apogee the dynamical mean sun moves ahead of the true sun. The maximum separation of about 2° (8 minutes) occurs about 1 October. The two suns are again coincident at perigee about 1 January.

The eccentricity component of the equation of time is shown in figure 1809b. The obliquity component of the equation of time can now be found by comparing a dynamical mean sun moving uniformly along the ecliptic with an astronomical mean sun also moving uniformly at the same rate in the plane of the celestial equator.

With the dynamical mean sun and the astronomical mean sun coincident at the first point of Aries and each moving uniformly at the same rate along their respective paths, following the time of the vernal equinox the positions of the two suns are such that the celestial longitude of the dynamical mean sun equals the right ascension of the astronomical mean sun. As shown in figure 1809c, $\Upsilon D = \Upsilon M$. As is also shown in this figure, following the vernal equinox the right ascension of the astronomical mean sun is greater than the right ascension of the dynamical mean sun. Thus, during this period that part of the equation of time due to the obliquity of the orbit is a negative value.

When the celestial longitude of the dynamical mean sun has increased to 90°, the right ascension of the astronomical mean sun will also be 90°. At the time of the summer solstice, the hour circles of the two suns are coincident; the elevated pole, the ecliptic pole, and the two suns all lie on the same great circle. Therefore, at the summer solstice that part of the equation of time due to the obliquity of the orbit is zero. Halfway between the time of the vernal equinox and the summer solstice that

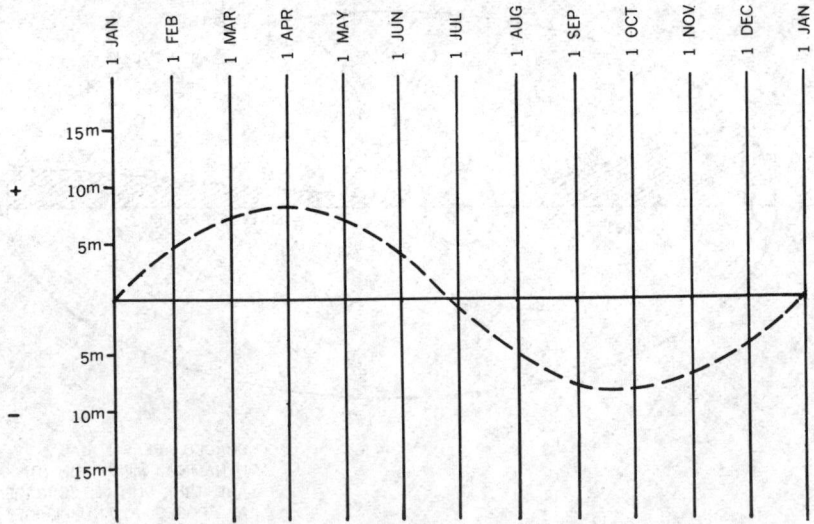

FIGURE 1809b.—Eccentricity component.

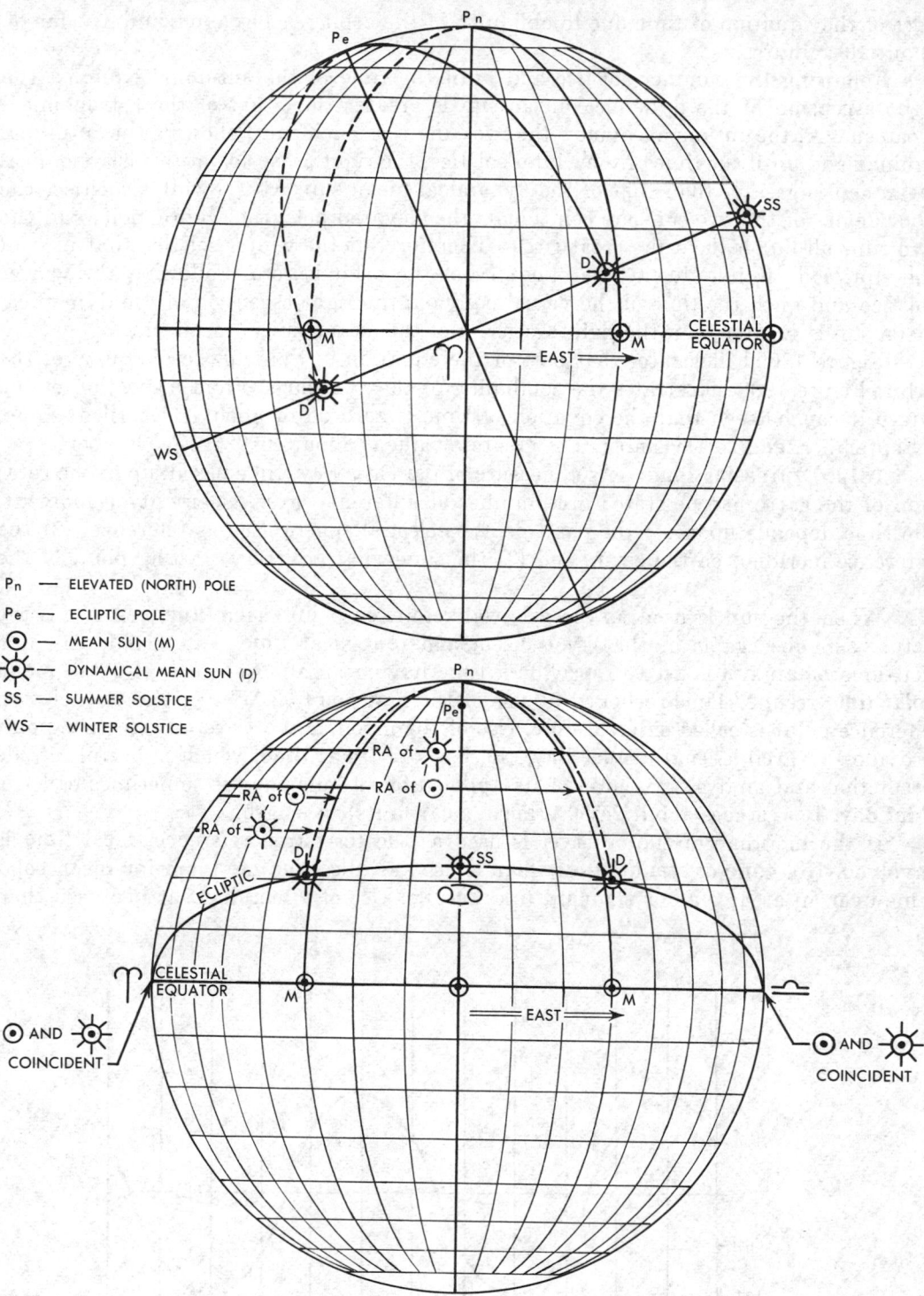

Pn — ELEVATED (NORTH) POLE
Pe — ECLIPTIC POLE
⊙ — MEAN SUN (M)
☀ — DYNAMICAL MEAN SUN (D)
SS — SUMMER SOLSTICE
WS — WINTER SOLSTICE

FIGURE 1809c.—Right ascensions of dynamical and astronomical mean suns.

part of the equation of time due to obliquity of the orbit reaches a maximum value of about 10 minutes.

Following the summer solstice and until the time of the autumnal equinox, the right ascension of the dynamical mean sun is greater than that of the astronomical mean sun. At the autumnal equinox, the two suns are coincident. Following the autumnal equinox and until the time of the winter solstice, the right ascension of the astronomical mean sun is greater than that of the dynamical mean sun. At the winter solstice, the hour angles of the two suns are coincident; the elevated pole, the ecliptic pole, and the two suns all lie on the same great circle. Therefore, at the winter solstice that part of the equation of time due to the obliquity of the orbit is zero. Following the winter solstice and until the time of the vernal equinox, the right ascension of the dynamical mean sun is greater than the right ascension of the astronomical mean sun.

Figure 1809d illustrates that part of the equation of time due to obliquity of the orbit. Figure 1809e illustrates the combining of the two parts. From inspection of the curve it can be seen that the equation of time is zero on or about 15 April, 14 June, 1 September, and 24 December. The greatest value is about 16^m22^s in November.

1810. Expressing time.—As a measure of part of a day, time based upon the rotation of the earth can be stated in a number of different ways. At any given moment, the time depends upon (1) the point on the celestial sphere used as reference, (2) the reference meridian on the earth, and (3) the somewhat arbitrary starting point of the day.

When the sun is used as the celestial reference point, **solar time** results. If the actual sun observable in the sky is used, **apparent solar time** is involved, and if a fictitious **mean sun** is used to provide a time having an almost constant rate, **mean solar time** results. Time reckoned by use of the first point of Aries (Υ) as the celestial reference point is called **sidereal time.** Use of the moon as the celestial reference point provides a variable-length **lunar day,** the basis of **lunar time,** which is useful in tide prediction and analysis. Because of its application, a lunar day is sometimes called a **tidal day.** It averages about 24^h50^m (mean solar units) in length.

If the meridian of the observer is used as the terrestrial reference, **local time** is involved. If a **zone** or **standard meridian** is used as the **time meridian** for mean solar time over an area, **zone** or **standard time** results. Use of a meridian farther east than

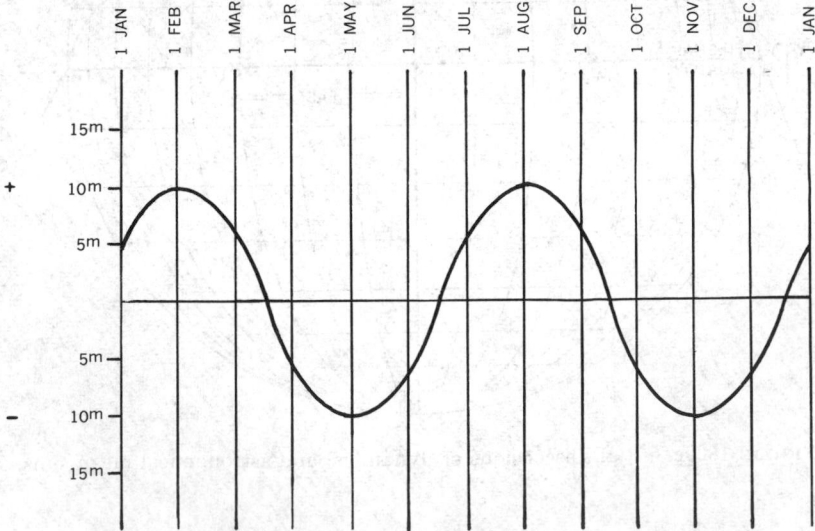

FIGURE 1809d.—Obliquity component.

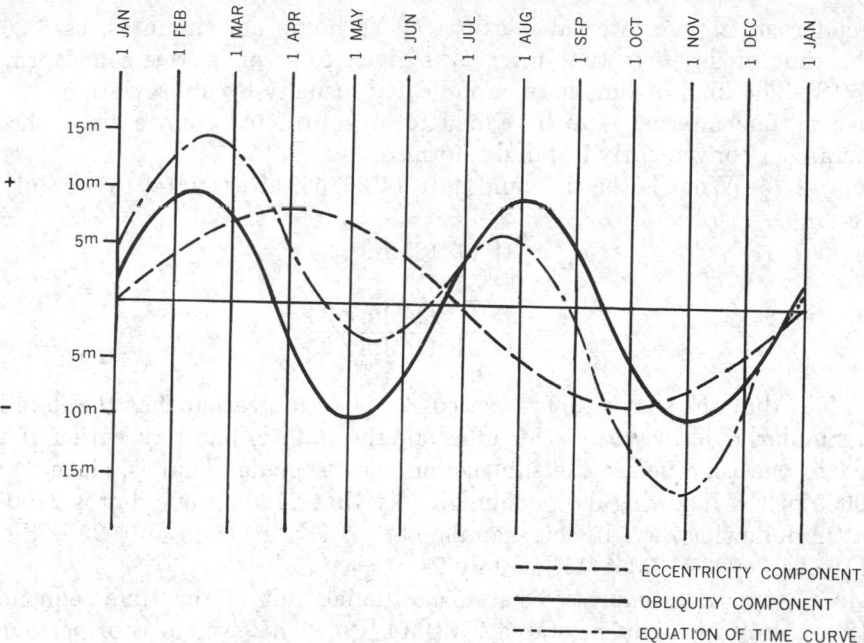

FIGURE 1809e.—Equation of time curve constructed from eccentricity and obliquity components.

would normally be used, so that the period of daylight is shifted later in the day produces a form of zone time called **daylight saving** or **summer time.** Time based upon the Greenwich meridian is called **Greenwich time. Greenwich mean time (GMT)** is of particular interest to a navigator because it is the principal entering argument for the almanacs.

One complete revolution of the earth with respect to a celestial reference point is called a **day.** In modern usage every kind of solar time has its zero or starting point at **midnight,** when the celestial reference point is directly over the *lower branch* of the terrestrial reference meridian. This has not always been so. Until January 1, 1925, the **astronomical day** began at *noon,* 12 hours *later* than the start of the calendar day of the same date. The **nautical day** began at *noon,* 12 hours *earlier* than the calendar day, or 24 hours earlier than the astronomical day of the same date. The **sidereal day** begins at **sidereal noon,** when the first point of Aries is over the *upper branch* of the reference meridian. There is no sidereal date.

Time is customarily expressed in time units, from 0^h through 24^h. To the nearest 1^m it is generally stated by navigators in a four-digit unit without punctuation. Thus, 0000 is midnight at the start of the day. One minute later the time is 0001. Half an hour after the start of the day the time is 0030, at one hour the time is 0100, at one hour and four minutes it is 0104, at 19 minutes after noon (solar time) it is 1219, at four hours and 23 minutes after (solar) noon it is 1623, etc. The term "hours" is sometimes used with the four-digit system to indicate that the number refers to the time or "hour" of the day. However, in those few occasions when any reasonable doubt may exist as to whether time is indicated, the fact can better be indicated in another way. Thus, the expression "1600 hours" to indicate "1600" or "16 hours" is not strictly correct, and is better avoided. **Watch time (WT),** indicated by a watch or clock having a 12-hour dial, and **chronometer time (C)** are expressed on a 12-hour basis, with designations AM (ante meridian) and PM (post meridian), as in ordinary civil life ashore.

In contrast, a time interval is expressed as hours and minutes, as 5^h26^m. When either the time of day or a time interval is given to seconds, this same form is used, as $21^h15^m18^s$. The kind of time may be indicated, usually by abbreviation.

When a time interval is to be added to or subtracted from a time, the solution can be arranged conveniently in tabular form.

Example 1.—What is the time and date $14^h36^m53^s$ after $21^h14^m18^s$ on July 24?

Solution.—

$$
\begin{aligned}
21^h14^m18^s &\text{ July 24} \\
14^h36^m53^s & \\
\hline
35^h51^m11^s &\text{ July 24} \\
=11^h51^m11^s &\text{ July 25}
\end{aligned}
$$

The fact that the sum of hours exceeds 24 is an indication that the date increases by one. Similarly, in *subtracting* an interval, the date is one day earlier if 24^h must be added to the time before the subtraction can be made. That is, since 2400 of one day is 0000 of the following day, one might say that 2700 on one day is $2700-2400=$ 0300 on the following day. In the example above, $11^h51^m11^s$ on July 25 is the same as $11^h51^m11^s+24^h00^m00^s=35^h51^m11^s$ on July 24.

Date is sometimes expressed as an additional unit of the time sequence. Thus, $21^h14^m18^s$ on July 24 might be stated $24^d21^h14^m18^s$. This system is of particular value when an interval of several days is to be added or subtracted.

Example 2.—What is the time and date $9^d16^h35^m04^s$ before $5^h11^m33^s$ on September 15?

Solution.—

$$
\begin{aligned}
15^d05^h11^m33^s & \\
9^d16^h35^m04^s & \\
\hline
5^d12^h36^m29^s &\text{ or } 12^h36^m29^s \text{ on Sept. 5.}
\end{aligned}
$$

By this method the month and day, if of significance, are recorded separately, or they, too, can be added to the sequence.

Example 3.—What is the time and date 3 years, 6 months, 25 days, 12 hours, 19 minutes, and 44 seconds after $7^h52^m24^s$ on November 14, 1958?

Solution.—

$$
\begin{aligned}
1958^y11^m14^d07^h52^m24^s & \\
3^y06^m25^d12^h19^m44^s & \\
\hline
1962^y06^m08^d20^h12^m08^s &=20^h12^m08^s \text{ on June 8, 1962.}
\end{aligned}
$$

Since a month may contain a variable number of days, both the months and days should be solved together. Thus, in the example above, the answer would be 17 months, 39 days. If 12 months are converted to one year, this becomes five months, 39 days. Since the fifth month is May, this might be stated as May 39. Since there are 31 days in May, this is $39-31=8$ days into the next month, or June 8.

A simpler method of determining the number of elapsed *days* between any two dates is to use the **Julian day** of each date, if the information is available. This also eliminates possible error due to change of calendar if long intervals are involved. The Julian day is the consecutive number of the day starting at 1200 on January 1, 4713 BC. Julian day is listed in the *American Ephemeris and Nautical Almanac*.

1811. Time and arc.—The time of day is an indication of the interval since the day began. One day represents one complete rotation of 360° of the earth with respect to a selected celestial point. Each day is divided into 24 **hours** of 60 **minutes,** each minute having 60 **seconds.** Thus, each day has $24\times60=1{,}440$ minutes or $1{,}440\times60=$ 86,400 seconds. This is time regardless of the celestial reference point used, and since the various references are in motion with respect to each other, as "seen" from the earth, apparent solar, mean solar, and sidereal days are of different lengths. Since they all have the same number and kind of fractional parts, these parts are themselves of different length in the different kinds of time. Mean solar units are customarily used to indicate time intervals. The smallest unit normally used in celestial navigation is the second, but in some electronic equipment the **millisecond** (one-thousandth of a second), **microsecond** (one-millionth of a second), and the **millimicrosecond** or **nanosecond** (one-billionth of a second) are used.

Time of day is an indication of the *phase* of rotation of the earth. That is, it indicates how much of a day has elapsed, or what part of a rotation has been completed. Thus, at zero hours the day begins. One hour later, the earth has turned through 1/24 of a day, or 1/24 of 360°, or $\frac{360°}{24}=15°$. Six hours after the day begins, it has turned through 6/24=1/4 day, or $\frac{360°}{4}=90°$. Twelve hours after the start of the day, the day is half gone, having turned through 180°. Smaller intervals can also be stated in angular units, for since one hour or 60 minutes is equivalent to 15°, one minute of time is equivalent to $\frac{15°}{60}=0°.25=15'$, and one second of time is equivalent to $\frac{15'}{60}=$ $0'.25=15''$. Thus,

$$
\begin{array}{rl}
 & Time \quad Arc \\
 & 1^d=24^h=360°=1 \text{ circle} \\
60^m= & 1^h=15° \\
 & 4^m=1°=60' \\
60^s= & 1^m=15' \\
 & 4^s=1'=60'' \\
 & 1^s=15''=0'.25
\end{array}
$$

Any time interval can be expressed as an angle of rotation, and vice versa. Interconversion of these units can be made by the relationships indicated above.

To convert time to arc:

1. Multiply the hours by 15 to obtain degrees.

2. Divide the minutes of time by four to obtain degrees, and multiply the remainder by 15 to obtain minutes of arc.

3. Divide the seconds of time by four to obtain minutes and tenths of minutes of arc, or multiply the remainder by 15 to obtain seconds of arc.

4. Add degrees, minutes, and tenths (or seconds).

Example 1.—Convert $14^h21^m39^s$ to arc units.

Solution.—

(1) $14^h \times 15=210°$

(2) $21^m \div 4= \quad 5°15'$ (remainder $1^m \times 15=15'$)

(3) $39^s \div 4= \quad\quad 9'45''$ (remainder $3^s \times 15=45''$)

(4) $14^h21^m39^s=\overline{215°24'45''}=215°24'.8$ (to the nearest $0'.1$).

To convert arc to time:

1. Divide the degrees by 15 to obtain hours, and multiply the remainder by four to obtain minutes of time.

2. Divide the minutes of arc by 15 to obtain minutes of time, and multiply the remainder by four to obtain seconds of time.

3. Divide the seconds of arc by 15 to obtain seconds of time.

4. Add hours, minutes, and seconds.

Example 2.—Convert 215°24′45″ to time units.
Solution.—

   (1) 215° ÷ 15=14ʰ20ᵐ   (remainder 5°×4=20ᵐ)
   (2)   24′ ÷ 15=   1ᵐ36ˢ (remainder 9′×4=36ˢ)
   (3)   45″ ÷ 15=   3ˢ
   (4) 215°24′45″=14ʰ21ᵐ39ˢ

Example 3.—Convert 161°53′.7 to time units.
Solution.—

   (1) 161° ÷ 15=10ʰ44ᵐ   (remainder 11°×4=44ᵐ)
   (2) 53′.7 ÷ 15=   3ᵐ34ˢ.8 (remainder 8′.7×4=34ˢ.8)
   (3)   161°53′.7=10ʰ47ᵐ34ˢ.8 =10ʰ47ᵐ35ˢ.

The navigator should be able to make these solutions mentally, writing only the answer. As a check, the answer can be converted back to the original value. Solution can also be made by means of arc to time tables in the almanacs. In the *Nautical Almanac* the table, given near the back of the volume (app. F), is in two parts, permitting separate entries with degrees, minutes, and quarter minutes of arc. The table is arranged in this manner because the navigator is confronted with the problem of converting arc to time more often than the reverse.

Example 4.—Convert 334°18′22″ to time units, using the *Nautical Almanac* arc to time conversion table.
Solution.—

$$334°=22^h16^m$$
$$18'.25=\quad 1^m13^s$$
$$334°18'22''=22^h17^m13^s$$

The 22″ are converted to the nearest quarter minute of arc for solution to the nearest second of time. Interpolation can be used if more precise results are required, since exact relationships are tabulated in the *Nautical Almanac* conversion table.

Example 5.—Convert 83°29′.6 to time units, using the *Nautical Almanac* arc to time conversion table.
Solution.—

$$83°=5^h32^m$$
$$29'.6=\quad 1^m58^s.4$$
$$83°29'.6=5^h33^m58^s.4$$

In this solution, 58ˢ.4 was obtained by eye interpolation in the quarter-minute part of the table.

Example 6.—Convert 17ʰ09ᵐ42ˢ to arc units, using the *Nautical Almanac* arc to time conversion table.
Solution.—

$$17^h08^m=257°$$
$$1^m42^s=\quad 25'.5$$
$$17^h09^m42^s=257°25'.5$$

A similar table appears near the back of the *Air Almanac* (app. G); however, quarter minutes of arc are not included.

Example 7.—Convert 334°47′.2 to time units, using the *Air Almanac* arc to time conversion table.

Solution.—

$$334° - 180° = 154° = 10^h 16^m$$
$$47'.2 = \qquad 3^m 09^s$$
$$154°47'.2 = \overline{10^h 19^m 09^s}$$
$$334°47'.2 = 22^h 19^m 09^s$$

Example 8.—Convert $15^h 13^m 18^s$ to arc units, using the *Air Almanac* arc to time conversion table.

Solution.—

$$15^h 12^m = 228°$$
$$1^m 18^s = \qquad 19'.5$$
$$15^h 13^m 18^s = \overline{228°19'.5}$$

Because the almanac conversion tables are exact relationships, interpolation in them can be carried to any degree of precision desired without introducing an error.

1812. Time and longitude.—As indicated in the preceding article, time is a measure of rotation of the earth, and any given time interval can be represented by a corresponding angle through which the earth turns. Suppose the celestial reference point were directly over a certain reference of the earth. An hour later the earth would have turned through 15°, and the celestial reference would be directly over a meridian 15° farther west. Any difference of longitude is a measure of the angle through which the earth must rotate for the local time at the western meridian to become what it was at the eastern meridian before the rotation took place. Therefore, places to the eastward of an observer have *later* time, and those to the westward have *earlier* time, and the difference is exactly equal to the difference in longitude, expressed in time units. When a meridian other than the local meridian is used as the time reference, the difference in time of two places is equal to the difference of longitude of their time reference meridians.

1813. The date line.—Since time becomes later toward the east, and earlier toward the west, time at the lower branch of one's meridian is 12 hours earlier or later depending upon the direction of reckoning. A traveler making a trip around the world gains or loses an entire day. To prevent the *date* from being in error, and to provide a starting place for each day, a **date line** is fixed by international agreement. This line coincides with the 180th meridian over most of its length. In crossing this line, one alters his date by one day. In effect, this changes his time 24 hours to compensate for the slow change during a trip around the world. Therefore, it is applied in the opposite direction to the change of time. Thus, if a person is traveling *eastward* from east longitude to west longitude, time is becoming *later*, and when the date line is crossed, the date becomes one day *earlier*. That is, at any moment the date immediately to the *west* of the date line (east longitude) is one day *later* than the date immediately to the *east* of the line, except at GMT 1200, when the (mean time) date is the same all over the world. At any other time two dates occur, one boundary between dates being the date line, and the other being the midnight line along the lower branch of the meridian over which the mean sun is located. At GMT 1200 these two boundaries coincide. In the solution of problems, error can sometimes be avoided by converting local time to Greenwich time, and then converting this to local time on the opposite side of the date line. Examples are given in following articles.

1814. Zone time.—At sea, as well as ashore, watches and clocks are normally set approximately to some form of **zone time** (**ZT**). At sea the *nearest* meridian exactly divisible by 15° is usually used as the **time meridian** or **zone meridian**. Thus, within a **time zone** extending 7°.5 on each side of each time meridian the time is the same, and time in consecutive zones differs by exactly one hour. The time is changed as con-

476 TIME

venient, usually at a whole hour, near the time of crossing the boundary between zones. Each time zone is identified by the number of times the longitude of its zone meridian is divisible by 15°, positive in west longitude and negative in east longitude. This number and its sign, called the **zone description (ZD),** is the number of whole *hours* that are added to or subtracted from the zone time to obtain **Greenwich mean time (GMT),** which is the zone time at the Greenwich (0°) meridian, and is often called **Universal Time (UT).** The mean sun is the celestial reference point for zone time.

Example 1.—For an observer at long. 141°18′4W the ZT is $6^h18^m24^s$.
Required.—(1) Zone description.
(2) GMT.
Solution.—(1) The nearest meridian exactly divisible by 15° is 135°W, into which 15° will go nine times. Since longitude is west, ZD is (+) 9.

$$
\begin{array}{ll}
\text{ZT} & 6^h18^m24^s \\
\text{ZD} \quad (+) & 9 \\
\hline
(2) \ \text{GMT} & 15^h18^m24^s
\end{array}
$$

In converting GMT to ZT, a positive ZD is *subtracted*, and a negative one *added*, but its sign remains the same, being part of the description. The word "reversed" (rev.) is written to the right in the work form to indicate that the "reverse" process is to be performed.

Example 2.—The GMT is $15^h27^m09^s$.
Required.—(1) ZT at long. 156°24′4 W.
(2) ZT at 39°04′8 E.
Solution.—

$$
\begin{array}{llll} \quad\quad
(1) \ \text{GMT} & 15^h27^m09^s & \quad (2) \ \text{GMT} & 15^h27^m09^s \\
\text{ZD} \ (+)10 & \text{(rev.)} & \text{ZD} \ (-) \ 3 & \text{(rev.)} \\
\hline
\text{ZT} \quad 5^h27^m09^s & & \text{ZT} \quad 18^h27^m09^s
\end{array}
$$

When time at one place is converted to that at another, the date should be watched carefully. If a sum exceeds 24 hours, subtract this amount and add one day. If 24 hours are added before a subtraction is made, the date at the place is one day *earlier*.

Example 3.—At long. 73°29′2 W the ZT is $21^h12^m53^s$ on May 14.
Required.—(1) GMT and date.
(2) ZT and date at long. 107°15′7 W.
Solution.—

$$
\begin{array}{lll}
\text{ZT} & 21^h12^m53^s & \text{May 14} \\
\text{ZD} \ (+) & 5 & \\
\hline
(1) \ \text{GMT} & 2^h12^m53^s & \text{May 15} \\
\text{ZD} \ (+) & 7 & \text{(rev.)} \\
\hline
(2) \quad \text{ZT} & 19^h12^m53^s & \text{May 14}
\end{array}
$$

The second part of this problem might have been solved by using the *difference* in zone description. Since the second place is two zones farther west, its time is two hours earlier. Problems involving zone times at various places generally involve nothing more than addition or subtraction of one small number, so solutions can generally be made mentally. However, when this forms part of a larger problem, or when a record of the solution is desired, the full solution should be recorded, including labels.

Example 4.—On November 30 the 1430 DR long. of a ship is 51°32′4 W. Ten hours later the DR long. is 53°07′2 W.
Required.—ZT and date of arrival at the second longitude.

Solution.—

ZT		1430 Nov. 30
ZD	(+)	3
GMT		1730 Nov. 30
int.		10
GMT		0330 Dec. 1
ZD	(+)	4 (rev.)
ZT		2330 Nov. 30

If a time zone boundary had not been crossed, there would have been no need to find GMT. It is particularly helpful to retain this step when the date line is crossed. This line is the *center* of a time zone, the western (east longitude) half being designated (−) 12, and the eastern (west longitude) half (+) 12.

*Example 5.—*On December 31 the 0800 DR long. of a ship is 177°23ʹ9E. Forty hours later the DR long. is 171°53ʹ9 W.

*Required.—*ZT and date of arrival at the second longitude.

Solution.—

Alternative solution

ZT		0800 Dec. 31	ZT	$31^d08^h00^m$
ZD	(−)	12	ZD	(−)12
GMT		2000 Dec. 30	GMT	$30^d20^h00^m$
int.		40	int.	1^d16^h
GMT		1200 Jan. 1	GMT	$1^d12^h00^m$
ZD	(+)	11 (rev.)	ZD	(+)11 (rev.)
ZT		0100 Jan. 1	ZT	$1^d01^h00^m$

For certain communication purposes it is sometimes convenient to designate a time zone by a single letter. The system used is shown in figure 1814.

Use of time zones on land began in 1883, when railroads adopted four standard zones for the continental United States. The division of the United States into time zones was not officially adopted by Congress, however, until March 19, 1918, when a fifth zone was also established for Alaska. The system of time zones is now used almost universally throughout the world, although on land the zone boundaries are generally altered somewhat for convenience. In a few places, half-hour zones are used but these are not standard time zones.

On land, normal zone time is usually called **standard time,** often with an adjective to indicate the zone, as **eastern standard time.** In some areas timepieces are *advanced* one or more hours during the summer to provide greater use of daylight. This "fast" time is called **daylight saving time** in the United States, and **summer time** elsewhere. When time is one hour fast, the zone description is (algebraically) one *less* than normal. When daylight saving or summer time is specified, an advance of one hour is understood unless a greater number is indicated.

*Example 6.—*What is the standard time and date at Tokyo, long. 140°E, when the daylight saving time at Washington, D.C., long. 77°W, is 1600 on Oct. 5?

Solution.—

ZT		1600 Oct. 5
ZD	(+)	4
GMT		2000 Oct. 5
ZD	(−)	9 (rev.)
ZT		0500 Oct. 6

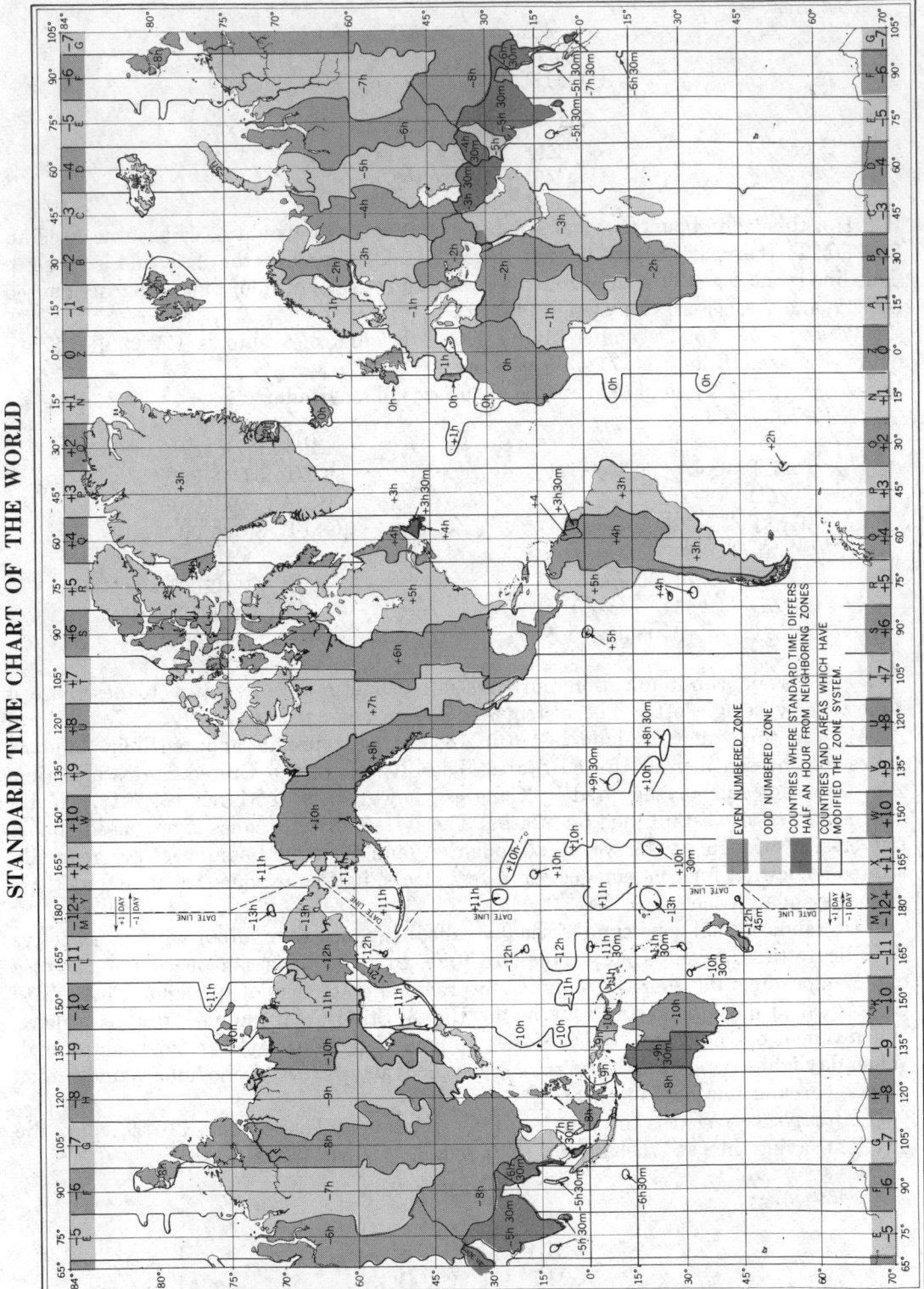

STANDARD TIME CHART OF THE WORLD

FIGURE 1814.—Time zone chart of the world.

During hostilities daylight saving time may be kept all year long throughout a nation, and designated **war time.**

1815. Chronometer time (C) is time indicated by a chronometer. Since a chronometer is set approximately to GMT, and not reset until it is overhauled and cleaned, perhaps three years later (art. 1514), there is nearly always a **chronometer error (CE)**, either *fast* (F) or *slow* (S). The change in chronometer error in 24 hours is called **chronometer rate,** or **daily rate,** and designated *gaining* or *losing*. With a consistent rate of 1^s per day for three years, the chronometer error would be approximately 18^m. Since chronometer error is subject to change, it should be determined from time to time, preferably daily at sea. Chronometer error is found by radio time signal (art. 1826), by comparison with another timepiece of known error, or by applying chronometer rate to previous readings of the same instrument. It is recorded to the nearest whole or half second. Chronometer rate is recorded to the nearest $0.^s1$.

Example 1.—At GMT 1200 on May 12 the chronometer reads $12^h04^m21^s$. At GMT 1600 on May 18 it reads $4^h04^m25^s$.

Required.—(1) Chronometer error at both comparisons.

(2) Chronometer rate.

(3) Chronometer error at GMT 0530 on May 27.

Solution.—

$$
\begin{array}{ll}
\text{GMT} & 12^h00^m00^s \text{ May 12} \\
\text{C} & 12^h04^m21^s \\
\hline
(1)\ \text{CE} & (\text{F})\ 4^m21^s
\end{array}
$$

$$
\begin{array}{ll}
\text{GMT} & 16^h00^m00^s \text{ May 18} \\
\text{C} & 4^h04^m25^s \\
\hline
(1)\ \text{CE} & (\text{F})\ 4^m25^s
\end{array}
$$

$$
\begin{array}{ll}
\text{GMT} & 12^d12^h \\
\text{GMT} & 18^d16^h \\
\hline
\text{diff.} & 6^d04^h = 6.^d2
\end{array}
$$

$$
\begin{array}{lll}
\text{CE} & (\text{F})\ 4^m21^s & 1200 \text{ May 12} \\
\text{CE} & (\text{F})\ 4^m25^s & 1600 \text{ May 18} \\
\hline
\text{diff.} & 4^s \text{ gained} \\
(2)\ \text{daily rate} & 0.^s6 \text{ per day, gaining.} & (4^s \div 6.^d2)
\end{array}
$$

$$
\begin{array}{ll}
\text{GMT} & 18^d16^h00^m \\
\text{GMT} & 27^d05^h30^m \\
\hline
\text{diff.} & 8^d13^h30^m = 8.^d5
\end{array}
$$

$$
\begin{array}{lll}
\text{CE} & (\text{F})\ 4^m25^s & 1600 \text{ May 18} \\
\text{corr.} & (+)5^s & (8.^d5 \times 0.^s6 \text{ per day}) \\
\hline
(3)\ \text{CE} & (\text{F})\ 4^m30^s & 0530 \text{ May 27}
\end{array}
$$

Because GMT is stated on a 24-hour basis, and chronometer time on a 12-hour basis, a 12-hour ambiguity exists. This is ignored in finding chronometer error. However, if chronometer error is applied to chronometer time to find GMT, a possible 12-hour error can result. This can be resolved by mentally applying zone description to local time to obtain approximate GMT. A time diagram can be used for resolving doubt as to approximate GMT and Greenwich date. If the sun for the kind of time used (mean or apparent) is between the *lower* branches of two time meridians (as the standard meridian for local time, and the Greenwich meridian for GMT), the date at the place farther *east* is one day *later* than at the place farther *west*.

Example 2.—On August 14 the DR long. of a ship is about 124° E, and the zone time is about 0500. Chronometer error is 12^m27^s slow.

Required.—GMT and date when the chronometer reads $8^h44^m22^s$.

Solution.—

approx.	ZT	0500	Aug. 14
	ZD	(—)8	
approx.	GMT	2100	Aug. 13

C	$8^h44^m22^s$	
CE	(S) 12^m27^s	
GMT	$20^h56^m49^s$	Aug. 13

The *A* chronometer, usually the best (having the most nearly uniform rate), is compared directly with the time signal (art. 1826). Other chronometers, designated *B, C*, etc., may then be compared with the *A* chronometer.

Example 3.—At GMT 1400 chronometer *A* is checked by time signal, and found to read $1^h57^m09^s$. A little later, when it reads $2^h05^m00^s$, chronometer *B* reads $2^h11^m38^s$.

Required.—(1) Error of chronometer *A*.

(2) Error of chronometer *B*.

Solution.—

	GMT	$14^h00^m00^s$
	C_A	$1^h57^m09^s$
(1)	CE_A	(S) 2^m51^s
	C_A	$2^h05^m00^s$
	GMT	$14^h07^m51^s$
	C_B	$2^h11^m38^s$
(2)	CE_B	(F) 3^m47^s

If time signals are not available at the chronometer, a good comparing watch (art. 1516) should be compared with the radio signal, and this watch used to determine chronometer error, as indicated in example 3, substituting the watch for chronometer *A*.

1816. Watch time (WT) is time indicated by a watch. This is usually an approximation of zone time, except that for timing celestial observations it is good practice to set a comparing watch (art. 1516) to GMT. If the watch has a second setting hand, the watch can be set exactly to ZT or GMT, and the time is so designated. If the watch is not set exactly to one of these times, the difference is known as **watch error (WE)**, labeled *fast* (F) or *slow* (S) to indicate whether the watch is ahead of or behind the correct time, respectively.

If a watch is to be set exactly to ZT or GMT, it is set to some whole minute slightly ahead of the correct time, and stopped. When the set time arrives, the watch is started. It should then be checked for accuracy.

Example 1.—A chronometer 9^m46^s fast on GMT reads approximately 7^h23^m. At the next whole five minutes of GMT a comparing watch is to be set to GMT exactly.

Required.—(1) What should the watch read at the moment of starting?

(2) What should the chronometer read?

Solution.—

	C	$7^h23^m00^s$	
	CE	(F) 9^m46^s	
	GMT	$7^h13^m14^s$	
(1)	GMT	$7^h15^m00^s$	(next whole 5^m)
	CE	(F) 9^m46^s	
(2)	C	$7^h24^m46^s$	

The GMT may be in error by 12^h, but if the watch is graduated to 12 hours, this will not be reflected. If a watch with a 24-hour dial is used, the actual GMT should be determined.

If watch error is to be determined, it is done by comparing the reading of the watch with that of the chronometer at a selected moment. This may be at some selected GMT, as in example 1.

Example 2.—If, in example 1, the watch had read $7^h14^m48^s$ at the moment the chronometer read $7^h24^m46^s$, what would be the watch error on GMT?

Solution.—

$$
\begin{array}{ll}
\text{GMT} & 7^h15^m00^s \\
\text{WT} & 7^h14^m48^s \\
\text{WE} & \text{(S)} \ \overline{12^s} \\
\end{array}
$$

A more convenient chronometer time might be selected, as a whole minute.

Example 3.—A watch is set to zone time approximately. The longitude is about 48°W. The watch is compared with a chronometer which is 19^m44^s fast on GMT. When the chronometer reads $5^h22^m00^s$, the watch reads $2^h01^m53^s$.

Required.—Watch error on zone time.

Solution.—

$$
\begin{array}{lll}
\text{C} & 5^h22^m00^s & \\
\text{CE} & \text{(F)} \ 19^m44^s & \\
\text{GMT} & \overline{5^h02^m16^s} & \\
\text{ZD(+)3} & & \text{(rev.)} \\
\text{ZT} & \overline{2^h02^m16^s} & \\
\text{WT} & 2^h01^m53^s & \\
\text{WE} & \text{(S)} \ \overline{23^s} & \\
\end{array}
$$

The possible 12^h error is not of significance. When such a watch is used for determining GMT, however, as for entering an almanac, the 12-hour ambiguity is important. Unless a watch is graduated to 24 hours, its time is designated AM before noon and PM after noon.

Example 4.—On January 3 the DR long. is 94°14′.7E. An observation of the sun is made when the watch reads $12^h16^m23^s$ PM. The watch is 22^s fast on zone time.

Required.—GMT and date.

Solution.—

$$
\begin{array}{lll}
\text{WT} & 12^h16^m23^s & \text{PM Jan. 3} \\
\text{WE} & \text{(F)} \ 22^s & \\
\text{ZT} & \overline{12^h16^m01^s} & \\
\text{ZD(}-\text{)6} & & \\
\text{GMT} & \overline{6^h16^m01^s} & \text{Jan. 3} \\
\end{array}
$$

Note that between 1200 and 1300 watch designations are PM. Between 0000 and 0100 they are AM.

Comparison of a watch and chronometer should be made carefully. If two observers are available, one can give a warning "stand-by" a few seconds before the selected time, and a "mark" at the appointed moment, while the other notes the time of the watch. A single observer can make a satisfactory comparison by counting with the chronometer. Chronometers beat in half seconds, with an audible "tick." Ten seconds before the selected time (perhaps a whole minute), the observer starts counting with the beats, as he watches the chronometer second hand, "50, and, 1, and, 2, and, 3, and, ... 9, and, mark." During the count the observer shifts his view from the chronometer to the second hand of the watch, continuing to count in cadence with the chronometer beats. At the "mark," the second, minute, and hour hands of the watch are read in that order, and the time recorded. A comparison of this time with the GMT or ZT corresponding to the selected chronometer time indicates the watch error.

Even though a watch is set to zone time approximately, its error on GMT can be determined and used for timing observations. In this case the 12-hour ambiguity in GMT should be resolved, and a time diagram used to avoid possible error. This method requires additional work, and presents a greater probability of error, without compensating advantages.

Still another method of determining GMT, generally used before zone time came into common use at sea, is to *subtract* watch time from chronometer time, to find C − WT. This is then *added* to the watch time of an observation to obtain chronometer time (C−WT+WT=C). Chronometer error is then applied to the result to obtain GMT. A time diagram should *always* be used with this method, to resolve the 12-hour ambiguity and to be sure of the correct Greenwich date, unless an auxiliary solution is made using approximate ZT and ZD. This method has little to recommend it.

If a watch has a **watch rate** of more than a few seconds per day, watch error should be determined both before and after a round of sights, and any difference distributed proportionally among observations.

If a stopwatch is used for timing observations, it should be started at some convenient GMT, as a whole 5^m or 10^m. The time of each observation is then this GMT *plus* the reading of the watch.

1817. Local mean time (LMT), like zone time, uses the mean sun as the celestial reference point. It differs from zone time in that the local meridian is used as the terrestrial reference, rather than a zone meridian. Thus, the local mean time at each meridian differs from that of every other meridian, the difference being equal to the difference of longitude, expressed in time units. At each zone meridian, including 0°, LMT and ZT are identical.

Example 1.—At long. 124°37′.2W the LMT is $17^h24^m18^s$ on March 21.

Required.—(1) GMT and date.

(2) ZT and date at the place.

Solution.—

	LMT	$17^h24^m18^s$	Mar. 21
	λ	$8^h18^m29^sW$	
(1)	GMT	$1^h42^m47^s$	Mar. 22
	ZD (+)	8	(rev.)
(2)	ZT	$17^h42^m47^s$	Mar. 21

In navigation the principal use of LMT is in rising, setting, and twilight tables. The problem is usually one of converting the LMT taken from the table to ZT. At sea, the difference between these times is normally not more than 30^m, and the conversion is made directly, without finding GMT as an intermediate step. This is done by applying a correction equal to the difference of longitude (dλ). If the observer is *west* of his time meridian, the correction is *added*, and if *east* of it, the correction is *subtracted*. If Greenwich time is desired, it is found from ZT.

Example 2.—At long. 63°24′.4E the LMT is 0525 on January 2.

Required.—(1) ZT and date.

(2) GMT and date.

Solution.—

$$
\begin{array}{llll}
 & \text{LMT} & 0525 & \text{Jan. 2} \\
 & d\lambda & (-)\ 14 & \\
\text{(1)} & \text{ZT} & \overline{0511} & \text{Jan. 2} \\
 & \text{ZD} & (-)4 & \\
\text{(2)} & \text{GMT} & \overline{0111} & \text{Jan. 2} \\
\end{array}
$$

On land, with an irregular zone boundary, the longitude may differ by more than $7°.5\ (30^m)$ from the time meridian.

If LMT is to be corrected to daylight saving time, the difference in longitude between the local and time merdian can be used, or the ZT can first be found and then increased by one hour.

Conversion of ZT (including GMT) to LMT is the same as conversion in the opposite direction, except that the sign of $d\lambda$ is reversed. This problem is not normally encountered in navigation.

1818. Apparent time utilizes the **apparent** (real) **sun** as its celestial reference, and a meridian as the terrestrial reference. **Local apparent time** (**LAT**) uses the local meridian. The LAT at the 0° meridian is called **Greenwich apparent time** (**GAT**).

The LAT at one meridian differs from that at any other by the difference in longitude of the two places, the place to the eastward having the later time, and conversion is the same as converting LMT at one place to LMT at another.

Use of the apparent sun as a celestial reference point for time results in time of nonconstant rate for at least three reasons. First, revolution of the earth in its orbit is not constant. Second, motion of the apparent sun is along the ecliptic, which is tilted with respect to the celestial equator, along which time is measured. Third, rotation of the earth on its axis is not constant. The effect due by this third cause is extremely small.

For the various forms of mean time, the apparent sun is replaced by a fictitious **mean sun** conceived as moving eastward along the *celestial equator* at a uniform speed equal to the average speed of the apparent sun along the ecliptic, thus providing a nearly uniform measure of time equal to the approximate average apparent time. At any moment the accumulated difference between LAT and LMT is indicated by the **equation of time** (**Eq. T**), which reaches a maximum value of about $16^m.4$ in November. This quantity is tabulated at 12-hour intervals at the bottom of the right-hand daily page of the *Nautical Almanac*. In the United States, the sign is considered positive $(+)$ if the time of sun's "Mer. Pass." is earlier than 1200, and negative $(-)$ if later than 1200. If the "Mer. Pass." is given as 1200 (as on June 12–14, 1975), the sign is positive if the GHA at GMT 1200 is between 0° and 1°, and negative if it is greater than 359°. The sign is correct for conversion of GMT to GAT. In Great Britain, this convention is reversed. Since GMT is the entering argument for the almanacs, interconversion of apparent and mean time should preferably be made from Greenwich time, rather than from local time.

Example.—Find the LAT and date at ZT $15^h10^m40^s$ on May 31, 1975, for long. $73°18'.4$ W.

Solution.—

$$
\begin{array}{lll}
\text{ZT} & 15^h10^m40^s & \text{May 31} \\
\text{ZD}(+) & 5 & \\
\text{GMT} & \overline{20^h10^m40^s} & \text{May 31} \\
\text{Eq. T}(+) & 2^m25^s & \\
\text{GAT} & \overline{20^h13^m05^s} & \text{May 31} \\
\lambda & 4^h53^m14^s\ \text{W} & \\
\text{LAT} & \overline{15^h19^m51^s} & \text{May 31} \\
\end{array}
$$

In conversion from apparent to mean time, a second solution may be needed if the equation of time is large and changing rapidly, using the GAT for entering the almanac for the first solution, and using the GMT from this solution as the almanac entry value for the second solution.

Apparent time can also be found by converting hour angle to time units, and adding or subtracting 12 hours. If LAT is required, but not GAT, conversion of arc to time should be made from LHA, rather than GHA, to avoid the need for conversion of longitude to time units. Equation of time can be found by *subtracting* mean time from apparent time at the same meridian. This method of finding apparent time and equation of time is the only one available with the *Air Almanac*, which does not tabulate equation of time.

The navigator has little or no use for apparent time, as such. However, it can be used for finding the time of **local apparent noon** (**LAN**), when the apparent sun is on the celestial meridian.

The mean sun averages out the irregularities in time due to the variations of the speed of revolution of the earth in its orbit and the fact that the apparent sun moves in the ecliptic while hour angle is measured along the celestial equator. It does not eliminate the error due to slight variations in the *rotational* speed of the earth. When a correction for the accumulated error from this source is applied to mean time, **Ephemeris Time** results. This time is of interest to astronomers, but is not used directly by the navigator.

1819. Sidereal time uses the first point of Aries (vernal equinox) as the celestial reference point. Since the earth revolves around the sun, and since the direction of the earth's rotation and revolution are the same, it completes a rotation with respect to the stars in less time (about $3^m56\overset{s}{.}6$ of mean solar units) than with respect to the sun, and during one revolution about the sun (one year) it makes one complete rotation more with respect to the stars than with the sun. This accounts for the daily shift of the stars nearly 1° westward each night. Hence, sidereal days are shorter than solar days, and its hours, minutes, and seconds are correspondingly shorter. Because of nutation (art. 1417) sidereal time is not quite constant in rate. Time based upon the average rate is called **mean sidereal time,** when it is to be distinguished from the slightly irregular sidereal time. The ratio of mean solar time units to mean sidereal time units is 1:1.00273791.

The sidereal *day* begins when the first point of Aries is over the *upper* branch of the meridian, and extends through 24 hours of sidereal time. The sun is at the first point of Aries at the time of the vernal equinox, about March 21. However, since the solar day begins when the sun is over the *lower* branch of the meridian, apparent solar and sidereal times differ by 12 hours at the vernal equinox. Each month thereafter, sidereal time *gains* about two hours on solar time. By the time of the summer solstice, about June 21, sidereal time is 18 hours *ahead* or six hours *behind* solar time. By the time of the autumnal equinox, about September 23, the two times are together, and by the time of the winter solstice, about December 22, the sidereal time is six hours *ahead* of solar time. There need be no confusion of the date, for there is no sidereal date.

Local sidereal time (**LST**) uses the local meridian as the terrestrial reference. At the prime meridian this is called **Greenwich sidereal time** (**GST**). The difference between LST at two meridians is equal to the difference of longitude between them, the place to the eastward having the later time. Local sidereal time is LHA♈ expressed in time units. To determine LST at any given moment, find GHA♈ by means of an almanac, and then apply the longitude to convert it to LHA♈. Then convert LHA♈ in arc to LST in time units.

Example.—Find LST at ZT 8ʰ25ᵐ51ˢ on May 31, 1975, for long. 103°16ʹ3 E.

Solution.—

ZT	8ʰ25ᵐ51ˢ May 31
ZD(−)7	
GMT	1ʰ25ᵐ51ˢ May 31
1ʰ	262°54ʹ8
25ᵐ51ˢ	6°28ʹ8
GHA♈	269°23ʹ6
λ	103°16ʹ3 E
LHA♈	12°39ʹ9
LST	0ʰ50ᵐ40ˢ

Unless GST is required, conversion from arc to time units should be made from LHA♈, rather than from GHA♈, to avoid the need for converting longitude from arc to time units.

Conversion of sidereal to solar time is the reverse. Local sidereal time is converted to arc (LHA♈), and the longitude is applied to find GHA♈. This is used as an argument for entering the almanac to determine GMT, which can then be converted to any other kind of time desired. This is similar to one method of finding time of meridian transit, described in article 2104. Normally, the problem is not encountered by the navigator.

Sidereal time, as such, is little used by the navigator. It is the basis of star charts (art. 2204) and star finders (art. 2210), and certain sight reduction methods (notably Pub. No. 249), but generally in the form LHA♈. This kind of time is used for these purposes because its celestial reference point remains almost fixed in relation to the stars. Sidereal time is used by astronomers to regulate mean time. Timepieces regulated to sidereal time can be purchased.

1820. Time and hour angle.—Both time and hour angle are a measure of the phase of rotation of the earth, since both indicate the angular distance of a celestial reference point *west* of a terrestrial reference meridian. Hour angle, however, applies to *any* point on the celestial sphere. Time might be used in this respect, but only the apparent sun, mean sun, the first point of Aries, and occasionally the moon are commonly used.

Hour angles are usually expressed in arc units, and are measured from the upper branch of the celestial meridian. Time is customarily expressed in time units. Sidereal time is measured from the upper branch of the celestial meridian, like hour angle, but solar time is measured from the lower branch. Thus, LMT=LHA mean sun plus or minus 180°, LAT=LHA apparent sun plus or minus 180°, and LST=LHA♈.

As with time, **local hour angle (LHA),** based upon the local celestial meridian, at two places differs by the longitude between them, and LHA at longitude 0° is called **Greenwich hour angle (GHA).** In addition, it is often convenient to express hour angle in terms of the *shorter* arc between the local celestial meridian and the body. This is similar to measurement of longitude from the Greenwich meridian. Local hour angle measured in this way is called **meridian angle (t),** which is labeled *east* or *west*, like longitude, to indicate the direction of measurement. A westerly meridian angle is numerically equal to LHA, while an easterly meridian angle is equal to 360°−LHA; also, LHA=t (W), and LHA=360°−t (E). Meridian angle is used in the solution of the navigational triangle (art. 1433).

Example 1.—Find LHA and t of the sun at GMT 3ʰ24ᵐ16ˢ on June 1, 1975, for long. 118°48ʹ2W.

Solution.—

$$\begin{array}{ll} \text{GMT} & 3^\text{h}24^\text{m}16^\text{s}\ \text{June 1} \\ 3^\text{h} & \overline{225°35.'7} \\ 24^\text{m}16^\text{s} & 6°04.'0 \\ \text{GHA} & \overline{231°39.'7} \\ \lambda & 118°48.'2\ \text{W} \\ \text{LHA} & \overline{112°51.'5} \\ t & 112°51.'5\ \text{W} \end{array}$$

Example 2.—Find LHA and t of Kochab at ZT $18^\text{h}24^\text{m}47^\text{s}$ on May 31, 1975, for long. 55°27.'3W.

Solution.—

$$\begin{array}{ll} & \text{Kochab} \\ \text{ZT} & \overline{18^\text{h}24^\text{m}47^\text{s}}\ \text{May 31} \\ \text{ZD}\ (+) & 4 \\ \text{GMT} & \overline{22^\text{h}24^\text{m}47^\text{s}}\ \text{May 31} \\ 22^\text{h} & \overline{218°46.'5} \\ 24^\text{m}47^\text{s} & 6°12.'8 \\ \text{SHA} & 137°17.'7 \\ \text{GHA} & \overline{2°17.'0} \\ \lambda & 55°27.'3\ \text{W} \\ \text{LHA} & \overline{306°49.'7} \\ t & 53°10.'3\ \text{E} \end{array}$$

1821. The legal basis of standard time in the United States is contained in the "Uniform Time Act of 1966" (Public Law 89–387) and the U. S. Code, Title 15. This act reiterates the policy of the United States to "promote the adoption and observance of uniform time within prescribed Standard Time Zones . . ." and establishes the annual advancement and retardation of standard time by 1 hour the last Sunday of April and October, respectively. The Department of Transportation is the agency designated for enforcement of the law.

The "Uniform Time Act" establishes 8 Standard Time Zones for the United States (fig. 1821) and notes that standard time is based on the mean solar time of specified longitudes. The reference meridians are spaced 15° apart in longitude beginning with the meridian through Greenwich, England. Time zones extend 7½° in longitude on each side with considerable variation in boundaries to conform to political or geographic boundaries or both. Since the time zones are 15° apart, the time difference between two adjacent zones is one hour.

A comprehensive delineation of these zones is given in the **Code of Federal Regulations,** entitled "Standard Time Zone Boundaries."

This system of time zones is now used almost universally throughout the world, although on land the zone boundaries are generally altered somewhat for convenience (fig. 1814). In a few places, half-hour zones are used.

The standard times used in various countries and places are tabulated in the almanacs.

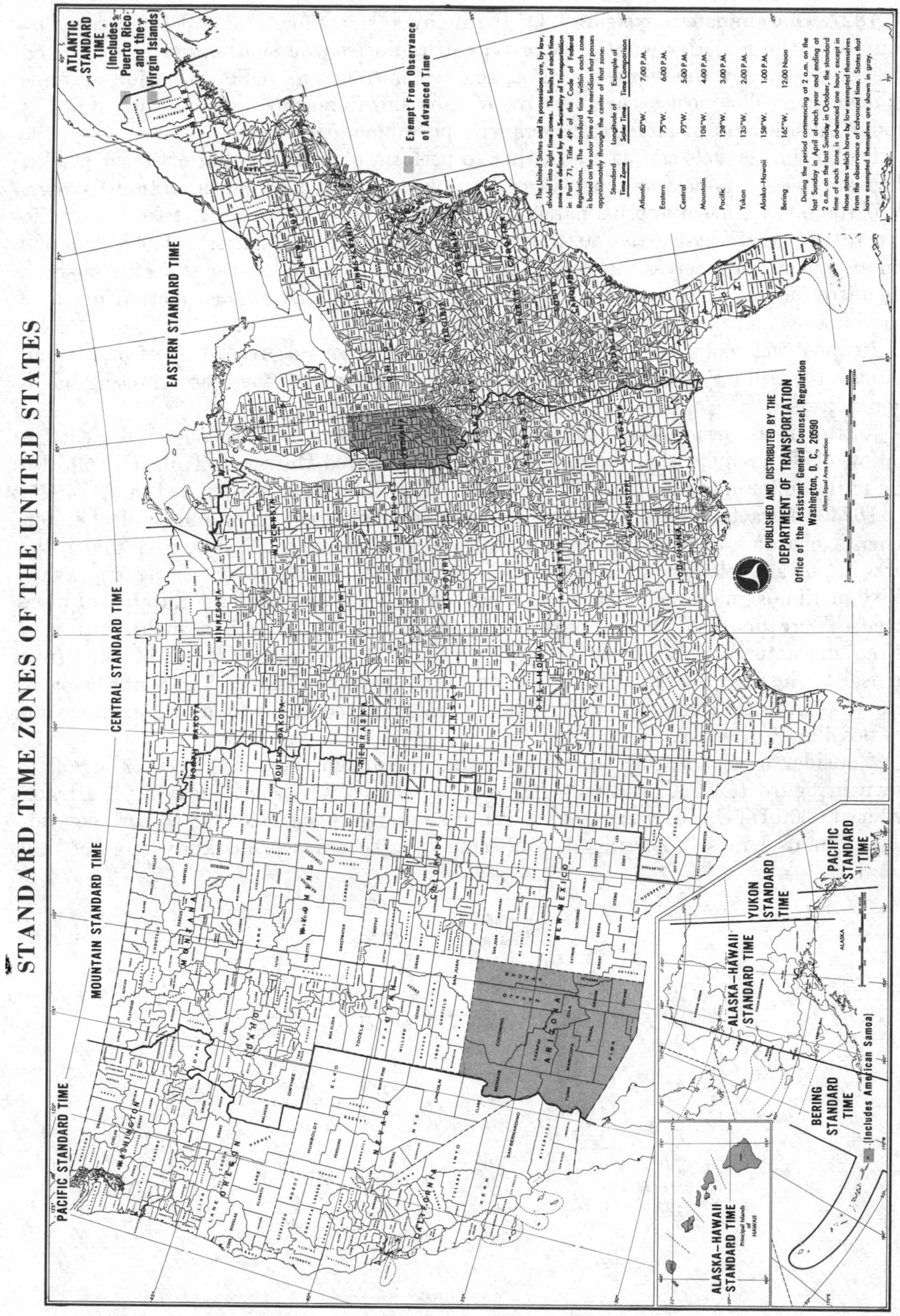

STANDARD TIME ZONES OF THE UNITED STATES

FIGURE 1821.—Standard Time Zones of the United States of America.

Radio Dissemination of Time Signals

1822. Dissemination systems.—Of the many systems for time and frequency dissemination, the majority employ some type of radio transmission, either in dedicated time and frequency emissions or established systems such as radionavigation systems and television. The most accurate means of time and frequency dissemination today is through on site visits or aircraft flyovers with portable atomic clocks.

Radio time signals can be used either to perform a clock function or to set clocks. When one uses a radio wave instead of a clock, however, new considerations evolve. One is the delay time of approximately 3 microseconds per kilometer it takes the radio wave to propagate and arrive at the reception point. Thus, a user 1,000 kilometers from a transmitter receives the time signal about 3 milliseconds later than the on-time transmitter signal. If time is needed to better than 3 milliseconds, correction must be made for the signal to pass through the receiver.

In most cases standard time and frequency emissions as received are more than adequate for ordinary needs. However, many systems exist for the more exacting scientific requirements.

Astronomers, geodesists, navigators, and others using time based on the earth's rotation (UT1) require that the emissions of Coordinated Universal Time (UTC) also include the difference between UTC and UT1. This difference is discussed in art. 1827.

1823. Characteristic elements of dissemination systems.—A number of common elements characterize most time and frequency dissemination systems. Among the more important elements are accuracy, ambiguity, repeatability, coverage, availability of time signal, reliability, ease of use, cost to the user, and the number of users served. There does not now appear to be any single system which incorporates all desired characteristics. The relative importance of these characteristics will vary from one user to the next, and the kind of compromise solution for one user may not be satisfactory to another. These common elements are discussed in the following examination of a possible radio signal.

Consider a very simple system consisting of an unmodulated 10-kHz signal as shown in figure 1823. A positive going zero-crossing of this signal, leaving the transmitter at 0000 UTC, will reach the receiver at a later time equivalent to the propagation delay. The user must know this delay because the accuracy of his knowledge of time

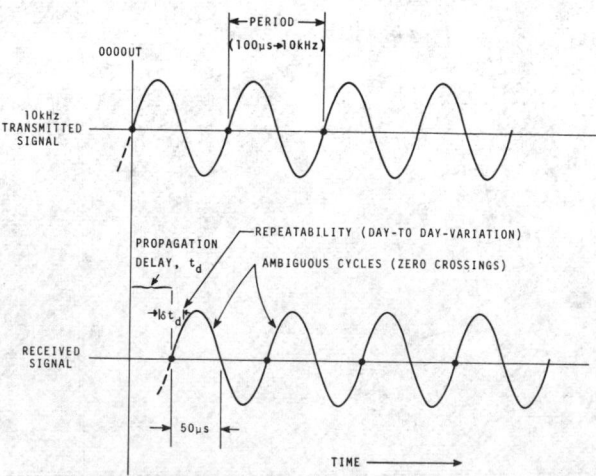

FIGURE 1823.—Single tone time dissemination.

can be no better than the degree to which this delay is known. (By *accuracy* is meant the degree of conformity to some specified value or definition.) Since all cycles of the signal are identical, the signal is *ambiguous* and the user must somehow decide which cycle is the "on time" cycle. This means, in the case of the hypothetical 10-kHz signal, that the user must know the time to ± 50 microseconds (half the period of the signal). Further, the user may desire to use this system, say once a day, for an extended period of time to check his clock or frequency standard. However, it may be that the delay will vary from one day to the next, and if the user is unaware of this variation, his accuracy will be limited by the lack of *repeatability* of the signal arrival time.

Many users are interested in making time coordinated measurements over large geographic areas. They would like all measurements to be referenced to one time system to eliminate corrections for different time systems used at scattered or remote locations. This is a very important practical consideration when measurements are undertaken in the field. In addition, a one reference system, such as a single time broadcast, increases confidence that all measurements can be related to each other in some known way. Thus, the *coverage* of a system is an important concept. Another important characteristic of a timing system is the *percent of time available*. The man on the street who has to keep an appointment needs to know the time perhaps to a minute or so. Although he requires only coarse time information, he wants it on demand so he carries a wristwatch that gives the time to him 24 hours a day. On the other hand, a user who needs time to a few microseconds employs a very good clock which only needs an occasional update, perhaps only once or twice a day. An additional characteristic of time and frequency dissemination is *reliability*, i.e., the likelihood that a time signal will be available when scheduled. Propagation fadeout can sometimes prevent reception of HF signals.

1824. Radio propagation factors.—Radio has offered good means of transferring standard time and frequency signals since the early 1900's. As opposed to the physical transfer of time via portable clocks, the transfer of information by radio entails propagation of electromagnetic energy through some propagation medium from a transmitter to a distant receiver.

In a typical standard frequency and time broadcast, the signals are directly related to some master clock and are transmitted with little or no degradation in accuracy. In a vacuum and noise free background, the signals should be received at a distant point essentially as transmitted, except for a constant path delay with the radio wave propagating near the speed of light (i.e., 299,773 kilometers per second). The propagation media, including the earth, atmosphere, and ionosphere, as well as physical and electrical characteristics of transmitters and receivers, influence the stability and accuracy of received radio signals, dependent upon the frequency of the transmission and length of signal path. Propagation delays are affected in varying degrees by extraneous radiations in the propagation media, solar disturbances, diurnal effects, and weather conditions, among others.

Radio dissemination systems can be classified in a number of different ways. One way is to divide those carrier frequencies low enough to be reflected by the ionosphere (below 30 MHz) from those sufficiently high to penetrate the ionosphere (above 30 MHz). The former can be observed at great distances from the transmitter but suffer from ionospheric propagation anomalies that limit accuracy; the latter are restricted to line-of-sight applications but show little or no signal deterioration caused by propagation anomalies. The most accurate systems tend to be those which use the higher, line-of-sight frequencies, while broadcasts of the lower carrier frequencies show the greatest number of users.

1825. Standard time broadcasts.—The World Administrative Radio Council (WARC) has allocated certain frequencies in five bands for standard frequency and time signal emission as shown in table 1825. For such dedicated standard frequency transmissions, the International Radio Consultative Committee (CCIR) recommends that carrier frequencies be maintained so that the average daily fractional frequency deviations from the internationally designated standard for measurement of time interval should not exceed 1×10^{-10}. The U. S. Naval Observatory *Time Service Announcement Series 1, No. 2*, gives characteristics of standard time signals that are assigned to allocated bands, as reported by the CCIR.

1826. Time signals.—The usual method of determining chronometer error and daily rate is by radio time signals, popularly called **time ticks.** Most maritime nations broadcast time signals several times daily from one or more stations, and a vessel equipped with radio receiving equipment normally has no difficulty in obtaining a time tick anywhere in the world. Normally, the time transmitted is maintained virtually uniform with respect to atomic clocks. The Coordinated Universal Time (UTC) as received by a vessel may differ from UT1 (GMT) by as much as $0\overset{s}{.}9$ (art. 1828).

The majority of radio time signals are transmitted automatically, being controlled by the standard clock of an astronomical observatory. Absolute reliance may be had in these signals, and they should be correct to 0.05 second. Some stations transmit by a combination of hand and automatic signals, and care should be exercised to differentiate between the two at the time of actual comparison of the chronometer.

Other radio stations, however, have no automatic transmission system installed, and the signals are given by hand. In this instance the operator is guided by the standard clock at the station. The clock is checked by either astronomical observations or by reliable time signals. The hand transmission should be correct to 0.25 second.

At sea the spring-driven chronometer should be checked daily by radio time signal, and in port daily checks should be maintained, or begun at least three days prior to departure, if conditions permit. Error and rate are entered in the chronometer record book (or record sheet) each time they are determined.

The various time signal systems used throughout the world are discussed in Pubs. Nos. 117A and 117B, *Radio Navigational Aids*, and volume 5 of *Admiralty List of Radio Signals*. Only the United States signals are discussed here.

Band No.	Designation	Frequency Range
4	VLF (Very Low Frequency).	20.0 kHz±50 Hz.
6	MF (Medium Frequency).	2.5 MHz±5 kHz.
7	HF (High Frequency)	5.0 MHz±5 kHz. 10.0 MHz±5 kHz. 15.0 MHz±10 kHz. 20.0 MHz±10 kHz. 25.0 MHz±10 kHz.
9	UHF (Ultra High Frequency).	400.1 MHz±25 kHz (satellite).
10	SHF (Super High Frequency).	4.202 GHz±2 MHz (satellite-space to earth). 6.427 GHz±2 MHz (satellite-earth to space).

TABLE 1825.—International standard time and frequency radio assignments.

The U. S. Naval Observatory at Washington, D.C., controls the transmissions of time signals from U. S. Naval radio stations. Beginning at 5 minutes before each even hour of GMT, dashes are transmitted on every second, except the 29th and certain others near the end of each minute, as shown in the following diagram:

Minutes	Seconds										
	50	51	52	53	54	55	56	57	58	59	60
55	—		—	—	—	—					
56	—	—		—	—	—					—
57	—	—	—		—	—					—
58	—	—	—	—		—					—
59	—										——

The seconds marked "60" indicate the start of the next minute. The final dash, marking the hour, is considerably longer than any of the others. The number of dashes in the group near the end of any minute indicates the number of minutes before the hour. This is known as the **United States system.** In all cases the beginnings of the dashes indicate the beginning of the seconds, and the ends of the dashes are without significance.

Although the broadcasts of the National Bureau of Standards (NSB) stations WWV and WWVH are intended primarily for dissemination of frequency and time *interval* for scientific purposes, time ticks are also provided.

Station WWV broadcasts from Fort Collins, Colorado at the international allocated frequencies of 2.5, 5.0, 10.0, 15.0, 20.0, and 25.0 MHz; station WWVH transmits from Kauai, Hawaii on the same frequencies with the exclusion of 25.0 MHz. The hourly broadcast formats are shown in figure 1826. The broadcast signals include standard time and frequencies and various voice announcements. Details of these broadcasts are given in NBS Special Publication 236, *NBS Frequency and Time Broadcast Services*. Both HF emissions are directly controlled by cesium beam frequency standards with periodic reference to the NBS atomic frequency and time standards; corrections are published monthly.

The time ticks in the WWV and WWVH emissions are shown in figure 1826. The 1-second UTC markers are transmitted continuously by WWV and WWVH, except for omission of the 29th and 59th marker each minute. With the exception of the beginning tone at each minute (800 milliseconds) all 1-second markers are of 5 milliseconds duration. Each pulse is preceded by 10 milliseconds of silence and followed by 25 milliseconds of silence. Time voice announcements are given also at 1-minute intervals. All time announcements are UTC.

1827. Codes for the transmission of DUT1.—The difference between UTC and and UT1 is known as DUT1, the relationship being DUT1=UT1−UTC. By means of a coding system incorporated in the actual emissions, primary time signal sources promulgate DUT1 in integral multiples of 100 milliseconds.

The CCIR standard format is in the form of emphasized second markers utilizing the first 15 seconds following the minute marker. The emphasis of the second markers can take the form of lengthening, doubling, splitting, or tone modulation of the normal seconds markers. Each emphasized second represents a DUT1 value of $0^s.1$.

A positive value of DUT1 is indicated by emphasizing a number (n) of consecutive seconds markers following the minute marker from seconds markers one to seconds marker (n) inclusive; (n) is an integer from 1 to 8 inclusive (fig. 1827a).

$$DUT1 = (n \times 0.1)s.$$

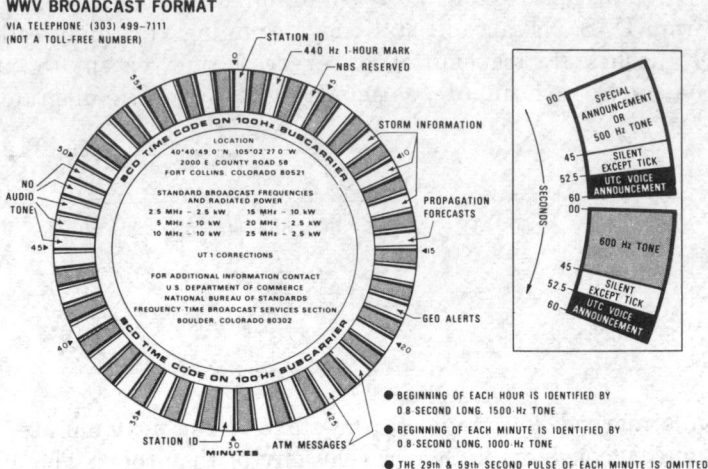

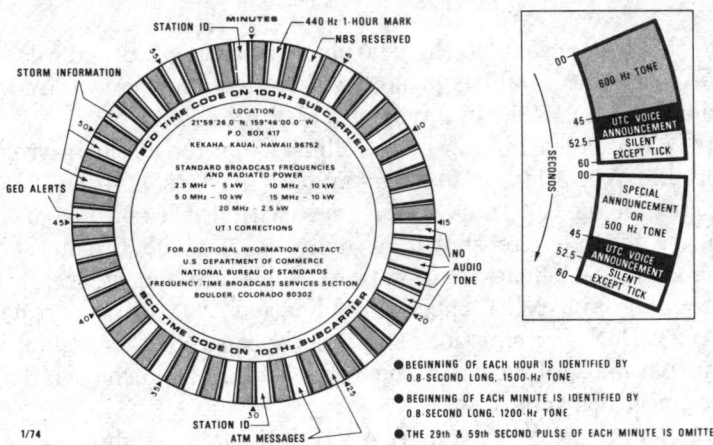

FIGURE 1826.—Broadcast format of stations WWV and WWVH.

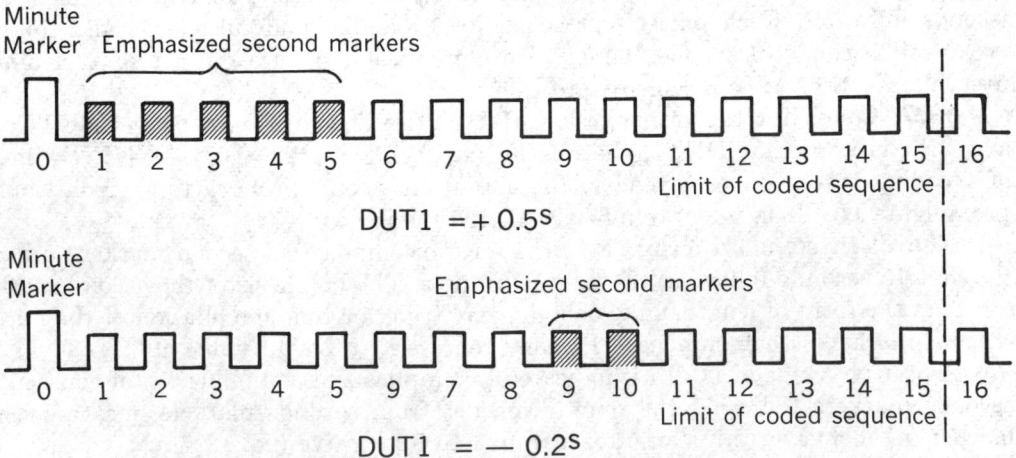

FIGURE 1827a.—CCIR code for transmission of DUT1.

A negative value of DUT1 is indicated by emphasizing a number (m) of consecutive seconds markers following the minute marker from seconds marker nine to seconds marker (8+m) inclusive; (m) is an integer from 1 to 8 inclusive.

$$DUT1 = -(m \times 0.1)s.$$

A zero value of DUT1 is indicated by the absence of emphasized seconds markers.

The National Bureau of Standards stations WWV and WWVH transmit DUT1 using the CCIR standard format. The CCIR standard format is used by most coordinated stations, including CHU, Canada.

In the **USSR extended format,** the CCIR format is followed for DUT1. In addition dUT1 is given to specify more precisely the difference UT1−UTC to multiples of $0°02$, the total value of the correction being DUT1+dUT1. Positive values of dUT1 are transmitted by the marking of p second markers between the 21st and 24th second (fig. 1827b) so that $dUT1 = (p \times 0.02)s$. Negative values of dUT1 are transmitted by the marking of q second markers between the 31st and 34th second, so that $dUT1 = -(q \times 0.02)s$.

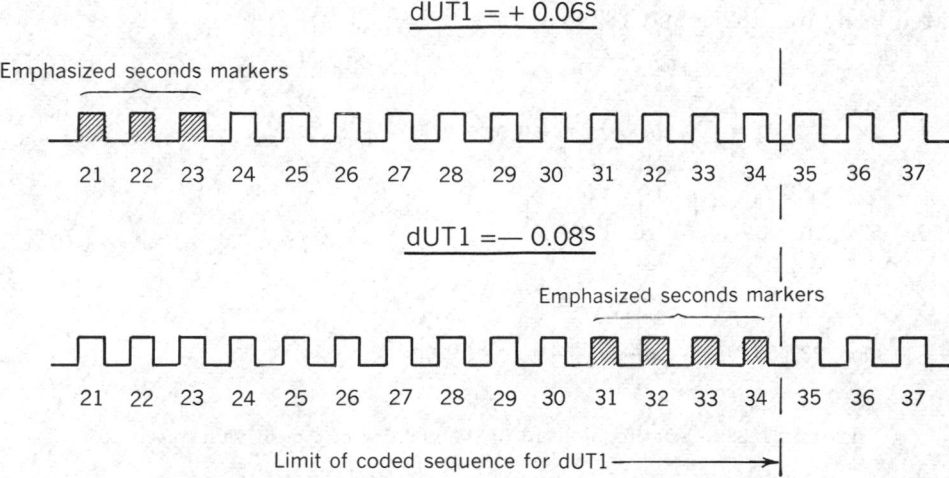

FIGURE 1827b.—USSR extended format for transmission of dUT1.

DUT1 may also be given by voice announcement or in Morse code. In the **Morse code method,** U. S. Naval Radio Stations use standard Morse code (15 words per minute) between seconds 56 and 59 inclusive of each minute not used for time ticks to indicate the sign and value in tenths of a second of DUT1. Positive values are indicated by the letter "A" and the appropriate digit; negative values are indicated by the letter "S" and the appropriate digit.

Standard Morse

A	. _	S	. . .
1	. _ _ _ _	6	_ . . . .
2	. . _ _ _	7	_ _ . . .
3	. . . _ _	8	_ _ _ . .
4	. . . . _	9	_ _ _ _ .
5	. . . . .	0	_ _ _ _ _

For example:

"...   . _ _ _ _" means DUT1$= -0°1$ and UT1=UTC$-0°1$.

Pubs. Nos. 117A and 117B, *Radio Navigational Aids*, should be referred to for up-to-date information on time signals.

1828. Leap-second adjustments.—By international agreement, UTC is maintained within about 0.9 of the celestial navigator's time scale, UT1. The introduction of **leap seconds** allows a good clock to keep approximate step with the sun. Because of the variations in the rate of rotation of the earth, however, the occurrences of the leap seconds are not predictable in detail.

The Bureau International de l'Heure (BIH) decides upon and announces the introduction of a leap second. The BIH announces the new leap second at least several weeks in advance. A positive or negative leap second is introduced the last second of a UTC month, but first preference is given to the end of December and June, and second preference is given to the end of March and September. A positive leap second begins at $23^h59^m60^s$ and ends at $00^h00^m00^s$ of the first day of the following month. In the case of a negative leap second, $23^h59^m58^s$ is followed one second later by $00^h00^m00^s$ of the first day of the following month.

The dating of events in the vicinity of a leap second is effected in the manner indicated in figures 1828a and 1828b.

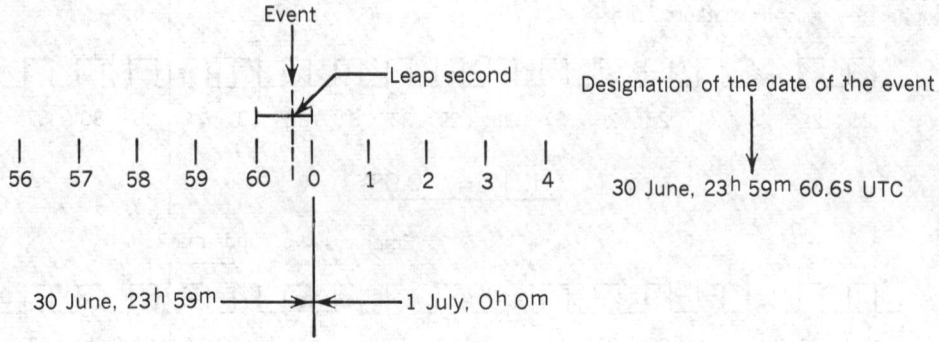

FIGURE 1828a.—Dating of event in the vicinity of a positive leap second.

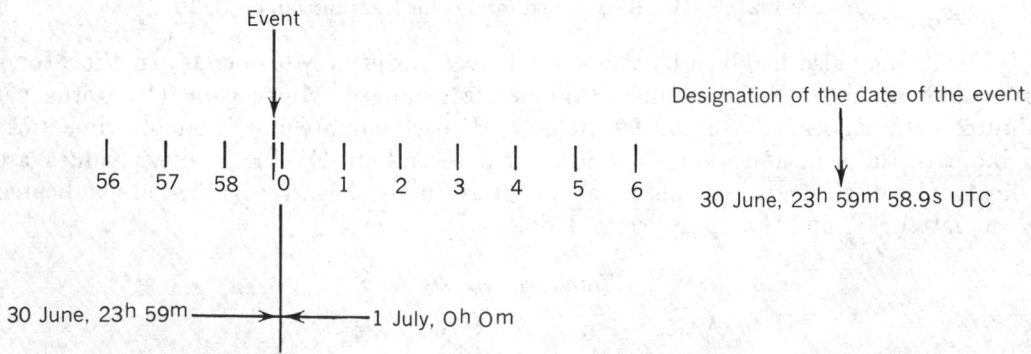

FIGURE 1828b.—Dating of event in the vicinity of a negative leap second.

Whenever leap second adjustments are to be made to UTC, mariners are advised by HYDROLANT/HYDROPAC messages originated by the Defense Mapping Agency Hydrographic Center.

Problems

1810a. What is the time and date $9^h13^m29^s$ before $3^h16^m34^s$ May 9?

Answer.—T $18^h03^m05^s$ May 8.

1810b. What is the time and date $4^d19^h22^m50^s$ after $9^h31^m04^s$ on December 25?

Answer.—T $4^h53^m54^s$ on Dec. 30.

1810c. What is the time and date 2 years, 11 months, 16 days, 10 hours, 23 minutes, and 48 seconds before $2^h46^m17^s$ on October 4, 1958?

Answer.—T $16^h22^m29^s$ on Oct. 17, 1955.

1810d. What is the time and date 412 days, 15 hours, 6 minutes, and 56 seconds after $22^h27^m03^s$ on March 16, 1958?

Answer.—T $13^h33^m59^s$ on May 3, 1959.

1811a. Convert $6^h28^m31^s$ to arc units, without use of a conversion table.

Answer.—$97°07'45''$ or $97°07'.8$.

1811b. Convert $217°28'.8$ to time units, without use of a conversion table.

Answer.—$14^h29^m55^s.2$ or $14^h29^m55^s$.

1811c. Convert $196°21'46''$ to time units, without use of a conversion table.

Answer.—$13^h05^m27^s.1$ or $13^h05^m27^s$.

1811d. Convert $107°49'44''$ to time units, using appendix F.

Answer.—$7^h11^m19^s$.

1811e. Convert $211°37'.3$ to time units, using appendix F.

Answer.—$14^h06^m29^s.2$.

1811f. Convert $8^h49^m33^s$ to arc units, using appendix F.

Answer.—$132°23'.2$.

1811g. Convert $251°09'.2$ to time units, using appendix G.

Answer.—$16^h44^m37^s$.

1811h. Convert $23^h07^m38^s$ to arc units, using appendix G.

Answer.—$346°54'.5$.

1814a. For an observer at long. $97°24'.6$E the ZT is $19^h10^m26^s$.

Required.—(1) Zone description.

(2) GMT.

Answers.—(1) ZD (−) 6, (2) GMT $13^h10^m26^s$.

1814b. The GMT is $11^h32^m07^s$.

Required.—(1) ZT at long. $133°24'.7$W.

(2) ZT at long. $111°43'.9$E.

Answers.—(1) ZT $2^h32^m07^s$, (2) ZT $18^h32^m07^s$.

1814c. At long. $165°18'.2$E the ZT is $17^h08^m51^s$ on July 11.

Required.—(1) GMT and date.

(2) ZT and date at long. $125°36'.7$W.

Answers.—(1) GMT $6^h08^m51^s$ on July 11, (2) ZT $22^h08^m51^s$ on July 10.

1814d. On January 26 the 0800 DR long. of a ship is $128°03'.2$E. Twenty-six hours later the EP long. is $125°01'.4$E.

Required.—ZT and date of arrival at the second longitude.

Answer.—ZT 0900 Jan. 27.

1814e. On April 1 the 1200 running fix long. of a ship is $179°55'.2$W. Eight hours later the DR long. is $178°48'.9$E.

Required.—ZT and date of arrival at the second longitude.

Answer.—ZT 2000 Apr. 2.

1814f. Inch'ŏn, long. 137°E, uses ZD (−) 8^h30^m for standard time. Find the standard time and date at San Francisco, long. 122°W, when the summer time at Inch'ŏn is 2000 on August 9.

Answer.—ZT 0230 Aug. 9.

1815a. At GMT 1400 on July 2 the chronometer reads $1^h42^m28^s$. At GMT 0800 on July 12 it reads $7^h42^m40^s$.

Required.—(1) Chronometer error at GMT 1400 on July 2.

(2) Chronometer error at GMT 0800 on July 12.

(3) Chronometer rate.

(4) Chronometer time at ZT 1800 July 20, at long. 153°21′.7W.

Answers.—(1) CE 17^m32^s slow, (2) CE 17^m20^s slow, (3) rate $1^s.2$ gaining, (4) C $3^h42^m51^s$.

1815b. On March 5 the DR long. of a ship is about 151°E, and the zone time is about 1800. Chronometer error is 6^m40^s fast.

Required.—GMT and date when the chronometer reads $8^h02^m23^s$.

Answer.—GMT $7^h55^m43^s$ on Mar. 5.

1815c. On November 7 the EP long. of a ship is about 71°W, and the zone time is about 1900. Chronometer error is 1^m18^s slow.

Required.—GMT and date when the chronometer reads (1) $11^h55^m20^s$, (2) $11^h59^m50^s$.

Answers.—(1) GMT $23^h56^m38^s$ Nov. 7, (2) GMT $0^h01^m08^s$ Nov. 8.

1815d. At GMT 2200 a comparing watch is checked by time signal, and found to read $10^h00^m05^s$. The chronometer errors are then determined by means of the comparing watch. When the watch reads $10^h06^m00^s$, chronometer *A* reads $10^h11^m17^s$, and when the watch reads $10^h08^m00^s$, chronometer *B* reads $9^h59^m06^s$.

Required.—(1) Watch error.

(2) Error of chronometer *A*.

(3) Error of chronometer *B*.

Answers.—(1) WE 5^s fast on GMT, (2) CE_A 5^m22^s fast, (3) CE_B 8^m49^s slow.

1816a. A chronometer 7^m22^s slow on GMT reads approximately 3^h45^m. About two minutes later, when the GMT is a whole minute, a comparing watch will be set to GMT exactly.

Required.—(1) Reading of the watch at starting.

(2) Reading of the chronometer.

Answers.—(1) WT $3^h54^m00^s$, (2) C $3^h46^m38^s$.

1816b. A chronometer 5^m10^s fast on GMT reads approximately 5^h50^m. About one minute later, when the GMT is a whole minute, a comparing watch with a 24-hour dial will be set to GMT exactly. The ZT is approximately 1145 and the long. 94°W.

Required.—(1) Reading of the watch at starting.

(2) Reading of the chronometer.

(3) Watch error if, instead of being set to GMT, the watch setting is unchanged and the watch reads $17^h45^m32^s$ at comparison.

Answers.—(1) WT $17^h46^m00^s$, (2) C $5^h51^m10^s$, (3) WE 28^s slow on GMT.

1816c. A watch is set to zone time, approximately. The long. is about 160°E. The watch is compared with a chronometer which is 3^m16^s fast on GMT. When the chronometer reads $1^h48^m00^s$, the watch reads $12^h45^m02^s$.

Required.—Watch error on zone time.

Answer.—WE 18^s fast on ZT.

1816d. On February 14 the DR long. is 63°46′.1W. An observation of Dubhe is made when the watch reads $6^h07^m30^s$ PM. The watch is 11^s slow on zone time.

Required.—GMT and date.

Answer.—GMT $22^h07^m41^s$ Feb. 14.

1816e. On December 11 a watch is set to zone time, approximately. The long. is 137°W. The chronometer is 3ᵐ36ˢ fast on GMT. When the chronometer reads 4ʰ40ᵐ00ˢ, the watch reads 7ʰ36ᵐ06ˢ PM.

Required.—(1) Watch error on GMT.

(2) GMT and date about 20 minutes later, when the watch reads 7ʰ55ᵐ52ˢ.

Answers.—(1) WE 2ʰ59ᵐ42ˢ fast on GMT, (2) GMT 4ʰ56ᵐ10ˢ Dec. 12.

1816f. Shortly before taking morning sights on January 17 the navigator compares his watch with the chronometer. When the chronometer reads 2ʰ30ᵐ00ˢ, the watch reads 6ʰ13ᵐ12ˢ AM. The chronometer is 17ᵐ15ˢ fast on GMT. The long. is 118°W.

Required.—(1) C−WT.

(2) GMT and date a little later when Regulus is observed at W 6ʰ28ᵐ47ˢ AM.

Answers.—(1) C−WT 8ʰ16ᵐ48ˢ, (2) GMT 14ʰ28ᵐ20ˢ Jan. 17.

1817a. At long. 138°09′.3E the LMT is 0ʰ09ᵐ57ˢ on April 23.

Required.—(1) GMT and date.

(2) ZT and date at the place.

Answers.—(1) GMT 14ʰ57ᵐ20ˢ Apr. 22, (2) ZT 23ʰ57ᵐ20ˢ Apr. 22.

1817b. At long. 157°18′.4W the LMT is 1931 on June 29.

Required.—(1) ZT and date.

(2) GMT and date.

Answers.—(1) ZT 2000 June 29, (2) GMT 0600 June 30.

1817c. At long. 99°35′.7W the daylight saving time is 21ʰ29ᵐ45ˢ on August 31.

Required.—(1) Standard time and date.

(2) LMT and date.

Answers.—(1) Standard time 20ʰ29ᵐ45ˢ Aug. 31, (2) LMT 20ʰ51ᵐ22ˢ Aug. 31.

1818a. Find the LAT and date at ZT 5ʰ26ᵐ13ˢ on June 12, 1975, for long. 9°28′.1E.

Answer.—LAT 5ʰ04ᵐ21ˢ June 12.

1818b. At long. 77°15′.5W the LAT is 1500 on June 13, 1975.

Required.—(1) ZT.

(2) LMT.

Answers.—(1) ZT 15ʰ08ᵐ56ˢ, (2) LMT 14ʰ59ᵐ54ˢ.

1818c. Using the *Air Almanac*, find (1) LAT at long. 117°55′W, and (2) the Eq. T, at ZT 20ʰ43ᵐ09ˢ on June 1, 1975.

Answers.—(1) LAT 20ʰ53ᵐ44ˢ, (2) Eq. T (+) 2ᵐ15ˢ.

1819a. Find LST at ZT 19ʰ24ᵐ26ˢ on June 1, 1975, for long. 87°51′.2E.

Answer.—LST 11ʰ53ᵐ29ˢ.

1819b. Find the ZT at LST 21ʰ20ᵐ07ˢ on May 31, 1975, for long. 54°21′.3W.

Answer.—ZT 4ʰ24ᵐ40ˢ.

CHAPTER XIX

THE ALMANAC

1901. Introduction.—A requirement of celestial navigation is the availability of accurate predictions of the positions of the celestial bodies used. These predictions, with respect to the celestial equator system of coordinates (art. 1428), are contained in three publications of the United States Naval Observatory. The solution for a celestial line of position consists principally of the conversion of tabulated coordinates to those on the horizon system of coordinates (art. 1430).

The *American Ephemeris and Nautical Almanac* gives, to a high precision, detailed information on a large number of celestial bodies. This annual publication is arranged to suit the convenience of the astronomer, for whom it is primarily intended. The ephemeris is not needed for ordinary purposes of navigation, although it contains some information of general interest, such as various astronomical constants, details of eclipses, information on planetary configurations (art. 1422), and miscellaneous phenomena. Each volume of the ephemeris contains instructions for its use.

With the editions for 1960, *The American Ephemeris and Nautical Almanac* issued by the Nautical Almanac Office, United States Naval Observatory, and *The Astronomical Ephemeris* issued by H. M. Nautical Almanac Office, Royal Greenwich Observatory, were unified. With the exception of the introductory pages i, ii and vi–viii, the two publications are identical; they are printed separately in the two countries, from reproducible material prepared partly in the United States and partly in the United Kingdom.

The title *The Astronomical Ephemeris* replaced, without loss of continuity of content, the previous title of *The Nautical Almanac and Astronomical Ephemeris* (usually abbreviated to *The Nautical Almanac*), which was introduced by Nevil Maskelyne for the original British edition of 1767; the title *The Nautical Almanac* is now used, in both the United Kingdom and the United States, for the unified edition of the Almanacs for surface navigation previously entitled *The Abridged Nautical Almanac* and *The American Nautical Almanac* respectively.

The *Nautical Almanac,* an annual publication, contains the astronomical information needed by the marine navigator. It is conveniently arranged to suit his needs, and the information is tabulated to a practical degree of precision, in general to the nearest $0\overset{\prime}{.}1$ of arc and 1^s of time, at hourly intervals. Beginning with the edition for 1958, this volume is a joint publication of the U. S. Naval Observatory and H. M. Nautical Almanac Office, Royal Greenwich Observatory, and incorporates a number of changes from previous editions. Extracts from the *Nautical Almanac* for 1975 are given in appendix F. These extracts, illustrating the various features of that publication, can be used in the solution of the various illustrative and sample problems of the present volume.

The *Air Almanac,* published two times per year, is intended primarily for air navigators. In general, the information is similar to that of the *Nautical Almanac,* but is given to a precision of $1'$ of arc and 1^s of time, at intervals of 10^m (values for the sun and Aries are given to a precision of $0\overset{\prime}{.}1$). This publication is suitable for ordinary navigation at sea, but may lack the precision that is sometimes needed. The *Air Almanac* is a joint publication of the U. S. Naval Observatory and H. M. Nautical Almanac

498

Office, Royal Greenwich Observatory. Extracts from the *Air Almanac* are given in appendix G.

A highly abbreviated, long-term almanac is given in appendix H. Because of the large intervals between entries, and the fact that no provision is made for nutation, information taken from this almanac may be of reduced accuracy. Although this accuracy is sufficient for most purposes of navigation, the almanac is not as convenient to use as either of those published by the U. S. Naval Observatory, and is not recommended when one of them is available. Instructions for its use are included in appendix H.

The *Explanatory Supplement to the Astronomical Ephemeris and to the American Ephemeris and Nautical Almanac*, first published in 1961, contains detailed explanations of the basis and derivation of each ephemeris in the edition for 1960; it also contains historical notes and other useful information and permanent tables that are not given in the almanacs. The second edition, published in 1974, contains footnotes indicating the changes that have been introduced into the ephemerides since 1960. It also includes a reprint of *The Supplement to A.E.* 1968, which gives an account of the introduction of the IAU System of Astronomical Constants. The *Explanatory Supplement* is published by H.M. Stationery Office, London.

1902. *Nautical Almanac*.—The major portion of the *Nautical Almanac* is devoted to hourly tabulation of Greenwich hour angle and declination, to the nearest $0\!'\!.1$ of arc. On each set of facing pages, information is given for three consecutive days. On the left-hand page, successive columns give GHA of Aries and both GHA and declination of Venus, Mars, Jupiter, and Saturn, followed by the SHA and declination of 57 stars. The GHA and declination of the sun and moon, and the horizontal parallax of the moon, are given on the right-hand page. Where applicable, the quantities v and d are given to assist in interpolation. The quantity v is the difference between the actual change of GHA in one hour and a constant value used in the interpolation tables, while d is the change in declination in one hour. Both v and d are given to the nearest $0\!'\!.1$. To the right of the moon data is given the LMT (art. 1817) of sunrise, sunset, and beginning and ending of nautical and civil twilight for various latitudes from 72°N to 60°S. The LMT of moonrise and moonset at the same latitudes is given for each of the three days for which other information is given, and for the following day. Magnitude (art. 1405) of each planet at GMT 1200 of the middle day is given at the top of the column. The GMT (art. 1814) of transit across the celestial meridian of Greenwich is given as "Mer. Pass." The value for the first point of Aries for the middle of the three days is given to the nearest $0^m\!.1$ at the bottom of the Aries column. The time of transit of the planets for the middle day is given to the nearest whole minute, with SHA (at GMT 0000 of the middle day) to the nearest $0\!'\!.1$, below the list of stars. For the sun and moon, the time of transit to the nearest whole minute is given for each day. For the moon, both upper and lower transits are given. This information is tabulated below the rising, setting, and twilight information. Given there, also, are the equation of time for 0^h and 12^h, and the age and phase of the moon (art. 1423). Equation of time is given, without sign, to the nearest whole second. Age is given to the nearest whole day. Phase is given by symbol.

The main tabulation is preceded by a list of religious and civil holidays, phases of the moon, a calendar, information on eclipses occurring during the year, and notes and a diagram giving information on the planets.

The main tabulation is followed by explanation and examples. Next are four pages of standard times (zone descriptions) in use in various places in the world. Star charts are given next, followed by a list of 173 stars in order of increasing sidereal hour angle. This list includes the stars given on the daily pages. It gives the SHA and declination each month, and the magnitude. Stars are listed by Bayer's name and also by popular name where there is one. Following the star list are three pages of Polaris tables giving the azimuth and the corrections to be applied to the observed altitude to find the latitude. Next is a table for converting arc to time units. This is followed by a 30-page table called "Increments and Corrections," used for interpolation of Greenwich hour angle and declination. This table is printed on tinted paper, for quick location. Then come tables for interpolating for times of rising, setting, and twilight; followed by two indices of the 57 stars listed on the daily pages, one index being in alphabetical order, and the other in order of decreasing SHA.

Sextant altitude corrections are given at the front and back of the almanac. Tables for the sun, stars, and planets, and a dip table, are given on the inside front cover and facing page, with an additional correction for nonstandard temperature and atmospheric pressure on the following page. Tables for the moon, and an abbreviated dip table, are given on the inside back cover and facing page. Use of the altitude correction tables is explained in chapter XVI. Corrections for the sun, stars, and planets for altitudes greater than 10°, and the dip table, are repeated on one side of a loose bookmark. The star indices are repeated on the other side.

1903. Air Almanac.—As in the *Nautical Almanac*, the major portion of the *Air Almanac* is devoted to a tabulation of GHA and declination. However, in the *Air Almanac* values are given at intervals of ten minutes, to a precision of 0́.1 for the sun and Aries and to a precision of 1′ for the moon and the planets. Values are given for the sun, first point of Aries (GHA only), the three navigational planets most favorably located for observation, and the moon. The magnitude of each planet listed is given at the top of its column, and the phase of the moon is given at the top of its column. Values for the first 12 hours of the day are given on the right-hand page, and those for the second half of the day on the back. In addition, the right-hand page has a table of the moon's parallax in altitude, and below this the semidiameter of the sun, and both the semidiameter and age of the moon (art. 1423). Each daily page includes the LMT of moonrise and moonset; and a difference column for finding the time of moonrise and moonset at any longitude.

Critical tables for interpolation for GHA are given on the inside front cover, which also has an alphabetical listing of the stars, with the number, magnitude, SHA, and declination of each. The same interpolation table and star list are printed on a flap which follows the daily pages. This flap also contains a star chart, a star index in order of decreasing SHA, and a table for interpolation of the LMT of moonrise and moonset for longitude.

Following the flap are instructions for the use of the almanac; a list of symbols and abbreviations in English, French, and Spanish; a list of time differences between Greenwich and various other places; a number of sky diagrams (art. 2212); a planet location diagram (art. 2209); star recognition diagrams for periscopic sextants; sunrise, sunset, and civil twilight tables; rising, setting, and depression graphs; semiduration graphs of sunlight, twilight, and moonlight in high latitudes; list of 173 stars by number and Bayer's name (also popular name where there is one), giving the SHA and declination each month (to a precision of 0́.1), and the magnitude; tables for interpolation of GHA sun and GHA Aries; a table for converting arc to time; a single Polaris correction table; an aircraft standard dome refraction table; a refraction correction table; a Coriolis correction table; and on the inside back cover a correction table for dip of the horizon.

1904. Use of the almanacs.—The time used as an entering argument in the almanacs is $12^h +$ Greenwich hour angle of the mean sun and is denoted by GMT. This scale may differ from the broadcast time signals by an amount which, if ignored, will introduce an error of up to 0ʹ.2 in longitude determined from astronomical observations. The difference arises because the time argument depends on the variable rate of rotation of the earth while the broadcast time signals are now based on an atomic time-scale. Step adjustments of exactly one second are made to the time signals as required (primarily at 24ʰ on December 31 and June 30) so that the difference between the time signals and GMT, as used in the almanacs, may not exceed 0ˢ.9. Those who require to reduce observations to a precision of better than 1ˢ must therefore obtain the correction to the time signals from coding in the signal, or from other sources. The correction may be applied to each of the times of observation. Alternatively, the longitude, when determined from astronomical observations, may be corrected by the corresponding amount shown in the following table:

Correction to time signals	Correction to longitude
−0ˢ.7 to −0ˢ.9	0ʹ.2 to east
−0ˢ.6 to −0ˢ.3	0ʹ.1 to east
−0ˢ.2 to +0ˢ.2	no correction
+0ˢ.3 to +0ˢ.6	0ʹ.1 to west
+0ˢ.7 to +0ˢ.9	0ʹ.2 to west

The main contents of the almanacs consist of data from which the Greenwich hour angle (GHA) and the declination (Dec.) of all the bodies used for navigation can be obtained for any instant of Greenwich mean time (GMT). The local hour angle (LHA) can then be obtained by means of the formula:

$$LHA = GHA \begin{array}{c} - \text{ west} \\ \\ + \text{ east} \end{array} \text{longitude.}$$

For the sun, moon, and the four navigational planets, the GHA and declination are tabulated directly in the *Nautical Almanac* for each hour of GMT throughout the year; in the *Air Almanac*, the values are tabulated for each whole 10ᵐ of GMT. For the stars the sidereal hour angle (SHA) is given, and the GHA is obtained from:

$$\text{GHA Star} = \text{GHA Aries} + \text{SHA Star.}$$

The SHA and declination of the stars change slowly and may be regarded as constant over periods of several days or even months if lesser accuracy is required. The SHA and declination of stars tabulated in the *Air Almanac* may be considered constant to a precision of 1ʹ.5 to 2ʹ for the period covered by each of the volumes providing the data for a whole year, with most data being closer to the smaller value. GHA Aries, or the Greenwich hour angle of the first point of Aries (the vernal equinox), is tabulated for each hour of GMT in the *Nautical Almanac* and for each whole 10ᵐ of GMT in the *Air Almanac*. Permanent tables give the appropriate increments to the tabulated values of GHA and declination for the minutes and seconds of GMT.

In the *Nautical Almanac*, the permanent table for increments also includes corrections for v, the difference between the actual change of GHA in one hour and a constant value used in the interpolation tables and d, the change in declination in one hour.

In the *Nautical Almanac*, v is always positive unless a negative sign (−) is given. This can occur only in the case of Venus. For the sun, the tabulated values of GHA have been adjusted to reduce to a minimum the error caused by treating v as negligible; there is no v tabulated for the sun.

No sign is given for tabulated values of d, which is positive if declination is increasing, and negative if it is decreasing. The sign of a v or d value is given also to the related correction.

In the *Air Almanac*, the tabular values of the GHA of the moon are adjusted so that use of an interpolation table based on a fixed rate of change gives rise to negligible error; no such adjustment is necessary for the sun and planets. The tabulated declination values, except for the sun, are those for the *middle* of the interval between the time indicated and the next *following* time for which a value is given, making interpolation unnecessary. Thus, it is always important to take out the GHA and declination for the tabular GMT immediately before the time of observation.

In the *Air Almanac*, GHA Aries and the GHA and declination of the sun are tabulated to a precision of 0'.1. If these values are extracted with the tabular precision, the "Interpolation of GHA" table on the inside front cover (and flap) should not be used; use the "Interpolation of GHA Sun" and "Interpolation of GHA Aries" tables, as appropriate. These tables for interpolation to a precision of 0'.1 just precede the Polaris Table.

The instructions in the explanation of each volume to ignore the decimal in smaller type when extracting GHA Aries and GHA and declination of the sun to a precision of 1' instead of rounding-off in the normal way are intended for the air navigator.

1905. Finding GHA and declination of the sun.—*Nautical Almanac.* Enter the daily-page table with the whole hour next preceding the given GMT, unless this time is itself a whole hour, and take out the tabulated GHA and declination. Record, also, the *d* value given at the bottom of the declination column. Next, enter the increments and corrections table for the number of minutes of GMT. If there are seconds, use the next *earlier* whole minute. On the line corresponding to the seconds of GMT take the value from the sun-planets column. Add this to the value of GHA from the daily page to find GHA at the given time. Next, enter the correction table for the same minute with the *d* value, and take out the correction. Give this the sign of the *d* value, and apply it to the declination from the daily page. The result is the declination at the given time.

Example 1.—Find the GHA and declination of the sun at GMT $18^h24^m37^s$ on June 1, 1975, using the *Nautical Almanac*.

Solution.—

	Sun			Sun
GMT	$18^h24^m37^s$ June 1	GMT	$18^h24^m37^s$ June 1
18^h	90°34'.3	18^h	22°02'.5N $d(+)0'.3$
24^m37^s	6°09'.3	d corr.	$(+)0'.1$
GHA	96°43'.6	Dec.	22°02'.6N

The correction table for GHA of the sun is based upon a rate of change of 15° per hour, the average rate during a year. At most times the rate differs slightly from this. The slight error thus introduced is minimized by adjustment of the tabular values.

The *d* value is the amount that the declination changes between 1200 and 1300 on the middle day of the three shown.

Air Almanac. Enter the daily page with the whole 10^m next preceding the given GMT, unless the time is itself a whole 10^m, and extract the tabulated GHA. The declination is extracted, without interpolation, from the same line as the tabulated GHA or, in the case of planets, the top line of the block of six. If the values extracted are rounded to the nearest minute, next enter the "Interpolation of GHA" table on the inside front cover (and flap), using the "Sun, etc." entry column, and take out the value for the remaining minutes and seconds of GMT. If the entry time is an exact tabulated value, use the correction given half a line *above* the entry time. Add this correction to the GHA taken from the daily page to find the GHA at the given time. No adjustment of declination is needed. If the values are extracted with a precision of 0'.1, the table for interpolating the GHA of the sun to a precision of 0.́1 must be used. No adjustment of declination is needed.

Example 2.—Find the GHA and declination of the sun at GMT 18ʰ24ᵐ37ˢ on June 1, 1975, using the *Air Almanac*.

Solution.—

	Sun				Sun	
GMT	18ʰ24ᵐ37ˢ	June 1		GMT	18ʰ24ᵐ37ˢ	June 1
18ʰ20ᵐ	95°34′			18ʰ20ᵐ	95°34.́3	
4ᵐ37ˢ	1°09′			4ᵐ37ˢ	1°09.́3	
GHA	96°43′			GHA	96°43.́6	
Dec.	22°03′N			Dec.	22°02.́6N	

1906. Finding GHA and declination of the moon.—*Nautical Almanac.* Enter the daily-page table with the whole hour next preceding the given GMT, unless this time is itself a whole hour, and take out the tabulated GHA and declination. Record, also, the corresponding *v* and *d* values tabulated on the same line, and determine the sign of the *d* value. The *v* value of the moon is always positive (+), and is not marked in the almanac. Next, enter the increments and corrections table for the minutes of GMT, and on the line for the seconds of GMT take the GHA correction from the moon column. Then, enter the correction table for the same minute with the *v* value, and extract the correction. Add both of these corrections to the GHA from the daily page to obtain the GHA at the given time. Then, enter the same correction table with the *d* value, and extract the correction. Give this correction the sign of the *d* value, and apply it to the declination from the daily page to find the declination at the given time.

Example 1.—Find the GHA and declination of the moon at GMT 21ʰ25ᵐ44ˢ on June 1, 1975, using the *Nautical Almanac*.

Solution.—

	Moon				Moon	
GMT	21ʰ25ᵐ44ˢ	June 1		GMT	21ʰ25ᵐ44ˢ	June 1
21ʰ	225°28.́1			21ʰ	3°06.́8S	*d*(−)10.́7
25ᵐ44ˢ	6°08.́4	*v*(+)15.́8		*d* corr.	(−)4.́5	
v corr.	(+)6.́7			Dec.	3°02.́3S	
GHA	231°43.́2					

The correction table for GHA of the moon is based upon the *minimum* rate at which the moon's GHA increases, 14°19.́0 per hour. The *v* correction makes the adjustment for the actual rate. The *v* value itself is the difference between the minimum rate and the actual rate during the hour following the tabulated time. The *d* value is the amount that the declination changes during the hour following the tabulated time.

Air Almanac. Enter the daily page with the whole 10ᵐ next preceding the given GMT, unless this time is itself a whole 10ᵐ, and take out the tabulated GHA and the declination, without interpolation. Next, enter the "Interpolation of GHA" table on the inside front cover, using the "moon" entry column, and take out the value for the remaining minutes and seconds of GMT. If the entry time is an exact tabulated value, use the correction given half a line *above* the entry time. Add this correction to the GHA taken from the daily page to find the GHA at the given time. No adjustment of declination is needed.

Example 2.—Find the GHA and declination of the moon at GMT 21ʰ25ᵐ44ˢ on June 1, 1975, using the *Air Almanac*.

Solution.—

Moon

GMT	$21^h25^m44^s$ June 1
21^h20^m	$230°20'$
5^m44^s	$1°23'$
GHA	$231°43'$
Dec.	$3°02'$S

The declination given in the table is correct for the time *five minutes later than tabulated*, so that it can be used for the ten-minute interval without interpolation, to an accuracy to meet most requirements. If greater accuracy is needed, it can be obtained by interpolation, remembering to allow for the five minutes indicated above.

1907. Finding GHA and declination of a planet.—*Nautical Almanac.* Enter the daily-page table with the whole hour next preceding the given GMT, unless the time itself is a whole hour, and take out the tabulated GHA and declination. Record, also, the *v* value given at the bottom of each of these columns. Next, enter the increments and corrections table for the minutes of GMT, and on the line for the seconds of GMT take the GHA correction from the sun-planets column. Next, enter the correction table with the *v* value and extract the correction, giving it the sign of the *v* value. Add the first correction to the GHA from the daily page, and apply the second correction in accordance with its sign, to obtain the GHA at the given time. Then, enter the correction table for the same minute with the *d* value, and extract the correction. Give this correction the sign of the *d* value, and apply it to the declination from the daily page to find the declination at the given time.

Example 1.—Find the GHA and declination of Venus at GMT $5^h24^m07^s$ on June 2, 1975, using the *Nautical Almanac.*

Solution.—

Venus			Venus		
GMT	$5^h24^m07^s$ June 2		GMT	$5^h24^m07^s$ June 2	
5^h	$206°59'.4$		5^h	$23°30'.8$N d $(-)0'.5$	
24^m07^s	$6°01'.8$ v $(-)0'.4$		d corr.	$(-)0'.2$	
v corr.	$(-)0'.2$		Dec.	$23°30'.6$N	
GHA	$213°01'.0$				

The correction table for GHA of planets is based upon the mean rate of the sun, 15° per hour. The *v* value is the difference between 15° and the change of GHA of the planet between 1200 and 1300 on the middle day of the three shown. The *d* value is the amount that the declination changes between 1200 and 1300 on the middle day. ◀

Venus is the only body listed which ever has a negative *v* value.

Air Almanac. Enter the daily page with the whole 10^m next preceding the given GMT, unless this time is itself a whole 10^m, and extract the tabulated GHA and declination, without interpolation. The tabulated declination is correct for the time 30^m later than tabulated, so that interpolation during the hour following tabulation is not needed for most purposes. Next, enter the "Interpolation of GHA" table on the inside front cover, using the "sun, etc." column, and take out the value for the remaining minutes and seconds of GMT. If the entry time is an exact tabulated value, use the correction half a line *above* the entry time. Add this correction to the GHA from the daily page to find the GHA at the given time. No adjustment of declination is needed.

Example 2.—Find the GHA and declination of Venus at GMT $5^h48^m45^s$ on June 2, 1975, using the *Air Almanac.*

Solution.—

Venus

GMT	$5^h48^m45^s$ June 2
5^h40^m	216°59′
8^m45^s	2°11′
GHA	219°10′
Dec.	23°31′N

The declination is taken for the next *earlier* tabulated time, and is correct for GMT 5^h45^m.

1908. Finding GHA and declination of a star.—If the GHA and declination of each navigational star were tabulated separately, the almanacs would be several times their present size. But since the sidereal hour angle (art. 1426) and the declination are nearly constant over several days (to the nearest 0′.1) or months (to the nearest 1′), separate tabulations are not needed. Instead, the GHA of the first point of Aries, from which SHA is measured, is tabulated on the daily pages, and a single listing of SHA and declination is given for each double page of the *Nautical Almanac*, and for an entire volume of the *Air Almanac*. The finding of GHA ♈ is similar to finding GHA of the sun, moon, and planets.

Nautical Almanac. Enter the daily-page table with the whole hour next preceding the given GMT, unless this time is itself a whole hour, and take out the tabulated GHA ♈. Record, also, the tabulated SHA and declination of the star from the listing on the left-hand daily page. Next, enter the increments and corrections table for the minutes of GMT, and on the line for the seconds of GMT take the GHA correction from the Aries column. Add this correction and the SHA of the star to the GHA ♈ of the daily page to find the GHA of the star at the given time. No adjustment of declination is needed.

Example 1.—Find the GHA and declination of Canopus at GMT $3^h24^m33^s$ on June 2, 1975, using the *Nautical Almanac*.

Solution.—

Canopus

GMT	$3^h24^m33^s$ June 2
3^h	294°58′.0
24^m33^s	6°09′.3
SHA	264°09′.3
GHA	205°16′.6
Dec.	52°41′.1S

The SHA and declination of 173 stars, including Polaris and the 57 listed on the daily pages, are given for the middle of each month, on almanac pages 268–273. For a star not listed on the daily pages this is the only almanac source of this information. Interpolation in this table is not necessary for ordinary purposes of navigation, but is sometimes needed for precise results. Thus, if the SHA and declination of β *Crucis* (Mimosa) are desired for March 1, 1975, they are found by simple eye interpolation to by SHA 168°25′.2 and Dec. 59°33′.2S.

If GHA ♈ is desired, it is found as indicated in example 1, but omitting the addition of SHA of a star. In the example GHA ♈ is 294°58′.0+6°09′.3=301°07′.3.

Air Almanac. Enter the daily page with the whole 10^m next preceding the given GMT, unless this is itself a whole 10^m, and extract the tabulated GHA♈. Next, enter the "Interpolation of GHA" table on the inside front cover, using the "sun, etc." entry column, and take out the value for the remaining minutes and seconds of GMT. If the entry time is an exact tabulated value, use the correction given half a line *above* the entry time. From the tabulation at the left side of the same page, extract the SHA and declination of the star. Add the GHA from the daily page and the two values taken from the inside front cover to find the GHA at the given time. No adjustment of declination is needed.

Example 2.—Find the GHA and declination of Peacock at GMT $12^h17^m58^s$ on June 1, 1975, using the *Air Almanac*.

Solution.—

	Peacock	
	Peacock	
GMT	$12^h17^m58^s$ June 1
12^h10^m	$71°52'$
7^m58^s	$2°00'$
SHA	$54°03'$
GHA	$127°55'$
Dec.	$56°49'S$

Rising, Setting, and Twilight

1909. Rising, setting, and twilight.—In both almanacs the times of sunrise, sunset, moonrise, moonset, and twilight information at various latitudes between 72°N and 60°S are given to the nearest whole minute. By definition, rising or setting occurs when the *upper* limb of the body is on the *visible* horizon, assuming standard refraction for zero height of eye. Because of variations in refraction and height of eye, computation to a greater precision than 1^m is not justified.

In high latitudes some of the phenomena do not occur during certain periods. The symbols used to indicate this condition are:

  ▭ Sun or moon does not set, but remains continuously above the horizon.

  ■ Sun or moon does not rise, but remains continuously below the horizon.

  //// Twilight lasts all night.

The *Nautical Almanac* makes no provision for finding the times of rising, setting, or twilight in polar regions. The *Air Almanac* has graphs for this purpose.

In the *Nautical Almanac*, sunrise, sunset, and twilight tables are given only once for the middle of the three days on each page opening. For most purposes this information can be used for all three days. Both almanacs have moonrise and moonset tables for each day.

The tabulations are in local mean time (art. 1817). On the zone meridian, this is the zone time (ZT). For every 15' of longitude that the observer's position differs from that of the zone meridian, the zone time of the phenomena differs by 1^m, being *later* if the observer is *west* of the zone meridian, and *earlier* if he is *east* of the zone meridian. The local mean time of the phenomena varies with latitude of the observer, declination of the body, and hour angle of the body relative to that of the mean sun.

Sunrise and sunset are also tabulated in the tide tables (from 76°N to 60°S) and in a supplement to the American ephemeris of 1946 entitled *Tables of Sunrise, Sunset, and Twilight* (from 75°N to 75°S). The meridian angle of any body at the time of its rising and setting can be computed by the formulas given in article 715 of volume II. The data concerning the rising and setting of the sun and moon and the duration of twilight for high southern latitudes are published as graphs in United States Naval Observatory Circular No. 147, *Sunlight, Moonlight, and Twilight for Antarctica;* these graphs are similar to the graphs in the *Air Almanac* for northern latitudes (art. 1912).

1910. Finding time of sunrise and sunset.—*Nautical Almanac.* Enter the table on the daily page, and extract the LMT for the tabulated latitude next *smaller* than the observer's latitude (unless this is an exact tabulated value). Apply a correction from table I on almanac page xxxii to interpolate for latitude, determining the sign of the correction by inspection. Then convert LMT to ZT by means of the difference in longitude (dλ) between the local and zone meridians.

Example.—Find the zone time of sunrise and sunset at lat. 43°31′.4N, long. 36° 14′.3W on June 1, 1975.

Solution.—

L 43°31′.4N June 1
λ 36°14′.3W

Sunrise			Sunset	
40°	0433		40°	1922
T I (−)	11		T I (+)	11
LMT	0422		LMT	1933
dλ (+)	25		dλ (+)	25
ZT	0447		ZT	1958

Air Almanac. The procedure is the same as that for the *Nautical Almanac*, except that the LMT is extracted from the tables of sunrise and sunset instead of the daily page, and latitude correction is by linear interpolation.

The tabulated times are for the Greenwich meridian. Except in high latitudes near the times of the equinoxes, the time of sunrise and sunset varies so little from day to day that no interpolation is needed for longitude. If such an interpolation is considered justified, it can be made in the same manner as for the moon (art. 1912).

In high latitudes, interpolation is not always possible. For instance, on June 1, 1975, sunrise at latitude 66°N occurs at 0115, but at latitude 68°N the sun does not set. Between these two latitudes the time of sunrise might be found from the graphs in the *Air Almanac,* or by computation, as explained in article 715 of volume II. However, in such a marginal situation, the time of sunrise itself is uncertain, being greatly affected by a relatively small change of refraction or height of eye.

1911. Finding time of twilight.—Morning twilight *ends* at sunrise, and evening twilight *begins* at sunset. The time of the darker limit can be found from the almanacs. The *time* of the darker limits of both *civil* and *nautical* twilights (center of the sun 6° and 12°, respectively, below the celestial horizon) is given in the *Nautical Almanac.* The *Air Almanac* provides tabulations of civil twilight from 60°S to 72°N. The brightness of the sky at any given depression of the sun below the horizon may vary considerably from day to day, depending upon the amount of cloudiness and other atmospheric conditions. In general, however, the most effective period for observing stars and planets occurs when the center of the sun is between about 3° and 9° below the celestial horizon. Hence, the darker limit of civil twilight occurs at about the mid point of this period. At the darker limit of nautical twilight the horizon is generally too dark for good observations. At the darker limit of *astronomical twilight* (center of the sun 18° below the celestial horizon) full night has set in. The time of this twilight is given in the ephemeris. Its approximate value can be determined by extrapolation (art. 207, vol. II) in the *Nautical Almanac,* noting that the duration of the different kinds of twilight is not proportional to the number of degrees of depression at the darker limit. More precise determination of the time at which the center of the sun is any given number of degrees below the celestial horizon can be determined by a large-scale diagram on the plane of the celestial meridan (art. 1432) or by computation (art. 715, vol. II). Duration of twilight in latitudes higher than 65°N is given in a graph in the *Air Almanac.*

Nautical Almanac. The method of finding the darker limit of twilight is the same as that for sunrise and sunset (art. 1910).

Example 1.—Find the zone time of beginning of morning nautical twilight and ending of evening nautical twilight at lat. 21°54ʹ7S, long. 109°34ʹ2E on June 1, 1975.
Solution.—

L 21°54ʹ7S June 1
λ 109°34ʹ2E

	Nautical twilight			Nautical twilight
20°S	0537		20°S	1819
T I	(+)3		T I	(−)3
LMT	0540		LMT	1816
dλ	(−)18		dλ	(−)18
ZT	0522		ZT	1758

Air Almanac. The method of finding the darker limit of twilight is the same as that for sunrise and sunset as explained in article 1910.

Example 2.—Find the zone time of beginning of morning civil twilight and ending of evening civil twilight at lat. 47°18ʹ8S, long. 87°28ʹ3W on June 1, 1975.
Solution.—

L 47°18ʹ8S June 1
λ 87°28ʹ3W

Civil Twilight			Civil Twilight		
45°S	0654		45°S	1701	
corr.	(+)7		corr.	(−)7	
LMT	0701		LMT	1654	
dλ	(−)10		dλ	(−)10	
ZT	0651	(twilight)	ZT	1644	(twilight)

Sometimes in high latitudes the sun does not rise but twilight occurs. This is indicated in the *Air Almanac* by the symbol ■ in the sunrise and sunset column. To find the time of beginning of morning twilight, *subtract* half the duration of twilight as obtained from the duration of twilight graph from the time of meridian transit of the sun; and for the time of ending of evening twilight, *add* it to the time of meridian transit. The LMT of meridian transit never differs by more than 16^m4 (approximately) from 1200. The actual time on any date can be determined from the almanac.

1912. Finding time of moonrise and moonset is similar to finding time of sunrise and sunset, with one important difference. Because of the moon's rapid change of declination, and its fast eastward motion relative to the sun, the time of moonrise and moonset varies considerably from day to day. These changes of position on the celestial sphere (art. 1403) are continuous, as moonrise and moonset occur successively at various longitudes around the earth. Therefore, the change in time is distributed over all longitudes. For precise results, it would be necessary to compute the time of the phenomena at any given place, by the method described in article 715 of volume II. For ordinary purposes of navigation, however, it is sufficiently accurate to interpolate between consecutive moonrises or moonsets at the Greenwich meridian. Since apparent motion of the moon is westward, relative to an observer on the earth, interpolation in west longitude is between the phenomenon on the given date and the *following* one. In east longitude it is between the phenomenon on the given date and the *preceding* one.

Nautical Almanac. For the given date, enter the daily-page table with latitude, and extract the LMT for the tabulated latitude next *smaller* than the observer's latitude (unless this is an exact tabulated value). Apply a correction from table I of the almanac

"Tables for Interpolating Sunrise, Moonrise, etc." to interpolate for latitude, determining the sign of the correction by inspection. Repeat this procedure for the day following the given date, if in west longitude; or for the day preceding, if in east longitude. Using the difference between these two times, and the longitude, enter table II of the almanac "Tables for Interpolating Sunrise, Sunset, etc." and take out the correction. Apply this correction to the LMT of moonrise or moonset at the Greenwich meridian on the given date to find the LMT at the position of the observer. The sign to be given the correction is such as to make the corrected time fall between the times for the two dates between which interpolation is being made. This is nearly always positive (+) in west longitude and negative (−) in east longitude. Convert the corrected LMT to ZT.

Example 1.—Find the zone time of moonrise and moonset at lat. 58°23.'6N, long. 144°07.'5W on June 1, 1975, using the *Nautical Almanac.*

Solution.—

$$L\ 58°23.'6N\ \text{June 1}$$
$$\lambda\ 144°07.'5W$$

Moonrise				Moonset		
58°N	0007	June 1		58°N	1110	June 1
T I	(+)1			T I	(−)1	
LMT (G)	0008	June 1		LMT (G)	1109	June 1
58°N	0021	June 2		58°N	1221	June 2
T I	0			T I	0	
LMT (G)	0021	June 2		LMT (G)	1221	June 2
LMT (G)	0008	June 1		LMT (G)	1109	June 1
diff.	13			diff.	72	
T II	(+)5			T II	(+)28	
LMT (G)	0008	June 1		LMT (G)	1109	June 1
LMT	0013	June 1		LMT	1137	June 1
dλ	(−)24			dλ	(−)24	
ZT	2349	May 31		ZT	1113	June 1

Air Almanac. For the given date, determine LMT for the observer's latitude at the Greenwich meridian, in the same manner as with the *Nautical Almanac*, except that linear interpolation is made directly from the main tabulation, since no interpolation table is provided. Extract, also, the value from the "Diff." column to the right of the moonrise and moonset column, interpolating if necessary. This "Diff." is one-fourth of one-half of the daily difference. The error introduced by this approximation is generally not more than a few minutes, although it increases with latitude. Using this difference, and the longitude, enter the "Interpolation of Moonrise, Moonset" table on flap F4 of the *Air Almanac* and take out the correction. The *Air Almanac* recommends the taking of the correction from this table without interpolation. The results thus obtained are sufficiently accurate for ordinary purposes of navigation. If greater accuracy is desired, the correction can be taken by interpolation. However, since the "Diff." itself is an approximation, the *Nautical Almanac* or computation (art. 715, vol. II) should be used if accuracy is a consideration. Apply the correction to the LMT of moonrise or moonset at the Greenwich meridian on the given date to find the LMT at the position of the observer. The correction is positive (+) for west longitude, and negative (−) for east longitude, unless the "Diff." on the daily page is preceded by a negative sign (−), when the correction is negative (−) for west longitude, and positive

(+) for east longitude. If the time is near midnight, record the date at each step, as in the *Nautical Almanac* solution.

  Example 2.—Find the zone time of moonrise and moonset at lat. 58°23′.6N, long. 144°07′.5W on June 1, 1975, using the *Air Almanac*.

  Solution.—

L 58°23′.6N June 1
λ 144°07′.5W

	Moonrise			Moonset	
diff.	(+)07		diff.	(+)36	
58°N	0007		58°N	1110	
corr.	(+)1		corr.	(−)1	
LMT (G)	0008		LMT (G)	1109	
corr.	(+)4		corr.	(+)29	
LMT	0012		LMT	1138	
dλ	(−)24		dλ	(−)24	
ZT	2348 May 31		ZT	1114	

As with the sun, there are times in high latitudes when interpolation is inaccurate or impossible. At such periods, the times of the phenomena themselves are uncertain, but an approximate answer can be obtained by moonlight graph in the *Air Almanac* or by computation, as explained in article 715 of volume II. With the moon, this condition occurs when the moon rises or sets at one latitude, but not at the next higher tabulated latitude, as with the sun. It also occurs when the moon rises or sets on one day but not on the preceding or following day. This latter condition is indicated in the *Air Almanac* by the symbol ✳ in the "Diff." column.

  Because of the eastward revolution of the moon around the earth, there is one day each synodical month (29½ days) when the moon does not rise, and one day when it does not set. These occur near last quarter and first quarter, respectively. Since this day is not the same at all latitudes or at all longitudes, the time of moonrise or moonset found from the almanac may occasionally be the preceding or succeeding one to that desired. When interpolating near midnight, one should exercise caution to prevent an error.

  Refer to the right-hand daily page of the *Nautical Almanac* for June 12, 13, 14 (app. F). On June 13 moonset occurs at 2350 at latitude 70°N, and at 0031 at latitude 72°N. These are *not* the same moonset, the one at 0031 occurring approximately one day *later* than the one occurring at 2350. This is indicated by the two times, which differ by nearly 24 hours. The table indicates that with increasing northerly latitude, moonset occurs *later*. Between 70°N and 72°N the time crosses midnight *to the following* day. Hence, between these latitudes interpolation should be made between 2350 on June 13 and 0007 on June 14.

  The effect of the revolution of the moon around the earth is to cause the moon to rise or set *later* from day to day. The daily retardation due to this effect does not differ greatly from 50ᵐ. The change in declination of the moon may increase or decrease this effect. The effect due to change of declination increases with latitude, and in extreme conditions it may be greater than the effect due to revolution of the moon. Hence, the interval between successive moonrises or moonsets is more erratic in high latitudes than in low latitudes. When the two effects act in the same direction, daily differences can be quite large. Thus, at latitude 72°N the moon rises at 0550 on June 13, and at 0806 on June 14. When they act in opposite directions, they are small, and when the effect due to change in declination is larger than that due to revolution, the moon sets *earlier* on succeeding days. Thus, at latitude 72°N the moon sets at 0031 on June 13, and at 0007 on June 14. This condition is reflected in the *Air Almanac* by a negative "Diff." If this happens near last quarter or first quarter, two moonrises or moonsets might occur on the same day, one a few minutes after the day begins, and the other a few minutes before it ends. On June 14, 1975, for instance, at latitude 72°N, the moon sets at 0007, rises at 0806, and sets again at 2350 the same day. On those days on which no moonrise or no moonset occurs, the next succeeding one is shown with 24^h added to the time. Thus, at latitude 68°N the moon rises at 2342 on May 25, while the next moonrise occurs 24^h45^m later, at 0027 on May 27. This is listed both as 2427 on May 26 and as 0027 on May 27 (not shown in app. F).

Interpolation for longitude is always made between *consecutive* moonrises or moonsets, regardless of the days on which they fall.

Example 3.—Find the zone time of moonset at lat. 71°38′.7N, long. 56°21′.8W during the night of June 13–14, 1975, using the *Nautical Almanac*.

Solution.—

$$
\begin{array}{ll}
\text{L } 71°38'.7\text{N} & \text{June 13–14} \\
\lambda\ 56°21'.8\text{W} & \\
& \text{Moonset} \\
70°\text{N} & 2350 \text{ June 13} \\
\text{T I } (+)15 & \\
\text{LMT (G)} & \overline{0005} \text{ June 14} \\
& \\
70°\text{N} & 2342 \text{ June 14} \\
\text{T I } (+)7 & \\
\text{LMT (G)} & \overline{2349} \text{ June 14} \\
\text{LMT (G)} & \underline{0005} \text{ June 14} \\
\text{diff.} & \overline{16} \\
\text{T II } (-)2 & \\
\text{LMT (G)} & 0005 \text{ June 14} \\
\text{LMT} & 0003 \text{ June 14} \\
d\lambda\ (-)15 & \\
\text{ZT} & \overline{2348} \text{ June 13}
\end{array}
$$

Interpolation for the first entry is between 2350 on June 13 (lat. 70°N) and 0007 on June 14 (lat. 72°N); for the second entry, between 2342 on June 14 and 2350 on June 14.

Beyond the northern limits of the almanacs the values can be obtained from a series of graphs given near the back of the *Air Almanac*. These graphs are shown in appendix G. For high latitudes, graphs are used instead of tables because graphs give a clearer picture of conditions, which may change radically with relatively little change in position or date. Under these conditions interpolation to practical precision is simpler by graph than by table. In those parts of the graph which are difficult to read, the times of the phenomena's occurrence are themselves uncertain, being altered considerably by a relatively small change in refraction or height of eye.

On all of these graphs any given latitude is represented by a horizontal line, and any given date by a vertical line. At the intersection of these two lines the duration is read from the curves, interpolating by eye between curves.

The "Semiduration of Sunlight" graph gives the number of hours between sunrise and meridian transit or between meridian transit and sunset. The dot scale near the top of the graph indicates the LMT of meridian transit, the time represented by the minute dot nearest the vertical dateline being used. If the intersection occurs in the area marked "sun above horizon," the sun does not set; and if in the area marked "sun below horizon," the sun does not rise.

Example 1.—Find the zone time of sunrise and sunset at lat. 71°30′.0N, long. 10°00′.0W near Jan Mayen Island, on August 25, 1975.

Solution.—

$$
\begin{array}{rll}
 & \text{August 25} & \\
\text{LMT} & 1202 & \text{LAN, from top of graph} \\
\text{d}\lambda & (-)20 & \\
\text{ZT} & 1142 & \text{LAN} \\
\text{semidur.} & 840 & \text{from graph} \\
\text{ZT} & 0302 & \text{sunrise } (-\text{semidur.}) \\
\text{ZT} & 2022 & \text{sunset } (+\text{semidur.})
\end{array}
$$

A vertical line through August 25 passes nearest the dot representing LAN 1202 on the scale near the top of the graph. This is LMT; at longitude 10°00′.0 W the ZT is 20^m earlier, or at 1142. The intersection of the vertical dateline with the horizontal latitude line occurs between the 8^h and 9^h curves, at approximately 8^h40^m. Hence, sunrise occurs at this interval before LAN and sunset at this interval after LAN.

The "Duration of Twilight" graph gives the number of hours between the beginning of morning *civil* twilight (center of sun 6° below the horizon) and sunrise, or between sunset and the end of evening civil twilight. If the sun does not rise, but twilight does occur, the time taken from the graph is half the total length of the single twilight period, or the number of hours from beginning of morning twilight to LAN, or from LAN to end of evening twilight. If the intersection occurs in the area marked "continuous twilight or sunlight," the center of the sun does not get more than 6° below the horizon, and if in the area marked "no twilight nor sunlight," the sun remains more than 6° below the horizon throughout the entire day.

Example 2.—Find the zone time of beginning of morning twilight and ending of evening twilight at the place and date of example 1.

Solution.—

Twilight	Twilight
ZT 0302 sunrise, from example 1	ZT 2022 sunset, from example 1
dur. 153 from graph	dur. 153 from graph
ZT 0109 morning twilight	ZT 2215 evening twilight

The intersection of the vertical dateline and the horizontal latitude line occurs approximately one-sixth of the distance from the 2^h line toward the 1^h20^m line; or at about 1^h53^m. Morning twilight begins at this interval before sunrise, and evening twilight ends at this interval after sunset.

The "Semiduration of Moonlight" graph gives the number of hours between moonrise and meridian transit or between meridian transit and moonset. The dot scale near the top of the graph indicates the LMT of meridian transit, each dot representing one hour. The phase symbols indicate the date on which the principal moon phases occur, the open circle indicating full moon and the dark circle indicating new moon. If the intersection of the vertical dateline and the horizontal latitude line falls in the "moon above horizon" or "moon below horizon" area, the moon remains above or below the horizon, respectively, for the entire 24 hours of the day.

If approximations of the times of moonrise and moonset are sufficient, the values of semiduration taken from the graph can be used without adjustment. For more accurate results, the times on the required date and the adjacent date (the following date in west longitude and the preceding date in east longitude) should be determined, and an interpolation made for longitude, as in any latitude, since the intervals given are for the Greenwich meridian.

Example 3.—Find the zone time of moonrise and moonset at lat. 74°00′.0N, long. 108°00′.0W on May 8, 1975, and the phase of the moon on this date.

Solution.—

	May 8			May 9	
LMT	0923		LMT	1006	meridian transit, from graph
dλ	(+)12		dλ	(+)12	
ZT	0935		ZT	1018	meridian transit
semidur.	7^{h}59^m		semidur.	9^{h}15^m	from graph
ZT	0136		ZT	0103	(moonrise−semidur.)
ZT	1734		ZT	1933	(moonset+semidur.)

	Moonrise			Moonset	
ZT	0136 May 8		ZT	1734 May 8	
ZT	0103 May 9		ZT	1933 May 9	
diff.	(−)33		diff.	(+)119	
33×108.0/360	(−)10		119×108.0/360	(+) 36	
ZT	0126		ZT	1810	

The phase is crescent, about two days before new moon. The LMT of meridian transits are found by noting the intersections of the vertical datelines with the dot scale near the top of the graph, interpolating by eye. At longitude 108°00′.0W the ZT is 12^m later. The semiduration is found by noting the position, with respect to the semiduration curves, of the intersection of the vertical dateline with the horizontal latitude line. This interval is subtracted from the time of meridian transit to obtain moonrise, and added to obtain moonset. These solutions are made for both May 8 and 9, and the difference determined in minutes. The adjustment to be applied to the ZT on May 8 at Greenwich is determined by multiplying this difference by the ratio λ/360. The phase is determined by noting the position of the vertical dateline with respect to the phase symbols. If the answer indicates that the phenomenon occurs on a date differing from that desired, a new solution should be made, adjusting the starting date accordingly. The phenomenon may occur twice on the same day, or it may not occur at all. In high latitudes the effect on the time of moonrise and moonset of a relatively small change in declination is considerably greater than in lower latitudes, resulting in greater differences from day to day.

Sunlight, twilight, and moonlight graphs are not given for south latitudes. Beyond latitude 65°S, the northern hemisphere graphs can be used for determining the semiduration or duration, by using the vertical dateline for a day when the declination has the same numerical value but opposite sign. The time of meridian transit and the phase of the moon are determined as explained above, using the correct date. Between latitudes 60°S and 65°S solution is made by interpolation between the tables and the graphs.

Several other methods of solution of these phenomena are available. The *Tide Tables* tabulate sunrise and sunset from latitude 76°N to 60°S. A supplement to the American Ephemeris of 1946, entitled *Tables of Sunrise, Sunset, and Twilight*, provides tabulations from latitude 75°N to 75°S and graphs for semiduration of sunlight and duration of twilight, with separate graphs for civil, nautical, and astronomical twilights. Semiduration or duration can be determined graphically by means of a diagram on the plane of the celestial meridian (art. 1432), or by computation. When computation is used, solution is made for the meridian angle at which the required negative altitude occurs. The meridian angle expressed in time units is the semiduration in the case of sunrise, sunset, moonrise, and moonset; and the semiduration of the combined sunlight and twilight, or the time from meridian transit at which morning twilight begins or evening twilight ends. For sunrise and sunset the altitude used is $(-)50'$. Allowance for height of eye can be made by algebraically subtracting (numerically adding) the dip correction from this altitude. The altitude used for twilight is $(-)6°$, $(-)12°$, or $(-)18°$ for civil, nautical, or astronomical twilight, respectively. The altitude used for moonrise and moonset is $-34' - SD + HP$, where SD is semidiameter and HP is horizontal parallax, from the daily pages of the *Nautical Almanac*.

1913. Rising, setting, and twilight at a moving craft.—Instructions given in the preceding three articles relate to a fixed position on the earth. Aboard a moving craft the problem is complicated somewhat by the fact that time of occurrence depends upon position of the craft, and vice versa. At ship speeds, it is generally sufficiently accurate to make an approximate mental solution, and use the position of the vessel at this time to make a more accurate solution. If higher accuracy is required, the position at the time indicated in the second solution can be used for a third solution. If desired, this process can be repeated until the same answer is obtained from two consecutive solutions. However, it is generally sufficient to alter the first solution by 1^m for each $15'$ of longitude that the position of the craft differs from that used in the solution, adding if west of the estimated position, and subtracting if east of it. In applying this rule, use both longitudes to the nearest $15'$. The first solution is known as the first estimate; the second solution is the second estimate.

CHAPTER XX

SIGHT REDUCTION

2001. Introduction.—The process of deriving from a celestial observation the information needed for establishing a line of position is called **sight reduction.** The observation itself consists of measuring the altitude of a celestial body and noting the time. The process of finding such a line of position may be divided into six steps:

1. Correction of sextant altitude (ch. XVI).
2. Determination of GHA and declination (ch. XIX).
3. Selection of assumed position and finding local hour angle or meridian angle at that point.
4. Computation of altitude and azimuth.
5. Comparison of computed and observed altitudes.
6. Plot of the line of position.

Broadly speaking, tables which assist in any of these steps can be considered **sight reduction tables.** However, the expression is generally limited to tables intended primarily for computation of altitude and azimuth. A great variety of such tables exists. In chapter XXI various methods of sight reduction, including graphical and mechanical solutions, are contrasted. All are based, directly or indirectly, upon solution of the navigational triangle (art. 1433). Thus, the process of sight reduction, in its limited sense, is one of converting coordinates of the celestial equator system (art. 1428) to those of the horizon system (art. 1430).

The correction of the sextant altitude (hs) to find observed altitude (Ho) is not necessarily performed first. If any form of time other than GMT is used for timing the observation, it is first converted to GMT because this is the kind of time used for entering the almanacs. From the almanac, the GHA and declination are determined.

2002. Selection of the assumed position (AP).—The following variables are needed to compute the altitude and azimuth:

1. Latitude (L).
2. Declination (d or Dec.).
3. Local hour angle (LHA) or meridian angle (t).

Except for declination, these variables are dependent upon the position from which the altitude and azimuth are to be computed for the time of the observation. Although the dead reckoning or estimated position can be used, unnecessary interpolation can be avoided when using modern sight reduction tables by selecting an AP for the reduction that will result in two of the three variables being exact entry values or table arguments. In these tables altitudes and azimuth angles are given for each whole degree of latitude and each whole degree of either meridian angle or local hour angle. Since the assumed position should be within 30′ of the actual position, the whole degree of latitude *nearest* to the DR or EP at the time of the sight is selected as the **assumed latitude** (aL). The **assumed longitude** (aλ) is also selected within 30′ of the DR or EP so that no minutes of arc will remain after it is applied to GHA. This means that in west longitude the minutes of aλ must be the same as those of GHA; while in east longitude the minutes of aλ must be equal to 60′ minus the minutes of GHA.

2003. Finding the local hour angle and meridian angle.—Meridian angle is the angular distance that the celestial body is east or west of the celestial meridian. It is found from local hour angle (LHA), which, in turn, is found from Greenwich hour angle by adding east longitude or subtracting west longitude. A time diagram (art. 1428) is useful in visualizing this relationship.

Example 1.—The GHA is 168°42′6.

Required.—The LHA and t at (1) long. 137°24′6W, and (2) 158°24′7E.

Solution.—

	(1) GHA	168°42′6		(2) GHA	168°42′6
	λ	137°24′6W		λ	158°24′7E
LHA		31°18′0	LHA		327°07′3
t		31°18′0W	t		32°52′7E

In west longitude, if GHA is less than longitude, add 360° to GHA before subtracting. In east longitude, if the sum exceeds 360°, subtract this amount. If LHA is less than 180°, it is numerically equal to meridian angle, which is labeled W (west). If LHA is greater than 180°, t is 360°—LHA and is labeled E (east).

Example 2.—The GHA is 168°42′6; observations are made at (1) long. 137°24′6W, and (2) long. 158°24′7E.

Required.—The aλ providing whole degrees of LHA and t.

Solution.—

	(1) GHA	168°42′6		(2) GHA	168°42′6
	aλ	137°42′6W		aλ	158°17′4E
LHA		31°00′0	LHA		327°00′0
t		31°00′0W	t		33°00′0E

2004. Comparison of computed and observed altitudes.—After appropriate corrections are applied to the **sextant altitude (hs),** the **observed altitude (Ho)** is obtained. For the instant of observation, the altitude and azimuth at some convenient **assumed position (AP)** near the actual position of the observer are determined by calculation or equivalent process. The difference between this **computed altitude (Hc)** and Ho is the **altitude intercept (a),** sometimes called **altitude difference.**

Since a is the difference in altitude at the assumed and actual positions, it is also the difference in zenith distance, and therefore the difference in radii of the circles of equal altitude at the two places. The position having the greater altitude is on the circle of smaller radius, and hence is closer to the GP of the body. In figure 2004 the AP is shown on the inner circle. Hence, Hc is greater than Ho.

The altitude intercept, the numerical difference between Hc and Ho, is customarily expressed in nautical miles (minutes of arc), and labeled **T** or **A** to indicate whether the line of position is **toward** or **away** from the GP, as measured from the AP.

Two useful aids in labeling the intercept are: **C**oast **G**uard **A**cademy for **C**omputed **G**reater **A**way, and **Ho Mo To** for **Ho Mo**re **To**ward.

For example,

	Hc	37°51′6		Hc	61°57′3
	Ho	37°43′9		Ho	62°12′7
a		7.7A	a		15.4T

2005. Plot of the line of position.—The line of position can be plotted using part of the information within the broken circle of figure 2004, as shown in figure 2005. First, the AP is plotted. The circle of equal altitude through this position is not needed, and is not plotted. From the AP the azimuth line is measured toward or away from the GP as appropriate, and the altitude intercept is measured along this line. At the point thus

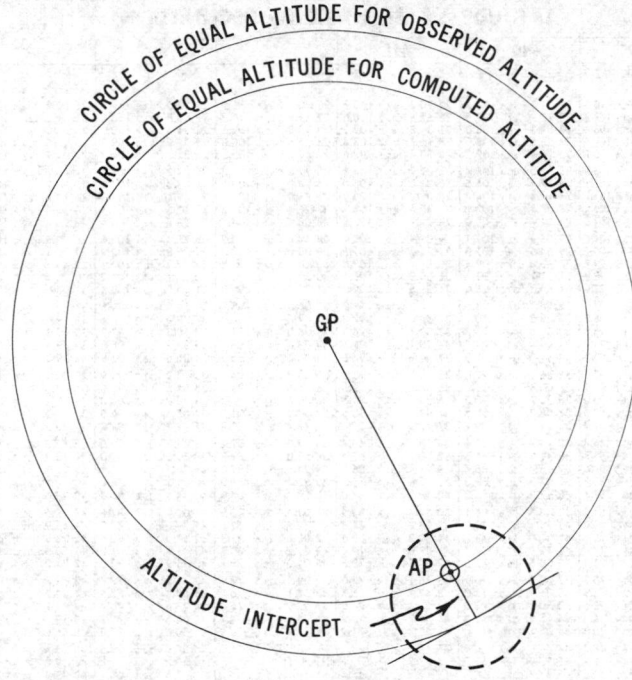

FIGURE 2004.—The basis for the line of position from a celestial observation.

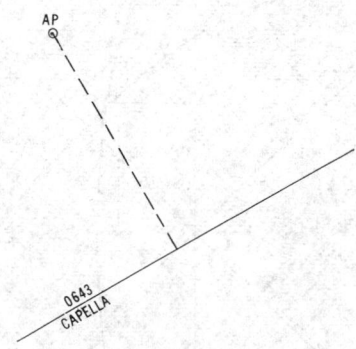

FIGURE 2005.—A line of position from observation of the star Capella at 0643.

located, a line is drawn perpendicular to the azimuth line. This perpendicular is the line of position.

2006. Computation of altitude and azimuth.—In modern practice, solutions of the navigational triangle for altitude and azimuth are usually effected by means of sight reduction tables of the inspection type. These inspection tables may contain tabulations of altitude and azimuth angle for arguments of local hour angle (or meridian angle), declination, and latitude, or tabulations of altitude and azimuth of selected stars for arguments of epoch, latitude, and sidereal time (LHA♈). Values are taken directly from the tables, without need for logarithms, auxiliary functions, or mathematical solutions (except interpolation).

Mathematical solutions of altitude and azimuth angle are presented in chapter VII of volume II. Chapter IX of volume II contains examples of the use of logarithms and auxiliary functions in sight reduction.

60°, 300° L.H.A.   LATITUDE **SAME** NAME AS DECLINATION

N. Lat. { L.H.A. greater than 180°......Zn=Z
{ L.H.A. less than 180°............Zn=360°−Z

Dec.	38° Hc	d	Z	39° Hc	d	Z	40° Hc	d	Z	41° Hc	d	Z	42° Hc	d	Z	43° Hc	d	Z	44° Hc	d	Z	45° Hc	d	Z	Dec.
0	23 12.2	+40.1	109.6	22 51.9	+40.9	110.0	22 31.3	+41.6	110.4	22 10.2	+42.4	110.7	21 48.8	+43.1	111.1	21 27.0	+43.8	111.5	21 04.8	+44.6	111.9	20 42.3	+45.3	112.2	0
1	23 52.3	39.8	108.8	23 32.8	40.6	109.2	23 12.9	41.4	109.6	22 52.6	42.2	110.0	22 31.9	42.9	110.4	22 10.8	43.7	110.8	21 49.4	44.4	111.1	21 27.6	45.0	111.5	1
2	24 32.1	39.5	107.9	24 13.4	40.4	108.4	23 54.3	41.2	108.8	23 34.8	41.9	109.2	23 14.8	42.7	109.6	22 54.5	43.4	110.0	22 33.8	44.2	110.4	22 12.6	45.0	110.8	2
3	25 11.6	39.3	107.1	24 53.8	40.1	107.6	24 35.5	40.9	108.0	24 16.7	41.7	108.4	23 57.5	42.5	108.8	23 37.9	43.3	109.3	23 18.0	43.9	109.7	22 57.6	44.7	110.1	3
4	25 50.9	39.0	106.3	25 33.9	39.8	106.7	25 16.4	40.6	107.2	24 58.4	41.5	107.6	24 40.0	42.3	108.1	24 21.2	43.0	108.5	24 01.9	43.8	108.9	23 42.3	44.5	109.3	4
5	26 29.9	+38.6	105.4	26 13.7	+39.5	105.9	25 57.0	+40.4	106.4	25 39.9	+41.1	106.8	25 22.3	+41.9	107.3	25 04.2	+42.8	107.7	24 45.7	+43.5	108.2	24 26.8	+44.3	108.6	5
6	27 08.5	38.4	104.6	26 53.2	39.2	105.1	26 37.4	40.0	105.5	26 21.0	40.9	106.0	26 04.2	41.8	106.5	25 47.0	42.5	107.0	25 29.2	43.3	107.4	25 11.1	44.0	107.9	6
7	27 46.9	38.0	103.7	27 32.4	38.9	104.2	27 17.4	39.8	104.7	27 01.9	40.7	105.2	26 46.0	41.4	105.7	26 29.5	42.3	106.2	26 12.5	43.1	106.7	25 55.1	43.8	107.1	7
8	28 24.9	37.7	102.8	28 11.3	38.6	103.3	27 57.2	39.5	103.9	27 42.6	40.0	104.4	27 27.4	41.2	104.9	27 11.8	41.9	105.4	26 55.6	42.8	105.9	26 38.9	43.6	106.4	8
9	29 02.6	37.3	101.9	28 49.9	38.2	102.5	28 36.7	39.1	103.0	28 22.9	40.0	103.5	28 08.6	40.8	104.1	27 53.7	41.7	104.6	27 38.4	42.5	105.1	27 22.5	43.3	105.6	9
10	29 39.9	+37.0	101.0	29 28.1	+37.9	101.6	29 15.8	+38.8	102.1	29 02.9	+39.7	102.7	28 49.4	+40.6	103.2	28 35.4	+41.4	103.8	28 20.9	+42.2	104.3	28 05.8	+43.1	104.8	10
11	30 16.9	36.5	100.1	30 06.0	37.5	100.7	29 54.6	38.4	101.3	29 42.6	39.3	101.8	29 30.0	40.2	102.4	29 16.8	41.1	102.9	29 03.1	42.0	103.5	28 48.9	42.8	104.0	11
12	30 53.4	36.2	99.2	30 43.5	37.2	99.8	30 33.0	38.1	100.4	30 21.9	39.0	101.0	30 10.2	39.9	101.5	29 57.9	40.8	102.1	29 45.1	41.6	102.7	29 31.7	42.4	103.2	12
13	31 29.6	35.8	98.3	31 20.7	36.7	98.9	31 11.1	37.7	99.5	31 00.9	38.6	100.1	30 50.1	39.6	100.7	30 38.7	40.5	101.2	30 26.7	41.3	101.8	30 14.1	42.2	102.4	13
14	32 05.4	35.3	97.3	31 57.4	36.3	97.9	31 48.8	37.3	98.6	31 39.5	38.3	99.2	31 29.7	39.1	99.8	31 19.2	40.0	100.4	31 08.0	41.0	101.0	30 56.3	41.9	101.6	14
15	32 40.7	+34.9	96.4	32 33.7	+35.9	97.0	32 26.1	+36.9	97.6	32 17.8	+37.8	98.3	32 08.8	+38.8	98.9	31 59.2	+39.8	99.5	31 49.0	+40.6	100.1	31 38.2	+41.5	100.7	15
16	33 15.6	34.5	95.4	33 09.6	35.5	96.1	33 03.0	36.4	96.7	32 55.6	37.5	97.3	32 47.6	38.4	98.0	32 39.0	39.3	98.6	32 29.6	40.3	99.3	32 19.7	41.1	99.9	16
17	33 50.1	33.9	94.4	33 45.1	35.0	95.1	33 39.4	36.0	95.7	33 33.1	37.0	96.4	33 26.0	38.0	97.1	33 18.3	38.9	97.7	33 09.9	39.9	98.4	33 00.8	40.8	99.0	17
18	34 24.0	33.5	93.4	34 20.1	34.5	94.1	34 15.4	35.6	94.8	34 10.1	36.5	95.5	34 04.0	37.6	96.1	33 57.2	38.6	96.8	33 49.8	39.5	97.5	33 41.6	40.5	98.1	18
19	34 57.5	33.0	92.4	34 54.6	34.0	93.1	34 51.0	35.1	93.8	34 46.6	36.1	94.5	34 41.6	37.1	95.2	34 35.8	38.1	95.9	34 29.3	39.1	96.6	34 22.1	40.0	97.2	19
20	35 30.5	+32.4	91.4	35 28.6	+33.6	92.1	35 26.1	+34.5	92.8	35 22.7	+35.7	93.5	35 18.7	+36.6	94.2	35 13.9	+37.7	94.9	35 08.4	+38.6	95.6	35 02.1	+39.6	96.3	20
21	36 02.9	31.9	90.4	36 02.2	32.9	91.1	36 00.6	34.1	91.8	35 58.4	35.1	92.5	35 55.3	36.2	93.3	35 51.6	37.2	94.0	35 47.0	38.2	94.7	35 41.7	39.2	95.4	21
22	36 34.8	31.3	89.3	36 35.1	32.5	90.0	36 34.7	33.6	90.8	36 33.5	34.6	91.5	36 31.5	35.7	92.3	36 28.8	36.7	93.0	36 25.2	37.8	93.7	36 20.9	38.8	94.5	22
23	37 06.1	30.8	88.2	37 07.6	31.9	89.0	37 08.3	32.9	89.8	37 08.1	34.1	90.5	37 07.2	35.2	91.3	37 05.5	36.2	92.0	37 03.0	37.2	92.8	36 59.7	38.2	93.5	23
24	37 36.9	30.2	87.2	37 39.5	31.3	87.9	37 41.2	32.5	88.7	37 42.2	33.5	89.5	37 42.4	34.6	90.2	37 41.7	35.7	91.0	37 40.2	36.8	91.8	37 37.9	37.8	92.6	24
25	38 07.1	+29.5	86.1	38 10.8	+30.7	86.8	38 13.7	+31.8	87.6	38 15.7	+33.0	88.4	38 17.0	+34.0	89.2	38 17.4	+35.2	90.0	38 17.0	+36.2	90.8	38 15.7	+37.3	91.6	25
26	38 36.6	28.9	85.0	38 41.5	30.0	85.7	38 45.5	31.2	86.5	38 48.7	32.4	87.4	38 51.0	33.5	88.2	38 52.6	34.6	89.0	38 53.2	35.7	89.8	38 53.0	36.8	90.6	26
27	39 05.5	28.3	83.8	39 11.5	29.5	84.6	39 16.7	30.6	85.4	39 21.1	31.7	86.3	39 24.5	32.9	87.1	39 27.2	34.0	87.9	39 28.9	35.2	88.7	39 29.8	36.3	89.6	27
28	39 33.8	27.5	82.7	39 41.0	28.7	83.5	39 47.3	30.0	84.3	39 52.8	31.1	85.2	39 57.4	32.3	86.0	40 01.2	33.4	86.8	40 04.1	34.5	87.7	40 06.1	35.6	88.5	28
29	40 01.3	26.9	81.5	40 09.7	28.1	82.4	40 17.3	29.2	83.2	40 23.9	30.5	84.0	40 29.7	31.7	84.9	40 34.6	32.8	85.7	40 38.6	34.0	86.6	40 41.7	35.1	87.5	29
30	40 28.2	+26.1	80.4	40 37.8	+27.4	81.2	40 46.5	+28.6	82.1	40 54.4	+29.8	82.9	41 01.4	+30.9	83.8	41 07.4	+32.2	84.6	41 12.6	+33.3	85.5	41 16.8	+34.5	86.4	30
31	40 54.3	25.5	79.2	41 05.2	26.6	80.0	41 15.1	27.9	80.9	41 24.2	29.1	81.8	41 32.3	30.3	82.6	41 39.6	31.4	83.5	41 45.9	32.6	84.4	41 51.3	33.8	85.3	31
32	41 19.8	24.6	78.0	41 31.8	25.9	78.8	41 43.0	27.1	79.7	41 53.3	28.3	80.6	42 02.6	29.6	81.5	42 11.0	30.8	82.4	42 18.5	32.0	83.3	42 25.1	33.2	84.2	32
33	41 44.4	23.9	76.8	41 57.7	25.1	77.6	42 10.1	26.4	78.5	42 21.6	27.6	79.4	42 32.2	28.8	80.3	42 41.8	30.1	81.2	42 50.5	31.3	82.1	42 58.3	32.5	83.0	33
34	42 08.3	23.0	75.5	42 22.8	24.4	76.4	42 36.5	25.6	77.3	42 49.2	26.9	78.2	43 01.0	28.1	79.1	43 11.9	29.3	80.0	43 21.8	30.6	81.0	43 30.8	31.8	81.9	34
35	42 31.3	+22.3	74.3	42 47.2	+23.5	75.2	43 02.1	+24.8	76.1	43 16.1	+26.0	77.0	43 29.1	+27.3	77.9	43 41.2	+28.6	78.8	43 52.4	+29.9	79.8	44 02.6	+31.0	80.7	35
36	42 53.6	21.4	73.0	43 10.7	22.7	73.9	43 26.9	23.9	74.8	43 42.1	25.3	75.7	43 56.4	26.5	76.7	44 09.8	27.8	77.6	44 22.2	29.0	78.6	44 33.6	30.3	79.5	36
37	43 15.0	20.5	71.7	43 33.4	21.8	72.6	43 50.8	23.1	73.5	44 07.4	24.3	74.5	44 22.9	25.7	75.4	44 37.6	26.9	76.4	44 51.2	28.3	77.3	45 03.9	29.5	78.3	37
38	43 35.5	19.7	70.4	43 55.2	20.9	71.3	44 13.9	22.2	72.3	44 31.7	23.6	73.2	44 48.6	24.8	74.1	45 04.5	26.1	75.1	45 19.5	27.4	76.1	45 33.4	28.7	77.1	38
39	43 55.2	18.7	69.1	44 16.1	20.0	70.0	44 36.1	21.4	71.0	44 55.3	22.6	71.9	45 13.4	24.0	72.9	45 30.6	25.3	73.8	45 46.9	26.6	74.8	46 02.1	27.8	75.8	39
40	44 13.9	+17.8	67.8	44 36.1	+19.2	68.7	44 57.5	+20.4	69.6	45 17.9		71.5	45 55.9	+24.3	72.5	46 13.4	+25.6	73.5	46 29.9	+27.0	74.5				40
41	44 31.7	16.9	66.5	44 55.3	18.1	67.4	45 17.9	19.5	68.3				46 20.2	23.4	71.2	46 39.0	24.8	72.2	46 56.9	26.0	73.2				41
42	44 48.6	15.9	65.1	45 13.4	17.2	66.0	45 37.4	18.5					46 22.5	22.5	69.9	47 03.8	23.8	70.9	47 22.9	25.2	71.9				42
43	45 04.5	15.0	63.8	45 30.6	16.3	64.7	45 55.9						46 45.0	21.5	68.5	47 27.6	22.8	69.5	47 48.1	24.1	70.5				43
44	45 19.5	13.9	62.4	45 46.9	15.2	63.3	46 13						47 06.5	20.5	67.1	47 50.4	21.8	68.1	48 12.2	23.2	69.2				44
45	45 33.4	+12.9	61.0	46 02.1	+14.2	61.9							47 26.9	+19.5	65.7	48 12.2	+20.8	66.8	48 35.4	+22.2	67.8				45
46	45 46.3	11.9	59.6	46 16.3	13.1	60.5							47 46.4	18.4	64.3	48 33.0	19.8	65.3	48 57.6	21.1	66.4				46
47	45 58.2	10.9	58.2	46 29.4	12.1	59.1							48 04.8	17.3	62.8	48 52.8	18.7	63.9	49 18.7	20.0	65.0				47
48	46 09.1	9.7	56.8	46 41.5	11.1	57.6							48 22.1	16.2	61.4	49 11.5	17.6	62.5	49 38.7	19.0	63.5				48
49	46 18.8	8.8	55.3	46 52.6	9.9								48 38.3	15.1	59.9	49 29.1	16.4	61.0	49 57.7	17.8	62.0				49
50	46 27.6	+7.6	53.9	47 02.5	+ 8.									+15.3	59.5	50 15.5	+16.7	60.5							50
51	46 35.2	6.5	52.5	47 11.4										14.2	58.0	50 32.2	15.4	59.0							51
52	46 41.7	5.5	51.0	47 19.1										12.9	56.5	50 47.6	14.3	57.5							52
53	46 47.2	4.3	49.6	47 25.8										11.5	55.0	51 01.9	13.0	56.0							53
54	46 51.5	3.3	48.1	47 31.											53.4	51 14.9	11.8	54.4							54
55	46 54.8	+2.1	46.6	47 3										51.9	51 26.7	+10.6	52.8							55
56	46 56.9	+1.0	45.2	47 3										50.3	51 37.3	9.2	51.3							56
57	46 57.9	−0.2	43.7	47										48.7	51 46.5	7.9	49.7							57
58	46 57.7	1.2	42.3	47									7.1	47.1	51 54.4	6.7	48.1							58
59	46 56.5	2.4	40.8	47									5.5	45.4	52 01.1	5.3	46.4							59
60	46 54.1	−3.5	39.3											.9	52 06.4	−3.9	44.8							60
61	46 50.6	4.6	37.9											.3	52 10.3	2.6	43.2							61
62	46 46.0	5.7	36.4											.4	52 12.9	1.3	41.6							62
63	46 40.3	6.8	35.0											.5	52 14.2	−0.1	39.9							63
64	46 33.5	7.9	33.5											.5	52 14.1	5	38.3							64
65	46 25.6	−9.0	32.1											.9	52 12.7	−2.8	36.7							65
66	46 16.6	10.0	30.6											.3	52 09.9	4.1	35.0							66
67	46 06.6	11.1	29.2											.7	52 05.8	5.5	33.4							67
68	45 55.5	12.1	27.8											.1	52 00.3	6.8	31.8							68
69	45 43.4	13.2	26.4	46										.6	51 53.5	8.1	30.2							69
70	45 30.2	−14.2	25.0	46										3.0	51 45.4	−9.4	28.6							70
71	45 16.0	15.1	23.6	46										4.3	51 36.0	10.7	27.0							71
72	45 00.9	16.2	22.2	45 4										24.9	51 25.3	12.0	25.4							72
73	44 44.7	17.1	20.9	45 4										23.4	51 13.3	13.2	23.8							73
74	44 27.6	18.0	19.5	45 24										21.8	51 00.1	14.4	22.3							74
75	44 09.6	−19.0	18.2	45 06.5										20.3	50 45.7	−15.6	20.8							75
76	43 50.6	19.8	16.9	44 48.0										18.8	50 30.1	16.9	19.2							76
77	43 30.8	20.8	15.6	44 28.5										17.4	50 13.2	17.9	17.7							77
78	43 10.0	21.6	14.3	44 08.1										15.9	49 55.3	19.1	16.2							78
79	42 48.4	22.4	13.0	43 46.8										14.5	49 36.2	20.2	14.8							79
80	42 26.0	−23.3	11.8	43 24.7	−23.0								17.6	−21.6	13.1	49 16.0	−21.2	13.3							80
81	42 02.7	24.0	10.5	43 01.7	23.8								56.0	22.1	11.7	48 54.8	22.3	11.9							81
82	41 38.7	24.9	9.3	42 37.9	24.7								47 33.4	23.5	10.3	48 32.5	23.3	10.5							82
83	41 13.8	25.6	8.1	42 13.2	25.4	8.2							47 09.9	24.5	8.9	48 09.2	24.3	9.1							83
84	40 48.2	26.3	6.9	41 47.8	26.2	7.0							46 45.4	25.4	7.6	47 44.9	25.3	7.7							84
85	40 21.9	−27.0	5.7	41 21.6	−26.9	5.8	42 21.						46 20.0	−26.3	6.3	47 19.6	−26.2	6.4							85
86	39 54.9	27.7	4.5	40 54.7	27.7	4.6	41 54.5						45 53.7	27.2	5.0	46 53.4	27.1	5.1							86
87	39 27.2	28.5	3.4	40 27.0	28.3	3.4	41 26.9	28.2					45 26.5	28.1	3.7	46 26.3	27.9	3.8							87
88	38 58.7	29.0	2.2	39 58.7	29.0	2.3	40 58.7	29.0					44 58.4	28.8	2.4	45 58.4	28.8	2.5							88
89	38 29.7	29.7	1.1	39 29.7	29.7	1.1	40 29.7	29.7	1.1	41			43 29.6	29.6	1.2	44 29.6	29.6	1.2							89
90	38 00.0	−30.3	0.0	39 00.0	−30.3	0.0	40 00.0	−30.3	0.0	41 00.0	−30.3	0.0	42 00.0	−30.3	0.0	43 00.0	−30.4	0.0	44 00.0	−30.4	0.0	45 00.0	−30.4	0.0	90

60°, 300° L.H.A.   LATITUDE **SAME** NAME AS DECLINATION

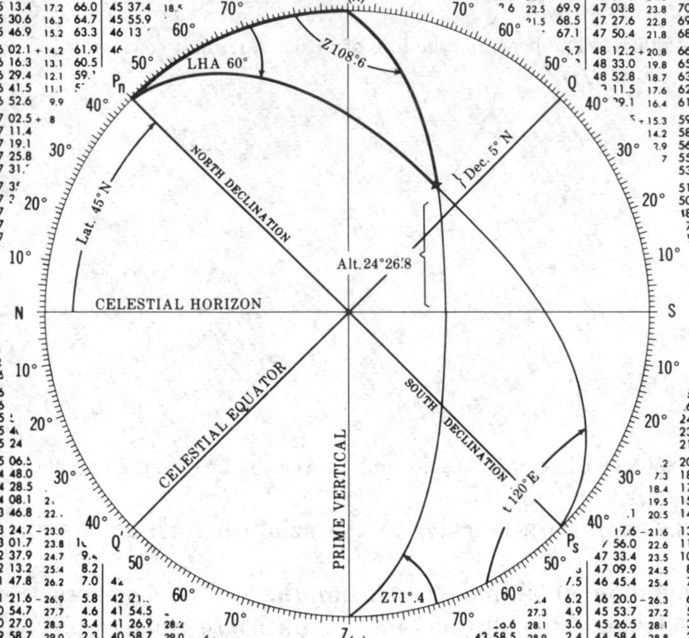

| 38° | 39° | 40° | 41° | 42° | 43° | 44° | 45° |

FIGURE 2007a.—Left-hand page of opening of volume 3 of Pub. No. 229.

LATITUDE CONTRARY NAME TO DECLINATION   L.H.A. 60°, 300°

Dec.	38° Hc	d	Z	39° Hc	d	Z	40° Hc	d	Z	41° Hc	d	Z	42° Hc	d	Z	43° Hc	d	Z	44° Hc	d	Z	45° Hc	d	Z	Dec.
0	23 12.2	−40.3	109.6	22 51.9	−41.1	110.0	22 31.3	−41.9	110.4	22 10.2	−42.6	110.7	21 48.8	−43.4	111.1	21 27.0	−44.1	111.5	21 04.8	−44.8	111.9	20 42.3	−45.5	112.2	0
1	22 31.9	40.5	110.4	22 10.8	41.3	110.8	21 49.4	42.1	111.1	21 27.6	42.8	111.5	21 05.4	43.5	111.9	20 42.9	44.2	112.2	20 20.0	44.9	112.6	19 56.8	45.6	112.9	1
2	21 51.4	40.8	111.2	21 29.5	41.5	111.5	21 07.3	42.4	111.9	20 44.8	43.0	112.3	20 21.9	43.7	112.6	19 58.7	44.5	112.9	19 35.1	45.1	113.3	19 11.2	45.7	113.6	2
3	21 10.6	41.0	112.0	20 48.0	41.8	112.3	20 25.0	42.4	112.7	20 01.8	43.2	113.0	19 38.2	43.9	113.3	19 14.2	44.5	113.7	18 50.0	45.2	114.0	18 25.5	45.9	114.3	3
4	20 29.6	41.2	112.7	20 06.2	41.9	113.1	19 42.6	42.7	113.4	19 18.6	43.4	113.7	18 54.3	44.1	114.1	18 29.7	44.8	114.4	18 04.8	45.4	114.8	17 39.6	46.0	115.0	4
5	19 48.4	−41.4	113.5	19 24.3	−42.1	113.8	18 59.9	−42.8	114.2	18 35.2	−43.5	114.5	18 10.2	−44.2	114.8	17 44.9	−44.9	115.1	17 19.4	−45.6	115.3	16 53.6	−46.2	115.6	5
6	19 07.0	41.6	114.3	18 42.2	42.3	114.6	18 17.1	43.0	114.9	17 51.7	43.7	115.2	17 26.0	44.4	115.5	17 00.0	45.0	115.8	16 33.8	45.6	116.0	16 07.4	46.3	116.3	6
7	18 25.4	41.8	115.0	17 59.9	42.5	115.3	17 34.1	43.0	115.6	17 08.0	43.9	115.9	16 41.6	44.5	116.2	16 15.0	45.1	116.4	15 48.2	45.8	116.7	15 21.1	46.4	117.0	7
8	17 43.6	41.9	115.8	17 17.4	42.6	116.1	16 50.9	43.3	116.4	16 24.1	44.0	116.6	15 57.1	44.6	116.9	15 29.9	45.3	117.1	15 02.4	45.9	117.3	14 34.7	46.5	117.6	8
9	17 01.7	42.1	116.5	16 34.8	42.8	116.8	16 07.6	43.5	117.1	15 40.1	44.1	117.3	15 12.5	44.8	117.6	14 44.6	45.4	117.8	14 16.5	46.0	118.0	13 48.2	46.6	118.3	9
10	16 19.6	−42.3	117.3	15 52.0	−43.0	117.5	15 24.1	−43.6	117.8	14 56.0	−44.2	118.0	14 27.7	−44.9	118.3	13 59.2	−45.5	118.5	13 30.5	−46.1	118.7	13 01.6	−46.7	118.9	10
11	15 37.3	42.4	118.0	15 09.0	43.1	118.3	14 40.5	43.7	118.5	14 11.8	44.4	118.7	13 42.8	45.0	118.9	13 13.7	45.6	119.2	12 44.4	46.3	119.4	12 14.9	46.9	119.6	11
12	14 54.9	42.5	118.8	14 25.9	43.2	119.0	13 56.8	43.9	119.2	13 27.4	44.5	119.4	12 57.8	45.1	119.6	12 28.1	45.7	119.8	11 58.1	46.3	120.0	11 28.0	46.8	120.2	12
13	14 12.4	42.7	119.5	13 42.7	43.3	119.7	13 12.9	44.0	119.9	12 42.9	44.6	120.1	12 12.7	45.2	120.3	11 42.4	45.8	120.5	11 11.8	46.4	120.7	10 41.2	47.0	120.8	13
14	13 29.7	42.8	120.2	12 59.4	43.4	120.4	12 28.9	44.0	120.6	11 58.3	44.7	120.8	11 27.5	45.3	121.0	10 56.6	45.9	121.1	10 25.4	46.4	121.3	9 54.2	47.0	121.5	14
15	12 46.9	−42.9	120.9	12 16.0	−43.6	121.1	11 44.9	−44.2	121.3	11 13.6	−44.5	121.3	10 42.2	−45.4	121.6	10 10.7	−46.0	121.8	9 39.0	−46.6	121.9	9 07.2	−47.1	122.1	15
16	12 04.0	43.1	121.6	11 32.4	43.6	121.8	11 00.7	44.3	122.0	10 28.8	44.8	122.2	9 56.8	45.3	122.3	9 24.7	46.0	122.5	8 52.4	46.6	122.6	8 20.1	47.2	122.7	16
17	11 20.9	43.1	122.4	10 48.8	43.8	122.5	10 16.4	44.3	122.7	9 44.0	44.8	122.8	9 11.4	45.6	123.0	8 38.7	46.1	123.1	8 05.8	46.6	123.2	7 32.9	47.2	123.3	17
18	10 37.8	43.2	123.1	10 05.0	43.8	123.2	9 32.1	44.5	123.4	8 59.0	45.0	123.5	8 25.8	45.6	123.6	7 52.6	46.2	123.7	7 19.2	46.7	123.9	6 45.7	47.3	124.0	18
19	9 54.6	43.3	123.8	9 21.2	43.9	123.9	8 47.6	44.5	124.0	8 14.0	45.1	124.2	7 40.2	45.6	124.3	7 06.4	46.2	124.4	6 32.5	46.8	124.5	5 58.4	47.2	124.6	19
20	9 11.3	−43.4	124.5	8 37.3	−44.0	124.6	8 03.1	−44.4	124.7	7 28.9	−45.1	124.8	6 54.6	−45.7	124.9	6 20.2	−46.3	125.0	5 45.7	−46.8	125.1	5 11.2	−47.4	125.2	20
21	8 27.9	43.5	125.2	7 53.3	44.1	125.3	7 18.6	44.7	125.3	6 43.8	45.2	125.5	6 08.9	45.8	125.6	5 33.9	46.3	125.7	4 58.9	46.8	125.8	4 23.8	47.3	125.8	21
22	7 44.4	43.5	125.9	7 09.2	44.1	126.0	6 33.9	44.7	126.1	5 58.6	45.3	126.2	5 23.1	45.8	126.2	4 47.6	46.3	126.3	4 12.1	46.9	126.4	3 36.5	47.4	126.4	22
23	7 00.9	43.6	126.6	6 25.1	44.2	126.7	5 49.2	44.7	126.7	5 13.3	45.3	126.8	4 37.3	45.8	126.9	4 01.3	46.4	127.0	3 25.2	46.9	127.0	2 49.1	47.4	127.0	23
24	6 17.3	43.7	127.3	5 40.9	44.2	127.3	5 04.5	44.8	127.4	4 28.0	45.3	127.5	3 51.5	45.9	127.5	3 14.9	46.4	127.6	2 38.3	46.9	127.6	2 01.7	47.5	127.7	24
25	5 33.6	−43.7	127.9	4 56.7	−44.2	128.0	4 19.7	−44.8	128.1	3 42.7	−45.3	128.1	3 05.6	−45.9	128.2	2 28.5	−46.4	128.2	1 51.4	−46.9	128.3	1 14.2	−47.4	128.3	25
26	4 49.9	43.8	128.6	4 12.5	44.3	128.7	3 34.9	44.8	128.7	2 57.4	45.4	128.8	2 19.7	45.9	128.8	1 42.1	46.4	128.9	1 04.5	47.0	128.9	0 26.8	−47.4	128.9	26
27	4 06.2	43.8	129.3	3 28.2	44.4	129.4	2 50.1	44.9	129.4	2 12.0	45.4	129.4	1 33.8	45.9	129.5	0 55.7	46.4	129.5	0 17.5	−46.9	129.5	0 20.6	+47.5	50.5	27
28	3 22.4	43.8	130.0	2 43.8	44.3	130.0	2 05.2	44.9	130.1	1 26.6	45.4	130.1	0 47.9	45.9	130.1	0 09.3	−46.5	130.1	C—S Line			1 08.1	47.4	49.9	28
29	2 38.6	43.8	130.7	1 59.5	44.4	130.7	1 20.3	44.8	130.7	0 41.2	45.4	130.8	0 02.0	−45.9	130.8	0 37.2	+46.4	(Contrary—Same Line)		1 55.5	47.4	49.3	29
30	1 54.8	−43.8	131.4	1 15.1	−44.3	131.4	0 35.5	−44.9	131.4	0 04.2	+45.4	48.6	0 43.9	+45.4	48.6	1 23.6	+46.4	47.4	2 03.3	+46.9	47.4	2 42.9	+47.4	48.7	30
31	1 11.0	43.9	132.1	0 30.8	−44.3	132.1	0 09.4	+44.9	47.9	0 49.6	45.4	47.9	1 29.8	45.9	48.0	2 10.0	46.4	48.0	2 50.2	46.9	48.0	3 30.3	47.4	48.0	31
32	0 27.1	−43.9	132.7	0 13.6	+44.4	47.3	0 54.3	44.9	47.3	1 35.0	45.4	47.3	2 15.7	45.9	47.3	2 56.4	46.3	47.3	3 37.1	46.8	47.4	4 17.7	47.3	47.4	32
33	0 16.8	+43.8	46.6	0 58.0	44.4	46.6	1 39.2	44.6	46.6	2 20.4	45.4	46.6	3 01.6	45.9	46.7	3 42.8	46.3	46.7	4 23.9	46.8	46.8	5 05.0	47.3	46.8	33
34	1 00.6	43.8	45.9	1 42.4	44.3	45.9	2 24.1	44.8	45.9	3 05.8	45.4	46.0	3 47.5	45.8	46.0	4 29.1	46.3	46.1	5 10.7	46.8	46.1	5 52.3	47.3	46.2	34
35	1 44.4	+43.9	45.2	2 26.7	+44.3	45.2	3 08.9	+44.9	45.3	3 51.2	+45.3	45.3	4 33.3	+45.8	45.4	5 15.5	+46.2	45.4	5 57.5	+46.8	45.5	6 39.6	+47.2	45.6	35
36	2 28.3	43.8	44.5	3 11.0	44.3	44.6	3 53.8	44.8	44.6	4 36.5	45.3	44.7	5 19.1	45.6	44.7	6 01.7	46.3	44.8	6 44.3	46.7	44.9	7 26.8	47.1	45.0	36
37	3 12.1	43.8	43.8	3 55.3	44.3	43.8	4 38.6	44.7	44.0	5 21.8	45.2	44.0	6 04.9	45.7	44.1	6 48.0	46.1	44.1	7 31.0	46.6	44.2	8 13.9	47.1	44.3	37
38	3 55.9	43.7	43.2	4 39.6	44.3	43.2	5 23.3	44.7	43.3	6 07.0	45.2	43.3	6 50.6	45.7	43.4	7 34.1	46.2	43.5	8 17.6	46.6	43.6	9 01.0	47.1	43.7	38
39	4 39.6	43.7	42.5	5 23.9	44.1	42.5	6 08.0	44.4	42.7	6 52.2	45.1	42.7	7 36.3	45.6	42.8	8 20.2	46.0	42.8	9 04.2	46.5	43.0	9 48.1	47.0	43.1	39
40	5 23.3	+43.7	41.8	6 08.0	+44.2	41.9	6 52.7	+44.6	41.9	7 37			8 2			9 06.3	+46.0	42.2	9 50.7	+46.5	42.3	10 35.1	+46.9	42.4	40
41	6 07.0	43.6	41.1	6 52.2	44.1	41.2	7 37.3	44.5	41.9							9 52.3	46.0	41.7	10 37.2	46.4	41.7	11 22.0	46.8	41.8	41
42	6 50.6	43.5	40.4	7 36.3	44.0	40.5	8 21.9	44.4									45.8	40.9	11 23.6	46.2	41.0	12 08.8	46.7	41.2	42
43	7 34.1	43.4	39.7	8 20.3	43.9	39.8	9 06.3										45.7	39.6	12 09.8	46.2	40.4	12 55.5	46.6	40.5	43
44	8 17.6	43.4	39.0	9 04.2	43.9	39.1	9 50									12 56.0	46.1	39.7	12 56.0	46.1	39.7	13 42.1	46.6	39.9	44
45	9 01.0	+43.4	38.3	9 48.1	+43.8	38.4											45.9	39.1	14 28.0	45.9	39.1	14 28.7	46.4	39.1	45
46	9 44.4	43.2	37.6	10 31.9	43.7	37.7										15 11.5	45.9	38.6	15 15.1	46.3	38.6	15 15.1	46.3	38.6	46
47	10 27.6	43.2	36.9	11 15.6	43.6	37.0										15 57.7	45.7	37.9	16 01.4	46.2	37.9	16 01.4	46.2	37.9	47
48	11 10.8	43.0	36.2	11 59.2	43.4	36.2											45.5	37.3	16 47.6	46.0	37.3	16 47.6	46.0	37.3	48
49	11 53.8	43.0	35.5	12 42.6	43.4											36.4		17 33.6	45.9	36.6	17 33.6	45.9	36.6	49
50	12 36.8	+42.8	34.8	13 26.0	+43												35.0		18 19.5	+45.8	35.9	18 19.5	+45.8	35.9	50
51	13 19.6	42.7	34.1	14 09.3													34.3		19 05.3	45.6	35.2	19 05.3	45.6	35.2	51
52	14 02.3	42.6	33.3	14 52.4													33.6		19 50.9	45.5	34.5	19 50.9	45.5	34.5	52
53	14 44.9	42.4	32.6	15 35.4													33.8		20 36.4	45.3	33.8	20 36.4	45.3	33.8	53
54	15 27.3	42.3	31.9	16 18.1													33.1		21 21.7	45.1	33.1	21 21.7	45.1	33.1	54
55	16 09.6	+42.2	31.1	17 00												32.2		22 06.8	+44.9	32.4	22 06.8	+44.9	32.4	55
56	16 51.8	42.0	30.4	17 42												31.5		22 51.7	44.8	31.7	22 51.7	44.8	31.7	56
57	17 33.8	41.8	29.7	18												30.8		23 36.5	44.5	31.0	23 36.5	44.5	31.0	57
58	18 15.6	41.6	28.9	19												30.0		24 21.0	44.3	30.2	24 21.0	44.3	30.2	58
59	18 57.2	41.4	28.1	19												29.3		25 05.3	44.1	29.5	25 05.3	44.1	29.5	59
60	19 38.6	+41.3	27.4	2												28.5		25 49.4	+43.8	28.8	25 49.4	+43.8	28.8	60
61	20 19.9	41.0	26.6	2												27.0		26 33.2	43.7	28.0	26 33.2	43.7	28.0	61
62	21 00.9	40.9	25.8	2														27 16.9	43.2	27.2	27 16.9	43.2	27.2	62
63	21 41.8	40.6	25.0	2														28 00.2	43.1	26.4	28 00.2	43.1	26.4	63
64	22 22.4	40.3	24.2	2														28 43.3	42.8	25.7	28 43.3	42.8	25.7	64
65	23 02.7	+40.2	23.4	N														29 26.1	+42.5	24.9	29 26.1	+42.5	24.9	65
66	23 42.9	39.8	22.6	2														30 08.6	42.2	24.0	30 08.6	42.2	24.0	66
67	24 22.7	39.6	21.8	2														30 50.8	41.9	23.2	30 50.8	41.9	23.2	67
68	25 02.3	39.4	21.0	2														31 32.7	41.6	22.4	31 32.7	41.6	22.4	68
69	25 41.7	39.0	20.1	2														32 14.3	41.2	21.5	32 14.3	41.2	21.5	69
70	26 20.7	+38.7	19.3	27														32 55.5	+40.9	20.7	32 55.5	+40.9	20.7	70
71	26 59.4	38.5	18.4	27														33 36.4	40.4	19.8	33 36.4	40.4	19.8	71
72	27 37.9	38.1	17.6	28														34 16.8	40.1	18.9	34 16.8	40.1	18.9	72
73	28 16.0	37.7	16.7	28														34 56.9	39.7	18.0	34 56.9	39.7	18.0	73
74	28 53.7	37.4	15.8	29														35 36.6	39.2	17.1	35 36.6	39.2	17.1	74
75	29 31.1	+37.1	14.9	30 29														36 15.8	+38.8	16.1	36 15.8	+38.8	16.1	75
76	30 08.2	36.6	14.0	31 06.4														36 54.6	38.4	15.2	36 54.6	38.4	15.2	76
77	30 44.8	36.3	13.1	31 43.3												37 33.0	37.9	14.2	37 33.0	37.9	14.2	37 33.0	37.9	14.2	77
78	31 21.1	35.9	12.2	32 19.7												38 10.9	37.3	13.2	38 10.9	37.3	13.2	38 10.9	37.3	13.2	78
79	31 57.0	35.3	11.2	32 55.8												38 48.2	37.0	12.3	38 48.2	37.0	12.3	38 48.2	37.0	12.3	79
80	32 32.4	+35.0	10.3	33 31.4	+35.2											39 25.1	+36.3	11.2	39 25.1	+36.3	11.2	39 25.1	+36.3	11.2	80
81	33 07.4	34.6	9.3	34 06.6	34.7											40 01.4	35.7	10.2	40 01.4	35.7	10.2	40 01.4	35.7	10.2	81
82	33 42.0	34.0	8.3	34 41.3	34.2											40 37.1	35.2	9.1	40 37.1	35.2	9.1	40 37.1	35.2	9.1	82
83	34 16.0	33.6	7.3	35 15.5	33.8	7.4										41 12.3	34.5	8.1	40 12.9	34.4	7.9	41 12.3	34.5	8.1	83
84	34 49.6	33.1	6.3	35 49.3	33.2	6.4										40 47.3	33.7	6.9	40 47.3	33.7	6.9	41 46.8	33.9	7.0	84
85	35 22.7	+32.6	5.3	36 22.5	+32.6	5.4	37								60	41 21.0	+33.2	5.8	42 20.7	+33.3	5.9	42 20.7	+33.3	5.9	85
86	35 55.3	32.0	4.3	36 55.1	32.1	4.3	37 55.							32.4	4.6	41 54.2	32.5	4.7	42 54.0	32.6	4.7	42 54.0	32.6	4.7	86
87	36 27.3	31.5	3.2	37 27.2	31.6	3.3	38 58.7	31.0						31.8	3.5	42 26.7	31.8	3.5	43 26.6	31.9	3.6	43 26.6	31.9	3.6	87
88	36 58.8	30.9	2.2	37 58.8	30.9	2.2	38 58.7	31.0			58.6	31.0	2.3			42 58.5	31.1	2.4	43 58.5	31.1	2.4	43 58.5	31.1	2.4	88
89	37 29.7	30.3	1.1	38 29.7	30.3	1.1	39 29.7	30.3	1.1		42 29.6	30.4	1.2			43 29.6	30.4	1.2	44 29.6	30.4	1.2	44 29.6	30.4	1.2	89
90	38 00.0	+29.7	0.0	39 00.0	+29.7	0.0	40 00.0	+29.7	0.0	41 00.0	+...		43 00.0	+29.6	0.0	43 00.0	+29.6	0.0	44 00.0	+29.6	0.0	45 00.0	+29.6	0.0	90
	38°			39°			40°			41°			42°			43°			44°			45°			

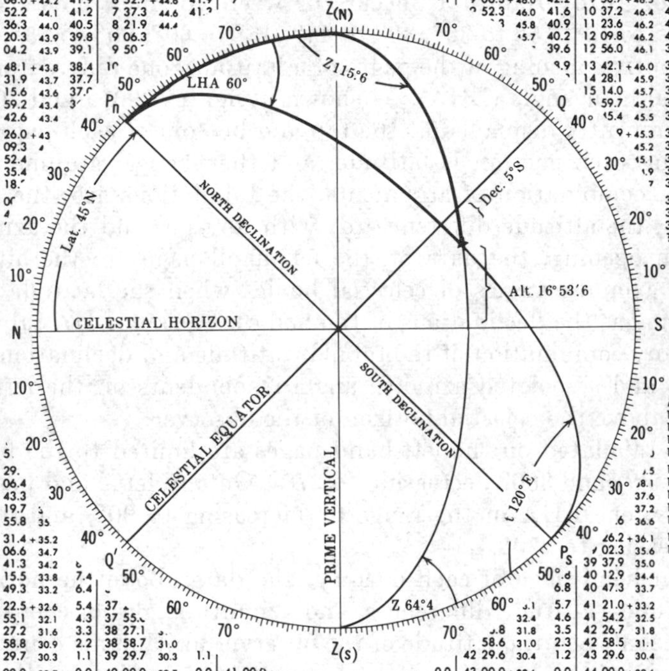

S. Lat. { L.H.A. greater than 180°......Zn=180°−Z
         { L.H.A. less than 180°............Zn=180°+Z

LATITUDE SAME NAME AS DECLINATION   L.H.A. 120°, 240°

FIGURE 2007b.—Right-hand page of opening of volume 3 of Pub. No. 229.

The principal inspection tables are Pub. No. 229, *Sight Reduction Tables for Marine Navigation;* Pub. No. 249, *Sight Reduction Tables for Air Navigation;* and Pub. No. 214, *Tables of Computed Altitude and Azimuth.*

2007. ***Sight Reduction Tables for Marine Navigation*** (**Pub. No. 229**).—These tables are published by the Defense Mapping Agency Hydrographic Center to facilitate the practice of celestial navigation at sea. A secondary purpose of the tables is to provide, within the limitations of the tabular precision and interval, a table of the solutions of the spherical triangle of which two sides and the included angle are known and it is necessary to find the values of the third side and adjacent angle.

The tables have been designed primarily for use with the Marcq St.-Hilaire or intercept method of sight reduction, utilizing a position assumed or chosen so that interpolation for latitude and local hour angle is not required. For entering arguments of integral degrees of latitude, declination, and local hour angle, altitudes and their differences are tabulated to the nearest tenth of a minute, azimuth angles to the nearest tenth of a degree. But the tables are designed for precise interpolation of altitude for declination only by means of interpolation tables which facilitate linear interpolation and provide additionally for the effect of second differences (art. 2008). The data are applicable to the solutions of sights of all celestial bodies; there are no limiting values of altitude, latitude, hour angle, or declination.

The tables are divided into six volumes, each of which includes two eight-degree zones of latitude. An overlap of 1° occurs between volumes. The six volumes cover latitude bands 0° to 15°, 15° to 30°, 30° to 45°, 45° to 60°, 60° to 75°, and 75° to 90°.

Each consecutive opening of the pages of a latitude zone differs from the preceding one by 1° of local hour angle (LHA). As shown in figures 2007a and 2007b, the values of LHA are prominently displayed at the top and bottom of each page; the horizontal argument heading each column is latitude, and the vertical argument is declination (Dec.). For each combination of arguments, the tabulations are: the tabular altitude (ht or Tab. Hc), the altitude difference (d) with its sign, and the azimuth angle (Z).

Within each opening, the data on the left-hand page are the altitudes, altitude differences, and azimuth angles of celestial bodies when the latitude of the observer has the same name as the declinations of the bodies. For any LHA tabulated on a left-hand page and any combination of the tabular latitude and declination arguments, the tabular altitude and associated azimuth angle respondents on the left-hand page are those of a body above the celestial horizon of the observer.

The LHA's tabulated on the left-hand pages are limited to the following ranges: 0° increasing to 90°, and 360° decreasing to 270°. On any left-hand page there are two tabulated LHA's, one LHA in the range 0° increasing to 90°, and the second in the range 360° decreasing to 270°.

On the right-hand page of each opening, the data above the horizontal rules are the tabular altitudes, altitude differences, and azimuth angles of celestial bodies above the celestial horizon when the latitude of the observer has a name contrary to the name of the declinations of the bodies and the LHA's of the bodies are those tabulated at the top of the page. The data below the horizontal rules are the tabular altitudes, altitude differences, and azimuth angles of celestial bodies above the celestial horizon when the latitude of the observer has the same name as the declinations of the bodies, and the LHA's of the bodies are those tabulated at the bottom of the page.

The LHA's tabulated at the top of a right-hand page are the same as those tabulated on the left-hand page of the opening. The LHA's tabulated at the bottom of the right-hand page are limited to the range 90° increasing to 270°, one of the two LHA's at the bottom of the page is in the range 90° increasing to 180°; the other LHA is in the range 180° increasing to 270°; the LHA in the range 90° increasing to 180° is the supplement of the LHA at the top of the page in the range 0° increasing to 90°. When the LHA is 90°, the left and right-hand pages are identical.

The horizontal rules, known as the **Contrary-Same Line** or **C–S Line,** indicate the degree of declination in which the celestial horizon occurs.

Figure 2007c illustrates four of the eight possible celestial triangles for specific numerical values of latitude and declination, and the LHA's tabulated on the left and right-hand pages of an opening of the tables (figs. 2007a and 2007b). The diagram on the plane of the celestial meridian at the upper left of figure 2007c indicates that the celestial body always lies above the celestial horizon when the observer's latitude has the same name as the declination of the body and the values of LHA are those tabulated on the left-hand page of an opening of the tables. The diagram at the upper right reveals that for the various combinations of arguments on the right-hand page, including whether the name of the observer's latitude is the same as or contrary to the name of the declination, the numerical value of the declination governs whether the body is above or below the celestial horizon. For example, the following arguments are used for entering the tables:

> LHA   60°
> Latitude   45°N (Contrary Name to Declination)
> Declination 5°S

The respondents are:

> Tabular altitude,   ht (Tab. Hc) 16°53′6
> Altitude difference, d   (−)46′2
> Azimuth angle,   Z   115°6

As can be verified by an inspection of the upper-right diagram, the altitude respondent is for a body 16°53′6 above the celestial horizon. Further inspection of the tabular data (fig. 2007b) and the diagram reveals that with the LHA and latitude (Contrary Name) remaining constant, the altitude of the body decreases as the declination increases in numerical value. Between values of declination 26° and 27° the body crosses the celestial horizon. When the declination reaches 35°, the altitude is 6°39′6 below the celestial horizon; the tabular azimuth angle is the supplement of the actual azimuth angle of 134°4.

As an additional example, the following arguments are used for entering the tables:

> LHA   240°   (t 120°E)
> Latitude   45°S (Same Name as Declination)
> Declination 5°S

The respondents are:

> Tabular altitude,   ht (Tab. Hc) 16°53′6
> Altitude difference, d   (−)46′2
> Azimuth angle,   Z   115°6

However, inspection of the diagram on the plane of the celestial meridian at the lower right of figure 2007c reveals that the altitude is 16°53′6 *below* the celestial horizon; the tabular azimuth angle is the *supplement* of the actual azimuth angle of 64°4. Further inspection of the tabular data and the diagram reveals that with the LHA and latitude (Same Name) remaining constant, the altitude of the body increases as the

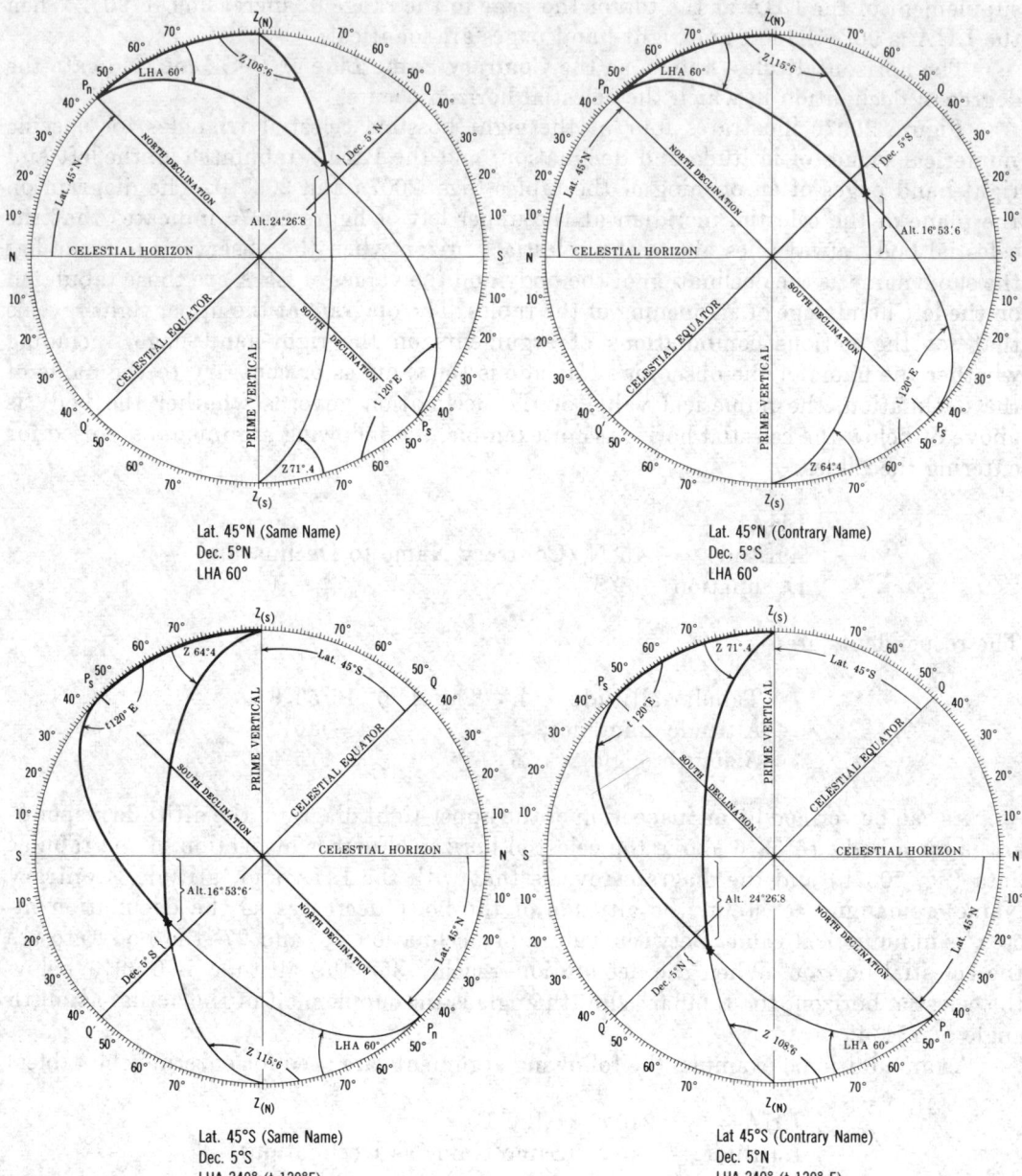

Lat. 45°N (Same Name)
Dec. 5°N
LHA 60°

Lat. 45°N (Contrary Name)
Dec. 5°S
LHA 60°

Lat. 45°S (Same Name)
Dec. 5°S
LHA 240° (t 120°E)

Lat 45°S (Contrary Name)
Dec. 5°N
LHA 240° (t 120° E)

FIGURE 2007c.—Diagrams on the plane of the celestial meridian.

declination increases numerically. Between values of declination of 26° and 27° the body crosses the celestial horizon. When the declination reaches 35°, the altitude is 6°39ʹ6 above the celestial horizon; the tabular azimuth angle is the actual azimuth angle of 45°6.

Inspection of figures 2007a, 2007b, and 2007c reveals that if the left-hand page of an opening of the tables is entered with latitude of contrary name and one of the LHA's tabulated at the bottom of the facing page, the tabular altitudes are negative; the tabular azimuth angles are the supplements of the actual azimuth angles.

2008. Pub. No. 229 interpolation.—In the normal use of the tables with the Marcq St.-Hilaire method, it is only necessary to interpolate the tabular altitude and azimuth angle for the excess of the actual declination of the celestial body over the integral declination argument. When the tabular altitude is less than 60°, the required interpolation can always be effected through the use of the tabulated altitude differences. When the tabular altitude is in excess of 60°, it may be necessary to include the effects of second diffcrences. When the tabular altitude difference is printed in italic type followed by a small dot, the effects of the second differences should be included in the interpolation. Although the effects of second differences may not be required, these effects can always be included in the interpolation whenever it is desired to obtain greater accuracy.

If the sight reduction is from a position such that interpolation for latitude and local hour angle increments is necessary, the required additional interpolation of the altitude can be effected by graphical means.

The data in the column for latitude 45° (Same Name as Declination) as contained in figure 2007a is rearranged in table 2008 to illustrate the first and second differences.

Table 2008 illustrates that the **first differences** are the differences between successive altitudes in a latitude column; the **second differences** are the differences between successive first differences.

LHA 60°, Lat. 45° (Same Name as Declination)

Dec.	ht (Tab. Hc)	First Difference	Second Difference
4°	23°42′3		
		+44′5	
5°	24°26′8		−0′2
		+44′3	
6°	25°11′1		−0′3
		+44′0	
7°	25°55′1		

TABLE 2008.—First and second differences of tabular altitudes.

The usual case is that the change of altitude with 60′ increase in declination is nearly linear as illustrated in figure 2008. In this case, the required interpolation can be effected by multiplying the altitude difference (a first difference) by the excess of the actual declination over the integral declination argument divided by 60′. This excess of declination in minutes and tenths of minutes of arc is referred to as the **declination increment** and is abbreviated **Dec. Inc.**

Using the data of table 2008, the computed altitude when the LHA is 60°, the latitude (Same Name) is 45°, and the declination is 5°45′5 is determined as follows:

$$\text{Correction} = \text{Altitude difference} \times \frac{\text{Dec. Inc.}}{60'} = (+)44'3 \times \frac{45'5}{60'} = 33'6$$
$$\text{Hc} = \text{ht} + \text{correction} = 24°26'8 + 33'6 = 25°00'4.$$

2009. Pub. No. 229 Interpolation Table.—The main part of the four-page Interpolation Table is basically a multiplication table providing tabulations of:

$$\text{Altitude Difference} \times \frac{\text{Declination Increment}}{60'}.$$

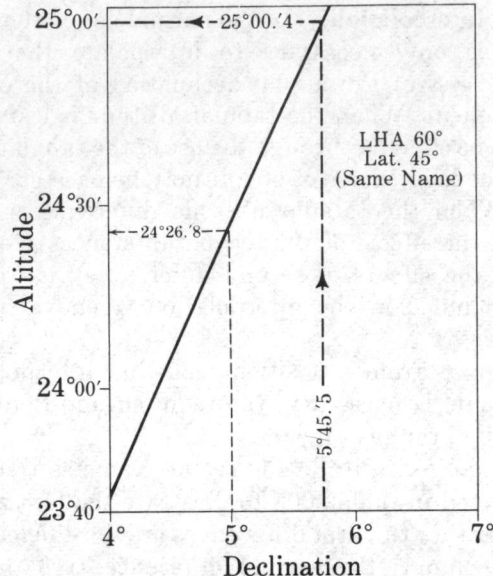

FIGURE 2008.—Linear interpolation by graph.

The design of the Interpolation Table is such that the desired product must be derived from component parts of the altitude difference. The first part is a multiple of 10′ (10′, 20′, 30′, 40′, or 50′) of the altitude difference; the second part is the remainder in the range 0′.0 to 9′.9. For example, the component parts of altitude difference 44′.3 are 40′ and 4′.3.

In the use of the first part of the altitude difference, the Interpolation Table arguments are Dec. Inc. and the integral multiple of 10′ in the altitude difference, d. As shown in figure 2009a, the respondent is:

$$\text{Tens} \times \frac{\text{Dec. Inc.}}{60'}.$$

In the use of the second part of the altitude difference, the Interpolation Table arguments are the nearest Dec. Inc. ending in 0′.5 and Units and Decimals. The respondent is:

$$\text{Units and Decimals} \times \frac{\text{Dec. Inc.}}{60'}.$$

In computing the table, the values in the Tens part of the multiplication table were modified by small quantities varying from −0′.042 to +0′.033 before rounding to the tabular precision to compensate for any difference between the actual Dec. Inc. and the nearest Dec. Inc. ending in 0′.5 when using the Units and Decimals part of the table.

As an example of the use of the Interpolation Table, the computed altitude and true azimuth are determined for Lat. 45°N, LHA 60°, and Dec. 5°45′.5N. Data are exhibited in figure 2009b.

The respondents for the entering arguments (Lat. 45° Same Name as Declination, LHA 60°, and Dec. 5°) are:

Tabular altitude,	ht	24°26′.8
Altitude difference,	d	(+)44′.3
Tabular azimuth angle,	Z	108°.6

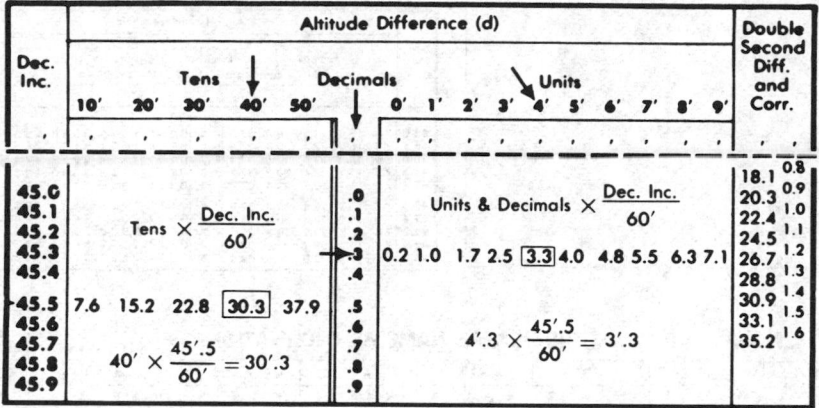

FIGURE 2009a.—Interpolation Table.

Note that Dec. Inc. 45ʹ5 is the vertical argument for entering the Interpolation Table to extract the correction for tens of minutes of altitude difference, d, and that it also indicates the subtable where the correction for minutes and tenths of minutes (Units and Decimals) of altitude difference, d, is found. Entering the Interpolation Table with Dec. Inc. 45ʹ5 as the vertical argument, the correction for 40ʹ of the altitude difference is 30ʹ3; the correction for 4ʹ3 of the altitude difference is 3ʹ3. Adding the two parts, the correction is (+)33ʹ6, the sign of the correction being in accordance with the sign of the altitude difference, d.

No special table is provided for interpolation of the azimuth angle, and the differences are not tabulated. With latitude and local hour angle constant, the successive azimuth angle differences corresponding to 1° increase in declination are less than 10°0 for altitudes less than 84°, and can easily be found by inspection. If formal interpolation of azimuth angle is desired, the degrees and tenths of degrees of azimuth angle difference are treated as minutes and tenths of minutes in obtaining the required correction from the Units and Decimals subtable to the right of the declination increment. But for most practical applications, interpolation by inspection usually suffices. In this example of formal interpolation, using an azimuth angle difference of −0°7 and a Dec. Inc. of 45ʹ5, the correction as extracted from the Units and Decimals subtable to the right of the Dec. Inc. is −0°5. Therefore, the azimuth angle as interpolated for declination increment is 108°1 (108°6−0°5). In summary,

Tabular altitude	ht	24°26ʹ8
Correction for 40ʹ of alt. diff.		(+)30ʹ3
Correction for 4ʹ3 of alt. diff		(+)3ʹ3
Computed altitude	Hc	25°00ʹ4

(See figures 2008 and 2009b)

Tabular azimuth angle	Z	108°6
Correction for Dec. Inc. 45ʹ5		(−)0°5
Interpolated azimuth angle	Z	N108°1W
True azimuth	Zn	251°9

INTERPOLATION TABLE

Dec. Inc.	Altitude Difference (d)																Double Second Diff. and Corr.
	Tens					Decimals	Units										
	10'	20'	30'	40'	50'		0'	1'	2'	3'	4'	5'	6'	7'	8'	9'	
45.0	7.5	15.0	22.5	30.0	37.5	.0	0.0 0.8	1.5 2.3	3.0 3.8	4.5 5.3	6.1 6.8						18.1 08
45.1	7.5	15.0	22.5	30.0	37.6	.1	0.1 0.8	1.6 2.4	3.1 3.9	4.6 5.4	6.1 6.9						20.3 09
45.2	7.5	15.0	22.6	30.1	37.6	.2	0.2 0.9	1.7 2.4	3.2 3.9	4.7 5.5	6.2 7.0						22.4 10
45.3	7.5	15.1	22.6	30.2	37.7	.3	0.2 1.0	1.7 2.5	3.3 4.0	4.8 5.5	6.3 7.1						24.5 11
45.4	7.6	15.1	22.7	30.3	37.8	.4	0.3 1.1	1.8 2.6	3.3 4.1	4.9 5.6	6.4 7.1						26.7 12
45.5	7.6	15.2	22.8	30.3	37.9	.5	0.4 1.1	1.9 2.7	3.4 4.2	4.9 5.7	6.4 7.2						28.8 13
45.6	7.6	15.2	22.8	30.4	38.0	.6	0.5 1.2	2.0 2.7	3.5 4.2	5.0 5.8	6.5 7.3						30.9 14
45.7	7.6	15.3	22.9	30.5	38.1	.7	0.5 1.3	2.0 2.8	3.6 4.3	5.1 5.8	6.6 7.4						33.1 15
45.8	7.7	15.3	22.9	30.6	38.2	.8	0.6 1.4	2.1 2.9	3.6 4.4	5.2 5.9	6.7 7.4						35.2 16
45.9	7.7	15.3	23.0	30.6	38.3	.9	0.7 1.4	2.2 3.0	3.7 4.5	5.2 6.0	6.7 7.5						

60°, 300° L.H.A.   LATITUDE SAME NAME AS DECLINATION

N. Lat { LHA greater than 180°......Zn=Z ; LHA less than 180°......Zn=360°−Z }

Dec.	38°			39°			40°			41°			42°			43°			44°			45°			Dec.
	Hc	d	Z	Hc	d	Z	Hc	d	Z	Hc	d	Z	Hc	d	Z	Hc	d	Z	Hc	d	Z	Hc	d	Z	
0	23 12.2	−40.1	109.6	22 51.9	−40.9	110.0	22 31.3	−41.6	110.4	22 10.2	−42.4	110.7	21 48.8	−43.1	111.1	21 27.0	−43.8	111.5	21 04.8	−44.6	111.9	20 42.3	−45.3	112.2	0
1	23 52.3	39.8	108.8	23 32.8	40.6	109.2	23 12.9	41.4	109.6	22 52.6	42.2	110.0	22 31.9	42.9	110.4	22 10.8	43.7	110.8	21 49.4	44.4	111.1	21 27.6	45.0	111.5	1
2	24 32.1	39.5	107.9	24 13.4	40.4	108.4	23 54.3	41.2	108.8	23 34.8	41.9	109.2	23 14.8	42.7	109.6	22 54.5	43.4	110.0	22 33.8	44.2	110.4	22 12.6	45.0	110.8	2
3	25 11.6	39.3	107.1	24 53.8	40.1	107.6	24 35.5	40.9	108.0	24 16.7	41.7	108.4	23 57.5	42.5	108.8	23 37.9	43.3	109.3	23 18.0	43.9	109.7	22 57.6	44.7	110.1	3
4	25 50.9	39.0	106.3	25 33.9	39.8	106.7	25 16.4	40.6	107.2	24 58.4	41.5	107.6	24 40.0	42.3	108.1	24 21.2	43.0	108.5	24 01.9	43.8	108.9	23 42.3	44.5	109.3	4
5	26 29.9	−38.6	105.4	26 13.7	−39.5	105.9	25 57.0	−40.4	106.4	25 39.9	−41.1	106.8	25 22.3	−41.9	107.3	25 04.2	−42.8	107.7	24 45.7	−43.5	108.2	24 26.8	−44.3	108.6	5
6	27 08.5	38.4	104.6	26 53.2	39.2	105.1	26 37.4	40.0	105.5	26 21.0	40.9	106.0	26 04.2	41.8	106.5	25 47.0	42.5	107.0	25 29.2	43.3	107.4	25 11.1	44.0	107.9	6
7	27 46.9	38.0	103.7	27 32.4	38.9	104.2	27 17.4	39.8	104.7	27 01.9	40.7	105.2	26 46.0	41.4	105.7	26 29.5	42.3	106.2	26 12.5	43.1	106.7	25 55.1	43.8	107.1	7
8	28 24.9	37.7	102.8	28 11.3	38.6	103.3	27 57.2	39.5	103.9	27 42.6	40.3	104.4	27 27.4	41.2	104.9	27 11.8	41.9	105.4	26 55.6	42.8	105.9	26 38.9	43.6	106.4	8
9	29 02.6	37.3	101.9	28 49.9	38.2	102.5	28 36.7	39.1	103.0	28 22.9	40.0	103.5	28 08.6	40.8	104.1	27 53.7	41.7	104.6	27 38.4	42.5	105.1	27 22.5	43.3	105.6	9

FIGURE 2009b.—Data from main tables and Interpolation Table.

2010. Pub. No. 229 interpolation when second differences are required.—The accuracy of linear interpolation usually decreases as the altitude increases. At altitudes above 60° it may be necessary to include the effect of second differences in the interpolation. When the altitude difference, d, is printed in italic type followed by a small dot, the second-difference correction may exceed 0′.25, and should normally be applied. The need for a second-difference correction is illustrated by the graph of table 2010 data in figure 2010a.

Other than graphically, the required correction for the effects of second differences is obtained from the appropriate subtable of the Interpolation Table. However, before the Interpolation Table can be used for this purpose, what is known as the double-second difference must be formed. The **double-second difference (DSD)** is the sum of two successive second differences. Although second differences are not tabulated, the DSD can be formed readily by subtracting, algebraically, the tabular altitude difference immediately above the respondent altitude difference from the tabular altitude difference immediately below. The result will always be a negative value.

As shown in figure 2010b, that compartment of the DSD table opposite the block in which the Dec. Inc. is found is entered with the DSD to obtain the DSD correction

LHA 38°, Lat. 45° (Same Name as Declination)

Dec.	ht (Tab. Hc)	First Difference	Second Difference
50°	64°08′.2		
		+2′.8·	
51°	64°11′.0		−2′.3
		+0′.5·	
52°	64°11′.5		−2′.1
		−1′.6·	
53°	64°09′.9		

TABLE 2010.—First and second differences of tabular altitudes.

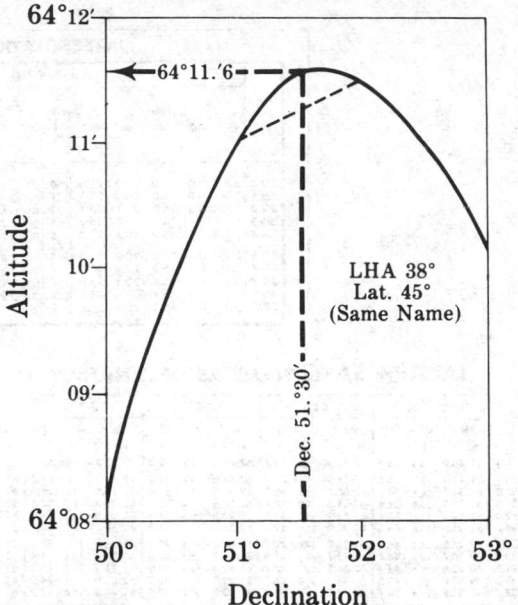

FIGURE 2010a.—Nonlinear interpolation by graph.

to the altitude. The correction is always plus. Therefore, the sign of the DSD need not be recorded. When the DSD entry corresponds to an exact tabular value, always use the upper of the two possible corrections.

As an example of the use of the double-second difference, the computed altitude and true azimuth are determined for Lat. 45°N, LHA 38°, and Dec. 51°30′.0N. Data are exhibited in figure 2010b.

The respondents for the entering arguments (Lat. 45° Same Name as Declination, LHA 38°, and Dec. 51°) are:

Tabular altitude,	ht	64°11′.0
Altitude difference,	d	(+)0′.5·
Azimuth angle,	Z	62°.8

The linear interpolation correction to the tabular altitude for Dec. Inc. 30′.0 is (+)0′.3.

Hc=ht+linear correction=64°11′.0+0′.3=64°11′.3.

However, by inspection of figure 2010a, illustrating this solution graphically, the computed altitude should be 64°11′.6. The actual change in altitude with an increase in declination is nonlinear. The altitude value lies on the curve between the points for declination 51° and declination 52° instead of the straight line connecting these points.

The DSD is formed by subtracting, algebraically, the tabular altitude difference immediately above the respondent altitude difference from the tabular altitude difference immediately below. Thus, the DSD is formed by algebraically subtracting (+)2′.8 from (−)1′.6; the result is (−)4′.4.

As shown in figure 2010b, that compartment of the DSD table opposite the block in which the Dec. Inc. (30′.0) is found is entered with the DSD (4′.4) to obtain the DSD correction to the altitude. The correction is 0′.3. The correction is always plus.

Hc=ht+linear correction+DSD correction
Hc=64°11′.0+0′.3+0′.3=64°11′.6.

INTERPOLATION TABLE

Dec. Inc.	Altitude Difference (d)															Double Second Diff. and Corr.
	Tens					Decimals	Units									
	10'	20'	30'	40'	50'		0'	1'	2'	3'	4'	5'	6'	7'	8'	9'	
30.0	5.0	10.0	15.0	20.0	25.0	.0	0.0	0.5	1.0	1.5	2.0	2.5	3.0	3.6	4.1	4.6	0.8 0.1
30.1	5.0	10.0	15.0	20.0	25.1	.1	0.1	0.6	1.1	1.6	2.1	2.6	3.1	3.6	4.1	4.6	2.4 0.1
30.2	5.0	10.0	15.1	20.1	25.1	.2	0.1	0.6	1.1	1.6	2.1	2.6	3.2	3.7	4.2	4.7	4.0 0.2
30.3	5.0	10.1	15.1	20.2	25.2	.3	0.2	0.7	1.2	1.7	2.2	2.7	3.2	3.7	4.2	4.7	5.6 0.3
30.4	5.1	10.1	15.2	20.3	25.3	.4	0.2	0.7	1.2	1.7	2.2	2.7	3.3	3.8	4.3	4.8	7.2 0.4
30.5	5.1	10.2	15.3	20.3	25.4	.5	0.3	0.8	1.3	1.8	2.3	2.8	3.3	3.8	4.3	4.8	8.8 0.5
30.6	5.1	10.2	15.3	20.4	25.5	.6	0.3	0.8	1.3	1.8	2.3	2.8	3.4	3.9	4.4	4.9	10.4 0.6
30.7	5.1	10.3	15.4	20.5	25.6	.7	0.4	0.9	1.4	1.9	2.4	2.9	3.4	3.9	4.4	4.9	12.0 0.7
30.8	5.2	10.3	15.4	20.6	25.7	.8	0.4	0.9	1.4	1.9	2.4	2.9	3.5	4.0	4.5	5.0	13.6 0.8
30.9	5.2	10.3	15.5	20.6	25.8	.9	0.5	1.0	1.5	2.0	2.5	3.0	3.5	4.0	4.5	5.0	15.2 0.9
																	16.8 1.0

38°, 322° L.H.A.   LATITUDE SAME NAME AS DECLINATION   N. Lat. { L.H.A. greater than 180°......Zn=Z / L.H.A. less than 180°......Zn=360°−Z

Dec.	38° Hc	d	Z	39° Hc	d	Z	40° Hc	d	Z	41° Hc	d	Z	42° Hc	d	Z	43° Hc	d	Z	44° Hc	d	Z	45° Hc	d	Z	Dec.
49	60 41.7	8.8	55.6	61 15.0	7.1	57.1	61 46.9	5.3	58.7	62 17.3	3.3*	60.3	62 46.3−	1.4*	62.0	63 13.7+	0.6*	63.7	63 39.4	2.7*	65.5	64 03.4	4.8*	67.4	49
50	60 32.9	-10.7	53.6	61 07.9	-9.0	55.1	61 41.6	-7.2	56.6	62 14.0−	5.4*	58.2	62 44.9−	3.4*	59.8	63 14.3−	1.4*	61.5	63 42.1+	0.6*	63.3	64 08.2+	2.8*	65.1	50
51	60 22.2	12.4	51.6	60 58.9	10.8	53.0	61 34.4	9.1	54.5	62 08.6	7.3	56.0	62 41.5	5.5*	57.6	63 12.9	3.6*	59.3	63 42.7−	1.5*	61.0	64 11.0−	0.5*	62.8	51
52	60 09.8	14.1	49.6	60 48.1	12.6	51.0	61 25.3	10.9	52.4	62 01.3	9.2	53.9	62 36.0	7.6*	55.5	63 09.3	5.5*	57.1	63 41.2	3.6*	58.8	64 11.5−	1.6*	60.5	52
53	59 55.7	15.9	47.7	60 35.5	14.3	49.0	61 14.4	12.8	50.4	61 52.1	11.2	51.8	62 28.6	9.5	53.3	63 03.8	7.7*	54.9	63 37.6	5.7*	56.5	64 09.9	3.7*	58.2	53
54	59 39.8	17.5	45.8	60 21.2	16.1	47.0	61 01.6	14.6	48.3	61 40.9	13.0	49.7	62 19.1	11.3	51.2	62 56.1	9.6	52.7	63 31.9	7.8*	54.3	64 06.2	5.9*	56.0	54
55	59 22.3	-19.1	43.9	60 05.1	-17.8	45.1	60 47.0	-16.3	46.3	61 27.9	-14.8	47.7	62 07.8−	13.3	49.1	62 46.5	-11.6	50.5	63 24.1	-9.9*	52.1	64 00.3	-8.0*	53.7	55
56	59 03.2	20.7	42.0	59 47.3	19.3	43.2	60 30.7	18.1	44.4	61 13.1	16.6	45.6	61 54.5	15.1	47.0	62 34.9	13.5	48.5	63 14.2	11.8*	49.9	63 52.3	10.1*	51.4	56
57	58 42.5	22.2	40.2	59 28.0	21.0	41.3	60 12.6	19.6	42.4	60 56.5	18.3	43.7	61 39.4	16.9	44.9	62 21.4	15.4	46.3	63 02.4	13.9	47.7	63 42.2	12.7*	49.2	57
58	58 20.3	23.6	38.4	59 07.0	22.5	39.5	59 53.0	21.3	40.6	60 38.2	20.0	41.7	61 22.5	18.6	42.9	62 06.0	17.2	44.2	62 48.5	15.7	45.6	63 30.0	14.1	47.0	58
59	57 56.7	25.0	36.7	58 44.5	23.9	37.7	59 31.7	22.8	38.7	60 18.2	21.6	39.8	61 03.9	20.4	40.9	61 48.8	19.0	42.2	62 32.8	17.6	43.5	63 15.9	16.1	44.8	59

FIGURE 2010b.—Data from main tables and Interpolation Table.

2011. Complete solution by Pub. No. 229 and _Nautical Almanac_.—The complete solution includes all of the parts listed in article 2001. Because of the various alternatives available for the separate parts, a large number of variations might be used in the complete solution.

It is good practice to have a standard work form. If this is not printed, or on a rubber stamp, it should be copied in its entirety before the solution is started. The first step should then be to fill in the known information. If the solution for observed altitude is made first, this value can then be copied in the main solution, so that it will be ready for comparison when Hc is determined. The best form to use is that which the individual navigator finds most logical and least likely to result in errors.

Some navigators include a time diagram (art. 1428) in the form as a check both on the time and meridian angle computation.

There is a growing tendency among navigators to keep the navigational watch set to GMT. This is particularly helpful when a number of observations are made, as during twilight, to eliminate the need for repeated application of watch error and zone description, and determination of Greenwich date.

Example.—On June 2, 1975, the 1742 dead reckoning position of a ship is lat. 41°10′S, long. 128°00′E. The ship is on course 315°, speed 20 knots. Observations are made from a height of eye of 31 feet using a sextant having an index correction of (−)1.0 as indicated below. Determine the 1742 fix.

Body	GMT	Sextant Altitude	SHA	Declination
Spica	08h24m03s	32°30′.4	159°01′.1	11°02′.2S
Regulus	08h29m58s	36°57′.1	208°13′.9	12°05′.2N
Procyon	08h35m59s	35°05′.1	245°29′.8	5°17′.2N
Canopus	08h41m55s	52°47′.7	264°09′.3	52°41′.1S

		Spica		*Regulus*
GMT (June 2)		08ʰ24ᵐ03ˢ		08ʰ29ᵐ58ˢ
GHA ♈ for 8ʰ GMT		10°10ʹ3		10°10ʹ3
Increments	24ᵐ03ˢ	6°01ʹ7	29ᵐ58ˢ	7°30ʹ7
SHA☆		159°01ʹ1		208°13ʹ9
GHA☆		175°13ʹ1		225°54ʹ9
aλ		127°46ʹ9E		128°05ʹ1E
LHA☆		303°00ʹ0		354°00ʹ0
Dec		11°02ʹ2S		12°05ʹ2N
Dec. Inc		02ʹ2		05ʹ2
aL		41°00ʹ0S		41°00ʹ0S
ht (Tab. Hc)		31°55ʹ0		36°42ʹ6
d and correction	(+)39ʹ7	(+)1ʹ5	(−)59ʹ7	(−)5ʹ2
Hc		31°56ʹ5		36°37ʹ4
Ho		32°22ʹ5		36°49ʹ4
a		26. 0T		12. 0T
Z and Zn	S104°1E	075°9	S172°7E	007°3

		Procyon		*Canopus*
GMT (June 2)		08ʰ35ᵐ59ˢ		08ʰ41ᵐ55ˢ
GHA ♈ for 8ʰ GMT		10°10ʹ3		10°10ʹ3
Increments	35ᵐ59ˢ	9°01ʹ2	41ᵐ55ˢ	10°30ʹ5
SHA☆		245°29ʹ8		264°09ʹ3
GHA☆		264°41ʹ3		284°50ʹ1
aλ		128°18ʹ7E		128°09ʹ9E
LHA☆		33°00ʹ0		53°00ʹ0
Dec		5°17ʹ2N		52°41ʹ1S
Dec. Inc		17ʹ2		41ʹ1
aL		41°00ʹ0S		41°00ʹ0S
ht (Tab. Hc)		34°59ʹ1		52°48ʹ5
d and correction	(−)52ʹ0	(−)14ʹ9	(+)3ʹ8	2ʹ6
Hc		34°44ʹ2		52°51ʹ1
Ho		34°57ʹ3		52°40ʹ6
a		13. 1T		10. 5A
Z and Zn	S138°7W	318°7	S53°3W	233°3

2012. Sight Reduction Tables for Air Navigation (Pub. No. 249).—Although these tables are designed to satisfy the needs of the air navigator, they are frequently used for sight reduction at sea. The following description and explanation of the use of the tables is limited to the marine application.

Volume I contains tabulations of altitude (to the nearest 1′) and azimuth (to the nearest 1°) in parallel columns. For each 1° of latitude a two-page table (one-page above 69°) is given. For each 1° (2° beyond latitude 69°) of LHA ♈, altitude and azimuth are given for seven stars carefully selected with regard to azimuth, magnitude, altitude, and continuity. Stars of the first magnitude are shown in capital letters, and those of second and third magnitude in lower case with initial capital. After each 15 entries a break occurs and a new listing of stars is given, whether or not there are any

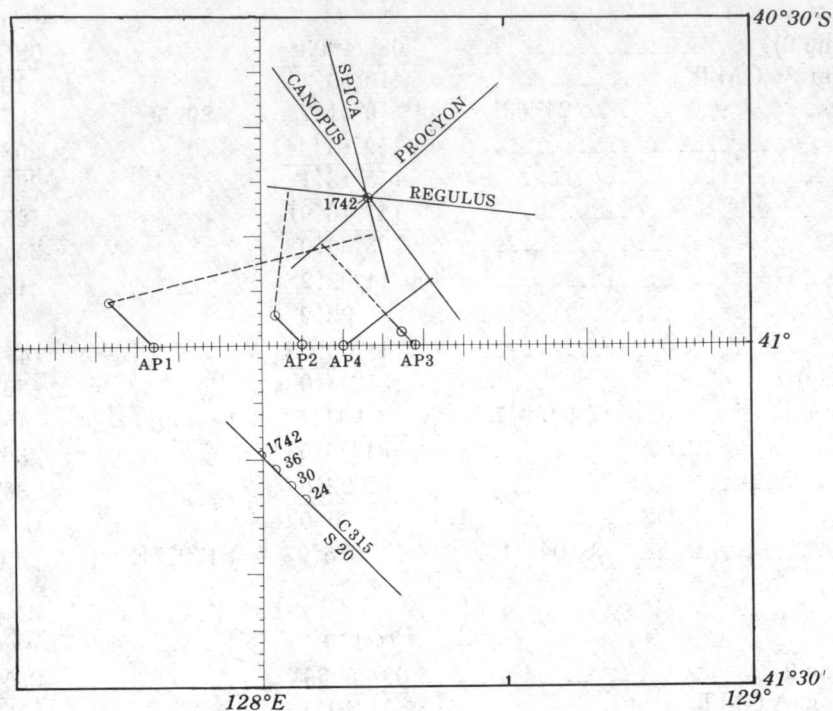

changes from the previous list. Stars are listed in the order of increasing azimuth at
the beginning of each period. Forty-one stars are included, 19 of which are of the first
magnitude, 17 of the second magnitude, and 5 of the third magnitude. The tables
are intended for use with an assumed position selected so that latitude and LHA♈
are each the nearest whole degree (nearest *even* degree of LHA♈ at latitudes higher
than 69°).

Volume I, for selected stars, is arranged for entering with latitude, LHA ♈,
and the appropriate star name. This arrangement minimizes the time and effort required
in sight reduction. Progressive changes in the coordinates affecting the tabulated data
necessitate recomputation at approximately five-year intervals in order to reduce the
effects of this source of cumulative error. Of the seven stars selected for each 15° of
LHA ♈, the three marked by the diamond symbol (♦) provide sets favorably situated
in altitude and azimuth for the three-body fix normally used in *air navigation*. The
volume for epoch 1980.0 will replace the volume for epoch 1975.0.

Tabulation by name of the star eliminates the need for finding the declination,
but a correction for precession of the equinoxes (art. 1419) and nutation (art. 1417)
may be needed. This is given in an auxiliary table near the back of the volume. The
correction which may reach a value as high as 3′ is applied to the fix, not to each
altitude.

Tabulation of *azimuth* (not azimuth angle) eliminates the need for conversion.

Tabulation by LHA♈ instead of meridian angle of the star eliminates the need
for finding and applying SHA. It also makes of the tables a star finder for the *seven*
stars given, since all values given for any entry of LHA♈ are for the *same time*.

An almanac giving GHA♈ is included for use should the *Air Almanac* or *Nautical
Almanac* not be available.

Example 1.—During evening twilight on June 2, 1975, the 1724 DR position of a ship is lat. 40°39'.2S, long. 128°01'.2E. At GMT 8ʰ24ᵐ03ˢ the navigator observes Canopus with a marine sextant having no IC, from a height of eye of 38 feet. The hs is 55°57'.1.

Required.—The *a*, Zn, and AP, using Pub. No. 249 (epoch 1975.0), vol. I, and the *Air Almanac.*

Solution.—

	June 2		Canopus		+ ☆ −	
GMT	8ʰ24ᵐ03ˢ	June 2		IC	−	−
8ʰ20ᵐ	15°11'			D		6'
4ᵐ03ˢ	1°01'			R		1'
GHA ♈	16°12'			sum	−	7'
*a*λ	127°48'E			corr.		(−) 7'
LHA ♈	144°00'			hs		55°57'
*a*L	41°00'S			Ho		55°50'
Hc	55°48'					
Ho	55°50'					
a	2 T		*a*L 41°00'S			
Zn	233°		*a*λ 127°48'E			

Example 2.—During evening twilight on June 2, 1975, the 1724 DR position of a ship is lat. 40°39'.2S, long. 128°01'.2E. At GMT 8ʰ24ᵐ03ˢ the navigator observes Canopus with a marine sextant having no IC, from a height of eye of 38 feet. The hs is 55°57'.1.

Required.—The *a*, Zn, and AP, using Pub. No. 249 (epoch 1975.0), vol. I, and the *Nautical Almanac.*

Solution.—

	June 2		Canopus		+ ☆ −	
GMT	8ʰ24ᵐ03ˢ	June 2		IC	−	−
8ʰ00ᵐ	10°10'.3			D		6'.0
24ᵐ03ˢ	6°01'.7			R		0'.7
GHA ♈	16°12'.0			sum	−	6'.7
*a*λ	127°48'.0E			corr.		(−) 6'.7
LHA ♈	144°00'.0			hs		55°57'.1
*a*L	41°00'.0S			Ho		55°50'.4
Hc	55°48'.0					
Ho	55°50'.4					
a	2.4T		*a*L 41°00'S			
Zn	233°		*a*λ 127°48'E			

Volumes II and III are somewhat similar in many respects to Pub. No. 229. Altitude and azimuth angle are given in parallel columns for every whole degree of latitude (0° to 89°), every whole degree of declination (0° to 29°), and every whole degree (2° beyond lat. 69°) of LHA for all values at which the altitude is greater than several degrees *below* the celestial horizon. The values for latitude and declination contrary name are tabulated with values of meridian angle (LHA less than 180°) increasing *upward* on the page, as in some older tables such as Pub. No. 260 (art. 719, vol. II). This permits better utilization of space where same- and contrary-name tabulations are given on the same page. It also serves to emphasize the difference between the same- and contrary-name tabulations, the contrary-name tabulation being given in a "contrary" manner on the page. A more convenient arrangement of declination entries is provided by having the "top" of each page of the tables along the left side, requiring the turning of the page through 90°.

The altitude difference (labeled d) is tabulated between the altitude and azimuth angle to facilitate interpolation of altitude for declination. No interpolation is needed for latitude and LHA because the assumed position is selected so that these are the nearest whole degree (nearest *even* degree of LHA beyond latitude 69°). The altitude difference is the difference in minutes, with sign, between the accompanying altitude and that for declination 1° *greater*, at the same latitude and LHA. It is used for entering an auxiliary table for determining the correction to be applied to altitude for minutes of declination, Dec. Inc. Interpolation is normally made in the direction of increasing declination.

Volume II covers latitudes 0° to 39°, and volume III contains similar information for latitudes 40° to 89°. Since these tables are entered with LHA of the celestial body, they do not become inaccurate in succeeding years, and no correction is needed for precession and nutation, as in volume I. In contrast with volume I, azimuth angle is tabulated instead of azimuth. A long-term almanac giving the GHA and declination of the sun is included in both volumes for use should the *Air Almanac* or *Nautical Almanac* not be available. These volumes are intended for solution of observations of the sun, moon, planets, and any stars within the declination range.

Example 3.—During morning twilight on June 2, 1975, the 0724 DR position of a ship is lat. 40°39′.2S, long. 131°01′.2E. At GMT 22ʰ24ᵐ03ˢ (June 1) the navigator observes Alpheratz with a marine sextant having no IC, from a height of eye of 38 feet. The hs is 20°15′.3.

Required.—The a, Zn, and AP, using Pub. No. 249, vol. III, and the *Air Almanac*.

Solution.—

	June 2	Alpheratz		+ ☆ −
GMT	22ʰ24ᵐ03ˢ June 1		IC	— —
22ʰ20ᵐ	224°46′		D	6′
4ᵐ03ˢ	1°01′		R	3′
SHA	358°13′		sum	— 9′
GHA	224°00′		corr.	(−)9′
aλ	131°00′E		hs	20°15′
LHA	355°00′		Ho	20°06′
d	28°57′N	Dec. Inc. 57′		
aL	41°00′S			
ht	20°51′	d (−) 60		Z S175°E
corr.	(−)57′			
Hc	19°54′			
Ho	20°06′			
a	12T	aL 41°00′S		
Zn	005°	aλ 130°40′E		

Example 4.—During morning twilight on June 2, 1975, the 0724 DR position of a ship is lat. 40°39′.2S, long. 131°01′.2E. At GMT 22ʰ24ᵐ03ˢ (June 1) the navigator observes Alpheratz with a marine sextant having no IC, from a height of eye of 38 feet. The hs is 20°15′.3.

Required.—The *a*, Zn, and AP, using Pub. No. 249, vol. III, and the *Nautical Almanac*.

Solution.—

	June 2		Alpheratz		+	☆	−
GMT	22ʰ24ᵐ03ˢ	June 1		IC	−		−
22ʰ	219°45ʹ7			D		6ʹ0	
24ᵐ03ˢ	6°01ʹ7			☆-P		2ʹ6	
SHA	358°13ʹ2			sum	−	8ʹ6	
GHA	224°00ʹ6			corr.		(−)8ʹ6	
aλ	130°59ʹ4E			hs		20°15ʹ3	
LHA	355°00ʹ0			Ho		20°06ʹ7	
d	28°57ʹ2N		Dec. Inc. 57′				
aL	41°00ʹ0S						
ht	20°51ʹ0		*d* (−)60			Z S175°E	
corr.	(−)57ʹ0						
Hc	19°54ʹ0						
Ho	20°06ʹ7						
a	12.7T		aL 41°00ʹ0S				
Zn	005°		aλ 130°59ʹ4E				

2013. *Tables of Computed Altitude and Azimuth* (Pub. No. 214).—The publication of these sight reduction tables has been discontinued by the Defense Mapping Agency Hydrographic Center. However, it is expected that navigators will use the volumes they possess for many years to come. The tables were published in nine volumes, each covering 10° of latitude in increments of 1°. For each degree of latitude there is a series of tables, with cutaway tabs providing quick reference to the first page of the tables for that latitude. Declination entries are given at intervals of 0°5 from 0° to 29°. Beyond this, 37 selected declination entries are given to provide solutions for all of the stars listed on the daily pages of the almanacs, and most of the additional stars listed near the back of the *Nautical Almanac*. A total of 96 declination entries are given for each latitude, arranged eight to a page. Each declination entry is given at the top of a column. The third variable, meridian angle, is given in the column at the extreme left and right sides of each page. These columns are labeled "H.A.," the abbreviation for "hour angle," the expression formerly used for meridian angle, but replaced because of confusion with *local* hour angle, *Greenwich* hour angle, etc. Meridian angle entries are given at intervals of 1° from 0° at the top of the page to the maximum value at which the altitude is 5° or greater.

At most page openings, separate tables are given for declination having the *same* name (N or S) as the latitude and those having *contrary* name (one N, the other S). That is, declination values on the left-hand page (same name) are duplicated on the right-hand page (contrary name). A maximum of ninety-one meridian angle entries (0°–90°) are given on the left-hand page (same name). As either the declination or the latitude increases, the number of same-name entries increases, and the number of contrary-name entries decreases. When the same-name entries exceed 90° of meridian angle, the additional ones are placed on the right-hand page, below the contrary-name entries. At extreme values of declination and latitude there are no contrary-name entries, the same-name entries occupying both pages.

In each declination column there are four sets of figures. The first, given in bold type, is the altitude (labeled "Alt.") to the nearest 0ʹ1. Following this is Δd in small type. This is the change of altitude for a unit change of declination. Except when the value is 1.0, entries are given in hundredths of a unit, although the position of the decimal point is not shown. Following Δd, and also in small type, is Δt, the change of altitude for a unit change of meridian angle. This is given in the same form as Δd. The last set of figures in the column is the azimuth angle (labeled "Az."), to the nearest $0°.1$. The current abbreviation for azimuth angle, Z, is used in example solutions.

At latitude $0°$ the arrangement is modified because there is no "same" or "contrary" name of declination. Here a single set of declination entries is given. Declination replaces latitude as the prefix label for azimuth angle.

Following the altitude-azimuth section of each latitude is a two-page star identification table. The use of this table is explained in article 2213.

On the inside front cover and its facing page is a speed-time-distance table, which is useful in advancing or retiring lines of position, as well as for other purposes. This table contains information similar to that in table 19, but in somewhat different form. Volume VIII and older printings of other volumes have sextant altitude correction tables on these pages.

Following the speed-time-distance table is an arc to time conversion table.

Following the title page and preface are given a description of the tables, and sample problems.

On the inside back cover and facing page is given a "multiplication table" to multiply Δd or Δt by the number of minutes between the declination or meridian angle and the value used for entering the main table. This is used in interpolating the altitude for declination or meridian angle.

On the two pages next preceding the multiplication table is given a somewhat similar table to provide easy interpolation for latitude.

The use of the various parts of Pub. No. 214 is explained in articles 2014–2016 and 2213. The primary purpose of Pub. No. 214 is to provide an easy method of sight reduction for use with the *Nautical Almanac* aboard ship. It may also be used with the *Air Almanac*, and for solution of any spherical triangle for which entry values are given. Therefore, it can be used in great-circle sailing for determining the initial course and the distance.

2014. Pub. No. 214 solution by Δd only.—If interpolation is made for all three variables—latitude, declination, and meridian angle—a triple interpolation is needed. A simpler solution, almost universally used with Pub. No. 214, is to select an assumed position that will eliminate interpolation for latitude and meridian angle, leaving a simple interpolation for declination.

Example.—Find computed altitude (Hc) and azimuth (Zn) if aL is $41°00'.0$N, d is $22°14'.3$N, and t is $36°00'.0$W.

Solution.—

t	$36°00'.0$W		
d	$22°14'.3$N	d diff. $14'.3$	
aL	$41°00'.0$N		
ht	$54°16'.8$	Δd $(+)$ 0.65	Z N$111°.0$W
corr.	$(+)$ $9'.3$		
Hc	$54°26'.1$		
Zn	$249°.0$		

The main table is entered with the three variables, t, d, and aL (being sure to note whether d and aL are of same or contrary name); and the values of ht (tabulated altitude, labeled "Alt." in Pub. No. 214), Δd, and Z are taken directly from the table, without interpolation. The tabulated altitude (ht) is the computed altitude (Hc) for the values used for entering the table. The designation ht is used to distinguish it from the Hc obtained by applying a correction to the value taken from the table.

The declination entry argument used should be the tabulated entry nearest the declination for which a solution is sought, normally differing by not more than half a degree. The difference between this value and the actual declination is recorded as "d diff." No sign (+ or −) is assigned to this value. It is good practice to show Δd as a decimal, even though it is not tabulated in this way. The sign of this value should be determined carefully by inspection of the main table of Pub. No. 214. Interpolation of altitude for declination is made between the base value taken from the table and the value given on the same line in the next column to the right or left. The choice of the second column depends upon the actual declination. If it is *greater* than the value used for entering the table, use the next column to the *right*, and if less, use the next column to the *left*. If the value in the second column is greater than the base value, the sign is plus (+), and if less, the sign is minus (−). The accuracy of this important step can be checked by comparing the computed altitude (Hc) with the altitudes given in the main table of Pub. No. 214. If Δd has been given the correct sign (and applied correctly), Hc should lie between the tabulated altitudes in the columns for tabulated declination next smaller and next larger than the actual declination.

The azimuth angle is given a prefix N or S to agree with the latitude, and a suffix E or W to agree with the meridian angle. For this reason it is good practice to label these values *when they are recorded*.

The next step is to multiply Δd by d diff., to interpolate between the altitude entries for consecutive declination columns. In most instances, the easiest way to do this is to use the multiplication table on the inside back cover of Pub. No. 214 and its facing page, entering separately with minutes and tenths of minutes of Δd and adding the two parts. The correction, which is recorded below ht, is given the sign of Δd. The correction is then added or subtracted, in accordance with its sign, to ht. The answer is computed altitude (Hc).

Azimuth (Zn), which is recorded below Hc, is found by converting azimuth angle (Z) in accordance with its labels, as explained in article 1430. Usually, azimuth angle is found without interpolation.

If Δd is changing rapidly, or when it changes sign (at the maximum altitude for the given meridian angle and latitude), interpolation may be somewhat less accurate than in other parts of the tables, but this should not introduce a large error unless the celestial body is near the zenith, when the method of Pub. No. 214 is not recommended.

2015. Pub. No. 214 solution by Δd and Δt is similar to that using Δd only, but with the additional step of interpolating between the altitude entries for consecutive meridian angle entries, in a similar manner to interpolation for declination.

Example.—Find computed altitude and azimuth if aL is 41°00ʹ.0N, d is 20°48ʹ.7S, and t is 22°14ʹ.0E.

Solution.—

t 22°14ʹ.0E	t diff. 14ʹ.0	t corr. (−) 4ʹ.2
d 20°48ʹ.7S	d diff. 11ʹ.3	d corr. (+) 10ʹ.8
aL 41°00ʹ.0N		corr. (+) 6ʹ.6
ht 24°43ʹ.1	Δd (+) 0.95 Δt (−) 0.30	Z N157°.4E
corr. (+)6ʹ.6		
Hc 24°49ʹ.7		
Zn 157°.4		

In this solution, t diff. is the difference between the meridian angle and the nearest whole degree of t used for entering the table. The t corr. is t diff.×Δt, found by using the same multiplication table used for the d corr. The sign of Δt is found by inspection of the main table. In this example interpolation is between the base altitude for t 22°, and the altitude for t 23°. Since the altitude for t 23° is less than that for t 22°, the correction should be subtracted, so that the interpolated value will lie between the two values between which interpolation is being made. The sign of Δd is found by comparing the altitude for d 21°00′ with that for d 20°30′. The total correction is the algebraic sum of the t corr. and d corr.

The principal advantage of this solution is that a round of sights can be worked and plotted from the same assumed position. However, this advantage is offset by the additional length of the solution. The method is little used.

2016. Pub. No. 214 solution by Δd, Δt, and ΔL.—If the altitude and azimuth at a particular place are desired, interpolation should be made for all three variables, t, d, and L, if needed. The change in altitude for a change of latitude of 1′ (ΔL) is not tabulated. The table on the two pages *preceding* the multiplication table of Pub. No. 214 is used for finding the correction for latitude.

Example 1.—Find computed altitude and azimuth if aL is 41°12′.8S, d is 21°32′.5S, and t is 8°52′.3W.

Solution.—

				+	−
t 8°52′.3W	t diff. 7′.7				
d 21°32′.5S	d diff. 2′.5		t corr. 2′.4		
aL 41°12′.8S	L diff. 12′.8		d corr. 2′.4		
ht 69°04′.0	Δd (+)0.94	Δt (+)0.32	L corr.		11′.7
corr. (−)6′.9			sum 4′.8		11′.7
Hc 68°57′.1			corr. (−)6′.9		
Zn 336°.0			Z S156°.0W		

The corrections for meridian angle and declination are found as explained in articles 2014 and 2015. The L corr. is found by entering the correction table with azimuth angle and L diff., the difference between the latitude of the assumed position and the nearest whole degree used for entering the main table. It is customary to interpolate in this table, where applicable, but the error introduced by not doing so is always less than 0′.3 if the *nearest* whole degree of azimuth angle is used. The sign of the latitude correction is determined by the rules given at the bottom of the correction table. The total correction is the algebraic sum of the three individual corrections.

All of these are *altitude* corrections. The azimuth is that corresponding to the values used for entering the main table. If the exact value at the place is desired, it can be found by interpolation. If such an interpolation is made, the interpolated value should be used for entering the latitude correction table for altitude interpolation.

In sight reduction for plotting lines of position, it is not customary to interpolate for azimuth angle when Pub. No. 214 is used. However, if greater accuracy is desired, as for determining compass error, triple interpolation should be made. This is customarily accomplished by entering the main table of Pub. No. 214 with the *nearest* values of t, d, and L, and taking out the corresponding tabulated value. Simple eye interpolation is then used to determine separately the correction for each of the three variables. The algebraic sum of these is the correction applied to the base value. The Δd, Δt, and ΔL corrections are not used because these refer to the *altitude*, not the azimuth. Corrections are made to azimuth angle *before* it is converted to azimuth.

Interpolation for azimuth is discussed in more detail in article 2028.

The complete solution includes all of the parts listed in article 2001. Because of the various alternatives available for the separate parts, a large number of variations might be used in the complete solution.

Example 2.—During morning twilight on June 1, 1975, the 0624 EP of a ship is lat. 41°12.3S, long. 178°39.2E. At ZT 6^h24^m57^s the navigator observes Mars with a marine sextant having an IC of (−) 1.0, from a height of eye of 53 feet. The hs is 41°45.9.

Required.—The *a*, Zn, and AP, using Pub. No. 214 (Δd, Δt, ΔL) and the *Nautical Almanac.*

Solution.—

	June 1	Mars		+ M −	
ZT	6^h24^m57^s	18^h 1°34.4N *d* (+)0.7	IC		1.0
ZD (−)	12	corr. 0.3	D		7.1
GMT	18^h24^m57^s May 31	*d* 1°34.7N	☆-P		1.0
18^h	150°48.3		add'l. 0.1		
24^m57^s	6°14.3	*v*(+) 0.8	sum 0.1		9.1
v corr.	(+)0.3		corr.		(−)9.0
GHA	157°02.9		hs		41°45.9
*a*λ	178°39.2E		Ho		41°36.9
LHA	335°42.1				
t	24°17.9E	t diff. 17.9	+	−	
d	1°34.7N	d diff. 4.7	t corr.	7.5	
*a*L	41°12.3S	L diff. 12.3	d corr.	4.2	
ht	42°13.1	Δd(−) 0.91 Δt(−)0.42	L corr.	10.3	
corr.	(−)22.0		sum	22.0	
Hc	41°51.1		corr.	(−)22.0	
Ho	41°36.9		Z	S146.7E	
a	14.2A	*a*L 41°12.3S			
Zn	033.3	*a*λ 178°39.2E			

Special Techniques

2017. Adjustment of straight line of position.—Table 4 gives the corrections to the straight line of position (LOP) as drawn on a chart or plotting sheet to provide a closer approximation to the arc of the circle of equal altitude, a small circle of radius equal to the zenith distance. As shown in figure 2017, the corrections are offsets of points on the LOP and are drawn at right angles to the LOP in the direction of the observed body. The offset points are joined to obtain the arc of the small circle. Usually the desired approximation to the arc of the small circle can be obtained by drawing a straight line through two offset points. The magnitudes of the offsets are dependent upon altitude and the distance of the offset point from the intercept.

2018. Graphical interpolation of altitude for latitude and local hour angle.—In principle the graphical method for interpolating altitude for latitude and local hour angle is the measurement of the difference of the radii of two circles of equal altitude corresponding to the altitudes of a celestial body from two positions at the same instant. One circle passes through the assumed position (integral latitude and that longitude providing an integral LHA), and the second circle passes through the dead reckoning position or other position from which the computed altitude is required.

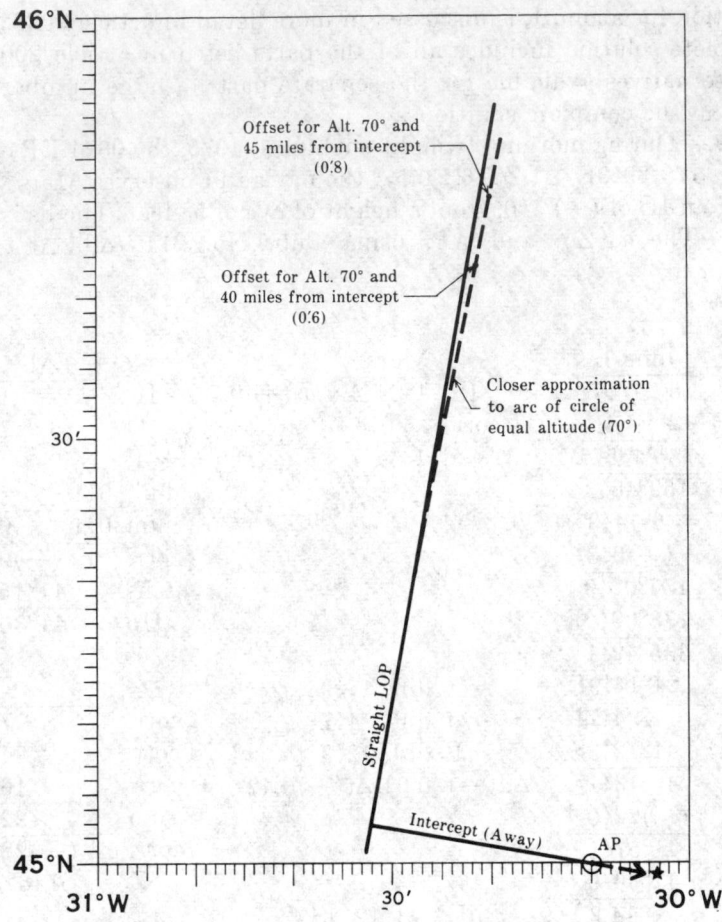

FIGURE 2017.—Adjustment of straight line of position.

The measurement, which is the difference in zenith distances as measured from the zenith of the assumed position and the zenith of some nearby position, is effected as follows:

1. Draw the azimuth line from the assumed position (AP) as shown in figure 2018 (the azimuth angle is interpolated for declination increment before conversion to true azimuth).

2. From the position (DR) for which the computed altitude is required, draw a line perpendicular to the azimuth line or its extension. This line approximates the arc of the circle of equal altitude passing through the DR.

3. Measure the distance from the foot of the perpendicular to the DR in nautical miles.

4. Enter table 4 with the distance of the DR from the foot of the perpendicular, and the altitude of the body as interpolated for declination increment; extract the offset.

5. From the foot of the perpendicular and in a direction away from the celestial body, lay off the offset on the azimuth line or its extension.

6. As shown in figure 2018, a closer approximation to the arc of the circle of equal altitude through the DR is made by drawing a straight line from the offset point to the DR.

7. The required correction, in units of minutes of latitude, for the latitude and LHA increments is the length along the azimuth line between the AP and the arc of the circle of equal altitude through the DR.

If the arc of the circle of equal altitude through the DR crosses the azimuth line between the AP and the body, the correction is to be added to the altitude interpolated for declination increment; otherwise the correction is to be subtracted. The method will give highly satisfactory results except when plotting on a Mercator chart in high latitudes.

Example.—

Computed altitude from AP	Hc	70°05′.0
Observed altitude	Ho	70°00′.0
Intercept	*a*	5. 0A
Computed altitude from AP	Hc	70°05′.0
Difference of the radii		20′.4
Computed altitude from DR	Hc	69°44′.6
Computed altitude from DR	Hc	69°44′.6
Observed altitude	Ho	70°00′.0
Intercept	*a*	15. 4T

The basic method should have most frequent application in great-circle solutions.

2019. Pub. No. 229 interpolation near the horizon.—This discussion is restricted to the interpolation of altitude for declination within the 1° interval containing the horizon, indicated by the horizontal segments of the C–S Line. Interpolation of altitude in the interval under consideration is accomplished by using the last tabular altitude and altitude difference appearing above the C–S Line. Since the last tabular altitude above the C–S Line indicates the body's altitude above the horizon for LHA at top of page, for the pertinent latitude, and for the last integral declination above the horizontal segment of the C–S Line pertaining to that particular latitude, interpolation resulting in positive altitudes may be carried out for increments of declination of contrary name so long as the interpolated altitude correction does not exceed the last tabular altitude above the C–S Line; for the LHA at bottom of page, positive altitudes will result when interpolating altitude for increments of declination of same name so long as the interpolated altitude correction exceeds the last tabular value above the C–S Line. Interpolation for declinations and increments of declination in excess of the above limits results in negative altitudes.

The tabular azimuth angle pertinent to this one-degree interval of declination is that immediately above or that immediately below the C–S Line, according as the entering arguments are contrary or same name, respectively. The difference in azimuth angle for the interval is determined by taking the value of tabular azimuth angle, on the same side of the C–S Line as the LHA argument, from the supplement of that on the opposite side of the line.

2020. Pub. No. 229 interpolation of negative altitudes.—This paragraph is restricted to tabular and interpolated altitudes for declinations other than one-degree intervals of declination containing the C–S Line. For all local hour angles at the top of the right-hand page, all tabular or interpolated altitudes on that page for declinations below the C–S Line are negative; also for any local hour angle at the bottom of the right-hand page, all tabular or interpolated altitudes for declinations above the C–S Line

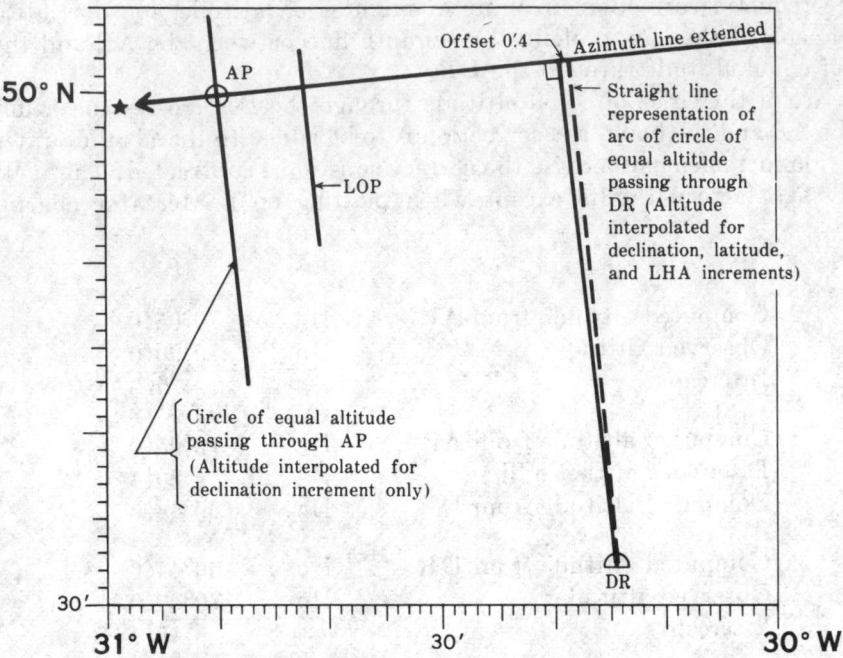

FIGURE 2018.—Graphical interpolation of altitude.

are negative; additionally, for these same local hour angles and latitudes changed to
Contrary Name, the tabular or interpolated altitudes on the left-hand page are negative.
Interpolation of altitudes for declination increments within these areas of negative
altitude should, however, be accomplished as if the altitudes were positive, adhering
strictly to the sign given d. Then, after interpolation, regard the results as negative.
In all instances involving negative altitudes, except the one-degree interval of declination
which includes the C–S Line, the supplement of the pertinent tabular azimuth angle
is that to be converted to true azimuth by the rules to be found on each opening of the
basic tables.

    2021. Interpolation near the zenith.—In the region within 4° of the zenith where
normal interpolation methods are inadequate, the following method can usually be
used to interpolate both altitude and azimuth angle. The Interpolation Table is employed in carrying out the desired interpolation, but the values of altitude and azimuth
angle extracted from the basic tables constitute data which require independent dif-
ferencing; the tabular altitude difference, d, is not used.

    To carry out the altitude interpolation, the basic tables are entered with the per-
tinent LHA and Dec., and with the integral degree of Lat. so chosen that, when increased by the declination increment, it is within 30′ of the known or DR latitude;
this practice will prevent long intercepts. For these entering arguments and for a latitude
and declination one degree more than the above referenced latitude and declination,
respectively, extract the tabular altitudes and azimuth angles. The altitudes and
azimuth angles are then differenced and with these differences interpolation of altitude
and azimuth angle for the desired declination is made, utilizing the Interpolation
Table. The computed altitude is then compared with that observed to determine the
intercept, which together with the interpolated azimuth angle converted to true azimuth
makes possible the construction of a line of position, which is plotted from the assumed

longitude, and from the latitude of the entering argument, augmented by the declination increment.

Example 1.—

	LHA	Lat.	Dec.	Ho
	3°27′	31°06′N	28°35′.1N	86°05′.5

Lat.	Dec.	Tab. Hc	diff.	Tab. Z	diff.
31°	28°	86°01′.4		138°.2	
			(+)1′.0		(+)0°.3
32°	29°	86°02′.4		138°.5	

Interpolate to Dec.=28°35′.1
Dec. Inc.=35′.1, diff.=(+)1′.0, Z diff.=(+)0°.3

Tab. Hc		86°01′.4		Tab. Z	138°.2
Correction		(+)0′.6			(+)0°.2
	Hc	86°02′.0		Z	138°.4
	Ho	86°05′.5			
Intercept		3.5T		Zn	221°.6

Plot from Lat. 31°35′.1N

Example 2.—

	LHA	Lat.	Dec.	Ho
	357°19′	37°58′S	36°13′.1S	87°14′.2

Lat.	Dec.	Tab. Hc	diff.	Tab. Z	diff.
38°	36°	86°52′.8		128°.9	
			(+)1′.4		(+)0°.4
39°	37°	86°54′.2		129°.3	

Interpolate to Dec.=36°13′.1
Dec. Inc.=13′.1, diff.=(+)1′.4, Z diff.=(+)0°.4

Tab. Hc		86°52′.8		Tab. Z	128°.9
Correction		(+)0′.3			(+)0°.1
	Hc	86°53′.1		Z	129°.0
	Ho	87°14′.2			
Intercept		21.1T		Zn	051°.0

Plot from Lat. 38°13′.1S

2022. Precomputation.—Sometimes it is desired to determine computed altitude *before* the observation, generally for the purpose of obtaining a line of position quickly after the observation has been completed. This is called **precomputation.** When it is done, sextant altitude corrections are generally applied *with reversed sign* to Hc to obtain **precomputed altitude (Hp),** which is then compared directly with hs to obtain the altitude intercept for plotting a line of position. Where altitude is needed for entering correction tables, the computed altitude (Hc) is used. The error introduced by this practice is negligible except at low altitudes, where the corrections should be adjusted by using the Hp to reenter the tables. If greater accuracy is required, limit precomputation to Hc and Zn, and apply corrections to the sextent altitude after observation.

Example.—On June 2, 1975, the 1025 DR position of a ship is lat. 42°21′.4S, long. 118°47′.1W. The navigator plans to observe the lower limb of the sun at this time with a marine sextant having an IC of (+)2′.5, from a height of eye of 25 feet.

Required.—(1) Precomputed altitude by Pub. No. 214, Δd only, (2) the *a*, Zn, and AP if hs is 22°23′.6. Use *Nautical Almanac.*

Solution.—

	June 2			Sun			+ ☉ −	
ZT	10ʰ25ᵐ00ˢ		18ʰ	22°10ʹ5N	d(+)0ʹ3	IC	2ʹ5	
ZD	(+)8		d corr.	(+)0ʹ1		D		4ʹ9
GMT	18ʰ25ᵐ00ˢ June 2		d	22°10ʹ6N		☉	13ʹ7	
18ʰ	90°32ʹ0					sum	16ʹ2	4ʹ9
25ᵐ00ˢ	6°15ʹ0					corr.	(+)11ʹ3	
GHA	96°47ʹ0							
aλ	118°47ʹ0W							
LHA	338°00ʹ0							
t	22°00ʹ0E							
d	22°11ʹ5N		d diff.	10ʹ6				
aL	42°00ʹ0S							
ht	22°50ʹ5		Δd	(−)0.95		Z	S157°9E	
corr.	(−)10ʹ1							
Hc	22°40ʹ4							
corr.	(+)11ʹ3 (rev.)							
(1) Hp	22°29ʹ1							
hs	22°23ʹ6							
(2) a	5.5A		aL 42°00ʹ0S					
Zn	022°1		aλ 118°47ʹ0W					

At the AP used in the calculation, Hp is correct only for the time used. However, if the observation is made early or late, the same Hp and Zn can be used by moving the AP along the parallel of latitude, eastward for early observations, or westward for late observations, a distance equal to 0ʹ25 of longitude for each second (15ʹ0 for each minute) difference between actual and predicted times. This adjustment is based upon the assumptions that the apparent motion of the body is westward at the rate of 15° per hour, and the declination is constant. Over the seconds or minutes likely to be involved, these assumptions and the possible increased length of the plotted lines do not introduce a significant error, except possibly for the moon.

2023. Low altitudes.—When Hc is determined by inspection tables such as Pub. No. 214, a minimum tabulated altitude may be available. In Pub. No. 214, altitudes below 5° are not given. These tables can be used for low-altitude observations by selection of an AP that will result in Hc being 5° or greater. To do this, proceed as follows: At the time of observation, note the approximate azimuth of the celestial body. Plot the azimuth line through the DR or EP and measure off, toward the celestial body, a distance equal to 6°−hs (or 6°−Ho). Select the AP in relation to this point as if it were the DR or EP. Occasionally it may be necessary to use 7°−hs (or 7°−Ho). The increased length of the altitude intercept line does not introduce a significant error over the distance that a rhumb line can be considered identical to a great circle. Only in high latitudes is this a problem, and here the error can be virtually eliminated by using a chart projection on which a great circle plots as a straight line or approximately so. The error introduced by using a rhumb line to represent the circle of equal altitude (the line of position) is not increased because the AP selected is near the azimuth line.

Example.—On June 1, 1975, the 1625 DR position of a ship is lat. 43°39ʹ7S, long. 15°07ʹ0W. At GMT 17ʰ24ᵐ22ˢ the navigator observes the lower limb of the sun as it breaks out below an overcast, shortly before setting. He uses a marine sextant having no IC, and makes his observation from a height of eye of 52 feet. The hs is

1°01′.6, air temperature (art. 807, vol. II) 24°F, and the atmospheric pressure (art. 808, vol. II) 30.16 inches. The sun's azimuth is approximately 305°.

Required.—The *a*, Zn, and AP using Pub. No. 214 (Δd only), the *Nautical Almanac*, and tables 23 and 24.

Solution.—

	June 1		Sun			+ ☉ −
GMT	17ʰ24ᵐ22ˢ June 1	17ʰ	22°02′.1N *d*(+)0′.3	IC	−	−
17ʰ	75°34′.4	*d* corr.	(+) 0′.1	D		7′.0
24ᵐ22ˢ	6°05′.5	*d*	22°02′.2N	sum	−	7′.0
GHA	81°39′.9			corr.		(−)7′.0
*a*λ	20°39′.9W			hs		1°01′.6
LHA	61°00′.0			ha		0°54′.6
t	61°00′.0W					
d	22°02′.2N		d diff. 2′.2	☉		9′.1
*a*L	41°00′.0S			T		1′.3
ht	5°21′.8	Δd(−)0.75	Z S125°.5W	B		0′.3
corr.	(−)1′.7			sum	−	10′.7
Hc	5°20′.1			corr.		(−)10′.7
Ho	0°43′.9			ha		0°54′.6
a	276.2A		*a*L 41°00′.0S	Ho		0°43′.9
Zn	305°.5		*a*λ 20°39′.9W			

Refer to figure 2023. From the 1625 DR position, the approximate azimuth of 305° is plotted, as shown by the broken line. Along this line a distance of 6°00′.0 − 0°43′.9=5°16′.1, or 316.1 miles, is measured, locating the point labeled A. The AP is selected with respect to this point as if it were the DR position. The sight is plotted from this AP as in any observation. If it makes the plot easier, record *a* in the solution in degrees and minutes of arc instead of in miles (5°20′.1 − 0°43′.9=4°36′.2=276′.2= 276.2 miles).

Large altitude differences can be avoided by using a method of solution that provides for low altitudes. Among such methods are Pub. Nos. 229 and 249; nearly any trigonometric method such as the cosine-haversine formula, the Ageton Method (table 35); and most graphical and mechanical methods. All of these methods are discussed in chapter XXI. If a trigonometric method is used, the *signs* of the various functions (or special rules) should be used if there is a possibility of Hc being negative. The need for special care can be eliminated by using an assumed position about half a degree or more from the DR position or EP, in the direction of the celestial body, if the altitude is less than 0°30′.

By any method of solution, if *either* Hc or Ho (but not both) is negative, the altitude intercept is found by numerically *adding* the two altitudes. Thus, if Hc is (+)0°12′.6 and Ho is (−)0°03°.2, the altitude intercept, *a*, is 15′.8, or 15.8 miles. The positive altitude is greater than the negative one. Therefore, the *a* in this case is *away*. If *both* Hc and Ho are negative, the difference is found by subtraction, but in this case the one which is numerically smaller is the greater altitude. Thus, if Hc is (−)0°09′.6 and Ho is (−)0°04′.3, the altitude intercept is 5.3T.

2024. High altitudes are usually avoided for at least two reasons. First, bodies near the zenith are difficult to observe. A star or planet is difficult to "bring down" to the horizon. It is not always easy to determine the azimuth accurately, and when near the zenith, a body may be changing azimuth rapidly. On the other hand, such observations are little affected by astronomical refraction. The second reason for avoiding high altitudes is one of geometry. As the altitude increases, the radius of

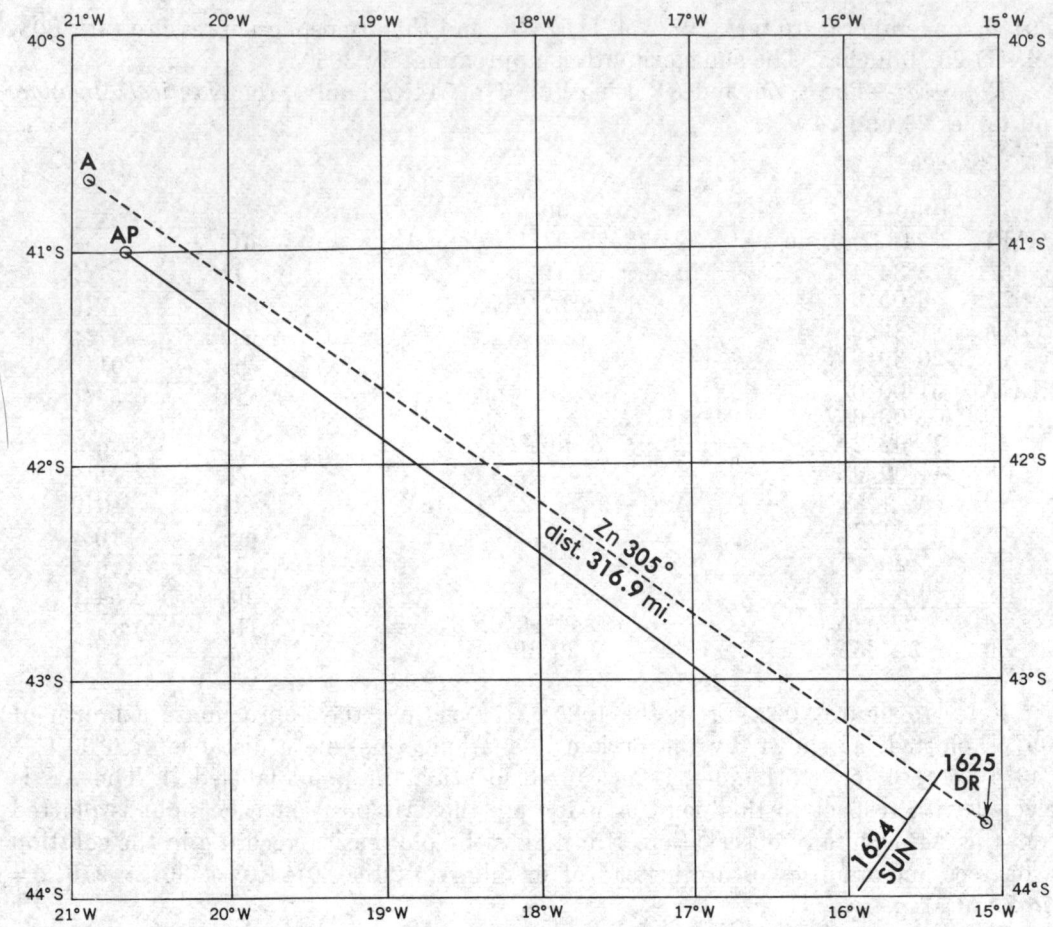

FIGURE 2023.—Selecting an AP for low-altitude solutions by Pub. No. 214.

the circle of position decreases. For a body near the zenith, the radius is so small that the use of a straight line to approximate the circle may introduce serious error.

With higher altitudes, it is good practice to avoid use of lines of position extending a considerable distance from the azimuth line. Since the decrease in radius is gradual, there is no one altitude at which the curvature becomes excessive. However, a safe general rule, if one is needed, is to use the DR position or EP as the assumed position, and interpolate for azimuth angle, for all altitudes greater than 70°. The purpose of this is not primarily to decrease the altitude intercept, as sometimes suggested, but to decrease the length of the line of position.

Within perhaps three degrees of the zenith, the curvature of the circle of position becomes so great that even for a short distance a straight line is not an adequate representation of the circle. At these altitudes, it is good practice to plot the line of position as a circle. This is done by using the geographical position (GP) of the celestial body as the center, and the zenith distance as the radius. Hence, no sight reduction tables are needed. The same body can be used for obtaining a fix from two observations separated by several minutes. In celestial navigation, as in piloting, a circle of position is advanced or retired by moving its center.

Example.—On May 31, 1975, the 1224 DR position of a ship is lat. 20°17ʹ4N, long. 50°07ʹ4W. The ship is on course 127°, speed 18 knots. Using a marine sextant having no IC, the navigator observes the lower limb of the sun twice, from a height of eye of 65 feet. The first observation is made at GMT $15^h15^m15^s$, and hs is 88°01′.1. The second observation is made at GMT $15^h24^m13^s$, and hs is 87°34′.7. The GHA of the sun at GMT $15^h15^m15^s$ is 49°25′.6. Use the same declination as at GMT $15^h24^m13^s$.

Required.—The 1224 fix.

Solution.—

	May 31		Sun			+	⊙	−
GMT	$15^h15^m15^s$ May 31		d 21°53′.1N		IC	—		—
GHA	49°25′.6				D			7′.8
					⊙	15′.9		
GP L₁	21°53′.1N				sum	15′.9		7′.8
GP λ₁	49°25′.6W				corr.	(+)8′.1		
radius	110.8 mi.				hs	88°01′.1		
					Ho	88°09′.2		
					z	1°50′.8		

	May 31		Sun			+	⊙	−
GMT	$15^h24^m13^s$ May 31	15^h 21°53′.0N d (+)0′.3	IC	—		—
15^h	45°36′.8	d corr. (+)0′.1	D			7′.8
24^m13^s	6°03′.3	d 21°53′.1N	⊙	15′.9		
GHA	51°40′.1		sum	15′.9		7′.8
			corr.	(+)8′.1		
GP L₂	21°53′.1N		hs	87°34′.7		
GP λ₂	51°40′.1W		Ho	87°42′.8		
radius	137.2 mi.		z	2°17′.2		

Answer.—1224 fix: L 20°09′.0N, λ 50°06′.0W.

The plot of this problem is shown in figure 2024. No significant error would be introduced by assuming the same declination and sextant altitude correction for both observations, and a change of GHA equal to the arc equivalent of the time difference between observations (art. 1811). In east longitude the GP longitude would be 360°−GHA.

Latitude by Meridian Transit

2025. Meridian altitudes.—The latitude of a place on the surface of the earth, being its angular distance from the equator, is measured by an arc of the meridian between the zenith and the equator, and hence is equal to the declination of the zenith; therefore, if the zenith distance of any heavenly body when on the meridian be known, together with the declination of the body, the latitude can be found.

Figure 2025a shows the celestial sphere surrounding the earth: P_nMP_s is the upper branch of a celestial meridian and LL′ a portion of the corresponding geographic meridian. The declination of a body at M (arc QM) is numerically equal to the latitude of its geographical position at GP. The zenith distance of a body is equivalent to the distance on earth between the geographical position of the body and the position of the observer. In figure 2025a the zenith distance of M is 30° and its declination is 20°N. If the body is on the meridian, the GP is also on the meridian. Since P_n, Z, and M are all on the celestial meridian, the navigational triangle flattens out to a line. The observer is 30° *north* of the GP (L 50°N) if the body is seen to bear south, or 30° *south* of the GP (L′ 10°S) if the body is seen to bear *north*. The navigator knows whether the GP is north or south, because it is the same as the direction he faces when making his observation.

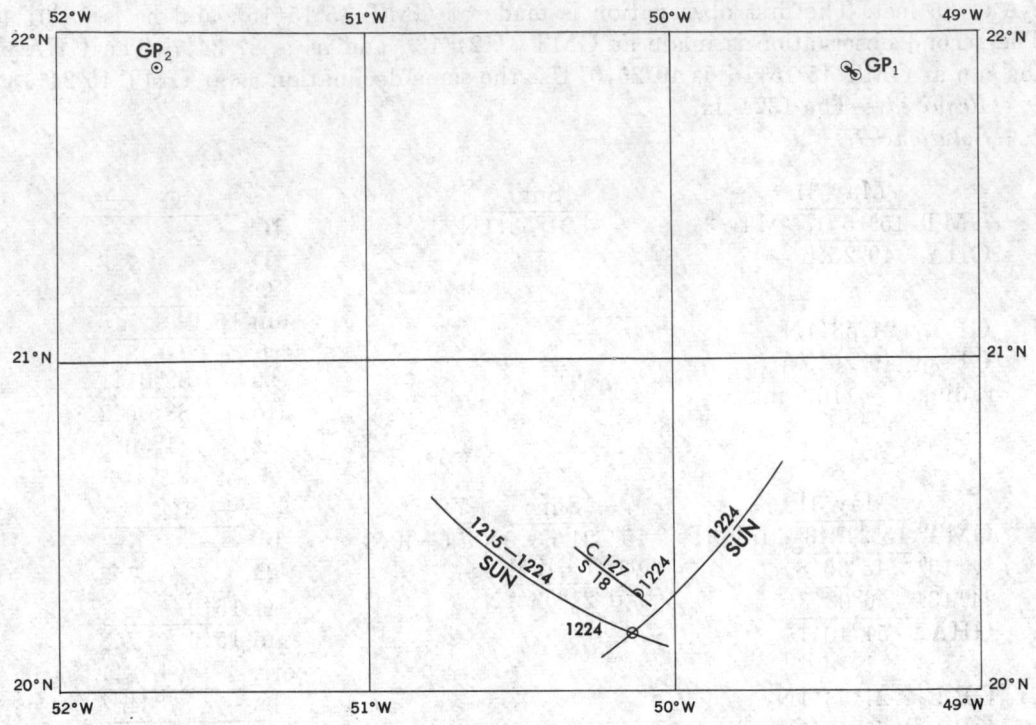

FIGURE 2024.—Plotting high-altitude observations.

In the diagram on the plane of the celestial meridian shown in figure 2025b, M is the position of a celestial body north of the equator but south of the zenith; QM is the declination of the body; SM is the altitude (h); and MZ is the zenith distance (z).

From the diagram:

$$QZ=QM+MZ, \text{ or } L=d+z.$$

With attention to the direction of the GP and the name of the declination, the above equation may be considered general for any position of the body at upper transit, as M, M′, M″.

When the body is below the pole, as at M‴—that is, at its lower transit—the same formula may be used by substituting 180°−d for d. Another solution is given in this case by observing that:

$$NP_n=P_nM'''+NM''', \text{ or } L=p+h.$$

By drawing that half of the diagram on the plane of the celestial meridian containing the zenith, the proper combination of zenith distance and declination is made obvious, as shown in the following examples:

Example 1.—The navigator observes the sun on the meridian, bearing south. The declination of the sun is 10°00′.0N; the corrected sextant altitude (Ho) is 60°00′.0.

Required.—The latitude.

Solution.— L=z+d.

	90°00′.0
Ho	60°00′.0
z	30°00′.0
d	10°00′.0N
L	40°00′.0N

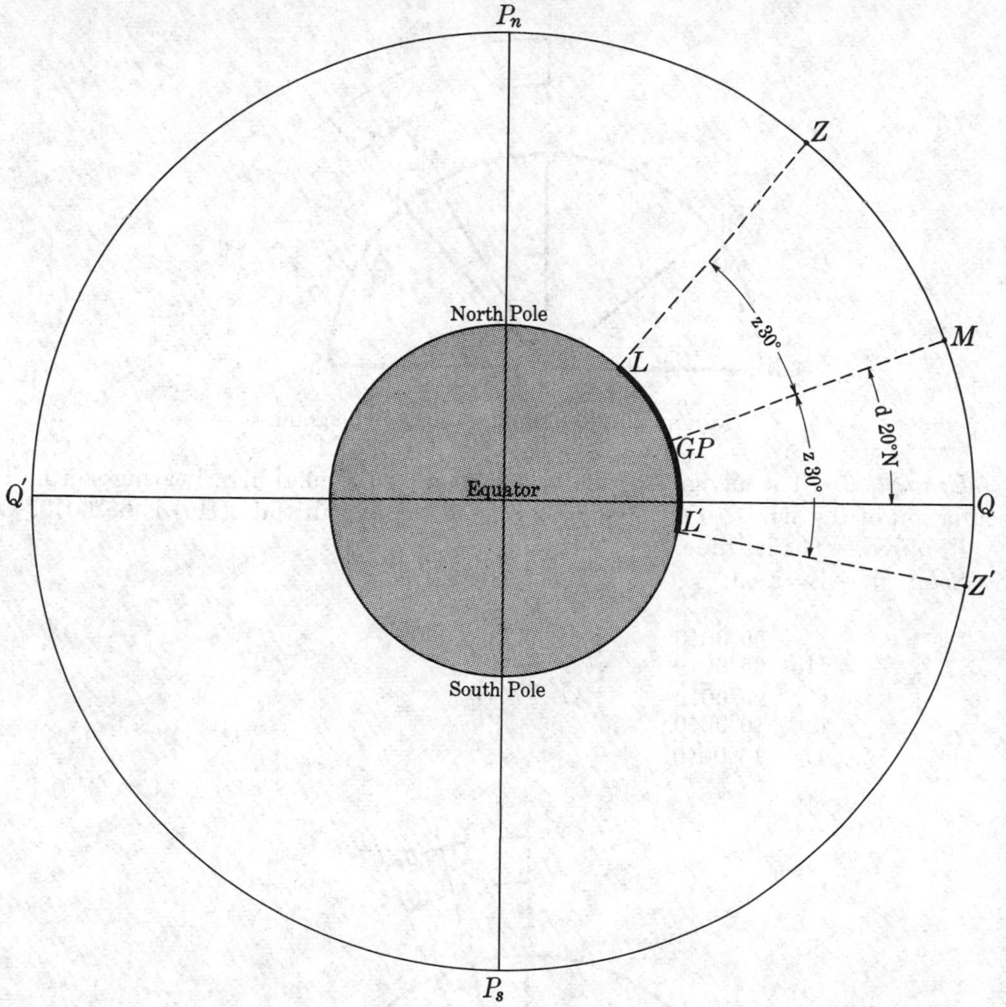

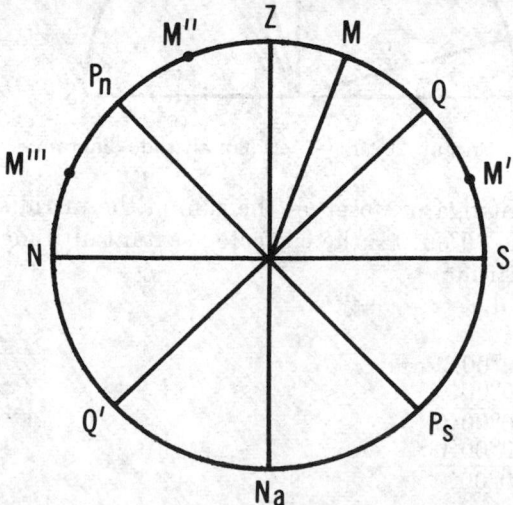

FIGURE 2025a.—Body on celestial meridian.

FIGURE 2025b.—Diagram on the plane of the celestial meridian.

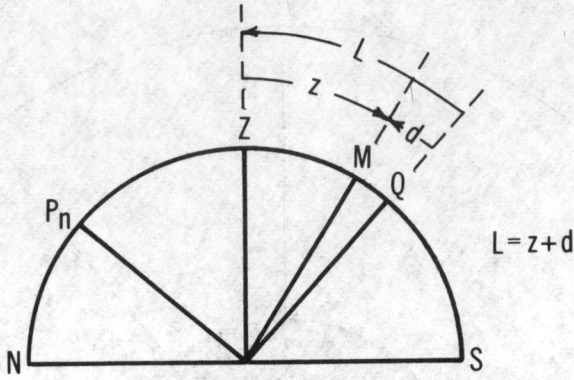

FIGURE 2025c.—Meridian altitude diagram.

Example 2.—The navigator observes the sun on the meridian, bearing south. The declination of the sun is 10°00′.0S; the corrected sextant altitude (Ho) is 65°00′.0.

Required.—The latitude.

Solution.— L=z−d.

	90°00′.0
Ho	65°00′.0
z	25°00′.0
d	10°00′.0S
L	15°00′.0N

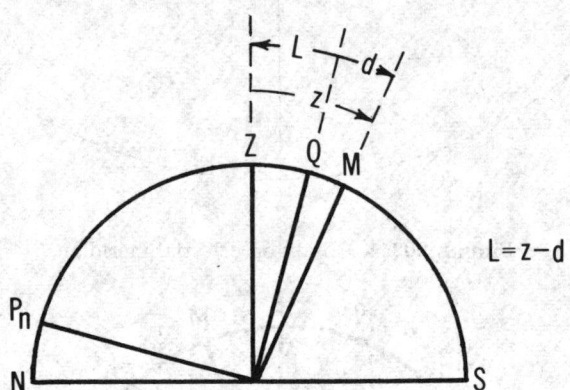

FIGURE 2025d.—Meridian altitude diagram.

Example 3.—The navigator observes the sun on the meridian, bearing north. The declination of the sun is 20°00′.0S; the corrected sextant altitude (Ho) is 60°00′.0.

Required.—The latitude.

Solution.— L=z+d.

	90°00′.0
Ho	60°00′.0
z	30°00′.0
d	20°00′.0S
L	50°00′.0S

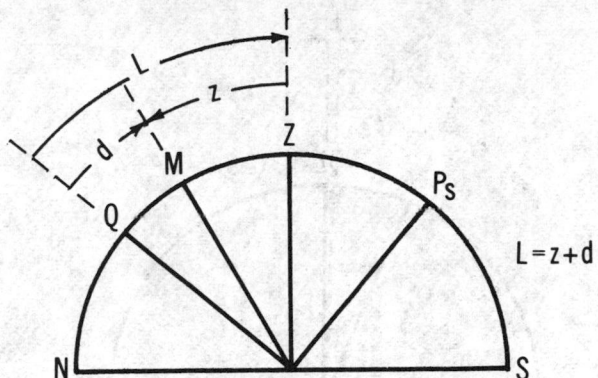

FIGURE 2025e.—Meridian altitude diagram.

Example 4.—The navigator observes the sun on the meridian, bearing north. The declination of the sun is 23°00′.0N; the corrected sextant altitude (Ho) is 72°00′.0.

Required.—The latitude.

Solution.— L=d−z.

	90°00′.0
Ho	72°00′.0
z	18°00′.0
d	23°00′.0N
L	5°00′.0N

Example 5.—In the vicinity of the equator, the navigator observes the sun on the meridian, bearing north. The declination of the sun is 22°05′.0N; the corrected sextant altitude (Ho) is 67°45′.0.

Required.—The latitude.

Solution.— L=z−d.

	90°00′.0
Ho	67°45′.0
z	22°15′.0
d	22°05′.0N
L	0°10′.0S

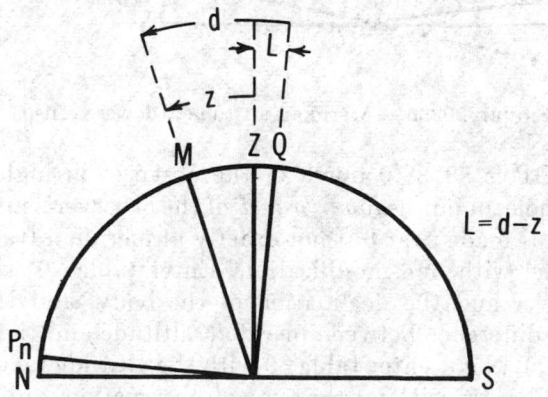

FIGURE 2025f.—Meridian altitude diagram.

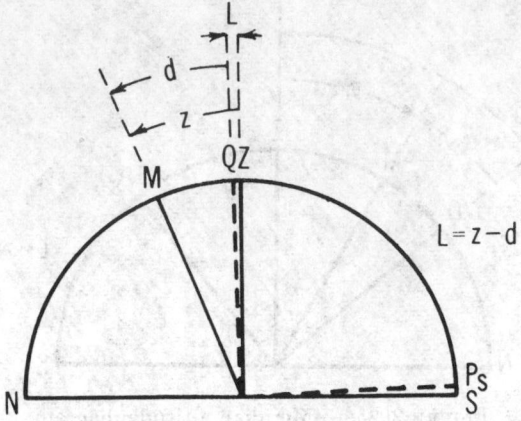

FIGURE 2025g.—Meridian transit in the vicinity of the equator.

Example 6.—The navigator in high northern latitudes observes the sun on the celestial meridian, bearing north. The declination of the sun is 18°46′.0N; the corrected sextant altitude (Ho) is 6°22′.0.
   Required.—The latitude.
   Solution.— L=(180°−d)−z, or
                L=p+h.

	90°00′.0
Ho	6°22′.0
z	83°38′.0
180°−d	161°14′.0N
L	77°36′.0N

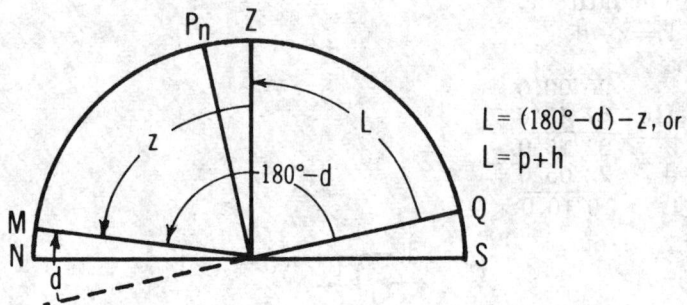

FIGURE 2025h.—Meridian altitude at lower transit.

Since the sun's GP is 83°38′.0 north of the observer in high northern latitudes, the GP is beyond the pole, or on the *lower branch* of the observer's meridian.
   If an observation is made near but not exactly at meridian transit, it can be solved as a meridian altitude, with one modification. Enter table 29 with the approximate latitude of the observer and the declination of the body, and take out the **altitude factor (*a*).** This is the difference between meridian altitude and the altitude one minute of time later (or earlier). Next, enter table 30 with the altitude factor and the difference of time between meridian transit and the time of observation, and take out the correction. *Add* this value to Ho if near upper transit, or *subtract* it from Ho if near lower transit. Then proceed as for a meridian altitude, remembering that the value obtained is the latitude at the time of observation, not at the time of meridian transit. This

method should not be used beyond the limits of table 30 unless reduced accuracy is acceptable. This process is called **reduction to the meridian,** the altitude before adjustment an **ex-meridian altitude,** and the observation an **ex-meridian observation.** It requires knowledge of the meridian angle, which depends upon knowledge of longitude.

2026. Finding time of meridian transit.—If a meridian altitude is to be observed other than by chance, a knowledge of the time of transit of the body across the meridian is needed.

On a slow-moving vessel, or one traveling approximately east or west, the time need not be known with great accuracy. The right-hand daily page of the *Nautical Almanac* gives the GMT of transit of the sun and moon across the Greenwich meridian (approximately LMT of transit across the local meridian) under the heading "Mer. Pass." In the case of the moon, an interpolation should be made for longitude. This is performed in the same manner as finding the LMT of moonrise and moonset (art. 1912). In the case of planets, the tabulated accuracy is normally sufficient without interpolation. The time of transit of the navigational planets is given at the lower right-hand corner of each left-hand daily page of the *Nautical Almanac*. The tabulated values are for the middle day of the page. These times are the GMT of transit across the Greenwich meridian, but are approximately correct for the LMT of transit across the local meridian. Observations are started several minutes in advance and continued until the altitude reaches a maximum and starts to decrease (a minimum and starts to increase for lower transit). The greatest altitude occurs at upper transit (and the least at lower transit). This method is not reliable if there is a large northerly or southerly component of the vessel's motion, because the altitude at meridian transit changes slowly, particularly at low altitudes. At this time the change due to the vessel's motion may be considerably greater than that due to apparent motion of the body (rotation of the earth), so that the highest altitude occurs several minutes before or after meridian transit.

If the moment at which the azimuth is 000° or 180° can be determined accurately, the observation can be made at this time. However, this generally does not provide a high order of accuracy.

If the longitude is known with sufficient accuracy, the time of transit can be computed. A number of methods of computation have been devised, but perhaps the simplest is to consider the GHA of the body equal to the longitude if west, or $360° - \lambda$ if east, and find the time at which this occurs.

Example 1.—Find the zone time of meridian transit of the sun at longitude 156° 44′.2W on May 31, 1975.

Solution.—

		May 31	
λ		156°44′.2W	
GHA		156°44′.2	
22^h		150°36′.1	
24^{m}32^s		6°08′.1	
GMT		22^{h}24^{m}32^s	May 31
ZD	(+)10		(rev.)
ZT		12^{h}24^{m}32^s	

This solution is the reverse of finding GHA. The largest tabulated value of GHA that does not exceed the desired GHA is found in the tabulation for the day, and recorded, with its time. The difference between this value and the desired GHA is then used to enter the "Increments and Corrections" table. The time interval corresponding to this value is added to the time taken from the daily page. If there is a *v* correction, it is subtracted from the GHA difference before the time interval is determined. The GMT can be converted to any other kind of time desired. If the Greenwich date differs from the local date at the time of transit (for the sun this can occur only near the 180th meridian), a second solution may be needed. This possibility can often be avoided by making an approximate mental solution in advance. As the basis for this approximate solution, it is convenient to remember that the GMT of Greenwich transit (GHA 0°) is about the same as the LMT of local transit. To find the time of transit of a star, subtract its SHA from the desired GHA to find the desired GHA♈. Determine the time corresponding to GHA♈, as explained above for the sun.

Aboard a moving vessel, the longitude at transit usually depends upon the time of transit. An approximate mental solution may provide a time sufficiently close. In the absence of better information, use ZT 1200 for the sun. Find the time of transit for the position at this time, and then make an adjustment, if necessary, for the sun between 1200 and the time found by computation. This adjustment is equal to four seconds for each minute of longitude involved. If the ship is *west* of the 1200 position at the computed time of transit, *add* the correction; and if *east*, *subtract* it. The result is the **first estimate** of the zone time of **local apparent noon (LAN)** or of meridian transit. For high accuracy a second adjustment may occasionally be needed, but this is seldom justified because of the uncertainty of the vessel's position. If the second adjustment is made, the result is the **second estimate.**

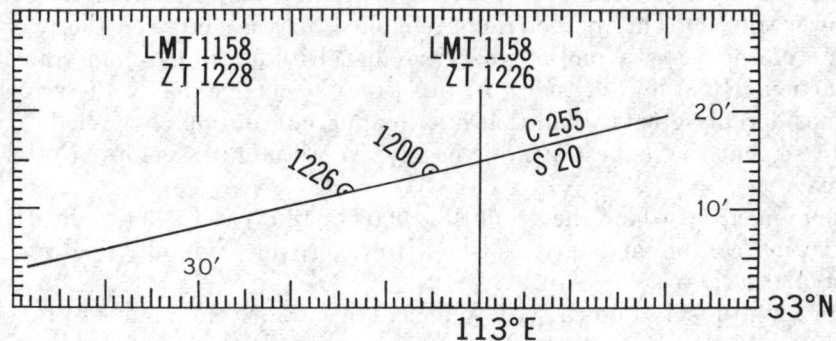

FIGURE 2026.—Time of meridian passage.

The time of transit of the sun can also be found by means of apparent time (art. 1818). Meridian transit occurs at LAT $12^h00^m00^s$. This can be converted to any other kind of time desired.

Example 2.—Find the zone time of meridian transit of the sun as observed aboard a ship steaming at 20 knots on course 255° on May 31, 1975, using the positional data given in figure 2026.

Solution.—

$$
\begin{array}{rll}
 & \text{May 31} & \\
 & \overline{360°00'\!\!.0} & \\
\lambda & 112°55'\!\!.0\text{E} & \\
\text{GHA} & \overline{247°05'\!\!.0} & \\
4^h & 240°37'\!\!.7 & \\
25^m49^s & \overline{6°27'\!\!.3} & \\
\text{GMT} & \overline{4^h25^m49^s} & \text{May 31} \\
\text{ZD} \, (-)8 & & \text{(rev.)} \\
\text{ZT} & \overline{12^h25^m49^s} & \\
d\lambda & (+) \, 0^m36^s & \\
\text{ZT} & \overline{12^h26^m25^s} & \text{(first estimate)}
\end{array}
$$

The second estimate of the zone time of meridian transit is found by plotting the DR position for the first estimate of the zone time of transit and then applying the dλ between this DR and the 1200 DR to the time found by computation.

$$
\begin{array}{ll}
\text{ZT} & 12^{\text{h}}25^{\text{m}}49^{\text{s}} \\
\text{d}\lambda & (+)0^{\text{m}}37^{\text{s}} \\
\text{ZT} & 12^{\text{h}}26^{\text{m}}26^{\text{s}} \ \text{(second estimate)}
\end{array}
$$

As shown in figure 2026, the zone times of meridian transit are noted on several successive meridians. This is accomplished by extracting the LMT of meridian transit from the daily page of the *Nautical Almanac* and converting this time to the zone time for each meridian. The time when the ship and the sun are on the same meridian can then be obtained by inspection to within approximately one-half minute.

Polaris

2027. Latitude by Polaris.—Another special method of finding latitude, available in most of the Northern Hemisphere, utilizes the fact that Polaris is less than 1° from the north celestial pole. As indicated in article 1432, the altitude of the elevated pole above the celestial horizon is equal to the latitude. Since Polaris is never far from the pole, its observed altitude (Ho), with suitable correction, is the latitude.

The nature of this correction as tabulated in the *Air Almanac* is suggested by inspection of figure 2027b in which the circle represents the path of Polaris around the north celestial pole (P_n), as seen by an observer on earth looking along the axis P_sP_n (fig. 2027a). The line *ab* represents a small portion of the observer's meridian. Polaris is at upper transit at *a* and at lower transit at *b*. This is also shown in figure 2027b, to larger scale. Latitude is equal to the altitude *minus* the polar distance (*p*) when Polaris is at *a* and *plus* the polar distance when it is at *b*. When the star is at any point *c*, the Polaris correction is polar distance times the cosine of the local hour angle (corr.=*p* cos LHA). Thus, the correction is a function of LHA of the star, and hence also of LHA ♈, insofar as the difference between these quantities (the SHA) can be considered constant.

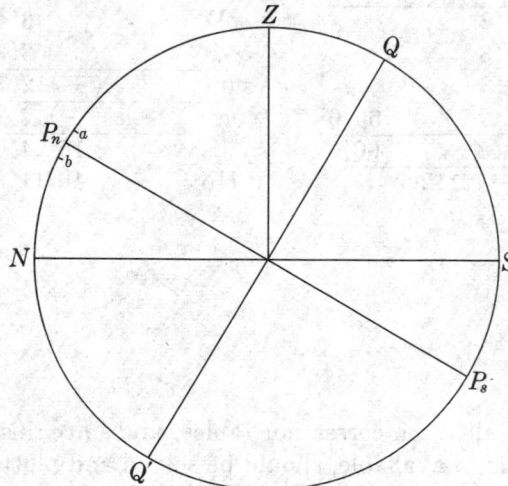

FIGURE 2027a.—Latitude is equal to the (1) declination of the zenith and (2) the altitude of the elevated pole. Compare with figure 2027b.

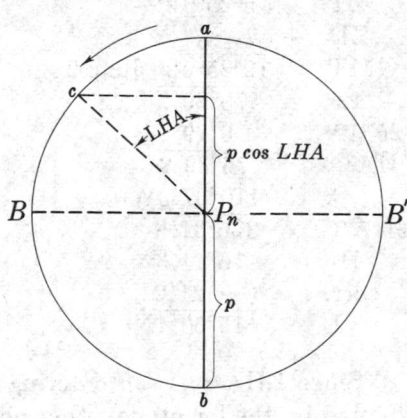

FIGURE 2027b.—The correction is (−)*aPn* when Polaris is at *a* and (+)*bPn* when at *b*. At any point *c* the correction is *p* cos LHA. At *B* or *B'* the correction is zero.

Although the above method usually provides sufficient accuracy for air navigation, a higher degree of accuracy may be obtained by use of Polaris correction tables included in the *Nautical Almanac*. These tables are based on the following formula:

Latitude—corrected sextant altitude$=-p\cos h+\frac{1}{2}\,p\sin p\sin^2 h\,\tan$ (latitude),
where $p=$polar distance of *Polaris*$=90°-$Dec.
$h=$local hour angle of *Polaris*$=$LHA Aries$+$SHA.

The value a_0, which is a function of LHA Aries only, is the value of both terms of the above formula calculated for mean values of the SHA and Dec. of Polaris, for a mean latitude of 50°, and adjusted by the addition of a constant (58.'8). The value a_1, which is a function of LHA Aries and latitude, is the excess of the value of the second term over its mean value for latitude 50°, increased by a constant (0.'6) to make it always positive. The value a_2, which is a function of LHA Aries and date, is the correction to the first term for the variation of Polaris from its adopted mean position; it is increased by a constant (0.'6) to make it positive. The sum of the added constants is 1°, so that:

Latitude$=$corrected sextant altitude$-1°+a_0+a_1+a_2$.

The table at the top of each Polaris correction page is entered with LHA Aries, and the first correction (a_0) is taken out by single interpolation. The second and third corrections (a_1 and a_2, respectively) are taken from the double entry tables without interpolation, using the LHA Aries column with the latitude for the second correction and with the month for the third correction.

Example 1.—During morning twilight on June 2, 1975, the 0525 DR position of a ship is lat. 15°43.'6N, long. 110°07.'3W. At watch time $5^h24^m49^s$ AM the navigator observes Polaris with a marine sextant having an IC of $(-)3.'0$, from a height of eye of 44 feet. The watch is 23^s slow on zone time. The hs is 16°24.'0.

Required.—The latitude.

Solution.—

	June 2		Polaris			$+$	☆	$-$
			$+$	$-$				
WT	$5^h24^m49^s$ AM				IC			3.'0
WE	(S)23^s	a_0	38.'2		D			6.'4
ZT	$5^h25^m12^s$	a_1	0.'3		☆-P			3.'3
ZD (+) 7		a_2	0.'3		sum			$(-)12.'7$
GMT	$12^h25^m12^s$ June 2	add'l		60.'0	corr.			$(-)12.'7$
12^h	70°20.'2	sum	38.'8	60.'0	hs			16°24.'0
25^m12^s	6°19.'0	corr.	$(-)21.'2$		Ho			16°11.'3
GHA ♈	76°39.'2							
λ	110°07.'3W							
LHA ♈	326°31.'9							
Ho	16°11.'3							
corr.	$(-)21.'2$							
L	15°50.'1N							

Since LHA ♈ is an entering value in all three correction tables, and since this is affected by the longitude, other observations, if available, should be solved and plotted first, to obtain a good longitude for the Polaris solution. For greater accuracy, particularly in higher latitudes, and especially if considerable doubt exists as to the longitude, it is good practice to find the azimuth of Polaris and draw the line of position perpendicular to it, through the point defined by the latitude found in the computation and the longitude used in the solution. The azimuth at various latitudes to 65°N is given below the Polaris corrections. This table can be extrapolated to higher latitudes, but Polaris would not ordinarily be used much beyond latitude 65°. In the example given above the azimuth is 000°.8.

The *Air Almanac* provides only the first correction, which it designates Q.

Polaris observations can be solved like those of other celestial bodies, using the declination and SHA given in the tabulation near the back of the *Nautical Almanac*.

The Polaris correction table in the *Air Almanac* lists the correction Q to be applied to the sextant altitude of Polaris to give the latitude of the observer. The correction is given in a critical table, with argument LHA Aries (♈) obtained from the daily pages. The effect of refraction is not included and so the sextant altitude must be fully corrected before use.

Example 2.—On 1 June 1975 at GMT $02^h53^m32^s$ in longitude 49°18'W, the corrected sextant altitude of Polaris is 54°46'.

Required.—The latitude.

Solution.—

GMT	$2^h53^m32^s$ June 1		Corr. sextant altitude		54°46'
2^h50^m	291°28'		Q (LHA ♈, 243°03')	(+)	44'
3^m32^s	0°53'		Latitude		55°30'
GHA ♈	292°21'				
λ	49°18'W				
LHA ♈	243°03'				

2028. Azimuth by tables.—One of the more frequent applications of sight reduction tables is their use in computing the azimuth of a celestial body for comparison with an observed azimuth in order to determine the error of the compass. In computing the azimuth of a celestial body, for the time and place of observation, it is normally necessary to interpolate the tabular azimuth angle as extracted from the tables for the differences between the table arguments and the actual values of declination, latitude, and local hour angle. The required triple interpolation of the azimuth angle using Pub. No. 229, *Sight Reduction Tables for Marine Navigation*, is effected as follows:

1. Refer to figure 2028a. The main tables are entered with the nearest integral values of declination, latitude, and local hour angle. For these arguments, a base azimuth angle is extracted.

2. The tables are reentered with the same latitude and LHA arguments but with the declination argument 1° greater or less than the base declination argument depending upon whether the actual declination is greater or less than the base argument. The difference between the respondent azimuth angle and the base azimuth angle establishes the azimuth angle difference (Z Diff.) for the increment of declination.

3. The tables are reentered with the base declination and LHA arguments but with the latitude argument 1° greater or less than the base latitude argument depending upon whether the actual (usually DR) latitude is greater or less than the base argument to find the Z Diff. for the increment of latitude.

4. The tables are reentered with the base declination and latitude arguments but with the LHA argument 1° greater or less than the base LHA argument depending upon whether the actual LHA is greater or less than the base argument to find the Z Diff. for the increment of LHA.

5. The correction to the base azimuth angle for each increment is Z Diff. $\times \dfrac{\text{Inc.}}{60'}$.

43°, 317° L.H.A. — LATITUDE SAME NAME AS DECLINATION

Dec.	30°			31°			32°			33°			34°			35°			Dec.
	Hc	d	Z	Hc	d	Z	Hc	d	Z	Hc	d	Z	Hc	d	Z	Hc	d	Z	
°	°			°			°			°			°			°			°
20	50 00.7	+23.2	94.2	49 55.7	+24.6	95.4	49 49.4	+26.1	96.6	49 41.9	+27.5	97.8	49 33.2	+28.9	98.9	49 23.3	+30.3	100.1	20
21	50 23.9	22.0	92.8	50 20.3	23.6	94.0	50 15.5	25.0	95.2	50 09.4	26.6	96.4	50 02.1	28.0	97.6	49 53.6	29.4	98.8	21

44°, 316° L.H.A. — LATITUDE SAME NAME AS DECLINATION

Dec.	30°			31°			32°			33°			34°			35°			Dec.
	Hc	d	Z	Hc	d	Z	Hc	d	Z	Hc	d	Z	Hc	d	Z	Hc	d	Z	
°	°			°			°			°			°			°			°
20	49 08.9	+23.0	93.7	49 04.5	+24.5	94.8	48 58.8	+26.0	96.0	48 52.0	+27.4	97.1	48 44.0	+28.8	98.2	48 34.8	+30.2	99.4	20
21	49 31.9	22.0	92.2	49 29.0	23.5	93.4	49 24.8	25.0	94.6	49 19.4	26.4	95.7	49 12.8	27.8	96.9	49 05.0	29.2	98.0	21

FIGURE 2028a.—Extracts from Pub. No. 229.

The auxiliary interpolation table (art. 206, vol. II) can normally be used for computing this value because the successive azimuth angle differences are less than 10.°0 for altitudes less than 84°.

Example 1.—In DR lat. 33°24.′0N, the azimuth of the sun is observed as 096.°5 pgc. At the time of the observation, the declination of the sun is 20°13.′8N; the local hour angle of the sun is 316°41.′2.

Required.—The gyro error.

Solution.—By Pub. No. 229:

The error of the gyrocompass is found as shown in figure 2028b.

	Actual	Base Arguments	Base Z	Tab* Z	Z Diff.	Increments	Correction (Z Diff × Inc. ÷ 60)
Dec.	20°13.′8N	20°	97.°8	96.°4	−1.°4	13.′8	−0.°3
DR Lat.	33°24.′0N	33°(Same)	97.°8	98.°9	+1.°1	24.′0	+0.°4
LHA	316°41.′2	317°	97.°8	97.°1	−0.°7	18.′8	−0.°2

Base Z	97.°8
Corr.	(−) 0.°1
Z	N 97.°7E
Zn	097.°7
Zn pgc	096.°5
Gyro Error	1.°2E

Total Corr.	−0.°1

*Respondent for two base arguments and 1° change from third base argument, in vertical order of Dec., DR Lat., and LHA.

FIGURE 2028b.—Azimuth by Pub. No. 229.

Using Pub. No. 214, *Tables of Computed Altitudes and Azimuth*, to determine the azimuth from the tabular values which are actually azimuth angles, interpolation is made for meridian angle, declination, and latitude.

Example 2.—In DR lat. 41°25.′9S, the azimuth of the sun is observed as 016.°0 pgc. At the time of the observation, the declination of the sun is 22°19.′6N; the meridian angle of the sun is 17°22.′4E.

Required.—The gyro error.

Solution.—By Pub. No. 214:

(1) Refer to appendix N. In this example the tabular azimuth angle used as base Z is compared with the tabular azimuth angle for the base declination and latitude, but meridian angle 18° to determine the Z Diff. for meridian angle. Similarly, the base Z is compared with the tabular value for the base meridian angle and latitude, but declination 22° to determine the Z Diff. for declination; and with the base value of meridian angle and declination, but latitude 42° to determine the Z Diff. for latitude.

(2) Interpolation is between whole degrees of meridian angle and latitude, but between half degrees of declination when the declination is 29° or less. For declinations of more than 29°, the interpolation interval for declination varies.

$$\text{t corr.} = \text{Z Diff.} \times \frac{\text{Increments}}{1°} = (-)1°0 \times \frac{0°4}{1°0} = (-)0°4.$$

$$\text{d corr.} = \text{Z Diff.} \times \frac{\text{Increments}}{0°5} = (-)0°1 \times \frac{0°2}{0°5} = (+)0°0.$$

$$\text{L corr.} = \text{Z Diff.} \times \frac{\text{Increments}}{1°} = (+)0°2 \times \frac{0°4}{1°0} = (+)0°1.$$

	Actual	Base Arguments	Base Z	Tab* Z	Z Diff.	Increments	Correction +	Correction −
t	17°.4E	17°	162°.7	161°.7	(−) 1°.0	0°.4		0°.4
d	22°.3N	22°30′	162°.7	162°.6	(−) 0°.1	0°.2	0°.0	
L	41°.4S	41°(Contrary)	162°.7	162°.9	(+) 0°.2	0°.4	· 0°.1	

Base Z	162°.7	Total Corr.	(−) 0°.3
Corr.	(−) 0°.3		
Z	S 162°.4E		
Zn	017°.6		
Znpgc	016°.0		
Gyro Error	1°.6E		

*Respondent for two base arguments and 1° (30′ for d) change from the third base argument, in vertical order of t, d, and L.

FIGURE 2028c.—Azimuth by Pub. No. 214.

The error of the gyrocompass is found as shown in figure 2028c.

Solutions for azimuth are discussed in more detail in chapter VII of volume II.

2029. Amplitudes.—For checking the compass, an azimuth observation of a celestial body at low altitude is desirable because it can be measured easiest and most accurately. If the body is observed when its center is on the *celestial* horizon, the **amplitude (A)**, which is the arc of the horizon between the prime vertical and the body, can be taken directly from table 27.

The amplitude is given the prefix E (east) if the body is rising and W (west) if setting. It is given the suffix N if the body rises or sets north of the prime vertical (which it does if it has northerly declination) and S if it rises or sets south of the prime vertical (having southerly declination). The suffix is given to agree with the declination of the body. Interconversion of amplitude and azimuth is similar to that of azimuth angle and azimuth. Thus, if A=E15°S, the body is 15° south of east or 90°+15°=105°. For any given body, the numerical value of amplitude would be the same at rising and setting if the declination did not change.

When the center of the sun is on the celestial horizon, its *lower limb* is about two-thirds of a diameter above the visible horizon. When the center of the moon is on the celestial horizon, its *upper limb* is on the visible horizon. When planets and stars are on the celestial horizon, they are a little more than one sun diameter above the visible horizon. In high latitudes, amplitudes should be observed on the visible horizon.

If the body is observed when its center is on the *visible horizon*, the *observed* value should be corrected by the value from table 28, using the rules given with the table, before comparison with the value taken from table 27. If preferred, the correction can be applied with reversed sign to the value taken from table 27 and compared with the uncorrected observed value. This is the procedure used if amplitude or azimuth is desired when the celestial body is on the visible horizon.

Amplitudes are discussed in more detail in article 740 of volume II.

CHAPTER XXI

COMPARISON OF VARIOUS METHODS OF SIGHT REDUCTION

2101. Introduction.—Before the development of a means of determining accurate time at sea (art. 127), longitude could not be found by celestial observation. Celestial bodies were used for determination of latitude, and as an indication of direction, often in a very general way. The development of the marine chronometer opened up a whole new vista to the navigator. Immediately, methods began to appear to utilize this new dimension of navigation. During the two centuries that have elapsed, many of the best minds have been directed to the problem of providing easier or more adequate methods of "reducing" the observations to a form suitable for determination of position.

2102. Kinds of methods.—Various "special" methods have been devised to take advantage of some unique relationship to provide a simplified solution. The most widely used are **latitude methods** for determination of latitude by meridian altitude or observation of Polaris, and **longitude methods** for determination of longitude by observation of a body near the prime vertical. Both latitude and longitude methods have now been largely superseded by the **altitude method,** based upon the discovery of the altitude intercept, or difference, by the Frenchman Marcq St.-Hilaire (art. 131). Most modern methods are of this type, although some latitude and longitude methods are still in use.

The most commonly used methods utilize computation for determining certain information which is then plotted as a line of position, two or more such lines being needed for a fix. The "method" might consist of one or more formulas to be solved by general mathematical tables, a set of special tables conveniently arranged for use with the formulas, or a set of tables constituting a list of computed answers. A method which determines latitude or longitude separately requires no plot. In fact, a plot would be misleading unless the celestial body were almost exactly on the celestial meridian or prime vertical, or unless the azimuth were considered. While a number of methods determine latitude and longitude by computation, without plotting, other methods substitute a graphical or mechanical solution for computation.

2103. Meridian altitudes.—If a celestial body is on the celestial meridian at the time of observation, a modification of the high-altitude method (art. 2024) can be used at any altitude, without plotting the GP. Both GP and observer are on the same meridian, and the difference of latitude between them is the zenith distance of the body (90°—Ho). The direction of the GP is the direction faced during observation (unless a backsight is made). The line of position is a latitude line.

Several hundred years ago, when longitude could not be found accurately, and logarithms had not been invented, the finding of latitude furnished the only reliable navigation available on long sea voyages. Since most of these were in a generally easterly or westerly direction, it became common practice to sail first to the latitude of destination ("run down the latitude") and then to follow this parallel until landfall was made. The meridian observation of the sun at local apparent noon was the most important navigational event of the day, and became a well-established routine. On the basis of this observation at "high noon," clocks were reset, and a new day, the **nautical day,** began. Intentional meridian altitudes of other celestial bodies were not as widely used as those of the sun.

As accurate time became available at sea, and then more convenient tables and more accurate almanacs appeared, the noon sight lost its importance. Since the modern inspection table has been available, the use of meridian altitudes has decreased rapidly, and reduction to the meridian has all but disappeared. True, the solution of a meridian altitude is simple and quick, but this is more than offset by the need for determining the time at which to make the observation (art. 2025), the dislike of many mariners for having to make an observation at a predetermined time, the inconvenience sometimes experienced when local apparent noon occurs at a time when other activities conflict with observation, and the possibility of missing the observation because of overcast conditions. The practice of observing a body when a line of position is desired, and solving those which happen to have a meridian angle of 0° or 180° in the same manner as other observations, is a growing practice that eliminates the need for remembering a separate procedure for bodies on the celestial meridian. The modern navigator thinks primarily in terms of lines of position, rather than of latitude and longitude observations.

Meridian altitudes are discussed in more detail in article 2025.

2104. Ex-meridian altitudes.—If an observation is made near but not exactly at meridian transit, it can be solved as a meridian altitude, with one modification. Enter table 29 with the approximate latitude of the observer and the declination of the body, and take out the **altitude factor** (*a*). This is the difference between meridian altitude and the altitude one minute of time later (or earlier). Next, enter table 30 with the altitude factor and the difference of time between meridian transit and the time of observation, and take out the correction. *Add* this value to Ho if near upper transit, or *subtract* it from Ho if near lower transit. Then proceed as for a meridian altitude, remembering that the value obtained is the latitude at the time of observation, not at the time of meridian transit. This method should not be used beyond the limits of table 30 unless reduced accuracy is acceptable. This process is called **reduction to the meridian,** the altitude before adjustment an **ex-meridian altitude,** and the observation an **ex-meridian observation.** It requires knowledge of the meridian angle, which depends upon knowledge of longitude. If reasonable doubt exists regarding the longitude, the azimuth of the body at the time of observation should be determined, and the line of position drawn perpendicular to it (through the point defined by the "observed" latitude and the assumed longitude), rather than as a latitude line. There are alternative methods available. A correction to latitude can be applied, using the factor f from table 26. In 1899 A. A. Vilkitskiy, a captain in the Russian Navy, developed a mechanical device for determining the correction to be applied for reduction to the meridian.

2105. Latitude by Polaris.—Another special method of finding latitude, available in most of the Northern Hemisphere, utilizes the fact that Polaris is less than 1° from the north celestial pole. As indicated in article 1432, the altitude of the elevated pole above the celestial horizon is equal to the latitude. Since Polaris is never far from the pole, its observed altitude (Ho), with suitable correction, is the latitude.

Like other special solutions, latitude by Polaris has lost much of its popularity since modern inspection tables have become available. Being of magnitude 2.1, Polaris is not a bright star. It is normally considered available to the mariner only during twilight, when the azimuths of various celestial bodies relative to each other are of more interest than an "easy" solution which is little, if at all, simpler than the usual solution by inspection table. If provision were made for solution of Polaris sights by inspection table, the special method would no longer be needed for ordinary navigation.

2106. Longitude methods.—A celestial observation for a line of position, whether reduction is to be by longitude method or by latitude method, consists of measurement of the altitude of a body with the noting of the time. If sight reduction is to be by the longitude method, the latitude must be known, or the best estimate used. With altitude, latitude, and declination (from the almanac), one is able to solve the navigational triangle (art. 1433) for meridian angle. This is converted to local hour angle. The Greenwich hour angle at the time of observation is determined by means of the almanac. The difference between the GHA and LHA is the longitude. A time diagram (art. 1428) is useful in establishing the correct relationship.

Longitude can also be determined by establishing the exact time of meridian transit, at which time the GHA (or 360°−GHA) is the longitude.

If the latitude is known accurately, the longitude method provides a direct and relatively simple solution for position. However, since latitude is rarely known to the desired accuracy, a line of position is usually needed. This is obtained by either (1) solving for longitude at two or more assumed latitudes, and drawing a straight line through the points thus found (the Sumner method), or (2) solving for longitude at one point, determining the azimuth at this point, and drawing the line of position through the single point thus found, perpendicular to the azimuth of the body.

The error introduced in the computed longitude as a result of an inaccurate latitude used in the solution increases as the celestial body departs from the prime vertical. If it is learned that an incorrect latitude has been used in the solution, a correction can be applied, using the factor F from table 26. If the body is near the celestial meridian, a small error in the latitude introduces a large error in the longitude. At any location, the azimuth of the body can be determined by observation or computation, and a line of position drawn perpendicular to it, through the position defined by the latitude used in the computation, and the calculated longitude. Alternatively, solution can be made at two or more latitudes, and the line of position drawn through the two positions. It was the use of this second method in 1837 by Captain Thomas H. Sumner, when his latitude was in doubt, that led to the discovery of the line of position from celestial observation (art. 131).

No longitude method is more accurate than the GMT used for timing the observation. Before chronometers (art. 1514) and time signals (art. 1826) were available, relatively few navigators attempted to determine longitude, and it was never established reliably. The search for a method of "discovering" longitude at sea was primarily a search for a means of determining time at the Greenwich meridian (arts. 126, 127).

If the longitude is to be determined, most accurate results are obtained, by observation of a body on the prime vertical. The observation having been made, sight reduction can be made by time sight or, more conveniently, by an ordinary solution for a line of position, using an inspection table such as Pub. No. 229. Any general method of sight reduction can be used, without need for a special solution.

Solution by the longitude method is usually called a **time sight.** The various longitude methods are all basically the same, differing only in choice of formulas and arrangement of tables. The basic formula is

$$\cos\ t = \frac{\sin h - \sin L \sin d}{\cos L \cos d},$$

in which t is the meridian angle, h is the altitude, L is the latitude, and d is the declination. Early tables for solution of meridian angle were called **horary tables.**

The time sight came into use following the development of the marine chronometer in 1763. Solution for meridian angle is usually by the formula

$$\text{hav } t = \sec L \csc p \cos S \sin (S-h),$$

in which p=90°−d if L and d have same name, and 90°+d if L and d have contrary names; and S=½(h+L+p).

When azimuth angle is used with the method, it is usually computed by one of the formulas

$$\sin Z = \sin t \cos d \sec h$$

or

$$\text{hav} (180° - Z) = \sec h \sec L \cos S \cos (S-p).$$

There are no rules with this method, but it is subject to possible large errors in high latitudes or if the body has a high declination. Various special tables have appeared for solution of the time sight:

Cassini. The first "inspection tables" were probably prepared by M. Cassini, a Frenchman, in 1770. These "horary tables" provided tabulated solutions for meridian angle.

Lalande. The horary tables prepared in 1793 by Jerome Lalande, a Frenchman, provided tabulated solution for meridian angle for the sun and stars for all latitudes to 61°.

Lynn Horary Tables, by Thomas Lynn, a commander of the East India Company Service, were published in 1827. These 242-page tables consisted of tabulated solutions of meridian angle computed by the time sight formula. Two years later they were followed by a volume of 364 pages of azimuth angle (*Lynn Azimuth Tables*) computed by the haversine azimuth formula. Entries are given for whole degrees of latitude to 60°, declination to 24°, and altitude to 60° (later 90°). The tables are accurate and well arranged, but the triple interpolation is tedious.

Hommey. Louis Hommey's *Table d'angles horaires* (horary tables), published in two volumes in France in 1863, contained more than 40,000 hour angles calculated for "all latitudes." These tables were an improvement on those of Cassini and Lalande.

Martelli. In 1873 a small volume of 49 pages by G. F. Martelli, an Italian, was published in New Orleans. This book, called simply *Tables of Logarithms*, provided a relatively, short, fast solution for meridian angle, with very few rules and only one interpolation. Martelli abandoned the inspection table and provided five short tables for a four-place logarithmic solution by the formula

$$\text{hav } t = \frac{\cos (L \sim d) - \cos z}{2 \cos L \cos d}.$$

Solution required six book openings, six table entries, and four mathematical steps. Hour angles were given only to eight hours, and no provision was made for azimuth.

This method proved very popular, and is still used among navigators of several countries. A 1932 edition was published in Glasgow, Scotland, with explanations in French, Dutch, Italian, and Spanish, as well as in English. A 1944 edition added provision for finding azimuth angle, and for solution by the altitude method.

Thomson. A table of only nine pages by Sir William Thomson, better known as Lord Kelvin, was published in London in 1876 to provide a solution for the longitude method. This very thin volume, called *Tables for Facilitating Sumner's Method at Sea*, contains the first known solution by dividing the navigational triangle into two right triangles. In 1849 Towson (art. 2126) had divided the triangle in the same manner, but this solution was for reduction to the meridian. Lord Kelvin divided the triangle by dropping a perpendicular from the celestial body to the celestial meridian of the observer, as shown in figure 2111. He used a for the length of the perpendicular v, b' for x, and b for w (of fig. 2111). His solution uses the formulas

$$\sin\ t = \frac{\sin a}{\cos d},$$

$$\cos\ b = \frac{\sin d}{\cos a},$$

$$\sin\ h = \cos\ a\ \cos\ b',$$

$$\sin\ z = \frac{\sin a}{\cos h}.$$

The tables are entered with *half* the colatitude (using colatitude to the nearest whole degree) in column *b*. With a pair of dividers, search is made in the "cohypo" column for two numbers, one agreeing with the altitude, and the other with the declination. The number in column *A* opposite the altitude in the cohypo column is the azimuth angle, and that opposite the declination is the meridian angle, interpolation being used if needed. The line of position is adjusted for the difference between the interpolated altitude and the observed altitude.

Although the tables are among the shortest of the various methods, their manipulation is difficult. In 1880 Kortazzi, a Russian astronomer, attempted to modify the tables to provide an easier solution, but without great success.

Davis' *Chronometer Tables,* providing a solution for the longitude method, were published in 1897 in London. They are similar to Lynn's tables, using his values but providing assistance in interpolation by adding values of change with latitude, declination, and altitude. As with Lynn, a separate volume is given for azimuth angle, in which there is no interpolation. Originally Davis' tables were limited to latitude 50° and declination 24°, but later tables were published for declinations 23° to 64°. A limited number of altitude entries is given.

Blackburne. Tables by H. S. Blackburne, a New Zealander, were published in London in 1914 under the title *The Excelsior Azimuth and Position Finding Table.* The tables, providing a solution by the longitude method, are similar to *Lynn Horary Tables* and Davis' *Chronometer Tables* but with a new determination of azimuth based upon the ratio of variation of latitude to variation of meridian angle. Azimuth angles (ten pages) are given in a separate tabulation in the same volume with meridian angles (242 pages).

Blackburne's arrangement is more modern than that of Davis. This was the first publication to include columns for variations of t for 1′ of declination, latitude, and altitude. Meridian angles are given to $0^{s}.1$. Latitude is limited to 30°, and declination to 23°.

Rust. In 1918 the *Practical Tables for Navigators and Aviators,* by Captain Armistead Rust, USN, were published in Philadelphia. This small volume of 37 pages of tables reverted to a logarithmic solution, as did Martelli's, using the following formula for determining meridian angle:

$$\log \text{hav}\ t = \log \sec L + \log \sec d + \log\ \tfrac{1}{2}\ [\cos\ (L \sim d) - \sin\ h].$$

The volume has three tables. Table *A* tabulates log secants for obtaining the first two terms of the formula. Table *B* is a double-entry table giving log $\frac{1}{2}$ [cos (L$\sim$d) $-$sin h]. Table *C* gives log haversines. Values are given to four places.

Azimuth angle is obtained from an original diagram computed from the well-known formula

$$\sin Z = \sin\ t\ \cos\ d\ \sec\ h.$$

This diagram had been given in a volume of ex-meridian tables by Rust published in 1908. In the *Practical Tables* an auxiliary diagram was added to indicate the meridian angle when the celestial body is on the prime vertical. The purpose of the diagram is to resolve possible ambiguities when the azimuth angle is near 90°. The Rust azimuth diagram was used later by Goodwin and Weems, and in the Italian *Tavole H* (art. 2110).

Goodwin. *The Alpha, Beta, Gamma Navigation Tables* of H. B. Goodwin, an Englishman, were first published in London in 1921. This is a small volume having two tables with a total of 34 pages. Meridian angle is found from the formula

$$\text{ver } t = \frac{\cos (L \sim d) - \cos z}{\cos L \cos d}.$$

Table I has two values, α being the angle in seconds of arc, and β being four-place natural cosines multiplied by 1,000 to eliminate the decimal. Table II provides γ, the logarithms for the values of versine t.

The Rust diagram is used for determining azimuth angle.

Instructions are included for use of the tables for altitude method of solution, and for reduction to the meridian.

H.O. Pubs. Nos. 203 and 204 (Littlehales), *The Sumner Line of Position of Celestial Bodies,* were published by the U. S. Navy Hydrographic Office in 1923. These tables, prepared by George W. Littlehales, provide in two large volumes (847 and 675 pages, respectively) tabulated solutions of the meridian angle and azimuth angle, using the general time sight formulas. The arrangement is similar to that of Davis and Blackburne, but t and Z are tabulated together in consecutive columns. Latitude is limited to 60°, and declination to 27° in H.O. Pub. No. 203 and to 64° in H.O. Pub. No. 204. Interpolation for latitude is avoided by using the nearest whole degree, and shifting the line of position for the difference between the altitude at this latitude and the observed altitude.

These publications are no longer in print.

Soule and Dreisonstok. In 1932 these two Americans prepared a small volume providing a logarithmic solution of the longitude method, using the formulas

$$\frac{1}{\text{hav } t} = \frac{\sec S \csc (S-h)}{\sec L \csc p}$$

and

$$\frac{1}{\text{hav } (180° - Z)} = \frac{\sec S \sec (S-p)}{\sec L \sec h},$$

where $S = \frac{1}{2} (h+L+p)$ and $p = 90° \pm d$.

The "azimuth" determined in this way is the direction of the line of position $(Z \pm 90°)$ rather than that of the celestial body.

Weems' *Secant Time Sight* was published in 1944 by Captain P. V. H. Weems, USN (Ret.), to provide a short solution based entirely upon secants and cosecants, using the formulas

$$\csc^2 \frac{1}{2} t = \frac{\sec S \csc (S-h)}{\sec L \sec d}$$

and

$$\csc Z = \frac{\csc t \sec d}{\sec h},$$

where $S = \frac{1}{2} (h+L+p)$. A Rust azimuth diagram is included for those who prefer a diagrammatic solution.

2107. Finding time on prime vertical.—Best results by time sight are obtained when the celestial body is on the prime vertical. As explained in article 1432, a celestial body having a declination of opposite name to the latitude crosses the prime vertical below the horizon. Its nearest visible approach is at the time of rising and setting.

If a celestial body has a declination of the same name as the latitude, but is numerically *greater*, it does not cross the prime vertical. Its nearest approach (in azimuth) is at the point at which its azimuth angle is maximum. At this point the meridian angle is given by the formula

$$\sec t = \tan d \cot L,$$

and its altitude by the formula

$$\csc h = \sin d \csc L.$$

A celestial body having a declination of the same name as the latitude, and numerically *smaller*, crosses the prime vertical at some point before it reaches the celestial meridian, and again after meridian transit. At these two crossings of the prime vertical, the meridian angles are equal and are always less than 90°. They are given by the formula

$$\cos t = \tan d \cot L.$$

The altitudes are also equal, and are given by the formula

$$\sin h = \sin d \csc L.$$

Meridian angle and altitude of bodies on the prime vertical, and similar data for the nearest approach (in azimuth) of those bodies of same name which do not cross the prime vertical, are given in table 25 for various latitudes, and for declinations from 0° to 23°, inclusive. Similar information can be determined by means of Pub. No. 214, entering with latitude and declination, and finding the meridian angle and altitude corresponding to an azimuth angle of 90° (or the maximum azimuth angle for nearest approach). Since this information is generally not required to great accuracy, interpolation is not needed.

To find the *time* of crossing the prime vertical, convert t to LHA, and add west longitude or subtract east longitude to find GHA. The GMT at which this GHA occurs can be found and converted to any other time desired.

Example.—Determine (1) the approximate zone time, and (2) the approximate altitude of the sun when it crosses the prime vertical during the afternoon of May 30, 1975, at lat. 51°32ʹ3N, long. 160°21ʹ7W, using table 25 and the *Nautical Almanac.*

Solution.—

		May 30	
t		71°6W	(from table 25)
LHA		71°6	
λ		160°4W	
GHA		232°0	
3ʰ		225°6	
26ᵐ		6°4	
GMT		0326	May 31
ZD(+)11			(rev.)
(1) ZT		1626	May 30
(2) h		28°4	(from table 25)

At the time of crossing the prime vertical, or at nearest approach (in azimuth), a celestial body is changing azimuth slowly, and therefore this is considered a good time to check compass deviation or to swing ship.

The prime vertical at any place is the celestial horizon of a point 90° away, on the same meridian. Therefore, a celestial body crosses the prime vertical at approximately the same time it rises and sets at the point 90° away. Thus, if one is at latitude 35°N, the sun crosses his prime vertical at about the same time it rises or sets at latitude 55°S. If time of sunrise and sunset are to be obtained accurately by this method, corrections must be applied for semidiameter and refraction.

2108. Altitude methods, like longitude methods, require an accurately timed observed altitude of a celestial body. Usually, in both types of solution, the navigational triangle is solved, but in the altitude method, t, d, and L are used in solving for altitude. The method is based upon the concept of circles of equal altitude explained by Commander Marcq St.-Hilaire, a Frenchman, in 1875 (art. 131). For this reason it is often called the **Marcq St.-Hilaire method.** It may also be called the **altitude intercept method** because it uses the difference between computed and observed altitudes, a value called an **altitude intercept.**

The altitude method has largely replaced the latitude and longitude methods, although some navigators still prefer the older methods. The principal advantage of the altitude method is that it provides a universal solution that is equally reliable in all latitudes, with all values of declination, and with all values of meridan angle. Even for observations of celestial bodies near the zenith the altitude method is applicable, although in this case an arc of the circle itself is plotted, without the use of the altitude intercept (art. 2024). However, the formulas selected for some of the "short methods" do impose some limitations when those methods are used.

For many years following introduction of the altitude method, the concept was termed the "new navigation," an expression now seldom heard. At first, an attempt was made to adapt existing tables to the altitude method. Some were more readily adaptable than others. In due course, various methods designed for use with the altitude method made their appearance. These methods may be grouped in six classifications: those which do not divide the triangle, those which divide it by dropping a perpendicular from each of the three vertices, those which do not use the navigational triangle, and the modern "inspection table." However, not all inspection tables are for altitude methods. In practice, the dropping of a perpendicular from the pole has not been used except in great-circle sailing (art. 903). This would result in dividing both the meridian angle and zenith distance into two parts, a condition that has not proved attractive.

2109. Altitude methods, triangle not divided.—The basic formula for solution of the undivided navigational triangle is

$$\sin h = \sin L \sin d + \cos L \cos d \cos t,$$

derived from the law of cosines. A number of special tables have been prepared for solution of the undivided triangle:

Davis' *Requisite Tables,* published in London in 1905, introduced the **cosine-haversine formula** to navigation, although it had been used previously by astronomers. This formula is

$$\text{hav } z = \text{hav } (L \sim d) + \cos L \cos d \text{ hav } t,$$

in which z is zenith distance (90°−h). This is sometimes written

$$\text{hav } z = \text{hav } (L \sim d) + \text{hav } \theta,$$

in which hav $\theta = \cos$ L cos d hav t. It might also be written entirely in haversines:

$$\text{hav } z = \text{hav } (d-L) + \text{hav } t \,[\text{hav } (180°-L-d) - \text{hav } (d-L)].$$

In this formula the sign of d is reversed if L and d are of contrary name. The haversine of an angle is positive whether the angle is positive or negative.

These tables were the first to give log haversines and natural haversines in one table. The method was little used at first, but later proved very popular, and as haversines became available from additional sources, the formula was used even more widely. Davis' original tables made no provision for azimuth.

Since the cosine-haversine formula can be used for solution with tables 33 and 34, an example is given below, with solution of azimuth by the formula

$$\sin Z = \sin t \cos d \sec h.$$

Example.—A celestial body a little to the south of west is observed, with the following results: t 80°45ʹ9W, aL 41°12ʹ3S, d 21°50ʹ7S.

Required.—The Hc and Zn by the formulas given above.

Solution.—

t 80°45ʹ9W	l hav 9.62300	l sin 9.99434
aL 41°12ʹ3S	l cos 9.87643	
d 21°50ʹ7S	l cos 9.96764	l cos 9.96764
θ —	l hav 9.46707	
L∼d 19°21ʹ6		n hav 0.29313
z 69°04ʹ3		n hav 0.02827
Hc 20°55ʹ7		n hav 0.32140
Zn 258°8		l sec 10.02964
	Z S78°47ʹ0W	l sin 9.99162

This is typical of logarithmic solutions, except that there are no "rules" for the altitude computation. As pointed out in article 2125, the formula used for azimuth angle does not indicate whether the body is north or south of the prime vertical.

Ball. In 1907 Rev. Frederick Ball's *Altitude or Position Line Tables* were published in London. There are two volumes of 244 and 240 (later 313) pages, respectively, the first volume having tables for latitude 0° to 30°, and the second, 31° to 60° (later editions 24° to 60°). These were the first inspection tables for the altitude method. The tabulated altitudes were computed by the haversine formula. The assumed position is selected so that latitude and meridian angle are the nearest whole degree, but no assistance is given for interpolation of altitude for declination.

Azimuth angle is not tabulated, being found by the altitude tables, interchanging altitude and declination, and finding azimuth angle (in hours and minutes) in the meridian angle columns. Since declination is limited to 24° in the first edition and 60° in later editions, this method is not available for azimuth if altitude is greater than this amount. In this case azimuth angle is found by the formula

$$\sin Z = \frac{\sec L \times \Delta h \ (\text{for } 8^m)}{120}.$$

This formula had not previously been used in navigation.

Davis' *Alt-Azimuth Tables* were published in London in 1917. This volume lists both altitude and azimuth together for the first time. Latitudes included are from 30° to 64°, and declinations from 0° to 24°. In 1921 a second volume was pubished for latitudes 0° to 30°. Entries are for each whole degree of latitude and declination, and for each 4^m (1°) of meridian angle. However, for each meridian angle, altitude *or* azimuth angle is given alternately. Thus, azimuth angle is given for meridian angles of 0^m, 8^m, 16^m, 24^m, etc., and altitude for meridian angles of 4^m, 12^m, 20^m, 28^m, etc. Altitudes are given in bold type. All declination entries (0° to 24°) are given on facing pages. Tables for latitude and declination of the same name are given in the first part of the book and those for contrary names in the last part, the two parts being separated by several auxiliary tables. Altitude is given to the nearest 1', and azimuth angle to the nearest 0°.1. Altitudes are carried down to the horizon, and the local apparent times of sunrise and sunset are also given, with the azimuth angle at these times. Because of the 8^m interval between altitude entries, and the use of an assumed position to avoid interpolation for change in meridian angle, large altitude differences sometimes arise.

H.O. Pub. No. 201, *Simultaneous Altitudes and Azimuths of Celestial Bodies*, was published by the U. S. Navy Hydrographic Office in 1919. In this volume of 606 pages, altitudes and azimuths were tabulated in parallel columns for the first time. Latitude is limited to 60° and declination to 24°. Virtually all altitudes above the horizon are included. The tables are well arranged and very legible, but no assistance is given for interpolation of altitude or azimuth angle for a change of declination. Meridian angles are given at intervals of 10^m (2°.5). Since the assumed position is selected to avoid interpolation of altitude or azimuth for meridian angle, large altitude differences result in some instances. This publication is no longer in print.

Yonemura. In 1920 S. Yonemura's *Tables for Calculating Altitude and Azimuth of Celestial Bodies* were published in Japan. This small table of 39 pages contains logarithms of haversines and secants, arranged for convenient solution of the formulas

$$\text{hav } (90°-h)-\text{hav } (L\sim d)=\text{hav } \theta,$$

$$\log \frac{1}{\text{hav } \theta} - (\log \sec L + \log \sec d) = \log \frac{1}{\text{hav } t},$$

$$\log \csc Z = \log \csc t + \log \sec d - \log \sec h.$$

The method is similar to that of **Davis'** *Requisite Tables* but includes solution for azimuth angle. The table is included in the book of Ogura's tables (art. 2110).

Braga. The *Táboas de Alturas* by Romêo Braga, a Brazilian, were published in 1924 in Paris. This is a table of natural haversines arranged for solution of the formula in which

$$\text{hav } (90°-h)=A+B,$$

in which $A=\text{hav } t-[\text{hav } (L+d) \text{ hav } t]$

and $B=\text{hav } (L-d)-[\text{hav } (L-d) \text{ hav } t].$

The first table of 108 pages is for solution for A and B. The second table of nine pages is for finding h.

The assumed latitude is selected so that (L+d) is a whole degree. The assumed longitude is selected so that t is a whole degree.

No provision is made for azimuth.

Japanese H.O. Pub. No. 601, *Celestial Navigation Computation Tables,* was published in 1942. The method is similar to that of Yonemura, the triangle not being divided and a modification of the cosine-haversine formula being used for altitude.

Waller. In 1946 George W. D. Waller, a naval officer on duty as a navigation instructor at the U. S. Naval Academy, proposed a solution by means of Gaussian logarithms, commonly called "addition and subtraction logs." The formula

$$\csc h = \frac{\csc d \csc L}{1 + \dfrac{\csc d \csc L}{\sec d \sec L \sec t}}$$

was derived from the basic formula given above,

and

$$\csc Z = \frac{\csc t \sec d}{\sec h}$$

was derived from the time and altitude azimuth formula given in article 2125.

A single table of 30 pages would contain in consecutive columns the following values:

$$
\begin{aligned}
A\ &=\log \text{secant} \\
B\ &=\log \text{cosecant} \\
C-&=\log (\text{cosecant}+1)-\log \text{cosecant} \\
C+&=\log \text{cosecant}-\log (\text{cosecant}-1).
\end{aligned}
$$

All values would be multiplied by 100,000 to eliminate decimals. One additional page would contain A and B values for all whole degrees from $0°$ to $180°$. The values C+ and C− are the Gaussian logs.

The method is reasonably short and simple. Its publication as the "A, B, C Method," with suitable explanation, was prevented by the untimely death of its originator.

Hugon. *Nouvelles Tables Pour le Calcul de la Droite de Hauteur a Partir du Point Estimé,* by the French hydrographic engineer, Professor P. Hugon, were published in 1947. This logarithmic solution is based upon the fundamental formula

$$\sin h = \sin L \sin d + \cos L \cos d \cos t,$$

from which the following is derived:

$$\text{hav } z = Xy + Yx$$

in which

$$
\begin{aligned}
X &= \text{hav } (180°-t) = \text{cohav } t \\
y &= \text{hav } (d-L) \\
Y &= \text{hav } t \\
x &= \text{hav } [180°-(d+L)] = \text{cohav } (d+L).
\end{aligned}
$$

The formula for z may then be written

$$\text{hav } z = A + B$$

in which

$$
\begin{aligned}
\log A &= \log X + \log y \\
\log B &= \log Y + \log x.
\end{aligned}
$$

Solution is by means of a table of 90 pages which lists in parallel columns values of log cohav, log hav, and natural hav for every minute of arc from $0°$ to $180°$. The solution requires six book openings, seven table entries, and five mathematical steps.

Azimuth is found from a diagram in a pocket on the inside back cover. This diagram is designed to solve the formula

$$M = \alpha X + \beta Y,$$

in which

$$M = \cos h \cos Z$$
$$\alpha = \sin (d-L)$$
$$X = \cos^2 \frac{t}{2}$$
$$\beta = \sin (d+L)$$
$$Y = \sin^2 \frac{t}{2}.$$

Chiesa. About 1948 the *Tavole nautiche e Tavole dei Semisenoversi* of the Italian Stefano Chiesa were published in Genova, Italy. These include tables for computation of altitude by the cosine-haversine formula, and "A, B, C" tables for computation of azimuth angle by the formula

$$\text{hav } Z = [\text{hav } p - \text{hav}(L-h)] \sec L \sec h.$$

Rose. In 1952 the *Nautische Tafeln* of G. Rose were published in Germany. This volume has a convenient table for computation of the altitude by the cosine-haversine formula. It also includes the "A, B, C" azimuth tables of Lecky (art. 2126). Various other tables are included, a number of them having been taken from an earlier work of the same name by Dr. Otto Fulst, published in numerous editions since 1860.

Doniol. The *Miniature Navigation Table for Altitude and Azimuth*, by R. Doniol, a Frenchman, was published in 1955. This is undoubtedly the shortest of all sight reduction tables, consisting of only two pages. The formula for altitude was derived from the basic formula given above. The formula used is

$$\sin h = n - (n+m)\, a,$$

in which $n = \cos (L-d)$, $m = \cos (L+d)$, and $a = \text{hav } t$.
The formula for Z was derived from the formula

$$\cot Z = \frac{\tan d \cos L - \cos t \sin L}{\sin t}.$$

The formula used is

$$\tan Z = \frac{\cos d}{\gamma},$$

in which $\gamma = f\Delta_M + f'\Delta_N$. In this expression, $f = \dfrac{\tan \frac{1}{2} t}{2 \sin 1'}$, $f' = \dfrac{\cot \frac{1}{2} t}{2 \sin 1'}$, $\Delta_M = \sin (d+L)\sin 1'$, and $\Delta_N = \sin (d-L)\sin 1'$.

The first of the two tables gives sines and cosines for each half degree, and tangents for half degrees of 45° and more. Interpolation is performed by means of a tabulated Δ value which is the change of sine or cosine for 1'. Interpolation is minimized by selecting an assumed position so that t and either (L+d) or (L−d) are an exact half degree.

The second table gives the value of t in degrees, minutes, and seconds, and the values of f and f′ corresponding to selected values of a (natural haversines). The interval between consecutive tabulated values of haversine varies from 0.0002 to 0.005.

The solution is generally accurate to 0.'1 of altitude and 0°.1 of azimuth, but the method requires a number of relatively simple mathematical steps, making it somewhat longer than most "short" solutions.

2110. Altitude methods, perpendicular from zenith.—In figure 2110 the navigational triangle is shown in heavy lines on a diagram on the plane of the celestial meridian (art. 1432). The broken line is a perpendicular from the zenith to the hour circle of the celestial body. This perpendicular may fall outside the triangle. In figure 2110 it divides both the azimuth angle (at Z) and the codeclination side into two parts. The length of the perpendicular is designated v and the two parts of the codeclination are designated w and x. By means of Napier's rules (art. 142, vol. II), the following basic formulas can be derived:

$$\sin v = \cos L \sin t \tag{1}$$
$$\cos w = \sin L \sec v, \text{ or } \tan w = \cot L \cos t \tag{2}$$
$$\sin Z' = \sin w \sec L, \text{ or } \cot Z' = \sin L \tan t \tag{3}$$
$$\sin h = \cos v \cos x \tag{4}$$
$$\sin Z'' = \sin x \sec h, \text{ or } \cos Z'' = \tan v \tan h, \tag{5}$$

in which $x = 90° - (d + w)$.

This basic method has been modified in a number of ways, having proved the most popular altitude method.

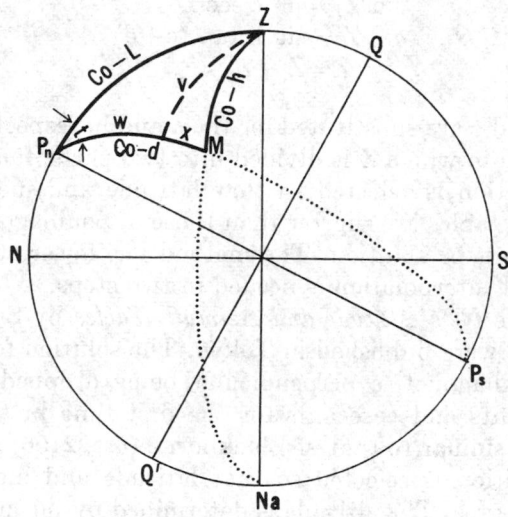

FIGURE 2110.—Navigational triangle with perpendicular from zenith to hour circle.

Souillagouet, a French professor of hydrography, was the first to divide the navigational triangle by dropping a perpendicular from the zenith. His *Tables du Point Auxiliare* were published in France in 1891. He designates various parts of the diagram of figure 2110 as follows:

v is designated a
w is designated b
x is designated $90° - (d \sim b)$.

His formulas for altitude are

$$\tan b = \cot L \cos t$$
$$\sin a = \cos L \sin t$$
$$\sin h = \cos a \sin (d \sim b).$$

For azimuth angle, the perpendicular is dropped from the celestial body to the celestial meridian, a being the perpendicular and b that part of the celestial meridian from the pole to the foot of the perpendicular. The following formulas are used:

$$\tan b = \cos t \cot d$$
$$\sin a = \sin t \cos d$$
$$\cot Z = \cos (L+b) \cot a.$$

The assumed position is selected so that latitude is the nearest 15′ and meridian angle is the nearest 1^m or 15′ (2^m or 30′ for latitudes greater than 60°). There are four separate tables with a total of 408 pages. The method requires five book openings, seven table entries, and six mathematical steps. Interpolation is not needed.

Bertin. A French professor of hydrography, Charles Bertin, devised tables similar to those of Souillagouet, which were published in Paris in 1919 under the title *Tablette de Point Sphérique*. Bertin used Souillagouet's formulas for altitude, but for azimuth angle he dropped the perpendicular from the zenith, as for altitude, and used the following formulas:

$$\sin Z_1 = \sin c \sec L$$
$$\cot Z_2 = \sin b \tan (c+d)$$
$$Z = Z_1 + Z_2.$$

In these formulas, b and c are substituted for the a and b, respectively, of Souillagouet. This is the first method in which Z is divided into two parts, found separately.

The assumed position is selected so that latitude and meridian angle are each to the nearest 20′. The tables are shorter than those of Souillagouet, having 324 pages, but still bulky for this type solution. The method has fewer steps and requires only two book openings, but interpolation is needed in two steps.

Ogura. In 1920 the *New Altitude and Azimuth Tables* by Sinkiti Ogura, Japanese hydrographic engineer, were published in Tokyo. The solution for altitude is generally similar to that of Souillagouet, a perpendicular being dropped from the zenith, but Ogura introduced secants and cosecants for the first time in this type solution. His solution for azimuth is similar to that of Blackburne (art. 2106) and Lecky (art. 2126).

The assumed position is selected so that latitude and meridian angle are each to the nearest whole degree. The altitude is determined by means of two tables (A and B–C) of a total of 27 pages, and azimuth by means of three additional tables (D, E, F) of a total of 29 pages. The altitude can be obtained to an accuracy of 0′.6 without interpolation. Latitude and declination are limited to 65°. The rules are numerous and complicated.

Both the Ogura and Yonemura (art. 2109) tables are given in the same book, the Japanese Hydrographic Office Pub. No. 225. An English edition, with slight modifications in the Ogura method, was published in 1924.

The Ogura tables have been widely copied.

Smart and Shearme's *Position Line Tables* were published in London in 1922, based upon a division of the triangle by a perpendicular from the zenith. The altitude formulas of Souillagouet were used, but the arrangement of the earlier tables was improved. It is somewhat similar to that of Ogura, but with the positions of meridian angle and latitude interchanged, providing a better arrangement when solutions of several observations are made simultaneously. Solution requires a log sine table which is not provided. There is no solution for azimuth. The assumed position is selected so that the meridian angle and latitude are each the nearest whole degree. No interpolation is needed.

Newton and Pinto. The *Navegação Moderna* of J. A. Newton and J. C. Pinto was published in Lisbon, Portugal, in 1924, providing a solution by dropping a perpendicular from the zenith. The method is based upon ideas expressed by Newton in 1912 and 1913. The formulas for altitude are almost the same as those of Souillagouet. The method of finding azimuth angle resembles somewhat the method of Bertin, but with the use of auxiliary angles. There are only two tables, the first occupying 120 pages, and the second two pages. The assumed position is selected so that latitude and meridian angle are each to the nearest 30'. No interpolation is needed, but the rules are somewhat complicated.

Weems' *Line of Position Book,* published in 1927, combines the Ogura altitude tables and the Rust azimuth diagram (art. 2106).

H.O. Pub. No. 208 (Dreisonstok), *Navigation Tables for Mariners and Aviators,* was published by the U. S. Navy Hydrographic Office in 1928 to provide a solution by the method of dropping a perpendicular from the zenith. The method, devised by Lieutenant Commander J. Y. Dreisonstok, USN, is similar to Ogura's. For altitude, it uses the Souillagouet formula inverted so as to be in secants and cosecants. For azimuth angle the formula is similar to that of Newton and Pinto, except that it does not use the parallactic angle at the celestial body. In the first edition the latitude was limited to 65°. There were two tables, one of 45 pages and the other of 18 pages. Later, a 23-page addition to the first table extended the coverage to the poles.

The assumed position is selected so that the latitude and meridian angle are each the nearest whole degree. The method requires four book openings, eight table entries, and six mathematical steps. Although values are usually obtained by relatively easy interpolation, altitude accuracy of 0'.5 can be obtained without interpolation.

As with H.O. Pub. No. 211 (art. 2111), the rules for this method were made on the assumption that only bodies above the celestial horizon would be observed. The rules may be restated to allow for both positive and negative altitudes, as follows:

If t is less then 90°, give b same name as latitude.

If t is greater than 90°, give b opposite name to latitude, and mark Z' minus.

If (d+b) is numerically greater than 90°, mark Z″ minus.

If (d+b) is contrary name to latitude, the altitude is negative; use the supplement of Z″.

If Z is minus, subtract from 360° and mark plus.

The value labeled "t" in the tables is actually LHA. If t, east or west, is used, as in modern practice, the printed values greater than 180° can be ignored. The rules can be stated in abbreviated form on alternate pages, as follows:

At the top of each left-hand page of table I:

$$t < 90°,\ b\ \text{same name as L}.$$

At the top of each right-hand page of table I:

$$t > 90°,\ b\ \text{contrary name to L, Z'}\ (-).$$

At the top of each left-hand page of table II:

$$(d+b) > 90°,\ Z''\ (-).$$

At the top of each right-hand page of table II:

$$Z(-),\ \text{use}\ 360° - Z.$$

At the bottom of each page of table II (if desired):

(d+b) contrary name to L, Hc (−): use 180°−Z″.

If the D+B value used for finding Z″ exceeds 10,000, it is reduced by this amount, the remainder being used for entering table II. If desired, this can be stated in abbreviated form at the bottom of alternate pages of table II, as follows:

(C+D) >10,000, use (C+D)−10,000.

Like H.O. Pub. No. 211 (art. 2111), H.O. Pub. No. 208 has been largely superseded by those tables constituting a list of computed answers.

Gingrich. The *Aerial and Marine Navigation Tables*, by Lieutenant John E. Gingrich, USN, were published in 1931 to provide another solution by the method of dropping a perpendicular from the zenith. The formulas for altitude are similar to those of Ogura, and the formulas for azimuth are similar to those of Perrin (art. 2126). The first two tables, of 31 and seven pages, respectively, are similar to those of Ogura. A single third table of 13 pages is given for azimuth. The general arrangement is in many respects similar to that of H.O. Pub. No. 208, and as with the earlier method, the assumed position is selected so that latitude and meridian angle are each to the nearest whole degree. The precision of tabulation of K, an auxiliary function, is not consistent. Consequently, if the tables are used without interpolation, errors as great as 0.5 can arise in the computed altitude.

Weems' *New Line of Position Tables* are sometimes called the *Manuscript Tables* because they were in manuscript form from 1932 until they were published in 1943. They are similar to his earlier tables but arranged with the position of latitude and meridian angle values interchanged so that values for several observations can be taken from the tables with a single book opening. The latitude values are extended from the 65° given in earlier tables to 90°. As in the earlier edition, the Rust azimuth diagram (art. 2106) is included, but provision is also made for computation of azimuth angle. One part is found in terms of latitude and meridian angle, using the formula of H.O. Pub. No. 208, and the other part is found in terms of altitude and the perpendicular from the zenith. If the azimuth is required to a greater precision that 0.5, interpolation is needed. The assumed position is selected so that the latitude and meridian angle are each the nearest whole degree.

Collins. The *I. C. S. Altitude and Azimuth Tables for Air and Sea Navigation*, by Elmer B. Collins, formerly of the U. S. Navy Hydrographic Office, were published by the International Correspondence Schools in 1934. The tables and method of solution are generally similar to those of H.O. Pub. No. 208.

F-Tafel, published by the German Oberkommandos der Kriegsmarine about 1937, divides the triangle by a perpendicular from the zenith. The formulas of Souillagouet are used for altitude. Azimuth is found by the familiar formula

$$\sin Z = \sin t \cos d \sec h.$$

There are four tables. Latitude, declination, and altitude are limited to 70°. The assumed position is selected so that latitude and meridian angle are each to the nearest whole degree.

Comrie. In 1938 the *Hughes' Tables for Sea and Air Navigation*, by L. J. Comrie, former Superintendent, H. M. Nautical Almanac Office, were published in London. These tables are similar to those of H.O. Pub. No. 208, but arranged with the positions of latitude and meridian angle interchanged as in the Weems' *New Line of Position Tables*.

Myerscough and Hamilton. The *Rapid Navigation Tables*, by W. Myerscough and W. Hamilton, were published in London in 1939. A perpendicular is dropped from the zenith to the hour circle of the celestial body. With slight modification, the altitude formulas of Souillagouet and the azimuth formula of Gingrich are used. Six quantities are tabulated in a single table of 90 pages. Both declination and latitude are limited to 70°. In the 1950 edition, the limits of declination and latitude were extended to 89°. A revision of the 1950 edition was published in 1965 as *Rapid Navigation Tables for Mariners*, a table of 195 pages.

Ageton's *Manual of Celestial Navigation,* published in 1942, combines the first table of Weems' *New Line of Position Tables* as table I, and H.O. Pub. No. 211 (art. 2111) as table II. The basic formulas are restated in terms of secants and cosecants. The result is a short, easy solution without interpolation, involving four book openings, eight table entries, and four mathematical steps. Since the H.O. Pub. No. 211 table is included, the book can be used for Ageton's earlier method.

Benest and Timberlake. The *Astro-Navigation Tables for the Common Tangent Method* by two British professors, E. E. Benest and E. M. Timberlake, were published in 1945. In three tables of 61, 18, and 12 pages is given a logarithmic solution for altitude only, by dropping a perpendicular from the zenith. The formulas are slight modifications of those of Ogura.

The location of the line of position is somewhat similar to the method sometimes used in longitude method solutions such as H.O. Pubs. Nos. 203 and 204 (art. 2106). Two assumed positions are selected, usually 1° apart on the same meridian. The altitude intercept at each position is determined, and a circle, or arc of a circle, is drawn with the assumed position as the center, and the altitude intercept as the radius. The line of position is the common tangent to the two circles. Since there are four common tangents, the general direction of the body is required. Where doubt exists as to which of two or more answers is the correct one, additional solutions from other assumed positions may resolve the ambiguity. If the celestial body is near the meridian, the two assumed positions are better taken on the same parallel of latitude. Even with these precautions, there is danger of selection of the wrong line.

Tavole H (*I. I. 3113*), published by the Istituto Idrografico della Marina of Italy in 1947, combines table I of Ogura and table II of Weems' *New Line of Position Tables*, including, also, the Rust azimuth diagram (art. 2106). This table is a modification of an earlier *Tavole F*.

Čumbelić. In 1969 Captain Petar Čumbelić of Yugoslavia published his single volume and compact *Nautičke Tablice*. This method is based upon a triangle divided by dropping a perpendicular from the zenith. The table includes an English explanation.

2111. Altitude methods, perpendicular from body.—Figure 2111 is a diagram on the plane of the celestial meridian (art. 1432), with the navigational triangle shown in heavy lines. A perpendicular from the celestial body, M, to the celestial meridian divides the triangle into two right spherical triangles. In figure 2111 the length of the perpendicular is designated v and the two parts of the colatitude are designated w and x. By means of Napier's rules (art. 142, vol. II), the following basic formulas can be derived:

$$\sin v = \cos d \sin t \tag{1}$$
$$\cos w = \sin d \sec v, \text{ or } \sin w = \cot t \tan v \tag{2}$$
$$\sin h = \cos v \cos x \tag{3}$$
$$\sin Z = \sin v \sec h, \text{ or } \cos Z = \tan x \tan h \tag{4}$$

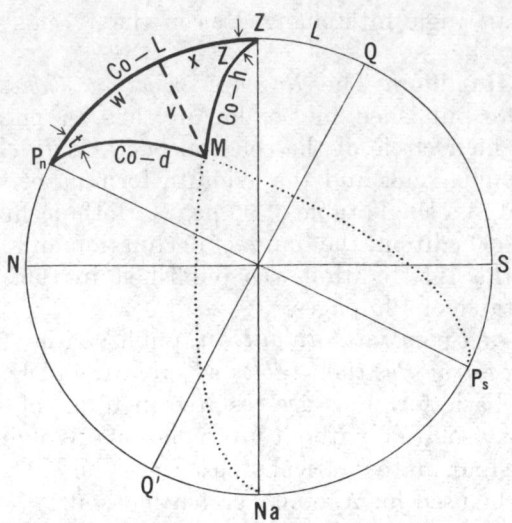

FIGURE 2111.—Navigational triangle with perpendicular from celestial body to celestial meridian.

Since $x=90°-(w+L)$, formula (3) can be written in terms of latitude, and w found from equation (2). Thus, both h and Z can be determined by means of t, d, and L and auxiliary functions found from them.

William Thomson (Lord Kelvin) was the first to divide the navigational triangle as shown in figure 2111 for sight reduction, but his method (art. 2106) was for determination of longitude. Various later methods made such a division for determination of altitude.

Fuss. The *Tables to Find Altitudes and Azimuths*, devised by V. E. Fuss, an astronomer at the Kronstadt (Russia) Naval Observatory, were published in 1901. In these tables a perpendicular is dropped from the celestial body, the following notation being used (fig. 2111):

v is designated a
w is designated $90°-b$
x is designated $B-90°$
$B=90°-L+b$ (if v falls between Z and Q).

Solution is by the following formulas:

$$\sin a = \cos d \sin t$$
$$\cot b = \cot d \cos t$$
$$\sin h = \cos a \sin B$$
$$\cot Z = \cot a \cos B.$$

The assumed latitude is selected to provide the nearest 15′ value of B. The assumed longitude is selected so that t will be the nearest whole 1^m ($0°25$). The tables are entered twice, first with t and d to find a and b, interpolating for d, and then with B and a to find h and Z, interpolating for a. The method involves two book openings, eight table entries, four interpolations, and ten mathematical steps. There are 144 pages of tables.

Aquino. The *Altitude and Azimuth Tables* of Radler de Aquino, a Brazilian naval officer, were first published in 1909. These were followed the next year by his *Sea and Air Navigation Tables*. Several later editions of both publications appeared with some modification, principally of the auxiliary material given. Aquino dropped a perpendicular from the celestial body to the celestial meridian, and used the same formulas as Fuss and generally the same arrangement, except that longitude is assumed so as to provide a meridian angle to the nearest whole degree.

H.O. Pub. No. 209 (Pierce), *Position Tables for Aerial and Surface Navigation,* was published by the U. S. Navy Hydrographic Office in 1930. These tables were devised by Commander M. R. Pierce, USN, in 1925, when he was navigator of the dirigible USS *Los Angeles.* The method is based upon a triangle divided by a perpendicular from the celestial body. It is generally similar to those designed by Fuss and Aquino, but the arrangement is somewhat different, requiring 206 pages of tables. This method was never widely used, and is now out of print.

H.O. Pub. No. 211 (Ageton), *Dead Reckoning Altitude and Azimuth Table,* was published by the U. S. Navy Hydrographic Office in 1931. This method, designed by Lieutenant Arthur A. Ageton, USN, while a student of the Post Graduate School, then at Annapolis, Maryland, is based upon a triangle divided by dropping a perpendicular from the celestial body. It is generally similar to those of Fuss and Aquino. However, Ageton modified the formulas so as to include only secants and cosecants. In terms of figure 2111, his notation is as follows:

v is designated R
w is designated $90° - K$
x is designated $K \sim L$
$K = x + L.$

Ageton's formulas are

$$\csc R = \csc t \sec d$$
$$\csc K = \frac{\csc d}{\sec R}$$
$$\csc h = \sec R \sec (K \sim L)$$
$$\csc Z = \frac{\csc R}{\sec h}.$$

A single table of 36 pages gives five-place log cosecants (labeled A) and log secants (labeled B), both multiplied by 100,000 to eliminate the decimal. These values are given in parallel columns for each $0\rlap{.}'5$ of angle from 0° to 180°. The table is well arranged and indexed for quick reference. The rules are relatively simple and well presented. The method can be used for solution from the dead reckoning or any other assumed position. The method is intended for use without interpolation. These features combined to make this a popular method, although solution is somewhat tedious, and large errors may be encountered if t is near 90°. The method has been largely superseded by those tables constituting a list of computed answers. However, the method is now published as table 35.

If a celestial body near the visible horizon is observed, it may be *below* the celestial horizon (zenith distance greater than 90°), because of refraction and dip. Under these conditions the *computed* altitude, Hc, is negative (art. 2023). In the solution by H.O. Pub. No. 211, Hc is negative if K is of the same name as L and greater than (90°+L), *or* if K is of contrary name to L and greater than (90°−L). Under the second of these conditions, Z is less than 90° and should be taken from the top of the table *if* K is greater than (180°−L).

Fontoura da Costa and Penteado's *Tabuas de Altura e Azimute* were published in Lisboa, Portugal, in 1936. These consist of 26 pages of log secant and log cosecant tables similar to those of H.O. Pub. No. 211. The method and formulas are slight modifications of those of H.O. Pub. No. 211 (table 35).

Tillman. The *Altitude Tables for Mariners and Aviators*, by E. Tillman, were published in 1936 in Sweden. Solution is by three tables using the basic formulas given above.

USSR tables. About 1940 the USSR replaced the Fuss tables with a method that is similar but uses a much shorter table. However, the solution is about the same length as with the Fuss tables, requiring six book openings, nine table entries, and five mathematical steps. Visual interpolation is used.

Japanese H.O. Pub. No. 602, *Brief Celestial Navigation Table,* was published in 1942. A perpendicular is dropped from the celestial body, as in figure 2111. Side *w* is designated K, and the following formulas are derived from the basic formulas given above:

$$\log \tan K = \log \cot d + \log \cos t$$

$$\log \cot Z = \log \cot t + \log \csc K + \log \cos (K+L)$$

$$\log \cot h = \log \cot (K+L) + \log \sec Z.$$

These formulas result in a simple solution, at the expense of some duplication in the three tables of 49 pages.

Hickerson. In 1944 Thomas F. Hickerson, professor of applied mathematics at the University of North Carolina, published a small volume called *Navigational Handbook with Tables,* in which the tables of H.O. Pub. No. 211 are given with the interval between entries reduced to 0.2. All values are given on 45 pages, by tabulating values only to 45° and interchanging the A and B values for angles between 45° and 90°. In 1947 a second edition was published under the title *Latitude, Longitude and Azimuth by the Sun or Stars.*

2112. Altitude methods without use of navigational triangle.—The navigational triangle is composed of arcs of three great circles: the celestial meridian of the observer, the hour circle of the celestial body, and the vertical circle of the celestial body. Arcs of other great circles might also be used in forming spherical triangles that can be solved to find altitude and azimuth.

Kotlarić. In 1954 Stjepo M. Kotlarić, scientific co-worker, Hydrographic Institute of the Yugoslav Navy, proposed a method and in 1958 published *Tables K1* based upon the solution of three right spherical triangles composed of arcs of great circles, as follows:

triangle 1—celestial horizon, hour circle, and celestial equator;
triangle 2—celestial horizon, hour circle, and celestial meridian (lower branch);
triangle 3—celestial horizon, hour circle, and vertical circle.

The formulas are derived from Napier's rules (F, M, and C are auxiliary parts):

$$\cos C = \cos L \sin t$$
$$\tan M = \cot L \cos t$$
$$\tan (Z+F) = - \sin L \tan t$$
$$\tan F = \cos C \tan (M+d)$$
$$\sin Hc = \sin C \sin (M+d)$$
$$Z = (Z+F) - F.$$

Hc and Z are solved from tables I and II, tables III and IV being the multiplication tables for obtaining the Hc corrections. The four tables total 190 pages. Table III is not used if the assumed position is selected so that latitude and meridian angle are the nearest whole or half degree. The pages could be reduced considerably if values for half degrees were not tabulated. With an assumed position selected as indicated above, the method requires only four table entries and three mathematical steps. All signs are printed in the heading of the tables. The computation is simple. *Tables K1* were reprinted in 1963 and 1971. The tables include a comprehensive English explanation.

2113. Modern inspection tables may contain lists of altitude or azimuth, or both. Another type tabulates the information needed for finding longitudes. Values are taken directly from the tables, without the need for logarithms, auxiliary functions, or mathematical solutions (except interpolation). Inspection tables are not new, the horary tables of Cassini in 1770, Lalande in 1793, Lynn in 1827, and Hommey in 1863 (art. 2106) being of this type. Other inspection tables include Davis' *Chronometer Tables*, Blackburne, H.O. Pubs. Nos. 203 and 204, Ball, Davis' *Alt-Azimuth Tables*, and H.O. Pub. No. 201 (arts. 2106 and 2109). None of these tables is used to any extent today, largely because interpolation is difficult, and coverage is limited. A short logarithmic solution with wide coverage has often proved more popular.

In contrast, the modern inspection table, made practicable by recent developments in computation techniques, has largely replaced the trigonometric solution. The principal modern inspection tables are:

Pub. No. 214, *Tables of Computed Altitude and Azimuth,* were published by the U. S. Navy Hydrographic Office between 1936 and 1946, in nine volumes. Between 1951 and 1953 the British Admiralty published identical tables (H.D. 486) in six volumes, with altered explanation to suit British practice. The first volume of an identical Spanish edition was published in Spain in 1953, and the second volume in 1956. Several volumes of an Italian edition based on Pub. No. 214 have also been published. Pub. No. 214 was superseded by Pub. No. 229, *Sight Reduction Tables for Marine Navigation.* Both tables are described in detail in chapter XX.

British Air Pub. 1618 (H.O. Pub. No. 218), *Astronomical Navigation Tables,* were published by the British Admiralty between 1938 and 1944 in 15 volumes (lat. 0°–79°). In 1941 the first 14 volumes (lat. 0°–69°) were republished by the U. S. Navy Hydrographic Office as H.O. Pub. No. 218. The tables are intended primarily for aviators.

These tables are similar to Pub. No. 249, but with several major differences. In A.P. 1618 values are given to the nearest whole minute for altitude, and the nearest whole degree for azimuth. The altitude values include allowance for refraction at a height of 5,000 feet. The minimum altitude in most cases is 10°. Provision is made for interpolation for declination only, and this always from the *next smaller* whole degree, instead of from the *nearest* whole degree. Declination is given for each whole degree from 0° to 28° only. In addition, values of altitude and azimuth angle are given for the declination (in 1940) of 22 stars. This part of the table is entered with the star name (or an arbitrarily-assigned number), so the declination of the body need not be known. An auxiliary table provides a correction for changes in declination during the years following 1940 (to the year 2000).

During World War II these tables were widely used by aviators. Some marine navigators also used them. Publication of these tables has been discontinued.

Japanese H.O. Pub. No. 351, *Celestial Navigation Observation Table,* was published in 1940–42, in seven volumes for latitudes 0°–70°. The original printing was classified "secret." The tables are similar to British Air Pub. 1618, with several differences. In H.O. Pub. No. 218 all star-name entry tables are given first, followed by all declination entry tables. In Pub. No. 351 the declination entry table for each degree of latitude is followed by the star-name entry table. Altitudes, including refraction at 4,000 meters (13,123 feet), are tabulated to a minimum value of 2°. Declination is extended to 29°. The latitude-declination contrary-name entries are inverted so that meridian angles increase *upward* on the page as in Pub. No. 260 (art. 719, vol. II), resulting in better utilization of space on the pages having both "same name" and "contrary name" entries. Twenty stars are used, the selection differing somewhat from that of H.O. Pub. No. 218. In H.O. Pub. No. 218 the stars are listed and numbered alphabetically. In Pub. No. 351 they are given in order of declination, from Dubhe, listed as 62°03′N, to Sirius, listed as 16°38′S.

Hoehne, In October 1941 George G. Hoehne, then a navigation instructor at the Pan American Airways Navigation School, Miami, Florida, submitted a set of *Star Air Navigation Tables* to the U. S. Navy Hydrographic Office which were superior to the star section of H.O. Pub. No. 218 in basic design. His manuscripts included the tabulation of the altitudes and true azimuths of carefully selected bright stars arranged in a format such that this data could be rapidly extracted for at least ten stars from two facing pages with but one opening of the tables. The use of LHA ♈ instead of the LHA of each star as a table argument simplified the sight reduction by: (1) eliminating the need to apply the SHA of a star to the GHA ♈ to obtain the LHA of a star; (2) enabling the optimum arrangement for rapid extraction of tabular values of altitude and true azimuth; and (3) providing for the selection of the best stars for observation for a given LHA ♈ at an assumed position. The use of LHA ♈ as a table argument with the data arranged in parallel columns so that the stars would be tabulated, from left to right, in increasing numerical order of true azimuth served to make the tables a star finder. The same basic format was later used with 360° of LHA ♈ per table opening for volume I of Pub. No. 249, *Sight Reduction Tables for Air Navigation.*

In early 1942, Hoehne was originally granted permission to use, in part, tabular values of altitude, azimuth angle, and pertinent data contained in the star section of H.O. Pub. No. 218 and ingeniously constructed his preliminary volume I of *Celestial Navigation Tables.* Its success led to his publication of volume II of *Practical Celestial Air Navigation Tables* in 1943. For the period 1942–1990, two simple correction tables prevent the tabulated altitudes from becoming inaccurate because of precession of the equinoxes (art. 1419). Refraction at altitude 5,000 feet is included as in H.O. Pub. No. 218.

Figures 2113a and 2113b illustrate facing pages on which data for at least 10 stars are tabulated for a 60° range of LHA ♈ (T).

The tabulated altitudes are corrected for annual change in declination using Table I on the inside of the front cover (fig. 2113c). This correction must be added or subtracted according to the sign prefixed to (t). The year at the bottom of each star column is the year before which this correction cannot exceed 1′.

GHA ♈ as obtained from the almanac is adjusted for the annual change in right ascension using Table VII at the back of the book (fig. 2113d). The correction obtained from this table can be readily combined with the increment to be added to the tabular GHA ♈ extracted from the almanac.

Example.—During morning twilight on June 1, 1975, the 0430 DR position of a ship is lat. 30°10′N, long. 45°02′W. At GMT 4ʰ32ᵐ30ˢ the navigator observes Fomalhaut with a marine sextant having no IC, from a height of eye of 38 feet. The hs is 24°58′.

Required.—The a, Zn, and AP, using volume II of *Practical Celestial Air Navigation Tables* and the *Air Almanac.*

Solution.—

	June 1	*Fomalhaut*		+ ☆ −
GMT	7^{h}32^{m}30^s June 1		IC	− −
7^{h}30^m	1°40′		D	6′
2^{m}30^s	0°38′		sum	− 6′
GHA ♈	362°18′		corr.	(−) 6′
1975 corr.	(−) 04′		hs	24°58′
adj. GHA ♈	362°14′		Ho	24°52′
aλ	45°14′W			
LHA ♈	317°00′			
aL	30°00′N			
ht	24°49′ t (+)17			
1975 corr.	(+) 10′			
Hc	24°59′			
Ho	24°52′			
a	7A	aL	30°00′N	
Zn	154°	aλ	45°14′W	

Since refraction at 5,000 feet is included in the tabulated altitudes, the sextant altitude is not corrected for refraction. An auxiliary table provides an additional refraction correction to be applied to low-altitude observations. For marine observations there is no correction for altitudes above 15°; the correction is (−)1′ for altitudes 6° to 10° and (−)2′ for altitude 4°. The correction is applied to the sextant altitude.

Japanese H.O. Pub. No. 603, *Simplified Celestial Observation Table,* was published in 1943. This publication is virtually the same as Pub. No. 351, except that eight additional stars are given, all farther south than those of Pub. No. 351. This extends the list to α *Crucis* (Acrux), given as declination 62°48′S.

Altitude and Azimuth Almanac was published by the Japanese Hydrographic Office, beginning in 1944. Originally, this was a secret publication. Several different versions were printed, and there were some modifications after the first editions. In each, however, the functions of almanac and sight reduction tables were combined. For each of several specific locations, the altitude and azimuth of one or more celestial bodies are tabulated for the date and time, usually at ten-minute intervals. In the earlier editions, the locations selected were important points in the western Pacific. From this practice, these publications are sometimes called "destination tables." Later editions used positions differing in latitude by 5°. These tables provided a quick solution for observations made at the tabulated times. On a worldwide basis such a system would involve a very voluminous tabulation each year, or cumbersome corrections. The *Altitude and Azimuth Almanac* is no longer published.

Hohentafeln nach Sternzeit, an official German table, was published in 1944 as an experimental edition with a very limited range of latitude. The tables were similar to those of Hoehne, but with six stars listed for each minute of local sidereal time.

Ménéclier and Chevalier. The *Cálculo del Punto* of Victor Ménéclier and Roberto Chevalier was published in 1945–49 by Aeronáutica Argentina. There are six volumes for latitudes 0° to 59° *south.* At intervals of 4^{m}LST (or 1° LHA♈) the altitude, correction factor, and azimuth (not azimuth angle) of selected stars are tabulated. Twelve columns are provided, but a number of blank areas appear, resulting in an average of about nine altitude-azimuth entries for each time entry. In most cases

30°N   **30°N**

T	CAPH Alt. (t)	Az	ANTARES / CAPELLA Alt. (t)	Az	ALPHERATZ Alt. (t)	Az	ARCTURUS / ALDEBARAN Alt. (t)	Az	FOMALHAUT Alt. (t)	Az	T
301	40 11− 3	36	13 38− 5	228	37 31+ 6	75	11 20− 9	286	17 28+15	142	301
302	40 42 3	36	12 59 5	229	38 21 6	75	10 30 9	287	17 59 15	142	302
303	41 13 3	36	12 20 5	230	39 11 6	76	9 41 9	287	18 31 15	143	303
304	41 44 4	36	11 41 5	230	40 01 6	76	8 42 9	287	19 02 15	144	304
305	42 14 4	36	11 01 5	231	40 52 6	76	8 03 9	288	19 32 16	145	305
306	42 44− 4	36	10 21− 5	231	41 42+ 5	77	7 14− 9	288	20 02+16	145	306
307	43 15 5	36	9 41 5	232	42 33 5	77	6 25 9	289	20 31 16	146	307
308	43 45 5	35	9 00 5	233	43 24 5	77	5 37− 9	289	20 59 16	147	308
309	44 15 5	35	8 19 5	233	44 14 5	78			21 27 16	148	309
310	44 45 6	35	7 38 5	234	45 05 5	78			21 55 16	149	310
311	45 14− 6	35	6 56− 5	234	45 56+ 5	78			22 21+16	149	311
312	45 44 6	34	6 14 5	235	46 47 5	79			22 48 17	150	312
313	46 14 7	34	5 32− 5	235	47 38 5	79			23 13 17	151	313
314	46 43 7	31			48 29 5	79			23 38 17	152	314
315	47 12 7	34			49 20 5	80			24 02 17	153	315
316	47 41− 8	33			50 11+ 5	80			24 26+17	153	316
317	48 09 8	33			51 02 5	80			24 49 17	154	317
318	48 37 8	33			51 53 4	81			25 11 17	155	318
319	49 06 9	32			52 45 4	81			25 32 17	156	319
320	49 33 9	32	CAPELLA		53 36 4	81			25 53 18	157	320
321	50 01− 9	32			54 27+ 4	82			26 13+18	158	321
322	50 28 10	31	5 35+ 2	39	55 19 4	82			26 32 18	159	322
323	50 55 10	31	6 08 2	39	56 10 4	82			26 50 18	160	323
324	51 22 11	31	6 40 2	40	57 02 4	82			27 08 18	161	324
325	51 48 11	30	7 13 2	40	57 53 4	83			27 25 18	161	325
326	52 14−11	30	7 46+ 2	41	58 45+ 4	83			27 41+18	162	326
327	52 40 12	29	8 20 2	41	59 36 4	83			27 56 18	163	327
328	53 05 12	29	8 54 2	41	60 28 4	84			28 11 18	164	328
329	53 30 12	28	9 29 2	42	61 19 4	84			28 24 18	165	329
330	53 54 13	28	10 03 2	42	62 11 4	84			28 37 19	166	330
331	54 18−13	27	10 38+ 2	43	63 03+ 4	85			28 49+19	167	331
332	54 42 13	26	11 13 2	43	63 55 3	85	ALDEBARAN		29 00 19	168	332
333	55 05 14	26	11 48 2	43	64 46 3	86			29 11 19	169	333
334	55 27 14	25	12 24 2	44	65 38 3	86			29 20 19	170	334
335	55 49 14	25	13 00 2	44	66 30 3	86	5 43+ 4	74	29 29 19	171	335
336	56 11−15	24	13 36+ 2	44	67 22+ 3	87	6 33+ 4	75	29 36+19	172	336
337	56 31 15	23	14 12 2	45	68 14 3	87	7 22 4	75	29 43 19	173	337
338	56 52 15	23	14 49 2	45	69 06 3	87	8 12 3	76	29 49 19	174	338
339	57 12 16	22	15 25 2	45	69 58 3	88	9 02 3	76	29 54 19	175	339
340	57 31 16	21	16 02 2	46	70 49 3	88	9 52 3	77	29 58 19	176	340
341	57 49−16	20	16 40+ 2	46	71 41+ 3	89	10 43+ 3	77	30 01+19	177	341
342	58 07 17	19	17 17 2	46	72 33 3	89	11 33 3	78	30 03 19	178	342
343	58 24 17	19	17 55 1	47	73 25 3	90	12 23 3	78	30 05 19	179	343
344	58 40 17	18	18 32 1	47	74 17 3	90	13 14 3	78	30 05 19	180	344
345	58 56 17	17	19 10 1	47	75 09 3	91	14 05 3	79	30 05 19	181	345
346	59 11−18	16	19 49+ 1	48	76 01+ 3	91	14 56+ 3	79	30 03+19	182	346
347	59 25 18	15	20 27 1	48	76 53 3	92	15 47 3	80	30 01 19	183	347
348	59 38 18	14	21 06 1	48	77 45 3	92	16 38 3	80	29 58 19	184	348
349	59 50 18	13	21 44 1	48	78 37 3	93	17 29 3	81	29 54 19	185	349
350	60 02 19	12	22 23 1	49	79 29+ 3	94	18 20 3	81	29 49 19	186	350
351	60 13−19	11	23 02+ 1	49			19 11+ 3	82	29 43+19	187	351
352	60 22 19	10	23 41 1	49			20 02 3	82	29 36 19	188	352
353	60 32 19	9	24 21 1	49			20 54 3	83	29 29 19	189	353
354	60 40 19	8	25 00 1	50			21 45 3	83	29 20 19	190	354
355	60 47 20	7	25 40 1	50			22 37 3	84	29 11 19	191	355
356	60 53−20	6	26 20+ 1	50			23 28+ 3	84	29 00+19	192	356
357	60 58 20	5	27 00 1	50			24 20 3	84	28 49 19	193	357
358	61 03 20	4	27 40 1	51			25 12 3	85	28 37 19	194	358
359	61 06 20	3	28 20 1	51			26 03 3	85	28 24 18	195	359
360	61 09−20	2	29 00+ 1	51			26 55+ 3	86	28 11+18	196	360
Year	1944		1948 / 1957		1944		1944 / 1949		1944		Year

FIGURE 2113a.—Left-hand page of opening of *Practical Celestial Air Navigation Tables.*

30°N — 30°N

T	ALTAIR Alt.	t	Az	RASALAGUE Alt.	t	Az	VEGA Alt.	t	Az	ETAMIN Alt.	t	Az	DENEB Alt.	t	Az	T
301	68 23+	9	191	50 49−	1	252	69 56−	1	302	58 03	0	321	73 21−11		23	301
302	68 12	9	193	50 00	1	253	69 11	1	301	57 31	0	321	73 41	12	20	302
303	67 59	9	196	49 10	1	253	68 27	1	300	56 58	0	320	73 58	12	18	303
304	67 44	9	199	48 20	1	254	67 42	1	300	56 25	0	320	74 13	12	16	304
305	67 26	9	201	47 30	1	255	66 56	1	299	55 51	0	319	74 26	12	13	305
306	67 07+	9	203	46 40−	1	256	66 11−	1	299	55 17	0	319	74 37−13		11	306
307	66 45	9	206	45 49	1	256	65 25	1	298	54 43	0	318	74 45	13	8	307
308	66 21	9	208	44 59	1	257	64 39	1	298	54 08	0	318	74 51	13	5	308
309	65 56	9	210	44 08	1	258	63 53	1	298	53 33	0	318	74 55	13	3	309
310	65 29	8	212	43 17	1	258	63 07	1	297	52 58	0	317	74 56	13	0	310
311	65 01+	8	214	42 26−	1	259	62 21−	1	297	52 23	0	317	74 55−13		357	311
312	64 30	8	216	41 35	1	260	61 35	0	297	51 51	0	317	74 51	13	355	312
313	63 59	8	218	40 44	1	260	60 48	0	297	51 11	0	316	74 45	13	352	313
314	63 26	8	220	39 53	1	261	60 02	0	296	50 36	0	316	74 37	13	349	314
315	62 52	8	222	39 01	1	262	59 15	0	296	49 59	0	316	74 26	12	347	315
316	62 16+	8	224	38 10−	1	262	58 29	0	296	49 23	0	315	74 13−12		344	316
317	61 40	7	225	37 18	1	263	57 42	0	296	48 47	0	315	73 58	12	342	317
318	61 02	7	227	36 27	1	263	56 55	0	296	48 10	0	315	73 41	12	340	318
319	60 24	7	229	35 35	1	264	56 09	0	296	47 34	0	315	73 21	11	337	319
320	59 45	7	230	34 44	1	264	55 22	0	296	46 57	0	315	73 01	11	335	320
321	59 04+	7	231	33 52−	1	265	54 35	0	296	46 20	0	315	72 38−11		333	321
322	58 23	7	233	33 00	1	266	53 48	0	296	45 43	0	315	72 14	10	331	322
323	57 42	7	234	32 08	1	266	53 02	0	296	45 06	0	314	71 48	10	329	323
324	56 59	7	235	31 17	1	267	52 15	0	296	44 29	0	314	71 21	10	328	324
325	56 16	7	237	30 25	1	267	51 28	0	296	43 52	0	314	70 53	9	326	325
326	55 32+	6	238	29 33−	1	268	50 41	0	296	43 15	0	314	70 23−	9	325	326
327	54 48	6	239	28 41	1	268	49 54	0	296	42 37	0	314	69 52	9	323	327
328	54 03	6	240	27 49	1	269	49 08	0	296	42 00	0	314	69 21	8	322	328
329	53 18	6	241	26 57	1	269	48 21	0	296	41 23	0	314	68 48	8	321	329
330	52 32	6	242	26 05	1	270	47 34	0	296	40 46	0	314	68 15	8	319	330
331	51 46+	6	243	25 13−	1	270	46 48	0	296	40 08	0	314	67 40−	7	318	331
332	51 00	6	244	24 22	1	271	46 01	0	296	39 31	0	314	67 05	7	317	332
333	50 13	6	245	23 30	1	271	45 15	0	296	38 54	0	314	66 30	7	316	333
334	49 25	6	246	22 38	1	272	44 28	0	296	38 16	0	314	65 54	7	315	334
335	48 38	6	247	21 46	1	272	43 42	0	297	37 39	0	314	65 17	6	314	335
336	47 50+	6	248	20 54−	1	273	42 55	0	297	37 02	0	314	64 39−	6	314	336
337	47 01	6	249	20 02	1	273	42 09	0	297	36 24	0	314	64 02	6	313	337
338	46 13	5	250	19 11	1	274	41 22+	1	297	35 47	0	314	63 23	5	312	338
339	45 24	5	250	18 19	1	274	40 36	1	297	35 10	0	314	62 45	5	312	339
340	44 35	5	251	17 27	1	275	39 50	1	297	34 33	0	314	62 06	5	311	340
341	43 46+	5	252	16 36−	1	275	39 04+	1	298	33 56	0	314	61 26−	5	310	341
342	42 56	5	253	15 44	1	276	38 18	1	298	33 19	0	315	60 47	4	310	342
343	42 07	5	253	14 53	1	276	37 32	1	298	32 42	0	315	60 07	4	309	343
344	41 17	5	254	14 01	1	277	36 46	1	298	32 05	0	315	59 27	4	309	344
345	40 27	5	255	13 10	1	277	36 00	1	298	31 28	0	315	58 46	4	309	345
346	39 37+	5	255	12 19−	1	277	35 15+	1	298	30 52	0	315	58 05−	3	308	346
347	38 46	5	256	11 27	1	278	34 29	1	299	30 15	0	315	57 25	3	308	347
348	37 56	5	257	10 36	1	278	33 44	1	299	29 38	0	315	56 43	3	308	348
349	37 05	5	257	9 45	1	279	32 58	1	299	29 02	0	315	56 02	3	307	349
350	36 14	5	258	8 54	1	279	32 13	1	299	28 26	0	316	55 21	3	307	350
351	35 23+	5	259	8 04−	1	280	31 28−	1	300	27 49	0	316	54 39−	2	307	351
352	34 32	5	259	7 13	1	280	30 43	1	300	27 13	0	316	53 58	2	307	352
353	33 41	5	260	6 23−	1	281	29 58	1	300	26 37	0	316	53 16	2	306	353
354	32 50	5	261				29 13	1	300	26 01	0	316	52 34	2	306	354
355	31 59	5	261				28 28	1	301	25 26	0	317	51 52	2	306	355
356	31 08+	5	262				27 43+	1	301	24 50	0	317	51 10−	1	306	356
357	30 16	5	262				26 59	1	301	24 15	0	317	50 28	1	306	357
358	29 25	5	263				26 14	1	301	23 39	0	317	49 46	1	306	358
359	28 33	5	263				25 30	1	302	23 04	0	317	49 04	1	306	359
360	27 42+	5	264				24 46+	1	302	22 29	0	318	48 21−	1	306	360
Year	1947			1963			1958						1945			Year

From Practical Celestial Air Navigation Tables, Volume II. Copyright 1942, 1943, 1969 & 1970, by Navigation Publishing Co., and by George G. Hoehne, Author. Used by permission.

FIGURE 2113b.—Right-hand page of opening of *Practical Celestial Air Navigation Tables.*

TABLE I.

t / Year	1	2	3	4	5	6	7	8	9	10	11	12	13	14	15	16	17	18	19	20	t / Year
1942	0	0	0	0	0	0	0	0	0	0	0	0	0	0	0	1	1	1	1	1	1942
1943	0	0	0	0	0	0	0	0	0	0	1	1	1	1	1	1	1	1	1	1	1943
1944	0	0	0	0	0	0	0	1	1	1	1	1	1	1	1	1	1	1	1	1	1944
1945	0	0	0	0	0	0	1	1	1	1	1	1	1	1	1	1	1	2	2	2	1945
1946	0	0	0	0	0	1	1	1	1	1	1	1	1	1	2	2	2	2	2	2	1946
1947	0	0	0	0	1	1	1	1	1	1	1	1	2	2	2	2	2	2	2	2	1947
1948	0	0	0	1	1	1	1	1	1	1	1	2	2	2	2	2	2	2	3	3	1948
1949	0	0	0	1	1	1	1	1	1	2	2	2	2	2	2	2	3	3	3	3	1949
1950	0	0	0	1	1	1	1	1	2	2	2	2	2	2	2	3	3	3	3	3	1950
1951	0	0	1	1	1	1	1	1	2	2	2	2	2	3	3	3	3	3	3	4	1951
1952	0	0	1	1	1	1	1	2	2	2	2	2	3	3	3	3	3	4	4	4	1952
1953	0	0	1	1	1	1	2	2	2	2	2	3	3	3	3	3	4	4	4	4	1953
1954	0	0	1	1	1	1	2	2	2	2	3	3	3	3	4	4	4	4	4	5	1954
1955	0	0	1	1	1	2	2	2	2	2	3	3	3	4	4	4	4	4	5	5	1955
1956	0	1	1	1	1	2	2	2	2	3	3	3	3	4	4	4	5	5	5	5	1956
1957	0	1	1	1	1	2	2	2	3	3	3	3	4	4	4	5	5	5	5	6	1957
1958	0	1	1	1	2	2	2	2	3	3	3	4	4	4	4	5	5	5	6	6	1958
1959	0	1	1	1	2	2	2	3	3	3	3	4	4	4	5	5	5	6	6	6	1959
1960	0	1	1	1	2	2	2	3	3	3	4	4	4	5	5	5	6	6	6	7	1960
1961	0	1	1	1	2	2	2	3	3	4	4	4	5	5	5	6	6	6	7	7	1961
1962	0	1	1	1	2	2	3	3	3	4	4	4	5	5	6	6	6	7	7	7	1962
1963	0	1	1	2	2	2	3	3	3	4	4	5	5	5	6	6	7	7	7	8	1963
1964	0	1	1	2	2	2	3	3	4	4	4	5	5	6	6	6	7	7	8	8	1964
1965	0	1	1	2	2	2	3	3	4	4	5	5	5	6	6	7	7	8	8	8	1965
1966	0	1	1	2	2	3	3	3	4	4	5	5	6	6	6	7	7	8	8	9	1966
1967	0	1	1	2	2	3	3	4	4	4	5	5	6	6	7	7	8	8	9	9	1967
1968	0	1	1	2	2	3	3	4	4	5	5	6	6	7	7	7	8	8	9	9	1968
1969	0	1	1	2	2	3	3	4	4	5	5	6	6	7	7	8	8	9	9	10	1969
1970	0	1	2	2	2	3	4	4	4	5	6	6	6	7	8	8	8	9	10	10	1970
1971	1	1	2	2	3	3	4	4	5	5	6	6	7	7	8	8	9	9	10	10	1971
1972	1	1	2	2	3	3	4	4	5	5	6	6	7	7	8	9	9	10	10	11	1972
1973	1	1	2	2	3	3	4	4	5	6	6	7	7	8	8	9	9	10	10	11	1973
1974	1	1	2	2	3	3	4	5	5	6	6	7	7	8	8	9	10	10	11	11	1974
1975	1	1	2	2	3	4	4	5	5	6	6	7	8	8	9	9	10	10	11	12	1975
1976	1	1	2	2	3	4	4	5	5	6	7	7	8	8	9	10	10	11	11	12	1976
1977	1	1	2	2	3	4	4	5	6	6	7	7	8	9	9	10	10	11	12	12	1977
1978	1	1	2	3	3	4	4	5	6	6	7	8	8	9	10	10	11	11	12	13	1978
1979	1	1	2	3	3	4	5	5	6	6	7	8	8	9	10	10	11	12	12	13	1979
1980	1	1	2	3	3	4	5	5	6	7	7	8	9	9	10	11	11	12	13	13	1980
1981	1	1	2	3	3	4	5	5	6	7	8	8	9	10	10	11	12	12	13	14	1981
1982	1	1	2	3	4	4	5	6	6	7	8	8	9	10	10	11	12	13	13	14	1982
1983	1	1	2	3	4	4	5	6	6	7	8	9	9	10	11	11	12	13	14	14	1983
1984	1	1	2	3	4	4	5	6	7	7	8	9	10	10	11	12	12	13	14	15	1994
1985	1	2	2	3	4	4	5	6	7	8	8	9	10	10	11	12	13	14	14	15	1985
1986	1	2	2	3	4	5	5	6	7	8	8	9	10	11	12	12	13	14	15	15	1986
1987	1	2	2	3	4	5	5	6	7	8	9	9	10	11	12	13	13	14	15	16	1987
1988	1	2	2	3	4	5	6	6	7	8	9	10	10	11	12	13	14	14	15	16	1988
1989	1	2	2	3	4	5	6	7	7	8	9	10	11	11	12	13	14	15	16	16	1989
1990	1	2	2	3	4	5	6	7	8	8	9	10	11	12	12	13	14	15	16	17	1990

FIGURE 2113c.—Correction to tabulated altitude due to annual change in declination of stars.

TABLE VII.

CORRECTION TO GHA ARIES DUE TO ANNUAL CHANGE IN RIGHT ASCENSION OF STARS

Name of Star	1. ALDEBARAN 2. ALPHERATZ 3. ALPHECCA 4. ALTAIR 5. ANTARES					6. ARCTURUS 7. BETELGEUX 8. CAPELLA 9. CAPH 10. CANOPUS					11. DENEB 12. DENEBOLA 13. DUBHE 14. ETAMIN 15. FOMALHAUT					16. POLLUX 17. PROCYON 18. RASALAGUE 19. REGULUS 20. RIGEL					21. SIRIUS 22. SPICA 23. VEGA			Name of Star
No.	1	2	3	4	5	6	7	8	9	10	11	12	13	14	15	16	17	18	19	20	21	22	23	No.
Year																								Year
1942	−09	+39	−04	+01	+32	−15	−01	−06	+29	+20	+08	+28	−03	+11	+23	+33	−04	−04	−19	+04	+21	+28	+15	1942
1943	10	38	04	00	31	16	01	07	28	20	08	28	03	11	22	33	05	04	20	03	21	27	15	1943
1944	11	38	05	−01	30	17	02	08	27	19	07	27	04	10	22	32	06	05	21	02	20	26	14	1944
1945	11	37	05	01	30	17	03	09	27	19	07	26	05	10	21	31	06	06	22	02	19	26	14	1945
1946	−12	+36	−06	−02	+29	−18	−04	−10	+26	+19	+06	+25	−06	+10	+20	+30	−07	−06	−22	+01	+18	+25	+13	1946
1947	13	35	07	03	28	19	05	12	25	18	06	25	07	09	19	29	08	07	23	00	18	24	13	1947
1948	14	35	07	04	27	19	05	13	24	18	05	24	08	09	18	28	09	08	24	−01	17	23	12	1948
1949	15	34	08	04	26	20	06	14	23	18	05	23	09	09	17	27	10	08	25	01	16	22	12	1949
1950	16	33	09	05	25	21	07	15	23	17	04	22	10	08	17	26	10	09	26	02	16	22	11	1950
1951	−17	+32	−09	−06	+24	−21	−08	−16	+22	+17	+04	+22	−11	+08	+16	+25	−11	−10	−26	−03	+15	+21	+11	1951
1952	17	31	10	07	23	22	09	17	21	17	03	21	12	08	15	24	12	11	27	03	15	20	10	1952
1953	18	31	10	07	22	23	09	18	20	16	03	20	13	07	14	23	13	11	28	04	14	19	10	1953
1954	19	30	11	08	21	23	10	19	19	16	02	19	14	07	13	22	14	12	29	05	13	19	09	1954
1955	20	29	12	09	20	24	11	20	19	16	02	19	15	07	12	22	14	13	30	06	13	18	09	1955
1956	−21	+28	−12	−10	+19	−25	−12	−21	+18	+15	+01	+18	−15	+06	+12	+21	−15	−13	−30	−06	+12	+17	+08	1956
1957	22	28	13	10	19	25	13	23	17	15	01	17	16	06	11	20	16	14	31	07	11	16	08	1957
1958	22	27	14	11	18	26	13	24	16	15	00	16	17	06	10	19	17	15	32	08	11	15	07	1958
1959	23	26	14	12	17	27	14	25	15	14	00	15	18	05	09	18	17	15	33	08	10	15	07	1959
1960	24	25	15	12	16	28	15	26	15	14	−01	15	19	05	08	17	18	16	34	09	09	14	06	1960
1961	−25	+25	−15	−13	+15	−28	−16	−27	+14	+14	−01	+14	−20	+05	+08	+16	−19	−17	−34	−10	+09	+13	+06	1961
1962	26	24	16	14	14	29	17	28	13	13	02	13	21	04	07	15	20	18	35	11	08	12	05	1962
1963	26	23	17	15	13	30	18	29	12	13	02	12	22	04	06	14	20	19	36	11	07	11	05	1963
1964	27	22	17	15	12	30	18	30	11	13	03	12	23	03	05	13	21	20	37	12	07	11	04	1964
1965	28	21	18	16	11	31	19	32	11	12	04	11	24	03	04	12	22	20	38	13	06	10	04	1965
1966	−29	+20	−19	−17	+10	−32	−20	−33	+10	+12	−04	+10	−25	+03	+03	+11	−23	−21	−38	−14	+05	+09	+03	1966
1967	30	20	19	18	09	32	21	34	09	12	05	09	26	02	03	11	24	22	39	14	05	08	03	1967
1968	31	19	20	18	08	33	22	35	08	11	05	09	27	02	02	10	24	22	40	15	04	07	02	1968
1969	32	18	21	19	07	34	22	36	07	11	06	08	27	02	+01	09	25	22	41	16	03	07	02	1969
1970	33	18	21	20	07	34	23	37	07	11	06	07	28	01	00	08	26	23	42	16	03	06	01	1970
1971	−34	+17	−22	−21	+06	−35	−24	−38	+06	+10	+07	+06	−29	+01	−01	+07	−27	−24	−42	−17	+02	+05	+01	1971
1972	34	16	22	21	05	36	25	39	05	10	07	06	30	01	02	06	28	24	43	18	01	04	00	1972
1973	35	15	23	22	04	36	26	40	04	10	08	05	31	00	02	05	28	25	44	19	01	03	00	1973
1974	36	14	24	23	03	37	26	41	03	09	08	04	32	00	03	04	29	26	45	19	00	03	−01	1974
1975	37	14	24	23	02	38	27	43	03	09	09	03	33	00	04	03	30	27	46	20	−01	02	01	1975
1976	−38	+13	−25	−24	+01	−39	−28	−44	+02	+09	−09	+02	−34	−01	−05	+02	−31	−27	−46	−21	−01	+01	−02	1976
1977	39	12	26	25	00	39	29	45	01	08	10	02	35	01	06	01	31	28	47	21	02	00	02	1977
1978	40	11	26	26	−01	40	30	46	00	08	10	01	36	01	07	00	32	29	48	22	03	00	03	1978
1979	40	11	27	26	02	41	31	47	−01	08	11	00	37	02	07	00	33	29	49	23	03	−01	03	1979
1980	41	10	28	27	03	41	31	48	01	07	11	−01	38	02	08	−01	34	30	50	24	04	02	04	1980
1981	−42	+09	−28	−28	−04	−42	−32	−49	−02	+07	−12	−01	−39	−02	−09	−02	−35	−31	−50	−24	−05	−03	−04	1981
1982	43	08	29	29	04	43	33	50	03	07	12	02	39	03	10	03	36	31	51	25	05	04	05	1982
1983	44	07	29	29	05	43	34	51	04	06	13	03	40	03	11	04	36	32	52	26	06	04	05	1983
1984	45	07	30	30	06	44	35	53	05	06	13	04	41	03	11	05	37	33	53	26	07	05	06	1984
1985	45	06	31	31	07	45	35	54	05	06	14	04	42	04	12	06	38	33	54	27	07	06	06	1985
1986	−46	+05	−31	−32	−08	−45	−36	−55	−06	+05	−14	−05	−43	−04	−13	−07	−39	−34	−54	−28	−08	−07	−07	1986
1987	47	04	32	32	09	46	37	56	07	05	15	06	44	05	14	08	39	35	55	29	09	08	07	1987
1988	48	04	33	33	10	47	38	57	08	05	15	07	45	05	15	09	40	36	56	29	09	08	08	1988
1989	49	03	33	34	11	47	39	58	09	04	16	07	46	05	16	10	41	36	57	30	10	09	09	1989
1990	−50	+02	−34	−34	−12	−48	−39	−59	−09	+04	−16	−08	−47	−06	−16	−11	−42	−37	−58	−31	−11	−10	−09	1990

Correction applied to GHA Aries in accordance with prefixed sign.

From Practical Celestial Air Navigation Tables, Volume II. Copyright 1942, 1943, 1969 & 1970, by Navigation Publishing Co., and by George G. Hoehne, Author. Used by permission.

FIGURE 2113d.—Correction to GHA ♈ due to annual change in right ascension of stars.

altitudes are carried to a minimum value of 5°, and azimuth to the horizon. These tables are similar to those of Hoehne and volume I of Pub. No. 249.

H.O. Pub. No. 230 (Goetz), *High Latitude Celestial Navigation Tables,* designed in 1945 by Roy F. Goetz, was published by the U. S. Navy Hydrographic Office in 1946.

The first section, called "Star Tables," is entered with the latitude to the nearest 1° from 70°N to 89°N, the name of the star (for ten selected stars), and LHA♈ at intervals of 2° for latitude 70° to 79°, 5° for 80° to 84°, and 10° for 85° to 89°. Altitude is tabulated to the nearest 1' and azimuth (not azimuth angle) to the nearest 0°.1. A "ΔH" value is given for use with an auxiliary table to interpolate for precession of the equinoxes (art. 1419).

In the second section, called "Declination Tables," declination is substituted for the name of the star. A separate table is given for each 1° declination from 0° to 28°. For each degree a "same name" section is given first, followed by a "contrary name" section (to declination 19°). The minimum altitude is 1°. The declination tables give "d" in place of "ΔH" for use with an auxiliary table to interpolate for declination.

Only 400 of these tables were published. They were intended only for use in military aircraft operating beyond the latitude range of H.O. Pub. No. 218. After Pub. No. 249 became available, H.O. Pub. No. 230 was canceled.

Pub. No. 249, *Sight Reduction Tables for Air Navigation,* in three volumes, are published by the Defense Mapping Agency Hydrographic Center. A preliminary edition of volume I for selected stars was published in 1947 under the title *Star Tables for Air Navigation,* using the principles and features of tables proposed previously by George G. Hoehne, Commander C. H. Hutchings, USN, and others. The altitudes of this edition were adjusted for refraction at a height of 10,000 feet. By the time the "first" edition was printed in 1951, for epoch 1955.0, more than 20,000 copies of the preliminary edition had been distributed. The 1951 edition dropped the refraction adjustment feature from the altitudes, and had an improved selection of stars. It was followed in 1952 with two volumes for declination entry at 1° intervals from 0° to 29°. In 1952 and 1953 a British edition was published with identical tables (A. P. 3270) but altered explanation. The tables have been accepted as standard by the air forces of Great Britain, Canada, Australia, New Zealand, and the United States.

Pub. No. 249 is described in detail in chapter XX.

Experimental Air Navigation Tables. During the early part of World War II the British Royal Air Force felt the need for an inspection table that would be faster than Air Pub. 1618 (H.O. Pub. No. 218), but free from the limitations of the astrograph (art. 2123). Wing Commander R. C. Alabaster suggested the addition of SHA to the hour angle (measured eastward) of the stars given in Air Pub. 1618, converted to time at the sidereal rate of 15°02'.5 per hour. This would give the time interval until the next meridan transit of the vernal equinox. Before observation, the time of passage of the vernal equinox across a convenient meridian would be marked on the chart or plotting sheet. After observation, the tables would be entered with assumed latitude and the nearest tabulated altitude. The (SHA+HA) corresponding to this altitude would be added to GMT at the time of observation. The result should be close to the time marked on the chart. The difference would be converted to arc units (or a time scale would be marked on the chart or plotting sheet) and the corresponding longitude determined. This point would serve as the assumed position. The difference between the observed altitude and that used for entering the table would be the altitude difference to be used with the azimuth for plotting the line of position.

Squadron Leaders A. Potter and A. J. Hagger suggested a method of printing a time scale on the chart or plotting sheet with an auxiliary table to assist in locating the assumed position.

Various modifications and conventions were later added to avoid negative values and other complications. As the method finally emerged, a quantity known as "scale time" was adopted. This value, designated T, would be equal to 26 hours plus the GMT of the next transit of the vernal equinox occurring after 0600 during the night of the flight. The GMT of observation would be designated t. The quantity $T-t$ would be the value tabulated.

Further attempts were made to simplify the conversion of mean to sidereal time so that the single setting might be used during an entire flight. One of these, called the "Astro-Scales," was suggested by Wing Commander E. W. Anderson in 1945. In 1953 he and D. H. Sadler suggested an improved version.

Although a considerable amount of thought was given to this method, and experimental tables were published for a limited band of latitude, the limitations of a longitude method and the inconvenience of converting mean time to sidereal time resulted in the method being discarded in favor of the less restrictive Pub No. 249 method.

Ashton. In 1943 Philip Ashton proposed a set of tables called *Astrograph-time Star Tables for Air Navigation*, based upon the principle of the *Experimental Air Navigation Tables*. A permanent table would be entered with the name of the star, latitude, and "astrograph mean time" (art. 2123), and altitude and azimuth would be taken from the table. A set of tables issued each year would list the values to be used with GMT each night to determine the astrograph mean time. Before take-off, the chart or plotting sheet would be marked to agree with the astrograph mean time, and a metal tape would then be used to convert mean time to sidereal time for finding the assumed position.

Heard. About 1950 John F. Heard, associate professor of astronomy at the University of Toronto, prepared a modification of the *Experimental Air Navigation Tables*. The tabulation would be altered so that altitude would be given in the left-hand column at intervals of 20'. A delta ("diff.") value would be tabulated and this used with the difference between entering and observed altitudes to enter an auxiliary table to determine a correction to be applied to $T-t$ so that the altitude difference need not be plotted. A correction for 60 minus seconds of T would also be applied. The "bearing" of the line of position (azimuth plus or minus 90°) would also be tabulated. The line of position would be plotted through the assumed position, in the direction indicated by the "bearing." For any given time three stars differing in azimuth by approximately 120° would be given. The part of the table to use would be determined by a rough computation of $T-t$.

Kotlarić. In 1976 Dr. Stjepo M. Kotlarić, (art. 2112 and 2116), then Assistant Director, Hydrographic Institute of the Yugoslav Navy, conceived and designed a set of inspection tables generally similar to Pub. No. 214 in format but differing considerably from the latter tables in the manner of tabulation.

Projected for publication in 1977, *Tables K21, Computed Results of Altitudes and Azimuths for all Latitudes and all Celestial Bodies*, are in three volumes, each covering a 30° band of latitude. The table arguments are latitude, meridian angle, and declination. The respondents are tabular altitude, index for altitude correction due to the excess of actual declination over the declination argument, and azimuth angle. Unlike Pub. No. 214 but like Pub. No. 229, the sign of the altitude correction is tabulated.

The altitude and azimuth angle data for each degree of latitude are arranged on nine successive openings of the volume. Meridian angle is the vertical argument and declination is the horizontal argument. As in Pub. No. 214, tabular altitudes and corresponding azimuth angles are limited to those of bodies approximately 5° and more above the horizon. Data for a body having declination of same name as latitude are tabulated on the left-hand page and continued on the right-hand page as necessary. Data for a body having declination of contrary name to the latitude are tabulated below on the right-hand page beginning with meridian angle 0° and continuing until the 5° altitude limitation is reached.

At each opening declination is tabulated in eight columns at 1° intervals from 0° to 30°; from 31°30′ to 89° the declinations and intervals are selected to provide those declinations required for the reduction of the selected stars. The declination in the right-hand column of each page is repeated in the first column of the pages of the next opening. This repetition of data is used as an aid to determining whether interpolation of azimuth angle for declination increment is required. There is no need to turn pages to determine the change in azimuth angle for 1° increase in declination.

The tables are intended for use with an assumed position selected so that interpolation for latitude and meridian angle is not required. Entering the tables with integral values of latitude, declination, and meridian angle, the respondents are found in a form which is a unique feature of *Tables K21*. The degrees and minutes of the tabulated altitude are printed as a two to four digit group without spacing between digits if four digits are used. For example: Tabular altitude 32°45′ is printed as 3245. Although the digital tabulation is only to the minute for tabular altitude and the index for altitude correction, and to the degree for azimuth angle, the addition of a decimal point following these values enables their extraction to a greater precision than that tabulated. The decimal point following the tabular altitude or the index for altitude correction means 0′.5; following the tabular azimuth angle, the decimal point means 0°.5. The table designer added this feature to include the maximum amount of data in the smallest space practicable and to give the user an option with respect to the precision of the data extracted. When using the decimal point option, the extracted values of altitude and index correction do not differ from values computed to the nearest 0′.1 by more than 0′.2; the extracted azimuth angle values do not differ from azimuth angles computed to the nearest 0°.1 by more than 0°.2.

The multiplication table is simple to use. It is entered with the index correction as the vertical argument and the declination increment (1′ to 59′ followed by decimal parts from 0′.1 to 0′.9) as the horizontal argument.

The tables include a comprehensive English explanation.

Davies. In 1974 Rear Admiral Thomas D. Davies, USN (Ret.) proposed the construction of tables listing for each degree of latitude the LHA♈ and azimuth of stars when their altitudes are integral degrees. The table entering arguments are assumed latitude and assumed altitude. A list of about 15 to 20 stars under the altitude heading approximating the observed altitude is examined to find the combination of LHA♈ and azimuth approximating the time and azimuth of the star observation.

The altitude intercept is plotted from an adjusted assumed position: the closest integral degree of latitude and the DR longitude offset by the difference between the tabulated LHA♈ and LHA♈ at the time of the observation.

The identity of the star observed need not be known.

Due to the high rate of change of LHA♈ with change in latitude and altitude when a body is near meridian transit, a simple modification of the normal procedure is required when stars are observed at or near meridian transit. When the star is near meridian transit, LHA♈ for meridian transit and a correction to the assumed altitude to give the altitude at transit are tabulated. The simple modification is clearly identified. A correction for precession of the equinoxes (art. 1419) and nutation (art. 1417) may be required.

The proposed method is called the Method of Assumed Altitude. The proposed tables are entitled *Star Sight Reduction and Identification Tables*.

2114. Azimuth methods.—Nearly all methods proposed for obtaining a line of position are based upon the use of altitudes. The azimuth might also be used if an instrument becomes available for measuring it to the required accuracy. The accuracy needed would depend upon the acceptable error of the line of position. The error would be proportional to the cosine of the altitude. For a celestial body on the celestial horizon an error of 1' in the azimuth would introduce an error of one mile in the line of position, the same as it does in an altitude observation. For any altitude greater than 0°, the error would be less.

Each method of determining a line of position by altitude has its counterpart in the azimuth problem. Thus, if it can be determined that a celestial body is exactly on the celestial meridian, the west longitude is the same as the GHA of the body. If the body is exactly on the prime vertical, the latitude can be computed. As a more general case, two points on a given azimuth line can be computed and joined by a straight line, by assuming two latitudes or two longitudes. However, if one such position is known, the azimuth line of position can be drawn through it in the direction of the azimuth. If the celestial body is sufficiently high, or if a small scale is acceptable and allowance is made for chart distortion, the azimuth line can be plotted directly, just as the circle of position can be drawn if the altitude is known. The difference between the observed azimuth and that computed for an assumed position can be used in a manner similar to the altitude difference. The azimuth difference in minutes multiplied by the cosine of the altitude would be the "intercept" measured off from the assumed position in a direction perpendicular to the computed azimuth. Through the point thus determined, a line would be drawn in the direction of the observed azimuth. For small differences, the line could be drawn perpendicular to the line from the assumed position. The relative values of the observed and computed azimuths would indicate the direction (right or left) to draw the line from the assumed position.

If the altitude and azimuth were both known to sufficient accuracy, a single celestial body would suffice for determining position by any combination of altitude and azimuth methods or by direct computation of latitude and longitude. The two lines of position would always be perpendicular to each other.

Double altitudes. For a stationary observer the longitude can be determined by observing the altitude shortly before meridian transit (either upper or lower), and noting the time when the altitude has returned to exactly the same value after meridian transit. If there has been no change in declination between observations, the mid time represents the moment of meridian transit, at which time the azimuth is 000° or 180°. The GHA (or 360° − GHA for east longitude) is the longitude of the observer. This method might be considered as either a longitude or an azimuth method. A variation is to observe a number of altitudes shortly before and after meridian transit. These are then plotted against time on cross-section paper and a smooth curve plotted through them. The time corresponding to the maximum altitude (minimum altitude for lower transit) is the moment of meridian transit.

Quilter. In 1950 Commander E. S. Quilter, USN, suggested a method based upon azimuth difference. He would measure and compute azimuth to the nearest 0°.01 (when the means for doing so became available) and express the azimuth difference to the same precision. A table would be provided to list values of K, a constant by which the azimuth difference would be multiplied for any given altitude to determine the "intercept" to measure off from the assumed position.

2115. Determination of latitude and longitude.—Most methods provide information needed for plotting a line of position. The fix is at the common intersection of two or more such lines. A line of position might be plotted in one of several ways. In the latitude and longitude methods, the lines are plotted at the computed coordinate. When one coordinate has been determined, the other can be computed without plotting. Thus, the longitude determined by time sight is generally correct only for the latitude used in its solution, and the plotting of a longitude line is misleading, unless the celestial body is on the prime vertical. A better procedure is to compute two points, using different latitudes (or longitudes, if latitude is being computed). These two points are on the line of position. A straight line connecting them is a good approximation of the circle of equal altitude. This was the method used by Captain Sumner when he discovered the line of position (art. 131), and the method of H.O. Pubs. Nos. 203 and 204 (art. 2106).

Another method is to compute one point and the azimuth (or $Zn \pm 90°$), and plot the line of position through the point. This is the method used by Soule and Dreisonstok (art. 2106).

If only the altitude difference is computed for two points, the line of position is a common tangent of circles of radius equal to the altitude difference at these two points. This is the method of Benest and Timberlake (art. 2110).

The most common modern method of plotting the line of position is by means of the assumed position, altitude intercept, and azimuth.

It is possible, too, to plot circles of position by using the geographical position of each body as the center of its circle, and the zenith distance as its radius. This is the method used for high-altitude observations (art. 2024), but is generally not practical for ordinary altitudes because of the small scale that would be needed, and the error that would be introduced by chart distortion, unless plotting were done on the surface of a sphere (art. 2124).

The use of a circle of equal altitude is similar to the use of a circle of position around a landmark of known range. The bearing of such a landmark also furnishes a line of position. Similarly, a line of position can be obtained by plotting the azimuth line of a celestial body, and a fix by plotting two such lines. This is generally not done because of the scale and chart limitations mentioned above, and also because the needed accuracy in observation is beyond the capability of equipment generally available to the navigator. Errors in both compass and measurement of azimuth are involved.

Various methods of determining position by computation from observations of two or more celestial bodies or four observations of a single celestial body are discussed in articles 2116 and 2117.

2116. Computed position from observation of two or more bodies.—Several methods have been proposed for computing the position directly from the observation of two or more celestial bodies. These generally consist of some combination of latitude and time sight methods. One form of automatic celestial navigation, proposed by Collins Radio Company, uses the principle of the planetarium in reverse, two bodies serving to position a horizontal-stabilized sphere (in principle) for latitude and local sidereal time. If the device is accurately set to Greenwich sidereal time, longitude is indicated.

Fox. In 1951 Charles Fox, associate professor of mathematics at McGill University, Montreal, proposed formulas for computing latitude and longitude if certain star pairs are observed, the two stars of each pair having almost the same SHA. Presumably, simultaneous observations would be needed. Five such star pairs are listed. Four of the stars in three of these pairs are dimmer than the third magnitude, and are not listed in the almanacs, either in the main tabulation or among the additional stars.

More involved formulas are suggested for use of the method with any three celestial bodies.

de Jonge. In 1945 Joost H. Kiewiet de Jonge, a lieutenant in the Netherlands East Indies Army Air Force, proposed a method of determining position from the observation of three stars. The U. S. Navy Hydrographic Office published experimental tables for several star pairs for latitudes 20° to 30° under the title *Three Star Position Tables for Aerial Navigation.* It was anticipated that if the method proved popular, all possible three-star combinations (of the stars in the main tabulation of the almanacs) would be given, so that the navigator would not be limited in his selection.

No assumed position is needed with the method. Three stars are observed at intervals of three minutes, the stars being observed in the order of listing in the main table. Table I is entered with the three altitudes, h_1, h_2, and h_3, and for each a value is taken from the table. These values are labeled H_1, H_2, and H_3, respectively. They are combined to form $H_1 + H_2 = H_{12}$, and $H_2 + H_3 = H_{23}$. These combined values, H_{12} and H_{23}, are then used to enter the main table, from which local sidereal time (in arc units) and latitude are obtained. Greenwich sidereal time minus local sidereal time equals longitude (measured westward). Delta values and auxiliary tables provide corrections for motion of the observer and observation intervals differing from three minutes. Mean corrections for both atmospheric refraction and Coriolis are included in the tables, which are limited to altitudes between 20° and 75°, and azimuth difference between consecutive stars to 165°.

Dozier. In 1949 Charles T. Dozier proposed a method based upon the simultaneous observation of two celestial bodies and the solution of two spherical triangles, with vertices as follows:

triangle 1—the two celestial bodies and the elevated pole,
triangle 2—the two celestial bodies and the zenith.

The method involves the successive solution of seven formulas:

$$\cos D = \sin d_1 \sin d_2 + \cos d_1 \cos d_2 \cos S \tag{1}$$

$$\sin (X_1 \pm A_1) = \frac{\sin S \cos d_2}{\sin D} \tag{2}$$

$$\cos A_1 = \frac{\sin h_2}{\cos h_1 \sin D} \pm \frac{\tan h_1}{\tan D} \tag{3}$$

$$X_1 = (X_1 \pm A_1) \mp A_1 \tag{4}$$

$$\sin L = \sin d_1 \sin h_1 + \cos d_1 \cos h_1 \cos X_1 \tag{5}$$

$$\sin t_1 = \frac{\sin X_1 \cos h_1}{\cos L} \tag{6}$$

$$\lambda = GHA_1 \pm t_1 \tag{7}$$

in which D is the great-circle distance (angular) between the two celestial bodies, d_1 is the declination of the first body, d_2 is the declination of the second body, S is the difference of SHA of the two bodies, X_1 is the parallactic angle of the first body, A_1 is the angle at the first body between its vertical circle and the great circle between it and the second body, h_1 is the altitude of the first body (Ho is used), h_2 is the altitude (Ho) of the second body, L is the latitude of the observer, t_1 is the meridian angle of the first body, λ is the longitude of the observer, and GHA is the Greenwich hour angle of the first body.

If the great circle joining the two celestial bodies is on that side of the zenith opposite the elevated pole (if Z is within the angle formed by the vertical circle and hour circle of the first body), (X_1+A_1) is used in formulas (2) and (4), the sign in formula (3) is positive $(+)$, and the sign of A_1 in formula (4) is negative $(-)$. These signs are all reversed if the line adjoining the celestial bodies is on the opposite side of the zenith (Z outside the angle). If the great circle joining the two bodies passes almost through the zenith, an error might be made in the selection of the sign, and it is well to select another star pair. In formula (7) the sign is positive if the first celestial body is east of the observer's celestial meridian, and negative if it is west. The answer is in longitude measured westward from the Greenwich meridian. If the value exceeds 180°, it is subtracted from 360°, and the longitude is east.

If the quadrant of angle $(X_1 \pm A_1)$ or if t_1 is in doubt, the following formulas are suggested to replace (2) or (6):

$$\cot\ (X_1 \pm A_1) = \frac{\cos d_1 \tan d_2 - \sin d_1 \cos S}{\sin S} \tag{2A}$$

$$\cot\ t_1 = \frac{\cos d_1 \tan h_1 - \sin d_1 \cos X_1}{\sin X_1}. \tag{6A}$$

In the presentation of the method it was suggested that simultaneous observations be obtained by a two-star tracker mounted on a stable platform, or by a double sextant. Several such sextants have been proposed, but none is in common use. Other possibilities would be to have two observers or to adjust the value of one observation for the change in altitude due to its apparent motion and the motion of the observer between observations.

It was proposed that values obtained by solution of formula (1) be published in a permanent table, since these values for various star pairs would be constant except for the very slight change due to proper motion (art. 1418). Since the values obtained by formula (2) change slowly with precession of the equinoxes (art. 1419), it was proposed that the angle (X_1+A_1) for a number of star pairs be published annually, perhaps in the almanacs. The other formulas would be solved after observation of the celestial bodies.

Kotlarić. In 1954 Stjepo M. Kotlarić (arts. 2112 and 2113), of Yugoslavia, proposed a method based upon the simultaneous observation of two selected stars and the solution of three spherical triangles with vertices as follows:

triangle 1—the two stars and the elevated pole,
triangle 2—the two stars and the zenith, and
triangle 3—the elevated pole, the zenith, and the second star.

The parallactic angle (X) of the second star is determined by solutions of triangles 1 and 2, using haversine formulas. The latitude and the local hour angle of the second star are then computed by solution of triangle 3, using observed altitude, parallactic angle, and declination of the second star as the known parts. By subtracting the GHA of the second star from its LHA, the longitude is obtained.

From triangle PnM_1M_2 (fig. 2116), angle A and the interstellar distance $(90°-V_x)$ are computed by means of the difference of sidereal hour angles (SHA$_1$ and SHA$_2$) of the two stars observed and their declinations (d_1 and d_2) from the formulas:

$$\sin^2 \frac{90°-V_x}{2} = \sin^2 \frac{d_2-d_1}{2} + \sin^2 \frac{SHA_1-SHA}{2} \cos d_2 \cos d_1 \tag{1}$$

$$\sin^2 \frac{A}{2} = \csc (90° - V_x) \sec d_2 \cos R \sin (R - d_1) \tag{2}$$

$$R = \frac{d_1 + (90° - V_x) + d_2}{2}.$$

From triangle ZM_1M_2, angle B is computed, using the two observed altitudes (Ho_1 and Ho_2) and the interstellar distance ($90° - V_x$) as the known parts, from the formula:

$$\sin^2 \frac{B}{2} = \csc (90° - V_x) \sec Ho_2 \cos R \sin (R - Ho_1) \tag{3}$$

$$R = \frac{Ho_1 + (90° - V_x) + Ho_2}{2}.$$

Angle B, combined with angle A, gives the parallactic angle (X) from one of the following relations, depending upon the relative positions of the zenith and the two stars:

$$X = A + B, \quad X = A - B, \quad X = 360° - (A + B). \tag{4}$$

From triangle $PnZM_2$ the local hour angle of the second star (LHA_2) and the latitude of the observer are computed, using d_2, Ho_2, and X as the known parts, from the formulas:

$$\sin^2 \frac{90° - L}{2} = \sin^2 \frac{Ho_2 - d_2}{2} + \sin^2 \frac{X}{2} \cos Ho_2 \cos d_2 \tag{5}$$

$$\sin^2 \frac{LHA_2}{2} = \csc (90° - d_2) \sec L \cos R \sin (R - Ho_2) \tag{6}$$

$$R = \frac{Ho_2 + (90° - d_2) + L}{2}.$$

The longitude of the observer and its sign (− for west longitude and + for east longitude) are found by subtracting the Greenwich hour angle of the second star (GHA_2) from the local hour angle of the same star (LHA_2). The second star should not be observed in the vicinity of the observer's meridian.

Nonsimultaneous observations, preferably not more than 4 minutes apart, may be used if corrections for the motions of the body and the observer are applied.

A modified version of this direct method of computation of latitude and longitude of the observer's position proposed in 1954 was published in 1971 as *Tables K11, Two-Star Fix Without Use of Altitude Difference Method*. In *Tables K11* the developed formulas were not used for tabulation of latitude and LHA_2 as suggested in 1954, but for the tabulation of correction indices and their signs. These indices are used through the multiplication table in obtaining corrections to the tabulated entering arguments (assumed latitude and LHA ♈) for the difference in declinations and sidereal hour angles between the constant values used in the tabulation and the values at the time of observation. Correction indices are also provided in the main table for use in obtaining corrections to the entering arguments for the difference between actual and tabulated altitudes in order to obtain accurate latitude and LHA ♈. The longitude is obtained by subtracting the GHA^2 from the sum of LHA♈ and tabulated SHA_2.

Tables K11 are unique among all other tabular methods as they give tabulated corrections to be applied to the assumed position in order to obtain the observed position without plotting lines of position. The method is simple; there are no rules for signs nor mental interpolations. The tabulated corrections are given on one page of the main tables at the opening for assumed latitude and LHA♈.

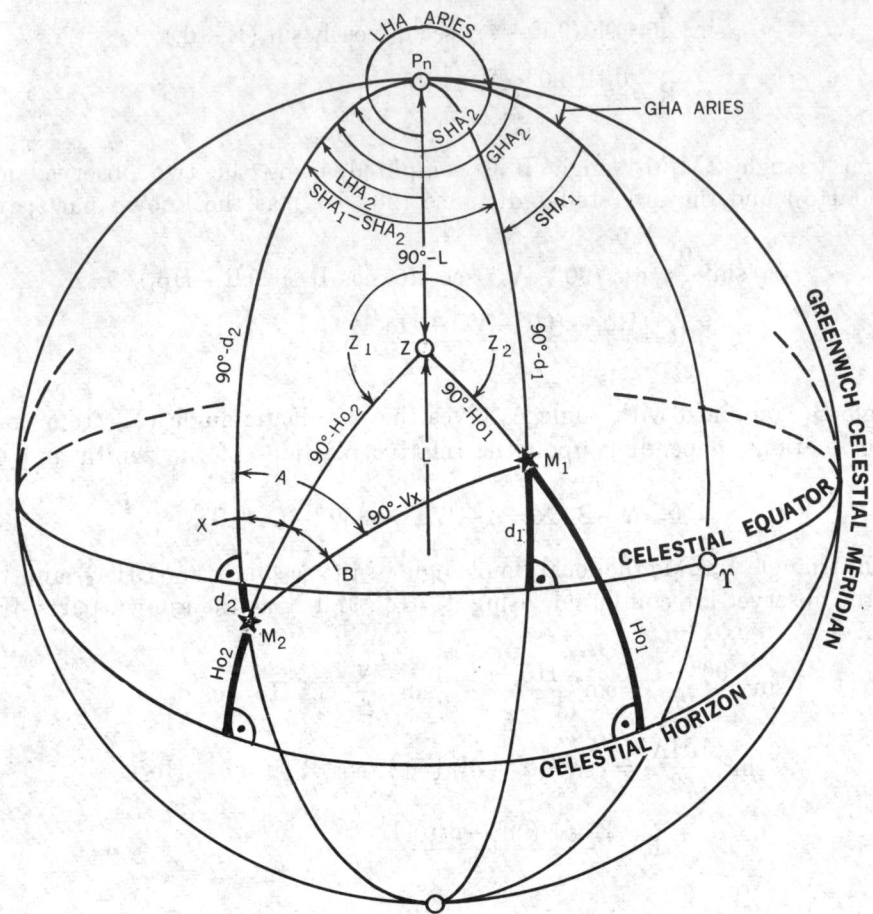

FIGURE 2116.—The spherical triangles on the celestial sphere used in Tables K11.

The tables are published in five volumes: Volume I N(lat. 0° to 9°30′N), in press; Volume II N(lat. 10° to 19°30′N), published 1975; Volume III N(lat. 20° to 29°30′N), published 1974; Volume IV N(lat. 30° to 39°30′N), published 1972; and Volume V N(lat. 40° to 49°30′N), published 1971.

Data for 37 stars in 155 star combinations are included in the tables. Each of the 360 pages of the main table of each volume contains tabulations for two star pairs for arguments of a single latitude (whole degrees or whole degrees and half degree) and a 20° range of LHA ♈ at half-degree intervals.

In 1974 Dr. Kotlarić simplified the correction procedure required when the star observations are nonsimultaneous; eliminating the need to observe the compass azimuth of the first star. Corrections for the elapsed time between observations are applied directly to the tabulated latitude and LHA ♈.

The modification is designed for the new edition in a way to double the number of star pairs without increasing the number of pages of each volume. To reach this goal four different star pairs will be tabulated on each page within the same 20° range of LHA ♈ but divided separately for each 10° range of LHA ♈. Eight different star pairs are given for each assumed position found at each opening of the tables. This is deemed quite satisfactory for the practice of navigation.

The tables include a comprehensive English explanation.

Uribe-White. A unique method of using two stars was suggested in 1952 by Enrique Uribe-White, of Colombia. A bubble sextant would be used to measure the altitude of one star, while a small, marine-type sextant attached to the bubble sextant would be used to measure simultaneously the angle at the star between the vertical circle and the great circle through this star and a second one. Prepared tables would give the great-circle distance between the two stars and also the angle between the great circle joining them and the hour circle of the first star. This angle, combined with the inclined angle which would be measured, constitute the parallactic angle (art. 1433). With this value, the observed altitude, and the declination of the first body, the latitude of the observer and the meridian angle of the first star could be computed by relatively simple formulas or by a mechanical computer proposed by the originator of the method. Meridian angle could be compared with GHA to determine longitude.

2117. Position from observation of single body.—If azimuth could be determined and plotted to sufficient accuracy, the altitude and azimuth of a single body could be used for establishing a fix. Any combination of altitude and azimuth methods (arts. 2108 and 2114) might be used, or the position could be computed without plotting. The following formulas might be used:

$$\sin t = \sin Z \cos h \sec d$$
$$\tan K_1 = \cos t \cot d$$
$$\tan K_2 = \cos Z \cot h$$
$$L = 90° - (K_1 + K_2) \quad \text{(Approximate latitude must be known).}$$

A single body can be used for a running fix, of course, and if the body is near the zenith, a relatively short time might be needed. This is the case for high-altitude observations (art. 2024) and has been used by a submarine measuring azimuth through its periscope when the sun is near the zenith.

Willis. Another method of determining position by a single body is by the use of altitude and rate of change of altitude. Three methods of doing this were suggested by Edward J. Willis in 1928.

Prime vertical observation. It can be shown by the use of differential calculus (art. 144, vol. II) that

$$\cos L = \frac{dh}{dt} \csc Z \tag{1}$$

when $\frac{dh}{dt}$ is the rate of change of altitude with respect to time, specifically the change of altitude in minutes of arc during a one-minute-of-arc (four-seconds-of-time) change of hour angle of the body. However, to obtain latitude accurately in this way it is necessary to determine $\frac{dh}{dt}$ to an accuracy of perhaps four decimal places, and Z to an accuracy of perhaps one minute of arc. Two possible methods of obtaining $\frac{dh}{dt}$ are given below, but present instrument limitations do not permit measurement of azimuth to the required accuracy. However, the cosecant of 90° is unity, so that if the observation is made when the celestial body is on the prime vertical, the formula becomes

$$\cos L = \frac{dh}{dt}. \tag{2}$$

Relatively little error is introduced if the body is within 1° of the prime vertical. The determination of position consists of the following steps:

1. Observe the altitude (h) and rate of change of altitude $\left(\dfrac{dh}{dt}\right)$ when the celestial body is within 1° of the prime vertical.

2. Compute latitude (L) by formula (2).

3. Determine longitude by any standard method, such as Pub. No. 214 or other line of position method, or by time sight (art. 2106).

Perpendicular lines of position. The great circle through the zenith and the celestial body (the vertical circle or azimuth line) furnishes an azimuth line of position that can be established if rate of change of altitude can be accurately determined. This line is perpendicular to the circle of equal altitude and therefore nearly perpendicular to the line of position determined in the usual manner. The intersection of the two lines is the position of the observer. The method involves the following steps:

1. Observe the altitude (h) and rate of change of altitude $\left(\dfrac{dh}{dt}\right)$.

2. Compute the direction of the great circle through the zenith and the celestial body (the vertical circle) at the point where the great circle crosses the celestial equator. This is the complement of the latitude of the vertex and so can be found from a modification of formula (2), which gives the latitude of the vertex:

$$\sin Z_0 = \frac{dh}{dt}. \tag{3}$$

3. Compute the longitude (λ_0) at which the vertical circle crosses the celestial equator, using the formula

$$\sin (\lambda_0 \sim \lambda_b) = \tan Z_0 \tan d. \tag{4}$$

The value λ_b is the longitude of the geographical position of the celestial body.

4. Solve for the latitude (L) at which the azimuth line of position crosses the meridian of the dead reckoning position, or for longitude (λ) at which the line crosses the parallel of latitude of the dead reckoning position, using one of the following formulas:

$$\tan L = \cot Z_0 \sin (\lambda_0 \sim \lambda_{DR}) \tag{5}$$

or

$$\sin (\lambda_0 \sim \lambda) = \tan Z_0 \tan L_{DR} \tag{6}$$

in which L_{DR} and λ_{DR} are the DR latitude and longitude, respectively. Any assumed position in the vicinity can be used in place of the DR. In general, it is preferable to use (5) if azimuth angle is between 45° and 135°, and (6) if it is outside these limits.

5. Solve for the direction (Z) of the azimuth line of position at the point determined in step (4), using the formula

$$\sin Z = \sin Z_0 \sec L. \tag{7}$$

If the DR position or the AP is near the actual position, the azimuth can be considered the same at both without appreciable error.

6. Plot the azimuth line of position through the point found in step (4), in the direction found in step (5).

7. Compute a and Zn by any method and plot the resulting line of position. The intersection of the two lines of position is the fix.

Latitude and longitude by computation. This method is independent of a dead reckoning position, and requires no plotting. It is free from limitations except that observations near meridian transit should be avoided. At this time the rate of change of altitude decreases to zero and then reverses, introducing a possible error. The steps by this method are:

1. Observe the altitude (h) and rate of change of altitude $\left(\dfrac{dh}{dt}\right)$.
2. Compute Z_0, using formula (3).
3. Compute the latitude (L) of the observer by the formula

$$\sin L = \cos Z_0 \cos\left[h \pm \sin^{-1}\left(\frac{\sin d}{\cos Z_0}\right)\right]. \tag{8}$$

In the solution of this equation, the angle whose sine is $\dfrac{\sin d}{\cos Z_0}$ is added to or subtracted from h. The cosine of this angle is then multiplied by $\cos Z_0$, and the result is the sine of the latitude of the observer. The sign is positive ($+$) unless L is greater than d and has the same name, when it is negative ($-$). However, if d is of the same name and greater, the angle to be added may be greater than 90°.

4. Compute the meridian angle of the observer by the formula

$$\sin t = \sin Z_0 \cos h \sec d \sec L. \tag{9}$$

5. Determine GHA for the time of observation.
6. Convert t to LHA, and compute longitude (λ) by the formula

$$\lambda = \text{GHA} - \text{LHA}. \tag{10}$$

If λ is greater than 180°, subtract it from 360° and label it E (east).

Formulas (8) and (10) yield a position on the circle of equal altitude regardless of the value of Z_0 used. The correct position is given only if the correct value of Z_0 is used.

Any of the three methods requires determination of $\dfrac{dh}{dt}$. Two methods are proposed:

In the first, the time needed for the sun (or moon) to change altitude an amount equal to its own diameter is measured. If the body is rising, the upper limb of the reflected image is brought a short distance below the horizon. As it makes contact with the horizon, a stopwatch is started. When the lower limb makes contact with the horizon (usually between 127.8 seconds, the minimum for a stationary observer, and ten minutes after the first contact) the watch is stopped, and the time is read to the nearest tenth of a second, if possible. If the body is setting, the lower limb of the reflected image is brought a short distance above the horizon and the watch started when the lower limb makes contact and stopped when the upper limb makes contact with the horizon. At sunrise or sunset no sextant is needed. Any lag in starting or stopping the watch will not affect the result if it is the same at both ends of the period. The diameter of the body, in minutes of arc, divided by one-fourth the number of seconds is $\dfrac{dh}{dt}$. Since semidiameter is tabulated, the most convenient procedure for determining $\dfrac{dh}{dt}$ is probably to solve the equation

$$\frac{dh}{dt} = \frac{8\,\text{SD}}{T},$$

where SD is the semidiameter of the body in minutes and T is the time interval in seconds. The semidiameter is given to the nearest 0′.1 in the *Nautical Alamanac*. More accurate results will be obtained if the value is taken from the *Ephemeris*, where semidiameter is given to the nearest 0″.01.

The motion of the observer introduces an error which can be corrected as follows: multiply *half* the run of the vessel between upper and lower limb contacts, expressed in nautical miles, by the cosine of the angle between the course of the vessel and the azimuth of the celestial body at the mid time of observation. If this angle is *less* than 90°, the correction is *added* to the tabulated semidiameter if the body is setting, and *subtracted* if it is rising. If the angle is *greater* than 90°, the correction is *added* if the body is rising and *subtracted* if it is setting.

Some practice may be needed to obtain an accurate measurement of the time interval. This practice might be obtained by making a number of observations at a known position and comparing these with values obtained by computation, using the formula

$$T = 8 \text{ SD cos h sec d sec L csc t,}$$

using Hc for h.

The time of an observation is at the middle of the interval between contacts. In correcting hs, the reading of the sextant, to obtain Ho, omit the correction for semidiameter. This might be done by correcting in the usual manner, with an additional correction equal to the semidiameter. The additional correction is negative (−) if the lower limb correction is applied, and positive (+) if the upper limb correction is applied. Another way is to apply neither the lower nor upper limb correction, but a value equal to the algebraic average of both.

The second method of determining $\frac{dh}{dt}$ is given as the more accurate of the two. It consists of observing three altitudes of the celestial body at exactly equal intervals of from 15 to 30 minutes. A shorter interval may result in too great an error in rate, while a longer one increases the time without advantage. If h_1, h_2, and h_3 are the three altitudes and t_1 and t_3 are the meridian angles at the times of the first and third observations, respectively, $\frac{dh}{dt}$ can be computed by means of the formula

$$\frac{dh}{dt} = \sin \tfrac{1}{2}(h_1 - h_3) \cos \tfrac{1}{2}(h_1 + h_3) \csc \tfrac{1}{2}(t_1 - t_3) \sec h_2.$$

If difficulty is experienced in making an accurate observation at a given time, better results might be obtained by computing the time for the third observation, by adding the interval between the first two observations to the time of the second observation, and then making several observations starting shortly before the computed time. These can then be plotted on cross-section paper with altitude as one coordinate and time as the other. The altitude indicated by the intersection of the line representing the required time and a line faired through the plotted points is used as the third altitude. A similar procedure might increase the accuracy of the first two observations. A quicker but less accurate way of determining the third altitude is to take one observation shortly before the required time and another shortly after it, and interpolating to find the altitude at the required time. Another variation is to take an altitude at *about* the required time and adjust the second altitude to the corresponding value midway between the first and third observations, using the mean value found by interpolating from the first or third observation and extrapolating (art. 207, vol. II) from the other. The time and altitude are those of the second observation.

This method assumes no change of declination between observations, and no change in the position of the observer. When the observer is not stationary, a correction is applied to h_1 and h_3 to convert them to the equivalent values at the position of the second observation. Assuming constant course and speed, this correction in minutes of arc is equal to the vessel's run between consecutive observations multiplied by the cosine of the angle between the course of the vessel and the average azimuth of the body. If the angle is *less* than 90°, the correction is *added* to h_1 and *subtracted* from h_3. If the angle is *greater* than 90°, the correction is *subtracted* from h_1 and *added* to h_3.

A possible variation of either method of determining $\dfrac{dh}{dt}$ would be to make a comparatively large number of observations (10 to 15) at short intervals and plot the altitudes versus time on cross-section paper. A point near each end of the line faired through the plotted points would then be corrected for the run of the vessel, as in the second method. Two points might then be selected, one near each end of the altitude-time line. The change in altitude, in minutes, divided by one-fourth the number of seconds between the two points is $\dfrac{dh}{dt}$. If preferred, three points might be selected at equal intervals and the formula of the second method used.

Rate determined by two individual observations a few minutes apart would not be sufficiently accurate for practical navigation.

None of the methods employing rate of change of altitude have proved popular, probably because of the difficulty of obtaining an accurate value of $\dfrac{dh}{dt}$. The use of azimuth and rate of change of azimuth, altitude and rate of change of azimuth, or azimuth and rate of change of altitude have been even less attractive because of the even greater difficulty of obtaining accurate measurements of azimuth or rate of change of azimuth. With the further development of automatic devices for continuously measuring altitude or azimuth, with allowance for motion of the observer, such methods might prove more attractive.

2118. Use of unique situations.—Various unique situations might be used for determining position or a line of position. As a general rule these have not been attractive because they could be used only when the conditions were met. As an example, if a celestial body of known coordinates were known to be in the zenith, the declination of the body would be the same as the latitude of the observer. His longitude would be the same as GHA of the body (360° − GHA in east longitude).

Near the geographical poles, the poles can be used as the assumed position. Here the declination of the body is the same as the computed altitude, and GHA replaces azimuth.

Meridian altitudes (art. 2103) and latitude by Polaris (art. 2105) are examples of methods depending upon unique situations. These have both been used extensively, but are decreasing in popularity because of their reliance upon unique conditions, without adequately compensating advantages.

Shchetkin. In 1899 N. O. Shchetkin proposed a method of computing latitude and meridian angle from measurement of the times at which two or more pairs of stars have the same altitude. Each star pair would provide, in effect, a single great-circle line of position. Variations of the method were proposed by Zinger, Pewzow, and W. W. Kawraisky, a Russian. The necessary tables for latitude 60°N to 80°N were published by the Astronomical Institute of Russia in 1936. A similar method was prepared by Simon Swahn in 1943.

Collins. In 1946 Oliver C. Collins, an astronomer at the University of Nebraska, proposed a variation of the method of Shchetkin, and extended it to include observations when two celestial bodies have the same azimuth.

McKee. In 1951 Lieutenant Merlin A. McKee, USMS, proposed a graphical solution of the same-altitude method of Collins.

Pierce. About 1951 Rear Admiral M. R. Pierce, USN (Ret.), suggested a method of establishing a line of position perpendicular to the course line when the altitude of a celestial body is observed at the moment it crosses the great circle through the observer and his destination.

2119. Graphical and mechanical solutions.—All of the methods described above require tables, either for a mathematical solution or to extract computed values of altitude and azimuth. The total number of possible tabular solutions must be very great. The number of graphical and mechanical solutions is almost endless. The ones selected for mention below are representative of the types that have been prepared or made available.

Graphical solutions are almost as old as tabular ones, having existed at least since 1790, when *Margetts' Horary Tables* appeared in graphical form. These were intended "for shewing by Inspection the Apparent Diurnal Motion of the Sun, Moon, and Stars, the Latitude of a Ship and the Azimuth, Time, or Altitude corresponding with any Celestial Object." They were intended primarily for use with the longitude method of laying down a line of position.

In general, graphical and mechanical solutions have not proved popular, for several reasons: First, they generally involve a small scale, yielding results of less accuracy than desired, even with careful work. Second, some of the methods must be used as a whole, and cannot be divided into parts to increase the scale. Third, such methods usually do not provide a record of the solution, and it is often difficult to check the results. Fourth, solutions requiring instruments are subject to errors due to lack of proper adjustment or mechanical damage which may not be apparent. Fifth, the required diagrams or instruments may be quite bulky, requiring considerable space for stowage and manipulation. Finally, in some cases the necessary instruments are expensive.

2120. Altitude and azimuth angle by graph.—One type of graphical solution is by means of a diagram that solves an equation.

d'Ocagne. Typical of such diagrams is that prepared by Maurice d'Ocagne, a Frenchman. Both altitude and azimuth angle can be found by means of this diagram, which is based upon the following formulas:

$$\text{hav } z = \text{hav } (L-d) + \{\text{hav } [180° - (L+d)] - \text{hav } (L-d)\} \text{ hav } t,$$
$$\text{hav } (90° \pm d) = \text{hav } (L-h) + \{\text{hav } [180° - (L+h)] - \text{hav } (L-h)\} \text{ hav } Z,$$

in which $z = 90° - h$.

The sides of a square are divided according to the haversines of angles, from 0° to 180°, and the corresponding graduations of opposite sides are connected with straight lines, forming a diagram as shown in figure 2120a. The graduations on the two sides run in opposite directions. To find the zenith distance, locate the value corresponding to (L−d) along the left of the diagram, and the value corresponding to (L+d) along the right of the diagram. Draw a straight line through these points. Locate the intersection of this line with the vertical line corresponding to meridian angle. A horizontal line from this intersection to the left edge indicates the zenith distance.

To find azimuth angle, draw a straight line between (L−h) at the left and (L+h) at the right. Locate the intersection of this line and the *horizontal* line corresponding to (90°−d). A *vertical* line from this intersection to the top of the diagram indicates the azimuth angle.

If the altitude, latitude, and declination are known, the first solution can be made in reverse for meridian angle, for a longitude method solution.

The diagram was first published in 1899 in *Traité de Nomographie* by d'Ocagne. Similar diagrams have since been published under the name *Spherical Triangle Nomo-*

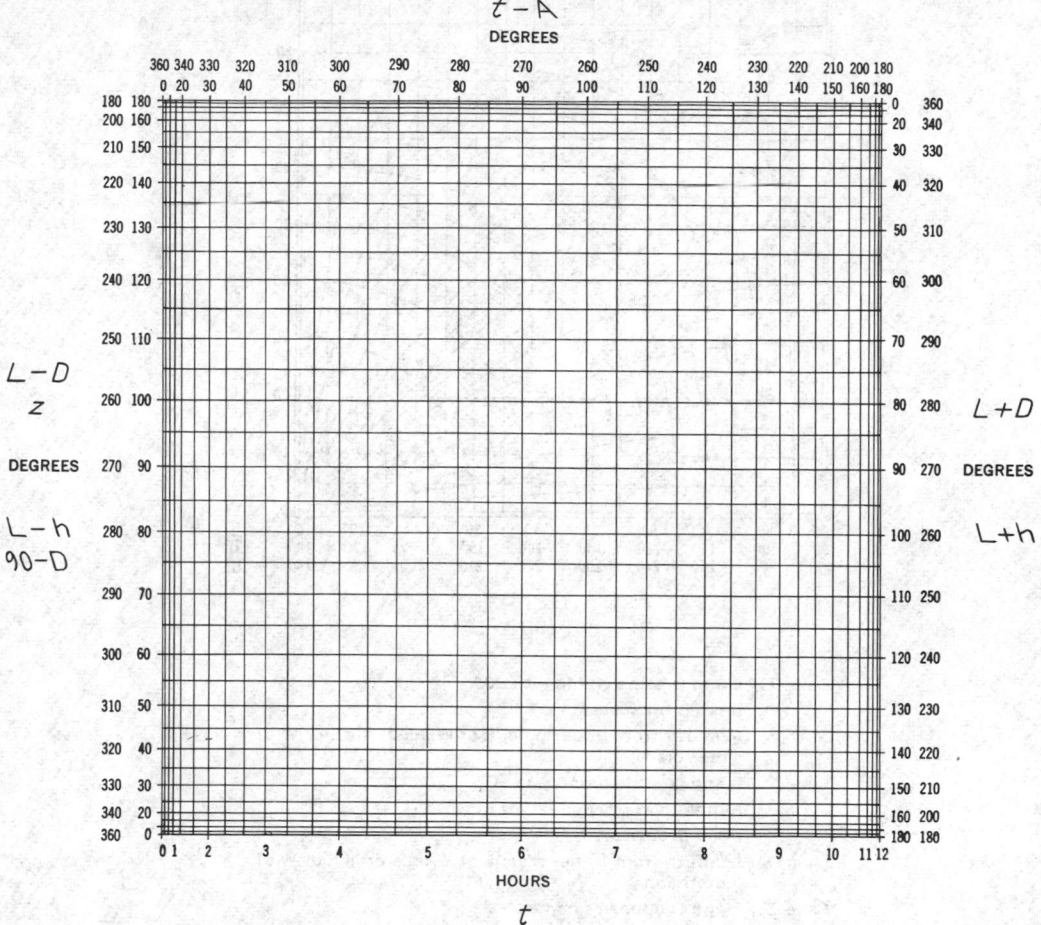

FIGURE 2120a.—The d'Ocagne diagram.

gram by Wimperis, and under the title *Altitude, Azimuth, and Hour Angle Diagram* by Littlehales in 1906, and by the U. S. Navy Hydrographic Office in 1917.

Favé and Rollet de l'Isle.—If a perpendicular is dropped from the celestial body to the celestial meridian, a diagram can be prepared to solve the basic formulas given in article 2111, or others derived from these. Such a diagram is shown in figure 2120b. This diagram was devised by the French engineers Favé and Rollet de l'Isle in 1892. The diagram represents only one-eighth of a sphere, additional sections being needed. An alternative is to show additional labels, as in figure 2120b. This results in three "cases" and several rules similar to those used with some logarithmic solutions. Solutions for both altitude and azimuth angle are made in two steps, plus one addition or subtraction. This diagram was reproduced by the Frenchman M. E. Pereire in 1894 and by another Frenchman, P. Constan, in 1906 as a method of finding azimuth

Jernæs.—In 1953 Leiv Jernæs, a Norwegian, invented a device he called a "Nauticator," which consists of various scales in a semicircle with radial scales on a plastic arm pivoted at the center of curvature of the semicircle. The device is used with a pair of dividers to solve various problems of spherical trigonometry to an accuracy of about 15′.

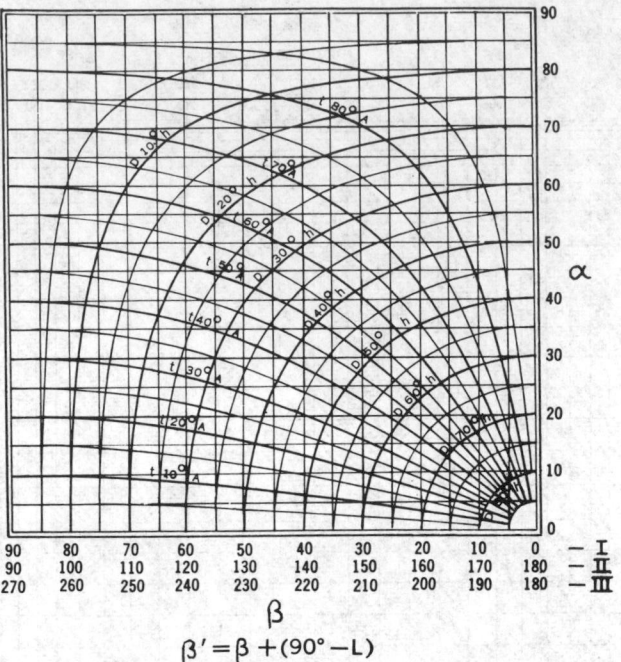

$$\beta' = \beta + (90° - L)$$

Case 1. L and D same Name —t<90°
Read β on scale II
Azimuth from upper pole, E or W as star is E or W of meridian

Case 2. L and D same name —t>90°
Read (180° —t) instead of t
Read β on scale I
Azimuth from upper pole, E or W as star is E or W of meridian

Case 3. L and D opposite names
Read β on scale I
Azimuth from lower pole, E or W as star is E or W of meridian

FIGURE 2120b.—The Favé diagram.

Bertin. In 1955 Rev. Maurice Bertin, a Frenchman, devised a graphical solution for the longitude method, using the formulas:

$$\tan^2 \tfrac{1}{2} t = \tan \tfrac{1}{2} (90° - \alpha) \tan \tfrac{1}{2} (90° - \beta) \qquad (1)$$

and

$$\tan^2 \tfrac{1}{2} Z = \frac{\tan \tfrac{1}{2} (90° - \alpha)}{\tan \tfrac{1}{2} (90° - \beta)} \qquad (2)$$

in which

$$\tan \tfrac{1}{2} \alpha = \tan \tfrac{1}{2} (h+d) \tan \tfrac{1}{2} (90° - L)$$

and

$$\tan \tfrac{1}{2} \beta = \frac{\tan \tfrac{1}{2} (h - d)}{\tan \tfrac{1}{2} (90° - L)}.$$

The diagram consists of three families of straight lines, one vertical, one horizontal, and the third at an angle of 45° to the others. The accuracy depends upon the scale of the diagram, but a large one is needed for navigational accuracy.

2121. Altitude and azimuth angle by computer.—Slide rules, like diagrams, have been devised to solve formulas. In the case of the navigational triangle, both suffer from the need for a scale that can be read to a subdivision at least as small as 1′. A number of such slide rules have been devised for use in reducing celestial observations.

Richer. In 1791 Jean Francisco Richer, a Frenchman, constructed a device composed of six arms, some hinged and some sliding, which won a prize offered by the Paris Academy of Science for a simple method of "clearing" lunar distances (art. 131) in the solution for longitude. The device solved a formula devised by the French mathematician Joseph Louis Lagrange, and was capable also of solving other problems involving spherical triangles, such as those related to time sight solution (art. 2106), computation of altitude, and great-circle sailing problems (art. 903).

Poor. A slide rule invented by Professor Charles L. Poor is shown in figure 2121a. This device, called the "Line of Position Computer," was designed to solve the cosine-haversine formula (art. 2109). Eight concentric circular scales are engraved on a metal disk about 15 inches in diameter. A plastic arm and circular sheet are pivoted at the center of the disk. The arm may be clamped to the plastic sheet. The seven outer scales are used in solving for altitude. The altitude scale is graduated at intervals of 10′, and further subdivisions can be estimated. The inner scale is used for determining azimuth angle. Several rules are needed, and the number of scales adds to the possibility of error.

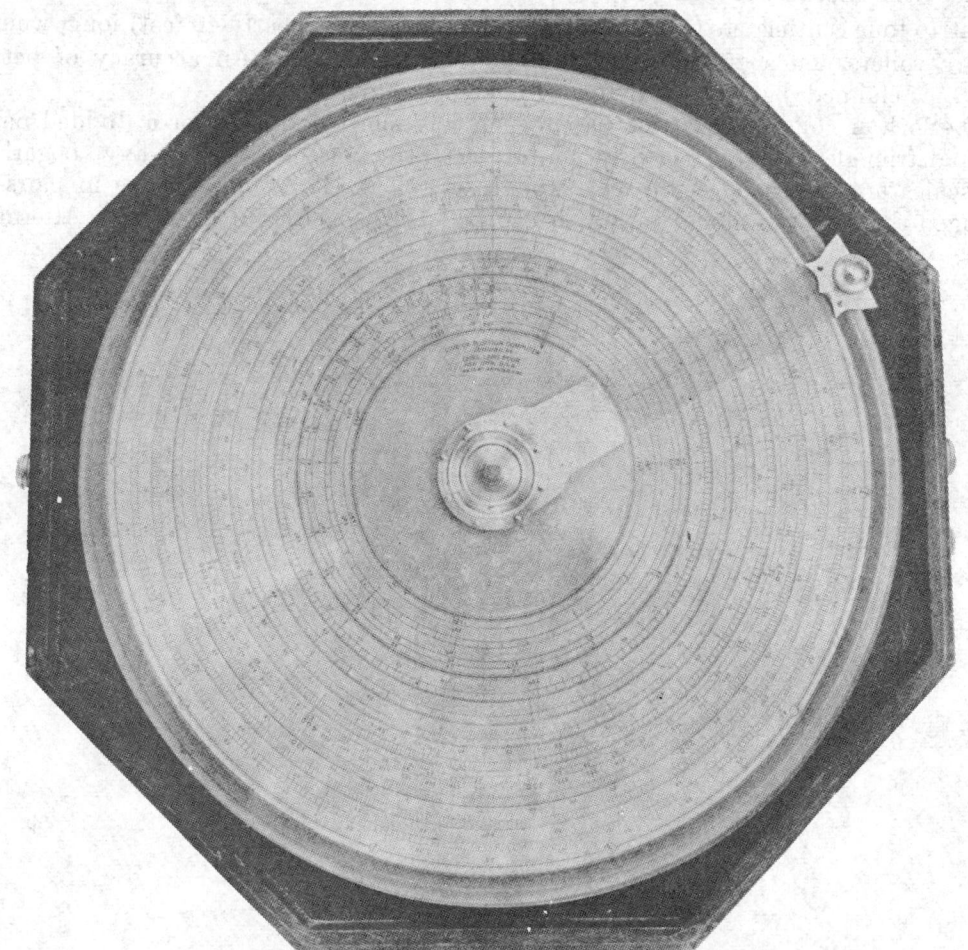

FIGURE 2121a.—The Poor Line of Position Computer.

Bygrave. A cylindrical slide rule was designed by the Englishman Bygrave to solve the navigational triangle divided by dropping a perpendicular from the celestial body to the celestial meridian (fig. 2111). This device, shown in figure 2121b, consists of three concentric tubes. The inner one has a spiral scale of logarithmic tangents, the middle one a spiral scale of logarithmic cosines, and the outer one a pointer for each scale. Solution is simple and relatively fast, but altered procedures are required if the azimuth angle is near 90°, or the meridian angle or declination is very small. The overall dimensions are about 2½ inches in diameter by nine inches long. An accuracy of about 1' or 2' is generally attainable.

Bertin. In 1955 Rev. Maurice Bertin devised an 18-inch slide rule to provide a solution of the longitude method to an accuracy of about 1°, using the formulas upon which his graphical solution (art. 2120) is based. He also devised a solution of the same formulas by a circular slide rule consisting essentially of two spirals. The inner one is on a disk 23 centimeters (9.2 inches) in diameter, and the outer one is on an annular ring 39 centimeters (15.6 inches) in outside diameter. The graduations are proportional to the log cotangents of half-angles. A window on a cover is provided with a radial line to serve as an index. Solution is facilitated if an approximation of the answer is known in advance. An accuracy of better than 3' is claimed for this device. Still another solution proposed at the same time is by a computer consisting of a strip four centimeters (1.6 inches) wide and 12 meters (nearly 40 feet) long, wound on two rollers and engraved with three sets of graduations. An accuracy of better than 1' is claimed, but several arithmetical steps are required.

LeSort. A computing device based upon solution of formulas for a divided navigational triangle was designed by Commander LeSort of the French Navy. Logarithmic scales are placed on eight films wound on rollers. The films operate in pairs so arranged that the two films of any pair can be locked together at any point. Alternate

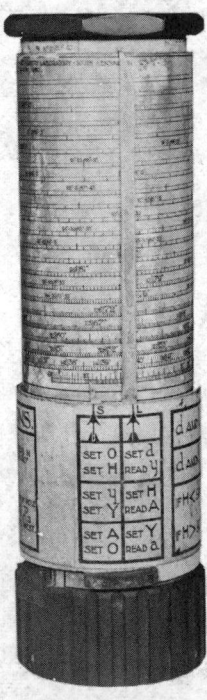

FIGURE 2121b.—The Bygrave slide rule.

films carry log cosine and log tangent scales. Although an accuracy of about 0.'2 can be obtained, the method is comparatively long and has no apparent advantage over modern inspection tables.

Desk computers. Several desk-type computers have been designed to solve the navigational triangle.

2122. Altitude and azimuth angle by map projection.—If the observer were to move along his meridian to the nearer pole, and the navigational triangle were to move with him without its proportions being changed, his zenith would coincide with the pole, and the vertical circle would coincide with some celestial meridian. Zenith distance or altitude could be read directly. Since both great circles forming the azimuth angle would now coincide with celestial meridians, the azimuth angle could also be determined directly.

Littlehales. To accomplish this with a sphere, to a useful accuracy, would require a sphere of impractical size for use by the navigator. However, the solution can be made by means of a map projection. George Littlehales, of the U. S. Navy Hydrographic Office, used the stereographic projection (art. 318) and a 12-foot sphere for this purpose. The projection is divided into 368 overlapping sheets which, with a key diagram, are bound together. An accuracy of about 1′ or 2′ can obtained by a rapid and simple process, but the volume is bulky and not particularly convenient.

Veater. Commander Veater of the British Royal Navy used the transverse Mercator projection (art. 309), with the observer's meridian as the fictitious equator.

Hyatt. A similar principle is utilized in the diagram on the plane of the celestial meridian (art. 1432). A mechanical device based upon this diagram can be made by drawing a hemisphere by equatorial orthographic (art. 319) or stereographic projection and pivoting at its center an identical hemisphere on transparent material. If the top hemisphere is rotated until the arc between poles of the two hemispheres is equal to the colatitude of the observer, the lines of one hemisphere represent coordinates of the celestial equator system (art. 1428), and those of the other, coordinates of the horizon system (art. 1430). Thus, if a body is located by meridian angle and declination on one set of lines, its altitude and azimuth angle can be read from the other set. If altitude and declination are used to locate the body, meridian angle can be read from the diagram. In the United States such a device, on both the orthographic and stereographic projections, has been prepared by Commander Delwyn Hyatt, USN, under the titles "Celestial Coordinator" and "Coordinate Transformer." It has also been produced in other countries, notably in Germany, France, and Russia, where, in addition to such a device, precision instruments based upon the same principle have been constructed. The scale of the German instrument is so small that an accuracy of about 5′ is about the best that can be expected. The Bastien-Morin (French) and Kavroyskyy (Russian) instruments might yield results of slightly greater accuracy. The plastic device, if carefully made, might be generally accurate to half a degree. It has been used primarily for instructional purposes.

Brown-Nassau. The Brown-Nassau "Navigational Computer" utilizes the same principle, but uses the azimuthal equidistant projection (art. 320) and increases the scale by limiting the device to an octant of the sphere, with separate solutions for altitude and azimuth, and various rules.

True. In his *Celestial Navigator for Aviators*, printed about 1943, Clarence H. True, of the Canal Zone, uses a single diagram on the orthographic projection. This serves as the basis for a solution by construction, claimed to be of sufficient accuracy for use in lifeboats. Various rules are needed.

Pierce. A series of diagrams on the azimuthal equidistant projection have been devised by Rear Admiral M. R. Pierce, USN (Ret.). The method is based upon the principle that angles are correctly represented at the point of tangency of this projection, and radial lines from this point represent great circles along which distances are represented by a uniform scale. A protractor is used for measuring the azimuth angle. Attached to the protractor is an arm with a linear scale graduated so that altitude can be read directly. The whole device is called a "Cadameter." The method is easy to use, and about as fast as modern inspection tables. With great care an accuracy of 1' can be obtained. The method suffers from the need for a number of diagrams which are somewhat bulky and more susceptible to damage than a book.

2123. Latitude and longitude by diagram.—A number of graphical and mechanical solutions have been devised to yield latitude and longitude directly.

Beij. One proposed in 1924 by K. Hilding Beij, of the U. S. Bureau of Standards, was based upon the fact that latitude and local sidereal time are completely defined by the simultaneous altitudes of two celestial bodies whose declination and SHA are known. A page of his proposed diagrams is shown in figure 2123a, in which latitude is the abscissa, and LST is the ordinate. Position on the graph is located by the intersection of the curves representing the altitude of the two celestial bodies observed. The vertical line through the intersection indicates the latitude, and the horizontal line the LST. The difference between GST and LST is the longitude. If a timepiece keeping GST is available, not even an almanac is needed.

The method is accurate, fast, and direct. The individual sheets can be drawn to any scale and cut to any size desired. For a large scale with sheets of a convenient size, a great many diagrams would be needed, but these might be bound together in convenient-size volumes, or placed on a tape wound around rollers, as originally proposed. A weakness of the method is the requirement for simultaneous observations. For

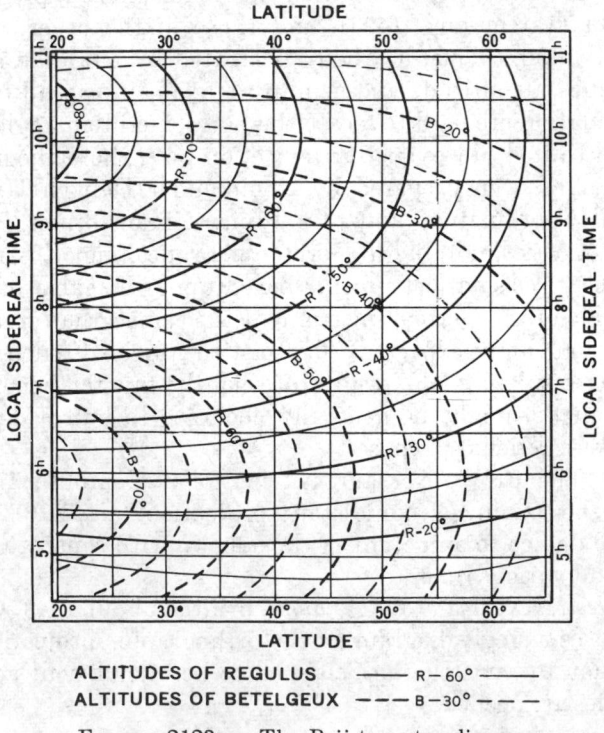

FIGURE 2123a.—The Beij two-star diagram.

nonsimultaneous observations a table might be provided to indicate the change in altitude during the interval between observations. Since the positions of the curves depend upon the declination and SHA of the body, the method is limited to celestial bodies whose coordinates are nearly constant, unless the curves are intended only for a particular time. Even for stars, the diagrams become out-of-date in a few years. The method is limited to the particular bodies for which curves are shown, although the number of curves need not be limited to two. This is a form of precomputation, since the computation is performed in locating the curves, rather than by the navigator. In a sense, it might be considered a graphical form of Pub. No. 249 (art. 2113).

Weems. If the Beij diagram is rotated through 90°, the parallels of latitude become horizontal, as customary on a chart. If they are spaced according to the Mercator projection, azimuth is indicated by the normal to a curve. This is the arrangement used by Captain P. V. H. Weems, USN (Ret.), in his *Star Altitude Curves*, the first volume of which was published in 1928. Later he added a third star, using a different color for each star, and included a correction for refraction at sea level. A separate volume is used for each 10° of latitude, and a correction is provided for precession of the equinoxes. Coverage extends from latitude 50°S to 70°N, with a separate volume for latitude 70°–90°N. The curves for 80°–90°N are on the polar stereographic projection. Any orthomorphic projection (art. 302) could be used at any latitude.

Lines representing observations at different times can be advanced or retired as on any chart of the same projection. In addition to the adjustment due to motion of the craft between observations, the lines are shifted right or left for the elapsed time between observations. An accuracy of about 1′ is attainable by interpolation between curves for each 10′ of altitude.

The star altitude curves are undoubtedly the most widely used of all the graphical and mechanical methods. Two-star curves similar to Weems' first edition were published in Germany in 1940.

Pritchard and Lamplough. In 1940 H. C. Pritchard and F. E. Lamplough, of the British Royal Aircraft Establishment, devised a method of reducing the work involved in the adjustment for elapsed time between observations. They placed the star altitude curves on film which is used in a projector called an **astrograph**. The curves are projected onto a Mercator plotting sheet and can be moved across it to allow for rotation of the earth. The adjustment is critical, the setting of the projector somewhat involved (a special "astrograph mean time" being needed), and a bulky and expensive projector is needed to prevent distortion. Because of these disadvantages and the fact that any advantage over short tabular methods is slight, the astrograph decreased in popularity following World War II.

Longley. In 1943 Flight Lieutenant C. D. N. Longley, RAF, suggested a "Star Computer" based upon the principle of the astrograph. A circular disk serving as a base plate would have a mean time scale around its circumference. Altitude curves of a limited number of stars would be printed on a template for each latitude. The circumference of each template would also carry a mean time scale. A radial cursor would aid in reading the device, which is set by means of the GMT at which LHA♈ is 0° at some convenient longitude, the time of observation, and observed altitude. Longitude is determined within a 10° band, the ambiguity being resolved by means of the dead reckoning position. With a modification of the procedure, the device can be used with the altitude method.

Baker. As early as 1919 Commander T. Y. Baker, RN, prepared altitude curves and their orthogonals (normals) on transparent tape which is wound on rollers in the "Baker Navigating Machine" (fig. 2123b). The transparent tape is moved across a Mercator plotting sheet, being oriented by means of a time scale set with respect

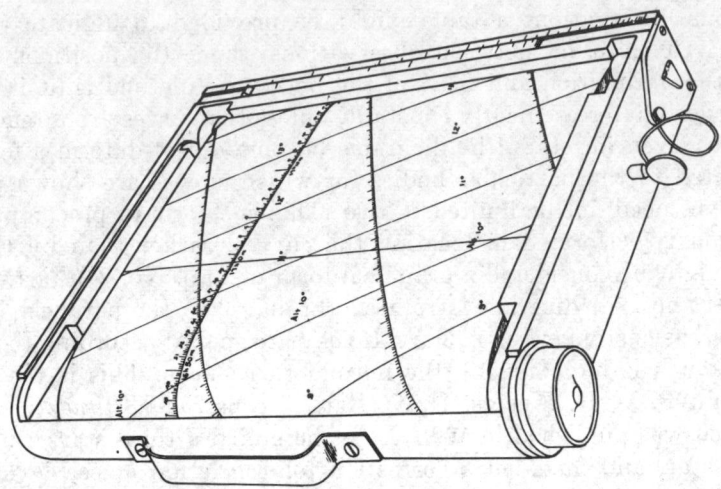

FIGURE 2123b.—The Baker Navigating Machine.

to a meridian. The line of position is transferred to the plotting sheet by means of carbon paper. A single tape has curves for several stars, and a separate tape for each 4° of declination from 24°N to 24°S permits use of the device with the sun and other bodies of the solar system. A rule attached to the machine (shown at the top of fig. 2123b) provides a correction for declination differing from that of the curves.

Weems. In 1955 Captain P. V. H. Weems, USN (Ret.), prepared a somewhat similar device called a "Polar Computer," using his star altitude curves.

Leick. In 1911 Dr. A. Leick, a German, prepared a diagram by which latitude and LST could be obtained by altitudes of Polaris and one other star. The diagram can be used for finding the correction to apply to the altitude of Polaris to determine the latitude, and then to find the LST in a second step.

Favé. In 1901 Favé devised a graphical solution based upon the Marcq St.-Hilaire principle (art. 2108). A chart on the stereographic projection (art. 318) is used. Tables of computed altitude and azimuth for the point of tangency are needed. The chart is on transparent material. An additional sheet has a set of arcs of circles, with a straight azimuth line drawn normal to them. The chart is placed over the curves with the straight azimuth line through the point of tangency and oriented in the direction of the celestial body. A large circle on the chart assists in this orientation. The chart is then moved along the azimuth line until the curve representing the computed altitude at the point of tangency is under that point. The curve representing the observed altitude is then correctly placed and a segment of it can be traced on the chart. However, due to chart distortion, error is introduced in this way. It can be removed by means of a nomogram which indicates the correct curve to use. A mark is placed on the chart at the intersection of the azimuth line and the curve representing the observed altitude. The chart is then moved along the azimuth line a second time until the correct curve is in place, and the arc is traced. This process is repeated for each celestial body observed. For stars, a one-page set of curves can be used instead of tables for determining altitude and azimuth at the point of tangency. Favé recommended use of five separate charts with points of tangency at 0°, 30°, 45°, 75°, and 90°, respectively. Each chart could be used as a plotting sheet for any longitude at the same latitude, requiring computed altitude and azimuth for only five places. Favé later put his method into instrumental form and used a special protractor and curved ruler.

Brill. In 1909 Dr. Alfred Brill, a German, invented a device based upon the same principle used by Favé, as shown in figure 2123c. In this device the plotting sheet is on the azimuthal equidistant projection (art. 320) and covers about 10° of latitude. Two sets of curves on separate sheets of tracing cloth are mounted below the plotting sheet. A handle turns the plotting sheet to the correct azimuth.

Voigt. The same principle used by Favé and Brill was used in the Voigt "Orion" instrument constructed in Germany in 1911. A plotting sheet on the azimuthal equidistant projection is engraved on aluminum. Each of the three plotting sheets, centered on latitudes 42°, 50°, and 55°, respectively, covers a spread of 10° of latitude. The line of position is drawn by means of a flexible ruler mounted on a bridge that can be clamped at any position over the plotting sheet. The curvature is controlled by means of gears, a scale being provided to indicate the correct value.

Vucetic. In 1921 a device called a "Toposcope" was prepared by Vucetic, a Frenchman. The device is identical with the Brill instrument except that a single set of curves is prepared and these are cut through the material as slots, and placed over the top of the plotting sheet.

Littlehales in 1918 suggested a method similar to that of Favé, but with a polyconic projection (art. 315).

Kahn. In 1928 Louis Kahn, a French naval architect, proposed that a set of navigational charts be prepared on the oblique Mercator projection (art. 310), a separate chart being provided for the great circle between various places on the earth. On each chart the small circles on the earth directly below the parallels of declination (that is, the daily paths of the geographical positions) of various navigational stars would be shown. These circles would be graduated in Greenwich sidereal time, so that the GP at any GST would be indicated. The distance from any assumed position to the GP at the instant of observation would be the zenith distance, and the direction of the line would be the azimuth. By comparing the observed zenith distance with that at the assumed position, the navigator could obtain the altitude difference, and plot the line of position. The common intersection of two or more such lines of position, advanced

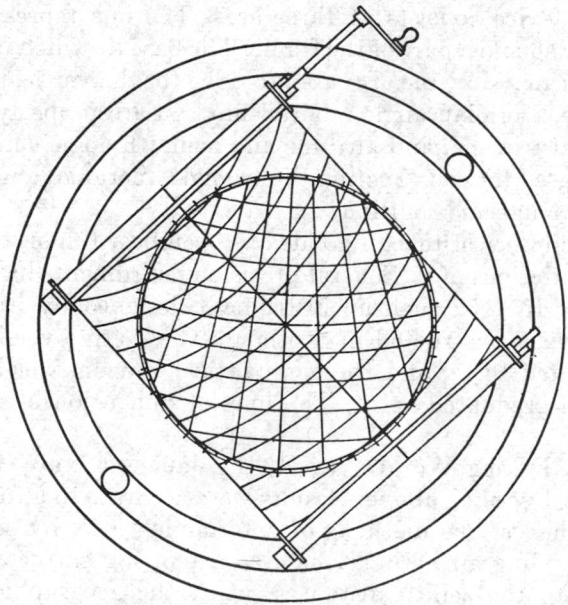

FIGURE 2123c.—The Brill device.

or retired to a common time if necessary, would define the position of the observer. The method would be limited to zenith distance within the range of the chart. A later version would produce greater accuracy, but with a little more trouble in making the measurements, by substituting the gnomonic projection (art. 317) for the oblique Mercator projection.

Dusinberre. In 1944 Lieutenant Commander H. W. Dunsinberre, USN, suggested a method using star diagrams. A diagram for each 1° of latitude and 1° of LHA ♈ would be provided. Each diagram would consist of a series of radial lines extending in the directions of the prominent stars favorable for observation. The 22 stars of H.O. Pub. No. 218 (art. 2113) were suggested. Until changed by precession of the equinoxes (art. 1419) the common origin of these lines would represent a definite altitude for each star. The altitude at the next higher whole degree or half degree, adjusted for refraction, would be indicated by a tick on the appropriate azimuth line. After observation, a transparent plotting board would be properly oriented over the appropriate star diagram, using LHA ♈ and adjusting for the run between observations. The line of position would then be drawn at the correct point, perpendicular to the azimuth line, using the tick as a guide. An LHA ♈ computer was proposed for determining LHA ♈ at the time of each observation from a single LHA ♈ for a time near the start of each set of observations. When all lines of position were plotted, the fix would be transferred to the chart or plotting sheet.

2124. Solution by sphere.—Solution of a spherical triangle directly on a spherical surface, or by means of arcs representing great circles on the surface of an imaginary sphere, must have occurred to man quite early. Pictures of ancient navigators surrounded by their instruments and accessories invariably show a sphere. Solution by sphere is still suggested from time to time. Although this method is relatively simple and easy, the problem of scale is even more acute than in the graphical solutions.

Spherical methods can be classified in three groups: (1) those which solve the navigational triangle for a single line of position, (2) those which solve two or more observations for a fix, and (3) those which combine observation and solution for a fix.

The first group constructs the navigational triangle with arcs of great circles. Essentially, such a device consists of three arcs. The one representing the celestial meridian is usually fixed and a part of the frame. The base to which it is attached usually carries the azimuth scale. Movable arcs are provided for the vertical circle and the hour circle. If the latitude, meridian angle, and declination are properly set, the three arcs form the navigational triangle, and altitude and azimuth angle can be read from their scales. If altitude is used for constructing the triangle, meridian angle can be read from the instrument for a longitude solution.

Willis. A large number of teaching aids has been based upon this design or one of the many possible variations of it. Several precision instruments have been proposed or actually constructed. In 1932 such an instrument designed by Edward J. Willis, an American engineer, was constructed in Scotland. The marine version, weighing about 27 pounds, is graduated to 1′; and the aeronautical version, weighing between seven and eight pounds, is graduated to 5′. The longest dimension of either version is 11 inches.

Japanese Navy. During World War II, the Japanese Navy used an instrument virtually in the form described above. Results were accurate to approximately 1′.

McMillen. Of the various methods of determining a fix by sphere, the most obvious is that of providing an actual sphere as a plotting surface, with provision for striking arcs equal to the zenith distances, using the geographical positions of the celestial bodies as centers. In 1943 such a method was proposed by D. A. McMillen, a

United States businessman in São Paulo, Brazil. His sphere, of a little more than 14 inches in diameter, had a scale of 8° (480 nautical miles) per inch along a great circle.

Hiltner. In 1945 Dr. W. F. Hiltner, a professor at Lehigh University, suggested a similar method using arcs of spheres and a billiard ball. This in effect, sets up two navigational triangles, locating the observer at the common zenith of both triangles. Simultaneous observations are needed.

U. S. Navy Training Device Center. About the same time, the Training Device Center of the U. S. Navy prepared a device called the "Sphereman Craft Positioner," combining the functions of the devices of both McMillen and Hiltner, and providing a plotting surface for dead reckoning. A line of position from a single observation can be drawn on the 17-inch aluminum globe, or the triangle of position from the observation of three stars can be mechanically set up. Provision is made for advancement or retirement of lines due to motion of the craft. The device was intended for training purposes.

Zerbee. In 1951 Louis J. Zerbee, of Bellfontaine, Ohio, proposed a device similar to that of Hiltner, but without the billiard ball. His instrument was called the "Zerbee Celestial Fix Finder." Like the Hiltner device, that of Zerbee makes no provision for nonsimultaneous observations (unless one of them is corrected to the value it would have if observed simultaneously with the other) or for a check by observation of additional bodies. Observations of bodies near the meridian or taken from high latitudes cannot be accommodated.

Combined sextant and computer. At least as early as 1895 an attempt was made to combine in a single instrument the functions of sextant and computer. Such instruments are fundamentally the same as those described above, except that they are set by alignment with one or more celestial bodies. If the instrument is level and accurately aligned with the meridian at the time of observation, the miniature sphere is oriented to the celestial sphere and the earth. If both the altitude and azimuth are used, a fix can be obtained by means of a single celestial body. If two bodies are observed simultaneously, accurate directional reference by compass is not needed.

The weakness of such methods is the need for a stable platform and either accurate directional reference or the need for observing two bodies simultaneously.

Beehler. In 1895 Lieutenant W. H. Beehler, USN, invented an instrument he called the "Solarometer," which was designed to furnish a position from observation of the sun. It requires a heavy cast iron base rigidly attached to the ship, with a bowl set in gimbals and filled with mercury. A float resting on the mercury carries the sighting instrument.

Hagner. In 1936 Fred Hagner, of San Antonio, Tex., invented a similar instrument he called the "Hagner Position Finder." This is a portable instrument operating on the same principle as the Solarometer, but obtaining the vertical by being hung from a suitable support, and therefore acting as a pendulum. This is reminiscent of the ancient astrolabe (art. 124).

Bedell. In 1953 A. L. Bedell, of St. Louis, Mo., proposed an instrument based upon simultaneous observation of two celestial bodies. The horizontal would be defined by spirit level.

2125. Azimuth.—Most of the methods described above provide for determination of both altitude and azimuth angle. Several provide only for altitude. The number of tables, diagrams, and devices providing solution for azimuth only is very great, approaching the number providing solution for both altitude and azimuth. The reason for this is that azimuth is needed for other purposes than sight reduction. One common use is for checking the compass. Since modern inspection tables have provided parallel columns of computed altitude and azimuth or azimuth angle, separate azimuth tables have decreased in popularity.

Azimuth can be determined by computation or by amplitudes (tab. 27, 28), as well as by azimuth table. The method of computation depends somewhat upon the information available. There are three general approaches:

Time azimuth is the name given an azimuth or azimuth angle computed with meridian angle (a function of time), latitude, and polar distance (or declination) as the known quantities.

Altitude azimuth is an azimuth or azimuth angle computed with altitude, latitude, and polar distance as the known quantities.

Time and altitude azimuth is computed with meridian angle, declination, and altitude as the known quantities, the most common formula being

$$\sin Z = \sin t \cos d \sec h.$$

The weakness of this method is that it does not indicate whether the celestial body is north or south of the prime vertical. Usually there is no question on this point, but if Z is near 90°, the quadrant may be in doubt. If this occurs, either the meridian angle or altitude when on the prime vertical can be determined from table 25 or by computation, using the formula

$$\cos t = \tan d \cot L$$
or
$$\sin h = \sin d \csc L.$$

If the altitude is *less*, or the meridian angle is *greater* than the value when the body is on the prime vertical, the azimuth angle should be labeled N or S to agree with the latitude. If h is *greater* or t is *less* than when on the prime vertical, Z should be given the contrary name (N or S) to that of the latitude.

Amplitudes. For checking the compass, a low altitude is desirable because it can be measured easiest and most accurately. If a celestial body is observed when its center is on the *celestial* horizon, the amplitude (art. 2029), which is the arc on the horizon between the prime vertical and the body, can be taken directly from table 27.

2126. Azimuth tables are numerous. Originally, they were designed primarily for use in determining compass error. Since the sun was the celestial body customarily used for this purpose, most of the tables were designed with the sun in mind. Meridian angle is commonly expressed in terms of local apparent time, in intervals varying from about one to 20 minutes. In many of the tables, meridian angle increases *upward* from the bottom of the page.

The following are some of the principal azimuth tables:

Wakeley. The first known azimuth tables for use of the navigator were *The Regiment of the Pole Star* by Andrew Wakeley. These tables were part of the author's *The Mariner's Compass Rectified*, published in London in 1665. These tables show the "true hour of the day" at which the sun is at the various points of the compass.

Lynn Azimuth Tables, by Thomas Lynn (art. 2106), were published in 1829. This 364-page table gives azimuth angle computed by the haversine formula of article 2106.

Towson and Atherton. The *Tables to Facilitate the Practice of Great Circle Sailing*, by the Englishmen John Thomas Towson and J. W. Atherton, were designed primarily for great-circle sailing, but since they indicate the course, they were easily adapted to finding azimuth angle. They were published in England in 1847.

Burdwood. The *Tables of Sun's True Bearing or Azimuth*, by Staff Commander John Burdwood, RN, were first published in 1852, with additional parts being added in 1858, 1862, 1864, and 1866. Captain John E. Davis, RN, and Percy L. H. Davis, of the British Nautical Almanac Office, later added to the tables, making them complete for all values of altitude and for declination between 64°N and 64°S. These tables were standard in Great Britain for more than a century. They have now been largely replaced by H.D. 486 (Pub. No. 214) for mariners and A.P. 3270 (Pub. No. 249) for aviators. Burdwood used modifications of the time azimuth formula.

Labrosse. Azimuth tables by the Frenchman F. Labrosse were published in London in 1868, and later in Paris. In 275 pages this *Table des Azimuts du Soleil* covers latitudes from 61°N to 61°S, and declinations from 0° to 30°N or S. The following formula was used:

$$\cot Z = \frac{\tan d \cos L}{\sin t} - \sin L \cot t.$$

Fifteen editions had been published by 1920.

Shortrede. In 1869 Captain Robert Shortrede's *Azimuth and Hour Angle for Latitude and Declination* and *Tables for Finding Azimuth at Sea* were published in London.

John E. Davis. The first azimuth tables by Captain John E. Davis were published in 1875. These were published as an extension of the Burdwood tables.

Perrin. In Paris the *Nouvelles Tables Destinées à Abréger les Calculs Nautiques*, by Ensign de Vaisseau E. Perrin, French Navy, were published first in 1876. These consist of three tables of nine, seven, and six pages, respectively, providing elements for determination of azimuth by a short computation. Several editions were published.

Kortazzi, a Russian, produced a volume appropriately called *Modification des Tables d'Azimuth de Thomson* (art. 2106). These were published in Paris in 1880.

H.O. Pub. No. 66 (**Schroeder and Wainwright**), *Arctic Azimuth Tables*. Lieutenants Seaton Schroeder and Richard Wainwright, USN, prepared azimuth tables for use of the USS *Rodgers* in her search for the arctic steamer *Jeanette*. These were published in 1881. Azimuths to the nearest 1' are given for each 10^m meridian angle between 4^h and 7^h, for latitudes between 70° and 88°, declination 0° to 23°, same name.

Decante. In 1882 Lieutenant de Vaisseau E. Decante, of the French Navy, prepared *Table du Cadran Solaire Azimutal*, which was published in 1904, in eight volumes for latitudes 1° to 66° and declinations 0° to 48°.

Pub. No. 260 (**Schroeder and Southerland**). The *Azimuths of the Sun* were prepared in 1882 by Lieutenant Seaton Schroeder, USN, and Master W. H. H. Southerland, USN. These are popularly called "Red Azimuth Tables," because of the red binding used for most printings. This designation distinguishes them from the "Blue Azimuth Tables" (Pub. No. 261). After 15 editions, these tables are still in use. Azimuth angles are given to the nearest 1', at 10^m intervals of local apparent time from "sunrise" to "sunset" (middle of the sun on the *celestial* horizon), with the LAT and the azimuth angle of these phenomena given at the bottom of each column. A separate table is given for each 1° of latitude from 0° to 70°. The first part of the book is a table for latitude 0°. The second part is devoted to tables of latitude and declination "same name." The third part gives "contrary name" tables. Declination entries are given at 1° intervals from 0° to 23°, with the approximate dates on which this is the declination of the sun. Extracts from these tables are given in volume II. Values are customarily taken by triple interpolation, using the right-hand "PM" LAT column as meridian angle.

Blackburne. The New Zealand nautical almanac for 1883 carried the 177-page "A and B" azimuth tables, by H. S. Blackburne. By 1911, after several modifications, these emerged as *"A, B, C" Tables for Azimuth, Great Circle Sailing, and Reduction to the Meridian.* The range of both the latitude and declination is from 90°N to 90°S.

Lecky. In 1892 Captain S. T. S. Lecky, an Englishman, modified the Blackburne tables and produced another set of "A, B, C" tables which have been widely used.

Ebsen. The *Azimut-Tabellen* of Julius Ebsen, published in Germany in 1896, uses the same formula as Labrosse, and is arranged like Pub. No. 260, except that azimuth angles are given to the nearest 0°.1, and the time and azimuth angle of sunrise and sunset are given at the top of the table, in place of the dates of Pub. No. 260. In two volumes, coverage is for latitudes 72°N to 72°S, and declinations 0° to 29°. Tables are for same name only, contrary-name situations being handled by using the supplement of meridian angle, and using the supplement of the value taken from the table, as in Pub. No. 261.

Johnson. A *Combined Time and Altitude Azimuth Table* for latitudes and declinations from 0° to 80°, by A. C. Johnson of the British Royal Navy, was published in London in 1900. In the same year, his *Short, Accurate, and Comprehensive Altitude-Azimuth Tables* were published. This publication consists of three tables for computation of azimuth for each degree of latitude and altitude from 0° to 75°, and each degree of declination from 30°N to 30°S.

Zhdanko. The Russian *Tables of Azimuth of the Sun*, by M. Zhdanko, published in 1900, supplied computed azimuth angles for latitudes between 61° and 75°. These were later expanded by Yustchenko.

Percy L. H. Davis. In 1900 Percy L. H. Davis took over the work previously done by Burdwood and John E. Davis, continuing to improve and extend the tables.

Pub. No. 261, *Azimuths of Celestial Bodies*, published by the U. S. Navy Hydrographic Office in 1902, extend the Pub. No. 260 tables by providing information in similar form (but with meridian angle increasing *downward* on the page) for declinations 24° to 70°. These are popularly called "Blue Azimuth Tables," from their blue binding. Tables for "same name" only are given. If latitude and declination are of contrary name, the tables are entered with the supplement of the meridian angle. The value taken from the table is then the supplement of the azimuth angle, which is labeled N or S to agree with the latitude and E or W to agree with the meridian angle. Extracts from Pub. No. 261 are given in volume II.

Symonds. The *Nautical Astronomy, with New Tables*, by W. P. Symonds, British Survey Commissioner, Bombay, includes azimuth tables. It was published in 1912.

Goodwin. *An Equatorial Azimuth-Table*, by H. B. Goodwin, was published in 1921.

Purey-Cust. *Azimuth by Logs*, by Admiral Sir H. E. Purey-Cust, RN, was published in England in 1929. It consists of a three-page table of the logarithms of the six principal trigonometric functions at 10′ intervals (5′ below 10°) for solution of the time azimuth and altitude azimuth formulas.

Yustchenko. In 1935 A. Yustchenko, a Russian, extended the Zhdanko tables to all latitudes, in the work entitled *Azimuty Svetil* (Azimuths of Celestial Bodies). For each 10° of latitude (5°, 15°, 25°, etc., to 85°) complete azimuth tables (to the nearest 0°.1) are given for each 1ᵐ of meridian angle and each 30′ of declination from 0° to 30°. At the bottom of each page are given corrections for 1° of latitude. This value is multiplied by the number of degrees between the actual latitude and the latitude for which the table was computed.

Cugle. *Cugle's Two-Minute Azimuths*, by Charles H. Cugle, were printed in 1935 in two large volumes. Coverage is for latitude 0° to 65° and declination 0° to 23° The arrangement is almost identical with that of Pub. No. 260, except that meridian angle increases *downward* on the page. The number of entries is multiplied by *five*, values being given for each 2^m of meridian angle.

Table 902. *Azimuts*, published in Paris in 1953, with the concurrence of the Marine Hydrographic Service, contains azimuth angles to the nearest $0°.1$ for each whole degree of latitude from 70°N to 70°S, each whole degree of declination from 0° to 30°, and each 10^m of meridian angle. The arrangement is similar to that of Pub. No. 260, except that meridian angle increases *downward* on the page.

2127. Azimuth diagrams have appeared in various forms, in addition to the general graphical and mechanical solutions discussed above. A graphical solution is generally more acceptable for azimuth than for altitude, because the accuracy requirement for azimuth is usually less.

Godfrey. A graphical solution has been available at least since 1858 when the *Time Azimuth Diagram* of Hugh Godfrey was published in London.

Weir. The *Azimuth Diagram* devised by Captain Patrick Weir, of the British Merchant Navy, was published in London in 1890, and by the U. S. Navy Hydrographic Office in 1891, under the title *Time Azimuth Diagram*.

Molfino. In 1901 the *Nomograma degli Azimut del Sole* of Molfino was published.

Constan. In 1906 P. Constan's *Tables Graphiques d'Azimut* were published in Paris. This was a reproduction of the graph of Favé and Rollet de l'Isle (art. 2120).

Alessio. The *Diagrammi Altazimutali* of A. Alessio was published in 1908 in Italy.

Rust. In 1908 the diagram of Lieutenant Commander Armistead Rust, USN, (art. 2106) was published. This diagram was later used by Goodwin (art. 2106) and Weems (arts. 2106 and 2110), and in the Italian *Tavole H* (art. 2110).

Cornet. The *Graphique d'Azimut* of Cornet was published in 1927.

Romanovsky. About 1933 A. A. Romanovsky, a Russian, devised a simple nomogram for determining azimuth.

German Oberkommandos der Kriegsmarine. A large volume called *Azimut-diagramme*, containing sets of diagrams for each whole degree of latitude (2° beyond 80°) for all azimuth angles and for all altitudes to 80°, was published by the German Oberkommandos der Kriegsmarine in 1944.

Hugon. The azimuth diagram of Professor P. Hugon (art. 2109) was published in 1947.

Hilsenrath. About 1948 Joseph Hilsenrath, of the University of Maryland, produced a mechanical device for solving azimuth angle by the method of Weir's diagram.

2128. Summary.—The methods of sight reduction discussed in this chapter are undoubtedly only a small fraction of the number of methods that have been proposed. They are considered representative of the effort that has been made to reduce the work of the navigator. Individual preferences have largely dictated the use of the various methods. Presentation and description of a method have been important factors in the relative popularity of various methods.

There is no single "best" method for all circumstances and all navigators. The one which produces the desired results easiest and with least possibility of mistake is the one that should be selected. However, two practical precautions should be observed. First, one should be thoroughly familiar with the *limitations* or *weaknesses* of the method he selects. Second, a prudent navigator will never limit himself to a single method, particularly one requiring a special table that might some day be unavailable, or a device that is subject to mechanical damage or loss. The slight bending of an arc might be too insignificant to be noticed, yet might introduce intolerably large errors in the result. A wise practice is to memorize, or write on something always carried, fundamental formulas that can be used when no "special" tables are available.

CHAPTER XXII

IDENTIFICATION OF CELESTIAL BODIES

2201. Introduction.—A basic requirement of celestial navigation is the ability to identify the bodies observed. This is not difficult because relatively few celestial bodies are commonly used for navigation, and various aids are available to assist in their identification, as explained in this chapter.

Many navigators consider it a matter of professional pride to have a more extensive acquaintance with the heavens than required by the relatively simple demands of navigation.

2202. Bodies of the solar system.—No problem is encountered in the identification of the sun and moon. However, the planets can be mistaken for stars. A person working continually with the night sky recognizes a planet by its changing position among the relatively fixed stars. He identifies the planets by noting their positions relative to each other, the sun, the moon, and the stars. He knows that they remain within the narrow limits of the zodiac (art. 1420)but are in almost constant motion relative to the stars. The magnitude and color may be helpful. The information he needs is found in the *Nautical Almanac*. The "Planet Notes" near the front of that volume are particularly useful.

Sometimes the light from a planet seems steadier than that from a star. This is because fluctuation of the unsteady atmosphere causes **scintillation** or **twinkling** of a star, which has no measurable diameter with even the most powerful telescopes. The navigational planets are less susceptible to twinkling because of the broader apparent area giving light.

Planets can also be identified by planet diagram (art. 2209), star finder (art. 2210), sky diagram (art. 2212), or by computation (art. 2213).

2203. Stars.—The average navigator regularly uses not more than perhaps 20 or 30 stars. The *Nautical Almanac* gives full navigational information on 19 first magnitude stars and 38 second magnitude stars, in addition to Polaris. Abbreviated information is given for 115 more. Additional stars are listed in *The American Ephemeris and Nautical Almanac* and in various star catalogs. About 6,000 stars of the sixth magnitude or brighter (on the entire celestial sphere) are visible to the unaided eye on a clear, dark night.

Stars are designated by one or more of the following:

Name. Most names of stars, as now used, were given by the ancient Arabs and some by the Greeks or Romans. One of the stars of the *Nautical Almanac*, Nunki, was named by the Babylonians. Only a relatively few stars have names. Several of the stars on the daily pages of the almanacs had no name prior to the 1953 edition, and were given coined names so that all stars listed on the daily pages might have names. The pronunciation, meaning, and other information of general interest regarding Polaris and the 57 stars listed on the daily pages of the *Nautical Almanac* are given in appendix J.

Bayer's name. Most bright stars, including those with names, have been given a designation consisting of a Greek letter followed by the possessive form of the name

616

of the constellation, as α *Cygni* (Deneb, the brightest star in the constellation *Cygnus*, the swan). Roman letters are used when there are not enough Greek letters. Usually, the letters are assigned in order of brightness within the constellation, but in some cases the letters are assigned in another order, where it seems logical to do so. An example is the Big Dipper, where the letters are assigned in order from the outer rim of the bowl to the end of the handle. This system of star designation was suggested by John Bayer of Augsburg, Germany, in 1603. All of the 173 stars included in the list near the back of the *Nautical Almanac* are given by Bayer's name as well as regular name, where there is one.

Flamsteed's number. A similar system, accommodating more stars, numbers them in each constellation, from west to east, the order in which they cross the celestial meridian. An example is 95 *Leonis*, the 95th star in the constellation *Leo*, the lion. This system was suggested by John Flamsteed (1646–1719), who was the first British Astronomer Royal.

Catalog number. Stars are sometimes designated by the name of a star catalog and the number of the star as given in that catalog, as A. G. Washington 632. In these catalogs stars are listed in order from west to east, without regard to constellation, starting with the hour circle of the vernal equinox. This system is used primarily for dimmer stars having no other designation. Navigators seldom have occasion to use this system.

The ability to identify stars by position relative to each other is useful to the navigator. A tabulation of the relative positions of the 57 stars given on the daily pages of the *Nautical Almanac*, and Polaris, is given in appendix I. A star chart (fig. 2204) is helpful in locating these relationships and others which may be useful. This method is limited to periods of relatively clear, dark skies with little or no overcast. Stars can also be identified by the *Air Almanac* sky diagram (art. 2212), star finder (art. 2210), Pub. No. 249 (art. 2211), or by computation (art. 2213).

2204. Star charts are based upon the celestial equator system of coordinates, using declination and sidereal hour angle (or right ascension). The zenith of the observer is at the intersection of the parallel of declination equal to his latitude, and the hour circle coinciding with his celestial meridian. This hour circle has an SHA equal to 360°−LHA ♈ (or RA=LHA♈). The horizon is everywhere 90° from the zenith. A **star globe** is similar to a terrestrial sphere, but with stars (and often constellations) shown instead of geographical positions. Star globes are used by British navigators, but not customarily by Americans. The *Nautical Almanac* includes adequate instructions for using this device. On a star globe the celestial sphere is shown as it would appear to an observer *outside* the sphere. Constellations appear reversed. Star charts may show a similar view, but more often they are based upon the view from *inside* the sphere, as seen from the earth. On these charts, north is at the top, as with maps, but east is to the *left* and west to the *right*. The directions seem correct when the chart is held overhead, with the top toward the north, so that the relationship is similar to that in the sky. Any map projection (ch. III) can be used, but some are more suitable than others.

The *Nautical Almanac* has four star charts. The two principal ones are on the polar azimuthal equidistant projection (art. 320), one centered on each celestial pole. Each chart extends from its pole to declination 10° (same name as pole). Below each polar chart is an auxiliary chart on the Mercator projection, from 30°N to 30°S. On any of these charts, the zenith can be located as indicated above, to determine which stars are overhead. The horizon is 90° from the zenith. The charts can also be used

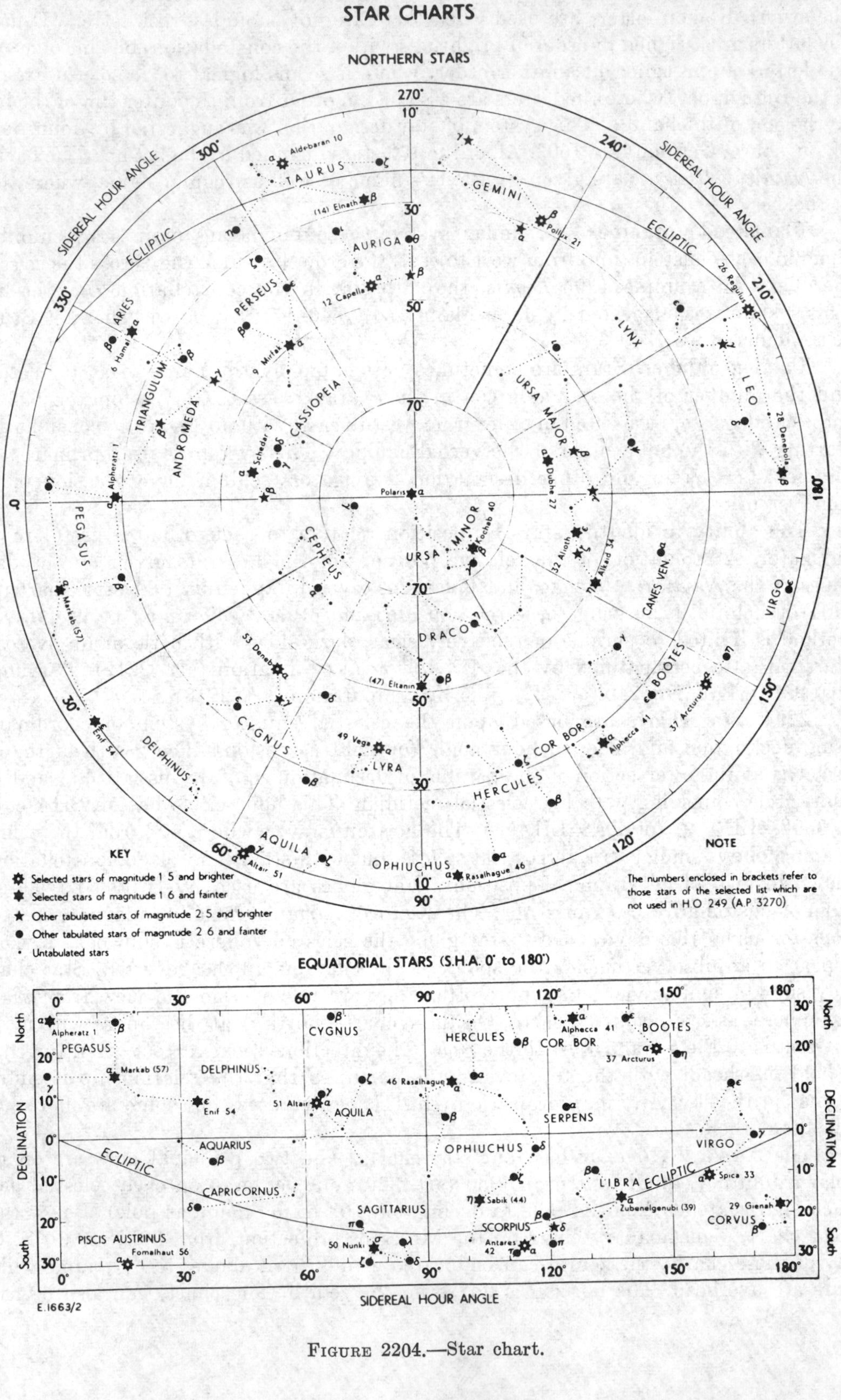

STAR CHARTS

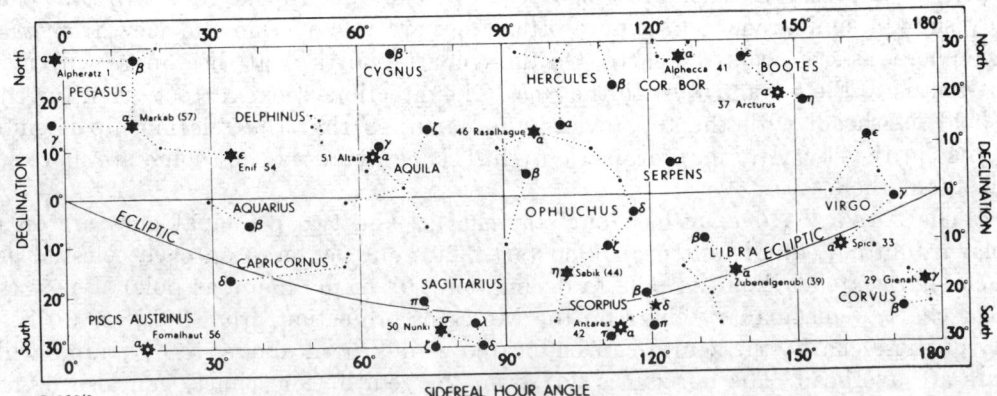

FIGURE 2204.—Star chart.

to determine the location of a star relative to surrounding stars. The *Air Almanac* has a fold-in chart near the back, on the rectangular projection (art. 311). This projection is suitable for indicating the coordinates of the stars, but excessive distortion occurs in regions of high declination. The celestial poles are represented by the top and bottom horizontal *lines* the same length as the celestial equator. To locate the horizon on this chart, first locate the zenith as indicated above, and then locate the four cardinal points. The north and south points are 90° from the zenith, along the celestial meridian. The distance to the elevated pole (having the same name as the latitude) is equal to the colatitude of the observer. The remainder of the 90° (the latitude) is measured *from* the same pole, along the *lower branch* of the celestial meridian, 180° from the upper branch containing the zenith. The east and west points are on the celestial equator at the hour circle 90° east and west (or 90° and 270° in the same direction) from the celestial meridian. The horizon is a sine curve (fig. 140b, vol. II) through the four cardinal points. Directions on this projection are distorted.

The star charts shown in figures 2205–2208, on the transverse Mercator projection (art. 309), are designed to assist one in learning the stars listed on the daily pages of the *Nautical Almanac,* and Polaris. Each chart extends about 20° beyond each celestial pole, and about 60° (four hours) each side of the central hour circle (at the celestial equator). Therefore, they do not coincide exactly with that half of the celestial sphere above the horizon at any one time or place. The zenith, and hence the horizon, varies with the position of the observer on the earth, and also with the rotation of the earth (apparent rotation of the celestial sphere). The charts show all stars of fifth magnitude and brighter as they appear in the sky, but with some distortion toward the right and left edges.

The overprinted lines add certain information of use in locating the stars. Only Polaris and the 57 stars listed on the daily pages of the *Nautical Almanac* are named on the charts. The almanac star charts should be used for locating the additional stars given near the back of the *Nautical Almanac* and the *Air Almanac*. The broken lines connect stars of some of the more prominent constellations. The solid lines indicate the celestial equator and certain useful relationships among stars in different constellations. The celestial poles are marked by crosses, and labeled. By means of the celestial equator and the poles, one can locate his zenith approximately along the mid hour circle, when this coincides with his celestial meridian, as shown in the table below. At any time earlier than those shown in the table the zenith is to the *right* of center, and at a later time it is to the *left*, approximately one-quarter of the distance from the center to the outer edge (at the celestial equator) for each hour that the time differs from that shown. The stars in the vicinity of the North Pole can be seen in proper perspective by inverting the chart, so that the zenith of an observer in the Northern Hemisphere is *up* from the pole.

	Fig. 2205	*Fig. 2206*	*Fig. 2207*	*Fig. 2208*
Local sidereal time	0000	0600	1200	1800
LMT 1800	Dec. 21	Mar. 22	June 22	Sept. 21
LMT 2000	Nov. 21	Feb. 20	May 22	Aug. 21
LMT 2200	Oct. 21	Jan. 20	Apr. 22	July 22
LMT 0000	Sept. 22	Dec. 22	Mar. 23	June 22
LMT 0200	Aug. 22	Nov. 22	Feb. 21	May 23
LMT 0400	July 23	Oct. 22	Jan. 21	Apr. 22
LMT 0600	June 22	Sept. 21	Dec. 22	Mar. 23

2205. Stars in the vicinity of *Pegasus* (fig. 2205).—In autumn the evening sky has few first magnitude stars. Most of these are near the southern horizon of an observer in the latitudes of the United States. A relatively large number of second and third magnitude stars seem conspicuous, perhaps because of the small number of brighter stars. High in the southern sky three third magnitude stars and one second magnitude star form a square with sides nearly 15° of arc in length. This is *Pegasus*, the winged horse, although to many modern men it more nearly resembles a baseball diamond, complete with catcher, pitcher, batter, umpire, base umpire near second base, infield and outfield; although there does seem to be a large number of outfielders. One may even see the next batter, bat boy, and coach.

Only Markab at the southwestern corner (third base) and Alpheratz at the northeastern corner (first base) are listed on the daily pages of the *Nautical Almanac*. Alpheratz is part of the constellation *Andromeda*, the princess, extending in an arc toward the northeast and terminating at Mirfak in *Perseus*, legendary rescuer of *Andromeda*.

A line extending northward through the eastern side (first-second base line) of the square of *Pegasus* passes through the leading (western) star of M-shaped (or W-shaped) *Cassiopeia*, the legendary mother of the princess *Andromeda*. The only star of this constellation listed on the daily pages of the *Nautical Almanac* is Schedar, the second star from the leading one as the configuration circles the pole in a counterclockwise direction. If the line through the eastern side of the square of *Pegasus* is continued on toward the north, it leads to second magnitude Polaris, the North Star (less than 1° from the north celestial pole) and brightest star of *Ursa Minor*, the Little Bear. Kochab, a second magnitude star at the other end of the Little Dipper, is also listed in the almanacs. At this season the Big Dipper is low in the northern sky, below the celestial pole. A line extending from Kochab through Polaris leads to Mirfak, assisting in its identification when *Pegasus* and *Andromeda* are near or below the horizon.

Deneb, in *Cygnus*, the swan, and Vega are bright, first magnitude stars in the northwestern sky. They are discussed in article 2208. Capella, a bright star in the northeastern sky, is discussed in article 2206.

The line through the eastern side of the square of *Pegasus* (first-second base line) approximates the hour circle of the vernal equinox, shown at ♈ on the celestial equator to the south. The sun is at ♈ on or about March 21, when it crosses the celestial equator from south to north. If the line through the eastern side of *Pegasus* is extended southward and curved slightly toward the east, it leads to second magnitude Diphda. A longer and straighter line southward through the western side (home plate-third base line) of *Pegasus* leads to first magnitude Fomalhaut. A line extending northeasterly from Fomalhaut through Diphda leads to Menkar, a third magnitude star, but the brightest in its vicinity. Ankaa, Diphda, and Fomalhaut form an isosceles triangle, with the apex at Diphda. Ankaa is near or below the southern horizon of observers in latitudes of the United States. Four stars farther south than Ankaa may be visible when on the celestial meridian, just above the horizon of observers in latitudes of the extreme southern part of the United States. These are Acamar, Achernar, Al Na'ir, and Peacock. These stars, with each other and with Ankaa, Fomalhaut, and Diphda, form a series of triangles as shown in figure 2205. Almanac stars near the bottom of figure 2205 are discussed in succeeding articles.

Two other almanac stars can be located by their positions relative to *Pegasus*. These are Hamal in the constellation *Aries*, the ram, east of *Pegasus*, and Enif, west of the southern part of the square, identified as shown in figure 2205. The line leading to Hamal, if continued, leads to the *Pleiades*, not used by navigators for celestial observations, but a prominent figure in the sky, heralding the approach of the many conspicuous stars of the winter evening sky, figure 2206.

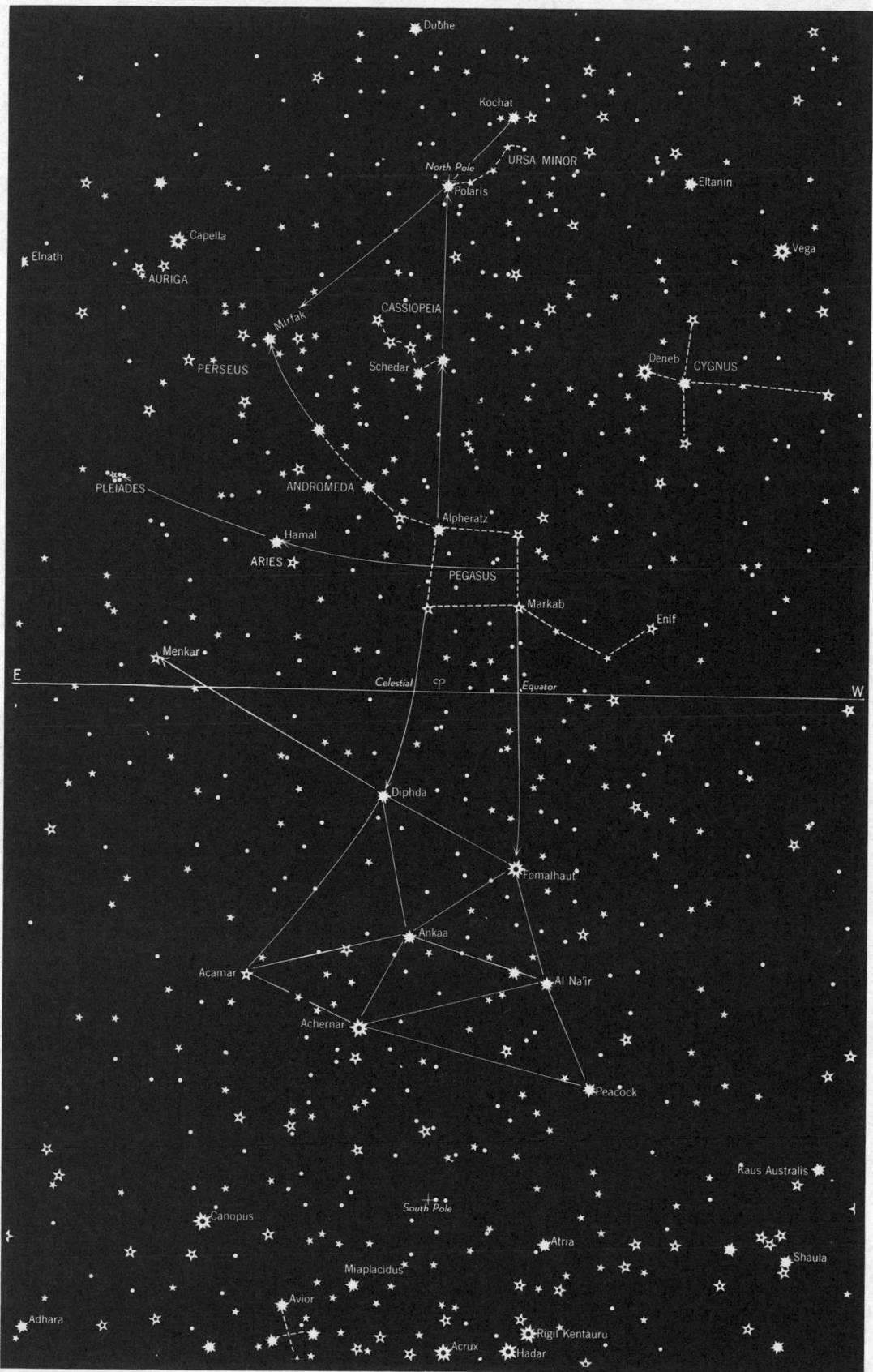

FIGURE 2205.—Stars in the vicinity of *Pegasus*.

Scale of magnitudes: 1st ✦   2nd ✹   3rd ✰   4th ✦   5th •

2206. Stars in the vicinity of Orion (fig. 2206).—As *Pegasus* leaves the meridian and moves into the western sky, *Orion*, the mighty hunter, rises in the east. With the possible exception of the Big Dipper, no other configuration of stars in the entire sky is as well known as *Orion* and its immediate surroundings. In no other part are there so many first magnitude stars.

The belt of *Orion*, being nearly on the celestial equator, is visible by an observer in virtually any latitude, rising and setting almost on the prime vertical, and dividing equally its time above and below the horizon. Of the three second magnitude stars forming the belt, only Alnilam, the middle one, is listed on the daily pages of the *Nautical Almanac*.

Four conspicuous stars form a box around the belt. To the south is Rigel, one of the hottest and bluest of the stars, in contrast with relatively cool, red, variable Betelgeuse, at approximately an equal distance to the north. Bellatrix, bright for a second magnitude star but overshadowed by its more brilliant neighbors, is a few degrees west of Betelgeuse. Neither the second magnitude star forming the southeastern corner of the box, nor any star of the dagger, is listed on the daily pages of the *Nautical Almanac*.

A line extending eastward from the belt of *Orion* and curving toward the south leads to Sirius, the brightest star in the entire heavens, having a magnitude of $(-)$ 1.6. Only Mars and Jupiter at or near their greatest brilliance, and the sun, moon, and Venus are brighter than Sirius. This is part of the constellation *Canis Major*, the large hunting dog of *Orion*. Starting at Sirius a curved line extends northward through first magnitude Procyon, in *Canis Minor*, the small hunting dog; first magnitude Pollux and second magnitude Castor (not listed on the daily pages of the *Nautical Almanac*), the twins of *Gemini;* brilliant Capella in *Auriga*, the charioteer; and back down to first magnitude Aldebaran, the follower, which trails the *Pleiades*, the seven sisters. Aldebaran, brightest star in the head of *Taurus*, the bull, may also be found by a curved line extending northwestward from the belt of *Orion*. The V-shaped figure forming the outline of the head and horns of *Taurus* points toward third magnitude Menkar. At the summer solstice the sun is between Pollux and Aldebaran.

If the curved line from *Orion's* belt southeastward to Sirius is continued, it leads to a conspicuous, small, nearly equilateral triangle of three bright second magnitude stars of nearly equal brilliancy. This is part of *Canis Major*. Only Adhara, the westernmost of the three stars, is listed on the daily pages of the *Nautical Almanac*. Continuing on with somewhat less curvature, the line leads to Canopus, second brightest star in the heavens and one of the two stars having a negative magnitude (-0.9). With Suhail and Miaplacidus, Canopus forms a large, equilateral triangle which partly encloses the false Southern Cross. The brightest star within this triangle is Avior, near its center. Canopus is also at one apex of a triangle formed with Adhara to the north and Suhail to the east, another triangle with Acamar to the west and Achernar to the southwest, and another with Achernar and Miaplacidus. Acamar, Achernar, and Ankaa form still another triangle toward the west. Because of chart distortion, these triangles do not appear in the sky in exactly the relationship shown on the star chart. Other daily-page almanac stars near the bottom of figure 2206 are discussed in succeeding articles.

During the winter evening sky the Big Dipper is east of Polaris, the Little Dipper is nearly below it, and *Cassiopeia* is west of it. Mirfak is northwest of Capella, nearly midway between it and *Cassiopeia*. Hamal is in the western sky. Regulus and Alphard are low in the eastern sky, heralding the approach of the configurations associated with the evening skies of spring.

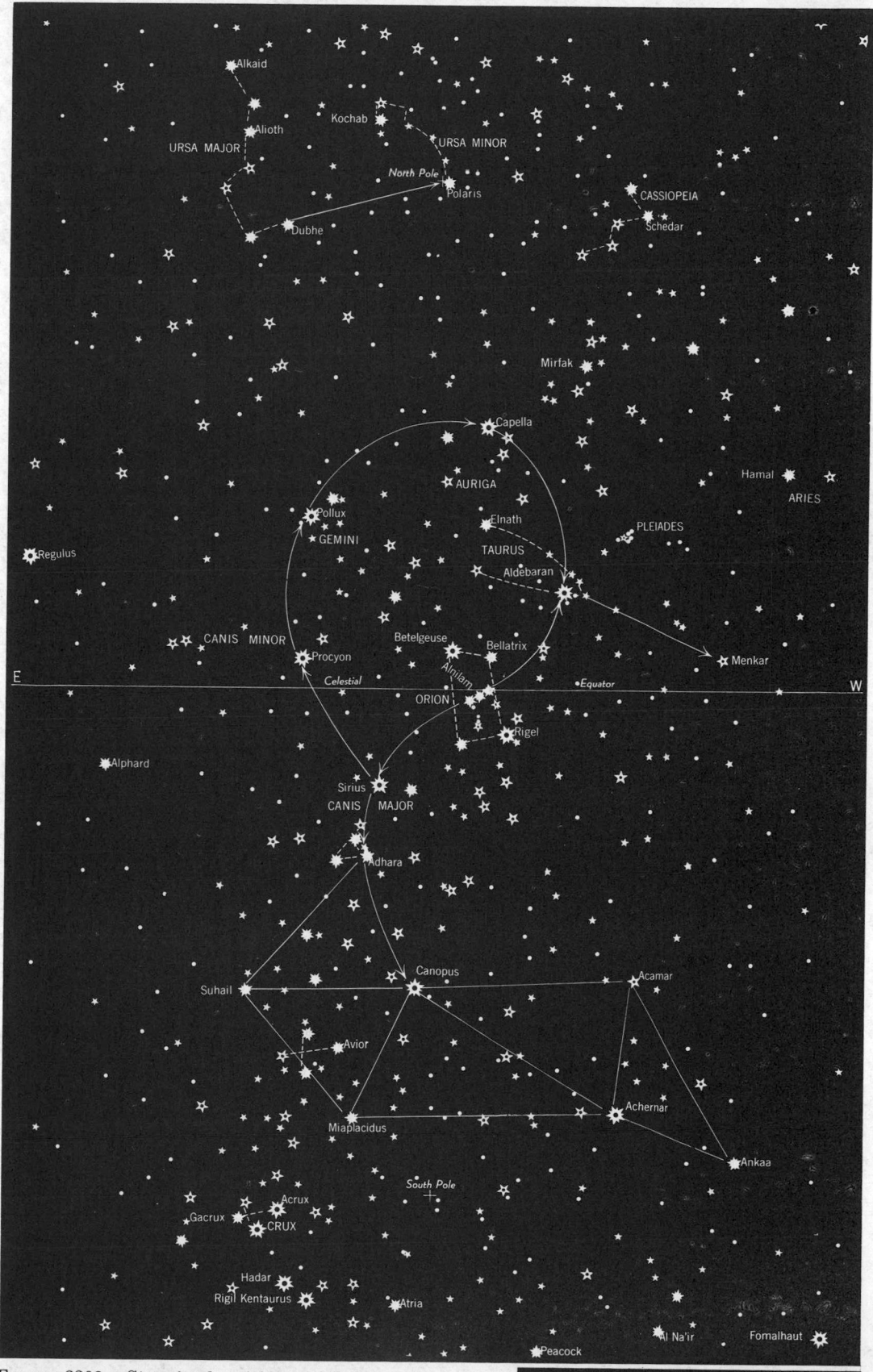

FIGURE 2206.—Stars in the vicinity of *Orion*.

2207. Stars in the vicinity of *Ursa Major* (fig. 2207).—As if to enhance the splendor of the sky in the vicinity of *Orion*, the region toward the east, like that toward the west, has few bright stars, except in the vicinity of the south celestial pole. However, as *Orion* sets in the west, leaving Capella and Pollux in the northwestern sky, a number of good navigational stars move into favorable positions for observation.

The Big Dipper, part of *Ursa Major*, the great bear, appears prominently *above* the north celestial pole, directly opposite *Cassiopeia* (only partly shown in fig. 2207), which appears as a W just above the northern horizon of most observers in latitudes of the United States. Of the seven stars forming the Big Dipper, only Dubhe, Alioth, and Alkaid are listed on the daily pages of the *Nautical Almanac*.

The two second magnitude stars forming the outer part of the bowl of the Big Dipper are often called the *pointers* because a line extending northward (*down* in spring evenings) through them points to Polaris. The Little Dipper, with Polaris at one end and Kochab at the other, is part of *Ursa Minor*, the Little Bear. Relative to its bowl, the handle of the Little Dipper curves in the opposite direction to that of the Big Dipper. Other almanac stars near the top of figure 2207 are discussed elsewhere.

A line extending southward through the pointers, and curving somewhat toward the west, leads to first magnitude Regulus, brightest star in *Leo*, the lion. The head, shoulders, and front legs of this constellation form a sickle, with Regulus at the end of the handle. Toward the east is second magnitude Denebola, the tail of the lion. On toward the southwest from Regulus is second magnitude Alphard, brightest star in *Hydra*, the sea serpent. A dark sky and considerable imagination are needed to trace the long, winding body of this figure.

A curved line extending the arc of the handle of the Big Dipper leads to first magnitude Arcturus. With Alkaid and Alphecca, brightest star in *Corona Borealis*, the Northern Crown, Arcturus forms a large, inconspicuous triangle. If the arc through Arcturus is continued, it leads next to first magnitude Spica and then to *Corvus*, the crow, which appears most like a gaff mainsail of a schooner. The brightest star in this constellation is Gienah, but three others are nearly as bright. At autumnal equinox the sun is on the celestial equator, about midway between Regulus and Spica.

A long, slightly curved line from Regulus east-southeasterly through Spica leads to Zubenelgenubi (zōō·běn′ěl·jě·nu′bē) at the southwestern corner of an inconspicuous box-like figure called *Libra*, the (weighing) scales.

Returning to *Corvus*, a line from Gienah, extending diagonally across the figure and then curving somewhat toward the east, leads to Menkent, just beyond *Hydra*.

Far to the south, below the horizon of most northern hemisphere observers, a group of bright stars is a prominent feature of the spring sky of the Southern Hemisphere. *Crux*, the Southern Cross, is about 40° south of *Corvus*. This is a small figure and a poor cross, and hence disappointing to many who view it for the first time. The "false cross" to the west is a better but less conspicuous cross. Acrux at the southern end of the Southern Cross, and Gacrux at the northern end, are listed on the daily pages of the *Nautical Almanac*.

The triangles formed by Suhail, Miaplacidus, and Canopus, and by Suhail, Adhara, and Canopus, are west of the Southern Cross, Suhail being in line with the horizontal arm of the Southern Cross at this time. A line from Canopus, through Miaplacidus, curved slightly toward the north, leads to Acrux. A line through the east-west arm of *Crux*, eastward and then curving toward the south, leads first to Hadar and then to Rigil Kentaurus, two very bright stars. Continuing on, the curved line leads to small *Triangulum Australe*, the Southern Triangle, the easternmost star of which is Atria.

Scorpius, the scorpion, Kaus Australis, and Peacock, in the southeastern sky of the Southern Hemisphere, are discussed in article 2208.

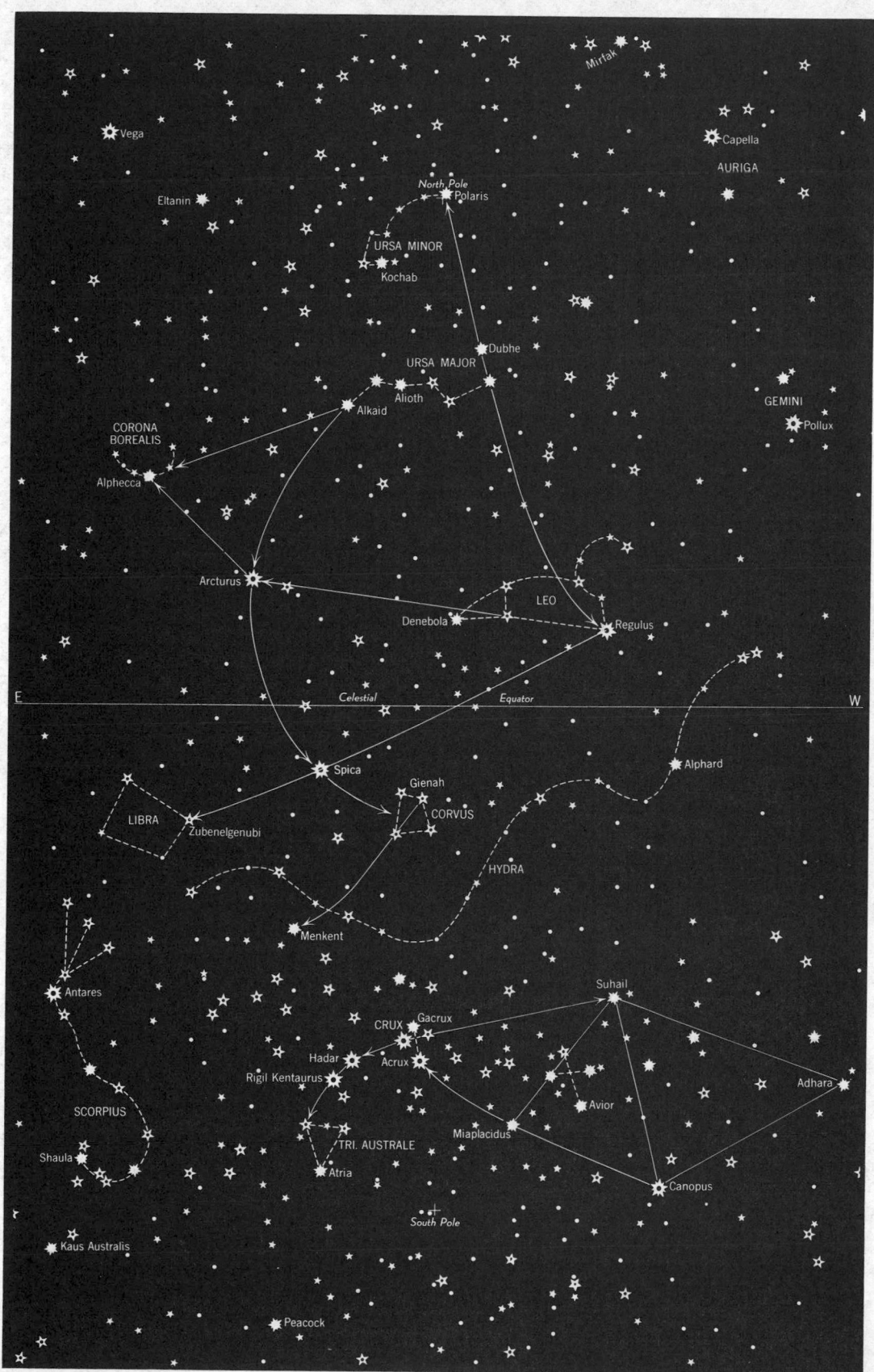

FIGURE 2207.—Stars in the vicinity of Ursa Major.

Scale of magnitudes: 1st 2nd 3rd 4th 5th

2208. Stars in the vicinity of *Cygnus* (fig. 2208).—As the celestial sphere continues in its apparent westward rotation, the stars familiar to a spring evening observer sink low in the western sky. By midsummer the Big Dipper has moved to a position to the left of the north celestial pole, and the line from the pointers to Polaris is nearly horizontal. The Little Dipper is standing on its handle, with Kochab above and to the left of the celestial pole. *Cassiopeia* is at the right of Polaris, opposite the handle of the Big Dipper.

The only first magnitude star in the western sky is Arcturus, which forms a large, inconspicuous triangle with Alkaid, the end of the handle of the Big Dipper, and Alphecca, the brightest star in *Corona Borealis*, the Northern Crown.

The eastern sky is dominated by three very bright stars. The westernmost of these is Vega, the brightest star north of the celestial equator, and third brightest star in the heavens. Its magnitude is 0.1. Having a declination of a little less than 39°N, this star passes through the zenith along a path across the central part of the United States, from Washington in the east to San Francisco on the Pacific coast. Vega forms a large but conspicuous triangle with its two bright neighbors, Deneb to the northeast and Altair to the southeast. The angle at Vega is nearly a right angle. Deneb is at the end of the tail of *Cygnus*, the swan. This configuration is sometimes called the Northern Cross, with Deneb at the head. To modern youth it more nearly resembles a dive bomber while it is still well toward the east, with Deneb at the nose of the fuselage. Altair has two fainter stars close by, on opposite sides. The line formed by Altair and its two fainter companions, if extended in a northwesterly direction, passes through Vega, and on to second magnitude Eltanin. The angular distance from Vega to Eltanin is about half that from Altair to Vega. Vega and Altair, with second magnitude Rasalhague to the west, form a large equilateral triangle. This is less conspicuous than the Vega-Deneb-Altair triangle because the brilliance of Rasalhague is much less than that of the three first magnitude stars, and the triangle is overshadowed by the brighter one.

Far to the south of Rasalhague, and a little toward the west, is a striking configuration called *Scorpius*, the scorpion. The brightest star, forming the head, is red Antares. At the tail is Shaula.

Antares is at the southwestern corner of an approximate parallelogram formed by Antares, Sabik, Nunki, and Kaus Australis. With the exception of Antares, these stars are only slightly brighter than a number of others nearby, and so this parallelogram is not a striking figure. At winter solstice the sun is a short distance northwest of Nunki.

Northwest of *Scorpius* is the box-like *Libra*, the (weighing) scales, in which Zubenelgenubi marks the southwest corner.

With Menkent and Rigil Kentaurus to the southwest, Antares forms a large but unimpressive triangle. For most observers in the latitudes of the United States, Antares is low in the southern sky, and the other two stars of the triangle are below the horizon. To an observer in the Southern Hemisphere *Crux*, the Southern Cross, is to the right of the south celestial pole, which is not marked by a conspicuous star. A long, curved line starting with the now-vertical arm of the Southern Cross and extending northward and then eastward passes successively through Hadar, Rigil Kentaurus, Peacock, and Al Na'ir.

Fomalhaut is low in the southeastern sky of the southern hemisphere observer, and Enif is low in the eastern sky at nearly any latitude. With the appearance of these stars it is not long before *Pegasus* will appear over the eastern horizon during the evening, and as the winged horse climbs evening by evening to a position higher in the sky, a new annual cycle approaches.

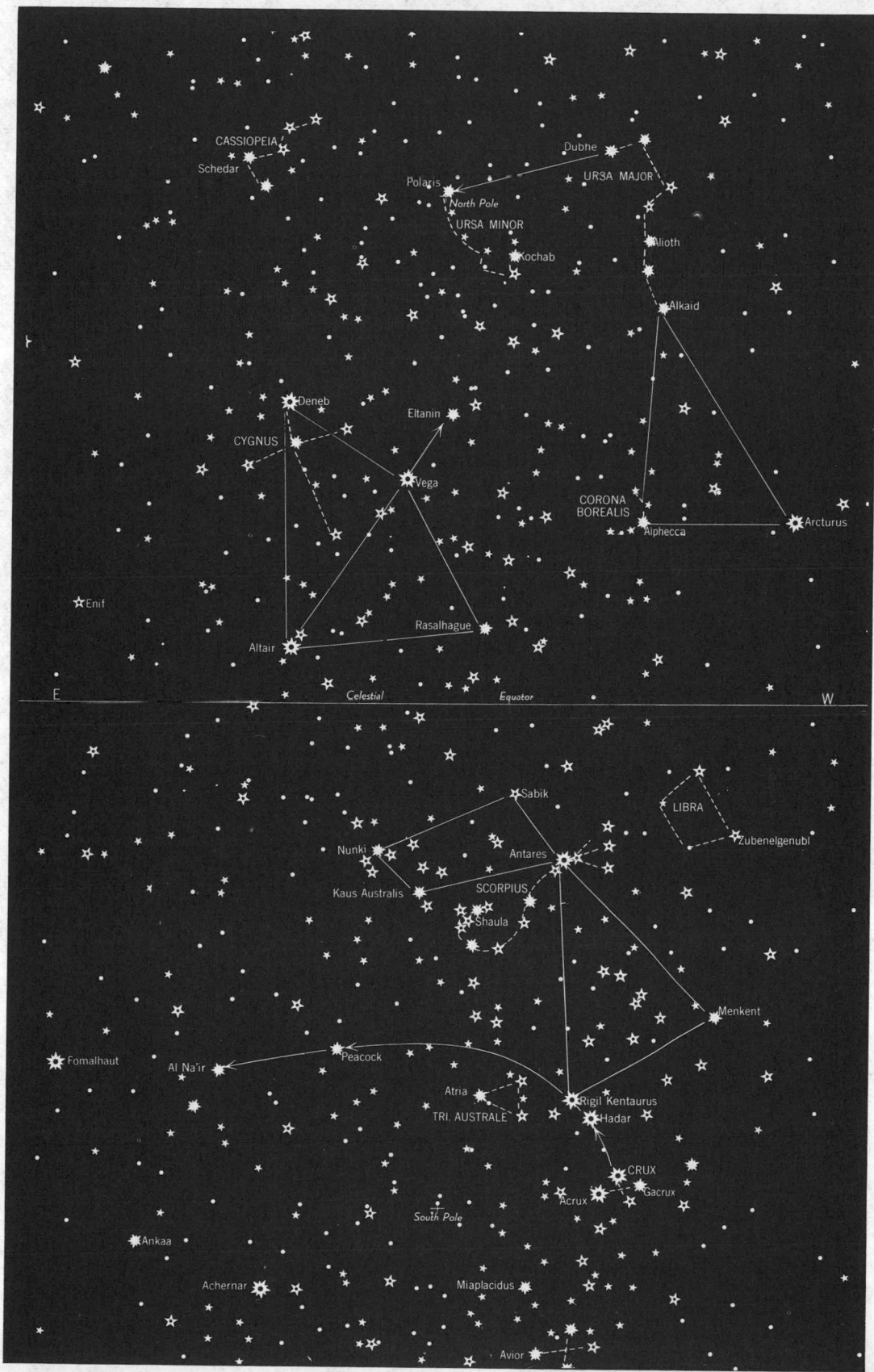

FIGURE 2208.—Stars in the vicinity of *Cygnus.*

Scale of magnitudes: 1st 2nd 3rd 4th 5th

2209. Planet diagram.—The planet diagram in the *Nautical Almanac* shows, in graphical form for any date during the year, the LMT of meridian passage of the sun, of the five planets Mercury, Venus, Mars, Jupiter, and Saturn, and of each 30° of SHA. The diagram provides a general picture of the availability of planets and stars for observation, and thus the following information:

1. whether a planet or star is too close to the sun for observation;
2. whether a planet is a morning or evening star;
3. some indication of the planet's position during twilight;
4. the proximity of other planets; and
5. whether a planet is visible from evening to morning twilight.

A band 45^m wide is shaded on each side of the curve marking the LMT of meridian passage of the sun. Any planet and most stars lying within the shaded area are too close to the sun for observation.

When the meridian passage occurs at midnight, the body is in opposition (art. 1422) to the sun and is visible all night; planets may be observable in both morning and evening twilights. As the time of meridian passage decreases, the body ceases to be observable in the morning, but its altitude above the eastern horizon during evening twilight gradually increases; this continues until the body is on the meridian at twilight. From then onwards the body is observable above the western horizon and its altitude at evening twilight gradually decreases; eventually the body comes too close to the sun for observation. When the body again becomes visible, it is seen as a morning star low in the east; its altitude at twilight increases until meridian passage occurs at the time of morning twilight. Then, as the time of meridian passage decreases to 0^h, the body is observable in the west in the morning twilight with a gradually decreasing altitude, until it once again reaches opposition.

Only about one half the region of the sky along the ecliptic as shown on the diagram is above the horizon at one time. At sunrise (LMT about 6^h) the sun and, hence, the region near the middle of the diagram are rising in the east; the region at the bottom of the diagram is setting in the west. The region half way between is on the meridian. At sunset (LMT about 18^h) the sun is setting in the west; the region at the top of the diagram is rising in the east. Marking the planet diagram of the *Nautical Almanac* so that east is at the top of the diagram and west is at the bottom can be useful to interpretation.

If the curve for a planet intersects the vertical line connecting the date graduations below the shaded area, the planet is a morning star; if the intersection is above the shaded area, the planet is an evening star.

A similar **planet location diagram** in the *Air Almanac* represents the region of the sky along the ecliptic within which the sun, moon, and planets always move; it shows, for each date, the sun in the center and the relative positions of the moon, the five planets Mercury, Venus, Mars, Jupiter, Saturn and the four first magnitude stars *Aldebaran*, *Antares*, *Spica*, and *Regulus*, and also the position on the ecliptic which is north of Sirius (i.e. Sirius is 40° south of this point). The first point of Aries is also shown for reference. The magnitudes of the planets are given at suitable intervals along the curves. The moon symbol shows the correct phase. A straight line joining the date on the left-hand side with the same date of the right-hand side represents a complete circle around the sky, the two ends of the line representing the point 180° from the sun; the intersections with the curves show the spacing of the bodies along the ecliptic on the date. The time scale indicates very approximately the local mean time at which an object will be on the observer's meridian.

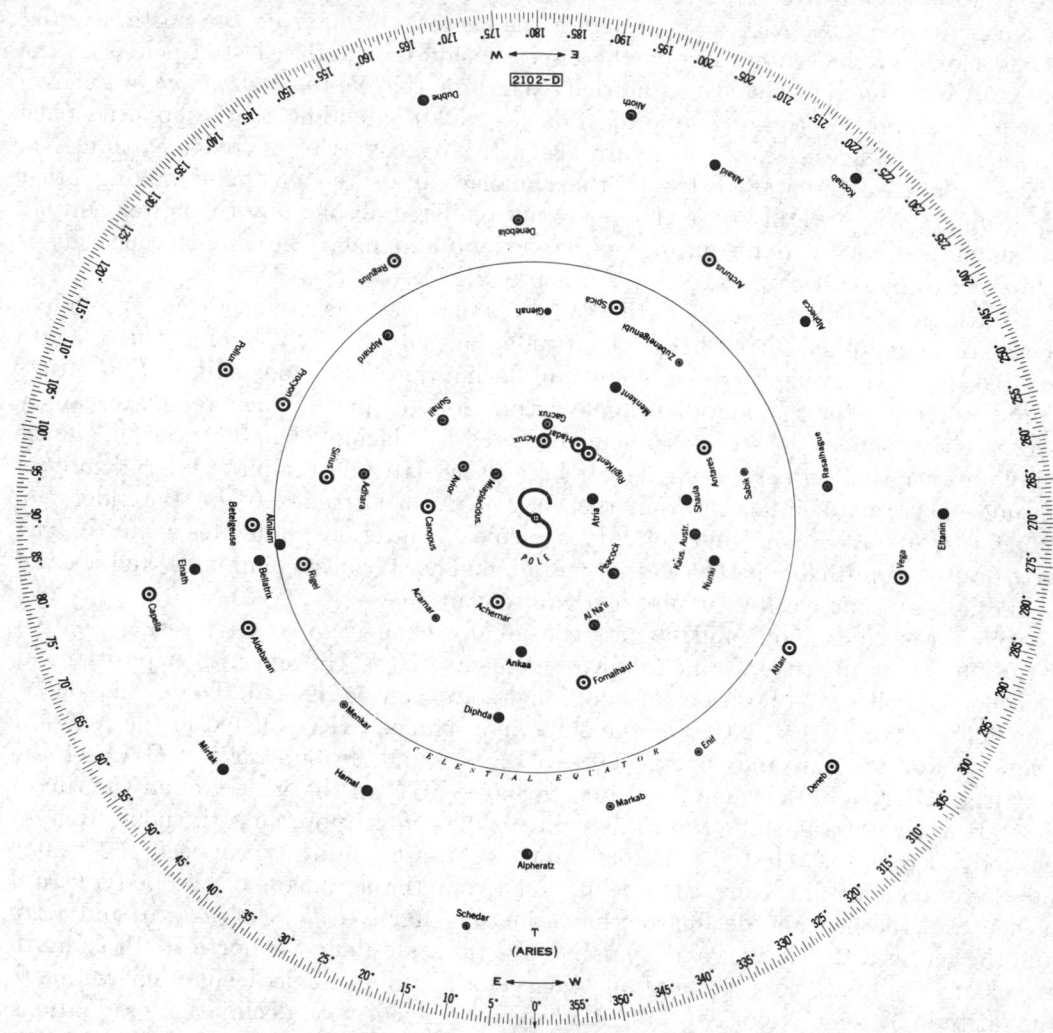

FIGURE 2210a.—The south pole side of the star base of No. 2102–D.

At any time only about half the region on the diagram is above the horizon. At sunrise the sun (and hence the region near the middle of the diagram) is rising in the east and the region at the end marked "West" is setting in the west; the region half-way between these extremes is on the meridian, as will be indicated by the local time (about 6^h). At the time of sunset (local time about 18^h) the sun is setting in the west, and the region at the end marked "East" is rising in the east.

The diagram should be used in conjunction with the *Sky Diagrams*.

2210. Star finders.—Various devices have been invented to help an observer locate and identify individual stars. The most widely used is the Star Finder and Identifier formerly published by the U. S. Navy Hydrographic Office and now published commercially. The current model, No. 2102–D, as well as the previous 2102–C model patented by E. B. Collins, employs the same basic principle as that used in the Rude Star Finder, which was patented by Captain G. T. Rude, USC&GS, and later sold to the Hydrographic Office. Successive models reflect various modifications to meet changing conditions and requirements.

The *star base* of No. 2102–D consists of a thin, white, opaque, plastic disk about 8½ inches in diameter, with a small peg in the center. On one side the north celestial pole is shown at the center, and on the opposite side the south celestial pole is at the center. All of the stars listed on the daily pages of the *Nautical Almanac* are shown on a polar azimuthal equidistant projection (art. 320) extending to the opposite pole. The south pole side is shown in figure 2210a. Many copies of an older edition, No. 2102–C, showing the stars listed in the almanacs prior to 1953, and having other minor differences, are still in use. These are not rendered obsolete by the newer edition, but should be corrected by means of the current almanac. The rim of each side is graduated to half a degree of LHA ♈ (or 360°—SHA).

Ten transparent *templates* of the same diameter as the star base are provided. There is one template for each 10° of latitude, labeled 5°, 15°, 25°, etc., plus a tenth (printed in red) showing meridian angle and declination. The older edition (No. 2102– C) did not have the red meridian angle-declination template. Each template can be used on either side of the star base, being centered by placing a small center hole in the template over the center peg of the star base. Each latitude template has a family of altitude curves at 5° intervals from the horizon (from altitude 10° on the older No. 2102–C) to 80°. A second family of curves, also at 5° intervals, indicates azimuth. The north-south azimuth line is the celestial meridian. The star base, templates, and a set of instructions are housed in a circular leatherette container.

Since the sun, moon, and planets continually change apparent position relative to the "fixed" stars, they are not shown on the star base. However, their positions at anytime, as well as the positions of additional stars, can be plotted. To do this, determine 360°—SHA of the body. For the stars and planets, SHA is listed in the *Nautical Almanac*. For the sun and moon, 360°—SHA is found by subtracting GHA of the body from GHA ♈ at the same time. Locate 360°—SHA on the scale around the rim of the star base. A straight line from this point to the center represents the hour circle of the body. From the celestial equator, shown as a circle midway between the center and the outer edge, measure the declination (from the almanac) of the body *toward* the center if the pole and declination have the *same* name (*both* N or *both* S), and *away* from the center if they are of *contrary* name. Use the scale along the north-south azimuth line of any template as a declination scale. The meridian angle-declination template (the latitude 5° template of No. 2102–C) has an open slot with declination graduations along one side, to assist in plotting positions, as shown in figure 2210b. In the illustration the celestial body being located has a 360°—SHA of 285°, and a declination of 14°.5S. It is not practical to attempt to plot to greater precision than the nearest 0°.1. Positions of Venus, Mars, Jupiter, and Saturn on June 1, 1975, are shown plotted on the star base in figure 2210c. It is sometimes desirable to plot positions of the sun and moon, to assist in planning. Plotted positions of stars need not be changed. Plotted positions of bodies of the solar system should be replotted from time to time, the more rapidly moving ones oftener than others. The satisfactory interval for each body can be determined by experience. It is good practice to record the date of each plotted position of a body of the solar system, to serve later as an indication of the interval since it was plotted.

To orient the template properly for any given time, proceed as follows: enter the almanac with GMT, and determine GHA ♈ at this time. Apply the longitude to GHA ♈, subtracting if west or adding if east, to determine LHA ♈. If LMT is substituted for GMT in entering the almanac, LHA ♈ can be taken directly from the almanac, to sufficient accuracy for orienting the star finder template. Select the template for the latitude nearest that of the observer, and center it over the star base,

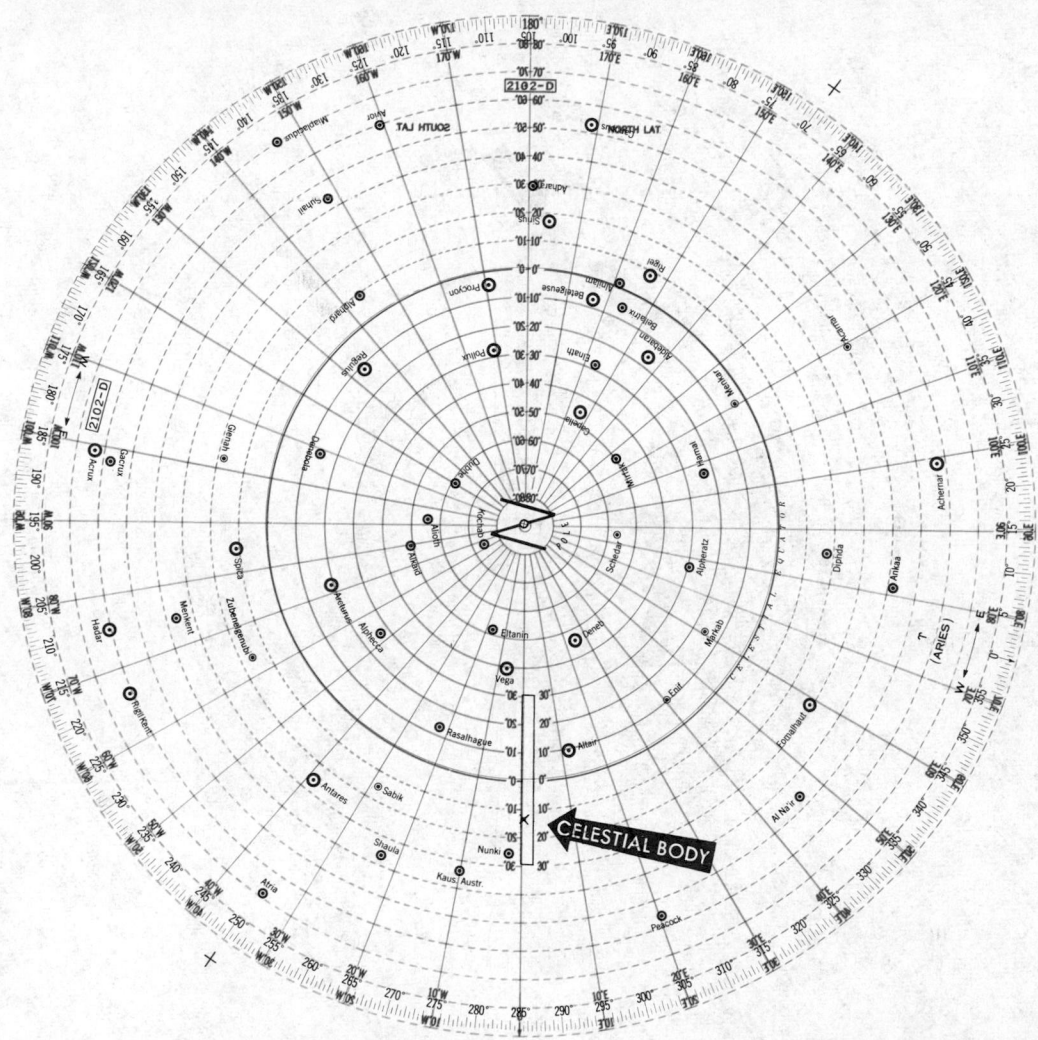

FIGURE 2210b.—Plotting a celestial body on the star base of No. 2102–D.

being careful that the correct sides (north or south to agree with the latitude) of both template and star base are used. Rotate the template relative to the star base until the arrow on the celestial meridian (the north-south azimuth line) is over LHA ♈ on the star base graduations. The small cross at the origin of both families of curves now represents the zenith of the observer. The approximate altitude and azimuth of the celestial bodies above the horizon can be read directly from the star finder, using eye interpolation. Consider Polaris, not shown as at the north celestial pole. For more accurate results, the template can be lifted clear of the center peg of the star base, and shifted along the celestial meridian until the latitude, on the altitude scale, is over the pole. This refinement is not needed for normal use of the device. It should not be used for a latitude differing more than 5° from that for which the curves were drawn. If the altitude and azimuth of an identified body shown on the star base are known, the template can be oriented by rotating it until it is in correct position relative to that body.

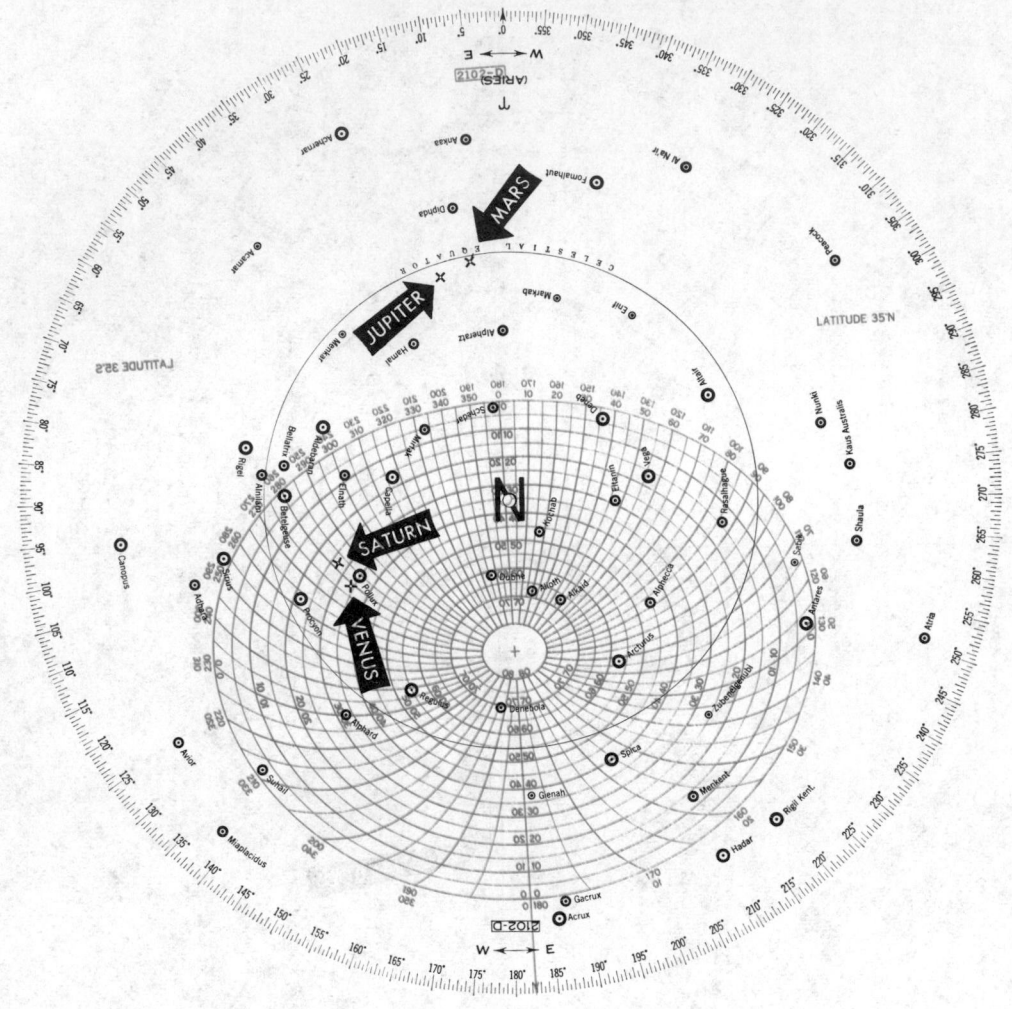

FIGURE 2210c.—A template in place over the star base of No. 2102–D.

Customarily, No. 2102–D is used in either of two ways:

1. To make an advance list of celestial bodies available for observation at a given time.

2. To identify an unknown celestial body which has been observed.

Example 1.—During evening twilight on June 1, 1975, the GMT 2324 DR position of a ship is lat. 34°12.′5N, long. 57°40.′0W.

Required.—The approximate altitude (h) and azimuth of each first magnitude star, and any planets, between altitudes 15° and 75°.

Solution (fig. 2210c).—(1) Plot the positions of the planets, as shown. The values used are those for GMT 0000 on June 1, as follows:

Planet	360°—SHA	Dec.
Venus	116°7	23°7N
Mars	8°0	1°8N
Jupiter	15°9	5°5N
Saturn	108°4	22°3N

(2) Determine LHA ♈ by means of the *Nautical Almanac*, as follows:

$$
\begin{array}{rl}
\text{GMT} & \underline{2324} \qquad \text{June 1} \\
23^{\text{h}} & 234°48'.2 \\
24^{\text{m}} & 6°01'.0 \\
\text{GHA ♈} & 240°49'.2 \\
\lambda & 57°40'.0\text{W} \\
\text{LHA ♈} & 183°09'.2
\end{array}
$$

(3) Select the template for latitude 35°, place it over the north side of the star base with "LATITUDE 35° N" appearing correctly, and orient it to 183°.2. It is customary to list the bodies in order of increasing azimuth, as follows:

Body	h	Zn
Vega	17°	054°
Arcturus	59°	111°
Spica	42°	157°
Regulus	53°	240°
Procyon	20°	262°
Venus	32°	278°
Saturn	25°	282°
Pollux	33°	284°
Capella	15°	316°

Example 2.—At the time and place of example 1, an unidentified celestial body is observed through a break in the clouds. Its sextant altitude is 15°27'.8, and its azimuth is 085°.

Required.—Identify the celestial body.

Solution (fig. 2210c).—Orient the template as in example 1. By means of its altitude and azimuth, identify the star as Rasalhague.

If no body appears at the measured altitude and azimuth, place the red meridian angle-declination template over the altitude-azimuth template and read off, by inspection, the declination and the 360°−SHA value of the body, and from this, determine its SHA. Using the SHA and declination, enter the list of stars near the back of the *Nautical Almanac*, and identify the body. If it is not found in this list, and no error has been made, one of the stars not listed in the almanac, or possibly the planet Mercury, has been observed. Unless a copy of *The American Ephemeris and Nautical Almanac* or another book containing the required information is available, the observation cannot be used. If right ascension (art. 1426) of the body is available, but not its SHA, the value taken from the star finder (360°−SHA) is converted to time units (art. 1811) and used directly, since RA=360°−SHA.

Example 3.—At the time and place of example 1 an unidentified celestial body is observed through a break in the clouds. Its altitude is 52°58'.9, and its azimuth is 170°.

Required.—Identify the celestial body.

Solution (fig. 2210c).—Orient the template as in example 1. Since no celestial body appears at the place indicated by its altitude and azimuth, the red meridian angle-declination template is placed over the altitude-azimuth template. The declination is found to be about 1°S. The 360°−SHA value is about 190°, and SHA is therefore about 170°. From the star list near the back of the *Nautical Almanac*, the star is identified as γ *Virginis*.

Kotlarić's Star Finder and Identifier, designed and patented by Dr. Stjepo M. Kotlarić, Assistant Director of the Hydrographic Institute of the Yugoslav Navy, is actually a booklet of 18 pairs of star charts with a plastic template enclosed. It depicts the 57 selected stars plus 125 other stars, for a total or 182 stars. All of the 173 stars listed in the *Nautical Almanac* are depicted. This star finder provides greater reliability in identification than No. 2102–D.

Each pair of star charts shows the Western and Eastern Hemispheres separately. The Western Hemisphere is shown using the stereographic projection (art. 318) on a plane tangent to the celestial equator at the west point; the Eastern Hemisphere is shown using the same projection on a plane tangent to the celestial equator at the east point.

The stars are plotted with different symbols, according to their magnitude. Selected stars are in black, and other stars in green. The stars in constellations are connected by a broken yellow line, while the "star-chasing" alignments are plotted with solid yellow lines. The names of the selected stars are shown in black capital letters, while all other stars are shown in green, using capital letters for popular names.

Since the list of stars near the back of the *Nautical Almanac* is not compiled in alphabetical order, an alphabetical index of stars with their rounded values of SHA and declination is included with the star finder to facilitate location of a star in the list.

Two 20° intervals of LHA♈, differing by 180°, are used for constructing each pair of star charts. The circle bordering the star chart (fig. 2210d) represents the observer's celestial meridian. The circle is graduated to permit orientation of the plastic template to the star chart, according to the observer's latitude, in order to portray the visible hemisphere in the horizon system of coordinates.

The latitude scale on the right-hand half is black, and that on the left half is red. By selecting the appropriate pair of star charts according to the values of LHA ♈ and the azimuth, printed on the star charts, and by placing the template over the selected star chart in such a way that their centers coincide and the zenith of the template is placed on the proper latitude value on the black border scale when the azimuth figures are in black type (or on the red border scale when the azimuth figures are in red type), the altitude and azimuth of a star can be determined. Also, with the observed altitude and azimuth the coordinates of the star in the celestial equator system can be determined.

Star symbols on all the star charts are plotted for odd tens of degrees of LHA ♈. A part of the star's path is plotted to a distance of 10° to the left and to the right of the star symbol's position. A 10° increase of LHA ♈ from the star symbol's position is plotted as a solid line path, and a 10° decrease of LHA ♈ is plotted as a dotted line path. These portions of the star paths facilitate the identification of stars and make for more certainty in identification. The position of a star, determined by means of altitude and azimuth on the template superimposed on this star chart, may be found from either the star symbol or the appropriate point on the star path when LHA ♈ at the time of the observation differs from the value of odd tens of degrees for which the star symbol is printed on the star chart.

Example 4.—Three unknown stars with the following data are observed from lat. 50°N:

Zn	h	LHA ♈
028°	22°48′	70°
029°5	25°00′	66°5
152°	26°16′	61°

Required.—Identify the stars.

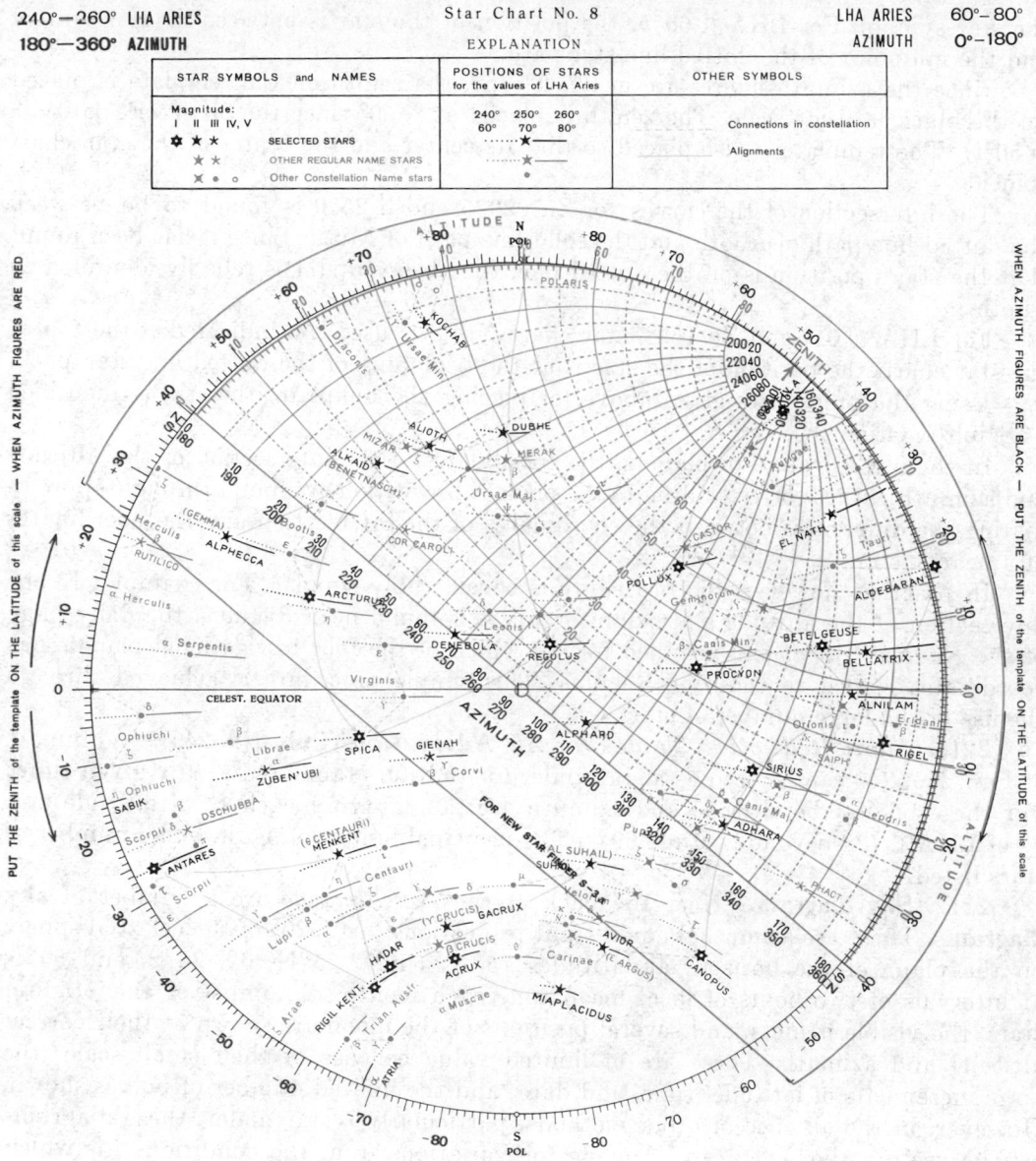

FIGURE 2210d.—Kotlarić's Star Finder and Identifier.

Solution.—For LHA ♈ 70° and Zn 028°, star chart No. 8 (fig. 2210d) is used. Since the azimuth figures are in black type, the zenith on the template is placed on the black latitude scale. The zenith is placed at +50° since the observer's latitude is 50°N. (If the observer's latitude were 50°S, the zenith on the template would be placed at −50°.) The template is also placed so that its center and the center of the star chart coincide.

At the intersection of the curves for Zn 028° and h 22°.8, the symbol for Mizar is found. The body is identified as Mizar.

For LHA ♈ 66°.5 and Zn 029°.5, star chart No. 8 is used. As indicated at the top of the star chart, the position of the star is on the dotted line path extending from the star symbol. For LHA♈ 66°5, the position of the star is between the star symbol and the midpoint of the dotted line star path.

Since the azimuth figures are in black type, the zenith on the template is placed on the black latitude scale. The zenith is placed at +50° since the observer's latitude is 50°N. The template is also placed so that its center and the center of the star chart coincide.

The intersection of the curves for Zn 029°5 and h 25°0 is found to be between the dotted line path of Alioth and the solid line path of Mizar. Since it has been found that the star's position is on the dotted line, the observed star is reliably identified as Alioth.

For LHA♈ 61° and Zn 152°, star chart No. 8 is used. As indicated at the top of the star chart, the position of the star is at the beginning of the dotted line star path. Using the procedures given above for placing the template, the star is identified as Saiph (κ Orionis).

In the identification of planets, the coordinates of the intersection of the altitude and azimuth curves corresponding to the planet observation are found through approximating the differences between the coordinates of the intersection and the coordinates of a nearby star.

In practice, however, the procedure is considerably simpler. For example: If the intersection of the altitude and azimuth curves is found near Regulus, the daily page of the *Nautical Almanac* is scanned to find which of the four navigational planets has coordinates closest to those of Regulus. This simple procedure is achieved through the use of the large number of stars.

2211. Sight Reduction Tables for Air Navigation (Pub. No. 249).—Volume I of Pub. No. 249 can be used as a star finder for the stars tabulated at any given time. For these bodies the altitude and azimuth are tabulated for each 1° of latitude and 1° of LHA♈ (2° beyond latitude 69°). The principal limitation is the small number of stars listed.

2212. Sky diagram.—Near the back of the *Air Almanac* are a number of **sky diagrams.** These are azimuthal equidistant projections (art. 320) of the celestial sphere on the plane of the horizon, at latitudes 75°N, 50°N, 25°N, 0°, 25°S, and 50°S, at intervals of two hours of local mean time each month. A number of the brighter stars, the visible planets, and several positions of the moon are shown at their correct altitude and azimuth. These are of limited value because of their small scale; the large increments of latitude, time, and date; and the limited number of bodies shown. However, in the absence of other methods, particularly a star finder, these diagrams can be useful. Allowance can be made for variations from the conditions for which each diagram is constructed. Instructions for use of the diagrams are included in the *Air Almanac.*

2213. Identification by computation.—If the altitude and azimuth of the celestial body, and the approximate latitude of the observer, are known, the navigational triangle (art. 1433) can be solved for meridian angle and declination. The meridian angle can be converted to LHA, and this to GHA. With this and GHA of Aries at the time of observation, the SHA of the body can be determined. With SHA and declination, one can identify the body by reference to an almanac. Any method of solving a spherical triangle, with two sides and the included angle being given, is suitable for this purpose. A large-scale, carefully-drawn diagram on the plane of the celestial meridian, using the refinement shown in figure 1432f, should yield satisfactory results. A simple method of computation is by Pub. No. 214. Following the tables of computed altitude and azimuth for each latitude, a two-page star identification table is given, as shown in appendix N. The example given below is based upon this extract.

The steps in solution by Pub. No. 214 are:

1. Convert Zn to Z.

2. With Z and h (usually the approximate value taken from the sextant, without correction) enter the Pub. No. 214 star identification pages for the nearest whole degree of latitude, and extract the declination and meridian angle, t (given as H.A. in the table). If the declination is given in roman type, above the heavy line, it has the *same* name as the latitude. If the declination is given in *italics*, below the heavy line, it has the *contrary* name to that of the latitude. When interpolating between roman and italic declinations, consider the italic value negative, using the arithmetical *sum* as the algebraic *difference* needed for interpolation. Extract values to the nearest whole degree.

3. Convert t to LHA.

4. Apply the longitude to LHA to find GHA, adding if in west longitude, and subtracting if in east longitude.

5. Enter the *Nautical Almanac* with GMT, and determine GHA Υ.

6. Subtract GHA Υ from GHA $\star$ to find SHA (since GHA$\star$=GHA Υ+SHA).

7. With the approximate SHA and d enter the *Nautical Almanac* star list and identify the body, checking first the SHA and then the declination. Do not overlook the possibility of having observed a planet or a star not listed in the almanac. For a planet, check first the declination. If this is approximately correct, check the GHA. It is not necessary to find the SHA of a planet.

Example.—On May 31, 1975, the 0425 DR position of a ship is lat. 41°13.'6N, long. 140°41.'7W. About this time the navigator observes an unknown star through a break in the clouds, as follows: GMT 13ʰ24ᵐ46ˢ, hs 15°01.'5, Zn 232°.

Required.—Identify the unknown celestial body, using Pub. No. 214.

Solution.—

	May 31			
GMT	13ʰ24ᵐ46ˢ May 31	Zn	232°	
13ʰ	83°24.'4	Z	N128°W	
24ᵐ46ˢ	6°12.'5	h	15°	
GHA Υ	89°36.'9 (subtract)	d	16°S	(from Pub. No. 214)
GHA $\star$	193°	t	52°W	(from Pub. No. 214)
SHA $\star$	103°	LHA	52°	
d	16°S	λ	141°W	
Body	Sabik	GHA	193°	

Although no formal star identification tables are included in Pub. No. 229, a simple approach to star identification is to scan the pages of the appropriate latitudes and observe the combination of arguments which give the altitude and azimuth angle of the observation. Thus the declination and LHA $\star$ are determined directly. The star's SHA is found from, SHA $\star$=LHA $\star$—LHA Υ. From these quantities the star can be identified from the *Nautical Almanac*.

Another solution is available through an interchange of arguments using the nearest integral values. The procedure consists of entering Pub. No. 229 with the observer's latitude (same name as declination), with the observed azimuth angle (converted from observed true azimuth as required) as LHA and the observed altitude as declination, and extracting from the tables the altitude and azimuth angle respondents. The extracted altitude becomes the body's declination; the extracted azimuth angle (or its supplement) is the meridian angle of the body. Note that the tables are always entered with latitude of same name as declination. In north latitudes the tables can be entered with true azimuth as LHA.

If the respondents are extracted from above the C–S Line on a right-hand page, the name of the latitude is actually contrary to that of the declination. Otherwise, the declination of the body has the same name as the latitude. If the azimuth angle respondent is extracted from above the C–S Line, the supplement of the tabular value is the meridian angle, t, of the body. If the body is east of the observer's meridian, LHA=360°−t; if the body is west of the meridian, LHA=t.

Problems

2210a. During morning twilight on June 3, 1975, the GMT 1825 (June 2) DR position of a ship is lat. 26°21′.4N, long. 157°17′.2E.

Required.—The approximate altitude and azimuth of each first magnitude star, and any planets, between altitudes 10° and 80°, using No. 2102–D.

Answer.—

Body	h	Zn
Jupiter	35°	101°
Mars	41°	111°
Fomalhaut	32°	160°
Altair	59°	242°
Vega	50°	301°
Deneb	67°	334°

2210b. At the time and place of problem 2210a an unidentified celestial body is observed through a break in the clouds. Its sextant altitude is 21°04′.1 and its azimuth is 044°.

Required.—Identify the celestial body, using No. 2102–D.

Answer.—Mirfak.

2210c. The dead reckoning latitude of a ship is 25°06′.4S. Two stars are observed in quick succession, as follows:

Star	h	Zn
Antares	57°	100°
Unidentified	52°	337°

Required.—Identify the unknown celestial body, using No. 2102–D.

Answer.— εVirginis.

2213. On June 2, 1975, the 1725 DR position of a ship is lat. 41°27′.3S, long. 158°36′.9E. About this time the navigator observes two unknown celestial bodies through breaks in the clouds, as follows: (1) GMT $6^h24^m15^s$, hs 16°34′.9, Zn 334°; (2) GMT $6^h25^m53^s$, hs 20°26′.0, Zn 334°. The second body appears to be of the first magnitude.

Required.—Identify the unknown celestial bodies, using Pub. No. 214.

Answers.—(1) Pollux, (2) Venus.

PART FOUR

THE PRACTICE OF NAVIGATION

PART FOUR

The Practice of Navigation

CHAPTER XXIII

THE PRACTICE OF MARINE NAVIGATION

2301. Introduction.—In the preceding 22 chapters, dead reckoning, piloting, and celestial navigation are discussed separately. In this chapter the interrelationship of the various elements of navigation, including radionavigation, are discussed. However, the most important element of successful navigation cannot be acquired from this book—nor from any book or instructor. The *science* of navigation can be taught, but the *art* of navigation must be acquired. Modern navigation is a blending of the two—a *scientific art*. The truly successful navigator is one who supplements his knowledge with judgment, utilizing every opportunity to improve his judgment through experience. Even with knowledge and judgment, the navigator cannot expect to be fully reliable unless he is alert, constantly evaluating the situation as it develops, avoiding dangerous situations before they arise, or recognizing them if they do occur, and always keeping "ahead of the vessel." The elements of successful navigation, then, are *knowledge*, *judgment*, and *alertness*. To the person possessing these, navigation can be a pleasure. A person who tries to navigate without them is at best a doubtful asset. He may be a menace to his vessel and shipmates.

It is not wise to attempt to reduce navigation to a series of steps that can be followed mechanically. The methods and techniques to be used are those which are applicable to the type of vessel, the equipment available, the training and experience of the navigator and any assistants, the local situation, etc. The navigation of a small craft proceeding up the Choptank River, for instance, might be quite different from that of an ocean liner entering New York harbor. Both might differ from the navigation of a naval vessel approaching an assigned anchorage. It is important that a navigator make an "estimate of the situation" and use the methods and techniques that are best adapted to the conditions at hand.

The discussion that follows is generally applicable to any vessel under average conditions, but is written primarily for an average ship which might be planning and executing an ocean voyage.

2302. Advance preparation.—The initial planning for an ocean passage includes careful study of the *Sailing Directions* (*Planning Guide*) and inspection of charts of appropriate scale with the objective of determining the route, the conditions expected to be encountered, and the speed of advance required if the passage is to be completed by a predetermined time. This planning may utilize the services of ship weather routing (ch. XXIV).

As the planning progresses, the navigator obtains an overview of the passage. When the planning is completed, the navigator has developed the intended track based upon prudent consideration of: (1) the capabilities and limitations of navigational methods and systems to be employed; (2) navigational hazards; and (3) the possibility of equipment failure and human error. The detailed planning for the approach and entry at the destination is usually deferred until some time during the transit but before making landfall.

Before getting underway, the navigator should familiarize himself with his equipment. Any defective or questionable instruments should be repaired or replaced. The necessary charts and publications should be on hand. If the voyage is to extend beyond the time range of any publication, such as an almanac or tide tables, the volume for the next period should be included, or provision should be made to acquire it before the expiration date of the current volume. Charts and light lists should be checked to see that they have been corrected through the lastest *Notice to Mariners*.

When all equipment is on hand and in suitable condition, the navigator should study his charts and publications. He should determine which soundings are in feet, which in fathoms, and whether other units are used. It is good practice to underline or circle with a colored pencil the statement of units as given on each chart. The various notes on the chart should be read, and applicable ones marked. The latitude and longitude scales should be observed and the units noted. The channels, currents, shoals, aids to navigation, and natural landmarks should be studied so that the general arrangement is familiar. Useful natural ranges should be located and marked. Where needed, turning bearings, danger angles, and danger bearings should be determined.

The tides and currents to be encountered should be determined from the tables and charts. The advice and warnings given in coast pilots or sailing directions should be read and pertinent parts marked or copied out. The light list should be studied, and the arcs of visual range for the usual height of eye drawn in. Characteristics, including shape and color of the structure, should be written on the chart, if not printed there, or in a notebook, to assist in identification. Useful radar targets, radiobeacons, Loran rates, etc., should be noted if equipment to utilize them is available. If a danger sounding is useful, it should be drawn in. The bottom configuration should be studied for distinctive features that will prove helpful in locating the position of the vessel, or keeping it in safe water. If foreign charts are to be used, the symbols should be understood.

The extent of the preliminary study depends somewhat upon the navigator's previous knowledge of the area. But however familiar he may be with local conditions, the navigator should not overlook the need for checking his equipment to be sure it is complete and up-to-date, nor to refresh his memory regarding critical items of information. The prudent navigator leaves nothing to chance and *assumes nothing that can be verified*.

In pilot waters with limited maneuvering space, the desired track might well be plotted in advance, and the predicted time between buoys, turns, etc., determined. Where repeated runs are made over the same routes, the entire track may be plotted in ink. Courses, distances between lights, visual range arcs, and other useful information might be prominently indicated. When this practice is followed, a positive routine should be set up to apply corrections and to bring these to the attention of all concerned.

2303. Getting underway.—Shortly before the ship gets underway the necessary charts, publications, and plotting equipment should be placed on the chart table. A check should be made to be sure that all marks (except those permanently plotted in ink or colored pencil) relating to a previous voyage have been erased from the charts. The navigator's binoculars should be checked to see that they are properly secured in their accustomed place on the bridge. The gyrocompasses should be started sufficiently in advance to insure proper operation, and should then be compared with the repeaters and the magnetic compass on the bridge. Gyro error should be determined before getting underway. The deviations of the magnetic compass may be unusually high because of cranes, cables, etc. A check should be made to see that the latest deviation tables are available, and that magnetic gear has not been left near the compass. Azimuth circles and peloruses should be in place and checked. The standard and emergency steering gear should be checked, as well as communication and signaling equipment. If practical, the mechanical log and electronic equipment such as radar, Loran, radio direction finder, and echo sounder should be started and checked. Radar and echo sounder errors should be determined prior to getting underway. The hand lead should be placed at a convenient location ready for immediate use. The anchor windlass should be tested. The sextant, chronometers, almanac, and tables should be checked to see that they are in their proper places. It is good practice for the navigator to prepare a check-off list to insure that nothing is overlooked. The checks should be made carefully by a responsible person who reports the results to the navigator.

Before getting underway the navigator should see that all navigational personnel are at their assigned stations and that each understands his duties. Aboard naval vessels a piloting team (normally composed of the navigator, plotter, recorder, bearing observers, echo sounder operator, and others) is usually employed when transiting restricted waters. Aboard merchant vessels in the same circumstances, the navigation may be performed by no more than the mate on watch and the helmsman. In any event, it is good practice to acquaint each person with the general plan of operation, for an informed person is less likely to make mistakes, and more likely to detect mistakes made by others.

2304. Leaving port.—In a harbor, the largest scale chart should be used for greatest accuracy and detail. The dead reckoning should be started as soon as the vessel steadies on its first course. If the desired track has not been plotted in advance, the dead reckoning is run ahead a short distance. In either event, the predicted time of arrival at the next turning bearing, or of passing the next aid to navigation is recorded on the chart. Predicted times of arrival at various points are of great importance in interpreting the information received and in avoiding dangerous situations. It is good practice to use *all* available information, and not rely solely upon a single aid. A good position should be maintained at all times. Fog may set in rapidly and without warning, obscuring landmarks before a round of bearings can be observed. Lights should be timed and identified by their characteristics. At a distance, the color and shape of buoys may not be apparent. Sometimes a sailboat can be mistaken for a buoy. Buoys may be out of position. Bearings and ranges on fixed objects are better than on floating aids which do not remain at fixed points. Soundings should be taken continuously in the vicinity of shoal water. It is good practice to check the compass and radar at convenient opportunities, as when on a range or passing between two headlands. Ranges are of great value for checking position or keeping on the desired track, and should be used whenever available.

By skillful navigation, one may be able to save many miles of steaming. However, it is possible to allow insufficient margin of safety. The navigator should always keep in mind the possibility of failure of some item of equipment, unexpected fog, or the need for maneuvering room if another vessel approaches too close. He should remember, too, that in pilot waters currents may be strong and variable.

A detailed record should be kept in a notebook. Entries should be made showing bearings and ranges, important soundings, all changes of course and speed, the times of passing important aids to navigation, and other pertinent information. The record should leave nothing in doubt, indicating whether bearings are true or by magnetic compass, whether soundings are in feet, fathoms, or meters. This record is useful in preparing the ship's log, providing guidance for future runs over the same area, establishing position if fog sets in, and in providing an acceptable record if the vessel experiences a mishap resulting in a later investigation.

The chart, also, should present a neat and intelligible record of the passage. Course lines and lines of position should be drawn boldly and neatly, and should be no longer than needed. Standard labels should be used wherever they contribute to an understanding of the plot. They should be so placed and worded that no doubt is left as to their applicability and meaning. If possible, lines and labels should not be drawn through chart symbols.

Outside the harbor, if the course is parallel to the coast, there may be advantages in remaining close enough to utilize major aids to navigation and other landmarks. However, a set toward the beach, particularly off the entrance to an estuary, can endanger the safety of a vessel. Many ships have grounded because a course was set too close to off-lying dangers.

2305. Taking departure.—When a vessel reaches the open sea and is about to leave the land astern, a last accurate position is obtained by means of landmarks available. This process is called **taking departure.** It marks the end of piloting and the beginning of the next phase of the navigation. The work of the navigator becomes less hurried, and fixes are obtained less frequently. Soundings become of less interest. The hand lead is secured. The position may be transferred from the chart to a plotting sheet. Courses and speeds will be maintained over relatively long periods. The sea routine begins. Even if the vessel is to follow the coast, it generally does so at such a distance that danger is some distance away, and fixing is an intermittent process rather than a continuous one.

2306. Navigation at sea, like piloting, varies somewhat from vessel to vessel depending upon the equipment available and the individual preferences of the navigator. A daily routine, called the **day's work,** is established by the navigator and carried out with such variations as dictated by circumstances. While details vary with the navigator, a typical minimum day's work is:

1. Plot of dead reckoning throughout the day.

2. Observation and reduction of celestial observations for a fix during morning twilight.

3. Winding of chronometers and determination of chronometer error.

4. Observation of the sun for a morning sunline (on or near the prime vertical if made at about the same time as 5).

5. Azimuth of the sun for a compass check, commonly made at about the same time as a morning sunline observation. This may be an amplitude observation at sunrise.

6. Observation of the sun at or near noon. This is crossed with a morning sunline, advanced, or with an observation of the moon or Venus to obtain a noon (ZT 1200) position.

7. Computation of the day's run (noon to noon, or midnight to midnight).

8. Observation of the sun during the afternoon (on or near the prime vertical if made at about the same time as 9). This is primarily for use with the advanced noon sunline, or with a moon or Venus line, if the skies are overcast during evening twilight.

9. Azimuth of the sun for a compass check. This is commonly made at about the same time as an afternoon sun observation, but may be an amplitude observation at sunset.

10. Computation of the time of sunset, sunrise, and twilight, and preparation of a list of stars and any planets in favorable positions for observation during each twilight period, with the approximate altitude and azimuth of each body.

11. Observation and reduction of celestial observations for a fix during evening twilight.

12. Computation of the time of moonrise and moonset (if required).

13. Use of Loran and any other available radionavigation aid on a regular schedule, as every hour.

The list of celestial bodies available for observation is customarily prepared with the aid of a star finder such as No. 2102–D (art. 2210) or volume I of Pub. No. 249.

This list is particularly helpful during evening twilight, when one desires to know where to look for the brightest stars or planets before the general pattern of stars becomes visible. Some navigators list or make a simple plot of the *relative* azimuths of the bodies, to assist in locating them. The brightest bodies may be visible at about the time of sunset, or even a little before.

In general, it is good practice to observe the brightest bodies as they appear in the evening, while the horizon is clear and sharp, and the dimmest first in the morning, before they fade from view. Cloud cover permitting, the normal practice of navigators is to observe stars in the eastern sky first. During morning twilight the eastern horizon becomes clearly defined first due to the rising sun; the dim stars above this horizon fade from view first because of the brighter eastern sky. During evening twilight the eastern horizon becomes indistinct first due to the setting sun, dictating observation of stars above this horizon first. Also, during evening twilight the bright stars in the darker eastern sky will be visible first.

Several observations should be made of each body, each sight being taken quickly to avoid eye fatigue. In general, it is better to use one good observation than to average several of questionable accuracy. At least five or six bodies should be observed. If the four most favorably situated ones provide a good fix, additional sights need not be reduced, but if doubt remains, information for obtaining additional lines is available. It is better to observe bodies all around the horizon than in the same semicircle. Thus, three bodies separated by 120° are better than three separated by 60°, for in the former case any constant error in altitude will be neutralized.

If a comparing watch is used, it should be compared with the chronometer or a time tick every time celestial observations are made. The index correction should be determined each time the sextant is used. If the horizon is used for this purpose, the measurement should be made *before* evening twilight observations and *after* morning twilight observations, while the horizon is sharp. If the horizon is not equally sharp in all directions, the best part should be used.

When skies clear after a prolonged period of overcast, or when clouds threaten to obscure the heavens, additional observations should be made, if available. During the day a series of sunlines might be obtained and advanced to a common time, or the moon or Venus might be available at a favorable azimuth. Sometimes observations can be made during the night, either by use of moonlight to illuminate the horizon, or by dark-adapting the eyes. At this time the moon, and bodies having an azimuth nearly the same as the moon, should be avoided because of the probability of false horizons on the illuminated water.

Sights may be reduced by any reliable method. The one most widely used by mariners is Pub. No. 229, used in conjunction with the *Nautical Almanac*. If a check is needed, a good practice is to use a different method and a different almanac, so that mistakes will not be repeated.

Before the development of modern sight reduction methods, celestial navigation was largely a matter of determining latitude by observation of bodies on or near the celestial meridian (including Polaris) and longitude by observation of bodies on or near the prime vertical. Longitude was computed by time sight. Frequently, this method of navigation was inconvenient. Often it produced misleading results, as when a north-south "longitude" line was used instead of the true line of position which might differ in direction by as much as 30° or more. Errors were introduced when an incorrect longitude was used for solving a reduction to the meridian, or an incorrect latitude for solving a time sight of a body some distance from the prime vertical. The use of azimuth with a time sight was an improvement, but was not well adapted to observations of celestial bodies near the celestial meridian. The modern navigator is freed from these restrictions. He is able to obtain a *line of position* extending in the correct direction almost any time a celestial body can be observed. He places no special significance upon latitude and longitude lines, and solves all sights by a common method of sight reduction.

It is good practice to use a workbook for the various solutions made at sea. This provides a valuable record which may be of inestimable value in the future. Entries should be neat, orderly, and intelligible to another navigator. All original data and computations should be included. The use of standard work forms is recommended. They are considered adequate but, for sight reduction of celestial observations, there is merit in using a form which uses a single column, so that several sights can be reduced in parallel columns. The *best* form for anyone to use is one he thoroughly understands and finds logical and least confusing. If an alteration in a work form reduces the number of errors made, it is a desirable change. Because of the difference of opinion among marine navigators, and the tendency to follow mechanically an established form without fully understanding the principles involved, a work form standardized for all navigators is probably undesirable, although such is widely used by air navigators, who use celestial navigation somewhat intermittently. When one has established the work forms he desires to use, he can have a rubber stamp made, or have the forms reproduced by printing. The former is probably preferable because it permits use of a bound workbook. However, printed forms can be punched for retention in a looseleaf binder.

At sea it is good practice to run the dead reckoning from fix to fix, determining set and drift of the current at each fix. The use of single lines of position and current to establish estimated positions is a matter of judgment. The ability to predict the difference between dead reckoning positions and fixes, which ability may be developed when the need is not apparent, can serve as a valuable asset when fixes are not available. In the U. S. Navy, the best position available is recorded in the log at 0800, 1200, and 2000. A typical plot of part of a day's run at sea (omitting possible radionavigation fixes) is shown in figure 2306.

It is good practice to compare the gyro repeaters with the steering magnetic compass each half hour and after each change of course at sea, to detect any discrepancy which may arise through malfunction. In making the comparison, one should not overlook changes in variation and deviation. The master gyrocompass should be compared with its repeaters from time to time.

One of the duties of the navigator is to inform the captain of the expected time of crossing time zone boundaries. The change of time is usually made at a convenient whole hour near the time of crossing a boundary, or during the night. Aboard some merchant ships the change is distributed equally through several watches, as 20 minutes during three consecutive watches.

It is common practice for the captain to maintain a **night order book.** Standing orders such as the conditions under which the captain is to be called, and the admonition to keep a sharp lookout, are usually given on the inside front cover. The orders for each night, if any, are recorded in order, over the captain's signature. They include items such as courses to be steered, speeds to be used, times and bearings of lights expected to be sighted, and any other pertinent navigational information. The navigator provides the captain with such information as he may require.

2307. Landfall.—After a voyage at sea, the first contact with land is of considerable importance. The accuracy with which one predicts the time and place of sighting land depends upon the accuracy of navigation. If consistent radionavigation fixes have been obtained at frequent intervals, and these positions are confirmed by a recent fix from celestial observations or other information, the prediction should be highly accurate.

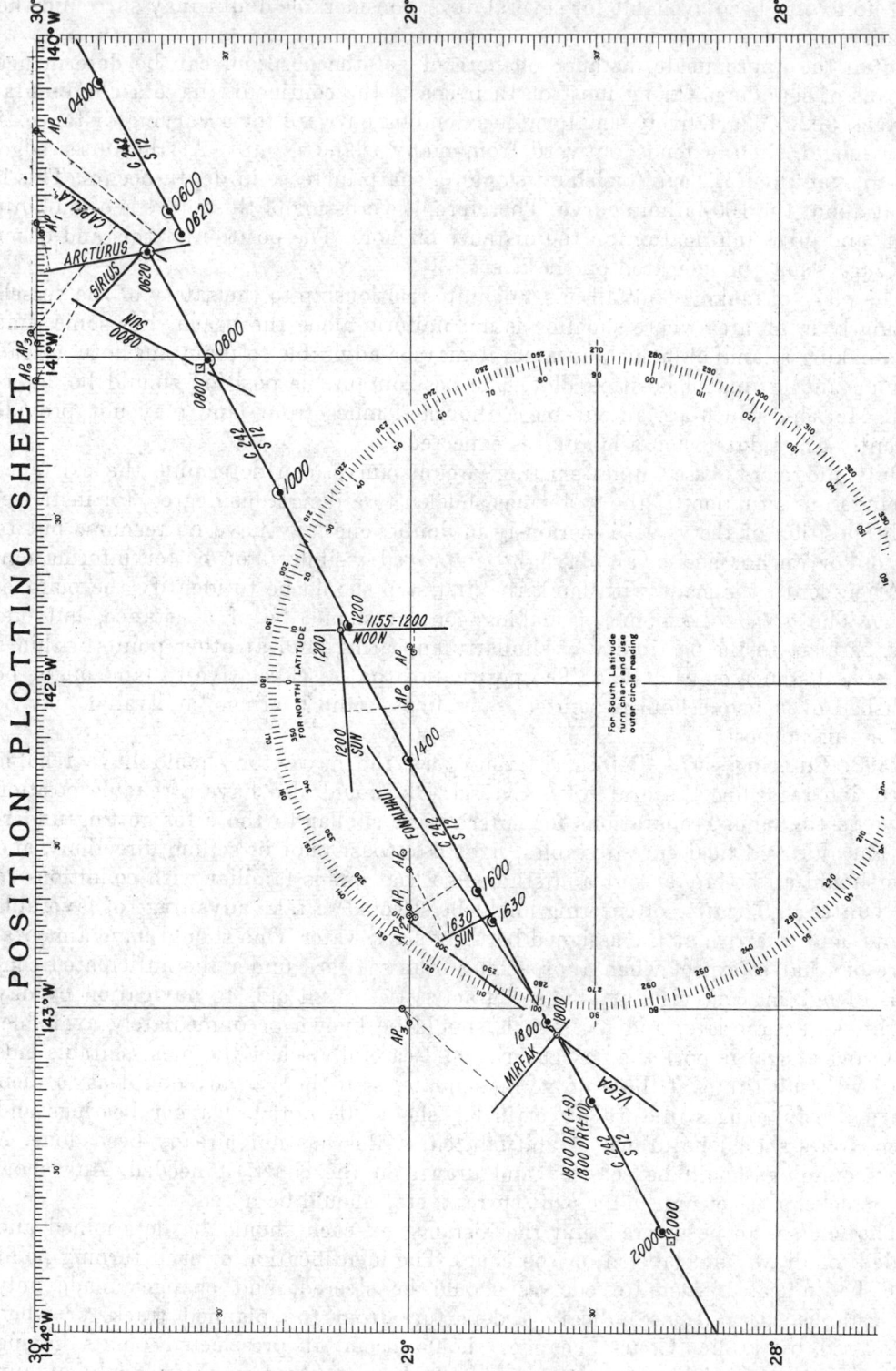

FIGURE 2306.—Typical minimum plot at sea (omitting possible radionavigation fixes).

But if no fix has been available for several days, considerable doubt may surround the landfall.

Often the approximate distance offshore, if not the position, can be determined by means of soundings. Along most of their coasts the continents have a **continental shelf** (art. 3022) of relatively shoal water extending outward for a varying distance. A similar **island shelf** extends outward from many island groups. At the outer edge, called the **continental slope** (or **island slope**), a sharp increase in depth occurs. This is often at about the 100-fathom curve. Therefore, the crossing of this curve is often quite abrupt, and gives information on the distance offshore. The position of this and other depth curves may be indicated on the chart.

The place of making landfall has a definite relationship to the safety of the vessel, particularly in an area where shoaling is not uniform along the beach. For some time before making a landfall in such an area, it may be advisable to maintain both a dead reckoning and estimated position plot. The best obtainable position should be determined. Methods which are acceptable a thousand miles from land may not provide sufficiently exact data when a landfall is expected.

Only judgment, based upon existing circumstances, can determine the existence of a dangerous situation. If the water has shoaled to a dangerous degree, for instance, and the position of the vessel is seriously in doubt, one may have no recourse but to stand off or anchor and await daylight, improved visibility, or better information.

When contact is made with land, the first step should be to identify the point of contact. The *anticipated* point of making contact should be of assistance, but one should be alert to the possibility of similarly appearing land at other points within a reasonable distance on each side. The position of the vessel relative to land might be established even before land is sighted. Soundings, radio bearings, and radar may be used for this purpose.

2308. Entering port.—Before entering port, the navigator should have reliable information regarding the draft of his vessel. He should also have a reliable position relative to the land. Preparations for entering are similar to those for getting underway. The tide and tidal current tables, light list, coast pilot or sailing directions, and charts should all be broken out and studied so that one is familiar with conditions to be encountered. The *time* of entering might be selected to take advantage of favorable currents, and to arrive at the assigned berth at slack water. One should have a mental picture of what to expect when approaching from seaward under the anticipated conditions of lighting and visibility. The characteristics of all aids to navigation by day or night, as appropriate, and fog signals should be known or immediately available. In entering a strange port the navigator should carefully select the most suitable aids to use, with substitutes if these prove inadequate, or if there is any doubt as to their identity. Useful ranges, natural or artificial, should be noted. Danger bearings and danger circles should be drawn in and labeled, if this has not already been done. A danger sounding should be selected and drawn on the chart, if needed. Any shoal areas, wrecks, areas of unusually swift current, etc., should be noted.

The courses to be steered and the distance on each should be determined and recorded, or drawn and labeled on the chart. The identification of each turning point should be indicated. Definite courses should be steered, and changes made only when established positions indicate a departure from the planned track, or when necessitated by traffic. Course changes should occur at preselected points having definite identification. The position should not be permitted to be in doubt at any time, even in ports which are familiar to the navigator and considered easy to enter. Most avoidable groundings are caused by erroneous assumptions which should have been verified. The position should be checked frequently, using the most reliable information available. This may seem to be an unnecessary refinement, but in an emergency a position might be needed at a time when it cannot be obtained. When changes of course are ordered, it is good practice to indicate the amount and direction of change, or the new course, to avoid the possibility of having one's attention diverted at the moment the order should be given to check the swing or steady on the new course. In general, course changes are best made when a given aid to navigation or other landmark is abeam, or when the ship is on a range.

If it becomes necessary to pass between visible dangers without suitable marks for obtaining fixes, a track midway between dangers can be followed by eye more accurately than one closer to either side. If a vessel is to pass near reefs or shoals, it is sometimes possible to observe these from a position aloft, particularly if the sun is astern.

The actual navigation while entering port is similar to that when leaving port. A typical plot in pilot waters is shown in figure 2308. The entering of pilot waters should be accompanied by a mental reorientation and an increased alertness. The use of a local pilot, unless this is a mandatory requirement, is a matter which should be decided in each case. Whether or not a pilot is used, local harbor regulations should be followed, for the presence of a pilot does not relieve the master of his responsibility. One should not forget to note the time of entering the area where local or inland rules of the road apply.

Speed in the vicinity of wharves, construction work, dredges, small boats, etc., should be carefully controlled to avoid damage to them.

If the vessel anchors, the anchorage should be selected carefully, considering local regulations as well as suitability and safety, including the holding qualities of the bottom. If there is any doubt as to the depth of water, a boat might be sent in ahead to take soundings. If space is limited, the approach to the anchorage should be planned and executed carefully. As soon as the anchor is let go, the position should be determined accurately. Bearings of a number of prominent landmarks and lights should be measured and recorded, as a guide in determining whether or not the vessel drags anchor. A **drag circle** is helpful. Using the position of the anchor as its center, the drag circle is constructed with a radius equal to the scope plus the distance from the hawsepipe to the point of observation. A **swing circle,** with radius equal to the scope plus vessel's length, may also be helpful.

2309. Fog.—During periods of reduced visibility, the navigator's work is more difficult. At sea he is prevented from making celestial observations. Even when the fog is so shallow that celestial bodies are visible, the horizon is not available as a reference. An artificial-horizon sextant may prove of some value at such a time, but unless the sea is almost a flat calm, the results are likely to be less reliable than the dead reckoning. Radio aids to navigation are affected little by fog. Unless the vessel is approaching land, there is generally no cause for concern regarding the navigation, the principal danger being one of collision with other vessels. Usually the navigator merely waits for the fog to lift.

When a coast is approached, however, a wait may be impractical. The safety of the vessel requires reliable positional information. Along a coast where the shoaling is gradual, the echo sounder can be of great assistance in indicating the distance off. But along a coast having abrupt shoaling, the first indication of shallow water may be obtained so close to the beach that action to avoid grounding is not possible. If radio aids such as Loran, radio direction finder, and radar are available, they can provide useful information. If the vessel is near enough to a shore with steep cliffs, the echo of the vessel's whistle may provide indication of the distance off.

The decision of whether to enter a fogbound harbor should be made carefully. Once committed to the channel, the vessel may have no alternative but to continue on

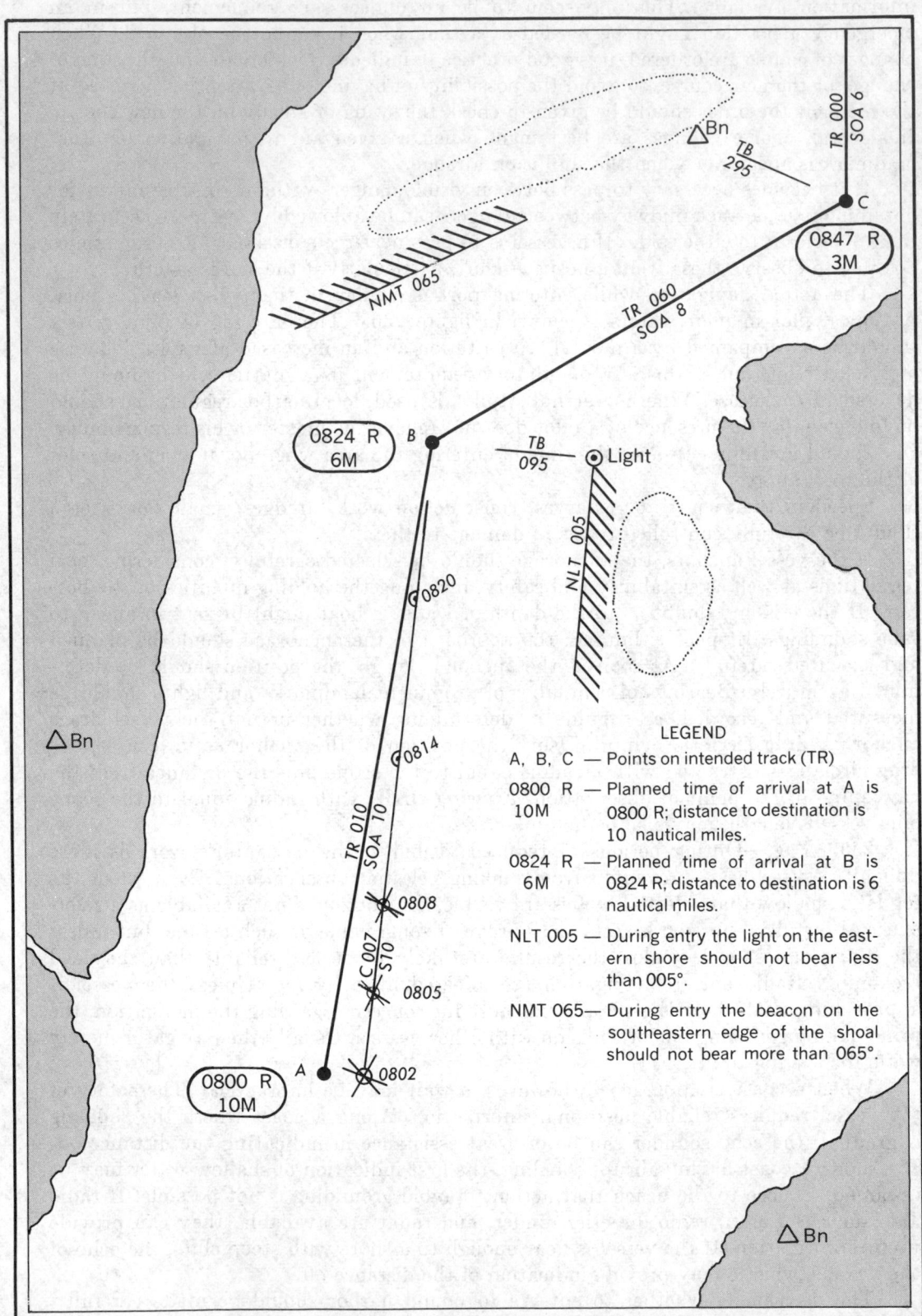

FIGURE 2308.—Typical plot in pilot waters.

to the anchorage or wharf, for in some areas there is not room to turn back, and anchoring is unsafe. It is sometimes wiser to stand off or anchor for a few hours than to risk danger of grounding or collision.

If the decision is made to enter, one should be prepared for any reasonable eventuality. The proximity of danger and the presence of currents make necessary the maintenance of a good position at all times. Fog limits the number of objects that can be used for fixing position, and destroys the overall view of the area. The radio direction finder and radar, both shipborne and shore-based, have done much to reduce the hazard due to fog, but they have not eliminated it. The need for special precautions and increased vigilance is still present.

During periods of reduced visibility the practice of steering exact courses, with precise changes at definite points, is of great assistance in pilot waters. If the vessel is following a channel, each buoy should be located successively. If the fog is dense, this requires careful steering and attention to all details, such as indications of current, changes of wind, etc. If a single buoy is missed, consideration should be given to anchoring and waiting for improved visibility.

With the possible exception of radar, the most important navigational aid during fog in pilot waters is the echo sounder or hand lead. Continuous soundings, compared with the chart, can provide valuable information on the position and safety of the vessel. The decision as to whether to plot a line of soundings on transparent material, or along the edge of a piece of paper, and compare this with the chart is a matter of judgment. In general, the procedure is valuable when approaching a harbor or proceeding in an open part of a large bay, but in a channel or other restricted waters the method is not needed and might prove distracting.

During fog one should keep a sharp lookout for any objects that might appear momentarily through thin places in the fog. It is well to have a lookout stationed aloft, and another in the bow, for the visibility may vary with height.

The lookouts and all persons on the bridge should listen intently for fog signals. As soon as such a signal is heard, an effort should be made to identify its source and determine its bearing. However, experience in the use of sound signals indicates that they are not wholly reliable. In particular, relative intensity of a sound is not a reliable indication of its distance, or whether the distance is increasing or decreasing. A signal may be totally inaudible in certain areas close to its source. Neither is its apparent direction always a correct indication of its actual direction. A fog signal may not be in operation when fog is present a short distance from a station but is unobserved from it. Transmission of sound through water is subject to uncertainties due principally to differences in density in different parts of the sea, causing the sound to be deflected.

It is well to remember that at reduced speed the relative effect of current is correspondingly greater, since the effect of current is proportional to time, not to the speed of the vessel.

2310. Navigation of small craft.—In principle, the navigation of small craft is the same as that of a large ship, but because of the shallower draft, greater maneuverability, and possible limitations of equipment of small craft, there are important differences. Small craft spend most of their time within sight of land, where navigation is largely a matter of piloting. They generally skirt the beach close enough to be able to reach safety in case of storm or fog, and since most of them are used primarily for pleasure, there is a natural tendency for the navigation to be a less continuous process than in larger craft.

The equipment carried and the type of navigation employed depend primarily upon the use of the craft and the preference of the user. If a rowboat, canoe, or small sailboat is to be used only close to the shore in good weather, "seaman's eye" might be sufficient for all navigational purposes. But if there is any possibility of the craft being out in a fog, or proceeding to greater distances from shore, fog-signalling apparatus, a compass, and some means of taking soundings should be carried.

A wide variety of equipment is available for yachts, and from this, suitable items can be selected. A minimum list should include a compass, pelorus, charts, plotting equipment (many types are available), means for determining speed or distance, log book, tide and tidal current tables, light list, coast pilot or sailing directions, hand lead, binoculars, flashlight, and fog-signal apparatus. A barometer and thermometer are useful.

Several items of electronic equipment, some of which are relatively inexpensive, are available for use in small craft, to aid in navigation and increase safety. The principal item of radio equipment, from the standpoint of safety, is a marine radiotelephone, which in addition to providing normal communication to other boats and the shore, permits the boat carrying it to call for help in distress, and assists in the location of the distressed vessel. The radio direction finder is a simple device requiring little power, an important factor on small craft. A multiband direction finder may be used as a second receiver in the broadcast and radiotelephone bands. Portable broadcast receivers permit reception of weather information on even the smallest boats. For larger craft, where ample power is available, radar and Loran may be good investments. In addition, every small craft should carry a corner reflector (art. 4201), so as more readily to reflect radar signals. In an emergency a metal bucket might be of some value as a reflector.

If the craft is to proceed out of sight of land for more than short intervals, celestial navigation equipment should be carried. This includes a sextant, an accurate timepiece, an almanac, sight reduction tables, and perhaps a star finder. If there is doubt as to advisability of including some item of equipment, the safer decision is to include it. It is better to have unused equipment than to risk danger of becoming lost because of lack of needed equipment.

The practice of navigation in small craft varies even more widely than the equipment carried. The variation extends from complete navigation similar to that of a large ocean steamer to no navigation other than by eye. The completeness of the navigation should fit the circumstances. There is an understandable tendency among small craft navigators of limited experience to underestimate the need for thorough and complete navigation. In general, it is good practice for the navigator of a small craft to establish the routine of always following definite courses from buoy to buoy or from landmark to landmark, so that the sudden onset of low visibility will not find him unable to proceed to safety without delay. He should change course at established points, maintain knowledge of his position at all times, and have reliable information on the deviation of his compass. There is a place in small craft navigation for a complete, accurate, neat plot. Where this is impractical because of heavy weather or limited plotting space, a careful log and dead reckoning by table 3 should be substituted.

The accounts given in yachting magazines, and the large number of calls for assistance received by the Coast Guard, indicate an inadequacy of the navigation of many small craft. Part of this is due to a lack of appreciation of the need for careful navigation. Much of it is due to lack of knowledge on the part of the small craft owner. The decision to omit some part of navigation should stem from knowledge, not ignorance. To the adequately informed, navigation can be part of the pleasure of yachting.

CHAPTER XXIV

SHIP WEATHER ROUTING

2401. Introduction.—*Ship weather routing* is a procedure whereby an optimum route is developed based on the forecasts of weather and seas and the ship's characteristics for a particular transit. Within specified limits of weather and sea conditions, the term optimum is used to mean maximum safety and crew comfort, minimum fuel consumption, minimum time underway, or any desired combination of these factors.

The ship routing agency, acting as an advisory service, attempts to avoid or reduce the effects of adverse weather and sea conditions on a ship by issuing initial route recommendations prior to sailing, recommendations for track changes while underway (diversions), and weather advisories to alert the commanding officer or master with respect to approaching unfavorable weather and sea conditions which cannot be effectively avoided by a diversion. Adverse weather and sea conditions are defined as those conditions which will cause a significant speed reduction or time loss, for example, speed reduced by one third or a lesser speed reduction causing a loss of at least 6 hours transit time.

The initial route recommendation is based on a survey of weather and sea forecasts between the point of departure and the destination and takes into account the hull type, speed capability, cargo, and loading conditions. The ship's progress is continually monitored and, if adverse weather and sea conditions are forecast along the ship's current track, a recommendation for a diversion is normally transmitted to the ship. By this process of initial route selection and continued monitoring of the ship's progress for possible change in relation to the forecast weather and sea conditions along a route, it is possible to maximize ship's speed and safety.

In providing optimum sailing conditions, the advisory service also attempts to reduce transit time by avoiding the adverse conditions which may be encountered on a shorter route; or if the forecasts permit, diverting to a shorter track to take advantage of favorable weather and sea conditions. The greatest potential advantage for this ship weather routing exists when: (1) the passage is relatively long, generally about 1500 miles or more; (2) the waters are navigationally unrestricted so that there is a choice of routes (alternatively, navigational restrictions are limiting but at the same time offer possible protection from adverse weather); and (3) weather is a factor in determining the route to be followed.

The use of this advisory service in no way should relieve the commanding officer or master of responsibility for prudent seamanship and safe navigation. There is no intent by the routing agency to inhibit the exercise of professional judgement, capabilities, and the prerogatives of commanding officers and masters.

The purpose of this chapter is to acquaint the mariner with the basic philosophy and procedures of ship weather routing as an aid to his understanding of the ship routing agency's recommendations. This information should enhance his ability to determine the correct course of action when encountering a hostile environment.

2402. Development.—Today, ship weather routing uses modern weather forecasting techniques and computer procedures to provide optimum routes. It has only been with the recent advent of extended range forecasting and the development of selective climatology that a ship routing system has been possible. The ability to effectively advise ships to take advantage of favorable wind, seas, and ocean currents had been hampered previously by forecast limitations and the lack of an effective communications system with which to advise the commanding officer or master.

Prior to World War II all development work was in the area of data accumulation and climatology. Benjamin Franklin, as deputy postmaster general of the British Colonies in North America produced a chart of the Gulf Stream from information supplied by masters of New England whaling ships. This first mapping of the Gulf Stream helped improve the mail packet service between the British Colonies and England. In some passages the sailing time was reduced by as much as 14 days over routes previously sailed. In the mid-19th century, Lieutenant Matthew Fontaine Maury, USN, compiled large amounts of atmospheric and oceanographic data from ships' log books (art. 117). For the first time a climatology of ocean weather and currents of the world was available to the mariner. This information was used by Maury to develop seasonally recommended routes for sailing ships and early steam powered vessels in the latter half of the century. In many cases, Maury's charts were proved correct by the savings in transit time. On one trade route alone, the average transit time from New York to California around Cape Horn was reduced from 183 days to 139 days with the use of his recommended seasonal routes.

In the 1950's the concept of ship weather routing was put into operation by several private meteorological groups and by the U. S. Navy. By applying the available surface and upper air forecasts to transoceanic shipping, it was possible to effectively avoid much of the heavy weather while generally sailing shorter routes than previously.

Optimum Track Ship Routing (OTSR), the ship routing service of the U. S. Navy, utilizes short range and extended range forecasting techniques in the route selection and surveillance procedures. The short range dynamic forecasts of 3 to 5 days are derived from the meteorological primitive equations. These forecasts are computed twice daily from a data base of northern hemisphere surface and upper air observations, and include surface pressure, upper air constant pressure heights, and the spectral wave values. A significant increase in data input, particularly from derived satellite information over ocean areas, can be expected to extend the time period for which these forecasts are useful.

For extended range forecasting, generally 3 to 14 days, a computer searches a library of historical northern hemisphere surface pressure and 500 millibar analyses for an analogous weather pattern. This is an attempt at selective climatology by matching the current weather pattern with past weather patterns and providing a logical sequence-of-events forecast for the 10- to 14-day period following the dynamic forecast. It is performed for both the Atlantic and Pacific Oceans using climatological data for the entire period of data stored on tape (30 years in use in 1977). For longer ocean transits, monthly climatological values of wind, seas, fog, and ocean currents are used to further extend the time range.

Aviation was first in applying the principle of minimum time tracks (MTT) to a changing wind field. But the problem of finding an MTT for a specific flight is much simpler than for a transoceanic ship passage. This is because aircraft flight time is only hours, while the ship transit time is usually 7 to 14 days or more. Thus, marine minimum time tracks require significantly longer range forecasts to effectively develop a best weather-least cost route.

Automation has enabled ship routing agencies to develop realistic minimum time tracks. Computation of minimum time tracks for proposed transits or ships already underway makes use of:

1. a navigation system to compute route distance, time enroute, estimated times

of arrival (ETA's), and to provide 6 hourly DR synoptic positions for the range of the dynamic forecasts for the ship's current track;

2. a surveillance system which surveys the environmental factors of wind, seas, fog, and ocean currents obtained from the dynamic and climatological fields;

3. an environmental constraint system imposed as part of the route selection and surveillance process. Constraints are the upper limits of wind and seas desired for the transit and are determined by the ship's loading, speed capability, and vulnerability. The constraint system is an important part of the route selection process and acts as a warning system when the weather and sea forecast along the present track is such that the ship is expected to transit an area which exceeds those predetermined limits;

4. ship performance curves, or speed curves, used to approximate ship's speed of advance (SOA) while transiting the forecast sea states.

Ship weather routing services are being offered as an aid to shipping by the governments of many nations. These include Japan, United Kingdom, Union of Soviet Socialist Republics, Netherlands, Federal Republic of Germany, and the United States. Also, several private firms provide the service to shipping industry clients.

2403. Ship and cargo considerations.—Ship and cargo characteristics have a significant influence on the application of ship weather routing. Ship size, speed capability, and type of cargo are important considerations in the route selection process prior to sailing and the surveillance procedure while underway. These ship characteristic factors help to identify the degree of vulnerability to potential adverse conditions and the ship's ability to effectively avoid the adverse weather and seas by diversion.

Generally, ships with higher speed capability and less cargo encumbrances will have shorter routes and be better able to maintain near normal SOA's than ships with lower speed capability or cargos which may generate unfavorable ship motions resulting from wind and sea conditions. Some routes are unique because of the type of ship or cargo. Avoiding one element of weather such as heavy head or beam seas to reduce pounding or rolling may be of prime importance. For example, a 20-knot ship with a deck cargo may be severely hampered in its ability to maintain a 20-knot SOA in any seas exceeding moderate head or beam seas because of the greater ship motions or other effects resulting from the deck load's characteristics. A similar ship without the deck load is not as vulnerable to these same or higher sea conditions and is able to nearly maintain the 20-knot SOA. In towing operations, a tug is more vulnerable to adverse weather and sea conditions, not only in consideration for the tow, but also because of its already limited speed capability and the difficulty in effectively avoiding adverse weather and sea conditions by a diversion.

Ship performance curves (speed curves) are used to estimate the ship's SOA while transiting the forecast sea states. The curves indicate the effect of head, beam, and following seas of various significant wave heights on the ship's speed. Figure 2403 is a performance curve prepared for an 18-knot vessel.

With the aid of the speed curves it is possible to determine just how costly a diversion will be in terms of the required distance and time. A diversion may not be necessary where the duration of the adverse conditions is limited. In this case, it may be better to ride out the weather and seas knowing that a diversion, even if able to maintain the normal SOA, will not overcome the increased distance and time required by the diversion.

At other times, the diversion track is less costly because it avoids an area of adverse weather and sea conditions while being able to maintain normal SOA even though the distance to destination is increased. Based on input data for environmental conditions and ship's behavior, route selection and surveillance techniques seek to achieve the optimum balance between time and distance and acceptable environmental and sea-

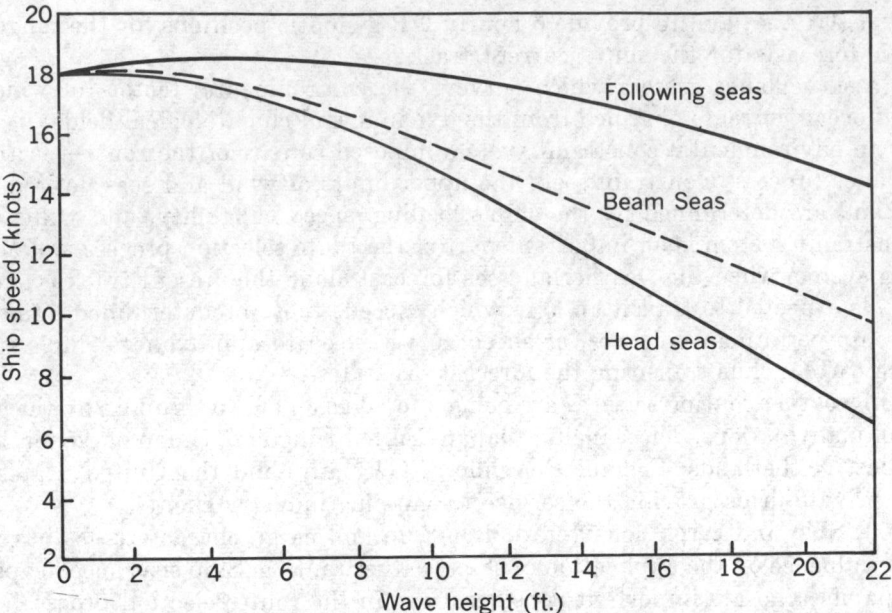

FIGURE 2403.—Performance curves for head, beam, and following seas (18-knot vessel).

keeping conditions. Although speed performance curves are an aid to the ship routing agency, the response by mariners to deteriorating weather and sea conditions is not uniform. Some reduce speed voluntarily or change heading sooner than others when unfavorable conditions are encountered. Certain waves with characteristics such that the ship's bow and stern are in successive crests and troughs present special problems for the mariner. Being nearly equal to the ship's length, such wavelengths may induce very dangerous stresses. The degree of hogging and sagging may be more apparent to the mariner than to the ship routing agency. Therefore, adjustment in course and speed for a more favorable ride may be initiated by the commanding officer or master when this situation is encountered.

    2404. Environmental factors of importance to ship weather routing are those elements of the atmosphere and ocean that may produce a change in the status of a ship transit. In ship routing, consideration is given to wind, seas, fog, ice, and ocean currents. While all of the environmental factors are important for route selection and surveillance, optimum routing is normally considered attained if the effects of wind and seas can be optimized.

    The effect of wind speed on ship performance is in some respects difficult to determine. In light winds (less than 20-knots), ships lose speed in headwinds and gain speed slightly in following winds. For higher wind speeds, ship speed is reduced in both head and following winds. This is due to the increased wave action and indicates the importance of sea conditions in determining ship performance. In dealing with wind, it is also necessary to know the ship's sail area. For example, high winds will have a greater adverse effect on a large, fully loaded container ship than a large, fully loaded tanker of similar length.

    Wave height is the major factor affecting ship performance. Wave action is responsible for ship motions that reduce propeller thrust. The relationship of ship speed to wave direction and height is similar to that of wind. Head seas reduce ship speed, while following seas increase ship speed only slightly. In heavy seas, exact performance may be difficult to predict because of the adjustments to course and speed for shiphandling and comfort. Although the effect of sea and swell is much greater than wind, it is difficult to separate the two in ship routing.

In an effort to provide a more detailed description of the actual and forecast sea state, Fleet Numerical Weather Central, Monterey, California, uses the Spectral Ocean Wave Model (SOWM) for the U. S. Navy's Optimum Track Ship Routing service. The spectral wave model provides energy values from 12 different directions (30° sectors) and 15 frequency bands for wave periods from 6 to 26 seconds with the total wave energy being propagated throughout the grid system as a function of direction and frequency. It is based on the analyzed and forecast planetary boundary layer model wind fields and is produced for the Northern Hemisphere. For OTSR purposes, primary and secondary waves are derived from the spectral wave program, where the primary wave train has the principal energy (direction and frequency), and the secondary has to be 20 percent of the primary.

Fog, while not directly affecting ship performance, should be avoided as much as feasible in order to maintain normal speed in safe conditions. Extensive areas of fog during summertime can be avoided by selecting a lower latitude route than one based solely upon wind and seas. Although the route may be longer, transit time may be less due to not having to reduce speed in areas of very low visibility for safety considerations.

Ocean currents do not present a significant routing problem, but they can be a determining factor in route selection and diversion. This is especially true when the points of departure and destination are at relatively low latitude. The important considerations to be evaluated are the difference in distance between a great-circle route and a route selected for optimum current, with the expected increase in SOA from the following current, and the decreased probability of a diversion for weather and seas at the lower latitude. For example, it has proven beneficial to remain equatorward of approximately 22°N for westbound passages between the Canal Zone and southwest Pacific ports. For eastbound passages, if the maximum latitude on a great-circle track from the southwest Pacific to the Canal Zone is below 24°N, a route passing near the axis of the Equatorial Countercurrent is practical because the increased distance is offset by favorable current. Direction and speed of ocean currents are more predictable than wind and seas, but some variableness is to be expected. Major ocean currents can be disrupted for several days by very intense weather systems such as hurricanes and typhoons.

The problem of ice is twofold: floating ice (icebergs) and deck ice (art. 3826). If possible, areas of icebergs or pack ice should be avoided because of the difficulty of detection and the potential for disaster. Deck ice may be more difficult to contend with from a ship routing point of view because it is caused by freezing weather associated with a large weather system. While mostly a nuisance factor on large ships, it may cause significant problems with the stability of small ships.

Generally, the higher the latitude of a route, even in the summer, the greater are the problems with the environment. Certain operations should benefit from seasonal planning as well as optimum routing. For example, towing operations poleward of about 40° latitude should be avoided in non-summer months as much as possible.

2405. Synoptic weather considerations.—A ship routing agency should direct its forecasting skills to avoiding or limiting the effect of weather and seas associated with extratropical low pressure systems in the mid or higher latitudes and the tropical systems in low latitudes by route selection and diversion. Seasonal or monsoon weather is also a definite factor in route selection and diversion in certain areas of the world's oceans.

Despite the amount of attention and publicity given to tropical cyclones, mid-latitude low pressure systems generally present more difficult problems to a ship routing agency. This is primarily due to the fact that major ship traffic is sailing in the latitudes of the migrating low pressure systems and the amount of potential exposure to intense weather systems, especially in winter, is much greater.

Low pressure systems weaker than gale intensity (winds less than 34 knots) are not a severe problem for most ships. However, a relatively weak system may generate prolonged periods of rough seas which are uncomfortable and may hamper normal work aboard ship. Ship weather routing can frequently limit rough conditions to short periods of time and provide more favorable conditions for most of the transit. Relatively small ships, tugs with tows, low powered ships, and ships with sensitive cargoes can be significantly affected by weather systems weaker than gale intensity. Use of a routing agency, or at least giving careful attention to the latest weather information, is considered very prudent and can be beneficial.

Gales (winds 34 to 47 knots) and storms (winds greater than 48 knots) are of such intensity that they generate very rough or high seas which force a reduction in speed in order to gain a more comfortable and safe ride. Because of the extensive geographic area covered by a well developed, intense, low pressure system, once ship's speed is reduced, the ability to improve the ship's situation is severely hampered. Thus, exposure to potential damage and danger is greatly increased. A recommendation for a diversion by a routing agency, well in advance of the intense weather and associated seas, will limit the duration of exposure of the ship to potential problems. If effective, ship speed will not be reduced and satisfactory progress will be maintained, even though the remaining distance to destination is increased. Overall transit time is usually shorter than if no track change had been made and the ship had remained in heavy weather. In some cases diversions are made to avoid adverse weather conditions and shorten the track at the same time. Significant savings can be the result.

In very intense low pressure systems with high winds and long duration over a long fetch, seas will be generated and propagated as swell over considerable distances. Even on a diversion, it is difficult to effectively avoid all unfavorable conditions. Generally, original routes for transoceanic passages issued by the U. S. Navy's ship routing service are equatorward of the 10% frequency isoline for gale force winds for the month of transit as interpreted from the *U. S. Navy Marine Climatic Atlas of the World*. These are shown in figures 2405a and 2405b for the Pacific. To avoid the area of significant gale activity in the Atlantic from October to April, the latitude of transit is generally in the lower thirties.

The areas and seasons and, to some degree, the probability of development of tropical cyclones are fairly well defined in climatological publications. In long range planning considerable benefit can be gained by limiting the exposure to the potential hazards of tropical systems.

For routing in the North Pacific it has proven very helpful to provide routes which avoid the areas with the greatest probability of tropical cyclone formation. Avoiding existing tropical cyclones with a history of 24 hours or more of 6-hourly warnings is in most cases relatively straightforward. The concern is largely the price to pay in added time and distance to maintain satisfactory conditions. However, when transiting the tropical cyclone generating area the ship under routing may provide the first report of environmental conditions indicating that a new disturbance is developing. In the eastern North Pacific the generating area for a high percentage of tropical cyclones is relatively compact (fig. 2405c). It has proven beneficial on certain ocean transits (Canal Zone to or from mid or western North Pacific ports) to remain equatorward of a line from lat. 9°N, long. 90°W to lat. 14°N, long. 115°W. In the western North Pacific, again depending on the point of departure or destination, it is advisable to hold north of 22°N when no tropical systems are known to exist (fig. 2405d).

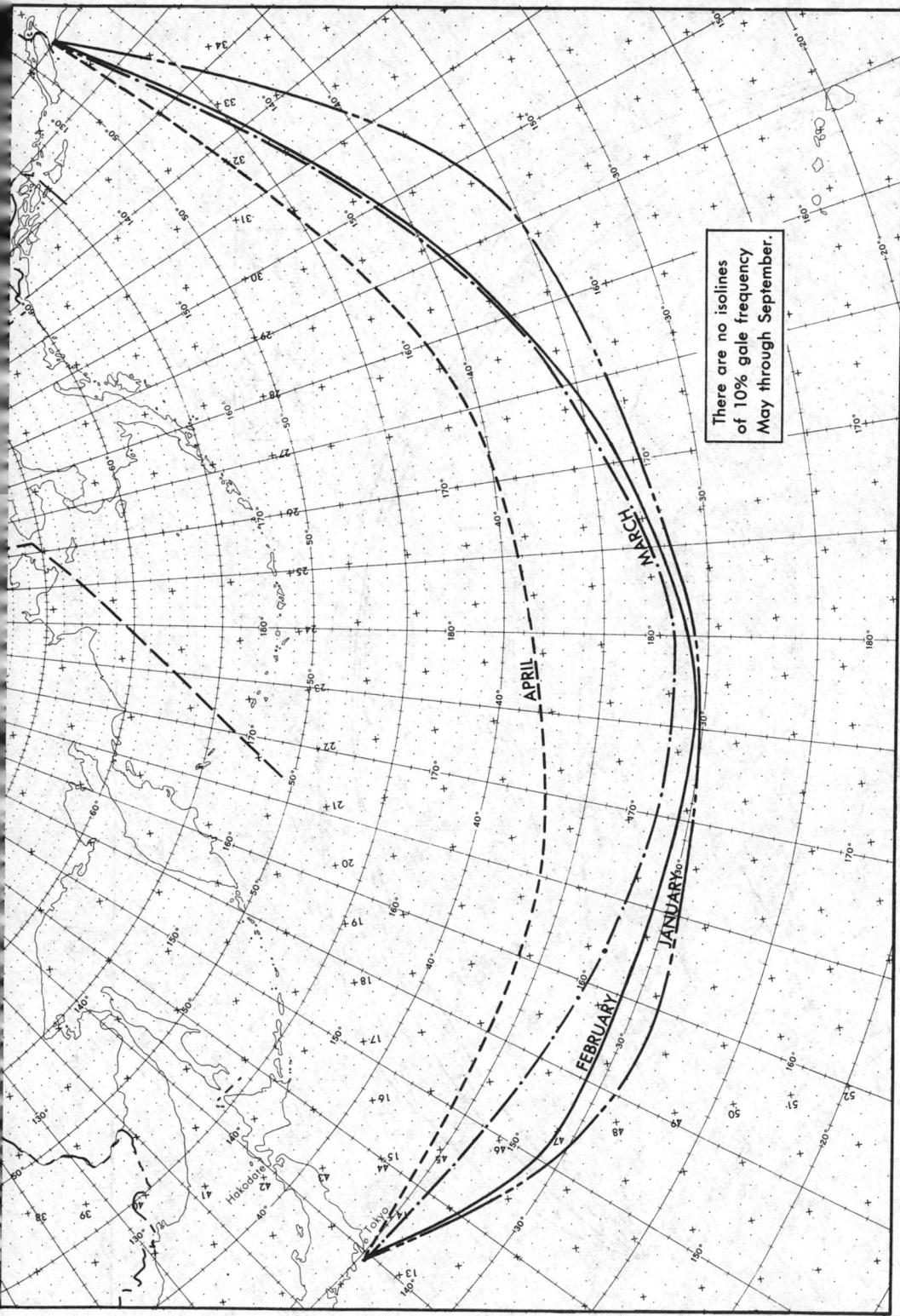

There are no isolines
of 10% gale frequency
May through September.

FIGURE 2405a.—Generalized 10% frequency isolines of gale force winds for January through April.

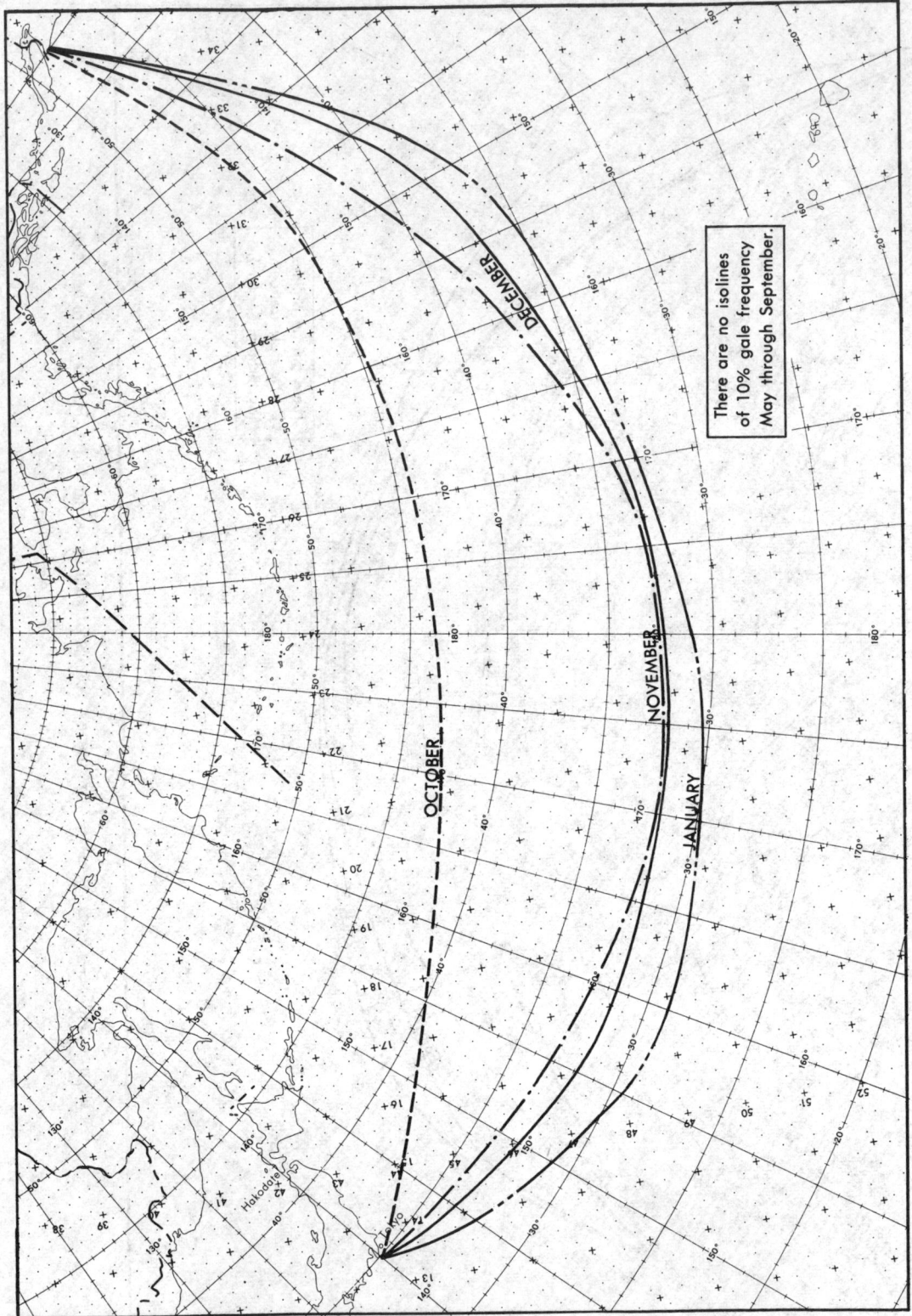

There are no isolines
of 10% gale frequency
May through September.

FIGURE 2405b.—Generalized 10% frequency isolines of gale force winds for October through April.

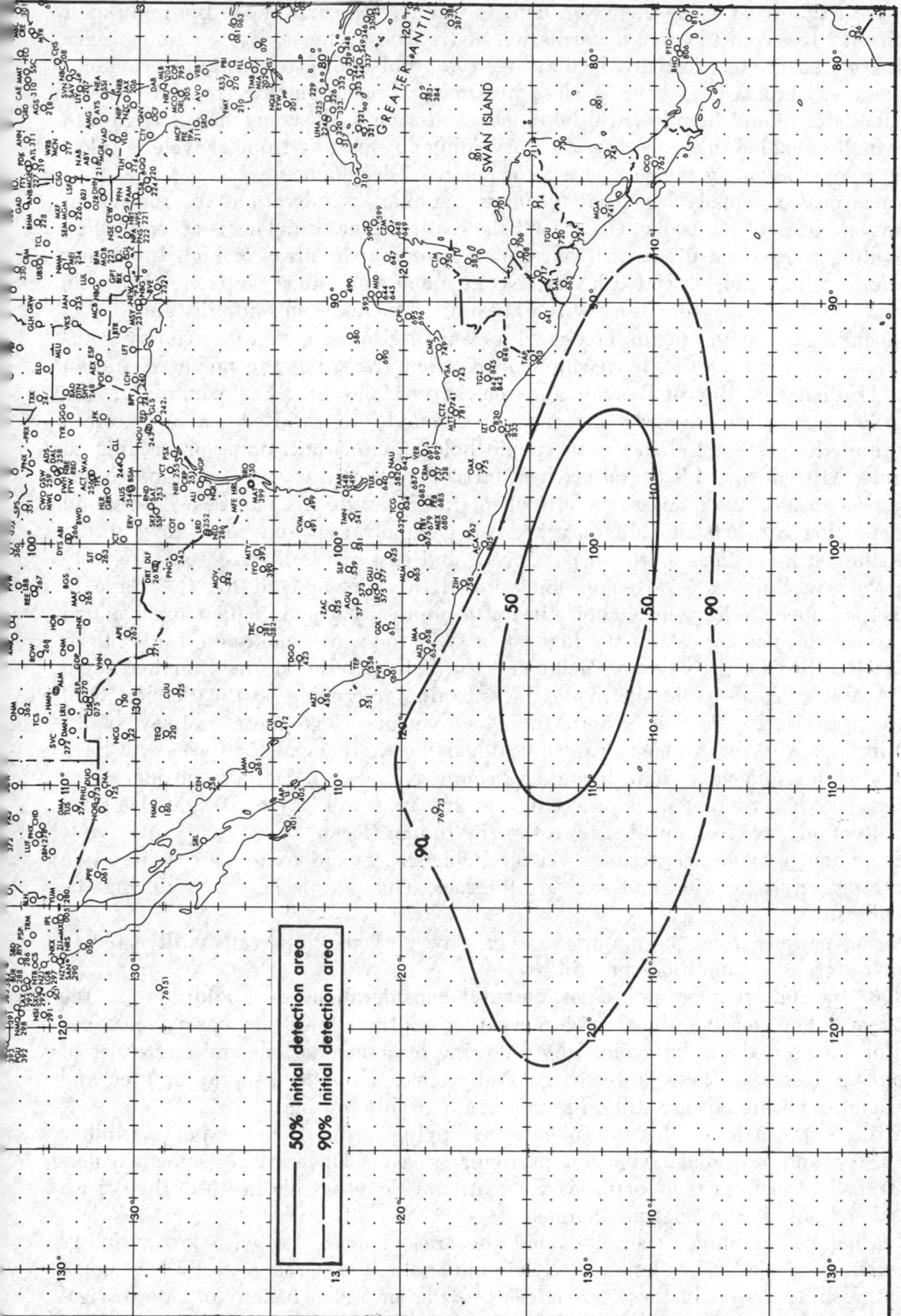

FIGURE 2405c.— Area of initial detection of high percentage of tropical cyclones which later developed to tropical storm or hurricane intensity, 1957–1974 (after Bowman and Renard).

In the Atlantic, it is considered prudent to sail near the axis of the Bermuda high or northward to avoid the area of formation of tropical cyclones. By remaining clear of these generating areas initially, it alleviates the problem of attempting to provide a diversion to a ship that may be in close proximity to a developing tropical system. Also, the distance and time lost will be much greater on a diversion than if the route had originally avoided the generating area. Avoiding any existing tropical cyclone takes precedence over avoiding the general area of potential development.

It has proven equally beneficial to employ similar considerations for routing in the monsoon areas of the Indian Ocean and the South China Sea. This is accomplished by providing routes and diversions that generally avoid the areas of high frequency of gale force winds and associated heavy seas as much as feasible. Ships are then able to remain in satisfactory conditions with only limited increases in route distance.

Depending upon the points of departure and destination, there are many combinations of routes that can be recommended when transiting the northern Indian Ocean (Arabian Sea, Bay of Bengal) and the South China Sea. For example, in the Arabian Sea during the summer monsoon, routes to and from the Red Sea, the western Pacific, and the eastern Indian Ocean should hold equatorward. Ships proceeding to the Persian Gulf during this period are held farther south and west, attempting to put the heaviest seas on the quarter or stern when transiting the Arabian Sea. Eastbound ships departing the Persian Gulf may proceed generally east southeast toward the Indian sub-continent then south, to pass north and east of the highest southwesterly seas in the Arabian Sea. Westbound ships out of the Persian Gulf for the Cape of Good Hope appear to have little choice in routes unless considerable distance is added to the transit by passing east of the highest seas. In the winter monsoon, routes to or from the Red Sea for the western Pacific and the Indian Ocean are held farther north in the Arabian Sea to avoid the highest seas. Ships proceeding to the Persian Gulf from the western Pacific and eastern Indian Ocean may hold more eastward when proceeding north in the Arabian Sea. Ships departing the Persian Gulf area will have considerably less difficulty than during the summer monsoon. Similar considerations can be given when routing ships proceeding to and from the Bay of Bengal. Refer to sailing directions for recommended routes in the Indian Ocean.

In the South China Sea, transits via the Palawan Passage are given consideration when strong, opposing wind and seas are forecast. This is especially true during the winter monsoon.

During periods when the major monsoon flow is slack, ships can be diverted to the shortest track as conditions permit.

2406. Special weather and environmental considerations.—In addition to the synoptic weather considerations in ship weather routing, there are special environmental problems that can be avoided by following recommendations and advisories of ship routing agencies. These problems generally cover a smaller geographic area and are seasonal in nature but are still quite important to ship routing.

In the North Atlantic, because of heavy shipping traffic, frequent poor visibility in rain or fog, and restricted navigation, particularly east of Dover Strait, some mariners prefer transit to or from the North Sea via Pentland Firth passing north of the British Isles rather than via the English Channel.

Weather routed ships generally avoid the area of dense fog with low visibility in the vicinity of the Grand Banks off Newfoundland and the area east of Japan north of 35°N. Fishing vessels in these two areas provide an added hazard to safe navigation. This condition exists primarily from June through August and sometimes into September. Arctic supply ships en route from the U. S. east coast to the Davis Strait-

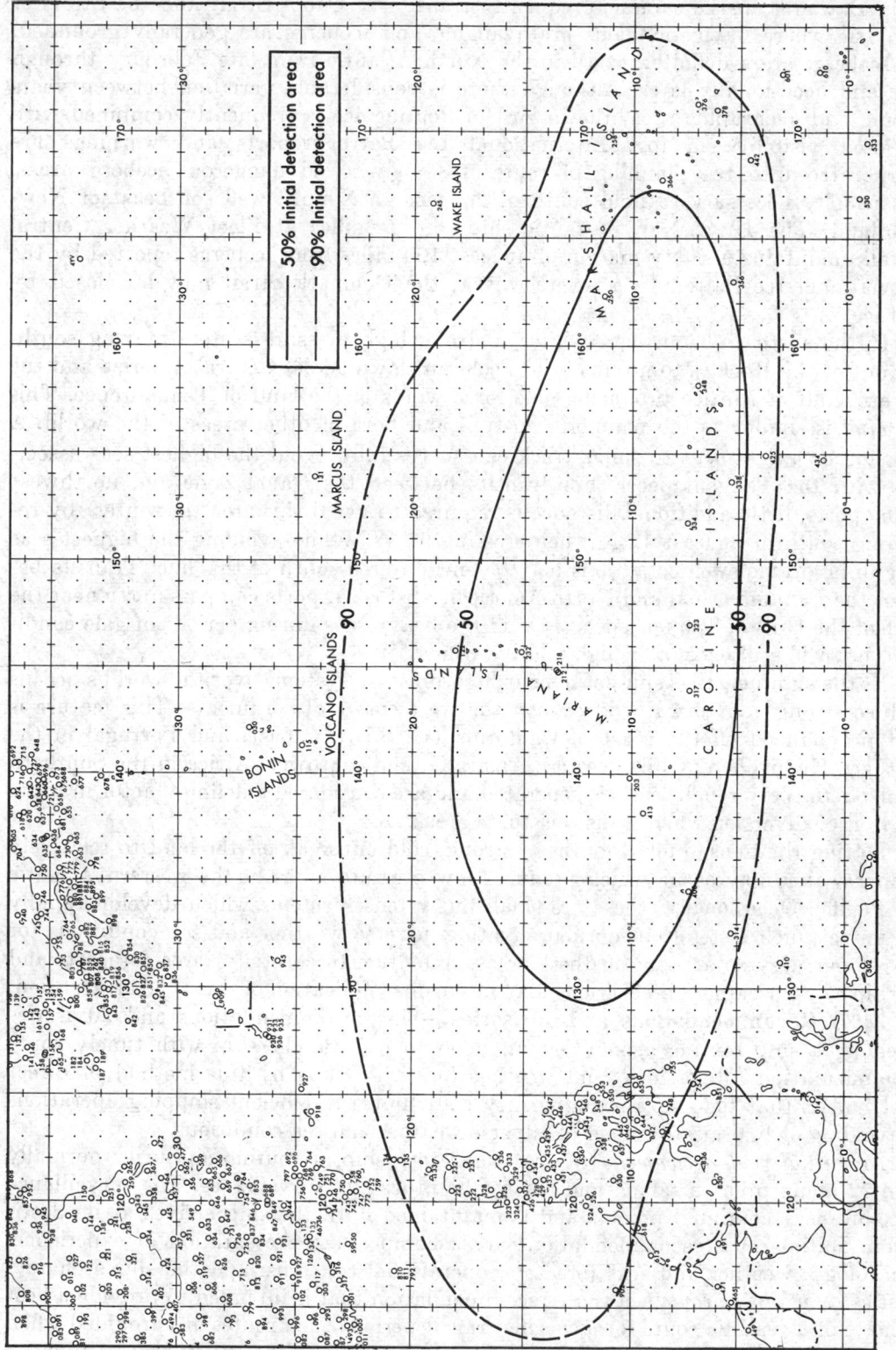

FIGURE 2405d. — Area of initial detection of high percentage of tropical cyclones which later developed to tropical storm or typhoon intensity, 1946–1973 (after Gray).

Baffin Bay area in the summer frequently transit via Cabot Strait and the Strait of Belle Isle where navigation aids are available and icebergs are generally grounded.

Icebergs are a definite hazard in the North Atlantic from late February through June and occasionally later. Although there is considerable variation between years in time and geographic area, the hazard of floating ice is frequently combined with restricted visibility in fog. International Ice Patrol reports and warnings are incorporated into the planning of routes to safely avoid dangerous iceberg areas. It is usually necessary to hold south of at least 45°N until well southeast of Newfoundland. The U. S. Navy Atlantic ship routing office at Fleet Weather Central Norfolk maintains a safety margin of at least 100 miles from icebergs reported by the International Ice Patrol. In a severe winter, the Denmark Strait may be closed by fixed ice.

In the northern hemisphere winter, a strong high pressure system moving southeast out of the Rocky Mountains brings cold air down across Central America and the western Gulf of Mexico producing gale force winds in the Gulf of Tehuantepec. This *fall wind* is similar to the pampero, mistral, and bora of other areas of the world. A diversion or adjustment to ship's track can successfully avoid the highest seas associated with the Tehuantepecer. For transits between the Canal Zone and northwest Pacific ports, little additional distance is required to avoid this area (in winter) by remaining south of at least 12°N when crossing 97°W. While avoiding the highest seas some unfavorable swell conditions may be encountered south of this line. Transits between the Panama Canal and North American west coast ports can pass north near the coast of the Gulf of Tehuantepec to avoid the heavy seas during periods of gale conditions, but will still encounter high relative winds.

In the summer, the semi-permanent high pressure systems over the world's oceans produce strong equatorward flow along the west coasts of continents. This feature is most pronounced off the coast of California (U. S. west coast) and Portugal in the Northern Hemisphere; Chile, western Australia, and southwest Africa in the Southern Hemisphere. Very rough seas are generated and are considered a definite factor in route selection or diversion when transiting these areas.

During the nonsummer months, a strong, cold outbreak off the land to relatively warmer water may occur which produces low pressure areas in the western Atlantic and Pacific. Occasionally, these are small but intense systems which develop rapidly and move much faster than normal, creating adverse weather and sea conditions for ships departing and arriving in these areas. Attention to coastal or area forecasts and the ship's own weather observations may be the first indication of this type of situation.

2407. Recommendations and advisories.—The recommendations and advisories issued by a ship routing agency are intended to provide the ship with timely route recommendations, diversions, and weather forecasts. It is by this method of direct involvement that the ship routing agency contributes to efficient shipping operations by avoiding or limiting the effect of adverse weather and sea conditions.

An *initial route recommendation* is issued to a ship or routing authority normally 48 to 72 hours prior to sailing and begins the process of surveillance. The surveillance procedure is a continual process and is maintained until the ship arrives at its destination. Initial route recommendations are a composite representation of experience, climatology, weather and seas forecasts, operational concerns, and the ship's characteristics. A *planning route* is a route recommendation that is intended to provide a best estimate of a realistic route for a specific transit period. Such routes are provided when estimated dates of departure (EDD's) are given to the routing agency well in advance of departure, usually a week to several months. Long range planning routes are based more on seasonal and climatological expectations than the current weather situation.

While planning routes are an attempt at making extended range (more than a week) or long range (more than a month) forecasts, these recommendations are likely to have some revision near the time of departure to reflect the current synoptic weather pattern. An initial route recommendation is more closely related to the current synoptic weather patterns by using the latest dynamic forecasts than are the planning route recommendations. These, too, are subject to revision prior to sailing if weather and sea conditions warrant.

Adjustment of departure time is a recommendation for delay in departure, or early departure if feasible, and is intended to avoid or significantly reduce the adverse weather and seas forecast on the first portion of the route if sailing on the original EDD. The initial route is not revised, only the timing of the ship's transit through an area with currently unfavorable weather conditions. Adjusting the departure time is an effective method of avoiding a potentially hazardous situation where there is no optimum route for sailing at the originally scheduled time.

A *diversion* is an underway adjustment in track and is intended to avoid or limit the effect of adverse weather conditions forecast to be encountered along the ship's current track. Ship's speed is expected to be reduced by the encounter with the heavy weather. In most cases the distance to destination is increased in attempting to avoid the adverse weather, but this is partially overcome by being able to maintain near normal SOA. Diversions should also be recommended where satisfactory weather and sea conditions are forecast on a shorter track.

Adjustment of SOA is a recommendation for slowing or increasing the ship's speed as much as practicable in an attempt to avoid an adverse weather situation by adjusting the timing of the encounter. This is also an effective means of maintaining maximum ship operating efficiency and not diverting from the present ship's track. By adjusting the SOA, a major weather system can sometimes be avoided with no increase in distance. The development of fast ships (SOA greater than 30 knots) gives the ship routing agency the potential to "make the ship's weather" by adjusting the ship's speed and track for encounter with favorable weather conditions or ship response factors.

Evasion is a recommendation to the commanding officer or master to take independent action to avoid, as much as possible, a potentially dangerous weather system. The ship routing meteorologist may recommend a general direction for safe evasion but does not specify an exact track. The recommendation for evasion is an indication that the weather and sea conditions have deteriorated to a point where shiphandling and safety are the primary considerations and progress toward destination has been temporarily suspended or is at least of secondary consideration.

A *weather advisory* is a transmission sent to the ship advising the commanding officer or master of expected adverse conditions, their duration, and geographic extent. It is initiated by the ship routing agency as a service and an aid to the ship. The best example of a situation for which a forecast will be helpful is when the ship is currently in good weather but adverse weather is expected within 24 hours for which a diversion is not being recommended or, a diversion where adverse weather conditions are still expected. This type of advisory may include a synoptic weather discussion and a wind, seas, or fog forecast.

The ability of the routing agency to achieve optimum conditions for the ship is aided by the commanding officer or master adjusting course and speed where necessary for an efficient and safe ride. At times, the local sea conditions may dictate that the commanding officer or master take independent action.

2408. Southern Hemisphere.—Available data on which to base analyses and forecasts is generally very limited in the Southern Hemisphere. Weather information obtained from satellites offers the possibility of improvement in southern hemisphere forecast products.

Passages south of the Cape of Good Hope and Cape Horn should be timed to avoid heavy weather as much as possible since intense and frequent low pressure systems are common in these areas. In particular, near the southeast coasts of Africa and South America, intense low pressure systems form in the lee of relatively high terrain near the coasts of both continents. Winter transits south of Cape Horn are difficult since the time required at relatively higher latitudes is longer than the typical time interval between storms. Remaining equatorward of about 35°S as much as practicable will limit exposure to adverse conditions. If the frequency of lows passing these areas is one every three or four days, the probability of encountering heavy weather is high.

Tropical cyclones in the Southern Hemisphere present a significant problem because of the sparse surface and upper air observations from which forecasts can be made. Satellites provide the most reliable means by which to obtain accurate positions of tropical systems and also give the first indication of tropical cyclone formation.

In the Southern Hemisphere, OTSR and other ship weather routing services are available but are limited in their full application because of sparse data reports from which reliable short range and extended range forecasts can be produced. Strong climatological consideration is usually given to any proposed southern hemisphere transit. OTSR procedures (art. 2402) for the Northern Hemisphere can be instituted in the Southern Hemisphere whenever justified by basic data input and available forecast models.

2409. Communications.—A vital part of a ship routing service is communications between the ship underway and the routing agency. Reports from the ship give the progress and ability to proceed in existing conditions. Weather reports enrich the basic data collection on which analyses are based and forecasts derived in turn.

Despite all efforts to achieve the best forecasts possible, the quality of forecasts does not always warrant maintaining the route selected prior to departure until reaching destination. In the U. S. Navy's ship routing program, experience shows that one-third of the ships routed receive some operational or weather dependent change while underway.

The routing agency needs reports of the ship's position and the ability to transmit recommendations for track change or weather advisories to the ship. The ship needs send and receive capability for the required information. Information on seakeeping changes initiated by the ship is desirable in a coordinated effort to provide optimum transit conditions.

2410. Benefits.—The benefits of ship weather routing services are basically cost reduction and safety. The savings in operating costs are derived from reductions in transit time, heavy weather encounters, fuel consumption, cargo and hull damage, and more efficient scheduling of dockside activities. The savings are further increased by fewer emergency repairs, more efficient use of personnel, improved topside working conditions, lower insurance rates as preferred risks under weather routing, and ultimately extended ship operating life.

An effective routing service maximizes safety by greatly reducing the probability of severe or catastrophic damage to the ship and injury to crew members.

2411. Conclusion.—The success of ship weather routing is dependent upon the validity of the forecasts and the routing agency's ability to make appropriate route recommendations and diversions. Anticipated improvements in a routing agency's recommendations will come from advancements in meteorology, technology, and the application of ocean wave forecast models.

Advancements in mathematical meteorology coupled with the continued application of computers will extend the time range and skill of the dynamic and statistical forecasts.

Technological advancements in the areas of satellite and automated communications, and onboard ship response systems will increase the amount and type of information to and from the ship with fewer delays. An onboard ship response system will enable the commanding officer or master to effectively select the course and speed required to conserve fuel and provide the best ride while making satisfactory progress on the track recommended by the routing agency. Ship response and performance data included with the ship's weather report will provide the routing agency with real time information with which to ascertain the actual state of the ship. Being able to predict a ship's response in most weather and sea conditions will result in improved routing procedures.

Shipboard and anchored wave measuring devices contribute to the development of ocean wave analysis and forecast models. Shipboard seakeeping instrumentation with input of measured wave conditions and predetermined ship response data for the particular hull enables a master or commanding officer to adjust course and speed for actual conditions.

Modern ship designs, exotic (nonstandard) cargoes, and sophisticated transport methods require individual attention to each ship's areas of vulnerability. Any improvement in the description of sea conditions by ocean wave models will improve the output from ship routing and seakeeping systems.

Advanced planning of a proposed transit combined with the study of expected weather conditions both before and during the voyage, as is done by ship routing agencies, and careful on board attention to seakeeping (with instrumentation if available) provide the greatest opportunity to achieve the goal of optimum environmental conditions for ocean transit.

References

Bijlsma, S. J. "On Minimal-Time Routing." Royal Netherlands Meteorological Institute, no. 94 (1975).

Bowman, W. N. and R. J. Renard. "Digest of Tropical Cyclones in the Eastern North Pacific." Environmental Prediction Research Facility, Monterey, California, Technical Paper (December 1975).

Bowman, W. N. and R. J. Renard. "The Climatology and Forecasting of Eastern North Pacific Tropical Cyclones." Environmental Prediction Research Facility, Monterey, California, Technical Paper 7–76 (July 1976).

Brand, S. and J. W. Bellock. "Typhoon Havens Handbook for the Western Pacific and Indian Oceans." Environmental Prediction Research Facility, Monterey, California, Technical Paper 5–76 (June 1976).

Cima, N. E. and W. F. Dupin. "Predicting Individual Ship Performance from Real Time Environmental Observations." Society of Naval Architects and Marine Engineers, (September 1974).

Clune, W. M. "Optimum Track Ship Routing at FNWC Monterey." *Mariner's Weather Log*, vol. 19, no. 1 (January 1975). National Oceanic and Atmospheric Administration.

Gray, W. M. "Tropical Cyclone Genesis in the Western North Pacific." Environmental Prediction Research Facility, Monterey, California, Technical Paper 16–75 (May 1975).

Harding, E. T. and W. J. Kotsch. *Heavy Weather Guide*. Annapolis, Maryland, United States Naval Institute, 1965.

Hoffman, D. "Fuel Conservation and Heavy Weather Avoidance." Lecture presented at Seminar on Maritime Fuel Conservation, May 8–9, 1975, at Webb Institute, Long Island, New York.

James, R. W. "Application of Wave Forecasts to Marine Navigation." U. S. Naval Oceanographic Office SP–1 (July 1957).

James, R. W. "Present Status of Ship Routing." Lecture presented at Interocean 70, (November 1970) Dusseldorf, Germany.

James, R. W. "Dangerous Waves Along North Wall of the Gulf Stream." *Mariner's Weather Log*, vol. 18, no. 3 (November 1974) National Oceanic and Atmospheric Administration.

Lazanoff, S. M. and N. M. Stevenson. "An Evaluation of a Hemispheric Operational Spectra Model." Fleet Numerical Weather Central, Monterey, California, Technical Note 75–3 (June 1975).

CHAPTER XXV

POLAR NAVIGATION

Polar Regions

2501. Introduction.—No single definition of the limits of the polar regions satisfies the needs of all who are interested in these areas. Astronomically, the parallels of latitude at which the sun becomes circumpolar (the Arctic and Antarctic Circles at about latitude 67°.5) are considered the lower limits. Meteorologically, the limits are irregular lines which, in the Arctic, coincides approximately with the tree line. For general purposes, the navigator may consider polar regions as extending from the geographical poles of the earth to latitude 70° (in the Arctic coinciding approximately with the northern coast of Alaska), with transitional **subpolar regions** extending for an additional 10° (in the Northern Hemisphere extending to the southern tip of Greenland).

This chapter deals primarily with marine navigation in high latitudes.

2502. Polar geography.—The north polar region, the **Arctic,** consists of an elongated central water area a little smaller than the United States, almost completely surrounded by land (fig. 2502a). Some of this land is high and rugged with permanent **ice caps,** but part of it is low and marshy when thawed. Underlying **permafrost,** permanently frozen ground, prevents adequate drainage, resulting in large numbers of lakes and ponds and extensive areas of **muskeg,** soft spongy ground with characteristic growths of certain types of moss and tufts of grass or sedge. There are also large areas of **tundra,** low treeless plains with vegetation consisting of mosses, lichens, shrubs, willows, etc., and usually having an underlying layer of permafrost. The northernmost point of land is Kap Morris Jessup, Greenland, about 380 nautical miles from the pole.

The central part of the **Arctic Ocean,** as the body of water is called, is a basin of about 12,000 feet average depth. However, the bottom is not level, having a number of seamounts and deeps. The greatest depth is probably a little more than 16,000 feet. At the North Pole the depth is 14,150 feet. Surrounding the polar basin is an extensive continental shelf, broken only in the area between Greenland and Svalbard (Spitsbergen). The many islands of the Canadian archipelago are on this shelf. The Greenland Sea, east of Greenland; Baffin Bay, west of Greenland; and the Bering Sea, north of the Aleutians, each has its independent basin. In a sense, the Arctic Ocean is an arm of the Atlantic, as shown in figure 2502a.

The south polar region, the **Antarctic,** is in marked contrast to the Arctic in physiographical features. Here a high, mountainous land mass about twice the area of the United States is surrounded by water (fig. 2502b). An extensive polar plateau covered with snow and ice is about 10,000 feet high. There are several mountain ranges with peaks rising to heights of more than 13,000 feet. The average height of Antarctica is about 6,000 feet, which is higher than any other continent. The height at the South Pole is about 9,500 feet. The barrier presented by land and tremendous **ice shelves** 500 to 1,000 feet thick prevent ships from reaching very high latitudes. Much of the coast of Antarctica is high and rugged, with few good harbors or anchorages.

2503. Navigation in polar regions.—Special techniques have been developed to adapt navigation to the unique conditions of polar regions. These conditions are largely the result of (1) high latitude, and (2) meteorological factors.

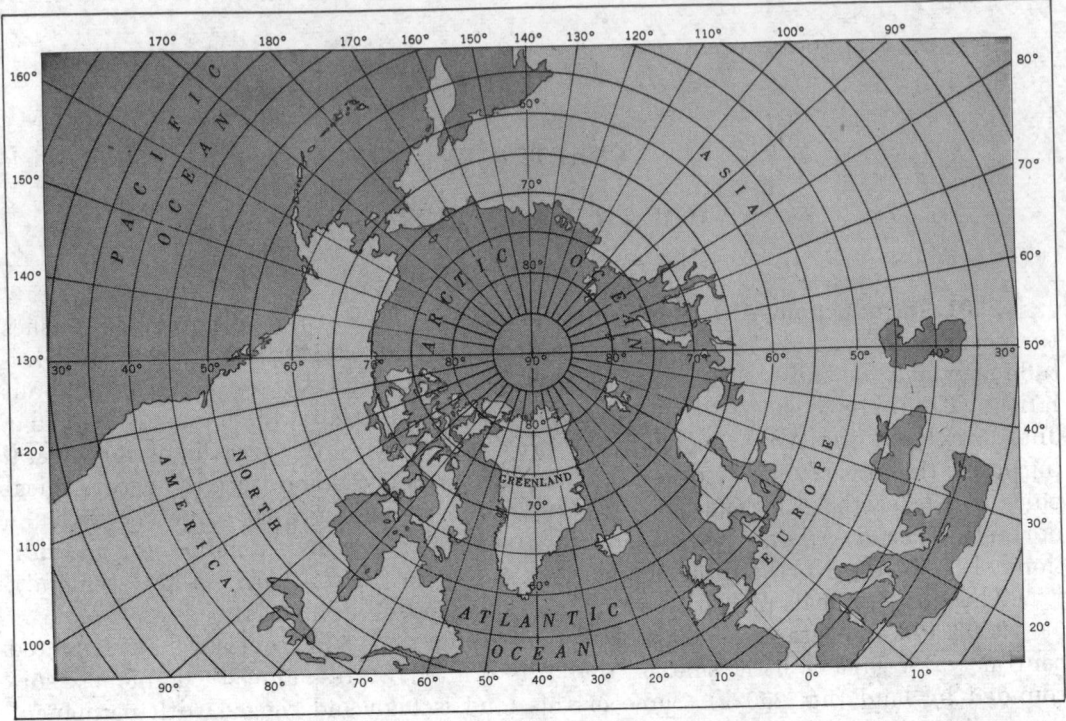

FIGURE 2502a.—The north polar region, or *Arctic*.

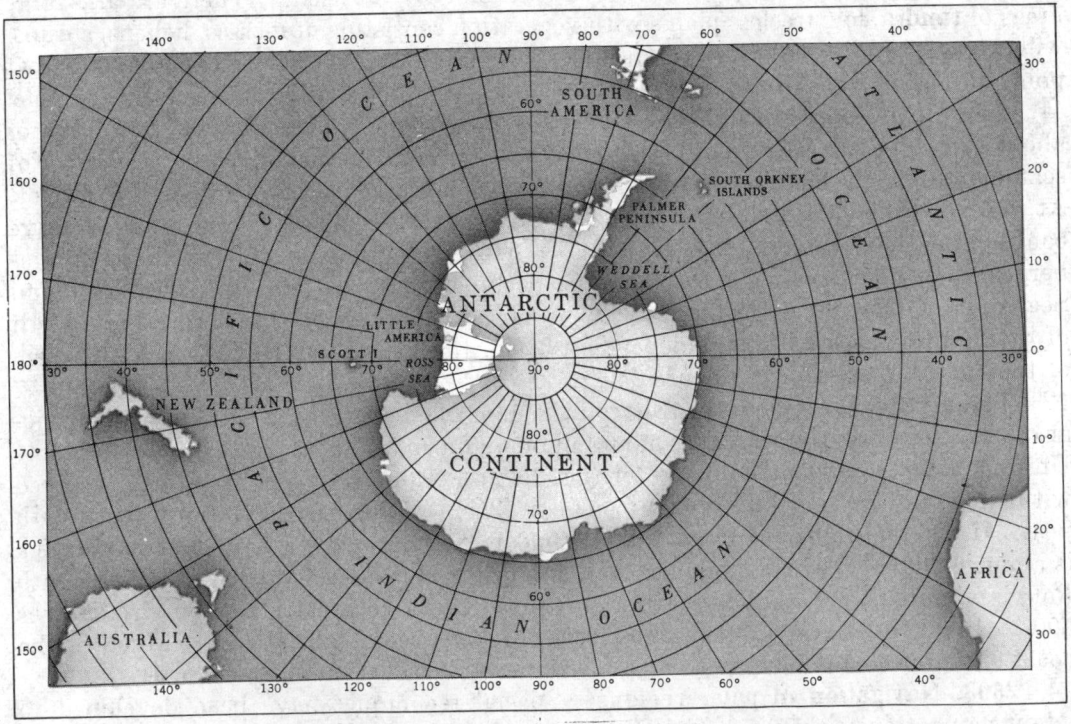

FIGURE 2502b.—The south polar region, or *Antarctic*.

2504. High-latitude effects.—Much of the thinking of the marine navigator is in terms of the "rectangular" world of the Mercator projection, on which the meridians are equally spaced, vertical lines perpendicular to the horizontal parallels of latitude. Directions are measured relative to the meridians, and are maintained by means of a magnetic or gyrocompass. A straight line on the chart is a rhumb line, the line used for ordinary purposes of navigation. Celestial bodies rise above the eastern horizon, climb to a maximum altitude often high in the sky as they cross the celestial meridian, and set below the western horizon. By this motion the sun divides the day naturally into two roughly equal periods of daylight and darkness, separated by relatively short transitional periods of twilight. The hour of the day is associated with this daily motion of the sun.

In polar regions conditions are different. Meridians all converge at the poles, which are centers of series of concentric circles constituting the parallels of latitude. The rapid convergence of the meridians renders the usual convention of direction inadequate for some purposes. A rhumb line is a curve which differs noticeably from a great circle, even for short distances. Even visual bearings cannot adequately be represented as rhumb lines. At the pole all directions are south or north, depending upon the pole. Direction in the usual sense is replaced by longitude.

At the pole the zenith and celestial pole coincide. Hence, the celestial horizon and celestial equator also coincide, and declination and computed altitude are the same. Therefore, celestial bodies change computed altitude only by changing declination. Stars circle the sky without noticeable change in altitude. Planets rise and set once each sidereal period (12 years for Jupiter, 30 years for Saturn). At the North Pole the sun rises about March 21, slowly spirals to a maximum altitude of about 23°27′ near June 21, slowly spirals downward to the horizon about September 23, and then disappears for another six months. At the South Pole a similar cycle takes place but during the opposite time of year. It requires about 32 hours for the sun to cross the horizon, during which time it circles the sky 1⅓ times. The twilight periods following sunset and preceding sunrise last for several *weeks*. The moon rises and sets about once each month. Only celestial bodies of north declination are visible at the North Pole; only bodies of south declination are visible at the South Pole.

The long polar night is not wholly dark. The full moon at this time rises relatively high in the sky. Light from the **aurora borealis** in the Arctic and the **aurora australis** in the Antarctic is often quite bright, occasionally exceeding that of the full moon. Even the planets and stars contribute an appreciable amount of light in this area where a snow cover provides an excellent reflecting surface.

All time zones, like all meridians, meet at the poles. *Local* time does not have its usual significance, since the hour of the day bears no relation to periods of light and darkness or to altitude of celestial bodies.

2505. Meteorological effects.—Polar regions are cold, but the temperature at sea is not as extreme as inland. The average winter temperature over the Arctic Ocean is (−)30°F to (−)40°F, with an extreme low value near (−)60°F. Colder temperatures have been recorded in Yellowstone National Park. During the summer the temperature remains above freezing over the ocean. Inland, extreme values are sometimes reached. At least one point on the Arctic Circle has experienced a temperature of 100°F. Few points on the Antarctic Continent have recorded temperatures above freezing, and the interior is probably the coldest part of the world.

Fog and clouds are common in polar regions, yet there is less precipitation than in some desert regions, since the cold air has small capacity for holding moisture. Very cold air over open water sometimes produces steaming of the surface, occasionally to a height of several hundred feet. This is called **frost smoke** or **sea smoke** (fig. 2505).

FIGURE 2505.—Frost smoke.

When there is no fog or frost smoke, the visibility is often excellent. Sounds can some-times be heard at great distances.

Sharp discontinuities or inversions in the temperature lapse rate sometimes produce a variety of mirages and extreme values of refraction. The sun has been known to rise several *days* before it was expected in the spring. False horizons are not uncommon.

Strong winds are common in the subarctic and in both the Antarctic and sub-antarctic. The belt of water surrounding Antarctica has been characterized as the stormiest in the world, being an area of high winds and high seas. Strong winds are not encountered over the Arctic Ocean.

In the polar and subpolar regions the principal hazard to ships is ice, both that formed at sea and land ice which has flowed into the sea in the form of glaciers. Many low land areas are ice-free in summer. Ice is considered in more detail in chapter XXXVI.

When snow obliterates surface features, and the sky is covered with a uniform layer of cirrostratus or altostratus clouds, so that there are no shadows, the horizon disappears and earth and sky blend together, forming an unbroken expanse of white, without features. Landmarks cannot be distinguished, and with complete lack of contrast, distance is virtually impossible to estimate. This is called **arctic** (or **antarctic**) **whiteout.** It is particularly prevalent in northern Alaska during late winter and early spring.

2506. Miscellaneous.—The cold surface water of the Arctic Ocean flows outward between Greenland and Svalbard and is replaced by warmer subsurface water from the Atlantic. The surface currents depend largely upon the winds, and are generally quite weak in the Arctic Ocean. However, there are a number of well-established currents flowing with considerable consistency throughout the year. The general circulation in the Arctic is clockwise on the American side and around islands, and counterclockwise on the Asian side. Tidal ranges in this area are generally small. In the restricted waters of the upper Canadian-Greenland area both tides and currents vary considerably from place to place. In the Baffin Bay-Davis Strait area the currents are strong and the tides are high, with a great difference between springs and neaps. In the Antarctic, currents are strong, and the general circulation offshore is eastward or *clockwise* around the continent. Close to the shore, a weaker westerly or *counterclockwise* current may be encountered, but there are many local variations.

Since both magnetic poles are situated within the polar regions, the horizontal intensity of the earth's magnetic field is so low that the magnetic compass is of reduced value, and even useless in some areas. The magnetic storms centered in the auroral zones (art. 4301) disrupt radio communications and alter magnetic compass errors. The frozen ground in polar regions is a poor conductor of electricity, another factor adversely affecting radio wave propagation.

2507. Summary of conditions in polar regions.—The more prominent characteristic features associated with large portions of the polar regions may be summarized as follows:

1. High latitude.
2. Rapid convergence of meridians.
3. Nearly horizontal diurnal motion of celestial bodies.
4. Long periods of daylight, twilight, and semidarkness.
5. Low mean temperatures.
6. Short, cool summers and long, cold winters.
7. High wind-chill factor.
8. Low evaporation rate.
9. Scant precipitation.
10. Dry air (low absolute humidity).
11. Excellent sound-transmitting conditions.
12. Periods of excellent visibility.
13. Extensive fog and clouds.
14. Large number and variety of mirages.
15. Extreme refraction and false horizons.
16. Winter freezing of rivers, lakes, and part of the sea.
17. Areas of permanent land and sea ice.
18. Areas of permanently frozen ground.
19. Large areas of tundra (Arctic).
20. Large areas of poor drainage, with many lakes and ponds (Arctic).
21. Large areas of muskeg (a grassy marsh when thawed) (Arctic).
22. Extensive auroral activity.
23. Large areas of low horizontal intensity of earth's magnetic field.
24. Intense magnetic storms.
25. Uncertain radio wave propagation.
26. Strong winds (Antarctic).
27. Frequent blizzards (Antarctic).
28. Large quantities of blowing snow.

Charts

2508. Projections.—In polar regions, as elsewhere, the chart is an important item of navigational equipment. The projections used for polar charts are considered in articles 321 and 322.

For ordinary navigation the Mercator projection has long been the overwhelming favorite of marine navigators, primarily because a rhumb line appears as a straight line on this projection. Even in high latitudes the mariner has exhibited an understandable partiality for Mercator charts, and these have been used virtually everywhere that ships have gone.

However, as the latitude increases, the superiority of the Mercator projection decreases, primarily because the value of the rhumb line becomes progressively less. At latitudes greater than 60° the decrease in utility begins to be noticeable, and beyond latitude 70° it becomes troublesome. In the clear polar atmosphere, visual bearings are observed at great distances, sometimes 50 miles or more. The use of a rhumb line to represent a bearing line introduces an error at any latitude, but at high latitudes this error becomes excessive.

Another objection to Mercator charts at high latitudes is the increasing rate of change of scale over a single chart. This results in distortion in the shape of land masses and errors in measuring distances.

At some latitude the disadvantages of the Mercator projection outweigh its advantages. The latitude at which this occurs depends upon the physical features of the area, the configuration and orientation of land and water areas, the nature of the operation, and, mostly, upon the previous experience and personal preference of the mariner. Because of differences of opinion in this matter, a transitional zone exists in which several projections may be encountered. The wise high-latitude navigator is prepared to use any of them, since coverage of his operating area may not be adequate on his favorite projection.

2509. Adequacy.—Charts of most polar areas are generally inferior to those of other regions in at least three respects:

1. *Lack of detail.* Polar regions have not been surveyed with the thoroughness needed to provide charts of the accustomed detail. Relatively few soundings are available and many of the coastal features are shown by their general outlines only. Large areas are perennially covered by ice, which presents a changing appearance as the amount, position, and the character of the ice change. Heavy covers of ice and snow prevent accurate determination of surface features of the earth beneath. Added to this is the similarity between adjacent land features where the hundreds of points and fiords in a rugged area or the extensive areas of treeless, flat coastal land in another look strikingly alike. The thousands of shallow lakes and ponds along a flat coastal plain lack distinctive features.

2. *Inaccuracy.* Polar charts are based upon incomplete surveys and reports of those who have been in the areas. These reports are less reliable than in other areas because icebergs are sometimes mistaken for islands, ice-covered islands are mistaken for grounded icebergs, shorelines are not easy to detect when snow covers both land and attached sea ice, inlets and sounds may be completely obscured by ice and snow, and meteorological conditions may introduce inaccuracy in determination of position. Consequently, many features are inaccurately shown in location, shape, and size, and there are numerous omissions. Isogonic lines, too, are based upon incomplete information, resulting in less than desired accuracy.

3. *Coverage.* Relatively few nautical charts of polar regions are available, and the limits of some of these are not convenient for some operations. As in other areas,

charts have been made as the need has arisen. Hence, large-scale charts of some areas are completely lacking. Aeronautical charts are sometimes quite helpful, as they often show more detail of land areas than do the nautical charts. However, aeronautical charts do not show soundings.

2510. Polar grid.—Because of the rapid convergence of the meridians in polar regions, the true direction of an oblique line near the pole may vary considerably over a relatively few miles. The meridians are radial lines meeting at the poles, instead of being parallel, as they appear on the familiar Mercator chart.

Near the pole the convenience of parallel meridians is attained by means of a **polar grid.** On the chart a number of lines are printed parallel to a selected reference meridian, usually that of Greenwich. On transverse Mercator charts the fictitious meridians may serve this purpose. Any straight line on the chart makes the same angle with all grid lines. On the transverse Mercator projection it is therefore a **fictitious rhumb line.** On any polar projection it is a close approximation to a great circle. If north along the reference meridian is selected as the reference direction, all parallel grid lines can be considered extending in the same direction. The constant direction relative to the grid lines is called **grid direction.** North along the Greenwich meridian is usually taken as grid north in both the Northern and Southern Hemispheres.

The value of grid directions is indicated in figure 2510. In this figure A and B are 400 miles apart. The true bearing of B from A is 023°, yet at B this bearing line, if continued, extends in true direction 163°, a change of 140° in 400 miles. The grid direction at any point along the bearing line is 103°.

When north along the Greenwich meridian is used as grid north, interconversion between grid and true directions is quite simple. Let G represent a grid direction and T the corresponding true direction. Then for the Arctic,

$$G = T + \lambda W.$$

That is, in the Western Hemisphere, in the Arctic, grid direction is found by *adding* the longitude to the true direction. From this it follows that

$$T = G - \lambda W,$$

and in the Eastern Hemisphere

$$G = T - \lambda E,$$
$$T = G + \lambda E.$$

In the Southern Hemisphere the signs (+ or −) of the longitude are reversed in all formulas.

If a magnetic compass is used to follow a grid direction, variation and convergency can be combined into a single correction called **grid variation** or **grivation.** It is customary to show lines of equal grivation on polar charts rather than lines of equal variation. Defense Mapping Agency Hydrographic Center chart 43 shows the **isogrivs** (lines of equal grivation) for the north and south polar areas.

With one modification the grid system of direction can be used in any latitude. Meridians 1° apart make an angle of 1° with each other where they meet at the pole. The **convergency** is one, and the 360° of longitude cover all 360° around the pole. At the equator the meridians are parallel and the convergency is zero. Between these two limits the convergency has some value between zero and one. On a sphere it is equal to the sine of the latitude. For practical navigation this relationship can be used on the spheroidal earth. On a simple conic or Lambert conformal chart a constant convergency is used over the entire chart, and is known as the **constant of the cone.** On a simple

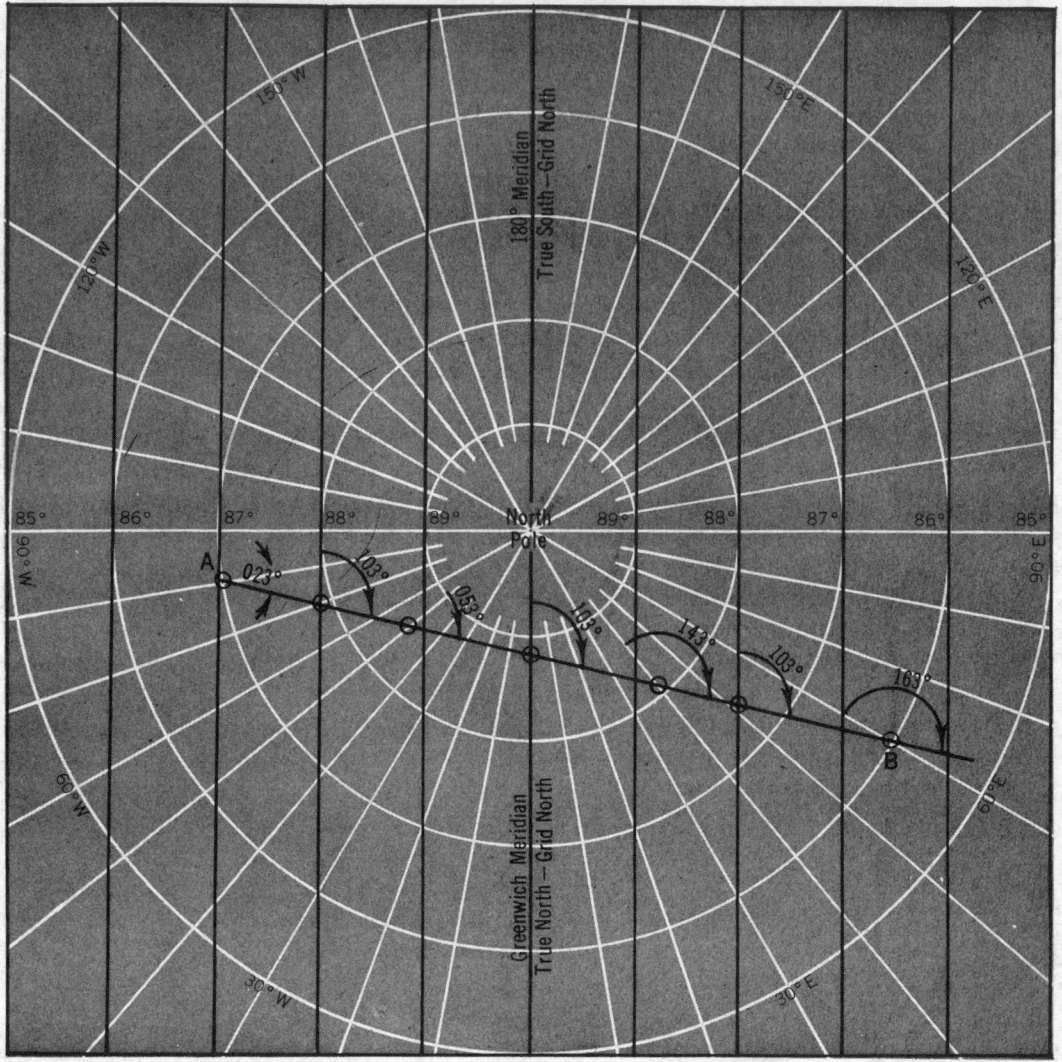

FIGURE 2510.—Polar grid navigation.

conic projection it is equal to the sine of the standard parallel. On a Lambert conformal projection it is equal (approximately) to the sine of the latitude midway between the two standard parallels. When convergency is printed on the chart, it is generally adjusted for ellipticity of the earth. If K is the constant of the cone,

$$K = \sin \tfrac{1}{2} (L_1 + L_2),$$

where L_1 and L_2 are the latitudes of the two standard parallels. On such a chart, grid navigation is conducted as explained above, except that in each of the formulas the longitude is multiplied by K:

$$G = T + K\lambda W,$$
$$T = G - K\lambda W,$$
$$G = T - K\lambda E,$$
$$T = G + K\lambda E.$$

Thus, a straight line on such a chart changes its true direction, not by 1° for each degree of longitude, but by $K°$. As in higher latitudes, convergency and variation can be combined.

In using grid navigation one should keep clearly in mind the fact that the grid lines are parallel *on the chart*. Since distortion varies on charts of different projections, and on charts of conic projections having different standard parallels, *the grid direction between any two given points is not the same on all charts*. For operations which are to be coordinated by means of grid directions, *it is important that all charts showing the grid be on a single graticule* (art. 303).

2511. Plotting on polar charts, as on other charts, involves the measurement of distance and direction. On a chart with converging meridians, as one on the Lambert conformal projection, distance is measured by means of the latitude scale, as on a Mercator chart, but this scale is so nearly constant that any part of it can be used without introducing a significant error. A mile scale is sometimes shown in or near the margin of such a chart, and can be used anywhere on that chart.

Since the meridians converge, a straight line makes a different angle with each meridian, as shown in figure 2510. For this reason, compass roses are not customarily shown on such a chart. If they do appear, *each one applies only to the meridian on which it is located*. The navigator accustomed to using a Mercator chart can easily forget this point, and hence will do well to ignore compass roses. If a drafting machine is used, it should be aligned with the correct meridian each time a measurement is made. Since this precaution can easily be overlooked, especially by a navigator accustomed to resetting his drafting machine only when the chart is moved, and since the resulting error may be too small to be apparent but too large to ignore, it is good practice to discard this instrument when the Mercator chart is replaced by one with converging meridians, unless positive steps are taken to prevent error.

The most nearly fool-proof and generally the most satisfactory method of measuring directions on a chart with converging meridians is to use a protractor, or some kind of plotter combining the features of a protractor and straightedge (fig. 2511a).

If a course is to be measured, the mid meridian of each leg should be used, as shown in figure 2511a. If a bearing is to be measured, the meridian nearest the point at which the bearing was determined should be used, as shown in figure 2511b. Thus, in the usual case of determining the bearing of a landmark from a ship, the meridian nearest the ship should be used. In using either of the plotters shown in figures 2511a or 2511b, note that the center hole is placed over the meridian used, the straightedge part is placed along the line to be drawn or measured, and the angle is read on the protractor at the same meridian which passes under the center hole. It is sometimes more convenient to invert the plotter, so that the protractor part extends on the opposite side of the straightedge.

For plotting grid directions, angles are measured from grid north, using *any* grid meridian. Any convenient method can be used. If a protractor or plotter is being used for plotting grid directions, it is usually desirable to use the same instrument for plotting true directions. The distance is the same whether grid or true directions are used.

Dead Reckoning

2512. Polar dead reckoning.—In polar regions, as elsewhere, dead reckoning involves measurement of direction and distance traveled, and the use of this information for determination of position.

Direction is normally determined by a compass, but in polar regions both magnetic and gyrocompasses are subject to certain limitations not encountered elsewhere.

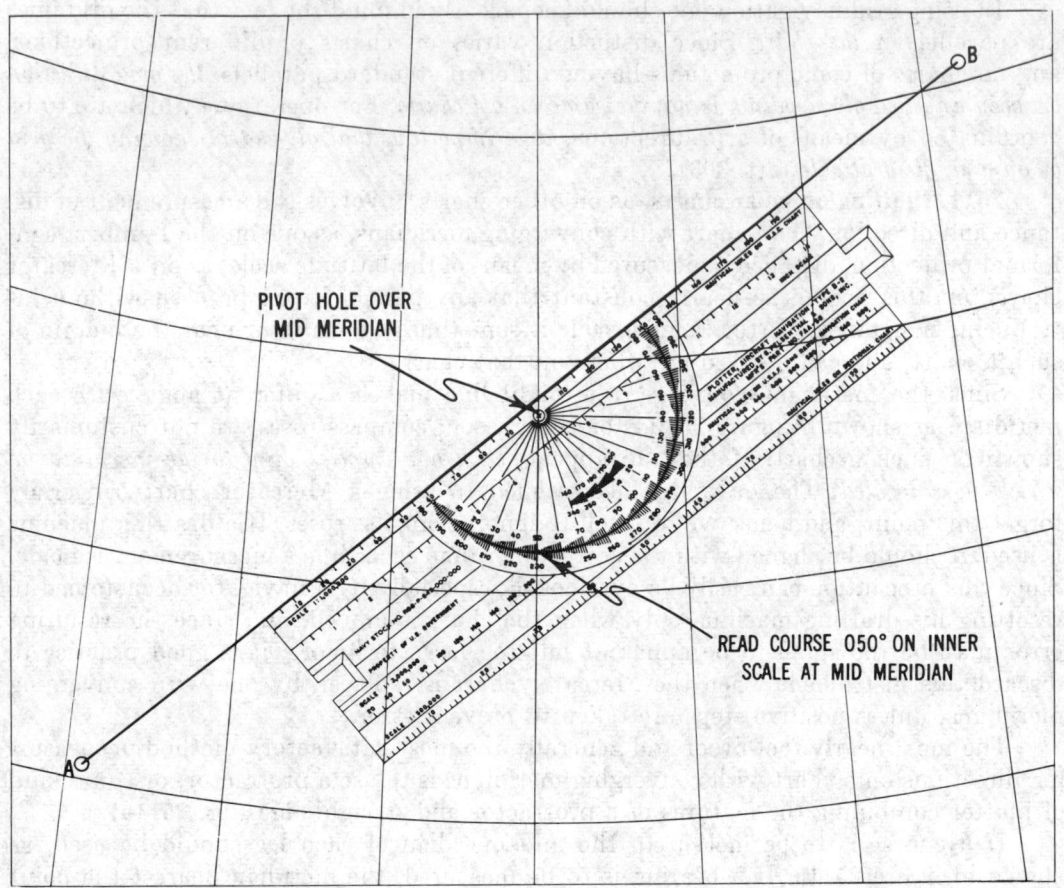

FIGURE 2511a.—Measuring a course on a Lambert conformal chart by B–2 aircraft plotter. Note that measurement is made at the mid meridian.

However, the navigator who thoroughly understands the use of these instruments in high latitudes can get much useful information from them. The polar navigator should not overlook the value of radar tracking or visual tracking for determining direction of motion. This is discussed in article 2515.

Speed or distance is normally measured by log or engine revolution counter, but these methods are not entirely suitable when the ship is operating in ice. The problem of determining speed or distance in ice is discussed in article 2515.

2513. The magnetic compass depends for its directive force upon the horizontal intensity of the magnetic field of the earth. As the magnetic poles are approached, this force becomes progressively weaker until at some point the magnetic compass becomes useless as a direction-measuring device. In a marginal area it is good practice to keep the magnetic compass under almost constant scrutiny, as it is somewhat erratic in dependability and its errors may change rapidly. Frequent compass checks by celestial observation or any other method available are wise precautions. A log of compass comparisons and observations is useful in predicting future reliability.

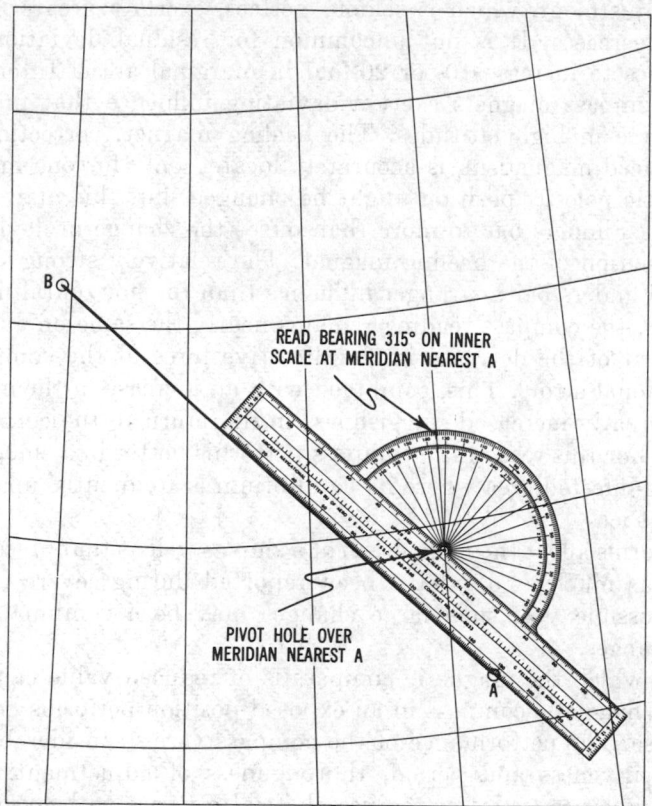

READ BEARING 315° ON INNER
SCALE AT MERIDIAN NEAREST A

PIVOT HOLE OVER
MERIDIAN NEAREST A

FIGURE 2511b.—Measuring a bearing on a Lambert conformal chart by AN plotter. Note that measurement is made at the meridian nearest the ship.

The magnetic poles themselves are somewhat elusive, since they participate in the normal diurnal, annual, and secular changes in the earth's field, as well as the more erratic changes caused by magnetic storms. Measurements indicate that the north magnetic pole moves within an elongated area of perhaps 100 miles in a generally north-south direction and somewhat less in an east-west direction. Normally, it is at the southern end of its area of movement at local noon and at the northern extremity twelve hours later, but during a severe magnetic storm this motion is upset and becomes highly erratic. Because of the motions of the poles, they are sometimes regarded as *areas* rather than points. There is some evidence to support the belief that several secondary poles exist, although such alleged poles may be anomalies (local attractions), possibly of intermittent or temporary existence. Various severe anomalies have been located in polar areas and others may exist.

The continual motion of the poles may account, at least in part, for the large diurnal changes in variation encountered in high latitudes. Changes as large as 10° have been reported.

Measurements of the earth's magnetic field in polar regions are neither numerous nor frequent. The isogonic lines in these areas are close together, resulting in rapid change in short distances in some directions, and their locations are imperfectly known. As a result, charted variation in polar regions is not of the same order of accuracy as elsewhere.

The decrease in horizontal intensity encountered near the magnetic poles, as well as magnetic storms, affects the deviation. Any deviating magnetic influence remaining after adjustment, which is seldom perfect, exerts a greater influence as the directive force decreases. It is not uncommon for residual deviation determined in moderate latitudes to increase 10- or 20-fold in marginal areas. Interactions between correctors and compass magnets exert a deviating influence that may increase to a troublesome degree in high latitudes. The heeling magnet, correcting for both permanent and induced magnetism, is accurately located only for one magnetic latitude. Near the magnetic pole its position might be changed, but this may induce sufficient magnetism in the Flinders bar to more than offset the change in deviation due to the change in the position of the heeling magnet. The relatively strong vertical intensity may render the Flinders bar a stronger influence than the horizontal field of the earth. When this occurs, the compass reading remains nearly the same on any heading.

Another effect of the decrease in the directive force of the compass is a greater influence of frictional errors. This, combined with an increase in the period of the compass, results in greatly increased sluggishness in its return to the correct reading after being disturbed. For this reason the compass performs better in a smooth sea free from ice than in an ice-infested area where its equilibrium is frequently upset by impact of the vessel against ice.

Magnetic storms affect the magnetism of a ship as well as that of the earth. Changes in deviation of as much as 45° have been reported during severe magnetic storms, although it is possible that such large changes may be a combination of deviation and variation changes.

The area in which the magnetic compass is of reduced value cannot be stated in specific terms. A magnetic compass in an exposed position performs better than one in a steel pilot house. The performance of the compass varies considerably with the type of compass, sensitiveness and period, thoroughness of adjustment, location on the vessel, and magnetic properties of the vessel. It also varies with local conditions.

In a very general sense the magnetic compass can be considered of reduced reliability when the horizontal intensity is less than 0.09 oersted, erratic when the field is less than 0.06 oersted, and useless when it is less than 0.03 oersted. The extent of these areas in the Northern Hemisphere is indicated in figure 2513. Similar areas extend around the south magnetic pole, which is located at latitude 68°S, longitude 139°E, not far from the eastern shore of the Ross Sea. Defense Mapping Agency Hydrographic Center chart 33 shows lines of equal horizontal intensity in the north and south polar regions, respectively. However, the effectiveness of the magnetic compass is influenced also by local conditions. A compass on a vessel making a voyage through the islands of the Canadian archipelago has been reported to give fair indication of direction in certain small areas where the horizontal intensity is less than 0.02 oersted, yet to be useless at some places where the horizontal intensity is greater than 0.04 oersted.

Despite its various limitations, the magnetic compass is a valuable instrument in much of the polar regions, where the gyrocompass is also of reduced reliability. With careful adjustment, frequent checks, and a record of previous behavior, the polar navigator can get much useful service from his instrument.

When a compass is subjected to extremely low temperatures, there is danger of the liquid freezing. Sufficient heat to prevent this can normally be obtained from the compass light, which should not be turned off during severe weather.

2514. The gyrocompass depends for its operation upon the rotation of the earth about its axis. Its maximum directive force is at the equator, where the axis of the compass is parallel to the axis of the earth. As the latitude increases, the angle between

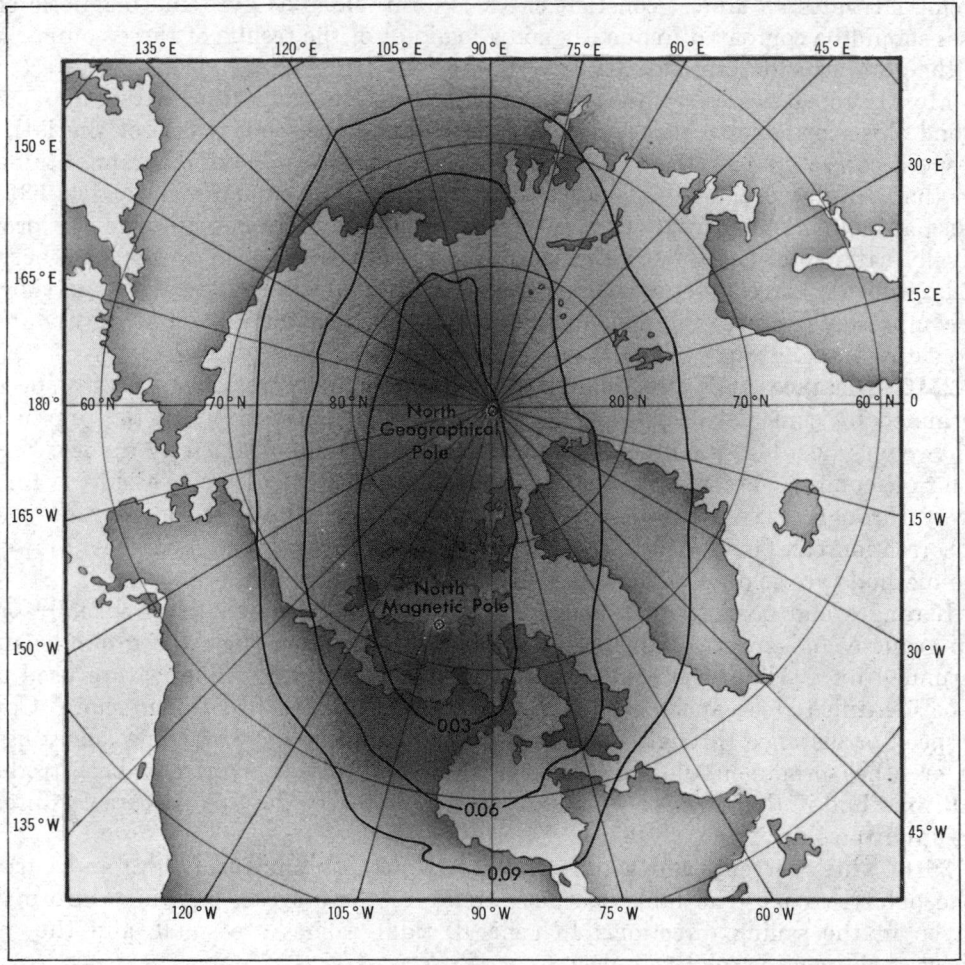

FIGURE 2513.—Arctic areas in which the magnetic compass is of reduced value. Inside the curves representing the 0.09, 0.06, and 0.03 oersted values of horizontal intensity the compass can be considered of reduced reliability, erratic, and useless, respectively.

these two axes increases. At the *geographical* poles the gyrocompass has no directive force.

The gyrocompass is generally reliable to latitude 70°. At higher latitudes the disturbing effect of imperfections in compass or adjustment is magnified. Latitude adjustment becomes critical. Speed error increases as the speed of the vessel approaches the rotational speed of the earth. Ballistic deflection error becomes large and the compass is slow to respond to correcting forces. Frequent changes of course and speed, often necessary when proceeding through ice, introduce errors which are slow to settle out. The impact of the vessel against ice deflects the gyrocompass, which does not return quickly to the correct reading.

The error increases and becomes more erratic as the vessel proceeds to higher latitudes. Extreme errors as large as 27° have been reported at latitudes greater than 82°. The gyrocompass probably becomes useless at about latitude 85°. At latitude 70° the gyro error should be determined frequently, perhaps every four hours, by means of celestial bodies when these are available. As the error increases and becomes more erratic, with higher latitude, it should be determined more frequently. In heavy ice at extreme latitudes an almost constant check is desirable. The gyro and magnetic compasses should be compared frequently and a log kept of the results of these comparisons and the gyro error determinations.

Most gyrocompasses are not provided with a latitude correction setting above 70°. Beyond this, correction can be made by either of two methods: (1) set the latitude and speed correctors to zero and apply a correction from a table or diagram obtainable from the manufacturer of the compass, or constructed as explained in article 639; or (2) use an equivalent latitude and speed setting. Both of these methods have proved generally satisfactory, although the second is considered superior to the first because it at least partly corrects for errors introduced by a change in course. In certain types of gyrocompasses, facilities for their operation in a high latitude mode up to about 86° and as directional gyros even to the poles is provided.

2515. Distance and direction in ice.—In ice-free waters, distance or speed is determined by some form of log or by engine revolution counter. In the presence of ice, however, most logs are inoperative or inaccurate due to clogging by the ice. Engine revolution counters are not accurate speed indicating devices when a ship is forcing its way through ice. With experience, one can estimate the speed in relation to ice, or a correction can be applied to speed by engine revolution counter. At best, however, these methods are seldom of the desired accuracy.

If ranges and bearings of a land feature can be determined either visually or by radar, course and speed of the vessel or distance traveled over the ground can be determined by tracking the landmark and plotting the results. The feature used need not be identified. Ice can be used if it is grounded or attached to the shore. Course and speed or distance through the water can be determined by tracking a floating iceberg or other prominent floating ice feature. However, an error may be introduced by this method if the effect of wind and current upon the floating feature is different than upon the ship.

2516. Tide, current, and wind.—Relatively little is known of tides and currents in the polar regions. The tables do not extend to these areas, but some information is given in the sailing directions. In general, tidal ranges are small, and the water in most anchorages is relatively deep.

Currents in many coastal areas are strong and somewhat variable. When a vessel is operating in ice, the current is often difficult to determine because of frequent changes in course and speed of the vessel and inaccuracies in the measurement of direction and distance traveled.

In the vicinity of land, and in the whole antarctic area, winds are variable in direction, gusty, and often strong. Offshore, in the Arctic Ocean, the winds are not strong and are steadier, but ships rarely operate in this area. The wind in polar regions, as elsewhere, has two primary navigational effects upon vessels. First, its direct effect is to produce leeway. When a vessel is operating in ice, the leeway may be different from that in open water. It is well to determine this effect for one's own vessel. The second effect is to produce wind currents in the sea.

2517. Keeping the dead reckoning.—Because of the lack of facilities for fixing the position of a vessel in polar regions, accurate dead reckoning is even more important than elsewhere. The problem is complicated by the fact that the *elements* of dead reckoning, direction and distance, are usually known with less certainty than in lower latitudes. This only heightens the need for *keeping* the dead reckoning with all the accuracy obtainable. This may usually be accomplished by careful hand plotting on the available charts or plotting sheets.

Piloting

2518. Piloting in high latitudes is basically no different from that elsewhere. However, in polar regions piloting is the primary method of marine navigation. As previously indicated, dead reckoning is difficult and generally less accurate than in lower latitudes.

Piloting is associated with proximity to land and shoal water. A ship in polar regions is seldom far from land, and the areas are not so accurately surveyed that the navigator can be sure that uncharted shoals are not nearby.

Piloting is characterized by an alertness not required when a vessel is far from danger of grounding. Nowhere is this alertness more necessary than in polar regions. Added to the usual reasons for constant vigilance are the uncertainties of charted information and the lack of detail, as discussed in article 2509.

2519. Natural landmarks are plentiful in some areas, but their usefulness is restricted by the difficulty in identifying them, or locating them on the chart. Along many of the coasts the various points and inlets bear a marked resemblance to each other. The appearance of a coast is often very different when many of its features are obliterated by a heavy covering of snow or ice than when it is ice-free.

2520. Bearings are useful, but have limitations. When bearings on more than two objects are taken, they may fail to intersect at a point because the objects may not be charted in their correct relation to each other. Even a point fix may be considerably in error geographically if all of the objects used are shown in correct relation to each other, but in the wrong position on the earth. However, in restricted waters it is usually more important to know the position of the vessel relative to nearby land and shoals than its latitude and longitude. The bearing and distance of even an unidentified or uncharted point are valuable.

When a position is established relative to nearby landmarks, it is good practice to use this to help establish the identity and location of some prominent feature a considerable distance ahead, so that this feature, in turn, can be used to establish future positions.

In high latitudes it is not unusual to make use of bearings on objects a considerable distance from the vessel. Because of the rapid convergence of the meridians in these areas, such bearings are not correctly represented by straight lines on a Mercator chart. If this projection is used, the bearings should be corrected in the same manner that radio bearings are corrected (using table 1), since both can be considered great circles. Neither visual nor radio bearings are corrected when plotted on a Lambert conformal or polar steorographic chart.

2521. Soundings are so important in polar regions that echo sounders are customarily operated continuously while the vessel is underway. It is good practice to have at least two such instruments, preferably those of the recording type and having a wide flexibility in the range of the recorder. In few parts of the polar regions have enough soundings been obtained and made available to charting agencies to permit adequate portrayal of the bottom configuration. However, since depth of water is a primary consideration in avoiding an unwanted grounding, a constant watch should be maintained to avoid unobserved shoaling.

Polar regions have relatively few shoals, but in some areas, notably along the Labrador coast, a number of pinnacles and ledges rise abruptly from the bottom. These constitute a real danger to vessels, since they are generally not surrounded by any apparent shoaling. In such an area, or when entering an unknown harbor or any area of questionable safety, it is good practice to send one or more small craft ahead with portable sounding gear.

In very deep water, of the order of 1,000 fathoms or more, the echo returned from the bottom is sometimes masked by the sound of ice coming in contact with the hull, but this is generally not a problem when the bottom is close enough to be menacing.

The hand lead is of little value to a ship underway in ice, because the ice generally prevents its effective use unless the vessel is stopped.

If a ship becomes **beset** by ice, so that steerage way is lost and the vessel drifts with the ice, it may be in danger of grounding as the ice moves over a shoal. Hence, it is important that soundings be continued even when beset. If necessary, a hole should be made in the ice and a hand lead used. A vessel with limited means for freeing itself may prudently save such means for use only when there is danger of grounding.

Useful information on the depth of water in the vicinity of a ship can sometimes be obtained by watching the ice. A stream of ice moving faster than surrounding ice, or a stretch of open water in loose pack ice often marks the main channel through shoal water. A patch of stationary ice in the midst of moving ice often marks a shoal.

Knowledge of earth formations may also prove helpful. The slope of land is often an indication of the underwater gradient. Shoal water is often found off low islands, spits, etc., but seldom near a steep shore. Where glaciation has occurred, the moraine deposits are likely to have formed a bar some distance offshore. Submerged rocks and pinnacles are more likely to be encountered off a rugged shore than near a low, sandy beach.

2522. Anchorages.—Because good anchorages are not plentiful in high latitudes, there is an understandable temptation to be less demanding in their selection. This is dangerous practice, for in polar regions some of the requirements are accentuated. The factors to be considered are:

1. *Holding quality of the bottom.* In polar regions a rocky bottom or one with only fair to poor holding qualities is not uncommon. Sometimes the bottom is steep or irregular. Since the nature of the bottom is seldom adequately shown on charts, a wise precaution is to sample the bottom, and sound in the vicinity before anchoring.

2. *Adequacy of room for swing.* Because high winds are frequent along polar shores, sometimes with little or no warning, long scopes of anchor chain are customarily used. Some harbors are otherwise suitable, but allow inadequate room for swing of the vessel at anchor, or even for its yaw in a high wind. If a vessel is to anchor in an unsurveyed area, the area should first be adequately covered by small boats with portable sounding gear to detect any obstructions.

3. *Protection from wind and sea.* In polar regions protection from wind is probably the most difficult requirement to meet. Generally, high land is accompanied by strong wind blowing directly down the side of the mountains. Polar winds are extremely variable, both in direction and speed. Shifts of 180° accompanied by an increase in speed of more than 50 knots in a few minutes have been reported. It is important that ground tackle be in good condition and that maximum-weight anchors be used. All available weather reports should be obtained and a continuous watch kept on the local weather. Whenever a heavy blow might reasonably be anticipated, the main engines should be kept in an operating condition and on a standby status. Heavy seas are seldom a problem.

4. *Availability of suitable exit in event of extreme weather.* In ice areas it is important that a continuous watch be kept to prevent blocking of the entrance by ice, or actual damage to the vessel by floating ice. However, in an unsurveyed area it may be dangerous to shift anchorage without first sounding the area. It is a wise precaution to do this in advance. Unless the vessel is immediately endangered by ice, it is generally safer to remain at anchor with optimum ground tackle and use of engines to assist

in preventing dragging, than to proceed to sea in a high wind, especially in the presence of icebergs and growlers, and particularly during darkness.

5. *Availability of objects for position determination.* The familiar polar problem of establishing a position by inaccurately charted or inadequately surveyed landmarks is accentuated when an accurate position is desired to establish the position of an anchor. Sometimes a trial and error method is needed, and it may be necessary to add landmarks located by radar or visual observation. Because of chart inadequacy, the suitability of an anchorage, from the standpoint of availability of suitable landmarks, cannot always be adequately predicted before arrival.

An unsurveyed harbor should be entered with caution at slow speed, with both the pilot house and engine room force alerted to possible radical changes in speed or course with little or no warning. The anchor should be kept ready for letting go on short notice and should be adequately attended. An engine combination providing full backing power should be maintained.

2523. Sailing directions for high latitudes contain a wealth of valuable information acquired by those who have previously visited the areas. However, since high latitudes have not been visited with the frequency of other areas, and since they are inadequately surveyed, the sailing directions for polar areas are neither as complete nor as accurate as for other areas, and information on unvisited areas is completely lacking. Until traffic in high latitudes increases and the sailing directions for these areas incorporate the additional information obtained, unusual caution should accompany their use. Each vessel that enters polar regions can help correct this condition by recording accurate information and sending it to the Defense Mapping Agency Hydrographic Center or its counterpart in other countries.

Electronics and Navigation

2524. Propagation.—In general, radio wave propagation in high latitudes follows the same principles that apply elsewhere, as described in chapter XL. However, certain anomalous conditions occur, and although these are but imperfectly understood, and experience to date has not always seemed consistent, there is much that has been established. An understanding of these conditions is important if maximum effective use is to be made of electronics in high latitudes. Such anomalous conditions are discussed in chapters XL and XLIII.

2525. Radar.—In polar regions, where fog and long periods of continuous daylight or darkness reduce the effectiveness of both celestial navigation and visual piloting, and where other electronic aids are generally not available, radar is particularly valuable. Its value is further enhanced by the fact that polar seas are generally smooth, resulting in relatively little oscillation of the shipborne antenna. When ice is not present, relatively little sea return is encountered from the calm sea.

However, certain limitations attend the use of radar in polar regions. Similarity of detail along the polar shore is even more apparent by radar than by visual observation. Lack of accurate detail on charts adds to the difficulty of identification. Identification is even more of a problem when the shoreline is beyond the radar horizon and accurate contours are not shown on the chart. When an extensive ice pack extends out from shore, accurate location of the shoreline is extremely difficult.

Good training and extensive experience are needed to interpret accurately the returns in polar regions where ice may cover both land and sea. A number of icebergs close to a shore may be too close together to be resolved, giving an altered appearance to a shoreline, or they may be mistaken for off-lying islands. The shadow of an iceberg or pressure ridge and the lack of return from an open lead in the ice may easily be confused. Smooth ice may look like open water. In making rendezvous, one might inadvertently close on an iceberg instead of a ship.

As with visual bearings, radar bearings need correction for convergency unless the objects observed are quite close to the ship.

2526. Long-range and worldwide radionavigation aids, such as Loran-C, Omega, and the Navy Navigation Satellite System, are particularly useful in the Arctic because of the scarcity of aids of shorter range. Such short range aids as may be in existence are subject to damage or failure by ice or storms, or other causes. Ice and storm damage may be widespread and require considerable time to repair. Isolated damage may exist for a long time without being discovered and reported.

2527. Other electronic aids are virtually nonexistent in polar regions.

The *radio direction finder* is useful when the few transmitting stations are within range. One of the principal uses of RDF in polar regions is to assist in locating other vessels, for rendezvous or other purposes. This is particularly true in an area of many icebergs, where radar may not distinguish between ships and icebergs.

Consol is available in the Norwegian Sea between Norway and Greenland.

The *echo sounder* is highly useful, as indicated in article 2521, and is operated continuously in high latitudes.

Sonar is useful primarily for detecting ice, particularly growlers. Since about ½ to ⅞ of the ice is under water, its presence can sometimes be detected by sonar when it is overlooked by radar or visual observation.

Celestial Navigation

2528. Celestial navigation in high latitudes.—Of the various types of navigation, celestial is perhaps least changed in polar regions. However, certain special considerations are applicable.

Because of the limitations of other forms of navigation, as discussed earlier in this chapter, celestial navigation provides the principal means of determining geographical position. However, as indicated in article 2520, position relative to nearby dangers is usually of more interest to the polar navigator than geographical position. Since ships in high latitudes are seldom far from land, and since celestial navigation is attended by several limitations, discussed in article 2529, its use in marine navigation is generally confined to the following applications:

1. navigation while proceeding to and from polar regions;
2. checking the accuracy of dead reckoning;
3. checking the accuracy of charted positions of landmarks, shoals, etc; and
4. providing a directional reference, either by means of a celestial compass or by providing a means of checking the magnetic or gyrocompass.

Although its applications are limited, celestial navigation is important in high latitudes. Application 3 above, and application 4, even more so, can be of great value to the polar navigator.

2529. Celestial observations.—The best celestial fixes are usually obtained by star observations during twilight. As the latitude increases, these periods become longer, providing additional time for observation. But with this increase comes longer periods when the sun is just below the horizon and the stars have not yet appeared. During this period, which in the extreme condition at the pole lasts for several *days*, no celestial observations may be available. The moon is sometimes above the horizon during this period and bright planets, notably Venus and Jupiter, may be visible. With practice, the brighter stars can be observed when the sun is 2° to 3° below the horizon.

Beyond the polar circles the sun remains above the horizon without setting during part of the summer. The length of this period increases with latitude. At Thule, Greenland, about 10° inside the Arctic Circle, the sun remains above the horizon for four months. During this period of continuous daylight the sun circles the sky, changing azimuth about 15° each hour. A careful observation, or the average of several observations, each two hours provides a series of running fixes. An even better check on position is provided by making hourly observations and establishing the most probable position at each observation. Sometimes the moon is above the horizon, but within several days of the new or full phase it provides lines of position nearly parallel to the sunlines and hence of limited value in establishing fixes.

During the long polar night the sun is not available and the horizon is often indistinct. However, the long twilight, a bright aurora, and other sources of polar light (art. 2504) shorten this period. By adapting their eyes to darkness, some navigators can make reasonably accurate observations throughout the polar night. The full moon in winter remains above the horizon more than half the time and attains higher altitudes than at other seasons.

In addition to the long periods of darkness in high latitudes, other conditions are sometimes present to complicate the problem of locating the horizon. During daylight the horizon is frequently obscured by low fog, frost smoke, or blowing snow, yet the sun may be clearly visible. Hummocked sea ice is sometimes a problem, particularly at low heights of eye. Nearby land or an extensive ice foot can also be troublesome. Extreme conditions of abnormal refraction are not uncommon in high latitudes, sometimes producing false horizons and always affecting the refraction and dip corrections.

Because of these conditions, it is advisable to be provided with an artificial-horizon sextant (art. 1513). This instrument is generally not used aboard ship because of the excessive acceleration error encountered as the ship rolls and pitches. However, in polar regions there is generally little such motion and in the ice there may be virtually none. Some practice is needed to obtain good results with an artificial-horizon sextant, but these results are sometimes superior to those obtainable with a marine sextant, and when some of the conditions mentioned above prevail, the artificial-horizon sextant may provide the only means of making an observation. Better results with this instrument can generally be obtained if the instrument is hung from some support, as it generally is when used in aircraft.

An artificial horizon (art. 1512) can sometimes be used effectively, even an improvised one, as by placing heavy lubricating oil in a bucket.

It is sometimes possible to make better observations by artificial-horizon sextant or artificial horizon from a nearby cake of ice than from the ship.

Clouds and high fog are frequent in high latitudes, but it is not uncommon, particularly in the Antarctic, for the fog to lift for brief periods, permitting an alert navigator to obtain observations.

As the latitude increases, an error of time has less effect upon altitude. At the equator an error of 4 seconds in time may result in an error in the location of the position line of as much as 1 mile. At latitude 60° a position error of this magnitude cannot occur unless the timing error is 8 seconds. At 70° nearly 12 seconds are needed, and at 80° about 23 seconds are needed for such a position error.

Polaris is of diminished value in high northern latitudes because of its high altitude. At high latitudes the second correction to observed altitude (a_1) becomes greater. The almanac makes no provision for applying this beyond latitude 68°. Bodies at high altitudes are not desirable for azimuth determination, but if Polaris is used, the use of the actual azimuth given at the bottom of the Polaris tables of the *Nautical Almanac* is of increased importance because of its larger variation from 000° in high latitudes. No azimuth is provided beyond latitude 65°.

In applying a sextant altitude correction for dip of the horizon, one should use height of eye *above the ice at the horizon*, instead of height above water. The difference between ice and water levels at the horizon can often be estimated by observing ice near the vessel.

2530. Low-altitude observations.—Because of large and variable refraction at low altitudes, navigators customarily avoid observations below some minimum, usually 5° to 15°, if higher bodies can be observed. In polar regions low-altitude observations are often the only ones available. The sun, moon, and planets remain low in the sky for relatively long periods, their diurnal motion being nearly horizontal. The only lower limit is that imposed by the horizon itself. In fact, good observations can sometimes be made without a sextant by noting the time at which either the upper or lower limb is tangent to the horizon. To such an observation sextant altitude corrections are applied as for a marine sextant without an index correction.

Correction of low-altitude observations made by marine sextant is discussed in article 1625. If a bubble or other artificial-horizon sextant is used, corrections are made as for higher altitudes, being careful to use the refraction value corrected for temperature, or to make a separate correction for air temperature. In addition, a correction for atmospheric pressure (tab. 24) is applied if of sufficient size to be of importance.

Solution of low-altitude observations is discussed in article 2023.

2531. Abnormal refraction and dip.—Tables of refraction correction are based upon a standard atmosphere. Variations in this atmosphere result in changes in the refraction, and since the atmosphere is seldom exactly standard, the mean refraction is seldom the same as shown in the tables. Variations from standard conditions are usually not great enough to be troublesome.

In polar regions, however, it is normal for the atmosphere to differ considerably from the standard, particularly near the surface. This affects both refraction and dip, as indicated in article 1605. Outside polar regions, variations in refraction seldom exceed 2′ or 3′, although extreme values of more than 30′ have been encountered. In polar regions refraction variations of several minutes are not uncommon and an extreme value of about 5° has been reported. This would produce an error of 300 miles in a line of position. The sun has been known to rise as much as ten *days* before it was expected.

Most celestial observations in polar regions produce satisfactory results, but the high-latitude navigator should be on the alert for abnormal conditions, since they occur more often than elsewhere, and have greater extreme values. A wise precaution is to apply corrections for air temperature (tab. 23) and atmospheric pressure (tab. 24), particularly for altitudes of less than 5°.

Abnormal dip affects the accuracy of celestial observations equally at any altitude, if the visible horizon is used. Such errors may be avoided in any *one* of four ways:

1. The artificial-horizon sextant may be used, as indicated in article 2529.

2. When stars are available, three stars may be observed at azimuth intervals of approximately 120°, (or four at 90° intervals, five at 72°, etc.). Any error in dip *or refraction* will alter the size of the enclosed figure, but will not change the location of its center unless the dip or refraction error varies in different directions. The stars should preferably be at the same altitude.

3. The altitude of a single body may be observed twice, facing in opposite directions. The sum of the two readings differs from 180° by twice the sum of the index and dip corrections (also personal and instrument corrections, if present). This method assumes that dip is the same in both directions, an assumption that is usually approximately cor-

rect. Also, the method requires that the arc of the sextant be sufficiently long and the altitude of the body sufficiently great to permit observation of the back sight in the opposite direction. In making such observations, it is necessary that allowance be made for the change of altitude between readings. This may be done by taking a direct sight, a back sight, and then another direct sight at equal intervals of time, and using the average of the two direct sights.

4. A correction for the difference between air and sea temperatures (art. 814, vol. II) may be applied to the sextant altitude. This will often provide reasonably good results. However, there is considerable disagreement in the manner in which temperature is to be measured, and in the factor to use for any given difference. Therefore, the validity of this correction is not fully established.

There is still much to be learned regarding refraction and even with all known precautions, results may occasionally be unsatisfactory.

2532. Sight reduction in polar regions is virtually the same as elsewhere. Computation can be made by nearly any method. In Pub. No. 214, tabulations are not extended below an altitude of 5°, but this method can be used for lower altitudes, which are not uncommon in polar regions, by selecting an assumed position some distance away, in the general direction of the body. Thus, if the altitude is 2°, an assumed position 3° (180 miles) nearer the body (4° is a better choice to allow for possible error in the dead reckoning and for adjustment for a convenient assumed position) should result in a computed altitude of 5° or more. This method will result in an unusually long altitude intercept, but the error introduced will be negligible *if* the assumed position is in the direction of the body, and the chart used is one on which a straight line is a close approximation to a great circle. A Lambert conformal chart is satisfactory for this purpose. An example of such a solution is given in article 2023.

One special method of considerable interest is conveniently applicable only within about 5° of the pole, a higher latitude than is usually attainable by ships. This is the method of using the pole as the assumed position. At this point the zenith and pole coincide and hence the celestial equator and celestial horizon also coincide, and the systems of coordinates based upon these two great circles of the celestial sphere become identical. The declination is computed altitude, and GHA replaces azimuth. A "toward" altitude intercept is plotted along the upper branch of the meridian over which the body is located, and an "away" intercept is plotted in the opposite direction, along the lower branch. Such a line or its AP is advanced or retired in the usual manner. This method is a special application of the meridian altitude sometimes used in lower latitudes. Beyond the limits of this method the meridian altitude can be used in the usual manner (art. 2025) without complications and with time of transit being less critical. However, table 29, for reduction to the meridian, extends only to latitude 60°.

2533. Plotting lines of position from celestial observations.—Lines of position from celestial observations in polar regions are plotted as elsewhere, using an assumed position, altitude intercept, and azimuth. If a Mercator chart is used, the error introduced by using rhumb lines for the azimuth line (a great circle) and line of position (a small circle) is accentuated. This can be overcome by using a chart on a more favorable projection.

If a chart with nonparallel meridians, such as the Lambert conformal, is used, the true azimuth should be plotted by protractor or plotter and measured at the meridian of the assumed position. On a chart having a grid overprint the true azimuth can be converted to grid azimuth, using the longitude of the assumed position, and the direction measured from any grid line. This method involves an additional step, with no real advantage.

Lines of position from high-altitude observations, to be plotted as circles with the geographical position as the center (art. 2024), should not be plotted on a Mercator chart because of the rapid change of scale, resulting in distortion of the circle as plotted on the chart.

Lines of position are advanced or retired as in any latitude. However, the movement of the line is no more accurate than the estimate of the direction and distance traveled, and in polar regions this estimate may be of less than usual accuracy. In addition to his problem of estimated direction of travel, the polar navigator may encounter difficulty in accurately plotting the direction determined. If an accurate gyrocompass is used, the ship follows a rhumb line, which is accurately shown only on a Mercator chart. If a magnetic compass is used, the rapid change in variation may be a disturbing factor. If the ship is in ice, the course line may be far from straight.

Because of the various possible sources of error involved, it is good practice to avoid advancing or retiring lines for a period longer than about two hours. When the sun is the only body available, best results can sometimes be obtained by making an observation every hour, retiring the most recent line one hour and advancing for one hour the line obtained two hours previously. The present position is then obtained by dead reckoning from the running fix of an hour before. Another technique is to advance the one or two previous lines to the present time for a running fix. A third method is to drop a perpendicular from the dead reckoning or estimated position to the line of position to obtain a new estimated position, from which a new dead reckoning plot is carried forward to the time of the next observation. A variation of this method is to evaluate the relative accuracy of the new line of position and the dead reckoning or estimated position run up from the previous position and take some point *between* them, halfway if no information is available on which to evaluate the relative accuracies. None of these techniques is suitable for determining set and drift of the current.

2534. Rising, setting, and twilight data are tabulated in the almanacs to latitude 72°N and 60°S. Within these limits the times of these phenomena are determined as explained in chapter XIX.

Beyond the northern limits of these tables the values can be obtained from a series of graphs given near the back of the *Air Almanac*. These graphs are shown in appendix G. For high latitudes, graphs are used instead of tables because graphs give a clearer picture of conditions, which may change radically with relatively little change in position or date. Under these conditions interpolation to practical precision is simpler by graph than by table. In those parts of the graph which are difficult to read, the times of the phenomena's occurrence are themselves uncertain, being altered considerably by a relatively small change in refraction or height of eye. The use of the graphs is explained in chapter XIX.

General

2535. Ice.—Several references have been made to ice. The almost constant presence of large quantities of ice is one of the distinctive features of polar regions, and is one of the primary considerations in any operations in these areas. The subject of ice in the sea is covered in chapter XXXVI.

2536. Knowledge of polar regions.—Operations in polar regions are attended by hazards and problems not encountered elsewhere. Lack of knowledge, sometimes accompanied by fear of the unknown, has prevented navigation in these areas from being conducted with the same confidence with which it is pursued in more familiar areas. As experience in high latitudes has increased, much of the mystery surrounding these areas has been dispelled, and operations there have become more predictable.

Before entering polar regions, the navigator will do well to acquaint himself with the experience of those who have preceded him into the areas and under the conditions he anticipates. This information can be found in a growing literature composed of the accounts of explorers, reports of previous operations in high latitudes, articles in professional journals, and several books on operations in polar regions. Some of it is given in various volumes of sailing directions.

The search for knowledge should not be confined to navigation. The wise polar navigator will seek information on living conditions, survival, geography, ice, climate and weather, and operational experience of others who have been to the same area. As elsewhere, knowledge and experience are valuable.

2537. Planning, important in any operation, is vital to the success of polar navigation. The first step to adequate planning is the acquisition of full knowledge, as discussed in article 2536. No item, however trivial, should escape attention. The ship should be provided with all the needed charts, publications, and special navigational material. All available data and information from previous operations in the area should be studied. Key personnel should be adequately instructed in polar navigation prior to departure or while en route to the polar regions. Forecasts on anticipated ice and weather conditions should be obtained before departure and after getting under way. All equipment should be put in top operating condition. All material should be carefully inspected for completeness and condition. The navigator should make certain that all items of equipment are familiar to those who will use them. This is particularly true of items not generally used at sea, such as charts on an unfamiliar projection, or a bubble sextant. Do not *assume* anything that can be *known*. On the adequacy and thoroughness of the advanced planning and preparation, perhaps more than anything else, will depend the success of polar navigation.

CHAPTER XXVI

LIFEBOAT NAVIGATION

Before Emergency Arises

2601. Introduction.—The methods and techniques used in lifeboat navigation are those available at the time. With full equipment, lifeboat navigation differs little from that aboard ship. More often, however, it is a matter of improvising equipment from available materials, and developing procedures from a knowledge of basic principles. Ingenuity is often essential. The officer who navigates by blindly "following the steps" may be of little more value in a lifeboat devoid of familiar navigational equipment than the man who has never set foot on the bridge of a ship. The wise officer becomes thoroughly familiar with the theory of navigation: the celestial triangle, the circle of equal altitude, and the other basic principles involved. He should be able to identify the most useful stars, and know how to solve his sights by any widely used method, because his favorite method may not be available. He should be able to construct a plotting sheet with a protractor, and use distress signaling equipment. Familiarity with the coordinates (latitude and longitude) of land points in the area of operations, ability to interpret wind and weather signs, knowledge of the ocean currents, and skill in handling a small boat are parts of the practical navigator's basic education which assume their greatest importance in an emergency. For the navigator prepared with such knowledge, and a determination to succeed, the situation is never hopeless. *Some* method of navigation is always available.

2602. Emergency navigation kit.—In time of national emergency, the prudent navigator will provide each lifeboat with a kit containing the equipment which it is practical to carry for emergency navigational purposes (art. 2603). Even in peacetime it is good practice to have one such kit permanently located in the chart house or the wheel house so that it can be quickly transferred to a lifeboat when needed.

The least preparation made should be a check-off list of items to be assembled if time permits, so that nothing will be overlooked. Such a list can be helpful even if one or more emergency kits have been provided. The list should be kept in a prominent place on the bridge or near the lifeboats, perhaps framed under glass. All officers should be familiar with its location and should be acquainted with the location and identity of each item listed.

Junior officers or reliable crew members should be assigned the duty of bringing to their stations, during abandon ship drill, emergency navigational equipment not permanently stowed in the boats. A senior officer should then check each item against the equipment check-off list to ascertain that nothing has been overlooked.

2603. Equipment.—If practicable, full navigational equipment should be provided. As many as possible of the items in the following list should be included. All of these except a timepiece, and possibly a sextant and radio, can be kept in the emergency navigation kit recommended in article 2602.

1. **Notebook** suitable for use as a deck log and for performing computations. Several items of information should be written in this notebook in advance, so as to be available when and if needed. Such items include the latitude and longitude of various places in the area of operation; any desired information on currents and weather; declination and SHA of several widely scattered stars, with any needed information

on identifying them; desired notes and tables from this chapter and elsewhere; any desired general information, such as a list of poisonous fish and those items which may prove useful for survival. This section of the notebook should be brief and the items limited to those most essential in time of emergency.

2. **Charts and other plotting materials.** A pilot chart is most suitable for lifeboat use, both for plotting and as a source of information on variation of the compass, shipping lanes, currents, winds, and weather. Charts for both the summer and winter seasons should be included. During World War II pilot charts were printed on waterproof material suitable for use in a lifeboat. **Plotting sheets** (art. 323) are useful but not essential if charts are available. The plotting sheets should cover the latitudes in which the ship operates. **Universal plotting sheets** (art. 324) may be preferred, particularly if the latitude coverage is large. Several **maneuvering boards,** and several sheets of **cross-section paper** (preferably with ten squares per inch) should be included, as these have many uses.

3. **Plotting equipment.** Pencils, erasers, straightedge, protractor, dividers and compasses (not essential, but useful), and a knife or pencil sharpener should be included. Preferably, the straightedge and protractor should be combined in a single device constituting some kind of **plotter** (art. 605). A ruler graduated in inches and fractions may be useful.

4. **Timepiece.** A good watch is needed if longitude is to be determined astronomically. This watch should be waterproof or kept in a waterproof container which permits reading and winding of the watch without exposing it to the elements. The watch should be wound regularly and a record kept of its error and rate of change. Even if one or more such watches are available, the possibility of taking along the chronometers should not be overlooked. The optimum timepiece is a quartz crystal watch.

5. **Sextant.** A marine sextant should be taken along if possible. However, since this may be impractical, a lifeboat sextant, or materials for constructing one, should be provided. The relatively inexpensive plastic sextants should be more than adequate for lifeboat use. They should be protected from the direct rays of the sun when not in use. Several commercially manufactured lifeboat sextants have been made available, particularly during wartime. A lifeboat sextant can be made of wood or other rigid material, two small mirrors, and a pivot. The graduations of the arc should be double those of a compass rose (an angle of 5° should be labeled 10°, etc.). It is not necessary to provide a vernier, or means of adjusting the sextant, since accuracy of 0°.1 is satisfactory for lifeboat use.

6. **Almanac.** A *Nautical Almanac* for the current year is desirable. In an emergency an almanac for another year can be used for stars and the sun without serious error by lifeboats standards, if suitable adjustment is made (art. 2617). Some form of long-term almanac, as that given in appendix H, might well be copied or pasted in the notebook suggested as item 1, above.

7. **Tables.** Some form of table will be needed for reducing celestial observations. The most suitable is one that does not require much space. If a table of trigonometric functions (either logarithmic or natural) is provided, formulas should be included with them. It is not wise to trust the memory for such vital information. A set of tables similar to Pub. No. 214 can be made at 5° intervals of the arguments. Only one page is needed for each latitude entry (5°) if declination is limited to about 30° (sufficient for bodies of the solar system and many stars), entries are given to the nearest 0°.1 for altitudes and 1° for azimuth, and the delta (Δ) values are omitted. **Traverse tables** and others given in this chapter are useful. Volume II provides tables of trigonometric functions (logarithmic and natural), formulas, a long-term almanac, traverse tables,

and a sight reduction table (table 35). Due to its contents, volume II would be very useful in a lifeboat.

8. **Compass.** Each lifeboat is required to carry a magnetic compass. A deviation table for each compass should be made while in port, with magnetic material in its normal place. It would be well to check the accuracy of each table periodically.

9. **Flashlight.** A flashlight is required to be carried in each lifeboat. The batteries should be replaced from time to time, as necessary. Extra batteries and bulbs might well be carried.

10. **Portable radio.** If a portable radio is available, be sure it is included. Whether this is one of the transmitting-receiving sets approved by the Federal Communications Commission for lifeboat use, or merely a small receiver of limited range owned by a crew member, do not overlook it, as it may be used as a radio direction finder.

2604. Position of ship.—A knowledge of the position of the vessel at the time it is abandoned is of great importance. The officer on watch on the bridge should never permit himself to become careless in the matter of keeping a mental note of the approximate position of the vessel. During wartime, or whenever the possibility of abandoning ship might reasonably be anticipated, the radio operator should be provided with a list of advance dead reckoning positions.

Abandoning Ship

2605. Before lowering boats.—The period between the decision to abandon ship and the actual leaving of the vessel is a highly important one. It is also a period of mental strain and possible confusion. The degree to which the crew can be prepared for the ordeal ahead depends upon the amount of time available and the thoroughness of the preparation that has been made. If there has been advance warning of the possibility of the decision, certain preparations can be made before the decision is reached. If time permits, after the decision to abandon ship has been made, the radio operator should send a final distress message, giving the ship's position and any other pertinent information. It will be important later to know whether an acknowledgment of receipt of the message was received. Any available time can be wisely used to check the navigational equipment in each boat and assemble missing items. There may be time to make a last minute check of position of the ship, position of any nearby land, set and drift of current, present and forecast weather, watch error, and date. These items should be written down. Perhaps the chart can be taken along. Equipment should be properly secured before lowering the boats. In a rough sea it may be desirable to lower the sextant, chronometer, and radio into the boat after it is afloat.

2606. Establishing command.—The identity of the person in command of each boat, and the over-all commander, should be firmly established. Almost invariably this will be the senior officer present. In a lifeboat, perhaps more than in any other circumstances, strong leadership is required if the confidence of the crew is to be maintained. The officer whom the crew respects as a *man*, admires as a *seaman*, and recognizes as a *gentleman* will have little or no trouble with discipline and cooperation of all on board.

Morale is a prime consideration, and it grows in importance with the passage of time. The person in command should be recognized as the final authority in all matters, but it is important that he give to each person an opportunity to be heard, and that he keep all hands fully informed of the bad as well as of the good. Decisions will be more acceptable if the crew has been informed of each consideration as it arises, and so has been somewhat prepared. Complete fairness and impartiality are essential.

2607. Estimate of the situation.—Perhaps the first item which should engage the attention of the person in command, after the lifeboat has cleared the stricken vessel, is the questioning of each person aboard to collect all the useful information available. It is well to determine what is known regarding the position of the ship, ocean currents, weather, astronomy, navigation, seamanship, sailing, etc. Find out who owns watches and what each owner knows about the error and rate of his watch. Establish a routine for winding and comparing them. No useful skill or knowledge should be overlooked; all should be fully considered in making the important decision of whether to remain in the vicinity of the disaster in the hope of rescue, or to attempt to reach land or a more heavily traveled shipping lane.

This decision of whether to stay or leave may be the most important one of the entire experience. Until comparatively recent times there was no problem. Because there was virtually no hope of assistance, the lifeboat crew had to rely upon itself. Since the development of modern communication and rescue facilities, however, it is often wiser to remain than to complicate the rescue problem by increasing the area to be searched.

The decision should not be made until careful consideration has been given to all factors, nor should it be delayed longer than necessary. Considerations vary with the circumstances, but certainly the following should be included:

Was a distress message sent before the ship was abandoned? Did it include the position of the ship? How accurate was the position? Is there any reasonable doubt that the message was received? If no message was sent, how soon will the ship be missed? What rescue facilities are available? How far away are they and how long will it be before help arrives? How conspicuous is the lifeboat? What facilities are available for attracting attention, either visually or by radar? How proficient is the crew in using such equipment? Is a radio transmitter available? What is the probable running time to the nearest land in several directions, considering the prevailing winds and currents, the motive power available (art. 2614), and the ability of the crew to use it? How long will the fresh water and rations last, and will they be sufficient to sustain the crew in the physical exertion required?

If the decision is to stay, how will the crew occupy its time, remembering the increased morale problem with an idle crew? How will position be maintained, or regained if the boat drifts? Would it be practical to wait two or three days, perhaps, in the hope of rescue, and then to set out for land if help does not come?

If the decision is to leave, where should the boat head? How soon can a well-traveled shipping lane be reached? In time of war, where is the enemy and where are friends? How large and conspicuous is the land in each direction, considering the low height of eye in a lifeboat? It may be better to head for conspicuous land 500 miles away than for a small, low island 200 miles away, particularly if the latter is in a direction of unfavorable winds or currents, or takes the boat farther away from shipping lanes.

Avoid, if possible, a hasty decision that will later be recognized as unwise. Discuss the matter thoroughly with the crew, and when the decision is made, inform them of the reason for it. Do this in a manner that will invite their confidence and support. Inform them of the best estimate of the situation.

2608. Selecting the route.—It is not always desirable to head directly for the objective. A longer route with favorable winds and currents may be quicker. A longer route by way of shipping lanes may enhance the possibility of rescue.

With clear skies, latitude can be found with relatively crude equipment. But unless accurate Greenwich time is available, longitude cannot be found astronomically, even with the best equipment; nor is a nonastronomical method likely to be available. In the absence of reliable longitude information, it is better to head for a point at the latitude of the destination but so far east or west of it that no reasonable doubt will exist as to the direction of land when that latitude is reached. The distance of the point from the destination depends upon the degree of uncertainty of the longitude, remembering that this uncertainty is likely to increase with time. This method of "parallel sailing" was used for centuries before a method of determining or "discovering" longitude at sea was developed.

If the objective has a considerable extent in a north-south direction, the need for a final east-west leg is less critical, and in attempting to reach a continent or very large island, one need not consider it at all. In the absence of better information, an east or west course should be selected from the outset, since most large land masses of the earth are oriented in a general north-south direction.

2609. Keeping boats together.—If more than one boat is launched, every effort should be made to keep them together. While the person in charge of each boat is responsible for decisions regarding his boat, considerable advantage is to be gained by keeping the boats together and recognizing one person, logically the senior officer present, as the over-all commander. Since navigational equipment and skill probably will differ widely from boat to boat, the benefits of any accurate navigation can be shared by all if the boats are close together. Other knowledge can be exchanged, equipment shared, and rations distributed equitably. It may be wise to shift some personnel among the boats, perhaps on a periodic basis, either to effect a better balance of skill and knowledge, or for morale purposes.

2610. Lookout.—Always there is the possibility of sighting another vessel. Hence, a lookout should be posted at all times. This becomes of even greater importance when approaching land, or if the location of all land along the route is not known. If it is possible to rig a metal object high in the boat, this should be done to enhance the possibility of detection by radar.

Dead Reckoning

2611. Importance of dead reckoning.—Of the various kinds of navigation, dead reckoning alone is always available in some form. It should never be neglected, but in a lifeboat it is of more than average importance. A close check should be kept on the direction and distance made good, and all disturbing elements such as wind and current should be carefully evaluated. Long voyages have been successfully completed by this method alone, and landfalls have been made with surprising accuracy. This is not meant to minimize the importance of other methods of determining position, but with the methods generally available in a lifeboat, one may well find that, during the first few days, his dead reckoning positions are more accurate than those determined by other methods. If the means of determining direction and distance—the elements of dead reckoning—are accurate, it might be well to make an adjustment to the dead reckoning only after consistent indication of the magnitude and direction of its error. The dropping of the dead reckoning at each uncertain "fix" is at best a questionable procedure. The conflicting information likely to be available calls for careful analysis and good judgment on the part of the navigator.

2612. Deck Log.—From the beginning a careful log should be kept. The date and time of abandoning ship should be the first entry, followed by navigational information available, and the various important decisions and the reasons for them. Since the conservation of paper may be important, record only the essentials of the important items, but do not overlook the recording in considerable detail of the selection of a commanding officer, changes in command, deaths, missing persons, and navigational information.

The best determination of the position of abandoning ship should be recorded, followed by a full account of courses, distances, positions, winds, currents, and leeway. No important navigational information should be left to memory if it can be recorded.

2613. Direction.—As one of the elements of dead reckoning, direction is an important item. As indicated in article 2603, a deviation table for each lifeboat compass should be determined in port, and checked periodically. At the first convenient opportunity after abandoning ship the accuracy should be checked on the course to be followed.

If an almanac, accurate Greenwich time, and the necessary tables are available, the azimuth of any celestial body can be computed and this value compared with the azimuth as measured by the compass. If it is difficult to observe the compass azimuth, select a body dead ahead and note the compass heading. The difference between computed and observed azimuths is compass error. This is of more immediate value than deviation, but if the latter is desired, it can be determined by applying to the compass error the variation, from the pilot chart.

Several unique astronomical situations occur, permitting determination of azimuth without computation:

Polaris is always within 2° of true north for observers between the equator and latitude 60°N. When this star is directly above or below the celestial pole, its azimuth is exactly north at any latitude. This occurs approximately when the *trailing* star of either *Cassiopeia* (ε *Cassiopeiae*) or the Big Dipper (Alkaid) is directly above or directly below Polaris (fig. 2621). When a line through the trailing stars and Polaris is horizontal, the maximum correction should be applied. Below latitude 50° this can be considered 1°; and between 50° and 65°, 2°. If *Cassiopeia* is to the *right* of Polaris, the azimuth is 001° (or 002°), and if to the left, 359° (or 358°). The *south* celestial pole is located approximately at the intersection of a line through the longer axis of the Southern Cross with a line from the northernmost star of *Triangulum Australe* perpendicular to the line joining the other two stars of the triangle. No conspicuous star marks this spot (figs. 2205–2208).

Meridian transit. Any celestial body bears due north or south at meridian transit, either upper or lower. This is the moment of maximum (or minimum) altitude of the body. However, since the altitude at this time is nearly constant during a considerable change of azimuth, the instant of meridian transit may be difficult to determine. If time and an almanac are available, and the longitude is known, the time of transit can be computed.

Body on prime vertical. If any method is available for determining when a body is on the prime vertical (due east or west), the compass azimuth at this time can be observed. Table 25 provides this information. Any body on the celestial equator (declination 0°) is on the prime vertical at the time of rising or setting. For the sun this occurs at the time of the equinoxes (art. 1419). The star Mintaka (δ *Orionis*), the *leading* star of *Orion's* belt, has a declination of approximately 0°.3S and can be considered on the celestial equator. For an observer near the equator, such a body is always nearly east or west. Because of refraction and dip, the azimuth should be noted when the center of the sun or a star is a little more than one sun diameter (half a degree) *above* the horizon. The moon should be observed when its *upper* limb is *on* the horizon.

Body at rising or setting. Except for the moon, the azimuth angle (art. 1428) of a body is almost the same at rising as at setting, except that the former is toward the *east* and the latter toward the *west*. If the azimuth is measured *both* at rising and setting, true south (or north) is midway between the two observed values, and the difference between this value and 180° (or 000°) is the compass error. Thus, if the compass azimuth of a body is 073° at rising, and 277° at setting, true south (180°) is at $\frac{073° + 277°}{2} = 175°$ by compass, and the compass error is 5°E. This method may be in error if the boat is moving rapidly in a north or south direction. If the declination and latitude are known, the true azimuth of any body at rising or setting can be determined by means of a diagram on the plane of the celestial meridian (art. 1432) or by computation (art. 2125). For this purpose the body (except the moon) should be considered as rising or setting when its center is a little more than one sun diameter (half a degree) above the horizon, because of refraction and dip.

The direction of the sun in relation to the hands of a watch is sometimes advocated, but the limitations of this method are too great to permit general application.

A simple nonastronomical method can be used for determining the *deviation*. An object that will float but not drift rapidly before the wind is thrown overboard. The boat is then steered as steadily as possible in the *opposite* direction to that desired. At a distance of perhaps half a mile, or more if the floating object is still clearly in view, the boat is turned around in the smallest practicable radius, and headed back toward the floating object. The *magnetic* course is midway between the course toward the object and the *reciprocal* of the course away from the object. Thus, if the boat is on compass course 151° while heading away from the object, and 337° while returning, the magnetic course is midway between 337° and $151° + 180° = 331°$, or $\frac{337° + 331°}{2} = 334°$. Since 334° magnetic is the same as 337° by compass, the deviation on this heading is 3°W.

If a compass is not available, any celestial body can be used to steer by, if its diurnal apparent motion is considered. A reasonably straight course can be steered by noting the direction of the wind, the movement of the clouds, the direction of the waves, or by watching the wake of the boat. A line can be secured to the side of the boat at a point amidships or forward. The line should tend parallel to the centerline of the boat if on a straight course. The angle between the centerline and the wake is an indication of the amount of leeway. The accuracy of the towed-object or wake method is affected adversely by a cross sea.

A body having a declination the same as the latitude of the destination is over the destination once each day, at the time when its hour angle is the same as the longitude, measured westward through 360°. At this time it should be dead ahead if the boat is following the great circle leading directly through the destination.

2614. Motive power.—A lifeboat is equipped with one or more of the following means of locomotion: oars, hand-operated propeller, motor, sail. Inflatable rafts usually have no means of locomotion other than paddles. Of these, only sail offers a practical means of travel over an extended period of time. Men living in an open boat, perhaps on reduced rations, should not attempt to expend their strength on hand locomotion, except for short periods. Likewise, the comparatively small fuel supply in a motorboat should be hoarded jealously. It may be desperately needed later, as for landing through a surf, preventing the boat from drifting onto a rocky coast, or making the land when a strong current is carrying the boat past an island.

A sail should be rigged, for in it lies the best hope of reaching distant land. If the standard lifeboat sail is not available, a substitute can usually be devised, using the boat cover, or even clothing, and oars.

2615. Distance can be determined directly between accurate fixes, but generally it is found by means of speed and elapsed time. A loaded lifeboat will not travel fast, under normal conditions. With fair wind and weather it may make good a speed of about two knots through the water. Hence the importance of wind and current. The navigator used to observing the sea from a high bridge usually overestimates his speed in a lifeboat, where he is only a few feet from the water. With practice, his ability should improve.

Speed may be determined by using a form of **chip log.** Attach a long line to a heavy, floating object. Put one knot in the line twelve or fifteen fathoms from the object, and another just ten fathoms (or any convenient distance) from the first. Stream the device over the side and let the line run out freely, noting the elapsed time between passage of the two knots through the hand. A variation of this is the **Dutchman's log.** A floating object is thrown overboard at the bow, and the elapsed time required for a known length along the centerline to pass it is noted. If a line is attached to the object, it may be used many times. With either variation, it is well to tie the bitter end of the line to the boat, to minimize danger of losing the whole device overboard.

With either the chip or Dutchman's log, the speed is determined by the formula:

$$S = \frac{60 \text{ seconds per minute} \times 60 \text{ minutes per hour} \times \text{feet between marks}}{6,000 \text{ feet per mile} \times \text{seconds of elapsed time}}.$$

This is equal to:

$$S = \frac{3,600 \times \text{feet between marks}}{6,000 \times \text{seconds of elapsed time}} = \frac{0.6 \times \text{feet between marks}}{\text{seconds of elapsed time}}.$$

Since the feet between marks is constant, a convenient number can be selected. Thus, if the length is 16⅔ feet, the formula becomes

$$S = \frac{10}{\text{seconds of elapsed time}}.$$

If the elasped time is ten seconds, the boat is traveling at one knot; if five seconds, at two knots; if eight seconds, at 1¼ knots, etc.

If a watch is not available, a simple pendulum may be devised to time the interval. A piece of string with a weight attached, of a length of 9.8 inches (to the center of gravity of the weight), will, when suspended, make a complete swing (back *and* forth) once every second. For a pendulum 39.1 inches long the period is two seconds. With practice, time can be estimated with fair accuracy.

It is not always possible to head directly along the course to the destination, because of adverse winds. It is better to make good progress in the general direction desired than none at all, and much better on morale. However, at times conditions, may be so adverse that it will be best to drop sail until the wind shifts or abates. At such a time a sea anchor should be streamed to minimize loss of precious mileage, and, in severe conditions, to keep the boat headed into the sea.

2616. Position by dead reckoning.—Plotting can be done directly on a pilot chart or plotting sheet. If this proves too difficult, or if an independent check is desired, some form of mathematical reckoning may be useful. Table 2616, a simplified traverse table, can be used for this purpose. This is a critical-type table, various factors being given for limiting values of certain angles. To find the difference or change of latitude,

ANGLE	0°	18°	31°	41°	49°	56°	63°	69°	75°	81°	87°	90°
FACTOR	1.0	0.9	0.8	0.7	0.6	0.5	0.4	0.3	0.2	0.1	0.0	

TABLE 2616.—Simplified traverse table.

in minutes, enter the table with course angle, reckoned from north or south toward the east or west. Multiply the distance run, in miles, by the factor. To find the departure, in miles, enter the table with the *complement* of the course angle. Multiply the distance run, in miles, by the factor. To convert departure to difference of longitude, in minutes, enter the table with mid latitude. Divide the departure by the factor.

Example.—A lifeboat travels 26 miles on course 205°, from L 41°44′N, λ56°21′W.

Required.—Latitude and longitude of the point of arrival.

Solution.—The course angle is 205°−180°=S25°W, and the complement is 90° −25°=65°. The factors corresponding to these angles are 0.9 and 0.4, respectively. The difference of latitude is 26×0.9=23′ (to the nearest minute) and the departure is 26×0.4=10 mi. Since the course is in the southwestern quadrant, in the Northern Hemisphere, the latitude of the point of arrival is 41°44′N−23′=41°21′N. The factor corresponding to the mid latitude 41°32′N is 0.7. The difference of longitude is 10 ÷0.7=14′. The longitude of the point of arrival is 56°21′W+14′=56°35′W.

Answer.—L41°21′N, λ56°35′W.

Celestial Navigation

2617. Celestial coordinates.—Almanac information, particularly declination and Greenwich hour angle of bodies, is important to celestial navigation. If the current *Nautical Almanac* is available, there is no problem. If the only copy available is for a previous year, it can be used for the sun, Aries, and stars without serious error, by lifeboat standards. However, for greater accuracy, proceed as follows: For declination of the sun, enter the almanac with a time that is *earlier* than the correct time by 5^h49^m times the number of years between the date of the almanac and the correct date, adding 24^h for each February 29 that occurs between the dates. If the date is February 29, use March 1 and reduce by one the number of 24^h periods added. For GHA of the sun or Aries determine the value for the correct time, adjusting the minutes and tenths of arc to agree with that at the time for which the declination is determined. Since the adjustment never exceeds half a degree, care should be used when the value is near a whole degree, to prevent the value from being in error by 1°. Appendix H is a long-term almanac giving values of GHA ♈, and GHA and declination of the sun. Instructions for its use are included in the appendix. A reproduction of this almanac might profitably be included in the navigational kit mentioned in article 2602.

If no almanac is available, a rough approximation of the declination of the sun can be obtained as follows: Count the days from the given date to the *nearer* solstice (June 21 or December 22). Divide this by the number of days from that solstice to the equinox (March 21 or September 23), using the equinox that will result in the given date being between it and the solstice. Multiply the result by 90°. Enter table 2616 with the angle so found, and extract the factor. Multiply this by 23°.45 to find the declination.

Example.1.—The date is August 24.

Required.—The approximate declination of the sun.

Solution.—The number of days from the given date to the nearer solstice (June 21) is 64. There are 94 days between June 21 and September 23. Dividing and multiplying by 90°,

$$\frac{64}{94}\times90°=61°.3.$$

The factor from table 2616 is 0.5. The declination is 23°.45×0.5=11°.7. It is known to be north because of the date.

Answer.—Dec. 11°.7N.

The accuracy of this solution can be improved by considering the factor of table 2616 as the value for the mid angle between the two limiting ones (except that 1.00 is correct for 0° and 0.00 is correct for 90°), and interpolating to one additional decimal. In this instance the interpolation would be between 0.50 at 59°5 and 0.40 at 66°. The interpolated value is 0.47, giving a declination of 11°0N. Still greater accuracy can be obtained by using a table of natural cosines instead of table 2616. By natural cosine the value is 11°3N.

If the latitude is known, the declination of any body can be determined by observing a meridian altitude. In a lifeboat it is usually best to make a number of observations shortly before and after transit, plot the values on cross-section paper, letting the ordinate (vertical scale) represent altitude, and the abscissa (horizontal scale) the time. The altitude is found by fairing a curve or drawing an arc of a circle through the points, and taking the highest value. A meridian altitude problem is then solved in reverse.

Example 2.—The latitude of a lifeboat is 40°16′S. The sun is observed on the meridian, bearing north. The *observed* altitude is 36°29′.

Required.—Declination of the sun.

Solution.—The zenith distance is 90°−36°29′=53°31′. The sun is 53°31′ north of the observer, or 13°15′ north of the equator. Hence, the declination is 13°15′N.

Answer.—Dec. 13°15′N.

The GHA ♈ can be determined approximately by considering it equal to GMT (in angular units) on September 23. To find GHA ♈ on any other date, add 1° for each day following September 23. The value is approximately 90° on December 22, 180° on March 21, and 270° on June 21. The values so found can be in error by as much as several *degrees*, and so should not be used if better information is available. An approximate check is provided by the great circle through Polaris, Caph (the leading star of *Cassiopeia*), and the eastern side of the square of *Pegasus*. When this great circle coincides with the meridian, LHA ♈ is approximately 0°. The hour angle of a body is equal to its SHA plus the hour angle of Aries.

If an error of as much as 4°, or a little more, is acceptable, the GHA of the sun can be considered equal to GMT±180° (12ʰ). For more accurate results, one can make a table of the equation of time from the *Nautical Almanac* perhaps at five- or ten-day intervals, and include this in the emergency navigation kit mentioned in article 2602. The equation of time is applied according to its sign to GMT±180° to find GHA.

2618. Altitude measurement.—If a sextant is available, either one from the pilot house or an emergency-type instrument, altitudes are measured in the usual manner. The sextant should be shielded as much as possible from wind and spray. If the sea is rough, the observer should brace himself against the mast and make his observation when on the crest of a wave, when the horizon is least likely to be obscured by nearby waves. It is usually good practice to make a number of observations and average both the altitudes and times, or plot on cross-section paper the altitudes versus time, using any convenient time and the corresponding altitude for solving the observation.

The improvisations which may be made in the absence of a sextant are so varied that in virtually any circumstances the application of a little ingenuity and some effort will produce a device for measuring altitude. The results obtained with any improvised method will be approximate at best, but if a number of observations are averaged, the accuracy should be improved. Almost always a measurement, however approximate, is better than an estimate. Two general classes of improvisation are available:

1. *By circle.* Any circular scale, such as a maneuvering board, compass rose, protractor, or plotter can be used to measure altitude or zenith distance directly. This is

the principle of the ancient astrolabe (art. 124). A maneuvering board or compass rose is usually handled best by mounting it on a flat board. A protractor or plotter may be so mounted or used directly. There are a number of variations of the technique of using such a device. Some of them are:

A peg or nail is placed at the center of the circle and perpendicular to it. A weight is hung from the 90° graduation, and a string for holding the device is attached at the 270° graduation. When it is held with the weight acting as a plumb bob, the 0°–180° line is horizontal (fig. 2618a). In this position the board is turned in azimuth until it is in line with the sun. The intersection of the shadow of the center peg with the arc of the circle indicates the altitude of the center of the sun.

The weight and loop can be omitted and pegs placed at the 0° and 180° points of the circle. While one observer sights along the line of pegs to the horizon, an assistant notes the altitude.

The weight can be attached to the center pin, and the three pins (0°, center, 180°) aligned with the celestial body. The reading is made at the point where the string holding the weight crosses the scale. The reading thus obtained is the zenith distance unless the graduations are labeled to indicate altitude. This method, illustrated in figure 2618b, is used for bodies other than the sun.

Whatever the technique it is good practice to reverse the device for half the readings of a series, to minimize errors of construction. Generally, the circle method produces more accurate results than the right triangle method, described below.

2. *By right triangle.* The principle of the ancient cross-staff can be used to establish one or more right triangles, which can be solved by measurement of the angle representing the altitude, either directly or by reconstructing the triangle. Another way of determining the altitude is to measure two of the sides of the triangle and divide one by the other to determine one of the trigonometric functions. This procedure, of course, requires a source of information on the values of trigonometric functions corresponding to various angles. If the cosine is found, table 2616 can be used. The tabulated factors can be considered correct to one additional decimal for the value midway between the

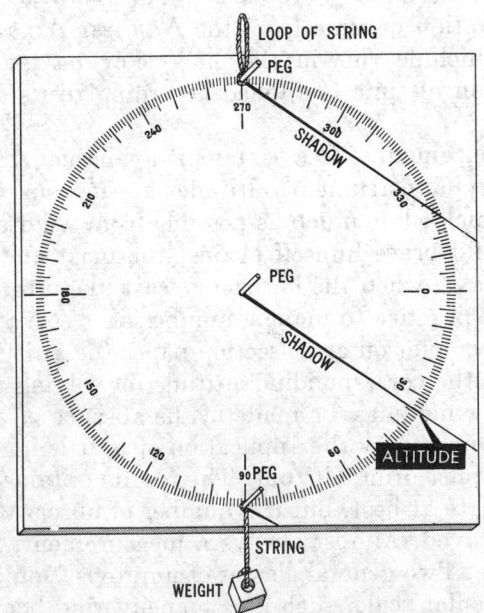

FIGURE 2618a.—Improvised astrolabe; shadow method. Pegs and board shown tilted for clarity.

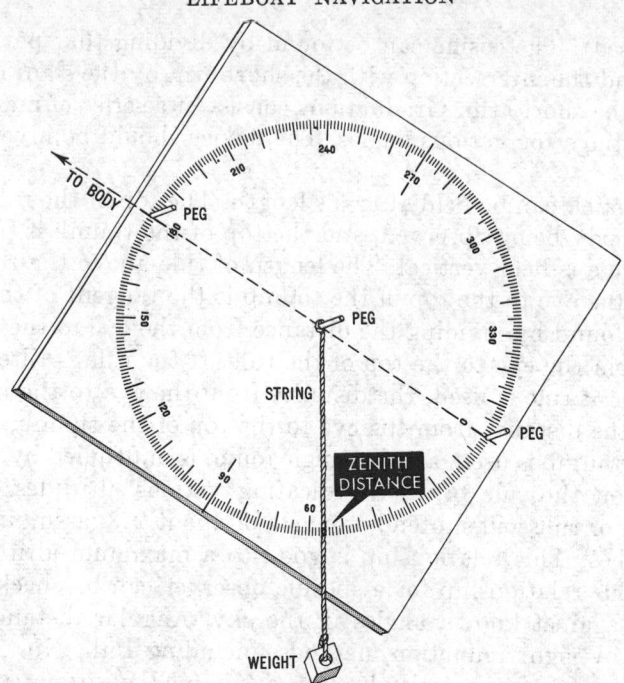

FIGURE 2618b.—Improvised astrolabe; direct sighting
method. Pegs and board shown tilted for clarity.

limiting values (except that 1.00 is the correct value for 0° and 0.00 is the correct value for
90°) without serious error by lifeboat standards. Interpolation can then be made between
such values. By either protractor or table, most devices can be graduated in advance so
that angles can be read directly. There are many variations of the right triangle method.
Some of these are:

Two straight pieces of wood can be attached to each other in such a way that the
shorter one can be moved along the longer, the two always being perpendicular to
each other. The shorter piece is attached at its center. One end of the longer arm is
held to the eye. The shorter arm is moved until its top edge is in line with the celestial
body, and its bottom edge is in line with the horizon. Thus, two right triangles are
used (the third sides being the slant distances between the ends of the arms) each representing half the altitude (fig. 2618c). For low altitudes, only one of the triangles is used,
the long arm being held in line with the horizon. The length of half the short arm,
divided by the length of that part of the long arm between the eye and the intersection
with the short arm, is the tangent of half the altitude (the whole altitude if only one

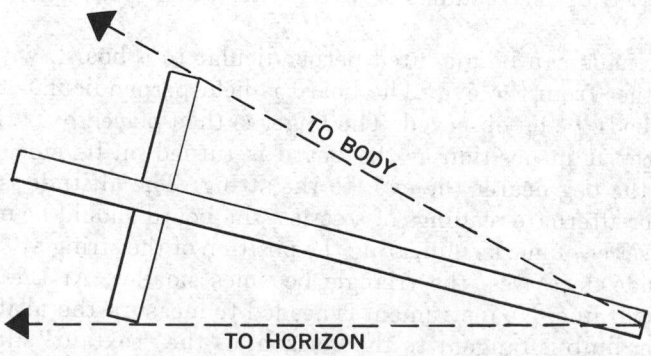

FIGURE 2618c.—Improvised cross-staff.

right triangle is used). The cosine can be found by dividing that part of the long arm between the eye and the intersection with the short arm by the slant distance from the eye to one end of the short arm. Graduations consist of a series of marks along the long arm indicating settings for various angles. The device should be inverted for alternate readings of a series.

A rule or any stick can be held at arm's length. The top of the rule is placed in line with the celestial body being observed, and the top of the thumb is placed in line with the horizon. The rule is held vertical. The length of rule above the thumb, divided by the distance from the eye to the top of the thumb is the tangent of the angle observed. The cosine can be found by dividing the distance from the eye to the top of the thumb by the distance from the eye to the top of the rule. If the rule is tilted toward the eye until the minimum of rule is used, the distance from the eye to the middle of the rule is substituted for the distance from the eye to the top of the thumb, *half* the length of the rule above the thumb is used, and the angle found is multiplied by two. Graduations consist of marks on the rule or stick indicating various altitudes. For the average observer each inch of rule will subtend an angle of about $2°.3$, assuming an eye-to-ruler distance of 25 inches. This relationship is good to a maximum altitude of about 20°. The accuracy of this relationship for a specific observer can be checked by comparing the measurement against known angles in the sky. Angular distances between stars can be computed by sight reduction methods, including Pub. No. 229, by using the declination of one star as the latitude of the assumed position, and the difference between the hour angles (or SHA's) of the two bodies as the local hour angle. The angular distance is the complement of the computed altitude. The angular distances between some well-known star pairs are: end stars of *Orion's* belt, $2°.7$; pointers of the Big Dipper, $5°.4$, Rigel to *Orion's* belt, $9°.0$; eastern side of the great square of *Pegasus*, $14°.0$; Dubhe (the pointer nearer Polaris) and Mizar (the second star in the Big Dipper, counting from the end of the handle), $19°.3$.

The angle between the lines of sight from each eye is, at arm's length, about 6°. By holding a pencil or finger horizontal, and placing the head on its side, one can estimate an angle of about 6° by closing first one eye and then the other, and noting how much the pencil or finger appears to move in the sky.

The length of the shadow of a peg or nail mounted perpendicular to a horizontal board can be used as one side of an altitude triangle. The other sides are the height of the peg and the slant distance from the top of the peg to the end of the shadow. The height of the peg, divided by the length of the shadow, is the tangent of the altitude of the center of the sun. The length of the shadow divided by the slant distance is the cosine. Graduations consist of a series of concentric circles indicating various altitudes, the peg being at the common center. The device is kept horizontal by floating it in a bucket of water. Half the readings of a series are taken with the board turned 180° in azimuth.

Two pegs or nails can be mounted perpendicular to a board, with a weight hung from the one farther from the eye. The board is held perpendicular and the two pegs aligned with the body being observed. The finger is then placed over the string holding the weight, to keep it in position as the board is turned on its side. A perpendicular is dropped from the peg nearer the eye, to the string. The altitude is the acute angle nearer the eye. For alternate readings of a series, the board should be inverted. Graduations consist of a series of marks indicating the position of the string at various altitudes.

As the altitude decreases, the triangle becomes smaller. At the celestial horizon it becomes a straight line. No instrument is needed to measure the altitude when either the upper or lower limb is tangent to the horizon, as the "sextant" altitude is then 0°.

2619. Sextant altitude corrections.—If altitudes are measured by a marine sextant, the usual sextant altitude corrections apply (ch. XVI). If the center of the sun or moon is observed, either by sighting at the center or by shadow, the lower-limb corrections should be applied, as usual, and an additional correction of (−)16′ applied. If the upper limb is observed, use (−)32′. If a weight is used as a plumb bob, or if the *length* of a shadow is measured, omit the dip (height of eye) correction.

If the almanac is not available for making corrections, each source of error can be corrected separately, as follows:

Index correction. If a sextant is used, the index correction should be determined and applied to all observations, or the sextant adjusted to eliminate index error.

Refraction is given to the nearest minute of arc in table 2619. The value for a horizon observation is 34′. If the nearest 0°.1 is sufficiently accurate, as with an improvised method of observing altitude, a correction of 0°.1 should be applied for altitudes between 5° and 18°, and no correction applied for greater altitudes. Refraction applies to all observations, and is always a minus (−) correction.

ALT.	5°	6°	7°	8°	10°	12°	15°	21°	33°	63°	90°
REFR.	9′	8′	7′	6′	5′	4′	3′	2′	1′	0	

TABLE 2619.—Refraction.

Dip, in minutes of arc, is approximately equal to the square root of the height of eye, in feet. The correction applies to all observations in which the horizon is used as the horizontal reference. It is always a minus (−) correction. If 0°.1 accuracy is used, no dip correction is needed for lifeboat heights of eye.

Semidiameter. The semidiameter of either the sun or moon does not differ greatly from 16′. The correction does not apply to other bodies or to observations of the center of the sun and moon, by whatever method, including shadow. The correction is plus (+) if the lower limb is observed, and minus (−) if the upper limb is observed.

Parallax. For lifeboat accuracy, parallax is applied to observations of the moon only. An approximate value, in minutes of arc, can be found by multiplying 57′ by the factor from table 2616, entering that table with altitude. For more accurate results the factors can be considered correct to one additional decimal for the altitude midway between the limiting values (except that 1.00 is correct for 0° and 0.00 is correct for 90°), and the values for other altitudes can be found by interpolation. This correction is always plus (+).

For observations of celestial bodies on the horizon, the total correction for zero height of eye is:

> *Sun.* Lower limb: (−)18′, upper limb: (−)50′.
> *Moon.* Lower limb: (+)39′, upper limb: (+)7′.
> *Planet or star.* (−)34′.

Dip should be added algebraically to these values.

Since the "sextant" altitude is zero, the "observed" altitude is equal to the total correction.

2620. Sight reduction.—If any tables designed for sight reduction, such as Pub. No. 229, are available, they should be safeguarded to prevent loss or damage. If trigonometric tables and the necessary formulas are available, they will serve the purpose. Speed in solution is seldom a factor in a lifeboat. A slow method might actually be an asset, from a morale standpoint, as it will provide occupation for a limited time for at least one crew member. The tables and formulas given in volume II would be useful.

If tables but no formulas are available, carefully determine the mathematical knowledge possessed by the crew. Someone may be able to provide the missing information. If the formulas are available, but no tables, approximate natural values of the various trigonometric functions can be obtained graphically by the method explained in article 139 of volume II. Graphical solution of the navigational triangle can be made by the orthographic method explained in article 1432. A maneuvering board might prove helpful in the graphical solution for either trigonometric functions or altitude and azimuth. Very careful work will be needed for useful results by either method.

Unless full navigational equipment is available, better results might be obtained by making separate determinations of latitude and longitude.

2621. Latitude determination.—Several methods are available for determining latitude, and in none of them is accurate time needed.

Meridian altitude. Latitude can be determined by means of a meridian altitude of any body, if its declination is known. The method is explained in article 2103. If accurate time, knowledge of the longitude, and an almanac are available, the observation can be made at the correct moment, as determined in advance. However, if any of these is lacking, or if an *accurate* altitude-measuring instrument is unavailable, better procedure is to make a number of altitude observations before and after meridian transit. A plot is then made of altitude versus time, if cross-section paper is available, and the highest (or lowest, for lower transit) altitude is scaled from a curve faired through the plotted points. At lifeboat speeds this procedure is not likely to introduce a significant error. The time used for plotting the observations need not be accurate, as *elapsed* time between observations is all that is needed, and this is not of critical accuracy. Thus, even a watch that has run down and then been rewound can be used without resetting. Any altitudes that are not consistent with others of the series should be discarded.

Polaris. Latitude by Polaris is explained in article 2105. In a lifeboat, only the first correction is of practical significance. If suitable tables are not available, this correction can be estimated. The trailing star of *Cassiopeia* (ε *Cassiopeiae*) and Polaris have almost exactly the same SHA. The trailing star of the Big Dipper (Alkaid) is nearly opposite Polaris and ε *Cassiopeiae*. These three stars, ε *Cassiopeiae*, Polaris, and Alkaid, form a line through the pole (approximately). When this line is horizontal,

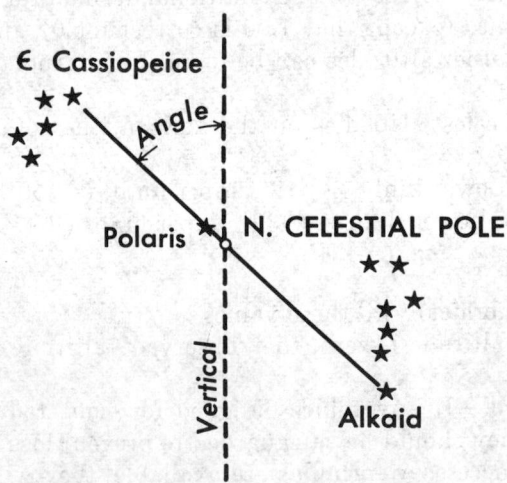

FIGURE 2621.—Relative positions of ε *Cassiopeiae*, Polaris, and Alkaid with respect to the north celestial pole.

there is no correction. When it is vertical, the maximum correction of 56′ applies. It should be added to the observed altitude if Alkaid is at the top, and subtracted if ε *Cassiopeiae* is at the top. For any other position, estimate the angle this line makes with the vertical (fig. 2621), and multiply the maximum correction (56′) by the factor from table 2616, adding if Alkaid is higher than ε *Cassiopeiae*, and subtracting if it is lower. For more accurate results, the factor from table 2616 can be considered accurate to one additional decimal for the mid value between those tabulated (except that 1.00 is correct for 0° and 0.00 for 90°). Other values can be found by interpolation.

Length of day. The length of the day varies with latitude. Hence, latitude can be determined if the elapsed time between sunrise and sunset can be observed. Correct the observed length of day by *adding* 1ᵐ for each 15′ of longitude traveled toward the east and *subtracting* 1ᵐ for each 15′ of longitude traveled toward the west. The latitude determined by length of day is the value for the time of meridian transit. Since meridian transit occurs approximately midway between sunrise and sunset, half the interval may be observed and doubled. If a sunrise and sunset table is not available, the length of daylight can be determined graphically by means of a diagram on the plane of the celestial meridian (art. 1432). A maneuvering board is useful for this purpose. This method cannot be used near the time of the equinoxes, and is of little value near the equator. The moon can be used if moonrise and moonset tables are available, but with the moon the half-interval method is of insufficient accuracy, and allowance should be made for the longitude correction.

Body in zenith. The declination of a body in the zenith is equal to the latitude of the observer. If no means are available for measuring the altitude, the position of the zenith may possibly be estimated in a calm sea by lying in the lifeboat and looking skyward. The accuracy of the results depends upon the ability to estimate the position of the zenith. Use of a plumb bob may help.

Variation of the compass can occasionally be used for determining latitude, as explained in article 2622.

2622. Longitude determination.—Unlike latitude, longitude requires accurate Greenwich time for its determination by astronomical means. All such methods consist of noting the Greenwich time at which a phenomenon occurs locally. In addition, a table indicating the time of occurrence of the same phenomenon at Greenwich, or equivalent information, is needed.

Time of transit. When a body is on the local celestial meridian, its GHA is the same as the longitude of the observer if in west longitude, or 360°−λ in east longitude. Thus, if the GMT of local transit is determined and a table of Greenwich hour angles (or time of transit of the Greenwich meridian) is available, longitude can be computed. If only the equation of time is available, the method can be used with the sun. This is the reverse of the problem of finding the time of transit of a body (art. 2104). The time of transit is not always apparent. If a curve is made of altitude versus time, as suggested in article 2621, the time corresponding to the highest altitude is used in the determination of longitude. Under some conditions it may be preferable to observe an altitude before meridian transit and then again after meridian transit, when the body has returned to the same altitude as at the first observation. Meridian transit occurs midway between these two times. A body in the zenith is on the celestial meridian. If accurate azimuth measurement is available, note the time when the azimuth is 000° or 180°.

Sunrise and sunset. The difference between the observed GMT of sunrise or sunset and the LMT tabulated in the almanac is the longitude in time units, which can then be converted to angular measure. If the *Nautical Almanac* is used, this information is tabulated for each third day only. Greater accuracy can be obtained if interpolation is used for determining intermediate values. Moonrise or moonset can be used if the tabulated LMT is corrected for longitude (art. 1812). Planets and stars can be used if the means are available for determining the time of rising or setting. This can be determined by computation (art. 2536) or, approximately, by means of a diagram on the plane of the celestial meridian (art. 1432).

Either of these methods can be used in reverse to set a watch that has run down, or to check the accuracy of a watch, if the longitude is known. In the case of a meridian transit the time need not be determined at the instant of transit. The watch is started and the altitude is then measured several times before and after transit, or at equal altitudes. The times of these observations are noted and from them the time of meridian transit is determined. The difference between this time and the correct time of transit can then be used as a correction to reset the watch. If a watch runs down and cannot be reset from other timepieces, the correct time should be determined at the first opportunity, if the longitude accuracy is likely to deteriorate.

Variation of the compass. If the deviation of the compass is known accurately and an accurate azimuth can be observed, it is possible to determine the variation. If this is compared with the variation shown on the pilot chart, an approximate line of position can be determined. Since in many areas these lines run in a generally north-south direction, this may be an indication of the longitude. However, if the line has a large east-west component, it should be considered as any other such line of position, rather than as a longitude line. In some areas it is more nearly a latitude line. The accuracy of the method depends upon the accuracy with which the variation can be determined, and the spacing between adjacent isogonic lines.

Time sight. If altitude of a celestial body is available, including zero "sextant" altitude at rising or setting (art. 2619), longitude can be found by time sight (art. 2106).

Approaching Land

2623. Signs of land.—There are a number of signs which may indicate that the lifeboat is approaching land.

The sky will sometimes indicate a break in the open sea. A small fixed cloud, when surrounding ones are in motion or absent, will usually be over or close to land. At high latitudes, a light-colored reflection in the sky might be over an ice area; a light green reflection in the tropical sky might indicate a shallow lagoon. Such indications may be even more apparent on the under side of a uniform cloud layer.

Birds most often fly away from land at dawn and toward it at dusk. A large number of birds may indicate the nearness of land.

Swell, properly interpreted, may be used as a guide to land. Consecutive swells travel parallel until they reach an island and then "bend" around it. Eddies are formed where the distorted swell meets beyond the island. This eddy line may be used as a bearing to land, sometimes at a considerable distance.

The color of the sea may act as a guide in finding land as the open sea generally appears dark blue or dark green, and a lighter shade indicates shallow water, which may be near land.

The sound of the surf is often heard while still a considerable distance from land. Other sounds may also be heard at great distances.

Odors, as from burning wood, sometimes carry a long way out to sea.

Sounds and odors may be particularly helpful in periods of reduced visibility.

2624. Distance off.—At sea in a lifeboat the navigator is handicapped by his limited range of visibility. Distance to the horizon, in nautical miles, is given approximately by the formula $1.15\sqrt{h}$, h being the height of eye in feet. Thus, distance in miles is approximately 1¼ times the square root of the height in feet. At an eye height of nine feet, the horizon is about 3½ miles away. A loaded Victory ship, whose greatest mast height is about 81 feet above the waterline, could be seen $1.15\sqrt{81}$ or 10.35 miles by an observer at zero height of eye. At a height of eye of nine feet the top of the mast should break the horizon when the ship is about 13.8 miles off.

If the height of an object above the horizon, or the distance between points on it is known, a simple proportion can be solved to determine the distance off by use of the cross-staff (art. 2618) or a similar device. To do this, align the two ends of the crosspiece with top and bottom, or two ends, of the object. The ratio of the length of the crosspiece to the length from this piece to the eye is the same as the ratio of the height (or length) of the object to its distance from the observer (fig. 2624). Thus, if the crosspiece is 18 inches and the intercepted length of the long piece is 31 inches, the distance to an island 1½ miles wide in the line of sight is found from the proportion

$$\frac{18}{31}=\frac{1.5}{D}, \text{ or } \frac{D}{1.5}=\frac{31}{18}$$

$$D=\frac{1.5\times31}{18}=2.6 \text{ miles.}$$

In this proportion the two parts of either fraction must be expressed in the same units if results are to be obtained without a conversion factor. Thus, both 18 and 31 are expressed in inches, and both 1.5 and 2.6 are in miles. For small or distant objects the crosspiece may be too long. In this case replace it with a shorter one, use half or less of it, or substitute some other device such as a rule held at arm's length. In the case of a height, only the visible part of the object is used if the horizon is between the observer and the object.

A variation of this method can produce approximate results rather quickly. Hold a pencil, stick, or finger vertical at arm's length. Close one eye and align the vertical member with one end of an object such as an island. Open the closed eye and close the other one. Estimate the distance the vertical member appears to move against the background. The distance of the background object is ten times the amount of apparent movement, in the same units. The actual ratio varies somewhat among individuals and can be determined by comparing the length of the outstretched arm with the distance between eyes—or by practice on objects of known size at known distances. For vertical objects hold the extended member horizontal and bend the head until it, also, is horizontal.

2625. Beaching the boat.—The beaching of a lifeboat may be one of the most dangerous parts of the entire experience. The approach to an island should be made

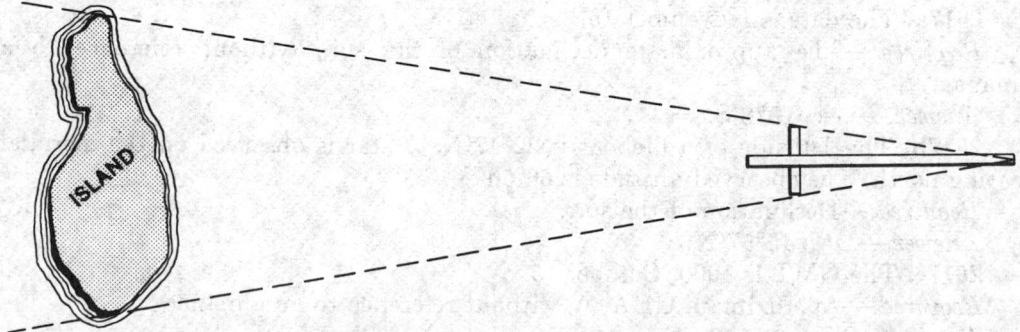

FIGURE 2624.—Using the cross-staff to measure distance.

on the lee side, if possible, and every effort should be made to attract the attention of any inhabitants so that advice on the best place to land, and perhaps assistance, might be obtained. If no help is available, sail parallel to the coast to study the terrain and determine the safest place to beach the boat. A lagoon or other sheltered area may be available. It may be necessary to delay the landing overnight to make a complete study of the terrain and to beach the boat by daylight. Surf appears less rough from the sea than from land. High spray indicates a rough surf.

If a steering oar is available, the rudder should be unshipped before the boat is brought in, as the steering oar will provide better control in the surf zone. The sea anchor should be used to lessen the possibility of broaching and capsizing. Storm oil should be used, if available, to reduce the roughness of the surf. It is possible that the course can be altered somewhat while heading in to the beach, to take advantage of a better opening, but care should be taken to avoid broaching. Additional information on handling a boat in a surf can be found in nearly any book on seamanship.

2626. Ashore.—Once the boat has been safely beached, the problem remains to lead the survivors to civilization. Perhaps the land will be heavily populated and the boat met by local people, or the way to safety may be indicated by a road or trail. But the boat may be beached at a deserted place where there are no signs of life.

Many of the methods used to determine position at sea may also be used ashore, and usually with greater accuracy due to the absence of motion.

Problems

2613a. The compass azimuth of the sun is 126° at rising and 252° at setting.
Required.—Compass error.
Answer.—CE 9°W.

2613b. A life preserver is thrown overboard from a lifeboat and the boat headed away on course 355°. At a distance of half a mile the boat turns and heads back for the life preserver. The return course is 169°. The variation is 5°W.
Required.—(1) True course back to the life preserver.
(2) Deviation on this heading.
Answers.—(1) TC 167°, (2) D 3°E.

2615. The two knots in the log line of an improvised chip log of a lifeboat are 16⅔ feet apart. The elapsed time between passage of the knots through the hands of the observer is four seconds.
Required.—Speed of the lifeboat.
Answer.—S 2.5 kn.

2616. A lifeboat travels 18 miles on course 110°, from lat. 35°15′S, long. 82°31′W.
Required.—Latitude and longitude of the point of arrival.
Answer.—L 35°20′S, λ 82°11′W.

2617a. The date is November 15.
Required.—The approximate declination of the sun, without reference to an almanac.
Answer.—Dec. 18°.8′S.

2617b. The latitude of a lifeboat is 22°47′N. A star is observed on the meridian, bearing north. The observed altitude is 66°50′.
Required.—Declination of the star.
Answer.—Dec. 45°57′N.

2617c. The GMT is 1000, October 15.
Required.—Approximate GHA ♈, without reference to an almanac.
Answer.—GHA ♈ 172°.

2624. Approaching land, the navigator wishes to determine his distance from a lighthouse situated on the coast. He holds a rule at arm's length and finds that ⅝ inch of the rule appears the same height as the top of the lighthouse above water. He estimates the distance from his eye to the rule as 24 inches, and the height of the top of the lighthouse as 150 feet above water.

Required.—Distance to the lighthouse.

Answer.—D 0.9 mi.

PART FIVE

NAVIGATIONAL SAFETY

PART FIVE

NAVIGATIONAL SAFETY

CHAPTER XXVII

NAVIGATIONAL SAFETY

2701. Introduction.—The discussion of navigational safety in this chapter *supplements* the discussions of safety matters in other chapters. For example, the *fallibility of floating aids to navigation* is discussed in chapter IV.

Where applicable, the mariner should always refer to the more detailed information given in the publications corrected by *Notice to Mariners*, e.g. Pubs. Nos. 117A and 117B, *Radio Navigational Aids*.

Published Warnings

2702. *Notice to Mariners* is published weekly by the Defense Mapping Agency Hydrographic Center and is prepared jointly with the National Ocean Survey and the U. S. Coast Guard. It is published to advise mariners of important matters affecting navigational safety, including new hydrographic discoveries, changes in channels and aids to navigation, etc. (U. S. Code Title 10, Secs. 7391 and 7392 and Title 44, Sec. 1336 refers). Besides keeping mariners informed generally, the information published in *Notice to Mariners* is particularly designed to simplify the correction aboard oceangoing ships of charts, sailing directions, light lists, and other publications produced by the Defense Mapping Agency Hydrographic Center, National Ocean Survey, and the U. S. Coast Guard. The Second and Ninth U. S. Coast Guard Districts are not included in the coverage of this Notice.

All corrections listed affect the safety of navigation, and it is the responsibility of users to decide which of their charts and publications require correction. In the interest of navigational safety, suitable records of *Notice to Mariners* corrections should be maintained to facilitate the updating of charts and publications prior to their use. Because of the sometimes transitory nature of aids to navigation, depths, and port information, local area sources should be consulted whenever possible.

Information for *Notice to Mariners* is contributed by the following agencies: Defense Mapping Agency Hydrographic Center (Department of Defense) for waters outside the territorial limits of the United States; National Ocean Survey (National Oceanic and Atmospheric Administration, Department of Commerce), which is charged with the surveys and charting of the coasts and harbors of the United States and its territories; the U. S. Coast Guard (Department of Transportation) which is responsible for the safety of life at sea and the establishment and operation of aids to navigation; and the Corps of Engineers, U. S. Army (Department of Defense) which is charged with the improvement of rivers and harbors of the United States. In addition, important contributions are made by foreign hydrographic offices and cooperating observers of all nationalities.

Notice to Mariners, relating to the *Great Lakes* and tributary waters west of Montreal, Canada, is published weekly by the U. S. Coast Guard. These Notices contain selected items from *Local Notices to Mariners* and other reported marine information and are intended primarily for use in correcting Great Lakes charts and related publications.

Mariners are requested to cooperate in the corrective maintenance of navigational charts and publications by reporting all discrepancies between published information and conditions actually observed or encountered, and by recommending appropriate additions, deletions, or improvements. A convenient reporting form is provided in the back of most issues of *Notice to Mariners*.

Information affecting National Ocean Survey charts and publications, or concerning coasts and waters of the United States and its territories should be sent to the Director, National Ocean Survey. Deficiencies in aids to navigation, either visual or electronic, on the coasts or waters of the United States or its territories should be reported to the nearest Coast Guard District Office. Suggestions regarding these aids should also be sent to the Coast Guard District Office.

Notice to Mariners No. 1 contains *important information* on a variety of subjects, amplifying information not usually found on charts or navigational publications. This information is promulgated as *Special Notice to Mariners Paragraphs* once each year in the interest of safe navigation. Additional items considered of interest to the mariner, including a selected listing of firing, bombing, and exercise areas, are also included in this Notice.

The *Summary of Corrections* published by the Defense Mapping Agency Hydrographic Center contains corrections to charts, *Sailing Directions*, and *United States Coast Pilots* previously published in *Notice to Mariners*. The weekly *Notice to Mariners* should be referred to for confirmation of the corrective material published in this Summary.

2703. The *Local Notice to Mariners* is issued by each U. S. Coast Guard District to disseminate important information affecting navigational safety within the District. This Notice reports changes to and deficiencies in aids to navigation maintained by and under the authority of the U. S. Coast Guard and such other marine information as new charts, channel depths, naval operations, regattas, etc. Since temporary information, known or expected to be of short duration, is not included in the weekly *Notice to Mariners* published by the Defense Mapping Agency Hydrographic Center, the appropriate *Local Notice to Mariners* may be the only source of such information. Small craft using the Intracoastal Waterway and other waterways and small harbors that are not normally used by oceangoing vessels need it to keep chart and related publications up-to-date.

If still significant at the time of publication, the U. S. Coast Guard's *Broadcast Notice to Mariners* (art. 2705) is included in the *Local Notice to Mariners*.

The *Local Notice to Mariners* is published as often as required; usually weekly. It may be obtained, free of charge, by making application to the appropriate Coast Guard District Commander. Vessels operating in ports and waterways in several districts will have to obtain the *Local Notice to Mariners* from each district in order to be fully informed.

2704. The *Daily Memorandum* provides navigators of ships in port with printed copy of HYDROLANTS or HYDROPACS (art. 2707) broadcast in the past 24 hours or since the previous working day.

The *Daily Memorandum* is published by the Defense Mapping Agency Hydrographic Center each working day in two editions: the Atlantic Edition and the Pacific Edition, both prepared at Washington, D.C.

The *Daily Memorandum* is sent to fleet operating bases, naval stations, custom houses, shipping company offices, etc., where it may be picked up by navigational personnel of vessels in port.

Radio Navigational Warning Systems

2705. Short range or local warnings.—One of the two distinct types of radio navigational warning systems is the short range or local radio navigational warnings for mariners plying nearby waters. Short range or local warnings are intended primarily to help local and coastal traffic. Usually, local or short range warnings are broadcast from a single coast station, frequently by voice as well as radiotelegraph. Examples of short range navigational warning systems are the radio navigational warning broadcasts of the various U. S. Coast Guard Districts. Most maritime nations broadcast short range warnings to notify local mariners of dangers in coastal and inland waters. Schedules and working particulars of many such stations throughout the world can be found in Pubs. Nos. 117A and 117B, *Radio Navigational Aids.*

Broadcast Notice to Mariners are originated by the U. S. Coast Guard and broadcast from U. S. Coast Guard, U. S. Navy, and some commercial radio stations to report deficiencies and changes in aids to navigation.

2706. Long range radio navigational warnings are primarily intended to assist mariners on the high seas by giving them navigational safety information in ports, harbors, coastlines, or areas at sea in major ocean areas. Such warnings are usually broadcast by means of radiotelegraph and radioteleprinter from several widely dispersed radio stations with sufficient power to ensure their availability to all ships in the oceanic area. The HYDROLANT and HYDROPAC system (art. 2707) of the Defense Mapping Agency Hydrographic Center, for the general Atlantic and Pacific areas, is typical of a long range radio navigational warning system. Long range warning systems are discussed in more detail in Pubs. Nos. 117A and 117B, *Radio Navigational Aids*, and volume V of *Admiralty List of Radio Signals.*

2707. The U.S. long range radio navigational warning system provides coverage outside NAVAREAS IV and XII (art. 2708) by HYDROLANT and HYDROPAC messages originated by the Defense Mapping Agency Hydrographic Center. The particulars of this system are discussed in detail in Pubs. Nos. 117A and 117B, *Radio Navigational Aids.*

HYDROLANTS and HYDROPACS are restricted to the more important marine incidents or navigational changes for which a delay in disseminating the information to mariners would adversely affect navigational safety. Many of these warnings are temporary in nature. Others might remain in force for long periods of time and ultimately be superseded by a numbered paragraph in *Notice to Mariners.*

Printed copies of HYDROLANTS and HYDROPACS are published each working day in the appropriate edition of the *Daily Memorandum.* The text of effective HYDROLANTS and HYDROPACS issued during a week is printed in the weekly *Notice to Mariners.*

It is important that the mariner retains the radio warning until the printed *Notice to Mariners* is received.

2708. NAVAREA Warnings, containing information which may affect the safety of navigation on the high seas, are broadcast in accordance with international obligations. The Defense Mapping Agency Hydrographic Center is responsible for disseminating navigational information for ocean areas designated as NAVAREAS IV and XII of Worldwide Navigational Warning System (fig. 2708).

As is the case with HYDROLANTS and HYDROPACS, warnings for NAVAREAS IV and XII may be superseded by a numbered paragraph in *Notice to Mariners.* Printed copies are published each working day in the appropriate edition of the *Daily Memorandum.* The text of effective warnings for NAVAREAS IV and XII is printed in the weekly *Notice to Mariners.*

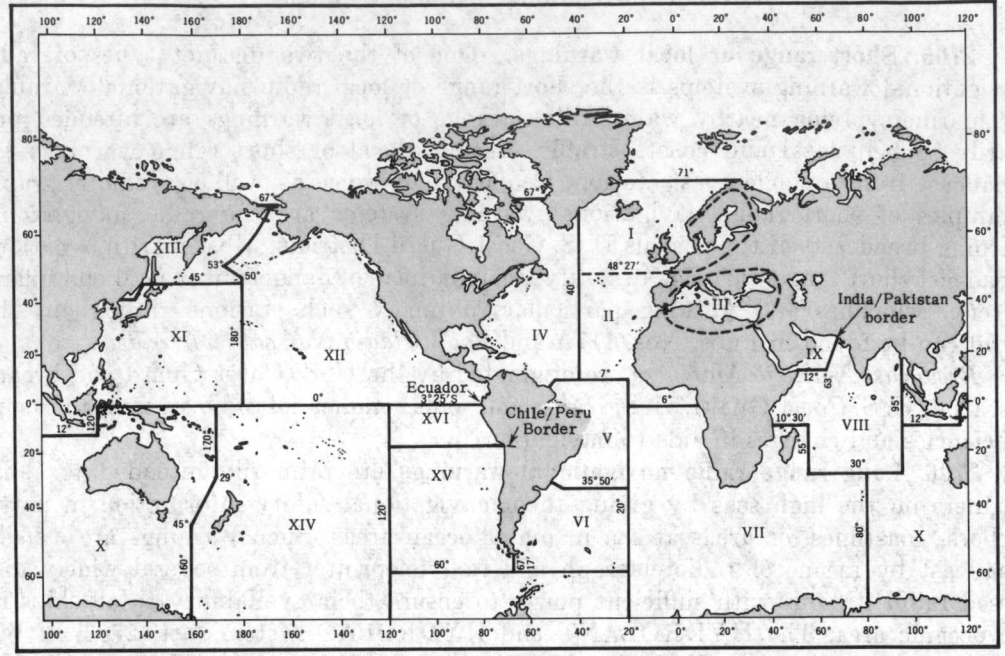

FIGURE 2708.—NAVAREAS of Worldwide Navigational Warning System.

2709. Special Warnings are broadcast by U. S. Navy and U. S. Coast Guard radio stations primarily for the dissemination of official U. S. Government proclamations affecting shipping. Special Warnings are published in all editions of the *Daily Memorandum* and in the weekly *Notice to Mariners*. Upon issuance the text of all effective Special Warnings are published in *Notice to Mariners No. 1*, annually.

Safety Information

2710. Traffic separation schemes.—To increase the safety of navigation, particularly in areas of high shipping density, routes incorporating traffic separation have, with the approval of the Inter-Governmental Maritime Consultative Organization (IMCO), been established in certain areas of the world. In the interest of safe navigation, it is recommended that through traffic use these routes, as far as circumstances permit, by day and by night and in all weather conditions. The routes, which are intended for use by all vessels, do not give any special rights to vessels using them.

General principles for navigation in Traffic Separation Schemes are as follows:

1. The *International Regulations for Preventing Collisions at Sea* apply to navigation in routing systems.

2. Routing systems are intended for use by day and by night in all weather, in ice-free waters or under light ice conditions where no extraordinary maneuvers or assistance by icebreaker(s) are required.

3. Routing systems are recommended for use by all ships unless stated otherwise.

4. A deep water route is primarily intended for use by ships which because of their draft in relation to the available depth of water in the area concerned require the use of such a route. Through traffic to which the above consideration does not apply should, if practicable, avoid following deep water routes. When using a deep water route mariners

should be aware of possible changes in the indicated depth of water due to meteorological or other effects.

5. A vessel using a traffic separation scheme shall:

(i) proceed in the appropriate traffic lane in the general direction of traffic flow for that lane;

(ii) so far as practicable keep clear of a traffic separation line or separation zone;

(iii) normally join or leave a traffic lane at the termination of the lane, but when joining or leaving from the side shall do so at as small an angle to the general direction of traffic flow as practicable.

6. A vessel shall so far as practicable avoid crossing traffic lanes, but if obliged to do so shall cross as nearly as practicable at right angles to the general direction of traffic flow.

7. Inshore traffic zones shall not normally be used by through traffic which can safely use the appropriate traffic lane within the adjacent traffic separation scheme.

8. A vessel, other than a crossing vessel, shall not normally enter a separation zone or cross a separation line except:

(i) in cases of emergency to avoid immediate danger;

(ii) to engage in fishing within a separation zone.

9. A vessel navigating in areas near the terminations of traffic separation schemes shall do so with particular caution.

10. A vessel shall so far as practicable avoid anchoring in a traffic separation scheme or in areas near its terminations.

11. A vessel not using a traffic separation scheme shall avoid it by as wide a margin as is practicable.

12. The arrows printed on charts merely indicate the general direction of traffic; ships need not set their courses strictly along the arrows.

13. The signal "YG" meaning "you appear not to be complying with the traffic separation scheme" is provided in the International Code of Signals for appropriate use.

2711. Offshore oil-well structures.—Caution should be exercised when navigating in waters contiguous to the U. S. and its territories, particularly in the Gulf of Mexico; Santa Barbara Channel, California; and Cook Inlet, Alaska, in order to avoid collision with oil structures and their associated mooring piles, anchor and mooring buoys, etc.

The identification of the oil-well structures is discussed in *Notice to Mariners No. 1*. Due to the number of oil wells in the Gulf of Mexico, Shipping Safety Fairways have been established, and while adherence to these fairways is not mandatory, mariners should take advantage of the safer passage ways made available.

The most accurate information regarding the position of oil-well structures is contained in the latest editions of the pertinent National Ocean Survey charts. (Additionally, an annually up-dated listing of Gulf of Mexico oil-well structures is published by the U. S. Coast Guard. Mariners desiring to receive issues of the publication should write to the District Commander (OAN), Eighth Coast Guard District, Hale Boggs Federal Building, 500 Camp Street, New Orleans, Louisiana 70115, requesting to be placed on their mailing list.)

Corrective information concerning the establishment, change, or discontinuance of the oil-well structures (with the exception of mobile drilling rigs) is published in the weekly *Notice to Mariners*. Movements of mobile drilling rigs and seismic survey operations are generally covered in HYDROLANT/HYDROPAC radio navigational warning broadcasts (art. 2707).

Daily updating of oil-well structure information is available on the Local Notice to Mariners broadcast. Refer to Pubs. Nos. 117A and 117B, *Radio Navigational Aids*, for additional details.

2712. Danger from submarine cables and pipelines.—Submarine cables or pipelines pass beneath various navigable waterways throughout the world. Installation of new submarine cables and pipelines may be reported in *Notice to Mariners;* their locations may or may not be charted. Where feasible, warning signs are often erected to warn the mariners of their existence.

In view of the serious consequences resulting from damage to submarine cables and pipelines, mariners should take special care when anchoring, fishing or engaging in underwater operations near areas where these cables or pipelines may exist or have been reported to exist.

Certain cables carry high voltages; many pipelines carry natural gas under high pressure, or petroleum products. Electrocution, fire, or explosion with injury or loss of life or a serious pollution incident could occur if they are penetrated.

Vessels fouling a submarine cable or pipeline should attempt to clear without undue strain. Anchors or gear that cannot be cleared should be slipped; no attempt should be made to cut a cable or pipeline.

2713. Artificial obstructions to navigation.—**Disposal areas** are designated by the Corps of Engineers for depositing dredged material where existing depths indicate that the deposits will not cause sufficient shoaling to create a danger to surface navigation. The areas are shown on National Ocean Survey charts without blue tint, and soundings and depth curves are retained.

Dumping grounds are areas established by federal regulation in which dumping of dredged material and other nonbuoyant objects is prohibited or in which such dumping is allowed with the permission of and under the supervision of the Corps of Engineers.

Spoil areas are for the purpose of depositing dredged material, usually near and parallel to dredged channels; *they are usually a hazard to navigation.* Spoil areas are usually charted from survey drawings from Corps of Engineers after-dredging surveys, though they may originate from private or other government agency surveys. Spoil areas are tinted blue on the chart and labeled, and all soundings and depth contours are omitted. *Navigators of even the smallest craft should avoid crossing spoil areas.*

Fish havens are established by private interests, usually sport fishermen, to simulate natural reefs and wrecks that attract fish. The reefs are constructed by dumping assorted junk, ranging from old trolley cars and barges to scrap building material in areas which may be of very small extent or may stretch a considerable distance along a depth contour; old automobile bodies are a commonly used material. The Corps of Engineers must issue a permit, specifying the location and depth over the reef, before such a reef may be built. However, the reef builders adherence to permit specifications can be checked only with a wire drag. Fish havens are outlined and labeled on the charts, but soundings and depth contours are usually retained and blue tinting is seldom used. *Navigators should be cautious about passing over fish havens or anchoring in their vicinity.*

Fishtrap areas are areas established by the Corps of Engineers in which traps may be built and maintained according to established regulations. The fish stakes which may exist in these areas are obstructions to navigation and may be dangerous. The limits of fishtrap areas and a cautionary note are usually charted. *Navigators should avoid these areas.*

2714. Net bottom clearances.—It is becoming increasingly evident that economic pressures are causing mariners to navigate through waters of barely adequate depth, with net bottom clearances (also known as **under-keel clearances**) being finely assessed from the charted depths, predicted tide levels, and depths recorded by echo sounders.

It cannot be too strongly emphasized that even charts based on modern surveys may not show all sea-bed obstructions or the least depths, and actual tide levels may be appreciably lower than those predicted.

In many ships an appreciable correction must be applied to shoal soundings recorded by echo sounders due to the horizontal distance between the transducers. This separation correction, which is the amount by which recorded depths exceed true depths, increases with decreasing depths to a maximum equal to half the distance apart of the transducers; at this maximum the transducers are aground. Mariners should have available a table of true and recorded depths.

Other appreciable corrections include the effects of water density, trim, list, squat (bodily sinkage and change of trim), heaving, rolling, and pitching.

The effects of water density, trim, and list upon bottom clearance are easily calculated assuming at-rest conditions. Squat, heaving, rolling, and pitching are dynamic phenomena and are more complex to predict singly or in combination.

Squat, which includes bodily sinkage and change of trim, is a result of the pressure distribution on the hull caused by the relative motion of water and hull. The effect begins to increase significantly at depth-to-draft ratios less than 2.5. It increases rapidly with speed and is augmented in narrow channels.

The effect of heaving, pitching, and rolling on net bottom clearance can be quite significant in critical combinations of wave height and period, ship dimensions, and angle of incidence. Passages over bars in exposed areas require adequate allowance for these factors.

2715. Controlling depths.—The **controlling depth** of a channel is the least depth within the limits of the channel; it restricts the safe use of the channel to drafts of less than that depth. The **centerline controlling depth** of a channel applies only to the channel centerline; lesser depths may exist in the remainder of the channel. The **mid-channel controlling depth** of a channel is the controlling depth of only the middle half of the channel. **Federal project depth** is the design dredging depth of a channel constructed by the Corps of Engineers, U. S. Army; the project depth *may or may not be the goal of maintenance dredging* after completion of the channel, and, for this reason, project depth must not be confused with controlling depth.

Depths alongside wharves usually have been reported by owners or operators of the waterfront facilities, and may not have been verified by government surveys. Since these depths may be subject to change, local authorities should be consulted for the latest controlling depths.

In general, the *Coast Pilot* gives the project depths for deep-draft ship channels maintained by the Corps of Engineers. The latest controlling depths are usually shown on the charts and published in *Notice to Mariners*. For other channels, the latest controlling depths available at the time of publication are given.

The most authoritative source for channel depths in U. S. ports is the field office of the Corps of Engineers in the vicinity. Addresses and telephone numbers are given in *Notice to Mariners No. 1.*

2716. Use of foreign charts.—Caution should be exercised in the use of foreign charts not maintained by *Notice to Mariners* published by the Defense Mapping Agency Hydrographic Center. Foreign charts are sometimes referred to in *Sailing Directions* published by this Center. The mariner is advised that when such foreign charts are used for navigation, it is his responsibility to maintain the charts by the Notice to Mariners of the country producing the charts.

The mariner is warned that the buoyage system, shapes, and colors used by other countries often have a different significance than the U. S. system.

2717. Nautical chart symbols and abbreviations.—The standard symbols and abbreviations approved for use on all regular nautical charts published by the Defense Mapping Agency Hydrographic Center and the National Ocean Survey are contained in Chart No. 1, *United States of America Nautical Chart Symbols and Abbreviations*. The mariner should insure that a copy of the latest edition of Chart No. 1 is readily available.

The symbols and abbreviations used by other countries often vary from those used by the United States. Charts produced by the Defense Mapping Agency Hydrographic Center will show the colors, lights, and other characteristics in use for the area of the individual chart. Certain reproductions of foreign charts published and distributed by this Center may also show the shapes and other distinctive features that will vary from those illustrated in Chart No. 1. Mariners who acquire and use foreign charts and reproductions of such charts are advised to procure the symbol sheet of the foreign chart agency.

2718. Unverified information.—Information received by the Defense Mapping Agency Hydrographic Center and the National Ocean Survey from various sources concerning depths, dangers, currents, facilities, and other subjects, which has not been verified by government surveys or inspections, is often included in *Sailing Directions* and *Coast Pilots;* such unverified information is qualified as "reported," and should be regarded with caution.

2719. International Ice Patrol.—Beginning in February or March and ending in August or September of each year depending upon ice conditions, the International Ice Patrol conducts its annual service of guarding the southeastern, southern, and southwestern limits of the regions of icebergs in the vicinity of the Grand Banks of Newfoundland for the purpose of informing passing ships of the extent of ice in this dangerous region. Ice Patrol Bulletins are sent via CW, voice and radiofacsimile broadcasts. Details are given in Pub. No. 117A, *Radio Navigational Aids*.

2720. Firing danger areas.—Firing and bombing practice takes place either ocassionally or regularly in numerous areas established for those purposes along the coasts of practically all maritime countries.

In view of difficulty in keeping these areas up-to-date on the charts, and since the responsibility to avoid accidents rests with the authorities using the areas for firing or bombing practice, these areas will not as a rule be shown on Defense Mapping Agency Hydrographic Center charts. The National Ocean Survey charts show firing and bombing practice areas as defined by the *Code of Federal Regulations* in United States waters.

Any aid to navigation that may be established to mark a danger area, any target, fixed or floating, that may constitute a danger to navigation, will be shown on the appropriate charts.

Danger areas that will be in force for some length of time will be published in *Notice to Mariners*.

Warning signals, usually consisting of red flags or red lights, are customarily displayed before and during practice, but the absence of such warnings cannot be accepted as evidence that a practice area does not exist.

Vessels should be on the lookout for local warnings and signals, and should whenever possible, avoid passing through an area in which practice is in progress, but if compelled to do so should endeavor to clear it at the earliest possible moment.

CHAPTER XXVIII

OCEANIC SOUNDINGS AND HYDROGRAPHIC REPORTS

General

2801. Introduction.—Maritime shipping continues to increase with the growth in volume of domestic and international commerce, and seagoing vessels continue to increase in number, size, and speed. Not only does this growth result in constant demands for expansion and improvement of harbor, port, and navigation facilities, but it also necessitates improvements in the quality, quantity, and display of all forms of navigation information.

Although both government agencies and private institutions operate as many oceanographic and hydrographic ships as their resources permit, the magnitude of requirements for information far exceeds the collection capabilities of these comparatively few vessels. It is not possible for any hydrographic institute to conduct a continuous worldwide survey. Consequently, the Defense Mapping Agency Hydrographic Center and the National Ocean Survey depend to a very great extent upon reports from voluntary seagoing observers for information pertaining to navigation and oceanography. Information from these reports and other sources is evaluated and used in the improvement, production, correction, and maintenance of charts and publications.

After careful analysis of a report and comparison with all other data concerning the same area or subject, appropriate action is taken. If the report is of sufficient importance to affect the immediate safety of navigation, the information will be broadcast as a navigational warning. Each bit of information, no matter how trivial it may seem, is coordinated with other reports and used in some way in the compilation, construction, and correction of charts and publications. It is only through the constant flow of new information that charts and publications can be kept accurate and up-to-date.

Discrepancies are sometimes found in source material, mainly as a result of comparison with the reports submitted by mariners who have recently visited the area. Often, errors in basic source material are of the type that would affect the safety of navigation. Several confirming ship reports will usually reveal these errors so that corrective action can be taken. The greater the volume of confirming ship reports, the greater is the accuracy of the finished product.

2802. Marine reports.—Frequently the most valuable information is recent information reported by a mariner, who records the information in the greatest detail possible and reports it promptly.

Depending on the type of report, certain items of information are absolutely essential for a correct evaluation. An example is the state of tide. State of tide is of paramount importance in a report of near shore shoals, but of no interest with respect to shoals reported beyond the continental shelf.

Several reasons have been found for hesitancy on the part of the mariner to report his observations. He is frequently in doubt as to what information, and in what detail, to report. He often believes that the data that he reports will be inconsequential to the Defense Mapping Agency Hydrographic Center since "they already receive the most recent information available, and they are already aware of this data," as one mariner put it.

Excellence in grammar is unnecessary. Reports, or supplemental information, such as port plans, obtained locally, may even be in a foreign language. Observations should be reported in the language of mariners since they will be evaluated by ex-mariners, who will make full and appropriate use of the information.

Reports by letter are just as acceptable as those prepared on regular forms. In some instances, a letter report will permit greater flexibility in reporting details, conclusions, or recommendations concerning the observation. When using the regular report forms, one should not hesitate to use additional sheets to complete the details of his observation. One should never be reluctant to report in detail.

The following general suggestions are offered as an aid to making reports that will be of maximum value.

1. The geographical position included in the report may be used in the correction of charts. Accordingly, it should be fixed by the most accurate method available. If practicable, the position should be verified by additional means.

2. The report should state the method by which the position was fixed, so that the degree of accuracy can be established.

3. When reporting the position of an object or condition that is not shown on the chart but is within sight of charted objects, the simplest and most accurate method is to express the position in terms of bearings and distances from charted objects.

4. Should geographical coordinates be used to report position, they should be made as precise as circumstances permit. Either tenths of a minute or seconds, depending upon the scale of the chart, should be included. Unfortunately, coordinates of all charts for a given area are not always in exact agreement. Accordingly, one should refer to the chart by number and include the edition number and the date of the printing being used. Both are shown in the bottom margin.

5. When describing the sectors in which a light is either visible or obscured, the limiting bearings from the ship toward the light should be given. Although this is just the reverse of the form used for locating objects, it is the standard method used by the hydrographic institutes of practically all countries.

6. All bearings used in reports should be *true* bearings, expressed in degrees. Should magnetic bearings be used, for any reason, such use should be stated in the report.

7. A report prepared by one person should, if practicable, be checked by another.

In most cases marine information can be adequately reported on one of various forms printed by the Defense Mapping Agency Hydrographic Center and shown in *Guide to Marine Observing and Reporting* (art. 2804) or by the reporting sheet in the weekly *Notice to Mariners*. However, in some cases it is both more convenient and more valuable to annotate information directly on the affected chart and mail the chart to the Defense Mapping Agency Hydrographic Center.

As an example, new construction, such as port facilities, may be drawn on the chart in cases where a written report would be inadequate. Another example would be a chart showing the trackline and pertinent soundings through a critical passage or strait when the ship's draft is close to the controlling depth of the water in the passage or strait. Information, such as times, state of tide, draft, and method by which fixes were obtained should also be included.

Whenever it is necessary to send a chart to amplify or explain a report, the Defense Mapping Agency Hydrographic Center, upon request, will replace the chart free of charge on a one-for-one basis.

2803. Urgent reports by radio.—The *International Convention for the Safety of Life at Sea* (1960), which is applicable to all U. S. flag ships, requires: "The master of every ship which meets with dangerous ice, or dangerous derelict, or any other direct danger to navigation, or a tropical storm, or encounters sub-freezing air temperatures associated with gale force winds causing severe ice accretion on superstructures, or winds of force 10 or above on the Beaufort scale for which no storm warning has been received, is bound to communicate the information by all the means at his disposal to ships in the vicinity, and also to the competent authorities at the first point on the coast with which he can communicate."

The master must first warn ships in the vicinity and must then report the danger to competent authorities at the first point on the coast with which radio contact can be made, using relay procedure if necessary. The report should be broadcast first on 500 kHz prefixed by the Safety Signal "TTT TTT TTT." This should be followed by transmission of the message to the proper authorities ashore.

Details on reporting via radio are contained in chapters 4 and 5 of Pubs. Nos. 117A and 117B, *Radio Navigational Aids*.

2804. *Guide to Marine Observing and Reporting*, Pub. 606, prepared jointly by the Naval Oceanographic Office, the Defense Mapping Agency Hydrographic Center, U. S. Coast Guard, and the National Oceanic and Atmospheric Administration, provides detailed guidance for submitting hydrographic and oceanographic reports. Where appropriate, this guidance includes check lists of key questions as a means of insuring that no essential fact will be missing from a report.

Oceanic Soundings

2805. Soundings.—Relatively little is known of the surface features of the nearly 71 percent of the earth covered by water. However, enough has been learned to indicate that the unseen topography beneath the oceans has all the features common to that above water. It is known that there are submerged mountains extending to greater heights above their surroundings than do the Rockies, and depressions deeper than the Grand Canyon.

While many of the general features are known, details are lacking. In any given area, a very large number of accurately located soundings are needed to provide sufficient information for mapping the ocean floor. If sufficient information is available, the relief can be depicted on bathymetric charts by means of contours. A simplified chart of this type is shown in the upper part of figure 2805. The lower part of the figure is a block diagram of the area shown on the chart. Only a relatively small part of the oceans has been sounded sufficiently to provide the detailed information needed for such a chart, mainly narrow strips along coasts, i.e., the continental shelves. In these areas, the soundings have the necessary accuracy and density to portray underwater relief.

As long as oceanic soundings could be made only by a vessel stopping and lowering a weight, a process which might require several hours for a single sounding in very deep water, it was impractical for most vessels to obtain very much depth information at sea. With the development of the echo sounder, however, this situation has changed. With a recording echo sounder, a ship can obtain a profile along its track from continent to continent without slowing, using about a yard of recording paper per day. Such information, if reliable, is of great assistance to charting agencies in preparing more adequate charts of the ocean areas.

2806. Sounding equipment.—While lead lines and sounding machines have been used at sea, almost all deep-sea soundings are now taken by echo sounder (art. 619). If a depth recording device is available, it should be used, as the profile thus produced is a better indication of the bottom than even the most closely spaced visual readings.

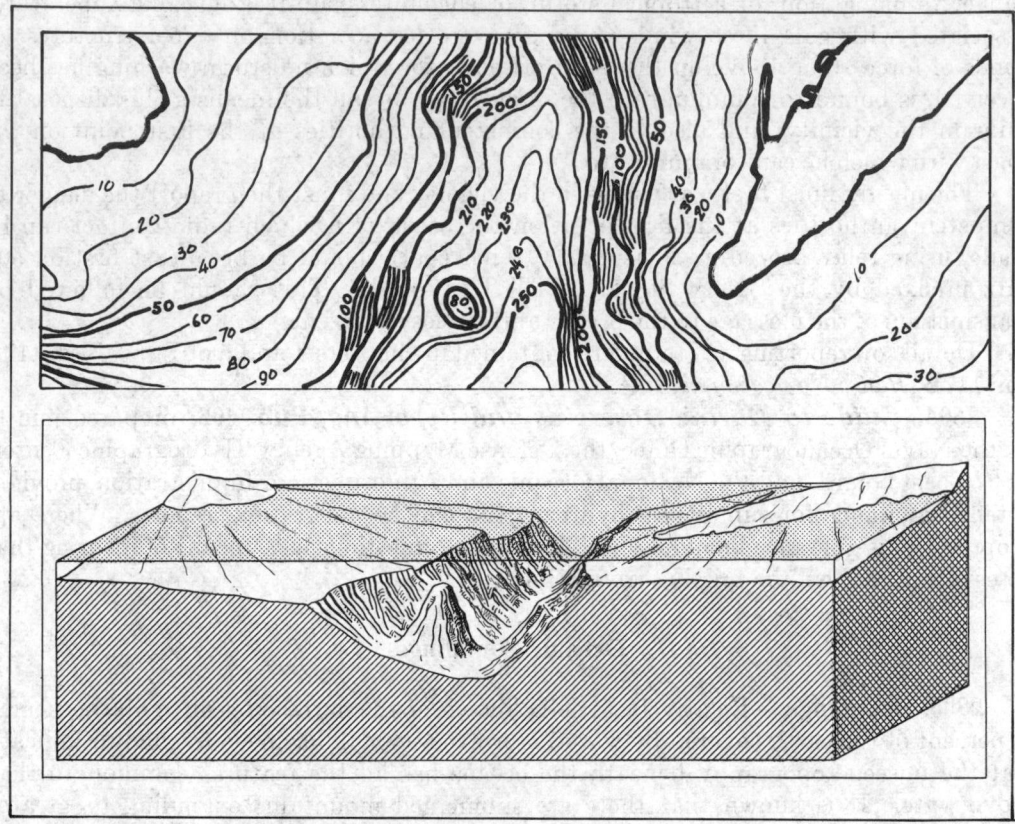

FIGURE 2805.—Contour lines and hachures (top) may be used to show underwater relief (bottom).

All echo sounding equipment is subject to certain errors unless the operator has a clear understanding of the operating characteristics and limitations of the instrument. The routine checks recommended by the manufacturer should be made at every change of the watch, or oftener. In addition, the operator should be alert for certain possible errors peculiar to his instrument. A close watch should be kept on the proper functioning of the stylus, recorder speed, the zero adjustment, and the frequency of the electric current. The percentage error in the recorded depth is the same as that of the electric current frequency. Thus, at 3,000 fathoms, the error of a 60-cycle echo sounder is 100 fathoms if the actual frequency is in error by two cycles.

2807. Evaluating results.—Inaccurate results may be worse than no information at all. Therefore, every effort should be made to obtain reliable data. Particularly, soundings which conflict with known or charted depths should be carefully analyzed. Even when the equipment is operating correctly, false returns might be received due to sources external to the vessel. A shoal "phantom bottom" may be due to marine life, there may be multiple echoes or interference, or no return may be received because of aeration of the water or suspended matter in it. Such errors are further discussed in article 3504. Unusual local conditions may be a source of error. If an error is believed probable, but no source is detected, full information should be submitted with the soundings, for the charting agency may be able to interpret the results. This action is particularly important where the measured depths are less than those shown on the chart. If no error can be found, the charting agency may have no alternative but to enter the shoal soundings upon the charts affected, and take the first opportunity to send a survey vessel to verify or disprove them.

The speed at which sound travels in water varies with the salinity, temperature, and pressure. When these are known, corrections can be applied to obtain more accurate results. However, this is normally done only for scientific purposes. Those soundings submitted to a charting agency should be the uncorrected values obtained by using an assumed standard speed of 4,800 feet or 1500 meters per second.

2808. Deep sea sounding lines.—Many deep sea soundings are obtained by ships proceeding between ports. Soundings should be taken at every opportunity. Those taken in well-surveyed areas can be of assistance to the navigator in locating his position. If they conflict with values shown on the chart, and no error is found, they should be sent to the appropriate charting agency, with full particulars. All soundings in areas for which little depth information is shown on the chart should be submitted.

In addition to reliable soundings, accurate positions are needed. Navigation should be in accordance with standard practice, using every practicable means to reduce error and provide frequent checks on position.

When two or more ships are operating together, they should steam on parallel courses about five miles apart. Each ship should collect and record its own navigational data for subsequent submission to the appropriate charting agency.

2809. Investigating small areas.—If a feature of particular interest, such as an isolated shoal or a seamount, is found or reported in the vicinity of the vessel, a service can be rendered by conducting a further investigation in the vicinity of the feature. Two methods are in common use for this purpose:

Radial. A system of radial lines 20° apart are laid out from a central control point, preferably at the center of the feature to be investigated. These are extended outward for a distance of about 30 miles, and the ends of alternate ones are connected, as shown in figure 2809a. These form a series of course lines as shown.

Parallel. A north-south, east-west square is laid out with perhaps 60-mile sides, the center of the feature of interest being at the center of the square. A series of course lines are drawn parallel to one side of the square, at intervals of about 5 miles. The ends of alternate parallel course lines are connected, as shown in figure 2809b.

During such an investigation, by either method, the best control of position can usually be obtained by anchoring a buoy, if practicable, at the center of the area. In some instances, several buoys might be used. Any rig having buoyancy adequate to support the necessary length of anchor cable is satisfactory. The type generally used consists of a steel drum or mooring buoy with a weight attached to a cable, in the case of a large buoy, or piano wire if the buoy is small and of insufficient buoyancy to support a cable. A chain is not generally used. Buoys of this type have been successfully anchored in depths to 2,500 fathoms. The position of the buoy is determined as accurately as practicable, using celestial navigation, Loran, or whatever means are available. Position of the vessel is determined relative to the buoy or buoys, using visual or radar bearings and ranges at intervals of half an hour or less. Beyond this range, the best available means are used. A balloon with a suspended radar reflector might be attached to the buoy to extend its range of usefulness. The securing line of the balloon should be at least 400 feet long, if practicable.

Sonar ranging, if available, should be used to assist in the location of shoal areas.

Sounding Reports

2810. Records.—Today much of the data processing necessary for compilation of nautical or bathymetric charts is accomplished by computers. Consequently, many of the laborious and time-consuming aspects of sounding report preparation have been eliminated. Computers, if given the proper information, can quickly and efficiently

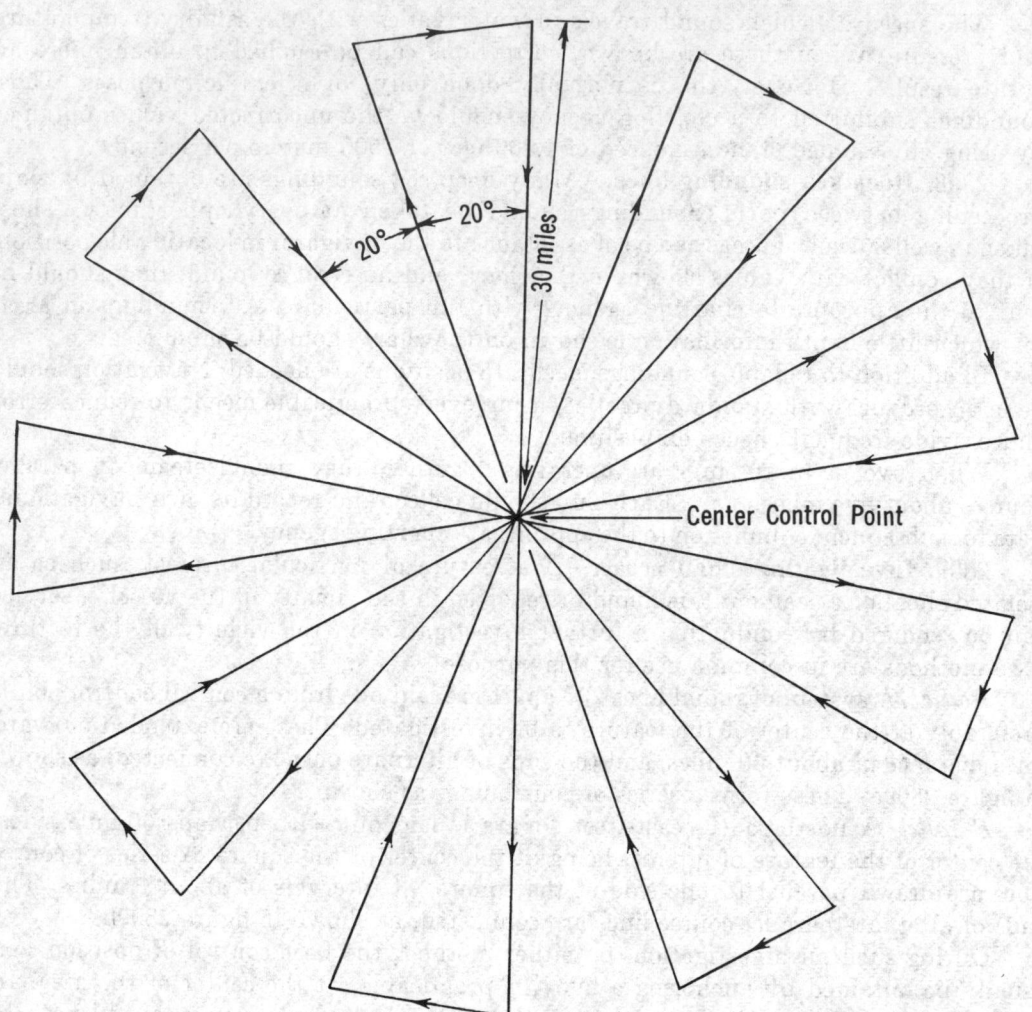

FIGURE 2809a.—Radial course line pattern.

perform all the routine data manipulation tasks formerly done manually by ocean-ographers and cartographers. However, it is still imperative that the mariner prepare his report accurately and completely, insuring that the basic elements of depth and position, both correlated with time, are included. Described below are the report records that best present these basic elements.

1. **Echograms.** Depth is best depicted by the echogram itself, a continuous analog record that serves not only as a report but also provides verification of the shipboard interpretation. There are many formats for echogram paper, but the essential information needed on an echogram is the following:

(i) *Ship Name.* Record at the beginning and end of each roll of echogram or portion thereof.

(ii) *Date.* Annotate at least once each day at 1200 and when starting and stopping echo sounder.

(iii) *Time.* The event marker should be activated and annotated with the correct time at the beginning of the echogram, at least once each watch thereafter, and at the end of the echogram.

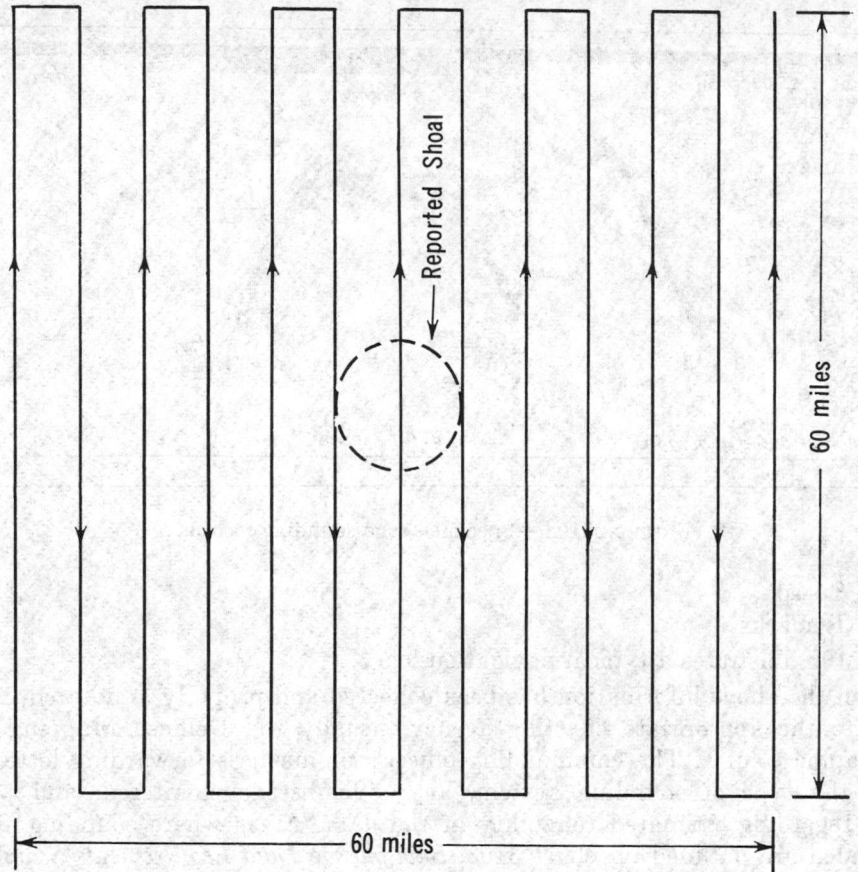

FIGURE 2809b.—Parallel course line pattern.

(iv) *Time Zones.* Greenwich mean time (GMT) should be used if practicable. In the event local time zones are used, annotate echogram whenever clocks are reset and identify time zone in use. Ambiguity of time zone is the most common cause of difficulty in relating a sounding trace to a ship's position.

(v) *Phase or Scale Changes.* Clearly label all depth phase (or depth scale) changes and the exact time they occur. Annotate the upper and lower limits of echograms if necessary.

(vi) *Transducer Depth.* The depth of the transducer beneath the surface and whether it is allowed for in the trace is necessary to compute true depth, especially in shoal areas. A specimen echo sounding record is shown in figure 2810a.

2. **Navigation Log.** In the past a smooth plotted track supplemented by the unadjusted plot was an essential part of a sounding report. The computer, with its tremendous capacity for data processing, has relieved the navigator of this monotonous and time-consuming task so that today only the navigation log is necessary. However, it is still important that the navigation log be accurate and contain all of the following information:

(i)   Date
(ii) Time (GMT)
(iii) Latitude and longitude
(iv) Type of navigational fix
(v)   Course

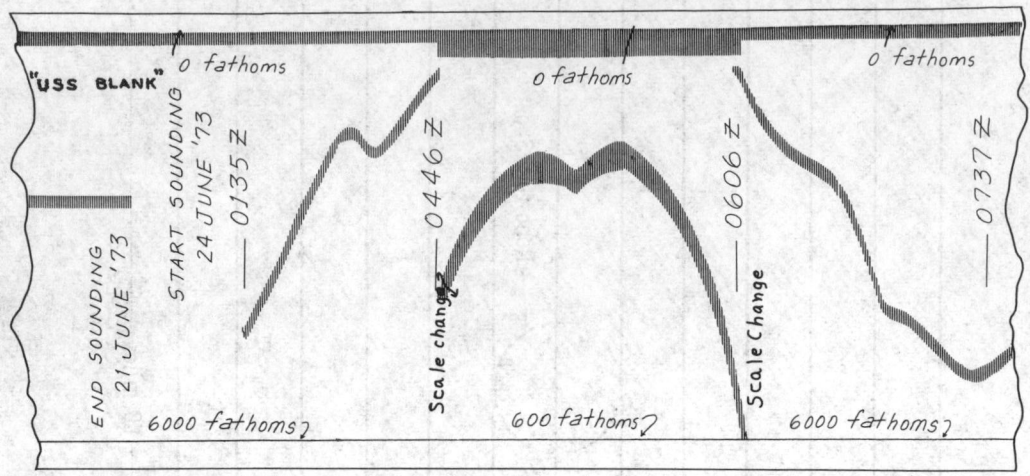

FIGURE 2810a.—Specimen echo sounding record.

(vi) Speed
(vii) Remarks

Figure 2810b illustrates a typical navigation log.

When the above information has been collected and properly annotated, it should be sent to the appropriate charting agency, usually the Defense Mapping Agency Hydrographic Center. The commanding officer's or master's forwarding letter should indicate the type of sounding system, any difficulties encountered, and pertinent remarks regarding estimated reliability of the data. Areas where sounding data are most needed are outlined on chart 5103, *Bathymetric Data Requirements,* which should be inspected prior to a voyage.

NAVIGATION LOG							REMARKS
DATE	TIME (GMT)	LAT.	LONG.	NAV. FIX	COURSE	SPEED	
11/2/73	0221	29°41'N	124°10'E	LORAN A	093°	12.3	
	0340				097°	12.3	CHANGE COURSE
	0400	29°40'N	124°35'E	NOON FIX	097°	12.3	
	0728	29°35'N	125°22'E	LORAN A	097°	12.3	
	0810				VARIOUS	8.2	REDUCE SPEED - MANUVERING TO AVOID FISHING BOATS
	0826	29°34'N	125°35.5E	LORAN A	097°	12.3	RESUME COURSE AND SPEED
	1011	29°32'N	125°56'E	EVENING STARS	097°	12.3	
	1620	29°23'N	127°22'E	LORAN A	102°	12.4	CHANGE COURSE
	2230	29°06.2N	128°48.5E	RADAR STAR	102°	12.5	
	2305				102°	10.1	REDUCE SPEED

FIGURE 2810b.—Typical navigation log.

CHAPTER XXIX

POSITION REPORTING SYSTEMS

2901. Introduction.—Several thousand merchant vessels are at sea at one time. These vessels have the proven potential for early arrival at a scene of distress. The purpose of a position reporting system is to make possible maximum efficiency in coordinating assistance by merchant vessels at a scene of distress in order to save life and property at sea.

It is important that information be readily available to Search and Rescue (SAR) coordinators immediately upon occurrence of an emergency so that potential assistance can be obtained effectively and with the least delay to those offering and needing aid. Establishing communications is sometimes difficult even when automatic alarms are used and determination of SAR capabilities and intentions of vessels is time-consuming, unless the essential information has been made readily available beforehand by their participation in a position reporting system.

Regulation 10, chapter V of the *Convention on Safety of Life at Sea* (SOLAS 1960) obligates the master of any vessel at sea who becomes aware of a distress incident to attempt to render assistance. He must proceed and assist until aware that other aid is at hand or until released by the distressed unit. Other international treaties and conventions impose the same requirement. Position reporting systems permit determination of the most appropriate early assistance, provide the means for a timely resolution of distress cases, and enable vessels responding to distress calls to continue their passage with a minimum amount of delay.

Recommendation 47 of IMCO's SOLAS 1960 Conference reads as follows:

"The Conference recommends that Contracting Governments should encourage all ships to report their positions when traveling in areas where arrangements are made to collect these positions for Search and Rescue (SAR) use. Each Government should arrange that such messages shall be free of cost to the ship concerned."

There are presently five vessel position reporting systems in operation throughout the world. These are: 1. Australian Ships Reporting System (AUSREP). 2. New Zealand System. 3. Greenland System. 4. Madagascar System. 5. Automated Mutual-assistance Vessel Rescue System (AMVER). The particulars of each system are given in publications of the Inter-Governmental Maritime Consultative Organization (IMCO).

Masters of vessels making offshore passages are requested by the U. S. Coast Guard to *always* participate in the AMVER System, and to participate in the *other* four systems whenever sailing within the areas covered by them.

2902. The Automated Mutual-assistance Vessel Rescue System (AMVER), operated by the United States Coast Guard, is a maritime mutual assistance program that provides important aid to the development and coordination of SAR efforts in the oceans of the world. Masters of merchant vessels of all nations making offshore passages of more than 24 hours are encouraged to send sail plans and periodic position reports to the AMVER Center in New York. There is no charge for these radio messages when they are sent through one of the cooperating AMVER radio stations (art. 2903). Information from these messages is entered into an electronic computer that generates and maintains dead reckoning positions of participating vessels throughout their voyages. The predicted locations and SAR characteristics of all vessels known to be within a given area are furnished upon request to recognized SAR agencies of any nation for use during an emergency. Predicted vessel locations are disclosed only for reasons related to maritime safety.

AMVER is a free and voluntary program. Benefits to shipping include: 1. Improved likelihood of rapid aid in emergencies; 2. reduced number of calls for assistance to vessels not favorably situated; 3. reduced time lost for vessels responding to calls for assistance. An AMVER participant is under no greater obligation to render assistance during an emergency than a vessel that is not participating.

In addition to the information calculated from sail plans and position reports, the AMVER Center stores data on the characteristics of merchant vessels. This data, reflecting SAR capability, includes the following: vessel name; international call sign; nation of registry; owner or operator; type of rig; type of propulsion; gross tonnage; length; normal cruising speed; radio schedule; medium, high, and very high frequency radio facilities; radio telephone installed; surface search radar installed; doctor normally carried. Vessels can assist the AMVER Center in keeping this data accurate by sending a complete report by message, letter, or by completing a SAR Capability Questionnaire (fig. 2905b) available from AMVER, and then sending corrections as the characteristics change. The corrections may easily be included in regular AMVER reports as remarks.

Although a vessel need not be departing or coming to the United States to be an AMVER participant there is an additional benefit for those whose destination is a U. S. port. AMVER participation via messages which include the necessary information is considered to meet the requirements of the United States Code of Federal Regulations, Title 33, Part 124.10; this requires, with certain exceptions, that the master or agent of each United States registered vessel and every foreign vessel arriving at a United States port (including the Great Lakes) from an offshore passage give advance notice to the U. S. Coast Guard at least 24 hours prior to arrival. The Code should be consulted to determine the exact current requirements, the exceptions, and the conditions of *constructive compliance*. The AMVER message must include the first port of call where a harbor entrance serves more than one port. The AMVER Center forwards pertinent information to the appropriate Coast Guard officials.

2903. AMVER System communications network.—An extensive radio station communications network supports the AMVER system and provides two routes for assistance messages as well as for AMVER messages: coast radio stations and Ocean Station Vessel radio facilities. Propagation conditions, location of vessel, and message density will normally determine which station may best be contacted to establish communications. To insure that no charge is applied, all AMVER messages should be passed through specified radio stations. Those which currently accept AMVER messages and apply no coast station, ship station, or landline charge are listed in each issue of the *AMVER Bulletin* (art. 2904) together with respective call sign, location, frequency bands, and hours of guard. Although AMVER messages may be sent through other stations, the Coast Guard cannot reimburse the sender for any charges applied.

2904. The *AMVER Bulletin,* published bimonthly by Commander, Atlantic Area, United States Coast Guard, Governors Island, New York, New York, 10004, provides information on the operation of the AMVER System of general interest to the mariner. It also provides up-to-date information on the AMVER communications network (art. 2903) and Radio Wave Propagation Charts which indicate recommended frequencies for contacting U. S. coast radio stations participating in the AMVER System, according to the time of day and the season of the year.

2905. AMVER participation.—Instructions guiding participation in the AMVER System are usually available in the following languages: Danish, Dutch, English,

French, German, Greek, Italian, Japanese, Polish, Norwegian, Portuguese, Russian, Spanish, and Swedish. They are available from: Commander, Atlantic Area, U. S. Coast Guard, Governors Island, New York, N.Y. 10004; Commander, Pacific Area, U. S. Coast Guard, 630 Sansome Street, San Francisco, California 94126; and at U. S. Coast Guard District Offices, Marine Inspection Offices, and Captain of the Port Offices in major U. S. ports. Requests for instructions should state the language desired if other than English.

Search and Rescue Operation procedures are contained in the *Merchant Ship Search and Rescue Manual (MERSAR)*, published by the Inter-Governmental Maritime Consultative Organization (IMCO).

A vessel is a participant in the AMVER program when its master sends a sail plan (fig. 2905a) to the AMVER Center upon leaving port, or as soon thereafter as possible. A participant is under no greater obligation to provide assistance during an emergency than a nonparticipant. There is no limitation on the size of a vessel that may participate in AMVER. Participation is determined by the nature of the passage and the communication capability aboard the vessel.

In connection with a vessel's first AMVER-plotted voyage, the master is requested to complete a questionnaire (fig. 2905b) providing the radio watch schedule, available

Form Approved
OMB No. 04-R3073

AMVER MESSAGE

Automated Mutual-assistance VEssel Rescue (AMVER) system
"that no call for help shall go unanswered"

1 NAME	2 CALL SIGN	3 REPORT TYPE
4 POSITION	5 DATE-TIME	GMT

6 SAILING ROUTE
6 SAILING ROUTE
6 SAILING ROUTE

7 SPEED	8 DESTINATION	9 ETA

To insure that no charge is applied, all AMVER messages should be passed through specified AMVER radio stations.

DEPT. OF TRANS., USCG, CG-4796 (REV. 8-75)
PREVIOUS EDITIONS MAY BE USED

DEPARTMENT OF TRANSPORTATION
UNITED STATES COAST GUARD

NAME 1	CALL SIGN 2	REPORT TYPE 3	POSITION 4	DATE-TIME 5	SAILING ROUTE 6	SPEED 7	DESTINATION 8	ETA 9
Name of vessel.	Radio call.	1, D, 2, or 3.	Latitude and longitude to nearest tenth degree *(name of point may be used where convenient, i.e. Ambrose).*	Date-Time GMT of position. *(Use 6 digit, i.e. 041800 where first 2 is date of month and last 4 are GMT hours and minutes.)*	Latitude and longitude to nearest 0.1 degree of each turn point along intended track. Use "RL" for rhumb line, or "GC" for great circle before each point to show method of sailing. When track is to be coastal, state "coastal" for that part of route.	To nearest 0.1 knot	Next port of call.	Estimated time of arrival at destination. Use GMT date and time.

Any vessel of any nation departing on an offshore passage of 24 hours duration or greater is encouraged to become a participant in the AMVER System by sending appropriate AMVER messages in four types of formats illustrated.

FIGURE 2905a.—Nine parts of AMVER message constituting a sail plan or movement report.

medical and communications facilities, and other useful characteristics. Stored in the AMVER computer, this information can be electronically processed with great speed in an emergency at the same time that a position is calculated.

Any vessel of any nation departing on an offshore passage of 24 hours duration or greater is encouraged to become a participant in the AMVER System by sending appropriate AMVER messages in four types of formats. The messages may be transmitted at any convenient time as long as the information is accurate and the data corresponds to the time specified. For example, the information may be estimated for a short time in the future, for the present, or for a short time past.

The four types of AMVER messages are:

Type 1. The complete Type 1 report (fig. 2905a) consists of nine parts and any pertinent remarks and contains the information necessary to initiate a plot. It is called an initial AMVER message and may be considered a movement report or sail plan. Type 1 reports may be sent immediately prior to departure, at departure, immediately after departure, or as soon as adequate communications can be established.

Type 2. The Type 2 report is considered a position report and includes the date and time of the position. It may contain additional entries and remarks. Experience has shown that occasional position reports are required during long passages to insure that the electronic computer will predict the positions within acceptable accuracy. It is not essential that these position reports be sent at any particular time or location, but it is suggested that they be prepared at intervals of approximately 15 degrees of latitude or longitude depending upon direction of advance. Positions are also extracted from weather reports made by ships participating in the international weather observation program since such position data is automatically forwarded to AMVER.

Type D. The Type D report is a deviation report and need include only information which differs from that previously reported. It is sent when the actual position will vary more than 25 miles from the position which would be predicted based upon data contained in previous reports. It may indicate a change of route, course, speed, or destination, and include any pertinent remarks.

Type 3. A Type 3 report is an arrival report, and is sent upon reaching the harbor entrance at port of destination. Parts 6, 7, 8, and 9 may be omitted from the message if desired. Remarks may be included. If communications cannot be established to permit sending the Type 3 report, the electronic computer will automatically terminate the plot at the predicted time of arrival at the destination. However, the report is desired to increase the accuracy of the plot. Type 3 reports are especially desired upon arrival at the harbor entrance of United States ports.

Only these four types of AMVER messages require specific formats. Other messages relating to a vessel's AMVER participation or data, such as facts on her SAR capabilities, may also be sent via the AMVER communications network.

Additional information concerning the AMVER System may be obtained by writing to Commandant, U. S. Coast Guard, Washington, D.C. 20590, or by writing or visiting Commander, Atlantic Area, U. S. Coast Guard, Governors Island, New York, N.Y. 10004.

The AMVER System is coordinated in the Pacific regions by Commander, Pacific Area, U. S. Coast Guard, U. S. Appraisers Bldg., 630 Sansome St., San Francisco, Calif. 94126.

Other countries such as Canada are a formal part of the AMVER System and provide radio stations for relay of AMVER reports as well as coordinating rescue efforts in certain regions. Applicable instructions have been promulgated by official publications of the participating countries.

Automated Mutual-assistance VEssel Rescue System

SAR CAPABILITY QUESTIONNAIRE FOR MERCHANT VESSELS
(PLEASE PRINT)

DATE _____

Present Name of Vessel _____ Call Sign _____ Year Built _____

Previous Name or Call
  Sign of Vessel _____ Manager or Owner _____

Propulsion Type _____ Type of Rig _____
         (see key below)   (see key below)

Length _____ Gross Tonnage _____ Average Speed _____
       (in feet)

Radio Watch Schedule _____ Radar _____ Doctor Normally carried _____
              (see key)   (Yes or No)   (Yes or No)

Radio Telephone (2182KHz) _____ VHF FM Radio (156.8 MHz) _____
                    (Yes or No)   (Yes or No)

Medium and/or High
Frequency Radio _____ Single Side Band _____
              (see key)   (Yes or No)

Nation of Registry _____

Remarks: _____
_____
_____

- -
(Fold on This Line)

TYPE OF RIG KEY   PROPULSION TYPE KEY

A   Academic or Training Vessel   DE   Diesel Electric
B   Cable Ship   GT   Gas Turbine
C   Cargo, Dry   HS   Hydrofoil Ship
D   Dredge   MV   Oil or Gas Engine
F   Fishing or Whaling Rig   NR   Nuclear Reactor
H   Hospital or Special Medical Facility SR   Steam Reciprocating
I   Icebreaker   SS   Steam Turbine
K   Car Carrier   TE   Turbo Electric
L   Log/Lumber Carrier
N   Naval Vessel   RADIO WATCH SCHEDULE KEY
O   Ore or Dry Bulk Cargo
P   Passenger   H24 24 Hour Continuous Service
R   Refrigerated Cargo   H16 16 Hour Service (ITU Schedule)
S   Salvage vessel, Tug or Tender   H8   8 Hour Service (ITU Schedule)
T   Tanker, or Liquid Bulk Carrier   HX   8 Hour Service, Schedule not
U   (Lash) Type Carrier   specified
W   Weather Station Vessel   N   No CW Operation (Radiotelephone only,
V   Van, or Container Carrier   unscheduled)
X   Miscellaneous, Research, Survey
    Ferry, etc.

RADIO FREQUENCY KEY: X Medium Frequency 405-535 KHz
                              Z High Frequency   4000-25110 KHz

Does vessel receive bi-monthly "AMVER Bulletin"? Yes ( ) No ( )
If not receiving "Bulletin", do you want vessel added to mailing list? Yes ( ) No ( )
(Please print complete mailing address on reverse, if Yes to above.)

NOTE: Please answer all questions; fold questionnaire so that address on the reverse
       side shows, staple or tape closed, apply postage of the country from which mailed.

DEPARTMENT OF TRANSPORTATION
U. S. COAST GUARD
FORM CAA 6 (REV 10-73)

FIGURE 2905b.—SAR Capability Questionnaire.

2906. AMVER plot information.—The information stored in the computer can be used to provide several types of display according to the needs of controllers at Rescue Coordination Centers. The surface picture (SURPIC) can be displayed as a **Radius SURPIC** (fig. 2906a). When requesting a Radius SURPIC, the controller specifies the date and time, a latitude and longitude to mark the center (P), the radius (in nautical miles) that the SURPIC should cover (R), whether the names of all ships are desired (or only those with doctors or just those heading either east or west).

A Radius SURPIC may be requested for any radius from 1 to 999 miles. A sample request is as follows:

"REQUEST 062100Z RADIUS SURPIC OF DOCTOR-SHIPS WITHIN 800 MILES OF 43.6N 030.2W FOR MEDICAL EVALUATION M/V SEVEN SEAS."

The **HI-LO SURPIC** (fig. 2906a) is obtained by the controller specifying the date, time, and two latitudes and two longitudes. The controller can limit the ships to be listed as with the Radius SURPIC. The computer responds with a listing of vessels within the boundaries specified.

There is no maximum or minimum size limitation on a HI–LO SURPIC.

A sample HI–LO SURPIC request is as follows:

"REQUEST 151300Z HI–LO SURPIC OF WESTBOUND SHIPS FROM 43N TO 31N LATITUDE AND FROM 130W TO 150W LONGITUDE FOR SHIP DISTRESS M/V EVENING SUN."

The **Trackline SURPIC** (fig. 2906a) is obtained by the controller specifying the date and time, two points (P–1 and P–2), whether the trackline should be rhumb line or great circle, what the half-width (D) coverage should be (in miles), and whether all ships are desired (or only doctor ships, or just those east or westbound). The half-width (D) specified should not exceed 100 miles. When received, the SURPIC will list ships in order from P–1 to P–2.

There is no maximum or minimum distance between P–1 and P–2.

A sample Trackline SURPIC request is as follows:

"REQUEST 310100Z GREAT CIRCLE TRACKLINE SURPIC OF ALL SHIPS WITHIN 50 MILES OF A LINE FROM 20.1N 150.2W TO 21.5N 158.0W FOR AIRCRAFT PRECAUTION."

A **Specific Advance** is not a SURPIC, as such. It is used to determine the location of a specific ship. It permits a controller to determine the position of an AMVER participant wherever located.

A sample Specific Advance request is as follows:

"REQUEST PRESENT POSITION, COURSE, AND SPEED OF M/V SOLID STATE/HIND."

A Radius SURPIC as it would be received by a rescue center, listing all ships within a 200-mile radius of 26.2N, 179.9W, is shown in figure 2906b.

2907. Uses of AMVER plot information.—An example of the use of a Radius SURPIC is depicted in figure 2907. In this situation rescue authorities believe that a ship in distress, or her survivors, will be found in the rectangular area. The Rescue Coordination Center requests a listing of all eastbound ships within 100 miles of a carefully chosen position. Once this list is received by the Rescue Coordination Center a few moments later, the names and call letters of those ships chosen to assist in the search can be passed to a powerful commercial radio station nearby for inclusion in their next regularly scheduled TRAFFIC LISTS (normally broadcast every 2 hours). These ships will be notified that rescue authorities are waiting to contact them on a given working frequency.

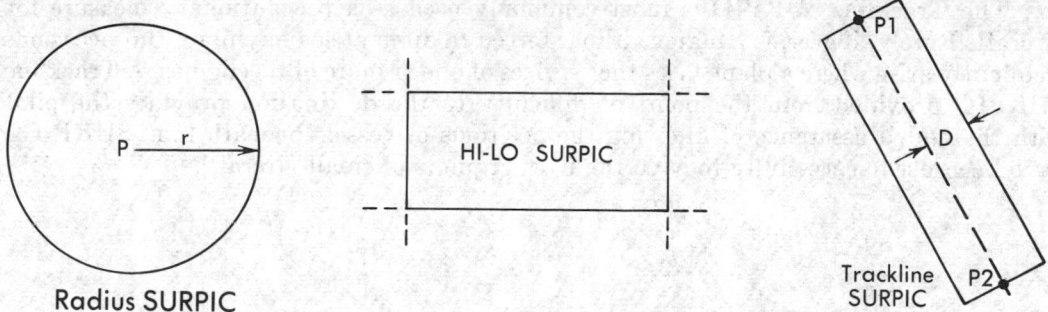

FIGURE 2906a.—Radius SURPIC, HI–LO SURPIC, and Trackline SURPIC.

Name	Call sign	Position	Course	Speed	SAR data							Destination and ETA	
CHILE MARU	JAYU	26.2N 179.9E	C294	12.5K	H 1 6 R	T		X Z				KOBE	11
CPA 258 DEG. 012 MI. 032000Z													
WILYAMA	LKBD	24.8N 179.1W	C106	14.0K	H X	R		T V X Z				BALBOA	21
CPA 152 DEG. 092 MI. 032000Z													
PRES CLEVELAND	WITM	25.5N 177.0W	C284	19.3K	H 2 4 R D T			X Z S				YKHAMA	08
CPA WILL PASS WITHIN 10 MI 040430Z													
AENEAS	GMRT	25.9N 176.9E	C285	.16.0K	H 8	R		N V X Z				YKHAMA	10
CPA 265 DEG. 175 MI. 03200Z													

FIGURE 2906b.—Radius SURPIC as received by a rescue center.

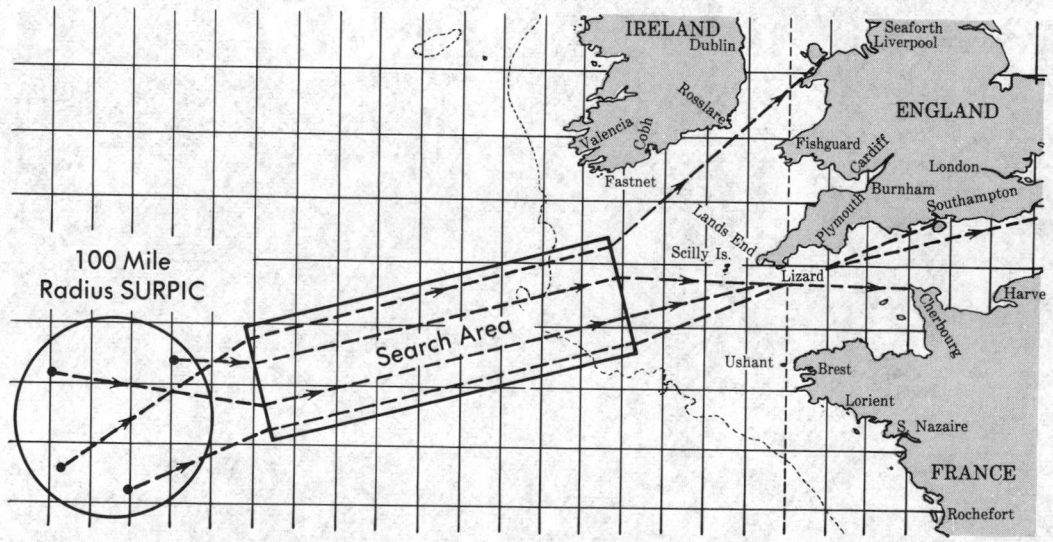

FIGURE 2907.—Use of Radius SURPIC.

Each ship contacted may be asked to sail a rhumb line between two specified points, one at the beginning of the search area and one at the end. By carefully assigning ships to areas of needed coverage, very little time need be lost from the sailing schedule of each cooperating ship. Those ships joining the search would report their positions every few hours to the Rescue Coordination Center, together with weather data and any significant sightings. In order to achieve saturation coverage, a westbound SURPIC at the eastern extremity of the search area would be used.

The Trackline SURPIC is most commonly used as a precautionary measure for aircraft. Rarely, if ever, is a major airliner forced to ditch at sea anymore. But occasions frequently arise where a plane loses the services of one or more of its engines. A Trackline SURPIC provided from the point of difficulty to the destination provides the pilot with the added assurance of knowing the positions of vessels beneath him. SURPIC's have been used successfully to save the lives of pilots of small aircraft.

PART SIX

OCEANOGRAPHY

PART SIX

OCEANOGRAPHY

CHAPTER XXX

THE OCEANS

3001. Introduction.—**Oceanography** is the application of the sciences to the phenomena of the oceans. It includes a study of their forms; physical, chemical, geological, and biological features; and phenomena. Thus, it embraces the widely separated fields of geography, geology, chemistry, physics, and biology. Many subdivisions of these sciences, such as sedimentation, ecology (biological relationship between organisms and their environment), bacteriology, biochemistry, hydrodynamics, acoustics, and optics, have been extensively studied in the oceans.

The oceans cover 70.8 percent of the surface of the earth. The Atlantic covers 16.2 percent, the Pacific 32.4 percent (3.2 percent more than the land area of the entire earth), the Indian Ocean 14.4 percent, and marginal and adjacent areas (of which the largest is the Arctic Ocean) 7.8 percent. Their extent alone makes them an important subject for study. However, greater incentive lies in their use for transportation, their influence upon weather and climate, and their potentiality as a source of power, food, freshwater, and mineral and organic substances.

3002. History of oceanography.—The earliest studies of the oceans were concerned principally with problems of navigation. Information concerning tides, currents, soundings, ice, and distances between ports was needed as ocean commerce increased. According to Posidonius, a depth of 1,000 fathoms had been measured in the Sea of Sardinia as early as the second century BC. About the middle of the 19th century, the Darwinian theories of evolution gave a great impetus to the collection of marine organisms, since it is believed by some that all terrestrial forms have evolved from oceanic ancestors. Later, the serious depletion of many fisheries called for investigation of the relation of the economically valuable organisms to the physical characteristics of their environment, especially in northwestern Europe and off Japan. Still later, the growing use of the oceans in warfare, particularly after the development of the submarine, required that much effort be expended in problems of detection and attack, resulting in the study of many previously neglected scientific aspects of the sea.

Oceanographic exploration. Exploration of the seas was primarily geographical until the 19th century, although the accumulated observations of seafarers, as recorded in the early charts and sailing directions, often included data on tides, currents, and other oceanographic phenomena. The great voyages of discovery, particularly those beginning in 1768 with Captain Cook, and continued by such commanders as La Pérouse, Bellingshausen, and Wilkes, included scientists in their complements. However, scientific work on the oceans at this period was severely limited by lack of suitable instruments for probing conditions below the surface. Meanwhile, Lieutenant Matthew Fontaine Maury, USN, working in the forerunner of the U. S. Navy Hydrographic Office in Washington, developed to a high degree of perfection the analysis of log-book observations. His first results, published in 1848, were of great importance to ship operations in the recommendation of favorable sailing routes, and they stimulated international cooperation in the fields of oceanography and marine meteorology.

In the rapid advances in technology after 1850, oceanographic instrumentation problems were not neglected, with the result that the British Navy in 1872–76 was able to send HMS *Challenger* around the world on the first purely deep-sea oceanographic expedition ever attempted. Her bottom samples, as analyzed by Sir John Murray, laid the foundation of geological oceanography, and 77 of her seawater samples, analyzed by C. R. Dittmar, proved for the first time that various constituents of the salts in seawater are everywhere in virtually the same proportions.

Since that time, the coastal waters and fishing banks of many nations have been extensively studied, and numerous vessels of various nationalities have conducted work on the high seas. Notable among these have been the American *Albatross* from 1882 to 1920; the Austrian *Pola* in the Mediterranean and Red Seas between 1890 and 1896; the Danish *Dana*, which during its voyages of 1920–22 discovered the breeding place of the European eels in the Sargasso Sea; the American *Carnegie* in 1927–29; the German *Meteor* in the Atlantic from 1928 to 1938; and the British *Discovery II* in the Antarctic between 1930 and 1939. Notable also were the drifts of the Norwegian vessels *Fram* and *Maud* in the arctic ice pack from 1893 to 1896 and 1918 to 1925, respectively; the attempt by Sir George Hubert Wilkins to operate under the ice in the British submarine *Nautilus* in 1931; and the Russian station set up at the North Pole in 1937, which made observations from the drifting pack ice.

At the same time, investigations pursued ashore provided the theoretical basis for the explanation of ocean currents, under the leadership of Helland-Hansen in Norway and Ekman and the Bjerknes in Sweden, while Martin Knudsen in Denmark worked out the precise details of the relationship between chlorinity, salinity, and density, enabling the theories to be verified by field observations.

During World War II, basic investigations were interrupted while work on purely military applications of oceanography was carried out. Deep-sea expeditions were renewed by the Swedish *Albatross* after the war, followed by the Danish *Galathea*, the second British *Challenger* (built in 1931), and *Discovery II* in the Antarctic, and vessels of the American Scripps Institution in the Pacific. Oceanographic work was carried out by Americans and Russians in the Arctic.

3003. Origin of the oceans.—Although many leading geologists still disagree with the conclusion that the structure of the continents is fundamentally different from that of the oceans, there is a growing body of evidence in support of the theory that the rocks underlying the ocean floors are more dense than those underlying the continents. According to this theory, all the earth's crust floats on a central liquid core, and the portions that make up the continents, being lighter, float with a higher freeboard. Thus, the thinner areas, composed of heavier rock, form natural basins where water has collected.

The shape of the oceans is constantly changing due to **continental drift.** The surface of the earth may be conceived as consisting of several "plates." These plates are joined along **fracture** or **fault lines.** There is constant and measurable movement of these plates.

The origin of the water in the oceans is also controversial. Although some geologists have postulated that all the water existed as vapor in the atmosphere of the primeval earth, and that it fell in great torrents of rain as soon as the earth cooled sufficiently, another school holds that the atmosphere of the original hot earth was lost, and that the water gradually accumulated as it was given off in steam by volcanoes or worked to the surface in hot springs.

Most of the water on the earth's crust is now in the oceans—about 328,000,000 cubic statute miles, or about 85 percent of the total. The mean depth of the ocean is 2,075 fathoms, and the total area is 139,000,000 square statute miles.

3004. Oceanographic chemistry may be divided into three main parts: the chemistry of (1) seawater, (2) marine sediments, and (3) organisms living in the sea. The first is of particular interest to the navigator.

Chemical properties of seawater are determined by analyzing samples of water obtained at various places and depths. Samples from below the surface are obtained by means of metal bottles designed for this purpose. The open bottles are attached at suitable intervals to a wire lowered into the sea. When they reach the desired depths, a metal ring or **messenger** is dropped down the wire. When the messenger arrives at the first bottle, it causes the bottle to close, trapping a sample of the water at that depth, and releasing a second messenger which travels on down the wire. The process is repeated at each bottle until all are closed, when they are hauled up and each bottle detached as it comes within reach. Of the various types devised, the **Nansen bottle** is the most widely known. It is equipped with a removable frame for attaching a thermometer.

3005. Physical properties of seawater are dependent primarily upon salinity, temperature, and pressure. However, factors like motion of the water and the amount of suspended matter affect such properties as color and transparency, conduction of heat, absorption of radiation, etc.

3006. Salinity is the amount of dissolved solid material in the water when carbonate has been converted to oxide, bromide and iodide to chloride, and organic material oxidized. It is usually expressed as parts per thousand (by weight), under certain standard conditions. This is not the same as **chlorinity,** which is equal approximately to the amount of chlorine, with bromides and oxides converted to chloride. (Actually the chlorine content is about 1.00045 times the chlorinity as determined by standard procedures.) The two have been found to be related empirically by the formula:

$$salinity = 0.03 + 1.805 \times chlorinity.$$

Historically the determination of salinity was a slow and difficult process, while chlorinity could be determined easily and accurately by titration with silver nitrate. It was customary to determine chlorinity and compute salinity by the formula given above. By this process, salinity could be determined with an error not exceeding 0.02 parts per thousand. Salinity can now be measured directly using a **salinometer** which measures changes in conductivity. Salinity generally varies between about 33 and 37 parts per thousand, the average being about 35 parts per thousand. However, when the water has been diluted, as near the mouth of a river or after a heavy rainfall, the salinity is somewhat less; and in areas of excessive evaporation, the salinity may be as high as 40 parts per thousand. In certain confined bodies of water, notably the Great Salt Lake in Utah, and the Dead Sea in Asia Minor, the salinity is several times this maximum. Chlorinity accounts for about 55 percent of salinity, the average being about 19 parts per thousand.

3007. Temperature in the ocean varies widely, both horizontally and with depth. Maximum values of about 90°F are encountered at the surface in the Persian Gulf in summer, and the lowest possible values of about 28°F (the usual minimum freezing point of seawater) occur in polar regions and near the ocean bottom everywhere, including the Tropics. Pub. No. 225, *World Atlas of Sea Surface Temperatures*, shows in detail the average sea surface temperatures for each month. The following tabulation gives the percentage distribution of temperatures for the world for the months of February and August, as derived from this source:

Surface temperature °F	Percentage of area of ocean	
	February	August
<35	12. 0	13. 1
35–40	6. 5	3. 3
40–45	4. 0	3. 0
45–50	4. 5	5. 0
50–55	4. 0	6. 5
55–60	5. 0	6. 0
60–65	5. 5	6. 3
65–70	8. 0	7. 0
70–75	10. 0	10. 4
75–80	17. 5	16. 5
80–85	23. 0	22. 7
85–90	0. 0	0. 2

The vertical distribution of temperature in the sea nearly everywhere shows a decrease of temperature with depth. Since colder water is denser (assuming the same salinity), it sinks below warmer water. This results in a temperature distribution just opposite to that of the earth's crust, where temperature increases with depth below the surface of the ground.

In general, in the sea there is usually a mixed layer of isothermal water below the surface, where the temperature is the same as that of the surface. This layer is caused by two physical processes: wind mixing, and convective overturning as surface water cools and becomes more dense. The layer is best developed in the Arctic and Antarctic regions and seas like the Baltic and Sea of Japan during the winter, where it may extend to the bottom of the ocean. In the Tropics, the wind-mixed layer may exist to a depth of 125 meters. The layer may exist throughout the year. Below this layer is a zone of rapid temperature decrease, called the **thermocline,** to the temperature of the deep oceans. At a depth greater than 200 fathoms, the temperature everywhere is below 60°F, and in the deeper layers, fed by cooled waters that have sunk from the surface in the Arctic and Antarctic, temperatures as low as 28°.5F exist.

In the colder regions the cooling creates the convective overturning and isothermal water in the winter; but in the summer a seasonal thermocline is created as the upper water becomes warmer.

A typical curve of temperature at various depths is shown in figure 3503a. Temperature at any desired depth can be determined by means of a **reversing thermometer** attached to a Nansen bottle (art. 3004). When the bottle closes, the thermometer measures the temperature to within 0°.04F, thus providing a reading for a particular time and point. Instruments with **thermistors** (devices that utilize the change in conductivity of a semiconductor with change in temperature) are commonly used to measure temperature. The STD (salinity-temperature-depth) is an instrument that provides continuous signals as it is lowered from the vessel; temperature is determined by means of a thermistor, salinity by conductivity, and depth by pressure. Continuous records of temperature were first obtained by an instrument called a **bathythermograph,** invented by Spilhaus in 1938. This device functioned to a depth of 75 meters.

The mechanical bathythermograph has been replaced almost entirely by the **expendable bathythermograph** (**XBT**), which uses a thermistor. The XBT is connected to the vessel by a fine wire. The wire is coiled inside the probe and as the probe free-falls in the ocean, the wire plays out. Depth is determined by elapsed time and a known sink rate. Depth range is determined by the amount of wire stored in the probe; the most common model has a depth range of 500 meters. At the end of the drop, the wire breaks and the probe falls to the ocean bottom. One instrument of this type is dropped from an aircraft, the data being relayed to the aircraft from a buoy to which the wire of the XBT is attached.

3008. Pressure.—In oceanographic work, pressure is generally expressed in units of the centimeter-gram-second system. The basic unit of this system is 1 dyne per square centimeter. This is a very small unit, one million constituting a practical unit called a bar, which is nearly equal to 1 atmosphere. Atmospheric pressure is often expressed in terms of **millibars,** 1,000 of these being equal to 1 bar. In oceanographic work, water pressure is commonly expressed in terms of **decibars,** 10 of these being equal to 1 bar. One decibar is equal to nearly 1½ pounds per square inch. This unit is convenient because it is very nearly the pressure exerted by 1 meter of water. Thus, the pressure in decibars is approximately the same as the depth in meters, the unit of depth customarily used in oceanographic research. In terms more familiar to the mariner, the pressure at various depths is as follows:

Depth in fathoms	Pressure in pounds per square inch
1,000	2,680
2,000	5,390
3,000	8,100
4,000	10,810
5,000	13,520

The increase in pressure with depth is nearly constant because water is only slightly compressible.

Although virtually all of the physical properties of seawater are affected to a measurable extent by pressure, the effect is not as great as those of salinity and temperature. Pressure is of particular importance to submarines, directly because of the stress it induces on the materials of the craft, and indirectly because of its effect upon buoyancy.

3009. Density is mass per unit volume. Oceanographers use the centimeter-gram-second system, in which density is expressed as grams per cubic centimeter. The ratio of the density of a substance to that of a standard substance under stated conditions is called **specific gravity.** By definition, the density of distilled water at $4°C(39°2 F)$ is 1 gram per milliliter (approximately 1 gram per cubic centimeter). Therefore, if this is used as the standard, as it is in oceanographic work, density and specific gravity are virtually identical numerically.

The density of seawater depends upon salinity, temperature, and pressure. At constant temperature and pressure, density varies with salinity or, because of the relationship between this and chlorinity, with the chlorinity. A temperature of 32°F and atmospheric pressure are considered standard for density determination. The effects of thermal expansion and compressibility are used to determine the density at other temperatures and pressures. The density at a particular pressure affects the buoyancy of submarines. It is also important in its relation to ocean currents.

The greatest changes in density of seawater occur at the surface, where the water is subject to influences not present at depths. Here density is decreased by precipitation, run-off from land, melting of ice, or heating. When the surface water becomes less dense, it tends to float on top of the more dense water below. There is little tendency for the water to mix, and so the condition is one of stability. The density of surface water is increased by evaporation, formation of sea ice, and by cooling. If the surface water becomes more dense than that below, it causes convective mixing. The more dense surface water sinks and mixes with less dense water below. The resultant layer of water is of intermediate density. This process continues until the density of the mixed layer becomes less than that of the water below. The convective circulation established as part of this process can create very deep uniform mixed layers. If the surface water becomes sufficiently dense, it sinks all the way to the bottom. If this occurs in an area where horizontal flow is unobstructed, the water which has descended spreads to other regions, creating a dense bottom layer. Since the greatest increase in density occurs in polar regions, where the air is cold and great quantities of ice form, the cold, dense polar water sinks to the bottom and then spreads to lower latitudes. In the Arctic Ocean region, the cold, dense water is confined by the Bering Strait and the underwater ridge from Greenland to Iceland to Europe. In the Antarctic, however, there are no similar geographic restrictions and large quantities of very cold, dense water formed there flow to the north along the ocean bottom. This process has continued for a sufficiently long period of time that the entire ocean floor is covered with this dense water, thus explaining the layer of cold water at great depths in all the oceans.

In some respects, oceanographic processes are similar to those occurring in the atmosphere (ch. XXXVIII). The convective circulation in the ocean is somewhat similar to that in the atmosphere. Water masses having nearly uniform characteristics are analogous to airmasses.

3010. Compressibility.—Seawater is nearly incompressible, its coefficient of compressibility being only 0.000046 per bar under standard conditions. This value changes slightly with changes of temperature or salinity. The effect of compression is to force the molecules of the substance closer together, causing it to become more dense. Even though the compressibility is low, its total effect is considerable because of the amount of water involved. If the compressibility of seawater were zero, sea level would be about 90 feet higher than it now is.

3011. Viscosity is resistance to flow. Seawater is slightly more viscous than freshwater. Its viscosity increases with greater salinity, but the effect is not nearly as marked as that occurring with decreasing temperature. The rate is not uniform, becoming greater as the temperature decreases. Because of the effect of temperature upon viscosity, an incompressible object might sink at a faster rate in warm surface water than in colder water below. However, for most objects, this effect may be more than offset by the compressibility of the object.

The actual relationships existing in the ocean are considerably more complicated than indicated by the simple explanation given above, because of turbulent motion within the sea. The disturbing effect is called **eddy viscosity.**

3012. Specific heat is the amount of heat required to raise the temperature of a unit mass of a substance a stated amount. In oceanographic work, specific heat is stated, in centimeter-gram-second units, as the number of calories needed to raise 1 gram of the substance 1°C. Specific heat at constant pressure is usually the quantity desired when liquids are involved, but occasionally the specific heat at constant volume is required. The ratio of these two quantities has a direct relationship to the speed of sound in seawater.

The specific heat of seawater decreases slightly as salinity increases. However, it is much greater than that of land. The ocean is a giant sink and source for heat. It can absorb large quantities of heat with very little change in temperature. This is partly due to the high specific heat of water and partly due to mixing in the ocean that distributes the heat throughout a layer. Land has a lower specific heat and, in addition, all heat is lost or gained from a thin layer at the surface. This accounts for the greater temperature range of land and the atmosphere above it, resulting in monsoons (art. 3810) and the familiar land and sea breezes of tropical and temperate regions (art. 3814).

3013. Thermal expansion.—One of the more interesting differences between salt- and freshwater relates to thermal expansion. Saltwater continues to become more dense as it cools to the freezing point; freshwater reaches maximum density at 4°C and then expands (becomes less dense) as the water cools to 0°C and freezes. This means that the convective mixing of freshwater stops at 4°C; freezing proceeds very rapidly beyond that point. The rate of expansion with increased temperature is greater in seawater than in freshwater. Thus, at temperature 15°C (59°F), and atmospheric pressure, the coefficient of thermal expansion is 0.000151 per degree Celsius for fresh- water and 0.000214 per degree Celsius for water of 35 parts per thousand salinity. The coefficient of thermal expansion increases not only with greater salinity, but also with increased temperature and pressure. At 35 parts per thousand, the coefficient of surface water increases from 0.000051 per degree Celsius at 0°C (32°F) to 0.000334 per degree Celsius at 30°C (86°F). At a constant temperature of 0°C (32°F) and a salinity of 34.85 parts per thousand, the coefficient increases to 0.000276 per degree Celsius at a pressure of 10,000 decibars (at a depth of approximately 10,000 meters).

3014. Thermal conductivity.—In water, as in other substances, one method of heat transfer is by conduction. Freshwater is a poor conductor of heat, having a coefficient of thermal conductivity of 0.00139 calories per second per centimeter per degree Celsius. For seawater it is slightly less but increases with greater temperature or pressure.

However, if turbulence is present, which it nearly always is to some extent in the ocean, the processes of heat transfer are altered. The effect of turbulence is to increase greatly the rate of heat transfer. The "eddy" coefficient used in place of the still-water coefficient is so many times larger, and so dependent upon the degree of turbulence that the effects of temperature and pressure are not important.

3015. Electrical conductivity.—Water without impurities is a very poor conductor of electricity. However, when salt is in solution in water, the salt molecules are ionized (art. 4107) and therefore are carriers of electricity. (What is commonly called fresh- water has many impurities and is a good conductor of electricity; only *pure* distilled water is a poor conductor of electricity.) Hence, the electrical conductivity of sea- water is directly proportional to the number of salt molecules in the water. For any given salinity, the conductivity increases with an increase in temperature.

3016. Radioactivity.—Although the amount of radioactive material in seawater is very small, this material is present in marine sediments to a greater extent than in the rocks of the earth's crust. This is probably due to precipitation of radium or other radioactive material from the water. The radioactivity of the top layers of sediment is less than that of deeper layers. This may be due to absorption of radioactive material in the soft tissues of marine organisms.

3017. Refractive index (art. 1613) of seawater increases as salinity becomes greater, or as temperature decreases. Since it varies with frequency of the radiant energy, the "D line" of sodium is usually used as the standard for comparison.

3018. Surface tension of water in dynes per square centimeter is approximately equal to $75.64 - 0.144T + 0.0399Cl$, where T is temperature in degrees Celsius (centi- grade) and Cl is the chlorinity of the water in parts per thousand. As indicated by the last term, the surface tension increases with chlorinity, and is therefore a little more for seawater than for freshwater. However, the presence of impurities causes it to be somewhat less than indicated by the formula.

3019. Transparency of seawater varies with the number, size, and nature of particles suspended in the water, as well as with the nature and intensity of illumina- tion. The rate of decrease of light energy with depth is called the "extinction coeffi- cient." The earliest method of measuring transparency was by means of a **Secchi disk,**

a white disk 30 centimeters (a little less than 1 foot) in diameter. This was lowered into the sea, and the depth at which it disappeared was recorded. In coastal waters the depth varies from about 5 to 25 meters (16 to 82 feet). Offshore, the depth is usually about 45 to 60 meters (148 to 197 feet). The greatest recorded depth at which the disk has disappeared is 66 meters (217 feet), in the Sargasso Sea.

Although the Secchi disk still affords a simple method of measuring transparency, more exact methods have been devised.

3020. Color.—The color of seawater varies considerably. Water of the Gulf Stream is a deep indigo blue, while a similar current off Japan was named Kuroshio (Black Stream) because of the dark color of its water. Along many coasts the water is green. In certain localities a brown or brownish-red water has been observed. Colors other than blue are caused by biological sources, such as plankton, or by suspended sediments from river runoff.

Offshore, some shade of blue is common, particularly in tropical or subtropical regions. It is due to scattering of sunlight by minute particles suspended in the water, or by molecules of the water itself. Because of its short wavelength, blue light is more effectively scattered than light of longer waves. Thus, the ocean appears blue for the same reason that the sky does (art. 3817). The green color often seen near the coast is a mixture of the blue due to scattering of light and a stable soluble yellow pigment associated with phytoplankton (art. 3024). Brown or brownish-red water receives its color from large quantities of certain types of **algae,** microscopic plants in the sea or from river runoff.

3021. Marine geology is a branch of oceanography dealing with bottom relief, particularly the characteristics of ocean basins and the geological processes that brought them into being and tend to alter them, as well as with marine sediments.

3022. Bottom relief.—Compared to land, relatively little is known of relief below the surface of the sea. Until recent years, the sea has proved an effective barrier to acquisition of knowledge of features below its surface. Although soundings of 1,000 fathoms were probably made as early as the second century BC (art. 3002), the number of deep sea soundings by means of a weight lowered to the bottom had been relatively few. The process was a time-consuming one requiring special equipment. Several hours were needed for a single sounding. Since the development of an effective echo sounder (art. 619) in 1922, the number of deep sea soundings has greatly increased. Later, a recording echo sounder was developed to permit the continuous tracing of a **bottom profile.** This has assisted materially in the acquisition of knowledge of bottom relief. By this means, many mountain ranges, and other features have been discovered. Although the main features are becoming known, a great many details are yet to be learned.

Along most of the coasts of the continents, the bottom slopes gradually downward to a depth of about 100 fathoms or somewhat less, where it falls away more rapidly to greater depths. This **continental shelf** (fig. 3022a) averages about 30 miles in width, but varies from nothing to about 800 miles, the widest part being off the Siberian arctic coast. A similar shelf extending outward from an island or group of islands is called an **island shelf.** At the outer edge of the shelf, the steeper slope of 2° to 4° is called the **continental slope,** or the **island slope,** according to whether it surrounds a continent or group of islands. The shelf itself is not uniform, but has numerous hills, ridges, terraces, and canyons, the largest being comparable in size to the Grand Canyon.

The relief of the ocean floor is comparable to that of land. Both have steep, rugged mountains, deep canyons, rolling hills, plains, etc. Most of the ocean floor is considered to be made up of a number of more-or-less circular or oval depressions called **basins,** surrounded by walls (sills) of lesser depth.

Undersea features (figs. 3022a and 3022b) are defined as follows:

Archipelagic apron or *apron*.—A gentle slope with a generally smooth surface on the sea floor, particularly as found around groups of islands or seamounts.

Bank.—An elevation of the sea floor located on a shelf and over which the depth of water is relatively shallow but sufficient for safe surface navigation.

Basin.—A depression of variable extent and more-or-less circular or oval in form.

Borderland or *continental borderland*.—A region adjacent to a continent, normally occupied by or bordering a shelf, that is highly irregular with depths well in excess of those typical of a shelf.

Canyon.—A relatively narrow, deep depression with steep slopes, the bottom of which generally grades downward.

Cone.—See FAN.

Continental borderland.—See BORDERLAND.

Continental margin.—The zone separating the emergent continent from the deep sea bottom, generally consisting of the rise, slope, and shelf.

Continental rise.—A gentle slope rising toward the foot of the continental slope. See RISE.

Continental shelf.—See SHELF.

Cordillera.—An entire mountain system including all the subordinate ranges, interior plateaus, and basins.

Escarpment or *scarp*.—An elongated and comparatively steep slope of the sea floor, separating flat or gently sloping areas.

Fan or *cone*.—A gently sloping, fan-shaped feature normally located near the lower termination of a canyon.

Fracture zone.—An extensive linear zone of unusually irregular topography of the sea floor characterized by large seamounts, steep-sided or asymmetrical ridges, troughs, or escarpments.

Gap.—A depression cutting transversely across a ridge or rise.

Hill.—A small elevation rising generally less than 200 meters from the sea floor.

Hole.—A small depression of the sea floor.

Knoll.—An elevation rising less than 1,000 meters from the sea floor and of limited extent across the summit.

Levee.—An embankment bordering either one or both sides of a seachannel or the low-gradient seaward part of a canyon or valley.

Moat.—An annual depression that may not be continuous, located at the base of many seamounts or islands.

Mountains.—A well delineated subdivision of a large and complex positive feature, generally part of a cordillera.

Peak.—An individual pointed top on a ridge or a complex seamount.

Plain.—A flat, gently sloping or nearly level region of the sea floor.

Plateau.—A comparatively flat-topped elevation of the sea floor of considerable extent across the summit and usually rising more than 200 meters on at least one side.

Province.—A region composed of a group of similar bathymetric features whose characteristics are markedly in contrast with surrounding areas.

Range.—A series of ridges or seamounts, generally parallel.

Reef.—An offshore consolidated rock hazard to navigation with a least depth of 20 meters (or 10 fathoms) or less.

Ridge.—A long, narrow elevation of the sea floor with steep sides.

Rise.—A long, broad elevation that rises gently and generally smoothly from the sea floor.

Saddle.—A low part on a ridge or between seamounts.

Seachannel.—A long, narrow, U-shaped, or V-shaped, shallow depression of the sea floor, usually occurring on a gently sloping plain or fan.

Seamount.—An elevation rising 1,000 meters or more from the sea floor, and of limited extent across the summit.

Shelf or *continental shelf.*—A zone adjacent to a continent or around an island, and extending from the low waterline to the depth at which there is usually a marked increase of slope to greater depth.

Shoal.—An offshore hazard to navigation with a least depth of 20 meters (or 10 fathoms) or less, composed of unconsolidated material.

Sill.—The low part of the ridge or rise separating ocean basins from one another or from the adjacent sea floor.

Slope or *continental slope.*—The declivity seaward from a shelf into greater depth.

Spur.—A subordinate elevation, ridge, or rise projecting from a larger feature.

Tablemount or *Guyot.*—A seamount having a comparatively smooth, flat top.

Terrace or *bench.*—A bench-like feature bordering an undersea feature.

Trench.—A long, narrow and deep depression of the sea floor, with relatively steep sides.

Trough.—A long depression of the sea floor, normally wider and shallower than a trench.

Valley.—A relatively shallow, wide depression with gentle slopes, the bottom of which generally grades continuously downward. This term is used for features that do not have canyon-like characteristics in any significant part of their extent.

The term **deep** may be used for a very deep part of the ocean, generally that part deeper than 3,000 fathoms.

The average depth of water in the oceans is 2,075 fathoms (12,450 feet), as compared to an average height of land above the sea of about 2,750 feet. The greatest known depth is 35,800 feet, in the Marianas Trench in the Pacific. The highest known land is Mount Everest, 29,002 feet. About 23 percent of the ocean is shallower than 10,000 feet, about 76 percent is between 10,000 and 20,000 feet, and a little more than 1 percent is deeper than 20,000 feet.

3023. Marine sediments.—The ocean floor is composed of material deposited there through the years. This material consists principally of (1) earth and rocks washed into the sea by streams and waves, (2) volcanic ashes and lava, and (3) the remains of marine organisms. Lesser amounts of land material are carried into the sea by glaciers, blown out to sea by wind, or deposited by chemical means. This latter process is responsible for the manganese nodules that cover some parts of the ocean floor. In the ocean, the material is transported by ocean currents, waves, and ice. Near shore the material is deposited at the rate of about 3 inches in 1,000 years, while in the deep water offshore the rate is only about half an inch in 1,000 years. Marine deposits in water deep enough to be relatively free from wave action are subject to little erosion. Recent studies have shown that some bottom currents are strong enough to move sediments. There are **turbidity currents,** similar to land slides, that move large masses of sediments. Turbidity currents have been known to rip apart large transoceanic cables on the ocean bottom. Because of this and the slow rate of deposit, marine sediments provide a better geological record than does the land.

Marine sediments are composed of individual particles of all sizes from the finest clay to large boulders. In general, the inorganic deposits near shore are relatively coarse (sand, gravel, shingle, etc.), while those in deep water are much finer (clay). In some areas the siliceous remains of marine organisms or the calcareous deposits (of either organic or inorganic origin) are sufficient to predominate on the ocean floor.

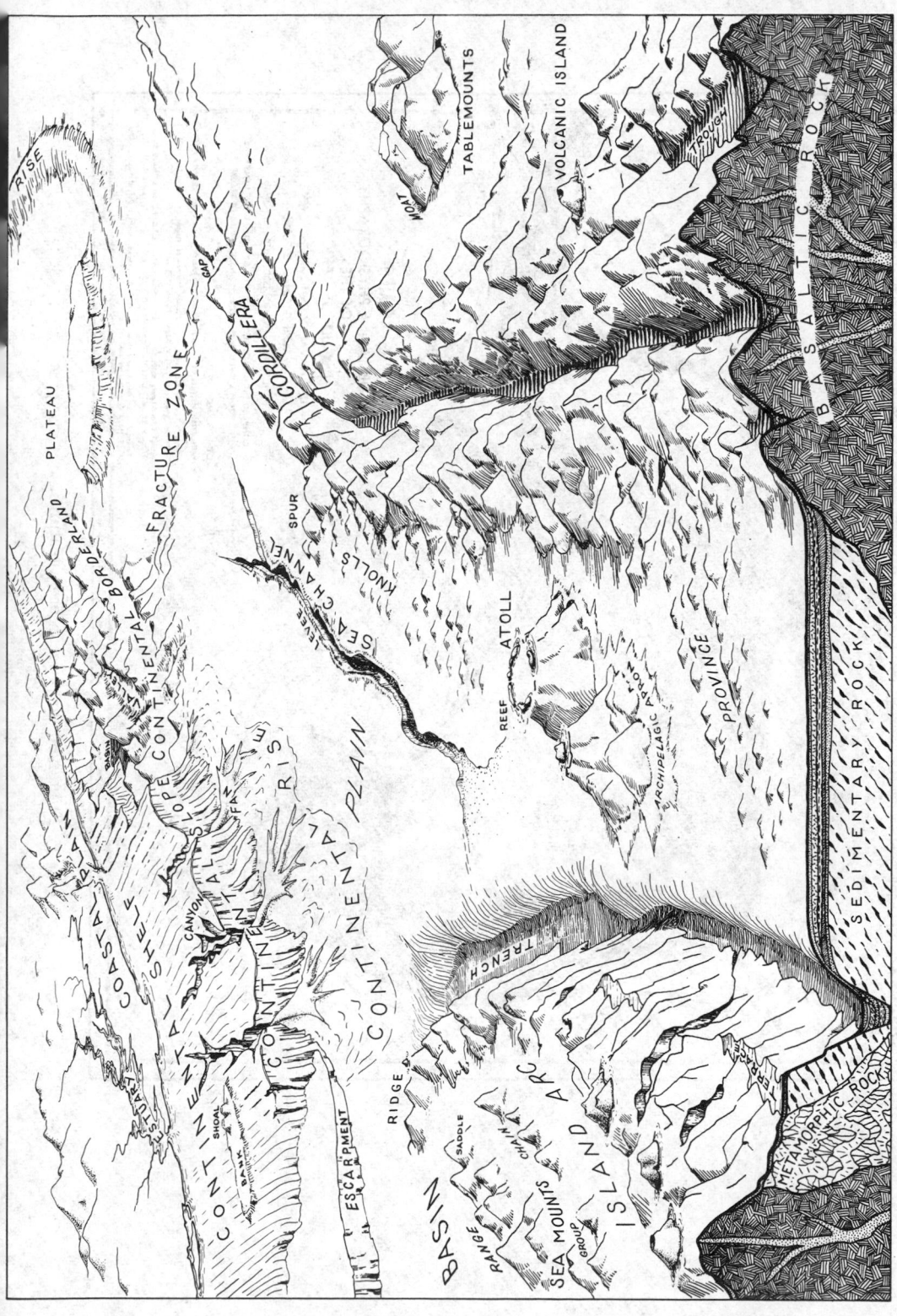

FIGURE 3022a.—Ocean basin features.

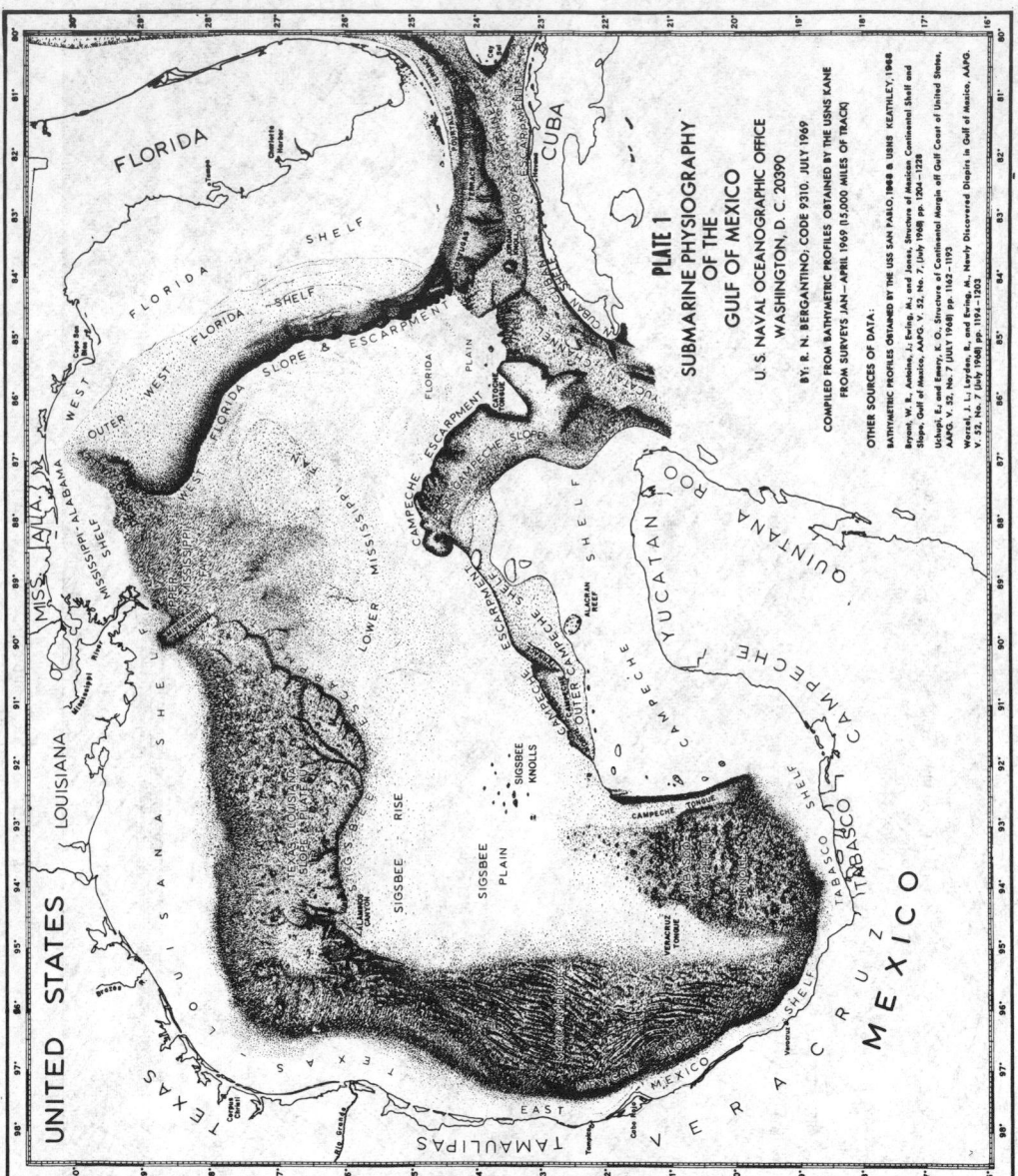

FIGURE 3022b.—Ocean basin features.

A wide range of colors is found in marine sediments. The lighter colors (white or a pale tint) are usually associated with coarse-grained quartz or limestone deposits. Darker colors (red, blue, green, etc.) are usually found in mud having a predominance of some mineral substance, such as an oxide of iron or manganese. Black mud is often found in an area that is little disturbed, such as at the bottom of an inlet or in a depression without free access to other areas.

Marine sediments are studied primarily by means of bottom samples. Samples of surface deposits are obtained by means of a **snapper** (for mud, sand, etc.) or "dredge" (usually for rocky material). If a sample of material below the bottom surface is desired, a "coring" device is used. This device consists essentially of a tube driven into the bottom by weights or explosives. A sample obtained in this way preserves the natural order of the various layers. Samples of more than 100 feet in depth have been obtained by means of coring devices. The bottom sample obtained by the mariner, by arming his lead with tallow or soap (art. 617), is an incomplete indication of bottom surface conditions.

3024. Synoptic oceanography.—Bathythermograph and sea surface temperature observations are reported directly to the Fleet Numerical Weather Central, Monterey, California. These synoptic reports are then analyzed by computer to determine ocean thermal conditions at any point in the Northern Hemisphere.

References

Crease, J. "The Origin of Ocean Currents." *Journal of the Institute of Navigation* (British), vol. 5, no. 3 (July 1952).

Day, A., Rear Admiral. "Navigation and Hydrography." *Journal of the Institute of Navigation* (British), vol. 6, no. 1 (January 1953).

Deacon, G. E. R. "Oceanographical Research and Navigation." *Journal of the Institute of Navigation* (British), vol. 4, no. 3 (July 1951).

Defant, A. *Physical Oceanography*. (2 vols.) New York, Pergamon, 1961.

Marmer, H. A. *The Scope of Oceanography*. James Johnstone Memorial Volume. Liverpool, University Press of Liverpool, 1934.

National Research Council. *Physics of the Earth—Oceanography*. Bulletin no. 85, Chapter V. Washington, The National Academy of Sciences, 1932.

Satow, P. G. "Some Problems of Underwater Navigation." *Journal of the Institute of Navigation* (British), vol. 4, no. 3 (July 1951).

Shepard, F. P. *Submarine Geology*. New York, Harper, 1948.

Sverdrup, H. U., M. W. Johnson, and R. H. Fleming. *The Oceans, Their Physics, Chemistry and General Biology*. New York, Prentice-Hall, 1942.

CHAPTER XXXI

TIDES AND TIDAL CURRENTS

General

3101. The tidal phenomenon is the periodic motion of the waters of the sea due to differences in the attractive forces of various celestial bodies, principally the moon and sun, upon different parts of the rotating earth. It can be either a help or hindrance to the mariner—the water's rise and fall may at certain times provide enough depth to clear a bar and at others may prevent him from entering or leaving a harbor. The flow of the current may help his progress or hinder it, may set him toward dangers or away from them. By understanding this phenomenon and by making intelligent use of predictions published in tide and tidal current tables and of descriptions in sailing directions, the mariner can set his course and schedule his passage to make the tide serve him, or at least to avoid its dangers.

3102. Tide and current.—In its rise and fall, the tide is accompanied by a periodic horizontal movement of the water called **tidal current.** The two movements, tide and tidal current, are intimately related, forming parts of the same phenomenon brought about by the tide-producing forces of the sun and moon, principally.

It is necessary, however, to distinguish clearly between tide and tidal current, for the relation between them is not a simple one nor is it everywhere the same. For the sake of clearness and to avoid misunderstanding, it is desirable that the mariner adopt the technical usage: **tide** for the vertical rise and fall of the water, and **tidal current** for the horizontal flow. The tide rises and falls, the tidal current floods and ebbs. In British usage, tidal current is called **tidal stream.**

3103. Cause.—It is often said of science that the ability to predict a natural event is indicative of understanding. Since tides are the most accurately predictable oceanographic phenomena, one could easily assume that physical oceanographers truly understand them. Unfortunately, this is not true; significant gaps remain. An examination of the details of this apparent contradiction gives insight into one of the most exciting areas of oceanography—ocean tides.

To facilitate this examination, it will be desirable, first of all, to discuss the fundamental tide-generating forces and the theoretical equilibrium tide they try to produce. The principal tide-generating forces on the surface of the earth result from the differential gravitational forces of the moon and sun. The moon is the main tide-generating body. Due to its greater distance, the effect of the sun is only 46 percent of the effect due to the moon. After the theoretical equilibrium tide produced by the sun and moon is discussed in this article, the actual tide as observed in nature is described in article 3104. Observed tides will differ considerably from the tides predicted by equilibrium theory since size, depth, and configuration of the basin or waterway, friction, land-masses, inertia of watermasses, Coriolis acceleration, and other factors are neglected in this theory. Nevertheless, equilibrium theory will be sufficient to describe the magnitude and distribution of the main tide-generating forces across the surface of the earth.

Tide-Generating Forces

Newton's universal law of gravitation governs both the orbits of celestial bodies and the tide-generating forces which occur on these bodies. The force of gravitational attraction between any two masses, m_1 and m_2, is given by

$$F = \frac{G m_1 m_2}{d^2},$$

where d is the distance between the two masses and G is a constant which depends upon the units employed. This law assumes that m_1 and m_2 are point masses. Newton was able to show that homogeneous spheres could be treated as point masses when determining their orbits. However, when computing differential gravitational forces, the actual dimensions of the masses must be taken into account.

Using the law of gravitation, it is found that the orbits of two point masses are conic sections about the barycenter of the two masses (art. 1407). If either one or both of the masses are homogenous spheres instead of point masses, the orbits are the same as the orbits which would result if all of the mass of the sphere were concentrated at a point at the center of the sphere. In the case of the earth-moon system, both the earth and the moon describe elliptical orbits about their barycenter if the simplifying assumption is made that both bodies are homogeneous spheres and the gravitational forces of the sun and other planets are neglected. The earth-moon barycenter is located at a distance of $0.74\,R_E$ from the earth's center, where R_E is the radius of the earth. This is approximately three-fourths of the distance from the center of the earth to the surface of the earth along the line connecting the centers of the earth and moon (fig. 3103a).

Thus, the center of mass of the earth describes a very small ellipse about the earth-moon barycenter whereas the center of mass of the moon describes a much larger ellipse about the same barycenter. If the gravitational forces of the other bodies of the solar system are neglected, Newton's law of gravitation also predicts that the earth-moon barycenter will describe an orbit which is approximately elliptical about the barycenter of the sun-earth-moon system. This barycentric point lies inside the sun (fig. 3103b).

The *differences* in gravitational attraction of various celestial bodies, principally the moon and sun, upon different parts of the rotating and revolving earth are the fundamental tide-generating forces. These *differential gravitational* forces are described here by considering first the effects of the moon only. The results will be general and can be applied directly to describe the differential gravitational forces of the sun.

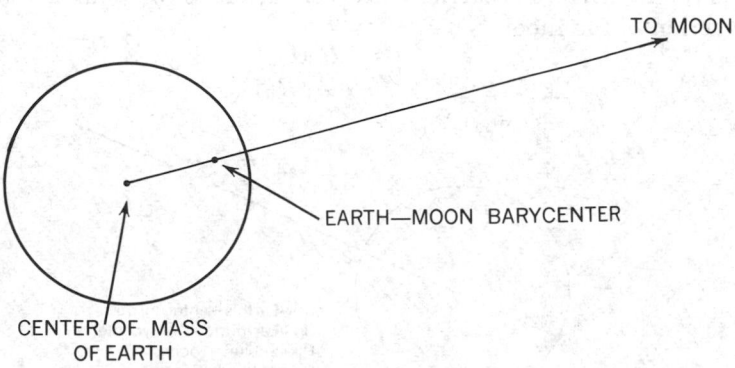

FIGURE 3103a.—Earth-moon barycenter.

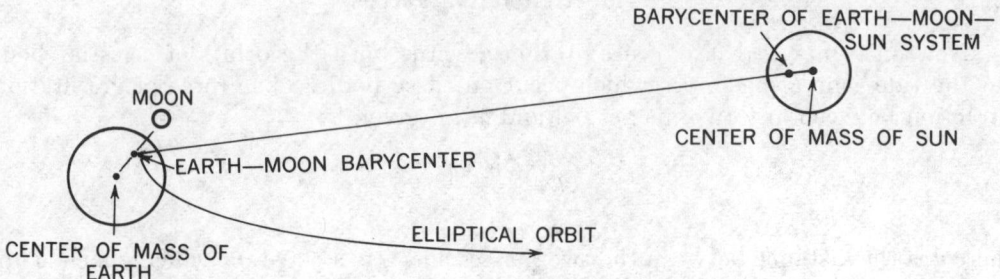

FIGURE 3103b.—Orbit of earth-moon barycenter (not to scale).

Earth-Moon System

When determining the orbit of the earth's center of mass about the earth-moon barycenter, the gravitational force exerted by the moon on the earth is given by

$$F = \frac{GM_E M_M}{d^2_M},$$

where M_E and M_M are the masses of the earth and moon, and d_M is the distance between their centers of mass. Acceleration and force are related by Newton's second law of motion, $F = ma$. The acceleration, a, of a mass, m, is then $a = F/m$. The terms "acceleration" and "force per unit mass" may be used interchangeably. Combining Newton's law of gravitation and his second law of motion, the acceleration of the earth's center of mass about the earth-moon barycenter is

$$a_c = \frac{GM_M}{d^2_M}.$$

In determining the direction and magnitude of tide-generating forces of the moon, the simplest case to treat is that of the sublunar point and its antipode on the earth. These two points are labeled P_1 and P_2 in figure 3103c.

The acceleration at the point P_1 due to the gravitational attraction of the moon is

$$a_1 = \frac{GM_M}{(d_M - R_E)^2},$$

where R_E is the radius of the earth. The acceleration at the point P_2 due to the gravitational attraction of the moon is

$$a_2 = \frac{GM_M}{(d_M + R_E)^2}.$$

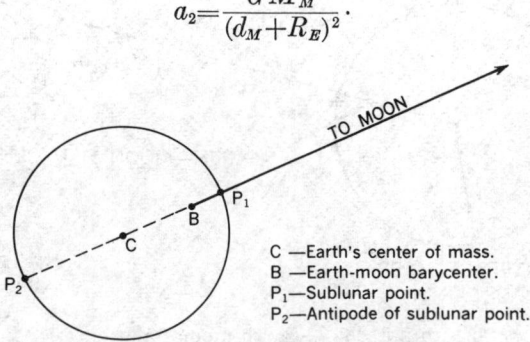

C —Earth's center of mass.
B —Earth-moon barycenter.
P_1—Sublunar point.
P_2—Antipode of sublunar point.

FIGURE 3103c.—Sublunar point and antipode.

The differential acceleration at P_1, that is, the acceleration at P_1 relative to the acceleration of the center of the earth, is

$$a_1 - a_c = \frac{GM_M}{(d_M - R_E)^2} - \frac{GM_M}{d^2{}_M}.$$

With some simplification, this expression becomes

$$a_1 - a_c = \frac{2GM_M R_E}{d^3{}_M}.$$

This is the differential acceleration or differential force per unit mass at the sublunar point P_1. In a similar manner, the differential acceleration at the antipode, point P_2, is found to be

$$a_2 - a_c = \frac{-2GM_M R_E}{d^3{}_M}.$$

Both the accelerations and the resulting differential accelerations or differential forces per unit mass are shown in figure 3103d.

Note that the differential gravitational force per unit mass at the antipode, point P_2, is negative. Thus, at both the sublunar point and the antipode, the moon's differential gravitational forces are vertical and directed away from the center of the earth.

A more complicated situation occurs when the moon's gravitational forces act on points of the earth's surface other than the sublunar point and the antipode. To find the differential accelerations at the sublunar point and the antipode, it was only necessary to take the algebraic difference between the accelerations at the surface and the acceleration of the earth's center. At other points on the surface, however, both the magnitude and direction of the moon's gravitational forces differ from that at the earth's center (figure 3103e). To obtain the differential accelerations at the other points, it is necessary to subtract the accelerations vectorially: $\overline{F}_D = \bar{a}_M - \bar{a}_C$, where $\overline{F}_D$ is the differential acceleration or differential force per unit mass at any point on the surface of the earth, $\bar{a}_C$ is the acceleration of the earth's center of mass, and $\bar{a}_M$ is the acceleration or force per unit mass at the point under consideration due to the moon's gravitational force acting at that point (figure 3103f).

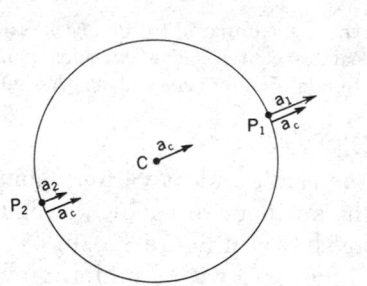

Differential gravitational force per unit mass at sublunar point P_1 is $a_1 - a_c$.

Differential gravitational force per unit mass at antipode, point P_2, is $a_2 - a_c$.

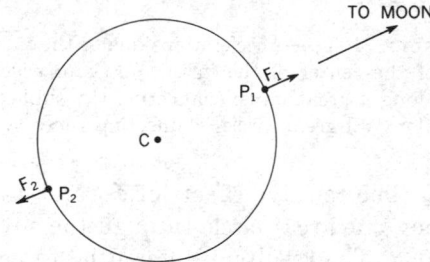

F_1 and F_2 represent the differential forces per unit mass at the sublunar point and the antipode, points P_1 and P_2, where
$F_1 = a_1 - a_c$
$F_2 = a_2 - a_c$

FIGURE 3103d.—Differential gravitational forces per unit mass at sublunar point and antipode.

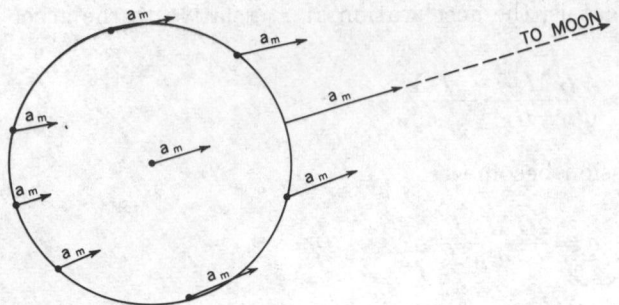

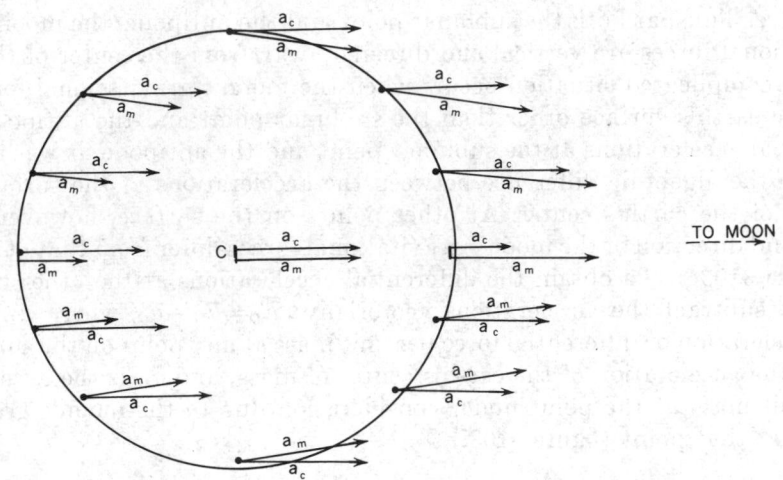

a_m is the acceleration or force per unit mass at various points on the earth's surface due the moon's gravitational forces at these points.

FIGURE 3103e.—Forces per unit mass on earth's surface due to moon's gravitational forces. Only the acceleration at the earth's center and the accelerations along one great circle through the sublunar point and the antipode are shown.

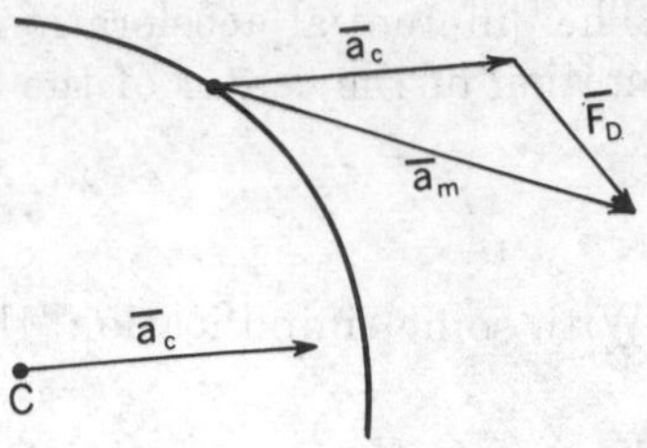

FIGURE 3103f.—Differential force per unit mass, $\overline{F}_D$, is the vector difference $\overline{a}_M - \overline{a}_C$.

FIGURE 3103g.—Accelerations due to the moon's gravitational forces, $\overline{a}_M$, compared to the acceleration of the center of the earth, $\overline{a}_C$. Comparisons are made at the earth's center and at various points along a great circle connecting the sublunar point and the antipode. The effects will be the same along all great circles connecting these two points.

The relative effects of $\overline{a}_M$ and $\overline{a}_C$ at the center of the earth and at various points along one great circle through the sublunar point and the antipode are shown in figure 3103g. The resultant differential forces per unit mass are shown in figure 3103h.

If it is assumed that the entire surface of the earth is covered with a uniform layer of water, the differential forces may be resolved into components perpendicular and parallel to the surface of the earth (fig. 3103i) to determine their effect.

The components of these differential forces which are perpendicular to the earth's surface have the effect of changing the weight of the mass on which they are acting. These vertical components do not contribute to the tidal effect. The horizontal components which are parallel to the earth's surface, although small, have the effect of moving the water in a horizontal direction towards the sublunar and antipodal points until an equilibrium position is found. The horizontal components of the differential forces are

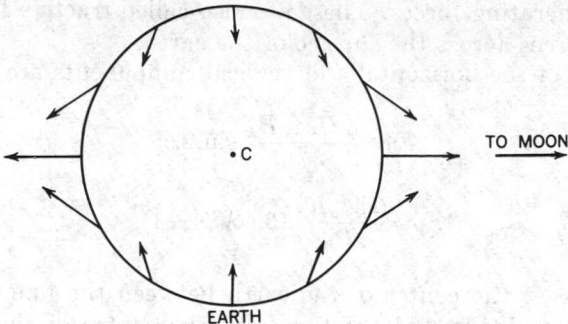

FIGURE 3103h.—Differential forces along a great circle connecting the sublunar point and antipode.

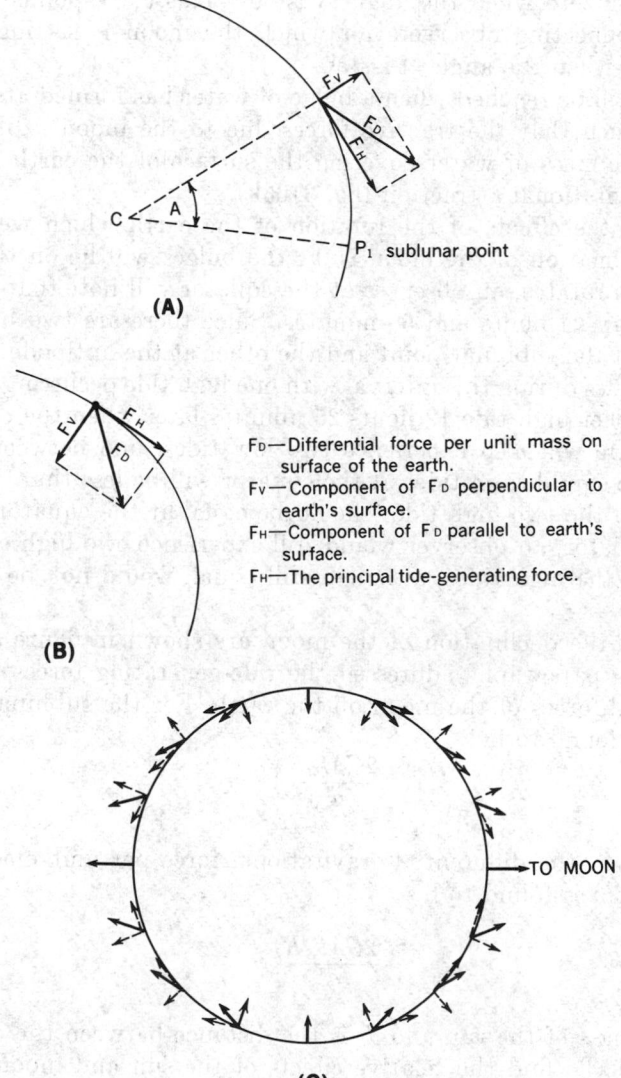

F_D—Differential force per unit mass on surface of the earth.

F_V—Component of F_D perpendicular to earth's surface.

F_H—Component of F_D parallel to earth's surface.

F_H—The principal tide-generating force.

FIGURE 3103i.—Differential force resolved into horizontal and vertical components. (A) F_D directed out of surface. (B) F_D directed into surface. (C) Varying directions of F_D along a great circle through sublunar point.

the principal tide-generating forces. These are also called **tractive forces.** Figure 3103j shows the tractive forces across the surface of the earth.

The magnitudes of the horizontal and vertical components are

$$F_H = \frac{3}{2} \frac{GM_M R_E}{d^3_M} \sin 2A$$

$$F_V = \frac{GM_M R_E}{d^3_M} (3 \cos^2 A - 1),$$

where A is the angle at the center of the earth between the line connecting the sublunar point and the antipode and the line from the center of the earth to the point under consideration (fig. 3103i). Thus, it can be seen that the horizontal component, which is the tide-generating force, is zero when the angle A is zero (sublunar point and antipode). It is also zero when the angle A is 90°. This corresponds approximately to the great circle connecting observers for which the moon is setting. The maximum value of F_H occurs when the angle A is 45°.

Equilibrium will be reached when a bulge of water has formed at the sublunar and antipodal points such that the tractive forces due to the moon's differential gravitational forces on the mass of water covering the surface of the earth are just balanced by the earth's gravitational attraction (fig. 3103k).

Consider now the effects of the rotation of the earth which were previously neglected. If the declination of the moon is 0°, the bulges will lie on the equator of the earth. As the earth rotates, an observer at the equator will note that the moon transits approximately every 24 hours and 50 minutes. Since there are two bulges of water on the equator, one at the sublunar point and the other at the antipode, the observer will also see two high tides during this interval with one high tide occurring when the moon is overhead and another high tide 12 hours 25 minutes later when the observer is located at the antipode. He will also experience two low tides, one between each high tide. The range of these equilibrium tides at the equator will be less than 1 meter.

The heights of the two high tides should be equal at the equator. At points north or south of the equator, an observer would still experience two high and two low tides, but the heights of the high tides, although still equal, would not be as great as they are at the equator.

The effects of the declination of the moon are shown in figure 3103l.

The preceding paragraphs addressed the tide-generating forces due to the differential gravitational forces of the moon on the earth. For the sublunar point, the force per unit mass was found to be

$$\frac{2GM_M R_E}{d^3_M}.$$

In a similar manner, the differential gravitational force per unit mass due to the sun at the subsolar point is found to be

$$\frac{2GM_S R_E}{d^3_S},$$

where M_S is the mass of the sun and d_S is the distance between the centers of mass of the sun and earth. To find the relative effects of the sun and moon, the ratio of the expressions can be used. This ratio is

$$\left(\frac{M_S}{M_M}\right)\left(\frac{d_M}{d_S}\right)^3.$$

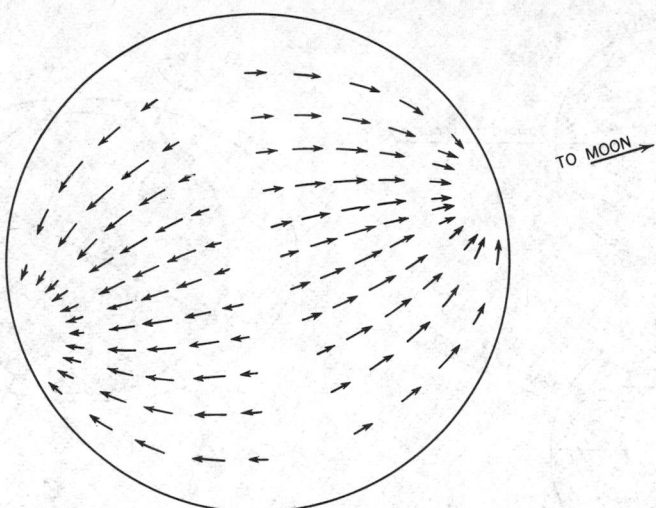

FIGURE 3103j.—Tractive forces across the surface of the earth. Tractive forces are zero at the sublunar and antipodal points and along the great circle halfway between these two points. Tractive forces are maximum along the small circles located 45° from the sublunar point and the antipode.

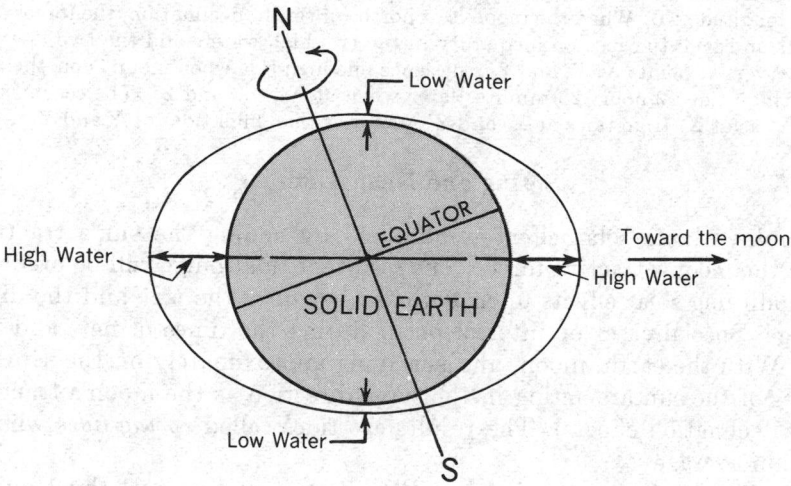

FIGURE 3103k.—Theoretical equilibrium configuration due to moon's differential gravitational forces. One bulge of the water envelope is located at the sublunar point, the other bulge at the antipode.

The numerical value of this ratio is 0.46. Thus, the effect of the moon is approximately two and one-quarter times greater than the effect of the sun even though the moon's mass is but a fraction of the sun's. This is due to the fact that the differential forces vary inversely as the *cube* of the distance. Thus the moon's smaller mass is offset by its much shorter distance to the earth.

The preceding discussion pertaining to the effects of the moon is equally valid when discussing the effects of the sun, taking into account that the magnitude of the solar effects are smaller than the lunar effects. Hence, the tides will also vary according to the sun's declination and its varying distance from the earth. A second envelope of water representing the equilibrium tides due to the sun would resemble the envelope shown in figure 3103k except that the heights of the high tides would be smaller.

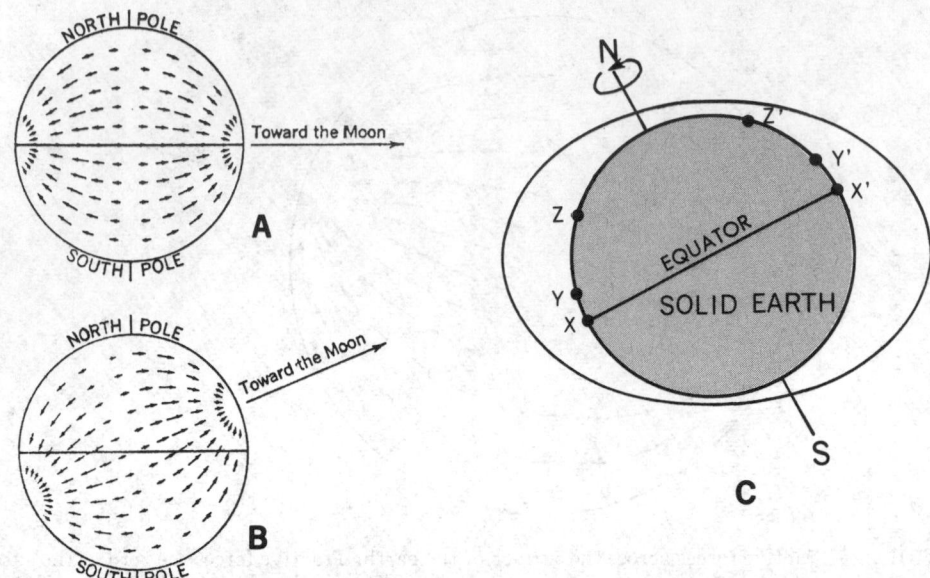

FIGURE 3103l.—Effects of the declination of the moon. (A) When the moon is in the plane of the equator, the forces are equal in magnitude at the two points on the same parallel of latitude and 180° apart in longitude. (B) When the moon is at north (or south) declination, the forces are unequal at such points and tend to cause an inequality in the two high waters and the two low waters of a day. (C) Observers at points *X*, *Y*, and *Z* experience one high tide when moon is on their meridian, then another high tide 12 hours 25 minutes later when at *X'*, *Y'*, and *Z'*. The second high tide is the same at *X'* as at *X*. High tides at *Y'* and *Z'* are lower than high tides at *Y* and *Z*.

Spring and Neap Tides

The combined lunar-solar effect is obtained by adding the sun's tractive forces vectorially to the moon's tractive forces. The resultant tidal bulge will be predominantly lunar with modifying solar effects upon both the height of the tide and the direction of the tidal bulge. Special cases of interest occur during the times of new and full moon (fig. 3103m). With the earth, moon, and sun lying approximately on the same line, the tractive forces of the sun are acting in the same direction as the moon's tractive forces (modified by declination effects). The results are tides called *spring tides* whose ranges are greater than average.

Another case of interest occurs when the moon is at first and third quarters. At those times, the tractive forces of the sun are acting at approximately right angles to the moon's tractive forces (fig. 3103m). The results are tides called *neap tides* whose ranges are less than average.

With the moon in positions between quadrature and new and full moon, the effect of the sun is to cause the tidal bulge to either lag or precede the moon (fig. 3103n). These effects are called *priming* and *lagging* the tides.

Tide

3104. General features.—**Tide** is the periodic rise and fall of the water accompanying the tidal phenomenon. At most places it occurs twice daily. The tide rises until it reaches a maximum height, called **high tide** or **high water,** and then falls to a minimum level called **low tide** or **low water.**

The rate of rise and fall is not uniform. From low water, the tide begins to rise slowly at first but at an increasing rate until it is about halfway to high water. The

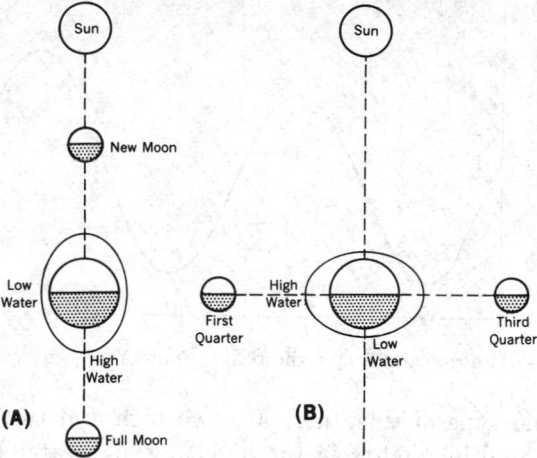

FIGURE 3103m.—(A) Spring tides occur at times of new and full moon. Range of tide is greater than average since solar and lunar tractive forces act in same direction. (B) Neap tides occur at times of first and third quarters. Range of tide is less than average since solar and lunar tractive forces act at right angles.

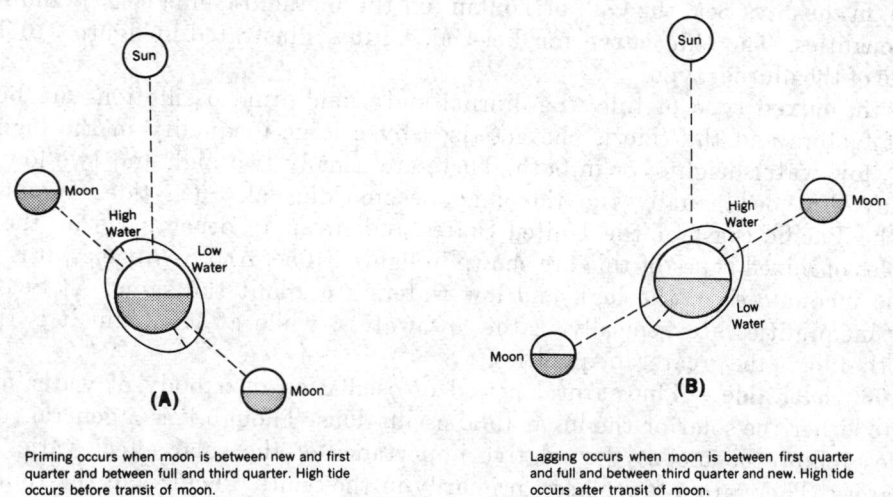

Priming occurs when moon is between new and first quarter and between full and third quarter. High tide occurs before transit of moon.

Lagging occurs when moon is between first quarter and full and between third quarter and new. High tide occurs after transit of moon.

FIGURE 3103n.—Priming and lagging the tides.

rate of rise then decreases until high water is reached and the rise ceases. The falling tide behaves in a similar manner. The period at high or low water during which there is no sensible change of level is called **stand.** The difference in height between consecutive high and low waters is the **range.**

Figure 3104 is a graphical representation of the rise and fall of the tide at New York during a 24-hour period. The tide curve has the general form of a sine curve.

3105. Types of tide.—A body of water has a natural period of oscillation that is dependent upon its dimensions. None of the oceans appears to be a single oscillating body, but rather each one is made up of a number of oscillating basins. As such basins are acted upon by the tide-producing forces, some respond more readily to daily or diurnal forces, others to semidiurnal forces, and others almost equally to both. Hence, tides at a place are classified as one of three types—**semidiurnal, diurnal,** or **mixed**—according to the characteristics of the tidal pattern occurring at the place.

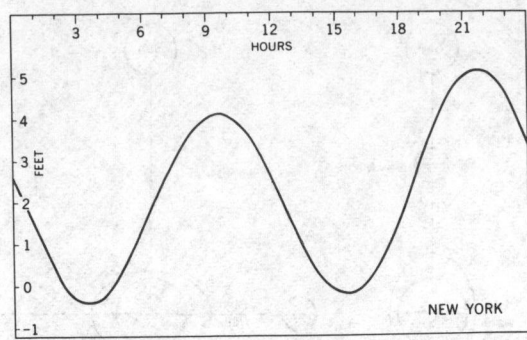

FIGURE 3104.—The rise and fall of the tide at New York, shown graphically.

In the **semidiurnal** type of tide, there are two high and two low waters each tidal day, with relatively small inequality in the high and low water heights. Tides on the Atlantic coast of the United States are representative of the semidiurnal type, which is illustrated in figure 3105a by the tide curve for Boston Harbor.

In the **diurnal** type of tide, only a single high and single low water occur each tidal day. Tides of the diurnal type occur along the northern shore of the Gulf of Mexico, in the Java Sea, the Gulf of Tonkin (off the Vietnam-China coast), and in a few other localities. The tide curve for Pei-Hai, China, illustrated in figure 3105b, is an example of the diurnal type.

In the **mixed** type of tide, the diurnal and semidiurnal oscillations are both important factors and the tide is characterized by a large inequality in the high water heights, low water heights, or in both. There are usually two high and two low waters each day, but occasionally the tide may become diurnal. Such tides are prevalent along the Pacific coast of the United States and in many other parts of the world. Examples of mixed types of tide are shown in figure 3105c. At Los Angeles, it is typical that the inequalities in the high and low waters are about the same. At Seattle the greater inequalities are typically in the low waters, while at Honolulu it is the high waters that have the greater inequalities.

3106. Solar tide.—The natural period of oscillation of a body of water may accentuate either the solar or the lunar tidal oscillations. Though it is a general rule that the tides follow the moon, the relative importance of the solar effect varies in different areas. There are a few places, primarily in the South Pacific and the Indonesian areas, where the solar oscillation is the more important, and at those places the high and low waters occur at about the same time each day. At Port Adelaide, Australia (fig. 3106), the solar and lunar semidiurnal oscillations are equal and nullify one another at neaps (art. 3108).

3107. Special effects.—As a progressive wave enters shallow water its speed is decreased. Since the trough is shallower than the crest, its retardation is greater, re-

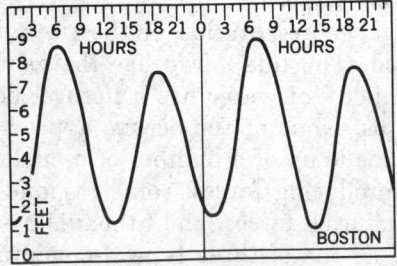

FIGURE 3105a.—Semidiurnal type of tide.

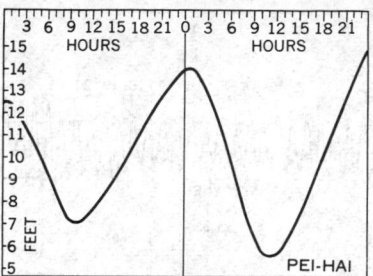

FIGURE 3105b.—Diurnal type of tide.

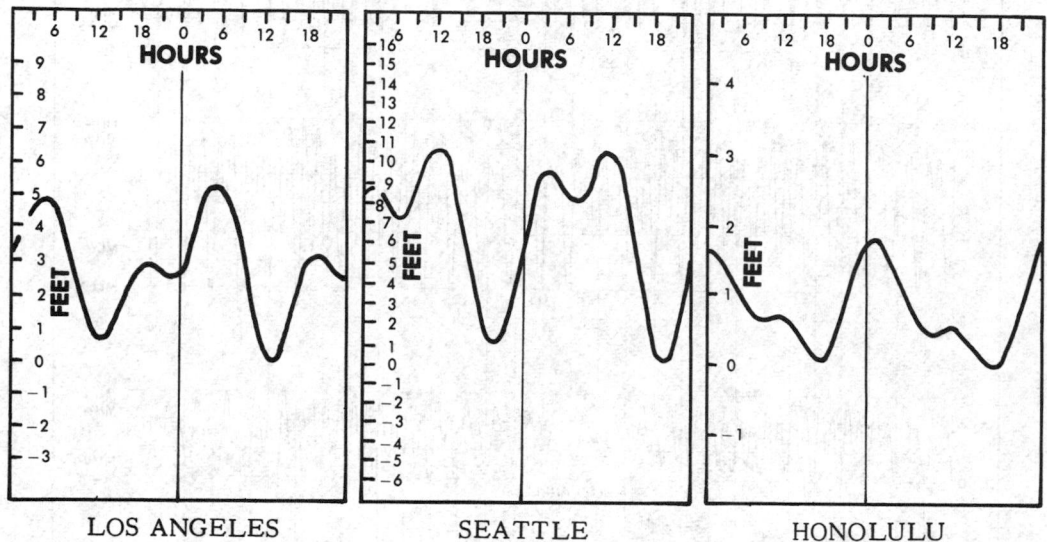

FIGURE 3105c.—Mixed type of tide.

sulting in a steepening of the wave front. Therefore, in many rivers, the duration of rise is considerably less than the duration of fall. In a few estuaries, the advance of the low water trough is so much retarded that the crest of the rising tide overtakes the low, and advances upstream as a churning, foaming wall of water called a **bore**. Bores that are large and dangerous at times of large tidal ranges may be mere ripples at those times of the month when the range is small. Examples occur in the Petitcodiac River in the Bay of Fundy, and at Haining, China, in the Tsientang Kaing. The tide tables indicate where bores occur.

Other special features are the **double low water** (as at Hoek Van Holland) and the **double high water** (as at Southampton, England). At such places there is often a slight fall or rise in the middle of the high or low water period. The practical effect is to create a longer period of stand at high or low tide. The tide tables direct attention to these and other peculiarities where they occur.

3108. Variations in range.—Though the tide at a particular place can be classified as to type, it exhibits many variations during the month (fig. 3106). The range of the tide varies in accordance with the intensity of the tide-producing force, though there may be a lag of a day or two (**age of tide**) between a particular astronomic cause and the tidal effect.

Thus, when the moon is at the point in its orbit nearest the earth (at *perigee*), the lunar semidiurnal range is increased and **perigean** tides occur; when the moon is farthest from the earth (at *apogee*), the smaller **apogean** tides occur. When the moon and sun are in line and pulling together, as at new and full moon, **spring** tides occur (the term

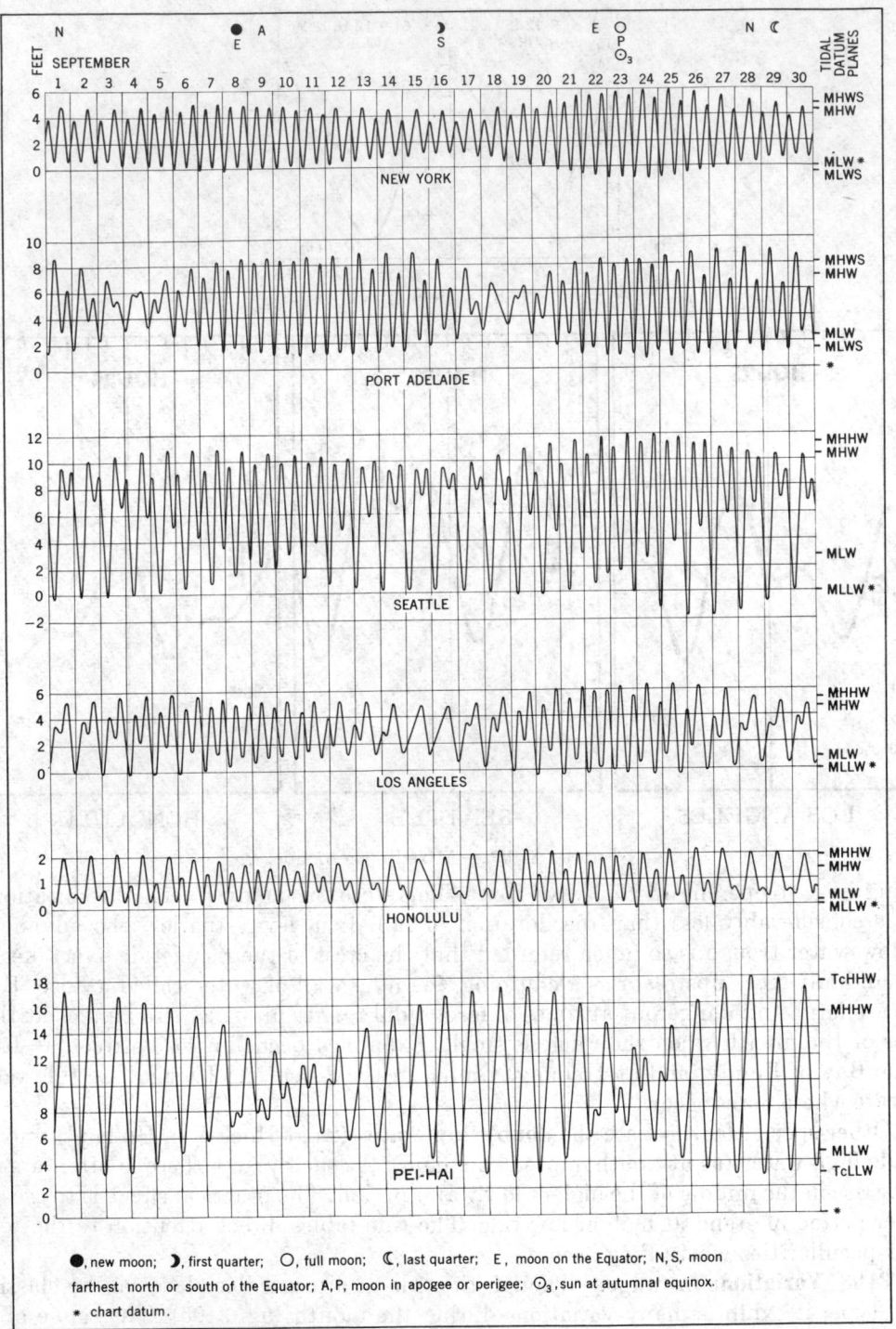

FIGURE 3106.—Tidal variations at various places during a month.

spring has nothing to do with the season of year); when the moon and sun oppose each other, as at the quadratures, the smaller **neap** tides occur.

When certain of these phenomena coincide, the great **perigean spring** tides, the small **apogean neap** tides, etc., occur.

These are variations in the semidiurnal portion of the tide. Variations in the diurnal portion occur as the moon and sun change declination. When the moon is at its maximum semi-monthly declination (either north or south), **tropic** tides occur in which the diurnal effect is at a maximum; when it crosses the equator, the diurnal effect is a minimum and **equatorial** tides occur.

It should be noted that when the range of tide is increased, as at spring tides, there is more water available only at *high* tide; at *low* tide there is less, for the high waters rise higher and the low waters fall lower at these times. There is more water at neap low water than at spring low water. With tropic tides, there is usually more depth at one low water during the day than at the other. While it is desirable to know the meanings of these terms, the best way of determining the height of the tide at any place and time is to examine the tide predictions for the place as given in the tide tables. Figure 3108 illustrates variations in the ranges and heights of tides in a locality such as the Indian Ocean where predicted and observed water levels are referenced to a chart sounding datum that will always cause them to be additive relative to the charted depth.

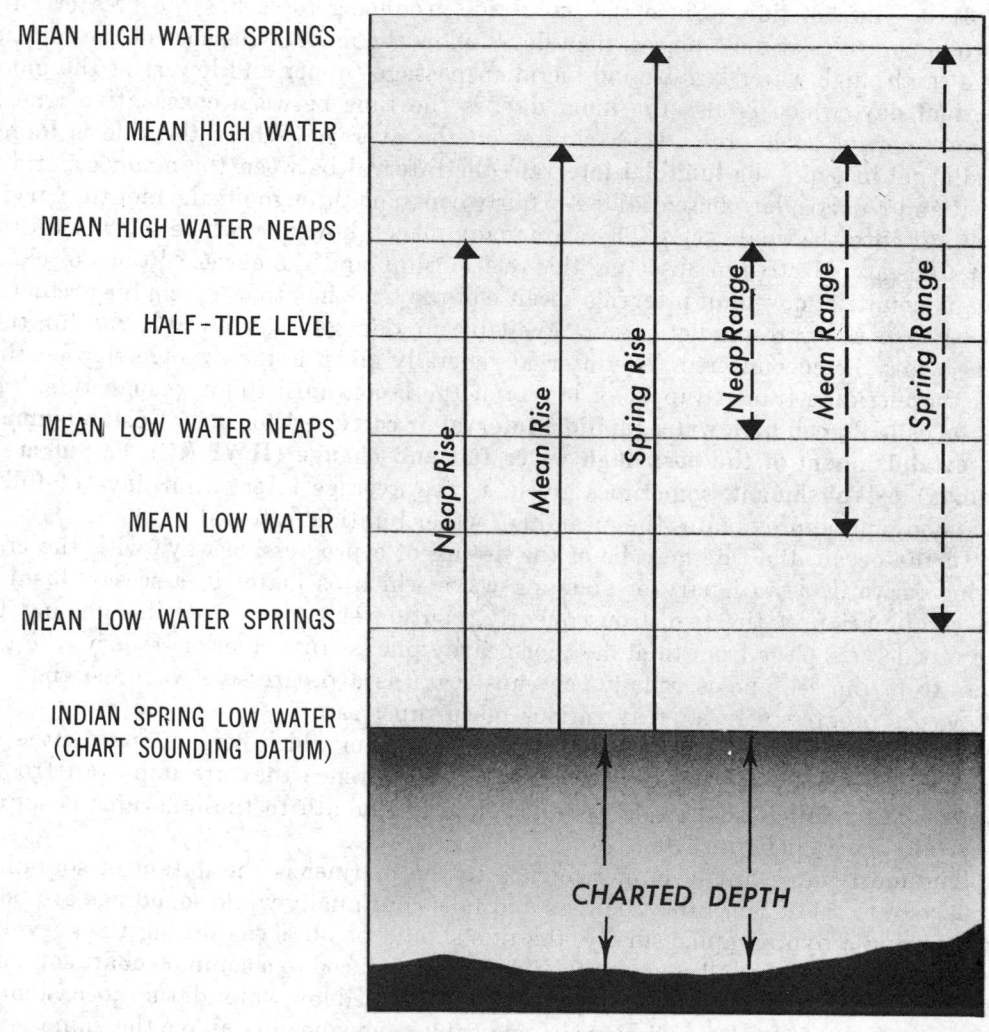

FIGURE 3108.—Variations in the ranges and heights of tide in a locality where the chart sounding datum is Indian Spring Low Water.

3109. Tidal cycles.—Tidal oscillations go through a number of cycles. The shortest cycle, completed in about 12 hours and 25 minutes for a semidiurnal tide, extends from any phase of the tide to the next recurrence of the same phase. During a **lunar day** (averaging 24 hours and 50 minutes) there are two highs and two lows (two of the shorter cycles) for a semidiurnal tide. The moon revolves around the earth with respect to the sun in a **synodical month** of about 29½ days, commonly called the **lunar month.** The effect of the phase variation is completed in one-half a synodical month or about 2 weeks as the moon varies from new to full or full to new. The effect of the moon's declination is also repeated in one-half of a **tropical month** of 27⅓ days or about each 2 weeks. The cycle involving the moon's distance requires an **anomalistic month** of about 27½ days. The sun's declination and distance cycles are respectively a half year and a year in length. An important lunar cycle, called the **nodal period,** is 18.6 years (usually expressed in round figures as 19 years). For a tidal value, particularly a range, to be considered a true mean, it must be either based upon observations extended over this period of time or adjusted to take account of variations known to occur during the cycle.

3110. Time of tide.—Since the lunar tide-producing force has the greater effect in producing tides at most places, the tides "follow the moon." Because of the rotation of the earth, high water lags behind meridian passage (upper and lower) of the moon. The **tidal day,** which is also the **lunar day,** is the time between consecutive transits of the moon, or 24 hours and 50 minutes on the average. Where the tide is largely semidiurnal in type, the **lunitidal interval**—the interval between the moon's meridian transit and a particular phase of tide—is fairly constant throughout the month, varying somewhat with the tidal cycles. There are many places, however, where solar or diurnal oscillations are effective in upsetting this relationship, and the newer editions of charts of many countries now omit intervals because of the tendency to use them for prediction even though accurate predictions are available in tide tables. However, the lunitidal interval may be encountered. The interval generally given is the average elapsed time from the meridian transit (upper or lower) of the moon until the next high tide. This may be called **mean high water lunitidal interval** or **corrected** (or **mean**) **establishment.** The **establishment of the port, high water full and change** (**HWF &C**), or **vulgar** (or **common**) **establishment,** sometimes given, is the average interval on days of full or new moon, and approximates the mean high water lunitidal interval.

In the ocean, the tide may be of the nature of a progressive wave with the crest moving forward, a stationary or standing wave which oscillates in a seesaw fashion, or a combination of the two. Consequently, caution should be used in inferring the time of tide at a place from tidal data for nearby places. In a river or estuary, the tide enters from the sea and is usually sent upstream as a progressive wave, so that the tide occurs progressively later at various places upstream.

3111. Tidal datums.—A **tidal datum** is a level from which heights and depths are measured. There are a number of such levels of reference that are important to the mariner. The relation of the tide each day during a month to these datums is shown, for certain places, in figure 3106.

The most important level of reference to the mariner is the datum of soundings on charts (art. 511). Since the tide rises and falls continually while soundings are being taken during a hydrographic survey, the tide should be observed during the survey so that soundings taken at all stages of the tide can be reduced to a common **chart sounding datum.** Soundings on charts show depths below a selected low water datum (occasionally mean sea level), and tide predictions in tide tables show heights above the same level. The depth of water available at any time is obtained by adding the height of the tide at the time in question to the charted depth, or by subtracting the predicted height if it is negative.

By international agreement, the level used as chart datum should be just low enough so that low waters do not go far below it. At most places, however, the level used is one determined from a mean of a number of low waters (usually over a 19-year period); therefore, some low waters can be expected to fall below it. The following are some of the datums in general use.

The highest low water datum in considerable use is **mean low water (MLW),** which is the average height of all low waters at a place. About half of the low waters fall below it. **Mean low water springs (MLWS),** usually shortened to **low water springs,** is the average level of the low waters that occur at the times of spring tides. **Mean lower low water (MLLW)** is the average height of the lower low waters of each tidal day. **Tropic lower low water (TcLLW)** is the average height of the lower low waters (or of the single daily low waters if the tide becomes diurnal) that occur when the moon is near maximum declination and the diurnal effect is most pronounced. This datum is not in common use as a tidal reference. **Indian spring low water (ISLW)** sometimes called **Indian tide plane** or **harmonic tide plane,** is a low water datum that includes the spring effect of the semi-diurnal portion of the tide and the tropic effect of the diurnal portion. It is about the level of lower low water of mixed tides at the time that the moon's maximum declination coincides with the time of new or full moon. **Mean lower low water springs** is the average level of the lower of the two low waters on the days of spring tides. Some still lower datums used on charts are determined from tide observations and some are determined arbitrarily and later referred to the tide. Most of them fall close to one or the other of the following two datums. **Lowest normal low water** is a datum that approximates the average height of monthly lowest low waters, discarding any tides disturbed by storms. **Lowest low water** is an extremely low datum. It conforms generally to the lowest tide observed, or even somewhat lower. Once a tidal datum is established, it is sometimes retained for an indefinite period, even though it might differ slightly from a better determination from later observations. When this occurs, the established datum may be called **low water datum, lower low water datum,** etc. These datums are used in a limited area and primarily for river and harbor engineering purposes. Examples are *Boston Harbor Low Water Datum* and *Columbia River Lower Low Water Datum.*

In some areas where there is little or no tide, such as the Baltic Sea, **mean sea level (MSL)** is used as chart datum. This is the average height of the surface of the sea for all stages of the tide over a 19-year period. This may differ slightly from **half-tide level,** which is the level midway between mean high water and mean low water.

Inconsistencies of terminology are found among charts of different countries and between charts issued at different times. For example, the spring effect as defined here is a feature of only the semidiurnal tide, yet it is sometimes used synonymously with tropic effect to refer to times of increased range of a diurnal tide. Such inconsistencies are being reduced through increased international cooperation.

Large-scale charts usually specify the datum of soundings and may contain a tide note giving mean heights of the tide at one or more places on the chart. These heights are intended merely as a rough guide to the change in depth to be expected under the specified conditions. They should not be used for the prediction of heights on any particular day. Such predictions should be obtained from *tide tables* (arts. 1203–1206).

3112. High water datums.—Heights of land features are usually referred on nautical charts to a high water datum. The one used on charts of the United States, its territories, and possessions, and widely used elswehere, is **mean high water (MHW),**

which is the average height of all high waters over a 19-year period. Any other high water datum in use on charts is likely to be higher than this. Other high water datums are **mean high water springs (MHWS),** which is the average level of the high waters that occur at the time of spring tides; **mean higher high water (MHHW),** which is the average height of the higher high waters of each tidal day; and **tropic higher high water (TcHHW),** which is the average height of the higher high waters (or the single daily high waters if the tide becomes diurnal) that occur when the moon is near maximum declination and the diurnal effect is most pronounced. A reference merely to "high water" leaves some doubt as to the specific level referred to, for the height of high water varies from day to day. Where the range is large, the variation during a 2-week period may be considerable.

As there are periodic and apparent secular trends in sea level, a specific 19-year cycle (the **National Tidal Datum Epoch**) is issued for all United States datums. The National Tidal Datum Epoch officially adopted by the National Ocean Survey is presently 1941 through 1959. The Epoch will be reviewed for consideration for revision at 25-year intervals.

3113. Observations and predictions.—Since the tide at different places responds differently to the tide-producing forces, the nature of the tide at any place can be determined most accurately by actual observation. The predictions in tide tables and the tidal data on nautical charts are based upon observations.

Tides are usually observed by means of a continuously recording gage. A year of observations is the minimum length desirable for determining the **harmonic constants** used in prediction. For establishing mean sea level and the long-time changes in the relative elevations of land and sea, as well as for other special uses, observations have been made over periods of 20, 30, and even 120 years at important locations. Observations for a month or less will establish the *type* of tide and suffice for comparison with a longer series of a similar type to determine tidal differences and constants.

Mathematically, the variations in the lunar and solar tide-producing forces, such as those due to changing phase, distance, and declination, are considered as separate constituent forces, and the **harmonic analysis** of observations reveals the response of each constituent of the tide to its corresponding force. At any one place this response remains constant and is shown for each constituent by **harmonic constants** which are in the form of a phase angle for the time relation and an amplitude for the height. Harmonic constants are used in making technical studies of the tide and predictions on computers and mechanical **tide predicting machines.** Most published tide predictions are made by computer.

3114. Tide tables are published annually by most of the maritime nations of the world. They consist primarily of two parts. One contains predictions of the time and height of each high and low water for every day of the year for many important ports called **reference stations.** The other part contains tidal differences and ratios for thousands of other places, called **subordinate stations,** and specifies the reference station to which the differences are to be applied in order to obtain time and height of tide for any day at the subordinate station. The type of tide at a subordinate station is the same as at its reference station. The use of tide tables is explained in articles 1203–1206.

3115. Meteorological effects.—The foregoing discussion of tide behavior assumes normal weather conditions. The level of the sea is affected by wind and atmospheric pressure. In general, onshore winds raise the level and offshore winds lower it, but the amount of change varies at different places. During periods of low atmospheric pressure, the water level tends to be higher than normal. For a stationary low, the increase in elevation can be found by the formula

$$R_0 = 0.0325(1010 - P),$$

in which R_0 is the increase in elevation in feet, and P is the atmospheric pressure in millibars. This is equal approximately to 1 centimeter per millibar depression, or 1 foot (13.6 inches) per inch depression. For a moving low, the increase in elevation is given by the formula

$$R = \frac{R_0}{1 - \dfrac{C^2}{gh}},$$

in which R is the increase in elevation in feet, R_0 is the increase in feet for a stationary low, C is the rate of motion of the low in feet per second, g is the acceleration due to gravity (32.2 feet per second per second), and h is the depth of water in feet.

Where the range of tide is very small, the meteorological effect may sometimes be greater than the normal tide.

Tidal Current

3116. Tidal and nontidal currents.—Horizontal movement of the water is **current.** It may be classified as "tidal" and "nontidal." **Tidal current** is the periodic horizontal flow of water accompanying the rise and fall of the tide, and results from the same cause. **Nontidal current** is any current not due to the tidal movement. Nontidal currents include the permanent currents in the general circulatory system of the oceans as well as temporary currents arising from meteorological conditions. The current experienced at any time is usually a combination of tidal and nontidal currents.

In navigation, the effect of the tidal current is often of more importance than the changing depth due to the tide, and many mariners speak of "the tide," when they have in mind the flow of the tidal current.

3117. General features.—Offshore, where the direction of flow is not restricted by any barriers, the tidal current is **rotary**; that is, it flows continuously, with the direction changing through all points of the compass during the tidal period. The tendency for the rotation in direction has its origin in the deflecting force of the earth's rotation, and unless modified by local conditions, the change is clockwise in the Northern Hemisphere and counterclockwise in the Southern Hemisphere. The speed usually varies throughout the tidal cycle, passing through two maximums in approximately opposite directions, and two minimums about halfway between the maximums in time and direction. Rotary currents can be depicted as in figure 3117a, by a series of arrows representing the direction and speed of the current at each hour. This is sometimes called a **current rose.** Because of the elliptical pattern formed by the ends of the arrows, it is also referred to as a **current ellipse.**

In rivers or straits, or where the direction of flow is more or less restricted to certain channels, the tidal current is **reversing**; that is, it flows alternately in approximately opposite directions with an instant or short period of little or no current, called **slack water,** at each reversal of the current. During the flow in each direction, the speed varies from zero at the time of slack water to a maximum, called **strength of flood** or **ebb,** about midway between the slacks. Reversing currents can be indicated graphically, as in figure 3117b, by arrows that represent the speed of the current at each hour. The flood is usually depicted above the slack waterline and the ebb below it. The tidal current curve formed by the ends of the arrows has the same characteristic sine form as the tide curve. (In illustrations for certain purposes, as in figures 3118b and 3120b, it is convenient to omit the arrows and show only the curve.)

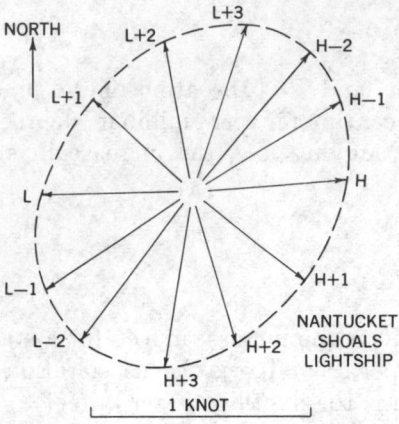

FIGURE 3117a.—Rotary tidal current. Times are hours before and after high and low tide at Nantucket Shoals Lightship. The bearing and length of each arrow represents the hourly direction and speed of the current. See figure 3120a.

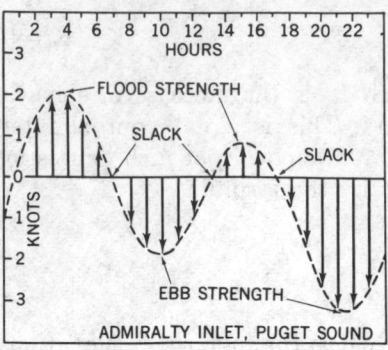

FIGURE 3117b.—Reversing tidal current. (Such graphs may show only the curved pattern without the arrows, as in figures 3118b and 3120b.) See figure 3120b.

A slight departure from the sine form is exhibited by the reversing current in a strait, such as East River, New York, that connects two tidal bodies of water. The tides at the two ends of a strait are seldom in phase or equal in range, and the current, called **hydraulic current,** is generated largely by the continuously changing difference in height of water at the two ends. The speed of a hydraulic current varies nearly as the square root of the difference in height. The speed reaches a maximum more quickly and remains at strength for a longer period than shown in figure 3117b, and the period of weak current near the time of slack is considerably shortened.

The current *direction* or **set** is the direction *toward* which the current flows. The *speed* is sometimes called the **drift.** The term "velocity" is often used as the equivalent of "speed" when referring to current, although strictly "velocity" implies direction as well as speed. The term "strength" is also used to refer to speed, but more often to greatest speed between consecutive slack waters. The movement toward shore or upstream is the **flood,** the movement away from shore or downstream is the **ebb.** In a purely semidiurnal type of current unaffected by nontidal flow, the flood and ebb each last about 6 hours and 13 minutes. But if there is either diurnal inequality or nontidal flow, the durations of flood and ebb may be quite unequal.

3118. Types of tidal current.—Tidal currents may be of the **semidiurnal, diurnal,** or **mixed** type; corresponding to a considerable degree to the type of tide at the place, but often with a stronger semidiurnal tendency.

The tidal currents in tidal estuaries along the Atlantic coast of the United States are examples of the semidiurnal type of reversing current. At Mobile Bay entrance they are almost purely diurnal. At most places, however, the type is mixed to a greater or lesser degree. At Tampa and Galveston entrances there is only one flood and one ebb each day when the moon is near its maximum declination, and two floods and two ebbs each day when the moon is near the equator. Along the Pacific coast of the United States there are generally two floods and two ebbs every day, but one of the floods or ebbs has a greater speed and longer duration than the other, the inequality varying with the declination of the moon. The inequalities in the current often differ considerably from place to place even within limited areas, such as adjacent passages in Puget Sound and various passages between the Aleutian Islands. Figure 3118a shows several types of reversing current. Figure 3118b shows how the flood disappears as the diurnal inequality increases at one station.

Offshore rotary currents that are purely semidiurnal repeat the elliptical pattern (fig. 3117a) each tidal cycle of 12 hours and 25 minutes. If there is considerable diurnal inequality, the plotted hourly current arrows describe a set of two ellipses of different sizes during a period of 24 hours and 50 minutes, as shown in figure 3118c, and the greater the diurnal inequality, the greater the difference between the sizes of the two ellipses. In a completely diurnal rotary current, the smaller ellipse disappears and only one ellipse is produced in 24 hours and 50 minutes.

3119. Variations and cycles.—Tidal currents have periods and cycles similar to those of the tides (art. 3109) and are subject to similar variations, but flood and ebb of the current do not necessarily occur at the same times as the rise and fall of the tide. The relationship is explained further in article 3121.

The speed at strength increases and decreases during the 2-week period, month, and year with the variations in the range of tide. Thus, the stronger **spring** and **perigean currents** occur near the times of new and full moon and near the times of the moon's perigee, or at times of spring and perigean tides (art. 3108); the weaker **neap** and **apogean**

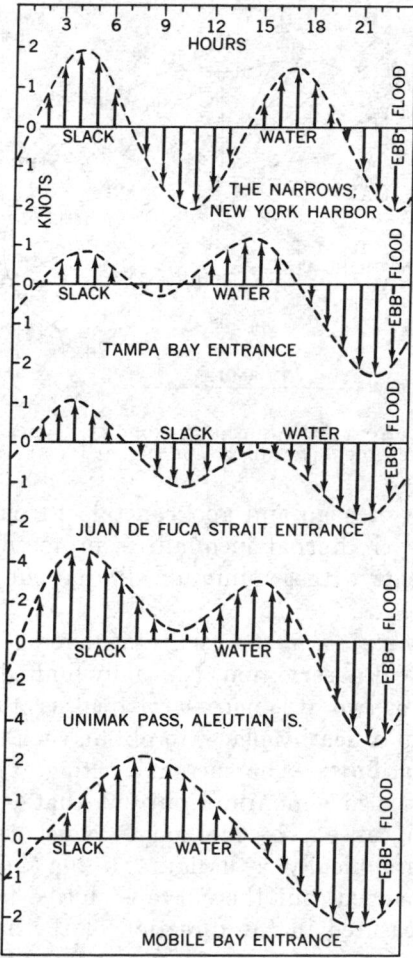

FIGURE 3118a.—Several types of reversing current. The pattern changes gradually from day to day, particularly for mixed types, passing through cycles somewhat similar to that shown for tides in figure 3106.

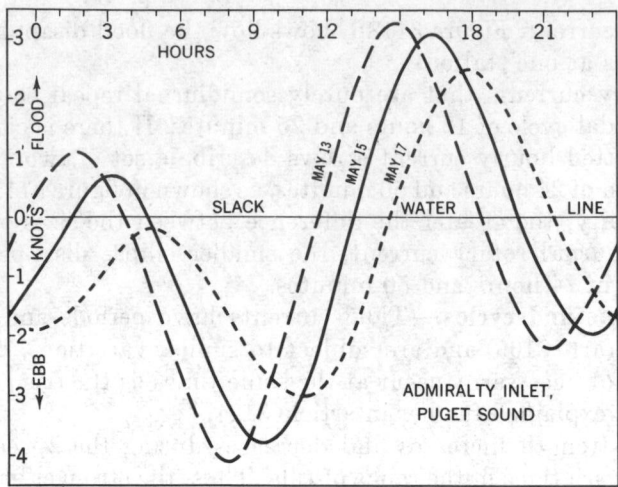

FIGURE 3118b.—Changes in a current of the mixed type. Note that each day as the inequality increases, the morning slacks draw together in time until on the 17th the morning flood disappears. On that day the current ebbs throughout the morning.

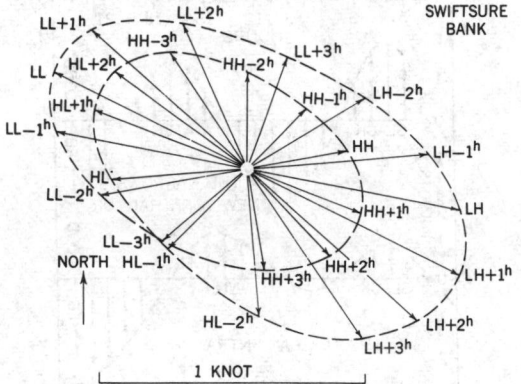

FIGURE 3118c.—Rotary tidal current with diurnal inequality. Times are in hours referred to tides (higher high, lower low, lower high, and higher low) at Swiftsure Bank.

currents occur at the times of neap and apogean tides; **tropic currents** with increased diurnal speeds or with larger diurnal inequalities in speed occur at times of tropic tides; and **equatorial currents** with a minimum diurnal effect occur at times of equatorial tides; etc.

As with the tide, a *mean value* represents an average obtained from a 19-year series. Since a series of current observations is usually limited to a few days, and seldom covers more than a month or two, it is necessary to adjust the observed values, usually by comparison with tides at a nearby place, to obtain such a mean.

3120. Effect of nontidal flow.—The current existing at any time is seldom purely tidal, but usually includes also a nontidal current that is due to drainage, oceanic circulation, wind, or other cause. The method in which tidal and nontidal currents combine is best explained graphically, as in figures 3120a and 3120b. The pattern of the tidal current remains unchanged, but the curve is shifted from the point or line from which the currents are measured in the direction of the nontidal current and by an amount equal to it. It is sometimes more convenient graphically merely to move the line or point of origin in the opposite direction.

Thus, the speed of the current flowing in the direction of the nontidal current is increased by an amount equal to the magnitude of the nontidal current, and the speed of the current flowing in the opposite direction is decreased by an equal amount. In figure 3120a a nontidal current is represented both in direction and speed by the vector *AO*. Since this is greater than the speed of the tidal current in the opposite direction, the point *A* is outside the ellipse. The direction and speed of the combined tidal and nontidal currents at any time is represented by a vector from *A* to that point on the curve representing the given time, and can be scaled from the graph. The strongest and weakest currents may no longer be in the directions of the maximum and minimum of the tidal current. In a reversing current (fig. 3120b), the effect is to advance the time of one slack and to retard the following one. If the speed of the nontidal current exceeds that of the reversing tidal current, the resultant current flows continuously in one direction without coming to a slack. In this case, the speed varies from a maximum to a minimum and back to a maximum in each tidal cycle. In figure 3120b the horizontal line *A* represents slack water if only tidal currents are present. Line *B* represents the effect of a 0.5-knot nontidal ebb, and line *C* the effect of a 1.0-knot nontidal ebb. With the condition shown at *C* there is only one flood each tidal day. If the nontidal ebb were to increase to approximately 2 knots, there would be no flood, two maximum ebbs and two minimum ebbs occurring during a tidal day.

3121. Relation between time of tidal current and time of tide.—At many places where current and tide are both semidiurnal, there is a definite relation between times of current and times of high and low water in the locality. Current atlases and notes on nautical charts often make use of this relationship by presenting for particular locations the direction and speed of the current at each succeeding hour after high and low water at a place for which tide predictions are available.

In localities where there is considerable diurnal inequality in tide or current, or where the type of current differs from the type of tide, the relationship is not constant, and it may be hazardous to try to predict the times of current from times of tide.

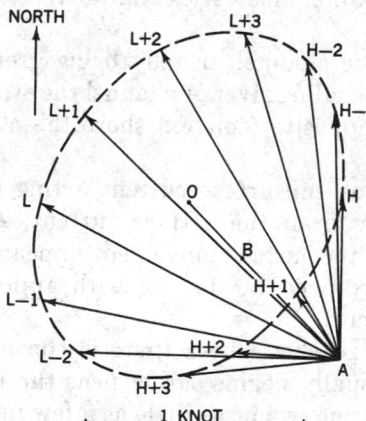

FIGURE 3120a.—Effect of nontidal current on the rotary tidal current of figure 3117a. If the nontidal current is northwest at 0.3 knot, it may be represented by *BO*, and all hourly directions and speeds will then be measured from *B*. If it is 1.0 knot, it will be represented by *AO* and the actual resultant hourly directions and speeds will be measured from *A*, as shown by the arrows.

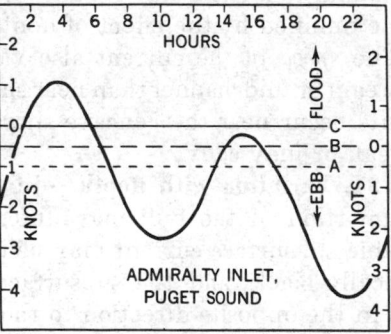

FIGURE 3120b.—Effect of nontidal current on the reversing tidal current of figure 3117b. If the nontidal current is 0.5 knot in the ebb direction, the ebb is increased by moving the slack water line from position *A* up 0.5 knot to position *B*. Speeds will then be measured from this broken line as shown by the scale on the right, and times of slack are changed. If the nontidal current is 1.0 knot in the ebb direction, as shown by line *C*, the speeds are as shown on the left, and the current will not reverse to a flood in the afternoon; it will merely slacken at about 1500.

Note the current curve for Unimak Pass in the Aleutians in figure 3118a. It shows the current as predicted in the tidal current tables. Predictions of high and low waters in the tide tables might have led one to expect the current to change from flood to ebb in the late morning, whereas actually the current continued to run flood with some strength at that time.

Since the relationship between times of tidal current and tide is not everywhere the same, and may be variable at the same place, one should exercise extreme caution in using general rules. The belief that slacks occur at local high and low tides and that the maximum flood and ebb occur when the tide is rising or falling most rapidly may be approximately true at the seaward entrance to, and in the upper reaches of, an inland tidal waterway. But generally this is not true in other parts of inland waterways. When an inland waterway is extensive or its entrance constricted, the slacks in some parts of the waterway often occur midway between the times of high and low tide. Usually in such waterways the relationship changes from place to place as one progresses upstream, slack water getting progressively closer in time to the local tide maximum until at the head of tidewater (the inland limit of water affected by a tide) the slacks occur at about the times of high and low tide.

3122. Relation between speed of current and range of tide.—The variation in the speed of the tidal current from place to place is not necessarily consistent with the range of tide. It may be the reverse. For example, currents are weak in the Gulf of Maine where the tides are large, and strong near Nantucket Island and in Nantucket Sound where the tides are small.

At any one place, however, the speed of the current at strength of flood and ebb varies during the month in about the same proportion as the range of tide, and one can use this relationship to determine the relative strength of currents on any day.

3123. Variation across an estuary.—In inland tidal waterways the *time* of tidal current varies across the channel from shore to shore. On the average, the current turns earlier near shore than in midstream, where the speed is greater. Differences of half an hour to an hour are not uncommon, but the difference varies and the relationship may be nullified by the effect of nontidal flow.

The *speed* of the current also varies across the channel, usually being greater in midstream or midchannel than near shore, but in a winding river or channel the strongest currents occur near the concave shore. Near the opposite (convex) shore the currents are weak or may eddy.

3124. Variation with depth.—In tidal rivers the subsurface current acting on the lower portion of the hull may differ considerably from the surface current. An appreciable subsurface current may be present when the surface movement appears to be practically slack, and the subsurface current may even be flowing with appreciable speed in the opposite direction to the surface current.

In a tidal estuary, particularly in the lower reaches where there is considerable difference in density from top to bottom, flood usually begins earlier near the bottom than at the surface. The differences may be an hour or two or as little as a few minutes, depending upon the estuary, the location in the estuary, and freshet conditions. Even when the freshwater runoff becomes so great as to prevent the surface current from flooding, it may still flood below the surface. The difference in time of ebb from surface to bottom is normally small but subject to variation with time and location.

The ebb speed at strength usually decreases gradually from top to bottom, but the speed of flood at strength often is stronger at subsurface depths than at the surface.

3125. Observations.—Observations of the current are made by means of a current meter or current pole and log line. In the past, most successful meters required a vessel and observers in continual attendance, as is necessary with the pole and line. Because of the difficulty and expense of such observations, they usually covered only a period of a day or two at a place. Observations of a month are the exception, and longer series were obtained only where ship and observers were available because of other duties, such as at lightships, where observations have been continued over a number of years.

Newer meters have been and are being developed that are suspended from a buoy and that record either in the buoy or send speed and direction impulses by radio to a base station on ship or land. With them, the period of observation has been increased so that in some recent surveys of United States harbors, the minimum period of observation was 1 week, with observations at several stations being continued over a period of 1 to 6 months.

3126. Tidal current tables and other sources of information.—The navigator should not attempt to predict currents without specific information for the locality in which he is interested. Such information is contained in various forms in many navigational publications.

Tidal current tables, issued annually, list daily predictions of the times and strengths of flood and ebb currents, and of the times of intervening slacks or minima. Due to lack of observational data, coverage is considerably more limited than for the tides. The tidal current tables do include supplemental data by which tidal current predictions can be determined for many places in addition to those for which daily predictions are given. The predictions are made by computers, using current harmonic constants that are obtained by analyzing current observations in the same manner as for tides (art. 3113). The use of tidal current tables is explained in articles 1207–1210.

Sailing directions and **coast pilots** issued by maritime nations include general descriptions of current behavior in various localities throughout the world.

Tidal current charts. A number of important harbors and waterways are covered by sets of tidal current charts showing graphically the hourly current movement.

Tidal Current Diagrams are a series of monthly diagrams used with the tidal current charts. The diagrams directly indicate the chart to use and the speed correction factor to apply to each chart.

The use of tables and charts for tide and current predictions is discussed in chapter XII.

References

Doodson, A. T., and H. D. Warburg. *Admiralty Manual of Tides.* London, H. M. Stationery Office, 1941.

Marmer, H. A. *The Tide.* New York, Appleton, 1926.

Schureman, Paul. *Manual of the Harmonic Analysis and Prediction of Tides.* Rev. ed. U. S. Coast and Geodic Survey Special Publication No. 98, Washington, U. S. Govt. Print. Off., 1940.

Schureman, Paul. *Tide and Current Glossary.* National Ocean Survey. Washington, U. S. Govt. Print. Off., 1975.

U. S. Coast and Geodetic Survey. *Manual of Current Observations.* Special Publication No. 215. Rev. ed. Washington, U. S. Govt. Print. Off., 1950.

U. S. Coast and Geodetic Survey. *Manual of Tide Observations.* Publication 30–1. Washington, U. S. Govt. Print. Off., 1965.

National Ocean Survey. *Tidal Current Charts* and *Tidal Current Diagrams.* Washington, several published periodically.

National Ocean Survey. *Tide Tables* and *Tidal Current Tables.* Washington, U. S. Govt. Print. Off., several volumes of each published annually.

CHAPTER XXXII

OCEAN CURRENTS

3201. Introduction.—The movement of water comprising the oceans is one of the principal sources of discrepancy between dead reckoning and actual positions of vessels. Water in essentially horizontal motion is called a **current,** the direction *toward* which it moves being the **set,** and its speed the **drift.** A well-defined current extending over a considerable region of the ocean is called an **ocean current.**

A **periodic current** is one the speed or direction of which changes cyclically at somewhat regular intervals, as a tidal current. A **seasonal current** is one which has large changes in speed or direction due to seasonal winds. A **permanent current** is one which experiences relatively little periodic or seasonal change.

A **coastal current** flows roughly parallel to a coast, outside the surf zone, while a **longshore current** is one parallel to a shore, inside the surf zone, and generated by waves striking the beach at an angle. Any current some distance from the shore may be called an **offshore current,** and one close to the shore an **inshore current.**

A **surface current** is one present at the surface, particularly one that does not extend more than a relatively few feet below the surface. A **subsurface current** is one which is present below the surface only.

There is evidence to indicate that the strongest ocean currents consist of relatively narrow, high-speed streams that follow winding, shifting courses. Often associated with these currents are secondary **countercurrents** flowing adjacent to them but in the opposite direction, and somewhat local, roughly circular, **eddy currents.** A relatively narrow, deep, fast-moving current is sometimes called a **stream current,** and a broad, shallow, slow-moving one a **drift current.**

3202. Causes of ocean currents.—Although man's knowledge of the processes which produce and maintain ocean currents is far from complete, he does have a general understanding of the principal factors involved. The primary generating forces are wind and the density differences in the water. In addition, such factors as depth of water, underwater topography, shape of the basin in which the current is running, extent and location of land, and deflection by the rotation of the earth all affect the oceanic circulation.

3203. Wind currents.—The stress of wind blowing across the sea causes the surface layer of water to move. This motion is transmitted to each succeeding layer below the surface, but due to internal friction within the water, the rate of motion decreases with depth. The current is called **Ekman wind current** or simply **wind current.** Although there are many variables, it is generally true that a steady wind for about 12 hours is needed to establish such a current.

A wind-driven current does not flow in the direction of the wind, being deflected by Coriolis force (art. 3803), due to rotation of the earth. This deflection is toward the *right* in the Northern Hemisphere, and toward the *left* in the Southern Hemisphere. The Coriolis force is greater in higher latitudes, and is more effective in deep water. In general, the difference between wind direction and surface wind-current direction varies from about 15° along shallow coastal areas to a maximum of 45° in the deep oceans. As the motion is transmitted to successive deeper layers, the Coriolis force continues to deflect the current. At several hundred fathoms the current may flow in the opposite direction to the surface current. This shift of current directions with depth combined with the decrease in velocity with depth is called the **Ekman spiral.**

.The speed of the current depends upon the speed of the wind, its constancy, the length of time it has blown, and other factors. In general, however, about 2 percent of the wind speed, or a little less, is a good average for deep water where the wind has been blowing steadily for at least 12 hours.

3204. Currents related to density differences.—As indicated in article 3009, the density of water varies with salinity, temperature, and pressure. At any given depth, the differences in density are due to differences in temperature and salinity. When suitable information is available, a map showing geographical density distribution at a certain depth could be drawn, with lines connecting points of equal density. These **isopycnic lines,** or lines connecting points at which a given density occurs at the same depth, would be similar to isobars on a weather map (art. 3827), and would serve an analogous purpose, showing areas of high density and those of low density. In an area of high density, the water surface is lower than in an area of low density, the maximum difference in height being of the order of 1 to 2 feet in 40 miles. Because of this difference, water tends to flow from an area of higher water (low density) to one of lower water (high density), but due to rotation of the earth, it is deflected toward the right in the Northern Hemisphere, and toward the left in the Southern Hemisphere. Thus, a circulation is set up similar to the cyclonic and anticyclonic circulation in the atmosphere. The greater the density gradient (rate of change with distance), the faster the related current.

3205. Oceanic circulation.—A number of ocean currents flow with great persistence, setting up a circulation that continues with relatively little change throughout the year. Because of the influence of wind in creating current (art. 3203), there is a relationship between this oceanic circulation and the general circulation of the atmosphere (art. 3804). The oceanic circulation is shown in figure 3205, with the names of the major ocean currents. Some differences in opinion exist regarding the names and limits of some of the currents, but those shown are representative. The spacing of the lines is a general indication of speed, but conditions vary somewhat with the season. This is particularly noticeable in the Indian Ocean and along the South China coast, where currents are influenced to a marked degree by the monsoons (art. 3810).

3206. Atlantic Ocean currents.—The trade winds (art. 3806), which blow with great persistence, set up a system of **equatorial currents** which at times extends over as much as 50° of latitude, or even more. There are two westerly flowing currents conforming generally with the areas of trade winds, separated by a weaker, easterly flowing countercurrent.

The **North Equatorial Current** originates to the northward of the Cape Verde Islands and flows almost due west at an average speed of about 0.7 knot.

The **South Equatorial Current** is more extensive. It starts off the west coast of Africa, south of the Gulf of Guinea, and flows in a generally westerly direction at an average speed of about 0.6 knot. However, the speed gradually increases until it may reach a value of 2.5 knots or more off the east coast of South America. As the current approaches Cabo de São Roque, the eastern extremity of South America, it divides, the southern part curving toward the south along the coast of Brazil, and the northern part being deflected by the continent of South America toward the north.

Between the North and South Equatorial Currents a weaker **Equatorial Countercurrent** sets toward the east in the general vicinity of the doldrums (art. 3805). This is fed by water from the two westerly flowing equatorial currents, particularly the South Equatorial Current. The extent and strength of the Equatorial Countercurrent changes with the seasonal variations of the wind. It reaches a maximum during July

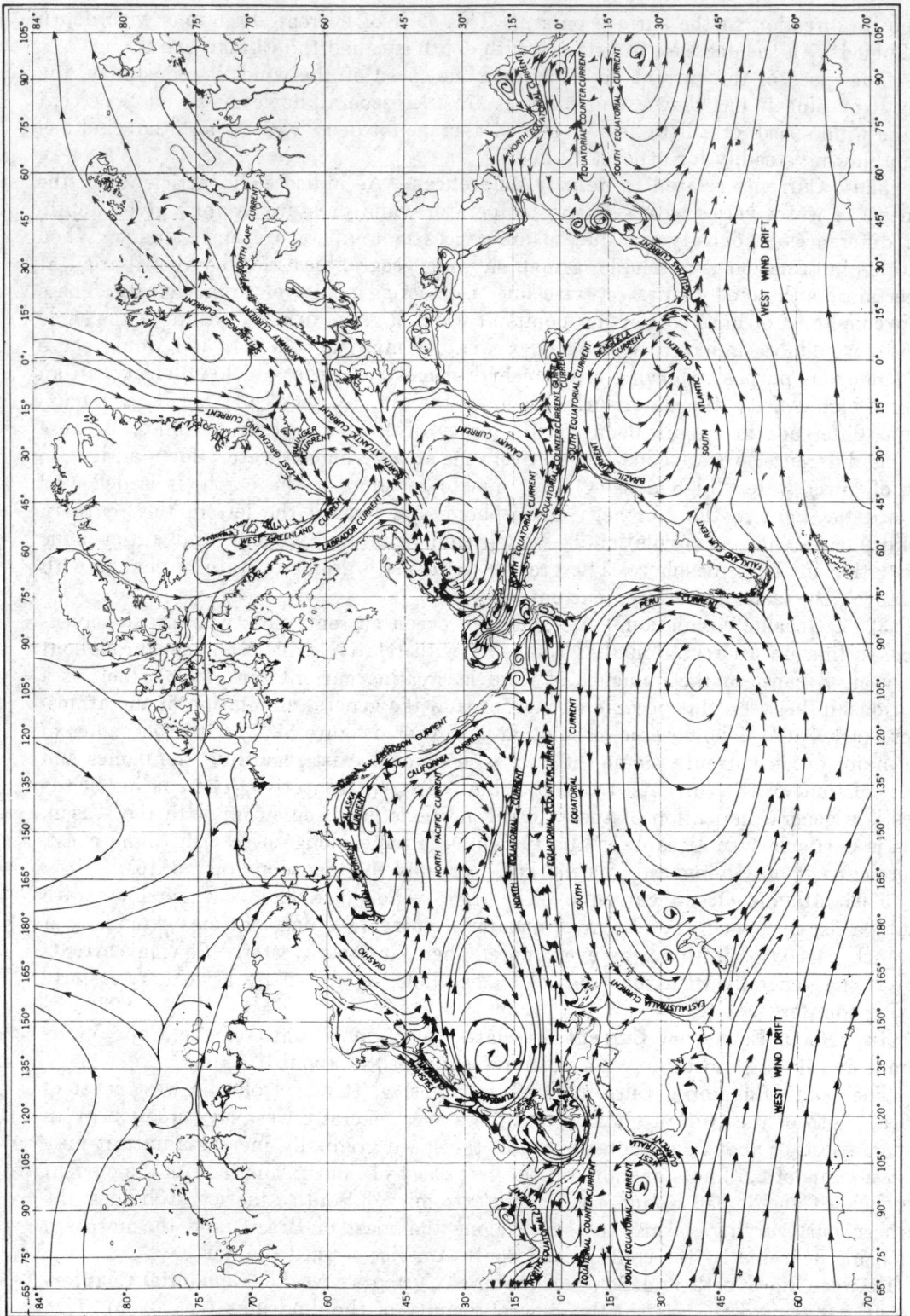

Figure 3205.—Major surface currents of the world (northern hemisphere winter).

and August, when it extends from about 50° west longitude to the Gulf of Guinea. During its minimum, in December and January, it is of very limited extent, the western portion disappearing altogether.

That part of the South Equatorial Current flowing along the northern coast of South America which does not feed the Equatorial Countercurrent unites with the North Equatorial Current at a point west of the Equatorial Countercurrent. A large part of the combined current flows through various passages between the Windward Islands, into the Caribbean Sea. It sets toward the west, and then somewhat north of west, finally arriving off the Yucatan peninsula. From here, some of the water curves toward the right, flowing some distance off the shore of the Gulf of Mexico, and part of it curves more sharply toward the east and flows directly toward the north coast of Cuba. These two parts reunite in the Straits of Florida to form the most remarkable of all ocean currents, the **Gulf Stream.** Off the southeast coast of Florida this current is augmented by a current flowing along the northern coasts of Puerto Rico, Hispaniola, and Cuba. Another current flowing eastward of the Bahamas joins the stream north of these islands.

The Gulf Stream follows generally along the east coast of North America, flowing around Florida, northward and then northeastward toward Cape Hatteras, and then curving toward the east and becoming broader and slower. After passing the Grand Banks, it turns more toward the north and becomes a broad drift current flowing across the North Atlantic. That part in the Straits of Florida is sometimes called the **Florida Current.**

A tremendous volume of water flows northward in the Gulf Stream. It can be distinguished by its deep indigo-blue color, which contrasts sharply with the dull green of the surrounding water. It is accompanied by frequent squalls. When the Gulf Stream encounters the cold water of the Labrador Current, principally in the vicinity of the Grand Banks, there is little mixing of the waters. Instead, the junction is marked by a sharp change in temperature. The line or surface along which this occurs is called the **cold wall.** When the warm Gulf Stream water encounters cold air, evaporation is so rapid that the rising vapor may be visible as frost smoke (art. 3815). The stream carries large quantities of gulfweed from the Tropics to higher latitudes.

Recent investigations have shown that the current itself is much narrower and faster than previously supposed, and considerably more variable in its position and speed. The maximum current off Florida ranges from about 2 to 4 knots. To the northward the speed is generally less, and decreases further after the current passes Cape Hatteras. As the stream meanders and shifts position, eddies sometimes break off and continue as separate, circular flows until they dissipate. Boats in the Bermuda Race have been known to be within sight of each other and be carried in opposite directions by different parts of the same current. As the current shifts position, its extent does not always coincide with the area of warm, blue water. When the sea is relatively smooth, the edges of the current are marked by ripples.

Information is not yet available to permit prediction of the position and speed of the current at any future time, but it has been found that tidal forces apparently influence the current, which reaches its daily maximum speed about 3 hours after transit of the moon. The current generally is faster at the time of neap tides than at spring tides. When the moon is over the equator, the stream is narrower and faster than at maximum northerly or southerly declination. Variations in the trade winds (art. 3806) also affect the current.

As the Gulf Stream continues eastward and northeastward beyond the Grand Banks, it gradually widens and decreases speed until it becomes a vast, slow-moving drift current known as the **North Atlantic Current,** in the general vicinity of the prevailing westerlies (art. 3808). In the eastern part of the Atlantic it divides into the **Northeast Drift Current** and the **Southeast Drift Current.**

The Northeast Drift Current continues in a generally northeasterly direction toward the Norwegian Sea. As it does so, it continues to widen and decrease speed. South of Iceland it branches to form the **Irminger Current** and the **Norway Current.** The Irminger Current curves toward the north and northwest to join the East Greenland Current southwest of Iceland. The Norway Current continues in a northeasterly direction along the coast of Norway. Part of it, the **North Cape Current,** rounds North Cape into the Barents Sea. The other part curves toward the north and becomes known as the **Spitsbergen Current.** Before reaching Svalbard (Spitsbergen), it curves toward the west and joins the cold **East Greenland Current** flowing southward in the Greenland Sea. As this current flows past Iceland, it is further augmented by the Irminger Current.

Off Kap Farvel, at the southern tip of Greenland, the East Greenland Current curves sharply to the northwest following the coastline. As it does so, it becomes known as the **West Greenland Current.** This current continues along the west coast of Greenland, through Davis Strait, and into Baffin Bay. Both East and West Greenland Currents are sometimes known by the single name **Greenland Current.**

In Baffin Bay the Greenland Current follows generally the coast, curving westward off Kap York to form the southerly flowing **Labrador Current.** This cold current flows southward off the coast of Baffin Island, through Davis Strait, along the coast of Labrador and Newfoundland, to the Grand Banks, carrying with it large quantities of ice (ch. XXXVI). Here it encounters the warm water of the Gulf Stream, creating the "cold wall." Some of the cold water flows southward along the east coast of North America, inshore of the Gulf Stream, as far as Cape Hatteras. The remainder curves toward the east and flows along the northern edge of the North Atlantic and Northeast Drift Currents, gradually merging with them.

The Southeast Drift Current curves toward the east, southeast, and then south as it is deflected by the coast of Europe. It flows past the Bay of Biscay, toward southeastern Europe and the Canary Islands, where it continues as the **Canary Current.** In the vicinity of the Cape Verde Islands, this current divides, part of it curving toward the west to help form the North Equatorial Current, and part of it curving toward the east to follow the coast of Africa into the Gulf of Guinea, where it is known as the **Guinea Current.** This current is augmented by the Equatorial Countercurrent and, in summer, it is strengthened by monsoon winds. It flows in close proximity to the South Equatorial Current, but in the opposite direction. As it curves toward the south, still following the African coast, it merges with the South Equatorial Current.

The clockwise circulation of the North Atlantic leaves a large central area having no well-defined currents. This area is known as the **Sargasso Sea,** from the large quantities of sargasso or gulfweed encountered there.

That branch of the South Equatorial Current which curves toward the south off the east coast of South America follows the coast as the warm, highly-saline **Brazil Current,** which in some respects resembles the Gulf Stream. Off Uruguay, it encounters the colder, less-salty Falkland Current and the two curve toward the east to form the broad, slow-moving **South Atlantic Current,** in the general vicinity of the prevailing westerlies (art. 3808). This current flows eastward to a point west of the Cape of Good Hope, where it curves northward to follow the west coast of Africa as the strong **Benguela Current,** augmented somewhat by part of the Agulhas Current flowing around the southern part of Africa from the Indian Ocean. As it continues northward, the current gradually widens and slows. At a point east of St. Helena Island it curves westward to continue as part of the South Equatorial Current, thus completing the counterclockwise circulation of the South Atlantic. The Benguela Current is augmented somewhat by the

West Wind Drift, a current which flows easterly around Antarctica. As the West Wind Drift flows past Cape Horn, that part in the immediate vicinity of the cape is called the **Cape Horn Current.** This current rounds the cape and flows in a northerly and northeasterly direction along the coast of South America as the **Falkland Current.**

3207. Pacific Ocean currents follow the general pattern of those in the Atlantic. The **North Equatorial Current** flows westward in the general area of the northeast trades, and the **South Equatorial Current** follows a similar path in the region of the southeast trades. Between these two, the weaker **Equatorial Countercurrent** sets toward the east, just north of the equator.

After passing the Mariana Islands, the major part of the North Equatorial Current curves somewhat toward the northwest, past the Philippines and Formosa. Here it is deflected further toward the north, where it becomes known as the **Kuroshio,** and then toward the northeast past the Nansei Shoto and Japan, and on in a more easterly direction. Part of the Kuroshio, called the **Tsushima Current,** flows through Tsushima Strait, between Japan and Korea, and the Sea of Japan, following generally the northwest coast of Japan. North of Japan it curves eastward and then southeastward to rejoin the main part of the Kuroshio. The limits and volume of the Kuroshio are influenced by the monsoons (art. 3810), being augmented during the season of southwesterly winds, and diminished when the northeasterly winds are prevalent.

The Kuroshio (Japanese for "Black Stream") is so named because of the dark color of its water. It is sometimes called the **Japan Stream.** In many respects it is similar to the Gulf Stream of the Atlantic. Like that current, it carries large quantities of warm tropical water to higher latitudes, and then curves toward the east as a major part of the general clockwise circulation in the Northern Hemisphere. As it does so, it widens and slows. A small part of it curves to the right to form a weak clockwise circulation west of the Hawaiian Islands. The major portion continues on between the Aleutians and the Hawaiian Islands, where it becomes known as the **North Pacific Current.**

As this current approaches the North American continent, most of it is deflected toward the right to form a clockwise circulation between the west coast of North America and the Hawaiian Islands. This part of the current has become so broad that the circulation is generally weak. A small part near the coast, however, joins the southern branch of the Aleutian Current, and flows southeastward as the **California Current.** The average speed of this current is about 0.8 knot. It is strongest near land. Near the southern end of Baja (Lower) California, this current curves sharply to the west and broadens to form the major portion of the North Equatorial Current.

During the winter, a weak countercurrent flows northwestward along the west coast of North America from southern California to Vancouver Island, inshore of the southeasterly flowing California Current. This is called the **Davidson Current.**

Off the west coast of Mexico, south of Baja California, the current flows southeastward, as a continuation of part of the California Current, during the winter. During the summer, the current in this area is northwestward, as a continuation of the Equatorial Countercurrent, before it turns westward to help form the North Equatorial Current.

As in the Atlantic, there is in the Pacific a counterclockwise circulation to the north of the clockwise circulation. Cold water flowing southward through the western part of Bering Strait between Alaska and Siberia is joined by water circulating counterclockwise in the Bering Sea to form the **Oyashio.** As the current leaves the strait, it curves toward the right and flows southwesterly along the coast of Siberia and the Kuril Islands. This current brings quantities of sea ice, but no icebergs. When it encounters the Kuroshio, the Oyashio curves southward and then eastward, the greater portion joining the Kuroshio and North Pacific Current. The northern portion continues eastward to join the curving Aleutian Current.

As this current approaches the west coast of North America, west of Vancouver Island, part of it curves toward the right and is joined by water from the North Pacific Current, to form the California Current. The northern branch of the Aleutian Current curves in a counterclockwise direction to form the **Alaska Current,** which generally follows the coast of Canada and Alaska. When it arrives off the Aleutian Islands, it becomes known as the **Aleutian Current.** Part of it flows along the southern side of these islands to about the 180th meridian, where it curves in a counterclockwise direction and becomes an easterly flowing current, being augmented by the northern part of the Oyashio. The other part of the Aleutian Current flows through various openings between the Aleutian Islands, into the Bering Sea. Here it flows in a general counterclockwise direction, most of it finally joining the southerly flowing Oyashio, and a small part of it flowing northward through the eastern side of the Bering Strait, into the Arctic Ocean.

The South Equatorial Current, extending in width between about 4°N latitude and 10°S, flows westward from South America to the western Pacific. After this current crosses the 180th meridian, the major part curves in a counterclockwise direction, entering the Coral Sea, and then curving more sharply toward the south along the east coast of Australia, where it is known as the **East Australia Current.** In the Tasman Sea, northeast of Tasmania, it is augmented by water from the West Wind Drift, flowing eastward south of Australia. It curves toward the southeast and then the east, gradually merging with the easterly flowing West Wind Drift, a broad, slow-moving current that circles Antarctica.

Near the southern extremity of South America, most of this current flows eastward into the Atlantic, but part of it curves toward the left and flows generally northward along the west coast of South America as the **Peru Current** or **Humboldt Current.** Occasionally a set directly toward land is encountered. At about Cabo Blanco, where the coast falls away to the right, the current curves toward the left, past the Galapagos Islands, where it takes a westerly set and constitutes the major portion of the South Equatorial Current, thus completing the counterclockwise circulation of the South Pacific.

During the northern hemisphere summer, a weak northern branch of the South Equatorial Current, known as the **Rossel Current,** continues on toward the west and northwest along both the southern and northeastern coasts of New Guinea. The southern part flows through Torres Strait, between New Guinea and Australia, into the Arafura Sea. Here, it gradually loses its identity, part of it flowing on toward the west as part of the South Equatorial Current of the Indian Ocean, and part of it following the coast of Australia and finally joining the easterly flowing West Wind Drift. The northern part of the Rossel Current curves in a clockwise direction to help form the Pacific Equatorial Countercurrent. During the northern hemisphere winter, the Rossel Current is replaced by an easterly flowing current from the Indian Ocean.

3208. Indian Ocean currents follow generally the pattern of the Atlantic and Pacific but with differences caused principally by the monsoons (art. 3810) and the more limited extent of water in the Northern Hemisphere. During the northern hemisphere winter, the **North Equatorial Current** and **South Equatorial Current** flow toward the west, with the weaker, easterly flowing **Equatorial Countercurrent** flowing between them, as in the Atlantic and Pacific (but somewhat south of the equator). But during the northern hemisphere summer, both the North Equatorial Current and the Equatorial Countercurrent are replaced by the **Monsoon Current,** which flows eastward and southeastward across the Arabian Sea and the Bay of Bengal. Near Sumatra, this current curves in a clockwise direction and flows westward, augmenting the South Equatorial Current and setting up a clockwise circulation in the northern part of the Indian Ocean.

As the South Equatorial Current approaches the coast of Africa, it curves toward the southwest, part of it flowing through the Mozambique Channel between Madagascar and the mainland, and part flowing along the east coast of Madagascar. At the southern end of this island the two join to form the strong **Agulhas Current,** which is analogous to the Gulf Stream.

A small part of the Agulhas Current rounds the southern end of Africa and helps form the Benguela Current. The major portion, however, curves sharply southward and then eastward to join the West Wind Drift. This junction is often marked by a broken and confused sea. During the northern hemisphere winter the northern part of this current curves in a counterclockwise direction to form the **West Australia Current,** which flows northward along the west coast of Australia. As it passes Northwest Cape, i t curves northwestward to help form the South Equatorial Current. During the northern hemisphere summer, the West Australia Current is replaced by a weak current flowing around the western part of Australia as an extension of the southern branch of the Rossel Current.

3209. Polar currents.—The waters of the North Atlantic enter the Arctic Ocean between Norway and Svalbard. The currents flow easterly north of Siberia to the region of the Novosibirskiye Ostrova, where they turn northerly across the North Pole and continue down the Greenland coast to form the **East Greenland Current.** On the American side of the arctic basin, there is a weak, continuous clockwise flow centered in the vicinity of 80°N, 150°W. A current north through Bering Strait along the American coast is balanced by an outward southerly flow along the Siberian coast, which eventually becomes part of the Oyashio. Each of the main islands or island groups in the Arctic, as far as is known, seems to have a clockwise nearshore circulation around it. The Barents Sea, Kara Sea, and Laptev Sea each have a weak counterclockwise circulation. A similar but weaker counterclockwise current system appears to exist in the East Siberian Sea.

In the Antarctic, the circulation is generally from west to east in a broad, slow-moving current extending completely around Antarctica. This is called the **West Wind Drift,** although it is formed partly by the strong westerly wind in this area and partly by density differences. This current is augmented by the Brazil and Falkland Currents in the Atlantic, the East Australia Current in the Pacific, and the Agulhas Current in the Indian Ocean. In return, part of it curves northward to form the Cape Horn, Falkland, and most of the Benguela Currents in the Atlantic, the Peru Current in the Pacific, and west Australia Current in the Indian Ocean.

3210. Ocean currents and climate.—Many of the ocean currents exert a marked influence upon the climate of the coastal regions along which they flow. Thus, warm water from the Gulf Stream, continuing as the North Atlantic, Northeast Drift, and Irminger Currents, arrives off the southwest coast of Iceland, warming it to the extent that Reykjavík has a higher average winter temperature than New York City, far to the south. Great Britain and Labrador are about the same latitude, but the climate of Great Britain is much milder because of the difference of temperature of currents. The west coast of the United States is cooled in the summer by the California Current, and warmed in the winter by the Davidson Current. As a result of this condition, partly, the range of monthly average temperature is comparatively small.

Currents exercise other influences besides those on temperature. The pressure pattern is affected materially, as air over a cold current contracts as it is cooled, and that over a warm current expands. As air cools above a cold ocean current, fog is likely to form. Frost smoke (art. 3815) is most prevalent over a warm current which flows into a colder region. Evaporation is greater from warm water than from cold water.

In these and other ways, the climate of the earth is closely associated with the ocean currents, although other factors, such as topography and prevailing winds, are also important.

References

Stream Drift Chart of the World—January. Defense Mapping Agency Hydrographic Center Pilot Charts (various editions).

Stream Drift Chart of the World—July. Defense Mapping Agency Hydrographic Center Pilot Charts (various editions).

Sverdrup, H. U., M. W. Johnson, and R. H. Fleming. *The Oceans, Their Physics, Chemistry and General Biology*. New York, Prentice-Hall, 1942.

CHAPTER XXXIII

OCEAN WAVES

3301. Introduction.—Undulations of the surface of the water, called **waves,** are perhaps the most widely observed phenomenon at sea, and possibly the least understood by the average seaman. The mariner equipped with a knowledge of the basic facts concerning waves is able to use them to his advantage, and either avoid hazardous conditions or operate with a minimum of danger if such conditions cannot be avoided.

3302. Causes of waves.—Waves on the surface of the sea are caused principally by wind, but other factors, such as submarine earthquakes, volcanic eruptions, and the tide, also cause waves. If a breeze of less than 2 knots starts to blow across smooth water, small wavelets called **ripples** form almost instantaneously. When the breeze dies, the ripples disappear as suddenly as they formed, the level surface being restored by surface tension of the water. If the wind speed exceeds 2 knots, more stable **gravity waves** gradually form, and progress with the wind.

While the generating wind blows, the resulting waves may be referred to as **sea.** When the wind stops or changes direction, the waves that continue on without relation to local winds are called **swell.**

Unlike wind and current, waves are not deflected appreciably by the rotation of the earth, but move in the direction in which the generating wind blows. When this wind ceases, friction and spreading cause the waves to be reduced in height, or **attenuated,** as they move across the surface. However, the reduction takes place so slowly that swell continues until it reaches some obstruction, such as a shore.

The Fleet Numerical Weather Central, Monterey, California, produces synoptic analyses and predictions of ocean wave heights using a spectral numerical model. The wave information consists of heights and directions for different periods and wavelengths. The model generates and propagates wave energy. Verification has been very good. Information from the model is provided to the U.S. Navy on a routine basis and is a vital input to the Optimum Track Ship Routing program (ch. XXIV).

3303. Wave characteristics.—Ocean waves are very nearly in the shape of an inverted **cycloid,** the figure formed by a point inside the rim of a wheel rolling along a level surface. This shape is shown in figure 3303a. The highest parts of waves are called **crests,** and the intervening lowest parts, **troughs.** Since the crests are steeper and narrower than the troughs, the mean or still water level is a little lower than half-way between the crests and troughs. The vertical distance between trough and crest is called **wave height,** labeled H in figure 3303a. The horizontal distance between successive crests, measured in the direction of travel, is called **wavelength,** labeled L. The time interval between passage of successive crests at a stationary point is called **wave period** (**P**). Wave height, length, and period depend upon a number of factors, such as the wind speed, the length of time it has blown, and its **fetch** (the straight distance it has traveled over the surface). Table 3303 indicates the relationship between wind

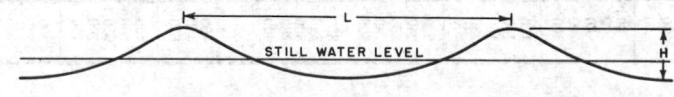

FIGURE 3303a.—A typical sea wave.

BEAUFORT NUMBER.

Fetch	11 P	11 H	11 T	10 P	10 H	10 T	9 P	9 H	9 T	8 P	8 H	8 T	7 P	7 H	7 T	6 P	6 H	6 T	5 P	5 H	5 T	4 P	4 H	4 T	3 P	3 H	3 T
10	5.0	10.0	1.8	4.2	10.0	1.9	4.1	8.0	2.0	3.9	7.3	2.3	3.4	6.0	2.5	3.1	5.0	2.7	2.8	3.5	3.2	2.4	2.6	3.7	2.1	1.8	4.4
20	5.9	16.0	3.0	5.2	14.0	3.2	5.5	12.0	3.5	4.4	10.0	3.9	4.3	8.6	4.2	3.8	7.0	4.7	3.3	4.9	5.4	2.9	3.2	6.2	2.5	2.0	7.1
30	6.3	19.8	4.1	6.0	18.0	4.4	5.5	15.5	4.7	5.4	12.1	5.2	4.6	10.0	5.8	4.2	8.0	6.2	3.7	5.8	7.2	3.3	3.8	8.3	3.0	2.0	8.0
40	6.7	22.5	5.1	6.3	21.0	5.4	5.9	17.7	5.8	5.4	14.0	6.5	4.9	11.2	7.1	4.6	9.0	7.8	4.1	6.2	8.9	3.6	3.9	10.3	3.2	2.0	9.8
50	7.1	25.0	6.1	6.7	23.0	6.4	6.0	19.8	6.9	5.6	15.7	7.7	5.2	12.2	8.4	4.8	9.8	9.1	4.4	6.5	11.0	3.8	4.0	12.4	3.2	2.0	12.0
60	7.5	27.5	7.0	7.0	25.0	7.4	6.5	21.0	8.0	6.0	17.0	8.7	5.5	13.9	9.6	5.1	10.3	10.2	4.6	6.8	12.0	4.0	4.0	14.0	3.5	2.0	16.0
70	7.7	29.5	7.8	7.3	26.5	8.3	6.8	22.5	9.0	6.4	18.0	9.9	5.7	14.5	10.5	5.4	10.8	11.9	4.8	7.0	13.5	4.1	4.0	15.8	3.7	2.0	18.0
80	7.9	31.5	8.6	7.7	28.0	9.3	7.1	24.0	10.0	6.6	18.9	11.0	6.0	15.0	12.0	5.6	11.2	13.0	4.9	7.2	15.0	4.2	4.0	17.0	3.8	2.0	20.6
90	8.2	34.0	9.5	7.9	30.0	10.2	7.2	25.0	11.0	6.7	20.0	12.0	6.3	15.5	13.0	5.8	11.3	14.1	5.1	7.3	16.5	4.3	4.0	18.0	3.9	2.0	23.6
100	8.5	35.0	10.3	8.1	32.0	11.0	7.6	26.5	11.9	6.9	20.5	12.8	6.5	15.5	14.0	6.0	11.4	15.1	5.3	7.3	17.5	4.4	4.0	20.0	4.0	2.0	27.1
120	8.8	37.5	11.5	8.4	33.5	12.3	7.9	27.5	13.1	7.3	21.5	14.5	6.7	16.0	15.9	6.2	11.7	17.0	5.4	7.8	20.0	4.7	4.1	22.4	4.2	2.0	31.1
140	9.2	40.0	13.0	8.8	35.5	13.9	8.3	29.0	14.6	7.6	22.0	16.0	7.0	16.5	17.6	6.4	11.9	19.1	5.8	7.9	22.5	4.9	4.2	25.4	4.5	2.0	36.6
160	9.6	42.5	14.5	9.1	37.0	15.1	8.7	30.5	16.4	8.0	23.0	18.0	7.3	16.5	19.5	6.6	12.0	21.1	6.0	7.9	24.3	5.2	4.2	28.4	4.9	2.0	43.2
180	10.0	44.5	16.0	9.5	38.5	16.5	9.0	31.5	18.0	8.3	23.5	19.9	7.5	17.0	21.3	6.8	12.1	23.1	6.2	8.0	27.0	5.4	4.3	30.9	4.9	2.0	50.0
200	10.3	46.0	17.1	9.8	40.0	18.1	9.2	32.5	19.3	8.5	23.5	21.5	7.7	17.5	23.1	7.1	12.2	25.4	6.4	8.0	29.0	5.6	4.3	33.5			
220	10.6	47.5	18.2	10.1	41.5	19.1	9.6	34.0	20.9	8.8	24.0	22.4	8.0	17.9	25.0	7.2	12.3	27.2	6.6	8.0	31.1	5.8	4.4	36.5			
240	10.8	49.0	19.5	10.3	43.0	20.5	9.8	34.5	22.0	9.0	24.5	24.4	8.2	17.9	26.8	7.3	12.4	29.0	6.8	8.0	33.1	5.9	4.4	39.2			
260	11.1	50.5	20.9	10.6	44.0	21.8	10.0	34.5	23.5	9.2	25.0	26.2	8.4	18.0	28.5	7.5	12.7	30.5	6.9	8.0	34.0	6.0	4.4	41.9			
280	11.3	51.5	22.0	10.9	45.0	23.0	10.2	35.0	25.0	9.4	25.0	27.7	8.5	18.0	29.5	7.8	12.9	32.4	7.0	8.0	36.8	6.2	4.4	44.5			
300	11.6	53.0	23.2	11.1	45.0	24.3	10.4	35.0	26.3	9.5	25.0	29.0	8.7	18.0	31.5	8.0	13.1	34.1	7.1	8.0	38.5	6.3	4.4	47.0			
320	11.8	54.0	24.5	11.2	45.5	25.5	10.6	35.5	27.6	9.6	25.0	30.2	8.9	18.0	33.0	8.3	13.3	36.0	7.2	8.0	40.5						
340	12.0	55.0	25.6	11.4	46.0	26.5	10.8	36.0	29.0	9.8	25.5	31.6	9.1	18.1	34.2	8.3	13.4	37.6	7.3	8.0	42.4						
360	12.2	55.5	26.6	11.6	46.5	27.7	10.9	36.5	30.0	9.9	25.5	33.0	9.3	18.1	35.7	8.4	13.4	38.8	7.4	8.0	44.2						
380	12.4	56.0	27.7	11.8	47.0	29.1	11.1	37.0	31.3	10.0	25.5	34.2	9.4	18.4	37.1	8.4	13.5	40.2	7.5	8.0	46.1						
400	12.6	56.5	28.9	12.0	47.5	30.2	11.2	37.0	32.5	10.2	26.0	35.6	9.5	18.4	38.8	8.6	13.5	42.2	7.7	8.0	48.0						
420	12.7	57.0	29.6	12.2	47.5	31.5	11.4	37.5	33.3	10.3	26.5	36.9	9.6	18.7	40.0	8.7	13.6	43.5	7.8	8.0	50.0						
440	12.9	57.5	30.9	12.3	48.0	32.5	11.5	37.5	34.8	10.4	27.0	38.1	9.7	18.8	41.3	8.8	13.7	44.7	7.9	8.0	52.0						
460	13.1	57.5	31.8	12.5	48.5	33.5	11.7	37.5	36.0	10.6	27.5	39.5	9.8	19.0	42.8	8.9	13.7	46.2	8.0	8.0	54.0						
480	13.2	57.5	32.7	12.6	49.0	34.5	11.8	38.0	37.0	10.8	27.5	41.0	9.9	19.0	44.0	9.0	13.7	47.8	8.1	8.0	56.0						
500	13.4	58.0	33.9	12.7	49.0	35.5	11.9	38.0	38.3	10.9	27.5	42.1	10.1	19.1	45.5	9.1	13.8	49.2	8.2	8.0	58.0						
550	13.7	59.0	36.5	13.0	50.0	38.2	12.2	38.5	41.0	11.1	27.5	44.9	10.3	19.5	48.5	9.3	13.8	53.0									
600	14.0	60.0	38.7	13.3	50.0	40.3	12.5	39.0	43.6	11.4	27.5	47.7	10.5	19.8	51.8	9.5	13.8	56.3									
650	14.2	60.0	41.0	13.7	50.5	43.5	12.8	40.0	46.4	11.6	27.5	50.3	10.7	19.8	55.0												
700	14.5	60.5	43.5	14.0	51.0	45.4	13.1	40.0	49.0	11.8	27.5	53.2	11.0	19.8	58.5												
750	14.8	61.0	45.8	14.2	51.0	48.0	13.3	40.0	51.0	12.1	27.5	56.2															
800	15.0	61.5	47.8	14.5	51.5	50.6	13.5	40.0	53.8	12.3	27.5	59.2															
850	15.2	62.0	50.0	14.6	52.0	52.5	13.8	40.0	56.2																		
900	15.5	62.5	52.0	14.9	52.0	54.6	14.0	40.0	58.2																		
950	15.7	63.0	54.0	15.1	52.0	57.2																					
1000	16.0	63.0	56.3	15.3	52.0	59.3																					

TABLE 3303.—Minimum Time (T) in hours that wind must blow to form waves of H significant height (in feet) and P period (in seconds). Fetch in nautical miles.

speed, fetch, length of time the wind blows, wave height, and wave period in deep water.

If the water is deeper than one-half the wavelength (L), this length in feet is theoretically related to period (P) in seconds by the formula

$$L = 5.12P^2.$$

The actual value has been found to be a little less than this for swell, and about two-thirds the length determined by this formula for sea. When the waves leave the generating area and continue as free waves, the wavelength and period continue to increase, while the height decreases. The rate of change gradually decreases.

The speed (S) of a free wave in deep water is nearly independent of its height or steepness. For swell, its relationship in knots to the period (P) in seconds is given by the formula

$$S = 3.03P.$$

The relationship for sea is not known.

The theoretical relationship between speed, wavelength, and period is shown in figure 3303b. As waves continue on beyond the generating area, the period, wavelength, and speed remains the same. Because the waves of each period have different speeds they tend to sort themselves by periods as they move away from the generating area. The longer period waves move at a greater speed and move ahead. At great enough distances from a storm area the waves will have sorted themselves into packets based on period.

All the waves are attenuated as they propagate but the short period waves attenuate faster so that at a long distance from a storm only the longer waves remain.

The time needed for a wave system to travel some distance is *double* that which would be indicated by the speed of individual waves. This is because the front wave gradually disappears and transfers its energy to succeeding waves. The process is

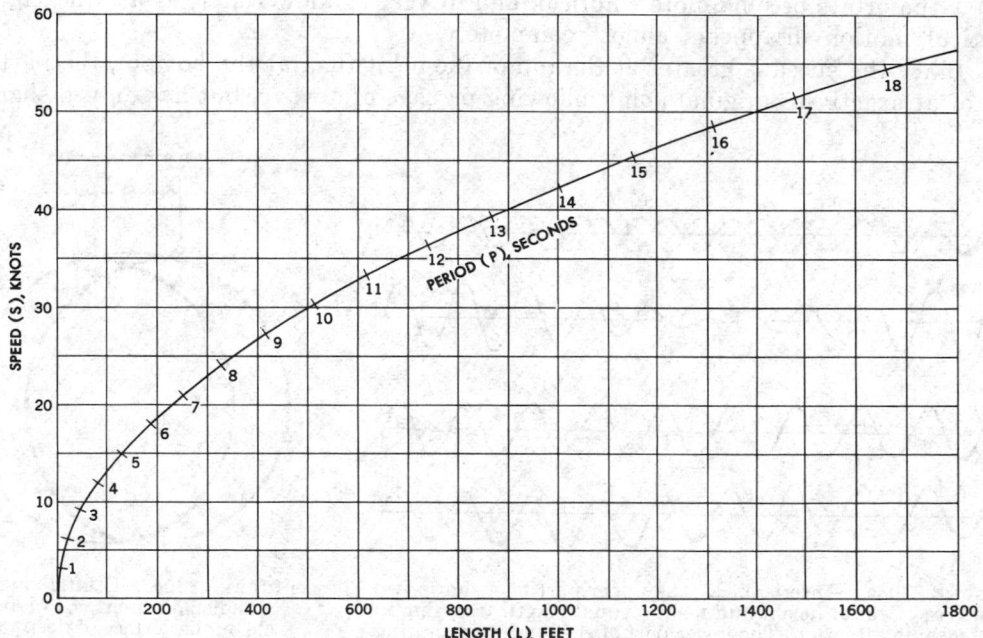

FIGURE 3303b.—Relationship between speed, length, and period of waves in deep water, based upon the theoretical relationship between period and length.

followed by each front wave in succession, at such a rate that the wave *system* advances at a speed which is just *half* that of *individual* waves. This process can be seen in the bow wave of a vessel. The speed at which the wave system advances is called **group velocity.**

Because of the existence of many independent wave systems at the same time, the sea surface acquires a complex and irregular pattern. Also, since the longer waves outrun the shorter ones, the resulting interference adds to the complexity of the pattern. The process of interference, illustrated in figure 3303c, is duplicated many times in the sea, being the principal reason that successive waves are not of the same height. The irregularity of the surface may be further accentuated by the presence of wave systems crossing at an angle to each other, producing peak-like rises.

In reporting average wave heights, the mariner has a tendency to neglect the lower ones. It has been found that the reported value is about the average for the highest one-third. This is sometimes called the "significant" wave height. The approximate relationship between this height and others, is as follows:

Wave	Relative height
Average	0.64
Significant	1.00
Highest 10 percent	1.29
Highest	1.87

3304. Path of water particles in a wave.—As shown in figure 3304, a particle of water on the surface of the ocean follows a somewhat circular orbit as a wave passes, but moves very little in the direction of motion of the wave. The common wave producing this action is called an **oscillatory wave.** As the crest passes, the particle moves forward, giving the water the appearance of moving with the wave. As the trough passes, the motion is in the opposite direction. The radius of the circular orbit decreases with depth, approaching zero at a depth equal to about half the wavelength. In shallower water the orbits become more elliptical, and in very shallow water, as at a beach, the vertical motion disappears almost completely.

Since the speed is greater at the top of the orbit than at the bottom, the particle is not at exactly its original point following passage of a wave, but has moved slightly

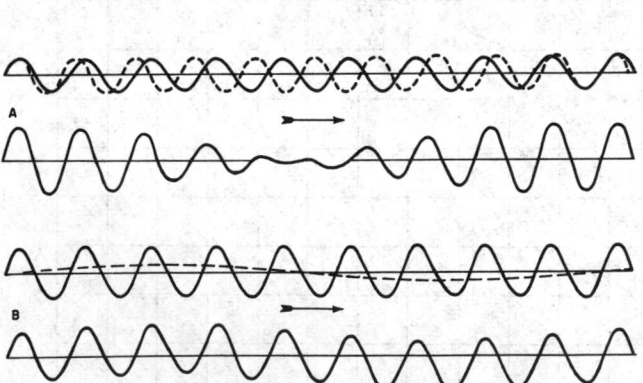

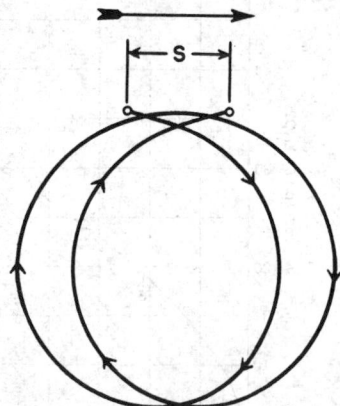

FIGURE 3303c.—Interference. The upper part of *A* shows two waves of equal height and nearly equal length traveling in the same direction. The lower part of *A* shows the resulting wave pattern. In *B* similar information is shown for short waves and long swell.

FIGURE 3304.—Orbital motion and displacement, *s*, of a particle on the surface of deep water during two wave periods.

in the direction of motion of the wave. However, since this advance is small in relation to the vertical displacement, a floating object is raised and lowered by passage of a wave, but moved little from its original position. If this were not so, a slow moving vessel might experience considerable difficulty in making way against a wave train. In figure 3304 the forward displacement is greatly exaggerated.

3305. Effects of currents on waves.—A following current increases wavelengths and decreases wave heights. An opposing current has the opposite effect, decreasing the length and increasing the height. A strong opposing current may cause the waves to break. The extent of wave alteration is dependent upon the ratio of the still-water wave speed to the speed of the current.

Moderate ocean currents running at oblique angles to wave directions appear to have little effect, but strong tidal currents perpendicular to a system of waves have been observed to completely destroy them in a short period of time.

3306. The effect of ice on waves.—When ice crystals form in seawater, internal friction is greatly increased. This results in smoothing of the sea surface. The effect of pack ice is even more pronounced. A vessel following a lead through such ice may be in smooth water even when a gale is blowing and heavy seas are beating against the outer edge of the pack. Hail is also effective in flattening the sea, even in a high wind.

3307. Waves and shallow water.—When a wave encounters shallow water, the movement of the individual particles of water is restricted by the bottom, resulting in reduced wave speed. In deep water wave speed is a function of period. In shallow water, the wave speed becomes a function of depth. The shallower the water the slower is the wave speed. As the wave speed slows, the period remains the same so the wavelength becomes shorter. Since the energy in the waves remains the same, the shortening of wavelengths results in increased heights. This process is called **shoaling.** If the wave approaches the shoal at an angle, each part is slowed successively as the depth decreases. This causes a change in direction of motion or **refraction,** the wave tending to become parallel to the depth curves. The effect is similar to the refraction of light and other forms of radiant energy (art. 1606).

As each wave slows, the next wave behind it, in deeper water, tends to catch up. As the wavelength decreases, the height generally becomes greater. The lower part of a wave, being nearest the bottom, is slowed more than the top. This may cause the wave to become unstable, the faster-moving top falling or **breaking.** Such a wave is called a **breaker,** and a series of breakers, **surf.** This subject is covered in greater detail in chapter XXXIV.

Swell passing over a shoal but not breaking undergoes a decrease in wavelength and speed, and an increase in height. Such **ground swell** may cause heavy rolling if it is on the beam and its period is the same as the period of roll of a vessel, even though the sea may appear relatively calm. Figure 3307 illustrates the approximate alteration of the characteristics of waves as they cross a shoal.

3308. Energy of waves.—The potential energy of a wave is related to the vertical distance of each particle from its still-water position, and therefore moves with the wave. In contrast, the kinetic energy of a wave is related to the speed of the particles, being distributed evenly along the entire wave.

The amount of kinetic energy in even a moderate wave is tremendous. A 4-foot, 10-second wave striking a coast expends more than 35,000 horsepower per mile of beach. For each 56 miles of coast, the energy expended equals the power generated at Hoover Dam. An increase in temperature of the water in the relatively narrow **surf zone** in which this energy is expended would seem to be indicated, but no pronounced increase has been measured. Apparently, any heat that may be generated is dissipated to the deeper water beyond the surf zone.

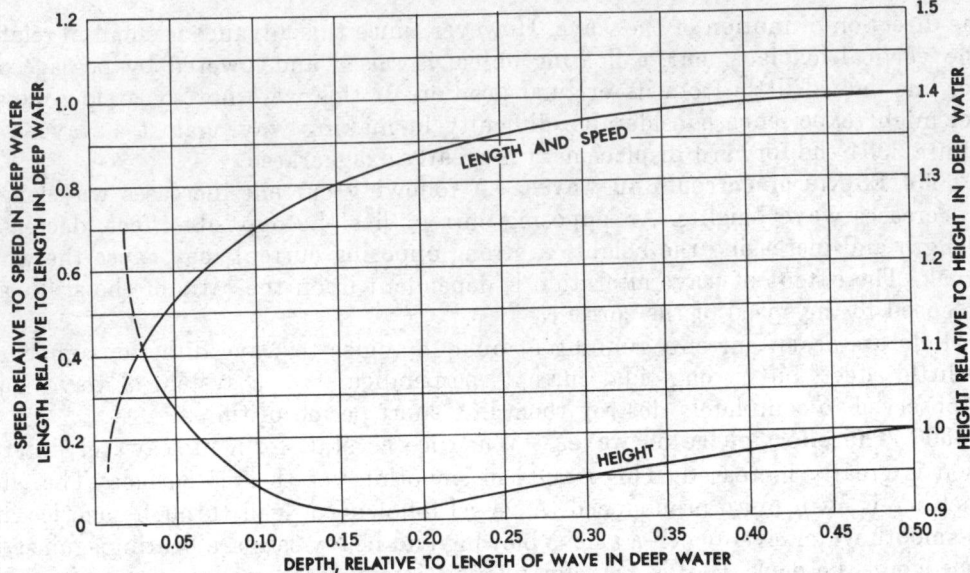

FIGURE 3307.—Alteration of the characteristics of waves as they cross a shoal.

3309. Wave measurement aboard ship.—With suitable equipment and adequate training, one can make reasonably reliable measurements of the height, length, period, and speed of waves. However, the mariner's estimates of height and length usually contain relatively large errors. There is a tendency to underestimate the heights of low waves, and overestimate the heights of high ones. There are numerous accounts of waves 75 to 80 feet high, or even higher, although waves more than 55 feet high are very rare. Wavelength is usually underestimated. The motions of the vessel from which measurements are made perhaps contribute to such errors.

Height. Measurement of wave height is particularly difficult. A microbarograph (art. 3705) can be used if the wave is long enough to permit the vessel to ride up and down with it. If the waves are approaching from dead ahead or dead astern, this requires a wavelength at least twice the length of the vessel. For most accurate results the instrument should be placed at the center of roll and pitch, to minimize the effects of these motions. Wave height can often be estimated with reasonable accuracy by comparing it with freeboard of the vessel. This is less accurate as wave height and vessel motion increase. If a point of observation can be found at which the top of a wave is in line with the horizon when the observer is in the trough, the wave height is equal to height of eye. However, if the vessel is rolling or pitching, this height at the moment of observation may be difficult to determine. The highest wave ever reliably reported was 112 feet observed from the USS *Ramapo* in 1933.

Length. The dimensions of the vessel can be used to determine wavelength. Errors are introduced by perspective and disturbance of the wave pattern by the vessel. These errors are minimized if observations are made from maximum height. Best results are obtained if the sea is from dead ahead or dead astern.

Period. If allowance is made for the motion of the vessel, wave period can be determined by measuring the interval between passages of wave crests past the observer. The correction for the motion of the vessel can be eliminated by timing the passage of successive wave crests past a patch of foam or a floating object at some distance from the vessel. Accuracy of results can be improved by averaging several observations.

Speed can be determined by timing the passage of the wave between measured points along the side of the ship, if corrections are applied for the direction of travel of the wave and the speed of the ship.

The length, period, and speed of waves are interrelated by the relationships indicated in article 3303. There is no definite mathematical relationship between wave height and length, period, or speed.

3310. Tsunamis are ocean waves produced by sudden, large-scale motion of a portion of the ocean floor or the shore, as by volcanic eruption, earthquake (sometimes called **seaquake** if it occurs at sea), or landslide. If they are caused by a submarine earthquake, they are usually called **seismic sea waves.** The point directly above the disturbance, at which the waves originate, is called the **epicenter.** Either a tsunami or a storm tide (art. 3311) that overflows the land is popularly called a **tidal wave,** although it bears no relation to the tide.

If a volcanic eruption occurs below the surface of the sea, the escaping gases cause a quantity of water to be pushed upward in the shape of a dome or mound. The same effect is caused by the sudden rising of a portion of the bottom. As this water settles back, it creates a wave which travels at high speed across the surface of the ocean.

Tsunamis are a series of waves. Near the epicenter, the first wave may be the highest. At greater distances, the highest wave usually occurs later in the series, commonly between the third and the eighth wave. Following the maximum, they again become smaller, but the tsunami may be detectable for several days.

In deep water the wave height of a tsunami is probably never greater than 2 or 3 feet. Since the wavelength is usually considerably more than 100 miles, the wave is not conspicuous at sea. In the Pacific, where most tsunamis occur, the wave period varies between about 15 and 60 *minutes*, and the speed in deep water is more than 400 knots. The approximate speed can be computed by the formula

$$S = 0.6 \sqrt{gd} = 3.4\sqrt{d},$$

where S is the speed in knots, g is the acceleration due to gravity (32.2 feet per second per second), and d is the depth of water in feet. This formula is applicable to any wave in water having a depth of less than half the wavelength. For most ocean waves it applies only in shallow water, because of the relatively short wavelength.

When a tsunami enters shoal water, it undergoes the same changes as other waves. The formula indicates that speed is proportional to depth of water. Because of the great speed of a tsunami when it is in relatively deep water, the slowing is relatively much greater than that of an ordinary wave crested by wind. Therefore, the increase in height is also much greater. The size of the wave depends upon the nature and intensity of the disturbance. The height and destructiveness of the wave arriving at any place depend upon its distance from the epicenter, topography of the ocean floor, and the coastline. The angle at which the wave arrives, the shape of the coastline, and the topography along the coast and offshore all have their effect. The position of the shore is also a factor, as it may be sheltered by intervening land, or be in a position where waves have a tendency to converge, either because of refraction or reflection, or both.

Tsunamis 50 feet in height or higher have reached the shore, inflicting widespread damage. On April 1, 1946, seismic sea waves originating at an epicenter near the Aleutians spread over the entire Pacific. Scotch Cap Light on Unimak Island, 57 feet above sea level, was completely destroyed. Traveling at an average speed of 490 miles per hour, the waves reached the Hawaiian Islands in 4 hours and 34 minutes, where they arrived as waves 50 feet above the high water level, and flooded a strip of coast more than 1,000 feet wide at some places. They left a death toll of 173, and property damage of $25,000,000. Less destructive waves reached the shores of North and South America, and Australia, 6,700 miles from the epicenter.

After this disaster, a tsunami warning system was set up in the Pacific, even though destructive waves are relatively rare (averaging about one in 20 years in the Hawaiian Islands).

In addition to seismic sea waves, earthquakes below the surface of the sea may produce a longitudinal wave that travels upward toward the surface, at the speed of sound. When a ship encounters such a wave, it is felt as a sudden shock which may be of such severity that the crew thinks the vessel has struck bottom. Because of such reports, some older charts indicated shoal areas at places where the depth is now known to be a thousand fathoms or more.

3311. Storm tides.—In relatively tideless seas like the Baltic and Mediterranean, winds cause the chief fluctuations in sea level. Elsewhere, the astronomical tide usually masks these variations. However, under exceptional conditions, either severe extra-tropical storms or tropical cyclones can produce changes in sea level that exceed the normal range of tide. Low sea level is of little concern except to shipping, but a rise above ordinary high-water mark, particularly when it is accompanied by high waves, can result in a catastrophe.

Although, like tsunamis, these **storm tides** or **storm surges** are popularly called **tidal waves,** they are not associated with the tide. They consist of a single wave crest and hence have no period or wavelength.

Three effects in a storm induce a rise in sea level. The first is wind stress on the sea surface, which results in a piling-up of water (sometimes called "wind set-up"). The second effect is the convergence of wind-driven currents, which elevates the sea surface along the convergence line. In shallow water, bottom friction and the effects of local topography cause this elevation to persist and may even intensify it. The low atmospheric pressure that accompanies severe storms causes the third effect, which is sometimes referred to as the "inverted barometer." An inch of mercury is equivalent to about 13.6 inches of water (art. 3115) and the adjustment of the sea surface to the reduced pressure can amount to several feet at equilibrium (art. 3911).

All three of these causes act independently, and if they happen to occur simultaneously, their effects are additive. In addition, the wave can be intensified or amplified by the effects of local topography. Storm tides may reach heights of 20 feet or more, and it is estimated that they cause three-fourths of the deaths attributed to hurricanes.

3312. Standing waves and seiches.—Previous articles in this chapter have dealt with **progressive waves** which appear to move regularly with time. When two systems of progressive waves having the same period travel in opposite directions across the same area, a series of **standing waves** may form. These appear to remain stationary.

Another type of standing wave, called a **seiche** (sāsh), sometimes occurs in a confined body of water. It is a long wave, usually having its crest at one end of the confined space, and its trough at the other. Its period may be anything from a few minutes to an hour or more, but somewhat less than the tidal period. Seiches are usually attributed to strong winds or differences in atmospheric pressure.

3313. Tide waves.—As indicated in chapter XXXI, there are, in general, two regions of high tide separated by two regions of low tide, and these regions move progressively westward around the earth as the moon revolves in its orbit. The high tides are the crests of these **tide waves,** and the low tides are the troughs. The wave is not noticeable at sea, but becomes apparent along the coasts, particularly in funnel-shaped estuaries. In certain river mouths or estuaries of particular configuration, the incoming wave of high water overtakes the preceding low tide, resulting in a high-crested, roaring wave which progresses upstream in one mighty surge called a **bore.**

3314. Internal waves.—Thus far, the discussion has been confined to waves on the surface of the sea, the boundary between air and water. **Internal waves,** or **boundary waves,** are created below the surface, at the boundaries between water strata of different densities. The density differences between adjacent water strata in the sea are considerably less than that between sea and air. Consequently, internal waves are much more easily formed than surface waves, and they are often much larger. The maximum height of wind waves on the surface is about 60 feet, but internal wave heights as great as 300 feet have been encountered.

Internal waves are detected by a number of observations of the vertical temperature distribution, using recording devices such as the bathythermograph (art. 3007). They have periods as short as a few minutes, and as long as 12 or 24 hours, these greater periods being associated with the tides.

A slow-moving ship operating in a freshwater layer having a depth approximating the draft of the vessel may produce short-period internal waves. This may occur off rivers emptying into the sea or in polar regions in the vicinity of melting ice. Under suitable conditions, the normal propulsion energy of the ship is expended in generating and maintaining these internal waves and the ship appears to "stick" in the water, becoming sluggish and making little headway. The phenomenon, known as **dead water,** disappears when speed is increased by a few knots.

The full significance of internal waves has not been determined, but it is known that they may cause submarines to rise and fall like a ship at the surface, and they may also affect sound transmission in the sea.

3315. Waves and ships.—The effects of waves on a ship vary considerably with the type ship, its course and speed, and the condition of the sea. A short vessel has a tendency to ride up one side of a wave and down the other side, while a larger vessel may tend to ride *through* the waves on an even keel. If the waves are of such length that the bow and stern of a vessel are alternately in successive crests and successive troughs, the vessel is subject to heavy sagging and hogging stresses, and under extreme conditions may break in two. A change of heading may reduce the danger. Because of the danger from sagging and hogging, a small vessel is sometimes better able to ride out a storm than a large one.

If successive waves strike the side of a vessel at the same phase of successive rolls, relatively small waves can cause heavy rolling. The effect is similar to that of swinging a child, where the strength of the push is not as important as its timing. The same effect, if applied to the bow or stern in time with the pitch, can cause heavy pitching. A change of either heading or speed can reduce the effect.

A wave having a length twice that of a ship places that ship in danger of falling off into the trough of the sea, particularly if it is a slow-moving vessel. The effect is especially pronounced if the sea is broad on the bow or broad on the quarter. An increase of speed reduces the hazard.

3316. Use of oil for modifying the effects of breaking waves.—Oil has proved effective in modifying the effects of breaking waves, and has proved useful to vessels at sea, whether making way or stopped, particularly when lowering or hoisting boats. Its effect is greatest in deep water, where a small quantity suffices if the oil can be made to spread to windward. In shallow water where the water is in motion over the bottom, oil is less effective but of some value.

The heaviest oils, notably animal and vegetable oils, are the most effective. Crude petroleum is useful, but its effectiveness can be improved by mixing it with animal and vegetable oils. Gasoline or kerosene are of little value. Oil spreads slowly. In cold weather it may need some thinning with petroleum to hasten the process and produce the desired spread before the vessel is too far away for the effect to be useful.

At sea, best results can be expected if the vessel drifts or runs slowly before the wind, with the oil being discharged on both sides from waste pipes or by other convenient method. If a sea anchor is used, oil can be distributed from a container inserted within it for this purpose. If such a container is not available, an oil bag can be fastened to an endless line rove through a block on the sea anchor. This permits distribution of oil to windward, and provides a means for hauling the bag aboard for refilling. If another vessel is being towed, the oil should be distributed from the towing vessel, forward and on both sides, so that both vessels will be benefited. If a drifting vessel is to be approached, the oil might be distributed from both sides of the drifting vessel or by the approaching vessel, which should distribute it to leeward of the drifting vessel so that that vessel will drift into it. If the vessel being approached is aground, the procedure best suiting the circumstances should be used.

If oil is needed in crossing a bar to enter a harbor, it can be floated in ahead of the vessel if a flood current is running. A considerable amount may be needed. During slack water a hose might be trailed over the bow and oil poured freely through it if no more convenient method is available. With an ebb current oil is of little use, unless it can be distributed from another vessel or in some other manner from the opposite side of the bar.

CHAPTER XXXIV

BREAKERS AND SURF

3401. Introduction.—The purpose of this chapter is to acquaint the navigator with the oceanographic factors affecting the safe navigation through the surf zone to the beach.

3402. Refraction.—As explained in article 3307, wave speed is slowed in shallow water, causing **refraction** if the waves approach the beach at an angle. Along a perfectly straight beach, with uniform shoaling, the wave fronts tend to become parallel to the shore. Any irregularities in the coastline or bottom contours, however, affect the refraction, causing irregularity. In the case of a ridge perpendicular to the beach, for instance, the shoaling is more rapid, causing greater refraction towards the ridge. The waves tend to align themselves with the bottom contours. Waves on both sides of the ridge have a component of motion toward the ridge. This **convergence** of wave energy toward the ridge causes an increase in wave or breaker height. A submarine canyon or valley perpendicular to the beach, on the other hand, produces **divergence,** with a decrease in wave or breaker height. These effects are illustrated in figure 3402. Bends in the coastline have a similar effect, convergence occuring at a *point,* and divergence if the coast is *concave* to the sea. Points act as focal areas for wave energy and experience large breakers. Concave bays have small breakers because the energy is spread out as the waves approach the beach.

Under suitable conditions, currents also cause refraction. This is of particular importance at entrances of tidal estuaries. When waves encounter a current running in the opposite direction, they become higher and shorter. This results in a choppy

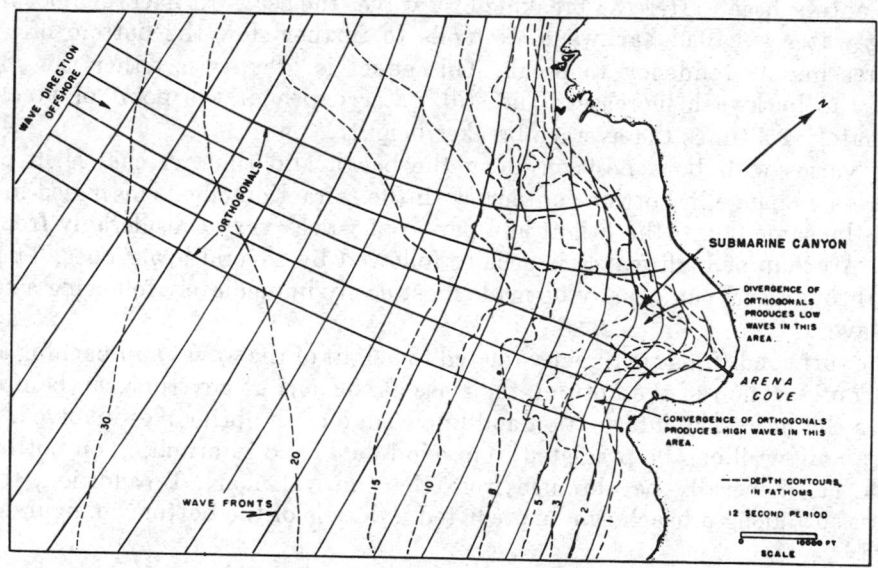

Courtesy of Robert L. Wiegel, Council on Wave Research, University of California.

Figure 3402.—The effect of bottom topography in causing wave convergence and wave divergence.

sea, often with breakers. When waves move in the same direction as current, they decrease in height, and become longer. Refraction occurs when waves encounter a current at an angle.

Refraction diagrams, useful in planning amphibious operations, can be prepared with the aid of nautical charts or aerial photographs. When computer facilities are available, complex computer programs are used to determine refraction diagrams, quickly and accurately.

3403. Breakers and surf.—In deep water, swell generally moves across the surface as somewhat regular, smooth undulations (ch. XXXIII). When shoal water is reached, the wave period remains the same, but the speed decreases. The amount of decrease is negligible until the depth of water becomes about one-half the wavelength, when the waves begin to "feel" bottom. There is a slight decrease in wave height, followed by a rapid increase, if the waves are traveling perpendicular to a straight coast with a uniformly sloping bottom. As the waves become higher and shorter, they also become steeper, and the crest becomes narrower. When the speed of individual particles at the crest becomes greater than that of the wave, the front face of the wave becomes steeper than the rear face. This process continues at an accelerating rate as the depth of water decreases. At some point the wave may become unstable, toppling forward to form a **breaker.**

There are three general classes of breakers. A **spilling breaker** breaks gradually over a considerable distance. A **plunging breaker** tends to curl over and break with a single crash. A **surging breaker** peaks up, but surges up the beach without spilling or plunging. It is classed as a breaker even though it does not actually break. The type of breaker is determined by the steepness of the beach and the steepness of the wave before it reaches shallow water, as illustrated in figure 3403.

Longer waves break in deeper water, and have a greater breaker height. The effect of a steeper beach is also to increase breaker height. The height of breakers is less if the waves approach the beach at an acute angle. With a steeper beach slope there is greater tendency of the breakers to plunge or surge. Following the **uprush** of water onto a beach after the breaking of a wave, the seaward **backrush** occurs. The returning water is called **backwash.** It tends to further slow the bottom of a wave, thus increasing its tendency to break. This effect is greater as either the speed or depth of the backwash increases. The still water depth at the point of breaking is approximately 1.3 times the average breaker height.

Surf varies with both position along the beach and time. A change in position often means a change in bottom contour, with the refraction effects discussed in article 3402. At the same point, the height and period of waves vary considerably from wave to wave. A group of high waves is usually followed by several lower ones. Therefore, passage through surf can usually be made most easily immediately following a series of higher waves.

Since surf conditions are directly related to height of the waves approaching a beach, and the configuration of the bottom, the state of the surf at any time can be predicted if one has the necessary information and knowledge of the principles involved. Height of the sea and swell can be predicted from wind data, and information on bottom configuration can generally be obtained from the nautical chart. In addition, the area of lightest surf along a beach can be predicted if details of the bottom configuration are available.

3404. Currents in the surf zone.—In and adjacent to the surf zone, currents are generated by waves approaching the bottom contours at an angle, and by irregularities in the bottom.

SPILLING BREAKER

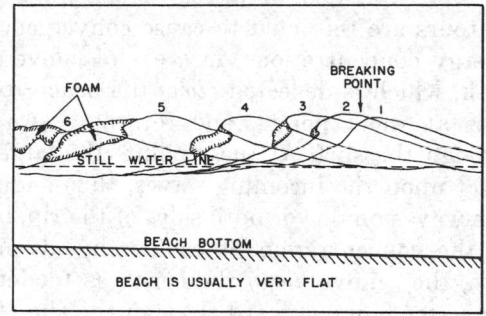

SKETCH SHOWING THE GENERAL CHARACTER
OF SPILLING BREAKERS

PLUNGING BREAKER

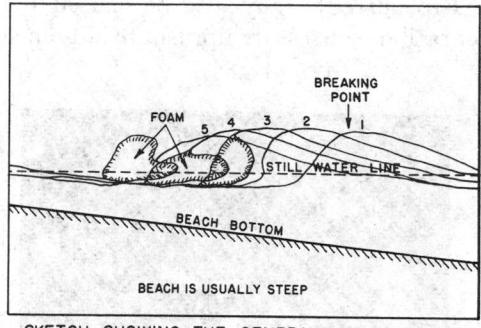

SKETCH SHOWING THE GENERAL CHARACTER
OF PLUNGING BREAKERS

SURGING BREAKER

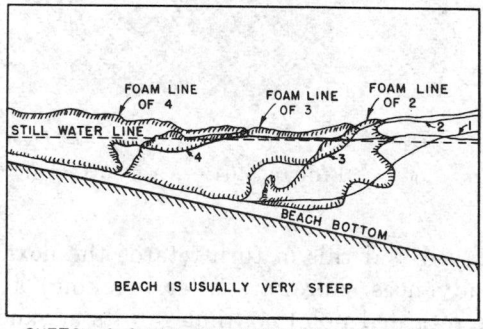

SKETCH SHOWING THE GENERAL CHARACTER
OF SURGING BREAKERS

Courtesy of Robert L. Wiegel, Council on Wave Research, University of California.

FIGURE 3403.—The three types of breakers.

Waves approaching at an angle produce a **longshore current** parallel to the beach, within the-surf zone. Longshore currents are most common along straight beaches. Their speeds increase with increasing breaker height, decreasing wave period, increasing angle of breaker line with the beach, and increasing beach slope. Speed seldom exceeds 1 knot, but sustained speeds as high as 3 knots have been recorded. Longshore currents are usually constant in direction. They increase the danger of landing craft broaching to.

As explained in article 3402, wave fronts advancing over nonparallel bottom contours are refracted to cause convergence or divergence of the energy of the waves. Energy concentrations, in areas of convergence, form barriers to the returning backwash, which is deflected *along* the beach to areas of less resistance. Backwash accumulates at weak points, and returns seaward in concentrations, forming **rip currents** through the surf. At these points the large volume of returning water has a retarding effect upon the incoming waves, thus adding to the condition causing the rip current. The waves on one or both sides of the rip, having greater energy and not being retarded by the concentration of backwash, advance faster and farther up the beach. From here, they move *along* the beach as **feeder currents.** At some point of low resistance, the water flows seaward through the surf, forming the **neck** of the rip current. Outside the breaker line the current widens and slackens, forming the **head.** The various parts of a rip current are shown in figure 3404.

Rip currents may also be caused by irregularities in the beach face. If a beach indentation causes an uprush to advance farther than the average, the backrush is

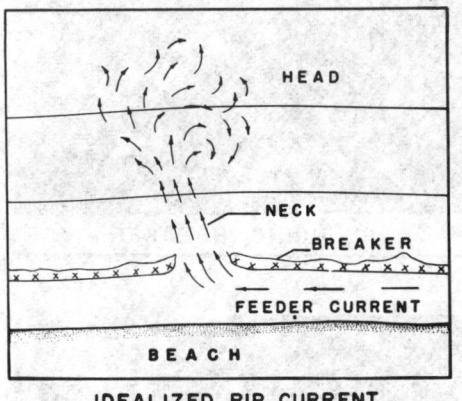

IDEALIZED RIP CURRENT

Courtesy of Robert L. Wiegel, Council on Wave Research, University of California.

FIGURE 3404.—A rip current (left) and a diagram of its parts (right).

delayed and this in turn retards the next incoming **foam line** (the front of a wave as it advances shoreward after breaking) at that point. The foam line on each side of the retarded point continues in its advance, however, and tends to fill in the retarded area, producing a rip current.

3405. Beach sediments.—In the surf zone, large amounts of sediment are suspended in the water. When the water motion decreases, the sediments are deposited as sand. The water motion can be either waves or currents. Promontories or points are rocky because the large breakers scour the points and small sediments are suspended in the water and carried away. Bays have sandy beaches because of the small wave conditions.

In the winter when storms create larger breakers and surf, the waves erode the beaches and carry the particles offshore where offshore sand bars form; sandy beaches tend to be narrower. In the summer the waves gradually move the sand back to the beaches and the offshore bars decrease; sandy beaches tend to be wider.

Longshore currents move large amounts of sand along the coast. These currents deposit sand on the upcurrent side of a jetty and erode the beach on the downcurrent side.

CHAPTER XXXV

SOUND IN THE SEA

3501. Underwater sound and the navigator.—The clarity with which the noises associated with weighing anchor, propelling a ship, and other underwater motions are heard below the waterline and near the skin of a vessel is an indication of the high sound-transmitting qualities of seawater. Water is a better conductor of sound than is air because it absorbs less energy from the sound. There are several ways in which underwater sound can be used in navigation.

The *direction* of travel of sound waves can be measured either by means of **binaural hearing** (hearing with two "ears"), or by equipment which has directional characteristics similar to those of a directional antenna used in radio (art. 4112). Either method can be used for determining the direction from which general noise is coming, but only the latter is used in active sonar equipment for determining direction and distance by reception of an echo from a directional signal, in a manner similar to radar (art. 4301).

Distance can be determined by (1) measuring the elapsed time between transmission of a signal and return of its echo, (2) measuring the elapsed time between transmission of a signal and its receipt at a second station, (3) measuring the time *difference* between reception of a signal transmitted through water and one transmitted through air, (4) measuring the difference in phase between two signals or change of phase of a signal when it returns as an echo, or (5) measuring the angle at which an echo is received from a signal produced at another place. The first method is used in active sonar and echo sounding equipment (art. 619). The fourth and fifth methods were used in early forms of echo sounders.

3502. Sources of sound in the ocean.—Underwater sounds intended for navigational use are produced in one of three basic ways: (1) by percussion, as the striking of a bell, gong, or the bottom of the vessel; (2) by oscillator, as the vibration of a diaphragm; (3) by explosion, as by small bomb or depth charge. Certain man-made noises ordinarily produced in water, such as those due to operation of the main engines of a vessel, can be detected by an appropriate listening device.

In addition, many noises are made by animals living in the ocean. Certain shrimp, great numbers of which inhabit some areas, make a snapping noise with their claws. Some fish make a noise by stridulating (scraping). When shellfish are being eaten, a sound is emitted as the shells are broken by the teeth of the fish which are feeding. Grunting noises are made by many kinds of fish, usually by means of their swim bladders. Porpoises produce sounds of a high pitch. Sounds of various frequency and amplitude are produced by other forms of marine life. Where sound-producing marine life is very abundant, it interferes with detection of man-made sounds, requiring a high signal-to-noise ratio. The effect is similar to that of a high atmospheric noise level in radio.

3503. Speed of sound in seawater.—Three variables govern the speed (S) of sound in a fluid. They are density (ρ), compressibility (β), and the ratio between the specific heats of the fluid at constant pressure and at constant volume (γ). The following formula is sufficiently accurate for most navigational purposes:

$$S=\sqrt{\frac{\gamma}{\rho\beta}}.$$

Density and specific heat are discussed in articles 3009 and 3012, respectively. Compressibility refers to the relative change in volume for a given change in pressure. The compressibility of water is low, and consequently the speed of sound in water is high. The specific heat ratio enters the formula because the energy of a sound impulse is briefly transformed into heat, and then reconverted (with slight loss) into kinetic energy. The ratio rarely exceeds 1.02 in seawater and is commonly taken as unity.

For atmospheric pressure 29.92 inches of mercury, temperature 60°F, and salinity 34.85 parts per thousand, the density of seawater is 64 pounds per cubic foot and the compressibility approximately 0.0000435 per atmosphere (one atmosphere equals 14.696 pounds per square inch). Using these values and 32.174 feet per second per second (the acceleration of gravity at latitude 45°) and 144 square inches per square foot, and taking γ equal to unity, one obtains:

$$S=\sqrt{\frac{1.0\times32.174\times14.696\times144}{64\times0.0000435}}=4945 \text{ ft./sec.}$$

The same formula can be used to determine the speed of sound in air. For atmospheric pressure 29.92 and temperature 60°F, the density of air is 0.0764 pound per cubic foot and, since air is a gas, the compressibility is the reciprocal of the pressure. Taking γ equal to 1.4, one obtains:

$$S=\sqrt{\frac{1.4\times32.174\times14.696\times144}{0.0764\times1}}=1117 \text{ ft./sec.}$$

The speed of sound in water is approximately 4.5 times its speed in air.

An increase in temperature decreases both density and compressibility, resulting in an increase in the speed of sound. In seawater, an increase in pressure or salinity produces a slight increase in density and a larger decrease in compressibility, resulting in a net increase in the speed of sound. Thus, in seawater, an increase in temperature, pressure, or salinity results in greater speed of sound. Of the three, temperature has the greatest influence on the speed of sound in seawater in the upper layers. At depth, pressure, and in coastal areas, changes in salinity, may have the greatest effect.

Normally, the change of these three elements is much more rapid in a vertical direction than in a horizontal direction. The change with depth varies with location. With respect to temperature, much of the ocean is considered to consist of three layers, a **mixed layer** influenced greatly by the temperature of the air above it, a **thermocline** of rapidly decreasing temperature, and a nearly uniform **deep-water layer.** Typical curves showing change of temperature and salinity with depth are shown in figure 3503a. The increase of pressure with depth is almost uniform, the pressure at 10,000 feet being approximately twice that at 5,000 feet, and 10 times that at 1,000 feet. A typical curve of speed of sound with depth is shown in figure 3503b. In this case there is little or no mixed layer and the temperature decreases rapidly from the surface; therefore, the sound velocity also decreases rapidly. Below the range of temperature decrease, the pressure effect becomes the primary factor and sound velocity starts to increase. Note that the minimum sound velocity is at 2,400 feet. This would be the depth of the deep sound channel.

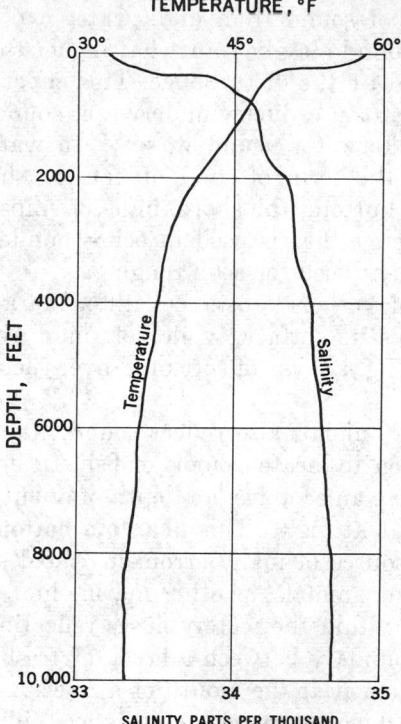

FIGURE 3503a.—Variation of temperature and salinity with depth at one locality.

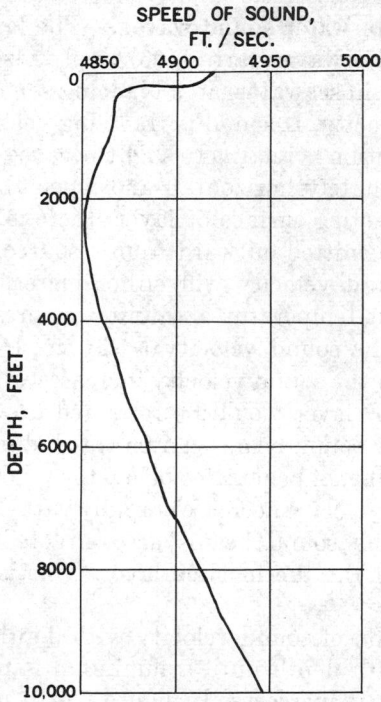

FIGURE 3503b.—Typical variation of speed of sound with depth in the ocean.

Study of transmission of sound from underwater explosions indicates that near the explosion the speed of sound may be somewhat higher than expected, probably due to increased pressure caused by the disturbance. This effect extends over such a short distance that it is insignificant in ordinary underwater sound transmission.

3504. Reflection of underwater sound waves.—In water, as in air, sound is reflected by obstructions in the form of solid objects or sharp discontinuities. Thus, sound is reflected from the bottom, the shore, hulls of ships, the surface of the water, etc. It is this reflecting energy that is used in echo sounders (art. 619) to determine depth, and in sonar equipment used for echo ranging.

Reflecting properties of various substances differ markedly. Rock reflects almost all of the sound that strikes its surface, while soft mud absorbs or is penetrated by sound. Thus, in echo sounding, a layer of soft mud over rock may result in two echoes, indicating two depths.

Fish and even tiny sea animals also reflect sound. As a result, echo sounders are widely used among fishermen to locate schools of fish. In deep water it is not unusual for an echo sounder to receive an echo from a depth of about 200 fathoms, although the depth is shallower somewhat at night. This **phantom bottom** or **deep scattering layer,** which is undoubtedly the source of many erroneous shoal sounding reports, is due to large numbers of tiny marine animals, or other marine life.

A sharp discontinuity within the water causes reflection of sound. Thus, an echo sounder may detect the boundary between a layer of freshwater overlying saltwater, a condition which might occur near the mouth of a river.

Sharp, distinct echoes denoting precise depths are difficult to obtain over rough-surfaced bottoms. Therefore, considerable discretion should be exercised in evaluating soundings taken over bottoms possessing a high degree of relief.

3505. Refraction of underwater sound waves.—The laws of refraction as applied to light (art. 1613) and radio waves (art. 4106) apply also to sound. Because of differences of velocity of sound in seawater, an advancing sound wave is refracted toward the area of slower sound velocity. If sound is traveling vertically downward, as in echo sounding, the effect of refraction is relatively slight because the layers of water in which velocity differs are approximately horizontal, and when the direction of travel of the sound is normal to the refracting surface or layer, there is no refraction.

If a sound beam is transmitted outward from a source, it will start at a particular sound velocity but the sound velocity will either increase or decrease as the beam moves into water of different temperatures, salinity, or pressure. The beam will refract toward the region where the sound velocity is slower. In a mixed surface layer the temperature is isothermal so the sound velocity increases with depth due to the pressure effect. A sound beam in that layer would be refracted upward to the surface where it would reflect off the surface. Sound beams can be trapped in the mixed layer and create a "surface sound duct." If a beam penetrates below the mixed layer into the thermocline it is in a region where sound velocity decreases rapidly with depth due to the temperature decrease. In the thermocline sound beams are refracted sharply downward. Sonar ranges can be very short in the thermocline layer. This is the region of the "shadow zone."

With typical distribution of sound velocity with depth, as shown in figure 3503b, sound velocity decreases with depth until a minimum is reached at some level below the surface, and below this it increases. In figure 3503b minimum velocity occurs at about 2,400 feet. In the Tropics this level of minimum velocity may be as deep as 6,000 feet, and in polar regions it may be at the surface. This level is referred to as the **deep sound channel.** Sound produced at any level tends to be refracted to the level of minimum speed, and to remain there, for as it attempts to leave this level, it is refracted back toward it, as shown in figure 3505. This, of course, does not refer to sound traveling vertically. If a sound is produced at this level, as by the explosion of a bomb or depth charge, the sound waves start to move outward as expanding spheres, but most of the rays are refracted back toward the minimum speed level. Because of this effect, such a sound may travel great distances with relatively little decrease in intensity. Listening gear placed at this level has detected sounds produced thousands of miles away.

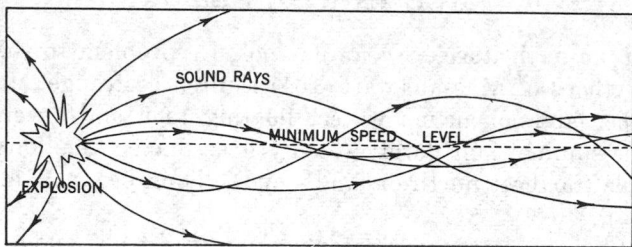

FIGURE 3505.—Transmission of sound rays along the minimum sound level.

Sound beams that penetrate the deep sound channel without being trapped continue on to regions of increased sound velocity. If the water is deep enough these beams will be refracted upwards towards the surface. If this occurs, the energy converges near the surface at ranges of about 30 nautical miles. This is the **convergence zone.** Convergence zone detection is significant in modern sonar applications.

3506. Attenuation of sound.—As sound is transmitted from a source, the energy is lost or *attenuated* due to reflection, spreading, and absorption. A sound beam reflected from the bottom or surface loses energy; although the sound energy is concentrated near the source, as the range increases the same energy is spread over a sphere whose radius is the range. The rate of absorption is a function of frequency; high frequency sound is absorbed more than sound of lower frequency.

CHAPTER XXXVI

ICE IN THE SEA

3601. Ice and the navigator.—*Sea ice* has posed a problem to the polar navigator since antiquity. Pytheas of Massalia (art. 104) sighted a strange substance which he described as "neither land nor air nor water" floating upon and covering the northern sea over which the summer sun barely set. Pytheas named this lonely region Thule, hence Ultima Thule (farthest north or land's end). Thus began over 20 centuries of polar exploration.

Ice is of direct concern to the navigator because it restricts and sometimes controls his movements, it affects his dead reckoning by forcing frequent and sometimes inaccurately determined changes of course and speed, it affects his piloting by altering the appearance or obliterating the features of landmarks and by rendering difficult the establishment and maintenance of aids to navigation, it affects his use of electronics by its effect upon propagation of radio waves and the changes it produces both in surface features and radar returns from such features, it affects his celestial navigation by altering the refraction and obscuring his horizon and celestial bodies either directly or by the weather it influences, and it affects his charts by introducing various difficulties to the hydrographic surveyor.

Because of his direct concern with ice, the prospective polar navigator will do well to acquaint himself with its nature and extent in the area he expects to navigate. To this end he should consult the sailing directions for the area, and whatever other literature may be available to him, including reports of previous operations in the same area.

3602. Formation of ice.—As it cools, water contracts until the temperature of maximum density is reached. Further cooling results in expansion. The maximum density of freshwater occurs at a temperature of $4°0C$ ($39°2F$), and freezing takes place at $0°C$ ($32°F$). The addition of salt lowers both the temperature of maximum density and, to a lesser extent, that of freezing. The relationships are shown in figure 3602. The two lines meet at a salinity of 24.7 parts per thousand, at which maximum density occurs at the freezing temperature of $-1°3C$ ($29°61F$). At this and greater salinities, the density increases right down to the freezing point. At a salinity of 35 parts per thousand, the approximate average for the oceans, the freezing point is $-1°88C$ ($28°6F$).

As the density of surface seawater increases with decreasing temperature, density currents are induced bringing warmer, less dense water to the surface. If the polar seas consisted of water with constant salinity, the entire water column would have to be cooled to the freezing point in this manner before ice would begin to form. This is not the case, however, in the polar regions where the vertical salinity distribution is such that the surface waters are underlaid at shallow depth by waters of higher salinity. In this instance density currents form a shallow mixed layer which subsequently cannot mix with the deep layer of warmer but saltier water. Ice will then begin forming at the water surface when density currents cease and the surface water reaches its freezing point. In shoal water, however, the mixing process can be sufficient to extend the freezing temperature from the surface to the bottom. Ice crystals can, therefore, form at any depth in this case. Because of their decreased density, they tend to rise to the surface unless they form at the bottom and attach themselves there. This ice, called **anchor ice,** may continue to grow as additional ice freezes to that already formed.

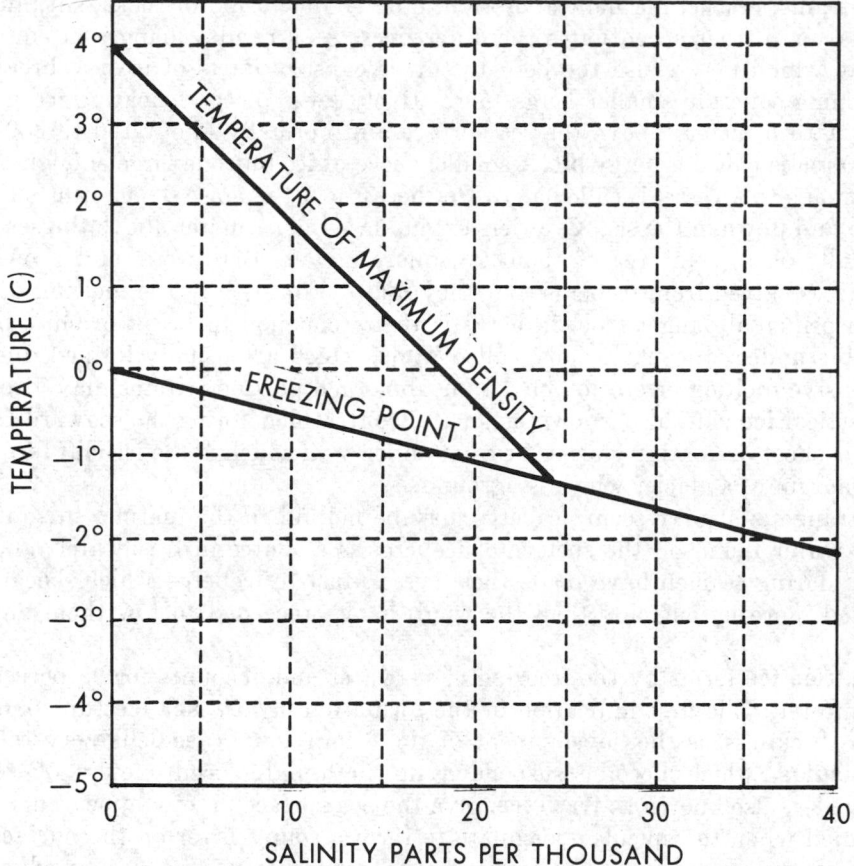

FIGURE 3602.—Relationship between temperature of maximum density and freezing point for water of varying salinity.

3603. Ice of land origin is formed on land by the freezing of freshwater or the compacting of snow as layer upon layer adds to the pressure on that beneath.

Under great pressure ice becomes slightly plastic and is forced outward and downward along an inclined surface. If a large area is relatively flat, as on the antarctic plateau, or if the outward flow is obstructed, as on Greenland, an **ice cap** forms and remains winter and summer. The thickness of these ice caps range from nearly 1 kilometer on Greenland to as much as 4.5 kilometers on the Antarctic Continent. Where ravines or mountain passes permit flow of the ice, a **glacier** is formed. This is a mass of snow and ice which continuously flows to lower levels, exhibiting many of the characteristics of rivers of water. The flow may be more than 30 meters per day, but is generally much less. When a glacier reaches a comparatively level area, it spreads out. When a glacier flows into the sea, the buoyant force of the water breaks off pieces from time to time, and these float away as **icebergs.** Icebergs may be described as dome shaped, sloping or pinnacled (fig. 3603a), tabular (fig. 3603b), glacier, or weathered.

An iceberg seldom melts uniformly because of lack of uniformity in the ice itself, differences in the temperature above and below the waterline, exposure of one side to the sun, strains, cracks, mechanical erosion, etc. The inclusion of rocks, silt, and other foreign matter further accentuates the differences. As a result, changes in equilibrium take place, which may cause the berg to tilt or capsize. Parts of it may break off or **calve,** forming separate smaller bergs. A relatively large piece of floating ice generally extending 1 to 5 meters above the sea surface and normally about 100 to 300 square meters in area is called a **bergy bit.** A smaller piece of ice but one large enough to inflict serious damage to a vessel is called a **growler** because of the noise it sometimes makes as it bobs up and down in the sea. Growlers extend less than 1 meter above the sea surface and normally occupy an area of about 20 square meters. Bergy bits and growlers are usually pieces calved from icebergs, but they may be formed by the melting of an iceberg. The principal danger from icebergs is their tendency to break or shift position, and possible underwater extensions, called **rams,** which are usually formed due to the more intensive melting or erosion of the unsubmerged portions. Rams may also extend from a vertical **ice cliff,** also known as an **ice front,** which forms the seaward face of a massive ice sheet or floating glacier; or from an **ice wall** which is the ice cliff forming the seaward margin of a glacier which is aground.

As strange as it may seem, icebergs may be helpful to the mariner in some ways. The melt water found on the surface of icebergs is a source of freshwater, and in the past some daring seamen have made their vessels fast to icebergs which, because they are affected more by currents than the wind, have proceeded to tow them out of the ice pack.

3604. Sea ice forms by the freezing of seawater and accounts for 95 percent of all ice encountered. The first indication of the formation of **new sea ice** (up to 10 centimeters in thickness) is the development of small individual, needlelike crystals of ice, called **spicules,** which become suspended in the top few centimeters of seawater. These spicules, also known as **frazil ice,** give the sea surface an oily appearance. **Grease ice** is formed when the spicules coagulate to form a soupy layer on the surface giving the sea a matte appearance. The next stage in sea ice formation occurs when **shuga,** an accumulation of spongy white ice lumps a few centimeters across, develops from grease ice. Upon further freezing, and depending upon wind exposure, seas, and salinity, shuga and grease ice develop into **nilas,** an elastic crust of high salinity up to 10 centimeters in thickness with a matte surface or into **ice rind,** a brittle, shiny crust of low salinity with a thickness up to approximately 5 centimeters. A layer of 5 centimeters of freshwater ice is brittle but strong enough to support the weight of a heavy man. In contrast, the same thickness of newly formed sea ice will support not more than about 10 percent of this weight, although its strength varies with the temperatures at which it is formed; very cold ice supports a greater weight than warmer ice. As it ages, sea ice becomes harder and more brittle.

New ice may also develop from **slush** which is formed when snow falls into seawater which is near its freezing point, but colder than the melting point of snow. The snow does not melt but floats on the surface, drifting with the wind into beds. If the temperature then drops below the freezing point of the seawater, the slush freezes quickly into a soft ice similar to shuga.

Sea ice is exposed to several forces, including currents, wave motion, tides, wind, and temperature differences. In its early stages, its plasticity permits it to conform readily to virtually any shape required by the forces acting upon it. As it becomes older, thicker, more brittle, and exposed to the influence of wind and wave action, new ice usually separates into circular pieces from 30 centimeters to 3 meters in diameter

FIGURE 3603a.—Pinnacled iceberg.

FIGURE 3603b.—A tabular iceberg.

and up to approximately 10 centimeters in thickness with raised edges due to individual pieces striking against each other. These circular pieces of ice are called **pancake ice**

FIGURE 3604a.—Pancake ice, with an iceberg in the background.

(fig. 3604a) and may break into smaller pieces with strong wave motion. Any single piece of relatively flat sea ice less than 20 meters across is called an **ice cake.** With continued low temperatures individual ice cakes and pancake ice will, depending on wind or wave motion, either freeze together to form a continuous sheet or unite into pieces of ice 20 meters or more across. These larger pieces are then called **ice floes** which may further freeze together to form an ice covered area greater than 10 kilometers across known as an **ice field.** In wind sheltered areas thickening ice usually forms a continuous sheet before it can develop into the characteristic ice cake form. When sea ice reaches a thickness of between 10 to 30 centimeters it is referred to as **grey** and **grey-white ice,** or collectively as **young ice,** and is the transition stage between nilas and **first-year ice.** First-year ice usually attains a thickness of between 30 centimeters and 2 meters in its first winter's growth.

Sea ice may grow to a thickness of 10 to 13 centimeters within 48 hours, after which it acts as an insulator between the ocean and the atmosphere progressively slowing its further growth. However, sea ice may grow to a thickness of between 2 to 3 meters in its first winter. Ice which has survived at least one summer's melt is classified as **old ice.** If it has survived only one summer's melt it is referred to as **second-year ice.** Because it is thicker and less dense than first-year ice, it stands higher out of the water. Old ice which has attained a thickness of 3 meters or more and has survived at least two summers' melt is known as **multiyear ice** and is almost salt free. Old ice may often be recognized by a bluish tone to its surface color in contrast to the greenish tint of first-year ice.

Greater thicknesses in both first and multiyear ice are attained through the deformation of the ice resulting from the movement and interaction of individual floes. Deformation processes occur after the development of new and young ice and are the direct consequence of the effects of winds, tides, and currents. These processes transform a relatively flat sheet of ice into **pressure ice** which has a readily observed roughness in its surface. **Bending,** which is the first stage in the formation of pressure ice, is the upward or downward motion of thin and very plastic ice. **Tenting** occurs when bending produces an upward displacement of ice forming a flat sided arch with a cavity beneath. More frequently, however, **rafting** takes place as one piece of new and young ice overrides another. When pieces of first-year ice are piled haphazardly over one another forming a wall or line of broken ice, referred to as a **ridge,** the process is known as **ridging.** Pressure ice with topography consisting of numerous mounds or hillocks is called **hummocked ice,** each mound being called a **hummock.**

The motion of adjacent floes is seldom equal. The rougher the surface, the greater is the effect of wind, since each piece extending above the surface acts as a sail. Some ice floes are in rotary motion as they tend to trim themselves into the wind. Since ridges extend below as well as above the surface, the deeper ones are influenced more by deep water currents. When a strong wind blows in the same direction for a considerable period, each floe exerts pressure on the next one, and as the distance increases, the pressure becomes tremendous. Ridges on sea ice are generally about 1 meter high and 5 meters deep, but under considerable pressure may attain heights of 30 meters and depths of 150 meters in extreme cases.

The alternate melting and growth of sea ice, combined with the continual motion of various floes that results in separation as well as consolidation, causes widely varying conditions within the ice cover itself. The mean areal density, or **concentration,** of pack ice in any given area is expressed in *oktas* (eighths). Concentrations range from: **open water** (total concentration of all ice does not exceed $\frac{1}{8}$), **very open pack** ($\frac{1}{8}$ to less than $\frac{3}{8}$ concentration), **open pack** ($\frac{3}{8}$ to less than $\frac{6}{8}$ concentration), **close pack** ($\frac{6}{8}$ to less than $\frac{7}{8}$ concentration), **very close pack** ($\frac{7}{8}$ to less than $\frac{8}{8}$ concentration), to **compact** or **consolidated pack** ($\frac{8}{8}$ or complete coverage). The extent to which an ice cover of varying concentrations can be penetrated by a vessel varies from place to place and with changing weather conditions. With a concentration of 1 to 2 oktas in a given area, an unreinforced vessel can generally navigate safely, but the danger of receiving heavy damage is always present. When the concentration increases to between 2 and 4 oktas, the area becomes only occasionally accessible to an unreinforced vessel depending upon the vagaries of wind and current. With concentrations of 4 to 6 oktas, the area becomes accessible only to ice strengthened vessels which on occasion will require icebreaker assistance. Navigation in areas with concentrations of 6 oktas or more should only be attempted by modern icebreakers.

Within the ice cover, openings may develop resulting from a number of deformation processes. Long, jagged cracks may appear first in the ice cover or through a single floe. When these cracks part and reach lengths of a few meters to many kilometers, they are referred to as **fractures.** If they widen further to permit passage of a ship, they are called **leads.** In winter, a thin coating of new ice may cover the water within a lead, but in summer the water usually remains ice-free until a shift in the movement forces the two sides together again. Before this occurs, lateral motion generally occurs between the floes, so that they no longer fit and unless the pressure is extreme, numerous large patches of open water remain. These nonlinear shaped openings enclosed in ice are called **polynyas.** Polynyas may contain small fragments of floating ice and may be covered with miles of new and young ice.

Sea ice which is formed in situ from seawater or by the freezing of pack ice of any age to the shore and which remains attached to the coast, to an ice wall, to an ice front, or between shoals is called **fast ice.** The width of this fast ice varies considerably and may extend for a few meters or several hundred kilometers. In bays and other sheltered areas, fast ice, often augmented by annual snow accumulations and the seaward extension of land ice, may attain a thickness of over 2 meters above the sea surface. When a floating sheet of ice grows to this or a greater thickness and extends over a great horizontal distance, it is called an **ice shelf.** Massive ice shelfs where the ice thickness reaches several hundred meters are found in both the Arctic and Antarctic.

The majority of the icebergs found in the Antarctic do not originate from glaciers as those found in the Arctic, but are calved from the outer edges of broad expanses of shelf ice. Icebergs formed in this manner are called **tabular icebergs,** having a boxlike shape with horizontal dimensions measured in kilometers, and heights above the sea surface approaching 60 meters. The largest antarctic ice shelves are found in the Ross and Weddell Seas. The expression "tabular iceberg" is not applied to bergs which break off from arctic ice shelves; similar formations there are called **ice islands.** These originate when shelf ice, such as that found on the northern coast of Greenland and in the bays of Ellesmere Island, breaks up. As a rule, arctic ice islands are not as large as the tabular icebergs found in the Antarctic. They attain a thickness of up to 55 meters and on the average extend 5 to 7 meters above the sea surface. Both tabular icebergs and ice islands possess a nearly level, but gently rolling surface. Because of their deep draft, they are influenced much more by current than wind. Both the United States and the U.S.S.R. have used arctic ice islands as floating scientific platforms from which polar research has been conducted.

3605. Thickness of sea ice.—Sea ice has been observed to grow to a thickness of almost 3 meters during its first year. However, the thickness of first-year ice that has not undergone deformation does not generally exceed 2 meters. In coastal areas where the melting rate is less than the freezing rate, the thickness may increase during succeeding winters, being augmented by compacted and frozen snow, until a maximum thickness of about 3.5 to 4.5 meters may eventually be reached. Old sea ice may also attain a thickness of over 4 meters in this manner, or when summer melt water from its surface or from snow cover runs off into the sea and refreezes under the ice where the seawater temperature is below the freezing point of the fresher melt water.

The growth of sea ice is dependent upon a number of meteorological and oceanographic parameters. Such parameters include air temperature, initial ice thickness, snow depth and density, wind speed, seawater salinity and density, and the specific heats of sea ice and seawater. Investigations, however, have shown that the most influential parameters affecting sea ice growth are air temperature, wind speed, snow depth and density, and initial ice thickness. Many complex equations have been formulated to predict ice growth using these five parameters. However, except for the first two, these parameters are not routinely observed for remote polar locations.

In the early 1940's a Russian geographical scientist, N. N. Zubov, formulated an ice growth equation as a function of air temperature alone and based on his empirical observations of ice formation along portions of the northern Russian arctic coast. Air temperatures are translated into accumulated frost degree days from which theoretical ice thicknesses are calculated using the equation:

$$T_j = \frac{-50 + \sqrt{2500 + 32 \sum_{i=1}^{j} DDi}}{2},$$

where T_j is the ice thickness in centimeters on day j and DDi is the frost degree day accumulation in degrees Celsius on day i.

A **frost degree day** is defined as a day with a mean temperature of 1° below an arbitrary base. The base most commonly used is the freezing point of freshwater (0°C). If, for example, the mean temperature on a given day is 5° below freezing, then five frost degree days are collected for that day. These frost degree days are then added to those collected the very next day to obtain an accumulated value, which is then added to the number of degree days collected the following day. This process is repeated daily throughout the ice growing season. Temperatures usually fluctuate above and below freezing for several days before remaining below freezing. Therefore, frost degree day accumulations are initiated on the first day of the period when temperatures remain below freezing. The relationship between frost degree day accumulations and theoretical ice growth curves at Point Barrow, Alaska is shown in figure 3605a. Similar curves for other arctic stations are contained in publications available from the U. S. Naval Oceanographic Office. Figure 3605b graphically depicts the relationship between accumulated frost degree days (°C) and ice thickness in centimeters.

During the winter the ice usually becomes covered with snow which insulates the ice beneath and tends to slow down its rate of growth. This thickness of snow cover varies considerably from region to region as a result of differing climatic conditions. Its depth may also vary widely within very short distances in response to variable winds and ice topography. While this snow cover persists, almost 90 percent of the incoming radiation is reflected back to space. Eventually, however, the snow begins to melt as the air temperature rises above 0° C in early summer and the resulting freshwater forms puddles on the surface. These puddles absorb about 90 percent of the incoming radiation and rapidly enlarge as they melt the surrounding snow or ice. Eventually the puddles penetrate to the bottom surface of the floes and are known as **thawholes.** This slow process is characteristic of ice in the Arctic Ocean and seas where movement is restricted by the coastline or islands. Where ice is free to drift into warmer waters (e.g., the Antarctic, East Greenland, and the Labrador Sea) decay is accelerated in response to wave erosion as well as warmer air and sea temperatures.

3606. Salinity of sea ice.—Sea ice forms first as salt-free crystals near the surface of the sea. As the process continues, these crystals are joined together and, as they do so, small quantities of brine are trapped within the ice. On the average, new ice 15 centimeters thick contains 5 to 10 parts of salt per thousand. With lower temperatures, freezing takes place faster. With faster freezing, a greater amount of salt is trapped in the ice.

Depending upon the temperature, the trapped brine may either freeze or remain liquid, but because its density is greater than that of the pure ice, it tends to settle down through the pure ice. As it does so, the ice gradually freshens, becoming clearer, stronger, and more brittle. At an age of 1 year, sea ice is sufficiently fresh that its melt water, if found in **puddles** of sufficient size, and not contaminated by spray from

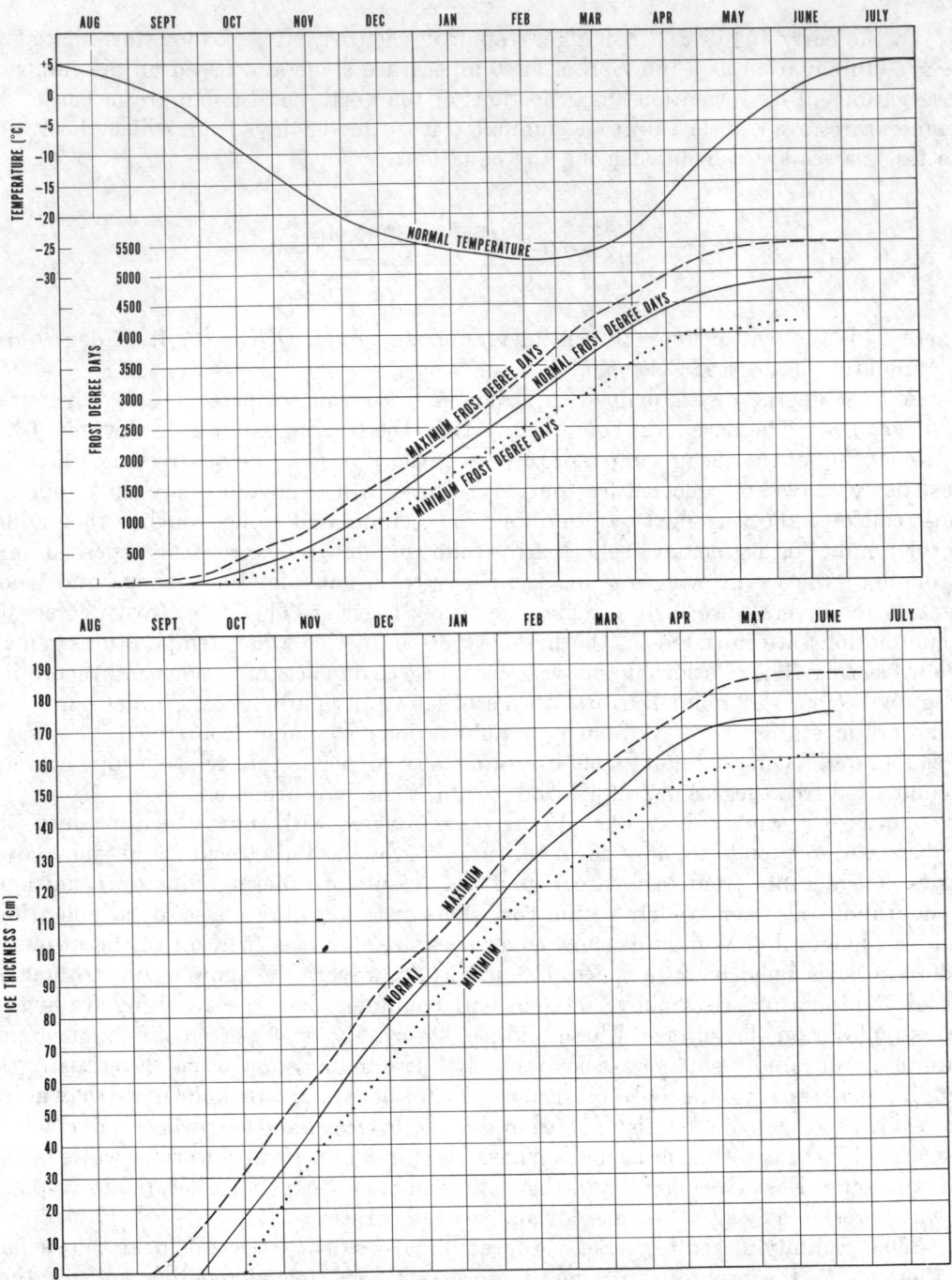

FIGURE 3605a.—Relationship between accumulated frost degree days and theoretical ice thickness at Point Barrow, Alaska.

the sea, can be used to replenish the freshwater supply of a ship. However, ponds of sufficient size to water ships are seldom found except in ice of great age, and then much of the melt water is from snow which has accumulated on the surface of the ice. When sea ice reaches an age of about 2 years, virtually all of the salt has been eliminated. Icebergs contain no salt, and uncontaminated melt water obtained from them is fresh.

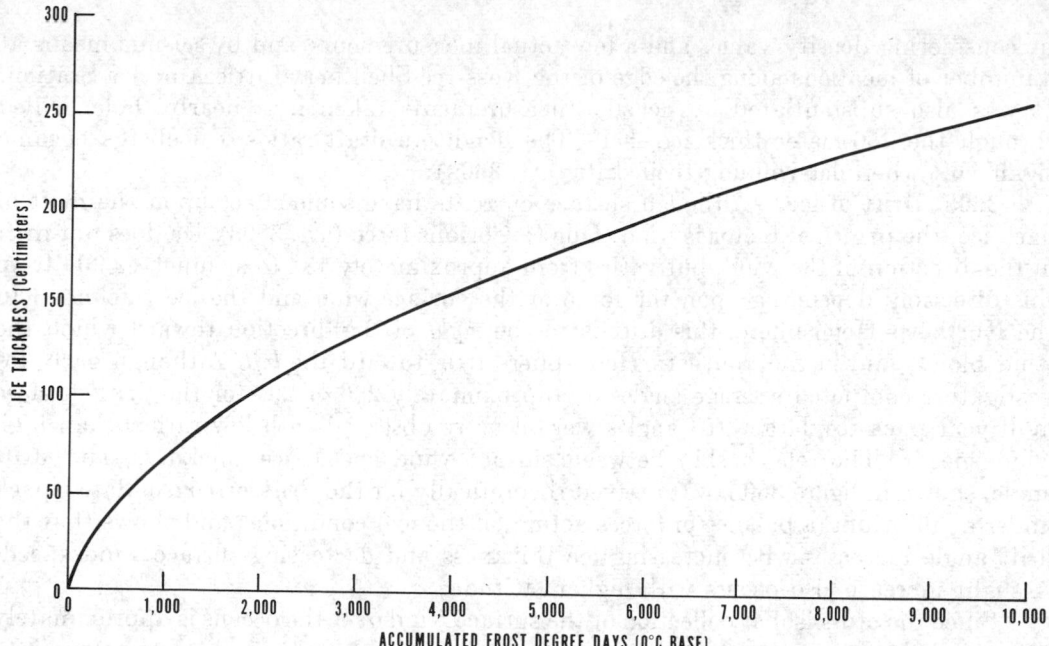

FIGURE 3605b.—Relationship between accumulated frost degree days (°C) and ice thickness (cm).

The settling out of the brine gives sea ice a honeycomb structure which greatly hastens its disintegration when the temperature rises above freezing. In this state, when it is called **rotten ice,** much more surface is exposed to warm air and water, and the rate of melting is increased. In a day's time, a floe of apparently solid ice several inches thick may disappear completely.

3607. Density of ice.—The density of freshwater ice at its freezing point is 0.917. Newly formed sea ice, due to its salt content, is more dense, 0.925 being a representative value. The density decreases as the ice freshens (art. 3606). By the time it has shed most of its salt, sea ice is less dense than freshwater ice, because ice formed in the sea contains more air bubbles. Ice having no salt but containing air to the extent of 8 percent by volume (an approximately maximum value for sea ice) has a density of 0.845.

The density of land ice varies over even wider limits. That formed by freezing of freshwater has a density of 0.917, as stated above. Much of the land ice, however, is formed by compacting of snow. This results in the entrapping of relatively large quantities of air. **Névé,** a snow which has become coarse grained and compact through temperature change, forming the transition stage to glacier ice, may have an air content of as much as 50 percent by volume. By the time the ice of a glacier reaches the sea, its density approaches that of freshwater ice. A sample taken from an iceberg on the Grand Banks had a density of 0.899.

When ice floats, part of it is above water and part is below the surface. The percentage of the mass below the surface can be found by dividing the average density of the ice by the density of the water in which it floats. Thus, if an iceberg of density 0.920 floats in water of density 1.028 (corresponding to a salinity of 35 parts per thousand and a temperature of −1°C, or 30°F), 89.5 percent of its mass will be below the surface. That is, about nine-tenths of the mass will be below the surface, and only about one-tenth will be above the surface.

The height to draft ratio for a blocky or tabular iceberg probably varies fairly closely about 1:5. This average ratio was computed for icebergs south of Newfoundland by considering density values and a few actual measurements, and by seismic means at a number of locations along the edge of the Ross Ice Shelf near Little America Station. It was also substantiated by density measurements taken in a nearby hole drilled through the 256-meter thick ice shelf. The height to draft ratios of icebergs become significant when determining their drift (art. 3609).

3608. Drift of ice.—Although surface currents have some effect upon the drift of pack ice, the principal factor is wind. Due to Coriolis force (art. 3803), ice does not drift in the direction of the wind, but varies from approximately 18° to as much as 90° from this direction, depending upon the force of the surface wind and the ice thickness. In the Northern Hemisphere, this drift is to the *right* of the direction toward which the wind blows, and in the Southern Hemisphere it is toward the *left*. Although early investigators computed average angles of approximately 28° or 29° for the drift of close multiyear pack ice, large drift angles were usually observed with low rather than high wind speeds. The relationship between surface wind speed, ice thickness, and drift angle, shown in figure 3608, was derived theoretically for the drift of consolidated pack under equilibrium (a balance of forces acting on the ice) conditions, and shows that the drift angle increases with increasing ice thickness and decreasing surface wind speed. A slight increase also occurs with higher latitude.

Since the cross-isobar deflection of the surface wind over the oceans is approximately 20°, the deflection of the ice varies from approximately along the isobars to as much as 70° to the right of the isobars, with low pressure on the left and high pressure on the right in the Northern Hemisphere. The positions of the low and high pressure areas are, of course, reversed in the Southern Hemisphere. The drift angles that are given in figure 3608a may be used for all ice concentrations and polar latitudes.

The rate of drift, compiled from observations of ice drift along the northern Russian coast bordering the Chukchi Sea, is presented in table 3608. Rates are given as a percentage of the surface wind speed and depend upon the roughness of the surface and the concentration of the ice. Percentages vary from approximately one quarter of 1 percent to almost 8 percent of the surface wind speed measured approximately 6 meters above the ice surface. Low concentrations of heavily ridged or hummocked floes drift faster than high concentrations of lightly ridged or hummocked floes with the same wind speed. From table 3608 it can be seen that sea ice of 6 to 7 okta concentrations and six tenths hummocking or close multiyear ice will drift at approximately 2 percent of the surface wind speed. Additionally, the response factors of 1 and 4 okta ice concentrations respectively, are approximately three times and twice the magnitude of the response factor for 7 okta ice concentrations with the same extent of surface roughness. Although a maximum ice drift to surface wind speed ratio of approximately 8 percent is indicated by table 3608, isolated ice floes have been observed to drift as fast as 10 percent to 12 percent of strong surface winds.

The rates with which sea ice drifts have been quantified through empirical observation. The drift angle, however, has been determined theoretically for 8 okta ice concentrations. This relationship presently is extended to the drift of all ice concentrations due to the lack of basic knowledge of the dynamic forces that act upon and result in redistributions of sea ice in the polar regions.

3609. Iceberg drift.—Icebergs extend a considerable distance below the surface and have relatively small "sail areas" compared to their subsurface mass. Therefore, the near-surface current is thought to be primarily responsible for drift; however, observations have shown that wind can be the dominant force that governs iceberg drift at a particular location or time. Also, the current and wind may contribute nearly equally to the resultant drift.

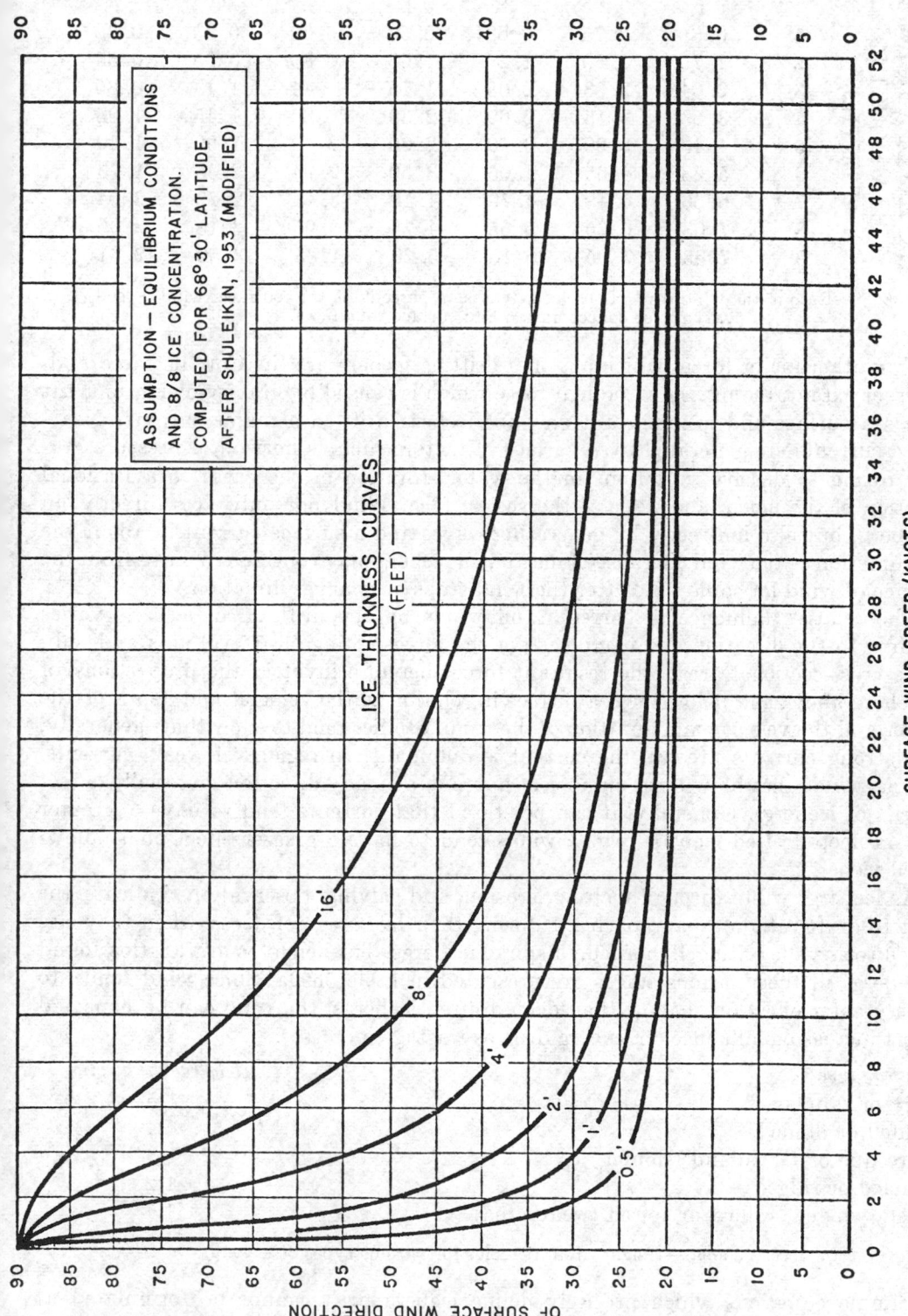

FIGURE 3608.—Ice drift direction for varying wind speed and ice thickness.

ICE CONCENTRATION (OKTAS)

EXTENT OF RIDGING & HUMMOCKING (TENTHS)		1	2	3	4	5	6	7
	1	0.88	0.75	0.63	0.50	0.39	0.33	0.26
	2	1.75	1.50	1.25	1.05	0.85	0.65	0.53
	3	2.64	2.33	2.05	1.75	1.44	1.13	0.85
	4	3.53	3.13	2.69	2.30	1.86	1.45	1.08
	5	4.40	3.90	3.40	2.90	2.40	1.90	1.40
	6	5.28	4.65	4.06	3.50	2.94	2.35	1.73
	7	6.66	5.48	4.79	4.10	3.41	2.73	2.04
	8	7.03	6.25	5.55	4.75	3.95	3.18	2.36
	9	7.93	7.05	6.10	5.20	4.35	3.50	2.61

TABLE 3608.—Rate of the wind drift of sea ice (given as a percent of the surface wind speed) for varying ice concentration and surface roughness.

Two other major forces which act on a drifting iceberg are the Coriolis force and, to a lesser extent, the pressure gradient force which is caused by gravity owing to a tilt of the sea surface and is important only for iceberg drift in a major current. Near-surface currents are generated by a variety of factors such as horizontal pressure gradients owing to density variations in the water, rotation of the earth, gravitational attraction of the moon, and slope of the sea surface. Wind not only acts directly on an iceberg, but also indirectly by generating waves and a surface current in about the same direction as the wind. Because of inertia, an iceberg may continue to move from the influence of wind for some time after the wind stops or changes direction.

The relative influence of currents and winds on the drift of an iceberg varies according to the direction and magnitude of the forces acting on its sail area and sub-surface cross-sectional area. The resultant force therefore involves the proportions of the iceberg above and below the sea surface in relation to the velocity and depth of the current, and the velocity and duration of the wind. Studies tend to show that, generally, where strong currents prevail, the current is dominant. In regions of weak currents, however, winds that blow for a number of hours in a steady direction materially affect the drift of icebergs. Generally, it can be stated that currents tend to have a greater effect, on deep-drafted icebergs, while winds tend to have a greater effect on shallow-drafted icebergs.

As icebergs waste through melting, erosion, and calving, observations indicate the height to draft ratio may approach 1:1 during their last stage of decay when they are referred to as valley, winged, horned, or spired icebergs. The height to draft ratios found for icebergs in their various stages are presented in table 3609a. Since wind tends to have a greater effect on shallow than deep-drafted icebergs, the wind can be expected to exert increasing influence on iceberg drift as wastage increases.

Iceberg type	Height to draft ratio
Blocky or tabular	1:5
Rounded or domed	1:4
Picturesque or Greenland (sloping)	1:3
Pinnacled or ridged.	1:2
Horned, winged, valley, or spired (weathered)	1:1

TABLE 3609a.—Height to draft ratios for various types of icebergs.

Simple equations which precisely define iceberg drift cannot be formulated at present because of the uncertainty in the water and air drag coefficients associated with iceberg motion. Values for these parameters not only vary from iceberg to iceberg, but they probably change for the same iceberg over its period of wastage.

Present investigations utilize an analytical approach facilitated by computer calculations in which the air and water drag coefficients are varied within reasonable limits. Combinations of these drag values are then used in several increasingly complex water models that try to duplicate observed iceberg trajectories. The results indicate that with a wind generated current, Coriolis force, and a uniform wind, but without a gradient current, small and medium icebergs will drift with the percentages of the wind as given in table 3609b. The drift will be to the right in the Northern Hemisphere and to the left in the Southern Hemisphere.

Wind Speed (knots)	Ice Speed/Wind Speed (percent)		Drift Angle (degrees)	
	Small Berg	Med. Berg	Small Berg	Med. Berg
10	3.6	2.2	12	69
20	3.8	3.1	14	55
30	4.1	3.4	17	36
40	4.4	3.5	19	33
50	4.5	3.6	23	32
60	4.9	3.7	24	31

TABLE 3609b.—Drift of iceberg as percentage of wind speed.

When gradient currents are introduced, trajectories vary considerably depending on the magnitude of the wind and current and whether they are in the same or opposite direction. When a 1-knot current and wind are in the same direction, drift is to the right of both wind and current with drift angles increasing linearly from approximately 5° at 10 knots to 22° at 60 knots. When the wind and a 1-knot current are in opposite directions, drift is to the left of the current with the angle increasing from approximately 3° at 10 knots, to 20° at 30 knots, and to 73° at 60 knots. As a limiting case for increasing wind speeds, drift may be approximately normal (to the right) to the wind direction. This indicates that the wind generated current is clearly dominating the drift. In general, the various models used demonstrated that a combination of the wind and current was responsible for the drift of icebergs.

3610. Extent of ice in the sea.—When an area of sea ice, no matter what form it takes or how it is disposed, is described, it is referred to as **pack ice.** In both polar regions the pack ice is a very dynamic feature with wide deviations in its areal extent dependent upon changing oceanographic and meteorological phenomena. In winter the arctic pack extends over the entire Arctic Ocean and for a varying distance outward from it; the limits receding considerably during the warmer summer months. Each year a large portion of the ice from the Arctic Ocean moves outward between Greenland and Spitsbergen, into the North Atlantic, and is replaced by new ice. Relatively little of the arctic pack ice is more than 10 years old. An example of the variance possible in the outer limit of the arctic ice pack is shown in figure 3610a where the average positions of the maximum and minimum extents of sea ice are plotted.

Ice covers a large portion of the antarctic waters and is probably the greatest single factor contributing to the isolation of the Antarctic Continent. During the austral winter (June through September), ice completely surrounds the continent, forming an almost impassable barrier that extends northward on the average to about 54°S in the Atlantic and to about 62°S in the Pacific. Disintegration of the pack ice during the austral summer months of December through March allows the limits of the ice edge to recede considerably opening some coastal areas of the Antarctic to navigation. The mean maximum and mean minimum positions of the antarctic ice limit are shown in figure 3610b.

Historical information on sea conditions for specific localities and time periods can be found in publications of the U. S. Naval Oceanographic Office and the Defense Mapping Agency Hydrographic Center. Such publications include sailing directions, forecasting guides, and ice atlases.

3611. Ice in the North Atlantic.—Sea level glaciers exist on a number of landmasses bordering the northern seas, including Alaska, Greenland, Svalbard (Spitsbergen), Zemlya Frantsa-Iosifa (Franz Josef Land), Noyaya Zemlya, and Severnaya Zemlya (Nicholas II Land). Except in Greenland, the rate of calving is relatively slow, and the few icebergs produced melt near their points of formation. Many of those produced along the coasts of Greenland, however, are eventually carried into the shipping lanes of the North Atlantic, where they constitute a major menace to ships.

Generally the majority of icebergs produced along the east coast of Greenland remain near their source of origin. However, a small number of bergy bits, growlers, and small icebergs are transported from this region by the East Greenland Current

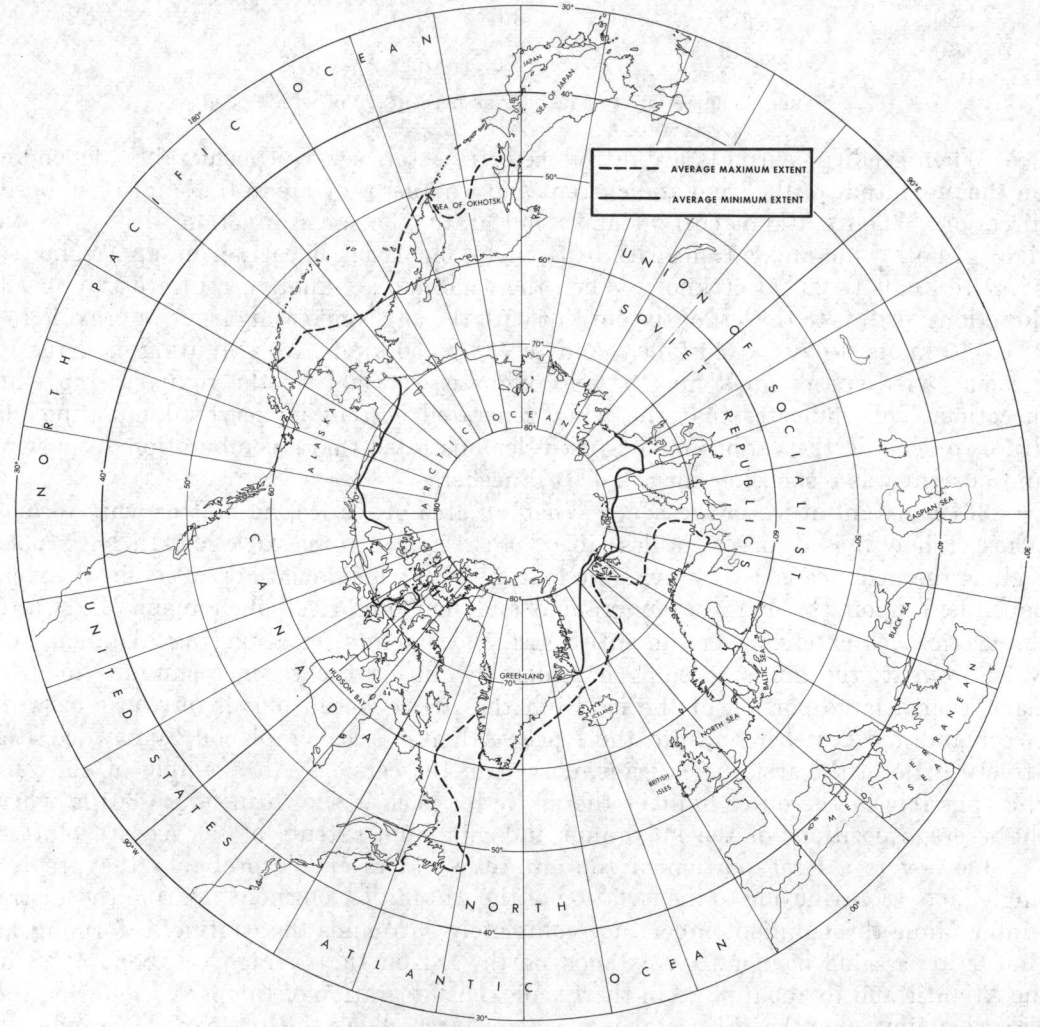

FIGURE 3610a.—Average maximum and minimum extent of arctic sea ice.

around Kap Farvel at the southern tip of Greenland and then northward by the West Greenland Current into Davis Strait to the vicinity of 67°N. Relatively few of these icebergs menace shipping but some are carried to the south and southeast of Kap Farvel by a counterclockwise current gyre centered near 57°N and 43°W.

The main source of the icebergs encountered in the North Atlantic is the west coast of Greenland between 67°N and 76°N where approximately 7,500 icebergs are formed each year. In this area there are about 100 low lying coastal glaciers, 20 of them being the principal producers of icebergs. Of these 20 major glaciers, 2 located in Disko Bugt between 69°N and 70°N are estimated to contribute 28 percent of all icebergs appearing in Baffin Bay and the Labrador Sea. The West Greenland Current carries icebergs from this area northward and then westward until they encounter the south flowing Labrador Current. West Greenland icebergs generally spend their first winter locked in the Baffin Bay pack ice; however, a large number can also be found within the sea ice extending along the entire Labrador coast by late winter. During the next spring and summer, when they are freed by the break up of the pack ice, they are transported further southward by the Labrador Current. The general drift patterns of icebergs that are prevalent in the eastern portion of the North American Arctic are shown in figure 3611a. Observations over a 69-year period show that an average of 365 icebergs per year reach latitudes south of 48°N, with approximately 10 percent of this

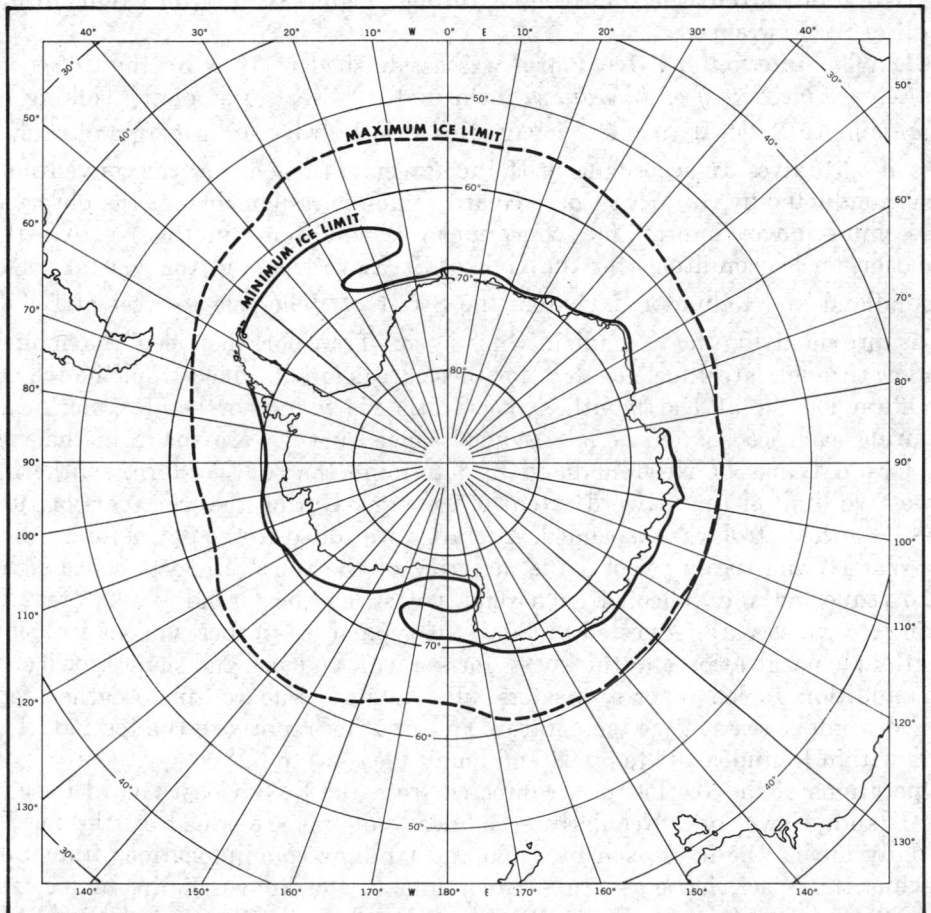

FIGURE 3610b.—Average maximum and minimum extent of antarctic sea ice.

total carried south of the Grand Banks (43°N) before they melt. Icebergs may be encountered during any part of the year, but in the Grand Banks area they are most numerous during spring. The maximum monthly average of iceberg sightings occur during April, May, and June, with May having the highest average of 124.

The variation from average conditions is considerable. More than 1,587 icebergs have been sighted south of latitude 48°N in a single year (1972), while in 1966 not a single iceberg was encountered in this area. In the years of 1940 and 1958 only one iceberg was observed south of 48°N. Although this variation has not been fully explained, it is apparently related to wind conditions, the distribution of pack ice in Davis Strait, and to the amount of pack ice off Labrador. It has been suggested that the distribution of the Davis Strait-Labrador Sea pack ice influences the effectiveness of this ice in holding back the icebergs. According to this theory, when pack ice is heavy along the Labrador coast, the icebergs are forced well offshore, where warmer water causes them to melt before they reach the North Atlantic shipping lanes; but when the pack ice is not sufficient for this, the icebergs drift closer to shore, where there is colder water which prolongs their existence.

Average iceberg and pack ice limits in this area during April, May, and June are shown in figures 3611b, 3611c, and 3611d. Icebergs have been observed in the vicinity of Bermuda, the Azores, and within 400 to 500 kilometers of Great Britain.

Pack ice may also be found in the North Atlantic, some having been brought south by the Labrador Current and some coming through Cabot Strait after having formed in the Gulf of St. Lawrence.

3612. The International Ice Patrol was established in 1914 by the *International Convention for the Safety of Life at Sea*, held in 1913 as a result of the sinking of the SS *Titanic* in 1912. On its maiden voyage this vessel struck an iceberg and sank with the loss of 1,513 lives. In accordance with the agreement reached at the convention, this patrol is conducted by the U. S. Coast Guard, which is responsible for the observations and dissemination of information concerning ice conditions in the North Atlantic. Information on ice conditions for the Gulf of St. Lawrence and the coastal waters of Newfoundland and Labrador, including the Strait of Belle Isle to west of Belle Isle itself, is provided by the Canadian Ministry of Transport between the months of December through late June. Ice data for these areas are obtained from the Ice Operations Officer located at Dartmouth, Nova Scotia via Sidney or Halifax marine radio.

During each ice season, aerial reconnaissance surveys are made in the vicinity of the Grand Banks of Newfoundland to determine the southeastern, southern, and southwestern limit of the seaward extent of icebergs. During the war years of 1916–18 and 1941–45 the patrol was suspended. Aircraft were added to the patrol force following World War II, and today perform the majority of the work. Reports of ice sightings are also requested and collected from ships transiting the Grand Banks area. When reporting ice, vessels are requested to detail the type of ice (icebergs or sea ice) sighted, its position, concentration and thickness (for sea ice), and size and shape (for icebergs).

In addition to ice reports, masters who do not issue routine weather reports, are urged to make sea surface temperature and weather reports to the Ice Patrol every 6 hours within latitudes 40° to 50°N and longitudes 42° to 60°W.

Operations of the Ice Patrol are directed from the U. S. Coast Guard Base, Governors Island, New York. Regularly scheduled bulletins are issued by the Ice Patrol twice daily during the ice season by radio and landline communications from Boston, Massachusetts. When icebergs are sighted outside the known limits of ice, special broadcasts are issued from St. Johns, Newfoundland, between those regularly scheduled. Iceberg positions in the ice bulletins are updated for drift at 12-hour intervals. A radio-facsimile chart is also broadcast once a day throughout the ice season. The Ice Patrol,

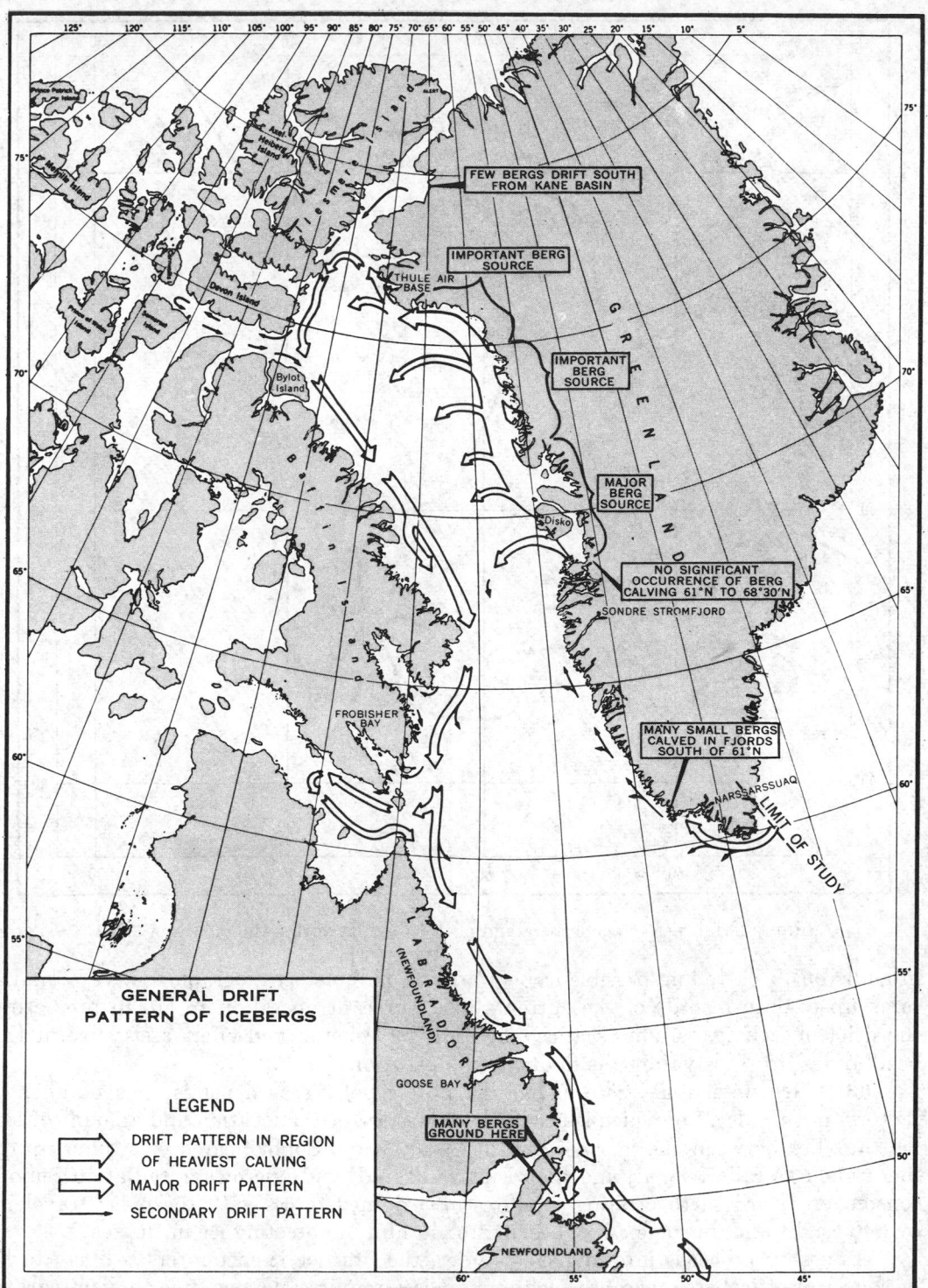

FIGURE 3611a.—General drift pattern of icebergs.

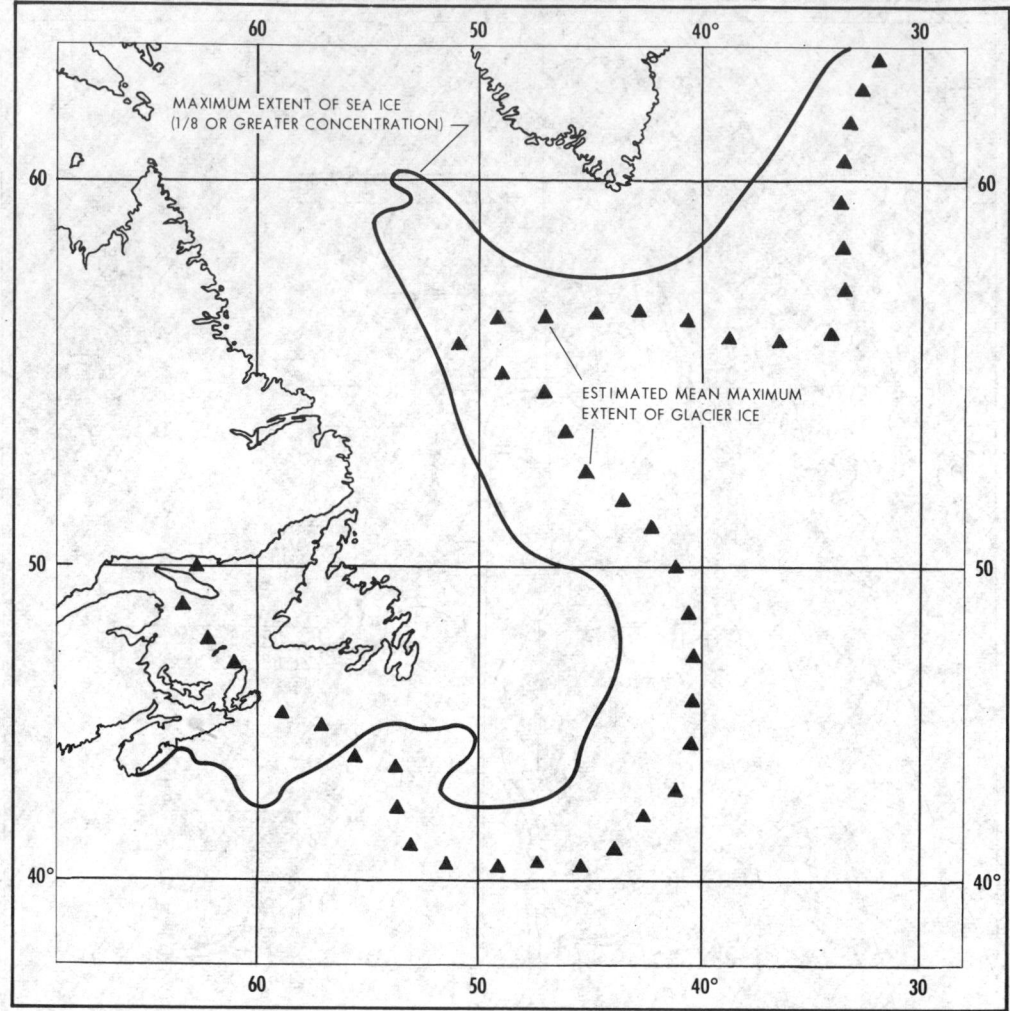

FIGURE 3611b.—Average iceberg and pack ice limits during the month of April.

in addition to patrolling possible iceberg areas, conducts oceanographic surveys, maintains up-to-date records of the currents in its area of operation to aid in predicting the drift of icebergs, studies sea ice conditions in general, and offers assistance, if the need arises, to ships within the limits of its operation.

3613. Ice detection.—Safe navigation in the polar seas depends on a number of factors, not the least of which is accurate knowledge of the location and amount of sea ice that lies between the mariner and his destination. Sophisticated electronic equipment such as radar, sonar, and the visible, infrared, and microwave radiation remote sensors on board earth orbiting satellites have joined forces with the polar traveler's own eyesight and, in some cases, hearing to aid him in detecting ice in the sea.

As a ship proceeds into higher latitudes, the first ice it encounters is likely to be in the form of icebergs, because such large pieces require a longer time to disintegrate. Icebergs can easily be avoided if detected soon enough. The distance at which an iceberg can be seen visually depends upon meteorological visibility, height of the iceberg, source and condition of lighting, and the observer. On a clear day with excellent visibility, a large iceberg, due to its brilliant luster, might be sighted at a distance of almost 35 kilometers. With a low-lying haze around the horizon, this distance may be

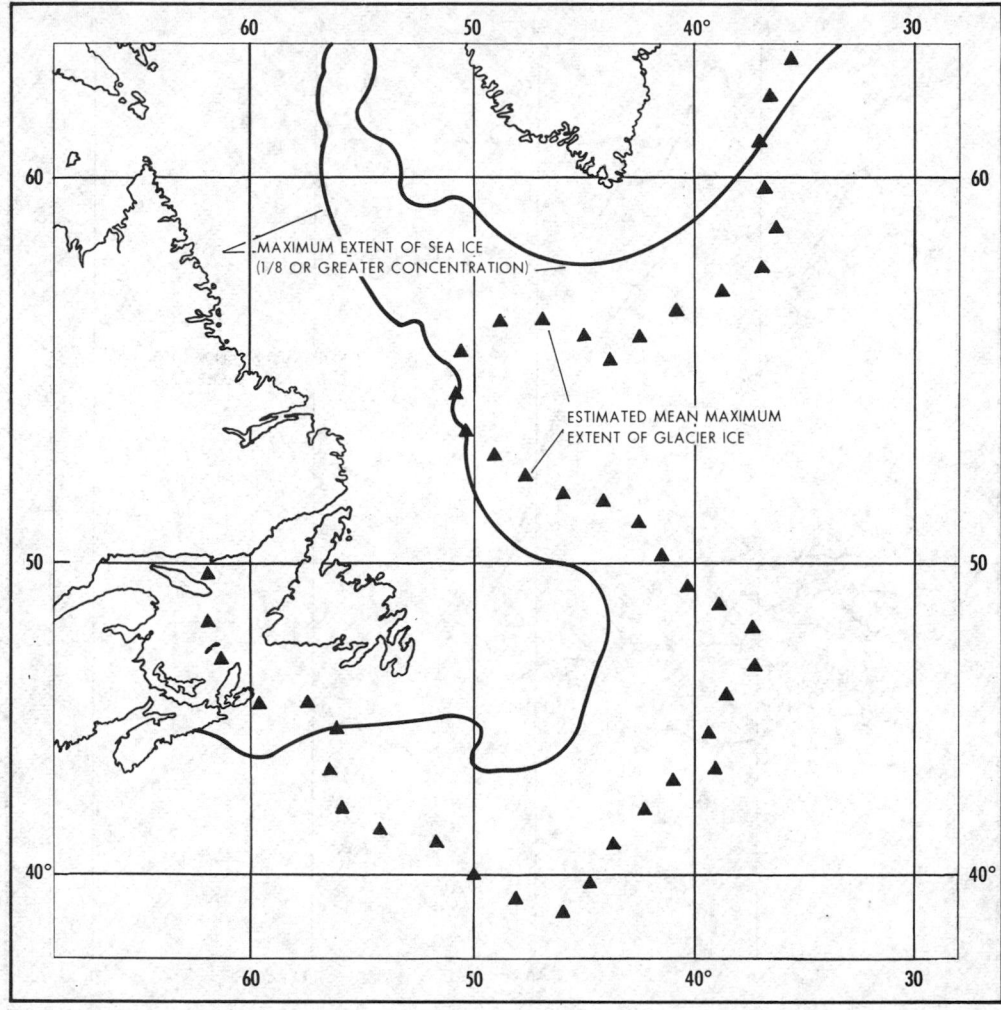

FIGURE 3611c.—Average iceberg and pack ice limits during the month of May.

reduced by one-half. In light fog or drizzle this distance is further reduced from 1,850 meters to 5.5 kilometers.

In a dense fog an iceberg may not be perceptible at a distance of over 100 meters or until it is close aboard where it will appear in the form of a luminous, white object if the sun is shining; or as a dark, somber mass with a narrow streak of blackness at the waterline if the sun is not shining. If the layer of fog is not too thick, an iceberg may be sighted from aloft sooner than from a point lower in the vessel, but this fact should not be considered justification for omitting a bow lookout. The diffusion of light in a fog will produce a blink, or area of whiteness, above and at the sides of an iceberg which will appear to increase the apparent size of its mass.

On dark, clear nights icebergs may be seen at a distance of from 1,850 meters to 4 kilometers, appearing either as white or black objects with an occasional light spot where a wave breaks against it. Under such conditions of visibility growlers are a greater menace to vessels, and the vessel's speed should be reduced and a sharp lookout maintained.

The moon may either help or hinder, depending upon its phase and position relative to ship and iceberg. A full moon in the direction of the iceberg interferes with

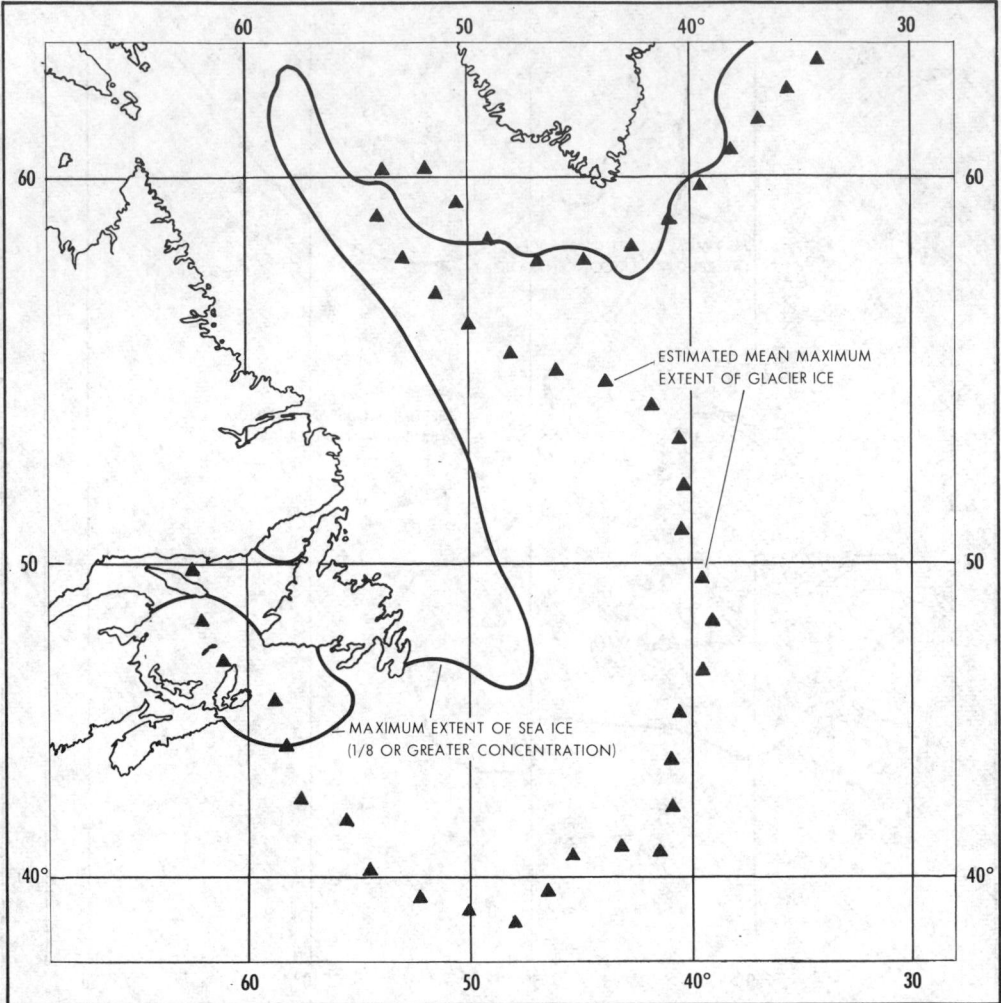

FIGURE 3611d.—Average iceberg and pack ice limits during the month of June.

its detection, while light from one in the opposite direction may produce a blink which renders the iceberg visible for a greater distance, possibly as much as 5.5 kilometers. A clouded sky at night, through which the moonlight is intermittent, also renders ice detection difficult. A night sky with heavy passing clouds may also dim or obscure any object which has been sighted, and fleecy cumulus and cumulonimbus clouds often may give the appearance of blink from icebergs.

If an iceberg is in the process of disintegration, its presence may be detected by the cracking sound as a piece breaks off, or by the thunderous roar as a large piece falls into the water. The appearance of smaller pieces of ice in the water often indicates the presence of an iceberg nearby. In calm weather such pieces may form a curved line with the parent iceberg on the concave side. Some of the pieces broken from an iceberg are themselves large enough to be a menace to ships.

As the ship moves closer towards areas known to contain sea ice, one of the most reliable signs that pack ice is being approached is the absence of swell or wave motion in a fresh breeze or a sudden flattening of the sea, especially from leeward. The observation of icebergs in itself is not a good indication that pack ice will be encountered soon, since icebergs may be found at great distances from pack ice. If the sea ice is approached from windward, it is usually compacted and the edge will be sharply defined. However, if it is approached from leeward, the ice is likely to be loose and somewhat scattered, often in long narrow arms.

Another reliable sign of the approach of pack ice, not yet in sight, is the appearance of a pattern, or **sky map,** on the horizon or on the underside of distant, extensive cloud areas, created by the varying amounts of light reflected from different materials on the sea or earth's surface. A bright white glare, or **snow blink,** will be observed above a snow covered surface. When the reflection on the underside of clouds is caused by an accumulation of distant ice, the glare is a little less bright and is referred to as an **ice blink.** A relatively dark pattern is reflected on the underside of clouds when it is over land that is not snow covered. This is known as a **land sky.** The darkest pattern will occur when the clouds are above an open water area, and is called a **water sky.** A mariner experienced in recognizing the sky maps detailed above will find them useful in avoiding ice or searching out openings which may permit his vessel to make progress while proceeding through an ice field.

Another indication of the presence of sea ice is the formation of thick bands of fog over the ice edge as moisture condenses from warm air as it passes over the colder ice. An abrupt change in air or sea temperature or seawater salinity is not a reliable sign of the approach of icebergs or pack ice. However, a drop in the seawater temperature to $1°.1C$ may be an indication that a ship is within 90 kilometers of pack ice.

The presence of certain species of animals and birds can also indicate that pack ice is in close proximity. The sighting of walruses, seals, or polar bears in the Arctic should warn the mariner that pack ice is close at hand. In the Antarctic, the usual precursors of sea ice are penguins, terns, fulmars, petrels, and skuas. The mariner will do well to observe the habits of all species encountered, for the information gained will be useful on subsequent journeys.

When visibility becomes limited, radar can prove to be an invaluable tool for the polar mariner. Although many icebergs will be observed visually on clear days before there is a return on the radarscope, radar under bad weather conditions will detect the average iceberg at a range of about 15 to 18 kilometers. The intensity of the return is a function of the nature of the iceberg's exposed surface (slope, surface roughness); however, it is unusual to find an iceberg which will not produce a detectable echo.

Large, vertical-sided tabular icebergs of the antarctic and arctic ice islands are usually detected by radar at ranges of 28 to 55 kilometers, with ranges of 68.5 kilometers having been reported.

Whereas a large iceberg is almost always detected by radar in time to be avoided, a growler large enough to be a serious menace to a vessel may be lost in the sea return and escape detection. If an iceberg or growler is detected by radar, tracking is sometimes necessary to distinguish it from a rock, islet, or another ship.

Radar can be of great assistance to one experienced in interpreting the radarscope. Smooth sea ice, like smooth water, returns little or no echo, but small floes of rough, hummocky sea ice capable of inflicting damage to a ship can be detected in a smooth sea at a range of about 4 to 6 kilometers. The return may be similar to sea return, but the same echoes appear at each sweep. A lead in smooth ice is clearly visible on a radarscope, even though a thin coating of new ice may have formed in the opening. A light covering of snow obliterating many of the features to the eye has little effect upon a radar return. The ranges at which ice can be detected by radar are somewhat dependent upon refraction, which is sometimes quite abnormal in polar regions. Adequate training and experience are essential if full benefit is to be realized from radar.

Echoes from the ship's whistle or horn will sometimes indicate the presence of icebergs. Such echoes can give an indication of direction. If the time interval between the sound and its echo is measured, the distance in meters can be determined by multi-plying the number of seconds by 168. However, echoes are not a reliable indication because only those pieces of ice with large vertical areas facing the ship return enough echo to be heard. Also, echoes might be received from land or a fog bank.

At relatively short ranges, sonar is sometimes helpful in locating ice. The initial detection of icebergs may be made at a distance of about 5 kilometers or more, but usually considerably less. Growlers may be detected at a distance of 900 meters to 2.5 kilometers, and even smaller pieces may be detected in time to avoid them. Since one-half to seven-eighths of the mass of an iceberg may lie below the surface, the underwater portion presents a better target than the portion above water.

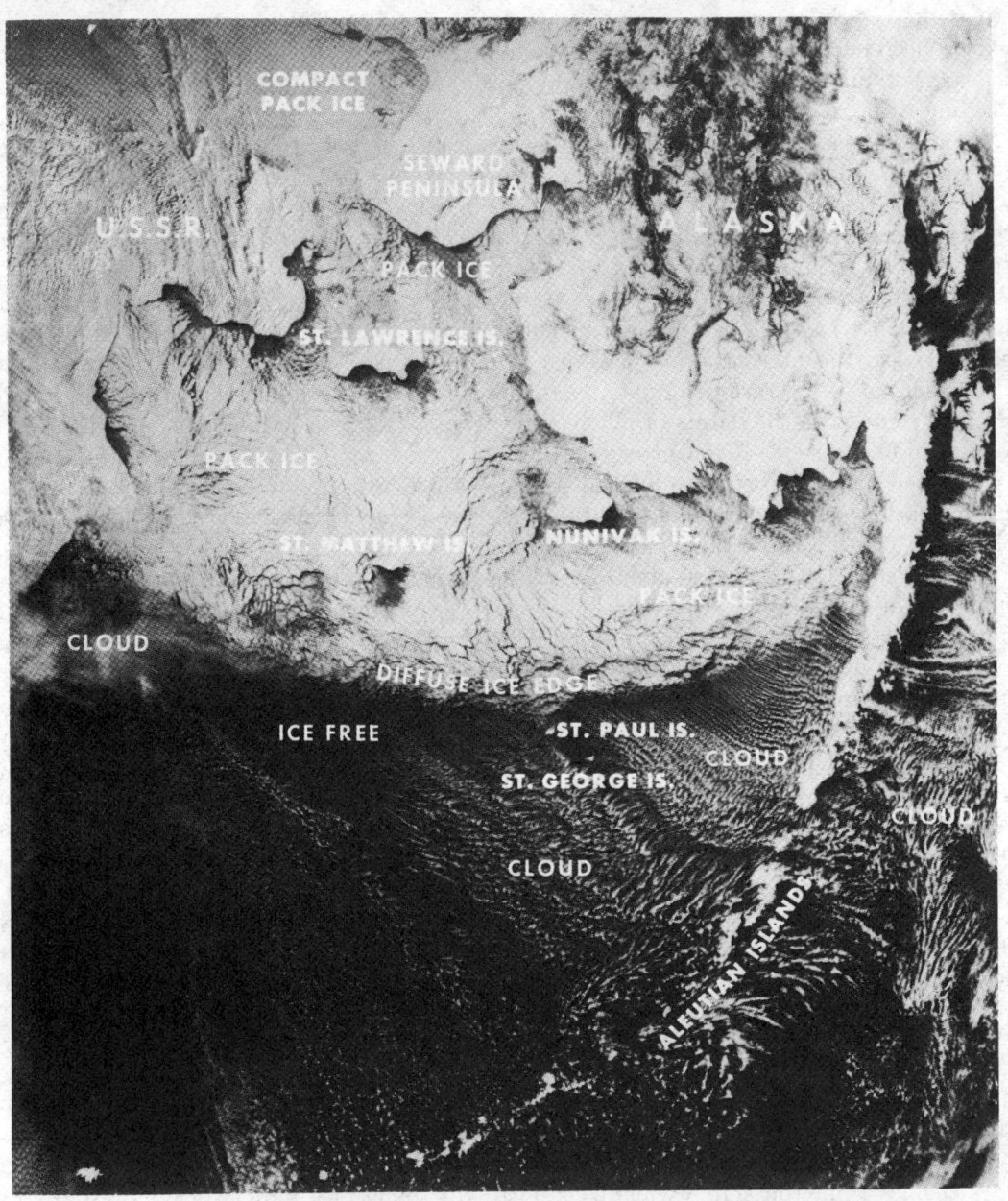

FIGURE 3613a.—Example of satellite imagery with a resolution of 0.9 kilometer.

Ice in the polar regions is best detected and observed from the air either from aircraft or by satellite remote sensing surveillance systems. Fixed-winged aircraft have been utilized extensively for obtaining detailed aerial ice reconnaissance information since the early 1930's and will no doubt continue to provide this invaluable service for many years to come. Some ships, particularly icebreakers, proceeding into high latitudes carry helicopters, which are invaluable in locating ice and determining the relative navigability of different portions of the ice pack. If these helicopters, their support vessels, or aircraft flying aerial reconnaissance can be contacted by radio, much useful information will be obtained from them. Ice reports from personnel at arctic and antarctic coastal shore stations can also prove valuable to the polar mariner.

The enormous ice reconnaissance capabilities of meteorological satellites were confirmed within hours of the launch by the National Aeronautics and Space Administration (NASA) of the first experimental meteorological satellite, TIROS I, on April 1, 1960. Although this satellite was placed in an equatorial orbit, it was able to detect ice covered waters in the Gulf of St. Lawrence-Newfoundland region. With the advent of the polar-orbiting meteorological satellites during the mid and late 1960's,

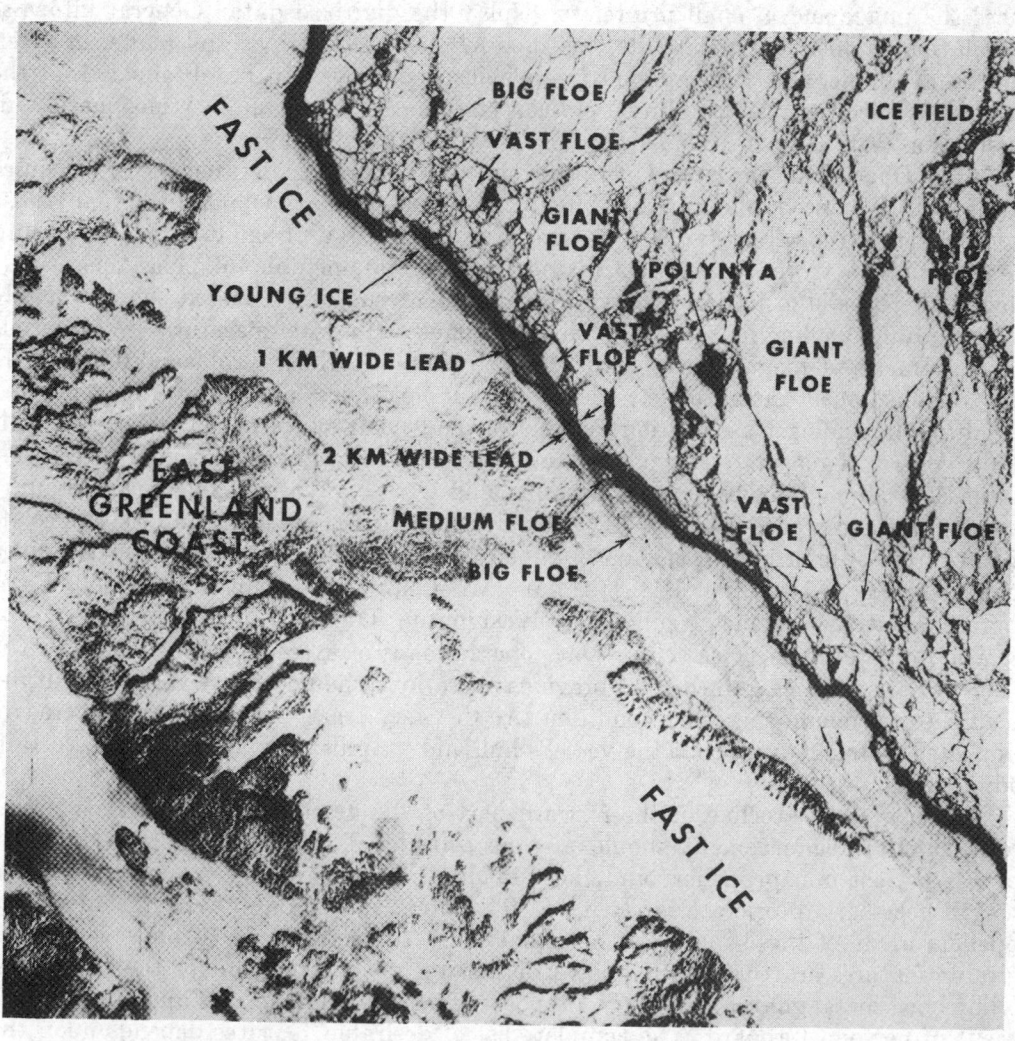

FIGURE 3613b.—Example of satellite imagery with a resolution of 80 meters.

the U. S. Navy initiated an operational satellite ice reconnaissance program which could, depending upon solar illumination, observe on a daily basis ice and its movement in any region of the globe. With the further addition of improved sensors such as high resolution infrared and visible scanning radiometers (SR); very high resolution radiometers (VHRR), also in the visible and infrared spectrum; and microwave systems; detailed global satellite ice data were made available under all weather and lighting conditions with resolutions in some cases below 100 meters. Examples of satellite imagery of ice covered waters are shown in figures 3613a and 3613b.

Utilizing portable Automatic Picture Transmission (APT) equipment, which can easily be installed aboard ships or aircraft, visible and infrared radiation data transmitted from operational satellites can be collected during a satellite's passage overhead. In this manner ice data from the satellite's scanning radiometers can be received by APT stations anywhere in the polar regions during the time they are in the line of sight of the satellite. Portable APT equipment is generally small and inexpensive, usually consisting of a receiver with a camera pack, a scanning radiometer adapter, a tape recorder for later data playback, and an omnidirectional antenna for ship and aircraft use. A printed display is available with the addition of a mini-computer that also enhances the image and a small printer to display the digitized data. General information relating to operational satellites, various APT systems, types and modes of satellite data available, and transmission frequencies and times can be obtained from the National Environmental Satellite Service, National Oceanic and Atmospheric Administration, Washington, D.C.

3614. Operations in ice.—Operations in the polar regions necessarily require considerable advanced planning and many more precautionary measures than those taken prior to a typical open ocean voyage. The crew, large or small, of a polar-bound vessel should be thoroughly indoctrinated in the fundamentals of polar operations, utilizing the best information sources available. The subjects covered should include training in shiphandling in ice, polar navigation, effects of low temperatures on materials and equipment, damage control procedures, communications problems inherent in polar regions, polar meteorology, sea ice terminology, ice observing and reporting procedures (including classification and codes) and polar survival. Training materials should consist of reports on previous arctic and antarctic voyages, sailing directions, ice atlases, training films on polar operations, and U. S. Navy service manuals detailing the recommended procedures.to follow during high latitude missions. Information relating to sources of information can be obtained from the Director, Naval Oceanography and Meteorology Command, Bay St. Louis, Mississippi, and from the Office of Polar Programs, National Science Foundation, Washington, D.C.

The preparation of a vessel for polar operations is of extreme importance and the considerable experience gained from previous operations should be drawn upon to bring the ship to optimum operating condition. At the very least, operations conducted in ice infested waters require that the vessel's hull and propulsion system undergo certain modifications.

The bow and waterline of the forward part of the vessel should be heavily reinforced. Similar reinforcement should also be considered for the propulsion spaces of the vessel. Cast iron propellers and those made of a bronze alloy do not possess the strength necessary to operate safely in ice. Therefore, it is strongly recommended that propellers made of these materials be replaced by those fabricated from steel. Other desirable features are the absence of vertical sides, deep placement of the propellers, a blunt bow, metal guards to protect propellers from ice damage, and lifeboats for 150 percent of personnel aboard. The complete list of desirable features depends upon the area of operations, types of ice to be encountered, length of stay in the vicinity of ice, anticipated assistance by icebreakers, and possibly other factors. Strength requirements and the minimum thicknesses deemed necessary for the vessel's frames and additional plating to be used as reinforcement, as well as other procedures needed to outfit a vessel for ice operations, can be obtained from the American Bureau of Shipping. For a more definitive and complete guide to the ice strengthening of ships, the mariner may desire to consult the procedures outlined in *Rules for Ice Strengthening of Ships*, from the Board of Navigation, Helsinki, Finland.

Equipment necessary to meet the basic needs of the crew and to insure the successful and safe completion of the polar voyage should not be overlooked. A minimum list of essential items should consist of polar clothing and footware, food, vitamins, medical supplies, fuel, storage batteries, antifreeze, explosives, detonators, fuses, meteorological supplies, and survival kits containing sleeping bags, trail rations, firearms, ammunition, fishing gear, emergency medical supplies, and a repair kit.

Whatever the nature of the vessel, it will be subjected to various hazards which may cause damage. Its safety depends largely upon the thoroughness of advance preparations, the alertness and skill of its crew, and their ability to make repairs if damage is incurred. Spare propellers, rudder assemblies, and patch materials, together with the equipment necessary to effect emergency repairs of structural damage should be carried. Examples of repair materials needed include quick setting cement, oakum, canvas, timbers, planks, pieces of iron of varying shapes, welding equipment, clamps, and an assortment of nuts, bolts, washers, screws, and nails.

Ice and snow accumulation on portions of the vessel poses a definite safety hazard. Therefore, mallets, hammers, and scrapers to aid in the removal of heavy accumulations of ice, together with a supply of snow shovels and stiff brooms for snow removal should be provided.

Navigation in polar waters is, even under optimum conditions, difficult and, during poor conditions, almost impossible. Environmental conditions encountered in the high latitudes such as fog, storms, compass anomalies, atmospheric effects, and, of course, ice, hinder polar operations. Also, deficiencies in the reliability and detail of hydrographic and geographical information presented on polar navigation charts coupled with a distinct lack of reliable bathymetry, current, and tidal data add to the problems of polar navigation. Much work is being carried out in the polar regions to improve the geodetic control, triangulation, and quality of hydrographic and topographic information necessary for accurate polar charts; however, until this massive task is completed, the only resource open to the polar navigator, especially during periods of poor environmental conditions, is to rely upon the basic principles of navigation and adapt them to unconventional methods when abnormal situations arise. A guide to polar navigation is presented in chapter XXV.

Upon the approach to pack ice, a careful decision is needed to determine the best action. Often it is possible to go around the ice, rather than through it. Unless the pack is quite loose, this action usually gains rather than loses time. When skirting an ice field or an iceberg, do so to windward, if a choice is available, to avoid projecting tongues of ice or individual pieces that have been blown away from the main body of ice.

When it becomes necessary to enter pack ice, a thorough examination of the distribution and extent of the ice conditions should be made beforehand from the highest possible location. Aircraft (particularly helicopters) and direct satellite readouts are of great value in determining the nature of the ice to be encountered. The most important features to be noted include the location of open water such as leads and polynyas which may be manifested by water sky, icebergs, and the presence or absence of both ice under pressure and rotten ice. Some protection may be offered the propeller and rudder assemblies by trimming the vessel down by the stern slightly (at no time more than 60 or 90 centimeters) prior to entering the ice; however, this precaution usually impairs the maneuvering characteristics of most vessels not specifically built for icebreaking.

Selection of the point of entry into the pack should be undertaken with great care; and if the ice boundary consists of closely packed ice or ice under pressure, it is advisable to skirt the edge until a more desirable point of entry is located. Seek areas with low ice concentrations, areas of rotten ice or those containing navigable leads, and if possible enter from leeward on a course perpendicular to the ice edge. It is also advisable to take into consideration the direction and force of the wind, and the set and drift of the prevailing currents when determining the point of entry and the course followed thereafter. Due to wind induced wave action, ice floes close to the periphery of the ice pack will take on a bouncing motion which can be quite hazardous to the hull of thin-skinned vessels. In addition, keep in mind that pack ice will drift slightly to the right of the lee of the true wind in the Northern Hemisphere and to the left of the lee in the Southern Hemisphere (art. 3608), and that leads opened by the force of the wind will appear perpendicular to the wind direction. If a suitable entry point cannot be located due to less than favorable conditions, one should be patient. Unfavorable conditions generally improve over a short period of time by a change in the wind, tide, or sea state.

Having entered the pack, *always work with the ice, not against it, and keep moving*, but do not rush the work of negotiating the pack. Patience may pay big dividends. Respect the ice but do not fear it. Proceed at slow speed at first, staying in open water or in areas of weak ice if possible. The vessel's speed may be safely increased after it has been ascertained how well it handles under the varying ice conditions encountered. Remember that it is always better to make good progress in the *general* direction desired than to fight large thick floes in the *exact* direction to be made good. However, avoid the temptation to proceed far to one side of the intended track; it is almost always better to back out and seek a more penetrable area. During those situations when it becomes necessary to back, always do so with extreme caution.

Ice conditions may change rapidly while a vessel is working in pack ice, necessitating some quick maneuvering. It must never be forgotten that conventional vessels, even though ice strengthened, are not built for ice navigation. The vessel should be conned to first attempt to place it in leads or polynyas, giving due consideration to wind conditions. The age, thickness, and size of ice which can be broken depends upon the type, size, strength, and shaft horsepower of the vessel employed. If contact with an ice floe is unavoidable, never strike it a glancing blow. This maneuver may cause the ship to veer off in a direction which will swing the stern into the ice. If possible seek weak spots in the floe and hit it head-on at slow speed. Unless the ice is rotten or very young, do not attempt to break through the floe, but rather make an attempt to swing it aside as speed is slowly increased. Keep clear of corners and projecting points of ice, but do so without making sharp turns which may throw the stern against the ice, resulting in a damaged propeller, propeller shaft, or rudder. The use of full rudder, in non-emergency situations, is not recommended because it may swing either the stern or mid-section of the vessel into the ice. Keep a sharp watch on the propellers and rudder, fending off with long ice poles pieces of ice which might damage these vital parts. Stop the propellers only if ice cannot be avoided.

Offshore winds may open relatively ice free navigable coastal leads, but such leads should not be entered without benefit of icebreaker escort. If it becomes necessary to enter coastal leads, narrow straits, or bays, an alert watch should be maintained since a shift in the wind may force drifting ice down upon the vessel. An increase in wind on the windward side of a prominent point, grounded iceberg, or land ice tongue extending into the sea will similarly endanger a vessel. It will always be wiser to seek out leads toward the windward side of the main body of the ice pack. In the event that the vessel is under imminent danger of being trapped close to shore by pack ice, immediately attempt to orient the vessel's bow seaward. This will help to take advantage of the little manuevering room available in the open water areas found between ice floes. Work carefully through these areas, easing the ice floes aside while maintaining a close watch on the general movement of the ice pack.

If the vessel is completely halted by pack ice, it is best to keep the rudder amidships and the propellers turning at slow speed. The wash of the propellers may help to clear ice away from the stern, making it possible to back down safely. When the vessel is stuck fast as is the case when the bow is forced up onto a massive ice floe, an attempt first should be made to free the vessel by going full speed astern. If this manuever proves ineffective, it may be possible to get the vessel's stern to move slightly, thereby causing the bow to shift, by shifting the rudder from one side to the other while going full speed ahead. Another attempt at going astern should then free the vessel. The vessel may also be freed by either transferring water from the ballast tanks causing the vessel to list, or by alternately flooding and emptying the fore and aft tanks. Men wielding crowbars may also be able to split the ice at the pressure points. If all these methods fail, the utilization of deadmen (2- to 4-meter lengths of timber buried in holes out in the ice and to which a vessel is moored) and ice anchors (a stockless, single-fluked hook embedded in the ice) may be helpful. With a deadman or ice anchors attached to the ice astern, the vessel may be warped off the ice by winching while the engines are going full astern. If all the foregoing methods fail, explosives placed in holes cut nearly to the bottom of the ice approximately 10 to 12 meters off the beam of the vessel and detonated while the engines are working full astern should succeed in freeing the vessel. A vessel may also be sawed out of the ice if the ambient air temperature is above the freezing point of seawater.

When a vessel becomes so closely surrounded by ice that all steering control is lost and it is unable to move, it is **beset.** It may then be carried by the drifting pack into shallow water or areas containing thicker ice or icebergs with their accompanying dangerous underwater projections. If ice forcibly presses itself against the hull, the vessel is said to be **nipped,** whether or not damage is sustained. When this occurs, the gradually increasing pressure may be capable of holing the vessel's bottom. When a vessel is beset or nipped, freedom may be achieved through the careful manuevering procedures, the physical efforts of the crew, or by the use of explosives similar to those previously detailed. Under severe conditions the mariner's best ally may be patience since there will be many times when nothing can be done to improve the vessel's plight until there is a change in meteorological conditions. It is a time to preserve fuel and perform any needed repairs to the vessel and its engines. Damage to the vessel while it is beset is usually attributable to collisions or pressure exerted between the vessel's hull, propellers, or rudder assembly and the sharp corners of ice floes. These collisions can be minimized greatly by attempting to align the vessel in such a manner as to insure that the pressure from the surrounding pack ice is distributed as evenly as possible over the hull. This is best accomplished when medium or large ice floes encircle the vessel.

In the vicinity of icebergs, either in or outside of the pack ice, a sharp lookout should be kept and all icebergs given a wide berth. The commanding officers and masters of all vessels, irrespective of their size, should treat all icebergs with due respect. The best locations for lookouts are generally in a crow's nest rigged in the foremast or housed in a shelter built specifically for a bow lookout in the eyes of a vessel. Telephone communications between these sites and the navigation bridge on larger vessels will prove invaluable. It is dangerous to approach close to an iceberg of any size because of the possibility of encountering underwater extensions, and because icebergs that are disintegrating may suddenly capsize or readjust their masses to new positions of equilibrium. In periods of low visibility the utmost caution is needed at all times. Vessel speed should be reduced and the watch prepared for quick maneuvering. Radar becomes an effective tool in this case, but does not negate the need for trained lookouts.

Since icebergs may have from eight to nine-tenths of their masses below the water surface, their drift (art. 3809) is generally influenced more by currents than winds, particularly under light wind conditions. The drift of pack ice, on the other hand, is usually dependent upon the wind. Under these conditions, icebergs within the pack may be found moving at a different rate and in a different direction from that of the pack ice. In regions of strong currents, icebergs should always be given a wide berth because they may often travel upwind at great speeds under the influence of contrary currents, wreaking heavy pack in their paths and endangering those vessels that are unable to work clear. In these situations, open water will generally be found leeward of the iceberg, with piled up pack ice to windward. Where currents are weak and a strong wind predominates, similar conditions will be observed as the wind driven ice pack overtakes an iceberg and piles up to windward with an open water area lying to leeward.

Under ice submarine operations require knowledge of prevailing and expected sea ice conditions to ensure maximum operational efficiency and safety. The most important ice features are the frequency and extent of downward projections (bummocks and ice keels) from the underside of the **ice canopy** (pack ice and enclosed water areas from the point of view of the submariner), the distribution of thin ice areas through which submarines can attempt to surface, and the probable location of the outer pack edge where submarines can remain surfaced during emergencies to rendezvous with surface ship or helicopter units.

Bummocks are the subsurface counterpart of hummocks, and **ice keels** are similarly related to ridges. When the physical nature of these ice features is considered, it is apparent that ice keels may have considerable horizontal extent whereas individual bummocks can be expected to have little horizontal extent. In shallow water lanes to the Arctic Basin such as the Bering Strait and the adjoining portions of the Bering Sea and Chukchi Sea, deep bummocks and ice keels may leave little vertical leeway for submarine passage. Widely separated bummocks may be circumnavigated but make for a hazardous passage. Extensive ice areas with numerous bummocks or ice keels which cross the lane, however, may effectively block passage to the Arctic Basin.

Bummocks and ice keels extend downward approximately five times their vertical extent above the ice surface. Therefore, observed ridges of approximately 10 meters may extend as much as 50 meters below sea level. Owing to the direct relation of the frequency and vertical extent between these surface features and their subsurface counterparts, aircraft reconnaissance of ice conditions over a planned submarine cruise track should be conducted before under ice operations are commenced.

Skylights are defined as thin places (usually less than 1 meter thick) in the ice canopy and appear from below as relatively light translucent patches in dark surroundings. The undersurface of a skylight is usually flat; not having been subjected to great pressure although the ice canopy may have a concentration of nearly 8 oktas. Skylights are called large if big enough for a submarine to attempt to surface through them; that is, have a linear extent of at least 120 meters. Skylights smaller than 120 meters are called small. An ice canopy along a submarine's track that contains a number of large skylights or other features such as leads and polynyas which permit a submarine to surface more frequently than 10 times per 56 kilometers is called **friendly ice.** An ice canopy containing no large skylights or other features which permit a submarine to surface is called **hostile ice.**

For a more comprehensive guide to operations in ice, it is recommended that the mariner refer to *Polar Operations*, by Captain Edwin A. MacDonald, USN (Ret.), published by the United States Naval Institute, Annapolis, Maryland.

3615. Great Lakes ice.—Large vessels have been navigating the Great Lakes since the early 1760's. This large expanse of navigable water has since become one of the world's busiest waterways. Due to the northern geographical location of the Great Lakes Basin and its susceptibility to arctic outbreaks of polar air during winter, the formation of ice plays a major role, albeit a disruptive one, in this region's economically vital marine industry. Because of the relatively large size of the five Great Lakes, the ice cover which forms on them is affected by the wind and currents to a greater degree than that on smaller lakes. The Great Lakes northern location results in a long ice growth season which in combination with the effect of wind and current imparts to their ice covers some of the characteristics and behavior of an arctic ice pack. For these reasons, this article is being included in this chapter on ice in the sea.

Since the five Great Lakes extend over a distance of approximately 800 kilometers in a north-south direction, each lake is influenced by varying degrees of meteorological parameters. These parameters, in combination with the fact that each lake also possesses differing hydrometeorological characteristics, materially affects the extent and distribution of their respective ice covers. The largest, deepest, and most northern of the five Great Lakes is Lake Superior. Ice not under pressure, especially along this lake's northern shores, can attain a thickness of between 70 to 100 centimeters which is equivalent to medium first-year ice. Winds and currents acting upon the ice have been known to cause ridging with heights approaching 10 meters. The great depth of Lake Superior, however, provides it with a large heat storage capacity which hinders the growth of ice somewhat, particularly during the period of initial ice formation. During a normal winter, it can be expected that 60 percent of the surface area of Lake Superior will become covered by ice. This value increases to 95 percent during a severe winter and decreases to 40 percent during a mild winter. Under average conditions, ice which presents an obstacle to navigation on Lake Superior appears during the last week of December along both the north and south shores with the maximum extent of ice cover occurring between March 30 and April 10.

Lake Michigan extends in a north-south direction for approximately 480 kilometers and possesses the third largest mean depth of the Great Lakes. Its north-south alignment causes ice to accumulate in the northern portions of the lake initially and then grow in a southerly direction as the winter progresses. Ice thickness ranges from an average of 10 to 20 centimeters (grey to grey-white ice) in the southern portion to 50 to 80 centimeters (thin to medium first-year ice) in the northern portion. The ice cover becomes a hazard to navigation in the northern sector of Lake Michigan during the last week of December with the average date of maximum extent of ice cover ranging from March 10 in the Chicago area to March 28 at the northern end of Green Bay. During a severe winter, 80 percent of Lake Michigan's surface area will be covered by ice. This value reduces to 40 percent for a normal winter and to only 10 percent during a mild winter.

Ice formation on Lake Huron generally commences along the northeastern and western shorelines during the last week in December of each year. The deep north central basin of the lake does not, except during severe winters, generally acquire even a partial ice cover. The ice on Lake Huron will on the average consist predominately of thin first-year ice (30-70 centimeters), with some medium first-year ice (70–120 centimeters) forming during a severe winter. The time interval between dates of the average maximum ice cover extent for this lake ranges from March 11 in the extreme southern portion to March 28 in the northern sector. The percent of lake surface area that will become ice covered is 60 percent for a normal winter, 40 percent for a mild winter, and 80 percent for a severe winter.

Lake Erie is the shallowest of the Great Lakes with a mean depth of just under 20 meters. Because of its shallowness, this lake is greatly influenced by seasonal temperature changes and will accumulate a considerable ice cover over a short period of time. Ice will begin to form first in the very shallow western portion of the lake during mid-December. During its growth period, the lake ice is acted upon by the prevailing winds and currents which concentrate it at the northeastern end of the lake. Generally, Lake Erie's ice cover is made up of a combination of grey-white ice (15–30 centimeters) and thin first-year ice (30–70 centimeters). The average dates on which the maximum extent of ice cover is attained on Lake Erie varies from March 5 in the western sector to March 15 for the northeastern portion of the lake. Since it reacts rapidly to the change in the seasons, Lake Erie will attain an ice cover that blankets 95 to 100 percent of its surface area during a normal winter. During a mild winter, the ice will occupy an area covering 50 percent of the surface area.

Lake Ontario has the smallest surface area of the five Great Lakes, but the second greatest mean depth, second only to Lake Superior. Like Lake Superior, its large mean depth gives Lake Ontario a large heat storage capacity which, in combination with its small surface area, causes the lake to respond slowly to changing meteorological conditions. This, in turn, produces the smallest amount of ice cover found on the Great Lakes. Ice will begin forming during mid-December in the northeastern section of the lake, and wind and current conditions similar to those found on Lake Erie will confine the majority of the ice cover to that section of the lake. The majority of the ice formed will consist of thin first-year ice (30–70 centimeters) with a small concentration of grey-white ice (15–30 centimeters). The date at which the ice cover on Lake Ontario reaches its maximum extent varies on the average from March 10 to March 20. During a mild winter only 8 percent of the lake surface area will be covered by ice. This value increases to 15 percent for a normal winter and to 25 percent for a severe winter.

The maximum ice cover distribution attained by each of the Great Lakes for a normal, mild, and severe winter are shown in figures 3615a, 3615b, and 3615c. It should be noted that although the average maximum ice cover distributions for all five lakes appear on a single chart, they occur during the average time periods detailed above for each lake.

Information concerning analyses, forecasts, and climatology of Great Lakes ice can be obtained from the Great Lakes Environmental Research Laboratory or the National Weather Service Forecast Office, both located in Ann Arbor, Michigan.

3616. Ice observing, reporting, and forecasting.—Advance knowledge of ice conditions to be encountered and knowledge of how these conditions will change over specified time periods are invaluable in both the planning and operational phases of a voyage undertaken in polar regions. Typical ice support services offered to the polar navigator generally include analyses of current ice conditions; short-range (24 to 48 hour), weekly (5 to 7 day), and long range (15 to 30 day) ice forecasts; seasonal long-range (60 to 90 day) ice outlooks which are ordinarily updated by 15 to 30 day forecasts as the season progresses; and ship weather routing service (ch. XXIV) through ice infested waters. Generally an ice analysis or forecast will depict the current or expected configuration and location of the pack ice edge, ice concentrations within the pack itself, and the locations of features such as leads, polynyas, fast ice, and areas of open water.

The single most important input into an ice forecast of any duration is an accurate, current, ice analysis based on the latest ice observations available. As stated previously, ice in the sea can be observed from vessels, fixed winged aircraft, helicopters, and by

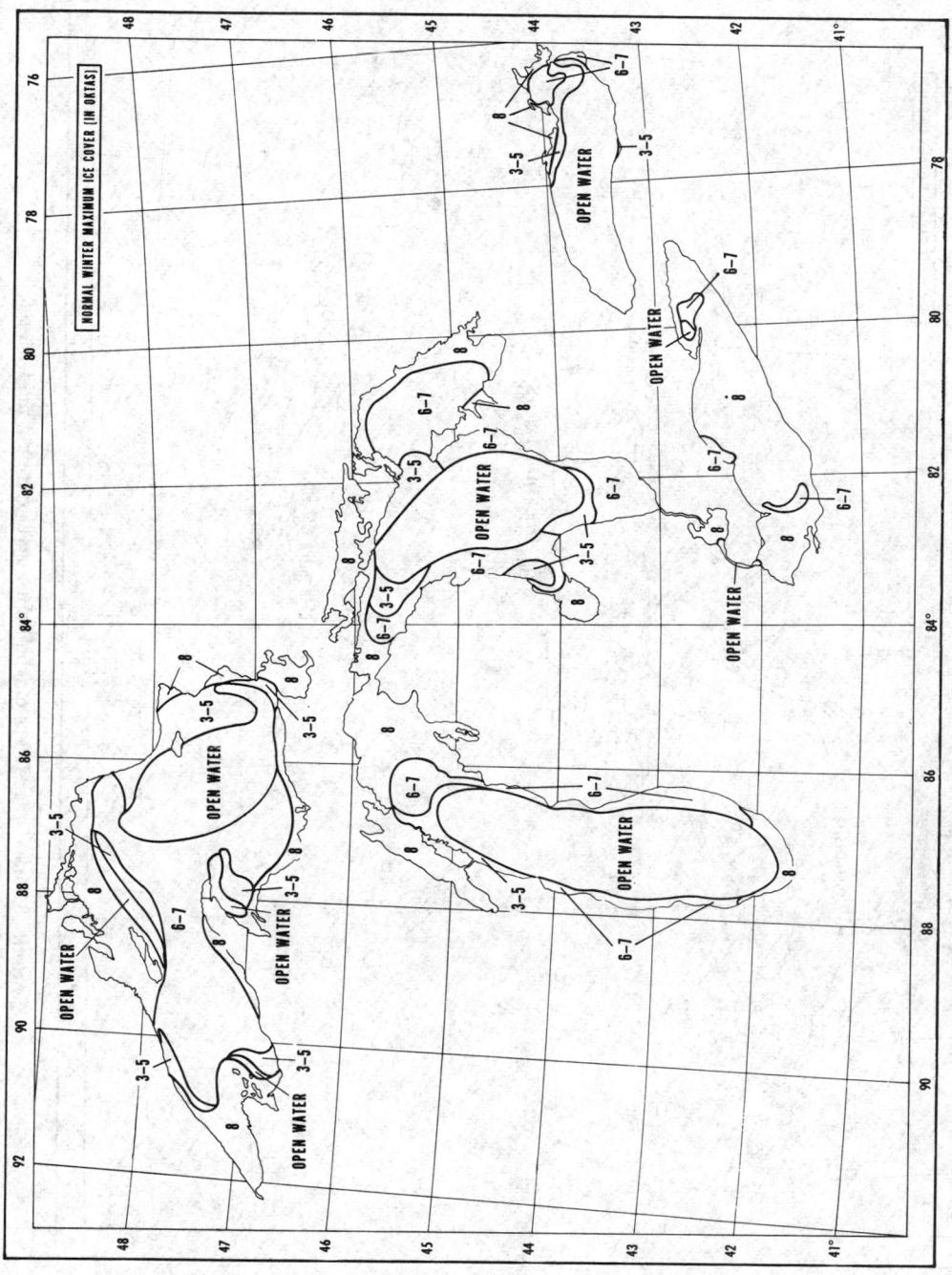

FIGURE 3615a.—Great Lakes maximum ice cover during a normal winter.

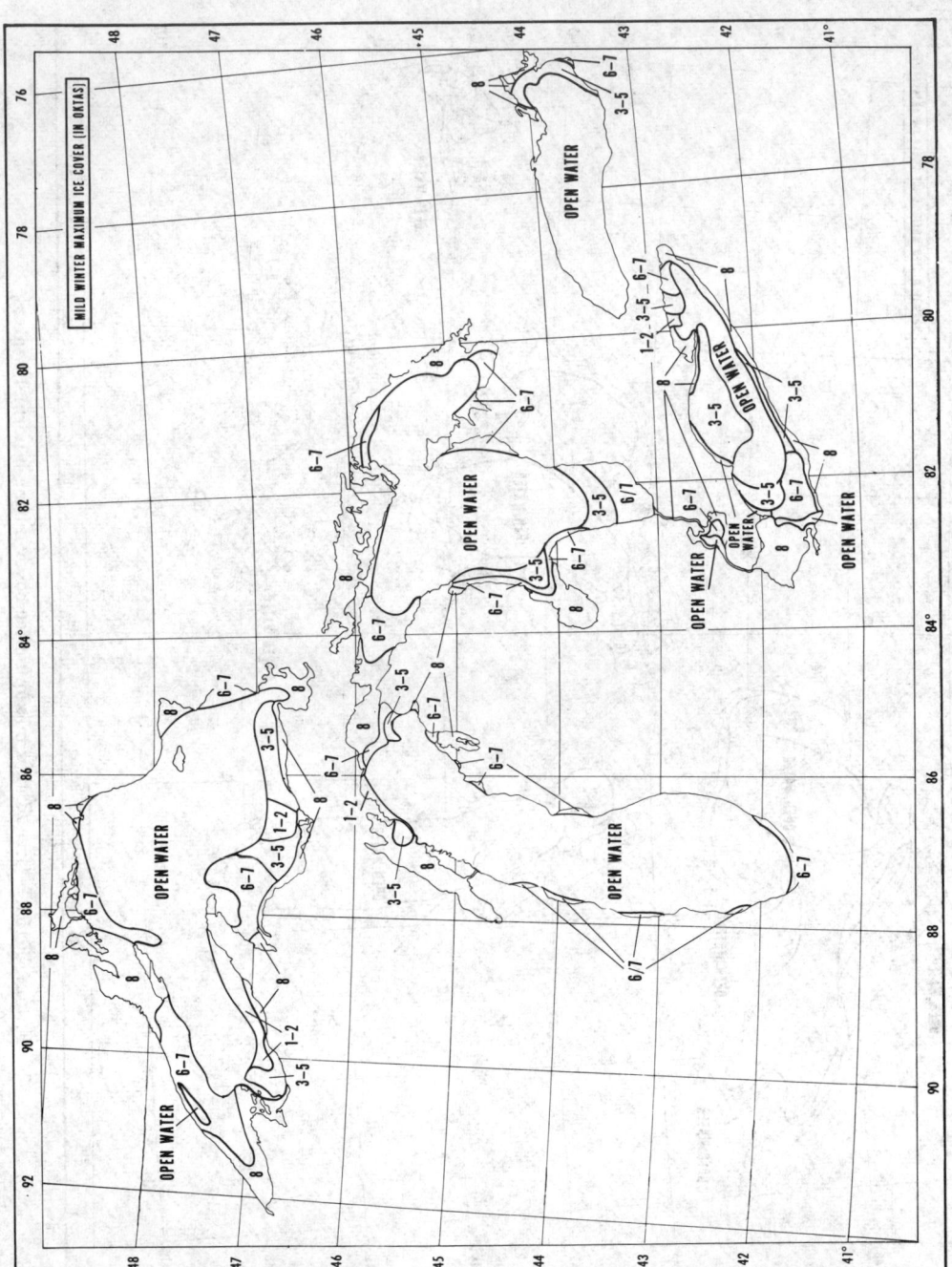

FIGURE 3615b.— Great Lakes maximum ice cover during a mild winter.

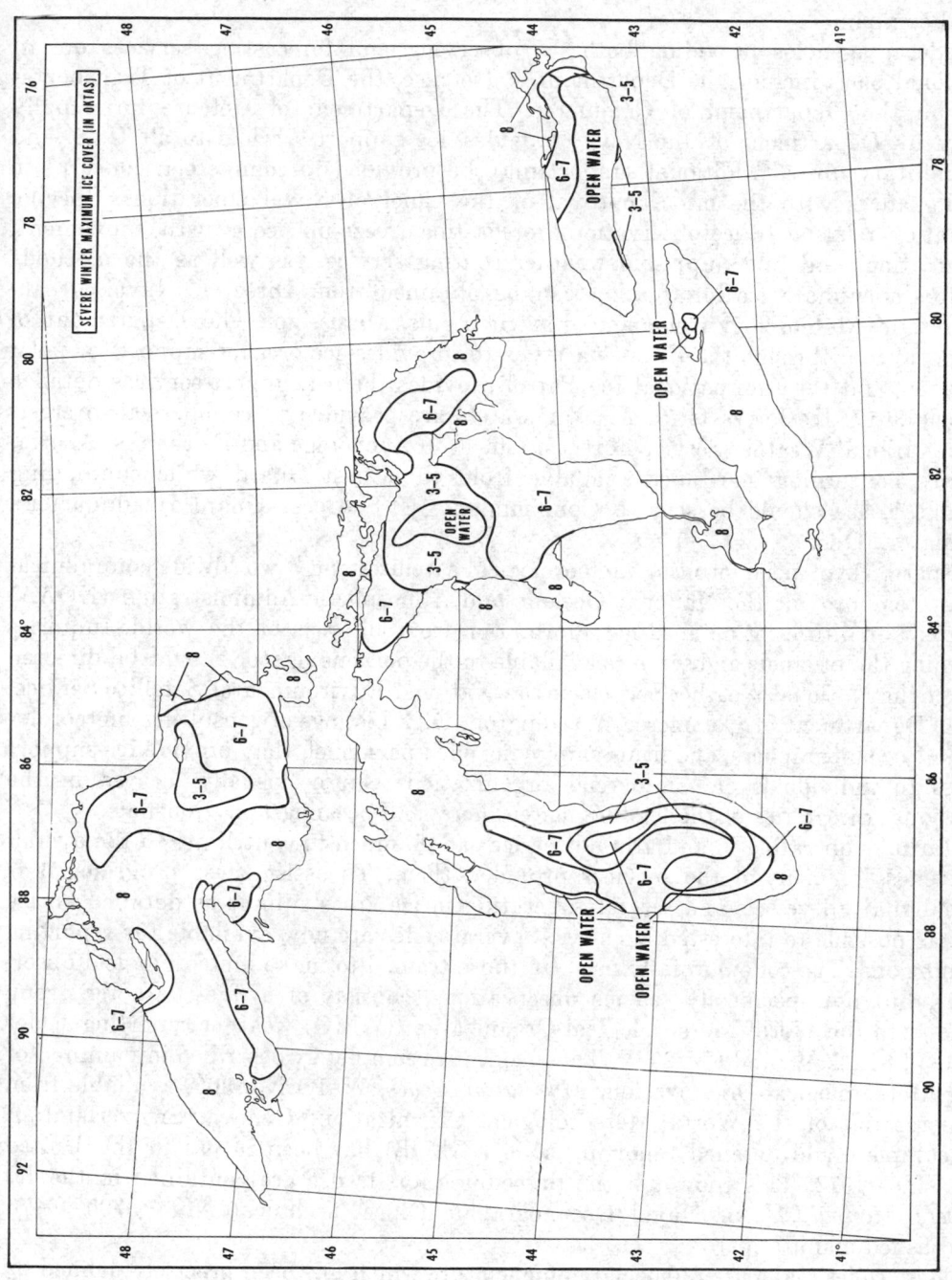

FIGURE 3615c.— Great Lakes maximum ice cover during a severe winter.

earth orbiting satellites, as well as by personnel at arctic and antarctic coastal shore stations. By means of modern communications networks, the reports of these observations are relayed to the offices of both federal government agencies and private commercial companies.

Federal agencies providing both ice observing and forecasting services on an operational basis include the Department of Defense, the Department of Transportation, and the Department of Commerce. The Department of Defense, principally through its Department of the Navy, provides ice support services to all U. S. and allied military units. Additional support may be provided to commercial concerns in some instances with the prior approval of the Chief of Naval Operations. Specific information relating to ice observation; forecasting freeze-up, ice growth, movement, concentration, and break-up; ship weather routing services; as well as the methods used to disseminate ice information can be obtained from Director, Naval Oceanography and Meteorology Command, Bay St. Louis, Mississippi. The Department of Transportation, through the U. S. Coast Guard, provides ice breaker support for polar operations, and the International Ice Patrol provides the ice support services detailed in article 3612. Ice forecasts for Alaskan waters are provided to commercial interests by the National Weather Service Forecast Offices in Anchorage and Fairbanks, Alaska. Inquiries concerning assistance available from the Coast Guard while conducting programs in ice should be sent to Commandant, U. S. Coast Guard Headquarters, Washington, D.C.

A network of polar orbiting meteorological satellites and a worldwide communications system provide the National Oceanic and Atmospheric Administration (NOAA) with great quantities of detailed ice information from all areas of the world. Inquiries concerning the products and services available to the polar navigator should be directed to either the National Weather Service or the National Environmental Satellite Service, NOAA, Department of Commerce, Washington, D.C. Listings of consulting meteorologists and oceanographers, and firms employing such personnel, that provide ice support services to individuals or commercial organizations can be usually located in the professional directories of the leading meteorology and oceanography journals.

Mariners operating in and around sea ice can do much to contribute to the overall effectiveness of many of the services provided them. To assist these programs it is essential that all vessels and aircraft operating in ice areas submit as detailed an ice report as possible to interested agencies. Several codes are now available for reporting ice conditions. The code normally used by those trained to make meteorological observations, but not specifically sea ice observations, consists of a five-character group appended to the World Meteorological Organization (WMO) weather reporting codes FM 21–V, FM 22–V, and FM 23–V. These codes are completely described in volume I of World Meteorological Organization, *Manual on Codes*, WMO No. 306, available from the Secretariat of the World Meteorological Organization, Geneva, Switzerland. A more complete and detailed reporting code.(ICEOB) has been in use in the United States since 1972. This code and the procedures for its use are contained in the *Ice Observers Manual*, U. S. Naval Oceanographic Office Technical Note 3700–49–76 (unpublished manuscript).

These codes make use of special nomenclature which has been precisely defined by the World Meteorological Organization in several languages. *Sea-Ice Nomenclature*, (WMO No. 259.TP.145) contains the nomenclature along with photography of most ice features. This publication is very useful for those who plan to submit ice condition reports.

In addition, *Guide to Meteorological Instruments and Observing Practices* (WMO No. 8.TP.31) contains a chapter on ice development, dynamic processes, and observing procedures and should also prove extremely useful.

The mariner who regularly sends as complete an ice report as possible contributes substantially to an increase in the knowledge of synoptic ice conditions and therefore to the accuracy and timeliness of subsequent ice analyses and forecasts.

PART SEVEN
WEATHER

CHAPTER XXXVII

WEATHER OBSERVATIONS

3701. Introduction.—Weather forecasts are generally based upon information acquired by observations made at a large number of stations. Ashore, these stations are located so as to provide adequate coverage of the area of interest. Most observations at sea are made by mariners, wherever they happen to be. Since the number of observations at sea is small compared to the number ashore, marine observations are of importance in areas where little or no information is available from other sources. Results of these observations are recorded in the deck log (art. 3719), or other appropriate form. Data recorded by designated vessels are sent by radio to centers ashore, where they are plotted, along with other observations, to provide data for drawing synoptic charts (art. 3826). These charts are used to make forecasts. Complete weather information gathered at sea is mailed to the appropriate meteorological services for use in the preparation of weather atlases and in marine climatological studies.

A special effort should be made to provide routine synoptic reports when transiting those areas where few ships are available to make and report weather observations. Such effort is particularly important when vessels are transiting the tropical regions. A vessel's synoptic weather report may be the first indication of a developing tropical cyclone.

In many instances, the analysis of the surface weather map and subsequent forecasts can be no better than the weather reports received.

A knowledge of *weather elements* and the instruments used to measure them is therefore of importance to the mariner who hopes to benefit from weather *broadcasts*.

3702. Atmospheric pressure measurement.—The sea of air surrounding the earth exerts a pressure of about 14.7 pounds per square inch on the surface of the earth. This **atmospheric pressure,** sometimes called **barometric pressure,** varies from place to place, and at the same place it varies with time.

Atmospheric pressure is one of the basic elements of a meteorological observation. When the pressure at each station is plotted on a synoptic chart, lines of equal atmospheric pressure, called **isobars,** are drawn to indicate the areas of high and low pressure and their centers. These are useful in making weather predictions, because certain types of weather are characteristic of each type area, and the wind patterns over large areas are deduced from the isobars.

Atmospheric pressure is measured by means of a **barometer. A mercurial barometer** does this by balancing the weight of a column of air against that of a column of mercury. The **aneroid barometer** has a partly evacuated, thin-metal cell which is compressed by atmospheric pressure, the amount of the compression being related to the pressure.

Early mercurial barometers were calibrated to indicate the height, usually in inches or millimeters, of the column of mercury needed to balance the column of air above the point of measurement. While the units **inches of mercury** and **millimeters of mercury** are still widely used, many modern barometers are calibrated to indicate the centimeter-gram-second unit of pressure, the **millibar,** which is equal to 1,000 dynes per square centimeter. A **dyne** is the force required to accelerate a mass of one gram at the rate of one centimeter per second per second. A reading in any of the three units of measurement can be converted to the equivalent reading in either of the other units by means of table 14, or the conversion factors given in appendix D. However, the pressure reading should always be reported in millibars.

3703. The mercurial barometer was invented by Evangelista Torricelli in 1643. In its simplest form it consists of a glass tube a little more than 30 inches in length and of uniform internal diameter; one end being closed, the tube is filled with mercury, and inverted into a cup of mercury. The mercury in the tube falls until the column is just supported by the pressure of the atmosphere on the open cup, leaving a vacuum at the upper end of the tube. The height of the column indicates atmospheric pressure, greater pressures supporting higher columns of mercury.

The mercurial barometer is subject to rapid variations in height, called **pumping,** due to pitch and roll of the vessel and temporary changes in atmospheric pressure in the vicinity of the barometer. Because of this, the care required in the reading of the instrument, its bulkiness, and its vulnerability to physical damage, the mercurial barometer has been replaced at sea by the aneroid barometer.

3704. The aneroid barometer (**fig. 3704**) measures atmospheric pressure by means of the force exerted by the pressure on a partly evacuated, thin-metal element called a **sylphon cell** (**aneroid capsule**). A small spring is used, either internally or externally, to partly counteract the tendency of the atmospheric pressure to crush the cell. Atmospheric pressure is indicated directly by a scale and a pointer connected to the cell by a combination of levers. The linkage provides considerable magnification of the slight motion of the cell, to permit readings to higher precision than could be obtained without it.

An aneroid barometer should be mounted permanently. Prior to installation, the barometer should be carefully set to station pressure (art. 3706). An adjustment screw is provided for this purpose. The error in the reading of the instrument is determined by comparison with a mercurial barometer or a standard precision aneroid barometer. If a qualified meteorologist is not available to make this adjustment, it is good practice to remove only one-half the apparent error. The case should then be tapped gently to assist the linkage to adjust itself, and the process repeated. If the remaining error is not more than half a millibar (0.015 inch), no attempt should be made to remove it by further adjustment. Instead, a correction should be applied to the readings. The accuracy of this correction should be checked from time to time.

3705. The barograph (**fig. 3705**) is a recording barometer. Basically, it is the same as a nonrecording aneroid barometer except that the pointer carries a pen at its outer end, and the scale is replaced by a slowly rotating cylinder around which a prepared chart is wrapped. A clock mechanism inside the cylinder rotates the cylinder so that a continuous line is traced on the chart to indicate the pressure at any time.

A **marine microbarograph** is a precision barograph with greater magnification of deformations due to pressure changes, and a correspondingly expanded chart. It is designed to maintain its precision through the varied and exacting conditions encountered in shipboard use. Two sylphon cells are used, one being mounted over the other in tandem. Minor fluctuations due to shocks or vibrations are eliminated by damping. Since oil-filled dashpots are used for this purpose, the instrument should not be inverted.

Ship motions are compensated by damping and spring loading which make it possible for the microbarograph to be tilted up to 22° without varying more than 0.3 millibars from true reading.

The barograph is usually mounted on a shelf or desk in a room open to the atmosphere, and in a location which minimizes the effect of the ship's vibration. Shock-

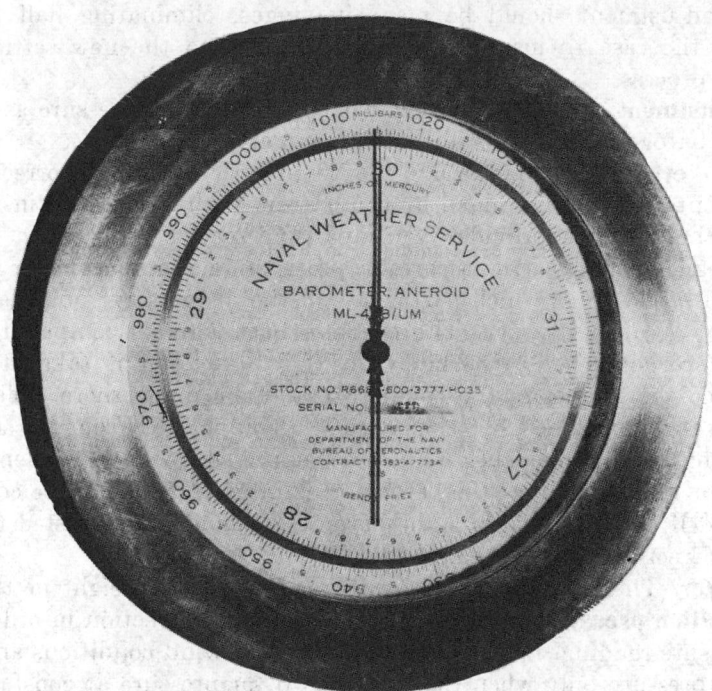

FIGURE 3704.—An aneroid barometer.

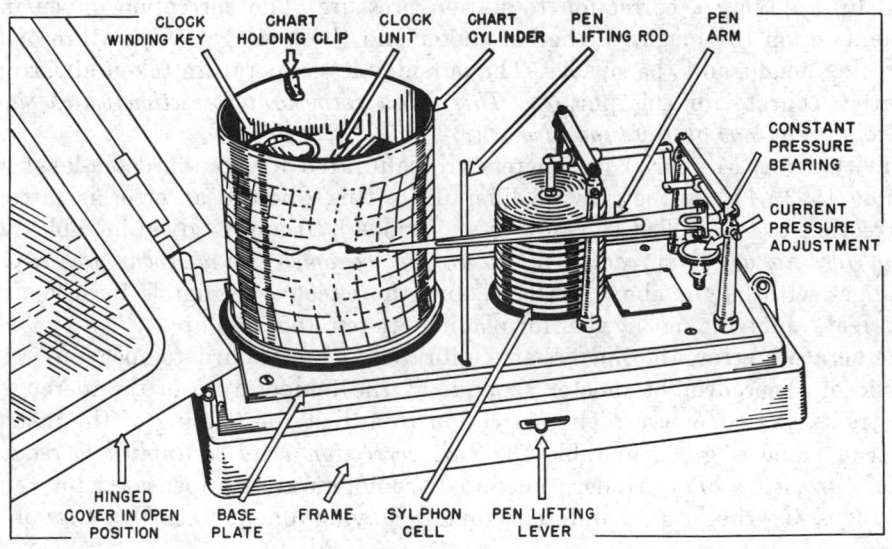

FIGURE 3705.—A barograph.

absorbing material such as sponge rubber is placed under the instrument to minimize the transmission of shocks.

The pen should be checked and the inkwell filled each time the chart is changed, every week in the case of the barograph, and each 4 days in the case of the microbarograph. The dashpots of the microbarograph should be kept filled with dashpot oil to within three-eighths inch of the top.

Both instruments require checking from time to time to insure correct indication of pressure. The position of the pen is adjusted by a small knob provided for this purpose. The adjustment should be made in stages, eliminating half the apparent error, tapping the case to insure linkage adjustment to the new setting, and then repeating the process.

3706. Adjustment of barometer readings.—Atmospheric pressure as indicated by a barometer or barograph may be subject to several errors, as follows:

Instrument error. Any inaccuracy due to imperfection or incorrect adjustment of the instrument can be determined by comparison with a precision instrument. The National Weather Service provides a comparison service. In certain U. S. ports a Port Meteorological Officer carries a portable precision aneroid barometer for barometer comparisons on board ships which participate in the cooperative observation program of the National Weather Service. The portable barometer is compared with station barometers before and after each ship visit. If a barometer is taken to a National Weather Service shore station, the comparison can be made there. The correct sea-level pressure can be obtained by telephone. The shipboard barometer should be corrected for height, as explained below, before comparison with this telephoned value. If there is reason to believe that the barometer is in error, it should be compared with a standard, and if an error is found, the barometer should be adjusted to the correct reading, or a correction applied to all readings.

Height error. The atmospheric pressure reading at the height of the barometer is called the **station pressure** and is subject to a height correction in order to make it a sea level pressure reading. Isobars adequately reflect wind conditions and geographic distribution of pressure only when they are drawn for pressure at constant height (or the varying height at which a constant pressure exists). On synoptic charts it is customary to show the equivalent pressure at sea level, called **sea level pressure.** This is found by applying a correction to station pressure. The correction, given in table 11, depends upon the height of the barometer and the average temperature of the air between this height and the surface. The outside air temperature taken aboard ship is sufficiently accurate for this purpose. *This is an important correction which should be applied to all readings of any type barometer.*

Gravity error. Mercurial barometers are calibrated for standard sea-level gravity at latitude 45°32′40″. If the gravity differs from this amount, an error is introduced. The correction to be applied to readings at various latitudes is given in table 12. *This correction does not apply to readings of an aneroid barometer or microbarograph.* Gravity also changes with height above sea level, but the effect is negligible for the first few hundred feet, and so is not needed for readings taken aboard ship.

Temperature error. Barometers are calibrated at a standard temperature of 32°F. The liquid of a mercurial barometer expands as the temperature of the mercury rises, and contracts as it decreases. The correction to adjust the reading of the instrument to the true value is given in table 13. *This correction is to be applied to readings of mercurial barometers only.* Modern aneroid barometers are compensated for temperature changes by the use of different metals having unequal coefficients of linear expansion.

3707. Wind measurement consists of determination of the direction *from* which the wind is blowing, and the speed of the wind. Wind direction is measured by a **wind vane,** and wind speed by an **anemometer.**

A wind vane consists of a device pivoted on a vertical shaft, with more surface area on one side of the pivot than on the other, so that the wind exerts more force on one side, causing the smaller end to point into the wind.

In its simplest form, an anemometer consists of a number of cups mounted on short horizontal arms attached to a longer vertical shaft which rotates as the wind blows against the cups. The speed at which the shaft rotates is directly proportional to the wind speed.

Several types of wind speed and direction recorders are available.

If no anemometer is available, wind speed can be estimated by its effect upon the sea and objects in its path, as explained in article 3709.

3708. True and apparent wind.—An observer aboard a vessel proceeding through still air experiences an **apparent wind** which is from dead ahead and has an apparent speed equal to the speed of the vessel. Thus, if the actual or **true wind** is zero and the speed of the vessel is 10 knots, the apparent wind is from dead ahead at 10 knots. If the true wind is from dead ahead at 15 knots, and the speed of the vessel is 10 knots, the apparent wind is 15+10=25 knots from dead ahead. If the vessel makes a 180° turn, the apparent wind is 15−10=5 knots from dead astern.

In any case, the apparent wind is the vector sum (art. 118, vol. II) of the true wind and the *reciprocal* of the vessel's course and speed vector. Since wind vanes and anemometers measure *apparent* wind, the usual problem aboard a vessel equipped with an anemometer is to convert this to true wind. There are several ways of doing this. Perhaps the simplest is by the graphical solution illustrated in the following example:

Example 1.—A ship is proceeding on course 150° at a speed of 17 knots. The apparent wind is from 40° off the starboard bow, speed 15 knots.

Required.—The relative direction, true direction, and speed of the true wind.

Solution (fig. 3708a).—Starting at the center of a manuevering board (art. 4212) or other suitable form, draw a line in the relative direction *from* which the apparent wind is blowing. Locate point 1 on this line, at a distance from the center equal to the speed of the apparent wind (2:1 scale is used in figure 3708a). From point 1, draw a line vertically *downward*. Locate point 2 on this line at a distance from point 1 equal to the speed of the vessel in knots, to the same scale as the first line. The relative direction of the true wind is *from* point 2 (120°) toward the center, and the speed of the true wind is the distance of point 2 from the center, to the same scale used previously (11 kn.). The true direction of the wind is the relative direction plus the true heading, or 120° +150°=270°.

Answers.—True wind from 120° relative, is 270° true, at 11 knots.

A quick solution can be made without an actual plot, in the following manner: On a maneuvering board, label the circles 5, 10, 15, 20, etc., from the center, and draw vertical lines tangent to these circles. Cut out the 5:1 scale and discard that part having graduations greater than the maximum speed of the vessel. Keep this equipment for all solutions. (For durability, the two parts can be mounted on cardboard or other suitable material.) To find true wind, spot in point 1 by eye. Place the zero of the 5:1 scale on this point and align the scale (inverted) by means of the vertical lines. Locate point 2 at the speed of the vessel as indicated on the 5:1 scale. It is always vertically *below* point 1. Read the relative direction and the speed of the true wind using eye interpolation if needed. The National Weather Service distributes a wind vector computer called a *Shipboard Wind Plotter* (fig. 3708b). Solution by means of this plotter is illustrated in the following example:

Example 2.—A ship is proceeding on course 270° at a speed of 14.5 knots. The apparent wind is from 40° off the starboard bow, speed 20 knots.

Required.—The relative direction, true direction, and speed of the true wind by Shipboard Wind Plotter.

Solution (fig. 3708b).—The true direction of the apparent wind is determined by adding the apparent wind direction to the ship's heading if the wind is from off the starboard bow and subtracting the apparent wind direction if the wind is from off the port bow. In this example, the true direction of the apparent wind is 310°. In this

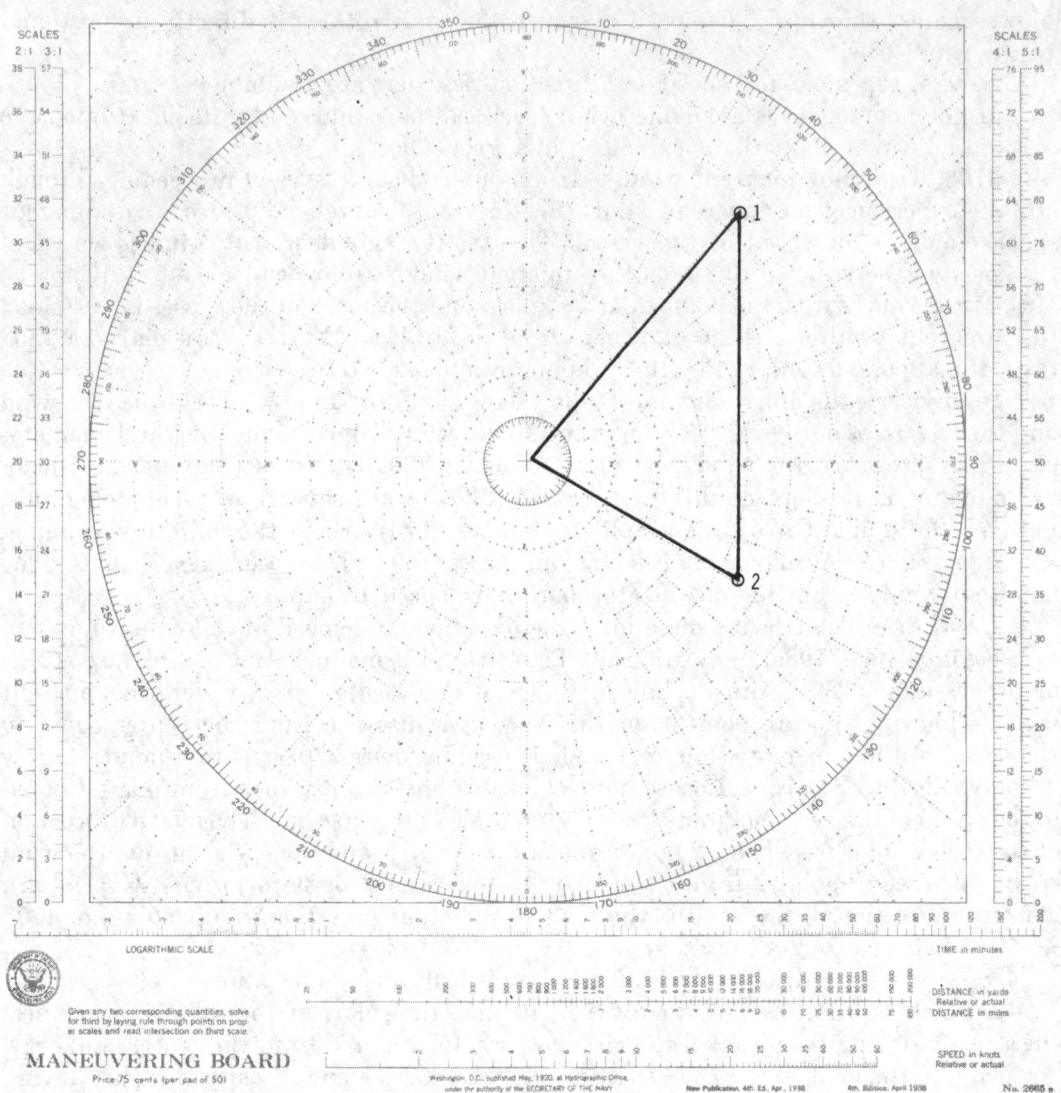

FIGURE 3708a.—Finding true wind by maneuvering board.

solution the red arrowhead is considered the top of the plotter. Set ship's course, 270°, to the top of the plotter by rotating the protractor disk to set 270° at the red arrow. Using a convenient linear scale, measure vertically downward from the center peg of the plotting board a distance equivalent to 14.5 knots. Mark this point "S" for ship. Rotate the protractor disk of the plotting board until 310° is at the red arrowhead at the top of the plotting board. Using the same linear scale as for ship's speed, plot vertically downward from the center peg of the plotting board a distance equivalent to 20 knots. Mark this point "W." Rotate the protractor disk until the "S" is vertically above the "W," using the vertical lines on the plotting board to line up the two points. Read the true wind direction at the top of the plotting board. The distance between points "S" and "W" is the true wind speed, using the same scale as in plotting points "S" and "W."

    Answers.—True wind direction is 357°, true wind speed is 13 knots.

    Such problems can be solved by the use of true directions and a regular vector solution, but the use of relative directions simplifies the plot because that component

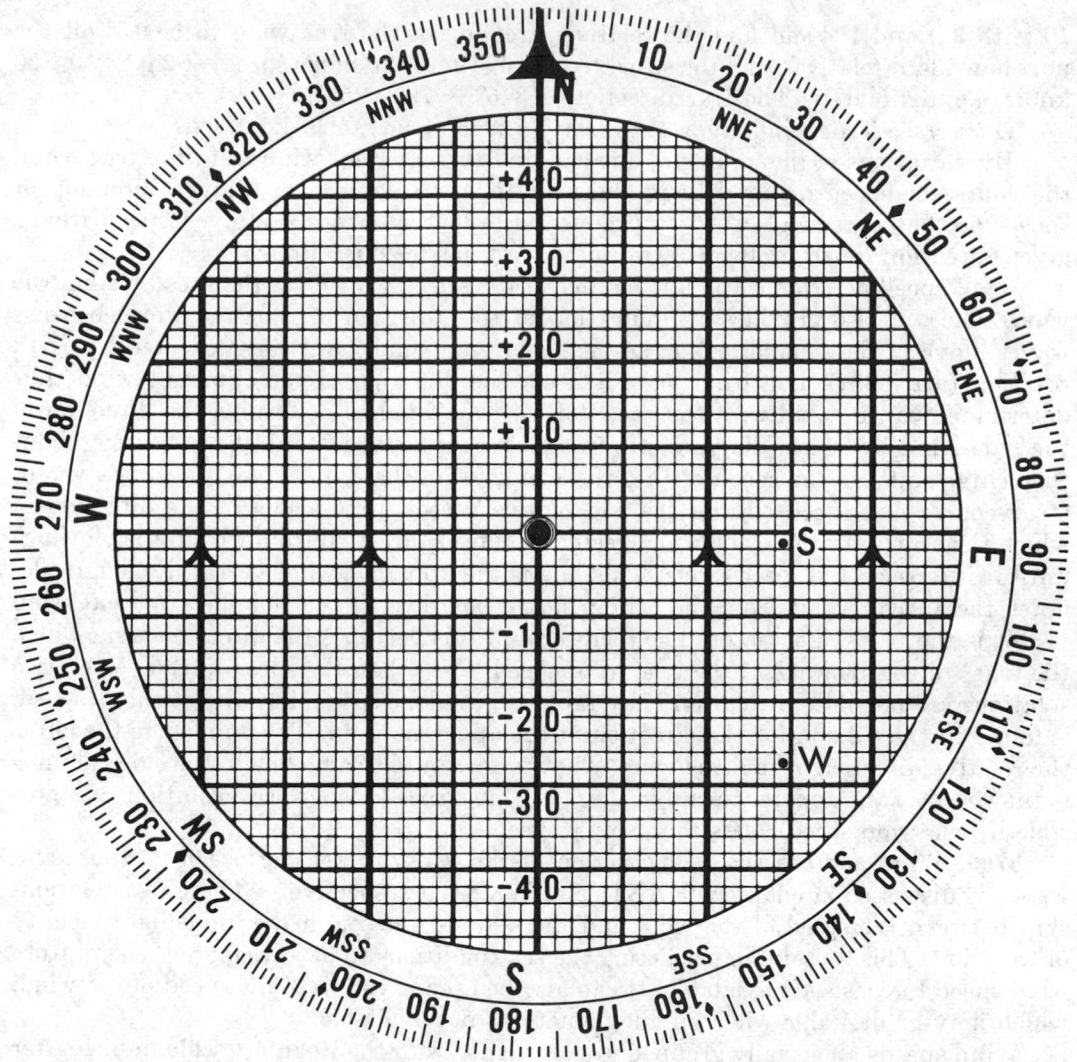

FIGURE 3708b.—Finding true wind by Shipboard Wind Plotter.

of the apparent wind due to the vessel's motion is always parallel (but reversed) to the vessel's motion, and the apparent wind is always *forward* of the true wind.

A tabular solution based upon the same principle can be made by means of table 10. The entering values for this table are the apparent wind speed *in units of ship's speed*, and the difference between the heading and the apparent wind direction. The values taken from the table are the relative direction (right or left) of the true wind, and the speed of the true wind *in units of ship's speed*. If a vessel is proceeding at 12 knots, 6 knots constitutes one-half (0.5) unit, 12 knots one unit, 18 knots 1.5 units, 24 knots two units, etc.

Example 3.—A ship is proceeding on course 270° at a speed of 10 knots. The apparent wind is from 10° off the port bow, speed 30 knots.

Required.—The relative direction, true direction, and speed of the true wind by table 10.

Solution.—The apparent wind speed is $\frac{30}{10}=3.0$ ship's speed units. Enter table

10 with 3.0 and 10° and find the relative direction of the true wind to be 15° off the port bow (345° relative), and the speed to be 2.02 times the ship's speed, or $2.02 \times 10 = 20$ knots, approximately. The true direction is $345° + 270° = 255°$.

Answers.—True wind from 345° relative, 255° true, at 20 knots.

By variations of this problem, one can find the apparent wind from the true wind, the course or speed required to produce an apparent wind from a given direction or speed, or the course and speed to produce an apparent wind of a given speed from a given direction. Such problems arise in aircraft carrier operations.

Wind speed determined by appearance of the sea (art. 3709) is the speed of the true wind. The sea also provides an indication of the direction of the true wind, because waves move in the same direction as the generating wind, not being deflected by earth rotation (art. 3302). If a wind vane is used, the direction of the apparent wind thus determined can be used with the speed of the true wind to determine the direction of the true wind by vector diagram. If a maneuvering board is used, draw a circle about the center equal to the speed of the true wind. From the center, plot the ship's vector (true course and speed). From the end of this vector draw a line in the direction in which the apparent wind is blowing (reciprocal of the direction from which it is blowing) until it intersects the speed circle. This line is the apparent wind vector, its length denotes the speed. A line from the center of the board to the end of the apparent wind vector is the true wind vector. The reciprocal of this vector is the direction from which the true wind is blowing. If the true wind speed is less than the speed of the vessel, two solutions are possible. If solution is by table 10, the true speed, in units of ship's speed, is found in the column for the direction of the apparent wind. The number to the left is the relative direction of the true wind. The number on the same line in the side columns is the speed of the apparent wind in units of ship's speed. Again, two solutions are possible if true wind speed is less than ship's speed.

3709. Wind and the sea.—The action of the wind in creating ocean currents and waves is discussed in chapters **XXXII** and **XXXIII**, respectively. There is a relationship between the speed of the wind and the state of the sea in the immediate vicinity of the wind. This is useful in predicting the sea conditions to be anticipated when future wind speed forecasts are available. It can also be used to estimate the speed of the wind, which may be desirable when an anemometer is not available.

Wind speeds are usually grouped in accordance with the **Beaufort scale** named after Admiral Sir Francis Beaufort, who devised it in 1806. As adopted in 1838, Beaufort numbers ranged from 0, calm, to 12, hurricane. The Beaufort scale, with certain other pertinent information, is given in appendix V. The appearance of the sea at different Beaufort scale numbers from 0 through 10 is shown in appendix W.

3710. Temperature is the intensity or degree of heat. It is measured in degrees. Several different temperature scales are in use.

On the **Fahrenheit** (**F**) scale pure water freezes at 32° and boils at 212°.

On the **Celsius** (**C**) scale commonly used with the metric system, the freezing point of pure water is 0° and the boiling point is 100°. This scale, has been known by various names in different countries. In the United States it was formerly called the **centigrade** scale. The Ninth General Conference of Weights and Measures, held in France in 1948, adopted the name Celsius to be consistent with the naming of other temperature scales after their inventors, and to avoid the use of different names in different countries. On the original Celsius scale, invented in 1742 by a Swedish astronomer named Anders Celsius, the numbering was the reverse of the modern scale, 0° representing the boiling point of water, and 100° its freezing point.

Absolute zero is considered to be the lowest possible temperature, at which there is no molecular motion and a body has no heat. For some purposes, it is convenient to express temperature by a scale at which 0° is absolute zero. This is called **absolute temperature**. If Fahrenheit degrees are used, it may be called **Rankine (R)** temperature; and if Celsius, **Kelvin (K)** temperature. The Kelvin scale is more widely used than the Rankine. Absolute zero is at (−) 459°69F or (−) 273°16C.

Temperature by one scale can be converted to that at another by means of the relationship that exists between the scales. Thus,

$$C=\frac{5}{9}(F-32),$$

$$F=\frac{9}{5}C+32,$$

and

$$K=C+273°16C.$$

A temperature of (−) 40° is the same by either the Celsius or Fahrenheit scale. Similar formulas can be made for conversion of other temperature scale readings. Table 15 gives the equivalent values of Fahrenheit, Celsius, and Kelvin temperatures.

The intensity or degree of heat (temperature) should not be confused with the *amount* of heat. If the temperature of air or some other substance is to be increased (the substance made hotter) by a given number of degrees, the amount of heat that must be added is dependent upon the amount of the substance to be heated. Also, equal amounts of different substances require the addition of unequal amounts of heat to effect equal increase in temperature because of their difference of specific heat (art. 3012). Units used for measurement of amount of heat are the **British thermal unit (BTU)**, the amount of heat needed to raise the temperature of 1 pound of water 1° Fahrenheit; and the **calorie**, the amount of heat needed to raise the temperature of 1 gram of water 1° Celsius.

3711. Temperature measurement is made by means of a **thermometer.** Most thermometers are based upon the principle that materials expand with increase of temperature, and contract as temperature decreases. In its most usual form a thermometer consists of a bulb filled with mercury and connected to a tube of very small cross-sectional area. The mercury only partly fills the tube. In the remainder is a vacuum created during construction of the instrument. The air is driven out by boiling the mercury, and the top of the tube is then sealed by a flame. As the mercury expands or contracts with changing temperature, the length of the mercury column in the tube changes. Temperature is indicated by the position of the top of the column of mercury with respect to a scale etched on the glass tube or placed on the thermometer support.

Temperature measuring equipment should be placed in a shelter which protects it from mechanical damage and direct rays of the sun. The shelter should have louvered sides to permit free access of air. Aboard ship, the shelter should be placed in an exposed position as far as practicable from metal bulkheads. On vessels where shelters are not available, the temperature measurement should be made in shade at an exposed position on the windward side.

Sea surface temperature observations are used in the forecasting of fog and furnish important information about the development and movement of tropical cyclones. Commercial fishermen are interested in the sea surface temperature as an aid in locating certain species of fish. There are several methods of determining seawater temperature. These include engine room intake readings, condenser intake readings, thermister probes attached to the hull, and readings from buckets recovered from over the side. Although the condenser intake method is not a true measure of surface water temperature, the error is generally small. Measurement should be made near the entrance of the intake.

If the temperature of the water at the surface is desired, a sample should be obtained by bucket, preferably a canvas bucket, from a forward position well clear of any discharge lines. The sample should be taken immediately to a place where it is sheltered from wind and sun. The water should then be stirred with the thermometer, keeping the bulb submerged, until an essentially constant reading is obtained.

A considerable variation in sea surface temperature can be experienced in a relatively short distance of travel. This is especially true when crossing major ocean currents such as the Gulf Stream and the Kuroshio. Significant variations also occur where large quantities of freshwater are discharged from rivers.

3712. Humidity is the condition of the atmosphere with reference to its water vapor content. **Relative humidity** is the ratio (stated as a percentage) of the pressure of water vapor present in the atmosphere to the saturation vapor pressure at the same temperature.

As air temperature decreases, the relative humidity increases. At some point, saturation takes place, and any further cooling results in condensation of some of the moisture. The temperature at which this occurs is called the **dew point,** and the moisture deposited upon natural objects is called **dew** if it forms in the liquid state, or **frost** if it forms in the frozen state.

The same process causes moisture to form on the outside of a container of cold liquid, the liquid cooling the air in the immediate vicinity of the container until it reaches the dew point. When moisture is deposited on man-made objects, it is usually called **sweat.** It occurs whenever the temperature of a surface is lower than the dew point of air in contact with it. It is of particular concern to the mariner because of its effect upon his instruments, and possible damage to his ship or its cargo. Lenses of optical instruments may sweat, usually with such small droplets that the surface has a "frosted" appearance. When this occurs, the instrument is said to "fog" or "fog up," and is useless until the moisture is removed. Damage is often caused by corrosion or direct water damage when pipes sweat and drip, or when the inside of the shell plates of a vessel sweat. Cargo may sweat if it is cooler than the dew point of the air. One of the principal problems of preserving ships of the reserve fleet is the protection against moisture. An important step is the draining of all water, sealing of compartments, and drying of the air.

Clouds and fog form by "sweating" of minute particles of dust, salt, etc., in the air. Each particle forms a nucleus around which a droplet of water forms. If air is completely free from solid particles on which water vapor may condense, the extra moisture remains in the vapor state, and the air is said to be **supersaturated.**

Relative humidity and dew point are measured by means of a **hygrometer.** The most common type, called a **psychrometer,** consists of two thermometers mounted together on a single strip of material, as shown in figure 3712a. One of the thermometers is mounted a little lower than the other, and has its bulb covered with muslin. When

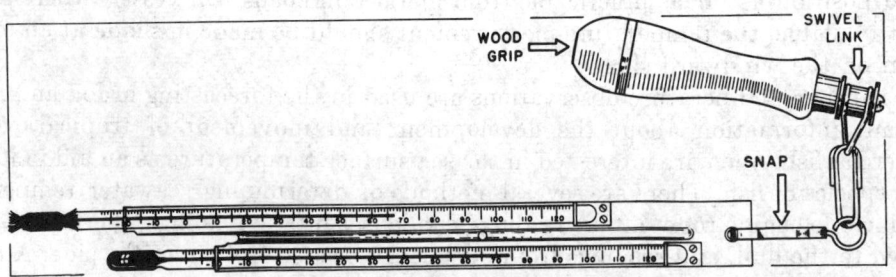

FIGURE 3712a.—A sling psychrometer.

the muslin covering is thoroughly moistened and the thermometer well ventilated, evaporation cools the bulb of the thermometer, causing it to indicate a lower reading than the other. A **sling psychrometer,** illustrated in figure 3712a, is ventilated by whirling the thermometers. **Dry-bulb temperature** is indicated by the uncovered **dry-bulb thermometer,** and **wet-bulb temperature** is indicated by the muslin-covered **wet-bulb thermometer.** The difference between these two temperatures, and the dry-bulb temperature, are used to enter **psychrometric tables** to find the relative humidity (tab. 16) and dew point (tab. 17). If the wet-bulb temperature is above freezing, reasonably accurate results can be obtained by a psychrometer consisting of wet- and dry-bulb thermometers mounted so that air can circulate freely around them without special ventilation. This type of installation is common aboard ship.

Example.—The dry-bulb temperature is 65°F and the wet-bulb temperature is 61°F.

Required.—(1) Relative humidity, (2) dew point.

Solution.—The difference between readings is 4°. Entering table 16 with this value and a dry-bulb temperature of 65°, the relative humidity is found to be 80 percent. From table 17 the dew point is found to be 58°.

Answers.—(1) Relative humidity 80 percent, (2) dew point 58°.

Also in use aboard many ships is the **electric psychrometer** (fig. 3712b). This is a handheld, battery operated instrument with two mercury thermometers for obtaining dry- and wet-bulb temperature readings. It consists of a plastic housing that holds the thermometers, batteries, motor, and fan. Although the electric psychrometer is constructed primarily of non-corrodible materials, prolonged exposure to the marine environment will shorten the life of the instrument.

3713. Clouds are visible assemblages of numerous tiny droplets of water, or ice crystals, formed by condensation of water vapor in the air, with the bases of the assemblages above the surface of the earth. **Fog** is a similar assemblage in contact with the surface of the earth.

The shape, size, height, thickness, and nature of a cloud depend upon the conditions under which it is formed. Therefore, clouds are indicators of various processes occurring in the atmosphere. The ability to recognize different types and a knowledge of the conditions associated with them are useful in predicting future weather.

Although the variety of clouds is virtually endless, they may be classified according to general type. Clouds are grouped generally into three "families" according to some common characteristic. **High clouds** are those having a mean lower level above 20,000 feet. They are composed principally of ice crystals. **Middle clouds** have a mean level between 6,500 and 20,000 feet. They are composed largely of water droplets, although the higher ones have a tendency toward ice particles. **Low clouds** have a mean lower level of less than 6,500 feet. These clouds are composed entirely of water droplets.

Within these 3 families are 10 principal cloud types. The names of these are composed of various combinations and forms of the following basic words, all from Latin:

Cirrus, meaning "curl, lock, or tuft of hair."

Cumulus, meaning "heap, a pile, an accumulation."

Stratus, meaning "spread out, flatten, cover with a layer."

Alto, meaning "high, upper air."

Nimbus, meaning "rainy cloud."

Individual cloud types recognize certain characteristics, variations, or combinations of these. The 10 principal cloud types are:

High clouds. **Cirrus (Ci)** are detached high clouds of delicate and fibrous appearance, without shading, generally white in color, and often of a silky appearance (figs. 3713a and 3713d). Their fibrous and feathery appearance is due to the fact that they

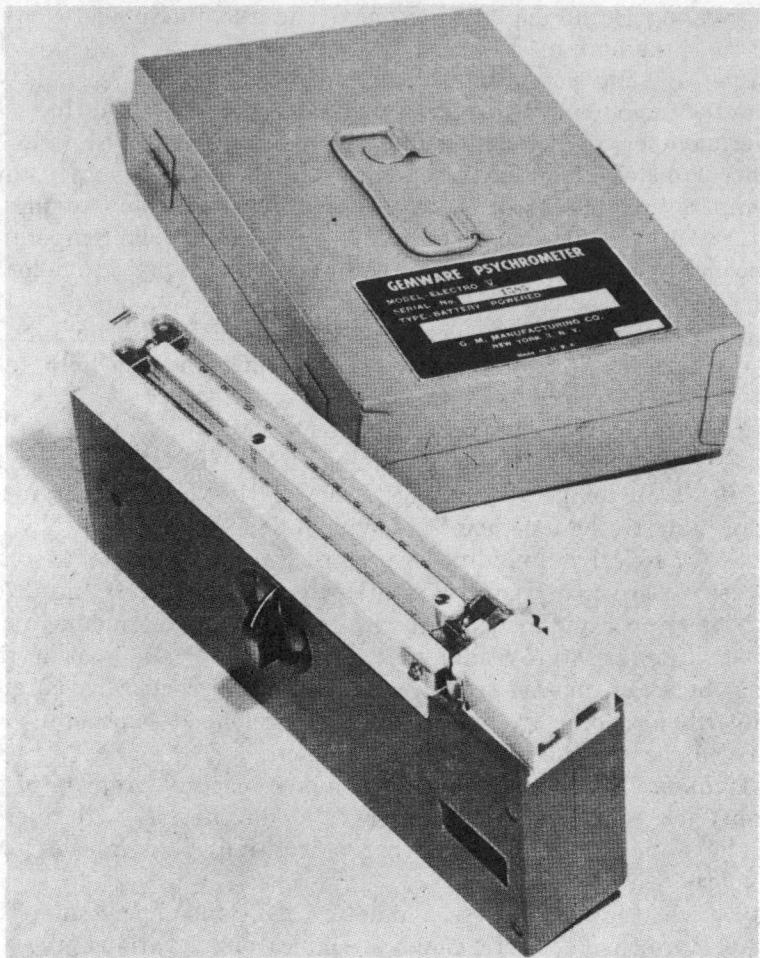

FIGURE 3712b.—Electric psychrometer.

are composed entirely of ice crystals. Cirrus appear in varied forms such as isolated tufts; long, thin lines across the sky; branching, feather-like plumes; curved wisps which may end in tufts, etc. These clouds may be arranged in parallel bands which cross the sky in great circles and appear to converge toward a point on the horizon. This may indicate, in a general way, the direction of a low pressure area. Cirrus may be brilliantly colored at sunrise and sunset. Because of their height, they become illuminated before other clouds in the morning, and remain lighted after others at sunset. Cirrus are generally associated with fair weather, but if they are followed by lower and thicker clouds, they are often the forerunner of rain or snow.

Cirrocumulus (Cc) are high clouds composed of small white flakes or scales, or of very small globular masses, usually without shadows and arranged in groups or lines, or more often in ripples resembling those of sand on the seashore (fig. 3713b). One form of cirrocumulus is popularly known as "mackerel sky" because the pattern resembles the scales on the back of a mackerel. Like cirrus, cirrocumulus are composed of ice crystals and are generally associated with fair weather, but may precede a storm if they thicken and lower. They may turn gray and appear hard before thickening.

Cirrostratus (Cs) are thin, whitish, high clouds (fig. 3713c) sometimes covering the sky completely and giving it a milky appearance and at other times presenting, more or less distinctly, a formation like a tangled web. The thin veil is not sufficiently dense to blur the outline of sun or moon. However, the ice crystals of which the cloud is composed refract the light passing through in such a way that halos (art. 3818) may form with the sun or moon at the center. Figure 3713d shows cirrus thickening and changing into cirrostratus. In this form it is popularly known as "mares' tails." If it continues to thicken and lower, the ice crystals melting to form water droplets, the cloud formation is known as altostratus. When this occurs, rain may normally be expected within 24 hours. The more brushlike the cirrus when the sky appears as in figure 3713d, the stronger the wind at the level of the cloud.

FIGURE 3713a.—Cirrus.

FIGURE 3713b.—Cirrocumulus.

FIGURE 3713c.—Cirrostratus.

FIGURE 3713d.—Cirrus and cirrostratus.

Middle clouds. **Altocumulus** (**Ac**) are middle clouds consisting of a layer of large, ball-like masses that tend to merge together. The balls or patches may vary in thickness and color from dazzling white to dark gray, but they are more or less regularly arranged. They may appear as distinct patches (fig. 3713e) similar to cirrocumulus (fig. 3713b) but can be distinguished by the fact that individual patches are generally larger, and show distinct shadows in some places. They are often mistaken for stratocumulus (fig. 3713i). If this form thickens and lowers, it may produce thundery weather and showers, but it does not bring prolonged bad weather. Sometimes the patches merge to form a series of big rolls that resemble ocean waves, but with streaks of blue sky (fig. 3713f). Because of perspective, the rolls appear to run together near the horizon. These regular parallel bands differ from cirrocumulus in that they occur in larger masses with shadows. These clouds move in the direction of the short dimension of the rolls, as do ocean waves. Sometimes altocumulus appear briefly in the form shown in figure 3713g, usually before a thunderstorm. They are generally arranged in a line with a flat horizontal base, giving the impression of turrets on a castle. The turreted tops may look like miniature cumulus and possess considerable depth and great length. These clouds usually indicate a change to chaotic, thundery skies.

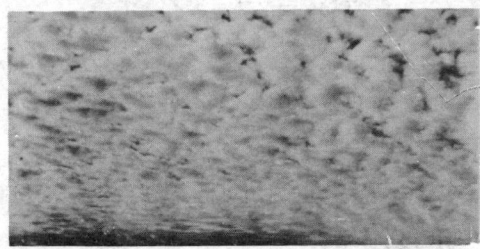

FIGURE 3713e.—Altocumulus in patches.

FIGURE 3713f.—Altocumulus in bands.

FIGURE 3713g.—Turreted altocumulus.

FIGURE 3713h.—Altostratus.

Altostratus (As) are middle clouds having the appearance of a grayish or bluish, fibrous veil or sheet (fig. 3713h). The sun or moon, when seen through these clouds, appears as if it were shining through ground glass, with a corona (art. 3819) around it. Halos are not formed. If these clouds thicken and lower, or if low, ragged "scud" or rain clouds (nimbostratus) form below them, continuous rain or snow may be expected within a few hours.

Low clouds. **Stratocumulus (Sc)** are low clouds composed of soft, gray, roll-shaped masses (fig. 3713i). They may be shaped in long, parallel rolls similar to altocumulus (fig. 3713f), moving forward with the wind. The motion is in the direction of their short dimension, like ocean waves. These clouds, which vary greatly in altitude, are the final product of the characteristic daily change that takes place in cumulus clouds. They are usually followed by clear skies during the night.

Stratus (St) is a low cloud in a uniform layer (fig. 3713j) resembling fog. Often the base is not more than 1,000 feet high. A veil of thin stratus gives the sky a hazy appearance. Stratus is often quite thick, permitting so little sunlight to penetrate that it appears dark to an observer below it. From above, it looks white. Light mist may descend from stratus. Strong wind sometimes breaks stratus into shreds called "fractostratus."

Nimbostratus (Ns) is a low, dark, shapeless cloud layer, usually nearly uniform, but sometimes with ragged, wet-looking bases. Nimbostratus is the typical rain cloud. The precipitation which falls from this cloud is steady or intermittent, but not showery.

Cumulus (Cu) are dense clouds with *vertical development* (clouds formed by rising air which is cooled as it reaches greater heights). They have a horizontal base and dome-shaped upper surface, with protuberances extending above the dome. Cumulus appear in small patches, and never cover the entire sky. When the vertical development is not great, the clouds appear in patches resembling tufts of cotton or wool, being popularly called "woolpack" clouds (fig. 3713k). The horizontal bases of such clouds may not be noticeable. These are called "fair weather" cumulus because they always accompany good weather. However, they may merge with altocumulus, or may grow to cumulonimbus before a thunderstorm. Since cumulus are formed by

FIGURE 3713i.—Stratocumulus.

FIGURE 3713j.—Stratus.

FIGURE 3713k.—Cumulus.

FIGURE 3713l.—Cumulonimbus.

updrafts, they are accompanied by turbulence, causing "bumpiness" in the air. The extent of turbulence is proportional to the vertical extent of the clouds. Cumulus are marked by strong contrasts of light and dark.

Cumulonimbus (Cb) is a massive cloud with great vertical development, rising in mountainous towers to great heights (fig. 3713l). The upper part consists of ice crystals, and often spreads out in the shape of an anvil which may be seen at such distances that the base may be below the horizon. Cumulonimbus often produces showers of rain, snow, or hail, frequently accompanied by thunder. Because of this, the cloud is often popularly called a "thundercloud" or "thunderhead." The base is horizontal, but as showers occur it lowers and becomes ragged.

3714. Cloud height measurement.—At sea, cloud heights are often determined by estimate. This is a difficult task, particularly at night.

The height of the base of clouds formed by vertical development (any form of cumulus), if formed in air that has risen from the surface of the earth, can be determined by psychrometer, because the height to which the air must rise before condensation takes place is proportional to the difference between surface air temperature and the dew point. At sea, this difference multiplied by 236 gives the height in feet. That is, for every degree difference between surface air temperature and the dew point, the air must rise 236 feet before condensation will take place. Thus, if the dry-bulb temperature is 80°F, and the wet-bulb temperature is 77°F, the dew point (from tab. 17) is

76°F, or 4° lower than the surface air temperature. The height of the cloud base is 4×236=944 feet.

3715. Visibility measurement.—**Visibility** is the extreme horizontal distance at which prominent objects can be seen and identified by the unaided eye. It is usually measured directly by the human eye. Ashore, the distances of various buildings, trees, lights, and other objects are measured and used as a guide in estimating the visibility. At sea, however, such an estimate is difficult to make with accuracy. Other ships and the horizon may be of some assistance.

Ashore, visibility is sometimes measured by a **transmissometer,** a device which measures the transparency of the atmosphere by passing a beam of light over a known short distance, and comparing it with a reference light.

3716. Upper air observations.—Upper air information provides the third dimension to the weather map. Unfortunately, the equipment necessary to obtain such information is quite expensive, and the observations are time consuming. Consequently, the network of observing stations is quite sparse compared to that for surface observations, particularly over the oceans and in isolated land areas. Where facilities exist, upper air observations are made by means of unmanned balloons in conjuction with theodolites, radiosondes, radar, and radio direction finders.

3717. Storm detection radar.—During World War II, it was found that certain radar equipment gave an indication of weather fronts (art. 3811) and precipitation areas. It was of particular value near hurricanes and typhoons. Since the close of that war a great amount of work has been done in perfecting radar equipment for use in weather observation. It has proved of immense value in detecting, tracking, and interpreting weather activity out to a distance of as much as 400 miles from the observing station.

3718. Automated weather stations and buoy systems provide regular transmissions of meteorological and oceanographic information by radio. They are generally used at isolated and relatively inaccessible locations from which weather and ocean data are of great importance. Depending on the type of system used, the elements usually measured include wind direction and speed, atmospheric pressure, air and sea surface temperature, spectral wave data, and a temperature profile from the sea surface to a predetermined depth.

3719. Recording observations.—Instructions for recording weather observations aboard vessels of the U. S. Navy are given in OPNAV Instruction 3140.37C, *Manual for Ship's Surface Weather Observations.* Instructions for recording observations aboard merchant vessels are given in Weather Service Observing Handbook No. 1, *Marine Surface Observations.*

Problems

3708a. A ship is proceeding on course 180° at a speed of 22 knots. The apparent wind is from 70° off the port bow, speed 20 knots.

Required.—The relative direction, true direction, and speed of the true wind by maneuvering board or the National Weather Service plotter.

Answers.—True wind from 231° relative, 051° true, at 24.3 knots.

3708b. A ship is proceeding on course 050° at a speed of 13.5 knots. The apparent wind is from broad on the starboard bow, speed 20 knots.

Required.—The relative direction, true direction, and speed of the true wind by table 10.

Answers.—True wind from 086° relative, 136° true, at 14.3 knots.

3708c. A ship is proceeding on course 020° at a speed of 16 knots. The true wind is estimated to be from 110° on the port bow, speed 10 knots.

Required.—The relative direction, true direction, and speed of the apparent wind by maneuvering board or the National Weather Service plotter.

Answers.—Apparent wind from 323° relative, 343° true, at 15.6 knots.

3708d. A ship is proceeding on course 190° at a speed of 14 knots. The true wind is estimated to be from broad on the starboard quarter, speed 20 knots.

Required.—The relative direction, true direction, and speed of the apparent wind by table 10.

Answers.—Apparent wind from 090° relative, 280° true, at 14.0 knots.

3708e. The true wind has been determined to be from 210°, speed 12 knots. The captain of an aircraft carrier desires an apparent wind of 30 knots from 10° on the port bow for launching aircraft.

Required.—The course and speed of the aircraft carrier.

Answers.—C 235°, S 18.6 kn. (The required apparent wind could also be produced by C 005°, S 40.5 kn.)

3708f. A ship is proceeding on course 255° at a speed of 15 knots. The wind vane indicates the apparent wind is broad on the starboard beam. From the appearance of the sea the navigator estimates the speed of the true wind as Beaufort 5 (19 knots).

Required.—(1) Relative and true directions of the true wind, (2) speed of the apparent wind. Use the maneuvering board.

Answers.—(1) True wind from 142° relative, 037° true; (2) apparent wind speed 11.6 knots.

3708g. A ship is proceeding on course 135° at a speed of 18 knots. The wind vane indicates the apparent wind is 40° on the starboard bow. From the appearance of the sea the navigator estimates the speed of the true wind as Beaufort 6 (24.5 knots).

Required.—(1) Relative and true directions of the true wind, (2) speed of the apparent wind. Use table 10.

Answers.—(1) True wind from 069° relative, 204° true; (2) apparent wind speed 36 knots.

3708h. A ship is proceeding on course 330° at a speed of 20 knots. The wind vane indicates the apparent wind is 30° on the port bow. From the appearance of the sea the navigator estimates the speed of the true wind as Beaufort 4 (13.5 knots).

Required.—(1) Relative and true directions of the true wind, (2) speed of the apparent wind. Solve first by maneuvering board and then by table 10.

Answers.—Graphical solution: (1) true wind from 199° relative, 169° true or from 282° relative, 252° true; (2) apparent wind speed 8.5 knots or 26.3 knots. Table 10 solution: (1) true wind from 197° relative, 167° true or from 283° relative, 253° true; (2) apparent wind speed 8.0 knots or 26.0 knots.

3712. The dry-bulb temperature is 41°F and the wet-bulb temperature is 35°F.

Required.—(1) Relative humidity, (2) dew point.

Answers.—(1) Relative humidity 53 percent, (2) dew point 26°.

3714a. The dry-bulb temperature is 72°F and the wet-bulb temperature is 58°F.

Required.—Height of the base of cumulonimbus clouds formed in air which has risen from the surface of the sea.

Answer.—Height 5,900 feet.

References

Kotsch, W. J. *Weather for the Mariner.* Annapolis, United States Naval Institute, 1970.

National Weather Service. *Marine Surface Observations,* Weather Service Observing Handbook No. 1. Washington, U. S. Govt. Print. Off., 1974.

Royal Meteorology Office. *Meteorology for Mariners.* London, Her Majesty's Stationery Office, 1967.

CHAPTER XXXVIII

WEATHER ELEMENTS

3801. Introduction.—**Weather** is the state of the earth's atmosphere with respect to temperature, humidity, precipitation, visibility, cloudiness, etc. In contrast, the term **climate** refers to the prevalent or characteristic meteorological conditions of a place or region.

All weather may be traced ultimately to the effect of the sun on the earth, including the lower portions of the atmosphere. Most changes in weather involve large-scale, approximately horizontal, motion of air. Air in such motion is called **wind.** This motion is produced by differences of atmospheric pressure, which are attributable both to differences of temperature and the nature of the motion itself.

The weather is of considerable interest to the mariner. The wind and state of the sea affect dead reckoning. Reduced horizontal visibility limits piloting. The state of the atmosphere affects electronic navigation and radio communication. If the skies are overcast, visual celestial observations are not available; and under certain conditions refraction and dip are disturbed. When wind was the primary motive power, knowledge of the areas of favorable winds was of great importance. This consideration led Matthew Fontaine Maury, more than a century ago, to seek information from ships' logs to establish speed and direction of prevailing winds over the various trade routes of the world. The information thus gathered was shown on pilot charts. By means of these charts, the mariner could select a suitable route for a favorable passage. Even power vessels are affected considerably by wind and sea. Less fuel consumption and a more comfortable passage are to be expected if wind and sea are moderate and favorable. Pilot charts are useful in selecting suitable routes.

Optimizing ship speed and safety by taking advantage of favorable wind and sea conditions has become practicable with the advent of extended range forecasting techniques. These techniques and the procedures used in ship weather routing are discussed in chapter XXIV.

3802. The atmosphere is a relatively thin shell of air, water vapor, dust, smoke, etc., surrounding the earth. The air is a mixture of transparent gases and, like any gas, is elastic and highly compressible. Although extremely light, it has a definite weight which can be measured. A cubic foot of air at standard sea-level temperature and pressure weighs 1.22 ounces, or about 1/817th part of the weight of an equal volume of water. Because of this weight, the atmosphere exerts a pressure upon the surface of the earth, amounting to about 15 pounds per square inch.

As altitude increases, less atmosphere extends upward, and pressure decreases. With less pressure, the density decreases. More than three-fourths of the air is concentrated within a layer averaging about 7 statute miles thick, called the **troposphere.** This is the region of most "weather," as the term is commonly understood.

The top of the troposphere is marked by a thin transition zone called the **tropopause,** immediately above which is the **stratosphere.** Beyond this lie several other layers having distinctive characteristics. The average height of the tropopause ranges from about 5 miles or less at high latitudes to about 10 miles at low latitudes.

The **standard atmosphere** is a conventional vertical structure of the atmosphere characterized by a standard sea-level pressure of 29.92 inches of mercury (1013.25

millibars) and a sea-level temperature of 59°F (15°C), the rate of temperature decreases with height (i.e., **standard lapse rate**) being a uniform 3°6F (2°C) per thousand feet to 11 kilometers (36,089 feet) and thereafter a constant temperature of (−)69°7F (−56°5C).

With the aid of *weather satellite observations*, meteorologists are continually learning more of the atmospheric processes in the troposphere and stratosphere as they affect weather at sea. In recent years research has indicated that the **jet stream** is an important entity in relation to the sequence of weather. The jet stream refers to relatively strong (≥60 knots) quasi-horizontal winds usually concentrated within a restricted layer of the atmosphere. Although jet stream winds can occur at any level and geographic location and from any direction, the term is most often associated with mid-latitude winds with maximum speeds from 270° (±45°). Such winds, called **polar jet stream winds,** average 90 knots maximum, but speeds up to 200 knots may occur in the winter season.

3803. General circulation of the atmosphere.—The heat required for warming the air is supplied originally by the sun. As radiant energy from the sun arrives at the earth, about 29 percent is reflected back into space by the earth and its atmosphere, 19 percent is absorbed by the atmosphere, and the remaining 52 percent is absorbed by the surface of the earth, much of which is reradiated back into space. This earth radiation is in comparatively long waves relative to the short-wave radiation from the sun, since it emanates from a cooler body. Long-wave radiation, being readily absorbed by the water vapor in the air, is primarily responsible for the warmth of the atmosphere near the earth's surface. Thus, the atmosphere acts much like the glass on the roof of a greenhouse. It allows part of the incoming solar radiation to reach the surface of the earth, but is heated by the terrestrial radiation passing outward. Over the entire earth and for long periods of time, the total outgoing energy must be equivalent to the incoming energy (minus any converted to another form and retained), or the temperature of the earth, including its atmosphere, would steadily increase or decrease. In local areas, or over relatively short periods of time, such a balance is not required, and in fact does not exist, resulting in changes such as those occurring from one year to another in different seasons and in different parts of the day.

As shown in figure 1419b, the more nearly perpendicular the rays of the sun strike the surface of the earth, the more heat energy per unit area is received at that place. Physical measurements show that in the Tropics more heat per unit area is received than is radiated away, and that in polar regions the opposite is true. Unless there were some process to transfer heat from the Tropics to polar regions, the Tropics would be much warmer than they are, and the polar regions would be much colder. Atmospheric motions bring about the required transfer of heat. The oceans also participate in the process, but to a lesser degree.

If the earth had a uniform surface and did not rotate on its axis, with the sun following its normal path across the sky (solar heating increasing with decreasing latitude), a simple circulation would result, as shown in figure 3803a. However, the surface of the earth is far from uniform, being covered with an irregular distribution of land of various heights, and water; the earth rotates about its axis once in approximately 24 hours, so that the portion heated by the sun continually changes; and the axis of rotation is tilted so that as the earth moves along its orbit about the sun, seasonal changes occur in the exposure of specific areas to the sun's rays, resulting in variations in the heat balance of these areas. These factors, coupled with others, result in constantly changing large-scale movements of air. For example, the rotation of the earth exerts an apparent force, known as **Coriolis force,** which diverts the air from a direct path between high and low pressure areas. The diversion of the air is toward the right in the Northern

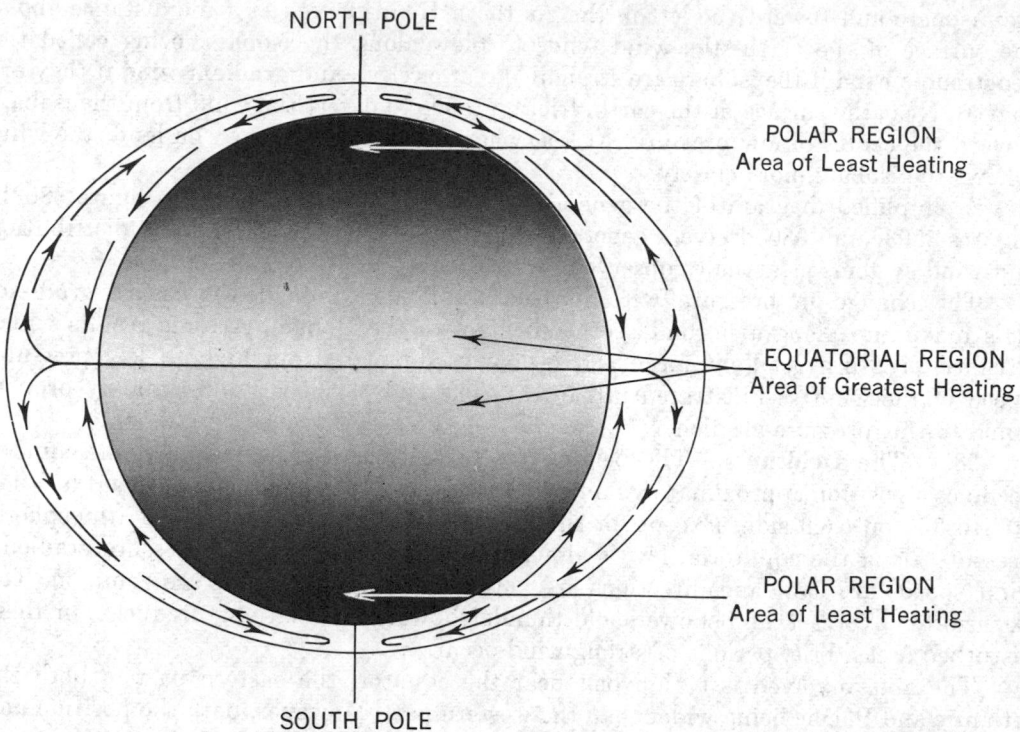

FIGURE 3803a.—Ideal atmospheric circulation for a uniform and nonrotating earth.

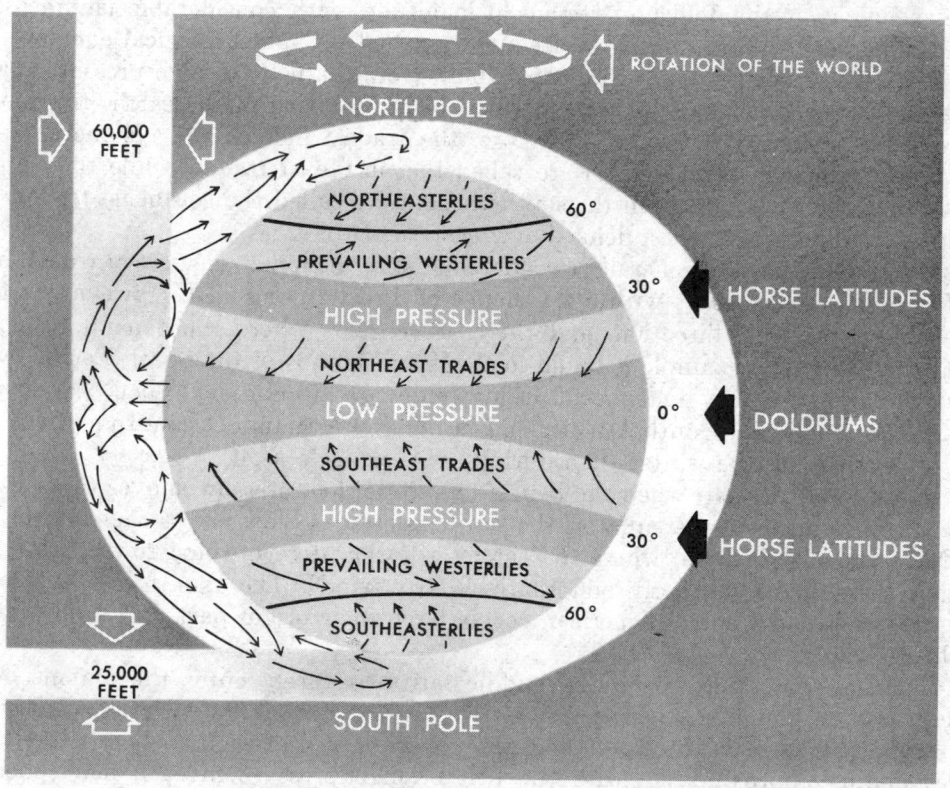

FIGURE 3803b.—Simplified diagram of the general circulation of the atmosphere.

Hemisphere and toward the left in the Southern Hemisphere. At some distance above the surface of the earth, the wind tends to blow along the isobars, being called the **geostrophic wind** if the isobars are straight (great circles), and **gradient wind** if they are curved. Near the surface of the earth, friction tends to divert the wind from the isobars toward the center of low pressure. At sea, where friction is less than on land, the wind follows the isobars more closely.

A simplified diagram of the general circulation pattern is shown in figure 3803b. Figures 3803c and 3803d give a generalized picture of the world's pressure distribution and wind systems as actually observed.

The change in pressure with horizontal distance is called **pressure gradient.** It is maximum along a normal (perpendicular) to the isobars. A force results which is called **pressure gradient force** and is always directed from high to low pressure. Speed of the wind as illustrated in figures 3803c and 3803d is approximately proportional to this pressure gradient.

3804. The Doldrums.—The belt of low pressure at the surface near the equator occupies a position approximately midway between high pressure belts at about latitude 30° to 35° on each side. Except for significant intradiurnal changes, the atmospheric pressure along the equatorial low is almost uniform. With minimal pressure gradient, wind speeds are light and directions are variable. Hot, sultry days are common. The sky is often overcast, and showers and thundershowers are relatively frequent; in these disturbed areas, brief periods of strong wind occur.

The area involved is a thin belt near the equator, the eastern part in both the Atlantic and Pacific being wider than the western part. However, both the position and extent of the belt vary with longitude and season. During all seasons in the Northern Hemisphere, the belt is centered in the eastern Atlantic and Pacific; however, there are wide excursions of the doldrums regions at longitudes with considerable landmass. On the average, the position is at 5°N, frequently called the **meteorological equator.**

3805. The trade winds at the surface blow from the belts of high pressure toward the equatorial belts of low pressure. Because of the rotation of the earth, the moving air is deflected toward the west. Therefore, the trade winds in the Northern Hemisphere are from the northeast and are called the **northeast trades,** while those in the Southern Hemisphere are from the southeast and are called the **southeast trades.** The trade-wind directions are best defined over eastern ocean areas.

The trade winds are generally considered among the most constant of winds, blowing for days or even weeks with little change of direction or speed. However, at times they weaken or shift direction, and there are regions where the general pattern is disrupted. A notable example is found in the island groups of the South Pacific, where the trades are practically nonexistent during January and February. Their best development is attained in the South Atlantic and in the South Indian Ocean. In general, they are stronger during the winter than during the summer season.

In July and August, when the belt of equatorial low pressure moves to a position some distance north of the equator, the southeast trades blow across the equator, into the Northern Hemisphere, where the earth's rotation diverts them toward the right, causing them to be southerly and southwesterly winds. The "southwest monsoons" of the African and Central American coasts have their origin partly in such diverted southeast trades.

Cyclones (art. 3812) from the middle latitudes rarely enter the regions of the trade winds, although tropical cyclones (ch. XXXIX) originate within these areas.

3806. The horse latitudes.—Along the poleward side of each trade-wind belt, and corresponding approximately with the belt of high pressure in each hemisphere, is another region with weak pressure gradients and correspondingly light, variable winds.

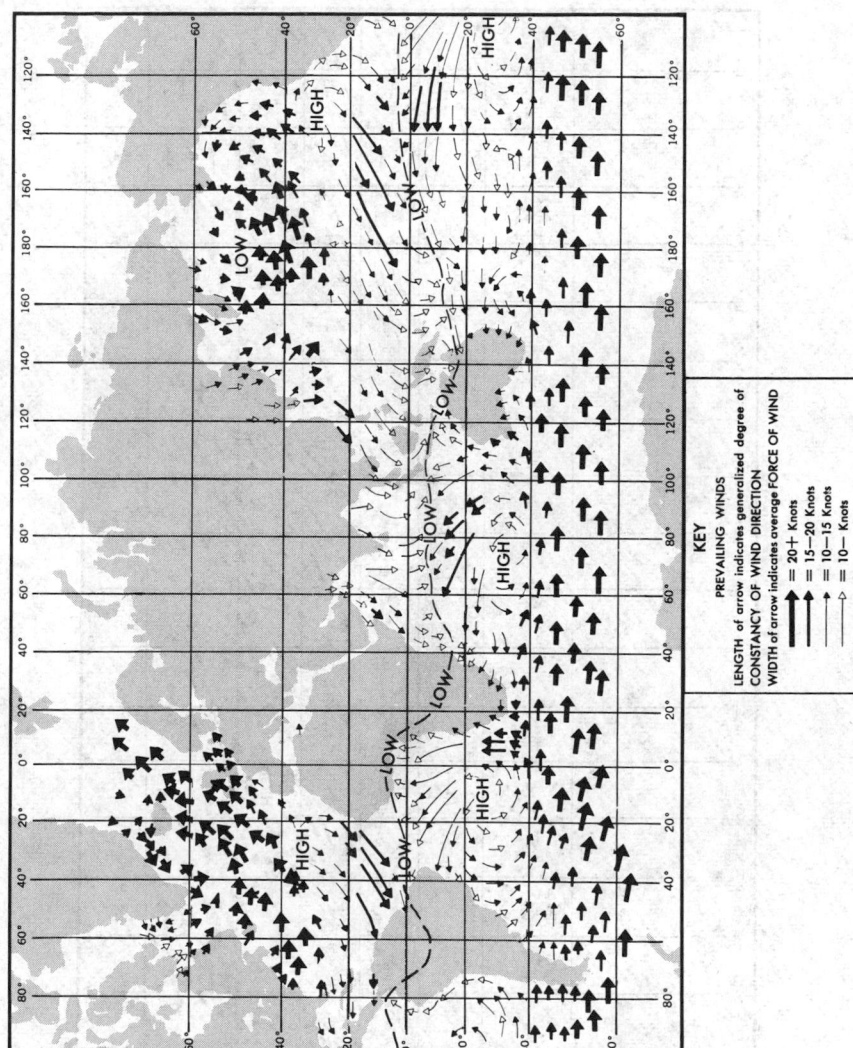

FIGURE 3803c.—Generalized pattern of actual surface winds in January and February.

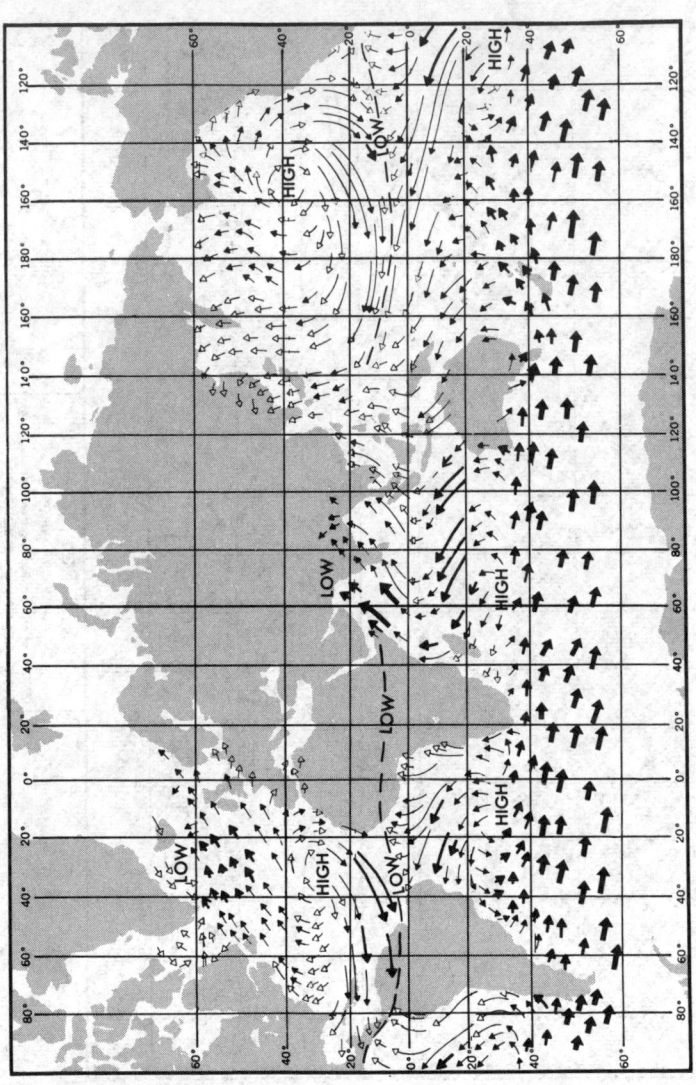

FIGURE 3803d.—Generalized pattern of actual surface winds in July and August. (See key with figure 3803c).

These are called the **horse latitudes.** The weather is generally good although low clouds are common. Compared to the doldrums, periods of stagnation in the horse latitudes are less persistent, being of a more intermittent nature. The difference is due primarily to the fact that rising currents of warm air in the equatorial low carry large amounts of moisture which condenses as the air cools at higher levels, while in the horse latitudes the air is apparently descending and becoming less humid as it is warmed at lower heights.

3807. The prevailing westerlies.—On the poleward side of the high pressure belt in each hemisphere the atmospheric pressure again diminishes. The currents of air set in motion along these gradients toward the poles are diverted by the earth's rotation toward the east, becoming southwesterly winds in the Northern Hemisphere and northwesterly in the Southern Hemisphere. These two wind systems are known as the **prevailing westerlies** of the temperate zones.

In the Northern Hemisphere this relatively simple pattern is distorted considerably by secondary wind circulations, due primarily to the presence of large landmasses. In the North Atlantic, between latitudes 40° and 50°, winds blow from some direction between south and northwest during 74 percent of the time, being somewhat more persistent in winter than in summer. They are stronger in winter, too, averaging about 25 knots (Beaufort 6) as compared with 14 knots (Beaufort 4) in the summer.

In the Southern Hemisphere the westerlies blow throughout the year with a steadiness approaching that of the trade winds (art. 3805). The speed, though variable, is generally between 17 and 27 knots (Beaufort 5 and 6). Latitudes 40°S to 50°S (or 55°S) where these boisterous winds occur, are called the **roaring forties.** These winds are strongest at about latitude 50°S.

The greater speed and persistence of the westerlies in the Southern Hemisphere are due to the difference in the atmospheric pressure pattern, and its variations, from that of the Northern Hemisphere. In the comparatively landless Southern Hemisphere, the average yearly atmospheric pressure diminishes much more rapidly on the poleward side of the high pressure belt, and has fewer irregularities due to continental interference, than in the Northern Hemisphere.

3808. Winds of polar regions.—Partly because of the low temperatures near the geographical poles of the earth, the surface pressure tends to remain higher than in surrounding regions. Consequently, the winds blow outward from the poles, and are deflected westward by the rotation of the earth, to become **northeasterlies** in the Arctic, and **southeasterlies** in the Antarctic. Where the polar easterlies meet the prevailing westerlies, near 50°N and 50°S on the average, a discontinuity in temperature and wind exists. This discontinuity is called the **polar front.** Here the warmer low-latitude air ascends over the colder polar air creating a zone of cloudiness and precipitation.

In the Arctic, the general circulation is greatly modified by surrounding landmasses. Winds over the Arctic Ocean are somewhat variable, and strong surface winds are rarely encountered.

In the Antarctic, on the other hand, a high central landmass is surrounded by water, a condition which augments, rather than diminishes, the general circulation. The high pressure, although weaker than in the horse latitudes, is stronger than in the Arctic, and of great persistence especially in eastern Antarctica. The cold air from the plateau areas moves outward and downward toward the sea and is deflected toward the west by the earth's rotation. The katabatic winds (art. 3813) remain strong throughout the year, frequently attaining hurricane force near the base of the mountains. These are some of the strongest surface winds encountered anywhere in the world, with the possible exception of those in well-developed tropical cyclones (ch. XXXIX).

3809. Modifications of the general circulation.—The general circulation of the atmosphere as described in articles 3803–3808 is greatly modified by various conditions.

The high pressure in the horse latitudes is not uniformly distributed around the belts, but tends to be accentuated at several points, as shown in figures 3803b and 3803c. These **semipermanent highs** remain at about the same places with great persistence.

Semipermanent lows also occur in various places, the most prominent ones being west of Iceland, and over the Aleutians (winter only) in the Northern Hemisphere, and in the Ross Sea and Weddell Sea in the antarctic areas. The regions occupied by these semipermanent lows are sometimes called the graveyards of the lows, since many lows move directly into these areas and lose their identity as they merge with and reinforce the semipermanent lows. The low pressure in these areas is maintained largely by the migratory lows which stall there, with topography also important, especially in Antarctica.

Another modifying influence is land, which undergoes greater temperature changes than does the sea. During the summer, a continent is warmer than its adjacent oceans. Therefore, low pressures tend to prevail over the land. If a climatological belt of high pressure encounters a continent, its pattern is distorted or interrupted, whereas a belt of low pressure is intensified over the same area. In winter, the opposite effect takes place, belts of high pressure being intensified over land and those of low pressure being weakened.

The most striking example of a wind system produced by the alternate heating and cooling of a landmass is the **monsoons** (seasonal wind) of the China Sea and Indian Ocean. A portion of this effect is shown in figures 3809a and 3809b. In the summer (fig. 3809a), low pressure prevails over the warm continent of Asia, and relatively higher pressure prevails over the adjacent sea. Between these two systems the wind blows in a nearly steady direction. The lower portion of the pattern is in the Southern Hemisphere, extending to about 10° south latitude. Here the rotation of the earth causes a deflection to the left, resulting in southeasterly winds. As they cross the equator, the deflection is in the opposite direction, causing them to curve toward the right, becoming southwesterly winds. In the winter (fig. 3809b), the positions of high and low pressure areas are interchanged, and the direction of flow is reversed.

In the China Sea the summer monsoon blows from the southwest, usually from May to September. The strong winds are accompanied by heavy squalls and thunderstorms, the rainfall being much heavier than during the winter monsoon. As the season advances, squalls and rain become less frequent. In some places the wind be-

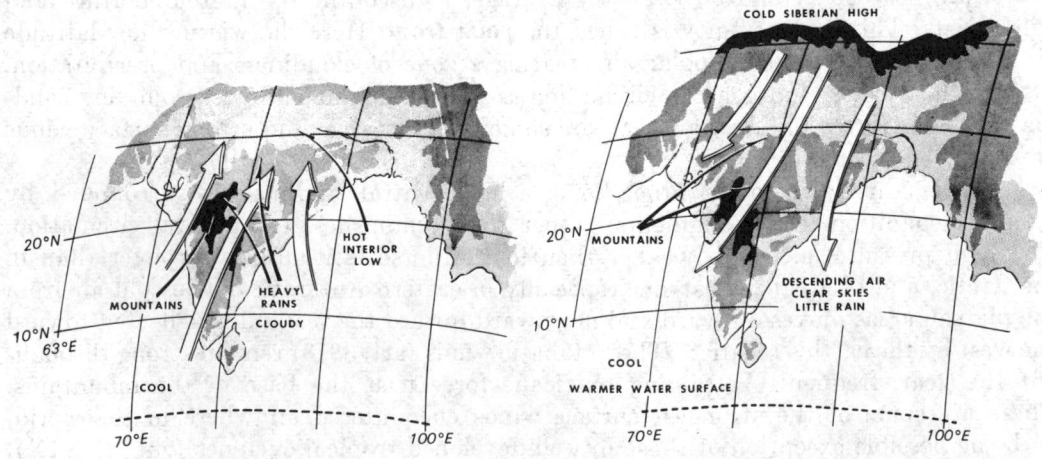

FIGURE 3809a.—The summer monsoon.   FIGURE 3809b.—The winter monsoon.

comes a light breeze which is unsteady in direction, or stops altogether, while in other places it continues almost undiminished, with changes in direction or calms being infrequent. The winter monsoon blows from the northeast, usually from October to April. It blows with a steadiness similar to that of the trade winds, often attaining the speed of a moderate gale (28–33 knots). Skies are generally clear during this season, and there is relatively little rain.

The general circulation is further modified by winds of cyclonic origin (art. 3812), and various local winds (art. 3813).

3810. Airmasses.—Because of large differences in physical characteristics of the earth's surface, particularly the oceanic and continental contrasts, the air overlying these surfaces acquires differing values of temperature and moisture. The processes of radiation and convection in the lower portions of the troposphere act in differing characteristic manners for a number of well-defined regions of the earth. The air overlying these regions acquires characteristics common to the particular area, but contrasting to those of other areas. Each distinctive part of the atmosphere, within which common characteristics prevail over a reasonably large area, is called an **airmass.**

Airmasses are named according to their source regions. Four such regions are generally recognized: (1) *equatorial* (E), the doldrum area between the north and south trades; (2) *tropical* (T), the trade wind and lower temperate regions; (3) *polar* (P), the higher temperate latitudes; and (4) *arctic or antarctic* (A), the north or south polar regions of ice and snow. This classification is a general indication of relative temperature, as well as latitude of origin.

Airmasses are further classified as maritime (m) or continental (c), depending upon whether they form over water or land. This classification is an indication of the relative moisture content of the airmass. Tropical air, then, might be designated maritime tropical (mT) or continental tropical (cT). Similarly, polar air may be either maritime polar (mP) or continental polar (cP). Arctic/antarctic air, due to the predominance of landmasses and ice fields in the high latitudes, is rarely maritime arctic (mA). Equatorial air is found exclusively over the ocean surface and is designated neither (cE) nor (mE), but simply (E).

A third classification sometimes applied to tropical and polar airmasses indicates whether the airmass is *warm* (w) or *cold* (k) relative to the underlying surface. Thus, the symbol mTw indicates maritime tropical air which is warmer than the underlying surface, and cPk indicates continental polar air which is colder than the underlying surface. The w and k classifications are primarily indications of stability (i.e., change of temperature with increasing height). If the air is cold relative to the surface, the lower portion of the airmass is being heated, resulting in instability (temperature markedly decreases with increasing height) as the warmer air tends to rise by convection. Conversely, if the air is warm relative to the surface, the lower portion of the airmass is cooled, tending to remain close to the surface. This is a stable condition (temperature increases with increasing height).

Two other types of airmasses are sometimes recognized. These are *monsoon* (M), a transitional form between cP and E; and *superior* (S), a special type formed in the free atmosphere by the sinking and consequent warming of air aloft.

3811. Fronts.—As airmasses move within the general circulation, they travel from their source regions and invade other areas dominated by air having different characteristics. Such a process leads to a zone of separation between the two airmasses. The gradients of thermal and moisture properties are maximized in the zone. Since the zone or discontinuity is so thin as to approach a sheet when viewed on a small scale map, it is called a **frontal surface.** The intersection of a frontal surface and a horizontal

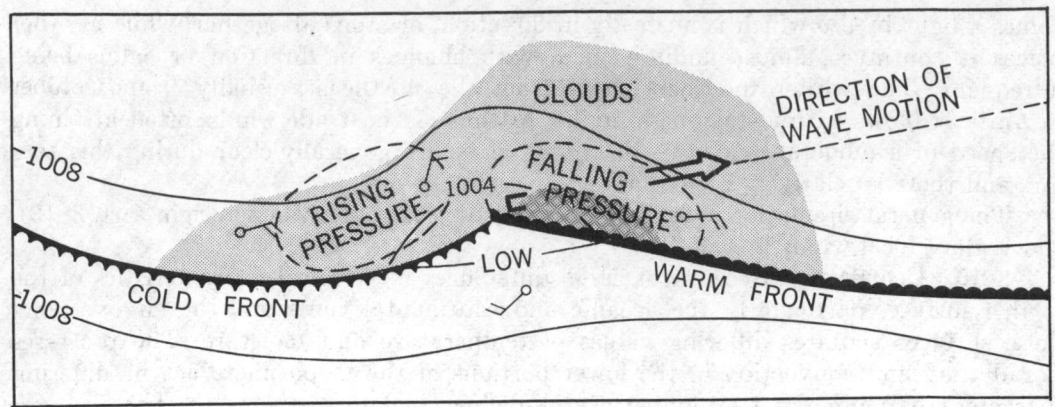

FIGURE 3811a.—First stage in the development of a frontal wave (top view).

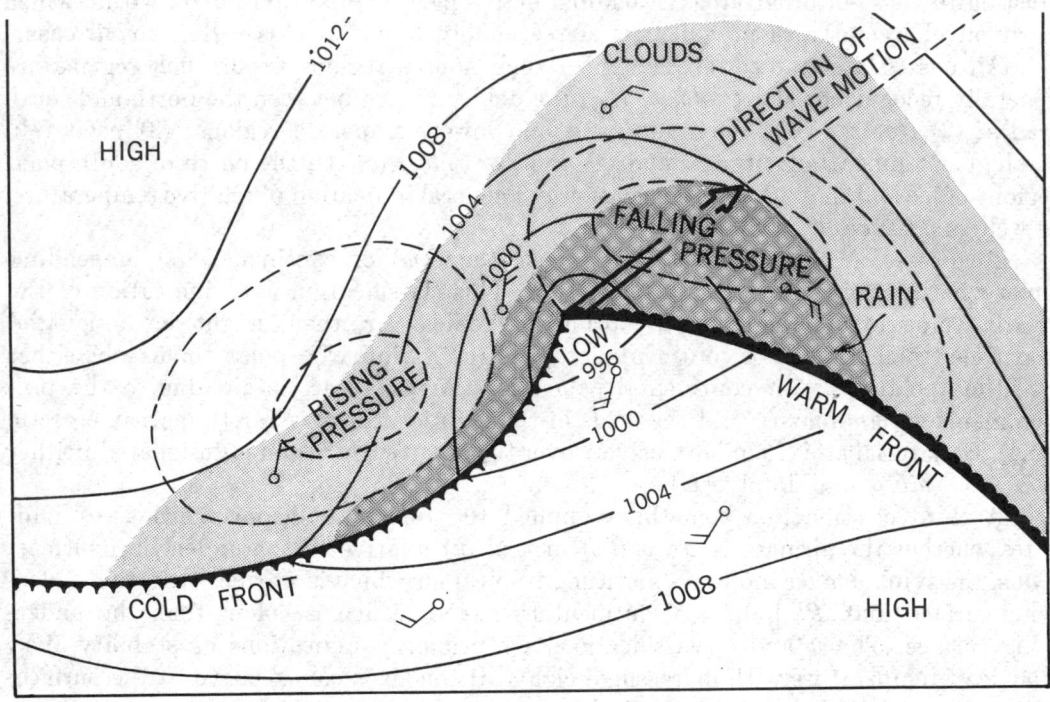

FIGURE 3811b.—A fully developed frontal wave (top view).

plane in a line is called a **front,** although the term "front" is commonly used as a short expression for "frontal surface" when this will not introduce an ambiguity.

Indicative of the differences in the motion of adjacent airmasses, the front takes a wave like character, hence the term "frontal wave."

Before the formation of frontal waves, the isobars (lines of equal atmospheric pressure) tend to run parallel to the fronts. As a wave is formed, the pattern is distorted somewhat, as shown in figure 3811a. In this illustration, colder air is north of warmer air. In figures 3811a–3811d isobars are drawn at 4-millibar intervals.

The wave tends to travel in the direction of the general circulation, which in the temperate latitudes is usually in a general easterly and slightly poleward direction.

Along the leading edge of the wave, warmer air is replacing colder air. This is called the **warm front.** The trailing edge is the **cold front,** where colder air is underrunning and displacing warmer air.

The warm air, being less dense, tends to ride up over the colder air it is replacing. The slope is gentle, varying between 1:100 and 1:300. Partly because of the replacement of cold, dense air with warm, light air, the pressure decreases. Since the slope is gentle, the upper part of a warm frontal surface may be many hundreds of miles ahead of the surface portion. The decreasing pressure, indicated by a "falling barometer," is often an indication of the approach of such a wave. In a slow-moving, well-developed wave, the barometer may begin to fall several *days* before the wave arrives. Thus, the amount and nature of the change of atmospheric pressure between observations, called **pressure tendency,** is of assistance in predicting the approach of such a system.

The advancing cold air, being more dense, tends to cut under the warmer air at the cold front, lifting it to greater heights. The slope here is such that the upper-air portion of the cold front is behind the surface position relative to its motion. The slope generally ranges from 1:25 to 1:100, being steeper than the warm front. After a cold front has passed, the pressure increases—a "rising barometer."

In the first stages, these effects are not marked, but as the wave continues to grow, they become more pronounced, as shown in figure 3811b. As the amplitude of the wave increases, pressure near the center usually decreases, and the "low" is said to "deepen." As it deepens, its forward speed generally decreases.

The approach of a well-developed warm front (i.e., when the warm air is mT) is usually heralded not only by falling pressure, but also by a more-or-less regular sequence of clouds. First, cirrus appear. These give way successively to cirrostratus, altostratus, altocumulus, and nimbostratus. Brief showers may precede the steady rain accompanying the nimbostratus.

As the warm front passes, the temperature rises, the wind shifts clockwise (in the Northern Hemisphere), and the steady rain stops. Drizzle may fall from low-lying stratus clouds, or there may be fog for some time after the wind shift. During passage of the **warm sector** between the warm front and the cold front, there is little change in temperature or pressure. However, if the wave is still growing and the low deepening, the pressure might slowly decrease. In the warm sector the skies are generally clear or partly cloudy, with cumulus or stratocumulus clouds most frequent. The warm air is usually moist, and haze or fog may often be present.

As the faster moving, steeper cold front passes, the wind shifts clockwise in the Northern Hemisphere (counterclockwise in the Southern Hemisphere), the temperature falls rapidly, and there are often brief and sometimes violent showers, frequently accompanied by thunder and lightning. Clouds are usually of the convective type. A cold front usually coincides with a well-defined **wind-shift line** (a line along which the wind shifts abruptly from southerly or southwesterly to northerly or northwesterly in the Northern Hemisphere and from northerly or northwesterly to southerly or southwesterly in the Southern Hemisphere). At sea a series of brief showers accompanied by strong, shifting winds may occur along or some distance (up to 200 miles) ahead of a cold front. These are called **squalls** (in common nautical use the term squall may be additionally applied to any severe local storm accompanied by gusty winds, precipitation, thunder, and lightning), and the line along which they occur is called a **squall line.**

Because of its greater speed and steeper slope, which may approach or even exceed the vertical near the earth's surface (due to friction), a cold front and its associated weather passes more quickly than a warm front. After a cold front passes, the pressure rises, often quite rapidly, the visibility usually improves, and the clouds tend to diminish.

As the wave progresses and the cold front approaches the slower moving warm front, the low becomes deeper and the warm sector becomes smaller. This is shown in figure 3811c.

Finally, the faster moving cold front overtakes the warm front (fig. 3811d), resulting in an **occluded front** at the surface, and an **upper front** aloft (fig. 3811e). When the two parts of the cold airmass meet, the warmer portion tends to rise above the colder part. The warm air continues to rise until the entire frontal system dissipates. As the warmer air is replaced by colder air, the pressure gradually rises, a process called "filling." This usually occurs within a few days after an occluded front forms. Finally, there results a **cold low,** or simply a low pressure system across which little or no gradient in temperature and moisture can be found.

The sequence of weather associated with a low depends greatly upon location with respect to the path of the center. That described above assumes that the observer is so located that he encounters each part of the system. If he is poleward of the path of the center of the low, the abrupt weather changes associated with the passage of fronts are not experienced. Instead, the change from the weather characteristically found ahead of a warm front to that behind a cold front takes place gradually, the exact sequence being dictated somewhat by distance from the center, as well as severity and age of the low.

Although each low follows generally the pattern given above, no two are ever exactly alike. Other centers of low pressure and high pressure and the airmasses associated with them, even though they may be 1,000 miles or more away, influence the formation and motion of individual low centers and their accompanying weather. Particularly, a high stalls or diverts a low. This is true of temporary highs as well as semipermanent highs.

3812. Cyclones and anticyclones.—An area of relatively low pressure, generally circular, is called a **cyclone.** Its counterpart for high pressure is called an **anticyclone.** These terms are used particularly in connection with the winds associated with such centers. Wind tends to blow from an area of high pressure to one of low pressure, but due to rotation of the earth, they are deflected toward the right in the Northern Hemisphere and toward the left in the Southern Hemisphere (art. 3803).

Because of the rotation of the earth, therefore, the circulation tends to be counterclockwise around areas of low pressure and clockwise around areas of high pressure in the Northern Hemisphere (figs. 3811c and 3811d), the speed being proportional to the spacing of isobars. In the Southern Hemisphere, the direction of circulation is reversed. Based upon this condition, a general rule (**Buys Ballot's Law**) can be stated thus:

If an observer in the Northern Hemisphere faces the surface wind, the center of low pressure is toward his right, somewhat behind him; and the center of high pressure is toward his left and somewhat in front of him.

If an observer in the Southern Hemisphere faces the surface wind, the center of low pressure is toward his left and somewhat behind him; and the center of high pressure is toward his right and somewhat in front of him.

In a general way, these relationships apply in the case of the general distribution of pressure, as well as to temporary local pressure systems.

The reason for the wind shift along a front is that the isobars have an abrupt change of direction along these lines, as shown in figures 3811a–3811d. Since the direction of the wind is directly related to the direction of isobars, any change in the latter results in a shift in the wind direction.

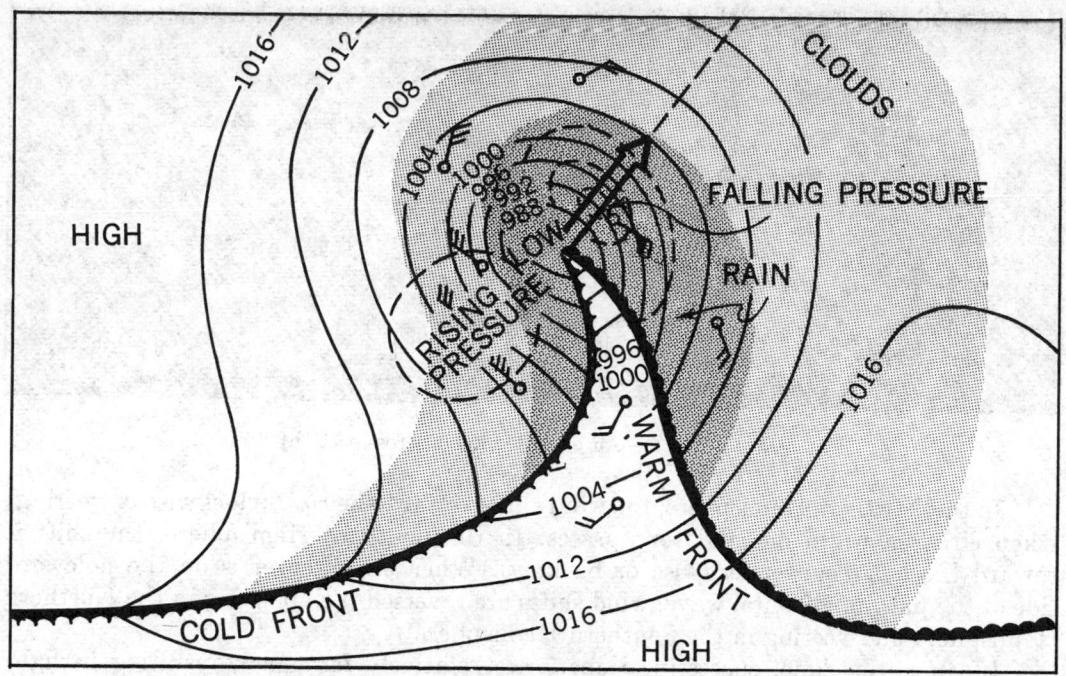

FIGURE 3811c.—A frontal wave nearing occlusion (top view).

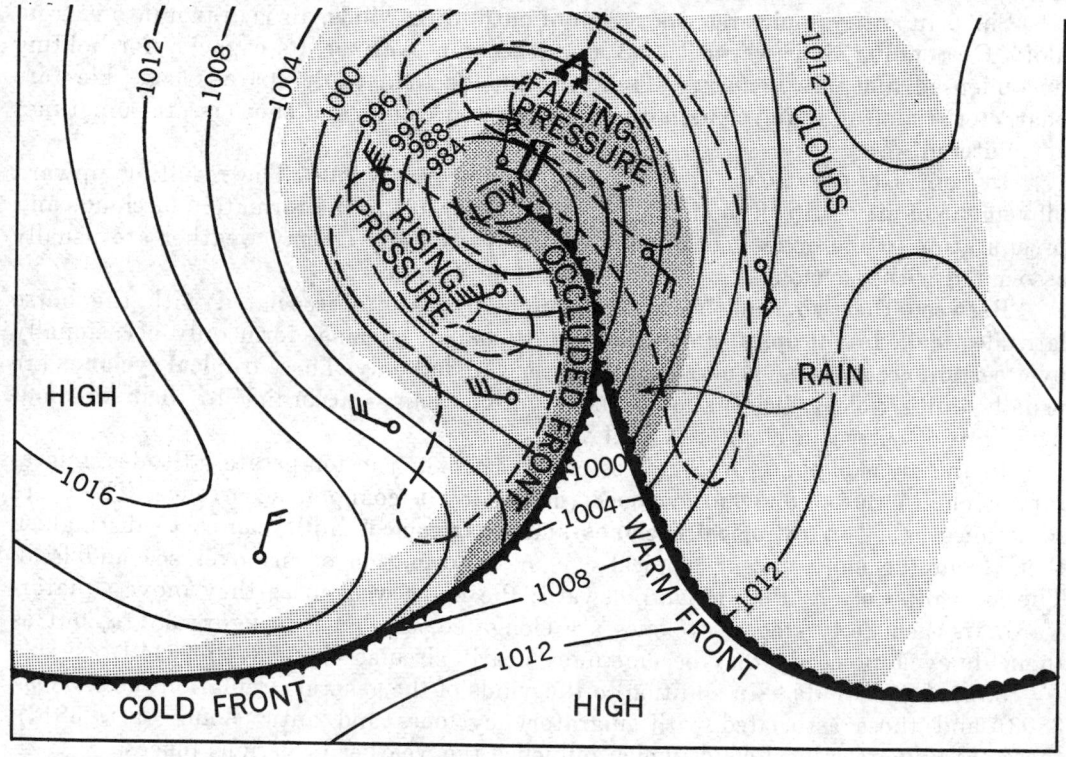

FIGURE 3811d.—An occluded front (top view).

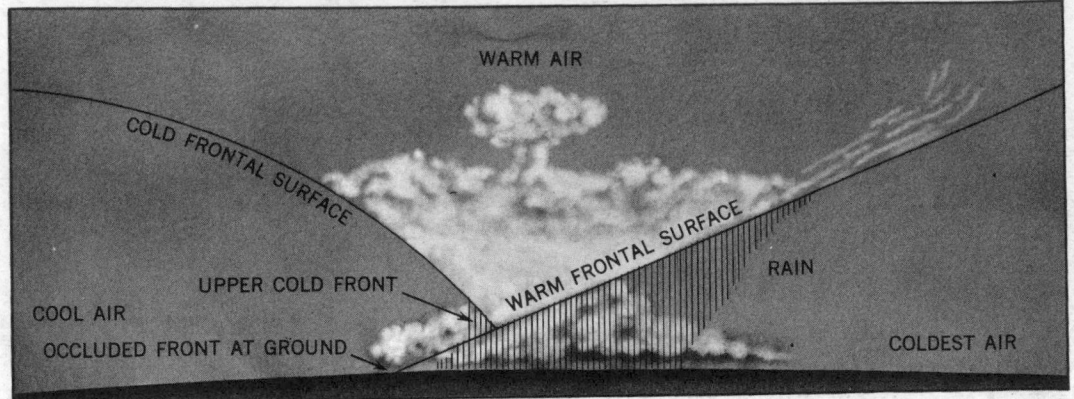

FIGURE 3811e.—An occluded front (cross section).

In the Northern Hemisphere, the wind shifts toward the *right* (clockwise or veering) when either a warm or cold front passes. In the Southern Hemisphere, the shift is toward the *left* (counterclockwise or backing). When an observer is on the poleward side of the path of a frontal wave, wind shifts are reversed (i.e., backing in the Northern Hemisphere and veering in the Southern Hemisphere).

In an anticyclone, successive isobars are relatively far apart, resulting in light winds. In a cyclone, the isobars are more closely spaced. With a steeper pressure gradient, the winds are stronger.

Since an anticyclonic area is a region of outflowing winds, air is drawn into it from aloft. Descending air is warmed, and as air becomes warmer, its capacity for holding uncondensed moisture increases. Therefore, clouds tend to dissipate. Clear skies are characteristic of an anticyclone, although scattered clouds and showers are sometimes encountered.

In contrast, a cyclonic area is one of converging winds. The resulting upward movement of air results in cooling, a condition favorable to the formation of clouds and precipitation. More or less continuous rain and generally stormy weather are usually associated with a cyclone.

Between the two hemispheric belts of high pressure associated with the horse latitudes, called **subtropical anticyclones** (art. 3806), cyclones form only occasionally over certain areas at sea, generally in summer and fall only. These **tropical cyclones** are usually quite violent, being known under various names according to their location. They are discussed in chapter XXXIX.

In the areas of the prevailing westerlies (art. 3807) in temperate latitudes, migratory cyclones (**lows**) and anticyclones (**highs**) are a common occurrence. These are sometimes called **extratropical cyclones** and **extratropical anticyclones** to distinguish them from the more violent tropical cyclones. Formation occurs over sea and land. The lows intensify as they move poleward; the highs weaken as they move equatorward. In their early stages, cyclones are elongated, as shown in figure 3811a, but as their life cycle proceeds, they become more nearly circular (figs. 3811b–3811d).

3813. Local winds.—In addition to the winds of the general circulation (arts. 3803–3808) and those associated with migratory cyclones and anticyclones (art. 3812), there are numerous local winds which influence the weather in various places.

The most common of these are the **land** and **sea breezes,** caused by alternate heating and cooling of land adjacent to water. The effect is similar to that which causes the monsoons (art. 3809), but on a much smaller scale, and over shorter periods. By day the land is warmer than the water, and by night it is cooler. This effect occurs along many coasts during the summer. Between about 0900 and 1100 the temperature of the land becomes greater than that of the adjacent water. The lower levels of air over the land are warmed, and the air rises, drawing in cooler air from the sea. This is the **sea breeze.** Late in the afternoon, when the sun is low in the sky, the temperature of the two surfaces equalizes and the breeze stops. After sunset, as the land cools below the sea temperature, the air above it is also cooled. The contracting cool air becomes more dense, increasing the pressure near the surface. This results in an outflow of winds to the sea. This is the **land breeze,** which blows during the night and dies away near sunrise. Since the atmospheric pressure changes associated with this cycle are not great, the accompanying winds generally do not exceed gentle to moderate breezes. The circulation is usually of limited extent, reaching a distance of perhaps 20 miles inland, and not more than 5 or 6 miles offshore, and to a height of a few hundred feet. In the doldrums and subtropics, this process is repeated with great regularity throughout most of the year. As the latitude increases, it becomes less prominent, being masked by winds of migratory cyclones and anticyclones (art. 3812). However, the effect often may be present to reinforce, retard, or deflect stronger prevailing winds.

Varying conditions of topography produce a large variety of local winds throughout the world. Winds tend to follow valleys, and to be deflected from high banks and shores. In mountain areas wind flows in response to temperature distribution and gravity. An **anabatic wind** is one that blows up an incline, usually as a result of surface heating. A **katabatic wind** is one which blows down an incline. There are two types, *foehn* and *fall wind.*

A dry wind with a downward component, warm for the season, is called a **foehn.** The foehn occurs when horizontally moving air encounters a mountain barrier. As it blows upward to clear the barrier, it is cooled below the dew point, resulting in loss of moisture by cloud formation and perhaps rain. As the air continues to rise, its rate of cooling is reduced because the condensing water vapor gives off heat to the surrounding atmosphere. After crossing the mountain barrier, the air flows downward along the leeward slope, being warmed by compression as it descends to lower levels. Thus, since it loses less heat on the ascent than it gains during descent, and since it loses moisture during ascent, it arrives at the bottom of the mountains as very warm, dry air. This accounts for the warm, arid regions along the eastern side of the Rocky Mountains and in similar areas. In the Rocky Mountain region this wind is known by the name **chinook.** It may occur at any season of the year, at any hour of the day or night, and have any speed from a gentle breeze to a gale. It may last for several days, or for a very short period. Its effect is most marked in winter, when it may cause the temperature to rise as much as 20° F to 30° F within 15 minutes, and cause snow and ice to melt within a few hours. On the west coast of the United States, a foehn wind, given the name **Santa Ana,** blows through a pass and down a valley by that name in Southern California. This wind may blow with such force that it endangers small craft immediately off the coast.

A cold wind blowing down an incline is called a **fall wind.** Although it is warmed somewhat during descent, as is the foehn, it remains cold relative to the surrounding air. It occurs when cold air is dammed up in great quantity on the windward side of a mountain and then spills over suddenly, usually as an overwhelming surge down the other side. It is usually quite violent, sometimes reaching hurricane force. A different name for this type wind is given at each place where it is common. The **tehuantepecer** of the Mexican and Central American coast, the **pampero** of the Argentine coast, the **mistral** of the western Mediterranean, and the **bora** of the eastern Mediterranean are examples of this type wind.

Many other local winds common to certain areas have been given distinctive names.

A **blizzard** is a violent, intensely cold wind laden with snow mostly or entirely picked up from the ground, although the term is often used popularly to refer to any heavy snowfall accompanied by strong wind. A **dust whirl** is a rotating column of air about 100 to 300 feet in height, carrying dust, leaves, and other light material. This wind, which is similar to a waterspout at sea (art. 3824), is given various local names such as **dust devil** in southwestern United States and **desert devil** in South Africa. A **gust** is a sudden, brief increase in wind speed followed by a slackening, or the violent wind or squall that accompanies a thunderstorm. A puff of wind or a light breeze affecting a small area, such as would cause patches of ripples on the surface of water, is called a **cat's paw.**

3814. Fog is a cloud (art. 3713) whose base is low enough to restrict visibility. Fog is composed of droplets of water, or ice crystals (**ice fog**) formed by condensation or crystallization of water vapor in the air.

Radiation fog forms over low-lying land on clear, calm nights. As the land radiates heat and becomes cooler, it cools the air immediately above the surface. This causes a **temperature inversion** to form, the temperature for some distance upward *increasing* with height. If the air is cooled to its dew point (art. 3712), fog forms. Often, cooler and more dense air drains down surrounding slopes to heighten the effect. Radiation fog is often quite shallow, and is usually densest at the surface. After sunrise the fog may "lift," as shown in figure 3814, and gradually dissipate, usually being entirely gone by noon. At sea the temperature of the water undergoes little change between day and night, and so radiation fog is seldom encountered more than 10 miles from shore.

Advection fog forms when warm, moist air blows over a colder surface and is cooled below its dew point. This type, most commonly encountered at sea, may be quite dense and often persists over relatively long periods. Advection fog is common over cold ocean currents. If the wind is strong enough to thoroughly mix the air, condensation may take place at some distance above the surface of the earth, forming low stratus clouds (art. 3713) rather than fog.

Off the coast of California, seasonal winds create an offshore current which displaces the warm surface water, causing an upwelling of colder water. Moist Pacific air is transported along the coast in the same wind system and is cooled by the relatively cold water. Advection fog results. In the coastal valleys, fog is sometimes formed when moist air blown inland during the afternoon is cooled by radiation during the night.

When very cold air moves over warmer water, wisps of visible water vapor may rise from the surface as the water "steams," as shown in figure 2505. In extreme cases this **frost smoke,** or **arctic sea smoke,** may rise to a height of several hundred feet, the portion near the surface constituting a dense fog which obscures the horizon and surface objects, but usually leaves the sky relatively clear.

Haze consists of fine dust or salt particles in the air, too small to be individually apparent, but in sufficient number to reduce horizontal visibility and cast a bluish or yellowish veil over the landscape, subduing its colors and making objects appear indistinct. This is sometimes called **dry haze** to distinguish it from **damp haze,** which consists of small water droplets or moist particles in the air, smaller and more scattered than light fog. In international meteorological practice, the term "haze" is used to refer to a condition of atmospheric obscurity caused by dust and smoke.

Mist is synonymous with **drizzle** in the United States but is often considered as intermediate between haze and fog in its properties.

A mixture of smoke and fog is called **smog.**

RADIATION FOG

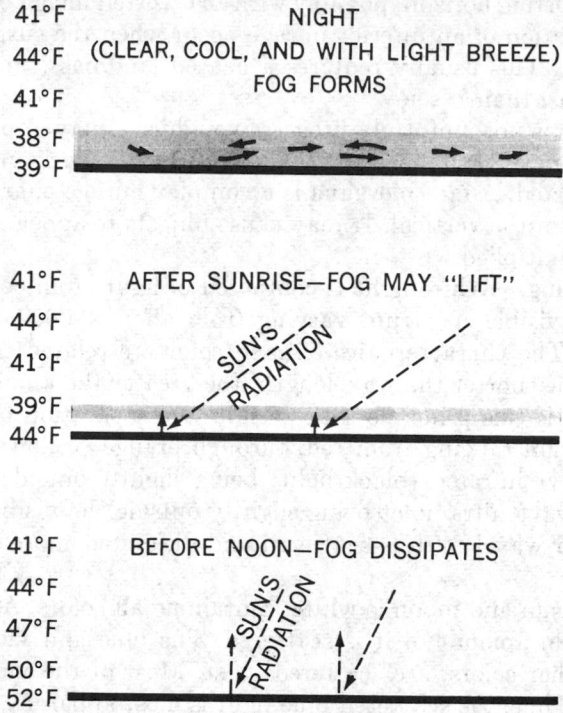

FIGURE 3814.—Formation and dissipation of radiation fog.

3815. Mirage.—As explained in article 1606, light is refracted as it passes through the atmosphere. When refraction is normal, objects appear slightly elevated, and the visible horizon is farther from the observer than it otherwise would be. Since the effects are uniformly progressive, they are not apparent to the observer. When refraction is not normal, some form of **mirage** may occur. A mirage is an optical phenomenon in which objects appear distorted, displaced (raised or lowered), magnified, multiplied, or inverted due to varying atmospheric refraction which occurs when a layer of air near the earth's surface differs greatly in density from surrounding air. This may occur when there is a rapid and sometimes irregular change of temperature or humidity with height.

If there is a temperature inversion (increase of temperature with height), particularly if accompanied by a rapid decrease in humidity, the refraction is greater than normal. Objects appear elevated, and the visible horizon is farther away. Objects which are normally below the horizon become visible. This is called **looming.** If the upper portion of an object is raised much more than the bottom part, the object appears taller than usual, an effect called **towering.** If the lower part of an object is raised more than the upper part, the object appears shorter, an effect called **stooping.** When the refraction is greater than normal, a **superior mirage** may occur. An inverted image is seen above the object, and sometimes an erect image appears over the inverted one, with the bases of the two images touching. Greater than normal refraction usually occurs when the water is much colder than the air above it.

If the temperature decrease with height is much greater than normal, refraction is less than normal, or may even cause bending in the opposite direction. Objects appear lower than normal, and the visible horizon is closer to the observer. This is called **sinking.** Towering or stooping may occur if conditions are suitable. When the refraction is reversed, an **inferior mirage** may occur. A ship or an island appears to be floating in the air above a shimmering horizon, possibly with an inverted image beneath it. Conditions suitable to the formation of an inferior mirage occur when the surface is much warmer than the air above it. This usually requires a heated landmass, and therefore is more common near the coast than at sea.

When refraction is not uniformly progressive, objects may appear distorted, taking an almost endless variety of shapes. The sun when near the horizon is one of the objects most noticeably affected. A **fata morgana** is a complex mirage characterized by marked distortion, generally in the vertical. It may cause objects to appear towering, magnified, and at times even multiplied.

3816. Sky coloring.—White light is composed of light of all colors. Color is related to wavelength, the visible spectrum varying from about 0.000038 to 0.000076 centimeters (art. 4003). The characteristics of each color are related to its wavelength (or frequency). Thus, the shorter the wavelength, the greater the amount of bending when light is refracted. It is this principle that permits the separation of light from celestial bodies into a **spectrum** ranging from red, through orange, yellow, green, and blue, to violet, with long-wave infrared (black light) being slightly outside the visible range at one end and short-wave ultraviolet being slightly outside the visible range at the other end. Light of shorter wavelength is scattered and diffracted more than that of longer wavelength.

Light from the sun and moon is white, containing all colors. As it enters the earth's atmosphere, a certain amount of it is scattered. The blue and violet, being of shorter wavelength than other colors, are scattered most. Most of the violet light is absorbed in the atmosphere. Thus, the scattered blue light is most apparent, and the sky appears blue. At great heights, above most of the atmosphere, it appears black.

When the sun is near the horizon, its light passes through more of the atmosphere than when higher in the sky, resulting in greater scattering and absorption of blue and green light, so that a larger percentage of the red and orange light penetrates to the observer. For this reason the sun and moon appear redder at this time, and when this light falls upon clouds, they appear colored. This accounts for the colors at sunset and sunrise. As the setting sun approaches the horizon, the sunset colors first appear as faint tints of yellow and orange. As the sun continues to set, the colors deepen. Contrasts occur, due principally to difference in height of clouds. As the sun sets, the clouds become a deeper red, first the lower clouds and then the higher ones, and finally they fade to a gray.

When there is a large quantity of smoke, dust, or other material in the sky, unusual effects may be observed. If the material in the atmosphere is of suitable substance and quantity to absorb the longer wave red, orange, and yellow radiations, the sky may have a greenish tint, and even the sun or moon may appear green. If the green light, too, is absorbed, the sun or moon may appear blue. A **green moon** or **blue moon** is most likely to occur when the sun is slightly below the horizon and the longer wavelength light from the sun is absorbed, resulting in green or blue light being cast upon the atmosphere in front of the moon. The effect is most apparent if the moon is on the same side of the sky as the sun.

3817. Rainbows.—The familiar arc of concentric colored bands seen when the sun shines on rain, mist, spray, etc., is caused by refraction, internal reflection, and diffraction of sunlight by the drops of water. The center of the arc is a point 180° from the sun, in the direction of a line from the sun, through the observer. The radius of the brightest rainbow is 42°. The colors are visible because of the difference in the amount of refraction of the different colors making up white light, the light being spread out to form a spectrum (art. 3816). Red is on the outer side and blue and violet on the inner side, with orange, yellow, and green between, in that order from red.

Sometimes a secondary rainbow is seen outside the primary one, at a radius of about 50°. The order of colors of this rainbow is reversed. On rare occasions a faint rainbow is seen on the same side as the sun. The radius of this rainbow and the order of colors are the same as those of the primary rainbow.

A similar arc formed by light from the moon (a lunar rainbow) is called a **moonbow.** The colors are usually very faint. A faint, white arc of about 39° radius is occasionally seen in fog opposite the sun. This is called a **fogbow,** although its origin is controversial, some considering it a halo (art. 3818).

3818. Halos.—Refraction, or a combination of refraction and reflection, of light by ice crystals in the atmosphere (cirrostratus clouds, art. 3713) may cause a **halo** to appear. The most common form is a ring of light of radius 22° or 46° with the sun or moon at the center. Occasionally a faint, white circle with a radius of 90° appears around the sun. This is called a **Hevelian halo.** It is probably caused by refraction and internal reflection of the sun's light by bipyramidal ice crystals. A halo formed by refraction is usually faintly colored like a rainbow (art. 3817), with red nearest the celestial body, and blue farthest from it.

A brilliant rainbow-colored arc of about a quarter of a circle with its center at the zenith, and the bottom of the arc about 46° above the sun, is called a **circumzenithal arc.** Red is on the outside of the arc, nearest the sun. It is produced by the refraction and dispersion of the sun's light striking the top of prismatic ice crystals in the atmosphere. It usually lasts for only about 5 minutes, but may be so brilliant as to be mistaken for an unusually bright rainbow. A similar arc formed 46° *below* the sun, with red on the upper side, is called a **circumhorizontal arc.** Any arc tangent to a heliocentric halo (one surrounding the sun) is called a **tangent arc.** As the sun increases in elevation, such arcs tangent to the halo of 22° gradually bend their ends toward each other. If they meet, the elongated curve enclosing the circular halo is called a **circumscribed halo.** The inner edge is red.

A halo consisting of a faint, white circle through the sun and parallel to the horizon is called a **parhelic circle.** A similar one through the moon is called a **paraselenic circle.** They are produced by reflection of sunlight or moonlight from vertical faces of ice crystals.

A **parhelion** (plural *parhelia*) is a form of halo consisting of an image of the sun at the same altitude and some distance from it, usually 22°, but occasionally 46°. A similar phenomenon occurring at an angular distance of 120° (sometimes 90° or 140°) from the sun is called a **paranthelion.** One at an angular distance of 180°, a rare occurrence, is called an **anthelion,** although this term is also used to refer to a luminous, colored ring or **glory** sometimes seen around the shadow of one's head on a cloud or fog bank. A parhelion is popularly called a **mock sun** or **sun dog.** Similar phenomena in relation to the moon are called **paraselene** (popularly a **mock moon** or **moon dog**), **parantiselene,** and **antiselene.** The term *parhelion* should not be confused with *perihelion*, that orbital point nearest the sun when the sun is the center of attraction (art. 1407).

A **sun pillar** is a glittering shaft of white or reddish light occasionally seen extending above and below the sun, usually when the sun is near the horizon. A phenomenon similar to a sun pillar, but observed in connection with the moon, is called a **moon pillar.** A rare form of halo in which horizontal and vertical shafts of light intersect at the sun is called a **sun cross.** It is probably due to the simultaneous occurrence of a sun pillar and a parhelic circle.

3819. Corona.—When the sun or moon is seen through altostratus clouds (art. 3713), its outline is indistinct, and it appears surrounded by a glow of light called a **corona.** This is somewhat similar in appearance to the corona seen around the sun during a solar eclipse (art. 1424). When the effect is due to clouds, however, the glow may be accompanied by one or more rainbow-colored rings of small radii, with the celestial body at the center. These can be distinguished from a halo by their much smaller radii and also by the fact that the order of the colors is reversed, red being on the inside, nearest the body, in the case of the halo, and on the outside, away from the body, in the case of the corona.

A corona is caused by diffraction of light by tiny droplets of water. The radius of a corona is inversely proportional to the size of the water droplets. A large corona indicates small droplets. If a corona decreases in size, the water droplets are becoming larger and the air more humid. This may be an indication of an approaching rainstorm.

The glow portion of a corona is called an **aureole.**

3820. The green flash.—As light from the sun passes through the atmosphere, it is refracted. Since the amount of bending is slightly different for each color, separate images of the sun are formed in each color of the spectrum. The effect is similar to that of imperfect color printing in which the various colors are slightly out of register. However, the difference is so slight that the effect is not usually noticeable. At the horizon, where refraction is maximum, the greatest difference, which occurs between violet at one end of the spectrum and red at the other, is about 10 seconds of arc. At latitudes of the United States, about 0.7 second of time is needed for the sun to change altitude by this amount when it is near the horizon. The red image, being bent least by refraction, is first to set and last to rise. The shorter wave blue and violet colors are scattered most by the atmosphere, giving it its characteristic blue color (art. 3816). Thus, as the sun sets, the green image may be the last of the colored images to drop out of sight. If the red, orange, and yellow images are below the horizon, and the blue and violet light is scattered and absorbed, the upper rim of the green image is the only part seen, and the sun appears green. This is the **green flash.** The shade of green varies, and occasionally the blue image is seen, either separately or following the green flash (at sunset). On rare occasions the violet image is also seen. These colors may also be seen at sunrise, but in reverse order. They are occasionally seen when the sun disappears behind a cloud or other obstruction.

The phenomenon is not observed at each sunrise or sunset, but under suitable conditions is far more common than generally supposed. Conditions favorable to observation of the green flash are a sharp horizon, clear atmosphere, a temperature inversion (art. 3814), and an attentive observer. Since these conditions are more frequently met when the horizon is formed by the sea than by land, the phenomenon is more common at sea. With a sharp sea horizon and clear atmosphere, an attentive observer may see the green flash at as many as 50 percent of sunsets and sunrises, although a telescope may be needed for some of the observations.

Duration of the green flash (including the time of blue and violet flashes) of as long as 10 seconds has been reported, but such length is rare. Usually it lasts for a period of about ½ second to 2½ seconds with about 1¼ seconds being average. This variability is probably due primarily to changes in the index of refraction (art. 1606) of the air near the horizon.

Under favorable conditions, a momentary green flash has been observed at the setting of Venus and Jupiter. A telescope improves the chances of seeing such a flash from a planet, but is not a necessity.

3821. Crepuscular rays are beams of light from the sun passing through openings in the clouds, and made visible by illumination of dust in the atmosphere along their paths. Actually, the rays are virtually parallel, but because of perspective, appear to diverge. Those appearing to extend downward are popularly called **backstays of the sun,** or **sun drawing water.** Those extending upward and across the sky, appearing to converge toward a point 180° from the sun, are called **anticrepuscular rays.**

3822. The atmosphere and radio waves.—Radio waves traveling through the atmosphere exhibit many of the properties of light, being refracted, reflected, diffracted, and scattered. These and other effects are discussed in chapter XL.

3823. Atmospheric electricity.—Various conditions induce the formation of electrical charges in the atmosphere. When this occurs, there is often a difference of electron charge between various parts of the atmosphere, and between the atmosphere and earth or terrestrial objects. When this difference exceeds a certain minimum value, depending upon the conditions, the static electricity is discharged, resulting in phenomena such as lightning or St. Elmo's fire.

Lightning is the discharge of electricity from one part of a thundercloud (art. 3713) to another, from one such cloud to another, or between such a cloud and the earth or a terrestrial object.

Enormous electrical stresses build up within thunderclouds, and between such clouds and the earth. At some point the resistance of the intervening air is overcome. At first the process is a progressive one, probably starting as a brush discharge (St. Elmo's fire) and growing by ionization. The breakdown follows an irregular path along the line of least resistance. A hundred or more individual discharges may be necessary to complete the path between points of opposite polarity. When this "leader stroke" reaches its destination, a heavy "main stroke" immediately follows in the opposite direction. This main stroke is the visible lightning, which may be tinted any color, depending upon the nature of the gases through which it passes. The illumination is due to the high degree of ionization of the air, which causes many of the atoms to be in excited states and emit radiation.

Thunder, the noise that accompanies lightning, is caused by the heating and ionizing of the air by lightning, which results in rapid expansion of the air along its path and the sending out of a compression wave. Thunder may be heard at a distance of as much as 15 miles, but generally does not carry that far. The elapsed time between the flash of lightning and reception of the accompanying sound of thunder is an indication of the distance, because of the difference in travel time of light and sound. Since the former is comparatively instantaneous, and the speed of sound is about 1,117 feet per second, the approximate distance in nautical miles is equal to the elapsed time in seconds, divided by 5.5. If the thunder accompanying lightning cannot be heard due to its distance, the lightning is called **heat lightning,** a phenomenon not unusual during continental "hot spells."

St. Elmo's fire is a luminous discharge of electricity from pointed objects such as the masts and yardarms of ships, lightning rods, steeples, mountain tops, blades of grass, human hair, arms, etc., when there is a considerable difference in the electrical charge between the object and the air. It appears most frequently during a storm. An object from which St. Elmo's fire emanates is in danger of being struck by lightning, since this type discharge may be the initial phase of the leader stroke. Throughout history those who have not understood St. Elmo's fire have regarded it with superstitious awe, considering it a supernatural manifestation. This view is reflected in the name **corposant** (from "corpo santo," meaning "body of a saint") sometimes given this phenomenon.

The **aurora** is a luminous glow appearing in varied forms in the thin atmosphere high above the earth in middle and high latitudes due to radiation emissions from gases in the high atmosphere.

3824. Waterspouts.—A waterspout is a small, whirling storm over the ocean or inland waters. Its chief characteristic is a funnel-shaped cloud; when fully developed it extends from the surface of the water to the base of a cumulus type cloud (fig. 3824). The water in a spout is mostly confined to its lower portion, and may be either salt spray drawn up by the sea surface, or freshwater resulting from condensation due to the lowered pressure in the center of the vortex creating the spout. The air in waterspouts may rotate clockwise or counterclockwise, depending on the manner of formation. They are found most frequently in tropical regions, but are not uncommon in higher latitudes.

There are two types of waterspouts: those derived from violent convective storms over land moving seaward, called **tornadoes,** and those formed over the sea and which are associated with fair or foul weather. The latter type is most common, lasts a maximum of 1 hour, and has variable strength. Many waterspouts are no stronger than dust whirlwinds, which they resemble; at other times they are strong enough to destroy small craft or to cause damage to larger vessels, although modern ocean-going vessels have little to fear from this type.

Waterspouts vary in diameter from a few feet to several hundred feet, and in height from a few hundred feet to several thousand feet. Sometimes they assume fantastic shapes; in early stages of development an hour glass shape between cloud and sea is common. Since a waterspout is often inclined to the vertical, its actual length may be much greater than indicated by its height.

3825. Deck ice.—Ships traveling through regions where the air temperature is below freezing may acquire thick deposits of ice as a result of salt spray freezing on the rigging or deck areas (fig. 3825). This accumulation of ice is called **ice accretion.** Also, precipitation may freeze to the superstructure and exposed areas of the vessel, increasing the load of ice.

On small vessels in heavy seas and freezing weather, deck ice may accumulate very rapidly and increase the topside weight to such an extent as to reduce seriously the stability of the vessel.

3826. Forecasting weather.—The prediction of weather at some future time is based upon an understanding of weather processes, and observations of present conditions. Thus, one learns that when there is a certain sequence of cloud types (art. 3713), rain usually can be expected to follow within a certain period. If the sky is cloudless, more heat will be received from the sun by day, and more heat will be radiated outward from the warm earth by night than if the sky is overcast. If the wind is in such a direction that warm, moist air will be transported over a colder surface, fog can be expected. A falling barometer indicates the approach of a "low," probably accompanied by stormy weather. Thus, before meteorology passed from an "art" to "science," many individuals learned to interpret certain atmospheric phenomena in terms of future weather, and to make reasonably accurate forecasts for short periods into the future.

With the establishment of weather observation stations, continuous and accurate weather information became available. As such observations expanded, and communication facilities improved, knowledge of simultaneous conditions over wider areas became available. This made possible the collection of these "synoptic" reports at civilian and military forecast centers.

The individual observations are made at government-operated stations on shore, and aboard vessels at sea. Observations aboard merchant ships at sea are made and transmitted on a voluntary and cooperative basis. The various national meteorological services supply shipmasters with blank forms, printed instructions, and other materials essential to the making, recording, and interpreting of observations. Any shipmaster

FIGURE 3824.—Waterspouts.

can render a particularly valuable service by reporting all unusual or non-normal weather occurrences.

Symbols and numbers are used to indicate on a **synoptic chart,** popularly called a **weather map,** the conditions at each observation station. Isobars are drawn through lines of equal atmospheric pressure, fronts are located and symbolically marked (fig. 3826), areas of precipitation and fog are indicated, etc.

Ordinarily, weather maps for surface observations are prepared every 6 (sometimes 3) hours. In addition, synoptic charts for selected heights are prepared every 12 (sometimes 6) hours. Knowledge of conditions aloft is of value in establishing the three-dimensional structure and motion of the atmosphere as input to the forecast.

FIGURE 3825.—Deck ice.

With the advent of the digital computer, highly sophisticated numerical models have been developed to analyze and prognosticate weather patterns. The civil and military weather centers prepare and disseminate vast numbers of weather charts (analyses and prognoses) daily to assist local forecasters in their efforts to provide users with accurate, predicted weather parameters. It must be remembered that in any area, the accuracy of forecasted parameters decreases with the length of the forecast period. Thus, a 12-hour forecast is likely to be more reliable than a 24-hour forecast. Long term forecasts for 2 weeks or a month in advance are limited to general statements. For example, a prediction is made as to which areas will have temperatures above or below normal, and how precipitation will compare with normal, but no attempt is made to state that rainfall will occur at a certain time and place.

Forecasts are issued for various areas. The national meteorological services of most maritime nations, including the United States, issue forecasts for ocean areas and warnings of the approach of storms. The efforts of the various nations are coordinated through the World Meteorological Organization.

3827. Dissemination of weather information is carried out in a number of ways. Forecasts are widely broadcast by commercial and government radio stations, and printed in newspapers. Shipping authorities on land are kept informed by telegraph and telephone. Visual storm warnings are displayed in various ports, and storm warnings are broadcast by radio.

Through the use of codes, a simplified version of synoptic weather charts is transmitted to various stations ashore and afloat. Rapid transmission of completed maps has been made possible by the development of facsimile transmitters and receivers. This system is based upon detailed scanning , by a photoelectric detector, of properly illuminated black and white copy. The varying degrees of light intensity are converted to electric energy which is transmitted to the receiver and converted back to a black and white presentation.

Complete information on dissemination of weather information by radio is provided in International Meteorological Codes 1972 and *World Wide Synoptic Broadcasts*,

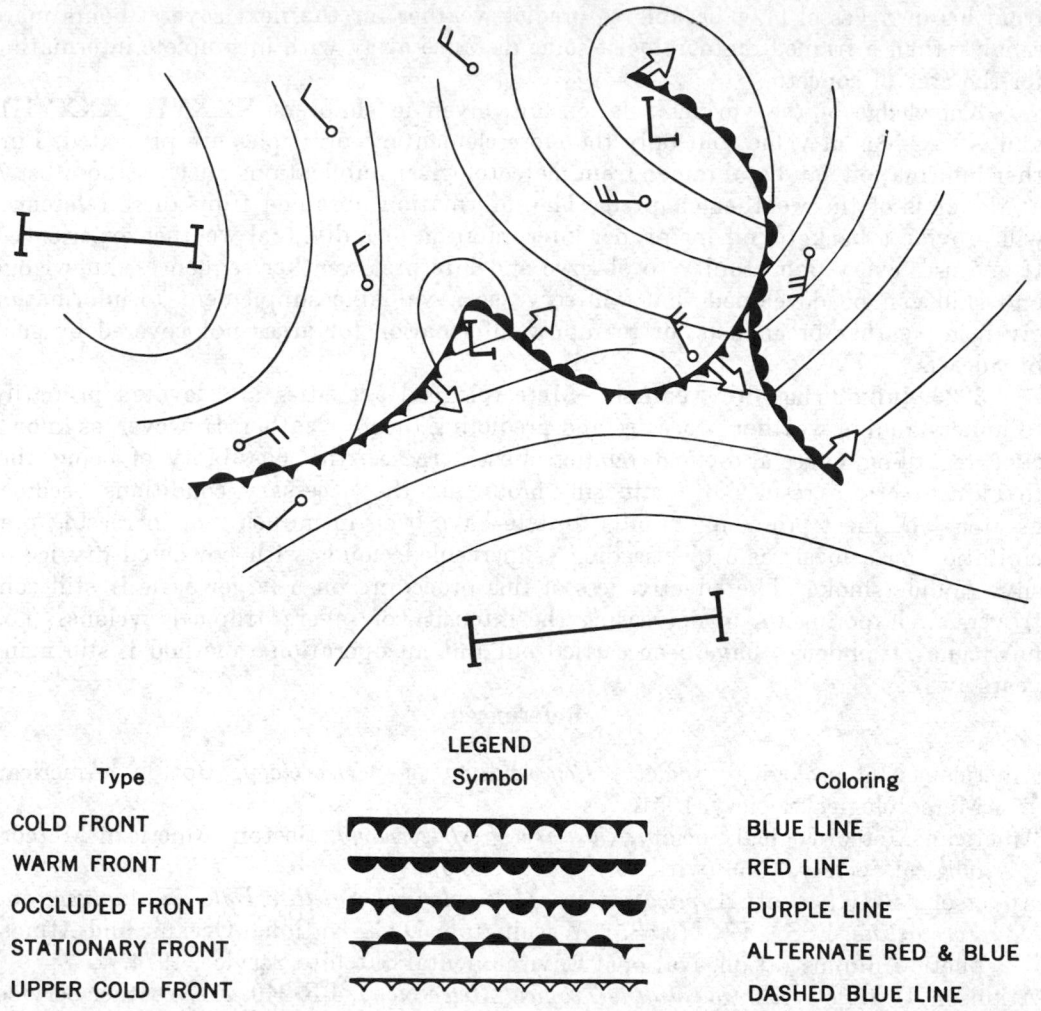

LEGEND

Type	Symbol	Coloring
COLD FRONT		BLUE LINE
WARM FRONT		RED LINE
OCCLUDED FRONT		PURPLE LINE
STATIONARY FRONT		ALTERNATE RED & BLUE
UPPER COLD FRONT		DASHED BLUE LINE

FIGURE 3826.—Designation of fronts on weather maps.

NAVAIR 50–1P–11, published by The Naval Weather Service Command. This publication lists broadcast schedules and weather codes. Information on day and night visual storm warnings is given in the various volumes of sailing directions and coast pilots.

3828. Interpreting the weather.—The factors which determine weather are numerous and varied. Ever-increasing knowledge regarding them makes possible a continually improving weather service. However, the ability to forecast is acquired through study and long practice, and therefore the services of a trained meteorologist should be utilized whenever available.

The value of a forecast is increased if one has access to the information upon which it is based, and understands the principles and processes involved. It is sometimes as important to know the various types of weather that *might* be experienced as it is to know which of several possibilities is *most likely* to occur.

At sea, reporting stations are unevenly distributed, sometimes leaving relatively large areas with incomplete reports, or none at all. Under these conditions, the locations of highs, lows, fronts, etc., are imperfectly known, and their very existence may even be in doubt. At such times the mariner who can interpret the observations made from his own vessel may be able to predict weather for the next several hours more reliably than a trained meteorologist some distance away with incomplete information for the area of concern.

Knowledge of the various relationships given in chapters XXXVII, XXXVIII, and XXXIX is of value, but only the more elementary principles are presented. Further information can be obtained from meteorological publications such as those listed at the ends of the weather chapters. The information obtained from these references will provide a background for proper interpretation of individual weather experiences. If one uses every opportunity to observe and interpret weather sequences, knowledge and skill can be developed that will serve as a valuable supplement to information given in weather broadcasts, or to supply information for areas not covered by such broadcasts.

3829. Influencing the weather.—Meteorological activities are devoted primarily to understanding weather processes and predicting future weather. However, as knowledge regarding cause-and-effect relationships increases, the possibility of being able to induce certain results by artificially producing the necessary conditions becomes greater. The most promising results to date have been in inducing or increasing precipitation on a local scale by "seeding" supercooled clouds with powdered dry ice or silver iodide smoke. The effectiveness of this procedure on a larger scale is still controversial. Experiments in decreasing the intensity of severe tropical cyclones (i.e., hurricanes, typhoons), have been carried out but an operational method is still many years away.

References

American Meteorological Society. *Compendium of Meteorology*. Boston, American Meteorological Society, 1951.

American Meteorological Society. *Glossary of Meteorology*. Boston, American Meteorological Society, 1959 (with corrections, 1970).

Anderson, R. K. et al. *Applications of Meteorological Satellite Data in Analysis and Forecasting*, ESSA TR NESS51. Washington, D.C., National Oceanic and Atmospheric Administration, National Environmental Satellite Service, 1974.

Atkinson, G. D. *Forecasting Guide to Tropical Meteorology*, TR 240, Air Weather Service, U. S. Air Force, 1971.

Berry, F. A. Jr., E. Bollay, and N. R. Beers. *Handbook of Meteorology*. New York, McGraw-Hill, 1945.

Byers, H. R. *General Meteorology*, 4th ed. New York, McGraw-Hill, 1974.

Donn, W. L. *Meteorology*, 4th ed. New York, McGraw-Hill, 1975.

Haltiner, G. J., and F. L. Martin. *Dynamical and Physical Meteorology*, New York, McGraw-Hill, 1957.

Kotsch, W. J. *Weather for the Mariner*, Annapolis, Maryland, Naval Institute Press, 1970.

Neuberger, H., and J. Cahir. *Principles of Climatology, A Manual on Earth Science*. New York, Holt, Rinehart and Winston, Inc., 1969.

Petterssen, S. *Introduction to Meteorology*, 3rd ed. New York, McGraw-Hill, 1969.

Riehl, H. *Tropical Meteorology*. New York, McGraw-Hill, 1954.

Trewartha, G. T. *An Introduction to Climate*, 4th ed. New York, McGraw-Hill, 1968.

U. S. Department of Commerce. *Mariners Weather Log*. National Oceanic and Atmospheric Administration, Environmental Data Service. (periodical).

U. S. Department of the Navy. *Numerical Environmental Products Manual*. NAVAIR 50–1G–522. Naval Weather Service Command, 1975.

U. S. Department of the Navy. *U. S. Navy Marine Climatic Atlas of the World*, vol. VIII, The World. NAVAIR 50–1C–54, Naval Weather Service Command, 1969.

U. S. Department of the Navy. *Aerographer's Mate 1 and C*, NAVEDTRA 10362–B. Naval Education and Training Command, 1974.

U. S. Department of the Navy. *Aerographer's Mate 3 and 2*, NAVEDTRA 10363–E, 1976.

Williams, J., J. J. Higginson, and J. D. Rohrbough. *Sea and Air, The Marine Environment*. Annapolis, Maryland, Naval Institute Press, 1973.

World Meteorological Organization. *The Preparation and Use of Weather Maps by Mariners*, TN72. Secretariat, World Meteorological Organization, Geneva, Switzerland, 1966.

CHAPTER XXXIX

TROPICAL CYCLONES

3901. Introduction.—A **tropical cyclone** is a cyclone (art. 3813) originating in the Tropics or subtropics. Although it generally resembles the extratropical cyclone originating in higher latitudes, there are important differences, the principal one being the concentration of a large amount of energy into a relatively small area. Tropical cyclones are infrequent in comparison with middle- and high-latitude storms, but they have a record of destruction far exceeding that of any other type of storm. Because of their fury, and the fact that they are predominantly oceanic, they merit the special attention of all mariners, whether professional or amateur.

Rarely does the mariner who has experienced a fully developed tropical cyclone at sea wish to encounter a second one. He has learned the wisdom of avoiding them if possible. The uninitiated may be misled by the deceptively small size of a tropical cyclone as it appears on a weather map, and by the fine weather experienced only a few hundred miles from the reported center of such a storm. The rapidity with which the weather can deteriorate with approach of the storm, and the violence of the fully developed tropical cyclone, are difficult to visualize if they have not been experienced.

On his second voyage to the New World, Columbus encountered a tropical storm. Although his vessels suffered no damage, this experience proved valuable during his fourth voyage when his vessels were threatened by a fully developed hurricane. Columbus read the signs of an approaching storm from the appearance of a southeasterly swell, the direction of the high cirrus clouds, and the hazy appearance of the atmosphere. He directed his vessels to shelter. The commander of another group, who did not heed the signs, lost most of his ships; more than 500 men in their crews perished.

3902. Definitions.—**Tropical cyclone** is the general term for cyclones originating in the Tropics or subtropics. These cyclones are classified by form and intensity as follows:

Tropical disturbance is a discrete system of apparently organized convection—generally 100 to 300 miles in diameter—having a nonfrontal migratory character, and having maintained its identity for 24 hours or more. It may or may not be associated with a detectable perturbation of the wind field. It has no strong winds and no closed isobars i.e., isobars that completely enclose the low. (In successive stages of intensification, the tropical cyclone may be classified as a tropical disturbance, tropical depression, tropical storm, and hurricane or typhoon.)

Tropical depression has one or more closed isobars and some rotary circulation at the surface. The highest sustained (1-minute mean) surface wind speed is 33 knots.

Tropical storm has closed isobars and a distinct rotary circulation. The highest sustained (1-minute mean) surface wind speed is 34 to 63 knots.

Hurricane or **typhoon** has closed isobars, a strong and very pronounced rotary circulation, and a sustained (1-minute mean) surface wind speed of 64 knots or higher.

3903. Areas of occurrence.—Tropical cyclones occur almost entirely in six rather distinct areas, four in the Northern Hemisphere and two in the Southern Hemisphere as shown in figure 3903. The name by which the tropical cyclone is commonly known varies somewhat with the locality, as follows:

North Atlantic. A tropical cyclone with winds of 64 knots or greater is called a **hurricane.**

Eastern North Pacific. The name **hurricane** is used as in the North Atlantic.

Western North Pacific. A fully developed storm with winds of 64 knots or greater is called a **typhoon** or, locally in the Philippines, a **baguio.**

North Indian Ocean. A tropical cyclone with winds of 34 knots or greater is called a **cyclonic storm.**

South Indian Ocean. A tropical cyclone with winds of 34 knots or greater is called a **cyclone.**

Southwest Pacific and Australian Area. The name **cyclone** is used as in the South Indian Ocean. A severe tropical cyclone originating in the Timor Sea and moving southwest and then southeast across the interior of northwestern Australia is called a **willy-willy.**

Tropical cyclones have not been observed in the South Atlantic or in the South Pacific east of 140°W.

3904. Origin, season, and frequency of occurrence of the tropical cyclones in the six areas are as follows:

North Atlantic tropical cyclones can affect the entire North Atlantic Ocean in any month. However, they are mostly a threat south of about 35°N from June through November; August, September, and October are the months of highest incidence (tab. 3904). About 9 or 10 tropical cyclones (tropical storms and hurricanes) form each season; 5 or 6 reach hurricane intensity (winds of 64 knots and higher). A few hurricanes have generated winds estimated as high as 200 knots. Early- and late-season storms usually develop west of 50°W; during August and September, this spawning ground extends to the Cape Verde Islands. These storms usually move westward or westnorthwestward at speeds of less than 15 knots in the lower latitudes. After moving into the northern Caribbean or Greater Antilles regions, they will usually either move toward the Gulf of Mexico or recurve and accelerate in the North Atlantic. Some will recurve after reaching the Gulf of Mexico, while others will continue westward to landfall (fig. 3904).

Eastern North Pacific season is from June through October, although a storm can form in any month. An average of 15 tropical cyclones (tropical storms and hurricanes) form each year with about 6 reaching hurricane strength. The most intense storms are often the early-and late-season ones; these form close to the coast and far south. Midseason storms form anywhere in a wide band from the Mexican-Central American coast to the Hawaiian Islands. August and September are the months of highest incidence. These storms differ from their North Atlantic counterparts in that they are usually smaller in size. However, they can be just as intense.

Western North Pacific. More tropical cyclones form in the tropical western North Pacific than anywhere else in the world. More than 25 (tropical storms and typhoons) develop each year, and about 18 become typhoons. These typhoons are the largest and most intense tropical cyclones in the world. Each year an average of five generate maximum winds over 130 knots; circulations covering more than 600 miles in diameter are not uncommon. Most of these storms form east of the Philippines, and move across the Pacific toward the Philippines, Japan, and China; a few storms form in the South China Sea. The season extends from April through December. However, tropical cyclones are more common in the off-season months in this area than anywhere else. The peak of the season is July through October, when nearly 70 percent of all typhoons develop. There is a noticeable seasonal shift in storm tracks in this region. From July

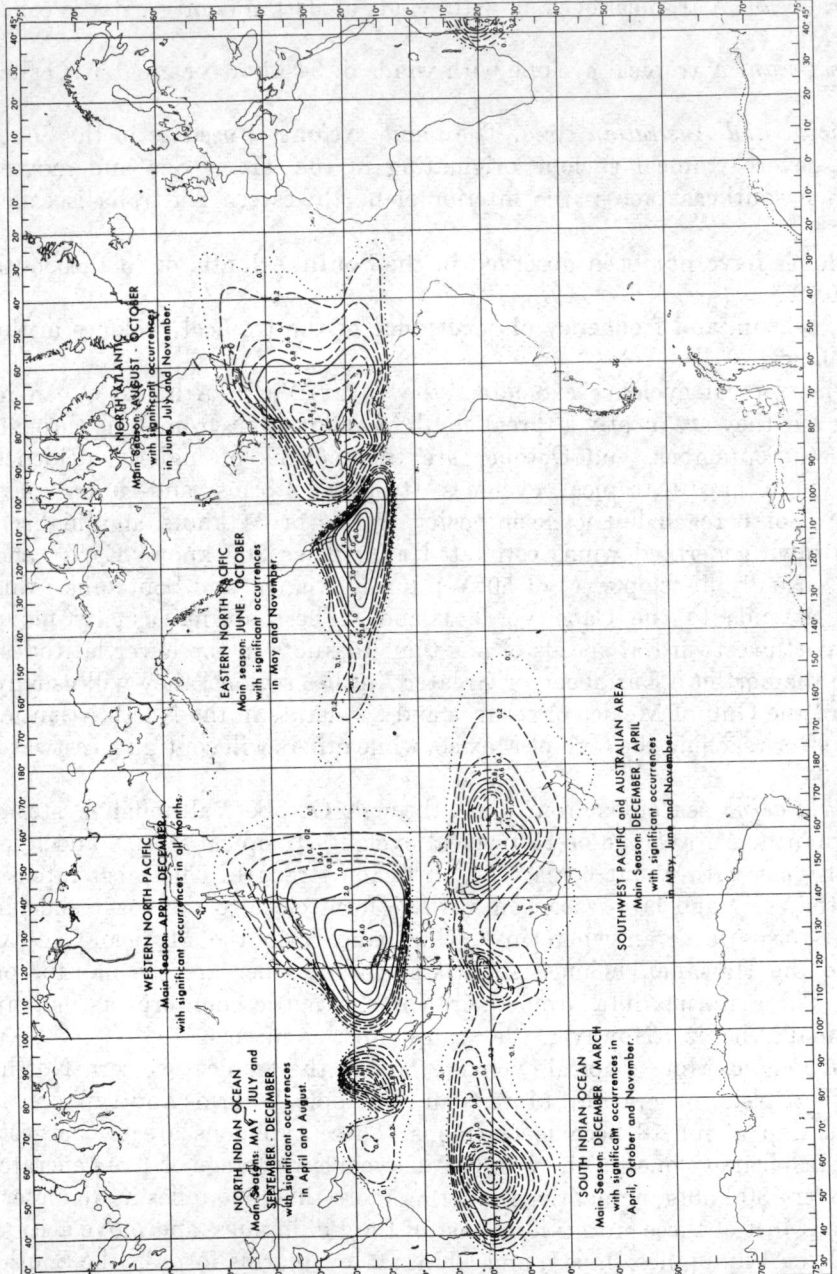

FIGURE 3903.—Areas in which tropical cyclones occur. The average number of tropical cyclones per 5° square has been analyzed for this figure. The main season for intense tropical storm activity is also shown for each major basin.

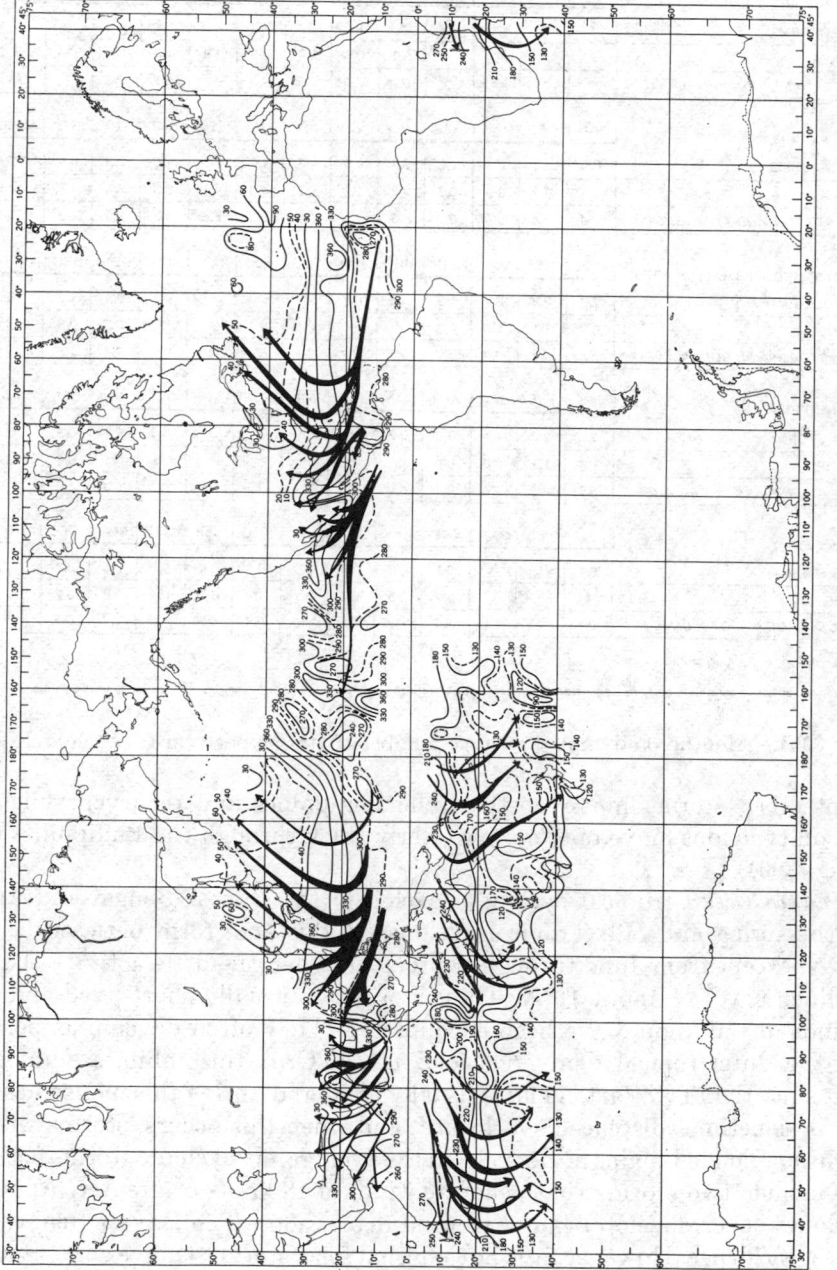

FIGURE 3904.—Storm tracks. The width of the arrow indicates the approximate frequency of storms; the wider the arrow the higher the frequency. Isolines on the base map show the resultant direction toward which storms moved. Data for the entire year has been summarized for this figure.

AREA AND STAGE	JAN	FEB	MAR	APR	MAY	JUN	JUL	AUG	SEP	OCT	NOV	DEC	ANNUAL
NORTH ATLANTIC													
TROPICAL STORMS	*	*	*	*	0.1	0.4	0.3	1.0	1.5	1.2	0.4	*	4.2
HURRICANES	*	*	*	*	*	0.3	0.4	1.5	2.7	1.3	0.3	*	5.2
TROPICAL STORMS AND HURRICANES	*	*	*	*	0.2	0.7	0.8	2.5	4.3	2.5	0.7	0.1	9.4
	JAN	FEB	MAR	APR	MAY	JUN	JUL	AUG	SEP	OCT	NOV	DEC	ANNUAL
EASTERN NORTH PACIFIC													
TROPICAL STORMS	*	*	*	*	*	1.5	2.8	2.3	2.3	1.2	0.3	*	9.3
HURRICANES	*	*	*	*	0.3	0.6	0.9	2.0	1.8	1.0	*	*	5.8
TROPICAL STORMS AND HURRICANES	*	*	*	*	0.3	2.0	3.6	4.5	4.1	2.2	0.3	*	15.2
	JAN	FEB	MAR	APR	MAY	JUN	JUL	AUG	SEP	OCT	NOV	DEC	ANNUAL
WESTERN NORTH PACIFIC													
TROPICAL STORMS	0.2	0.3	0.3	0.2	0.4	0.5	1.2	1.8	1.5	1.0	0.8	0.6	7.5
TYPHOONS	0.3	0.2	0.2	0.7	0.9	1.2	2.7	4.0	4.1	3.3	2.1	0.7	17.8
TROPICAL STORMS AND TYPHOONS	0.4	0.4	0.5	0.9	1.3	1.8	3.9	5.8	5.6	4.3	2.9	1.3	25.3
	JAN	FEB	MAR	APR	MAY	JUN	JUL	AUG	SEP	OCT	NOV	DEC	ANNUAL
SOUTHWEST PACIFIC AND AUSTRALIAN AREA													
TROPICAL STORMS	2.7	2.8	2.4	1.3	0.3	0.2	*	*	*	0.1	0.4	1.5	10.9
HURRICANES	0.7	1.1	1.3	0.3	*	*	0.1	0.1	*	*	0.3	0.5	3.8
TROPICAL STORMS AND HURRICANES	3.4	4.1	3.7	1.7	0.3	0.2	0.1	0.1	*	0.1	0.7	2.0	14.8
	JAN	FEB	MAR	APR	MAY	JUN	JUL	AUG	SEP	OCT	NOV	DEC	ANNUAL
SOUTHWEST INDIAN OCEAN													
TROPICAL STORMS	2.0	2.2	1.7	0.6	0.2	*	*	*	*	0.3	0.3	0.8	7.4
HURRICANES	1.3	1.1	0.8	0.4	*	*	*	*	*	*	*	0.5	3.8
TROPICAL STORMS AND HURRICANES	3.2	3.3	2.5	1.1	0.2	*	*	*	*	0.3	0.4	1.4	11.2
	JAN	FEB	MAR	APR	MAY	JUN	JUL	AUG	SEP	OCT	NOV	DEC	ANNUAL
NORTH INDIAN OCEAN													
TROPICAL STORMS	0.1	*	*	0.1	0.3	0.5	0.5	0.4	0.4	0.6	0.5	0.3	3.5
CYCLONES [1]	*	*	*	0.1	0.5	0.2	0.1	*	0.1	0.4	0.6	0.2	2.2
TROPICAL STORMS AND CYCLONES [1]	0.1	*	0.1	0.3	0.7	0.7	0.6	0.4	0.5	1.0	1.1	0.5	5.7

* Less than .05   [1] Winds ≥ 48 Kts.

Monthly values cannot be combined because single storms overlapping two months were counted once in each month and once in the annual.

TABLE 3904.—Monthly and annual average number of storms per year for each area.

through September, storms move north of the Philippines and recurve, while early- and late-season typhoons move on a more westerly track through the Philippines before recurving (fig. 3904).

North Indian Ocean tropical cyclones develop in the Bay of Bengal and Arabian Sea during the spring and fall. Tropical cyclones in this area form between latitudes 8°N and 15°N, except from June through September, when the little activity that does occur is confined north of about 15°N. These storms are usually short-lived and weak; however, winds of 130 knots have been encountered. They often develop as perturbations along the Intertropical Convergence Zone (ITCZ); this inhibits summertime development since the ITCZ (art. 3905) is usually over land during this monsoon season. However, it is sometimes displaced southward, and when this occurs, storms will form over the monsoon-flooded plains of Bengal. On the average, six cyclonic storms form each year. These include two storms that generate winds of 48 knots or greater. Another 10 tropical cyclones never develop beyond tropical depressions. The Bay of Bengal is the area of highest incidence. However, it is not unusual for a storm to move across southern India and reintensify in the Arabian Sea. This is particularly true during October— the month of highest incidence during the tropical cyclone season. It is also during this period that torrential rains from these storms dumped over already rain-soaked areas cause disastrous floods.

South Indian Ocean. Over the waters west of 100°E to the east African coast, an average of 11 tropical cyclones (tropical storms and hurricanes) form each season, and about 4 reach hurricane intensity. The season is from December through March, although it is possible for a storm to form in any month. Tropical cyclones in this region usually form south of 10°S. The latitude of recurvature usually migrates from about 20°S in January to around 15°S in April. After crossing 30°S, these storms sometimes become intense extratropical lows.

Southwest Pacific and Australian Area. These tropical waters spawn an annual average of 15 tropical cyclones (tropical storms and hurricanes), 4 of which reach hurricane intensity. The season extends from about December through April, although storms can form in any month. Activity is widespread in January and February, and it is in these months that tropical cyclones are most likely to affect Fiji, Samoa, and the other eastern islands.

Tropical cyclones usually form in the waters from 105°E to 160°W, between 5° and 20°S. Storms affecting northern and western Australia often develop in the Timor or Arafura Sea, while those that affect the east coast form in the Coral Sea. These storms are often small, but can develop winds in excess of 130 knots. New Zealand is sometimes reached by decaying Coral Sea storms; occasionally, it is reached by an intense hurricane. In general, tropical cyclones in this region move southwestward and then recurve southeastward (fig. 3904).

3905. Hurricane formation was once believed to result from an intensification of convective forces which produce the cumulonimbus towers of the doldrums. This view of hurricane generation held that surface heating caused warm moist air to ascend convectively to levels where condensation produced cumulonimbus clouds, which, after an inexplicable drop in atmospheric pressure, coalesced and were spun into a cyclonic motion by Coriolis force.

This hypothesis left much to be desired. Although some hurricanes develop from disturbances beginning in the doldrums (art. 3805), very few reach maturity in that region. Also, the high incidence of seemingly ideal convective situations does not match the low incidence of Atlantic hurricanes. Finally, the hypothesis did not explain the drop in atmospheric pressure, so essential to development of hurricane-force winds.

There is still no exact understanding of the triggering mechanism involved in hurricane generation, the balance of conditions needed to generate hurricane circulation, and the relationships between large- and small-scale atmospheric processes. But scientists today, treating the hurricane system as an atmospheric heat engine, present a more comprehensive and convincing view.

They begin with a starter mechanism in which either internal or external forces intensify the initial disturbance. The initial disturbance becomes a region into which low-level air from the surrounding area begins to flow, accelerating the convection already occurring inside the disturbance. The vertical circulation becomes increasingly well organized as water vapor in the ascending moist layer is condensed (releasing large amounts of heat energy to drive the wind system) and as the system is swept into a counterclockwise cyclonic spiral. But this incipient hurricane would soon fill up because of inflow at lower levels unless the chimney in which converging air surges upward is provided the exhaust mechanism of high-altitude winds.

These high-altitude winds (fig. 3905) pump ascending air out of the cyclonic system into a high-altitude anticyclone, which transports the air well away from the disturbance before sinking occurs. Thus, a large scale vertical circulation is set up in which low-level air is spiraled up the cyclonic twisting of the disturbance, and, after a trajectory over the sea, returned to lower altitudes some distance from the storm. This pumping action—and the heat released by the ascending air—may account for the sudden drop of atmospheric pressure at the surface, which produces the steep pressure gradient along which winds reach hurricane proportions.

It is believed that the interaction of low-level and high-altitude wind systems determines the intensity the hurricane will attain. If less air is pumped out than converges at low levels, the system will fill and die out. If more is pumped out than flows in, the circulation will be sustained and will intensify.

Research has shown that any process which increases the rate of low-level inflow is favorable for hurricane development, provided the inflowing air carries sufficient heat and moisture to fuel the hurricane's power system. It has also been shown that air above the developing disturbance at altitudes between 20,000 and 40,000 feet increases 1° to 3° in temperature about 24 hours before the disturbance develops into a hurricane. But it is not known whether low-level inflow and high-level warming *cause* hurricanes. They could very well be measurable symptoms of another effect which actually triggers the storm's increase to hurricane intensity.

The view of hurricanes as atmospheric engines is necessarily a general one. The exact role of each contributor is not completely understood. The engine seems to be both inefficient and unreliable; a myriad of delicate conditions must be satisfied for the atmosphere to produce a hurricane. Their relative infrequency indicates that many a potentially healthy hurricane ends early as a misfiring dud of a disturbance, somewhere over the sea.

3906. Portrait of a hurricane.—In the early life of the hurricane, the spiral covers an area averaging 100 miles in diameter with winds of 64 knots and greater, and spreads gale-force winds over a 400-mile diameter. The cyclonic spiral (fig. 3906) is marked by heavy cloud bands from which torrential rains fall, separated by areas of light rain or no rain at all. These spiral bands ascend in decks of cumulus and cumulonimbus clouds to the convective limit of cloud formation, where condensing water vapor is swept off as ice-crystal wisps of cirrus clouds. Thunderstorm electrical activity is observed in these bands, both as lightning and as tiny electrostatic discharge.

In the lower few thousand feet, air flows in through the cyclone, and is drawn upward through ascending columns of air near the center. The size and intensity decrease with altitude, the cyclonic circulation being gradually replaced above 40,000 feet by an anticyclonic circulation centered hundreds of miles away—the enormous high-altitude pump which is the exhaust system of the hurricane heat engine.

At lower levels, where the hurricane is more intense, winds on the rim of the storm follow a wide pattern, like the slower currents around the edge of a whirlpool; and, like those currents, these winds accelerate as they approach the center of the vortex. The

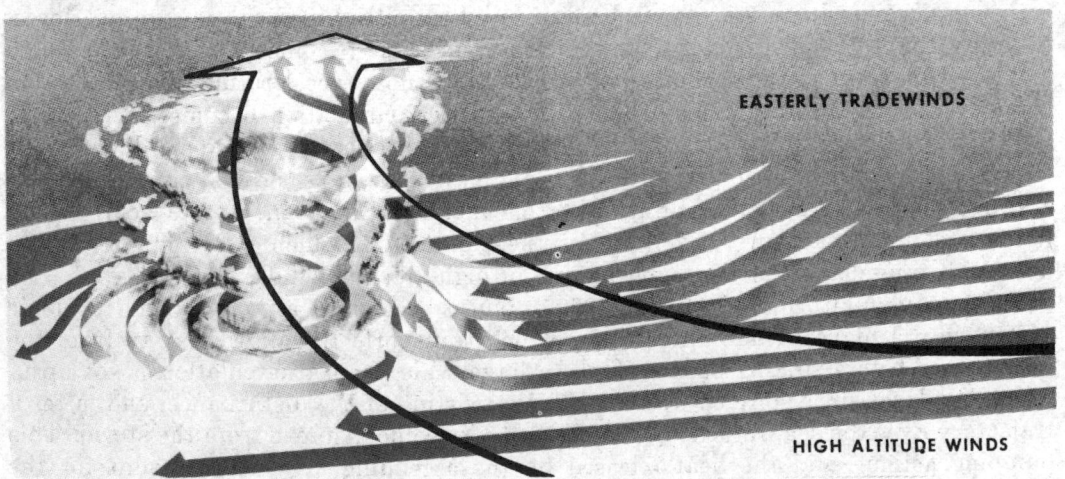

FIGURE 3905.—Pumping action of high altitude winds.

outer band has light winds at the rim of the storm, perhaps no more than 25 knots; within 30 miles of the center, winds may have velocities exceeding 130 knots. The inner band is the region of maximum wind velocity, where the storm's worst winds are felt, and where ascending air is chimneyed upward, releasing heat to drive the storm. In most hurricanes, these winds reach 85 knots and more than 170 knots in the more memorable ones.

In the hurricane, winds flow toward the low pressure in the warm, comparatively calm core. There, converging air is whirled upward by convection, the mechanical thrusting of other converging air, and the pumping action of high-altitude circulations. This spiral is marked by the thick cloud walls curling inward toward the storm center, releasing heavy precipitation and enormous quantities of heat energy. At the center, surrounded by a band in which this strong vertical circulation is greatest, is the **eye** of the hurricane.

The eye, like the spiral rainbands, is unique to the hurricane; no other atmospheric phenomenon has this calm core. On the average, eye diameter is about 14 miles, although diameters of 25 miles are not unusual. From the heated tower of maximum winds and cumulonimbus clouds, winds diminish rapidly to something less than 15 miles per hour in the eye; at the opposite wall, winds increase again, but come from the opposite direction because of the cyclonic circulation of the storm. This transformation of storm into comparative calm, and calm into violence from another quarter is spectacular. The eye's abrupt existence in the midst of opaque rainsqualls and hurricane winds, the intermittent bursts of blue sky and sunlight through light clouds in the core of the cyclone, and the galleried cumulus and cumulonimbus clouds are unforgettable.

That is how an average hurricane is structured. But every hurricane is individual, and the more or less orderly circulation described here omits the extreme variability and instability within the storm system. Pressure and temperature gradients fluctuate wildly across the storm as the hurricane maintains its erratic life in the face of forces

FIGURE 3906.—Cutaway view of a hurricane greatly exaggerated in vertical dimension. Actual hurricanes are less than 50,000 feet high and may have a diameter of several hundred miles.

which will ultimately destroy it. If it is an August storm, its average life expectancy is 12 days; if a July or November storm, it lives an average of 8 days.

3907. Life of a tropical cyclone.—Reports from ships in the vicinity of an **easterly wave** (a westward-moving trough of low pressure embedded in deep easterlies) indicate that the atmospheric pressure in the region has fallen more than 5 millibars in the past 24 hours. This is cause for alarm because in the Tropics pressure varies little; the normal diurnal pressure change is only about 3 millibars. Satellite pictures indicate thickening middle and high clouds, squalls are reported ahead of the easterly wave, and wind reports indicate a cyclonic circulation is forming. The former easterly wave—now classified a *tropical disturbance*—is moving westward at 10 knots under the canopy of a large high-pressure system aloft. Sea surface temperatures in the vicinity are in the mid-80°F range.

Within 48 hours winds increase to 25 knots near the center of definite circulation, and central pressure has dropped below 1000 millibars. The disturbance is now classified as a *tropical depression*. Soon the circulation extends out to 100 miles and upward to 20,000 feet. Winds near the center increase to gale force, central pressure falls below 990 millibars, and towering cumulonimbus clouds shield a developing eye; a *tropical storm* has developed.

Satellite photographs now reveal a tightly organized tropical cyclone, and reconnaissance reports indicate maximum winds of 80 knots around a central pressure of 980 millibars; a *hurricane* has developed. A ship to the right (left in the Southern Hemisphere) of the hurricane's center (looking toward the direction of storm movement) reports a 30-foot sea. The hurricane is fast maturing; it continues eastward.

A few days later the hurricane reaches its peak. The satellite photographs a textbook picture (fig. 3907), as 120-knot winds roar around a 940-millibar pressure center; hurricane-force winds extend 50 miles in all directions, and seas are reported up to 40 feet. There is no further deepening now, but the hurricane begins to expand. In 2 days, gales extend out to 200 miles, and hurricane winds out to 75 miles. Then the hurricane slows and begins to recurve; this turning marks the beginning of the end.

The hurricane accelerates, and, upon reaching the temperate latitudes, it begins to lose its tropical characteristics. The circulation continues to expand, but now cold air is intruding (cold air, cold water, dry air aloft, and land aid in the decay of a tropical cyclone). The warm core survives for a few more days before the transformation to a large extratropical low-pressure system is complete.

Not all tropical cyclones follow this ideal pattern. Most falter in the early stages, some dissipate over land, and others remain potent for several weeks.

The lowest-sea-level pressure ever recorded was 877 millibars in typhoon Ida, on September 24, 1958. The observation was taken by a reconnaissance aircraft dropsonde some 750 miles east of Luzon, Philippines. This observation was obtained again in typhoon Nora on October 6, 1973. The lowest barometric reading of record for the United States is 892.3 millibars obtained during a hurricane at Lower Matecumbe Key, Florida in September 1935, In hurricane Camille in 1969, a 905 millibar pressure was measured by reconnaissance aircraft. During a 1927 typhoon, the S. S. *Sapoeroea* recorded a pressure of 886.6 millibars, the lowest sea-level pressure reported from a ship. Pressure has been observed to drop more than 33 millibars per hour, with a pressure gradient amounting to a change of 3.7 millibars per mile.

3908. The marine weather broadcast is the most important tool the mariner has for avoiding the tropical cyclone. This broadcast, covering all tropical areas, provides information about the tropical cyclone's present location, maximum winds and seas, and future condition.

FIGURE 3907.—Satellite photograph of hurricane.

The U. S. Navy, the National Oceanic and Atmospheric Administration, ard the U. S. Air Force have developed a highly effective surveillance system for the tropical cyclone areas of the world. Routine and special weather reports (from land stations, ships at sea, aircraft; daytime weather satellite reports; radar reports from land stations; special reports from ships at sea; and the specially instrumented weather reconnaissance aircraft of National Oceanic and Atmospheric Administration and the U. S. Air Force) enable accurate detection, location, and tracking of tropical cyclones. International cooperation is good. In addition to improved satellites permitting nighttime surveillance, data buoys provide another new source of information for the protection of the mariner.

The tropical warning services have three principal functions:

1. the collection and analysis of the necessary observational data;
2. the preparation of timely and accurate forecasts and warnings; and
3. the rapid and efficient distribution of advisories, warnings, and all other pertinent information.

To provide timely and accurate information and warnings regarding tropical cyclones, the oceans have been divided into overlapping geographical areas of responsibility.

For detailed information on the areas of responsibility of the countries participating in the international forecasting and warning program, and radio aids, refer to *World-wide Marine Weather Broadcasts*, published jointly by the Naval Weather Service Command and the National Weather Service.

Although the areas of forecasting responsibility are fairly well defined for the Department of Defense, the international and domestic civilian system provides many overlaps and is dependent upon qualitative factors. For example, when a tropical storm or hurricane is traveling westward and crosses 35°W longitude, the continued issuance of forecasts and warnings to the general public, shipping interests, etc., becomes the responsibility of the National Hurricane Center of the National Weather Service at Miami, Florida. When a tropical storm or hurricane crosses 35°W longitude traveling from west to east, the National Hurricane Center ceases to issue formal public advisories, but will issue marine bulletins on any dangerous tropical cyclone in the North Atlantic, if it is of importance or constitutes a threat to shipping and other interests. These advisories are included in National Weather Service Marine Bulletins broadcast to ships four times daily at 0030, 0600, 1230, and 1830 GMT, over radio station NAM Norfolk, Virginia. Special advisories may be issued at any time.

In the eastern Pacific (east of longitude 140°W), responsibility for the issuance of tropical storm and hurricane advisories and warnings for the general public, merchant shipping, and other interests rests with the National Weather Service Eastern Pacific Hurricane Center, San Francisco, California. The Department of Defense responsibility rests with the U. S. Navy's Fleet Weather Central, Pearl Harbor, Hawaii. Formal advisories and warnings are issued at 0300, 0900, 1500, and 2100 GMT, and are included in the marine bulletins broadcast by radio stations KPH, KMI, KFS, NMC, ELH, DOE, NMQ, and KOU.

In the central Pacific (between the 180th meridian and longitude 140°W), the civilian responsibility rests with the National Weather Service Central Pacific Hurricane Center, Honolulu Hawaii. Department of Defense responsibility rests with the U. S. Navy's Fleet Weather Central, Pearl Harbor. Formal tropical storm and hurricane advisories and warnings are issued at 0300, 0900, 1500, and 2100 GMT, and are included in the marine bulletins broadcast by radio station KHK.

Tropical cyclone information messages generally contain position of the storm, intensity, direction and speed of movement, and a description of the area of strong winds. Also included is a forecast of future movement and intensity. When the storm is likely to affect any land area, details on when and where it will be felt, and data on tides, rain, floods, and maximum winds are also included. Figure 3908 provides an example of a marine advisory issued by the National Hurricane Center.

The U. S. Navy's Fleet Weather Central in Guam, with its built-in Joint (Navy and Air Force) Typhoon Warning Center (JTWC), has a primary area of responsibility for all U. S. tropical storm and typhoon advisories and warnings from the 180th meridian westward to the mainland of Asia. A secondary area of responsibility extends westward to longitude 90°E. Whenever a tropical cyclone is observed in the western North

NOAA/NATIONAL HURRICANE CENTER MARINE ADVISORY NUM-
BER 13 HURRICANE LADY 0400Z SEPTEMBER 21 19--.

HURRICANE WARNINGS ARE DISPLAYED FROM KEY LARGO TO
CAPE KENNEDY. GALE WARNINGS ARE DISPLAYED FROM KEY
WEST TO JACKSONVILLE AND FROM FLORIDAY BAY TO CEDAR KEY.

HURRICANE CENTER LOCATED NEAR LATITUDE 25.5 NORTH
LONGITUDE 78.5 WEST AT 21/0400Z. POSITION EXCELLENT AC-
CURATE WITHIN 10 MILES BASED ON AIR FORCE RECONNAISSANCE
AND SYNOPTIC REPORTS.

PRESENT MOVEMENT TOWARD THE WEST NORTHWEST OR 285
DEGREES AT 10 KT. MAX SUSTAINED WINDS OF 100 KT NEAR
CENTER WITH GUSTS TO 160 KT.
MAX WINDS OVER INLAND AREAS 35 KT.
RAD OF 65 KT WINDS 90 NE 60 SE 80 SW 90 NW QUAD.
RAD OF 50 KT WINDS 120 NE 70 SE 90 SW 120 NW QUAD.
RAD OF 30 KT WINDS 210 NE 210 SE 210 SW 210 NW QUAD.
REPEAT CENTER LOCATED 25.5N 78.3W at 21/0400Z.

12 HOUR FORECAST VALID 21/1600Z LATITUDE 26.0N LONGI-
TUDE 80.5W.
MAX WINDS OF 100 KT NEAR CENTER WITH GUSTS TO 160 KT.
MAX WINDS OVER INLAND AREAS 65 KT.
RADIUS OF 50KT WINDS 120 NE 70 SE 90 SW 120 NW QUAD.
24 HOUR FORECAST VALID 22/0400Z LATITUDE 26.0N
LONGITUDE 83.0W.
MAX WINDS OF 75 KT NEAR CENTER WITH GUSTS TO 120 KT.
MAX WINDS OVER INLAND AREAS 45 KT.
RADIUS OF 50 KT WINDS 120 NE 120 SE 120 SW 120 NW QUAD.

STORM TIDE OF 9 TO 12 FT SOUTHEAST FLA COAST GREATER
MIAMI AREA TO THE PALM BEACHES.

NEXT ADVISORY AT 21/1000Z.

FIGURE 3908.—Example of marine advisory issued by National Hurricane Center.

Pacific area, serially numbered warnings, bearing an immediate precedence are broadcast from the Fleet Weather Central/JTWC at 0000, 0600, 1200, and 1800 GMT.

The responsibility for issuing gale and storm warnings for the Indian Ocean,
Arabian Sea, Bay of Bengal, Western Pacific, and South Pacific rests with many
countries. In general, warnings of approaching tropical cyclones which may be hazardous will include the following information: storm type, central pressure given in millibars, windspeed observed within the storm, storm location, speed and direction of
movement, the extent of the affected area, visibility, and the state of the sea, as well
as any other pertinent information received. All storm warning messages commence
with the international call sign "TTT."

These warnings are broadcast on prespecified radio frequency bands immediately
upon receipt of the information and at specific intervals thereafter. Generally, the
broadcast interval is every 6 to 8 hours, depending upon receipt of new information.

Bulletins and forecasts are excellent guides to the present and future behavior of
the tropical cyclone, and a plot should be kept of all positions.

3909. The passage of a tropical cyclone at sea is an experience not soon to be
forgotten.

An early indication of the approach of such a storm is the presence of a long swell.
In the absence of a tropical cyclone, the crests of swell in the deep waters of the Atlantic
pass at the rate of perhaps eight per minute. Swell generated by a hurricane is about

twice as long, the crests passing at the rate of perhaps four per minute. Swell may be observed several days before arrival of the storm.

When the storm center is 500 to 1,000 miles away, the barometer usually rises a little, and the skies are relatively clear. Cumulus clouds, if present at all, are few in number and their vertical development appears suppressed. The barometer usually appears restless, **pumping** up and down a few hundredths of an inch.

As the tropical cyclone comes nearer, a cloud sequence begins which resembles that associated with the approach of a warm front in middle latitudes (art. 3811). Snow-white, fibrous "mare's tails" (cirrus) appear when the storm is about 300 to 600 miles away. Usually these seem to converge, more or less, in the direction from which the storm is approaching. This convergence is particularly apparent at about the time of sunrise and sunset.

Shortly after the cirrus appears, but sometimes before, the barometer starts a long, slow fall. At first the fall is so gradual that it only appears to alter somewhat the normal daily cycle (two maxima and two minima in the Tropics). As the rate of fall increases, the daily pattern is completely lost in the more or less steady fall.

The cirrus becomes more confused and tangled, and then gradually gives way to a continuous veil of cirrostratus. Below this veil, altostratus forms, and then strato-cumulus (art. 3713). These clouds gradually become more dense, and as they do so, the weather becomes unsettled. A fine, mist-like rain begins to fall, interrupted from time to time by showers. The barometer has fallen perhaps a tenth of an inch.

As the fall becomes more rapid, the wind increases in gustiness, and its speed becomes greater, reaching a value of perhaps 22 to 40 knots (Beaufort 6–8). On the horizon appears a dark wall of heavy cumulonimbus (art. 3713), the **bar** of the storm. Portions of this heavy cloud become detached from time to time and drift across the sky, accompanied by rainsqualls and wind of increasing speed. Between squalls, the cirrostratus can be seen through breaks in the stratocumulus.

As the bar approaches, the barometer falls more rapidly and wind speed increases. The seas, which have been gradually mounting, become tempestuous. Squall lines, one after the other, sweep past in ever increasing number and intensity.

With the arrival of the bar, the day becomes very dark, squalls become virtually continuous, and the barometer falls precipitously, with a rapid increase in wind speed. The center may still be 100 to 200 miles away in a fully developed tropical cyclone. As the center of the storm comes closer, the ever-stronger wind shrieks through the rigging and about the superstructure of the vessel. As the center approaches, rain falls in torrents. The wind fury increases. The seas become mountainous. The tops of huge waves are blown off to mingle with the rain and fill the air with water. Objects at a short distance are not visible. Even the largest and most seaworthy vessels become virtually unmanageable, and may sustain heavy damage. Less sturdy vessels may not survive. Navigation virtually stops as safety of the vessel becomes the prime con-sideration. The awesome fury of this condition can only be experienced. Words are inadequate to describe it.

If the eye of the storm passes over the vessel, the winds suddenly drop to a breeze as the wall of the eye passes. The rain stops, and the skies clear sufficiently to permit the sun to shine through holes in the comparatively thin cloud cover. Visibility im-proves. Mountainous seas approach from all sides, apparently in complete confusion. The barometer reaches its lowest point, which may be 1½ or 2 inches below normal in fully developed tropical cyclones. As the wall on the opposite side of the eye arrives, the full fury of the wind strikes as suddenly as it ceased, but from the opposite direction. The sequence of conditions that occurred during approach of the storm is reversed, and pass more quickly, as the various parts of the storm are not as wide in the rear of a storm as on its forward side.

Typical cloud formations associated with a hurricane are shown in figure 3909.

3910. Locating the center of a tropical cyclone.—If intelligent action is to be taken to avoid the full fury of a tropical cyclone, early determination of its location and direction of travel relative to the vessel is essential. The bulletins and forecasts are an excellent general guide, but they are not infallible and may be sufficiently in error to induce a mariner in a critical position to alter course so as to unwittingly increase the danger to his vessel. Often it is possible, using only those observations made aboard ship, to obtain a sufficiently close approximation to enable the vessel to maneuver to the best advantage.

As stated in article 3909, the presence of an exceptionally long swell is usually the first visible indication of the existence of a tropical cyclone. In deep water it approaches from the general direction of origin (the position of the storm center *when the swell was generated*). However, in shoaling water this is a less reliable indication because the direction is changed by refraction, the crests being more nearly parallel to the bottom contours.

When the cirrus clouds appear, their point of convergence provides an indication of the direction of the storm center. If the storm is to pass well to one side of the observer, the point of convergence shifts slowly in the direction of storm movement. If the storm center will pass near the observer, this point remains steady. When the bar (art. 3909) becomes visible, it appears to rest upon the horizon for several hours. The darkest part of this cloud is in the direction of the storm center. If the storm is to pass to one side, the bar appears to drift slowly along the horizon. If the storm is heading directly toward the observer, the position of the bar remains fixed. Once within the area of the dense, low clouds, one should observe their direction of movement, which is almost exactly along the isobars, with the center of the storm being 90° from the direction of cloud movement (left of direction of movement in the Northern Hemisphere, and right in the Southern Hemisphere).

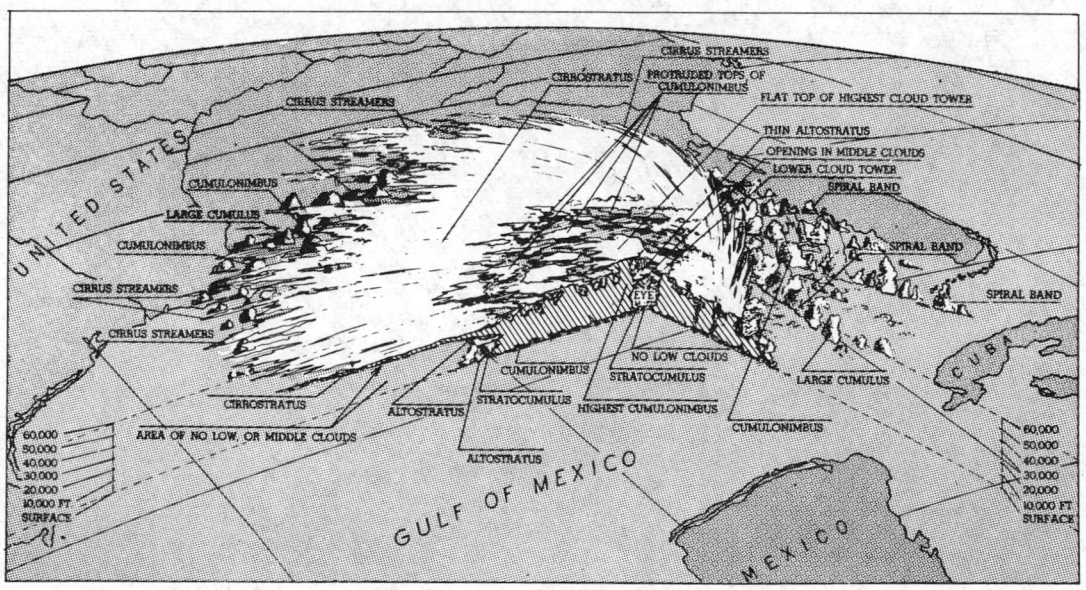

FIGURE 3909.—Typical hurricane cloud formations.

The winds are probably the best guide to the direction of the center of a tropical cyclone. The circulation is cyclonic (art. 3812), but because of the steep pressure gradient near the center, the winds there blow with greater violence and are more nearly circular than in extratropical cyclones.

According to Buys Ballot's law (art. 3812) an observer who faces into the wind has the center of the low pressure on his right in the Northern Hemisphere, and on his left in the Southern Hemisphere, and in each case somewhat behind him. If the wind followed circular isobars exactly, the center would be exactly 8 points, or 90°, from dead ahead when facing into the wind. However, the track of the wind is usually inclined somewhat toward the center, so that the angle from dead ahead varies between perhaps 8 and 12 points (90° to 135°). The inclination varies in different parts of the same storm. It is least in front of the storm, and greatest in the rear, since the actual wind is the vector sum of that due to the pressure gradient and the motion of the storm along the track. A good average is perhaps 10 points in front, and 11 or 12 points in the rear. These values apply when the storm center is still several hundred miles away. Closer to the center, the wind blows more nearly along the isobars, the inclination being reduced by one or two points at the wall of the eye. Since wind direc-

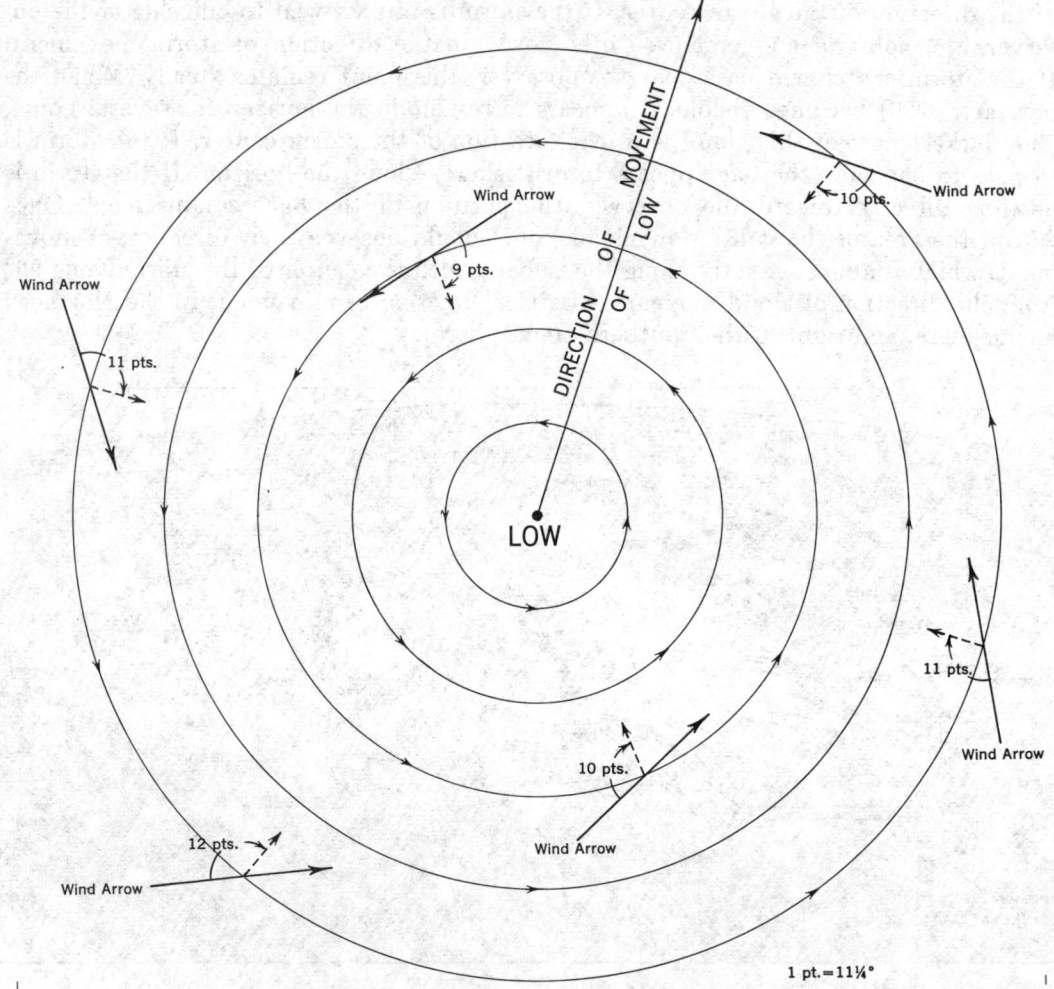

FIGURE 3910a.—Approximate relationship of wind to isobars and storm center in the Northern Hemisphere.

tion usually shifts temporarily during a squall, its direction at this time should not be used for determining the position of the center. The approximate relationship of wind to isobars and storm center in the Northern Hemisphere is shown in figure 3910a.

When the center is within radar range, it might be located by this equipment. However, since the radar return is predominantly from the rain, results can be deceptive, and other indications should not be neglected. Figure 3910b shows a radar PPI presentation of a tropical cyclone. If the eye is out of range, the spiral bands (fig. 3910b) may indicate its direction from the vessel. Tracking the eye or upwind portion of the spiral bands enables determining the direction and speed of movement; this should be done for at least 1 hour because the eye tends to oscillate. The tracking of individual cells, which tend to move tangentially around the eye, for 15 minutes or more, either at the end of the band or between bands, will provide an indication of the wind speed in that area of the storm.

Distance from the storm center is more difficult to determine than direction. Radar is perhaps the best guide. However, the rate of fall of the barometer is some indication.

3911. Maneuvering to avoid the storm center.—The safest procedure with respect to tropical cyclones is to avoid them. If action is taken sufficiently early, this is simply a matter of setting a course that will take the vessel well to one side of the probable track of the storm, and then continuing to plot the positions of the storm center, as given in the weather bulletins, revising the course as needed.

However, such action is not always possible. If one finds himself within the storm area, the proper action to take depends in part upon his position relative to the storm center and its direction of travel. It is customary to divide the circular area of the storm into two parts. In the Northern Hemisphere, that part to the *right* of the storm track (facing in the direction *toward* which the storm is moving) is called the **dangerous semicircle.** It is considered dangerous because (1) the actual wind *speed* is greater than that due to the pressure gradient alone, since it is augmented by the forward motion of the storm, and (2) the *direction* of the wind and sea is such as to carry a vessel into the path of the storm (in the forward part of the semicircle). The part to the left

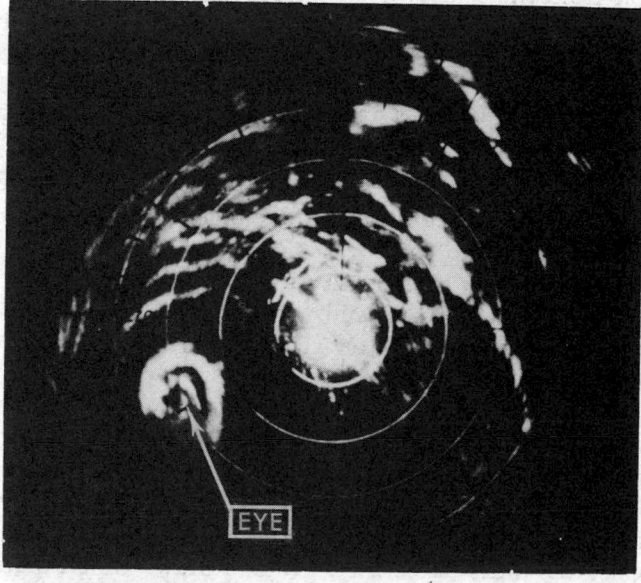

FIGURE 3910b.—Radar PPI presentation of a tropical cyclone.

of the storm track is called the **navigable semicircle.** In this part, the wind is decreased by the forward motion of the storm, and the wind blows vessels away from the storm track (in the forward part). Because of the greater wind speed in the dangerous semicircle, the seas are higher than in the navigable semicircle. In the Southern Hemisphere, the dangerous semicircle is to the left of the storm track, and the navigable semicircle is to the right of the storm track.

A plot of successive positions of the storm center should indicate the semicircle in which a vessel is located. However, if this is based upon weather bulletins, it is not a reliable guide because of the lag between the observations upon which the bulletin is based and the time of reception of the bulletin, with the ever present possibility of a change in the direction of motion of the storm. The use of one's radar eliminates this lag, but the return is not always a true indication of the center. Perhaps the most reliable guide is the wind. Within the cyclonic circulation, a *veering* wind (one changing direction to the right in the Northern Hemisphere and to the left in the Southern Hemisphere) indicates the vessel is probably in the dangerous semicircle, and a *backing* wind (one changing in a direction opposite to a veering wind) indicates the vessel is probably in the navigable semicircle. However, if a vessel is underway, its motion should be considered. If it is outrunning the storm or pulling rapidly toward one side (which is not difficult during the early stages of a storm, when its speed is low), the opposite effect occurs. This should usually be accompanied by a rise in atmospheric pressure, but if motion of the vessel is nearly along an isobar, this may not be a reliable indication. If in doubt, the safest action is usually to stop long enough to determine definitely the semicircle. The loss in valuable time may be more than offset by the minimizing of the possibility of taking the wrong action and increasing the danger to the vessel. If the wind direction remains steady (for a vessel which is stopped), with increasing speed and falling barometer, the vessel is in or near the path of the storm. If it remains steady with decreasing speed and rising barometer, the vessel is on the storm track, behind the center.

The first action to take if one finds himself within the cyclonic circulation, is to determine the position of his vessel with respect to the storm center. While the vessel can still make considerable way through the water, a course should be selected to take it as far as possible from the center. If the vessel can move faster than the storm, it is a relatively simple matter to outrun the storm if sea room permits. But when the storm is faster, the solution is not as simple. In this case, the vessel, if ahead of the storm, will approach nearer to the the center. The problem is to select a course that will produce the greatest possible minimum distance. This is best determined by means of a relative movement plot, as shown in the following example solved on a maneuvering board.

Example.—A tropical cyclone is estimated to be moving in direction 320° at 19 knots. Its center bears 170°, at an estimated distance of 200 miles from a vessel which has a maximum speed of 12 knots.

Required.—(1) The course to steer at 12 knots to produce the greatest possible minimum distance between the vessel and the storm center.

(2) The distance of the storm center at nearest approach.

(3) Elapsed time until nearest approach.

Solution (fig. 3911).—Consider the vessel remaining at the center of the plot throughout the solution, as on a radar PPI.

(1) Plot point C at a distance of 200 miles (scale 20:1) in direction 170° from the center of the diagram, to locate the position of the storm center relative to the vessel. From the center of the diagram, draw RA, the speed vector of the storm center, in direction 320°, speed 19 knots (scale 2:1). From A draw a line tangent to the 12-knot speed circle (labeled 6 at scale 2:1) *on the side opposite the storm center.* From the center

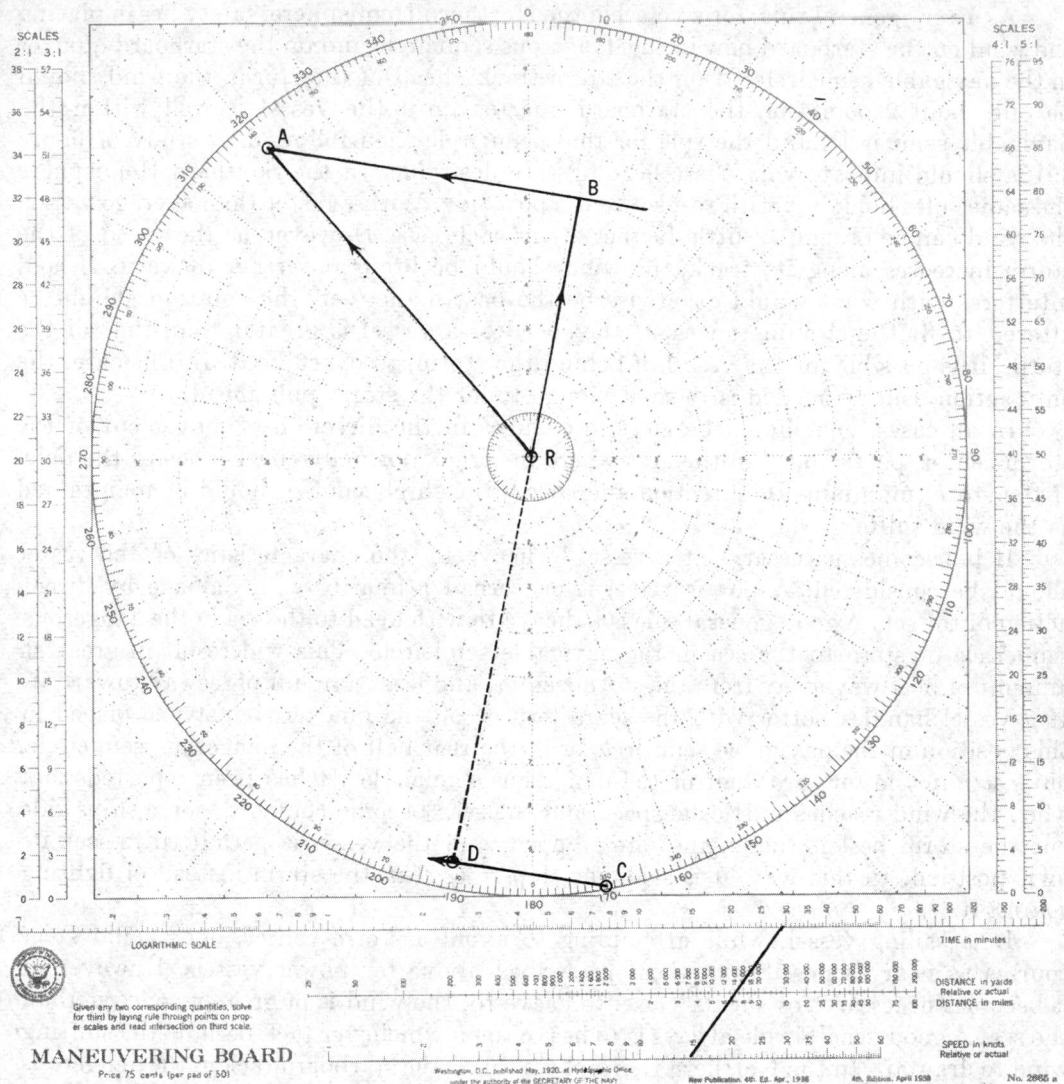

FIGURE 3911.—Solution to determine course for avoiding storm center.

of the diagram draw a perpendicular to this tangent line, locating point B. The line RB is the required speed vector for the vessel. Its direction, 011°, is the required course.

(2) The path of the storm center *relative to the vessel*, will be along a line from C in the direction BA, if both storm and vessel maintain course and speed. The point of nearest approach will be at D, the foot of a perpendicular from the center of the diagram. This distance, at scale 20:1, is 187 miles.

(3) The length of the vector BA (14.8 knots) is the speed of the storm with respect to the vessel. Mark this on the lowest scale of the nomogram at the bottom of the diagram. The relative distance $\dot{C}D$ is 72 miles, by measurement. Mark this (scale 10:1) on the middle scale at the bottom of the diagram. Draw a line between the two points and extend it to intersect the top scale at 29.2 (292 at 10:1 scale). The elapsed time is therefore 292 minutes, or 4 hours 52 minutes, or 5 hours, approximately.

Answers.—(1) C 011°, (2) D 187 mi., (3) t 5ʰ (approximately).

The storm center will be dead astern at its nearest approach.

As a very general rule, for a vessel in the Northern Hemisphere, safety lies in placing the wind on the starboard bow in the dangerous semicircle and on the starboard quarter in the navigable semicircle. If on the storm track ahead of the storm, the wind should be put about 2 points on the starboard quarter until the vessel is well within the navigable semicircle, and the rule for that semicircle then followed. A study of figure 3910a should indicate why these headings are desirable. In the Southern Hemisphere the same rules hold, but with respect to the port side. With a faster than average vessel, the wind can be brought a little farther aft in each case. However, as the speed of the storm increases along its track, the wind should be brought farther forward. If land interferes with what would otherwise be the best maneuver, the solution should be altered to fit the circumstances. If the speed of a vessel is greater than that of the storm, it is possible for the vessel, if behind the storm, to overtake it. In this case, the only action usually needed is to slow enough to let the storm pull ahead.

In all cases, one should be alert to changes in the direction of movement of the storm center, particularly in the area where the track normally curves toward the pole. If the storm maintains its direction and speed, the ship's course should be maintained as the wind shifts.

If it becomes necessary for a vessel to heave to, the characteristics of the vessel should be considered. A power vessel is concerned primarily with damage by direct action of the sea. A good general rule is to heave to with head to the sea in the dangerous semicircle or stern to the sea in the navigable semicircle. This will result in greatest amount of headway away from the storm center, and least amount of leeway toward it. If a vessel handles better with the sea astern or on the quarter, it may be placed in this position in the navigable semicircle or in the rear half of the dangerous semicircle, but *never* in the forward half of the dangerous semicircle. It has been reported that when the wind reaches hurricane speed and the seas become confused, some ships ride out the storm best if the engines are stopped, and the vessel is permitted to seek its own position. In this way, it is said, the ship rides *with* the storm instead of fighting *against* it.

In a sailing vessel, while attempting to avoid a storm center, one should steer courses as near as possible to those prescribed above for power vessels. However, if it becomes necessary for such a vessel to heave to, the wind is of greater concern than the sea. A good general rule always is to heave to on whichever tack permits the shifting wind to draw aft. In the Northern Hemisphere this is the starboard tack in the dangerous semicircle and the port tack in the navigable semicircle. In the Southern Hemisphere these are reversed.

While each storm requires its own analysis, and frequent or continual resurvey of the situation, the general rules for a steamer may be summarized as follows:

NORTHERN HEMISPHERE

Right or dangerous semicircle.—Bring the wind on the starboard bow (045° relative), hold course and make as much way as possible. If obliged to heave to, do so with head to the sea.

Left or navigable semicircle.—Bring the wind on the starboard quarter (135° relative), hold course and make as much way as possible. If obliged to heave to, do so with stern to the sea.

On storm track, ahead of center.—Bring the wind 2 points on the starboard quarter (about 160° relative), hold course and make as much way as possible. When well within the navigable semicircle, maneuver as indicated above.

On storm track, behind center.—Avoid the center by the best practicable course, keeping in mind the tendency of tropical cyclones to curve northward and eastward.

SOUTHERN HEMISPHERE

Left or dangerous semicircle.—Bring the wind on the port bow (315° relative), hold course and make as much way as possible. If obliged to heave to, do so with head to the sea.

Right or navigable semicircle.—Bring the wind on the port quarter (225° relative), hold course and make as much way as possible. If obliged to heave to, do so with stern to the sea.

On storm track, ahead of center.—Bring the wind 2 points on the port quarter (about 200° relative), hold course and make as much way as possible. When well within the navigable semicircle, maneuver as indicated above.

On storm track, behind center.—Avoid the center by the best practicable course, keeping in mind the tendency of tropical cyclones to curve southward and eastward.

Whenever a tropical cyclone is encountered, the wise procedure is to begin preparing the vessel for heavy weather in sufficient time to permit thorough preparation, so that damage may be minimized. One should be particularly careful to keep free surfaces of liquids to a minimum.

It is possible, particularly in temperate latitudes after the storm has recurved, that the dangerous semicircle is the left one in the Northern Hemisphere (right one in the Southern Hemisphere). This can occur if a large high lies north of the storm and causes a tightening of the pressure gradient in the region.

Typhoon Havens Handbook for the Western Pacific and Indian Oceans is published by the Naval Environmental Prediction Research Facility, Monterey, California, as an aid to commanders and commanding officers of ships in evaluating a typhoon situation and to assist them in deciding whether to sortie, to evade, or to remain in port to take shelter within a specific harbor.

3912. Effects.—The high winds of a tropical cyclone inflict widespread damage when such a storm leaves the ocean and crosses land. Aids to navigation may be blown out of position or destroyed. Craft in harbors, unless they are properly secured, drag anchor or are blown against obstructions. Ashore, trees are blown over, houses are damaged, power lines are blown down, etc. The greatest damage usually occurs in the dangerous semicircle a short distance from the center, where the strongest winds occur. As the storm continues on across land, its fury subsides faster than it would if it had remained over water.

Wind instruments are usually incapable of measuring the 175- to 200-knot winds of the more intense hurricanes; if the instrument holds up, often the supporting structure gives way.

Wind gusts, which are usually 30 to 50 percent higher than sustained winds, add significantly to the destructiveness of the tropical cyclone. Many tropical cyclones that reach hurricane intensity develop winds of more than 90 knots sometime during their lives, but few develop winds of more than 130 knots.

Tropical cyclones have produced some of the world's heaviest rainfalls. While average amounts range from 6 to 10 inches, totals near 100 inches over a 4-day period have been observed. A 24-hour world's record of 73.62 inches fell at Reunion Island during a tropical cyclone in 1952. Forward movement of the storm and land topography have a considerable influence on rainfall totals. Torrential rains can occur when a storm moves against a mountain range; this is common in the Philippines and Japan, where even weak tropical depressions produce considerable rainfall. A 24-hour total of 46 inches was recorded in the Philippines during a typhoon in 1911. As hurricane Camille crossed southern Virginia's Blue Ridge Mountains in August of 1969, there was nearly

30 inches of rain in about 8 hours. This caused some of the most disastrous floods in the state's history.

Flooding is an extremely destructive by-product of the tropical cyclone's torrential rains. Whether an area will be flooded depends on the physical characteristics of the drainage basin, rate and accumulation of precipitation, and river stages at the time the rains begin. When heavy rains fall over flat terrain, the countryside may lie underwater for a month or so, and while buildings, furnishings, and underground powerlines may be damaged, there are usually few fatalities. In mountainous or hill country, disastrous flood's develop rapidly and can cause a great loss of life.

There have been occasional reports in tropical cyclones of waves greater than 40 feet in height, and numerous reports in the 30- to 40- foot category. However, in tropical cyclones, strong winds rarely persist for a sufficiently long time or over a large enough area to permit enormous wave heights to develop. The direction and speed of the wind changes more rapidly in tropical cyclones than in extratropical storms. Thus, the maximum duration and fetch length for any wind condition is often less in tropical cyclones than in extratropical storms of similar intensity, and the waves accompanying any given local wind conditions are generally not so high as those expected, with similar local wind conditions, in the high-latitude-type storms. In hurricane Camille, significant waves of 43 feet were recorded; an extreme wave height reached 72 feet.

Exceptional conditions may arise when waves of certain dimensions travel within the storm at a speed equal to the storm's speed, thus, in effect, extending the duration and fetch of the wave and significantly increasing its height. This occurs most often to the right of the track in the Northern Hemisphere (left of the track in the Southern Hemisphere). Another condition that may give rise to exceptional wave heights is the intersection of waves from two or more distinct directions. This may lead to a zone of confused seas in which the heights of some waves will equal the sum in each individual wave train. This process can occur in any quadrant of the storm and so it should not be assumed that the highest waves will always be encountered to the right of the storm track in the Northern Hemisphere (left of the track in the Southern Hemisphere).

When these waves move beyond the influence of the generating winds, they become swell. They are recognized by their smooth, undulating form, in contrast to the steep, ragged crests of the winds' waves. This swell, particularly that generated by the right side of the storm, can travel a thousand miles or more and may produce tides 3 or 4 feet above normal along several hundred miles of coastline.

When a tropical cyclone moves close to a coast, wind often causes a rapid rise in water level, and along with the falling pressure may produce a storm **surge.** This surge is usually confined to the right of the track in the Northern Hemisphere (left of the track in the Southern Hemisphere) and to a relatively small section of the coastline. It most often occurs with the approach of the storm, but in some cases, where a surge moves into a long channel, the effect may be delayed. Occasionally, the greatest rise in water is observed on the opposite side of the track, when northerly winds funnel into a partially landlocked harbor. The surge could be 3 feet or less, or it could be 20 feet or more, depending on the combination of all the factors involved.

There have been reports of a "hurricane wave," described as a "wall of water," which moves rapidly toward the coastline. Authenticated cases are rare, but some of the world's greatest natural disasters have occurred as a result of this wave, which may be just a rapidly rising and abnormally high storm surge. In India, such a disaster occurred in 1876, between Calcutta and Chittagong, and drowned more than 100,000 persons.

Along the coast, particularly, greater damage may be inflicted by water than by the wind. There are at least four sources of water damage. First, the unusually high seas generated by the storm winds pound against shore installations and craft in their way. Second, the continued blowing of the wind toward land causes the water level to increase perhaps 3 to 10 feet above its normal level. This **storm tide,** which may begin when the storm center is 500 miles or even farther from the shore, gradually increases until the storm passes. The highest storm tides are caused by a slow-moving tropical cyclone of large diameter, because both of these effects result in greater duration of wind in the same direction. The effect is greatest in a partly enclosed body of water, such as the Gulf of Mexico, where the concave coastline does not readily permit the escape of water. It is least on small islands, which present little obstruction to the flow of water. Third, the furious winds which blow around the wall of the eye create a ridge of water called a **storm wave,** which strikes the coast and often inflicts heavy damage. The effect is similar to that of a **seismic sea wave,** caused by an earthquake in the ocean floor. Both of these waves are popularly called **tidal waves.** Storm waves of 20 feet or more have occurred. About 3 or 4 feet of this is due to the decrease of atmospheric pressure, and the rest to winds. Like the damage caused by wind, that due to high seas, the storm surge and tide, and the storm wave is greatest in the dangerous semicircle, near the center. The fourth source of water damage is the heavy rain that accompanies a tropical cyclone. This causes floods that add to the damage caused in other ways.

There have been many instances of tornadoes occurring within the circulation of tropical cyclones. Most of these have been associated with tropical cyclones of the North Atlantic Ocean and have occurred in the West Indies and along the gulf and Atlantic coasts of the United States. They are usually observed in the forward semicircle or along the advancing periphery of the storm. These tornadoes are usually short-lived and less intense than those that occur in the midwestern United States.

When proceeding along a shore recently visited by a tropical cyclone, a navigator should remember that time is required to restore aids to navigation which have been blown out of position or destroyed. In some instances the aid may remain but its light, sound apparatus, or radiobeacon may be inoperative. Landmarks may have been damaged or destroyed.

References

Australia Bureau of Meteorology. *Occurrence of Tropical Depressions and Cyclones in the Northeastern and Northwestern Australian Regions* (annual summary 1957–1962). Maribyrnong, Department of Supply, Central Drawing Office.

Australia Bureau of Meteorology. *Tropical Cyclones in the Northern Australian Regions* (annual summary 1962–1969). Maribyrnong, Department of Supply, Central Drawing Office.

Brand, S., and J. W. Blelloch. *Typhoon Havens Handbook for the Western Pacific and Indian Oceans.* Technical Paper 5–76, Naval Environmental Prediction Research Facility, Monterey, California, 1976.

Chin, P. C. *Tropical Cyclones in the Western Pacific and China Sea Area from 1884 to 1953.* Hong Kong, Royal Observatory, 1958.

Crutcher, H. L. and R. G. Quayle. *Mariners Worldwide Climatic Guide to Tropical Storms at Sea,* Naval Weather Service Command, U. S. Govt. Print. Off., 1974.

Cry, G. W. "Tropical Cyclones of the North Atlantic Ocean: Tracks and Frequencies of Hurricanes and Tropical Storms, 1871–1963," Technical Paper No. 55, Washington, U. S. Govt. Print. Off., 1965.

DeAngelis, R. M. "North Pacific Hurricanes: Timid or Treacherous?" *Mariners Weather Log,* vol. 11, No. 6 (November 1967), pp. 193–200.

Dunn, G. E. and B. I. Miller. *Atlantic Hurricanes.* Louisiana State University Press, 1960.

Environmental Science Services Administration. *Hurricane the greatest storm on earth.* Washington, U. S. Govt. Print. Off., 1967.

Harding, E. T. and Wm. J. Kotsch. *Heavy Weather Guide.* Annapolis, U. S. Naval Institute, 1965.

Harris, D. L. "Wave Patterns in Tropical Cyclones." *Mariners Weather Log,* vol. 6, No. 5 (September 1962) pp. 156–160.

Harris, D. L. "Characteristics of the Hurricane Storm Surge," Technical Paper No. 48. Washington, U. S. Govt. Print. Off., 1963.

Hodge, W. T. "North Pacific Typhoons Where and When Are They Most Frequent?" *Mariners Weather Log,* vol. 9, No. 3 (May 1965), pp. 73–76.

India Meteorological Department. *Tracks of Storms and Depressions in the Bay of Bengal and the Arabian Sea, 1877–1960.* New Delhi, India Meteorological Department, 1964.

Joint Typhoon Warning Center. *Annual Typhoon Reports 1959–1973.* Guam, U. S. Fleet Weather Central/Joint Typhoon Warning Center.

Mauritius Meteorological Department. *Annual Report of the Meteorological Department 1950–1966.* Port Louis, Mauritius Government Printer.

New Zealand Meteorological Service. *Annual Meteorological Summary 1957–1966.* Laucala Bay, Suva, Fiji Government Press.

Nimitz, Chester W., et. al. "Typhoon Doctrine." U. S. Naval Institute Proceedings, vol. 82, No. 1 (January 1956), pp. 83–93.

U. S. Weather Bureau. *Climatological and Oceanographic Atlas for Mariners,* Vol. I North Atlantic Ocean. Washington, U. S. Govt. Print. Off., 1959.

U. S. Weather Bureau. *Climatological and Oceanographic Atlas for Mariners,* Vol. II North Pacific Ocean. Washington, U. S. Govt. Print. Off., 1961.

PART EIGHT
ELECTRONICS AND NAVIGATION

PART EIGHT

ELECTRONICS AND NAVIGATION

CHAPTER XL

RADIO WAVES

4001. Source of radio waves.—All matter is made up of tiny particles called **atoms.** Each atom has a central **nucleus** composed principally of subatomic particles called **protons** and **neutrons.** One or more **electrons** revolve around the nucleus in orbits resembling those of planets around the sun (art. 1407). The number and arrangement of the particles constituting an atom of each element of matter determine the properties of that element. Electrons, each having a mass of only about 1/1,840 that of a proton or neutron, are kept in their orbits principally by means of an attractive electrical force, each electron carrying one negative "charge" and each proton one positive "charge." Like charges repel and unlike charges attract. This electrical attraction is additional to the gravitational attraction existing between all particles in the universe. The neutron is electrically neutral.

Under suitable conditions, some electrons become detached from their atoms. An excess or deficiency of electrons in a nonconductor is called **static electricity.** A substance which provides a path for electron movement with relatively little resistance is called a **conductor.** A *flow* of electrons along such a conductor constitutes an **electric current,** although the current direction is conventionally considered to be opposite to the direction of flow of the electrons. A **direct current** flows continuously in the same direction. If the strength of the current varies rhythmically but does not change direction, the current is said to be **pulsating.** If the direction of flow periodically reverses, an **alternating current** results.

In addition to its electrical and gravitational forces, a moving electron is accompanied by a **magnetic force.** As long as the flow is steady, the magnetic force is constant. If a conductor is in the region of influence or **field** of magnetism, there is no noticeable effect unless the strength of the field is changing, or relative motion exists between the conductor and the field, when an **induced current** flows in the conductor. The extent to which a substance has electrons free to move under suitable influence determines its value as a conductor. One which offers great resistance to such flow is called an **insulator.**

In a suitable electrical system, an electric charge creates a magnetic field which builds up to a maximum. If the electric current is then discontinued, the magnetic field collapses. This change in the strength of the magnetic field induces an electric current in the conductor, but in the opposite direction to the original current. This current creates a new magnetic field, and the cycle repeats. Thus, an alternating current is produced, the strength increasing to a maximum in one direction, decreasing to zero, increasing to a maximum in the opposite direction, and again decreasing to zero to start a new cycle. This cycle is repeated many times each second, the number depending upon the characteristics of the system. Such a system is called an **oscillating circuit.**

A relatively small amount of energy is dissipated as heat in overcoming the resistance of the circuit. The remainder continues to oscillate between electric and magnetic fields. The build-up and collapse of each field occurs at about the speed of light, which is approximately 186,000 statute miles (300,000,000 meters) per second. If a relatively long period of time is available for the cycle to occur, the energy is fully transferred before the next step occurs. However, if the cycle is speeded until the time needed for each field to build up or collapse is more than about one-half cycle, some of the energy becomes detached and is radiated into space, through which it travels at about the speed of light. This **electromagnetic radiation,** having both electrical and magnetic properties, is known as **radio waves,** if of a frequency suitable for radio communication.

4002. Radio wave terminology.—The build-up and collapse of the electric and magnetic fields are proportional to the *sine* of the portion of the cycle completed, as shown is figure 4002. This representation has led to the use of the term "wave" when referring to electromagnetic propagation. The highest point on the curve (in the direction considered positive) is the **crest,** the and lowest point the **trough.** Either point may be called the **peak,** considered positive or negative if a distinction is desired. The displacement of a peak from zero is called the **amplitude.** The forward side of any wave is called the **wave front.** For a nondirectional antenna each wave proceeds outward as an expanding sphere (or hemisphere).

One **cycle** is a complete sequence of values, as from crest to crest. The distance traveled by the energy during one cycle is the **wavelength,** usually expressed in metric units (meters, centimeters, etc.). The number of cycles repeated during unit time (usually one second) is the **frequency.** This is given in **hertz** (cycles per second). A **kilohertz (kHz)** is 1,000 cycles per second. A **megahertz (MHz)** is 1,000,000 cycles per second. Wavelength and frequency are inversely proportional. The approximate value of either may be found by dividing 300,000,000 by the other quantity, if wavelength is expressed in meters and frequency in hertz. Thus, if the frequency is 1,500 kilohertz (1,500,000 cycles per second), the wavelength is

$$\frac{300,000,000}{1,500,000} = 200 \text{ meters.}$$

If the wavelength is 10 centimeters (0.1 meter), the frequency is about

$$\frac{300,000,000}{0.1} = 3,000,000,000$$

cycles per second or 3 **gigahertz.** A more precise value for the speed of propagation in air is 299,708,000 meters per second. This is equivalent to 186,230 statute miles, or 161,829 nautical miles, per second. The exact value varies slightly with density of the medium through which the wave travels, and frequency. The speed in a vacuum is a little more than that in air.

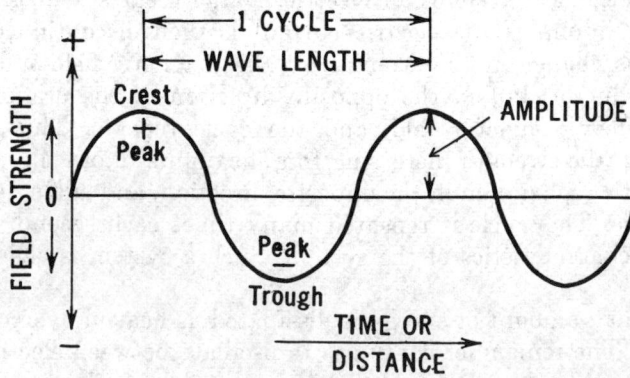

FIGURE 4002.—Radio wave terminology.

The **phase** of a wave is the amount by which the cycle has progressed from a specified origin. For most purposes it is stated in circular measure, a complete cycle being considered 360°. Generally, the origin is not important, principal interest being the phase relative to that of some other wave. Thus, two waves having crests one-fourth cycle apart are said to be 90° "out of phase." If the crest of one wave occurs at the trough of another, the two are 180° out of phase.

4003. Electromagnetic spectrum.—The entire range of electromagnetic radiation frequencies is called the **electromagnetic spectrum.** The range of frequencies suitable for radio transmission, called the **radio spectrum,** extends from 10 kilohertz to 300,000 megahertz, approximately. For convenience, it is divided into a number of **bands,** as shown in table 4003. Below the radio spectrum, but overlapping it, is the **audio frequency** band, extending from 20 to 20,000 hertz, approximately. This is the range of frequencies that can be heard by the human ear. Above the radio spectrum are heat and infrared, the visible spectrum (light in its various colors), ultraviolet, X-rays, gamma rays, and cosmic rays. These are included in table 4003. Waves shorter than 30 centimeters are usually called **microwaves.**

Band	Abbreviation	Range of frequency	Range of wavelength
Audio frequency	AF	20 to 20,000 Hz	15,000,000 to 15,000 m
Radio frequency	RF	10 kHz to 300,000 MHz	30,000 m to 0.1 cm
Very low frequency	VLF	10 to 30 kHz	30,000 to 10,000 m
Low frequency	LF	30 to 300 kHz	10,000 to 1,000 m
Medium frequency	MF	300 to 3,000 kHz	1,000 to 100 m
High frequency	HF	3 to 30 MHz	100 to 10 m
Very high frequency	VHF	30 to 300 MHz	10 to 1 m
Ultra high frequency	UHF	300 to 3,000 MHz	100 to 10 cm
Super high frequency	SHF	3,000 to 30,000 MHz	10 to 1 cm
Extremely high frequency	EHF	30,000 to 300,000 MHz	1 to 0.1 cm
Heat and infrared*		10^6 to 3.9×10^8 MHz	0.03 to 7.6×10^{-5} cm
Visible spectrum*		3.9×10^8 to 7.9×10^8 MHz	7.6×10^{-5} to 3.8×10^{-5} cm
Ultraviolet*		7.9×10^8 to 2.3×10^{10} MHz	3.8×10^{-5} to 1.3×10^{-6} cm
X-rays*		2.0×10^9 to 3.0×10^{13} MHz	1.5×10^{-5} to 1.0×10^{-9} cm
Gamma rays*		2.3×10^{12} to 3.0×10^{14} MHz	1.3×10^{-8} to 1.0×10^{-10} cm
Cosmic rays*		$> 4.8 \times 10^{15}$ MHz	$< 6.2 \times 10^{-12}$ cm

*Values approximate.

Table 4003.—Electromagnetic spectrum.

4004. Polarization.—As indicated in article 4001, radio waves have both electric and magnetic fields. The two fields are conceived as having direction associated with the orientation of the vibrations. The direction of the electric component of the field is called the **polarization** of the electromagnetic field. Thus, if the electric component is vertical, the wave is said to be "vertically polarized," and if horizontal, "horizontally polarized." A wave traveling through space may be polarized in any direction. One traveling along the surface of the earth is always vertically polarized because the earth, a conductor, short-circuits any horizontal component. The magnetic field and the electric field are always mutually perpendicular.

4005. Reflection.—When radio waves strike a surface, they are reflected in the same manner as light waves, if conditions are favorable. Radio waves of all frequencies are reflected by the surface of the earth. The strength of the **reflected wave** depends upon **grazing angle** (the angle between the incident ray and the horizontal), type of polarization, frequency, reflecting properties of the surface, and divergence of the reflected ray. Lower frequency results in greater penetration. At very low frequencies usable radio signals can be received some distance below the surface of the sea.

A change of phase takes place when a wave is reflected from the surface of the earth. The amount of the change varies with the conductivity of the earth and the polarization of the wave, reaching a maximum of 180° for a horizontally polarized wave reflected from seawater (considered to have infinite conductivity). When **direct waves** (those traveling from transmitter to receiver in a relatively straight line, without reflection) and reflected waves arrive at a receiver, the total signal is the vector sum of the two. If the signals are in phase, they reinforce each other, producing a stronger signal. If there is a phase difference, the signals tend to cancel each other, the cancellation being complete if the phase difference is 180° and the two signals have the same amplitude. This interaction of waves is called **wave interference.** A phase difference may occur because of the change of phase of a reflected wave, or because of the longer path followed by it. The second effect decreases with greater distance between transmitter and receiver, for under these conditions the difference in path lengths is smaller. At lower frequencies there is no practical solution to interference caused in this way. For VHF and higher frequencies the condition can be improved by elevating the antenna, if the wave is vertically polarized. Also, interference at higher frequencies can be more nearly eliminated because of the greater ease of beaming the signal to avoid reflection.

Reflections may also occur from mountains, trees, and other obstacles. Such reflection is negligible for lower frequencies, but becomes more prevalent as frequency increases. In radio communication it can be reduced by using directional antennas, but this solution is not always available for navigational systems.

Various reflecting surfaces occur in the atmosphere. At high frequencies, reflections take place from rain. At still higher frequencies, reflections are possible from clouds, particularly rain clouds. Reflections may even occur at a sharply defined boundary surface between airmasses, as when warm, moist air flows over cold, dry air. When such a surface is roughly parallel to the surface of the earth, radio waves may travel for greater distances than normal. A somewhat similar condition is described in article 4006. The principal source of reflection in the atmosphere is the ionosphere (arts. 4007, 4008).

4006. Refraction of radio waves is similar to that of light waves (art. 1606). Thus, as a signal passes from air of one density to that of a different density, the direction of travel is altered. The principal cause of refraction in the atmosphere is the difference in temperature and pressure occurring at various heights and in different airmasses.

Refraction occurs at all frequencies, but at those below 30 MHz the effect is small as compared with ionospheric effects (art. 4008), diffraction (art. 4009), and absorption (art. 4010). At higher frequencies, refraction in the lower layer of the atmosphere extends the **radio horizon** to a distance about 15 percent greater than the visible horizon. The effect is the same as if the radius of the earth were about one-third greater than it is, and there were no refraction.

Sometimes the lower portion of the atmosphere becomes stratified with horizontal layers of air having certain characteristics, resulting in nonstandard temperature and moisture changes with height. If there is a marked temperature inversion (art. 3814) or a sharp decrease in water vapor content with increased height, a horizontal radio **duct** may be formed. High frequency radio waves traveling horizontally within the duct are refracted to such an extent that they remain within the duct, following the curvature of the earth for phenomenal distances. This is called **super-refraction.** Maximum results are obtained when both transmitting and receiving antennas are within the duct. There is a lower limit to the frequency affected by ducts. It varies from about 200 MHz to more than 1,000 MHz.

At night, surface ducts may occur over land due to cooling of the surface. At sea, surface ducts about 50 feet thick may occur at any time in the trade wind belt. Surface ducts 100 feet or more in thickness may extend from land out to sea when warm air from the land flows over the cooler ocean surface. Elevated ducts from a few feet to more than 1,000 feet in thickness may occur at elevations of 1,000 to 5,000 feet, due to the settling of a large airmass. This is a frequent occurrence in Southern California and certain areas of the Pacific Ocean.

Refraction effects associated with the ionosphere are discussed in article 4008.

A bending in the horizontal plane occurs when a groundwave (art. 4008) crosses a coast at an oblique angle. This is due to a marked difference in the conducting and reflecting properties of the land and water over which the wave travels. The effect is known as **coastal refraction** or **land effect.**

4007. The ionosphere.—Since an atom normally has an equal number of negatively charged electrons and positively charged protons, it is electrically neutral. An **ion** is an atom or group or atoms which has become electrically charged, either positively or negatively, by the loss or gain of one or more electrons.

Loss of electrons may occur in a variety of ways. In the atmosphere, ions are usually formed by collision of atoms with rapidly moving particles, or by the action of cosmic rays or ultraviolet light. In the lower portion of the atmosphere, recombination soon occurs, leaving a small percentage of ions. In thin atmosphere far above the surface of the earth, however, atoms are widely separated and a large number of ions may be present. The region of numerous positive and negative ions and unattached electrons is called the **ionosphere.** The extent of ionization depends upon the kinds of atoms present in the atmosphere, the density of the atmosphere, and the position relative to the sun (time of day and season). After sunset, ions and electrons recombine faster than they are separated, decreasing the ionization of the atmosphere.

An electron can be separated from its atom only by the application of greater energy than that holding the electron. Since the energy of the electron depends primarily upon the kind of an atom of which it is a part, and its position relative to the nucleus of that atom, different kinds of radiation may cause ionization of different substances.

In the outermost regions of the atmosphere the density is so low that oxygen exists largely as separate atoms, rather than combining as molecules as it does nearer the surface of the earth. At great heights the energy level is low and ionization from solar radiation is intense. This is known as the **F layer.** Above this level the ionization decreases because of the lack of atoms to be ionized. Below this level it decreases because the ionizing agent of appropriate energy has already been absorbed. During daylight, two levels of maximum F ionization can be detected, the F_2 layer at about 125 statute miles above the surface of the earth, and the F_1 layer at about 90 statute miles. At night, these combine to form a single F layer.

At a height of about 60 statute miles the solar radiation not absorbed by the F layer encounters, for the first time, large numbers of oxygen *molecules*. A new maximum ionization occurs, known as the **E layer.** The height of this layer is quite constant, in contrast with the fluctuating F layer. At night the E layer becomes weaker by two orders of magnitude.

Below the E layer a weak **D layer** forms at a height of about 45 statute miles, where the incoming radiation encounters ozone (O_3) for the first time. The D layer is the principal source of absorption of HF waves, and of reflection of LF and VLF waves during daylight.

4008. The ionosphere and radio waves.—When a radio wave encounters a particle having an electric charge, it causes that particle to vibrate. The vibrating particle absorbs electromagnetic energy from the radio wave and reradiates it. The net effect is a change of polarization and an alteration of the path of the wave. That portion of the wave in a more highly ionized region travels faster, causing the wave front to tilt and the wave to be directed toward a region of less intense ionization.

Refer to figure 4008a, in which a single layer of the ionosphere is considered. Ray 1 enters the ionosphere at such an angle that its path is altered, but it passes on through and proceeds outward into space. As the angle with the horizontal decreases, a critical value is reached where the ray (2) is bent or reflected back toward the earth. As the angle is still further decreased, as at 3, the return to earth occurs at a greater distance from the transmitter.

A wave reaching a receiver by way of the ionosphere is called a **skywave.** This expression is also appropriately applied to a wave reflected from an airmass boundary. In common usage, however, it is generally associated with the ionosphere. The wave which travels along the surface of the earth is called a **groundwave.** At angles greater than the critical angle, no skywave signal is received. Therefore, there is a minimum distance from the transmitter at which skywaves can be received. This is called the **skip distance,** shown in figure 4008a. If the groundwave extends out for less distance than the skip distance, a **skip zone** occurs, in which no signal is received.

The critical radiation angle depends upon the intensity of ionization, and the frequency of the radio wave. As the frequency increases, the angle becomes smaller. At frequencies greater than about 30 MHz virtually all of the energy penetrates through or is absorbed by the ionosphere. Therefore, at any given receiver there is a maximum usable frequency if skywaves are to be utilized. The strongest signals are received at or slightly below this frequency. There is also a lower practical frequency beyond which signals are too weak to be of value. Within this band the optimum frequency can be selected to give best results. It cannot be too near the maximum usable frequency because this frequency fluctuates with changes of intensity within the ionosphere. During magnetic storms the ionosphere density decreases. The maximum usable frequency decreases, and the lower usable frequency increases. The band of usable frequencies is thus narrowed. Under extreme conditions it may be completely eliminated, isolating the receiver and causing a radio **blackout.**

Skywave signals reaching a given receiver may arrive by any of several paths, as shown in figure 4008b. A signal which undergoes a single reflection is called a "one-hop" signal, one which undergoes two reflections with a ground reflection between

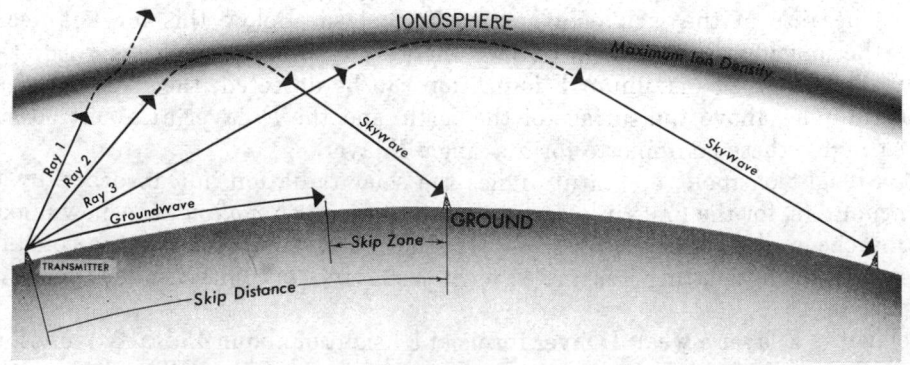

FIGURE 4008a.—The effect of the ionosphere on radio waves.

is called a "two-hop" signal, etc. A "multihop" signal undergoes several reflections. The layer at which the reflection occurs is usually indicated, also, as "one hop E," "two hop F," etc.

Because of the different paths and phase changes occurring at each reflection, the various signals arriving at a receiver have different phase relationships. Since the density of the ionosphere is continually fluctuating, the strength and phase relationships of the various signals may undergo an almost continuous change. Thus, the various signals may reinforce each other at one moment and cancel each other at the next, resulting in fluctuations of the strength of the total signal received. This is called **fading.** This phenomenon may also be caused by interaction of components within a single reflected wave, or changes in its strength due to changes in the reflecting surface. Ionospheric changes are associated with fluctuations in the radiation received from the sun, since this is the principal cause of ionization. Signals from the F layer are particularly erratic because of the rapidly fluctuating conditions within the layer itself.

The maximum distance at which a one-hop-E signal can be received is about 1,400 miles. At this distance the signal leaves the transmitter in approximately a horizontal direction. A one-hop-F signal can be received out to about 2,500 miles. At low frequencies groundwaves extend out for great distances.

A skywave may undergo a change of polarization during reflection from the ionosphere, accompanied by an alteration in the direction of travel of the wave. This is called **polarization error.** Near sunrise and sunset, when rapid changes are occurring in the ionosphere, reception may become erratic and polarization error a maximum. This is called **night effect.**

4009. Diffraction.—When a radio wave encounters an obstacle, its energy is reflected or absorbed, causing a **shadow** beyond the obstacle. However, some energy does enter the shadow area because of **diffraction.** This is explained by **Huygens' principle,** which states that *every point on the surface of a wave front is a source of radiation, transmitting energy in all directions ahead of the wave.* No noticeable effect of this principle is observed until the wave front encounters an obstacle, which intercepts a

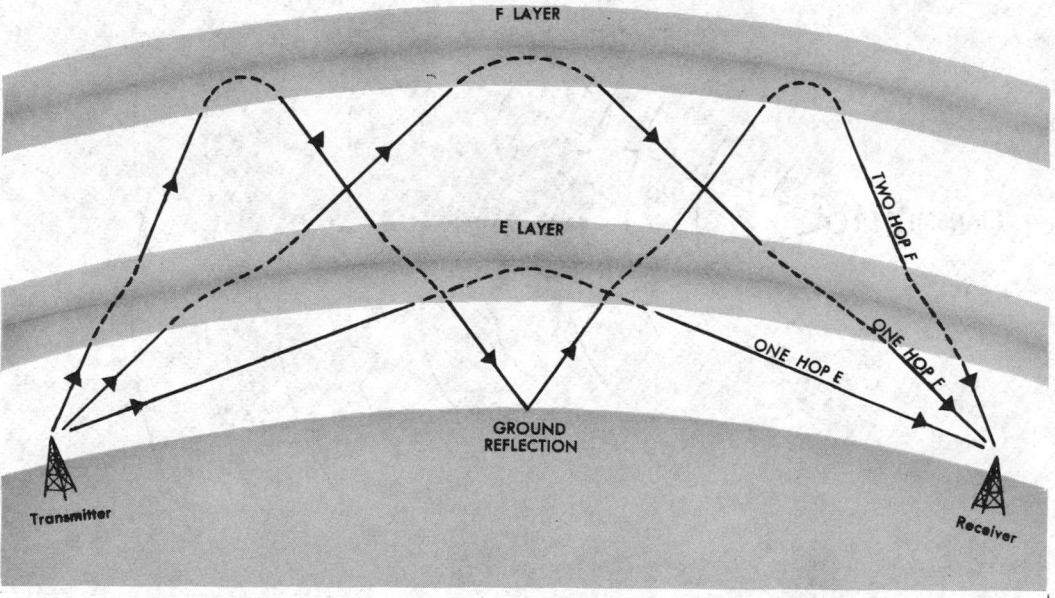

FIGURE 4008b.—Various paths by which a skywave signal might be received.

portion of the wave. From the edge of the obstacle, energy is radiated into the shadow area, and also outside of the area. The latter interacts with energy from other parts of the wave front, producing alternate bands in which the secondary radiation reinforces or tends to cancel the energy of the primary radiation. Thus, the practical effect of an obstacle is a greatly reduced signal strength in the shadow area, and a disturbed pattern for a short distance outside the shadow area. This is illustrated in figure 4009.

The amount of diffraction is inversely proportional to the frequency, being greatest at very low frequencies.

4010. Absorption and scattering.—The amplitude of a radio wave expanding outward through space varies inversely with distance. That is, it gets weaker with increased distance. The decrease of strength with distance is called **attenuation.** Under certain conditions the attenuation is greater than in free space.

A wave traveling along the surface of the earth loses a certain amount of energy to the earth. The wave is diffracted downward and absorbed by the earth. As a result of this absorption, the remainder of the wave front tilts downward, resulting in further absorption by the earth. Attenuation is greater over a surface that is a poor conductor. Relatively little absorption occurs over seawater, which is an excellent conductor at low frequencies, and low frequency groundwaves travel great distances over water.

A skywave suffers an attenuation loss in its encounter with the ionosphere. The amount depends upon the height and composition of the ionosphere, as well as the frequency of the radio wave. Maximum ionospheric absorption occurs at about 1,400 kHz.

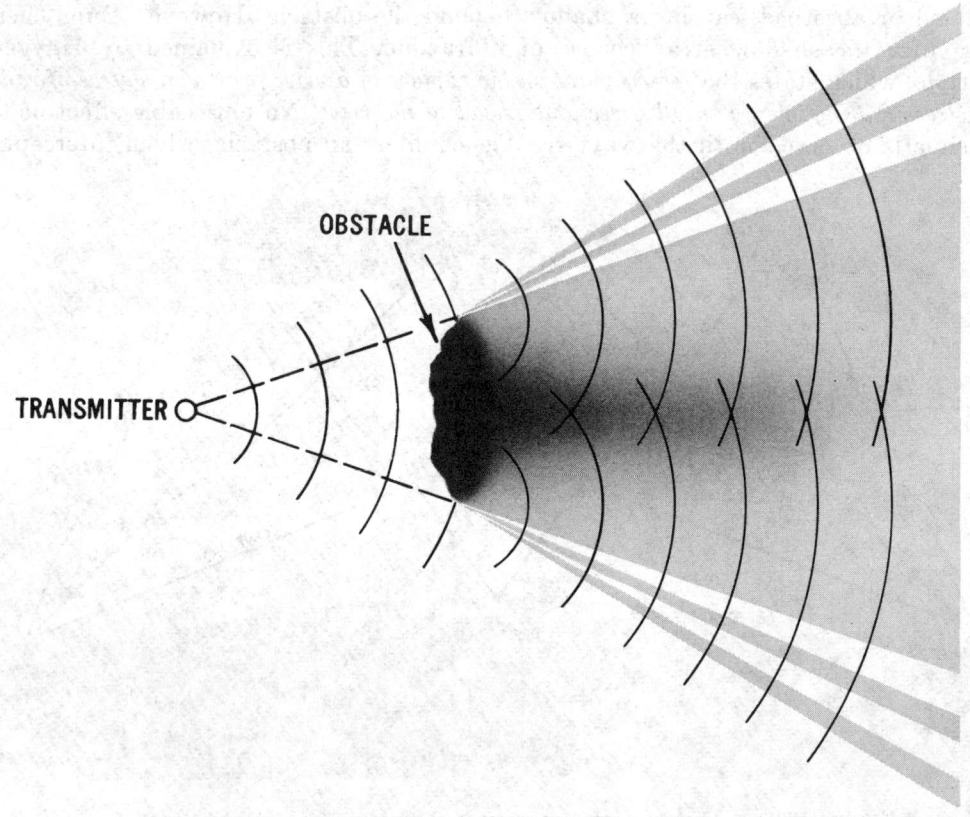

FIGURE 4009.—Diffraction.

In general, atmospheric absorption increases with frequency, being a problem only at SHF and EHF. At these frequencies, attenuation is further increased by **scattering** due to reflection by oxygen, water vapor, water droplets, and rain in the atmosphere.

4011. Noise.—Unwanted signals in a receiver are called **interference.** The intentional production of such interference to obstruct communication is called **jamming.** Unintentional interference is called **noise.**

Noise may originate within the receiver. **Hum** is usually the result of induction from neighboring circuits carrying alternating current. **Microphonic noise** is the result of vibration of elements in an electron tube. Irregular crackling or sizzling sounds may be caused by poor contacts or faulty components within the receiver. Electron movement in normal components causes some noise. This source sets the ultimate limit of sensitivity (art. 4018) that can be achieved in a receiver. It is the same at any frequency.

Noise originating outside the receiver may be either man-made or natural. Man-made noises originate in electrical appliances, motor and generator brushes, ignition systems, and other sources of sparks which transmit electromagnetic signals that are picked up by the receiving antenna.

Natural noise is caused principally by discharge of static electricity in the atmosphere. This is called **atmospheric noise, atmospherics,** or **static.** An extreme example is a thunderstorm. An exposed surface may acquire a considerable charge of static electricity. This may be caused by friction of water or solid particles blown against or along such a surface. It may also be caused by splitting of a water droplet which strikes the surface, one part of the droplet requiring a positive charge and the other a negative charge. These charges may be transferred to the surface. The charge tends to gather at points and ridges of the conducting surface, and when it accumulates to a sufficient extent to overcome the insulating properties of the atmosphere, it discharges into the atmosphere. Under suitable conditions this becomes visible and is known as **St. Elmo's fire,** which is sometimes seen at mastheads, the ends of yardarms, etc.

Atmospheric noise occurs to some extent at all frequencies, but decreases with higher frequencies. Above about 30 MHz it is not generally a problem.

Since most of the noise occurs at low frequencies, it travels great distances and the accumulation may reach troublesome proportions at these frequencies, particularly during the summer in mountainous regions.

4012. Antenna characteristics.—Antenna design and orientation have a marked effect upon radio wave propagation. For a single-wire antenna, strongest signals are transmitted along the perpendicular to the wire, and virtually no signal in the direction of the wire. For a vertical antenna, the signal strength is the same in all horizontal directions. Unless the polarization undergoes a change during transit, the strongest signal *received* from a vertical transmitting antenna occurs when the receiving antenna is also vertical.

For lower frequencies the radiation of a radio signal takes place by interaction between the antenna and the ground. For a vertical antenna, efficiency increases with greater length of the antenna. For a horizontal antenna, efficiency increases with greater distance between antenna and ground. Near-maximum efficiency is attained when this distance is one-half wavelength. This is the reason for elevating low frequency antennas to great heights. However, at the lowest frequencies, the required height becomes prohibitively great. At 10 kHz it would be about 8 nautical miles for a half-wavelength antenna. Therefore, lower frequency antennas are inherently inefficient. This is partly offset by the greater range of a low frequency signal of the same transmitted power as one of higher frequency.

At higher frequencies, the ground is not used, both conducting portions being included in a **dipole** antenna. Not only can such an antenna be made efficient, but it can also be made sharply directive, thus greatly increasing the strength of the signal transmitted in a desired direction.

The power received is inversely proportional to the square of the distance from the transmitter, assuming there is no attenuation due to absorption or scattering.

4013. Range.—The range at which a usable signal is received depends upon the power transmitted, the sensitivity of the receiver, frequency, route of travel, noise level, and perhaps other factors. For the same *transmitted* power, both the groundwave and skywave ranges are greatest at the lowest frequencies, but this is somewhat offset by the lesser efficiency of antennas for these frequencies. At higher frequencies, only direct waves are useful, and the effective range is greatly reduced. Attenuation, skip distance, ground reflection, wave interference, condition of the ionosphere, atmospheric noise level, and antenna design all affect the distance at which useful signals can be received.

4014. Frequency and radio wave propagation.—Frequency is an important consideration in radio wave propagation, as indicated previously. The following summary indicates the principal effects associated with the various frequency bands, starting with the lowest and progressing to the highest usable radio frequency.

Very low frequency (VLF, 10 to 30 kHz). The VLF signals propagate between the bounds of the ionosphere and the earth and are thus guided around the curvature of the earth to great distances with low attenuation and excellent stability. Diffraction is maximum. Because of the long wavelength, large antennas are needed, and even these are inefficient, permitting radiation of relatively small amounts of power. Magnetic storms have little effect upon transmission because of the efficiency of the "earth-ionosphere waveguide." During such storms, VLF signals may constitute the only source of radio communication over great distances. However, interference from atmospheric noise may be troublesome. Signals may be received from below the surface of the sea. The characteristics of VLF propagation are discussed in more detail in the coverage of the Omega Navigation System in chapter XLIII.

Low frequency (LF, 30 to 300 kHz). As frequency is increased to the LF band, diffraction decreases, there is greater attenuation with distance, and range for a given power output falls off rapidly. However this is partly offset by more efficient transmitting antennas, which can be of a size practical for use aboard ship. LF signals are most stable within groundwave distance of the transmitter. A wider bandwidth permits pulsed signals at 100 kHz. This allows separation of the stable groundwave pulse from the variable skywave pulse up to 1,500 km, and up to 2,000 km for overwater paths. The frequency for Loran-C (ch. XLIII) is in the LF band. This band is also useful for radio direction finding (ch. XLI), and time dissemination (ch. XVIII).

Medium frequency (MF, 300 to 3,000 kHz). Groundwaves provide dependable service, but the range for a given power is reduced greatly, varying from about 400 miles at the lower portion of the band to about 15 miles at the upper end for a transmitted signal of 1 kilowatt. These values are influenced, however, by the power of the transmitter, the directivity and efficiency of the antenna, and the nature of the terrain over which signals travel. Elevating the antenna to obtain direct waves may improve the transmission. At the lower frequencies of the band, skywaves are available both day and night. As the frequency is increased, ionospheric absorption increases to a maximum at about 1,400 kHz. At higher frequencies the absorption decreases, permitting increased use of skywaves. Since the ionosphere changes with the hour, season, and sunspot cycle, the reliability of skywave signals is variable. By careful selection of frequency, one can obtain ranges of as much as 8,000 miles with 1 kilowatt of transmitted power, using multihop signals. However, the frequency selection is critical. If it is too high, the signals penetrate the ionosphere and are lost in space. If it is too low, signals are too weak. In general, skywave reception is equally good by day or night, but lower frequencies are needed at night. The standard broadcast band for commercial stations (535 to 1,605 kHz) and the authorized frequencies for Loran-A (art. 4101) are in the MF band.

High frequency (HF, 3 to 30 MHz). As with higher medium frequencies, the groundwave range of HF signals is limited to a few miles, but the elevation of the antenna may increase the direct-wave distance of transmission. Also, the height of the antenna does have an important effect upon skywave transmission because the antenna has an "image" within the conducting earth. The distance between antenna and image is related to the height of the antenna, and this distance is as critical as the distance between elements of an antenna system. Maximum usable frequencies (art. 4008) fall generally within the HF band. By day this may be 10 to 30 MHz, but during the night it may drop to 8 to 10 MHz. The HF band is widely used for ship-to-ship and ship-to-shore communication.

Very high frequency (VHF, 30 to 300 MHz). Communication is limited primarily to the direct wave, or the direct wave plus a ground-reflected wave. Elevating the antenna to increase the distance at which direct waves can be used results in increased distance of reception, even though some wave interference between direct and ground-reflected waves is present. Diffraction is much less than with lower frequencies, but is most evident when signals cross sharp mountain peaks or ridges. Under suitable conditions, reflections from the ionosphere are sufficiently strong to be useful, but generally they are unavailable. There is relatively little interference from atmospheric noise in this band. Reasonably efficient directional antennas are possible with VHF. The VHF band is much used for communication.

Ultra high frequency (UHF, 300 to 3,000 MHz). Skywaves are not used in the UHF band because the ionosphere is not sufficiently dense to reflect the waves, which pass through it into space. Groundwaves and ground-reflected waves are used, although there is some wave interference. Diffraction is negligible, but the radio horizon extends about 15 percent beyond the visible horizon, due principally to refraction. Reception of UHF signals is virtually free from fading and interference by atmospheric noise. Sharply directive antennas can be produced for transmission in this band, which is widely used for ship-to-ship and ship-to-shore communication.

Super high frequency (SHF, 3,000 to 30,000 MHz). In the SHF band, also known as the *microwave* or as the *centimeter wave band*, there are no skywaves, transmission being entirely by direct and ground-reflected waves. Diffraction and interference by atmospheric noise are virtually nonexistent. Highly efficient, sharply directive antennas can be produced. Thus, transmission in this band is similar to that of UHF, but with the effects of shorter waves being greater. Reflection by clouds, water droplets, dust particles, etc., increases, causing greater scattering, increased wave interference, and fading. The SHF band is used for marine navigational radar.

Extremely high frequency (EHF, 30,000 to 300,000 MHz). The effects of shorter waves are more pronounced in the EHF band, transmission being free from wave interference, diffraction, fading, and interference by atmospheric noise. Only direct and ground-reflected waves are available. Scattering and absorption in the atmosphere are pronounced and may produce an upper limit to the frequency useful in radio communication.

4015. Regulation of frequency use.—While the characteristics of various frequencies are important to the selection of the most suitable one for any given purpose, these are not the only considerations. Confusion and extensive interference would result if every user had complete freedom of selection. Some form of regulation is needed.

The allocation of various frequency bands to particular uses is a matter of international agreement. Within the United States, the Federal Communications Commission has responsibility for authorizing use of particular frequencies. In come cases a given frequency is allocated to several widely separated transmitters, but only under conditions which minimize interference, as during daylight hours. Interference between stations is further reduced by the use of **channels,** each of a narrow band of frequencies. That is, assigned frequencies are separated by an arbitrary band of frequencies that are not authorized for use. In the case of radio aids to navigation, ship communications, etc., bands of several channels are allocated, permitting selection of band and channel by the user.

4016. Kinds of radio transmission.—A series of waves transmitted at constant frequency and amplitude is called a **continuous wave** (**CW**). This cannot be heard except at the very lowest radio frequencies, when it may produce, in a receiver, an audible hum of high pitch.

Although a continuous wave may be used directly, as in radio direction finding (art. 4101) or Decca (art. 4301), it is more commonly modified in some manner. This is called **modulation.** When this occurs, the continuous wave serves as a **carrier wave** for information. Any of several types of modulation may be used.

In **amplitude modulation** (**AM**) the amplitude of the carrier wave is altered in accordance with the amplitude of a **modulating wave,** usually of audio frequency, as shown in figure 4016a. In the receiver the signal is **demodulated** by removing the modulating wave and converting it back to its original form. This form of modulation is widely used in voice radio, as in the standard broadcast band of commercial broadcasting.

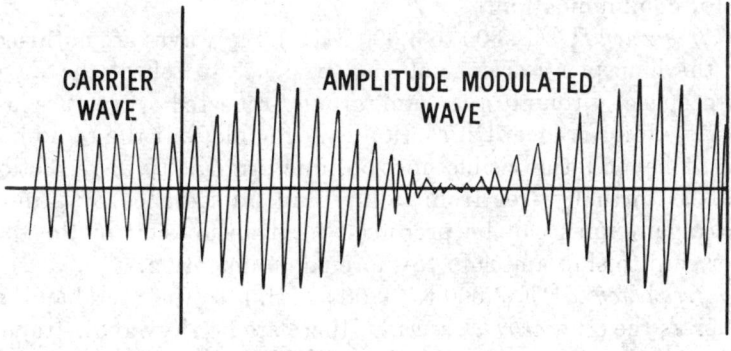

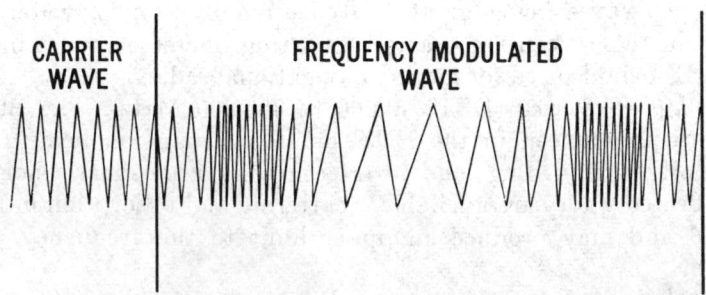

SAME INFORMATION TRANSMITTED BY
AMPLITUDE AND FREQUENCY MODULATED WAVES

FIGURE 4016a.—Amplitude modulation (upper figure) and frequency modulation (lower figure) by the same modulating wave.

If the *frequency* instead of the *amplitude* is altered in accordance with the amplitude of the impressed signal, as shown in figure 4016a, **frequency modulation** (**FM**) occurs. This is used for FM broadcasts and the sound portion of television broadcasts.

Pulse modulation (**PM**) is somewhat different, there being no impressed modulating wave. In this form of transmission, very short bursts of carrier wave are transmitted, separated by relatively long periods of "silence," during which there is no transmission. This type of transmission, illustrated in figure 4016b, is used in some common radio navigational aids, including radar (art. 4201) and Loran (art. 4301).

NO TRANSMISSION   NO TRANSMISSION

FIGURE 4016b.—Pulse modulation.

4017. Transmitters.—A radio **transmitter** consists essentially of (1) a **power supply** to furnish direct current, (2) an **oscillator** to convert direct current into radio-frequency oscillations (the carrier wave), (3) a device to control the generated signal, (4) an **amplifier** to increase the output of the oscillator. For some transmitters a **microphone** is needed with a **modulator** and final amplifier to modulate the carrier wave. In addition, an **antenna** and **ground** (for lower frequencies) are needed to produce electromagnetic radiation. These components are illustrated diagrammatically in figure 4017.

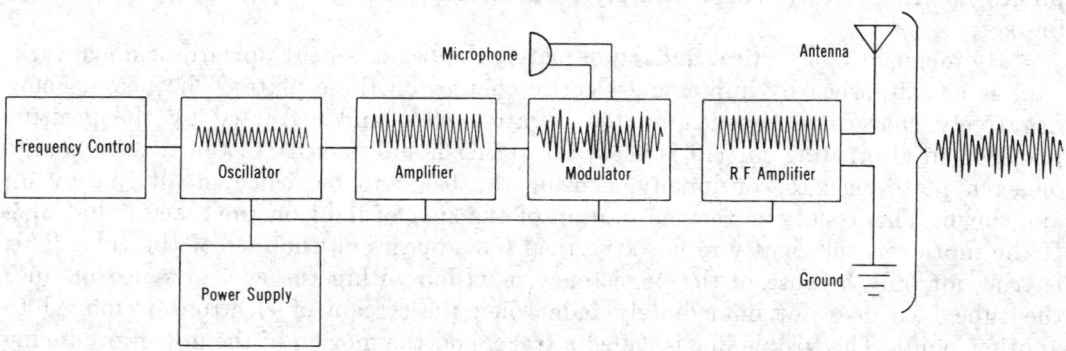

FIGURE 4017.—Components of a radio transmitter.

4018. Receivers.—When a radio wave passes a conductor, a current is induced in that conductor. A radio **receiver** is a device which accepts the power thus generated in an antenna, and transforms it into usable form. It should be able to select signals of a single frequency (actually a narrow band of frequencies) from among the many which may reach the receiving antenna. If necessary, the receiver should be able to demodulate the signal, and always it should provide adequate amplification. The output of a receiver may be presented audibly by earphones or loudspeaker; or visually on a dial, cathode-ray tube (art. 4019), counter, or other display. Thus, the useful reception of radio signals requires three components: (1) an antenna, (2) a receiver, and (3) a display unit.

Radio receivers differ mainly in (1) **frequency range,** the range of frequencies to which they can be tuned; (2) **selectivity,** the ability to confine reception to signals of the desired frequency and avoid others of nearly the same frequency; (3) **sensitivity,** the ability to amplify a weak signal to usable strength against a background of noise; (4) **stability,** the ability to resist drift from conditions or values to which set; and (5)

fidelity, the completeness with which the essential characteristics of the original signal are reproduced. Receivers may have additional features such as an automatic frequency control, automatic noise limiter, etc.

Some of these characteristics are interrelated. For instance, if a receiver lacks selectivity, signals of a frequency differing slightly from those to which the receiver is tuned may be received. This condition is called **spillover,** and the resulting interference is called **crosstalk.** If the selectivity is increased sufficiently to prevent spillover, it may not permit receipt of a great enough band of frequencies to obtain the full range of those of the desired signal. Thus, the fidelity may be reduced.

A **transponder** is a transmitter-receiver capable of accepting the challenge of an interrogator and automatically transmitting an appropriate reply.

4019. The cathode-ray tube is a useful device for presenting certain types of information. This tube, with its associated controls, is often called an **oscilloscope,** or **scope** for short. In television receivers it is usually called the **picture tube.**

The essential components of a cathode-ray tube are shown in figure 4019. At the left is a **cathode** which serves as a source of electrons. In this usage it is called an **electron gun.** The electrons are collected and focused into a beam by a **focusing anode,** and then speeded up by an **accelerating anode.** If there were no other controls, the beam of electrons would travel the remainder of the length of the tube and strike the enlarged, curved surface of the tube **face** at its center, approximately. The inside of the face is coated with a material known as a **phosphor** (such as zinc sulphide or calcium sulphide) which become luminous (**phosphorescent**) where a beam of electrons impinges upon it. If the beam is sharply focused, a dot of light appears at the point of impact.

By means of the **vertical deflection plates,** the beam is bent upward or downward. This is accomplished by impressing electric charges on these plates. The beam, being negatively charged, is repelled by the negative plate and attracted by the positive plate. If an alternating current is used, the strength and polarity of the electric charge on each plate changes continually, causing the beam to be deflected alternately up and down. This results in vertical motion of the spot of light on the face of the tube. If the motion is sufficiently rapid, a vertical *line* appears on the face of the tube. This is true not only because of the persistency of vision within the eye, but also because the tube face does not immediately fade when the stream of electrons is moved to another point. This visible line is called a **trace,** and the motion of the dot in producing it, a **sweep.** A horizontal trace can be made by means of the **horizontal deflection plates** which operate in a manner similar to that of the vertical deflection plates.

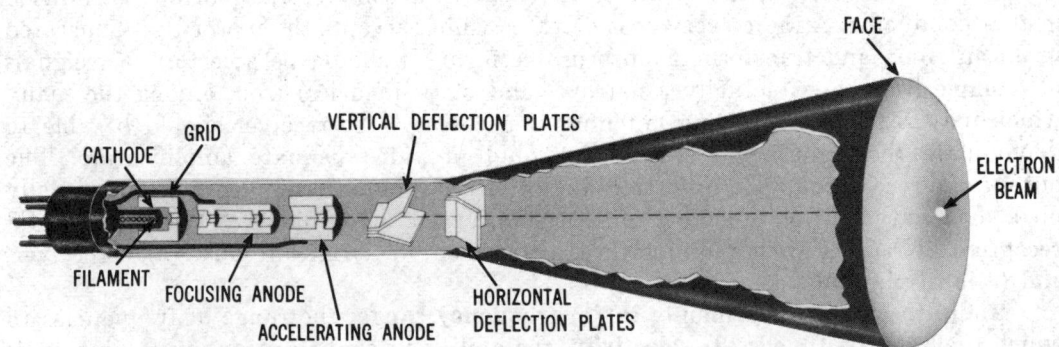

FIGURE 4019.—A cathode-ray tube.

If both sets of plates are energized at the same time, the spot of light can be moved to various places on the face of the tube. If two alternating currents are properly synchronized, the spot can be made to trace repeatedly some pattern, such as a sine wave. It is generally desirable to have one trace repeated in accordance with a pre-arranged plan, having the deflection such that motion in one direction across the face of the tube is relatively slow, and that in the opposite direction is very fast, so that the return of the spot to a starting point is almost instantaneous. Such a return is called **flyback,** and the faint trace that may be visible is called a **retrace.** The position of the spot along the trace can be used as a measurement of elapsed time since the spot was at some reference point. This is usually accomplished by having a received signal impress a momentary charge on the *other* set of deflecting plates, causing a deflection of the trace as the spot is momentarily moved to one side of the line; or by causing the received signal to intensify the spot, causing it to glow brighter.

By suitable controls, the trace can be divided into two or more parts, made to rotate, or take any of a great variety of motions and shapes.

In a **dark trace tube** the spot appears dark on a lighter background.

The cathode-ray tube has many applications in electronic navigational equipment.

CHAPTER XLI

RADIO DIRECTION FINDING

4101. Introduction.—Medium frequency radio direction finders on board ships enable measurement of the bearings of radio transmissions from other ships, aircraft, shore stations, marine radiobeacons, aeronautical radiobeacons, and the coastal stations of the radio communications network.

Depending upon the design of the **radio direction finder (RDF),** the bearings of the radio transmissions are measured as relative bearings or as both relative and true bearings. In one design, the true bearing dial is manually set with respect to the relative bearing dial in accordance with the ship's heading. In another design, the true bearing dial is rotated electrically in accordance with a course input from the gyrocompass. In some of the earlier designs, the RDF is mounted over the ship's compass so as to permit the bearings to be read directly from the compass card.

Whatever means is used to read the bearings, corrections for errors of radio bearings (art. 4104) must be applied. In some designs two distinct means are employed for automatic error compensation. An electrical compensating system provides for automatic compensation of errors which are symmetrically distributed, fore-and-aft or athwartship. A mechanical compensating system provides for automatic compensation of residual errors up to a limiting value. The mechanical compensator may consist of a stationary cam which is cut for each calibration (art. 4107), a movable roller, and associated linkage for causing the goniometer (art. 4103) pointer to lead or lag the actual goniometer setting.

When plotting radio bearings on a Mercator chart, conversion angle (art. 1403, vol. II) must be applied to convert the radio bearing (great-circle direction) to the equivalent rhumb line bearing. Conversion angles are given in table 1.

4102. Radiobeacons established to be of primary usefulness to mariners are known as **marine radiobeacons;** beacons established to be of primary usefulness to airmen are known as **aeronautical radiobeacons;** other beacons established for both classes of user are sometimes known as **aeromarine radiobeacons.** The most common type of marine radiobeacon transmits radio waves of approximately uniform strength in all directions. These *omnidirectional* beacons are known as **circular radiobeacons.**

Directional radiobeacons transmit radio waves within a narrow sector. Compared with the circular radiobeacon, the transmissions from the directional radiobeacons have relatively short range. The rotating loop radiobeacon is discussed in article 4111.

Most United States and Canadian radiobeacons are grouped together on the same operating frequency and are assigned a specific sequence of transmission within this group. This reduces station interference and undesirable retuning. Normally the stations operate in groups of six, each station in a group of **sequenced radiobeacons** using the same frequency and transmitting for 1 minute in its proper sequence. A few radiobeacons transmit for 1 minute with 2 minutes of silence, and some radiobeacons transmit continuously without interruption.

Except for **calibration radiobeacons,** radiobeacons operate during all periods either sequenced or continuously, regardless of weather conditions.

Simple combinations of dots and dashes are used for station identification. These combinations and the duration of the dots, dashes, and spaces are chosen for ease of identification. Where applicable, the Morse equivalent character or characters are shown in conjunction with the station characteristic. All radiobeacons superimpose the characteristic on a carrier which is on continuously during the period of transmission. This extends the usefulness of marine radiobeacons to an airborne or marine user of an **automatic radio direction finder** (**ADF**). Users of the "aural null" type radio direction finder will notice no change in quality of service. A 10-second dash is incorporated in the characteristic signal to enable the user of the aural null type of radio direction finder to refine his bearing.

Aeronautical radiobeacons are sometimes used by marine navigators for determining lines of position when marine radiobeacons are not available. Since it is not possible to predict the extent to which land effect (art. 4104) may render mariners' observations of the bearings of these beacons unreliable, their inclusion in Pubs. Nos. 117A and 117B, *Radio Navigational Aids*, does not imply that the beacons have been found reliable for marine use. Those aeronautical radiobeacons included in Pubs. Nos. 117A and 117B may be useful to the marine navigator who recognizes their limitations. These aeronautical aids become less trustworthy, so far as marine applications are concerned, as they are situated farther inland or when high land intervenes between them and the coast.

Pubs. Nos. 117A and 117B, *Radio Navigational Aids*, include in the details of many radiobeacons located at or near light stations a statement of the distance and bearing of the radiobeacon transmitting antenna from the light tower. Use should be made of this information when calibrating (art. 4107) the radio direction finder.

4103. Direction measurement at the receiving site is accomplished by means of a directional antenna. Nearly all antennas have some directional properties, but in the usual antenna used for radio communication, these properties are not sufficiently critical for navigational use.

A widely used directional antenna is in the form of a loop. Suppose a transmitted radio signal encounters such a loop oriented in the direction of travel of the radio signal, as shown in figure 4103a. If the diameter of the loop is half the wavelength, the crest of one wave arrives at one side of the loop at the same time that the trough arrives at the opposite side, as shown. Thus, the currents induced in the two sides reinforce each other, causing maximum output from the antenna. A short time later, as the wave continues to move past the antenna, the crest reaches the other side of the loop, and a new trough reaches the approach side. A maximum current now flows in the opposite direction. Therefore, with the antenna in this orientation, an alternating current flows in the loop. If the loop diameter is less than half a wavelength, the current is less than maximum.

If the antenna is rotated 90°, the alternate crests and troughs arrive at both sides at the same time, tending to cause currents to flow in opposite directions around the loop. Under these conditions the two parts cancel each other, resulting in zero antenna output. This condition is called a **null.**

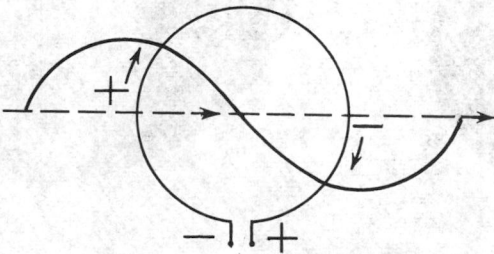

FIGURE 4103a.—Principle of the loop antenna.

As the antenna is rotated, its output varies with the angle relative to the direction of motion of the radio signal. This condition is illustrated in figure 4103b. The length of a line from the center to the outer edge of the shaded area represents the strength of the antenna output at that bearing, relative to the direction of motion of the radio wave. Thus, when it is in line, *with either side of the loop toward the approaching signal*, the output is maximum, and at 90° it is minimum. Since the change with bearing is most rapid near the region of minimum signal, this is the portion used for determination of direction.

Because of the characteristics of the simple loop antenna, a 180° **ambiguity** exists. That is, a signal approaching from either of two directions 180° apart would cause the same antenna output. This ambiguity can be resolved by using a vertical **sense antenna** in connection with a loop. The output from this wire, if the direction of motion of the signal is horizontal, is the same in all directions. Therefore, the polar diagram of its output is a circle, with the same polarity in all directions. If this output is exactly equal to the maximum of the loop, it will cancel the output from one side and double that from the other, since the polarity in the two sides is opposite. The resulting diagram of antenna output is shown in figure 4103c. With this arrangement, a single minimum exists, permitting the determination of which of the two reciprocal bearings is correct, thereby removing the ambiguity. The loop antenna is then used for making the reading. This is the type of equipment commonly used with a radio direction finder.

Two variations of the loop antenna are also used in radio direction finders. In one of these, the **crossed loop** type, two loops are rigidly mounted in such manner that one is rotated 90° with respect to the other. The *relative* output of the two antennas is related to the orientation of each with respect to the direction of travel of the radio wave, and is measured by a device called a **goniometer.** This is the type antenna used in an automatic direction finder. In the other variation, the **rotating loop** type, a single loop is

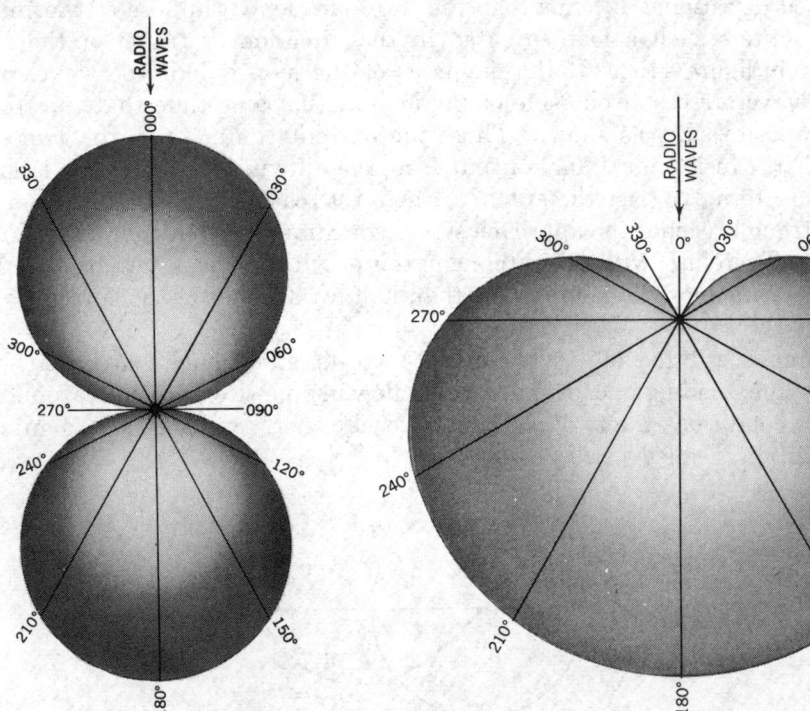

FIGURE 4103b.—Polar diagram   FIGURE 4103c.—Polar diagram of output of loop antenna
of output of loop antenna.   with vertical sense antenna.

kept in rapid rotation by means of a motor. The antenna output is shown on a cathode-ray tube, and the resulting display shows the direction of the signal.

4104. Errors of radio bearings.—Bearings obtained by radio direction finder are subject to certain errors, as follows:

Quadrantal error. When radio waves arrive at a receiver, they are influenced somewhat by the environment. An erroneous radio direction finder bearing results from currents induced in the direction finder antenna by re-radiation from the structural features of the vessel's superstructure and distortion of the radio wave front due to the physical dimensions and contour of the vessel's hull. This quadrantal error is a function of the *relative* bearing, normally being maximum for bearings broad on the bow and broad on the quarter. Its value for various bearings can be determined, and a **calibration table** made (art. 4107).

Coastal refraction. As indicated in article 4006, a radio wave crossing a coastline at an oblique angle undergoes a change of direction due to difference in conducting and reflecting properties of land and water. This is sometimes called **land effect.** It is avoided by not using, or regarding as of doubtful accuracy, bearings of waves which cross a shoreline at an oblique angle. Bearings within 15° to 20° of being parallel to a shoreline should not be trusted. If the transmitter is near the coast, negligible error is introduced because of the short distance the waves travel before undergoing refraction.

Polarization error. As indicated in article 4008, the direction of travel of radio waves may undergo an alteration during the confused period near sunrise or sunset, when great changes are taking place in the ionosphere. This error is sometimes called **night effect.** The error can be minimized by averaging several readings, but any radio bearings taken during this period should be considered of doubtful accuracy.

Reciprocal bearings. Unless a radio direction finder has a vertical sensing wire (art. 4103), there is a possible 180° ambiguity in the reading. If such an error is discovered, one should take the reciprocal of the *uncorrected* reading, and apply the correction for the new direction. If there is doubt as to which of the two possible directions is the correct one, one should wait long enough for the bearing to change appreciably and take another reading. The transmitter should draw *aft* between readings. If the reciprocal is used, the station will appear to have drawn *forward*. A reciprocal bearing furnished by a direction finder station should not be used because the quadrantal error is not known, either on the given bearing or its reciprocal.

4105. Accuracy of radio bearings.—In general, good radio bearings should not be in error by more than 2° for distances under 150 nautical miles. However, conditions vary considerably, and skill is an important factor. By observing the technical instructions for the equipment and practicing frequently when results can be checked by visual observation or by other means, one can develop skill and learn to what extent radio bearings can be relied upon under various conditions.

Other factors affecting accuracy include the errors discussed in article 4104, range, the condition of the equipment, and the accuracy of the calibration (art. 4107). Errors in bearing can result if the selectivity (art. 4106) of a radio direction finder is poor.

4106. Factors affecting maximum range.—The service range of a radiobeacon is determined by the strength of the radiated signal. Field strength requirements for a given service range vary with latitude, being higher in the southern latitudes. The actual useful range may vary considerably from the service range with different types of radio direction finders and during varying atmospheric conditions.

Sensitivity is a measure of the ability of a receiver to detect transmissions. All direction finder receivers do not have the same sensitivity. Some will detect a radiobeacon signal at its rated range whereas others will not detect the same signal until such time that the distance to the beacon has decreased. For example, radio direction finders having a sensitivity of 75 microvolts per meter on the radiobeacon band should be capable of detecting a signal whose intensity is 75 microvolts per meter or more. A radio direction finder having a sensitivity of 120 microvolts per meter will be unable to receive a radiobeacon signal rated at 75 microvolts per meter at 100 miles until 56 miles from the radiobeacon. At 56 miles the signal strength of the transmitted signal is 120 microvolts per meter, which is equal to the sensitivity of the receiver. It follows that the sensitivity of a radio direction finder determines the degree to which the full range capability of the radiobeacon system can be utilized.

Selectivity is a measure of the ability of a receiver to choose one frequency and reject all others. The selectivity varies with the type of receiver and its condition. The transmitted radiobeacon signal is comprised of a band of frequencies, 286.000 kHz to 287.020 kHz for example. A radio direction finder capable of accepting only this narrow band of frequencies would be ideal. If a radio direction finder accepts a wide band of frequencies (280 to 292 kHz) when tuned to 286 kHz, it will admit more noise and signals than desired. This additional interference may reduce the usefulness of the desired signal, and effectively decrease the maximum range of reception of the radiobeacon.

4107. Calibration.—The reliability of a radio direction finder is largely dependent upon the accuracy of the calibration. A good initial calibration not only increases the reliability of operation but also reduces the need for repeated recalibration, provided the superstructure and rigging of the vessel are not altered. Correct radio direction finder calibration compensates for errors caused by induced currents and vessel configuration, i.e., quadrantal error (art. 4104), also known as **direction finder error.**

Proper preliminary procedures for this calibration include accurately aligning the vessel's pelorus fore-and-aft, providing adequate communications between the pelorus and the radio direction finder, developing a plan for coordination between the calibrator and conning officer, determining that the equipment is in proper operating condition, and determining that metal booms, cranes, antennas, etc., are in their normal positions.

While the vessel is enroute to the calibration site, it may be advisable to take a number of bearings on the station to be used for calibration and on one or more other charted stations whose relative bearings can be ascertained. If it is feasible to take an RDF bearing on such a station when it bears broad on the bow or quarter, the magnitude of the quadrantal error can be estimated. Then the electrical error compensator, if installed, should be set to correct the error. It is also desirable to take RDF bearings while the vessel is enroute to the calibration site on a station at 135°, 225°, and 315° from the vessel's heading. These additional readings serve to check the setting of the electrical error compensator and to indicate whether additional adjustment of the compensator is required. Generally, if the magnitudes of the bearing errors on 135°, 225°, and 315° are less than the initial error used to adjust the compensator, the setting should be left unaltered.

The source of the radio signals used in calibration may be a radiobeacon operating on schedule or on request.

Sequenced radiobeacons cannot broadcast at any time other than on their assigned operating minute for the purpose of enabling vessels to calibrate their radio direction finders without causing interference. Special radio direction finder calibration transmitters of short range are operated at certain localities to provide calibration service during specified periods or on request. These stations with information as to position, frequency, characteristic, times of service, requests for use, etc., are listed in Pubs. Nos. 117A and 117B, *Radio Navigational Aids* and the *Light List.*

The position given for the antenna is the point from which the radiobeacon signal is emitted.

The calibration must be made on approximately the same frequency or frequencies as will be used to take RDF bearings because the direction finder error for several frequencies is not likely to be the same. It is believed that one calibration curve or table is satisfactory for the normal radiobeacon frequency (285 to 325 kHz); but the instructions issued by the manufacturer of the particular radio direction finder to be calibrated should be studied in this respect.

The usual method of calibration is to obtain a series of simultaneous radio and visual bearings on a transmitter. This can be done while a vessel swings at anchor or more quickly by steaming in a circle at the greatest distance compatible with clear visual observation of the transmitter, preferably over 1 mile. The simultaneous bearings should be observed and recorded at least every 10°, preferably every 5°.

The difference between a radio bearing and a simultaneously observed visual bearing, using the same reference, is the direction finder error. The error is positive if the visual bearing is greater than the radio bearing; otherwise, the error is negative.

The quadrantal error being maximum, generally, when the station is broad on the bow or quarter, setting of the electrical error compensator for a correction equal to the error measured when the visual bearing is 45° or 315° should provide marked reduction in errors corresponding to visual bearings of 45°, 135°, 225°, and 315°. If the vessel is swung again and another set of visual and RDF bearings are observed, the errors computed from this swing should comprise primarily the residual nonsymmetrical error components. This residual error can be corrected by cutting a cam for the mechanical error compensator.

The radio direction finder should be recalibrated after any changes have been made in the set or its surroundings, whenever there is reason to believe that the previous calibration has become inaccurate, and also at periodic intervals.

While RDF bearings are being taken, other radio antennas on board must be in the same condition as they were when the calibration was made; movable parts of the ship's superstructure such as booms, davits, wire rigging, etc., must be secured in the positions which they occupied when the radio direction finder was calibrated. Unusual cargoes such as large quantities of metals and extraordinary conditions of loading may cause errors.

4108. Using radio bearings.—A bearing obtained by radio, like one determined in any other manner, provides means for establishing a line of position. By heading in the direction from which the signal is coming, one can proceed toward, or **home** on, the transmitter. In thick weather one should avoid heading directly toward the source of radiation unless he has reliable information to indicate that he is some distance away. In 1934 the Nantucket Lightship was rammed and sunk by a ship homing on its radiobeacon.

Due to the many factors which enter into the transmission and reception of radio signals, a mariner cannot practically estimate his distance from a radiobeacon either by the strength of the signals received or by the time at which the signals were first heard. Mariners should give this fact careful consideration in approaching radiobeacons. When approaching a lightship, large navigational buoy, ocean station vessel, or a station on a submarine site, on radio bearings, the risk of collision will be avoided by insuring that the radio bearing does not remain constant.

It should be borne in mind that most lightships and large buoys are anchored to a very long scope of chain and, as a result, the radius of their swinging circle is considerable. The charted position is the location of the anchor. Furthermore, under certain conditions of wind and current, they are subject to sudden and unexpected sheers which are certain to hazard a vessel attempting to pass close aboard.

Radio waves, like light, travel along great circles. Except in high latitudes, visual bearings can usually be plotted as straight lines on a Mercator chart, without significant error. Radio bearings, however, are often observed at such positions with respect to the transmitter that the use of a rhumb line is not satisfactory. Under these conditions it is customary to apply the **conversion angle** (art. 1403, vol. II) as a correction to the observed angle, to find the equivalent rhumb line. Such a correction is not needed when a bearing is plotted on a gnomonic chart or one on which a straight line is a good approximation of a great circle. In other situations, a correction may be necessary.

If the transmitter and receiver are on the same meridian, or are both on the equator, no correction is needed because rhumb lines and great circles coincide under these conditions. The size of the correction increases with degree of departure from these conditions, and with greater distance between transmitter and receiver.

Conversion angles are given in table 1. This table is used to convert great circle to rhumb line directions. If the difference of longitude is not more than 4°5, and the mid-latitude between transmitter and receiver is not more than 85°, the first part of the table should be used. The simplifying assumptions used in the computation of this part of the table do not introduce a significant error within the limits of the table.

The sign of the correction can be determined by referring to the rules given at the bottom of each page of table 1. These follow from the fact that the great circle is nearer the pole than the rhumb line.

Before taking bearings on a commercial broadcasting station, the mariner should consider the following:

1. The operating frequency of the commercial station may differ widely from the frequency for which the radio direction finder is calibrated.

2. The broadcast antenna may be remote from the broadcast station.

3. The commercial stations are usually inland.

Accordingly, the use of commercial broadcasting stations to obtain a direction finder bearing is not recommended. If these stations are used, the mariner should recognize the limitations of the bearings obtained.

4109. Radio direction finder stations.—Radio direction finder stations are stations equipped with special apparatus for determining the direction of radio signals transmitted by ships and other stations. The bearings taken by radio direction finder stations, and reported to ships, are corrected for all determinable errors except conversion angle.

The bearings are normally accurate within 2° for distances under 150 nautical miles. The best bearings are obtained on ships whose signals are steady, clear, and strong. Therefore, the ship's transmitter should be finely tuned to the frequency of the transmitter. If the ship's transmitter is not finely tuned, it is difficult for the station to obtain bearings sufficiently accurate for navigational purposes.

Where bearing lines intersect an intervening coastline at an oblique angle or cross high intervening land, errors of from 4° to 5° may be expected due to refraction (art. 4104). However, the sectors in which such refraction may be expected is normally known by station personnel. Such sectors may not be included in the published sectors of calibration or are indicated as **sectors of uncertain calibration.**

The **sector of calibration** of a radio direction finder station is the sector about the receiving coil of the station in which the deviation of radio bearings is known. In Pubs. Nos. 117A and 117B, *Radio Navigational Aids*, the sectors are measured clockwise from 0° (true north) to 360° and are given looking from the station to seaward. Bearings which do not lie within the sector of calibration of a station should be considered unreliable.

4110. Distance finding stations.—At some locations a radio signal is synchronized with a sound signal which may be transmitted through either air or water or both. The travel time of the radio signal is negligible compared to that of the sound signal. Consequently, the difference in time between reception of the two signals is proportional to the distance from the station. The distance in nautical miles is equal to the number of seconds of time interval divided by $5\frac{1}{2}$ if the sound travels through air, or by $1\frac{1}{4}$ if through water (or multiplied by 0.18 or 0.8, respectively). The distance so found is from the origin of the *sound* signal, which might differ somewhat from that of the radio signal. Table 4110 can be used for finding the distance in nautical miles from a sound signal source.

Interval in seconds	Distance in nautical miles from sound signal source	
	Air	Submarine
1	0.18	0.8
2	.36	1.6
3	.54	2.4
4	.72	3.2
5	.90	4.0
6	1.08	4.8
7	1.26	5.6
8	1.44	6.4
9	1.62	7.2
10	1.80	8.0
20	3.60	16.0
30	5.40	24.0
40	7.20	
50	9.00	
60	10.80	

TABLE 4110.—Table for finding distance from a sound source.

The speed of sound travel is influenced by a number of conditions making it impracticable to state a factor that will give exact results under all conditions. The results obtained by the methods described may be accepted as being accurate to within 10 percent of the distance.

Ordinarily, the sound signals do not operate during the transmission period of the radio signal in clear weather. The methods in use employ, as a rule, distinctive signals to indicate the point of synchronization. Methods of synchronizing the signals vary and are described or illustrated in official announcements regarding them. It is essential to note carefully the point of synchronization used so that no error will be made through taking time on the wrong signal or the wrong part of it.

An example of the synchronized signals is shown in figure 4110. In this example, the beginning of the 10-second radio dash and the beginning of the 5-second fog signal blast are synchronized. The observer may use as the time interval the interval from the time of hearing the beginning of the long radio dash to the instant of hearing the beginning of the long blast of the fog signal.

FIGURE 4110.—Synchronized radio and fog signals.

In observing air signals it is usually sufficient to use a watch with second hand, although a stopwatch is helpful. For submarine signals where the interval is shorter and a time error correspondingly more important, it is essential that a stopwatch or other timing device be used. Where the radiobeacon and submarine signals are not received at the same point on the vessel, means of instant communication between two observers should be available or synchronized stopwatches provided for each.

In the case of some sound signals a series of short radio dashes is transmitted at intervals following the synchronizing point, so that by counting the number of such short dashes heard after the distinctive radio signal and before hearing the corresponding distinctive sound signal, the observer obtains his distance, in miles equal to the number of dashes counted, from the sound signal apparatus unless stated otherwise.

Ships not equipped with an RDF receiver can take advantage of the distance finding feature of a radiobeacon station, if equipped with a radio receiver capable of receiving the transmission. In the case of obtaining distance from a radiobeacon station which is synchronized with a submarine sound signal, the ship must also be equipped with a device for picking up submarine sound signals.

4111. Rotating loop radiobeacon.—The rotating loop radiobeacon *used in Japanese waters* consists of a rotating loop transmitter having directional properties by which an observer in a ship can obtain his bearing from the beacon without the use of a radio direction finder. Any radio receiving set capable of being tuned to the radiobeacon frequency can be used. The only other equipment required is a reliable stopwatch with a sweep second hand. Stopwatches and clocks with dials graduated in degrees can be used, from which bearings can be read off directly without any mathematical calculation.

During each revolution of the beacon, the signals received by the observer will rise and fall in intensity, passing through a maximum and a minimum twice each minute. The positions of minimum intensity, which occur at intervals of 30 seconds from one another, are very sharp and can be accurately observed. These are, therefore, used for navigation purposes.

The beacon may be regarded as having a line or beam of minimum intensity which rotates at a uniform speed of 360° in 1 minute (i.e. 6° in 1 second) based on the true meridian as starting point. Therefore, if the observer can (1) identify the beacon and (2) measure the number of seconds which this minimum beam takes to reach his position starting from the true meridian, this number multiplied by six will give his true bearing from the beacon or its reciprocal.

Each transmission (fig. 4111) from the beacon lasts for 4 minutes, and automatically starts again at the end of the silent period. Each transmission consists of two parts: (1) the identification signal of the station set at a slow speed for the first minute, commencing when the minimum beam is true east and west and followed by a long dash of about 12 seconds duration and (2) the signal group commencing when the minimum beam is approaching the true meridian and consisting of (i) the north starting signal, which is Morse V followed by two dots (... _ ..); (ii) a long dash of about 12 seconds duration; (iii) the east starting signal, which is Morse B followed by two dots (_ .. ..); and (iv) a long dash for about 42 seconds.

The navigation signals are repeated during the remainder of the transmission and signals cease when the minimum beam is in the east-west position.

4112. Using the rotating loop radiobeacon.—Procedures for using the rotating loop radiobeacon are as follows:

1. Set stopwatch to zero.
2. Listen for identification signal.

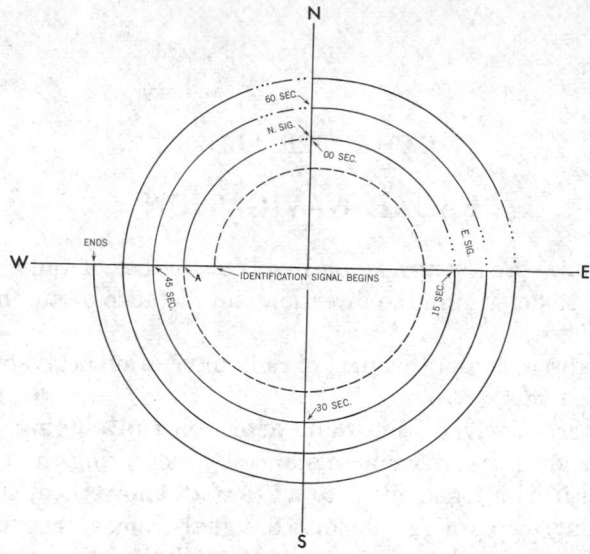

FIGURE 4111.—Transmissions from rotating loop radiobeacon.

3. When the first long dash begins (at A of figure 4111) standby for the north starting signal (Morse V followed by two dots); start stopwatch exactly at beginning of long dash (00ˢ of figure 4111), counting "one"-"two" with the two preceding dots and "three" for the start of the stopwatch.

4. Listen for minimum and record its exact time by stopwatch.

5. Multiply the number of seconds by 6° for bearing.

6. Determine whether bearing is reciprocal or direct.

7. If the north signal is faint, use the east signal but add 90° to the bearing.

The true bearing established is *from* the beacon. Therefore, if conversion angle (art. 1403, vol. II) is to be used it should be applied to the true bearing of the observer *from* the beacon, as in correcting bearings obtained by shore direction finder stations for conversion angle.

The following precautions should be observed:

1. Stopwatch should be started exactly at the beginning of the long dash.

2. The time of the minimum should be observed to the nearest fifth of a second, if possible.

3. Be sure to determine whether the bearing is the direct bearing to the beacon or its reciprocal.

4. If the east signal is used, be sure to add 90°.

5. The stopwatch should be checked before use. This can be done by checking the time by stopwatch of the complete revolution of the beacon transmission. A comparatively large bearing error can result from inaccurate timing.

CHAPTER XLII

RADAR NAVIGATION

4201. Introduction.—*Radar navigation* involves the use of radio waves, usually in the centimeter band, to determine the direction and distance of an object reflecting the waves to the sender.

A more detailed discussion of this part of radionavigation is given in Pub. No. 1310, *Radar Navigation Manual.*

4202. Radar, a term derived from **ra**dio **d**etection **a**nd **r**anging, is applied to electronic equipment designed to determine distance by measuring the time required for a radio signal to travel from a transmitter to a "target" and return, either as a reflected "echo" (**primary radar**) or as a retransmitted signal from a transponder (art. 4018) triggered by the original signal (**secondary radar**). Since primary radar uses a directional antenna, the direction of the target is also determined, but with somewhat less accuracy than the distance.

In the usual design for marine navigation applications, the radio signal is *pulse modulated* (art. 4016). Signals are generated in a transmitter by a timing circuit so that energy leaves the antenna in very short bursts or "pulses." During transmission of a pulse, the antenna is connected to the transmitter but not the receiver. As soon as the pulse leaves, an electronic switch disconnects the antenna from the transmitter and connects it to the receiver. Another pulse is not transmitted until after the preceding one has had time to travel to the most distant target within range, and return. Since the interval between pulses is long compared with the length of a pulse, strong signals can be provided with low *average* power. The duration or length of a single pulse is called **pulse length, pulse duration,** or **pulse width.**

From the receiver, the return signal goes to the indicator. This consists of a cathode-ray tube (art. 4019) and appropriate circuits. Many types of display have been devised, a number of them to meet specialized requirements. For navigational use, the earliest type of display was the **A-scope.** The principle of this scope is illustrated in figure 4202a. At *A* a pulse leaves the antenna of a ship, and a vertical deflection appears at the start of the horizontal trace on the scope face. At *B* the pulse has traveled some distance outward from the antenna. A short horizontal line appears after the vertical deflection on the scope face. The length of this line is directly proportional to the distance traveled by the pulse. At *C* the pulse encounters a target with a reflecting surface. At *D* the original pulse has moved on beyond the target, but part of its energy has been reflected back toward the transmitter. At *E* the echo has arrived back at the transmitting craft, causing a vertical deflection of the horizontal trace. The height of this deflection is directly proportional to the strength of the returning signal. At *F* the echo has proceeded on past the transmitting ship, and the trace is completed.

This sequence is repeated a great many times, perhaps 1,000 per second, the rate being called the **pulse repetition rate** (**PRR**) or **pulse recurrence rate.** The start of each trace is synchronized with transmission of the signal so that each trace is a repetition of the previous one, if slight changes in relative positions of transmitting ship, target, and antenna orientation are neglected. Therefore, the trace and all deflections appear as a continuous line. The distance between leading edges of the vertical deflections, or "pips," is directly proportional to range. A change of range alters the

940

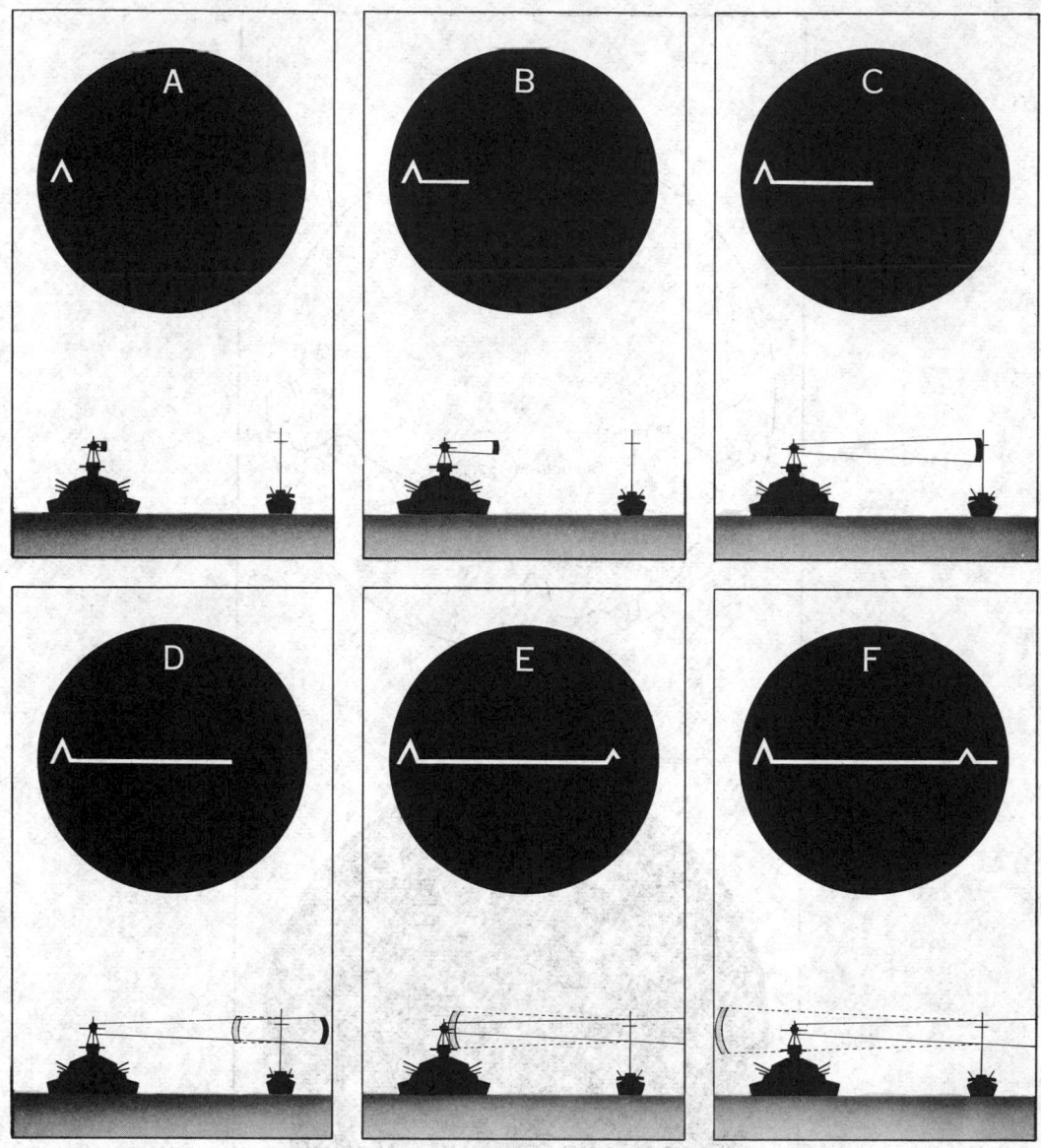

FIGURE 4202a.—A-scope.

positions of the second pip. The orientation of the antenna is an indication of direction. A pip appears only when the antenna is pointed toward the target.

The type of presentation now most commonly used for navigational radar is called the **plan position indicator** (**PPI**). On this presentation the sweep starts at the center of the tube face and moves outward along a radial line which rotates in synchronization with the antenna. Instead of being deflected, the trace glows with greater intensity (brightness) at the appropriate places. Because of the persistence of the tube face coating, the glow continues after the trace rotates on past the target, resulting in a maplike presentation on the scope. This presentation is shown in figure 4202b.

On a PPI, the range of a target is proportional to the distance of its echo signal from the center of the scope. This may be measured by a series of visible concentric circles at established distances from the center, or by means of an adjustable ring

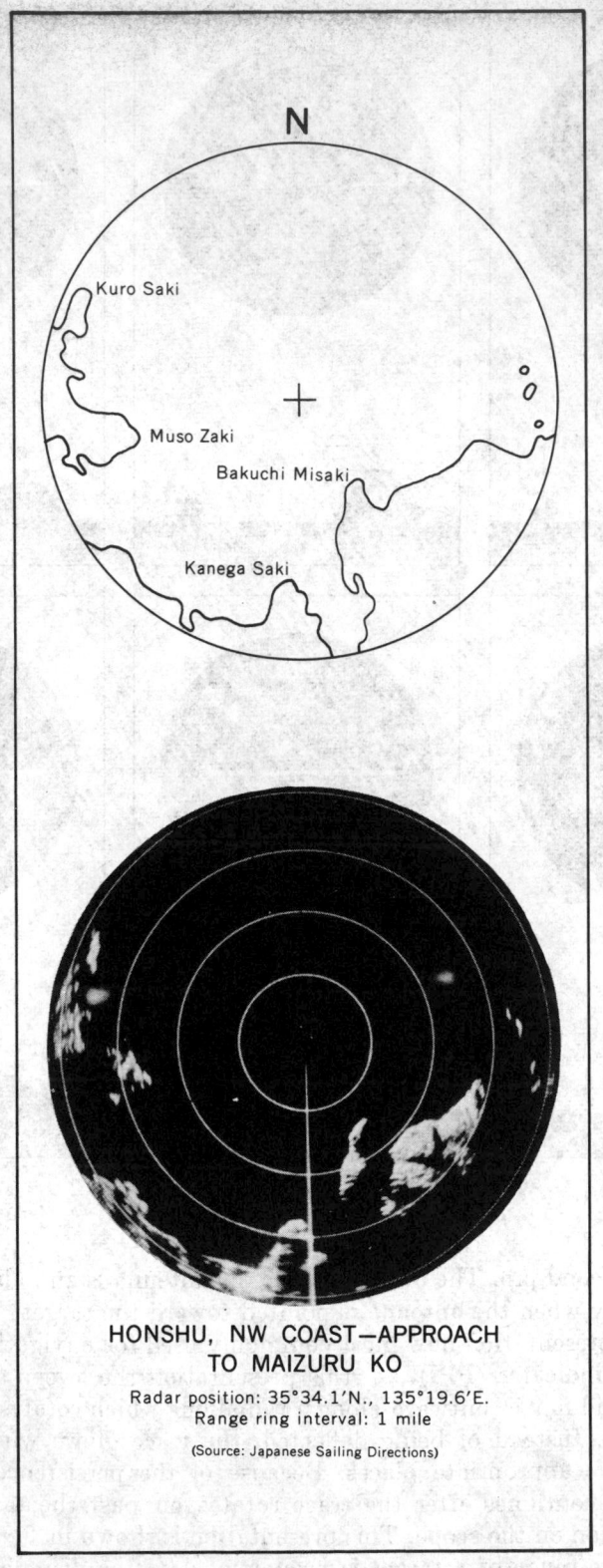

**HONSHU, NW COAST—APPROACH
TO MAIZURU KO**

Radar position: 35°34.1′N., 135°19.6′E.
Range ring interval: 1 mile

(Source: Japanese Sailing Directions)

FIGURE 4202b.—Plan position indicator display.

(**variable range marker**) synchronized with a counter. Bearing is indicated by the direction of an echo signal from the center of the scope. To facilitate measurement of direction, a movable, radial, guide line or **cursor** is provided, and a compass rose is placed around the outside of the scope. In the "heading-upward" presentation, relative bearings are indicated, the top of the scope representing the direction of the ship's head. In this *unstabilized* presentation, the orientation changes with changes in ship's heading. In the *stabilized* "north-upward" presentation, gyro north is always at the top, regardless of the heading. True bearings are indicated if there is no gyro error. On this type presentation a radial line is customarily provided at the heading of the vessel.

Provision may be made for offsetting the center of the PPI presentation from the center of the tube face, to permit large-scale observation of distant targets in one direction. With "true motion" radar, the center of the PPI continues to represent the same geographical position until reset. The actual motion of all moving objects, including one's own vessel, appears on the PPI, instead of the relative movement usually shown.

Other modifications have been devised. In some installations a **repeater** duplicates the presentation, making the information available at a distance from the radar.

4203. The radar beam.—The pulses of energy as emitted from a feedhorn at the focal point of a reflector or as emitted and radiated directly from the slots of a slotted waveguide antenna would, for the most part, form a single lobe-shaped pattern of radiation if emitted in free space. Figure 4203a shows this free space radiation pattern, including the undesirable minor lobes or side lobes associated with practical antenna design. Because of the large differences in the various dimensions of the radiation pattern, figure 4203a is necessarily distorted.

Although the radiated energy is concentrated or focused into a relatively narrow main beam by the antenna, similar to a beam of light from a flashlight, there is no clearly defined envelope of the energy radiated. Although the energy is concentrated along the axis of the beam, the strength of the energy decreases rapidly in directions away from the beam axis. The power in watts at points in the beam is inversely proportional to the square of the distance. Therefore, the power at 3 miles is only one-ninth of the power at 1 mile in a given direction. The field intensity in volts at points in the beam is inversely proportional to the distance. Therefore, the voltage at 2 miles is only one-half the voltage at 1 mile in a given direction. With the rapid decrease in the amount of radiated energy in directions away from the axis and in conjunction with the rapid decreases of this energy with distance, it follows that practical limits of power of voltage may be used to define the dimensions of the radar beam or to establish its envelope of useful energy.

The three-dimensional radar beam is normally defined by its *horizontal* and *vertical beam widths*. Beam width is the angular width of a radar beam between points within which the field strength or power is greater than arbitrarily selected lower limits of field strength or power.

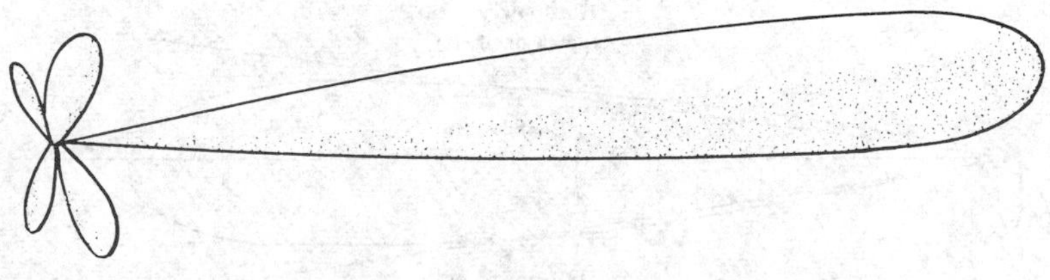

FIGURE 4203a.—Free space radiation pattern.

There are two limiting values, expressed either in terms of field intensity or power ratios, used conventionally to define beam width. One convention defines beam width as the angular width between points at which the field strength is 71 percent of its maximum value. Expressed in terms of power ratio, this convention defines beam width as the angular width between **half-power points.** The other convention defines beam width as the angular width between points at which the field strength is 50 percent of its maximum value. Expressed in terms of power ratio, the latter convention defines beam width as the angular width between **quarter-power points.**

The half-power ratio is the most frequently used convention. Which convention has been used in stating the beam width may be identified from the decibel (dB) figure normally included with the specifications of a radar set. Half-power and 71 percent field strength correspond to −3 dB; quarter-power and 50 percent field strength correspond to −6 dB.

The radiation diagram shown in figure 4203b depicts relative values of power in the same plane existing at the same distances from the antenna or the origin of the radar beam. Maximum power is in the direction of the axis of the beam. Power values diminish rapidly in directions away from the axis. The beam width in this case is taken as the angle between the half-power points.

For a given amount of transmitted power, the main lobe of the radar beam extends to a greater distance at a given power level with greater concentration of power in narrower beam widths. To increase maximum detection range capabilities, the energy is concentrated into as narrow a beam as is feasible. Because of practical considerations related to target detection and discrimination, only the horizontal beam width is quite narrow, typical values being between about 0°65 to 2°0. The vertical beam width is relatively broad, typical values being between about 15° to 30°.

The beam width is dependent upon the frequency or wavelength of the transmitted energy, antenna design, and the dimensions of the antenna.

For a given antenna size (antenna aperture), narrower beam widths are obtained when using shorter wavelengths. For a given wavelength, narrower beam widths are obtained when using larger antennas.

The slotted waveguide antenna has largely eliminated the side-lobe problem.

With radar waves being propagated in the vicinity of the surface of the sea, the main lobe of the radar beam, as a whole, is composed of a number of separate lobes as opposed to the single lobe-shaped pattern of radiation as emitted in free space. This phenomenon is the result of interference between radar waves directly transmitted and those waves which are reflected from the surface of the sea. The vertical beam widths of navigational radars are such that during normal transmission, radar waves will strike the surface of the sea at points from near the antenna to the radar horizon, depending upon antenna height and vertical beam width. The indirect waves (fig. 4203c) reflected from the surface of the sea may, on rejoining the direct waves, either reinforce or cancel the direct

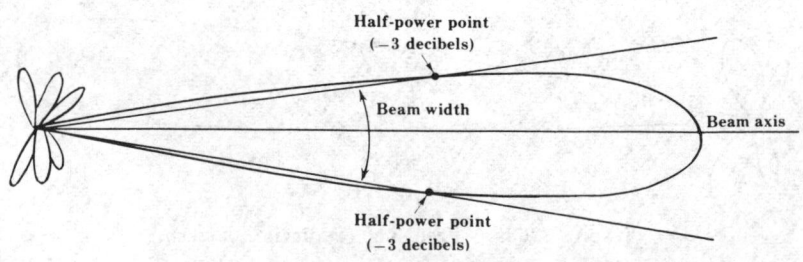

FIGURE 4203b.—Radiation diagram.

waves depending upon whether they are in phase or out of phase with the direct waves, respectively. Where the direct and indirect waves are exactly in phase, i.e., the crests and troughs of the waves coincide, hyperbolic lines of maximum radiation known as *lines of maxima* are produced. Where the direct and indirect waves are exactly of opposite phase, i.e., the trough of one wave coincides with the crest of the other wave, hyperbolic lines of minimum radiation known as *lines of minima* are produced. Along directions away from the antenna, the direct and indirect waves will gradually come into and pass out of phase, producing lobes of useful radiation separated by regions within which, for practical purposes, there is no useful radiation. Except for the fact that the phase of the indirect wave is reversed on being reflected from the surface of the sea, points on the lines of minima would correspond to differences in the lengths of the paths of the direct and indirect waves of an odd number of half wavelengths. Because of the reversal of the phase of the indirect wave on being reflected from the surface of the sea, points on the lines of minima correspond to differences in the lengths of the paths of the direct and indirect waves of an even number of half wavelengths.

Figure 4203d shows the lower region of the interference pattern of a respresentative navigational radar. Since the first line of minima is at the surface of the sea, the first region of minimum radiation or energy is adjacent to the sea's surface.

From this figure it should be obvious that if energy is to be reflected from a target, the target must extend somewhat above the radar horizon, the amount of extension being dependent upon the reflecting properties of the target.

A **vertical-plane coverage diagram** (fig. 4203d) is used by radar designers and analysts to predict regions in which targets will and will not be detected.

Of course, on the small page of a book it would be impossible to illustrate the coverage of a radar beam to scale with antenna height being in feet and the lengths of the various lobes of the interference pattern being in miles. In providing greater clarity of the presentation of the lobes, non-linear graduations of the arc of the vertical beam width are used.

The lengths of the various lobes shown in figures 4203d and 4203e should be given no special significance with respect to the range capabilities of a particular radar set. As with other coverage diagrams, the lobes are drawn to connect points of equal field intensities. Longer and broader lobes may be drawn connecting points of equal, but lesser, field intensities.

The vertical plane coverage diagram as shown in figure 4203e, while not representative of navigational radars, does indicate that at the lower frequencies the interference pattern is coarser than the patterns for higher frequencies. This particular diagram was constructed with the assumption that the free space useful range of the radar beam was 50 nautical miles. From this diagram it is seen that the ranges of the useful lobes are extended to considerably greater distance because of the reinforcement of the direct radar waves by the indirect radar waves. Also, the elevation of the lowest lobe is higher than it would be for a higher frequency. Figure 4203e also illustrates the vertical view of the undesirable side lobes associated with practical antenna design. In examining these

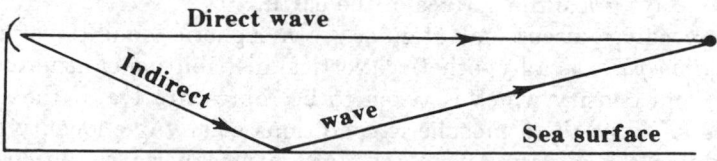

FIGURE 4203c.—Direct and indirect waves.

radiation coverage diagrams, the reader should keep in mind that the radiation pattern is three-dimensional.

Antenna height as well as frequency or wavelength governs the number of lobes in the interference pattern. The number of the lobes and the fineness of the interference pattern increase with antenna height. Increased antenna height as well as increases in frequency tends to lower the lobes of the interference pattern.

The pitch and roll of the ship radiating do not affect the structure of the interference pattern.

Diffraction is the bending of a wave as it passes an obstruction. Because of diffraction there is some illumination of the region behind an obstruction or target by the radar beam. Diffraction effects are greater at the lower frequencies. Thus, the radar beam of a lower frequency radar tends to illuminate more of the shadow region behind an obstruction than the beam of a radar of higher frequency or shorter wavelength.

Attenuation is the scattering and absorption of the energy in the radar beam as it passes through the atmosphere. It causes a decrease in echo strength. Attenuation is greater at the higher frequencies or shorter wavelengths.

While reflected echoes are much weaker than the transmitted pulses, the characteristics of their return to the source are similar to the characteristics of propagation. The strengths of these echoes are dependent upon the amount of transmitted energy striking the targets and the size and reflecting properties of the targets.

Refraction

If the radar waves actually traveled in straight lines or rays, the distance to the horizon grazed by these rays would be dependent only on the height of the antenna, assuming adequate power for the rays to reach this horizon. Without the effects of refraction, the distance to the **radar horizon** would be the same as that of the geometrical horizon for the antenna height. Like light rays, radar rays are subject to bending or refraction in the atmosphere resulting from travel through regions of different density. However, radar rays are refracted slightly more than light rays because of the frequencies used.

Where h is the height of the antenna in feet, the distance, d, to the radar horizon in nautical miles, assuming standard atmospheric conditions, may be found as follows:

$$d = 1.22\sqrt{h}.$$

With the distances to the geometrical and optical horizons being $1.06\sqrt{h}$ and $1.15\sqrt{h}$, respectively, the radar horizon exceeds the geometrical horizon by 15 percent and the optical horizon by 6 percent. Thus, like light rays in the standard atmosphere, radar rays are bent or refracted slightly downwards approximating the curvature of the earth.

The distance to the radar horizon does not in itself limit the distance from which echoes may be received from targets. Assuming that adequate power is transmitted, echoes may be received from targets beyond the radar horizon if their reflecting surfaces extend above it. Note that the distance to the radar horizon is the distance at which the radar rays graze the surface of the earth.

In the preceding discussion, standard atmospheric conditions were assumed. The *standard atmosphere* is a hypothetical vertical distribution of atmospheric temperature, pressure, and density which is taken to be representative of the atmosphere for various purposes. While the atmospheric conditions at any one locality during a given season may differ considerably from standard atmospheric conditions, the slightly downward bending of the light and radar rays may be described as the typical case.

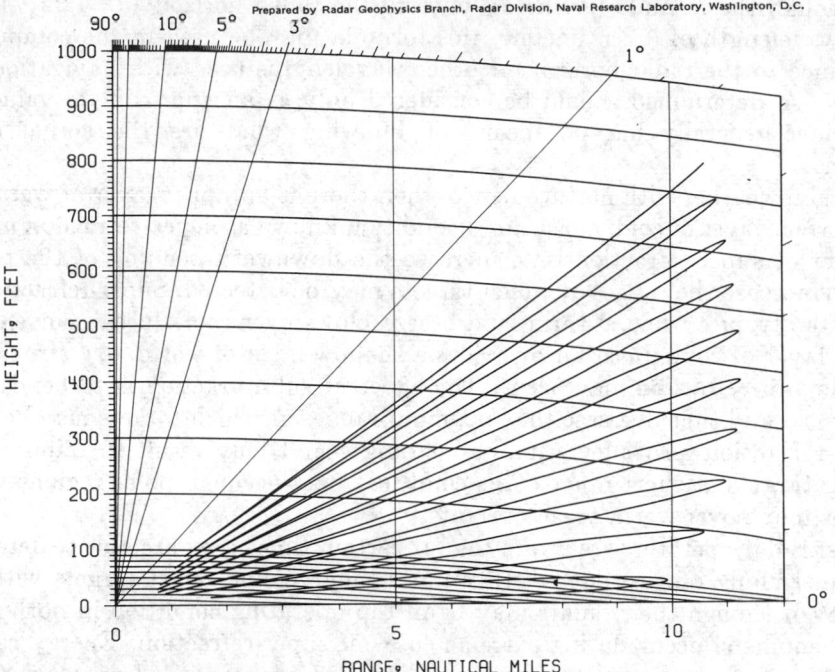

FIGURE 4203d.—Vertical-plane coverage diagram (3050 MHz, antenna height 125 feet, wave height 4 feet).

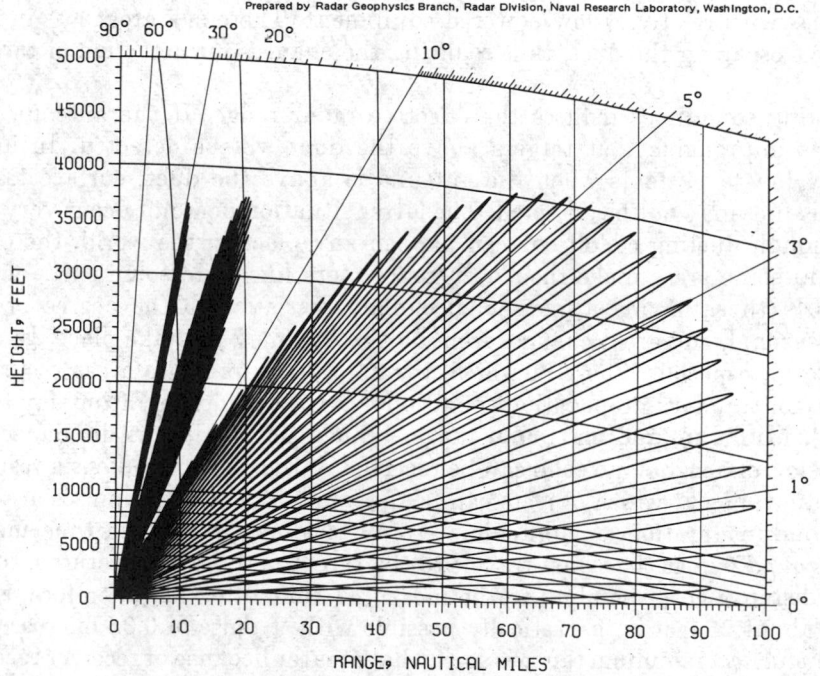

FIGURE 4203e.—Vertical-plane coverage diagram (1000 MHz, vertical beam width 10°, antenna height 80 feet, wave height 0 feet).

Although the formula for the distance to the radar horizon $(d=1.22\sqrt{h})$ is based upon a wavelength of 3 centimeters, this formula may be used in the computation of the distance to the radar horizon for other wavelengths used with navigational radar. The value so determined should be considered only as an approximate value because the mariner generally has no means of knowing what are the actual refraction conditions.

In calm weather with no turbulence when there is an upper layer of warm, dry air over a surface layer of cold, moist air, a condition known as **super-refraction** may occur. The effect of super-refraction is to increase the downward bending of the radar rays and thus increase the ranges at which targets may be detected. Super-refraction occurs often in the tropics when a warm land breeze blows over cooler ocean currents.

If a layer of cold, moist air overrides a shallow layer of warm, dry air, a condition known as **sub-refraction** may occur. The effect of sub-refraction is to bend the radar rays upward and thus decrease the maximum ranges at which targets may be detected.

Sub-refraction also affects minimum ranges and may result in failure to detect low lying targets at short range. This condition may occur in polar regions when cold airmasses move over warm ocean currents.

Most radar operators are aware that at certain times they are able to detect targets at extremely long ranges, but at other times they cannot detect targets within visual ranges, even though their radars may be in top operating condition in both instances. These phenomena occur during extreme cases of super-refraction. Energy radiated at angles of 1° or less may be trapped in a layer of the atmosphere called a **surface radio duct.** In the surface radio duct, the radar rays are refracted downward to the surface of the sea, reflected upward, refracted downward again within the duct, and so on continuously. The energy trapped by the duct suffers little loss; thus, targets may be detected at exceptionally long ranges. Surface targets have been detected at ranges in excess of 1,400 miles with relatively low-powered equipment. There is a great loss in the energy of the rays escaping the duct, thus reducing the chances for detection of targets above the duct.

Ducting sometimes reduces the effective radar range. If the antenna is below a duct, it is improbable that targets above the duct will be detected. In instances of extremely low-level ducts when the antenna is above the duct, surface targets lying below the duct may not be detected. The latter situation does not occur very often.

Although ducting conditions can happen any place in the world, the climate and weather in some areas make their occurrence more likely. In some parts of the world, particularly those having a monsoonal climate, variation in the degree of ducting is mainly seasonal, and great changes from day to day may not take place. In other parts of the world, especially those in which low barometric pressure areas recur often, the extent of nonstandard propagation conditions varies considerably from day to day.

4204. Minimum and maximum range.—Since the receiver is disconnected during transmission of a signal, no echo can be received during this period. As a result, there is a minimum range at which objects can be detected. The shortest pulses are about 0.05 microsecond in duration, or approximately 49 feet long. Since the time measurement is of the *round trip* as the signal travels to the target and the echo returns, the range is *half* the distance corresponding to the measured time interval. Therefore, a minimum range of about 25 feet is theoretically possible with a pulse of 0.05 microsecond. However, the *practical* minimum range is somewhat greater because of receiver recovery time, sea return, side-lobe echoes, and the vertical beam width.

1. *Recovery time* of the receiver extends the minimum range at which a target can be detected beyond the range determined by the pulse length.

2. *Sea return* or echoes received from waves may clutter the indicator within and beyond the minimum range established by the pulse length and recovery time.

3. When operating near land or large targets, *side-lobe echoes* (echoes from targets detected in the side-lobes of the antenna beam pattern) may clutter the indicator and prevent detection of close targets, without regard to the direction in which the antenna is trained.

4. Small surface targets may escape detection when close due to the limits of effective radiation established by the *vertical beam width*.

The *maximum range* is limited by the frequency, peak power, pulse length, pulse repetition rate, beam width, receiver sensitivity, antenna rotation rate, curvature of the earth, target characteristics, and weather.

1. Lower frequencies (longer wavelengths) generally provide longer detection ranges because the attenuation of the higher frequencies is greater, regardless of weather.

2. The range capability increases with increase in peak power. Doubling the peak power increases the range capability by about 25 percent.

3. As the pulse length is increased, the range capability also increases due to the greater amount of energy transmitted.

4. The pulse repetition rate (PRR) determines the maximum *measurable* range of the radar. Ample time must be allowed between pulses for an echo to return from any target located within the maximum workable range of the system. Otherwise, echoes returning from the more distant targets are blocked by succeeding transmitted pulses. This necessary time interval determines the highest PRR that can be used. The PRR must be high enough, however, that sufficient pulses hit the target, and enough echoes are returned to the radar.

5. The detection range increases as the radar beam becomes more concentrated.

6. The more sensitive receivers provide greater detection ranges.

7. The detection range increases as the antenna rotation rate decreases. For a radar set having a PRR of 1000 pulses per second, a horizontal beam width of $2°0$, and an antenna rotation rate of 6 RPM (1 revolution in 10 seconds or 36 scanning degrees per second), there is one pulse transmitted each $0°036$ of rotation. There are 56 pulses transmitted during the time required for the antenna to rotate through its beam width:

$$\frac{\text{Beam Width}}{\text{Degrees per Pulse}} = \frac{2°0}{0°036} = 56 \text{ pulses.}$$

With an antenna rotation rate of 15 RPM (1 revolution in 4 seconds or 90 scanning degrees per second), there is only one pulse transmitted each $0°090$ of rotation. There are only 22 pulses transmitted during the time required for the antenna to rotate through its beam width:

$$\frac{\text{Beam Width}}{\text{Degrees per Pulse}} = \frac{2°0}{0°090} = 22 \text{ pulses.}$$

From the foregoing it is apparent that at the higher antenna rotation rates, the maximum ranges at which targets, particularly small targets, may be detected are reduced.

8. Since radar operates in the higher frequencies that are essentially line-of-sight, the maximum range is limited by the curvature of the earth. The radar horizon, at which rays from the transmitting antenna graze the surface of the earth, is at a distance about 15 percent greater than that of the visible horizon (tab. 8). Under conditions of abnormal refraction (art. 4203), both visible and radar horizons may be extended to greater distances. Due to curvature of the earth, maximum range increases as either antenna or target height increases.

9. There are several target characteristics which will enable one target to be detected at a greater range than another, or for one target to produce a stronger echo than another target of similar size:

Height. Since radar wave propagation is almost line-of-sight, the height of the target is of prime importance. If the target does not rise above the radar horizon, the radar beam cannot be reflected from the target. Because of the interference pattern in the radar beam, the target must rise somewhat above the radar horizon.

Size. Up to certain limits, targets having larger reflecting areas return stronger echoes than targets having smaller reflecting areas. Should a target be wider than the horizontal beam width, the strength of the echoes is not increased on account of the greater width of the target because the area not exposed to the radar beam at any instant cannot, of course, reflect an echo. Since the vertical dimensions of most targets are small compared to the vertical beam width of marine navigational radars, the beam width limitation is not normally applicable to the vertical dimensions. However, there is a vertical dimension limitation in the case of sloping surfaces or stepped surfaces. In this case, only the projected vertical area lying within the distance equivalent of the pulse length can return echoes at any instant.

Aspect of a target is its orientation to the axis of the radar beam. With change in aspect, the effective reflecting area may change, depending upon the shape of the target. The nearer the angle between the reflecting area and the beam axis is 90°, the greater is the strength of the echo returned to the antenna.

Shape. Targets of identical shape may give echoes of varying strength, depending on aspect. Thus a flat surface at right angles to the radar beam, such as the side of a steel ship or a steep cliff along the shore, reflects very strong echoes. As the aspect changes, this flat surface tends to reflect more of the energy of the beam away from the antenna, and may give rather weak echoes. A concave surface tends to focus the radar beam back to the antenna while a convex surface tends to scatter the energy. A smooth conical surface does not reflect energy back to the antenna. However, echoes may be reflected to the antenna if the conical surface is rough.

Texture of the target may modify the effects of shape and aspect. A smooth texture tends to increase the reflection qualities, but unless the aspect and shape of the target are such that the reflection is focused directly back to the antenna, the smooth surface will give a poor radar echo because most of the energy is reflected in another direction. On the other hand, a rough surface tends to break up the reflection and improves the strength of echoes returned from those targets whose shape and aspect normally give weak echoes.

Composition. The ability of various substances to reflect radar pulses depends on the intrinsic electrical properties of those substances. Thus metal and water are good reflectors. Ice is a fair reflector, depending on aspect. Land areas vary in their reflection qualities depending on the amount and type of vegetation and the rock and mineral content. Wood and fiber glass boats are poor reflectors. It must be remembered that all of the characteristics interact with each other to determine the strength of the radar echo, and no factor can be singled out without considering the effects of the others.

10. The usual effects of weather are to reduce the ranges at which targets can be detected and to produce unwanted echoes on the radarscope which may obscure the returns from important targets or from targets which may be dangerous to one's ship.

The wind produces waves which reflect unwanted echos (art. 4206) which appear on the PPI as *sea return.* Sea return is normally greater in the direction from which the wind and seas are coming. Rain, hail, and snow storms all may return echoes which appear on the PPI as a blurred or cluttered area. In addition to masking targets which are within the storm area, heavy precipitation may absorb some of the strength of the pulse and decrease maximum detection range.

4205. Radarscope interpretation.—Radar may serve the navigator as a very valuable tool if its characteristics and limitations are understood. Although determining position through observation of the range and bearing of a charted, isolated, and well defined object having good reflecting properties is relatively simple, this task still requires that the navigator have an understanding of the characteristics and limitations of his radar. The more general task of using radar in observing a shoreline where the radar targets are not so obvious or well defined requires considerable expertise which may be gained only through an adequate understanding of the characteristics and limitations of the radar being used.

Although the plan position indicator does provide a chartlike presentation when a landmass is being scanned, the image painted by the sweep is not a true representation of the shoreline. But with practice, one can acquire considerable skill in interpreting the signals appearing on the radarscope. Some of the factors to be kept in mind in interpretation are the following:

Resolution in range. In part *A* of figure 4205a, a transmitted pulse has arrived at the second of two targets of insufficient size or density to absorb or reflect all of the energy of the pulse. While the pulse has traveled from the first to the second target, the echo from the first has traveled an equal distance in the opposite direction. At *B* the transmitted pulse has continued on beyond the second target, and the two echoes are returning toward the transmitter. The distance between leading edges of the two echoes is *twice* the distance between targets. The correct distance will be shown on the scope, which is calibrated to show *half* the distance traveled out and back. At *C* the targets are closer together and the pulse length has been increased. The two echoes merge, and on the scope will appear as a single, large target. At *D* the pulse length has been decreased, and the two echoes appear separated. The ability of a radar to separate targets close together on the same bearing is called **resolution in range.** It is related primarily to pulse length, the minimum distance between targets that can be distinguished as separate ones being *half* the pulse length. This (half the pulse length) is the apparent depth or thickness of a target presenting a flat perpendicular surface to the radar beam. Thus, several ships close together may appear as an island. Echoes from a number of small boats, piles, breakers, or even large ships close to the shore may blend with echoes from the shore, resulting in an incorrect indication of the position and shape of the shoreline.

Resolution in bearing is similar to that in range. A pulse proceeds outward along a narrow sector. As the beam rotates, energy is returned during the entire time that a target is "illuminated," the same as with a searchlight. A vertical target such as a mast is "seen" over the arc in which there is sufficient illumination to render it visible. On a radar PPI a target appears widened by an amount equal to the effective **beam width,** half the effective beam width being added to each side. Thus, the echoes from two or more targets close together at the same range may merge to form a single, wider echo. The ability to separate such targets is called **resolution in bearing.** In angular units it is dependent primarily upon beam width, a narrower beam having a higher resolution. In terms of distance between targets, range is also important, resolution increasing as range decreases.

Height of antenna and target. If the radar horizon (art. 4203) is between the transmitting vessel and the target, the lower part of the target will not be visible. A large vessel may appear as a small craft, a shoreline may appear at some distance inland. Areas within shadows may not be visible at all.

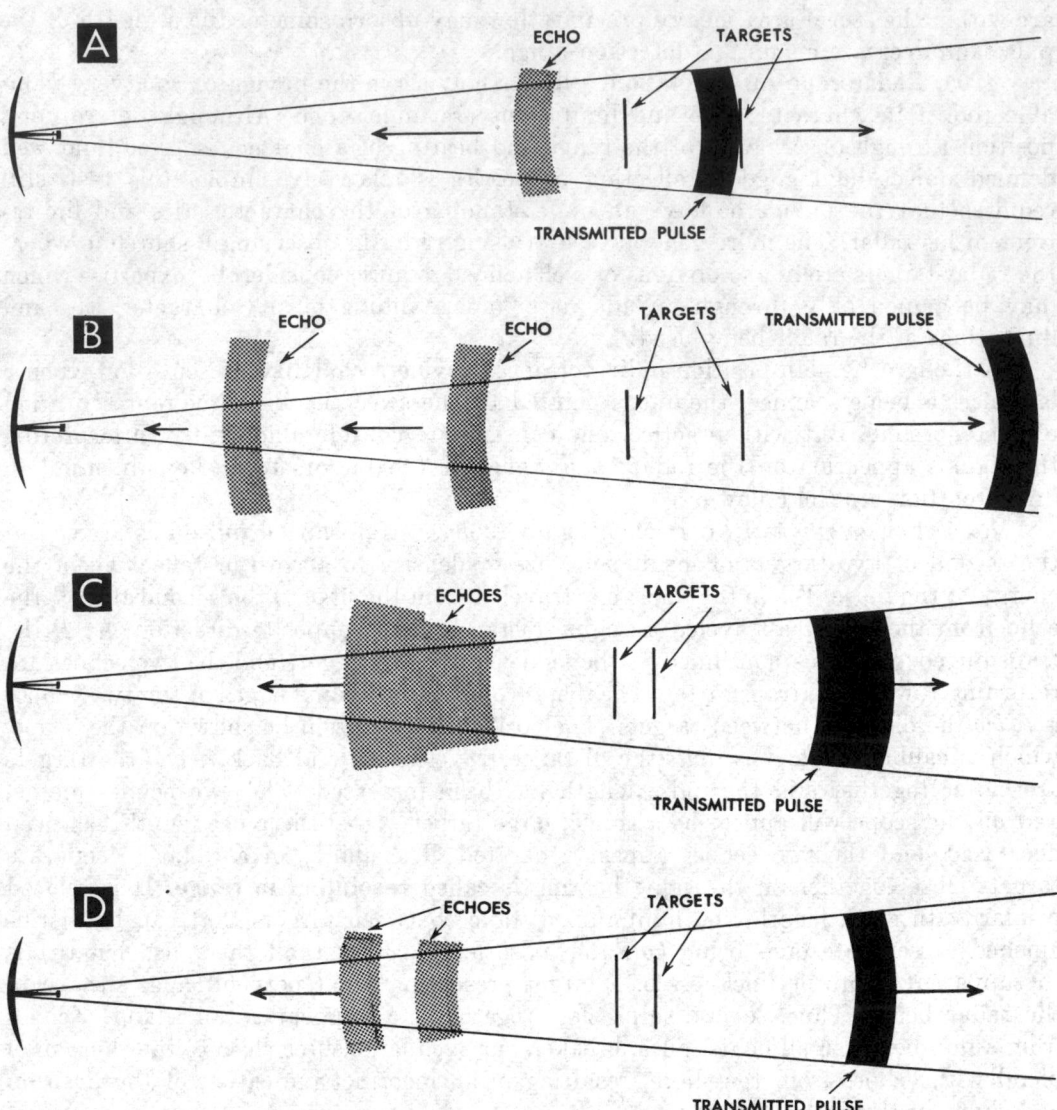

FIGURE 4205a.—Resolution in range.

Reflecting quality of target. Echoes from several targets of the same size may be quite different in appearance. A metal surface is a better reflector of radio waves than a wooden surface. A surface perpendicular to the beam returns a stronger echo than a nonperpendicular one. For this reason, a gently sloping beach may not be visible. A vessel encountered broadside returns a stronger echo than one heading toward or away from the radar vessel. In some instances, the strength of an echo can be increased by means of a corner reflector (art. 4207).

Frequency. As the frequency is increased, reflections occur from smaller targets. Thus, a 10-centimeter radar generally penetrates fog, rain, snow, etc., while a 3-centimeter radar receives returns from such obstacles.

Radarscope interpretation is complicated somewhat by the presence of unwanted signals from atmospheric noise, sea return, precipitation, etc. Collectively, this is called **clutter.** Generally, it is strongest near the vessel and gradually decreases with increased range, because of reduced sea return. Strong echoes can sometimes be detected by reducing the volume or "gain" of the receiver (not the image intensity of the indicator), so that weaker signals will not appear. Even when the amplitude of the clutter is about the same as that of desired signals, the latter can sometimes be detected by watching the scope during several rotations of the antenna. At each rotation the signals from targets remain at about the same place, and of about the same magnitude, while those from waves, noise, etc., fluctuate, appearing different on each revolution. Floating ice or a small boat may not be detected at any range if the waves are high. A rough surface returns a stronger echo than a smooth surface.

Sometimes a signal appears on a radar screen when there is no visible object at the point indicated, and no apparent source of the signal. This is called a **ghost.** It may be due to faulty operation of the radar set or to an actual echo returned from a discontinuity in the atmosphere. Sometimes such discontinuities reflect light, also, producing images or apparent images similar to mirages and of seeming apparent reality. A similar condition occasionally occurs in the sea. This phenomenon is undoubtedly the basis of many reports of strange objects sighted visually or by radar. Sometimes such apparent objects exhibit incredible speed or maneuverability.

The major problem is that of determining which features in the vicinity of the shoreline are actually reflecting the echoes "painted" on the radarscope. Particularly in cases where a low lying shore is being scanned, there may be considerable uncertainty.

An associated problem is the fact that certain features on the shore will not return echoes, even if they have good reflecting properties, simply because they are blocked from the radar beam by other physical features or obstructions. This factor in turn causes the chartlike image painted on the scope to differ from the chart of the area.

If the navigator is to be able to interpret the chartlike presentation on his radarscope, he must have at least an elementary understanding of the characteristics of radar propagation, the characteristics of his radar set, the reflecting properties of different types of radar targets, and the ability to analyze his chart to make an estimate of just which charted features are most likely to reflect the transmitted pulses or to be blocked from the radar beam. Although contour lines on the chart topography aid the navigator materially in the latter task, experience gained during clear weather comparison of the visual cross-bearing plot and the radarscope presentation is invaluable.

Observing experience gained during good weather transits of confined waters can be invaluable during later inclement weather transits, particularly if the navigator gives close attention to the identification of those features the reliable identification of which would be of material aid in effecting a safe transit.

On relative and true motion displays, landmasses are readily recognizable because of the generally steady brilliance of the relatively large areas painted on the PPI. Also land should be at positions expected from knowledge of the ship's navigational position. On relative motion displays, landmasses move in directions and at rates opposite and equal to the actual motion of the observer's ship. Individual pips do not move relative to one another. On true motion displays, landmasses do not move on the PPI if there is accurate compensation for set and drift. Without such compensation, i.e., when the true motion display is sea-stabilized, only slight movements of landmasses may be detected on the PPI.

Although landmasses are readily recognizable, the primary problem is the identification of specific features so that such features can be used for fixing the position of the observer's ship. Identification of specific features can be quite difficult because of various factors, including distortion resulting from beam width and pulse length, and uncertainty as to just which charted features are reflecting the echoes. The following hints may be used as an aid in identification:

1. *Sandspits* and *smooth, clear beaches* normally do not appear on the PPI at ranges beyond 1 or 2 miles because these targets have almost no area that can reflect energy back to the radar. Ranges determined from these targets are not reliable. If waves are breaking over a sandbar, echoes may be returned from the surf. Waves may, however, break well out from the actual shoreline, so that ranging on the surf may be misleading when a radar position is being determined relative to the shoreline.

2. *Mud flats* and *marshes* normally reflect radar pulses only a little better than a sandspit. The weak echoes received at low tide disappear at high tide. *Mangroves* and other *thick growth* may produce a strong echo. Areas that are indicated as swamps on a chart, therefore, may return either strong or weak echoes, depending on the density and size of the vegetation growing in the area.

3. When *sand dunes* are covered with vegetation and are well back from a low, smooth beach, the apparent shoreline determined by radar appears as the line of the dunes rather than the true shoreline. Under some conditions, sand dunes may return strong echo signals because the combination of the vertical surface of the vegetation and the horizontal beach may form a sort of corner reflector.

4. *Lagoons* and *inland lakes* usually appear as blank areas on a PPI because the smooth water surface returns no energy to the radar antenna In some instances, the sandbar or reef surrounding the lagoon may not appear on the PPI because it lies too low in the water.

5. *Coral atolls* and *long chains of islands* may produce long lines of echoes when the radar beam is directed perpendicular to the line of the islands. This indication is especially true when the islands are closely spaced. The reason is that the spreading resulting from the width of the radar beam causes the echoes to blend into continuous lines. When the chain of islands is viewed lengthwise, or obliquely, however, each island may produce a separate pip. *Surf breaking on a reef* around an atoll produces a ragged, variable line of echoes.

6. One or two *rocks* projecting above the surface of the water, or waves breaking over a reef, may appear on the PPI. When an object is submerged entirely and the sea is smooth over it, no indication is seen on the PPI.

7. *If the land rises in a gradual, regular manner from the shoreline*, no part of the terrain produces an echo that is stronger than the echo from any other part. As a result, a general haze of echoes appears on the PPI, and it is difficult to ascertain the range to any particular part of the land.

Land can be recognized by plotting the contact. Care must be exercised when plotting because, as a ship approaches or goes away from a shore behind which the land rises gradually, a plot of the ranges and bearings to the land may show an "apparent" course and speed.

8. Blotchy signals are returned from *hilly ground* because the crest of each hill returns a good echo although the valley beyond is in a shadow. If high receiver gain is used, the pattern may become solid except for the very deep shadows.

9. *Low islands* ordinarily produce small echoes. When thick *palm trees* or other foliage grow on the island, strong echoes often are produced because the horizontal surface of the water around the island forms a sort of corner reflector with the vertical surfaces of the trees. As a result, *wooded islands* give good echoes and can be detected at a much greater range than barren islands.

With the appearance of a small pip on the PPI, *its identification as a ship* can be aided by a process of elimination. A check of the navigational position can overrule the possibility of land. The size of the pip can be used to overrule the possibility of land or precipitation, both usually having a massive appearance on the PPI. The rate of movement of the pip on the PPI can overrule the possibility of aircraft.

Having eliminated the foregoing possibilities, the appearance of the pip on the PPI at a medium range as a bright, steady, and clearly defined image indicates a high probability that the target is a steel ship.

The pip of a ship target may brighten at times and then slowly decrease in brightness. Normally, the pip of a ship target fades from the PPI only when the range becomes too great.

Although PPI displays are approximately chartlike when landmasses are being scanned by the radar beam, there may be sizable areas missing from the display because of certain features being blocked from the radar beam by other features. A shoreline which is continuous on the PPI display when the ship is at one position may not be continuous when the ship is at another position and scanning the same shoreline. The radar beam may be blocked from a segment of this shoreline by an obstruction such as a promontory. An indentation in the shoreline, such as a cove or bay, appearing on the PPI when the ship is at one position may not appear when the ship is at another position nearby. Thus, **radar shadow** alone can cause considerable differences between the PPI display and the chart presentation. This effect in conjunction with beam width and pulse length distortion of the PPI display can cause even greater differences.

The pips of ships, rocks, and other targets close to shore may merge with the shoreline image on the PPI. This merging is due to the distortion effects of horizontal beam width and pulse length. Target images on the PPI always are distorted angularly by an amount equal to the effective horizontal beam width. Also, the target images always are distorted radially by an amount at least equal to one-half the pulse length (164 yards per microsecond of pulse length).

Figure 4205b illustrates the effects of ship's position, beam width, and pulse length on the radar shoreline. Because of beam width distortion, a straight, or nearly straight, shoreline often appears crescent-shaped on the PPI. This effect is greater with the wider beam widths. Note that this distortion increases as the angle between the beam axis and the shoreline decreases.

Figure 4205c illustrates the distortion effects of radar shadow, beam width, and pulse length. View A shows the actual shape of the shoreline and the land behind it. Note the steel tower on the low sand beach and the two ships at anchor close to shore. The heavy line in view B represents the shoreline on the PPI. The dotted lines represent the actual position and shape of all targets. Note in particular:

1. The low sand beach is not detected by the radar.

2. The tower on the low beach is detected, but it looks like a ship in a cove. At closer range the land would be detected and the cove-shaped area would begin to fill in; then the tower could not be seen without reducing the receiver gain.

3. The radar shadow behind both mountains. Distortion owing to radar shadows is responsible for more confusion that any other cause. The small island does not appear because it is in the radar shadow.

4. The spreading of the land in bearing caused by beam width distortion. Look at the upper shore of the peninsula. The shoreline distortion is greater to the west because the angle between the radar beam and the shore is smaller as the beam seeks out the more westerly shore.

5. Ship No. 1 appears as a small peninsula. Her pip has merged with the land because of the beam width distortion.

6. Ship No. 2 also merges with the shoreline and forms a bump. This bump is caused by pulse length and beam width distortion. Reducing receiver gain might cause the ship to separate from land, provided the ship is not too close to the shore. The Fast Time Constant (FTC) control could also be used to attempt to separate the ship from land.

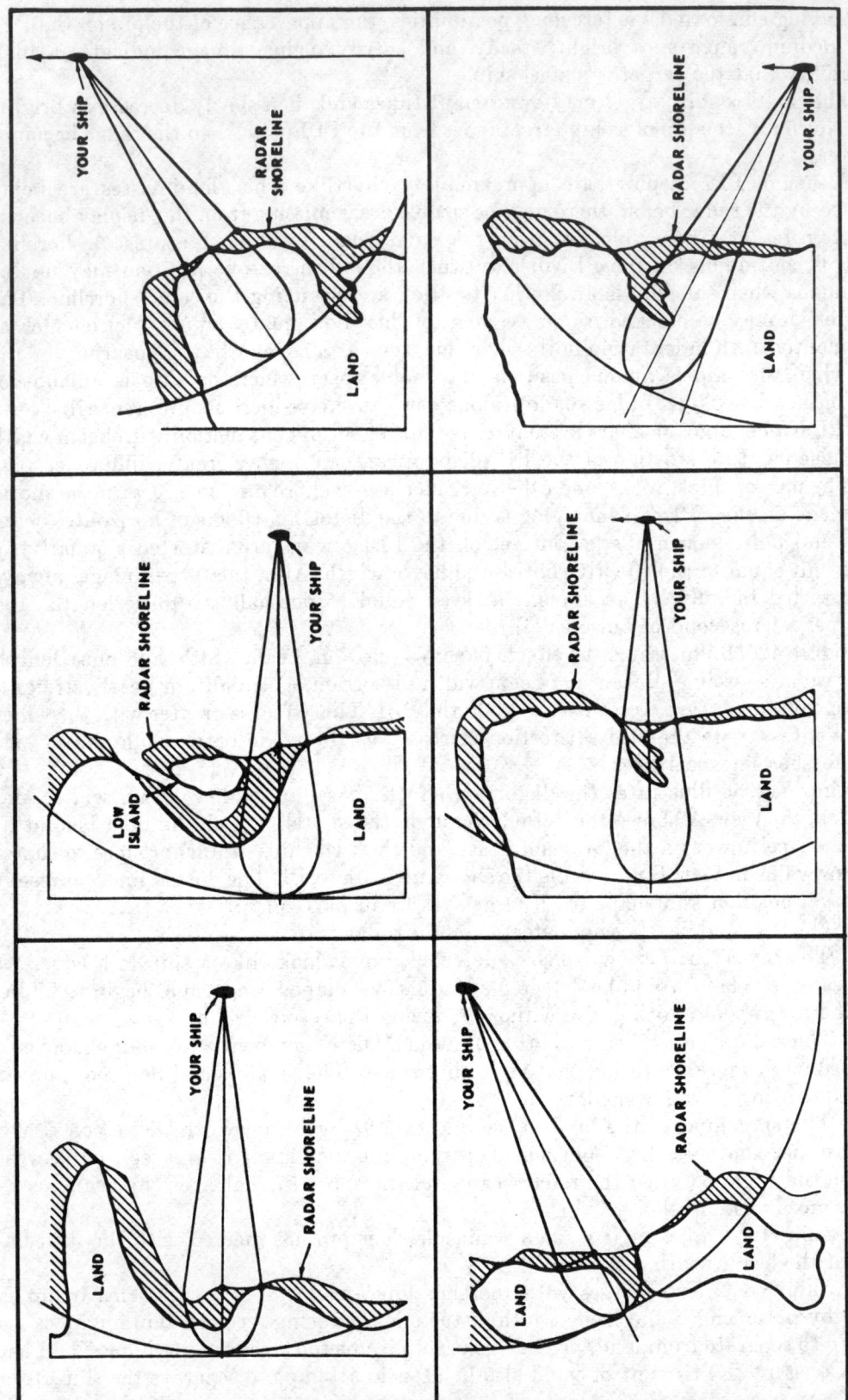

FIGURE 4205b.—Effects of ship's position, beam width, and pulse length on radar shoreline.

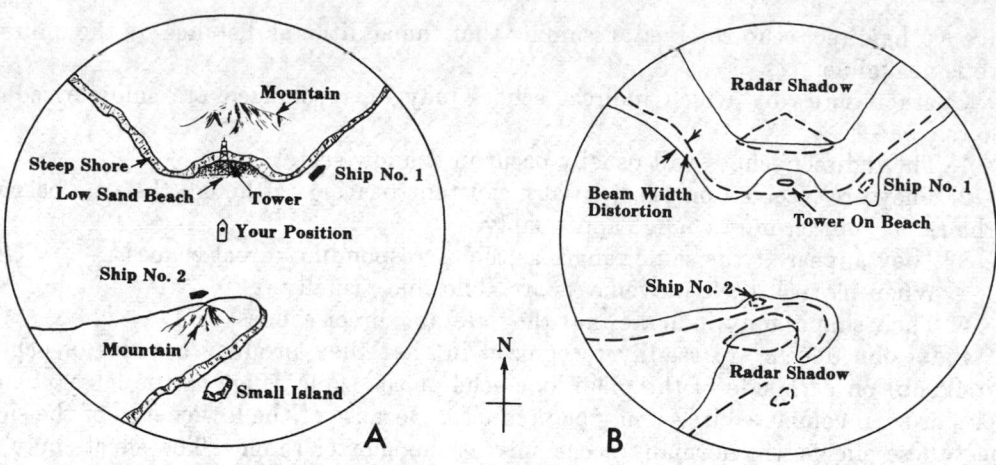

FIGURE 4205c.—Distortion effects of radar shadow, beam width, and pulse length.

4206. Recognition of unwanted echoes.—The navigator must be able to recognize various abnormal echoes and effects on the radarscope so as not to be confused by their presence.

Indirect or **false echoes** are caused by reflection of the main lobe of the radar beam off ship's structures such as stacks and kingposts. When such reflection does occur, the echo will return from a legitimate radar contact to the antenna by the same indirect path. Consequently, the echo will appear on the PPI at the bearing of the reflecting surface. As shown in figure 4206a, the indirect echo will appear on the PPI at the same

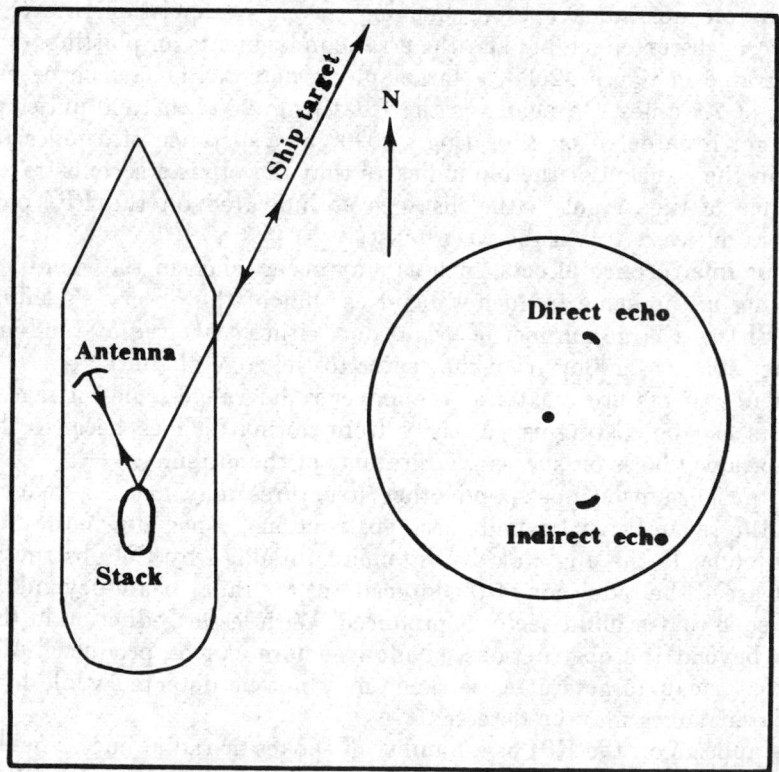

FIGURE 4206a.—Indirect echo.

range as the direct echo received, assuming that the additional distance by the indirect path is negligible.

Characteristics by which indirect echoes may be recognized are summarized as follows:

1. The indirect echoes will usually occur in shadow sectors.

2. They are received on substantially constant bearings although the true bearing of the radar contact may change appreciably.

3. They appear at the same ranges as the corresponding direct echoes.

4. When plotted, their movements are abnormal, usually.

5. Their shapes may indicate that they are not direct echoes.

Side-lobe effects are readily recognized in that they produce a series of echoes (fig. 4206b) on each side of the main lobe echo at the same range as the latter. Semi-circles or even complete circles may be produced. Because of the low energy of the side-lobes, these effects will normally occur only at the shorter ranges. The effects may be minimized or eliminated through use of the gain and anti-clutter controls. Slotted wave guide antennas have largely eliminated the side-lobe problem.

Multiple echoes may occur when a strong echo is received from another ship at close range. A second or third or more echoes may be observed on the radarscope at double, triple, or other multiples of the actual range of the radar contact (fig. 4206c).

Second-trace echoes (**multiple-trace echoes**) are echoes received from a contact at an actual range greater than the radar range setting. If an echo from a distant target is received after the following pulse has been transmitted, the echo will appear on the radarscope at the correct bearing but not at the true range. Second-trace echoes are unusual except under abnormal atmospheric conditions, or conditions under which super-refraction is present. Second-trace echoes may be recognized through changes in their positions on the radarscope on changing the pulse repetition rate (PRR); their hazy, streaky, or distorted shape; and the erratic movements on plotting.

As illustrated in figure 4206d, a target pip is detected on a true bearing of 090° at a distance of 7.5 miles. On changing the PRR from 2000 to 1800 pulses per second, the same target is detected on a bearing of 090° at a distance of 3 miles (fig. 4206e). The change in the position of the pip indicates that the pip is a second-trace echo. The actual distance of the target is the distance as indicated on the PPI plus half the distance the radar wave travels between pulses.

Electronic interference effects, such as may occur when in the vicinity of another radar operating in the same frequency band as that of the observer's ship, is usually seen on the PPI as a large number of bright dots either scattered at random or in the form of dotted lines extending from the center to the edge of the PPI.

Interference effects are greater at the longer radar range scale settings. The interference effects can be distinguished easily from normal echoes because they do not appear in the same places on successive rotations of the antenna.

Stacks, masts, samson posts, and other structures may cause a reduction in the intensity of the radar beam beyond these obstructions, especially if they are close to the radar antenna. If the angle at the antenna subtended by the obstruction is more than a few degrees, the reduction of the intensity of the radar beam beyond the obstruction may be such that a **blind sector** is produced. With lesser reduction in the intensity of the beam beyond the obstructions, **shadow sectors** can be produced. Within these shadow sectors, small targets at close range may not be detected while larger targets at much greater ranges may be detected.

Spoking appears on the PPI as a number of spokes or radial lines. Spoking is easily distinguished from interference effects because the lines are straight on all range-scale settings and are lines rather than a series of dots.

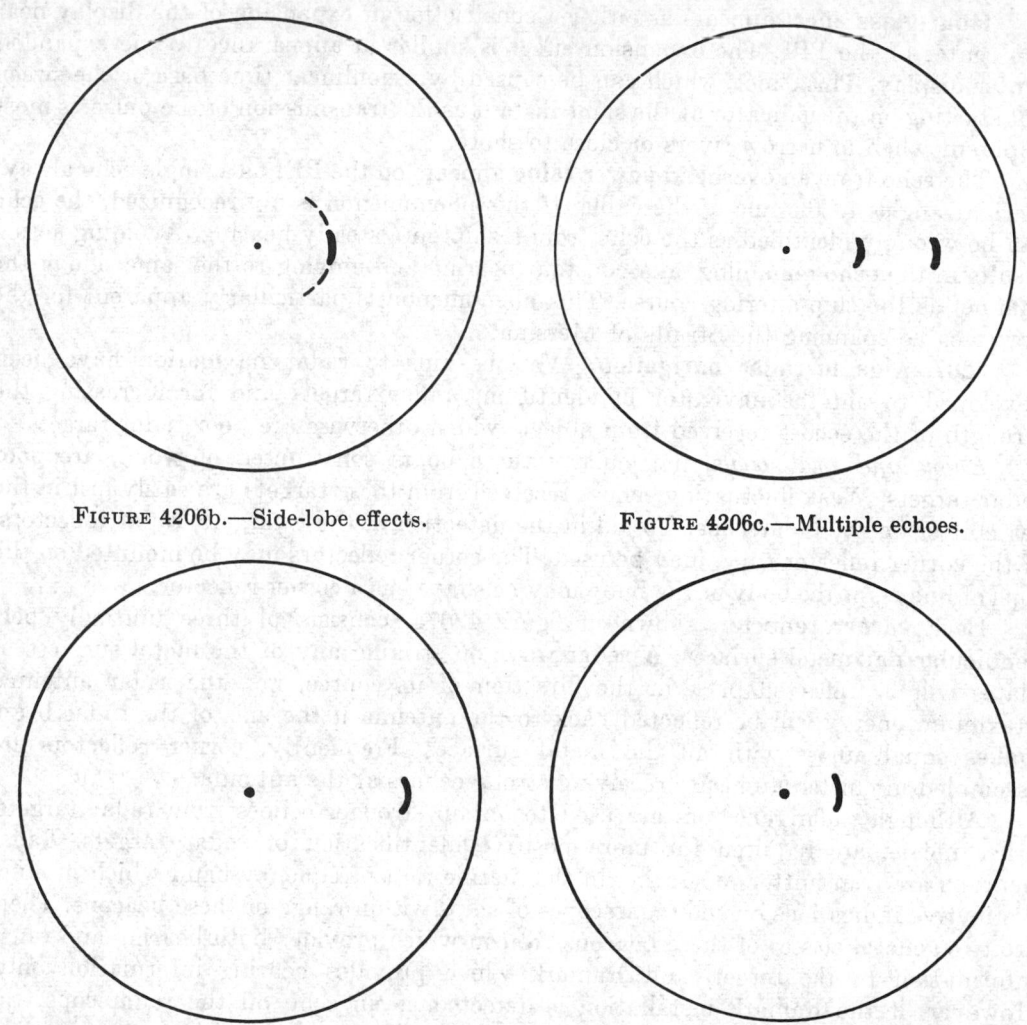

FIGURE 4206b.—Side-lobe effects.

FIGURE 4206c.—Multiple echoes.

FIGURE 4206d.—Second-trace echo on 12-mile range scale.

FIGURE 4206e.—Position of second-trace echo on 12-mile range scale after changing PRR.

The spokes may appear all around the PPI, or they may be confined to a sector. Should the spoking be confined to a narrow sector, the effect can be distinguished from a Ramark signal (art. 4207) of similar appearance through observation of the steady relative bearing of the spoke in a situation where the bearing of the Ramark signal should change.

The appearance of spoking is indicative of need for equipment maintenance.

The PPI display may appear as alternately normal and dark sectors. This **sectoring** phenomenon is usually due to the automatic frequency control being out of adjustment.

The appearance of **serrated range rings** is indicative of need for equipment maintenance.

After the radar set has been turned on, the display may not spread immediately to the whole of the PPI because of static electricity inside the CRT. Usually, the **static electricity effect,** which produces a distorted PPI display, lasts no longer than a few minutes.

Hour-glass effect appears as either a constriction or expansion of the display near the center of the PPI. The expansion effect is similar in appearance to the expanded center display. This effect, which can be caused by a nonlinear time base or the sweep not starting on the indicator at the same instant as the transmission of the pulse, is most apparent when in narrow rivers or close to shore.

The echo from an **overhead power cable** appears on the PPI as a single echo always at right angles to the line of the cable. If this phenomenon is not recognized, the echo can be wrongly identified as the echo from a ship on a steady bearing. Avoiding action results in the echo remaining on a constant bearing and moving to the same side of the channel as the ship altering course. This phenomenon is particularly apparent for the power cable spanning the Straits of Messina.

4207. Aids to radar navigation.—Various aids to radar navigation have been developed to aid the navigator in identifying radar targets and for increasing the strength of the echoes received from objects which otherwise are poor radar targets.

Buoys and small boats, particularly those boats constructed of wood, are poor radar targets. Weak fluctuating echoes received from these targets are easily lost in the sea clutter on the radarscope. To aid in the detection of these targets, radar reflectors, of the corner reflector type, may be used. The corner reflectors may be mounted on the tops of buoys, or the body of the buoy may be shaped as a corner reflector.

Each **corner reflector,** shown in figure 4207a, consists of three mutually perpendicular flat metal surfaces. A radar wave on striking any of the metal surfaces or plates will be reflected back in the direction of its source, i.e., the radar antenna. Maximum energy will be reflected back to the antenna if the axis of the radar beam makes equal angles with all the metal surfaces. Frequently, corner reflectors are assembled in clusters to insure receiving strong echoes at the antenna.

Although radar reflectors are used to obtain stronger echoes from radar targets, other means are required for more positive identification of radar targets. **Radar beacons** are transmitters operating in the marine radar frequency band which produce distinctive indications on the radarscopes of ships within range of these beacons. There are two general classes of these beacons: Racon which provides both bearing and range information to the target, and Ramark which provides bearing information only. However, if the Ramark installation is detected as an echo on the radarscope, the range will be available also.

Racon is a radar transponder which emits a characteristic signal when triggered by a ship's radar. The signal may be emitted on the same frequency as that of the triggering radar, in which case it is superimposed on the ship's radar display automatically. The signal may be emitted on a separate frequency, in which case to receive the signal the ship's radar receiver must be capable of being tuned to the beacon frequency or a special receiver must be used. In either case, the PPI will be blank except

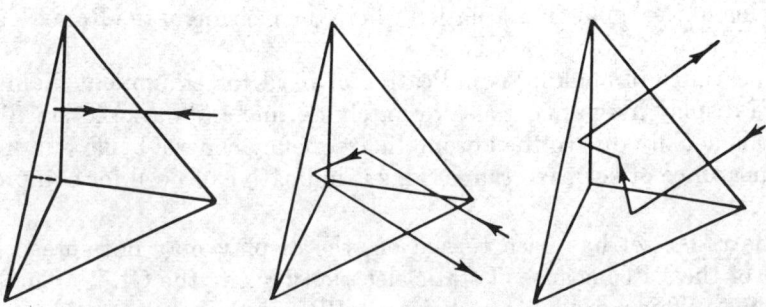

FIGURE 4207a.—Corner reflectors.

for the beacon signal. However, the only Racons in service are "in band" beacons which transmit in one of the marine radar bands, usually only the 3-centimeter band.

The Racon signal appears on the PPI as a radial line originating at a point just beyond the position of the radar beacon or as a Morse code signal (fig. 4207b) displayed radially from just beyond the beacon.

Ramark is a radar beacon which transmits either continuously or at intervals. The latter method of transmission is used so that the PPI can be inspected without any clutter introduced by the Ramark signal on the scope. The Ramark signal as it appears on the PPI is a radial line from the center. The radial line may be a continuous narrow line, a broken line (fig. 4207c), a series of dots, or a series of dots and dashes.

4208. Radar navigation.—Radar provides a means of establishing position, or keeping a vessel in safe water during periods of reduced visibility, or at considerable distance from shore, when other methods may not be available. Since both range and bearing can be obtained, a single identifiable object is needed. However, if a visual bearing is available, it should be more reliable than one obtained by radar. Since radar range is usually more accurate than radar bearing, a fix by two or more ranges is generally preferable to one obtained by two bearings or by range and bearing. However, accurate range requires reliable identification of the part of the target returning the echo. This is not always apparent when natural objects are used.

In addition to the usual methods of piloting, radar is adapted to several methods of somewhat limited application. If a single prominent target is available in an operating area, a series of concentric circles and radial lines can be drawn on the chart and suitably labeled. If bearing and distance are measured frequently, an almost continuous fix can be obtained by spotting in the positions by eye. If a polar plot is made on a piece of transparent material to the same scale as the chart, the ranges and bearings of a number of points can be plotted in quick succession, and the transparent material fitted to the chart by trial and error. The center of the plot is then the position of the radar.

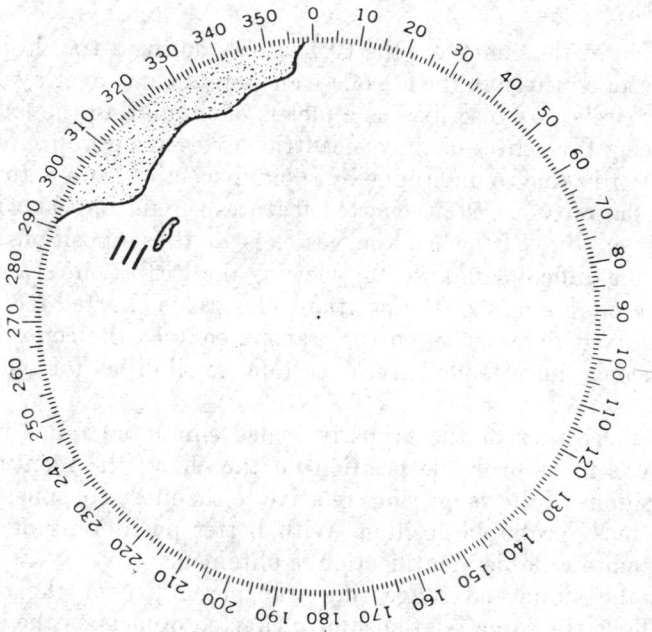

FIGURE 4207b.—Coded Racon signal.

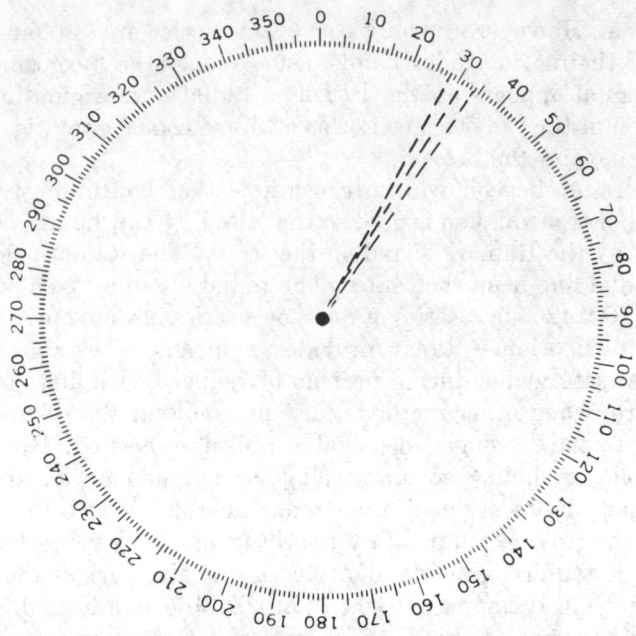

FIGURE 4207c.—Ramark signal appearing as a broken radial line.

In that the navigator of a radar-equipped vessel always must be prepared to use radar as his primary means of navigation in pilot waters, during the planning for a transit of these waters it behooves him to study the navigational situation with respect to any special techniques which can be employed to enhance the use of radar. The effectiveness of such techniques usually is dependent upon adequate preparation for their use, including special constructions on the chart or the preparation of transparent chart overlays.

The correlation of the chart and the PPI display during a transit of confined waters frequently can be aided through the use of a transparent chart overlay on which properly scaled concentric circles are inscribed as a means of simulating the fixed range rings on the PPI. By placing the center of the concentric circles at appropriate positions on the chart, the navigator is able to determine by rapid inspection, and with close approximation, just where the pips of certain charted features should appear with respect to the fixed range rings on the PPI when the vessel is at those positions. This technique compensates for the difficulty imposed by viewing the PPI at one scale and the chart at another scale. Through study of the positions of various charted features with respect to the simulated fixed range rings on the transparency as the center of the simulated rings is moved along the intended track, certain possibilities for unique observations may be revealed.

By placing the center of the properly scaled simulated range ring transparency over the observer's most probable position on the chart, the identification of echoes is aided. The positions of the range rings relative to the more conspicuous objects aid in establishing the most probable position. With better positioning of the center of the simulated rings, more reliable identification is obtained.

By placing the simulated range ring transparency over the chart so that the simulated rings have the same relationship to charted objects as the actual range rings have to the corresponding echoes, the observer's position is found at the center of the simulated range rings. Under some conditions, there may not be enough suitable objects and corresponding echoes to correlate with the range rings to obtain the desired accuracy.

This method of fixing should be particularly useful aboard small craft with limited navigational personnel, equipment, and plotting facilities. It should serve to overcome difficulties associated with unstabilized displays and lack of a variable range marker.

Preferably, radar fixes obtained through measuring the range and bearing to a single object should be limited to small, isolated fixed objects which can be identified with reasonable certainty. In many situations, this may be the only reliable method which can be employed. If possible, the fix should be based upon a radar range and visual gyro bearing because radar bearings are less accurate than visual gyro bearings. A primary advantage of the method is the rapidity with which a fix can be obtained. A disadvantage is that the fix is based upon only two intersecting lines of position, a bearing line and a range arc, obtained from observations of the same object. Identification mistakes can lead to disaster. *If the fix is based upon a floating aid, it should be treated with considerable caution.*

Generally, fixes obtained from radar bearings are less accurate than those obtained from intersecting range arcs. The accuracy of fixing by this method is greater when the center bearings of small, isolated, radar-conspicuous objects can be observed. The rapidity of the method affords a means for initially determining an approximate position for subsequent use in more reliable identification of objects for fixing by means of two or more ranges.

Fixing by tangent bearings is one of the least accurate methods. The use of tangent bearings with a range measurement can provide a fix of reasonably good accuracy. As illustrated in figure 4208a, the tangent bearing lines intersect at a range from the sland observed less than the range as measured because of beam width distortion. Right tangent bearings should be decreased by an estimate of half the horizontal beam width. Left tangent bearings should be increased by the same amount. The fix is taken as that point on the range arc midway between the bearing lines.

It is frequently quite difficult to correlate the left and right extremities of the island as charted with the island image on the PPI. Therefore, even with compensation for half of the beam width, the bearing lines usually will not intersect at the range arc.

In many situations, the more accurate radar fixes are determined from nearly simultaneous measurements of the ranges to two or more fixed objects. Preferably, at least three ranges should be used for the fix. The number of ranges which it is feasible to use in a particular situation is dependent upon the time required for identification and range measurements. In many situations, the use of more than three range arcs for the fix may introduce excessive time lag.

If the most rapidly changing range is measured first, the plot will indicate less progress along the intended track than if it were measured last. Thus, less lag in the radar plot from the vessel's actual position is obtained through measuring the most rapidly changing range last.

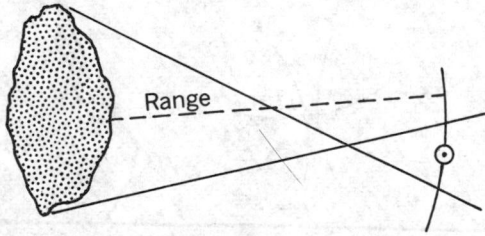

FIGURE 4208a.—Fixing by tangent bearings and radar range.

Similar to a visual cross-bearing fix, the accuracy of the radar fix is dependent upon the angles of cut of the intersecting lines of position (range arcs). For greater accuracy, the objects selected should provide range arcs with angles of cut as close to 90° as is possible. In cases where two identifiable objects lie in opposite or nearly opposite directions, their range arcs, even though they may intersect at a small angle of cut or may not actually intersect, in combination with another range arc intersecting them at an angle approaching 90°, may provide a fix of high accuracy (fig. 4208b). The near tangency of the two range arcs indicates accurate measurements and good reliability of the fix with respect to the distance off the land to port and starboard.

Small, isolated, radar-conspicuous fixed objects afford the most reliable and accurate means for radar fixing when they are so situated that their associated range arcs intersect at angles approaching 90°.

Figure 4208c shows a fix obtained by measuring the ranges to three radar-conspicuous objects well situated. The fix is based solely upon range measurements because radar ranges are more accurate than radar bearings even when small objects are observed. Note that in this rather ideal situation, a point fix was not obtained. Due to inherent radar errors, any point fix should be treated as an accident dependent upon plotting errors, the scale of the chart, etc.

Although observed radar bearings were not used in establishing the fix as such, the bearings were useful in the identification of the radar-conspicuous objects.

As the ship travels along its track, the three radar-conspicuous objects still afford good fixing capability until such time as the angles of cut of the range arcs have degraded appreciably. At such time, other radar-conspicuous objects should be selected to provide better angles of cut. Preferably, the first new object should be selected and observed before the angles of cut have degraded appreciably. Incorporating the range arc of the new object with range arcs of objects which have provided reliable fixes affords more positive identification of the new object.

While fixing by means of intersecting range arcs, the usual case is that two or more small, isolated, and conspicuous objects, which are well situated to provide good angles of cut, are not available. The navigator must exercise considerable skill in

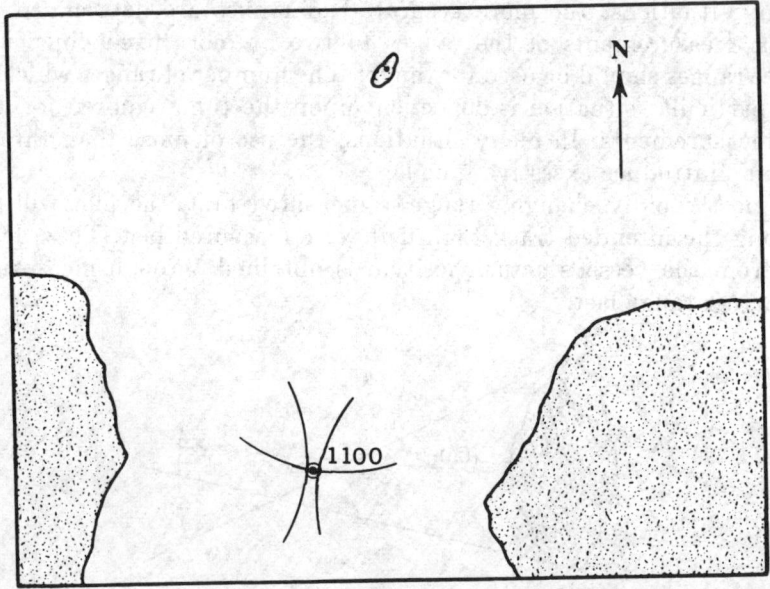

FIGURE 4208b.—Fixing by range arcs.

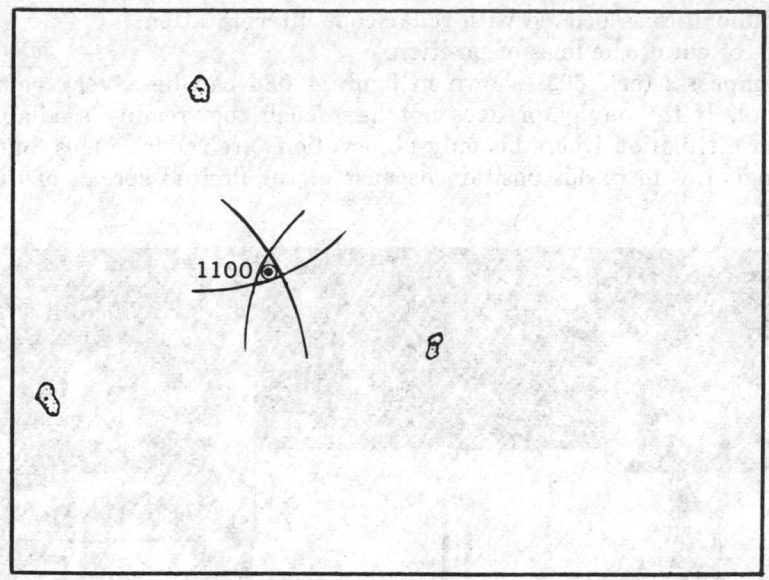

FIGURE 4208c.—Fix by small, isolated radar-conspicuous objects.

radarscope interpretation to estimate which charted features are actually displayed. If initially there are no well defined features displayed and there is considerable uncertainty as to the vessel's position, the navigator may observe the radar bearings of features tentatively identified as a step towards their more positive identification. If the cross-bearing fix does indicate that the features have been identified with some degree of accuracy, the estimate of the vessel's position obtained from the cross-bearing fix can be used as an aid in subsequent interpretation of the radar display. With better knowledge of the ship's position, the factors affecting the distortion of the radar display can be used more intelligently in the course of more accurate interpretation of the radar display.

Frequently there is at least one object available which, if correctly identified, can enable fixing by the range and bearing of a single object method. A fix so obtained can be used as an aid in radarscope interpretation for fixing by two or more intersecting range arcs.

The difficulties which may be encountered in radarscope interpretation during a transit may be so great that accurate fixing by means of range arcs is not obtainable. In such circumstances, range arcs having some degree of accuracy can be used to aid in the identification of objects used with the range and bearing method.

With correct identification of the object observed, the accuracy of the fix obtained by the range and bearing to single object method usually can be improved through the use of a visual gyro bearing instead of the radar bearing. Particularly during periods of low visibility, the navigator should be alert for visual bearings of opportunity.

Although the best method or combination of methods for a particular situation must be left to the good judgment of the experienced navigator, factors affecting method selection include:

1. The general need for redundancy—but not to such extent that too much is attempted with too little aid or means in too little time.

2. The characteristics of the radar set.

3. Individual skills.

4. The navigational situation, including the shipping situation.

5. The difficulties associated with radarscope interpretation.

6. Angles of cut of the lines of position.

Beam compasses (art. 602) shown in figure 4208d can be a very valuable radar navigation tool. If the navigator does not have such tool readily available, he may find himself in a situation where his only observations are radar ranges, but he cannot strike the range arcs to fix his position because of the limited spread of the points of his compasses.

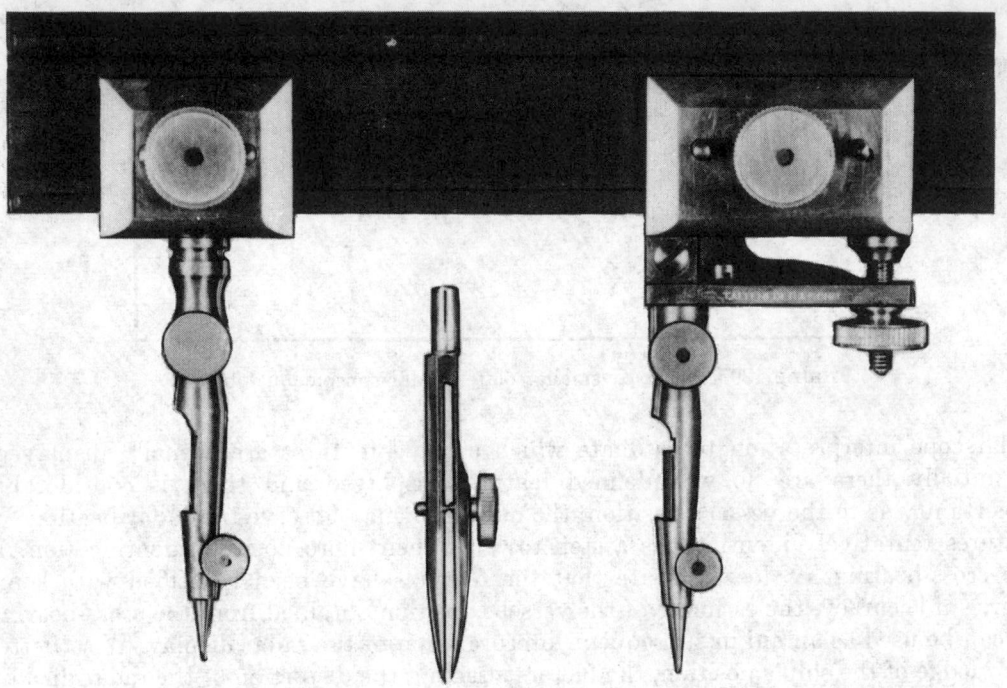

FIGURE 4208d.—Beam compasses.

CHAPTER XLIII

RADIONAVIGATION SYSTEMS

General

4301. Introduction.—Radionavigation systems are characterized with respect to their transmissions by the radiofrequency of the carrier wave, the power, and the signal type. These systems are also characterized by how the signals are analyzed upon reception, the nature of the lines of position they supply, their range or area of coverage, their availability to the user, their passivity, and their accuracy.

As discussed in article 4014, the frequency and power of the radio wave transmission are among the factors determining the effective range of a system. However, very low frequency (VLF) signals travel very long distances with relatively small amounts of power radiated. Although low frequency (LF) transmissions generally show greater attenuation with distance than VLF signals, the 100 kHz Loran-C (art. 4329) transmissions in particular, provide reliable groundwave reception at distances of about 800 to 1,200 nautical miles. The Decca Navigator System (art. 4344), also operating in the LF band at 70 to 130 kHz but at considerably less power than Loran-C, provides reliable groundwave reception at distances of more than 400 nautical miles during daylight under good reception conditions. At night this reception may be reduced significantly by skywave contamination of the groundwave. The very high frequency (VHF) transmission, as from navigational satellites (ch. XLIV); and the super high frequency (SHF) transmissions, as from navigational radar (ch. XLII), are limited to the line-of-sight.

The signal type affects how signals are analyzed upon reception. In general, the receivers of pulse modulated systems determine time intervals; the receivers of continuous wave (CW) systems compare phases. From the point of view of reception, these systems are designated as **time difference measuring systems** and **phase comparison systems.** This distinction is made despite the fact that both systems detect time intervals. The phase comparison consists in fact in determining the time shift of one wave with respect to another, taking as a unit of time the inverse of the frequency.

Using Loran–C as a specific example, however, the pulse type signal is processed in the receiver by both time difference and phase comparison methods.

The difference in the ranges of reliable reception of Loran–C and Decca signals is also due to the pulse modulation of the Loran–C signal. Multiple pulse formats raise the average power and thus increase the range. Other advantages to be derived from pulse modulation include:

1. freedom from lane ambiguities,

2. means to discriminate between groundwaves and skywaves,

3. suitable coding techniques can be used for groundwave and skywave discrimination even if the skywave of an earlier pulse coincides with the groundwave of a later pulse, and

4. the envelope of the pulse permits identification of a specific carrier wave cycle of a coherent radiofrequency signal for phase measurement purposes.

The use of continuous wave transmissions for wide area coverage from a single complex of stations results in two serious problems: (1) ambiguities in position determination, and (2) difficulties in discriminating against skywave contamination. Also, where high accuracy coverage of long coastlines and vast ocean areas is required, and where relatively few suitable sites for transmitting stations are available, continuous wave systems are generally unsatisfactory because of the limitations of the maximum permissible baseline lengths of the high accuracy continuous wave systems.

According to the nature of the lines of position provided, radionavigation systems may be described as **hyperbolic, ranging, azimuthal,** or **composite.**

Radionavigation systems may be described as **short range** if their positioning capability is limited to coastal regions, or the maximum useful range is limited to making landfall. Examples are radar and the radio direction finder. The systems may be described as **medium range** if their positioning is generally limited to ranges permitting reliable positioning for about 1 day prior to making landfall; Decca is an example.

Those radionavigation systems providing positioning capability on the high seas in areas well beyond the positioning capability of the medium range systems are described as **long range systems.** Examples of these systems are Loran-C and Omega. When the latter system is fully implemented, it may be described as a **worldwide** or **global system.** The Navy Navigation Satellite System is an example of the worldwide or global system. The worldwide or global system provides positioning capability wherever the observer may be located on navigable waters.

The maximum range of a radionavigation system depends upon the frequency, transmitter power, signal-to-noise ratio in the service area, receiver sensitivity, and losses over the signal path. The signal-to-noise ratio, often expressed in decibels (app. D), is a more realistic indicator of range capability than the field intensity of the groundwave.

Radionavigation systems may also be classified with respect to availability. Loran-C may be described as a **continuous system** because the user within the effective range of the system can use it at any time to determine his position. Omega signals as transmitted in the 10-second commutation pattern (tab. 4312) may be considered as continuously available. Therefore, for practical purposes positioning can be effected continuously. When using the Navy Navigation Satellite System (ch. XLIV) near the equator, the time between fixes may be well in excess of 1 hour because one of the satellites in near polar orbit is not available for observations. Therefore, the Navy Navigation Satellite is an example of a system that is *not* continuous.

Those systems whose operation does not require the user to transmit signals and can be used simultaneously by an unlimited number of users are described as *non-saturable.* **Saturable** systems are limited to a single user or a limited number of users on a time-shared basis.

Systems whose operation does not require the user to transmit a signal may be described as **passive.**

Due to varying accuracy requirements among users, accuracy (app. **Q**) classifications, such as high, medium, and low, have limited value. In this chapter Loran-C is described as a system of high accuracy when the groundwave is used; except for differential Omega (art. 4321), Omega is described as a system of medium accuracy; Consol is described as a system of low accuracy.

4302. Distance-difference measurement.—If synchronized signals from two stations are transmitted, the *difference* in distance from the stations can be measured, either by means of the elapsed time interval between the arrival of the two signals, or by measurement of the phase difference between the signals.

Refer to figure 4302. Let M and S be two stations. Synchronization is achieved by letting the signals of M, the **master,** control those of S, the **slave** or **secondary.** Circles $M1$, $M2$, $M3$, etc., are units of distance from M; and circles $S1$, $S2$, $S3$, etc., are units of

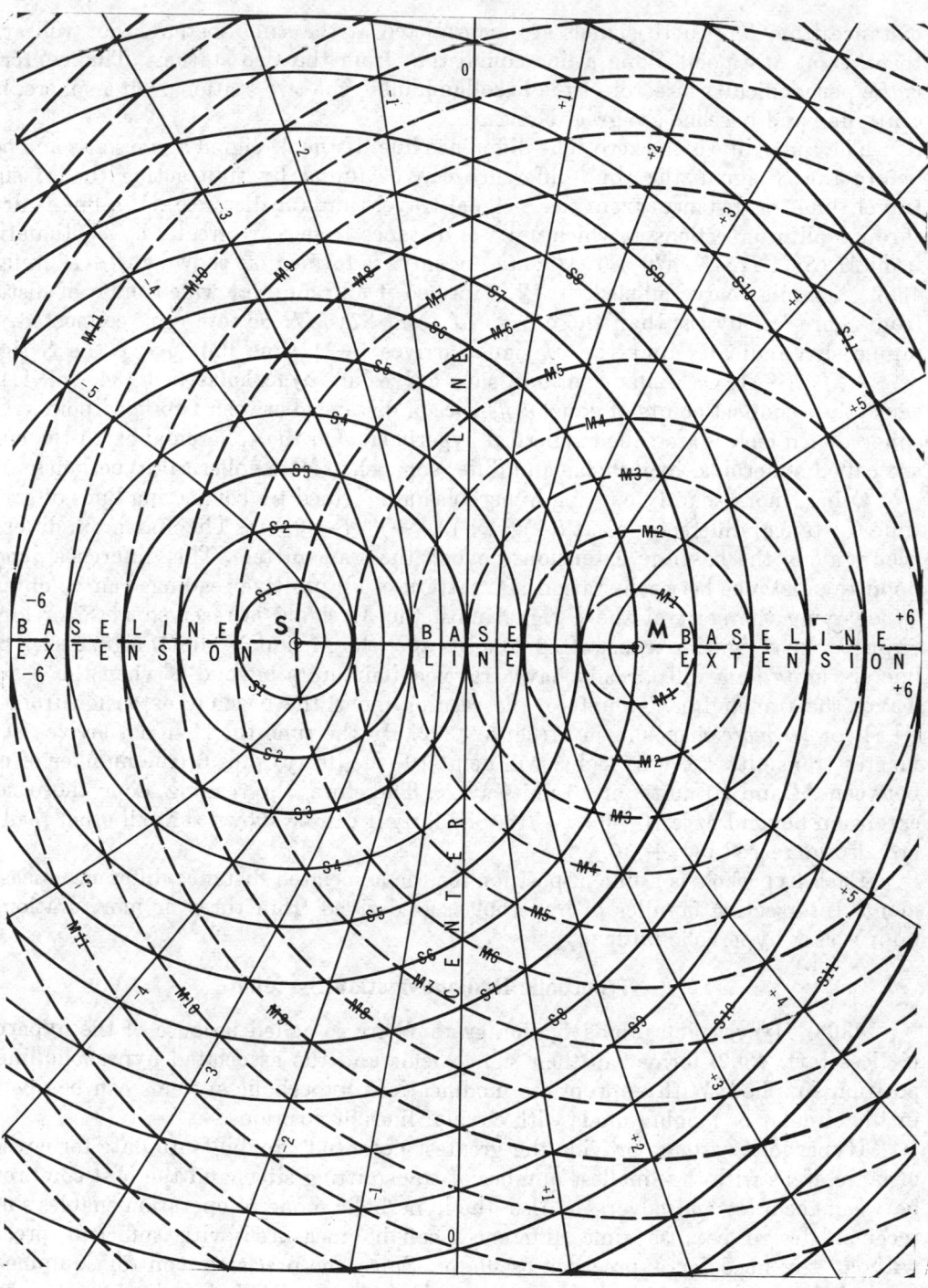

FIGURE 4302.—Hyperbolic lattice.

distance from S. If both signals are transmitted at the same instant, they will arrive together at any point along a line equidistant from the two stations. This **centerline** is the perpendicular bisector of the **baseline** joining the two stations. On a sphere, both centerline and baseline are great circles.

The centerline is the zero time difference line. If the M signal arrives at some point before the S signal, the time difference can be found by subtracting the M signal travel time (or distance) from the S signal travel time (or distance). If a line is drawn through all intersections at which units of distance from S are greater by *one* than those from M ($S8$, $M7$; $S7$, $M6$; $S6$, $M5$; etc.), a curve is formed, as shown at "+1" in figure 4302. A similar curve labeled "−1" is formed if all points at which units of distance from S are *less* by *one* than those from M ($M8$, $S7$; $M7$, $S6$; etc.) are connected. The minus sign indicates that the M signal arrives (−)1 time unit *before* the S signal, or $S-M=(-)1$. On a plane surface, such curves are **hyperbolas** (art 134, vol. II) because they connect points of equal *difference* of distance between two fixed points. On a sphere, such curves are called **spherical hyperbolas.** On the spheroidal earth the curves are called **spheroidal hyperbolas** and differ somewhat from spherical hyperbolas.

Other, more sharply curving hyperbolas are formed by connecting lines of greater time (distance) difference, as at (+)2, (−)2, (+)3, (−)3, etc. The maximum difference occurs along the **baseline extensions** beyond the transmitters. This difference depends upon the distance between stations. A pattern of all positive readings can be obtained by delaying the start of the S signal until the M signal is received at S, or longer. Suppose the S signal is transmitted 10 units *after* the M signal. The M signal for a baseline six units long will already have traveled four units beyond S when the S signal leaves the transmitter. Therefore, the reading along the baseline extension from S is (+)4, or 10 *more* than shown in figure 4302. By the time the S signal arrives at the master transmitter, the M signal will be at 10 (the delay) plus 6 (the number of units between M and S) units, or 16 units away. Therefore, the reading along the baseline extension beyond M is $10+6=(+)16$. Similarly it can be shown that all other readings are also increased by (+)10.

Each hyperbola is a line of position for the associated distance-difference measurement. Intersecting families of hyperbolas, as derived from three or more stations, is known as a hyperbolic **lattice.**

Hyperbolic Radionavigation Systems

4303. Hyperbolic radionavigation systems are so called because of the hyperbolic lattices (art. 4302) formed in their signal fields and the associated hyperbolic lines of position supplied. With appropriate modifications hyperbolic systems can be operated in the circular or ranging mode with circular lines of position.

Hyperbolic systems provide the greatest potential capability to date for coverage of large areas with the smallest number of transmitting sites, and the best compromise between accuracy and coverage. Also, the hyperbolic mode of operation enables simpler receiver design because time differences can be measured with sufficient precision without the need for a precision oscillator. Since the precision control equipment is located at the transmitting sites, user equipment can be designed to meet different requirements at reasonable cost. The systems are continuous, non-saturable, and passive (art. 4301).

The disadvantage of a hyperbolic system in needing two stations to provide a single family of hyperbolas (figure 4303) can be partly overcome by using a group or **chain** of stations that operates to form a lattice of intersecting families of hyperbolas.

The accuracy (app. Q) of the fix provided by a hyperbolic radionaviation system is dependent upon the accuracy of each line of position used to obtain the fix and the angle of cut of the lines of position. The accuracy of each line of position depends upon the following factors:

1. the precision with which the difference between the times of arrival of two signals can be measured;

2. the synchronization of the transmitting stations;

3. the accuracy of propagation predictions;

4. operational or receiver accuracy;

5. user's position relative to the transmitting stations; and

6. lattice table and charting accuracies, including the accuracies of the positions of the transmitting stations.

Since the velocity of propagation of radio energy is approximately 1 foot per nanosecond, for accuracies on the order of tens or hundreds of feet, measurements must be made to tens or hundreds of nanoseconds. If the time differences are to be converted to lines of position accurately, propagation conditions must be reliably predictable to tens or hundreds of nanoseconds. Receiver accuracy is dependent upon signal-to-noise ratio, operator skill, and instrumentation. The user's position relative to the transmitting stations governs the **gradient** or spacing between consecutive lines of position per unit time difference, as 1 microsecond. If the gradient is high a relatively small time-difference error will result in a relatively high position error. Lines are most closely spaced, giving highest accuracy, along the baseline between stations. As the distance between consecutive lines increases, the accuracy decreases, being so low along the baseline extensions that the use of this part of the lattice is normally avoided.

The undesirable divergence of the hyperbolic lines of position varies with the length of the baseline. However, each hyperbola becomes more nearly a straight line (great circle) as distance from the baseline increases. At a distance from the center of the baseline of five times the length of the baseline, the departure of the hyperbola from a great circle becomes very small. Thus, if the baseline is very short, as in Consol (art 4354), the system can be considered directional (azimuthal) beyond a distance of a few miles from the station.

The use of time-difference measurements to establish lines of position serves to minimize the effects on position accuracy of errors caused by propagation anomalies.

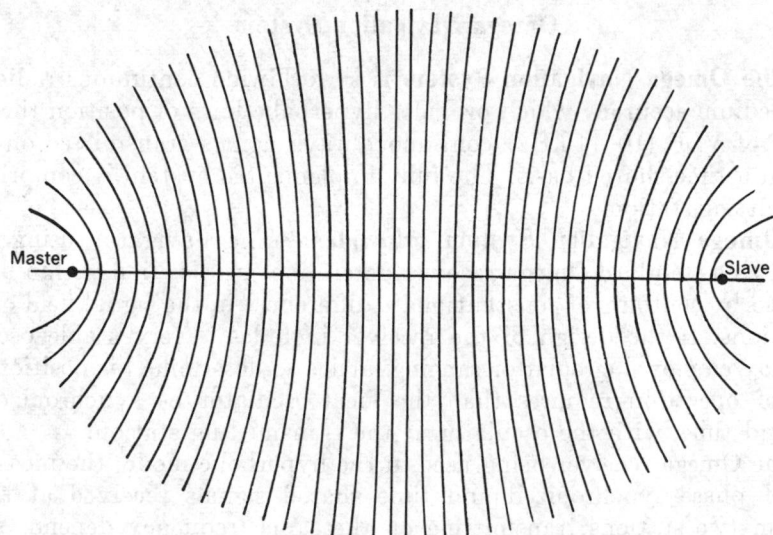

FIGURE 4303.—A family of hyperbolas. Each hyperbola is a line of position for the associated time-difference measurement.

4304. The ranging mode, often called the **Range-Range** or **Rho-Rho** mode, is that method of operation in which the times for the signals to travel from each transmitting station to the receiver are measured rather than their differences. Each time measurement (range measurement) provides a circular line of position.

The feasibility of ranging mode is dependent upon a stable frequency source, propagation predictability, and a stable time reference within the receiver. The range to a station is calculated from the difference in the known time of transmission and the measured time of arrival of the signal at the receiver. The user's time reference must be initially synchronized to the time standard at the transmitting station. Since perfect synchronization is, in general, not feasible, calibration of the user's time standard is required.

While the gradient (art. 4303) in the hyperbolic mode degrades with increasing distance from the transmitting stations, the gradient in the ranging mode is a constant equal to the propagation velocity. Therefore, the ranging mode overcomes the *geometric dilution* associated with the hyperbolic mode at extended ranges. Thus, the ranging mode can be used to increase the coverage area.

For a given service area and the associated transmitting station locations, the ranging mode may provide better system geometry, i.e. better angles of cut of the intersecting circles forming the lattice. Greater freedom in selecting stations for better system geometry is afforded by not having to use a master station, two intersecting lines of position being obtainable from two slave (secondary) stations. The ranging mode of operation can be used to extend the coverage area since the user must be within range of only two transmitting stations. Also the coverage area is extended by overcoming the geometric dilution of the hyperbolic mode.

When three stations can be received, the ranging mode is enhanced by redundant information since only two stations are needed. This redundancy serves to increase fix accuracy. With these circular lines of position, the fix determined by the intersection of one pair will, in general, be inconsistent with a fix determined by the intersection of a second pair. Since the inconsistency will be due to errors in the system, including drift in the time standard, the third (redundant) measurement can be used to estimate the errors. If the estimate is correct the three lines of position will intersect at a common point.

Omega Navigation System

4305. The Omega Navigation System is a worldwide continuous radionavigation system of medium accuracy which provides hyperbolic lines of position through phase comparisons of VLF (10–14 kHz) continuous wave signals transmitted on a common frequency on a time shared basis. The fully implemented system is comprised of only eight transmitting stations.

4306. Omega Navigation System principles.—The navigator using what may be described as a standard Omega receiver determines his position within a hyperbolic lattice formed by contours of constant phase differences in the signal field of the transmitting stations. If the design of the receiver includes a very stable oscillator, the navigator may employ a circular or ranging lattice to determine his position. However, this mode of operation requires that the local oscillator be synchronized, both in frequency and time, with the oscillator at the transmitting station.

With the Omega receiver being used in the hyperbolic mode, the measured phase difference of phase synchronized and time shared signals received at a particular position from two stations transmitting on the same frequency depends solely upon how much farther the position is from one transmitting station than the other. The term **phase synchronized** or **phase coherent** indicates that the phases of all trans-

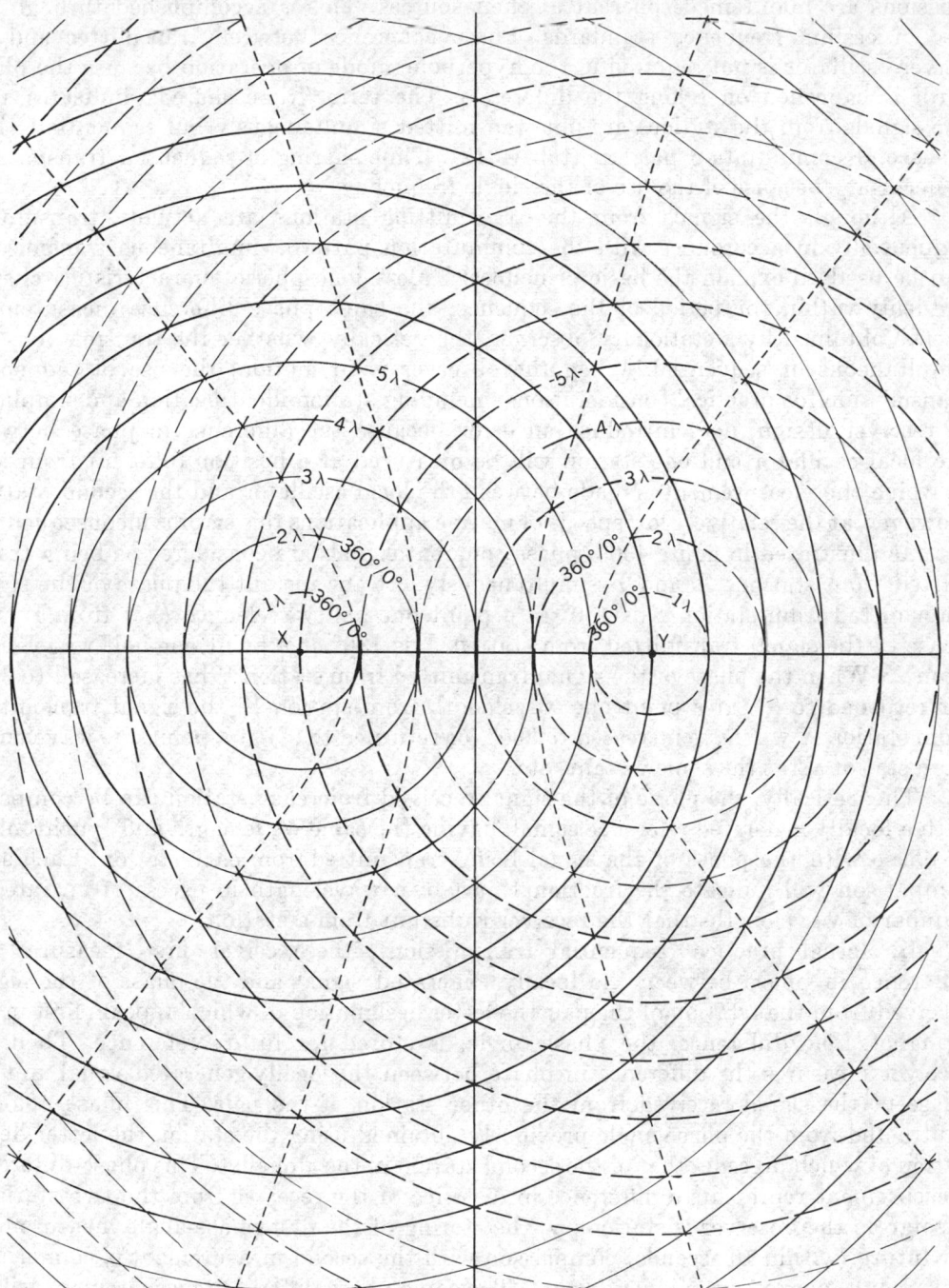

FIGURE 4306.—Phase coherent signals.

missions are maintained coherent at their sources. This is accomplished through the use of cesium frequency standards. Phase coherence between transmitter and receiver oscillator is not required in the hyperbolic mode of operation because the phase error is cancelled on taking the difference. The term "time shared" indicates that the signals from the stations are not transmitted simultaneously but sequentially in a 10-second commutation pattern (tab. 4312). Time sharing or sequential transmission is necessary because of the use of the single frequency.

Although the signals from the transmitting stations are actually transmitted sequentially in accordance with the commutation pattern, simultaneous transmission can be used to explain the basic principles. Unless ionospheric characteristics change suddenly within the period of the sequence, the same phase-difference measurement can be obtained by a stationary observer, theoretically, whether the transmissions are simultaneous or sequential. When the observer is in motion, the use of sequential transmission for practical considerations, including station identification and simplicity of receiver design, does introduce an error because the difference in phase between the local oscillator and one station will be measured at a position different from that at which the measurement is made between the local oscillator and the second station. However, at the relatively low speeds of marine applications this error is inconsequential.

As illustrated in figure 4306, phase coherent signals are considered as being transmitted from stations X and Y simultaneously. At the instant the phase of the signal transmitted from station Y is 180° at a point one-half wavelength ($\frac{1}{2}\lambda$) from Y, the phase of the signal transmitted from station X is 180° at a point one-half wavelength from X. When the phase of the signal transmitted from station Y has increased to 360° (or returned to 0°) at a point one wavelength from station Y, the signal transmitted from station X will have increased to 360° (or returned to 0°) at a point one wavelength from station X at the same instant, etc.

Theoretically, the phase of the signal received from each station can be compared with a locally generated reference signal, having the same wavelength and synchronized in phase with the phase of the signal being transmitted from each station. Each such comparison will indicate the fractional part of a wavelength in excess of an integral number of wavelengths that the receiver is distant from a station.

In actual practice (sequential transmission), the receiver first measures the difference in phase between the locally generated signal and the phase of the signal received from that station of the pair the letter designation of which appears first in the alphabet. The difference, the phase angle, is stored for future reference. Then the receiver measures the difference in phase between the locally generated signal and the phase of the signal received from the other station of the pair. This phase angle is subtracted from the phase angle previously obtained using the station the letter designation of which precedes that of the second station in the alphabet. This phase-difference measurement represents a difference in distance of the receiver from the two stations. Insofar as the observer is stationary, the storing of the first phase-angle measurement for future (within 10 seconds) comparison with the second measurement is comparable to a simultaneous transmission format. The same phase-difference measurement will be observed at all points which have the same difference in distance from the two transmitting stations. The locus of such points is a contour of constant phase (isophase contour) which is fixed on the surface of the earth with respect to the positions of the two transmitting stations.

By repeating measurements for another pair of stations, a second isophase contour or line of position is obtained. The intersection of the lines of position establishes the position of the observer.

4307. Omega lanes.—With the stations transmitting at 10.2 kHz, the wavelength is approximately 16 nautical miles. Thus, identical phase angles are repeated at 16-mile intervals. However, on the baseline between two transmitting stations a specific difference in the phase angles of the radio waves received from the two transmitting stations repeats itself every one-half wavelength or about every 8 miles.

As is obvious from inspection of figure 4307, isophase contours pass through all points which are an integral number of wavelengths distant from the two transmitting stations, X and Y. At points any integral number of wavelengths plus a half wavelength from the stations, the phase-difference is also zero. Thus, isophase contours pass through points on the baseline a half wavelength apart.

Since a representative baseline in the Omega system is about 5,000 nautical miles in length, or about 300 wavelengths at 10.2 kHz, specific phase-angle differences in the 10.2 kHz signal field are repeated about 600 times on the baseline. Hence, at 10.2 kHz there are about 600 points on the baseline at which the phase-angle differences are zero.

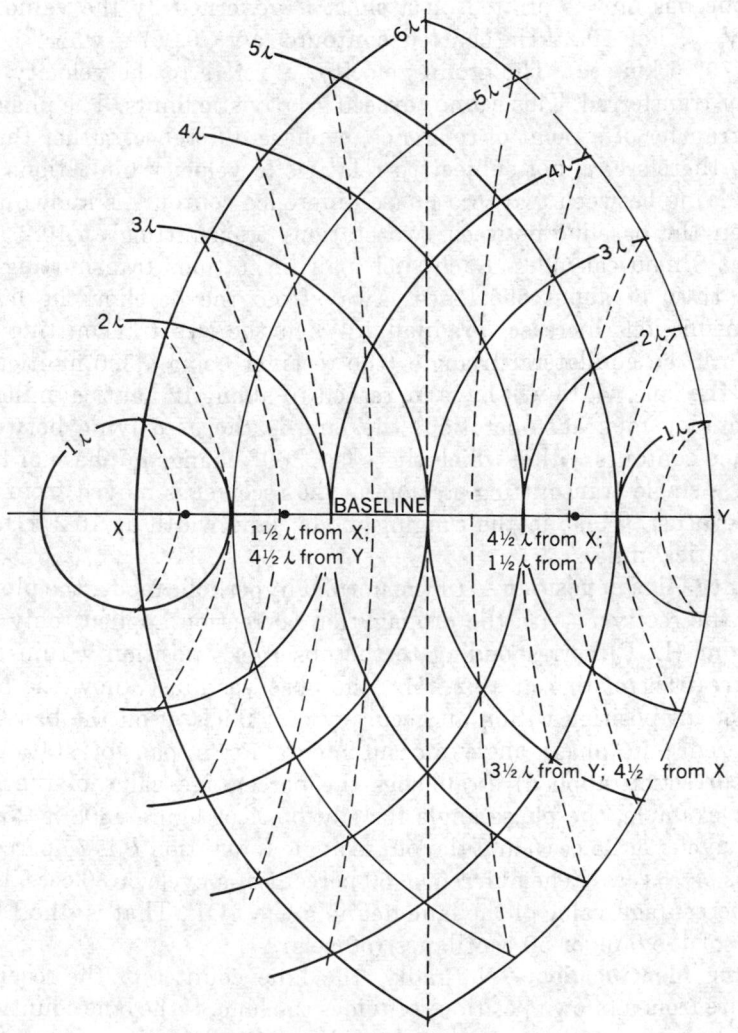

FIGURE 4307.—Isophase contours.

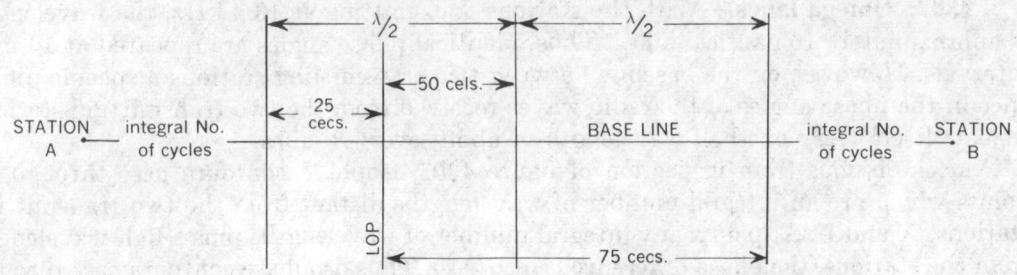

FIGURE 4308.—Omega line of position.

Contours connecting points in the signal field at which the phase-angle differences are zero are the constant phase or isophase contours plotted on Omega charts and tabulated in the Omega lattice tables. At 10.2 kHz each such contour is spaced at intervals of about 8 nautical miles on the baseline. Away from the baseline there is a small divergence of the hyperbolic contours. The exact spacing of the hyperbolic contours on the baseline as printed on a chart is governed by the value used for the phase velocity, v. For 10.2 kHz charted contours, $c/v=0.9974$, where c is the group velocity (299,792.5 km/sec). The group velocity, c, refers to the velocity at which the energy is being transferred. This cannot exceed relativistic limits. The phase velocity, v, refers to the transfer of a point of reference, a phase difference, rather than a physical quantity and, therefore, is not subject to relativistic velocity limitations.

The area lying between two zero phase-difference contours is known as an **Omega lane.** Thus, on the baseline between two stations transmitting at 10.2 kHz the lane width is about 8 nautical miles. Each such pair of stations transmitting at 10.2 kHz produces a pattern of about 600 lanes. Away from the baseline the lane width for 10.2 kHz transmissions increases gradually. When the two transmitting stations and the receiver form an equilateral triangle (the receiver being 4,300 nautical miles from the baseline), the lane width will have increased to about 12 nautical miles.

In the ranging mode of operation, the lane is the area lying between two zero phase-difference contours within which there is a 360° change in phase of the CW wave received from a single transmitting station as the receiver is moved from one isophase contour to the other. Thus, in the ranging mode, lane width at 10.2 kHz is constant at about 16 nautical miles.

4308. Omega line of position.—In the normal hyperbolic mode, the phase-difference readout from the receiver (with the propagation correction applied) only indicates the isophase contour (LOP) corresponding to the observer's position within a lane. When the stations are transmitting at 10.2 kHz, the observer must know the lane in which he is located or his position within an accuracy of 4 miles, if on the baseline.

The difference in phase angle measurements for a pair of stations (with the propagation correction applied) establishes the percentage value of the lane defining the LOP. For example, the phase angle for station A of figure 4308 is 25 percent of a cycle (25 centicycles or 25 cecs) and the phase angle for station B is 75 percent of a cycle (75 centicycles or 75 cecs). The difference, 50 percent of a cycle or 50 cecs, is numerically equal to the percentage value of the lane defining the LOP. That is, the LOP is defined by 50 percent of the lane or 50 centilanes (50 cels).

4309. Lane identification.—Normally, the lane counter of the receiver, which is set on departure from a known position, provides the lane. If the lane counting capability of the equipment is lost for any reason, such as temporary equipment failure, the navigator usually can determine the lane he is in by dead reckoning or other navigational means.

Should there be any ambiguity with respect to the lane, the multiple Omega frequencies can be used to determine the lane by obtaining fixes on two or more pairs of stations if the user has a multi-channel receiver. Any two stations can be used as a pair rather than a particular master and slave as in the Loran concept.

If one of the Omega frequencies were 3.4 kHz, the wavelength would be 48 nautical miles; the lane width on the baseline would be 24 nautical miles or three times the lane width at 10.2 kHz. The difference between the 13.6 kHz and 10.2 kHz Omega frequencies is 3.4 kHz. By observing the difference in the phase-difference readings at 10.2 kHz and 13.6 kHz, it is possible to form a *coarse lane* corresponding to a frequency of 3.4 kHz, neglecting the slight difference in propagational velocities at 10.2 kHz and 13.6 kHz. With the coarse lane so formed, the navigator now need only to know his position within an accuracy of 12 miles to identify the coarse lane without ambiguity. Since the 3.4 kHz coarse lane is formed by three 10.2 kHz *fine lanes* as shown in figure 4309, the correct fine lane can be identified by means of the equivalent of the phase-difference reading for 3.4 kHz. The equivalent phase reading is obtained by subtracting the 10.2 kHz phase reading from the 13.6 kHz phase reading and then applying a 3.4 kHz correction. *The use of this technique is dependent upon the availability of a multi-channel receiver and propagation corrections for 10.2 kHz and 3.4 kHz.* With the correct 10.2 kHz lane so identified without ambiguity, it is then possible to determine a more exact line of position within the fine lane by means of a phase reading at 10.2 kHz.

4310. Identification of coarse lane.—Since the equivalent of the 3.4 kHz coarse lane is formed by three 10.2 kHz fine lanes, the first step is to inspect the 10.2 kHz isophase contours on the chart to determine which lane numbers are multiples of three, or which numbers on the contours can be divided exactly by three. Having identified the coarse lane or lanes in which the observer might be located, the next step is to apply the equivalent of the phase-difference reading for 3.4 kHz. If the correct coarse lane has been selected, the isophase contour (LOP) as plotted within the coarse lane will lie within 12 miles of the DR position, assuming that such position is not in error by more than 12 miles. The LOP will establish in which of the three fine lanes the observer is located. If the LOP as plotted within the coarse lane does not lie within 12 miles of the DR position, an adjacent coarse lane should be selected for use in identification of the fine 10.2 kHz lane.

The lane resolution process can be extended further by using even lower difference frequencies. By taking the difference of 11.333 kHz and 10.2 kHz Omega frequencies to obtain a difference frequency of 1.133 kHz, a coarse lane having a width of 72 nautical miles on the baseline can be used.

4311. Station locations and coverage.—The Omega stations, their letter designators, and approximate locations are given in figure 4311. The Omega coverage diagram, not shown here but generally similar to the Loran–C coverage diagram (fig. 4340),

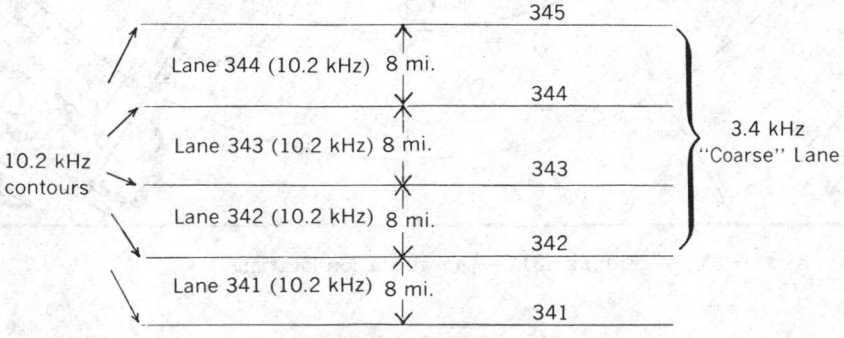

FIGURE 4309.—The coarse lane.

Letter Designation	Station Name	Approximate Location General	Latitude	Longitude
A	OMEGA Norway	Norwegian Coast at Arctic Circle	66°N	13°E
B	OMEGA Liberia	Monrovia, Liberia	6°N	11°W
C	OMEGA Hawaii	Oahu, Hawaii	21°N	158°W
D	OMEGA North Dakota	La Moure, North Dakota	46°N	98°W
E	OMEGA Reunion	La Reunion Island, France	21°S	55°E
F	OMEGA Argentina	Golfo Nuevo, Argentina	43°S	65°W
G				
H	OMEGA Japan	Tsushima, Japan	35°N	129°E

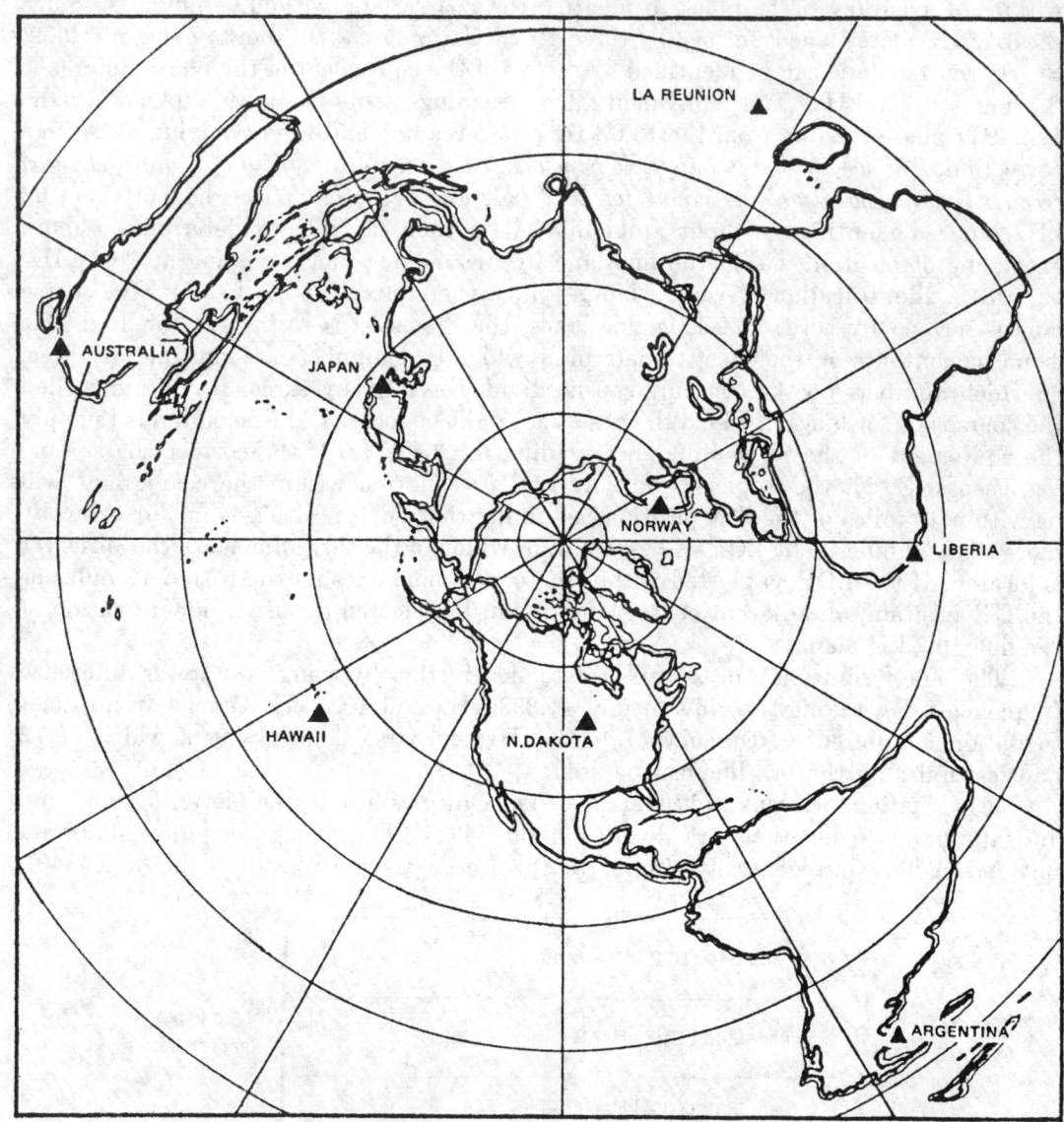

FIGURE 4311.—Omega station locations.

provides the repeatable accuracy for different regions expressed in terms of d_{rms} (arts. Q7 and Q8). The accuracy is determined using a standard deviation of 4 centilanes for each of the two lines of position making up the fix.

4312. Characteristics of the Omega transmission.—Omega is a VLF, continuous wave, time shared radionavigation system with all stations transmitting at the same frequencies. The stations always transmit in the same order, with the length of each transmission varying between 0.9, 1.0, 1.1, and 1.2 seconds from station to station. The order and lengths of the station transmissions at 10.2 kHz, in accordance with the Omega station identification code, are contained in table 4312.

Station	A	B	C	D	E	F	G	H
Length of transmission in seconds_____	0.9	1.0	1.1	1.2	1.1	0.9	1.2	1.0

TABLE 4312.—Omega commutation pattern.

4313. Signal format.—As shown in figure 4313, the order of transmission is such that when station A transmits at 10.2 kHz, stations G and H transmit at 11.33 kHz and 13.6 kHz, respectively, for the same time duration that station A transmits at 10.2 kHz. When station B transmits at 10.2 kHz, stations A and H transmit at 13.6 kHz and 11.33 kHz, respectively, for the same time duration that station B transmits at 10.2 kHz, and so on until the whole sequence of transmissions has been completed. Since there is a time interval of 0.2 second between transmissions, the entire cycle of the commutation pattern is repeated every 10 seconds. The start of one of the segments of the 10-second cycle is sufficiently close to Coordinated Universal Time (art. 1805) to permit station identification while listening to UTC.

The 0.2-second interval between transmissions rules out the possibility of over-lapping of the signals received from different stations. The 0.2-second interval between transmissions also eases the requirement for perfect alignment of the receiver commutator. A 0.1-second error in setting the commutator cycle has negligible effect.

4314. Identification of the Omega signal.—Depending upon the observer's distance from the various transmitters, the Omega signals are of differing amplitude or strength.

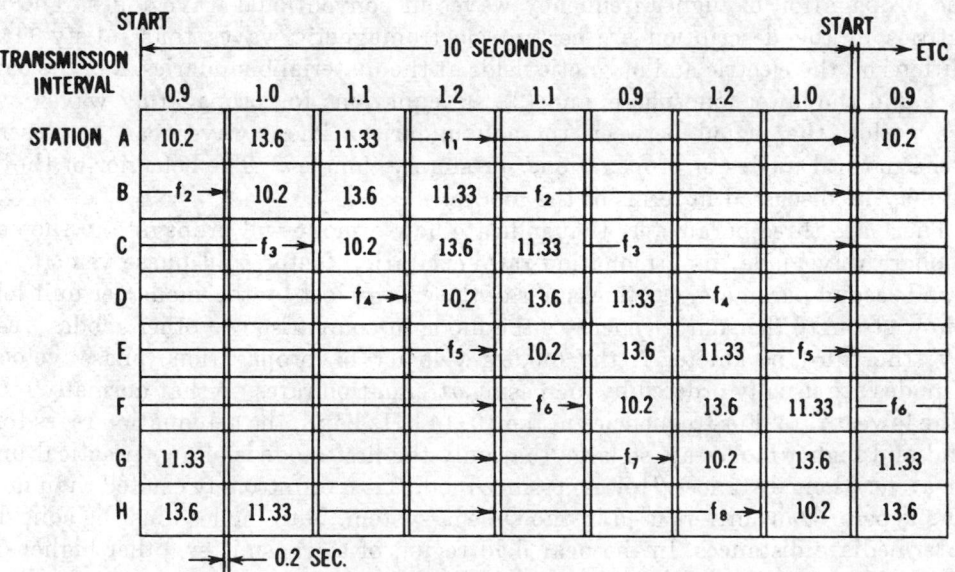

FIGURE 4313.—Signal format.

The relative strengths of the signals received and the time sequence of transmission can be used to identify the Omega signal.

By the signal strength method of identification, the various stations can be recognized either by the relative sound levels or by the heights of the signals on an oscilloscope. In identifying the stations aurally, the signals from the nearer stations will sound relatively loud, whereas the signals from the more distant stations will be relatively weak, or they may not be heard. On an oscilloscope display, the amplitudes of the signals from the nearer stations will be relatively large whereas the amplitudes of the signals from the more distant stations will be relatively small, or the signals may not be seen. It should be kept in mind, however, these methods depend upon observing or listening to the entire signal format. The transmission from any single transmitter can be distorted by propagation effects, and unless all the signals are taken into consideration, an erroneous lane count can be established. Also, "long path" signals, or signals which travel the longer of the two possible great-circle paths from the transmitter, degrade this technique.

Each of the eight transmissions during the 10-second period of transmitting the complete sequence of signals is called a *time segment*. The first transmission in the sequence is segment A, the second is segment B, etc. (the time segment designation should not be confused with the station designations). A particular station can be identified by observing the relative time of its transmissions in the segment sequence. The 13.6 kHz transmission from station B occurs during time segment C, the 13.6 kHz transmission from station C occurs during time segment D (the commutation cycle in the receiver must be synchronized so that this condition occurs). By reference to standard time transmissions (WWV, WWVH, etc.), the start of the sequence of transmissions can be determined. Through identification of the various time segments, the various stations can be identified.

Some Omega receivers are designed for automatically adjusting the receiver's internal timing circuits to agree with the Omega transmission pattern.

4315. Characteristics of Omega propagation.—The propagation of very low frequency (VLF) electromagnetic waves in the region between the lower portion of the ionosphere and the surface of the earth may be described in much the same manner as the propagation of higher frequency waves in conventional waveguides. The basic quantities in the description are certain electromagnetic waves that satisfy (1) the conditions on the electric and magnetic fields at the material boundaries, i.e., the earth's surface and the lower ionosphere; and (2) the equations for propagating waves everywhere within the region between these boundaries. These waves can be described by "the natural modes of propagation," or simply "modes." The behavior of the VLF wave may be discussed in terms of the modes.

There are three parameters that indicate how a mode will propagate in the earth-ionosphere waveguide: its attenuation rate, excitation factor, and phase velocity. The first and second parameters are measures of the energy lost by the mode per unit length and how strongly the source generates the mode in comparison to other modes, respectively; the third parameter is the mode's velocity of propagation (phase velocity). The modes are usually ordered by increasing attenuation rates, so that normally mode 1 has the lowest rate. For frequencies in the 10–14 kHz band, the attenuation rates for the second and higher modes are so large that only the first mode is of any practical importance at very long distances. However, since mode 2 is more strongly excited than mode 1 by the type of transmitters used in the Omega system, both modes must be considered at intermediate distances. In the near field region of a transmitter, other higher-order modes may have to be taken into account.

Another consideration of some importance is the fact that the modes have different phase velocities. In particular, mode 2 has a higher phase velocity than mode 1. Thus, as these modes propagate outward from the transmitter, they move in and out of phase with one another, so that the strength of the vertical electric field of the signal displays "dips" or "nulls" at several points on a radial from the transmitter. These nulls gradually disappear, however, as mode 2 attenuates, so that the strength behaves in a smooth and regular manner at long distances (where mode 1 dominates). However, within about 450 nautical miles of a transmitter the modal interference is such that the use of Omega is not generally reliable.

Since the degree of modal interference is also dependent upon factors other than proximity to the transmitter, e.g. path geomagnetic latitude and bearing, the minimum distance for reliable use is variable. For applications sensitive to spatial irregularities, such as lane resolution, separations greater than 450 miles may be required. Lesser separations may be adequate for daylight path propagation at 10.2 kHz. As a warning, the Omega LOPs depicted on charts are dashed within 450 nautical miles of a station.

Since the characteristics of the Omega signal are largely determined by the electromagnetic properties of the lower ionosphere and the surface of the earth, any change in these properties along a propagation path will generally affect the behavior of these signals. Of course, the changes will not all produce the same effect. Some will lead to small effects due to a relatively insensitive relationship between the signal characteristics and the corresponding properties. For Omega signals, one of the most important properties in this category is the effective height of the ionosphere. This height is about 90 kilometers (km) at night, but decreases quite rapidly to about 70 km soon after sunrise due to the ionization produced by solar radiation. As expected, it increases again after sunset.

The phase velocity of mode 1 is critically dependent on this height, increasing as the height decreases or vice versa. Since the phase of the Omega signal at long distances is inversely proportional to this velocity, it will readily increase or decrease in step with the effective height. In other words, the phase will be advanced or retarded as the effective height changes. One therefore expects regular diurnal changes in the phase from day to day, and studies have shown that this is indeed the case, although the exact shape and magnitude of this diurnal variation depends on several factors, including the geographic position of the receiver and transmitter and the orientation of the path relative to the boundary between the day and night hemispheres.

In general, however, if an initially all-night path is partially illuminated by the sun, starting at the transmitter, the phase will decrease, i.e. be advanced, from the night value to the nominal day value; while the opposite change will take place on an all-day path that moves into the night hemisphere starting at the transmitter. Moreover, the transition from night to day values of phase, or vice versa, will be relatively long for east-west paths, and will become shorter as the propagation path approaches a north-south orientation. Clearly, these changes will have an important effect on uncompensated LOPs. Since one wavelength is the distance covered by a wave (traveling with a given phase velocity) in one period, the LOPs constructed from the measured phase-difference will be squeezed together in going from all day to all night conditions over the propagation path, and stretched out for night to day transitions, relative to the *charted* LOPs.

Finally, while the diurnal variation in phase represents the major time-variation in the characteristics of the Omega signal at long distances, the presence of a boundary between the day and night hemispheres may produce an additional variation that arises in the following manner. In the night hemisphere, both mode 1 and mode 2 are usually present. In the day hemisphere, however, only mode 1 is usually present.

Hence, as the signal passes from the night to the day hemisphere, mode 2 will be converted into the daytime mode 1 at the day-night boundary. This resultant mode 1 may then interfere with the nighttime mode 1 that passes unchanged into the day hemisphere. Thus, some additional variation in the characteristics may be present due to such interference.

4316. Geophysical parameters.—Effects less pronounced than those associated with diurnal phase shift are produced by various geophysical parameters including:

ground conductivity. Very high attenuation is incurred with propagation over freshwater ice caps.

earth's magnetic field. Propagation towards magnetic west is attenuated more than propagation towards magnetic east.

solar activity. See Sudden Ionospheric Disturbances (art. 4317) and Polar Cap Absorption (art. 4318).

latitude. The height of the ionosphere varies with latitude, being slightly higher over the higher latitudes than over the lower latitudes during the summer.

solar zenith angle. The height of the ionosphere varies with the solar zenith angle. For example, the ionosphere is higher in the summer than in the winter of the Northern Hemisphere.

4317. Sudden Ionospheric Disturbances (SIDs) occur when there is a very sudden and large increase in X-ray flux emitted from the sun, usually during a solar flare. SIDs also occur during flares called "X-ray flares" that produce large X-ray flux, but which have no components in the visible light spectrum. The effect, which is restricted to sunlit propagation paths, causes a phase advance and is known as a **sudden phase anomaly** (SPA). The SID effects are related to the solar zenith angle, and consequently, occur mostly in lower latitude regions. Usually there is a fast advance over a period of 5 to 10 minutes followed by a recovery over a period of about 30 to 60 minutes. Significant SIDs could cause position errors of about 2 to 3 miles.

4318. The polar cap disturbance (PCD) is an ionospheric disturbance which is in no way dependent on the ice cap in the polar region. It is the result of the focusing effect the earth's magnetic field has on particles released from the sun during a solar proton event. The effect concentrates high-energy particles in the region of the magnetic pole with the result that normal VLF transmission is disrupted.

The effect on radio waves is known as **polar cap absorption** (PCA). Historically, PCDs produced large or total absorption of high frequency radio waves crossing the polar region, hence the term polor cap absorption. The amount of transmission anomaly depends on how much of the total transmission path actually crosses the region of the magnetic pole and its associated auroral zone. A transmission path which is entirely outside the Arctic region will be unaffected by the PCD. Although the occurrence of a PCD is random and unpredictable, the probability of PCD incidence increases during periods of high solar activity. The *Omega Propagation Correction Tables* make no allowance for this phenomenon which is random in occurrence, although the frequency of occurrence increases during those years of peak solar activity.

The PCDs, often called PCA events (PCAs), may persist for a week or more although a duration of only a few days is more common. HYDROLANT/HYDROPAC messages are originated by the Defense Mapping Agency Hydrographic Center if significant PCDs are detected.

The position error that will be experienced for a given LOP will depend upon the transmitting stations used and the effect of the PCD on each signal. In some cases the effect will tend to be cancelled out if the navigator is using the hyperbolic mode and has chosen station pairs whose transmission paths through the auroral zone are similar. However, no cancellation will be realized if the ranging mode is used. Using circular

LOPs in this case, the position error will depend upon the severity of the PCD and the propagation path geometry involved. Phase shifts of as much as 50 cecs for a given signal have been observed. At 10.2 kHz in the ranging mode, this would correspond to a position error of approximately 8 nautical miles.

4319. Arctic paths.—The predicted propagation corrections include allowance for propagation over regions of very poor conductivity such as Greenland and parts of Iceland. Little data are available for these areas, hence even the best estimates are uncertain. In particular, rather rapid attenuation of the signal with position occurs as one passes into the "shadow" of the Greenland ice cap.

4320. Auroral zones.—Paths which intercept the auroral zones surrounding the north and south geomagnetic poles are known to affect the phase of Omega signals. Auroral effects are believed to arise from electron precipitation in the higher regions of the ionosphere which serves as a source of ionization for the D-region of the ionosphere. Although the visual auroral zone is generally oval in shape, it is now thought that the shape of the effective region producing ionization of the D-region is circular about the geomagnetic poles. Thus, auroral effects occur in a circular band between 60° and 80° north and south geomagnetic latitude. In terms of phase velocity, the nighttime auroral variation is about four times that of the daytime variation. The actual effect on Omega signals for paths intersecting this region is a decrease in phase, i.e. a phase advance with respect to nominal values.

4321. Spatial and dispersive correlation.—Over very long transmission paths from a transmitting station to various points within a limited area, approximately the same errors will be accumulated along segments of the different paths. It follows that within this limited area, two Omega receivers will exhibit similar errors. This spatial correlation results in Omega having excellent rendezvous capability. **Differential Omega,** in which a propagation correction as accurately determined at a fixed site is broadcast to Omega users within the immediate area (radius up to about 300 nautical miles), makes use of this spatial correlation.

Over the same propagation path, fluctuations on 10.2 kHz are usually closely related to those on 13.6 kHz. This dispersive correlation generally reduces errors associated with the use of the two frequencies in lane resolution.

4322. The stability of propagation has been demonstrated by long term monitoring of Omega signals at fixed sites by the Naval Electronics Laboratory Center (NELC) and others. The monitoring verifies that the standard deviation of an LOP derived from a station pair is on the order of 4 cels. This monitoring also indicates that the phase-difference measurement is dependent upon the time of day. During the day the required propagation corrections are relatively small but undergo more variations than the required nighttime corrections; during the nighttime, the required corrections are relatively large but more nearly constant. During the daytime the actual and charted Omega lanes differ than during the night.

4323. Propagation prediction.—The practicality of the Omega Navigation System is dependent upon the fact that the radio signals in the VLF band have very good phase stability over extremely long distances. The accuracy of the system is dependent upon this inherent stability and the predictability of the phase variations along the propagation path. Long term studies indicate that the Omega signal phase, which varies diurnally in response to diurnal changes in the ionosphere, can be predicted with enough accuracy to enable positioning to within 1 to 2 nautical miles d_{rms} (app. Q).

The model for propagation predictions, based on theoretical and empirical physical principles, is revised periodically to account for changes in solar activity and other propagation anomalies. It is necessary to update the propagation correction tables about every 2 years. Through force fitting, the tabular corrections are adjusted in accordance with local prediction errors determined by monitoring phase data at the transmitting stations and other sites.

4324. The *Omega Propagation Correction Tables* contain the necessary data for correcting Omega receiver readouts, affected by the prevailing propagation conditions, to the standard conditions on which all Omega hyperbolic charts and tables are based. Propagation corrections are *always* necessary.

The corrections are presented in the single station (range) mode so that the navigator only need acquire the tables for the stations and areas desired. Each table contains propagation corrections for the station and area listed on the cover.

The publication number, pertinent suffix followed by the letter C, and the designator of the single stations for which they are computed fully identify each propagation correction table. Using Pub. No. 224 (109–C) D shown in figure 4324a as an example, the 224 designates an Omega publication; the first digit of the suffix (109) identifies the frequency as 10.2 kHz (2 denotes 3.4 kHz); the last two digits of the suffix identify the area of coverage of the table as 09 (fig. 4324b); the letter C indicates that the table is a PPC table as opposed to a lattice table; and the station designator (D) completes the full identification of the table.

Pub. 224 (109-C) D

OMEGA PROPAGATION
CORRECTION TABLES

FOR 10.2 kHz

AREA 09

NORTHWEST PACIFIC

STATION D (NORTH DAKOTA)

Prepared and published by the
DEFENSE MAPPING AGENCY HYDROGRAPHIC CENTER
Washington, D. C. 20390
Reprinted 1976

For sale by authorized Sales Agents of the Defense Mapping Agency Hydrographic Center
DMA STOCK NO. OMPUB224109CD

FIGURE 4324a.—*Omega Propagation Correction Tables.*

Propagation corrections are tabulated for each grid point of a grid constructed for 4° intervals for latitudes between 0° and 45°. The longitude interval is increased to 6° for latitudes between 45° and 60°, and to 8° for latitudes between 60° and 80°. Additionally, propagation corrections for the north and south polar areas between 70° and 90° are tabulated at intervals of 4° of latitude and 20° of longitude.

The corrections for a given coverage area are arranged in order of increasing west longitude and increasing north latitude as shown in figure 4324c. The numbers in the centers of the small quadrangles of this figure are the page numbers of the table in which the corrections are tabulated. Also, the centers of these quadrangles are the grid points at which sets of corrections are computed. As shown in figure 4324d, each set contains a matrix of propagation correction values arranged horizontally by Greenwich mean time (GMT) and vertically in semimonthly periods.

4325. The propagation corrections effect a conversion from the prevailing propagation conditions to the standard conditions on which the Omega charts and lattice tables are based.

The values as extracted from the tables are in units of centicycles (cecs). The centicycle (cec) is equal to 1 percent of a cycle. Note, however, that the difference in cecs of the phase readings of a station pair is numerically equal to the percentage value of the lane defining the LOP, i.e., the difference in cecs is numerically equal to the number of cels defining the LOP within the lane.

To obtain the propagation correction for a station pair, the correction for each station is determined first. Following such determinations, the correction for the station the designator of which follows the designator of the other station in the alphabet is subtracted algebraically from the propagation correction of the other

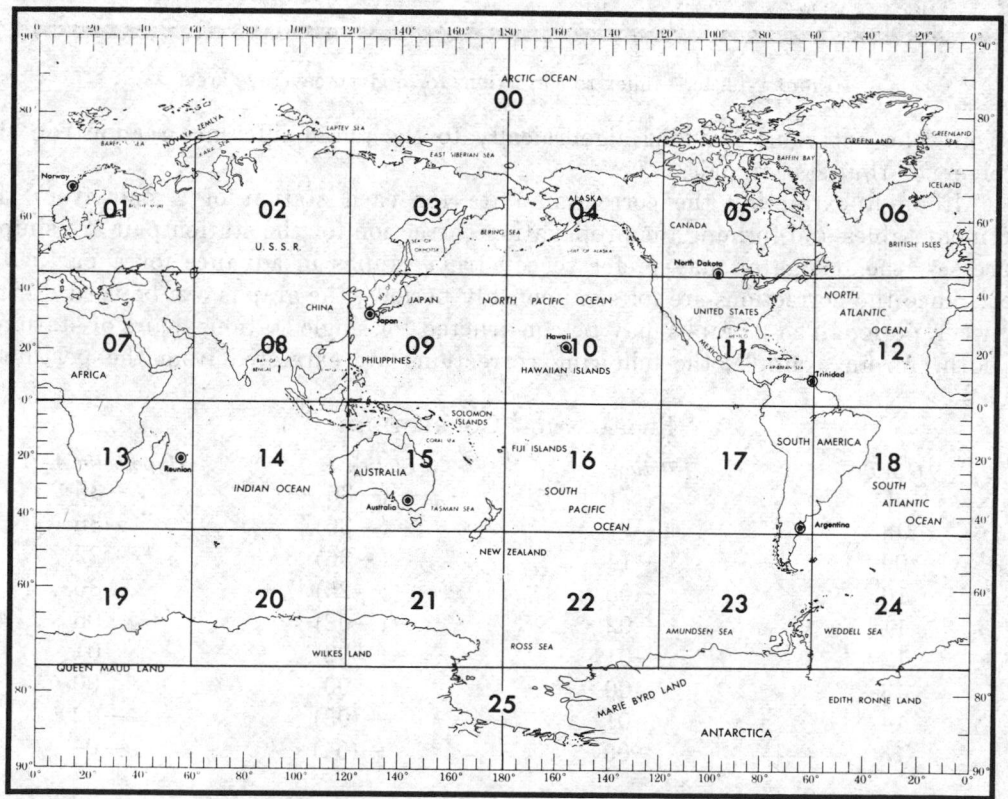

FIGURE 4324b.—Omega table areas.

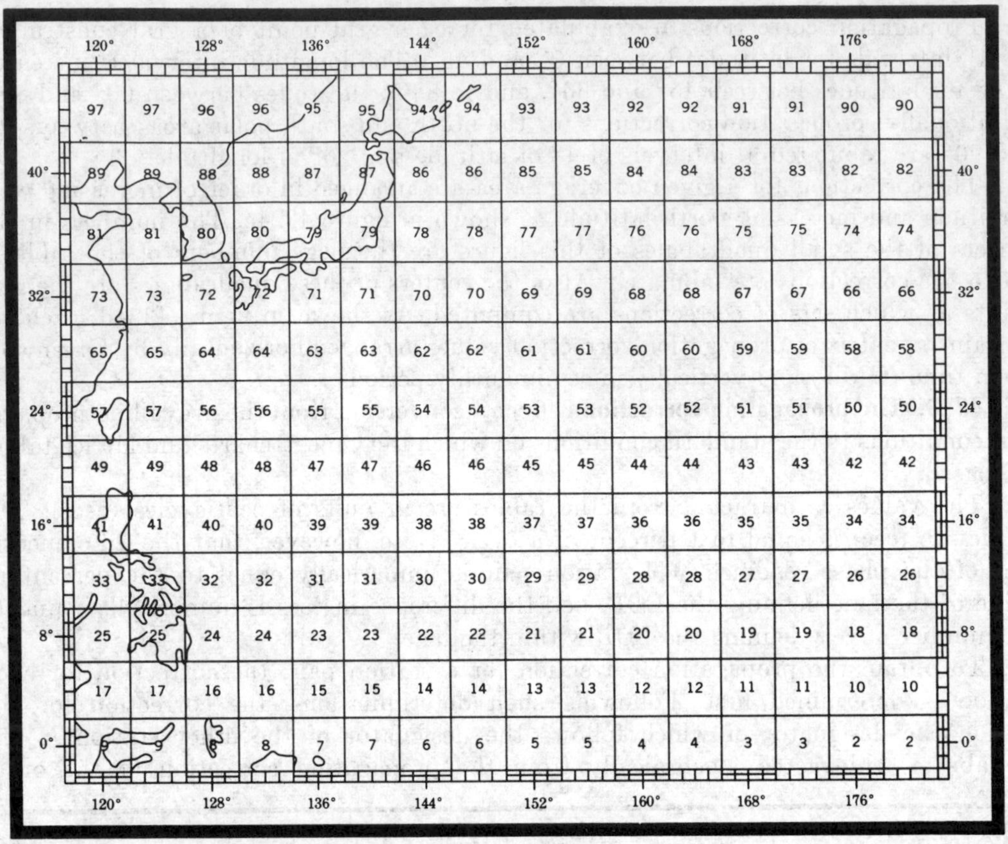

FIGURE 4324c.—Index to corrections for a given coverage area.

station. The net value is added algebraically to the phase-difference readout on the receiver for that station pair.

Although extracting the correction data for each station of a pair from the pertinent tables and forming the propagation correction for the station pair are simple processes, the navigator may prefer to construct graphs in advance for a particular area. Since the corrections are for semimonthly periods, the graphs can be used during a 2-week period. These graphs may be constructed for single stations, pairs of stations, or both. As an example, the following corrections are extracted from the pertinent tables:

PROPAGATION CORRECTIONS

GMT	Station A	Station B	Hyperbolic A–B
07	−71	−(−36)	−35
08	−71	−(−36)	−35
09	−14	−(−36)	22
10	−05	−(−25)	30
11	−02	−(−08)	06
12	−01	−(−02)	01
13	00	00	00
14	01	−(03)	−02
15	00	−(04)	−04

Note that since B follows A in the alphabet, the correction for station B is subtracted algebraically from the correction for station A.

LOCATION 20.0 N 160.0 E
STATION D NORTH DAKOTA

DATE	00	01	02	03	04	05	06	07	08	09	10	11 (GMT)	12	13	14	15	16	17	18	19	20	21	22	23	24
1-15 JAN	-19	-26	-35	-46	-58	-71	-87	-98	-101	-103	-103	-103	-103	-103	-104	-103	-90	-80	-68	-54	-28	-7	-9	-8	-13
16-31 JAN	-15	-23	-33	-42	-54	-68	-84	-97	-101	-102	-103	-103	-103	-104	-102	-88	-78	-65	-50	-25	-5	-7	-5	-7	-15
1-14 FEB	-8	-19	-28	-38	-49	-63	-80	-95	-100	-102	-103	-103	-103	-103	-98	-85	-73	-61	-45	-20	-3	-4	-2	-3	-8
15-29 FEB	-3	-12	-22	-33	-45	-59	-76	-92	-99	-102	-103	-103	-103	-92	-78	-68	-56	-38	-13	-2	-2	1	1	-3	
1-15 MAR	1	-7	-18	-28	-41	-55	-72	-90	-99	-102	-103	-103	-103	-100	-85	-73	-61	-43	-20	-7	-1	0	3	4	1
16-31 MAR	4	-2	-12	-24	-36	-50	-68	-87	-98	-101	-103	-103	-93	-79	-69	-58	-44	-24	-2	0	2	5	6	4	
1-15 APR	7	2	-8	-19	-31	-45	-63	-84	-97	-101	-102	-103	-99	-84	-73	-63	-51	-37	-16	0	2	5	7	8	7
16-30 APR	8	4	-4	-15	-27	-41	-58	-80	-96	-100	-102	-103	-92	-79	-67	-58	-46	-30	-10	1	3	6	8	9	8
1-15 MAY	9	7	0	-11	-23	-37	-54	-77	-94	-99	-102	-99	-85	-73	-63	-53	-40	-26	-6	2	4	8	9	10	9
16-31 MAY	10	8	2	-8	-20	-33	-49	-72	-92	-99	-101	-93	-81	-69	-60	-50	-37	-23	-3	2	5	8	10	11	10
1-15 JUN	11	9	3	-5	-17	-30	-46	-68	-89	-98	-100	-90	-78	-67	-59	-49	-37	-21	-3	2	6	9	11	11	11
16-30 JUN	11	9	4	-4	-16	-29	-43	-66	-88	-97	-100	-90	-78	-67	-60	-49	-37	-21	-3	2	5	9	11	11	11
1-15 JUL	11	9	4	-5	-16	-29	-44	-66	-88	-97	-100	-91	-79	-69	-60	-51	-37	-23	-5	2	5	8	10	11	11
16-31 JUL	10	9	3	-6	-18	-31	-46	-68	-89	-98	-101	-96	-83	-72	-62	-51	-42	-25	-7	2	5	8	10	11	10
1-15 AUG	10	7	1	-10	-22	-35	-51	-74	-92	-99	-102	-101	-87	-76	-66	-55	-45	-29	-10	1	4	7	9	10	10
16-31 AUG	8	5	-3	-15	-27	-40	-57	-79	-95	-100	-102	-103	-93	-80	-69	-57	-44	-33	-13	1	3	6	8	9	8
1-15 SEP	6	1	-9	-20	-33	-47	-65	-86	-97	-101	-102	-103	-99	-84	-74	-63	-51	-36	-15	0	2	4	7	7	6
16-30 SEP	3	-4	-15	-27	-39	-54	-73	-91	-99	-102	-103	-103	-90	-77	-65	-55	-39	-19	0	0	3	5	5	3	
1-15 OCT	-2	-11	-22	-33	-46	-61	-80	-95	-100	-102	-103	-103	-96	-82	-71	-59	-44	-24	-1	-1	1	3	3	-2	
16-31 OCT	-7	-18	-28	-39	-52	-67	-85	-97	-101	-102	-103	-103	-103	-100	-85	-76	-63	-49	-28	-3	-3	-1	1	-1	-7
1-15 NOV	-14	-24	-34	-44	-57	-72	-89	-99	-101	-103	-103	-103	-103	-92	-79	-69	-55	-36	-7	-5	-4	-3	-6	-14	
16-30 NOV	-19	-27	-36	-48	-60	-75	-90	-99	-102	-103	-103	-103	-104	-96	-85	-73	-61	-43	-11	-7	-7	-6	-11	-19	
1-15 DEC	-21	-29	-38	-49	-61	-75	-91	-99	-102	-103	-103	-103	-104	-100	-88	-77	-66	-48	-18	-8	-9	-8	-16	-21	
16-31 DEC	-20	-28	-38	-48	-60	-74	-89	-99	-102	-103	-103	-103	-104	-102	-91	-79	-68	-52	-26	-8	-10	-9	-15	-20	

LOCATION 20.0 N 160.0 E
STATION H JAPAN

DATE	00	01	02	03	04	05	06	07	08	09	10	11 (GMT)	12	13	14	15	16	17	18	19	20	21	22	23	24
1-15 JAN	-9	-8	-7	-7	-8	-9	-11	-21	-36	-43	-46	-47	-48	-48	-48	-48	-48	-48	-48	-48	-39	-21	-9	-10	-9
16-31 JAN	-9	-8	-7	-7	-7	-8	-10	-18	-33	-43	-46	-47	-48	-48	-48	-48	-48	-48	-48	-48	-39	-21	-8	-10	-9
1-14 FEB	-9	-7	-6	-6	-7	-8	-9	-15	-30	-41	-45	-47	-48	-48	-48	-48	-48	-48	-48	-48	-37	-19	-8	-10	-9
15-29 FEB	-8	-6	-6	-5	-6	-7	-9	-14	-27	-39	-44	-47	-47	-48	-48	-48	-48	-48	-48	-48	-33	-14	-8	-10	-8
1-15 MAR	-7	-6	-5	-5	-5	-7	-8	-12	-25	-38	-44	-46	-47	-48	-48	-48	-48	-48	-48	-48	-28	-9	-9	-9	-7
16-31 MAR	-7	-5	-4	-4	-5	-6	-8	-11	-23	-36	-43	-46	-47	-48	-48	-48	-48	-48	-46	-46	-22	-6	-9	-9	-7
1-15 APR	-6	-5	-4	-4	-5	-6	-8	-11	-21	-34	-43	-46	-47	-48	-48	-48	-48	-48	-41	-15	-7	-10	-8	-6	
16-30 APR	-5	-4	-4	-4	-4	-6	-7	-10	-19	-33	-42	-45	-47	-48	-48	-48	-48	-48	-48	-35	-8	-9	-9	-7	-5
1-15 MAY	-5	-4	-3	-3	-4	-5	-7	-10	-18	-31	-41	-45	-47	-48	-48	-48	-48	-48	-48	-28	-6	-9	-9	-7	-5
16-31 MAY	-5	-4	-3	-3	-4	-5	-7	-9	-17	-29	-39	-45	-47	-47	-48	-48	-48	-48	-24	-6	-10	-9	-7	-5	
1-15 JUN	-5	-4	-3	-3	-4	-5	-7	-9	-15	-27	-38	-44	-46	-47	-48	-48	-48	-48	-22	-7	-10	-9	-7	-5	
16-30 JUN	-5	-4	-3	-3	-4	-5	-7	-9	-15	-26	-37	-44	-46	-47	-48	-48	-48	-48	-23	-7	-10	-9	-7	-5	
1-15 JUL	-5	-4	-3	-3	-4	-5	-7	-9	-14	-26	-38	-44	-46	-47	-48	-48	-48	-48	-24	-6	-10	-9	-7	-5	
16-31 JUL	-5	-4	-3	-3	-4	-5	-7	-9	-15	-27	-38	-44	-46	-47	-48	-48	-48	-48	-29	-6	-9	-9	-7	-5	
1-15 AUG	-5	-4	-3	-3	-4	-5	-7	-9	-16	-29	-40	-45	-47	-47	-48	-48	-48	-48	-34	-8	-9	-10	-7	-5	
16-31 AUG	-6	-4	-4	-4	-4	-5	-7	-10	-19	-32	-41	-45	-47	-48	-48	-48	-48	-48	-38	-11	-8	-10	-7	-6	
1-15 SEP	-6	-5	-4	-4	-5	-6	-8	-11	-22	-36	-43	-46	-47	-48	-48	-48	-48	-48	-40	-15	-7	-10	-8	-6	
16-30 SEP	-6	-5	-4	-4	-5	-7	-8	-13	-26	-39	-44	-46	-47	-48	-48	-48	-48	-48	-42	-18	-7	-9	-8	-6	
1-15 OCT	-7	-5	-5	-5	-6	-7	-9	-16	-31	-41	-45	-47	-48	-48	-48	-48	-48	-48	-43	-20	-7	-9	-9	-7	
16-31 OCT	-7	-6	-6	-6	-7	-8	-10	-20	-34	-43	-46	-47	-48	-48	-48	-48	-48	-48	-45	-24	-9	-9	-9	-7	
1-15 NOV	-8	-7	-6	-6	-7	-9	-12	-23	-37	-44	-46	-47	-48	-48	-48	-48	-48	-48	-47	-28	-12	-9	-10	-8	
16-30 NOV	-9	-7	-7	-7	-8	-9	-13	-25	-38	-44	-46	-47	-48	-48	-48	-48	-48	-48	-47	-30	-13	-9	-10	-9	
1-15 DEC	-9	-8	-7	-7	-8	-9	-13	-25	-38	-44	-46	-47	-48	-48	-48	-48	-48	-48	-48	-35	-18	-9	-10	-9	
16-31 DEC	-9	-8	-7	-7	-8	-9	-12	-24	-38	-44	-46	-47	-48	-48	-48	-48	-48	-48	-48	-37	-19	-9	-10	-9	

FIGURE 4324d.—Extracts from *Omega Propagation Correction Tables*.

As illustrated in figure 4325a, a simple graph can be constructed which simplifies any interpolation that might be required and depicts any rapid variations in the corrections indicating uncertainty in the validity of the correction. In this graph propagation changes occur quite rapidly about 0830Z. Station A (Norway) corrections only are graphed in figure 4325b. These corrections for 10 January are for a grid point (lat. 16°N, long. 40°W) at which the sun rises at about the same time as at station A. Hence, propagation changes over most of the 2,300 nautical mile propagation path from northern Norway to 16°N, 40°W occur quite rapidly about 0830Z. The prudent procedure would be to use a different station pair at this time for obtaining an LOP.

When forming the 3.4 kHz coarse lane from the 10.2 kHz and 13.6 kHz transmissions from a station pair and determining in which 10.2 kHz fine lane the observer is located by means of the equivalent 3.4 kHz phase-difference reading, the phase-difference reading at 10.2 kHz is subtracted from the phase difference reading at 13.6 kHz. The correction as extracted from the *Omega Propagation Correction Tables* for 10.2 kHz is subtracted algebraically from the correction extracted from the tables for 13.6 kHz. The algebraic difference of the corrections so found for each station of the pair is then applied to the phase difference reading.

4326. Omega plotting charts.—Several series of charts have either been produced or are under development for use with the Omega system. The 7600 and 7700 series, designed to give global coverage on the Mercator projection with a scale of 1:2,187,400

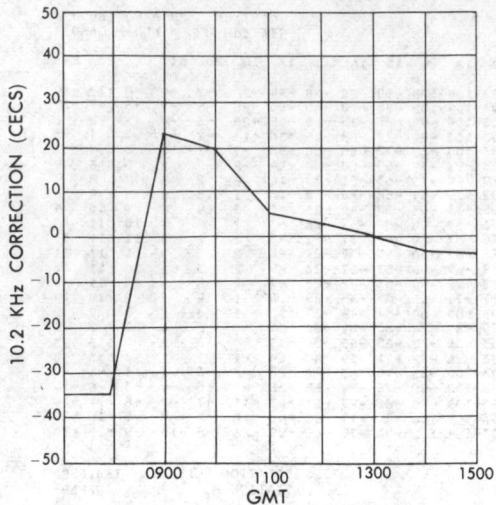

FIGURE 4325a.—Diurnal effects.

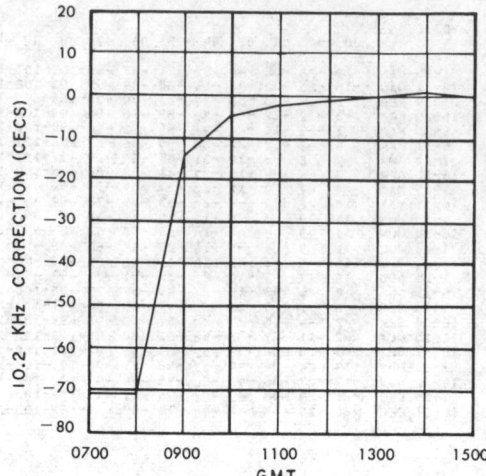

FIGURE 4325b.—Diurnal effects.

(1 inch=30 nautical miles), are plotting sheets overprinted with Omega zero phase-difference contours for standard propagation conditions.

On these plotting charts the LOP for a corrected receiver reading of a station pair is constructed by graphical linear interpolation between the charted LOPs.

Notice to Mariners are not issued for changes to hydrographic information on these plotting charts. The mariner should consult the nautical charts covering the same area for hydrographic information.

4327. Lattice tables.—It is not feasible to provide the great number of large-scale charts required for every application of the Omega System. The counterpart to the Omega chart is the lattice table (Omega charting coordinate table) contained in the Pub. 224 Series. Through use of this table, Omega lines of position can be plotted on a suitable plotting sheet or chart having a scale as large as 1:800,000.

Because all Omega frequencies are integral multiples of a common base frequency (1.133 kHz), there is no real need to publish lattice tables for frequencies other than 10.2 kHz. For instance, every third 10.2 kHz hyperbola is also a 3.4 kHz hyperbola; every fourth 13.6 kHz hyperbola is also a 3.4 kHz hyperbola. The tables are computed for hyperbolic lanes at a frequency of 10.2 kHz. Every 10.2 kHz hyperbola, exactly divisible by three (897,900,903, etc.) is also a 3.4 kHz hyperbola.

The numbering of the lanes established by a station pair increases in the direction away from that station of the pair the designator of which appears first in the alphabet; the 10.2 kHz lane at the perpendicular bisector of the baseline of the pair is assigned a value of 900. A fictitious minimum lane count is inserted in the lattice computations to provide this 10.2 kHz lane count of 900 lanes on the perpendicular bisector of the baseline.

For each coverage area as shown in figure 4324b there is a separate Omega Table (lattice table) for each station pair that can be used in that area.

The publication number, pertinent suffix, and station pair fully identify each lattice table. Using Pub. No. 224 (109), Pair D–H, as an example, the 224 designates an Omega publication; the first digit of the suffix (109) identifies the frequency as 10.2 kHz; the last two digits of the suffix identify the area of coverage of the table as area 09; the station pair (D–H) completes the full identification of the table.

T Lat	D-H 1090		D-H 1091		D-H 1092		D-H 1093		D-H 1094		T Long
° '	° '	Δ	° '	Δ	° '	Δ	° '	Δ	° '	Δ	° '
0	162 16.2E	-121	162 04.0E	-121	161 51.9E	-122	161 39.6E	-122	161 27.4E	-122	
1 N	162 18.7E	-120	162 06.5E	-121	161 54.4E	-121	161 42.3E	-121	161 30.1E	-121	
2 N	162 20.7E	-120	162 08.7E	-120	161 56.6E	-120	161 44.5E	-120	161 32.5E	-120	
3 N	162 22.4E	-119	162 10.4E	-119	161 58.5E	-119	161 46.4E	-120	161 34.4E	-120	
4 N	162 23.7E	-119	162 11.8E	-119	161 59.9E	-119	161 47.9E	-119	161 36.0E	-119	
5 N	162 24.6E	-118	162 12.8E	-118	162 00.9E	-118	161 49.0E	-118	161 37.1E	-118	
6 N	162 25.1E	-117	162 13.4E	-117	162 01.6E	-118	161 49.7E	-118	161 37.9E	-118	
7 N	162 25.2E	-116	162 13.6E	-117	162 01.8E	-117	161 50.0E	-117	161 38.3E	-117	
8 N	162 24.9E	-116	162 13.3E	-116	162 01.6E	-116	161 49.9E	-117	161 38.2E	-117	
9 N	162 24.2E	-115	162 12.6E	-115	162 01.0E	-116	161 49.3E	-116	161 37.7E	-116	
10 N	162 23.0E	-115	162 11.5E	-115	161 59.9E	-115	161 48.3E	-115	161 36.7E	-115	
11 N	162 21.4E	-114	162 09.9E	-115	161 58.3E	-115	161 46.8E	-115	161 35.3E	-115	
12 N	162 19.2E	-114	162 07.8E	-114	161 56.3E	-114	161 44.8E	-114	161 33.3E	-114	
13 N	162 16.6E	-113	162 05.3E	-114	161 53.8E	-114	161 42.3E	-114	161 30.9E	-114	
14 N	162 13.5E	-113	162 02.2E	-113	161 50.8E	-114	161 39.3E	-114	161 27.9E	-114	
15 N	162 09.8E	-113	161 58.5E	-113	161 47.2E	-113	161 35.8E	-113	161 24.5E	-113	
16 N	162 05.6E	-112	161 54.3E	-112	161 43.0E	-112	161 31.7E	-112	161 20.4E	-112	
17 N	162 00.8E	-112	161 49.5E	-112	161 38.2E	-112	161 27.0E	-112	161 15.7E	-112	
18 N	161 55.3E	-112	161 44.1E	-112	161 32.9E	-111	161 21.7E	-112	161 10.4E	-112	
19 N	161 49.2E	-111	161 38.1E	-111	161 26.9E	-112	161 15.6E	-112	161 04.4E	-111	
20 N	161 42.4E	-111	161 31.3E	-111	161 20.1E	-111	161 09.0E	-111	160 57.8E	-111	
21 N	161 34.9E	-110	161 23.8E	-111	161 12.7E	-111	161 01.6E	-111	160 50.4E	-111	
22 N	161 26.7E	-110	161 15.6E	-110	161 04.5E	-111	160 53.4E	-111	160 42.3E	-111	
23 N	161 17.6E	-110	161 06.6E	-110	160 55.5E	-111	160 44.3E	-111	160 33.3E	-110	
24 N	161 07.7E	-110	160 56.6E	-110	160 45.6E	-110	160 34.5E	-111	160 23.3E	-111	
25 N	160 56.9E	-110	160 45.9E	-110	160 34.8E	-111	160 23.6E	-110	160 12.6E	-110	
26 N	160 45.1E	-110	160 34.1E	-110	160 23.0E	-111	160 11.9E	-110	160 00.8E	-110	
27 N	160 32.3E	-110	160 21.3E	-110	160 10.1E	-110	159 59.0E	-110	159 48.0E	-110	
28 N	160 18.4E	-110	160 07.3E	-110	159 56.2E	-111	159 45.1E	-111	159 34.0E	-110	
29 N	160 03.3E	-110	159 52.2E	-111	159 41.0E	-111	159 29.9E	-111	159 18.8E	-110	
30 N	159 46.9E	-110	159 35.8E	-111	159 24.6E	-111	159 13.4E	-111	159 02.3E	-111	
31 N	159 29.2E	-111	159 18.0E	-111	159 06.8E	-112	158 55.6E	-111	158 44.4E	-111	
32 N	159 10.0E	-112	158 58.8E	-112	158 47.5E	-112	158 36.3E	-112	158 25.1E	-112	
33 N	158 49.3E	-112	158 37.9E	-113	158 26.6E	-112	158 15.3E	-112	158 04.1E	-113	
34 N	158 26.8E	-113	158 15.4E	-114	158 04.0E	-113	157 52.6E	-113	157 41.3E	-113	
35 N	158 02.4E	-114	157 50.9E	-114	157 39.5E	-114	157 28.0E	-114	157 16.5E	-115	
36 N	157 36.1E	-116	157 24.4E	-115	157 12.9E	-115	157 01.4E	-115	156 49.7E	-116	
37 N	157 07.5E	-117	156 55.8E	-116	156 44.1E	-116	156 32.4E	-117	156 20.7E	-117	
38 N	156 36.5E	-118	156 24.7E	-118	156 12.9E	-118	156 01.0E	-119	155 49.1E	-118	
39 N	156 03.0E	-119	155 51.0E	-120	155 38.9E	-120	155 26.8E	-120	155 14.8E	-120	
40 N	155 26.5E	-121	155 14.3E	-122	155 02.0E	-122	154 49.7E	-122	154 37.4E	-122	
41 N	154 46.8E	-124	154 34.3E	-125	154 21.7E	-125	154 09.2E	-124	153 56.8E	-125	
42 N	154 03.5E	-127	153 50.7E	-128	153 37.8E	-128	153 25.1E	-127	153 12.2E	-128	
43 N	153 16.1E	-131	153 03.0E	-131	152 49.9E	-131	152 36.7E	-132	152 23.5E	-132	
44 N	152 24.4E	-134	152 10.9E	-135	151 57.3E	-135	151 43.7E	-135	151 30.1E	-136	
45 N	151 27.5E	-139	151 13.5E	-140	150 59.4E	-140	150 45.3E	-140	150 31.2E	-141	
T	D-H 1090		D-H 1091		D-H 1092		D-H 1093		D-H 1094		T

FIGURE 4327.—Extract from Omega Table.

As shown in figure 4327, the columns are headed by lane values at intervals of one lane in most cases. Lane values corresponding to the baseline extensions are so marked.

Because Omega isophase contours fan out in all directions, it is sometimes necessary to tabulate the latitude at which the contours intersect meridians; at other times it is necessary to tabulate the longitudes at which the contours intersect parallels of latitude. The tables are arranged so that the latitude always appears to the left of the longitude.

For the entire area of coverage, points on the isophase contours are tabulated at intervals of 1° of latitude or longitude from the equator to 60° north and south. From 60° latitude to 80° latitude, the points are tabulated at intervals of 1° of latitude or 2° of longitude. From 80° latitude to the pole, the points are tabulated at intervals of 1° of latitude or 5° of longitude.

Close to the transmitting stations where the hyperbolic contours curve sharply, additional points are tabulated at intervals of 15 minutes of arc. The spacing of the points is such that the navigator can safely use a straight line between any two adjacent tabulated points as an approximation of the hyperbola. Within approximately *20 miles* of a transmitting station, the curvature of the hyperbolic contours is excessive. The navigator is *cautioned* that *straight line segments* will introduce *appreciable errors*. A plot of three consecutive points will indicate the amount of curvature and the actual contour. When operating within *450 nautical miles* from a transmitting station, *caution* should be exercised because transmissions from the station may not be reliable. The use of the signals when within 450 nautical miles of a transmitting station should be avoided if possible.

4328. Interpolation.—The usual situation is that the LOP corresponding to a corrected receiver reading lies *within* a lane, i.e., the LOP usually lies between adjacent zero phase-difference contours for standard propagation conditions. Since the lattice table tabulations are points on these contours, interpolation is usually required.

To facilitate linear interpolation in the lattice tables, the rate of change of latitude or longitude per lane is tabulated immediately to the right of each tabulated point on the zero phase-difference contour or lane boundary. This Δ value is only an average rate of change for a two-lane band. It is assumed to be correct at the tabulated point of the middle hyperbola. For this reason it is always necessary to interpolate from the nearest tabulated lane value, T. The difference between the corrected receiver reading and tabular lane is multiplied by Δ. This product is added algebraically to the value of latitude or longitude tabulated under the column headed by T. Either Δ or the difference between the corrected receiver reading and the tabulated lane value (T) can be negative.

The Δ value is in units of minutes of arc, the last digit being tenths of minutes of arc. However, the decimal is not shown in the tabulation.

As the baseline extensions are approached, accurate interpolation is impossible. In these areas, values for Δ have been omitted.

Example.—The 0400Z DR position of a ship on 5 February is latitude 21°36′N, longitude 161°15′E. The 0400Z Omega reading for station pair D–H is as follows:

0400Z Pair D–H 1090.15.

Required.—The 0400Z Omega LOP.

Solution.—The appropriate predicted propagation correction (PPC) must be applied to the observed receiver reading to obtain the corrected receiver reading. Therefore, enter the PPC tables for the pertinent stations with the DR position. Select the PPC for the closest geographic intersection to the ship's DR position for the proper time and date. Combine the PPC's for the individual stations comprising the pair by algebraically subtracting the correction for the second station alphabetically of the pair from the correction for the first station. Apply the correction to the uncorrected receiver reading. Enter the lattice table in the T column nearest to the value of the corrected receiver reading and with the latitudes or longitudes closest to and on each side of the DR position. Extract the corresponding longitudes or latitudes for these two points. Interpolate if necessary. Plot the two points thus obtained. Connect these two points with a straight line to determine the Omega LOP.

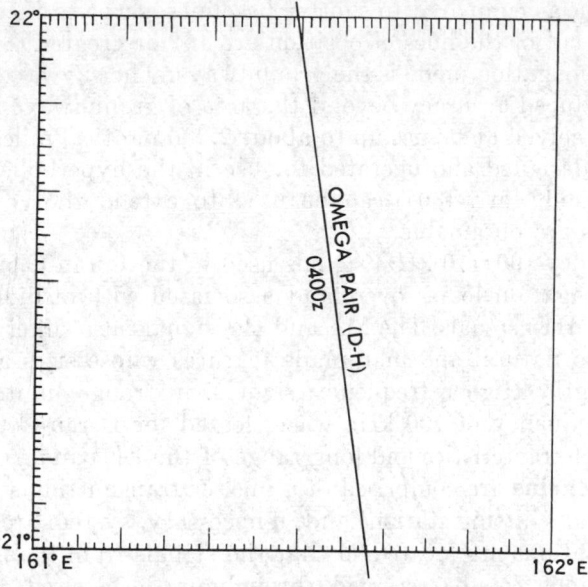

FIGURE 4328.—Plot of Omega line of position.

PPC table excerpts for Stations D and H are as follows (see figure 4324d):

PPC for Station D _____ —.49
PPC for Station H _____ —.07
PPC for Pair D–H=(—.49)–(—.07) _____ —.42

Pair D–H lattice table excerpt (see figure 4327):

Receiver reading (uncorrected) _____ 1090.15
PPC for Pair D–H _____ —.42
Corrected receiver reading _____ 1089.73
T _____ 1090.00
Diff _____ —.27

Latitude	Tabulated longitude	Δ
21°N	161°34.′9E	—11.0
22°N	161°26.′7E	—11.0

Longitude change (diff.×Δ)	Interpolated longitude
(—.27)×(—11.0)=+3.′0	161°37.′9E
(—.27)×(—11.0)=+3.′0	161°29.′7E

Answer.—The LOP is plotted through the following positions: latitude 21°N, longitude 161°37.′9E, and latitude 22°N, longitude 161°29.′7E (see figure 4328).

Loran–C

4329. Loran-C is a long range hyperbolic radionavigation system of high accuracy which processes a pulsed LF (100 kHz) signal by both the time difference and phase comparison methods. Ranges of 800 to 1,200 nautical miles are obtainable when using the groundwave, depending upon transmitter power, signal-to-noise ratio in the service area, receiver sensitivity, and losses over the signal path. Wide coverage areas are made possible by the low propagation losses of LF groundwaves, by the use of pulse groups to increase the average power without any increase in the peak power, and by the use of long baselines which, as compared to shorter baselines, serve to increase the total area where the angles of cut of the lines of position are 15° or greater.

The normal propagation mode is the groundwave. The skywave propagation mode can be used with reduced accuracy beyond the area of groundwave reception. One-hop skywaves may be received at ranges up to about 2,300 nautical miles.

Although it is designed and operated for use in the hyperbolic mode, Loran-C in the Range-Range mode (art. 4304) can be used to extend the coverage area within which accurate fixes are obtainable.

The low frequency (90–110 kHz) signals used in the Loran-C system do not suffer from the high propagation losses over land associated with medium frequency (MF) and high frequency (HF) signals. The MF and HF signals also suffer loss of propagation predictability due to natural and man-made features whose sizes are significant fractions of a wavelength. Higher frequency signals are range limited to line-of-sight. Thus, the center frequency of 100 kHz was selected for Loran-C to benefit from the stable propagation characteristics and long range of the LF band.

4330. Loran-C chains are comprised of a master transmitting station, two or more secondary (slave) transmitting stations and, if necessary, system area monitor stations. The transmitting stations are located so that the signals from the master and at least two secondary stations can be received throughout the desired coverage or service area. For convenience, the master station is designated by the letter M and the secondary stations are designated W, X, Y, or Z. Thus, a particular master-secondary pair and the time difference (TD) which it produces can be referred to by the letter designations of both stations or just that of the secondary, e.g. MX time difference or TDX (fig. 4330).

4331. The Loran-C signal format.—The transmitting stations of a Loran-C chain transmit groups of pulses at a specified **group repetition interval (GRI).** Each pulse has a 100 kHz carrier and is of the shape shown in figure 4331a. The shape is such that 99 percent of the radiated energy is contained between the frequencies of 90 and 110 kHz. For each chain a minimum GRI is selected of sufficient length so that it contains time for transmission of the pulse group from each station (10,000 microseconds for the master and 8,000 microseconds for each secondary) plus time between each pulse group so that signals from two or more stations cannot overlap in time anywhere in the coverage area (fig. 4331b). Thus, with respect to the time of arrival of the master, a secondary station will delay its own transmissions for a specified time, called the **secondary coding delay.** The minimum GRI is therefore a direct function of the number of stations and the distance between them. A GRI for the chain is then selected so that adjacent chains do not cause mutual (cross-rate) interference. Possible values for GRI are listed in table 4331a. The GRI is defined to begin coincident with the start of the first pulse of the master group.

Each station transmits one pulse group per GRI. The master pulse group consists of eight pulses spaced 1,000 microseconds apart, and a ninth pulse 2,000 microseconds after the eighth. Secondary pulse groups contain eight pulses spaced 1,000 microseconds apart. Multiple pulses are used so that more signal energy is available at the receiver, improving significantly the signal-to-noise ratio without having to increase the peak transmitted power capability of the transmitters. The master's ninth pulse is used for visual identification of the master, and for blink. **Blink,** used to warn users that there is an error in the transmissions of a particular station, is accomplished by turning the ninth pulse on and off in a specified code as shown in table 4331b. The secondary station of the unusable pair also blinks by turning its first two pulses on and off. Most modern receivers automatically detect secondary station blink only, as this is sufficient to trigger alarm indicators.

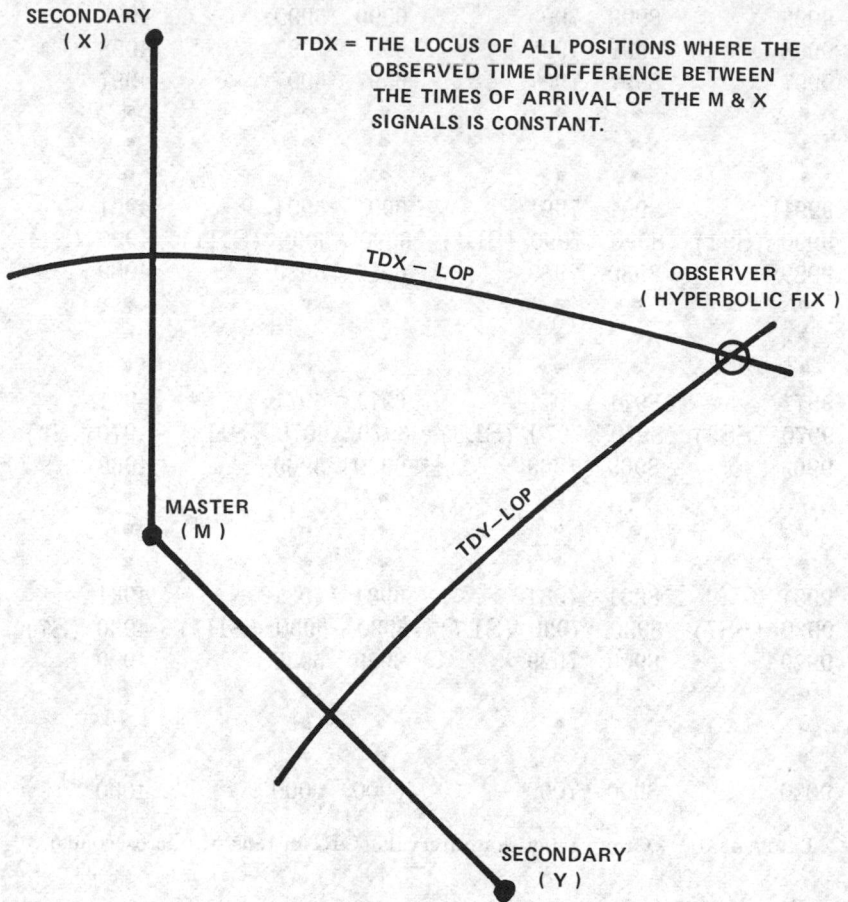

SECONDARY
(X)

TDX = THE LOCUS OF ALL POSITIONS WHERE THE
OBSERVED TIME DIFFERENCE BETWEEN
THE TIMES OF ARRIVAL OF THE M & X
SIGNALS IS CONSTANT.

TDX – LOP

OBSERVER
(HYPERBOLIC FIX)

MASTER
(M)

TDY–LOP

SECONDARY
(Y)

FIGURE 4330.—Loran-C chain.

The rate structure for Loran-C is limited in theory to GRIs of 00010 to 99990 microseconds in 10 microsecond steps. In actual practice the GRIs are between 40000 and 99990 microseconds with limits placed on rates actually selected. The designation of a Loran-C rate is by the first four digits of the specific GRI. This is a newly expanded rate structure. The old rate structure consisted of those GRIs with old rate designations shown in parentheses (thus rate SS7 is now referred to as 9930).

4332. Avoiding skywave contamination.—A skywave may arrive at a receiver as little as 35 microseconds (μs) or as much as 1,000 μs after the groundwave. In the first case, the skywave will overlap its own groundwave while in the second case the skywave will overlap the groundwave of the succeeding pulse. Either case will cause distortion of the received signal in the form of fading and pulse shape changes. Large positional errors would result if these conditions were not accounted for in the selection of the Loran-C signal format, and the design of the receivers.

The early arriving skywave is overcome by making time of arrival measurements on the first part of the pulse. This ability is enhanced by the fast-rising pulse (fig. 4331a), achieving high power prior to the arrival of the skywaves. The shape of the pulse also allows the receiver to identify one particular cycle of the 100–kHz carrier. This is essential to prevent whole cycle ambiguities in the time-difference measurement and allows the high accuracy of the phase measurement system to be achieved.

To prevent the long-delay skywaves from affecting the time-difference measurement, the phase of the 100–kHz carrier is changed in each pulse of a group in accord-

9999		8999	7999		6999	5999		4999	
9998		8998	7998		6998	5998		4998	
9997		8997	7997		6997	5997		4997	
•		•	•		•	•		•	
•		•	•		•	•		•	
•		•	•		•	•		•	
9991		8991	7991		6991	5991		4991	
9990	(SS1)	8990	7990	(SL1)	6990	5990	(SH1)	4990	(S1)
9989		8989	7989		6989	5989		4989	
•		•	•		•	•		•	
•		•	•		•	•		•	
•		•	•		•	•		•	
9971		8971	7971		6971	5971		4971	
9970	(SS3)	8970	7970	(SL3)	6970	5970	(SH3)	4970	(S3)
9969		8969	7969		6969	5969		4969	
•		•	•		•	•		•	
•		•	•		•	•		•	
•		•	•		•	•		•	
9931		8931	7931		6931	5931		4931	
9930	(SS7)	8930	7930	(SL7)	6930	5930	(SH7)	4930	(S7)
9929		8929	7929		6929	5929		4929	
•		•	•		•	•		•	
•		•	•		•	•		•	
•		•	•		•	•		•	
9000		8000	7000		6000	5000		4000	

TABLE 4331a.—Group repetition intervals (GRI in tens of microseconds).

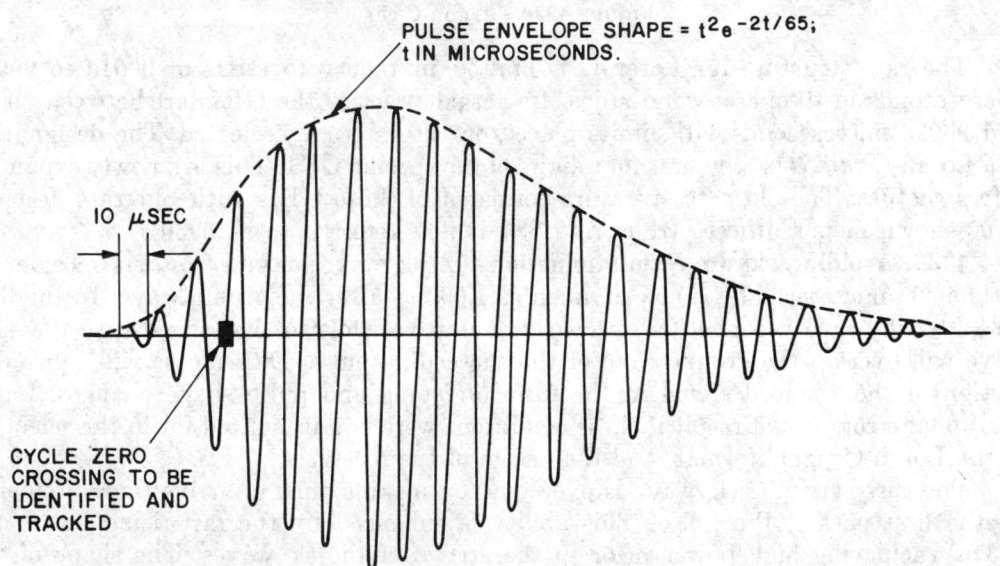

FIGURE 4331a.—Loran-C pulse.

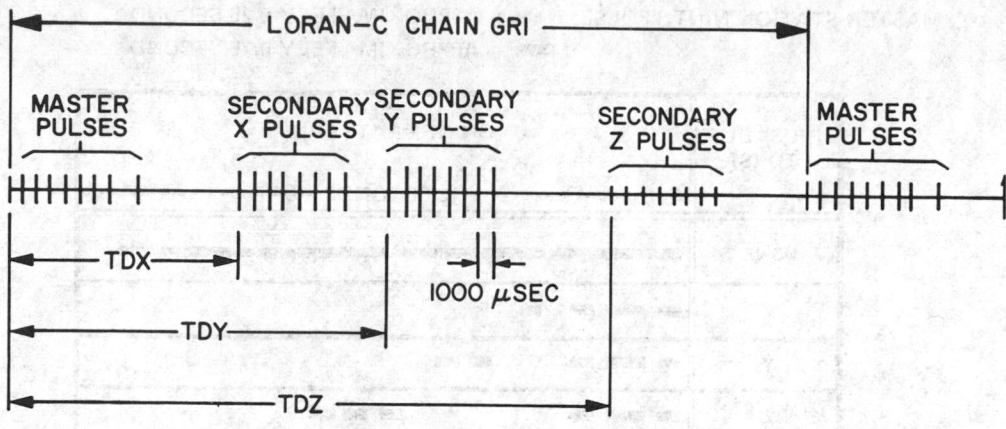

FIGURE 4331b.—Loran-C signal format.

ance with a predetermined pattern. The phase codes for Loran-C are shown in table 4331c. The different phase codes for the master and secondary signals also allow automatic receivers to use the code for master and secondary station identification.

4333. Synchronization control.—All transmitting stations are equipped with cesium frequency standards. The high stability and accuracy of these standards permit each station to derive its own time of transmission without reference to another station.

The objective for control of a Loran-C chain is to maintain constant the observed time difference (TD) of each master-secondary pair throughout the coverage area. Frequency offsets in the cesium standards and changes in propagation conditions can cause the observed TD to vary. Therefore, one or more **system area monitor** (**SAM**) stations with precision receiving equipment are established in the coverage area to monitor continuously the TDs of the master-secondary pairs. In some cases a transmitting station is suitably located and performs the SAM function. A control TD is established through calibration (art. 4334). When the observed TD varies from the control TD by one-half of the prescribed control tolerance, the SAM directs a change in the timing of the secondary station to remove the error. The control tolerance is plus or minus 200 nanoseconds or better. If the observed TD differs from the control TD by more than the control tolerance, "blink" (art. 4331) is ordered to advise users that the TD is unusable.

The Loran-C system as it operates today (1977) has maintained a record of 99.7 percent availability, not including scheduled off-air maintenance, which reduces that figure to about 99 percent. New equipment is being developed which will permit on-air maintenance, and also improve the system availability, with a goal of better than 99.7 percent, including all interruptions of service.

4334. System calibration.—When a Loran-C chain is established (or when a secondary is added) and periodically thereafter, chain calibration is conducted. The purpose of the calibration is to record the Loran-C time differences at a number of known geographical points in the coverage area. This information is then used to:

1. verify the initial chain synchronization to ensure that the chain performs as advertised;

2. establish the control time differences, which are then used as the reference for measuring synchronization control;

3. ensure the accuracy of existing control time differences;

4. provide survey data for accurate charting and for use in determining surface conductivities.

MASTER STATION NINTH PULSE: ■■ = APPROXIMATELY 0.25 SECOND

▬▬ = APPROXIMATELY 0.75 SECOND

UNUSABLE TD (S)	ON-OFF PATTERN ← 12 SECONDS →
NONE	▬▬▬▬▬▬▬▬▬▬▬▬▬▬
X	■■ ■■ ■■ ■■
Y	■■ ■■ ■■ ■■ ■■
Z	■■ ■■ ■■ ■■ ■■ ■■
W	■■ ■■ ■■ ■■ ■■ ■■ ■■
XY	■■ ■■ ■■ ■■ ■■ ■■
XZ	■■ ■■ ■■ ■■ ■■ ■■ ■■
XW	■■ ■■ ■■ ■■ ■■ ■■ ■■ ■■
YZ	■■ ■■ ■■ ■■ ■■ ■■ ■■
YW	■■ ■■ ■■ ■■ ■■ ■■ ■■ ■■
ZW	■■ ■■ ■■ ■■ ■■ ■■ ■■ ■■ ■■
XYZ	■■ ■■ ■■ ■■ ■■ ■■ ■■ ■■ ■■
XYW	■■ ■■ ■■ ■■ ■■ ■■ ■■ ■■ ■■ ■■
XZW	■■ ■■ ■■ ■■ ■■ ■■ ■■ ■■ ■■ ■■
YZW	■■ ■■ ■■ ■■ ■■ ■■ ■■ ■■ ■■ ■■
XYZW	■■ ■■ ■■ ■■ ■■ ■■ ■■ ■■ ■■ ■■ ■■

SECONDARY STATION FIRST TWO PULSES:

TURNED ON (BLINKED) FOR APPROXIMATELY 0.25 SECONDS EVERY 4.0 SECONDS. ALL SECONDARIES USE SAME CODE, AUTOMATICALLY RECOGNIZED BY MOST MODERN LORAN—C RECEIVERS.

TABLE 4331b.—Loran-C blink code.

   In performing a calibration, an effort is made to distribute the monitor sites uniformly over the coverage area. Each site is visited for a minimum period of 4 hours, during which time the Loran-C signals are monitored precisely and the average value for the period is determined. The transmitting stations and the station for which the control time differences are to be established are also required to conduct precise monitoring. The geographic location of the monitor site (if not already known) is determined at the same time by use of satellite positioning. The calibration data is then reduced to establish or check the control time differences, and to estimate surface conductivities throughout the coverage area. This improves the ability to predict the time differences at particular locations.

	MASTER	EACH SECONDARY
GRI A	++--+-+- +	+++++--+
GRI B	+--+++++ -	+-+-++--

NOTE: (+)   INDICATES ZERO DEGREE CARRIER PHASE

(–)   INDICATES 180° CARRIER PHASE

LORAN—C INTERVALS A&B ALTERNATE IN TIME

TABLE 4331c.—Loran-C phase codes.

4335. Receiver characteristics.—A "true" low-cost Loran-C receiver which will be useful to the limits of the U. S. Coast Guard's advertised coverage area for the Coastal Confluence Zone has the following characteristics:

1. It acquires the Loran-C signals automatically, without the use of an oscilloscope.

2. It accomplishes cycle matching on all pulses to take advantage of the maximum accuracy of the system.

3. It automatically tracks the signals once they have been acquired.

4. It displays two time-difference readings.

There are many combined Loran-A/C receivers on the market, exhibiting varying degrees of performance. Few of these receivers are known to meet all of the above requirements. There is no guarantee that all Loran-A/C receivers will accurately measure the received Loran-C signals out to the limits of the advertised coverage area, since most of them use pulse envelope matching techniques and little or no cycle matching. Some receivers perform all of the desired functions except that they depend on the operator using an oscilloscope for signal acquisitions. In a "noisy" environment (e.g. where the atmospheric or man-made noise level is high compared to that of the desired Loran-C signals), this will be extremely difficult, again limiting the area in which that receiver can be used.

4336. Interference filters.—Like all radionavigation systems, Loran-C can be adversely affected by interference. The effect of interference is to make it difficult to acquire the Loran-C signals or to make the readings fluctuate more than usual or both. Most manufacturers provide tuneable filters which can be used to minimize such interference. If a user is to remain always in the same general area (about 100-mile radius from a center point) it will probably never be necessary to readjust these filters once they are properly set by the manufacturer or his local representative.

If the user is to travel great distances, it will be necessary for him to learn how to readjust the filters. This is not a difficult task following some initial training.

4337. Signal acquisition.—To acquire the Loran-C signals it is important to enter into the receiver the GRI of the local Loran-C chain. Usually, the GRI will remain unchanged as long as the vessel stays on the same coast of the United States.

The speed at which the receiver will find the Loran-C signals depends upon the signal strength and how much noise is present. In some receivers, the user can expedite the process by preselecting the approximate Loran-C readings he expects to read. Most modern receivers will be automatically tracking within 5 minutes of initial turn-on, and will continue to track until the receiver is turned off. If a user is at a known location (at a pier and ready for departure, for example) it will be obvious to him when the receiver is providing the correct information. In any event, most receivers show some type of an alarm which remains lighted until the receiver is tracking properly.

Initially acquiring Loran-C signals when arriving from far out (several hundred miles or more) at sea is a more difficult problem than the one of a vessel at a pier where the Loran-C readings are known. Thus, the receiver may take more time to acquire the signals. When first entering a Loran-C coverage area, the receiver should be checked frequently to ensure that all the alarms are extinguished. Sometimes, due to weak signals and high noise, the receiver alarms will go out even though the receiver is not tracking precisely. However, as the vessel continues to enter the stronger signal area, the receiver will automatically recognize that it has made an error and will give the user an alarm light. This should occur well before the vessel enters the CCZ.

4338. Lattice tables provide the coordinates necessary for the construction of straight line representations of segments of the hyperbolic lines of position. Except when the user of the Loran-C system is within about 20 nautical miles of a transmitting station, the straight line segment joining any two adjacent tabulated points can be used without appreciable error. Should there be doubt about the accuracy of the line of position with regard to curvature, the amount of error can be resolved by plotting an adjoining straight line segment of the line of position.

Pub. 221, *Loran-C Table*, is a series of lattice tables published by the Defense Mapping Agency Hydrographic Center. In this series there is a separate lattice table for each station pair of a chain. Each table is identified by the publication number (221), pertinent suffix, and station pair. For example, Pub. 221 (2013) Pair 7960–X is the lattice table for the 7960–X pair in the Gulf of Alaska chain.

Points on hyperbolas separated by 10 microseconds of time difference are tabulated in the lattice tables (fig. 4338a) at intervals of whole degrees of latitude or longitude except in areas close to transmitting stations. In such areas, points are tabulated at intervals of whole degrees or quarter degrees, depending upon the degree of curvature of the line. A separate column is given for each tabulated reading, at 10-microsecond intervals. An auxiliary tabulation labeled Δ (delta) gives the change in longitude or latitude (to $0\rlap{.}'01$) for a 1-microsecond change in the time-difference reading. Also, points on the baseline extension are tabulated in a column headed by the time-difference reading on the baseline extension.

Tabulated readings are for groundwaves. Skywave readings are corrected to the equivalent groundwave readings before entering the tables. A groundwave reading is designated T_G, and a skywave reading T_S. If a groundwave is matched with a skywave, the reading is labeled T_{GS} if the groundwave is from the master station, and T_{SG} if from the secondary (slave) station.

The Loran-C lattice table is entered with the groundwave reading in microseconds, and the latitude *or* longitude. For a line running in a generally north-south direction, the table is entered with the latitude, and the corresponding longitude is taken from the table. For an east-west line, the table is entered with longitude, and latitude is taken from the table. Two such points are thus determined and plotted, one on each side of the dead reckoning position. The straight line connecting them is an approximation of a small segment of the line of position.

Interpolation is usually required. For each latitude *or* longitude argument, the lattice table is entered with the tabulated time-difference (T) *nearest* to the groundwave reading. The longitudes *or* latitudes extracted are then corrected by the amounts of the products of (T_G-T) and Δ, the change in longitude *or* latitude for 1-microsecond change in T. Careful attention must be given to the signs of Δ and (T_G-T). The sign of Δ is found by inspection. The sign of (T_G-T) is found by *always* algebraically subtracting T from T_G.

Example 1.—The 1530 DR position of a ship is lat. 48°35′N, long. 30°17′W. Loran-C readings are obtained, as follows:

1530	7930–X	T_G 29523.8
1530	7930–Z	T_G 48635.7

Required.—The 1530 Loran-C fix.

Solution.—Enter the lattice tables (fig. 4338a) in the T (time difference) column nearest to the value of T_G and with the latitudes or longitudes closest to and on each side of the DR position. Extract the corresponding longitudes or latitudes for these two points. Interpolate if necessary. Plot the two points thus obtained. Connect these two points with a straight line to determine a segment of the hyperbolic line of position. The intersection of two lines for different pairs determines the Loran-C fix (fig. 4338b).

Pair 7930–X	Lati-tude	Tabulated longitude	Δ	Longitude change $(T_G-T)\times(\Delta)$	Interpolated longitude
T_____ 29520					
T_G_____ 29523.8	48°N	30°24′.3W	+22	$(+3.8)\times(+.22)=+0′.8$	30°25′.1W
T_G–T___ +3.8	49°N	30°21′.5W	+21	$(+3.8)\times(+.21)=+0′.8$	30°22′.3W

Pair 7930–Z	Longi-tude	Tabulated latitude	Δ	Latitude change $(T_G-T)\times(\Delta)$	Interpolated latitude
T_____ 48640					
T_G_____ 48635.7	30°W	48°24′.3N	+20	$(-4.3)\times(+.20)=-0′.9$	48°23′.4N
T_G–T___ −4.3	31°W	48°47′.5N	+19	$(-4.3)\times(+.19)=-0′.8$	48°46′.7N

Loran-C lines of position are plotted through the following positions: lat. 48°N′ long. 30°25′.1W; lat. 49°N, long. 30°22′.3W; and lat. 48°23′.4N, long. 30°W; lat. 48°46′.7N, long. 31°W.

Answer.—lat. 48°32′.7N, long. 30°23′.6W.

When it is possible to match two groundwaves, never match a groundwave with a skywave. Under the best conditions for matching groundwaves to skywaves, the value obtained may be uncertain by an amount equivalent to several miles in position. As is the case with matching two skywaves, the error may be very large when the user is within 200 microseconds of the baseline extensions.

When receiving a skywave signal from one Loran-C station and strong groundwave and skywave signals from a second Loran-C station, the practical procedure is to match the skywave from the first station with the groundwave from the second station. This situation would be encountered when the receiver is located far from the first station and near to the second station. The use of an all skywave match in this situation may cause large errors because of large uncertainties in the skywave correction for the near station.

Example 2.—The 2130 DR position of a ship is lat. 48°35′N, long. 46°45′W. Loran-C readings are obtained as follows:

2130	7930–X	T_S 33114.3
2130	7930–Z	T_{SG} 54632.2

(240) GF   7930-X

T	29500		29520		29540		29560		29580		T
Lat		Δ		Δ		Δ		Δ		Δ	Long
° '	° '		° '		° '		° '		° '		° '
25 N	31 39.6W	36	31 46.8W	35	31 53.9W	35	32 01.1W	36	32 08.3W	36	
26 N	31 36.1W	35	31 43.3W	35	31 50.4W	35	31 57.5W	35	32 04.5W	35	
27 N	31 32.8W	34	31 39.7W	34	31 46.8W	35	31 53.8W	35	32 00.8W	34	
28 N	31 29.4W	34	31 36.3W	34	31 43.2W	34	31 50.0W	34	31 57.0W	34	
29 N	31 25.9W	34	31 32.8W	33	31 39.5W	33	31 46.3W	34	31 53.1W	34	
30 N	31 22.4W	33	31 29.1W	33	31 35.8W	33	31 42.6W	33	31 49.3W	33	
31 N	31 19.0W	32	31 25.5W	32	31 32.1W	32	31 38.7W	33	31 45.4W	33	
32 N	31 15.4W	32	31 21.9W	32	31 28.4W	32	31 34.9W	32	31 41.4W	32	
33 N	31 11.9W	31	31 18.2W	31	31 24.6W	31	31 31.0W	32	31 37.5W	31	
34 N	31 08.3W	31	31 14.6W	31	31 20.8W	31	31 27.1W	31	31 33.4W	31	
35 N	31 04.7W	30	31 10.9W	30	31 17.0W	30	31 23.2W	31	31 29.4W	30	
36 N	31 01.1W	30	31 07.1W	30	31 13.1W	30	31 19.2W	30	31 25.3W	30	
37 N	30 57.5W	29	31 03.4W	29	31 09.3W	29	31 15.3W	29	31 21.3W	29	
38 N	30 53.8W	29	30 59.6W	28	31 05.4W	29	31 11.3W	29	31 17.2W	29	
39 N	30 50.2W	28	30 55.9W	28	31 01.6W	28	31 07.2W	28	31 13.0W	28	
40 N	30 46.6W	27	30 52.1W	27	30 57.6W	27	31 03.3W	28	31 08.9W	27	
41 N	30 42.9W	27	30 48.4W	27	30 53.8W	27	30 59.3W	27	31 04.8W	27	
42 N	30 39.3W	26	30 44.7W	26	30 50.0W	26	30 55.3W	26	31 00.7W	26	
43 N	30 35.7W	26	30 41.0W	26	30 46.2W	26	30 51.4W	25	30 56.6W	26	
44 N	30 32.3W	25	30 37.4W	25	30 42.5W	25	30 47.5W	25	30 52.6W	25	
45 N	30 28.9W	24	30 33.9W	24	30 38.8W	24	30 43.7W	24	30 48.7W	25	
46 N	30 25.7W	24	30 30.5W	23	30 35.3W	24	30 40.1W	24	30 45.0W	24	
47 N	30 22.6W	23	30 27.3W	23	30 31.9W	23	30 36.6W	23	30 41.4W	23	
48 N	30 19.7W	22	30 24.3W	22	30 28.9W	22	30 33.4W	22	30 37.9W	22	
49 N	30 17.2W	22	30 21.5W	21	30 25.9W	22	30 30.4W	22	30 34.8W	22	

7930-Z   GR (197)

T	48600		48620		48640		48660		48680		T
Lat		Δ		Δ		Δ		Δ		Δ	Long
° '	° '		° '		° '		° '		° '		° '
	47 51.8N	21	47 56.0N	21	48 00.3N	21	48 04.5N	21	48 08.7N	21	29 W
	48 16.2N	20	48 20.3N	20	48 24.3N	20	48 28.3N	20	48 32.3N	20	30 W
	48 39.9N	19	48 43.7N	19	48 47.5N	19	48 51.3N	19	48 55.1N	19	31 W
	49 02.7N	18	49 06.3N	18	49 09.9N	18	49 13.6N	18	49 17.2N	17	32 W
	49 24.7N	17	49 28.1N	17	49 31.5N	17	49 35.0N	17	49 38.4N	17	33 W
	49 45.9N	16	49 49.2N	16	49 52.4N	16	49 55.7N	16	49 58.9N	16	34 W
	50 06.4N	15	50 09.5N	15	50 12.5N	15	50 15.6N	15	50 18.7N	15	35 W
	50 26.1N	14	50 29.1N	14	50 32.0N	14	50 34.9N	14	50 37.8N	14	36 W
	50 45.2N	13	50 48.0N	13	50 50.8N	13	50 53.5N	13	50 56.2N	13	37 W
	51 03.6N	13	51 06.2N	13	51 08.9N	13	51 11.5N	12	51 14.0N	13	38 W
	51 21.3N	12	51 23.9N	12	51 26.3N	12	51 28.8N	12	51 31.3N	12	39 W
	51 38.5N	11	51 40.8N	11	51 43.2N	11	51 45.6N	11	51 47.9N	11	40 W
	51 55.0N	11	51 57.3N	11	51 59.6N	11	52 01.8N	10	52 04.0N	11	41 W
	52 11.1N	10	52 13.2N	10	52 15.3N	10	52 17.5N	10	52 19.6N	10	42 W
	52 26.6N	10	52 23.6N	10	52 30.6N	10	52 32.7N	10	52 34.7N	9	43 W

FIGURE 4338a.—Extracts from lattice tables.

Required.—The 2130 Loran-C fix.

Solution.—The observed skywave reading (T_S) must be corrected to an equivalent groundwave reading (T_G). Preceding each time-difference table are conventional "Skywave Correction" tables for daytime (ionosphere height=73 kilometers) and for nighttime (h=91 km.). Enter the pertinent table (fig. 4338c) (in this example, nighttime—since the Loran-C readings are taken at 2130) with the DR position and obtain the skywave correction. Interpolate if necessary. Apply the correction to the observed T_S to determine T_G.

If a skywave and a groundwave are matched, the observed reading (T_{SG} or T_{GS}) must also be corrected to an equivalent groundwave reading (T_G). Special "Ground-

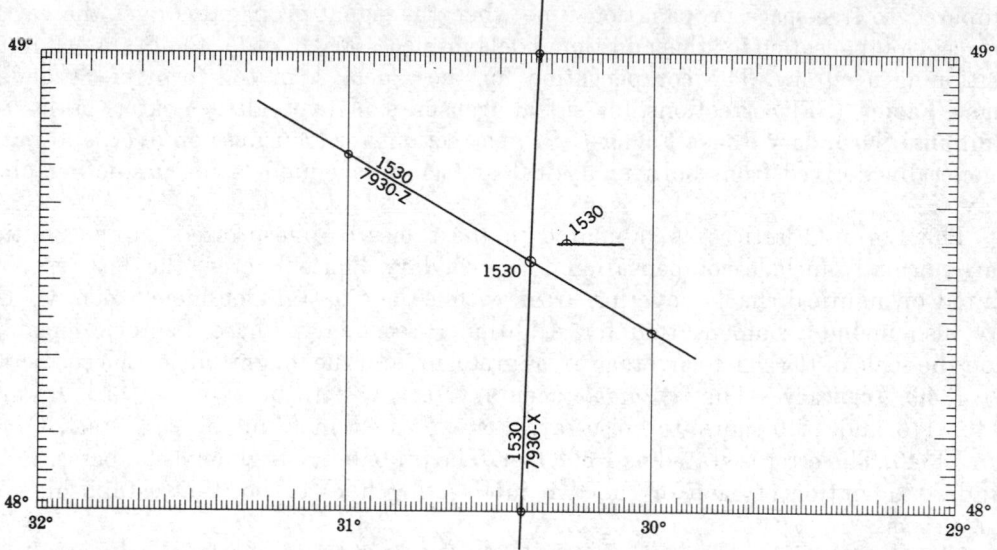

FIGURE 4338b.—Loran-C fix.

wave to Skywave Correction" tables (fig. 4338d) precede the time-difference tables. Enter the appropriate special correction table (in this example, nighttime) and obtain the special correction. To determine T_G, apply this correction to the observed T_{SG} or T_{GS} reading.

After T_G is determined, the remainder of the solution follows that of example 1. Extracts from the lattice table are given in figure 4338e.

Pair 7930–X

T_S	33114. 3
Conventional Corr	+8. 1
T_G	33122. 4

Pair 7930–X

T	33120
T_G	33122. 4
T_G–T	+2. 4

Latitude	Tabulated longitude	Δ	Longitude change $(T_G-T)\times(\Delta)$	Interpolated longitude
48°N	46°59'.5W	+40	(+2.4)×(+.40)=+1'.0	47°00'.5W
49°N	46°20'.5W	+38	(+2.4)×(+.38)=+0'.9	46°21'.4W

Pair 7930–Z

T_{SG}	45632. 2
Special Corr	+62
T_G	45694. 2

Pair 7930–Z

T	45700
T_G	45694. 2
T_G–T	−5. 8

Longitude	Tabulated latitude	Δ	Latitude change $(T_G-T)\times(\Delta)$	Interpolated latitude
46°W	48°10'.9N	+13	(−5.8)×(+.13)=−0'.8	48°10'.1N
47°W	48°41'.8N	+11	(−5.8)×(+.11)=−0'.6	48°41'.2N

Answer.—Following the procedure for plotting lines of position as shown in example 1, the 2130 Loran-C fix is lat. 48°31'.3N, long. 46°40'.2W.

4339. Propagation prediction.—The accuracy of the lattice tables or of the lattices overprinted on the nautical chart is dependent upon knowledge of the LF signal transit time between a transmitting station and receiver. The signal propagation velocity in free-space is well known; however, there exists an additional time (or phase) delay compared to free-space propagation time when the signal propagates over the earth's surface. Compensation for this additional delay is necessary in order to obtain maximum positioning accuracy. The compensation for these delays, in the form of **Secondary Phase Factor** (SF) corrections for signal transmission over all seawater paths and **Additional Secondary Phase Factor** (ASF) corrections for transmission over land paths, is generally derived from both analytical and empirical models for predicting phase delay.

The Loran-C lattices as tabulated in the tables or overprinted on the nautical chart normally include compensation for Secondary Phase Factor; the lattices over-printed on nautical charts covering areas within the Coastal Confluence Zone (CCZ) may also include compensation for Additional Secondary Phase Factor, depending upon the scale of the chart, coverage area, gradient, and the magnitude of the correction.

4340. Accuracy.—The *repeatable* accuracy (art. Q8) to be expected of a Loran-C fix for 1:3 and 1:10 signal-to-noise ratios is expressed in terms of $2d_{rms}$ (art. Q7) in figure 4340. The error is stated as 1,500 feet. The probability is given as 95 percent. The standard deviation of each of the two intersecting lines of position establishing the fix is 0.1 μs.

The repeatable accuracy is affected by systematic and random errors (arts. Q3 and Q4). The systematic errors are largely due to errors in propagation prediction (art. 4339).

4341. Ranging mode.—With the user's receiver appropriately modified to enable time measurements with respect to a local time reference, the Loran-C system can be operated in the ranging or Range-Range mode, which is discussed in more detail in article 4304.

4342. Loran-D, designed for military tactical use, is a lower power, shorter range version of Loran-C. Since the stations are readily transportable, the system provides the potential for filling any gaps in the higher power Loran-C coverage.

4343. The U. S. Coastal Confluence Zone (CCZ) as defined by the *National Plan for Navigation*, promulgated by the Secretary of Transportation, is that area of water extending outward from the shore for 50 nautical miles or to the 100-fathom curve, whichever is farther from the shore. The inner boundary is the harbor entrance. It is the area where transoceanic traffic converges and interport traffic exists.

After extensive study, the U. S. Coast Guard recommended and the Secretary of Transportation approved in 1974 the selection of Loran-C as the government sponsored navigation system for the CCZ.

Within the limits of the CCZ, users of "true" Loran-C receivers (art. 4335) should obtain a repeatable accuracy (art. Q8) of 0.25 nautical mile with a probability of 95 percent. That is, only 1 fix in 20 should deviate from the mean of a large number of positions that could be established by the Loran-C system at a given place and time by more than 0.25 nautical mile.

Loran-C coverage in the CCZ as planned in 1977 is shown in figure 4343.

Decca

4344. The Decca Navigator System, commonly referred to as **Decca,** is a short to medium range hyperbolic radionavigation system which utilizes phase comparisons of low frequency (70–130 kHz), unmodulated, continuous-wave transmissions to provide fixes of high accuracy. The simplicity and speed in fixing is an important characteristic of the system. A fix can be obtained in less than 1 minute by reading two relevant position coordinate values indicated by two of the three coordinate meters of the receiver and then referring them to the appropriate navigational chart overprinted with the Decca lattice.

SKYWAVE CORRECTION

7930-X GF

NIGHTTIME (h = 91 km.)

Longitude—59°W to 45°W

LAT	59	58	57	56	55	54	53	52	51	50	49	48	47	46	45	LAT
89																89
88																88
87																87
86																86
85																85
84																84
83									0.0	0.0	0.0					83
82	0.0	0.0	0.0	0.0	0.0	0.3	0.3	0.3	0.1	0.1	0.1	0.0	0.0	0.0	0.0	82
81	0.2	0.2	0.2	0.2	0.3	0.3	0.3	0.3	0.2	0.2	0.2	0.2	0.1	0.1	0.1	81
80	0.4	0.5	0.5	0.5	0.5	0.5	0.4	0.4	0.4	0.3	0.3	0.3	0.2	0.2	0.2	80
			ADD					ADD					ADD			
79	0.7	0.7	0.7	0.7	0.7	0.6	0.6	0.6	0.5	0.5	0.5	0.4	0.4	0.4	0.3	79
78	1.0	1.0	1.0	0.9	0.9	0.9	0.9	0.8	0.8	0.8	0.7	0.7	0.6	0.6	0.5	78
77	1.3	1.3	1.3	1.3	1.3	1.2	1.2	1.2	1.1	1.1	1.1	1.0	1.0	0.9	0.8	77
76	1.7	1.7	1.7	1.7	1.7	1.7	1.7	1.6	1.6	1.6	1.5	1.5	1.4	1.3	1.3	76
75	2.3	2.3	2.3	2.3	2.3	2.3	2.3	2.3	2.2	2.2	2.2	2.1	2.0	2.0	1.9	75
74	2.9	3.0	3.0	3.1	3.1	3.1	3.1	3.1	3.1	3.1	3.0	3.0	2.9	2.8	2.7	74
73	3.8	3.9	4.0	4.0	4.1	4.2	4.2	4.2	4.2	4.2	4.2	4.1	4.1	4.0	3.9	73
72	4.9	5.0	5.2	5.3	5.4	5.5	5.6	5.7	5.7	5.7	5.7	5.7	5.6	5.5	5.4	72
71	6.2	6.4	6.7	6.9	7.1	7.3	7.4	7.6	7.7	7.7	7.8	7.8	7.7	7.6	7.5	71
70	7.8	8.1	8.5	8.8	9.2	9.5	9.8	10	10	10	10	10	10	10	10	70
			ADD					ADD					ADD			
69	9.7	10	11	11	12	12	13	13	13	14	14	14	14	14	14	69
68	12	13	14	14	15	16	17	17	18	18	19	19	19	19	19	68
67	15	16	17	18	19	20	21	22	23	24	25	25	26	26	26	67
66	17	19	20	22	24	26	27	29	31	32	33	34	35	35	35	66
65	20	22	25	27	30	32	35	38	40	43	45	47	48	49	49	65
64	23	26	29	32	36	40	44	48	53	57	61	65				64
63	26	29	33	38	42	48	54	61								63
62	28	32	36	42	48	56	64									62
61	29	33	38	45	52	61					DO NOT USE					61
60	29	33	38	45	52	62					SKYWAVES					60
			ADD								IN THIS AREA					
59	27	31	36	42	50	58										59
58	25	29	33	38	44	52	60									58
57	22	25	29	33	38	44	50	57	65							57
56	19	22	25	28	32	36	40	45	50	56	61	65				56
55	16	18	21	23	26	29	32	35	39	42	45	48	50	51	51	55
54	13	15	17	19	21	23	25	27	30	32	34	35	37	37	37	54
53	11	12	14	15	17	18	20	21	23	24	26	27	27	28	28	53
52	9.0	10	11	12	13	14	15	17	18	19	19	20	21	21	21	52
51	7.3	8.0	8.8	9.6	10	11	12	13	14	14	15	15	16	16	16	51
50	5.8	6.4	7.0	7.6	8.2	8.8	9.4	10	11	11	11	12	12	12	12	50
			ADD					ADD					ADD			
49	4.6	5.0	5.5	5.9	6.4	6.8	7.3	7.7	8.1	8.4	8.7	9.0	9.1	9.2	9.3	49
48	3.6	3.9	4.3	4.6	5.0	5.3	5.6	5.9	6.2	6.5	6.7	6.9	7.0	7.0	7.1	48
47	2.8	3.1	3.3	3.6	3.8	4.1	4.3	4.6	4.8	4.9	5.1	5.2	5.3	5.4	5.4	47
46	2.2	2.4	2.6	2.7	2.9	3.1	3.3	3.5	3.6	3.8	3.9	4.0	4.0	4.1	4.1	46
45	1.6	1.8	1.9	2.1	2.2	2.4	2.5	2.6	2.7	2.8	2.9	3.0	3.0	3.1	3.1	45
44	1.2	1.3	1.5	1.6	1.7	1.8	1.9	2.0	2.1	2.1	2.2	2.3	2.3	2.3	2.3	44
43	0.9	1.0	1.1	1.2	1.2	1.3	1.4	1.5	1.5	1.6	1.6	1.7	1.7	1.7	1.7	43
42	0.6	0.7	0.8	0.8	0.9	0.9	1.0	1.1	1.1	1.2	1.2	1.2	1.2	1.2	1.3	42
41	0.4	0.4	0.5	0.5	0.6	0.6	0.7	0.7	0.8	0.8	0.8	0.9	0.9	0.9	0.9	41
40	0.1	0.2	0.2	0.3	0.3	0.4	0.4	0.5	0.5	0.5	0.5	0.6	0.6	0.6	0.6	40
			ADD					ADD					ADD			
39	0.0	0.0	0.0	0.1	0.1	0.1	0.2	0.2	0.2	0.3	0.3	0.3	0.3	0.3	0.3	39
38				0.0	0.0	0.0	0.0	0.0	0.0	0.0	0.1	0.1	0.1	0.1	0.1	38
37											0.0	0.0	0.0	0.0	0.0	37
36																36
35																35
34																34
33																33
32																32
31																31
30																30
	59	58	57	56	55	54	53	52	51	50	49	48	47	46	45	

Longitude—59°W to 45°W

NIGHTTIME

LXV

FIGURE 4338c.—Conventional skywave correction table.

GROUNDWAVE TO SKYWAVE CORRECTION

7930-Z   **GR**

NIGHTTIME (h = 91 km.)

Groundwave from Slave (R) to First-hop Skywave from Master (G)

Longitude—59°W to 45°W

Latitude	59	58	57	56	55	54	53	52	51	50	49	48	47	46	45	Latitude
69																69
68																68
67																67
66																66
65																65
64																64
63																63
62																62
61																61
60																60
59																59
58																58
57																57
56																56
55																55
54	68	ADD 69	71	73												54
53	65	66	68	69	71	72										53
52	63	64	65	66	67	68	70	71	72	73						52
51	61	62	63	64	65	65	66	67	68	68	69	69	70	70	70	51
50	60	60	61	62	62	63	63	64	65	65	66	66	66	66	66	50
49	59	59	60	60 ADD	60	61	61	62	62	63 ADD	63	63	63	63	63	49
48	58	58	58	59	59	59	60	60	60	61	61	61	61	61	61	48
47	57	57	57	58	58	58	58	59	59	59	59	59	59	59	59	47
46	56	56	57	57	57	57	57	58	58	58	58	58	58	58	58	46
45	56	56	56	56	56	56	57	57	57	57	57	57	57	57	57	45
44	55	ADD 55	56	56	56	56	56	ADD 56	56	56	ADD 56	56	56	56	56	44
43	55	55	55	55	55	55	55	56	55	56	56	56	56	56	56	43
42	55	55	55	55	55	55	55	55	55	55	55	55	55	55	55	42
41	54	55	55	55	55	55	55	55	55	55	55	55	55	55	55	41
40	54	54	54	54	54	54	55	55	55	55	55	55	55			40
39			54	54	ADD 54	54	54	54	54	54						39
38																38
37																37
36																36
35																35
34																34
33																33
32																32
31																31
30																30

NORTH   NORTH

59	58	57	56	55	54	53	52	51	50	49	48	47	46	45

Longitude—59°W to 45°W

Groundwave from Slave (R) to First-hop Skywave from Master (G)

NIGHTTIME

XLVII

FIGURE 4338d.—Special groundwave to skywave correction table.

328 GF | 7930-X

T	33100			33120			33140			33160			33180			T
Lat																Long
° '	°	'	Δ	°	'	Δ	°	'	Δ	°	'	Δ	°	'	Δ	° '
34 N	54	29.0W	56	54	40.5W	57	54	51.9W	57	55	03.5W	58	55	15.1W	58	
35 N	54	01.1W	55	54	12.3W	56	54	23.6W	56	54	35.0W	57	54	46.5W	57	
36 N	53	32.6W	54	53	43.5W	55	53	54.7W	55	54	05.8W	56	54	17.2W	56	
37 N	53	03.4W	53	53	14.1W	54	53	25.1W	54	53	36.0W	55	53	47.2W	55	
38 N	52	33.4W	52	52	44.1W	53	52	54.8W	53	53	05.6W	54	53	16.5W	54	
39 N	52	02.9W	51	52	13.3W	52	52	23.8W	52	52	34.3W	53	52	45.0W	53	
40 N	51	31.5W	50	51	41.7W	51	51	52.0W	51	52	02.4W	51	52	12.8W	52	
41 N	50	59.5W	49	51	09.4W	49	51	19.5W	50	51	29.5W	50	51	39.8W	51	
42 N	50	26.5W	48	50	36.3W	48	50	46.0W	49	50	56.0W	49	51	05.9W	50	
43 N	49	52.8W	47	50	02.3W	47	50	11.8W	47	50	21.5W	48	50	31.2W	48	
44 N	49	18.3W	45	49	27.5W	46	49	36.7W	46	49	46.1W	47	49	55.6W	47	
45 N	48	42.9W	44	48	51.8W	44	49	00.8W	45	49	09.9W	45	49	19.1W	46	
46 N	48	06.6W	43	48	15.2W	43	48	23.9W	43	48	32.8W	44	48	41.6W	44	
47 N	47	29.5W	41	47	37.8W	41	47	46.2W	42	47	54.7W	42	48	03.3W	42	
48 N	46	51.5W	39	46	59.5W	40	47	07.7W	40	47	15.8W	40	47	24.1W	41	
49 N	46	12.9W	38	46	20.5W	38	46	28.3W	38	46	36.1W	39	46	44.0W	39	
50 N	45	33.6W	36	45	40.9W	36	45	48.3W	37	45	55.7W	37	46	03.3W	37	
51 N	44	53.8W	34	45	00.8W	34	45	07.7W	35	45	14.8W	35	45	21.9W	35	
52 N	44	13.9W	32	44	20.5W	32	44	27.0W	33	44	33.7W	33	44	40.4W	33	
53 N	43	34.2W	30	43	40.4W	30	43	46.5W	30	43	52.8W	31	43	59.0W	31	

7930-Z | GR 97

T	45700			45720			45740			45760			45780			T
Lat																Long
° '	°	'	Δ	°	'	Δ	°	'	Δ	°	'	Δ	°	'	Δ	° '
	46	57.7N	16	47	01.0N	16	47	04.3N	15	47	07.6N	15	47	10.8N	16	44 W
	47	36.2N	14	47	39.2N	14	47	42.1N	14	47	45.0N	14	47	47.8N	14	45 W
	48	10.9N	13	48	13.6N	13	48	16.2N	12	48	18.7N	12	48	21.3N	12	46 W
	48	41.8N	11	48	44.2N	11	48	46.5N	11	48	48.8N	11	48	51.1N	11	47 W
	49	08.9N	10	49	11.0N	10	49	13.1N	10	49	15.2N	10	49	17.2N	10	48 W
	49	32.1N	9	49	34.0N	9	49	36.0N	9	49	37.9N	9	49	39.8N	9	49 W
	49	37.3N	9	49	39.2N	9	49	41.1N	9	49	43.0N	9	49	44.9N	9	49 15W
	49	42.3N	9	49	44.2N	9	49	46.0N	9	49	47.9N	9	49	49.8N	9	49 30W
	49	47.0N	9	49	48.9N	9	49	50.8N	9	49	52.6N	8	49	54.4N	9	49 45W
	49	51.6N	8	49	53.4N	9	49	55.2N	9	49	57.1N	9	49	58.8N	8	50 W
	49	56.0N	8	49	57.7N	8	49	59.4N	8	50	01.3N	9	50	03.1N	8	50 15W
	50	00.0N	8	50	01.7N	8	50	03.5N	8	50	05.3N	8	50	07.0N	8	50 30W
	50	03.9N	8	50	05.6N	8	50	07.4N	8	50	09.1N	8	50	10.9N	8	50 45W
	50	07.6N	8	50	09.3N	8	50	11.0N	8	50	12.7N	8	50	14.5N	8	51 W
	50	11.0N	8	50	12.7N	8	50	14.4N	8	50	16.1N	8	50	17.9N	8	51 15W
	50	14.3N	8	50	15.9N	8	50	17.7N	8	50	19.4N	8	50	21.1N	8	51 30W
	50	17.6N	8	50	19.0N	8	50	20.7N	8	50	22.4N	8	50	24.1N	8	51 45W
	50	20.2N	8	50	21.9N	8	50	23.6N	8	50	25.2N	8	50	26.9N	8	52 W
	50	22.8N	8	50	24.5N	8	50	26.2N	8	50	27.9N	8	50	29.5N	8	52 15W
	50	25.3N	8	50	27.0N	8	50	28.7N	8	50	30.4N	8	50	32.0N	8	52 30W

FIGURE 4338e.—Extracts from lattice tables.

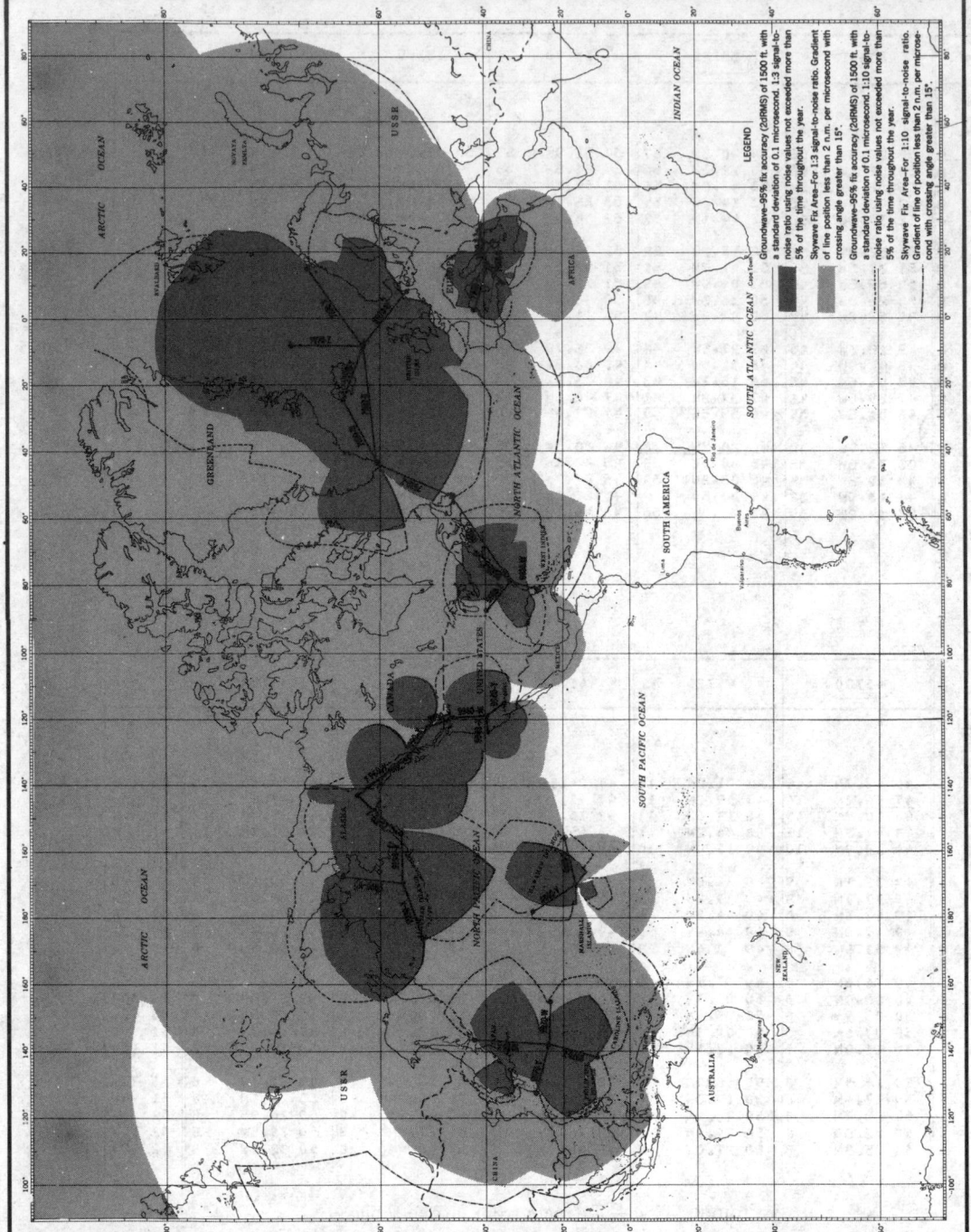

FIGURE 4340.—Loran-C coverage diagram.

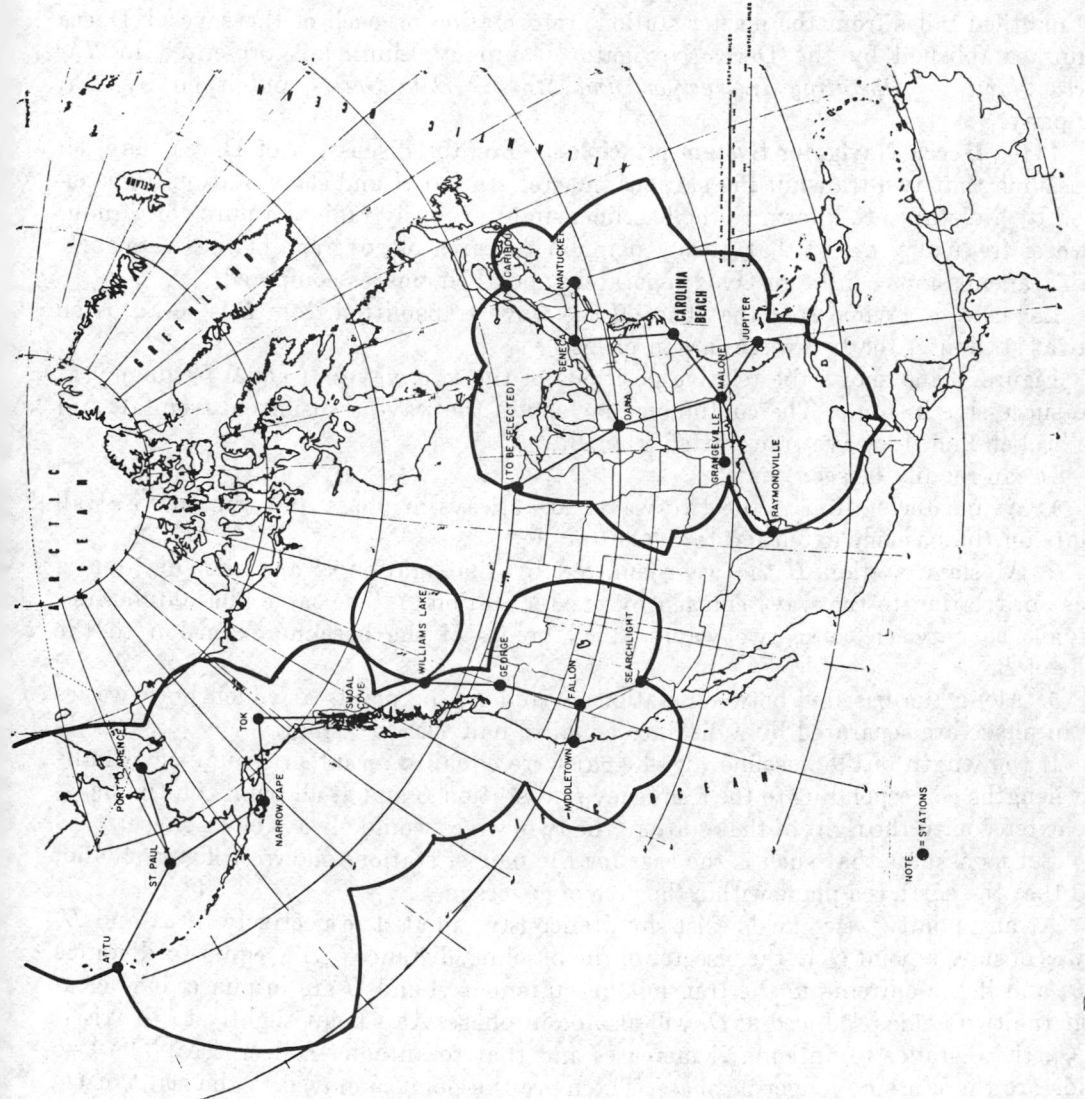

FIGURE 4343.—Loran-C coverage in the Coastal Confluence Zone as planned in 1977.

Developments of the Decca Navigator System used for special applications such as in narrow channels are not discussed in this chapter.

Like other hyperbolic systems, the Decca Navigator System is *continuous*, *passive*, and *non-saturable*.

4345. Decca chains.—Each of the several Decca chains usually consists of four transmitting stations operating in three pairs: master/red slave station, master/green slave station, and master/purple slave station. The slave station of the pair is so called because its function is to transmit a signal harmonically related and having a fixed phase relationship with the master signal. Each slave station is located about 60 to 120 nautical miles from the master station. Information on each of the several Decca chains established by the Decca Navigator Company Limited is presented in *The Decca Navigator Operating Instructions and Marine Data Sheets*, published by that company.

4346. Decca Navigator System principles.—For the discussion of Decca here, let us assume that two transmitting stations, master station A and slave station B, separated by a distance S, known as the baseline, simultaneously radiate a pure continuous wave of frequency f, and that at any point in the area of coverage of these stations, both transmissions can be received separately and their phases compared.

Let us also assume that the phase of the wave transmitted from B is so adjusted that at station A the two waves are in phase.

Figure 4346a shows the relative positions of the two waves of equal frequency at two successive instants. The continuous line shows the wave transmitted from A, and the broken line the wave transmitted from B.

It can readily be seen that:

1. At master station A the two waves are always in phase and remain so at all points on the baseline extension to the left of A.

2. At slave station B the wave emitted by that station is and remains out of phase in relation to the wave emitted by master station A. The same phase difference prevails as between these two waves at all points of the baseline extension to the right of B.

3. Along the baseline between stations A and B, the points at which both waves are in phase are separated by a distance equal to half the wavelength.

If the length of the baseline (fig. 4346a) were equal to an integral number of half-wavelengths corresponding to the frequency f, at station B and at all points on the baseline extension to the right of that station, the two waves would always be in phase.

Let us assume that such is the case for the pair of stations shown in figure 4346b, and that the earth is a plane within the area of coverage.

At any point Q, two fields exist simultaneously radiated respectively by A and B. If we consider a point Q_1 in the bisector of the baseline, distance Q_1A is equal to distance Q_1B, and if the currents in the transmitting antennas A and B are in phase, it is clear that the two fields produced at Q_1 will also be in phase. At a point slightly to the right of Q_1, the distance to antenna A increases and that to antenna B decreases. The two fields are therefore no longer in phase. The more the point is moved to the right of Q_1, the more the difference in phase increases. The phase difference may thus reach $360°$, which is equivalent to a phase difference of $0°$, and the two fields are once more in phase. This occurs in the case of a point Q_2 which is farther removed from A than from B by one wavelength.

If we now plot the hyperbola having A and B as its foci and passing through point Q_2, all points on the hyperbola (according to the actual definition of a hyperbola) will be one wavelength farther away from A than from B. Consequently, for all points on the hyperbola, both fields are in phase.

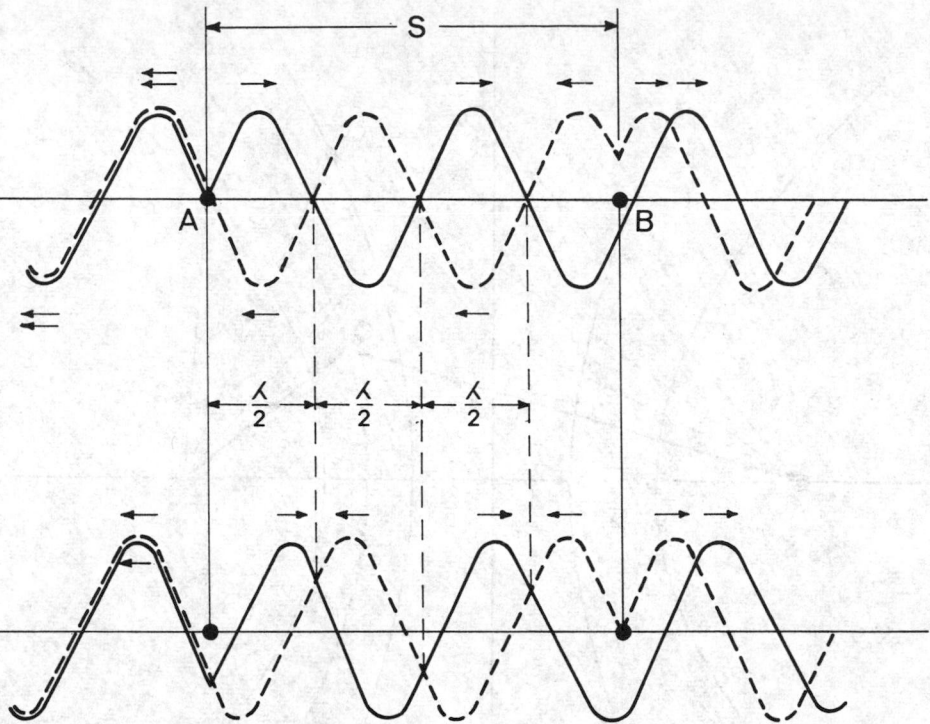

FIGURE 4346a.—Relative positions of two waves of equal frequency at two successive instants.

If point Q_3 is two wavelengths farther from A than from B, the phase difference between the two fields is 720° or twice 360°, i.e. 0° again. This is true for all points of the hyperbola passing through Q_3.

In practice the length of the baseline is not an integral number of wavelengths. The fixed relationship that the phase of the wave emitted by the slave station bears to that of the wave emitted by the master station is such that the waves are in-phase at the master station as shown in figure 4346a. Neither detail invalidates the basic principle.

The fixed phase relationship is maintained by **phase locking,** i.e. keeping the frequency emitted by the slave station at a constant phase angle relative to the stable frequency received from the master station.

Since it is impossible in practice to separate two waves of identical frequency at a receiver in order to measure their phase difference, as they would then combine into a single wave, recourse is made to a technical device which achieves the effect of transmitting signals of equal frequency from the master and slave stations. The effect of having waves sent from both stations to arrive at the phasemeter on an identical frequency, free from interference or wave distortion, is achieved by assigning harmonically-related values to the two frequencies actually transmitted so that multiplying circuits in the receiver can derive from each a common harmonic, the comparison frequency. As shown in table 4346, the master station transmits a signal of $6f$, the red slave $8f$, the green slave $9f$, and the purple slave $5f$, where the fundamental frequency, f, which is not transmitted, lies between 14.00 and 14.33 kHz. Thus the master and red slave signals are multipled to a common **comparison frequency** of $24f$. Geometrically the system functions as if the common frequency $24f$ were radiated from the two stations. The master/green and master/purple pairs function similarly by using the frequency values and multiplication factors shown in table 4346.

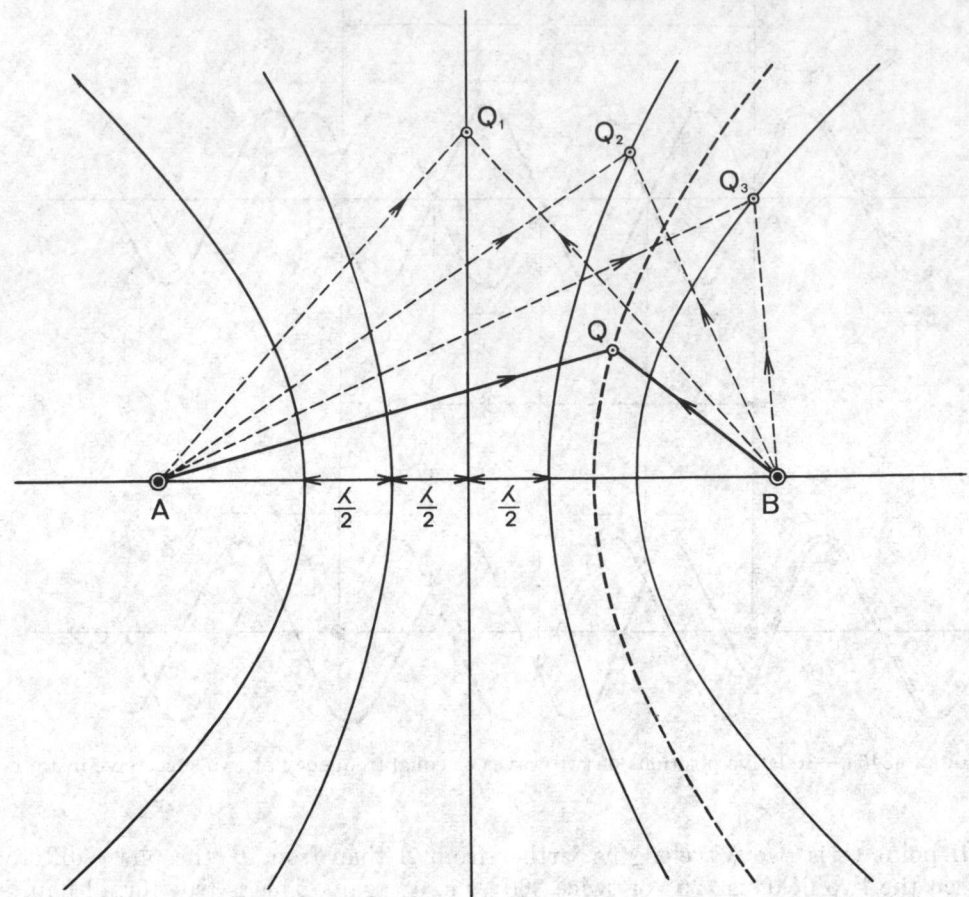

FIGURE 4346b.—Hyperbolas defined by phase-difference measurements.

	Master	Red	Green	Purple
Transmission frequency (kHz)	85. 000	113. 333	127. 500	70. 833
Harmonic	6f	8f	9f	5f
Phase comparison frequency		340. 000	255. 000	425. 000
Harmonic		24f	18f	30f
Lane width on baseline (meters)		440. 735	587. 647	352. 588
Comparison frequency for lane identification (1f)		14. 166	14. 166	14. 166
Zone width on baseline (km)		10. 56	10. 56	10. 56

TABLE 4346.—Transmission and comparison frequencies for a chain using a fundamental frequency of 14.166 kHz. The fundamental frequency f varies from chain to chain. The lane width on the baseline is for a propagation velocity of 299,700 kilometers per second.

4347. The Decca lattice.—Each hyperbola of the Decca lattice overprinted on the navigational chart in the color of its respective slave station is an in-phase or zero phase-difference hyperbola. The area between adjacent hyperbolas of zero phase difference is called a **lane**.

Each hyperbola *as charted* is based upon a velocity of propagation of the radio waves, assuming an all seawater path. As discussed in article 4339, an appropriate correction may be required when land intervenes.

4348. Decometers readings.—Since the phase-measuring equipment is sensitive to phase differences of the order of $3°$ to $3°5$, the number of hyperbolas that can be derived per lane is limited in practice to 100. Accordingly, the Decometer gives the fractional value of the lane in hundredths. Although the whole lane numbers are also given, the lane number must be initially set to the proper lane as established by other means. This is due to the lane ambiguity associated with the phase comparison method. As the vessel moves from one lane boundary to another, the fractional pointer of the Decometer makes one revolution.

The complete reading of the red, green, or purple Decometer consists of the Decometer color, the zone letter, the lane number, and the fractional value of the lane. The **zone** is a group of adjacent lanes used for lane identification purposes. Each zone contains 24 red, 18 green, or 30 purple lanes and is about 10 kilometers wide measured along the baseline. As is the case with the lane number, the zone letter must be initially set by manual means.

Since the zones are about 6 miles wide on the baseline, about 20 miles wide at 100 miles from the stations, and about 50 miles wide at the edge of the service area, there is seldom any problem in setting the zone indication on the Decometer.

The lanes in each family of hyperbolas are numbered differently: red 0–23, green 30–47, purple 50–79. These numbers recur in zones denoted by letters A to J. In cases where the master and slave are more than 10 zones apart, the zone lettering after J starts again at A.

4349. Lane identification within a known zone is obtained by a process essentially the same as that of determining the fractional value of a lane. As the vessel moves from one zone boundary to another, the lane identification pointer of the Decometer makes one revolution against a scale marked in lane numbers.

The lane identification transmissions emitted by Decca chains are classified as V1, V2, or Multipulse (MP). Most Decca chains emit either MP only or MP and V2 combined; a few chains emit V1 or V2 only. Decca Mark V receivers can receive V1 or V2 transmissions only; Mark 12 receivers can receive both MP and V-type transmissions; and Mark 21 receivers can receive only MP transmissions. Thus, when operating within the coverage area of chains emitting V-type transmissions, the users of Mark 21 receivers must ascertain the correct lane number by other means.

At distances in excess of 250 nautical miles from the stations of chains employing MP lane identification and 150 nautical miles in the case of stations employing V-type lane identification, skywave contamination may be of sufficient intensity to cause the lane identification meter to malfunction, resulting in *lane slip*. The effect is most pronounced at night or during the darker part of twilight. Lane slip or incorrect lane identification can also result from interruption or disturbance of the Decca transmission, incorrect initial referencing of the receiver, or from snow static or electrical storms.

Any interruption or disturbance of the normal transmissions of Decca stations is broadcast as a Decca Warning by the coast radio station in the vicinity.

The Decca Navigator Operating Instructions and Marine Data Sheets provide comprehensive information on lane identification according to receiver type.

In addition to providing initial lane identification within a known zone, lane identification provides an independent check on the lane counting process at any time.

4350. Chain numbers.—Each Decca chain is identified by a number from 0 to 10 used to denote a group of basic frequencies and a letter of A to F used to denote one of the six master frequencies in each group, except for group 10 which contains the A, B, and C frequencies only. Thus, there are 63 frequencies available for use with the several chains of the system. Mark V receivers can receive only the A, B, or C frequencies in groups 1 to 9, whereas Mark 12 and Mark 21 receivers can receive all 63 frequencies. Details are given in Pubs. Nos. 117A and 117B, *Radio Navigational Aids*, and volume 5 of *Admiralty List of Radio Signals*.

4351. Inter-chain fixing is positioning by means of intersecting hyperbolas obtained from different multipulse type chains in situations where a better angle of cut is obtained thereby. This method of operation is particularly advantageous at the longer ranges when the user is unable to resolve zone ambiguity. In such operation the reading from the second chain is obtained from the lane identification readout. Although the readout precision is only 0.1 lane, it is adequate for the purpose

The reliability of the multipulse lane identification is the main factor permitting interchain fixing, since the method would not be feasible if, on switching to the second chain, the correct lane number could not be ascertained immediately. Special charts overprinted with the appropriate pair of families of hyperbolas are available for certain areas where there is overlapping coverage from multipulse type chains. The transmitters for the two chains are not phase locked, and therefore it is not possible to use combinations of transmitters from the two chains to provide new families of hyperbolas.

4352. Accuracy and coverage.—The *repeatable* accuracy (art. Q8) to be expected of a Decca fix in a particular coverage area is given in diagrams in *The Decca Navigator Operating Instructions and Marine Data Sheets* and NP 275(5a), an appendix to volume 5 of the *Admiralty List of Radio Signals*. The accuracy is expressed in terms of d_{rms} (art. Q7). The assumed standard deviation of each line of position is 0.02 mean lane. The probability is given as 68 percent. The diagrams in the Decca publication present the repeatable accuracy according to time and season.

The repeatable accuracy is affected by both random and fixed (systematic) errors. The random errors (art. Q4) are largely due to skywave interference with the groundwave, resulting in incorrect Decometer readings. The fixed errors (art. Q3) are largely due to errors in propagation prediction (art. 4339). The Decca lattice as overprinted on the navigational chart does not reflect compensation for differences in the conductivities along the actual paths of the signals and the conductivity along an all seawater path. Although the fixed errors are generally small, there are certain regions (e.g. certain coastal waters) where consideration should be given to them when fixing the vessel's position. *The Decca Navigator Operating Instructions and Marine Data Sheets* include diagrams showing the known corrections which should be applied to the Decca readings. However, it should not be assumed that a fixed error does not exist when a correction is not given. The corrections as given on the diagrams may be too sparse to permit a valid assessment of the correction to apply to the Decometer reading. In such case not too much reliance should be placed on the absolute or predictable accuracy (art. Q8).

The repeatable accuracy of the system ranges from a few tens of meters by daytime in areas where the geometry is favorable to a few nautical miles in the presence of skywave interference by night at the limit of the range.

The coverage of a Decca chain is determined primarily by the effects of skywave contamination of the groundwave rather than factors of signal-to-noise ratio or system geometry, and varies with the low frequency propagation conditions characteristic of different regions of the world. Ranges of 175 nautical miles by night and 350 nautical miles by day may be taken as representative when the transmission paths lie over seawater.

4353. Decca Track Plotter.—It is possible to use an automatic track plotter with the Decca receivers, displaying and recording the track made good as a pen trace. This enables the vessel to follow any desired or intended track.

The hyperbolic lattice is represented on a special chart as a rectilinear inverse lattice so that, for example, the pen moves in response to the red pattern and the chart to the green. The pen therefore indicates the position of the vessel within the lattice and traces a continuous record of the **track made good.** Since the hyperbolas are represented as straight parallel lines intersecting at right angles, a certain amount of distortion occurs, but provision is made for reducing this distortion to an acceptable level. However, if a geographically straight track appears on the chart as a curve, steering the vessel so as to keep the pen on the curve will result in the intended track being made good.

Consol

4354. Consol is a long range azimuthal radionavigation system of low accuracy operated primarily for air navigation. Although not sufficiently accurate for coastal navigation or making landfall, the system can be useful to the marine navigator as an aid to ocean navigation.

A Consol station consists basically of a medium frequency (MF) radio transmitter with three antennas in line, equally spaced apart at a distance of the order of three times the wavelength of the transmitted frequency. The three antennas are fed with signals in such a manner that radial patterns of alternate dot and dash sectors are formed, separated by the **equisignal,** the whole pattern rotating through one sector width within a transmission cycle. An observer will therefore hear the equisignal between the dot and dash signals once per transmission cycle. A count of the dots and dashes will give the angular position within a sector. This sector has to be identified either by direction finding methods or some other form of navigation.

Since the radial sectors are not formed close to the transmitting site, there is a minimum range limitation within which the system cannot be used. This is usually taken to be 25 to 30 nautical miles from the site. There is also a sector 30° on either side of the baseline extension which is not usable because of pattern distortion.

The system is described as azimuthal even though it is basically a hyperbolic system. As discussed in article 4303, a system can be considered directional (azimuthal) beyond a distance of a few miles from the station if the baseline is very short.

Sometimes Consol is classified as a radiobeacon because of the frequency of operation and being azimuthal.

A modified form of Consol called **Consolan** was developed in the United States. In this system only two antennas are used.

In the U.S.S.R. a further modification of Consol is in use. This system, called BPM5, uses five antennas in the form of a cross to obtain narrower dot and dash sectors.

The main advantage of Consol is that the signal can be received on a standard communications receiver.

4355. The signal from the Consol transmitter consists of two parts, the transmission of the call sign, sometimes with a continuous wave signal, and the transmission of the rotating pattern (navigational period). The duration of the total transmitting cycle is not the same for all stations, but the navigational period has been standardized at 30 seconds. If the call sign only is sent in addition to the navigational cycle, the total signal duration is 40 seconds. When the continuous wave signal is incorporated, the total signal duration is 60 seconds. The call sign and the continuous wave signal are transmitted only from the center antenna in the Consol system. They can be used for coarse tuning or direction finding purposes.

The signals can be received by any medium frequency receiver operating in the maritime radionavigation band and suitable for receiving A1 telegraphy. The range and accuracy of the signal is affected by receiver selectivity, increasing as the selectivity increases, although above 100 Hz there is little increase in either range or accuracy. Some experience in the use of the system is found to be necessary to obtain the best results, especially if the signal is weak or there is excessive background noise.

Some special adaptors and receivers have been produced for use with the Consol system. These do aid in the counting of the dots and dashes. One such adaptor uses a meter indication in which dots give a deflection to one side of the center position and dashes give a deflection to the other side. An automatic Consol receiver displays a digital readout of the dot and dash count. This receiver can compensate, within certain limits, for missing characters when the equisignal condition is masked by noise.

4356. Method of use.—Procedures for using Consol and Consolan and the tables for converting dot and dash counts to true bearings *from* the station are given in Pubs. Nos. 117A and 117B, *Radio Navigational Aids*, and volume 5 of *Admiralty List of Radio Signals*. These bearings must be corrected for conversion angle (tab. 1) before plotting on the Mercator chart.

Figure 4356 shows what the observer will obtain in the receiver, depending on his position within a dash or dot sector. At the beginning of the keying cycle, the equisignal lines will be as shown, with the dash and dot sectors on either side. During the navigational period, these lines will rotate as shown, pushing the various sectors in front of them. There are 60 dots or dashes in each sector.

Consider first an observer at P_1 within a dash sector. As the pattern rotates a number of dashes will be heard before the equisignal condition. As the pattern continues to rotate, the equisignal will resolve into dots. By counting the number of dashes, the angular displacement from the equisignal line E_1 can be obtained.

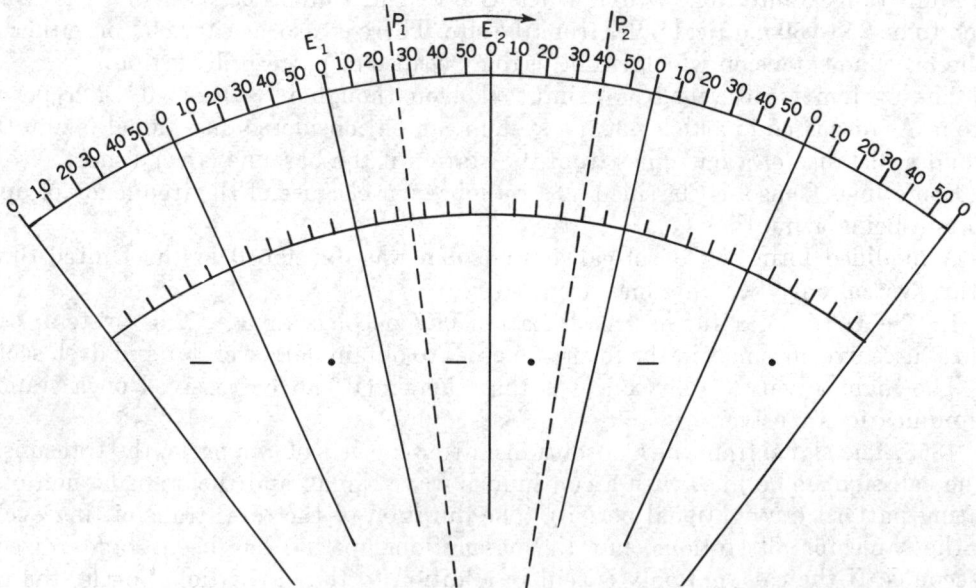

FIGURE 4356.—Signal reception.

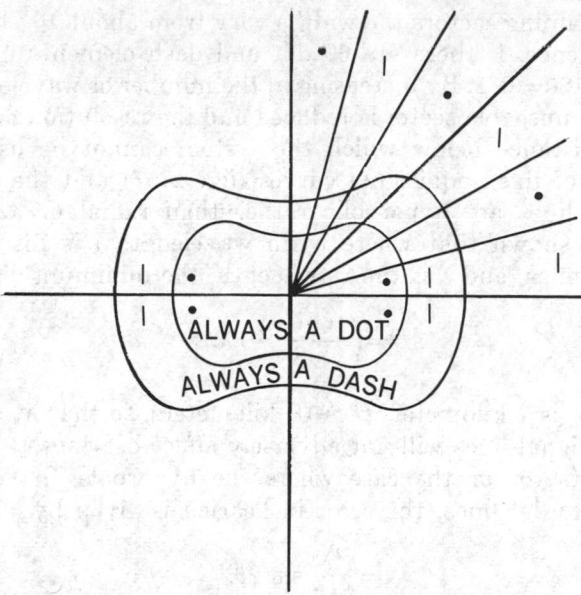

FIGURE 4357.—Fixed equisignal curves at close range.

Then consider an observer at P_2 within a dot sector. As the pattern rotates, a number of dots will be heard before the equisignal, followed by a number of dashes. In this case, the count of the number of dots will give the angular displacement with respect to the equisignal line E_2.

Due to the fact that the dots and dashes merge into the equisignal, it is difficult, in the equisignal, to distinguish between the dot and dash signals. In theory the total number of dashes and dots heard by the observers at P_1 and P_2 should in each case be 60. In practice this is not the case, there being a period of confusion around the equisignal time. In order to obtain an accurate assessment of the true count, the total number of dots and dashes heard during one navigational period is subtracted from the theoretical total count, that is 60. Half the resultant figures is then added to the original count of dots or dashes.

As an example, take the case where the theoretical dash count should be 25, but the actual count is 23 followed by a dot count of 33. This gives a total dot and dash count of 56. This is subtracted from the total theoretical count of 60 giving a figure of 4. Half this, 2, is added to the dash count of 23 to obtain the assessment of the true count of 25 from the equisignal line. This count is then referred to a Consol chart of tables to give the bearing from the station within the dash sector. The sector itself is identified either by radio direction finding or other navigational means.

4357. Accuracy.—The number of dot and dash sectors, and therefore the accuracy of the Consol line of position is dependent on the baseline length, $n\lambda$, between the inner and each outer antenna. Since the wavelength is fixed for each station, the number of sectors will therefore depend upon n. For any given value of n, there will be $8n$ equisignal lines in the full 360° coverage. For practical purposes the value of n is usually taken as three. In this case the equisignal lines will be at angles of 0°, ±9°6, ±19°5, ±30°, ±41°8, and ±90° from the normal to the baseline through the center antenna. In the last sector on each side, about 34° wide, the rotation speed of the equisingal line is not constant, especially at the beginning of the navigational cycle when it will be a maximum. The readings in these sectors are therefore normally taken as unreliable. In the remaining sectors the widths vary from about $10°$ to about $14°$, with an average of $12°$. Hence, if there are 60 dot and dash elements in each sector, the resolution will be $12°/120 = 0°.1$. By increasing n, the number of wavelengths in the baseline, the width of the unuseable sector is reduced and the resolution accuracy increased.

The minimum distance below which the system cannot be used is due to two factors, the presence of fixed equisignal curves (fig. 4357) and the fact that at close range the equisignal lines are hyperbolic rather than radial or azimuthal. For the first factor it can be shown that where n (in wavelengths) is distance between the center and outer antennas, and λ is the wavelength, the minimum distance is given by

$$D = \left(\frac{16n^2 - 1}{8}\right)\lambda.$$

Hence, if n is 3 and λ is 1 kilometer, D is 18 kilometers, so that at 20 kilometers and above, the fixed equisignal lines will not adversely affect bearings.

For the second factor or the case where the hyperbolas have not yet become asymptotic with the radial lines, the error in bearing is given by

$$\epsilon = \frac{n^2\lambda^2}{4D^2}\sin 2\theta,$$

where θ is the bearing. The bearing error ϵ always has the same sign in each quadrant as the error is always on the same side of the radial line. The error is maximum when bearing θ is $45°$ from the perpendicular bisectors. Table 4357a gives some values for the errors for different ranges and different bearings.

Table 4357a shows that the error is reduced with increase in range. At 50 kilometers the mean error is 2 minutes of arc; however, at the higher angles, this will be increased to 3 minutes of arc. When this error is combined with the minimum resolution error of $0°.1$, the minimum error becomes 8 minutes of arc. This minimum error will vary with the observer's position within the sector and his range and bearing from the station. This error is due entirely to the system itself, and will be the minimum system error. There are other factors which will affect the accuracy of the measured bearing.

Distance (D) (km)	Error in minutes of arc for angle of					Mean error in useable sector (minutes of arc)
	0°	15°	30°	45°	60°	
20	0	10	17	19	17	12
30	0	4	7.5	8.5	7.5	4.5
40	0	2	4	5	4	2.5
50	0	1.5	3	3	3	2
60	0	1	2	2	2	1
70	0	1	1	1.5	1	1
80	0	1	1	1	1	1

TABLE 4357a.—Values of error for different ranges and different bearings.

The overall accuracy of the system is dependent on a number of factors in addition to the system errors described above. These include asymmetrical phasing errors in the signals from the inner and outer antennas, phasing and amplitude errors in the signals from the outer antennas, propagation errors, and incorrect functioning of the receiver.

Phasing errors affect the width of the equisignal zone or its position, but these errors are normally corrected by a monitoring station.

Propagation conditions can introduce errors which cannot be corrected at the transmitting site. These are the errors which have the most effect on bearing accuracies. These errors can include:

1. those caused by a curved propagation path, giving a fixed bearing error;
2. those caused by a difference in propagation conditions between the outer antennas and the angular error which increases with bearing; and
3. those due to phase differences in groundwave and skywave path lengths.

At any receiving point, it is the stronger of the groundwave and skywave signals that will be detected. During daylight groundwaves predominate up to a range of about 150 nautical miles, while skywaves predominate at ranges greater than about 500 nautical miles. Between these two ranges is an area where skywave errors could cause problems.

In addition to the signal errors, it is also possible for the receiver on the vessel to introduce errors. If a loop antenna is used and it is set to a minimum signal condition as may be used for obtaining a direction finder bearing using the first part of the transmission, and readings are then taken during the navigational period of the transmission, large errors could result since the groundwave signal would be at a minimum while the skywave signal would be at a maximum, thus "swamping" the groundwaves. Therefore, it is essential that either the loop antenna be aligned for maximum signal during the navigational period or that a vertical antenna be used.

An automatic gain control in a receiver can cause difficulty in determining the equisignal. This determination is based upon the relative magnitudes of the two signals, while the function of the automatic gain control is to equalize the signal amplitudes if possible. Therefore, the observer should insure that the automatic gain control is not in operation during the period of counting the dots and dashes.

In general it is found that the bearing error increases with range, both day and night. The systematic errors are usually small except over rough ground. Skywave systematic errors, although large at some ranges, are usually smaller than the random errors. Table 4357b shows typical random errors of count under different conditions. The probability is given as 95 percent.

Day range (nautical miles)		Night range (nautical miles)				
Over land	Over sea	0–150	250	350	450	Over 550
4	2	2	8	14	10	4

TABLE 4357b.—Typical random errors of count under different conditions for a probability of 95 percent.

Table 4357c shows the 2 σ (art. Q6) errors of Consol lines of position.

Angle from normal	Day range (nautical miles)					Night range (nautical miles)		
	Over sea			Over land		100	300–1000	1500
	250	500	1000	250	500			
On normal	1.5	3	6	3	6	0.5	10	18
60°	3	6	12	6	12	1	20	36
75°	6	12	24	12	24	2	40	72

TABLE 4357c.—Errors of Consol lines of position in terms of 2 σ.

If a number of counts are taken sequentially and the mean value is used to obtain the bearing, the error should be less than shown in table 4357c.

4358. The operational range of the system is a function of the power transmitted from the three antennas. The total power from the transmitter is divided among the three antennas during the navigational period, the power from the center antenna being greater than that from the outer antennas by a factor of k. This factor then has an influence on the range. However, as k is increased the available power from the outer antennas is decreased, making it more difficult to count the dots and dashes in the presence of noise. For optimum operation of the system, the factor k is normally four.

The distance at which the signals can be used properly depends on propagation conditions as well as the ratio of signal to outside interference or to receiver noise.

Figure 4358 shows the field strength at different ranges in the case of a 1 kW, 275 kHz transmitter. Curves a, b, and c refer to groundwave propagation during daylight hours when skywaves at this frequency are heavily absorbed in the upper atmosphere. At night, however, the skywaves are reflected and can be received at great distances. It is much more difficult to predict field strengths under these conditions as the reflected waves are subject to variable absorption. However, curve d shows a typical mean level. It can be seen that, except at short ranges, the skywave signals received at night are in general stronger than the groundwaves received during the day.

The operational range of a Consol station depends not only on its output power and the time of day, but also on the receiver noise figure and outside interference levels. As an average, the maximum range is considered to be between 500 and 1,200 nautical miles by day and between 900 and 1,500 nautical miles by night.

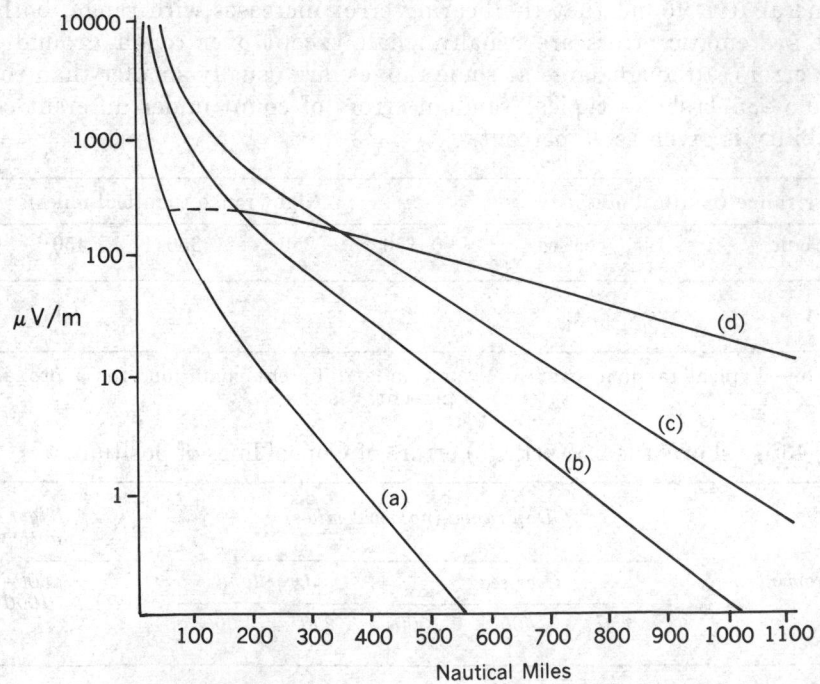

FIGURE 4358.—Typical field strength curves.

CHAPTER XLIV

SATELLITE NAVIGATION

4401. Introduction.—The Navy Navigation Satellite System (NAVSAT) is the operational satellite navigation system of the United States. It is all-weather, world-wide, and passive. The system's accuracy is better than 0.1 nautical mile anywhere in the world, on land and sea. It is available to all civilian users of the world. The system is used primarily for the navigation of surface ships and submarines; it has some application in air navigation. It is also used in hydrographic surveying and geodetic position determination. The system is also known as TRANSIT.

The NAVSAT system utilizes the doppler shift of radio signals transmitted from the satellite to measure the relative velocity between the satellite and the navigator. Knowing the satellite orbit precisely, the navigator's absolute position can be accurately determined from this time rate of change of range to the satellite. The satellites also transmit timing signals which provide time automatically. Frequency accuracy is better than one part in ten billion for precise determination of the doppler shift; the time is given in Coordinated Universal Time (UTC) to within 200 microseconds.

NAVSAT was conceived and developed by the Applied Physics Laboratory of the Johns Hopkins University for the U. S. Navy. The operation of the system is under the control of the U. S. Navy Astronautics Group with headquarters at Point Mugu, California.

System Configuration and Operation

4402. The Navy Navigation Satellite System (fig. 4402a) consists of a constellation of orbiting satellites, a network of tracking stations that continuously monitor the satellites and update the information they transmit, and any number of user equipments composed of receivers and computers.

Each navigation satellite is in a nominally circular polar orbit at an altitude of 450 to 700 nautical miles. The orbital planes of the satellites intersect at the earth's axis of rotation and are spaced apart in longitude. Thus, the orbital paths cross at the North and South Poles (fig. 4402b). Although the orbital planes remain nearly fixed in space, the satellites appear to traverse the longitudinal meridians as the earth rotates beneath them. There are usually five satellites operating in the system, and these provide navigation fixes anywhere on the earth on nearly an hourly basis. Five satellites in orbit provide redundancy; the minimum constellation for system operation is four. This redundancy allows for an unexpected failure of a satellite and the relatively long period of time desired to schedule, prepare for launch, and orbit a replacement satellite on an economical basis (not an emergency basis). This redundancy also provides for turning off a satellite when (on rare occasions) its orbital plane precesses near another satellite's plane, or when the timing (phasing) of several satellites in their orbits are temporarily such that many satellites pass nearly simultaneously near one of the poles.

Each satellite orbits the earth in approximately 108 minutes. Throughout its useful life, each satellite continuously transmits the following phase-modulated data as two messages on two radio frequency carriers (150 and 400 kHz): (1) two-minute mark synchronization signals, (2) a 400 Hz audible "beep" signal, and (3) fixed and variable parameters describing its own orbit. The fixed parameters describe the satellite's

Courtesy of Applied Physics Laboratory, The Johns Hopkins University.

FIGURE 4402a.—Navy Navigation Satellite System.

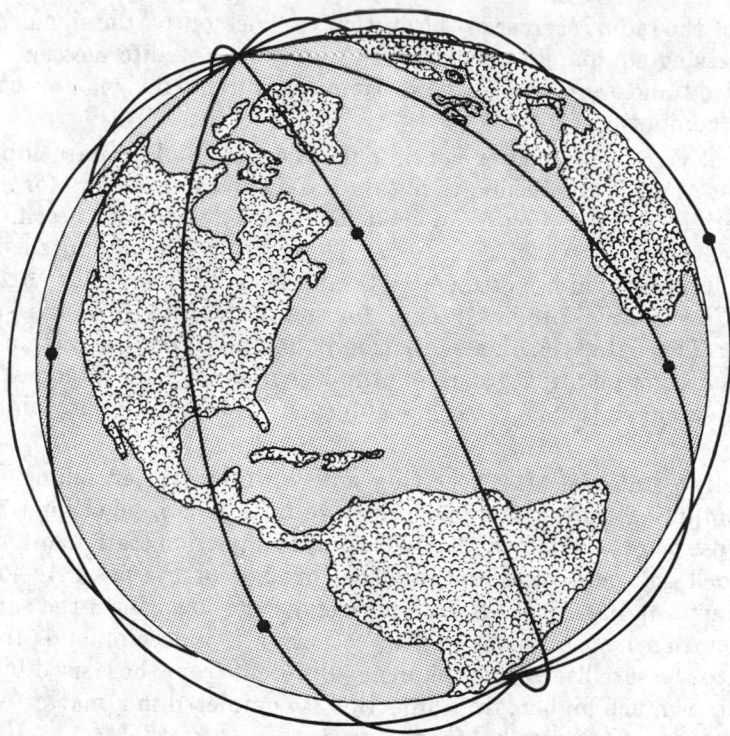

FIGURE 4402b.—Satellite orbital distribution.

approximate orbit and typically are used only for a 12- to 16-hour interval. The variable parameters describe the fine structure of the orbit as a function of time and are correct only for the time at which they are transmitted by the satellite. Thus, the satellite memory stores sufficient variable parameters to describe the orbit at 2-minute intervals between subsequent injections of data. Each transmission is timed so that the end of the 78th bit of each 2-minute message (the last bit of the synchronization signal), coincides with the integral 2 minutes of UTC. Thus, the satellite transmissions also serve as an accurate time reference for all navigators.

All data transmitted that does not change, such as synchronization and identification signals, etc., are "wired" into the satellite memory. All data that changes with time, such as the orbit parameters and the locations of the other satellites, are replaced at 12- to 16-hour intervals by a transmission from an **injection station.**

To determine accurately its present and future orbit for the 12- to 16-hour interval after data injection, each satellite is tracked as it passes within radio line-of-sight of each of the four fixed **tracking stations.** The tracking stations are located in Hawaii, California, Minnesota, and Maine. Each station includes equipments which receive and decode the satellite transmissions, and a directional antenna that is programmed to automatically point toward the satellite throughout the duration of the pass. The antenna directivity offers an additional measure of discrimination against spurious signals from local transmitters and ensures tracking of the selected satellite during those instances when two satellites converge within radio line-of-sight.

Programming data for pointing the station antennas either originate at the **central computing center** and are routed through the **control center** to the tracking station, or are locally derived at the tracking station. Just before the satellite time-of-rise, the antenna at the tracking station is pointed to acquire the satellite signals. As the satellite rises above the horizon, the antenna continues to follow the pass, enabling the frequency tracking loop of the radio receiver at the station to "lock onto" the signals. The receiver and data processing equipment decode and record the statellite message. The doppler signal is digitized and sent with satellite time measurements, via the control center, to the central computing center.

The central computing center continually accepts satellite data inputs from the four tracking stations. Periodically, to obtain the orbital parameters for a satellite, the central computing center computes an orbit for each satellite that best fits the doppler curves obtained from all tracking stations. Then, using the computed orbital shape, the central computing center extrapolates the position of the satellite at each integral 2 minutes in Coordinated Universal Time for the next 12 to 16 hours subsequent to data injection. The data, together with commands and time correction data for the satellite, and antenna-pointing orders for the injection station antennas, are supplied to the three injection stations located in California, Minnesota, and Maine via the control center.

The injection stations, after receiving and verifying the incoming message from the central computing center, store the message until it is needed for transmission to the satellite. Just before a satellite's time-of-rise, the injection station antenna is pointed to acquire, "lock on", and track the satellite throughout the pass. As soon as the receiving equipment at the injection station receives and locks onto the satellite signals, the injection station transmits the new injection data and commands to the satellite. Transmission to the satellite is on a frequency different from those used by the satellite, and the bit rate is much higher; thus, injection is completed in a matter of seconds and does not disturb use of the satellite for navigation.

The next integral 2-minute transmission by the satellite during the pass contains part of the newly injected data. In the injection station, this read-back is compared with the data that the satellite should be transmitting as a check for injection errors. Because most of the newly injected data (the variable parameters) will not be transmitted until the appropriate time during the satellite orbit, the initial read-back from the satellite includes parity check data. These data provide for error detection of the variable parameters so that the injection station can verify that the parameters were received correctly. If no errors are detected, injection is complete. If one or more errors are noted, injection is repeated at 2-minute intervals (updating the variable parameters as necessary) until the satellite transmission is verified as being correct or until the satellite is no longer available for data injection.

Once data injection is complete, the satellite continues to transmit its normal 2-minute messages. Any time corrections for the satellite clock and any commands for the satellite (such as changeover to the standby oscillator, cease transmission, etc.) also are performed during the period of data injection. These precautions ensure that the navigation equipment, which depends on accurate satellite data for determining its position, is provided the best possible data from each satellite. Any time that the satellite is within radio line-of-sight of the navigation equipment and has a maximum elevation at time of closest approach between 15° and 75°, the satellite transmission can be used to compute the exact position on earth of the navigator, although good data can be received frequently when the satellite is not within these elevation requirements.

4403. Navy Navigation Satellites are launched into nearly exact polar orbits from Vandenberg Air Force Base, California by four-stage, solid-fuel Scout rockets (fig. 4403). These polar orbits are nearly circular at altitudes of 450 to 700 nautical miles. The orbits are circular in order to attenuate acceleration and deceleration characteristics of elliptical orbits, and polar to reduce the precession of orbital planes which results in eventual overlap.

Courtesy of Applied Physics Laboratory,
The Johns Hopkins University.

FIGURE 4403.—Scout launch of Navy Navigation Satellite.

Although successive models may differ, each satellite contains: (1) receiver equipment to accept injection data and operational commands from the ground, (2) a decoder for digitizing the data, (3) switching logic and memory banks for sorting and storing the digital data, (4) control circuits to cause the data to be read out at specific times in the proper format, (5) an encoder to translate the digital data to phase modulation, (6) ultrastable 5 MHz oscillators, and (7) 1.5-watt transmitters to broadcast the 150- and 400-MHz oscillator-regulated frequencies that carry the data to earth.

4404. Configuration.—The satellites (sometimes called operational or Oscar satellites) weigh 140 pounds and have their antenna and solar cell panels configured for a nominal circular polar orbit at an altitude of about 600 nautical miles. Each satellite is an octagonal cylinder 18 inches wide and 12 inches high, and has four solar cell panels that extend from four of eight faces (fig. 4404). These four panels fold down around the fourth stage of the Scout rocket during launch, and are held by wires which also serve as a "yo-yo" despin mechanism after the fourth stage has fired. When released, the blades are erected into the position shown by swinging "door hinges." Subsequently, the external configuration is modified by extending a 100-foot boom from the top of the satellite. The boom has a 3-pound weight at the end in order to achieve gravity-gradient stabilization, so that the bottom of the satellite containing the antennas always points toward the ground.

4405. Stabilization.—The operational satellite and the last stage of the Scout rocket are despun soon after achieving orbit by the yo-yo technique (art. 4404). The yo-yo immediately reduces the spin to a few percent of the spin rate of the fourth stage (spin-stabilized) Scout rocket. This small residual spin is removed by incorporating long, thin rods of a magnetic material which exhibit substantial magnetic hysteresis in the solar panel blades. These hysteresis rods are inductively magnetized by the earth's magnetic field in alternate directions as the satellite spins. The hysteresis loss involved in this process takes energy from the satellite rotation and shows up as heat energy in the rods. This process slows the rotation rate to zero within less than a day. When the spin rate reaches zero, an electromagnet is activated along the vertical axis to align itself with the earth's magnetic field line. The hysteresis rods in the solar cell blades provide damping for the resulting magnetic attitudes stabilization. Within

FIGURE 4404.—Navy Navigation Satellite.

another day, the librations (oscillations) of the satellite about the local magnetic field have damped out sufficiently so that the satellite axis is always within 10° of the local magnetic field direction.

As the satellite passes over the north magnetic pole, it is vertical, with the bottom side of the satellite pointing toward the earth. At this point a command from the ground turns the electromagnet off, and the 100-foot boom is extended. Thus, during its time in orbit, the satellite always points its antennas toward the earth. This attitude is maintained because of the difference in the level of gravity at the satellite and at the end of the boom. In this "gravity-gradient" stabilization mode, the hysteresis rods provide enough damping to bring the librations below 10° within a day or two. This orientation makes it possible for the satellite to send most of its transmitted power toward the earth, and for circular polarization to be used so that no loss results from Faraday rotation in the ionosphere. In addition, the transmitter antenna shapes the beam so that more power is transmitted at large angles, so that at any moment the received power anywhere above the satellite's horizon is about the same.

4406. Power and thermal design.—The power system is based on solar cells that charge a set of sealed nickel-cadmium batteries and provide power during the dark portion of each orbit. The solar cells initially provide 30 watts of power when the satellite is launched. After 5 years of exposure to the radiation present in the space environment, 25 watts are still available, which is sufficient to power the satellite. A major problem with near-earth satellite design is caused by the variation in sunlight as the orbit plane precesses with respect to the terminator. A polar satellite near the earth has two extended periods each year during which the satellite is continuously in sunlight. This is often referred to as the **dawn orbit** since it corresponds to the time when the satellite passes overhead at approximately local sunrise (and, of course, sunset). At the other extreme, there are two periods each year during which the sun is nearly in the orbital plane; during this period, the satellite is in darkness for 33 percent of each orbit. This is known as the **noon orbit** because the satellite passes overhead near the time of local noon (and, of course, midnight). The satellite design assures that both the thermal balance and the power balance are acceptable under these two extreme situations.

For a gravity-gradient stabilized satellite, it is true that when the satellite is in constant sunlight (dawn orbit) the sun always "looks" at the side of the satellite whereas for the minimum sunlight case (noon orbit) the sun "looks" at the top and part of the edge of the satellite. Accordingly, by carefully choosing the ratio of the top area to the projected area of the sides, the total thermal input during a full orbit is approximately the same in both the dawn and noon orbits. Similarly, by canting the antenna blades on which the solar cells are mounted to the proper angle, the total power input from the solar cells is made approximately the same in both the dawn and noon orbit cases.

In the operational satellite the use of this technique has made it possible to provide automatic temperature control that is accurate to a few degrees by means of thermostats and heaters and, further, to have acceptable temperature limits even if the automatic temperature control system fails.

4407. Packaging techniques.—The operational navigation satellites are relatively simple from a mechanical standpoint. There are no tape recorders or television cameras and, in fact, no moving parts other than command relays, which are operated very infrequently. However, they do contain some 35,000 magnetic (memory) cores and 6,200 other electronic components. In order to reliably package this equipment within 140 lbs (a Scout rocket compatible payload), it is necessary to use modern packaging techniques. Welded "cordwood" construction with a package density of 50,000 parts per cubic foot is used wherever applicable. Of the 46,000 permanent electrical joints in the electronics, 40,000 are welds and only 6,000 are solder connections. Generally, except in telemetry functions which can be lost without destroying the operational usefulness, redundant wiring and redundant solder connections are used. The use of mechanical connectors (plugs) in electrical circuits is kept to an absolute minimum, and, where plugs must be used in critical circuitry, complete redundancy is provided. In most places where plugs would normally be used, wire-wrapped connections are used.

4408. Memory organization.—The information on satellite position required for navigation is stored in a magnetic core memory and transmitted as phase modulation on the two basic stable frequencies used to generate the doppler shift. The modulation pattern is quite symmetrical so as not to introduce an error in the measurement of doppler. The specific modulation patterns that are to be interpreted as "zero" or "one" are shown in figure 4408.

The memory, which is read out every 2 minutes, contains 156 words of 39 bits each, plus an additional 19 bits. The great majority of these words are not required for navigation but disseminate other information. The first two words are simply a fixed pattern of "zeros" and "ones" used to recognize the start of a message and to establish synchronization of the ground equipment with the satellite transmissions. Thereafter, the words with specific significance for navigation are a total of 19 words divided into 2 sets, an initial set of 8 so-called "ephemeral words" (consisting of word numbers 8, 14, 20, 26, 32, 38, 44, and 50) and a set of 11 fixed parameters that are changed only by injection.

Because of the departure of the earth's gravity field from that of an ideal spheroid, atmospheric drag, solar photon pressure, attraction by the sun and moon, etc., the satellite orbit cannot be given accurately by algebraic equations. However, there is an algebraic description using 11 orbit parameters which affords a good approximation and is simple to compute in navigation equipments. The deviations of the actual orbit from this 11-parameter algebraically described orbit are small and require relatively little satellite memory to store a complete set, each 2 minutes for 16 hours. The appropriate deviations of the actual orbit are transmitted each integral 2 minutes of UTC and are the eight ephemeral words mentioned above.

After injection, the main memory is simply read out serially every 2 minutes until a new injection takes place—all main memory words being unchanged during the interval between injections (usually about 12 hours). However, the ephemeral words must be advanced on every 2-minute memory readout, and are not stored in the main memory. Specifically, consider the memory readout that lasts from t minutes to $t+2$ minutes. The eight ephemeral words will contain the orbit deviations appropriate to the times $t-6$, $t-4$, $t-2$, t, $t+2$, $t+4$, $t+6$, and $t+8$, respectively. Thus, on each successive readout, the ephemeral words are moved upward (advanced) so that word number 8 in the previous readout is discarded and replaced by the previous word 14, the old word 14 is replaced by the old word 20, etc., and finally a new word 50 is transmitted. This new word is transferred from a separate memory in the satellite known as the ephemeral memory, which is filled at the time of injection. On each memory readout, a single 39-bit word is "transferred across" to fill word 50 in the main memory. The ephemeral memory contains 480 words, and since a fresh word is used every 2 minutes, the ephemeral memory is used up in $480 \times 2 = 960$ minutes, or 16 hours. Thus, a new injection must be made within 16 hours to prevent the ephemeral memory from running out. It should be noted that each word in the ephemeral memory is read out 8 successive times, first as word 50, then as word 44, etc., finally as word 8 and then is discarded. Notice also that a single 2-minute memory readout gives orbit information for a full 14-minute interval, spanning the time of readout symmetrically.

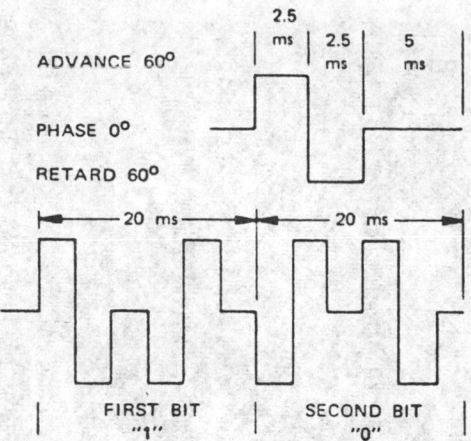

FIGURE 4408.—Phase modulation waveforms.

4409. Timing.—The orbit readout rate is controlled by counting down from the basic stable oscillator. However, in spite of the excellent stability of the satellite oscillator, there are long-term drifts that slowly change the basic oscillator frequency during the life of the satellite. Thus, to keep the memory readout period accurate at integral 2 minutes of UTC, it is necessary to modify the countdown of the oscillator. This is done by using the special bit of each 39-bit word in the main memory as a signal to determine whether or not to suppress a single count in the countdown process. This is done at a point where a single count has a value of $10\mu s$. Thus, a total variation of $156 \times 10\mu s = 1.56$ ms in each 2 minutes is available. With only this level of adjustment, time correction may not be sufficient for a 12 hour period. Thus, a fine adjustment is available by inserting an appropriate count suppression signal in the ephemeral memory. Each ephemeral memory correction bit is used only once and then discarded.

Use of the System

4410. Equipments developed for Navy Navigation Satellite System use include the AN/BRN–3, AN/SRN–9, AN/WRN–5, and AN/SRN–19 radionavigation sets. The AN/PRR–14 Geoceiver was developed for using NAVSAT for geodetic position determination.

AN/BRN–3 Radionavigation Set

4411. AN/BRN–3 Radionavigation Set was developed and deployed in the 1960's as a result of several programs and U. S. Navy contracts. Active development of major units was initiated by the Applied Physics Laboratory of The Johns Hopkins University in late 1960, with requests for technical proposals from industrial suppliers. In about

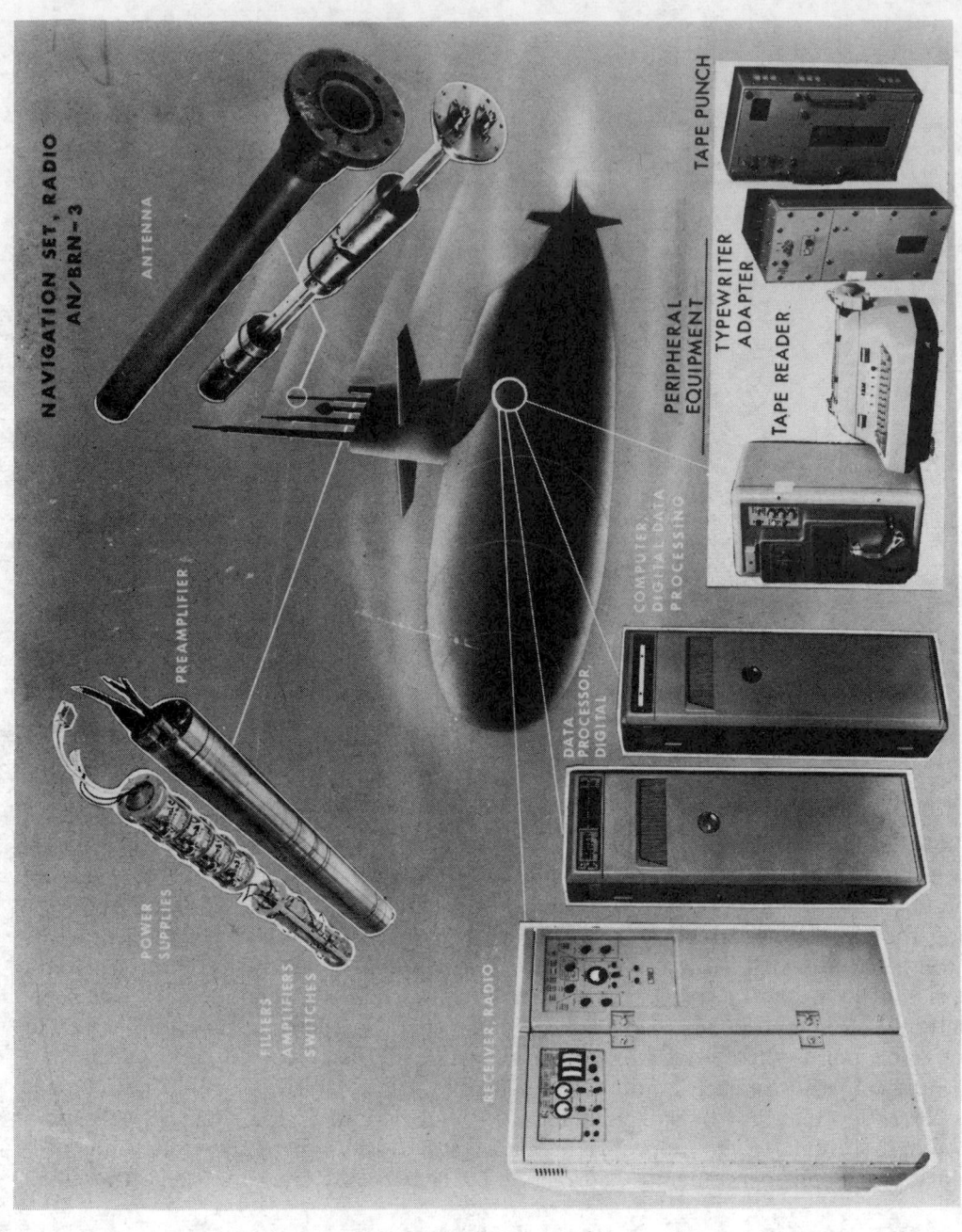

Courtesy of Applied Physics Laboratory, The Johns Hopkins University.

FIGURE 4411a.—AN/BRN–3 Radionavigation Set.

1 year the first prototype had been developed, tested, and delivered to the Applied Physics Laboratory to be used in the development of the total Navy Navigation Satellite System, and to be used as a standard for procurement control of follow-on prototype and production units. By 1964, the total system had matured and was operational with regular service being provided to the fleet ballistic missile (FBM) submarine forces while on patrol.

The AN/BRN–3 is a complex, multi-unit radionavigation aid whose purpose is to compute accurate ship's position using satellite orbital data and measurements of doppler shift to the received satellite reference signals. The position data are provided to the Navigation Control Console (NCC) via the Navigation Data Assimilation Computer (NAVDAC) for the calibration and adjustment of the Ship's Inertial Navigation System (SINS) so that continuous navigation is possible with accuracies sufficient for POLARIS or POSEIDON fleet ballistic missile (FBM) targeting. All units are designed for the special military environments prevailing in the FBM submarine application.

During the production years the Sperry Rand Corporation was designated the prime contractor for AN/BRN–3 procurement, deployment, and maintenance in the fleet. Applied Physics Laboratory of The Johns Hopkins University was retained and continues to provide technical services. The principal components of the system are: (1) radio receiver and RF amplifier/power supply, (2) RF antenna, (3) data processor/ computer, (4) tape punch and reader or magnetic tape unit, and (5) typewriters. Figure 4411a shows a typical FBM submarine installation.

The AN/BRN–3 Radionavigation Set, in conjunction with the SINS and other navigational aids, has a primary function of providing continuous submarine navigation with global, all-weather coverage and high accuracies sufficient to provide position references for POLARIS and POSEIDON missile targeting. The Navy Navigation Satellite System and the AN/BRN–3 provide highly accurate position fixes (at intermittent times dependent upon satellite availability in the local area and at the discretion of the submarine commander) from which a calibration of the SINS, relative to a standard earth coordinate system, can be made to indicate the compensating adjustments necessary to remove the effects of inertial system anomalies and drifts.

In addition to FBM submarine installations, the AN/BRN–3 has been used for special missions aboard surface ships. Several units are installed in training centers, instrumentation ships, and research centers.

In addition, each operational station of the navigation satellite ground support subsystem uses the AN/BRN–3 receiver for satellite tracking and orbit determination rather than for navigation. The AN/BRN–3 has been used as a standard for performance comparison with other alternative navigation sets and for performance evaluation of newly launched satellites prior to their acceptance into official Navy operational service.

The AN/BRN–3 receives navigation satellite signals on the 400 and 150 MHz channels from which it measures doppler shift versus time and recovers "message" data from the modulation. It receives ship's velocity information and position estimates from SINS, timing from the ship's clock, and operational commands from the ship's navigation center. Data other than the satellite signal-derived information are received via the ship's NAVDAC computer. The AN/BRN–3 computes from these inputs the ship's position at sea to a high accuracy and provides the information for printout at the Navigation Control Center (NCC).

In addition, the AN/BRN–3 computes from its data memory (which is updated by new message data recovered during each satellite pass reception interval actually taken), predictions, and information for the selection of usable future satellite passes from those that will be available within a time interval surrounding the next desired SINS calibration time. The prediction is based on a constellation of up to eight navigation satellites and the ship's estimated position. The information provided includes predictions of time of satellite rise (when the radio signal can be received) and the value of the doppler shift.

From a model of the total system, the AN/BRN–3 computes forcing functions for the enhancement of its own performance. It generates driving signals to assist the radio receiver in the acquisition and tracking of satellite radio signals so as to minimize the loss of information due to temporary failure to coherently track the signal as a result of its temporary disappearance due to spray and wavewash over the antenna at the sea surface. The system is decision directed and self-adaptive in the selection of operating mode and receiver tracking bandwidths. The AN/BRN–3 has self-diagnostic features for routine maintenance, pre-pass readiness checks to avoid abortive surfacing by the submarine for satellite reception, and for performance enhancement of the operational mode. The normal operation is completely automated although a full complement of controls and monitors are provided for manual operation.

Some of the important features and design characteristics of the AN/BRN–3 Radionavigation Set are:

1. For navigation the system uses iterative least squares curve fitting routines to match doppler information measured from received signals to doppler information that is predicted for the best estimate of the prevailing satellite-navigator dynamic geometry. A very large number of measurements are made on received signals to generate, in effect, a smoothed curve of observed doppler shift versus time.

2. Doppler measurements are made using the set's local clock to determine the time interval in microseconds that is required for a preset digital doppler shift counter to overflow when the doppler shift is offset about a reference frequency of 55 kHz. Each doppler information sample therefore constitutes a nominal short (1 second) count, the actual interval varying between about 0.8 to 1.4 seconds for satellites at an altitude of 600 nautical miles.

3. Provisions are made in the data processor for the validation and qualification of each doppler measurement sample and for selective grouping of qualified points to obtain a distribution versus time during the satellite pass which will provide the greatest efficiency in total time spanned and accuracy of the fix computation. Entry to the navigation fix computation routines requires 165 doppler data samples. After editing and grouping, 70 fully qualified data points are required for final fix computation—35 prior and 35 following the time of closest approach (TCA) between the satellite and submarine. This data processing is subject to software programming.

4. The radio receiver combines in analog circuitry the prevailing doppler shifts as received and reconstructed from each of the 400 and 150 MHz satellite carrier signals, thereby automatically compensating for refraction errors due to the electron density in the ionosphere (art. 4437). The analog combining circuitry generates a single signal for doppler measurement which is representative of signal propagation through nonrefracted vacuum. Due to the scaling factors employed, the magnitude of doppler shift presented for measurement is equivalent to that which would occur if the satellite transmitted a single carrier frequency at 687.5 MHz. The circuitry also provides an analog derivation of a refraction signal. This signal is a measure of the departure from exact mathematical coherency between the 400 and 150 MHz carrier signals as received. The refraction signal is used as a quality indicator—if the frequency of the refraction signal exceeds a threshold of 10 Hz for a sustained interval, the accompanying quantitative doppler data is deleted and not accepted to the navigation computing routines.

5. Data processing and computing routines are provided for the calibration of the local clock of the navigation set against epochs recovered from the satellite modulation and message formats.

6. One phase modulation decoder is provided in the radio receiver for the recovery of satellite timing, satellite orbital data, cross satellite alert, and other system data that are encoded in the 6,103 bits per 120 second repeatable satellite format which is transmitted by the satellite on each of the 400 and 150 MHz carrier signals. The phase modulation decoder is preceded by a proportional predetection combiner of the 500 kHz IF signals of the respective 400 and 150 MHz receiver channels.

7. After phase modulation detection of the combined satellite signals, information decoding is performed by the computing processor using majority voting and piecewise fitting routines to obtain at least one complete message from the several that occur within the interval of satellite signal reception.

8. There is an automatic search and satellite signal acquisition mode for the carrier tracking circuits of the radio receiver with the controls provided by the computer and data processor based upon predictions from a local memory of orbital parameters for up to eight satellites and the ship's inertial position data. Optional manual controls are also available at the receiver.

9. The system has built-in test features for the special analysis of the radio spectrum received by the antenna which can be used to identify and measure certain interfering and jamming signals at the sea surface.

10. The system has self-test features for equipment malfunction diagnosis and routine preventive maintenance covering the entire AN/BRN–3 system beginning at the antenna input terminals to the radio receiver. Software programs establish and control operational readiness tests prior to submarine surfacing while in a pre-pass period. The diagnostic analysis can extend to the smallest modular unit level.

The navigation accuracies that are obtained at sea depend in part upon the accuracies of inputs describing the ship's motion in the interval of the satellite pass when doppler data was measured.

The statistical accuracies achieved at a non-navigating fixed site, such as Station 110 located at Applied Physics Laboratory, using a typical operational software program, produce a circular probable error (CEP) of 0.017 nautical mile as shown in figure 4411b.

Integrated Doppler Tracking Equipment

4412. Developmental AN/SRN–9 equipment.—In the early stages of the development by the Applied Physics Laboratory of receiving equipment for use in the integrated doppler count method of navigation, the technical approach was centered around a single-frequency system. It was recognized that the use of a single-frequency system operating at the higher frequencies, i.e., 400 MHz, would result in a navigation error as large as 1 nautical mile because of the refraction effect of the ionosphere (art. 4437). The elimination of the requirements for a 150 MHz phase-locked receiver, for a more complex antenna with dual preamplifiers, and for refraction correction equipment appeared desirable in terms of the resultant equipment simplification and lower cost. The single-frequency system was built in breadboard form at the Laboratory, and the feasibility of the system demonstrated in mid-1961.

The design of a two-frequency system was begun by the Laboratory about the same time the single-frequency system reached its breadboard stage. This design effort disclosed that since the two received frequencies are always in constant ratio within a

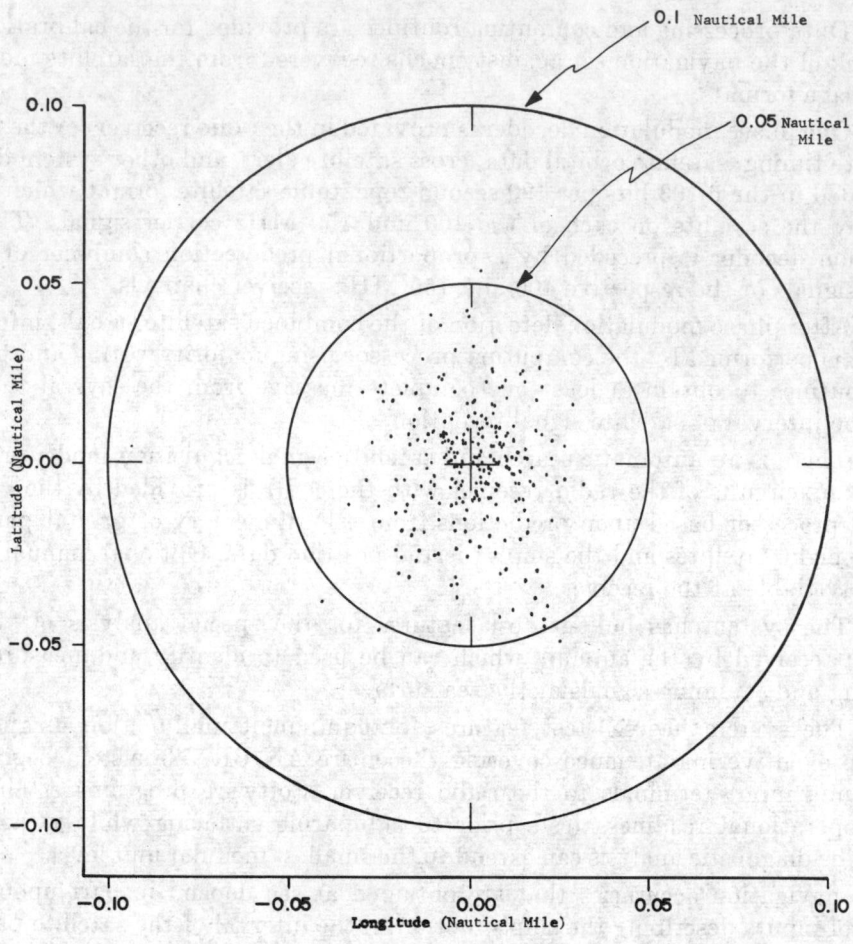

Courtesy of Applied Physics Laboratory,
The Johns Hopkins University.

FIGURE 4411b.—Accuracy results at Station 110 for October 1974.

few parts in 10^8 (the order of the refraction effect) the second receiver need not be a phase-locked receiver, but could be merely slaved to the 400 MHz phase-locked receiver. The two-frequency system design was developed and tested as an engineering model and subsequently developed into a prototype form designated XN–5 (fig. 4412). In the period between 1964 and 1967, a total of 23 prototype AN/SRN–9 (XN–5) sets were produced by the Laboratory and placed in service, primarily aboard attack aircraft carriers and oceanographic ships.

Basic to the design of both systems is the stable oscillator. Any bias in measuring frequency that is maintained over a pass (as opposed to point-to-point noise within a pass) produces a proportional error in position. The assumption is made, therefore, that the frequency of the local oscillator is an unknown (art. 4435). This assumption requires that the measurements and computations needed for a navigation fix be arranged to eliminate the value of the frequency of the oscillator. When this elimination is done properly, the only stability required is five parts in 10^{11} over a 2-minute period. Such stability can be achieved, and a carefully chosen crystal in a thermostatically controlled oven with a large thermal time constant is entirely adequate.

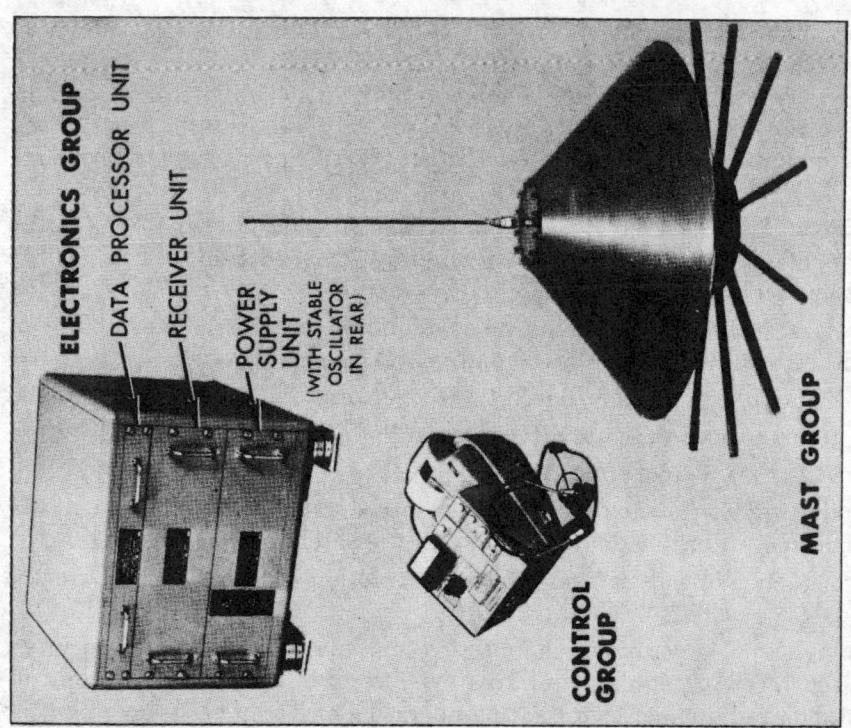

ELECTRONICS GROUP

DATA PROCESSOR UNIT

RECEIVER UNIT

POWER SUPPLY UNIT (WITH STABLE OSCILLATOR IN REAR)

CONTROL GROUP

MAST GROUP

AN SRN-9(XN-5) NAVIGATION RECEIVING SET

Courtesy of Applied Physics Laboratory, The Johns Hopkins University.

CP-827(XN-1)/SRN-9 DIGITAL COMPUTER

FIGURE 4412.—Developmental equipment.

The (XN–5) stable 5 MHz reference oscillator uses a design concept similar to those used in the satellite oscillator, i.e., a thermostatically controlled oven with a very long thermal time constant between the oven and a monel slug, which contains the critical circuits. Since the vacuum of space is not available for the earthbound oscillator, a great amount of thermal insulation is used, resulting in a relatively large physical size.

The AN/SRN–9 (XN–5) receiving equipment has five basic elements: (1) the antenna and preamplifiers, (2) the receiver-demodulator, (3) the digital section, (4) the control group (output section), and (5) the 5 MHz oscillator.

The antenna is a whip over a ground-plane mounted on the superstructure of the ship, along with preamplifiers for the 150 and 400 MHz signals.

The receiver-demodulator contains circuitry to perform the following functions:

1. selectively track a satellite signal after manual lock-on;

2. demodulate the binary data from the carriers;

3. provide timing signals to the digital section at the doublet (half bit) rate (one every 9.83 ms) as derived from the doublet coding in the satellite messages; and

4. produce a sequence of pulses from which a refraction corrected doppler count is obtained.

A precise timing signal based upon the message modulation rate is derived in an internal clock in the receiving equipment. This synchronized internal clock controls the decoding, printing, and doppler count gating operations with an accuracy of better than 0.2 ms. Because the operational satellites transmit the end of message work, two at each integral 2 minutes of UTC ($\pm 200 \mu$s), adequate time information is obtained from the satellite for navigation and doppler gating.

The digital section contains shift registers for accumulating the doppler count and for storing the serial binary data decoded from the satellite messages.

The digital section also contains an output register and the necessary counting and control logic to organize the satellite messages into words and digits (output format control). It also programs the data and other timing signals to the output terminals. The message data are extracted in four-bit groups (i.e., excess-three binary coded decimal format). Control signals are available to take all data (every word) or select only every sixth word (all that is necessary) for normal navigation.

From the control group, the navigator can monitor the operation of the equipment. In operation, the navigator remotely tunes the 400 MHz receiver from whence he obtains all necessary control functions.

In summary, for any satellite pass the following sequence of events will occur in the receiving equipment:

1. The receiver-demodulator is manually locked onto the satellite signals, and phase tracks during the satellite pass.

2. The receiver-demodulator begins decoding the binary data based on an arbitrary association of adjacent doublets.

3. The digital section monitors the decoded data, and properly pairs the demodulated doublets to form binary bits. When the proper pairing is achieved, the digital section energizes the bit synchronization line.

4. The counting and control logic is reset by the synchronization word in the satellite data format. The first time the synchronization word is received after bit synchronization, the digital section outputs a synchronization pulse. A 2 minute UTC pulse is

also generated each time the synchronization sequence (0111111111111111111111110) is received.

5. The counting and format control logic in the digital section governs the handling of the binary data from the satellite, and the accumulation and output of the doppler count.

6. The 2-minute doppler count and satellite message data are printed out in decimal form on the control group printer.

7. Whenever an interrupt in the satellite signal occurs, bit synchronization must be reestablished.

4413. Functional description.—The navigation program currently used in conjunction with the CP–827 computer has the following functional capabilities:

1. Processes data from the SRN–9 receiver in an "on line" mode (the receiver and computer are electrically interfaced, and satellite data collected by the receiver will be transferred and stored by the computer).

2. Formats and prints the receiver data on the Central Group.

3. Majority-votes satellite message data from several messages and modifies this data in the case of injection of new message data into the satellite.

4. Edits doppler data to $7^\circ.5$ provided at least four doppler counts are received. Additionally checks for monotonically increasing doppler counts and zero doppler counts.

5. Provides navigator's motion description in the form of constant course and speed or maneuvering with various options: distance north (DN) and distance east (DE) per 2 minutes, latitude, longitude, or range and bearing at the 2-minute time-marks.

6. Provides automatic satellite alert computation for the satellite just tracked. Alert computation for a single satellite may be performed at any time using message data from a previous satellite pass.

7. Renavigates satellite pass with different dopplers or different motion inputs.

8. A test satellite message can be navigated for test purposes.

4414. Accuracy.—The AN/SRN–9 (XN–5)/CP–827 produces an error at a fixed site of less than 50 meters (CEP). A bull's-eye plot of fixed site error is shown in figure 4414. The fixed site error is also given in table 4414. The difference in computed mean position and reference position is less than 17 meters. The shipboard accuracy at sea depends upon precise inputs of ship motion during a satellite pass. When SINS motion inputs are used, errors less than 0.1 nautical mile are obtained.

COMPUTED MEAN POSITION

Latitude: 39°09′.8124
Longitude: −76°53′.8408

FIX REFERENCE POSITION

Latitude: 39°09′.8214
Longitude: −76°53′.8410
Antenna Height: 106.00 meters

DIFFERENCE OF MEAN REFERENCE POSITION

D. Lat. −0.́0090	−0.0090 mi.
DLo 0.́0002	0.0002 mi.
Mean Radial Error about the Mean Position:	0.0284 mi.

DEVIATION ABOUT THE COMPUTED MEAN POSITION

Latitude:	0.0215 mi.
Longitude:	0.0226 mi.
Root Sum Square:	0.0312 mi.
Circular Probable Error (CEP):	0.0260 mi.

Total number of passes used: 32.

TABLE 4414.—Fixed site error of AN/SRN-9(XN-5)/CP-827.

4415. Status.—The AN/SRN-9 (XN-5) sets are, or have been, operational aboard U. S. Navy ships and oceanographic ships. On 1 April, 1974, the responsibility of the Applied Physics Laboratory for technical support of the AN/SRN-9 (XN-5)/CP-827 Radionavigation Set was transferred to the Naval Electronics System Engineering Center, San Diego, California. Prior to this date, the Laboratory had the continuing responsibility of providing field support. This included maintaining a repair facility, conducting personnel training programs, and supplying complete software programs.

Current Navy Navigation Satellite Equipment

4416. The AN/WRN-5 Radionavigation Set, a self contained navigation set consisting of preamplifier and receiver/computer assembly, is capable of automatic operation and utilizes short-count doppler data to provide navigation in a submarine environment. A synchro-to-digital interface allows interconnection with the SINS for the automatic inputting of ship's motion data. The set is fully militarized and uses the standard UHF submarine antenna for receiving 150 and 400 MHz signals from the Navy Navigation Satellites to obtain navigation fixes. The set is shown in figure 4416.

Modification of an AN/WRN-5 set is under way (1975) to enable the reception of PRN modulation (art. 4430) from improved NAVSAT satellites. This modification will give the AN/WRN-5 the capability of providing a standard doppler navigation fix, a range measurement navigation fix, or a combined doppler and range navigation fix. This capability offers the following advantages:

1. reduced antenna exposure time for a navigation fix,
2. more accurate time dissemination, and
3. fully refraction-corrected navigation using a single channel.

4417. Functional description.—The AN/WRN-5 Radionavigation Set consists of (1) antenna (uses the submarine's UHF antenna), (2) preamplifier, and (3) receiver assembly. The receiver assembly consists of the following subassemblies:

1. power supply,
2. radio receiver,
3. expanded data processor,

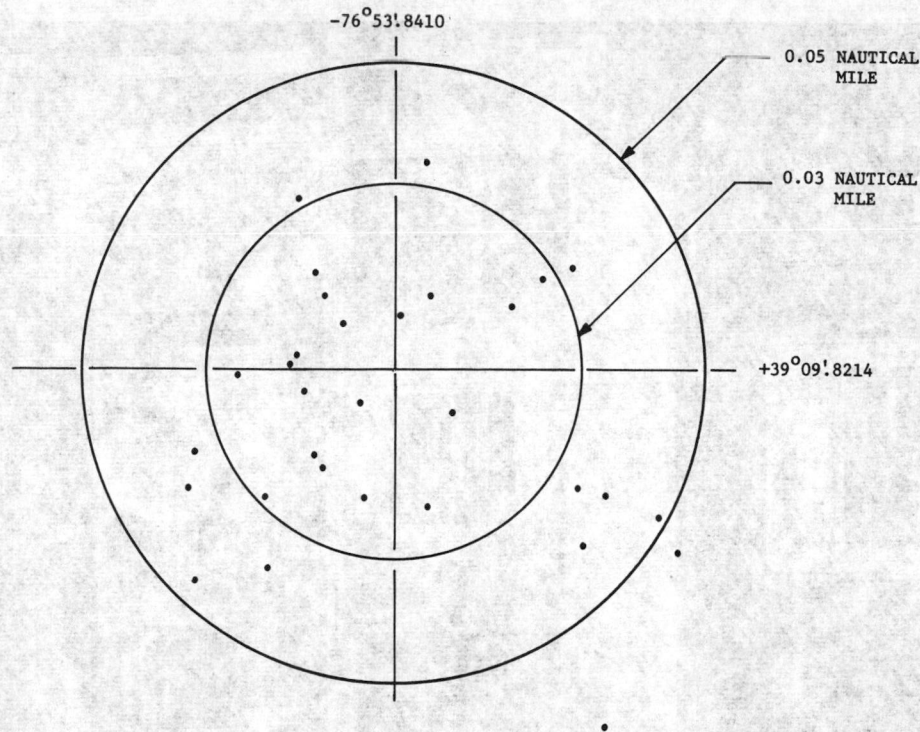

FIGURE 4414.—Bull's-eye plot of AN/SRN-9(XN-5)/CP827 navigation fixes at the Applied Physics Laboratory of The Johns Hopkins University.

4. RF test signal generator,
5. memory loader (tape cassette),
6. 5 MHz frequency standard,
7. remote video display,
8. software program.

The AN/WRN-5 set weighs 150 pounds and uses 350 watts of power.

4418. Design characteristics.—The AN/WRN-5 Radionavigation Set employs 150 and 400 MHz phase-locked tracking loops, and has the following features:

1. automatic acquisition,
2. short count (23 second nominal interval) 400 MHz and 150 MHz doppler data,
3. integral test set,
4. integral 5 MHz oscillator,
5. integral computer with 16K-word, 16-bit memory,
6. teletype interface,
7. SINS interface,
8. navigation fix display,
9. minimum exposure time,
10. latest navigation program.

The AN/WRN-5 set interfaces with a remote video display, printer, and teletype.

4419. Accuracy.—Fixed-site accuracy of the AN/WRN-5 is shown in tables 4419a, 4419b, and figure 4419. The evaluation was conducted during four modes of operation: (1) the normal mode-automatic acquisition, dual channel; (2) single channel, 400 MHz only; (3) single channel, 150 MHz only; and (4) dual channel, short exposure. In the short exposure mode, approximately 4 minutes of data were taken including at

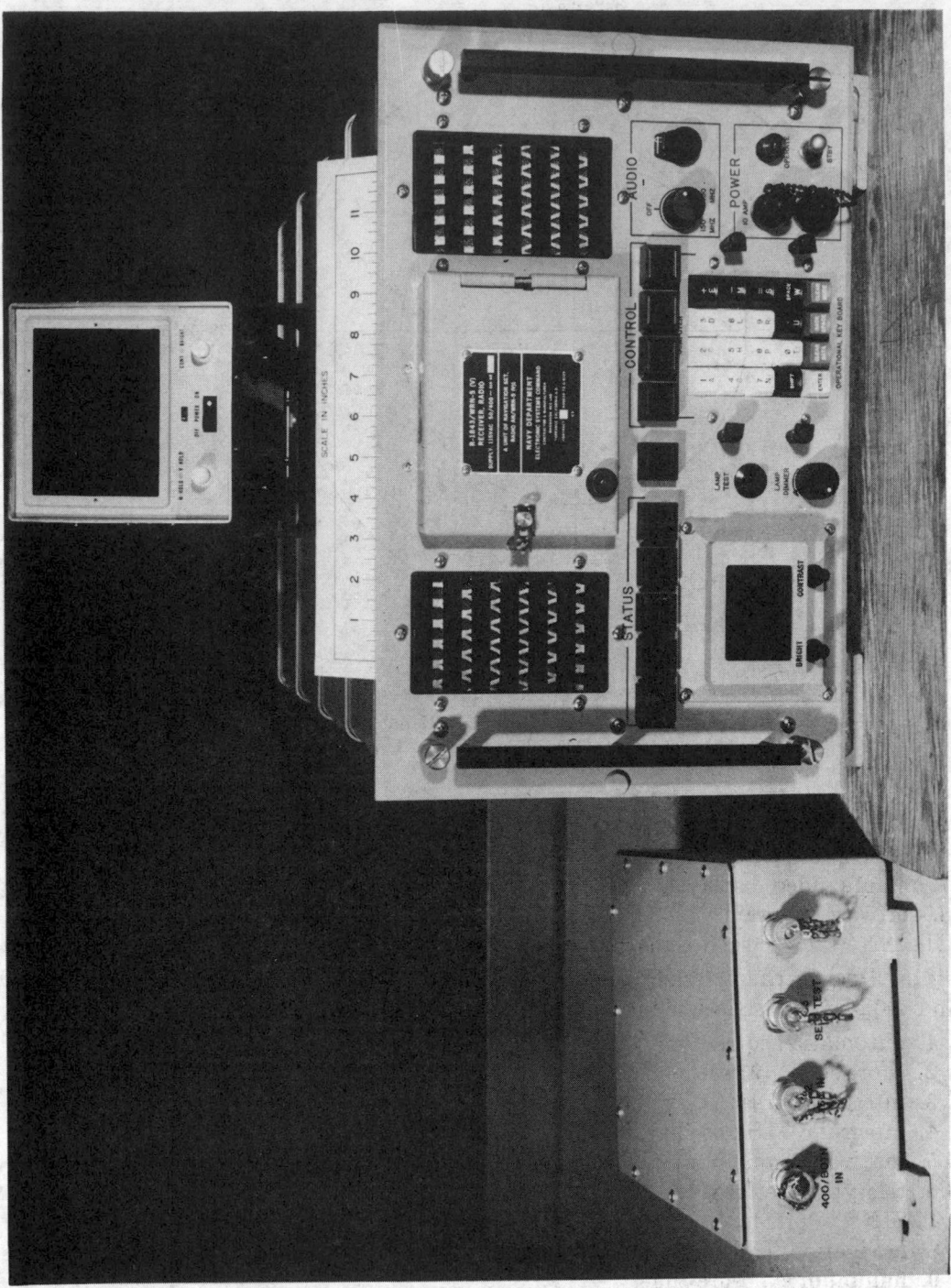

Courtesy of Applied Physics Laboratory, The Johns Hopkins University.

FIGURE 4416.—AN/WRN-5 Radionavigation Set.

least 2 minutes before the time of closest approach. In a few cases where lock was momentarily lost on one channel, data were taken for longer periods of time to allow a refraction corrected fix to be made.

DUAL CHANNEL, AUTOMATIC ACQUISITION

Number of Passes:	39 (ECA** 10°—70°)
Computed Mean Position*—	
Latitude:	39°09′.8158
Longitude:	−76°53′.8410
Difference of Mean Reference Position—	
Latitude:	−0. 0055 mi.
Longitude:	0. 0007 mi.
Mean Radial Error about Mean Position:	0. 0204 mi.
Deviation about Computed Mean—	
Latitude:	0. 0167 mi.
Longitude:	0. 0161 mi.
Root Sum Square:	0. 0232 mi.
Circular Probable Error (CEP):	0. 0193 mi.

SINGLE CHANNEL, 400 MHz

Number of Passes:	10 (ECA** 10°—70°)
Computed Mean Position*—	
Latitude:	39°09′.8144
Longitude:	−76°53′.8390
Difference of Mean Reference Position—	
Latitude:	0. 0070 mi.
Longitude:	0. 0016 mi.
Mean Radial Error about Mean Position:	0. 0491 mi.
Deviation about Computed Mean—	
Latitude:	0. 0195 mi.
Longitude:	0. 0477 mi.
Root Sum Square:	0. 0515 mi.
Circular Probable Error (CEP)	0. 0396 mi.

*Reference Position—Latitude: 39°09′.8214; Longitude: −76°53′.8410.
**ECA—Elevation at Closest Approach.

TABLE 4419a.—AN/WRN–5 fix results.

SINGLE CHANNEL, 150 MHz

Number of Passes:	14 (ECA** 10°—70°)
Computed Mean Position*—	
Latitude:	39°09′.8391
Longitude:	—76°54′.0482
Difference of Mean Reference Position—	
Latitude:	0. 0177 mi.
Longitude:	—0. 1612 mi.
Mean Radial Error about Mean Position:	0. 2676 mi.
Deviation about Computed Mean—	
Latitude:	0. 2662 mi.
Longitude:	0. 2175 mi.
Root Sum Square:	0. 3438 mi.
Circular Probable Error (CEP):	0. 2848 mi.

DUAL CHANNEL, SHORT EXPOSURE

Number of Passes:	20 (ECA** 10°—70°)
Computed Mean Position*—	
Latitude:	39°09′.7683
Longitude:	—76°53′.8468
Difference of Mean Reference Position—	
Latitude:	—0. 0530 mi.
Longitude:	—0. 0045 mi.
Mean Radial Error about Mean Position:	0. 1042 mi.
Deviation about Computed Mean—	
Latitude:	0. 1393 mi.
Longitude:	0. 0847 mi.
Root Sum Square:	0. 1630 mi.
Circular Probable Error (CEP):	0. 1319 mi.

*Fix Reference Position—Latitude: 39°09′.8214; Longitude: —76°53′.8410.
**ECA—Elevation at Closest Approach.

TABLE 4419b.—AN/WRN-5 fix results.

4420. Status.—A total of 32 AN/WRN-5 Radionavigation Sets (fig. 4416) have been procured (1975) by the Naval Electronics System Command for submarine use. Additional sets are being procured for installation in surface ships. The Applied Physics Laboratory served as technical advisor, assisting in the preparation of a technical specification for the equipment production contract and evaluating the AN/WRN-5 navigation program.

4421. AN/SRN-19 (XN-1) Radionavigation Set.—The radionavigation sets currently (1975) available for use with the NAVSAT, such as the AN/WRN-5, are rather sophisticated. They receive data on two satellite frequencies; they are more accurate; and they are relatively expensive. To meet the need for a low-cost simplified satellite navigation set for use aboard the smaller naval vessels, particularly destroyers, the Applied Physics Laboratory designed the AN/SRN-19 Radionavigation Set as a single

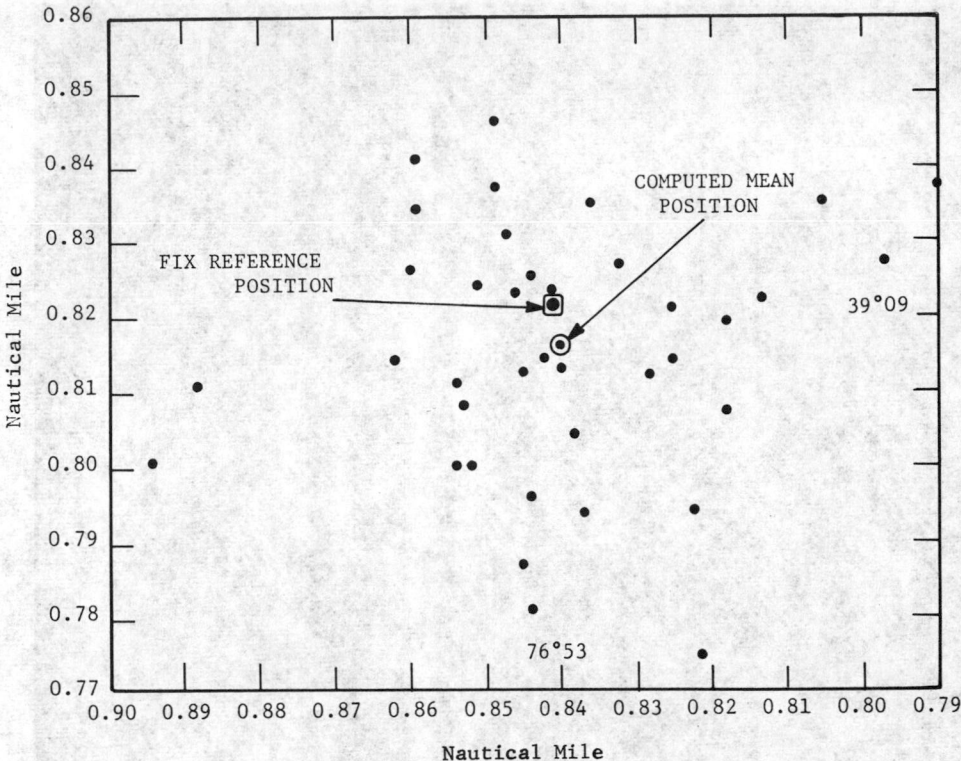

FIGURE 4419.—AN/WRN-5 receiver accuracy, dual channel operation.

channel integral doppler set that includes all of the units necessary to compute and display a navigation fix in one chassis and an external antenna/preamplifier unit. Developed in response to Advanced Development Objective (ADO) 3411, the AN/SRN-19 (XN-1) will enhance a vessel's navigation capabilities by providing regular position fixes and dead reckoning (between satellite fixes) anywhere in the world, day and night, in any weather. Design features of the set are such that is is expected to cost less than $10,000 in production quantities. It is intended for use on surface ships, especially those with an Anti Submarine Warfare mission, where the considerably higher cost of the AN/WRN-5 Radionavigation Set cannot be accommodated and where the extreme accuracy of the higher priced set is not required.

4422. Functional description.—Figure 4422 shows the AN/SRN-19 Radionavigation Set with its antenna/preamplifier and printer, which is optional. The set consists of a 400 MHz receiver; a 5 MHz oscillator; an 8,192 word, 16-bit data processor; power supplies; and 2 synchro-to-digital units mounted in its chassis. A display, keyboard, and a cassette recorder are mounted on the front panel of the chassis. Controls and monitoring devices are also on the front panel.

The receiver automatically searches for and locks onto a satellite's 400 MHz signal, and extracts from the signal two types of information. One is the reconstructed doppler shift of the satellite signal which results from the relative motion between the navigator and the satellite transmitting the signal. The other type of information is obtained by demodulation of the satellite carrier which is phase modulated with a message describing the satellite position in inertial space. These data along with the information on ship's motion during the satellite pass are used by the navigation program to compute the ship's position.

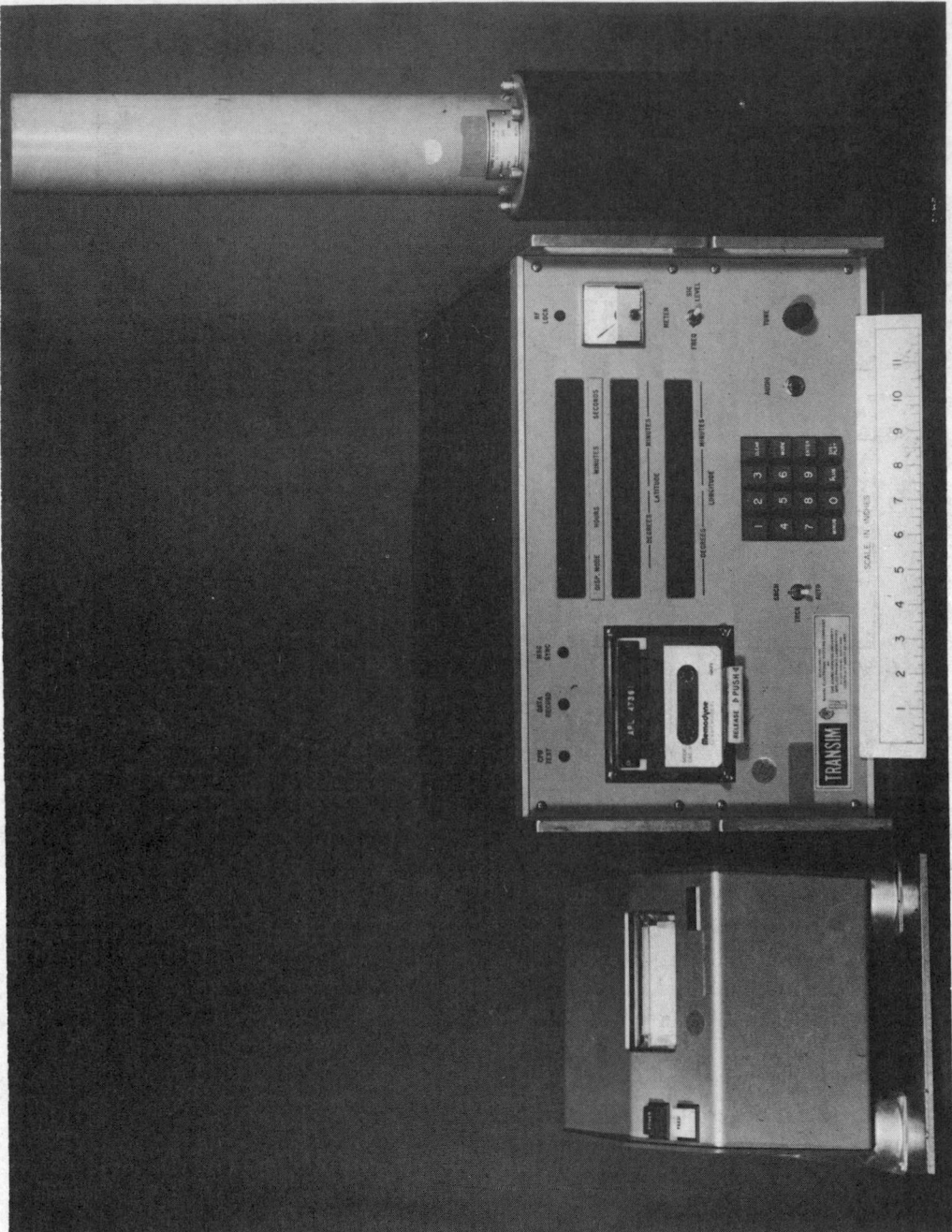

Courtesy of Applied Physics Laboratory, The Johns Hopkins University.

FIGURE 4422.—AN/SRN-19 (XN-1) Radionavigation Set.

The navigation program is permanently programmed on Read-Only-Memory (ROM) chips in the data processor. This program provides a continuous dead reckoning position using ship's course and speed through the two synchro-to-digital converters and updates the DR position periodically with a satellite navigation fix. Ship's position information in the form of time, latitude, and longitude is displayed on the AN/SRN–19 front panel and updated every 5 seconds. AN/SRN–19 time is kept by processing once per second interrupts to the data processor. The interrupts are provided by a count-down of the 5 MHz oscillator. This "clock" is initialized by the operator and corrected thereafter by satellite data.

The operator uses the keyboard to initialize the navigation program and to select special purpose routines that compute and display the desired information, e.g., ship's speed and heading, and satellite fix results. The cassette tape recorder records ship's position every 15 minutes for playback later at a shore facility.

The navigation program has the following capabilities:

1. Updates present latitude and longitude once per second by dead reckoning on ship's true speed and heading. The ship's position on the front panel display is refreshed every 5 seconds. True speed and heading are obtained by summing vectorially the speed and heading of the ship with respect to the water with the set and drift of the current in the area. The heading and speed of the ship with respect to the water are obtained automatically from the ship's Mark 19 Gyrocompass and electromagnetic underwater log through the AN/SRN–19 synchro-to-digital converters. The operator has the option of manually entering the set and drift of the ocean currents if they are known. If the ship does not have a Mark 19 Gyrocompass and electromagnetic log, the ship's heading and speed with respect to the water may be entered manually. The dead reckoning program continues to run once per second regardless of any other programs that may be executing (i.e., great circle program, satellite fix program, or alert program).

2. When the receiver locks onto a satellite signal, the program recognizes the beginning of a 2-minute data transmission interval, collects and majority votes the satellite message data, and computes a satellite fix provided there is sufficient satellite data. The fix is used to update automatically the dead reckoning position provided the following conditions are met:

    i. The satellite elevation at closest approach is between 10° and 80°.

    ii. The fix computation converges in five or less iterations and the total correction is less than 30 nautical miles.

If the above conditions are not met, the operator may manually enter the fix in the data processor to update the DR position.

The special purpose routines of the navigation program include the following:

1. A great circle program which will compute and display the great-circle distance and bearing from the ship's present position to any destination that has been entered by the operator.

2. A satellite alert program which computes and displays the next expected satellite rise time, and the elevation at closest approach of the satellite just tracked. A new alert is computed each time when the display button is depressed.

3. A keyboard/display program which is used to enter and display various parameters of interest.

4423. Accuracy.—The AN/SRN–19 (XN–1) has a fixed-site CEP of less than 120 meters. Figure 4423 shows plots of 24 satellite fixes taken at dockside aboard the USS *Forest Sherman* (DD–931) at Norfolk, Virginia.

During the period 24 April to 26 April 1974, an AN/SRN–19 was installed for a technical evaluation. The dockside RMS error for 24 navigation fixes was 0.076 nautical mile. The design goal was 0.1 nautical mile RMS at dockside. During at-sea tests,

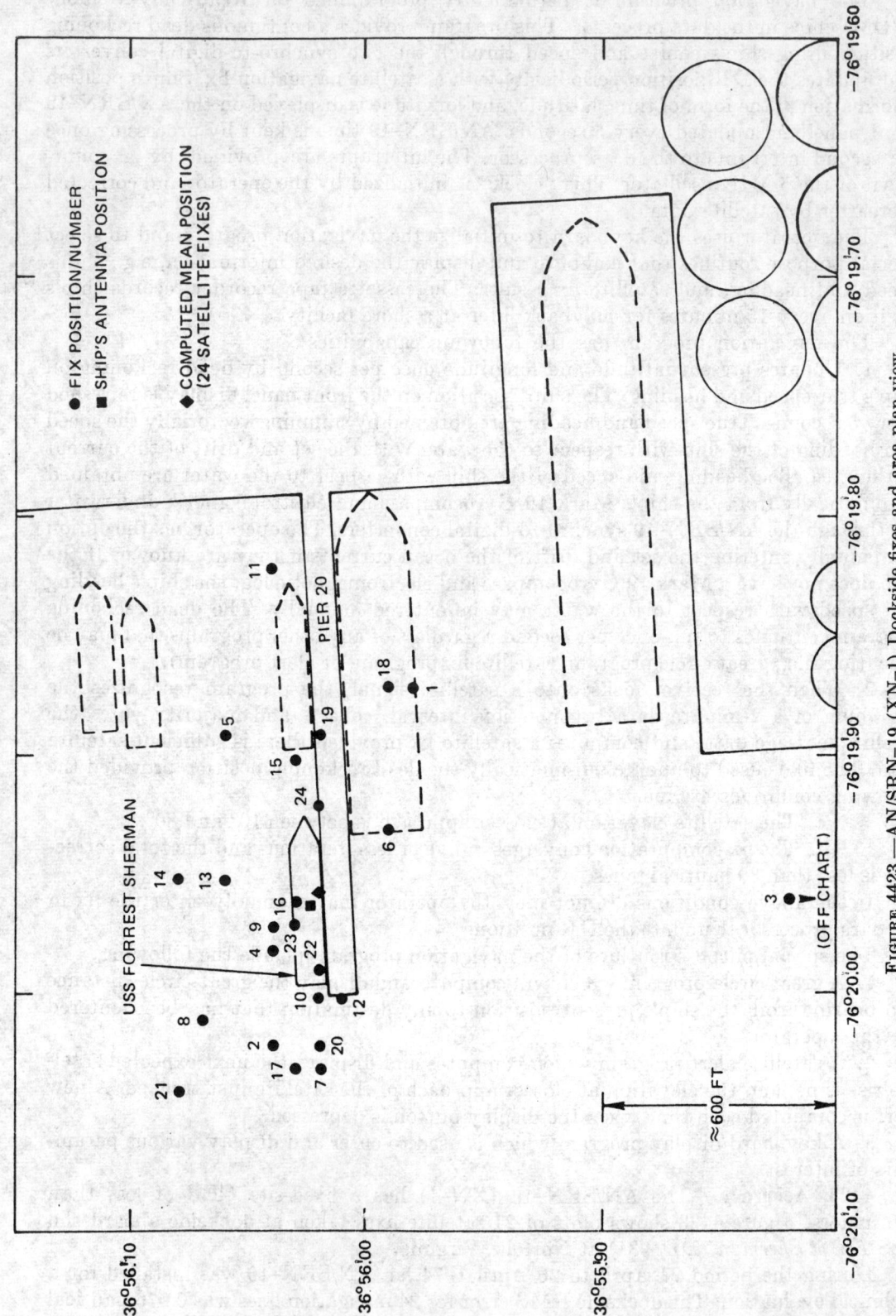

FIGURE 4423.—AN/SRN-19 (XN-1) Dockside fixes and area plan view.

automatic inputs of ship's course and speed were used. Based on eight satellite fixes obtained from the two at-sea tests, the RMS radial fix error of the AN/SRN–19 was 0.13 nautical mile. The design goal was 0.3 nautical mile RMS.

The DR velocity error is dependent upon the particular ship's motion measuring devices that are used. Fifty-three satellite navigation fixes were computed by the AN/SRN–19 located at the Applied Physics Laboratory with a 1-knot error intentionally inserted into the DR system. The RMS radial error of these 53 passes was 0.31 nautical mile.

4424. Status.—As of 1975, two AN/SRN–19 (XN–1) Radionavigation Sets have been fabricated. Modification of the S/N 01 set is under way to incorporate improvements preparatory to further technical evaluation; the S/N 02 set is being used for equipment checkout.

4425. AN/PRR–14 Geoceiver.—The basic purpose of the Geoceiver conceived at the Applied Physics Laboratory is to receive and record data for geodetic position determination. Secondary uses are for satellite orbit determination and shipboard navigation. The Geoceiver makes integrated doppler measurements from satellites radiating on 324 and 162 MHz frequency channels, as well as from the Navy navigation satellites radiating on the 400 and 150 MHz frequency.

4426. Functional description.—The received frequency pair may be selected manually or automatically. When in the automatic mode, the receiver alternately searches for the frequency pairs until satellite signals are acquired. Data processed by the Geoceiver—time, integrated doppler, and integrated refraction correction—are stored on punched paper tape which are subsequently transmitted to a computing center. Provision is also included for processing the Navy navigation satellite message with the doppler and refraction correction data to a computer for real-time navigation applications.

The main receiving unit of the Geoceiver is shown in figure 4426.

4427. Design characteristics.—The Geoceiver design specifications include the following:

1. double conversion 400/324 MHz channel,

2. double conversion slaved 150/162 MHz channel,

3. integrated doppler frequency measurements timed by a receiver clock (30-second or 60-second integration intervals),

4. receiver clock calibrated against received Navy navigation satellite time,

5. separate integrated refraction data from 150/162 MHz channel,

6. time, doppler, and refraction correction data recorded on punched paper tape with additional data entered from the receiver control panel,

7. Navy navigation satellite message, time, doppler, and refraction correction data available on a computer output to provide real-time navigation,

8. automatic search and acquisition of satellite signals with manual over-ride,

9. rapid resynchronization with satellite message and time if carrier tracking is lost for up to a minute,

10. built-in self-test and troubleshooting aids,

11. portable; small in size, weight and power consumption.

A suitable external computer is required for real-time navigation applications.

4428. Accuracy.—Table 4428 indicates single pass survey capabilities of the Geoceiver by using satellite orbits derived from tracked data as opposed to navigation results obtained from projected orbits.

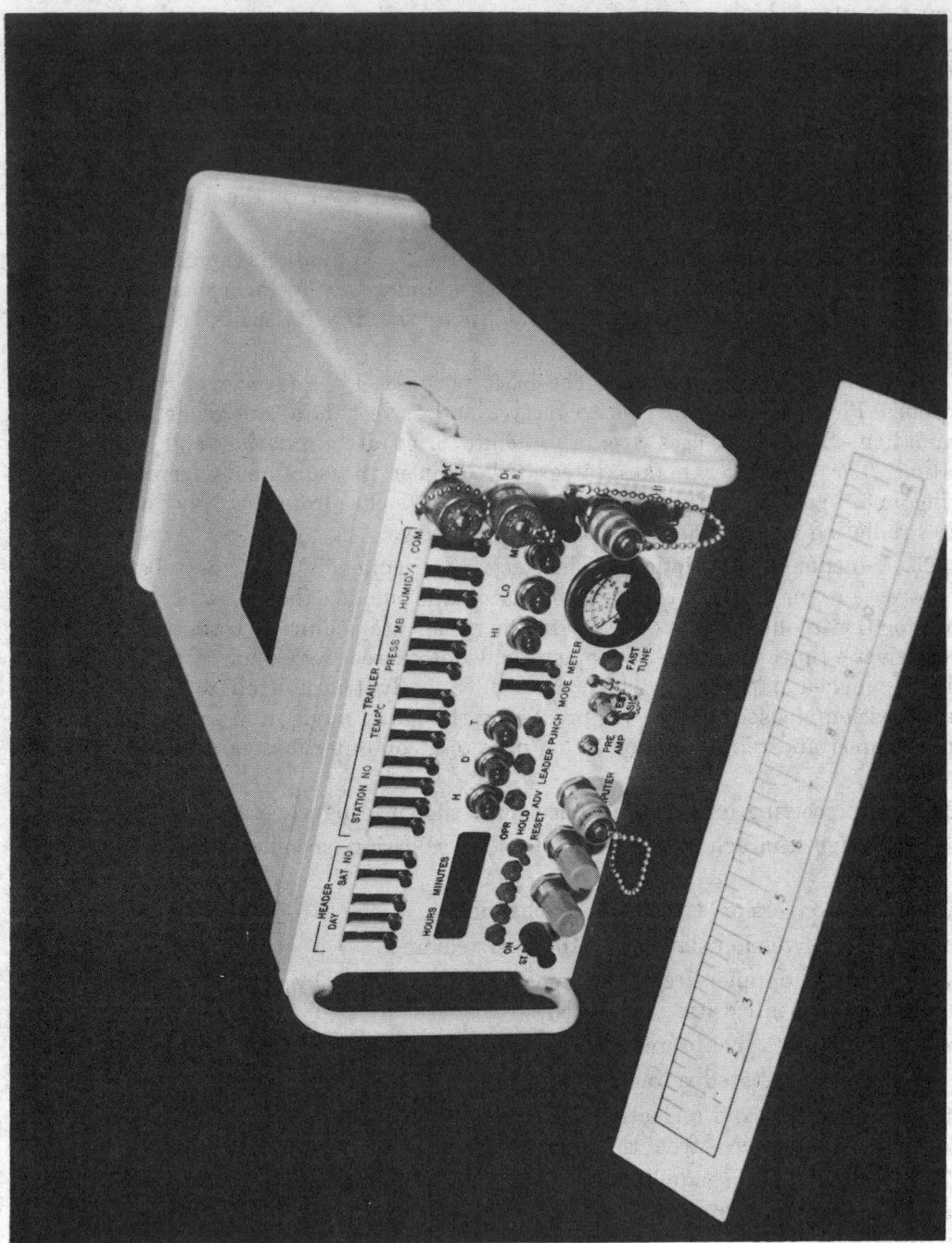

Courtesy of Applied Physics Laboratory, The Johns Hopkins University.

FIGURE 4426.—AN/PRR Receiver Unit.

Equipment	Satel-lite	No. Passes	Mean Error (Meters)		Standard Deviation (Meters)	
			Long.	Lat.	Long.	Lat.
Breadboard	30120	44	6. 2	−5. 1	8. 7	6. 1
Geoceiver	30130	53	8. 0	−3. 3	13. 7	5. 7
(Station 391)	30140	50	7. 6	−3. 1	8. 6	4. 9
	30180	44	8. 0	−5. 7	9. 3	6. 4
Prototype	30120	32	5. 7	−4. 3	12. 5	7. 5
Geoceiver	30130	37	8. 9	−3. 8	6. 6	3. 5
(Station 137)	30140	42	6. 3	−4. 2	7. 6	3. 9
	30180	42	6. 7	−5. 0	10. 8	6. 9
Breadboard	30120	7	13. 8	−1. 9	13. 2	9. 6
Geoceiver	30130	16	8. 0	−2. 9	9. 0	3. 9
(Station 136)	30140	14	7. 2	−2. 8	7. 3	6. 7
	30180	18	9. 7	−3. 3	11. 4	5. 7

Notes: 1. Obtained from NWL Technical Report TR–2338 dated September 1969.
2. Data obtained with antenna common to both the breadboard and prototype Geoceivers.

TABLE 4428.—Geoceiver survey data statistics for single pass solutions.

4429. Status.—The first Geoceiver was completed in January 1971. The second Geoceiver, S/N 02, was delivered to the Applied Physics Laboratory in February 1971 for evaluation. Currently (1975), Geoceivers S/N 03 and S/N 04 are at the Laboratory for data collection and evaluation. During 1971, a total of 33 Geoceivers were delivered to various users.

4430. Pseudo random noise modulation.—*A new generation of navigation satellites* was developed by the Applied Physics Laboratory as part of the Transit Improvement Program (TIP) to enable more accurate navigation fixes. A key element of TIP is a broadband **pseudo random noise** (**PRN**) **modulation** that provides the capability to recover satellite time epochs with greater precision than previously possible. The RF energy for the PRN modulation is spread over 3.3 MHz and is 45 dB down from the carrier so that the modulation is transparent to normal satellite navigation users.

The first satellite with PRN modulation was the TRIAD satellite launched in September 1972. Follow on TIP satellites will also include this PRN capability. Potential uses of this new modulation include navigation with PRN as a direct measurement of the range between the satellite and the navigator, navigation with single channel PRN and doppler measurements concurrently to eliminate the effects of refraction, evaluating the quality of the doppler data received, and synchronizing the navigator's clock to the satellite clock.

For satellite applications, the PRN technique offers significant advantages when compared to competing modulation techniques, namely:

1. It provides a solution to the problem of cross-satellite interference which is a problem at high latitudes with the six currently operational navigation satellites. PRN allows satellites to be tracked individually, even though their doppler frequencies

may cross. This capability remains regardless of the number of satellites in the constellation. PRN will also suppress other interfering signals.

2. The RF energy of the spread spectrum sidebands produced by PRN modulation is 45 dB down from the carrier frequency. This depressed and spread modulation obviates the need to obtain a new frequency allocation for the PRN system. PRN does not interfere with other users of the 150 and 400 MHz frequencies.

3. Satellite hardware and ground equipment modification requirements are no greater for PRN than for any other suggested timing system.

4. PRN modulation is transparent to the current navigation user equipment without modification or degradation of navigational fix accuracies.

5. The PRN ranging signals may be denied to unwanted users, thereby offering potential jamming immunity.

6. PRN provides maximum multipath suppression; this is especially important to the air navigation application.

In order to fully evaluate the PRN technique, an experimental ground system was developed at the Applied Physics Laboratory by using a suitably modified AN/SRN-9 receiver as the nucleus.

The experimental ground system was used to gather precision range and doppler data from the TRIAD satellite. Orbital satellite data were recorded on magnetic tape and subsequently analyzed on the IBM 360/91 computer at the Laboratory. Analytical software was developed to evaluate the capability of the PRN signals to meet the following objectives:

1. to reduce the time required to obtain a navigation fix during each pass by providing improved doppler count data,

2. to provide real-time reduction of interfering and multipath signals,

3. to provide experimental confirmation of the PRN techniques presently being considered for advanced navigation satellite systems.

The opportunity to demonstrate digital modulation techniques in general may be considered a secondary application of the system.

4431. Functional description.—The PRN ranging/time code is impressed on the 400 and 150 MHz carriers via a digital shift register and a two-stage phase modulator that operates directly at 400 and 150 MHz, having a peak phase deviation of 45°. The transmitted signal consists of 1 watt of the unmodulated carrier and 1 watt of PRN modulated side bands, the largest of which is 45 dB below the unmodulated carrier. Present navigation set users continue to navigate with the unmodulated carriers and are not affected by the ranging signal, since it is well below the minimum receiver threshold.

Reception of the PRN code requires a correlation type receiver in which a local replica of the code is generated and compared to the received code in a multiplier. The output voltage from the multiplier varies as the autocorrelation function of the code, and reaches a maximum value when the codes are in exact alignment. This voltage is fed back to a device which controls the delay of the locally generated code, keeping it aligned with the received code during the satellite pass.

A measurement subsystem consisting of a time-of-day (TOD) clock and an interpolater is a part of the system. Upon receipt of a PRN epoch pulse, the TOD clock is read out to a resolution of 1 miscrosecond. At the same time, an interpolation is made between the last microsecond recorded by the clock and the actual occurrence of the epoch pulse, to a resolution of 1 nanosecond. Both the 400 and 150 MHz epoch pulses are measured in this way and the data are subsequently used in the computer to calculate a single refraction-corrected range value.

The measurement subsystem also makes use of precision doppler counts. The counting technique used is patterned after the Geoceiver (AN/PRN–14) approach, wherein an exact number of doppler cycles are counted over continuous integration intervals. The TOD clock is read out to 1 microsecond at the beginning of each count. A doppler frequency is also obtained from the 150 MHz channel, scaled to 400 MHz, and counted in a similar manner. Both counts can be made and recorded at selectable intervals varying from 0.6 to 4.6 seconds during the pass, and subsequently used by the computer to generate a single refraction corrected doppler count.

4432. Accuracy.—Instrumentation accuracy is one factor contributing to the final range measurement accuracy of the system. Other factors must be considered, i.e., satellite and receiver oscillator instabilities, orbit prediction errors, higher order ionospheric effects, and similarly related effects. Data obtained from TRIAD have been used to demonstrate that:

1. Precise timing signals can be recovered and used to make counting and timing measurements of such high quality that accurate integral doppler navigation fixes can be obtained using only those measurements made within a relatively short interval of time centered about the closest approach of the satellite.

2. The timing signals can also provide the direct measurements of slant range for ranging fixes that are as accurate as integral doppler fixes.

3. A navigation fix free of the potentially large errors due to ionospheric refraction can be produced using only single frequency doppler and ranging measurements.

Demonstrated error levels from the ground system instrumentation, independent of the oscillator are listed below:

Time recovery errors (after refraction correction)—10 nsec rms, 10 nsec bias.

Doppler recovery errors (after refraction correction)—0.1 cycle rms.

4433. Status.—The SRN–9/PRN Ground Receiving System was first used to track the TRIAD satellite in the fall of 1972. Since then data from over 80 satellite passes have been obtained and analyzed.

The system has been used in TRIAD tracking to demonstrate successfully the time and frequency monitoring capabilities of PRN signals.

Basic Principles

4434. Design considerations.—A satellite navigation system is truly all weather when radio frequencies are utilized which are not sensitive to weather or atmospheric noise, and when frequencies are combined such as to obtain independence from ionospheric variations. The use of orbiting satellites makes the system inherently worldwide. Other attributes of a satellite navigation system depend upon other system design considerations such as the question of whether to utilize radio sextant techniques analogous to celestial navigation, whether to utilize simultaneous transmissions from multiple orbiting satellites in analogy with Loran or Omega, or whether to use an altogether new method which is more natural to artificial satellites than established techniques, e.g., taking advantage of the high speed of the satellite by using the doppler shift.

NAVSAT through its use of range rate by measurement of the doppler shift of satellite radio transmissions provides the following advantages:

1. There is no need for a large receiving antenna array as required by radio sextants.

2. Only one satellite need be utilized to obtain a position at a given time so that the complexity of maintaining cooperative satellites in orbit for simultaneous signal reception is avoided.

3. Doppler measurements are inherently open loop, that is, there is no need for transponding signals back and forth between the satellite and the observer as would

be necessary in measuring range directly. Therefore, NAVSAT is passive in that there are no radio transmissions from the observer's station.

4435. Basic doppler navigation principles.—Measurement of the satellite doppler curve in the vicinity of zero doppler shift allows a determination of the time and the line-of-sight range (slant range) to the closest point of approach of the satellite to the observer. This measurement enables determining the observer's position relative to the satellite in a coordinate system which is local to the satellite at the time of closest approach and whose axes are parallel and perpendicular to the direction the satellite travels over the earth at that time. Knowing the satellite's orbit, its subtrack over the earth's surface can be determined. Knowing the minimum slant range to the satellite and the altitude of the satellite, the distance from this subtrack can be found. This can be thought of as the cross-track coordinate of the observer relative to the satellite. Knowing the exact time when this minimum slant range occurred, the position of the satellite along its earth subtrack is known which can be considered the along-track coordinate of the observer relative to the satellite. Knowledge of the satellite orbit in detail tells how to transform the observer's relative along-track and cross-track coordinates to latitude and longitude.

While this method is adequate to determine the observer's position, other information in the doppler shift can be used to advantage. If the whole of the doppler shift is used, sufficient redundant information is obtained to overwhelm any error due to random noise such as receiver and atmospheric noise. Furthermore, one can tell which side of the satellite subtrack the navigator is on by utilizing the fact that the earth's rotation produces a slight difference between the doppler shift as received east of the satellite orbit and west of the orbit.

Effective utilization of the whole of the doppler shift as received by the observer also allows the navigated position to be essentially free of any momentary receiver "drop out," short term interference, etc., and some important potential system errors; for example, the error caused by an error in the frequency standard of the equipment. (The satellite frequency is maintained to an accuracy of better than one part in 10 billion but the navigator's local oscillator frequency can be in substantial error in some of the less expensive navigator equipments.) Figure 4435 shows the time dependence of the change in the received doppler shift for a set on the earth's equator which is changed by 1 kilometer in its along-track and cross-track components, respectively. It can be seen that the change in the along-track component produces a symmetric frequency change. Also, it can be seen that the change in cross-track component produces an anti-symmetric frequency change so that with doppler data only near the time of closest approach (zero relative time in figure 4435) along-track and cross-track components can be identified unambiguously. However, if a frequency standard error (local oscillator error) exists also, data only near closest approach will not allow unambiguous identification of both frequency and along-track changes. On the other hand, if the whole of the doppler shift is considered, the two errors can be easily differentiated since a change in frequency produces a constant frequency error, while a change in the along-track component produces a time dependent doppler error, the error being a maximum near the time of closest approach.

4436. Effect of random measurement errors.—Profiles of over-all system navigation error can be constructed assuming that only random doppler (frequency) errors are present. Figure 4436 shows a typical navigation error profile as the ground distance to the satellite subtrack changes. As is to be expected, the along-track error becomes relatively large when the satellite is on the horizon since it is not above the horizon sufficiently long to accurately establish separation of along-track error from the set's local oscillator error. The cross-track error becomes large when the satellite is nearly

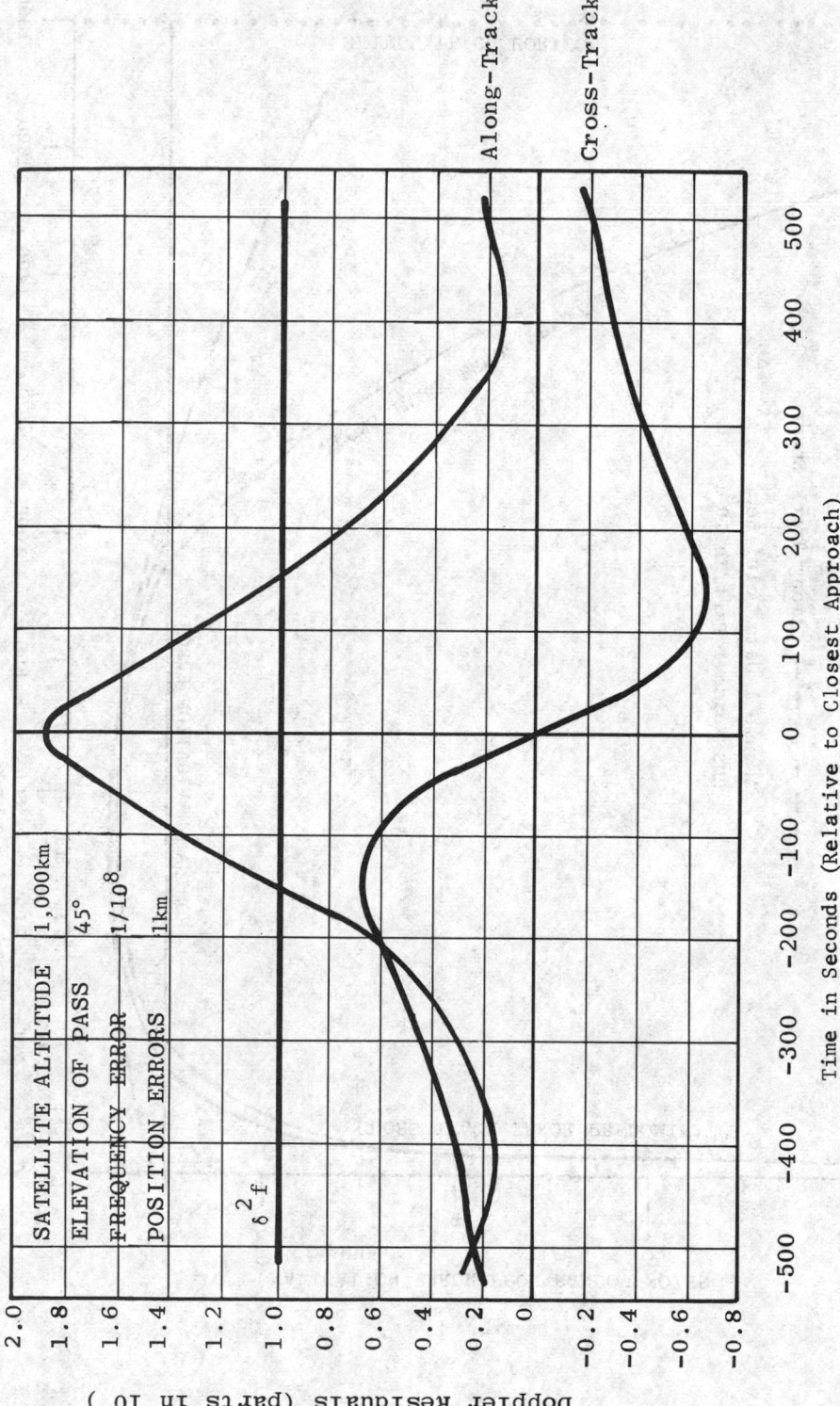

FIGURE 4435.—Two position parameters.

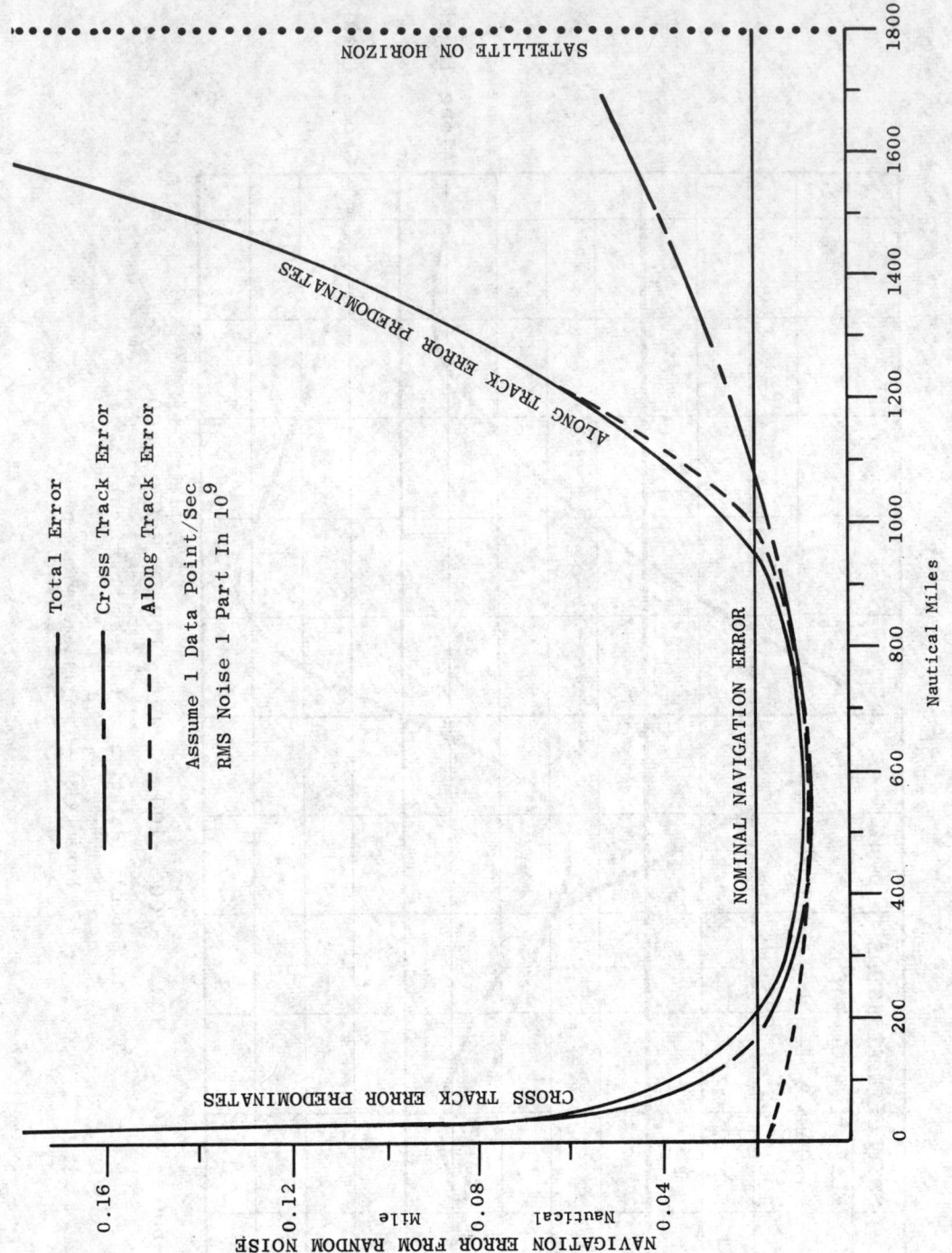

FIGURE 4436.—Ground range to satellite subtrack.

overhead since there is relatively small change in slant range to the satellite for a change in cross-track component when the satellite is overhead.

The error profiles like those in figure 4436 are pessimistic since they consider the navigation errors when many independent measurements of frequency are made, e.g., one each second. Modern techniques dictate that coherent measurements be taken so that any error in frequency which has an average error of zero is suppressed. With such techniques, the errors due to random noise are suppressed more than the square root of the number of measurements, but probably still less than the total length of time of reception itself. In other words, noise can be suppressed somewhere between a factor of 15 min. (average pass duration) $\times 60$ sec.$=900$ and

$$\sqrt{15 \times 60} = 30,$$

dependent upon other considerations.

One manner in which coherent measurements can be very conveniently utilized is by not measuring frequency per se but to maintain a running count of the number of zero crossings of the received signal to obtain the coherent integral of the doppler shift. Utilizing integral doppler data in this way yields more potential accuracy and can be easier to implement in the navigator's equipment. In doing this, the equipment does become more sensitive to intermittent signal dropouts, etc., so that the more reliable navigator's equipments utilize more sophisticated methods than this. However, several of the less expensive equipments, such as the AN/SRN–9 (art. 4412), utilize explicitly this technique, where the integral doppler value is read each time the satellite 2-minute time marker is received.

4437. Non-random error sources.—For all practical purposes, random-frequency errors in the doppler data will not cause significant navigation errors. This is not true of systematic errors. The major sources of error which have been found are related to ionospheric refraction, errors in knowledge of the gravity field acting on the navigation satellites, and errors in knowledge of ship's course and speed through the water.

A major potential source of error in all satellite radio navigation systems is ionospheric refraction. Navigation errors can result from the effect of refraction on the measurement of the doppler shift and from the errors in the satellite's orbit if refraction is not accurately accounted for in the satellite tracking. Since the doppler shift in the presence of the ionosphere is basically the time rate of change of the electromagnetic path length, the doppler shift is altered from what it would be in a vacuum. However, it can be shown that the ionosphere is **dispersive** (the amount of refraction is dependent upon the frequency) and for frequencies significantly above any ionospheric resonance frequency (usually less than 30 MHz) the dependence of the doppler shift with frequency is accurately known. For frequencies above 100 MHz, the dependence is inversely proportional to the frequency to very high accuracy. The refraction contribution can be eliminated by the proper mixing of the received doppler shift from two harmonically related frequencies (150 and 400 MHz for NAVSAT) to yield an accurate estimate of the vacuum doppler shift.

In addition, the two received doppler frequencies can be mixed to yield an experimentally measured effect of the ionosphere, and the probable error caused by the ionospheric contributions can be studied. Such studies show that the principal navigation error due to refraction is in the cross-track component; it typically can be several tenths of a nautical mile, and can be as large as 1 nautical mile. Unlike the mixing of local oscillator frequency error with the navigated along-track error, where use of the whole of the doppler curve allows both the along-track component and local oscillator frequency to be error determined, the ionospheric error has a time dependence during the pass of the satellite above the navigator's horizon which mimics the time dependence of the doppler signal for a cross-track error. In this case, the cross-track component and a parametric fit to ionospheric parameters does not yield negligible navigation errors. Consequently, except for the simplest navigator equipments, two frequencies are received to yield a navigation position via the vacuum doppler data. Figure 4437a shows the ionospheric contribution at 150 MHz which can be compared with the cross-track error of figure 4435.

Any error in the navigator's knowledge of the satellite position during the time doppler data is used feeds directly (and in nearly a one-to-one manner) into the navigation error. Consequently, every effort is made to reduce the navigation satellite orbit error to a minimum. The major contributor to this error is inadequate knowledge of the gravity field of the earth, i.e., the gravity forces acting on the satellite. In 1960 it was possible to determine the orbit of a satellite and then predict the orbit ahead in time for 1 day (for use by navigators) to an accuracy of 0.5 to 1.0 nautical mile due to errors in the gravity forces. Since that time extensive geodetic research utilizing research satellites, similar to the navigation satellites with added tracking capability by optical means, has resulted in a significant improvement in knowledge of the earth's gravity field and consequent improvement in navigation accuracy.

The technique for determining the gravity field is to accumulate a large amount of tracking data (primarily doppler and optical) as observed on a large number of satellites in orbits of varying inclinations. A gravity model is explicitly "parameterized" in

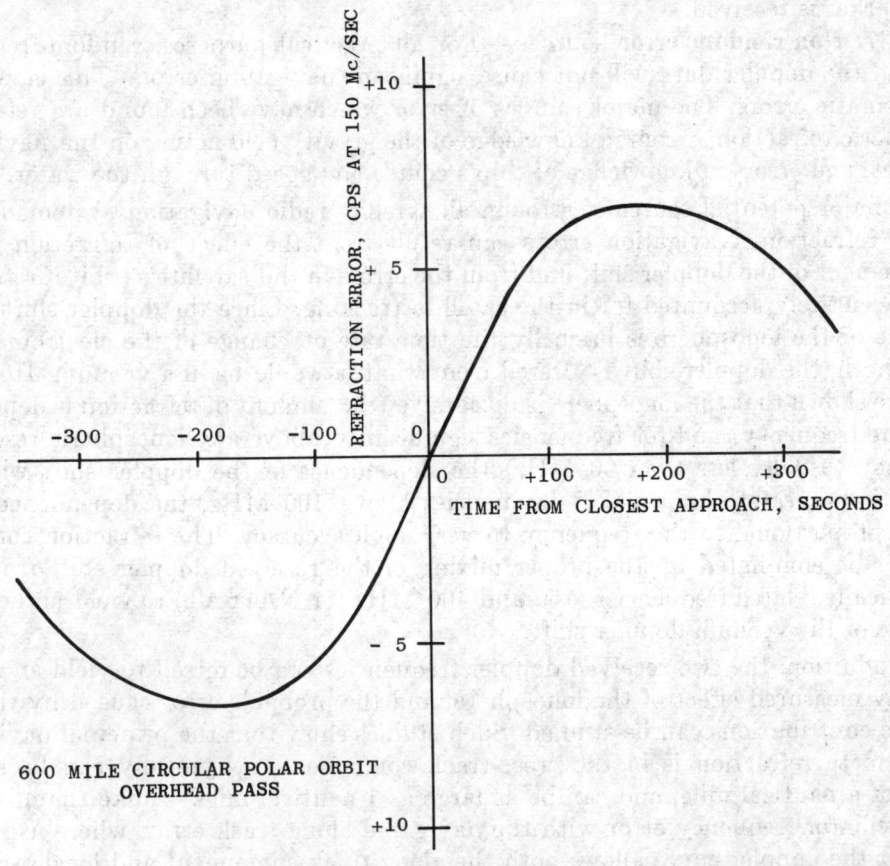

FIGURE 4437a.—First order theoretical refraction error.

terms of unknown coefficients in an expansion of the earth's gravity field. An over-all least squares fit of the tracking data is then made considering all of the satellite orbit parameters, all of the Legendre expansion coefficients of the gravity field, and the location of the tracking stations as unknowns. The gravity field which gradually emerged from such worldwide studies exhibited a complexity far beyond that ever suspected.

It is difficult to summarize the complex gravity field as it is known today. One fairly common method is to present contours of geoid heights. Such heights represent the height that water would rise or sink to—in seeking its own level—over and above that water level which would occur if the gravity field were a spherical mass (suitably modified for the equatorial bulge due to the earth's spinning). Consequently, such geoidal contour maps can indicate the departure of the earth's gravity field from what it was thought to be prior to the advent of satellite geodesy. Such a contour plot is shown in figure 4437b, which portrays the gravity field as known in 1968. With modern gravity models for the earth, satellite tracking error has been reduced from about ¼ mile to about 20 meters with commensurate reduction in the navigation error (orbit prediction error) caused by errors in the gravity forces acting on the satellite. As knowledge of the gravity field improves, errors due to this source will be further reduced.

The remaining large potential source of error is the error in the navigator's motion during the receipt of doppler data. Since the doppler shift is determined by the relative motion between satellite and navigator, any error in the navigator's motion will appear as an apparent error in the doppler data used to find the navigator's position. On the average this error causes about 400 yards navigation error for every knot of error in velocity. Navigator velocity error can become appreciable in aircraft navigation applications, and special techniques are used to bound this error in aircraft equipments. This error can become significant for high speed surface vessels and submarines in the most demanding applications. For such cases, inertial systems are usually used to determine vessel speed and aid in dead reckoning between satellite passes.

Other potential sources of error are usually negligible except for the most demanding applications. Sources of errors such as abnormal tropospheric refraction (e.g., navigation near a weather front); neglect of the variable height of the sea surface (e.g., ignore the geoidal height, figure 4437b, as an altitude correction of the navigator's antenna height); and even wander of the geographic position of the spin axis of the earth (the so called Chandler wobble) are errors which can and should be accounted for when highest accuracy is desired. With all such corrections, navigation accuracy rivals world surveying accuracy (art. 4425). For this reason, satellite navigation has brought attention to some large mapping errors. A good discussion of current navigation accuracy capability can be obtained in the bull's-eye plots shown for the navigation equipment discussed (figs. 4411b, 4414, and tab. 4428).

Integral Doppler Navigation

4438. AN/SRN–9 integral doppler navigation.—It is beyond the scope of this chapter to present details of the more sophisticated navigation techniques, e.g., the AN/BRN–3 coupled to SINS. However, the essentials and many of the details are similar for utilizing integral doppler data in the AN/SRN–9. Therefore, the navigation procedure is given for this equipment in more detail to provide one detailed example of satellite navigation.

The navigation fix obtained from the AN/SRN–9 is based upon the shift in frequency (doppler frequency shift) that occurs whenever the relative distance between a radio transmitter and receiver is changing. Such a change can be measured by a

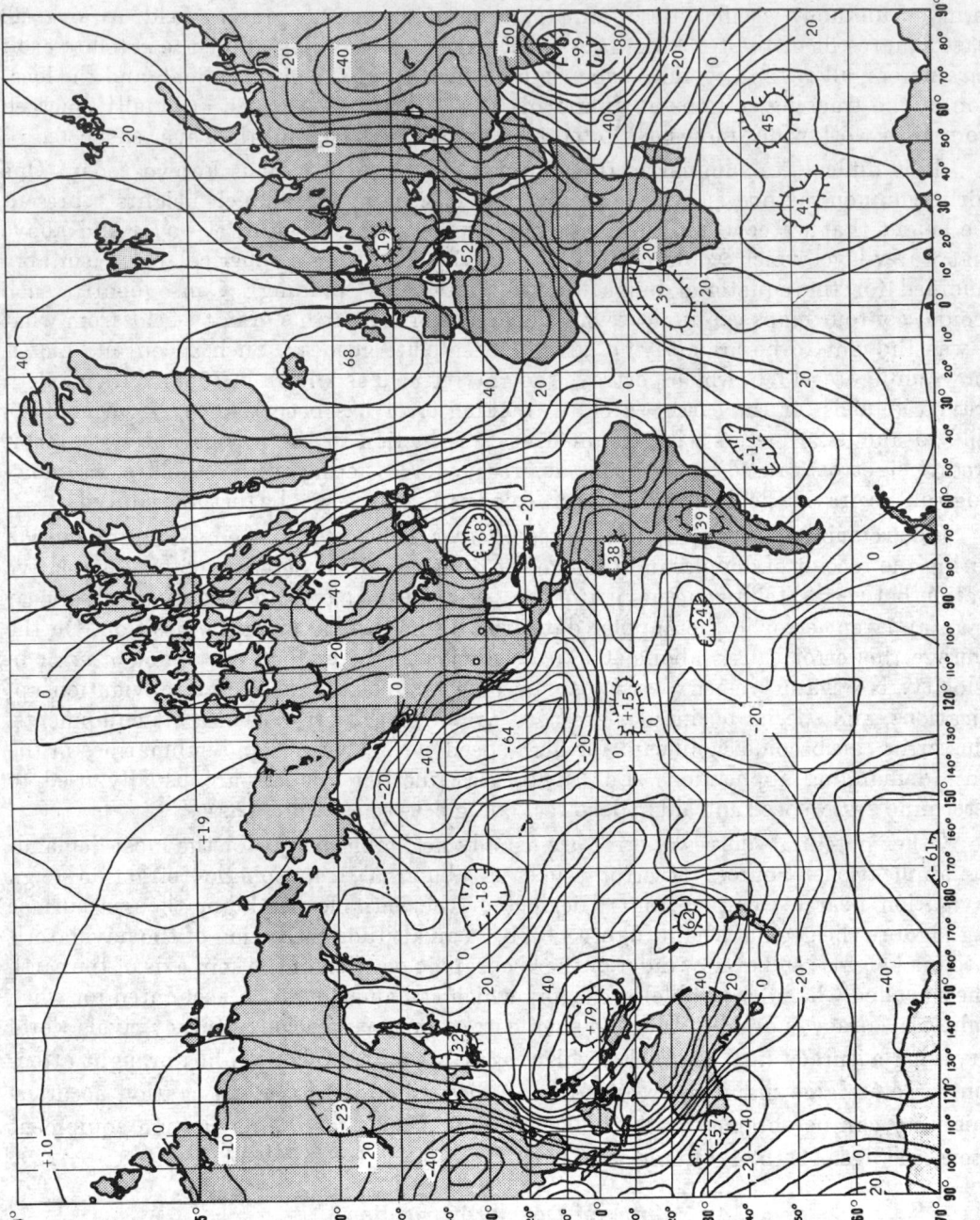

FIGURE 4437b.—Contour map of geoidal height (meters).

receiver whenever a transmitting navigation satellite passes within radio range, and is due to the combination of three effects:

1. motion of the satellite in its orbit,
2. motion of the navigator on the earth's surface, and
3. rotation of the earth (and therefore of the navigator) about the earth's axis.

It follows that the motion of the navigator must be properly measured or estimated and inserted into the computation if accurate fixes are to be obtained.

The integral of the doppler shift over a 2-minute interval (as measured by the AN/SRN–9 receiver, using a doppler frequency counter that is controlled by the 2-minute time markers received from the satellite) is a measure of how much the slant range from satellite to navigator has changed during this 2-minute interval. In order to derive his position, the navigator also needs to know the position of the satellite in its orbit every 2 minutes. The information required from computing a fix are as follows:

Data	*Obtained From*
Two-minute doppler frequency counts (integrated doppler).	AN/SRN–9 receiver, using self-contained frequency standard.
Satellite orbital position every 2 minutes____	AN/SRN–9 receiver recognition of satellite data bits plus subsequent computer operation (tab. 4438).
Own ship's *estimated* position every 2 minutes_	
Or	Ship's navigational aids (with DR plot if necessary).
Own ship's course and speed plus one estimate of ship's position at a stated time.	
Own ship's antenna height above geoid_____	See figure 4437b.

Figures 4438a and 4438b illustrate how the measurements are made and how the navigation fix is computed after the satellite pass is over. In figure 4438a, the positions of the satellite in its orbit are shown for times t_1 through t_4, which are the even minutes at which the satellite transmits its synchronization signal. The positions of the navigator, P_1 through P_4, refer to the times at which his AN/SRN–9 receiver recognizes the satellite synchronization signal, i.e., times $t_1 + \Delta t_1$ through $t_4 + \Delta t_4$. Note that the times of

Word number	Symbol	Meaning	Units
56	t_p	Time of perigee.	Min.
62	$\dot{M}$	Rate of change of mean anomaly.	Deg/Min.
68	$|\phi|$	Argument of perigee at t_p.	Deg.
74	$\dot{\phi}$	Rate of change of argument of perigee (absolute value).	Deg/Min.
80	ϵ	Eccentricity	
86	A_o	Semimajor axis.	Km.
92	Ω_N	Right ascension ascending node at t_p.	Deg.
98	$\dot{\Omega}$	Rate of change of Ω_N.	Deg/Min.
104	$\cos \psi$	Cosine of orbit inclination.	
110	Ω_G	Right Ascension Greenwich.	Deg.
128	$\sin \psi$	Sine of orbit inclination.	

TABLE 4438.—Satellite orbital information.

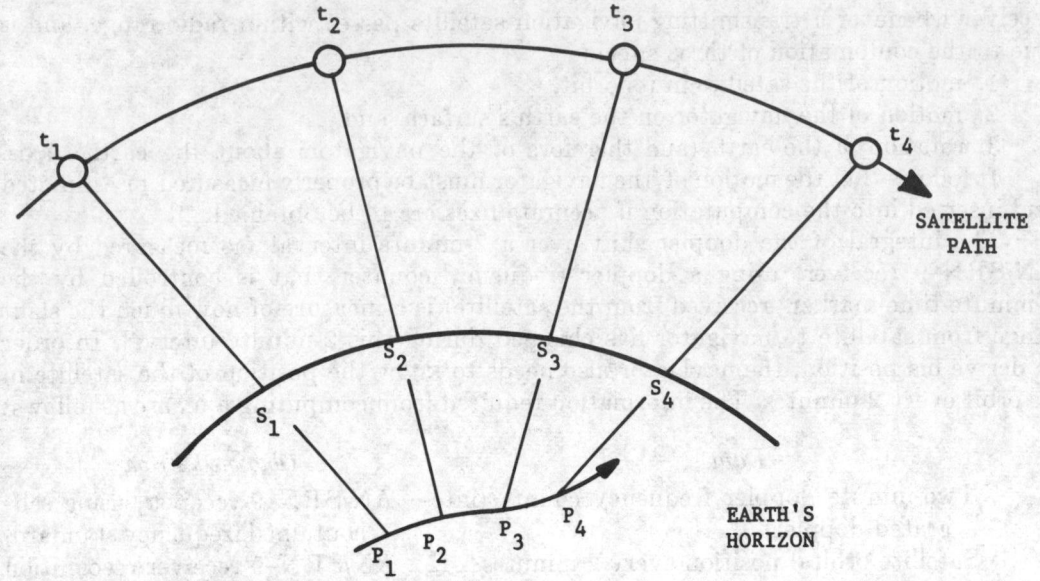

f_o = NOMINAL VALUE OF NAVIGATOR'S REFERENCE FREQUENCY

c = SPEED OF LIGHT

$\overline{f}$ = DIFFERENCE BETWEEN NAVIGATOR'S REFERENCE FREQUENCY AND SATELLITE TRANS-MISSION FREQUENCY

T = 2 MINUTES (i.e., $t_2 - t_1$, $t_3 - t_2$, etc.)

ϕ = LATITUDE

λ = LONGITUDE

t = TIME OF TRANSMISSION OF TIMING MARK

t+Δt = TIME OF RECEPTION OF TIMING MARK

N = DOPPLER COUNT

S = SLANT RANGE

$$N_{12} = \frac{f_o}{c}[S_2(\phi,\lambda) - S_1(\phi,\lambda)] + \Delta f \cdot T$$

$$N_{23} = \frac{f_o}{c}[S_3(\phi\ \lambda) - S_2(\phi,\lambda)] + \Delta f \cdot T$$

$$N_{34} = \frac{f_o}{c}[S_4(\phi,\lambda) - S_3(\phi,\lambda)] + \Delta f \cdot T$$

FIGURE 4438a.—Integrated doppler measurement.

reception are slightly later than the times of transmission because of the radio propagation time over the slant ranges S_1, S_2, S_3, and S_4. Also, since the propagation times Δt_1, Δt_2, Δt_3, and Δt_4 are not all equal, the time intervals over which the AN/SRN–9 makes its integral doppler measurements will differ slightly from the exact 2-minute value, being somewhat smaller prior to satellite closest approach (while S is decreasing). This fact, however, does not affect the result of the measurement because the number of RF cycles *transmitted* by the satellite between synchronization signals (exactly 2 minutes apart) must necessarily equal the number *received* by the navigator between receptions of the synchronization signals, since no RF cycles can be "lost" or "gained."

The integral doppler measurements are simply the count N_{12} of the number of doppler cycles received between $t_1 + \Delta t_1$ and $t_2 + \Delta t_2$, the count N_{23} of the number of doppler cycles between $t_2 + \Delta t_2$ and $t_3 + \Delta t_3$, and so on for all 2-minute intervals during

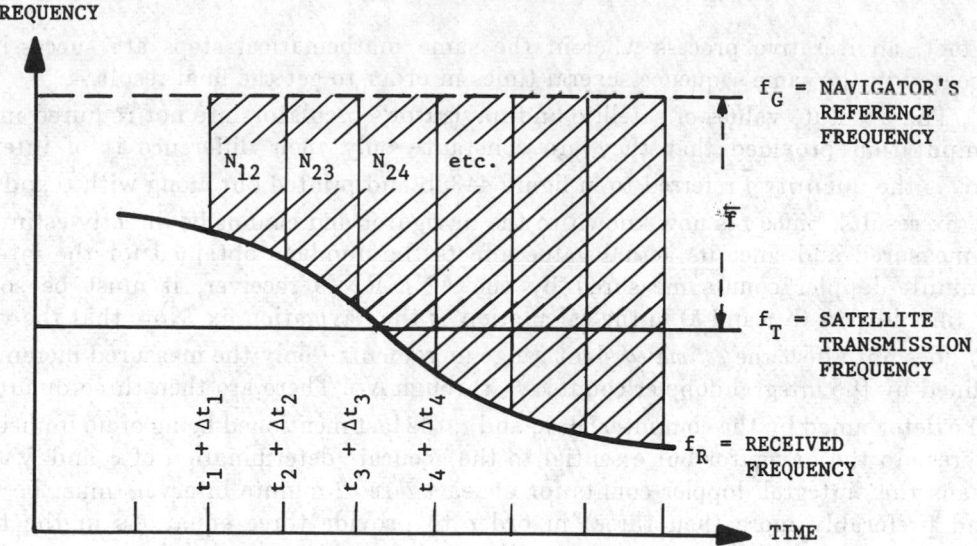

FIGURE 4438b.—Doppler frequency variation with time.

the satellite pass. These counts are a direct measure of the amount by which the slant range from satellite to navigator has changed (S_2-S_1, S_3-S_2, etc.) during the count intervals. This measure is quite accurate since each doppler count added (or subtracted) due to the relative motion means that S has decreased (or increased) by one wavelength, or by 0.75 meter at 400 MHz. Therefore, one of the required inputs to the fix computation (slant range increment over each 2-minute interval) is directly measured by the AN/SRN-9 integral doppler count, suitably scaled as indicated in figure 4438a. Note that the slant ranges S_1 through S_4 (and therefore their respective differences, or slant range increments) are all functions of the navigator's position (ϕ, λ). Since the satellite orbital positions can be calculated from the data recovered from the signal phase modulation by the AN/SRN-9 receiver, and since the navigator's *estimated* position every 2 minutes is available, values of *estimated* slant range from satellite to navigator can be computed. These estimated slant ranges are differenced to obtain *estimated* slant range increments, which then can be compared with the slant range increments *measured* by means of the integral doppler counts as already described.

Unless the navigator's estimate of his position happens to be exactly correct there will, of course, be a difference or residual when each *estimated* slant range increment is subtracted from the corresponding *measured* increment. The fix calculation then consists of changing the navigator's estimate of position (ϕ, λ) in small steps until the sum of the squares of the slant range residuals is minimized, at which point the closest achievable agreement exists between the (revised) estimates and the measures of slant range increment. The values of ϕ and λ so determined (i.e., the revised estimates that yield the smallest residual) are then the fix result, which is printed out at the end of the fix computation.

In practice, two factors complicate this simple explanation, and therefore represent extra computing steps in the fix computation:

1. The frequency of the satellite oscillator and also that of the reference oscillator used in the AN/SRN-9 receiver are constant but not precisely known to the navigator.

2. The process of minimizing the sum of the squares of the differences between the estimated and measured slant range differences calls for a number of different manipulations to be performed in the computer used to calculate the navigation fix and is,

in fact, an iterative process wherein the same mathematical steps are successively repeated in the same sequence several times in order to get the final result.

The absolute values of satellite and navigator's oscillators are not required in the computation provided that they are constant—only their difference is of interest. This is the quantity $\bar{f}$ referred to in figure 4438b and printed out along with ϕ and λ in the fix results. Since $\bar{f}$ is now known to the navigator and cannot be directly estimated or measured and since its actual value affects the numbers obtained for the integral 2-minute doppler counts measured by the AN/SRN–9 receiver, it must be solved for (in addition to ϕ and λ) in the calculation of the navigation fix. Note that the value of $\bar{f}$ does not affect the *estimated* slant range increments—only the measured increments defined by the integral doppler counts N_{12} through N_{34}. There are then three quantities to be determined by the computer: ϕ, λ, and $\bar{f}$, the last mentioned being of no immediate interest to the navigator but essential to the accurate determination of ϕ and λ. This means that integral doppler counts for at least *three* 2-minute intervals must be used (and preferably more than three) in order to provide three equations in the three unknowns, ϕ, λ, and $\bar{f}$.

That the integral doppler counts N_{12} and N_{34} are directly affected by $\bar{f}$ is illustrated in figure 4438b, wherein f_G is the (constant) frequency of the navigator's reference oscillator, f_T is the (constant) frequency of the satellite's transmitter, f_R is the received frequency containing the doppler component, and $\bar{f}=f_G-f_T$. The integral doppler counts, N_{12}, etc., are represented by the cross-hatched area in figure 4438b.

Since the values of three quantities (ϕ, λ, and $\bar{f}$) have to be simultaneously adjusted in minimizing the sum of the squares of the differences between estimated and measured slant range for three (or more) 2-minute intervals, the computations involve solution of a matrix whose general description can be illustrated as follows:

1. The *measured* slant range *increments* are calculated from the integral doppler counts for an assumed value of $\bar{f}$. Their rate of change as $\bar{f}$ changes is also determined.

2. The navigator's positions at the times t_1, t_2, etc., are calculated for an assumed initial position (ϕ, λ).

3. Using previously calculated satellite positions at t_1, t_2, etc., the estimated satellite-navigator slant range increments (for the assumed initial ϕ, λ are calculated).

4. The rate of change (partial derivative) of the estimated slant range increments (item 3 above) with respect to ϕ is determined.

5. The partial derivative of the estimated slant range increments with respect to λ is determined.

6. The differences (residuals) between *measured* slant range increments (item 1) and *estimated* slant range increments (item 3) are formed for each 2-minute interval.

7. Using the derivative of *measured* slant range increment with respect to $\bar{f}$, that of *estimated* slant range with respect to ϕ, and that of *estimated* slant range with respect to λ, new values of ϕ, λ, and $\bar{f}$ are calculated such that the sum of the squares of the residuals will be smaller than before these new values are used.

8. Steps 1 through 7 are repeated several times until the newly calculated values of $\bar{f}$, ϕ, and λ differ from the last values used by less than fixed threshold values. At this point the computing stops, and the last set of values of $\bar{f}$, ϕ, and λ is the final result.

4439. Computation algorithms.—In the computations the slant range is calculated for the beginning and end of each doppler counting interval based on the best estimates of the navigator's latitude, longitude, altitude above the geoid, and the transmitted satellite coordinates. Referring to figure 4438b, the doppler count N_{12} is repeated:

$$N_{12} = \int_{t_1+\Delta t_1}^{t_2+\Delta t_2} (f_G - f_R)dt. \tag{1}$$

It should be noted that the time $t_1 + \Delta t_1$ is the time of *receipt* of the satellite time mark which was transmitted at time Δt_1. Therefore, Δt_m, $m = 1, \ldots n$ ($n =$ the total number of 2-minute intervals observed during one pass) represent the propagation time delay for the time mark to travel the distance S_m from the satellite to the receiver. The propagation time delay is defined by the slant range distance divided by the speed of light:

$$\Delta t_m = S_m / C. \tag{2}$$

Rearranging equation (1):

$$N_{12} = \int_{t_1+\Delta t_1}^{t_2+\Delta t_2} f_G dt - \int_{t_1+\Delta t_1}^{t_2+\Delta t_2} f_R dt. \tag{3}$$

The first integral in equation 3 is of a constant frequency and its integration is simple. The second integral is of the changing frequency f_R and represents the number of cycles received between the message receipt of two timing marks. It should be noted that the number of cycles received must identically equal the number of cycles transmitted:

$$\int_{t_1+\Delta t_1}^{t_2+\Delta t_2} f_R dt = \int_{t_1}^{t_2} f_T dt. \tag{4}$$

Substituting this expression into equation 3:

$$N_{12} = \int_{t_1+\Delta t_1}^{t_2+\Delta t_2} f_G dt - \int_{t_1}^{t_2} f_T dt. \tag{5}$$

Since the frequency functions, f_G and f_T, are assumed constant during a satellite pass, the integration of equation 5 gives:

$$N_{12} = f_G[(t_2 - t_1) + (\Delta t_2 - \Delta t_1)] - f_T(t_2 - t_1). \tag{6}$$

Rearranging the terms in equation 6 gives:

$$N_{12} = (f_G - f_T)(t_2 - t_1) + f_G(\Delta t_2 - \Delta t_1). \tag{7}$$

The following comments apply to equation 7.
The quantity $f_G - f_T$ is assumed constant during a satellite pass:

$$f_G - f_T = \bar{f} \approx 32 \text{ kHz}, \tag{8}$$

and $f_G(\Delta t_2 - \Delta t_1)$ can be rewritten as:

$$f_G \frac{(S_2 - S_1)}{C}; \; \left(\Delta t_m = \frac{S_m}{C}\right), \tag{9}$$

defining L_G as the wavelength of the frequency f_G:

$$L_G = \frac{C}{f_G}; \; C = \text{speed of light in vacuum}, \tag{10}$$

and

$$\Delta T_{12} = t_2 - t_1.$$

Equation 7 becomes:

$$N_{12} = \bar{f}\Delta T_{12} + (1/L_G)\ (S_2 - S_1).$$ (11)

Defining $S_2 - S_1 = \hat{S}_{12}$ we have an expression for the *measured* slant range change in the kth counting interval:

$$\hat{S}_K = L_G N_K - L_G \bar{f} \Delta t_K.$$ (12)

The cartesian coordinates of a satellite are computed from the transmitted fixed and variable parameters of the satellite's position. Likewise, the navigator's cartesian coordinates are computed from his estimated position and geoidal height. The computed slant range at time t_K is then:

$$S_K = (X^2{}_K + Y^2{}_K + Z^2{}_K)^{1/2},$$ (13)

where, with subscripts N and S for the navigator and satellite respectively:

$$X_K = (X_{SK} - Y_{NK}),\ Y_K = (Y_{SK} - Y_{NK}),\ Z_K = (Z_{SK} - Z_{NK}).$$

The computed slant range change between times t_K and t_{K-1} is therefore $S_K - S_{K-1}$. Defining a residual:

$$R(\emptyset, \lambda, \bar{f})_K = \hat{S}_K - (S_K - S_{K-1}).$$

If M doppler intervals are to be used in the computation, M such functions may be computed and $F(\emptyset, \lambda, \bar{f})$, the sum of the squares of the residuals, may be computed:

$$F(\emptyset, \lambda, \bar{f}) = \sum_{K=1}^{M} R(\emptyset, \lambda, \bar{f})^2{}_K.$$ (14)

Expanding the residuals in a Taylor series about the initial estimates $\bar{f}_K$, $\emptyset_K$, and λ_K, then truncating the terms above first degree, this function becomes:

$$F = \sum_{K=1}^{M} \left[R_K - \frac{\partial(S_K - S_{K-1})}{\partial\emptyset}\Delta\emptyset - \frac{\partial(S_K - S_{K-1})}{\partial\lambda}\Delta\lambda + \frac{\partial}{\partial\bar{f}}\hat{S}_K\Delta\bar{f} \right]^2.$$ (15)

Since we have just shown that $\hat{S}_K$ is a function of $\bar{f}$, and S_K and S_{K-1} are both functions of $\emptyset$ and λ, or

$$F = \sum_{K=1}^{M} G^2{}_K,$$

where:

$$\Delta\bar{f} = \bar{f} - \bar{f}_K$$

$$\Delta\emptyset = \emptyset - \emptyset_K$$

$$\Delta\lambda = \lambda - \lambda_K$$

$$R_K = \hat{S}_K - (S_K - S_{K-1}),$$

and G_K symbolizes the bracketed function in equation 15.

To minimize $F(\phi, \lambda, \bar{f})$ with respect to $\phi, \lambda, \bar{f}$ equation 15 is differentiated partially with respect to $\phi, \lambda, \bar{f}$, the partials equated to zero, and the equations divided by 2.

$$\left. \begin{array}{l} \dfrac{\partial F}{\partial \phi} = 0 = -\displaystyle\sum_{K=1}^{M} G_K \dfrac{\partial(S_K - S_{K-1})}{\partial \phi} \\[4mm] \dfrac{\partial F}{\partial \lambda} = 0 = -\displaystyle\sum_{K=1}^{M} G_K \dfrac{\partial(S_K - S_{K-1})}{\partial \lambda} \\[4mm] \dfrac{\partial F}{\partial f} = 0 = \displaystyle\sum_{K=1}^{M} G_K \dfrac{\partial \hat{S}_K}{\partial \bar{f}} \end{array} \right\} \tag{16}$$

Define the A matrix

$$\{A\} = \begin{bmatrix} -\dfrac{\partial(S_1 - S_0)}{\partial \phi} & -\dfrac{\partial(S_1 - S_0)}{\partial \lambda} & \dfrac{\partial \hat{S}_1}{\partial \bar{f}} \\[4mm] -\dfrac{\partial(S_2 - S_1)}{\partial \phi} & -\dfrac{\partial(S_2 - S_1)}{\partial \lambda} & \dfrac{\partial \hat{S}_2}{\partial \bar{f}} \\ \cdot & \cdot & \cdot \\ \cdot & \cdot & \cdot \\ \cdot & \cdot & \cdot \\ -\dfrac{\partial(S_M - S_{M-1})}{\partial \phi} & -\dfrac{\partial(S_M - S_{M-1})}{\partial \lambda} & \dfrac{\partial \hat{S}_M}{\partial \bar{f}} \end{bmatrix}$$

and the residual matrix

$$R = \begin{bmatrix} R_1 \\ \cdot \\ \cdot \\ \cdot \\ R_M \end{bmatrix}$$

and an error matrix,

$$E = \begin{bmatrix} \Delta \phi \\ \Delta \lambda \\ \Delta \bar{f} \end{bmatrix}$$

and rewrite the G_K functions in matrix form.

$$G_1 = R_1 + \frac{\partial}{\partial \bar{f}} \hat{S}_1 \Delta \bar{f} - \frac{\partial(S_1 - S_0)}{\partial \phi} \Delta \phi - \frac{\partial(S_1 - S_0)}{\partial \lambda} \Delta \lambda$$

$$G_2 = R_2 + \frac{\partial}{\partial \bar{f}} \hat{S}_2 \Delta \bar{f} - \frac{\partial(S_2 - S_1)}{\partial \phi} \Delta \phi - \frac{\partial(S_2 - S_1)}{\partial \lambda} \Delta \lambda$$

$$G_3 = R_3 + \frac{\partial}{\partial \bar{f}} \hat{S}_3 \Delta \bar{f} - \frac{\partial(S_3 - S_2)}{\partial \phi} \Delta \phi - \frac{\partial(S_2 - S_1)}{\partial \lambda} \Delta \lambda$$

$$G_M = R_M + \frac{\partial}{\partial \bar{f}} \hat{S}_M \Delta \bar{f} - \frac{\partial(S_M - S_{M-1})}{\partial \phi} \Delta \phi - \frac{\partial(S_M - S_{M-1})}{\partial \lambda} \Delta \lambda$$

$$G = R + AE.$$

Then, in matrix notation:

$$A^T G = A^T [R + AE] = [0]$$

or

$$E = -[A^T A]^{-1} A^T R.$$

References

Dove, R. E., "Program Requirements for Short Count Integrated Doppler Satellite Navigation Solution," Applied Physics Laboratory, The John Hopkins University, TG–819–2, August 1974.

Guier, W. H. and G. C. Wieffenbach, "Theoretical Analysis of Doppler Radio Signals from Earth Satellites," Applied Physics Laboratory, The John Hopkins University, Laurel, Maryland, Bumblebee Series Report No. 276, April 1958.

Guier, W. H. and G. C. Wieffenbach, "A Satellite Doppler Navigation System," *Proceedings of the IRE*, vol. 48, No. 4, April 1960.

Guier, W. H., "Ionospheric Contributions to the Doppler Shift at VHF from Near-Earth Satellites," *Proceedings of the IRE*, vol. 49, No. 11, pp. 1680–1681, November 1961.

Guier, W. H., "Geodetic Problems and Satellite Orbits," Space Mathematics—part 2, vol. 6, Lectures in Applied Mathematics, American Mathematical Society, Providence, Rhode Island, 1966, p. 170 ff.

Guier, W. H., "Satellite Navigation using Integral Doppler Data: AN/SRN–9 Equipment," *Proceedings of the American Geophysical Union*, Washington, D.C., April 1965.

Hopfield, H. S., "The Effect of Tropospheric Refraction on the Doppler Shift of a Satellite Signal," *Journal of Geophysical Research*, vol. 68, pp. 5157–5168, 1963.

Hopfield, H. S., "Tropospheric Effect on Electromagnetically Measured Range: Prediction from Surface Weather Data," *Radio Science*, vol. 6, pp. 357–367, 1971.

Newton, R. R., "The U. S. Navy Doppler Geodetic System and Its Observational Accuracy," *Philosophical Transactions*, Royal Society of London, A, vol. 262, pp. 50–66, 1967.

Newton, R. R., and R. B. Kershner, "The Transit System," *Journal of the Institute of Navigation*, London, vol. 15, April 1962.

Yionoulis, S. M., F. T. Heuring, and W. H. Guier, "A Geopotential Model (APL 5.0–1967) Determined from Satellite Doppler Data at Seven Incl nations," *Journal of Geophysical Research*, vol. 77(20), 1972.

Yionoulis, S. M., "Determination of Coefficients Associated with the Geopotential Harmonics of Order Thirteen," *Journal of Geophysical Research*, vol. 71(6), 1966.

"Navy Navigation Satellite System User Equipment Handbook," prepared by the Space Development Department, Applied Physics Laboratory, The Johns Hopkins University, Laurel, Maryland, SDO–3100.

"The Navy Navigation Satellite System," U. S. Navy Astronautics Group, Point Mugu, California, January 1967.

CHAPTER XLV

DOPPLER SONAR NAVIGATION

4501. Introduction.—The *doppler effect*, first described by Christian Johann Doppler in 1842, is observed as a frequency shift resulting from relative motion between a transmitter and receiver or reflector of acoustic or electromagnetic energy. The effect on ultrasonic energy is used in **doppler sonar speed logs** to measure the relative motion between the vessel and the reflective sea bottom (for bottom return mode) or suspended particulate matter in the seawater itself (for volume reverberation mode). The velocity so obtained and integrated with respect to time is used in **doppler sonar navigators** to determine position with respect to a start point. The doppler effect is also used in **docking aids** which provide precise speed measurements.

The maximum safe docking speed of vessels exceeding about 100,000 dead weight tons is of the order of 0.2 feet per second; the berthing facility may collapse when the vessel makes contact at a speed in the region of 1 foot per second. When anchoring these large vessels without the aid of tugs, a speed of the order of 1 foot per second over the ground can result in the loss of the anchor and chain. Anchoring should be effected at speeds of less than 0.5 feet per second. Therefore, precise determination of the speed of these large vessels with respect to the bottom is essential to safe operation. The required speed-measurement increments are of the order of 0.01 knot.

4502. The Janus configuration (fig. 4502) normally used with doppler sonar speed logs and navigators employs four beams of ultrasonic energy, displaced laterally 90° from each other, and each directed obliquely (30° from the vertical) at the ocean floor, to obtain true ground speed in the fore and aft and athwartship directions. These speeds are measured as doppler frequency shifts in the reflected beams.

Under ideal operating conditions (i.e. a calm flat sea), the speeds are expressed as follows:

$$V_{fa} = \frac{F_f - F_a}{\dfrac{2F_s}{C}}$$

$$V_{st-p} = \frac{F_{st} - F_p}{\dfrac{2F_s}{C}},$$

where:

1. V_{fa} is the vessel's speed over the ground in the fore and aft direction;
2. V_{st-p} is the vessel's speed over the ground in the athwartship (starboard to port) direction;
3. F_f is the reflected forward beam frequency;
4. F_a is the reflected after beam frequency;
5. F_{st} is the reflected starboard beam frequency;
6. F_p is the reflected port beam frequency;
7. F_s is the transmitter operating frequency; and
8. C is the sound speed with respect to the water.

A development of the above simplified equations from the fundamental doppler equation for sound propagation is presented in article 4506.

1066

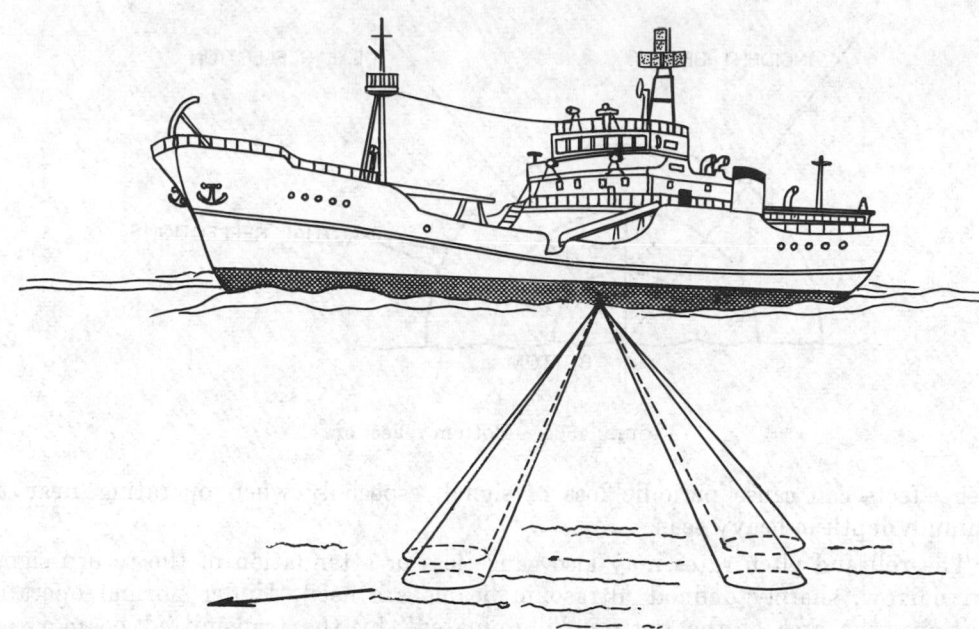

FIGURE 4502.—Janus configuration.

4503. Operational errors.—Under actual operating conditions, the deviations from the ideal or assumed conditions introduce additional terms and nonlinearities not shown in the simplified equations. These effects may be classified as *transducer orientation errors, vessel motion induced errors, velocity of sound errors,* and *power loss errors.*

Transducer orientation errors. If the transducers are not properly aligned with the vessel's velocity vector, the speed signal is reduced by the factor, cos α, where α is the angle between the transducer plane and the velocity vector. For example, if the transducers are aligned when the vessel has no trim, and the vessel is trimmed to angle α, the speed signal is reduced by a factor of cosine α. This error is generally small; for example, a trim (or list) of 8° will reduce the fore and aft (or starboard to port) speed signal by 1 percent.

Vessel motion induced errors. Even though the speed of sound is large compared to the vessels' speed, the vessel may roll or pitch a degree or two during the time between transmission and reception of a particular wave front. This difference in transmission and reception angles will introduce significant errors in single-beam systems. However, the Janus configuration (art. 4502) causes the errors to very nearly cancel. For a 2° difference between the transmission and reception angle, the error induced, using a Janus configuration, is less than 0.1 percent of the speed signal. The forward speed of a vessel will also cause differences in transmission and reception angles, but the resulting speed errors also tend to cancel.

The most significant speed error is caused by the fact that, as a vessel rolls or pitches, the respective speed signal is reduced by the cosine of the instantaneous roll or pitch angle. Since this cosine factor reduces the speed signal for both positive and negative values of angles, this error does not cancel. Assuming sinusoidal rolling with a maximum roll of 25°, the average roll over one-half cycle is 16°; the cosine factor is 0.9613. The starboard to port speed signal is reduced by nearly 4 percent.

Another effect of rolling and pitching is the variation in the amplitude of the return signal. As the beam on the high side of a roll or pitch tilts toward the horizon, the path length increases and more sound energy is lost in the water. In addition, the beam reflection angle is decreasing and less energy is back-scattered along the beam.

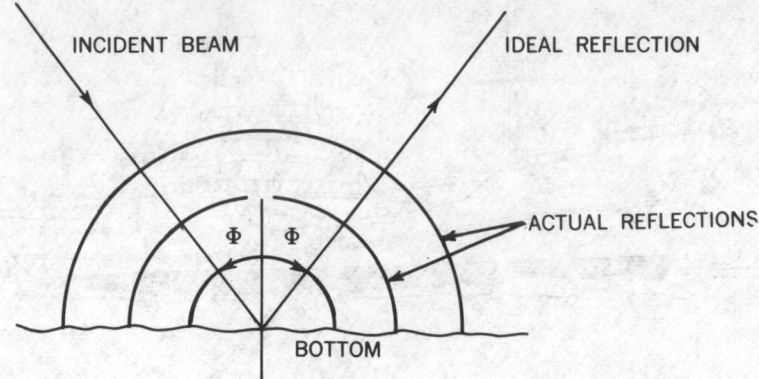

FIGURE 4503.—Bottom reflection.

These effects can cause periodic loss of signal, especially when operating near the maximum depth in heavy seas.

The roll and pitch rates may also cause loss or attenuation of the return signals when narrow, sharply defined ultrasonic beams are used. Under normal operating conditions, the area of the bottom "illuminated" by the transmitted beam is also "seen" by the receiving transducer. However, if the roll (or pitch) rate is very large, the receiving transducer may be rotated sufficiently to reduce the time it takes a wave front to travel to the bottom and back, so that it no longer "sees" the area illuminated by the transmitted beam. In water 400 feet deep and a 3° beam width, the roll rate must be less than 16° per second if the transmitted and received beams are to overlap at the half-power points.

Velocity of sound errors. The doppler frequency shifts are dependent upon the velocity of sound in water in the immediate vicinity of the transducer. The actual frequency changes occur as the sound pressure waves move from the face of the transducer into water undisturbed by the vessel's hull. Similarly, a received beam undergoes a frequency shift as the sound travels from the undisturbed water to the face of the receiving transducer.

One empirical formula for the speed of sound in seawater (ch. XXXV) is

$$C = 4422 + 11.25T - 0.0450T^2 + 0.0182d + 4.3\ (S-34),$$

where C is the velocity in feet per second, T is the temperature (°F), S is the salinity (parts per thousand), and d is the depth below the surface in feet. The velocity of sound in seawater is dependent primarily upon temperature which varies from about 28°F in polar regions to about 86°F in the Tropics. Over this temperature range, the velocity varies about 7 percent due to temperature alone. In the open sea, salinity varies from about 33 to 36 parts per thousand. However, the salinity in bays, inlets, and rivers varies from open-sea values to freshwater values. For example, as one goes from the Chesapeake Bay waters at Annapolis to the Atlantic Ocean, the salinity increases about 25 parts per thousand. This salinity change results in more than 1½ percent increase in velocity due to salinity alone.

Since the transmitter oscillator frequency is held constant, the calibration constant (art. 4506) should vary directly as the change in the velocity in seawater. In some doppler speed logs and navigators, the adjustment of the calibration constant may be limited to the effects of temperature change. In some installations a velocimeter may be used to determine the velocity of sound in the vicinity of the transducer.

Power loss errors. The speed information is contained in the frequency of the received signals. Therefore, the only power requirement is that the signal level be great enough for the receivers to separate it from the noise. If the speed signal is lost for very short periods at frequent intervals, there will be an erroneous speed indication. If the speed signal is lost for longer periods, the speed indication will drop to zero or the natural noise level. Commercial equipments have memory circuits that retain the last good speed signal until the next one is obtained to update the readout. This approach is not entirely satisfactory during tactical maneuvering.

Excluding internal system losses, there are two primary areas of power loss:
1. Power lost in the water during transit to and from the bottom.
2. Power lost at the bottom on reflection.

The losses in the water are caused by absorption, scatter, and normal inverse square spreading. The absorption and scatter losses are attenuation losses and are exponentially proportional to path length. The absorption loss is the energy lost to internal friction of the water. At the higher frequencies the loss is very nearly proportional to the square of the frequency but tends to become linear as the frequency decreases. The scattering loss is caused by the existence of suspended matter in the water that reflects or scatters the sound energy. This effect can be useful in that it may permit a doppler system to measure velocity with respect to water if the energy scattered back along the beam is sufficient to activate the receivers. Spreading losses are caused by the expansion or spreading of the wave front which then reduces the energy per unit area of the wave front. For spherical waves from a point source, the energy in a wave front, neglecting attenuation, is constant. Therefore, the energy density decreases inversely as the square of the distance from the source.

The losses on reflection from the bottom are caused by scatter and absorption. In general, the sound energy is reflected from the bottom in all directions, with the intensity of sound energy reflected in any particular direction being strongly dependent upon the angle of incidence and the character of the bottom.

For a perfectly smooth bottom, the incident sound beam would be reflected along the path labeled "ideal reflection" shown in figure 4503. This type of bottom would cause loss of a useful return. Actually, there is always a degree of back scatter. But for a very smooth mud bottom and a large angle of incidence, the back scatter along the incident beam is greatly reduced. The roughness of the bottom to a particular sound beam is dependent upon the wavelength of the sound. When the discontinuities of the bottom are much smaller than the wavelength, the bottom appears smooth and there is little back scatter.

The angle of incidence of the sound beam is dependent upon the slope of the bottom at the point of incidence. In general, the ocean bottom is similar to land areas with respect to valleys, hills, and similar terrain characteristics (art. 3022). Thus, the returned energy will vary greatly with the local slope of the bottom where the beam strikes it.

The sound energy absorbed on reflection depends largely on the material of the bottom. The average reflection coefficients for mud bottoms are approximately 0.16 to 0.17, whereas the reflection coefficients for sand bottoms are 0.51 to 0.82. Thus, when a system is operating near its maximum depth, a transition from a sand to a mud bottom could result in the loss of the signal reflected from the bottom.

This brief discussion of the factors affecting the power losses in underwater sound transmission and losses on reflection from the bottom indicates that the sound power level at the receiver will vary over many orders of magnitude due to environmental phenomena.

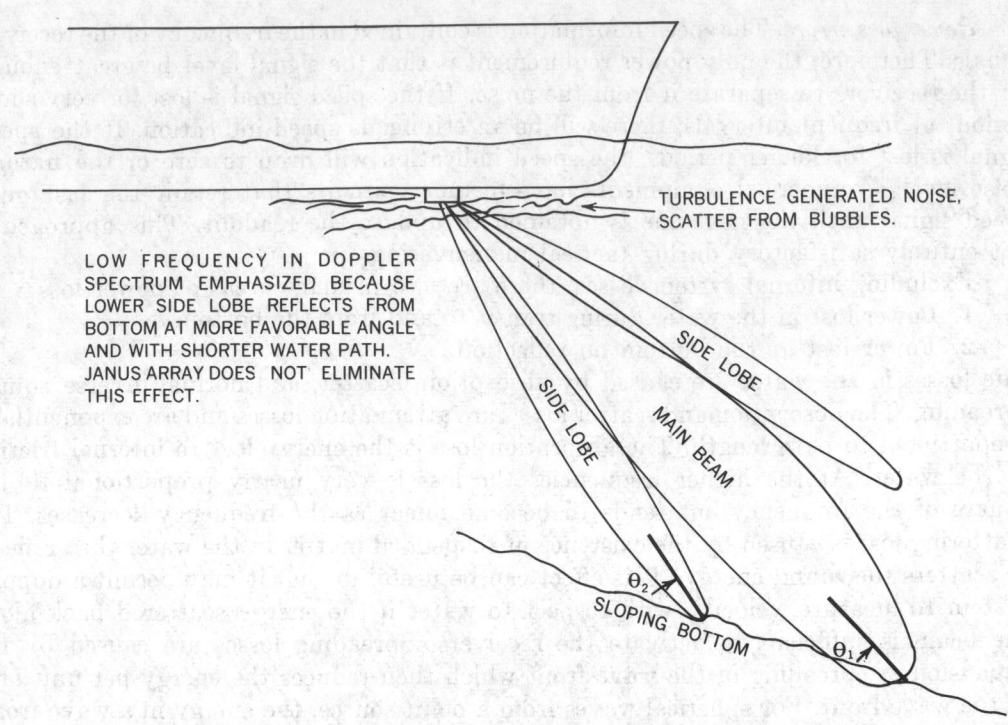

LOW FREQUENCY IN DOPPLER SPECTRUM EMPHASIZED BECAUSE LOWER SIDE LOBE REFLECTS FROM BOTTOM AT MORE FAVORABLE ANGLE AND WITH SHORTER WATER PATH. JANUS ARRAY DOES NOT ELIMINATE THIS EFFECT.

TURBULENCE GENERATED NOISE, SCATTER FROM BUBBLES.

SIDE LOBE

SIDE LOBE

MAIN BEAM

SLOPING BOTTOM

θ_2

θ_1

FIGURE 4504.—Side lobe reflection.

4504. Problems associated with beam geometry.—As shown in figure 4504, the side lobe reflects from the bottom at a more favorable angle with a shorter wave path than the main beam. It is evident from the development in article 4506 that if side lobe reception dominates over main beam reception, the result will be that the indicated speed will be lower than the actual speed. The Janus configuration does not eliminate this effect. This effect can be compensated for by transducer design tending to eliminate side-lobe effects. However, the beam width must be large enough (about 3° to 6°) to "illuminate" a sufficient area of the bottom to minimize the effects of bottom relief.

4505. Basic design considerations include the following:

Frequency. A high oscillator frequency is desirable for reducing transducer size and maximizing the doppler shift. However, at the higher frequencies the absorption loss (art. 4503) is very nearly proportional to the square of the frequency. As the frequency is decreased, the loss tends to become linear. As the frequency is reduced by the designer to obtain greater maximum depth of operation in the bottom return mode, he encounters transducer size problems. Improvement in operating depth diminishes near 100 kHz while transducer size has increased considerably. Also, as discussed in article 4503, the roughness of the bottom to a particular sound beam is dependent upon the wavelength of the sound. Therefore, the frequency selected by the designer is a trade off of desired maximum operating depth, transducer size, and bottom composition factors. The region between 150 and 600 kHz is finding the greatest application.

Sound transmission. The pulse transmission method permits the use of relatively high power for operating at greater depths in the bottom return mode. Continuous wave transmission, however, provides more precise velocity resolution permitting operation with very little clearance between the vessel's hull and the bottom. Therefore, a designer may select pulse transmission for a doppler sonar navigator but continuous wave transmission for a docking system to be used for precise speed measurements over a vessel operating with very little clearance.

4506. Development of expressions for the vessel's speed in the fore and aft and athwartship directions.—The doppler equation for sound propagation may be expressed as

$$F_o = F_s \left(\frac{C + V_m - V_o}{C + V_m - V_s} \right),$$

where F_o is the frequency detected by the observer, F_s is the frequency of the source, C is the speed of sound in the medium, V_m is the speed of the medium, V_o is the speed of the observer, and V_s is the speed of the source. All speeds are velocity components along the direction of sound propagation and are considered positive if moving in the same direction as the sound. Consider as shown in figure 4506a, the situation where the sound source (transmitter A) and observer (receiver A) are connected and moving at velocity V_A with respect to the ground. Similarly consider transmitter B and receiver B connected and moving at velocity V_B. V_W represents the water velocity with respect to the ground; C represents the sound velocity with respect to the water. If transmitter A has a frequency F_s, the frequency received by receiver B is given by

$$F_B = F_s \left(\frac{C + V_W - V_B}{C + V_W - V_A} \right).$$

Assuming that transmitter B always emits the same frequency received by receiver B, then receiver A receives a frequency given by

$$F_A = F_B \left(\frac{C + (-V_W) - (-V_A)}{C + (-V_W) - (-V_B)} \right).$$

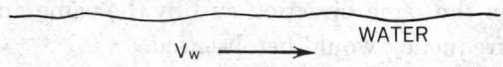

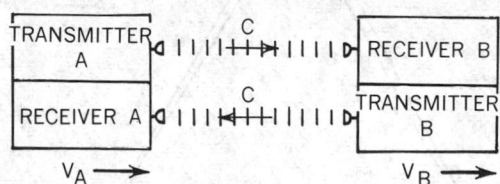

FIGURE 4506a.—Sound transmitters and receivers in a moving medium.

The signs of V_W, V_A, and V_B are negative because they are directed opposite the sound propagation between transmitter B and receiver A. Thus, the frequency received by receiver A may be written as

$$F_A = F_s \left(\frac{C + V_W - V_B}{C + V_W - V_A} \right) \left(\frac{C - V_W + V_A}{C - V_W + V_B} \right).$$

If the transmitter-receiver unit, B, is stationary with respect to the ground, $V_B = 0$. Then, receiver A will receive a frequency given by

$$F_A = F_s \left(\frac{C + V_W}{C + V_W - V_A} \right) \left(\frac{C - V_W + V_A}{C - V_W} \right).$$

If unit A is attached to a vessel's hull, and a reflector, the ocean bottom, is considered to act in the same manner as unit B, then the vessel's speed over the ground can be derived from the doppler shift, $F_s - F_A$.

Because the ultrasonic beam is not usually directed along the vessel's velocity vector and only a component of velocity along the beam results in a doppler shift, the doppler equation as given must be modified.

Inspection of the Janus arrangement shown in figure 4506b reveals that the components of the vessel's velocity (V_{fa}) and the water's velocity (V_W) in the fore and aft plane which cause doppler shifts are cosine projections along the ultrasonic beam. These components for the forward beam are $V_{fa} \cos \theta$ and $V_W \cos \theta$, respectively.

For forward velocities, the reflected forward beam frequency, F_f, is increased; and the reflected after beam frequency, F_a, is decreased. If there were vertical velocity components, their sine projections along the beams would cause doppler frequency shifts. However, for vertical velocities, the frequencies of both the forward and after beams would be shifted in the same direction and by the same amount. No significant change of the difference frequency would be observed.

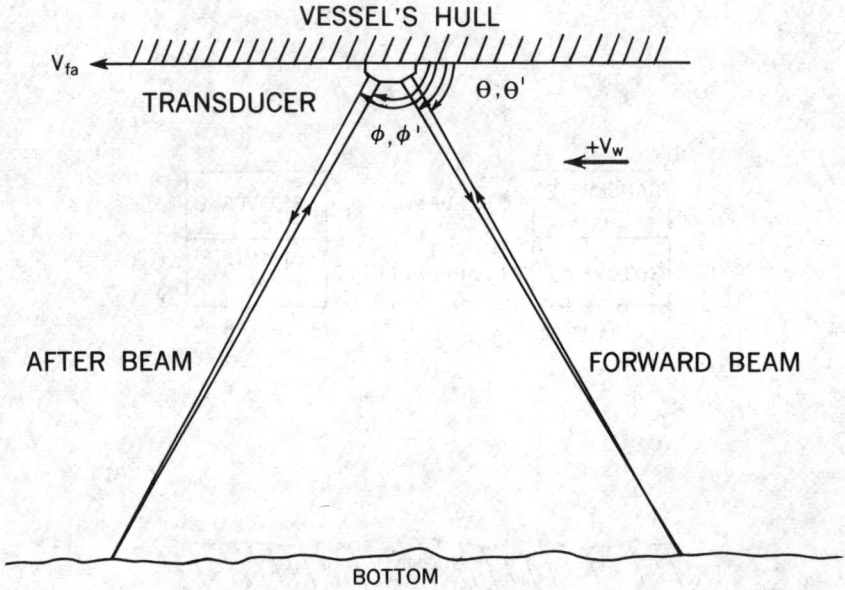

FIGURE 4506b.—Janus fore and aft beams.

If the vessel is pitching, the received signal will not return to the receiver at exactly the same angle at which it was transmitted. Thus, the reflected forward beam frequency is given by

$$F_f = F_s \left[\left(\frac{C + V_W \cos \theta}{C + V_W \cos \theta - V_{fa} \cos \theta} \right) \left(\frac{C - V_W \cos \theta' + V_{fa} \cos \theta'}{C - V_W \cos \theta'} \right) \right],$$

where θ is the beam angle with the vessel's fore and aft axis at transmission and θ' is the beam angle at reception.

The reflected after beam frequency is given by the same equation except that θ and θ' are replaced by ϕ and ϕ', respectively. The fact that the after beam is directed aft is accounted for in the cosine projections, i.e., $\cos \phi$ and $\cos \phi'$ are negative.

$$F_a = F_s \left[\left(\frac{C + V_W \cos \phi}{C + V_W \cos \phi - V_{fa} \cos \phi} \right) \left(\frac{C - V_W \cos \phi' + V_{fa} \cos \phi'}{C - V_W \cos \phi'} \right) \right].$$

Since the doppler shifts of the forward and after beams are in opposite directions, the difference between the frequencies of the two reflected beams is used to determine the vessel's fore and aft speed. If the sum of the frequencies were used, the doppler shifts would be cancelled. The difference frequency or speed signal is given by

$$F_f - F_a = F_s \left[\left(\frac{C + V_W \cos \theta}{C + V_W \cos \theta - V_{fa} \cos \theta} \right) \left(\frac{C - V_W \cos \theta' + V_{fa} \cos \theta'}{C - V_W \cos \theta'} \right) \right.$$

$$\left. - \left(\frac{C + V_W \cos \phi}{C + V_W \cos \phi - V_{fa} \cos \phi} \right) \left(\frac{C - V_W \cos \phi' + V_{fa} \cos \phi'}{C - V_W \cos \phi'} \right) \right].$$

Several approximations can be made to simplify this equation. Multiplying the two factors in the numerator of the first term gives

$$(C + V_W \cos \theta)(C - V_W \cos \theta' + V_{fa} \cos \theta') = C^2 - CV_W \cos \theta'$$

$$+ CV_{fa} \cos \theta' + CV_W \cos \theta - V^2_W \cos \theta \cos \theta' + V_{fa} V_W \cos \theta \cos \theta'.$$

Multiplying the two factors in the denominator of the first term by $1/C^2$ gives

$$(C + V_W \cos \theta - V_{fa} \cos \theta)(C - V_W \cos \theta') = C^2 - CV_W \cos \theta'$$

$$+ CV_W \cos \theta - V^2_W \cos \theta \cos \theta' - CV_{fa} \cos \theta + V_{fa} V_W \cos \theta \cos \theta'.$$

By multiplying both the numerator and the denominator of the first term by $1/C^2$ we obtain:

$$\frac{1/C^2 (C^2 - CV_W \cos \theta' + CV_{fa} \cos \theta' + CV_W \cos \theta - V^2_W \cos \theta \cos \theta' + V_{fa} \cos \theta \cos \theta')}{1/C^2 (C^2 + CV_W \cos \theta - CV_{fa} \cos \theta - CV_W \cos \theta' - V^2_W \cos \theta \cos \theta' + V_{fa} V_W \cos \theta \cos \theta')}.$$

Since $C \gg V_W$ or V_{fa}, terms containing V^2_W/C^2 and $V_{fa} V_W/C^2$, along with trigonometric functions can be neglected. The first term then becomes:

$$\frac{1/C^2 (C^2 - CV_W \cos \theta' + CV_{fa} \cos \theta' + CV_W \cos \theta)}{1/C^2 (C^2 + CV_W \cos \theta - CV_{fa} \cos \theta - CV_W \cos \theta')} = \frac{C(C + V_{fa} \cos \theta') + CV_W (\cos \theta - \cos \theta')}{C(C - V_{fa} \cos \theta) + CV_W (\cos \theta - \cos \theta')}$$

$$= \frac{(C + V_{fa} \cos \theta') + V_W (\cos \theta - \cos \theta')}{(C - V_{fa} \cos \theta) + V_W (\cos \theta - \cos \theta')}.$$

The second term of the equation can be simplified by similar approximations. The equation can then be written as:

$$F_f - F_a = F_s \left[\left\{ \frac{(C + V_{fa}\cos\theta') + V_W(\cos\theta - \cos\theta')}{(C - V_{fa}\cos\theta) + V_W(\cos\theta - \cos\theta')} \right\} \right.$$

$$\left. - \left\{ \frac{(C + V_{fa}\cos\phi')}{(C - V_{fa}\cos\phi)} + \frac{V_W(\cos\phi - \cos\phi')}{V_W(\cos\phi - \cos\phi')} \right\} \right].$$

Since the transmitted and received angles are very nearly the same, the cosine difference terms can also be neglected. Then,

$$F_f - F_a = F_s \left[\frac{(C + V_{fa}\cos\theta')}{(C - V_{fa}\cos\theta)} - \frac{(C + V_{fa}\cos\phi')}{(C - V_{fa}\cos\phi)} \right].$$

or

$$F_f - F_a = F_s \left[\left(1 + \frac{V_{fa}}{C}\cos\theta'\right)\left(1 - \frac{V_{fa}}{C}\cos\theta\right)^{-1} - \left(1 + \frac{V_{fa}}{C}\cos\phi'\right)\left(1 - \frac{V_{fa}}{C}\cos\phi\right)^{-1} \right].$$

Expanding the factors with the negative exponent in power series and multiplying gives:

$$F_f - F_a = F_s \left[\left(1 + \frac{V_{fa}}{C}\cos\theta'\right)\left(1 + \frac{V_{fa}}{C}\cos\theta + \frac{V^2_{fa}}{C^2}\cos^2\theta + \frac{V^3_{fa}}{C^3}\cos^3\theta + \ldots\right) \right.$$

$$\left. - \left(1 + \frac{V_{fa}}{C}\cos\phi'\right)\left(1 + \frac{V_{fa}}{C}\cos\phi + \frac{V^2_{fa}}{C^2}\cos^2\phi + \frac{V^3_{fa}}{C^3}\cos^3\phi + \ldots\right) \right].$$

Multiplying the factors and retaining only first order terms,

$$F_f - F_a = F_s \left[\frac{V_{fa}}{C}(\cos\theta + \cos\theta' - \cos\phi - \cos\phi') \right].$$

Assuming that $\theta \cong \theta'$ and $\phi \cong \phi'$, the cosines are very nearly equal. Then,

$$F_f - F_a = \frac{2F_s V_{fa}}{C}(\cos\theta - \cos\phi).$$

With $\theta = 60°$ and $\phi = 120°$,

$$F_f - F_a = \frac{2F_s}{C}V_{fa},$$

where V_{fa} is the vessel's velocity component in the fore and aft direction. A similar equation applies to the athwartship component:

$$F_{st} - F_p = \frac{2F_s}{C} \times V_{st-p}.$$

where F_{st} is the reflected starboard beam frequency, F_p is the reflected port beam frequency, and V_{st-p} is the athwartship (starboard to port) velocity.

The speed indication, S_i, is given by:

$$S_i = k\sqrt{(F_f - F_a)^2 + (F_{st} - F_p)^2}$$

$$= k\sqrt{\left(\frac{2F_s}{C}V_{fa}\right)^2 + \left(\frac{2F_s}{C}V_{st-p}\right)^2}$$

$$=k\frac{2F_s}{C}\sqrt{V^2_{fa}+V^2_{st-p}}$$

$$S_i=k\frac{2F_s}{C}V.$$

Thus, when the system calibration constant, k, has the value

$$k=\frac{C}{2F_s},$$

the speed indication is equal to the actual speed, V.

    The drift angle

$$=\tan^{-1}\left(\frac{V_{st-p}}{V_{fa}}\right)$$

$$=\tan^{-1}\left(\frac{F_{st}-F_p}{F_f-F_a}\right).$$

References

Kritz, Jack and Morton J. Howard. "Channel Navigation and Docking of Super-tankers." NAVIGATION: *Journal of the Institute of Navigation*, vol. 16, No. 1, April 1969.

Laster, D. R., and J. W. Fagan. "Exploratory Evaluation of Underwater Doppler Navigators." U. S. Navy Marine Engineering Laboratory Evaluation Report 8/65, October 1965.

CHAPTER XLVI

INTRODUCTION TO INERTIAL NAVIGATION

4601. Introduction.—*Inertial navigation* is the process of measuring a craft's velocity, attitude, and displacement from a known start point through sensing the accelerations acting on it in known directions by means of devices that mechanize Newton's laws of motion (art. 1407). Since these laws are expressed relative to inertial space (the fixed stars), the term "inertial" is applied to the process.

Inertial navigation is described as "self-contained," that is, independent of external aids to navigation. It is also described as "passive" because no energy is emitted to obtain information from an external source. Thus, inertial navigation is fundamentally different from other methods of navigation because it depends only on measurements made within the craft being navigated.

Inertial navigation is often referred to as a dead reckoning method because position is obtained by measuring displacements from a start point in accordance with the motion of the craft.

4602. The basic principle of inertial navigation is the measurement of the accelerations acting on a craft, other than those not associated with its orientation or motion with respect to the earth, and the double integration of these accelerations along known directions to obtain the displacement from the start point.

If the indicated acceleration of the craft from rest is constant, velocity and distance traveled can be found from the equations:

$$v = at,$$

and

$$s = 1/2\ at^2,$$

where a is the acceleration, v is the velocity, s is the distance, and t is the time. But the acceleration must be constant. The equations cannot be used for varying accelerations unless very small time increments are used, and the increments of velocity or distance are integrated (art. 147, vol. II). The equations, using the calculus notation are

$$v = \int a\ dt$$

$$s = \iint a\ dt,$$

where dt denotes a very small increment of time.

4603. Inertial sensors used in the mechanization of Newton's laws of motion, hereafter called the **inertial navigator** or **navigator,** are gyroscopes (art. 630) and accelerometers. The **gyroscopes** sense angular motions of the vessel. The **accelerometers** sense the vessel's linear accelerations which are changes in linear velocity. The inertial sensors are subject to all motions of the vessel in inertial space. Since some of these motions do not change the vessel's position or orientation on the earth and since the attitude and motion of the inertial navigator with respect to the earth is desired, it is necessary to apply certain corrections to the inertial motions (art. 4604) sensed in order to obtain the corresponding earth referenced values.

Although the gyroscope is discussed in some detail in article 630, the following discussion of this inertial sensor is written to meet the needs of an introductory treatment of inertial navigation.

The principle of **conservation of angular momentum** states that a system will maintain its angular momentum if no external forces are applied to it. Thus, the rotor (mass) of a gyroscope must maintain a constant angular momentum about its spin axis if no external forces are applied. Both the amplitude and direction of the angular momentum must be conserved. The spin axis, therefore, tends to maintain the same direction in inertial space. This property is called **gyroscopic inertia** or **rigidity in space.**

If a rotational or couple force is applied to the rotor through the gyroscope's supports, an additional angular momentum is introduced and the gyroscope's orientation will change to include this along with its original angular momentum about the spin axis and the axis of the applied force. This property of the gyroscope is called **precession.**

Precession causes the gyroscope to tend to align its spin axis with the axis of the applied torque (fig. 4603a). If the axis of applied torque is designated as the **input axis**, then the precession of the gyroscope can be determined by rotating the spin axis into the input axis through the smaller angle. Using this nomenclature the axis of precession is often called the **output axis.**

The rigidity of a gyroscope produces a phenomenon called **apparent precession.** This is due to the fact that as the gyroscope maintains its original orientation in space, the earth turns beneath it. As a result, to an observer on the earth, the gyroscope appears to turn or precess when actually it remains fixed in space. This apparent precession is shown in figure 4603b. If it is desired to have the gyroscope maintain an orientation referenced to the earth, it must be precessed (torqued) in such a manner as to remove the apparent precession.

The gyroscope described above is known as a **two-degree-of-freedom gyroscope.** It consists of an axially symmetric rotor supported in a case in such a way that one point on the axis is fixed relative to the case and the spin axis itself is free to assume any angular orientation relative to the case. A gimbal system supports the rotor within the case and provides angular freedom. An example of such an arrangement is shown in figure 4603c.

The spin axis has the ability to move about two axes with respect to the case (the enclosure not shown to which the gimbal system is attached). The gyroscope rotor is free to precess about either of the two supporting gimbal axes depending upon where the force is applied.

For practical application of the gyroscope to an inertial navigator it is more useful to design a gyroscope which is able to precess about only one axis called the output axis. Such a gyroscope will respond (precess) to rotations of the case about an axis known as the input axis. This allows the gyroscope to perform a control function with respect to an axis. With three such gyroscopes, mounted on a platform such that the input axes are mutually perpendicular, three-dimensional attitude control of the platform is obtained. Any component of rotation about the input axis causes a rotation about the output axis and can be sensed and used to control the orientation of the platform on which the gyroscope is mounted.

By attaching the outer gimbal of figure 4603c rigidly to the case such a configuration is obtained. The gyroscope now has just one axis of freedom with respect to the case about which it can precess. This is called a **single-degree-of-freedom gyroscope** (fig. 4603d).

Velocity is the linear rate of change of position. If the velocity is known it can be integrated with respect to time to determine the change in position. However, velocity

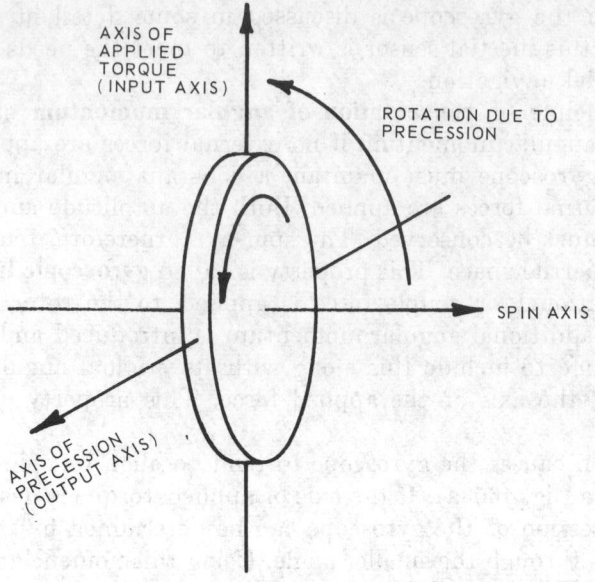

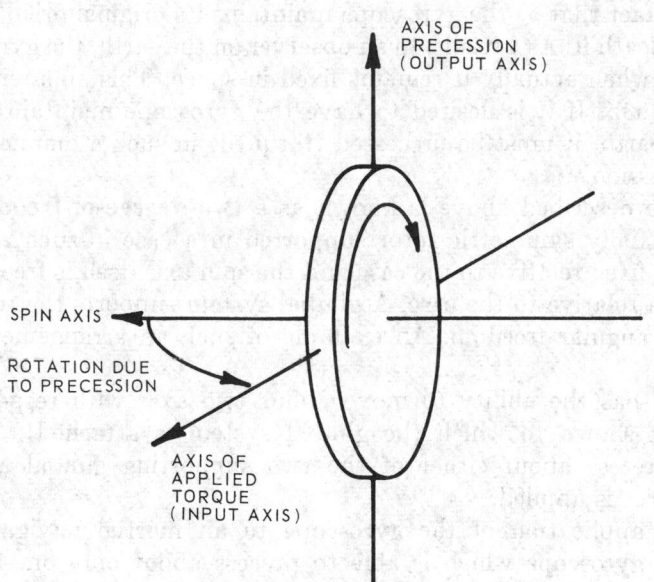

FIGURE 4603a.—Precession of a gyroscope.

cannot be sensed or measured with an inertial device since there is nothing inertially to distinguish one velocity from another.

A body at rest will remain at rest unless acted upon by an external force, and a body in motion will retain the motion unless acted upon by an external force. By measuring forces acting on a test mass, *changes* in velocity can be detected. This rate of change in velocity, called acceleration, is what accelerometers measure. The measuring device is properly called an accelerometer; but, since the integration is a simple step, the term **velocity meter** often is used.

In its simplest form, the accelerometer consists of a test mass, as shown in figure 4603e, constrained to measure accelerations in a particular direction (the **sensitive axis**)

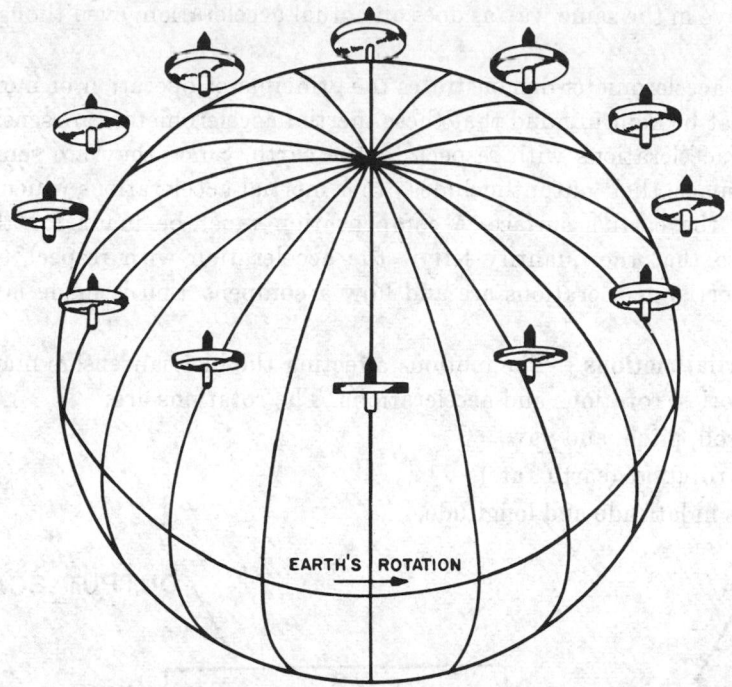

FIGURE 4603b.—Apparent precession.

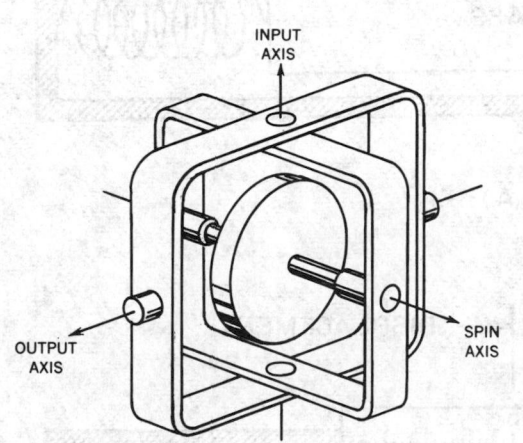

FIGURE 4603c.—Two-degree-of-freedom
gyroscope.

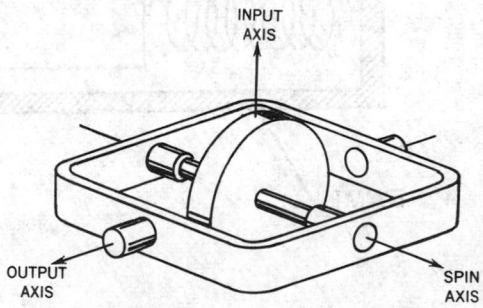

FIGURE 4603d.—Single-degree-of-freedom
gyroscope.

with a scale, or other appropriate device, to indicate its output. If the frame is accelerated to the right (fig. 4603e) the test mass lags behind since the acceleration is applied to the frame, not the test mass. The test mass displaces enough for the constraining springs to apply a force proportional to the acceleration. The test mass then moves with the case maintaining its constant displacement. When the acceleration is removed from the frame, the constraining springs cause the test mass to move (with respect to the case) back to the neutral position. Thus, a body at rest or a body at constant velocity (zero acceleration) causes no displacement, providing the accelerometer is held horizontal. If the accelerometer is tilted or placed on end, the force of gravity causes the mass to move in the same way as does an actual acceleration, even though the frame is at rest.

This basic accelerometer demonstrates the principle of operation of inertial accelerometers. It must be kept in mind that these inertial accelerometers are sensitive to more than just the accelerations with respect to the earth. Since they are sensitive to accelerations in space, their output includes other inertial accelerations which are not due to travel over the earth's surface. A compensation must be made for these inertial accelerations so that the quantity left is the acceleration with respect to the earth. What these inertial accelerations are and how a compensation is made is discussed in article 4604.

4604. Inertial motions.—The motions affecting the inertial sensors may be divided into two categories: rotations and accelerations. The rotations are:

1. craft's roll, pitch, and yaw,
2. earth's rotation (earth rate),
3. changes in latitude and longitude.

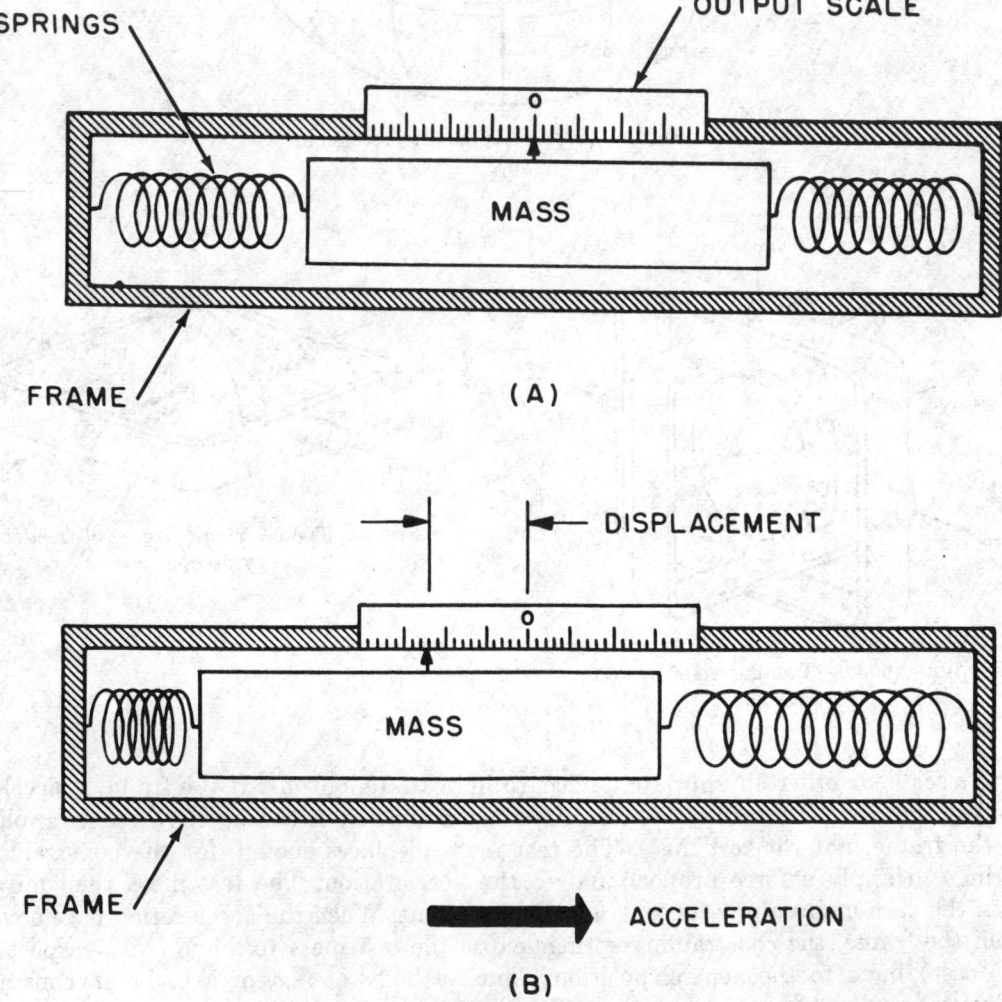

FIGURE 4603e.—Basic accelerometer.

The accelerations of concern are:

1. craft's acceleration with respect to the earth,
2. acceleration of gravity,
3. Coriolis acceleration.

Some of these motions are interrelated. For example, Coriolis acceleration results from the rotation of the earth. The rotation of the earth has an affect on gravity. There can be no latitude or longitude changes without acceleration with respect to the earth.

There are some inertial motions whose effects are negligible; that is, their effects are below the sensitivity level of the sensors. These motions are precession and nutation (art. 1419) and the acceleration of the earth in its orbit in accordance with Kepler's second law (art. 1407).

The revolution of the earth about the sun is included in the total earth rate, which equals the vector sum of the earth's rotation and revolution.

Since the inertial navigator deals with the earth referenced values of velocity, attitude, and position, and, since the gyroscopes maintain direction with respect to inertial space, it is necessary that the gyroscopes be controlled to maintain a reference with respect to the earth. In the discussion of the inertial navigator which follows, the earth reference used is the local vertical and an orientation with respect to true north.

The rotation of the earth causes the local vertical for a given position to change its direction in space. This change is not obvious to anyone on the earth because the local vertical maintains the same orientation with respect to the earth. To prevent the local vertical indication of the inertial navigator from being stationary in space due to rigidity in space (apparent precession), an earth rate torquing signal is applied so that the inertial navigator rotates about the earth's spin axis at the same rate that the earth does. As a result, the inertial navigator, which is controlled by the gyroscopes, maintains the desired orientation with respect to the earth as the earth rotates in inertial space.

The earth rate torquing signal is only one part of the total torquing signal going to each gyroscope. The change in position of the inertial navigator on the earth's surface also causes the local vertical to change direction in space. This is due to the fact that in going from one position to another the inertial navigator is changing from one local vertical to another. This is demonstrated in figure 4604a. As the inertial navigator travels over the earth's curved surface from position 1 to position 2, the "correct" orientation is shown by the solid line figure at position 2. The broken line figure represents the inertial navigator after the change in position without compensation for the change in the local vertical.

Each gyroscope must also be torqued because of its own internal drift with respect to inertial space. This precession can be caused by such factors as internal torques produced by friction and mass imbalance. The compensation applied for this drift is called **gyro bias.**

As shown in figure 4604a, the total angular change in the local vertical in moving from position 1 to position 2 is represented by θ. The value of θ, expressed in radians, is a function of the distance traveled, S, and the radius of the earth, R. Stated mathematically, this is:

$$\theta = \frac{S}{R}.$$

However, the quantity of interest in maintaining the correct orientation to the local vertical due to change in position is the rate of change of θ with respect to time. Assuming R to be constant,

$$\frac{d\theta}{dt} = \frac{1}{R}\frac{dS}{dt}.$$

Since the time rate of change of distance, S, is velocity, V,

$$\frac{d\theta}{dt} = \frac{V}{R}.$$

Thus, the appropriate gyroscopes must be torqued at this rate so that the vertical indication of the inertial navigator will remain correct as the craft moves over the curved surface of the earth. When the gyroscopes receive a properly calibrated signal to compensate for the change in the local vertical due to movement over the earth, the system is said to be *Schuler tuned*.

If the accelerometer is tilted, it will be affected by gravity. The output which would be produced would not be due to any acceleration of the inertial navigator with respect to the earth and so a compensation must be made. The simplest solution for elimination of the effect of gravity is to place the accelerometer so that its sensitive axis is perpendicular to gravity. Since all accelerations which result in a change in position are perpendicular to the local vertical, this orientation allows the accelerometer to measure these accelerations without being affected by gravity. Two accelerometers, then, are placed perpendicular to the local vertical and perpendicular to each other so that together they can measure any acceleration which will result in a change of position on the earth's surface. A third accelerometer is necessary to measure any accelerations of the navigator along the local vertical. This one also senses the total magnitude

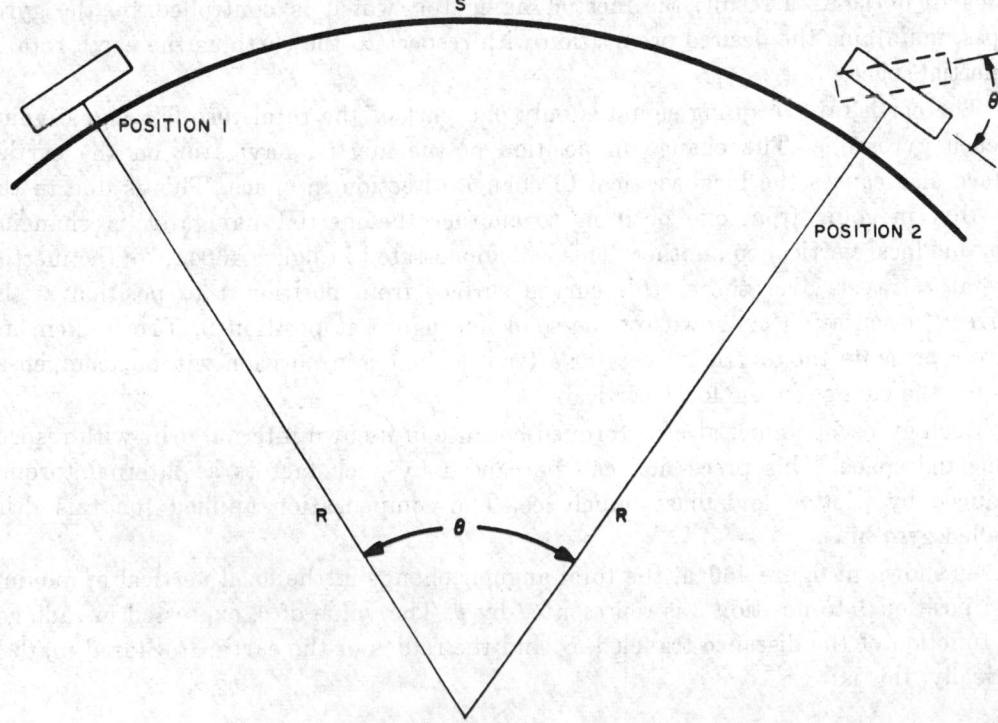

FIGURE 4604a.—Change in local vertical with movement over earth's surface.

of gravity acceleration which is compensated for in the computer of the inertial navigator.

Another acceleration occuring in inertial space which is not an acceleration with respect to the earth is **Coriolis acceleration.** Since the inertially oriented accelerometers produce outputs due to Coriolis acceleration, a compensation must be made. This is not a difficult problem because the Coriolis acceleration can be calculated and therefore removed from the output of an accelerometer before that output is used to provide inertial navigator values.

A body experiences Coriolis acceleration when it travels over a rotating surface in a direction perpendicular to the axis of rotation. The acceleration is not within the reference frame of the rotating body, but within the reference frame in which the body is rotating. A merry-go-round can be used to illustrate the often misunderstood Coriolis acceleration phenomenon.

If as shown in figure 4604b a ticket-taker starts from the center with a velocity, v, toward horse A, he will reach the horse at some finite time, t, later. With respect to the merry-go-round he traveled at a constant velocity and therefore did not accelerate. However, when using the ground below the merry-go-round as the reference in which to make the measurements of his motion, it can be seen that in the time it takes for the man to get to the horse, the horse has moved to position A'. This is due to the rotation, ω, of the merry-go-round. The path of the man with respect to the ground is shown as

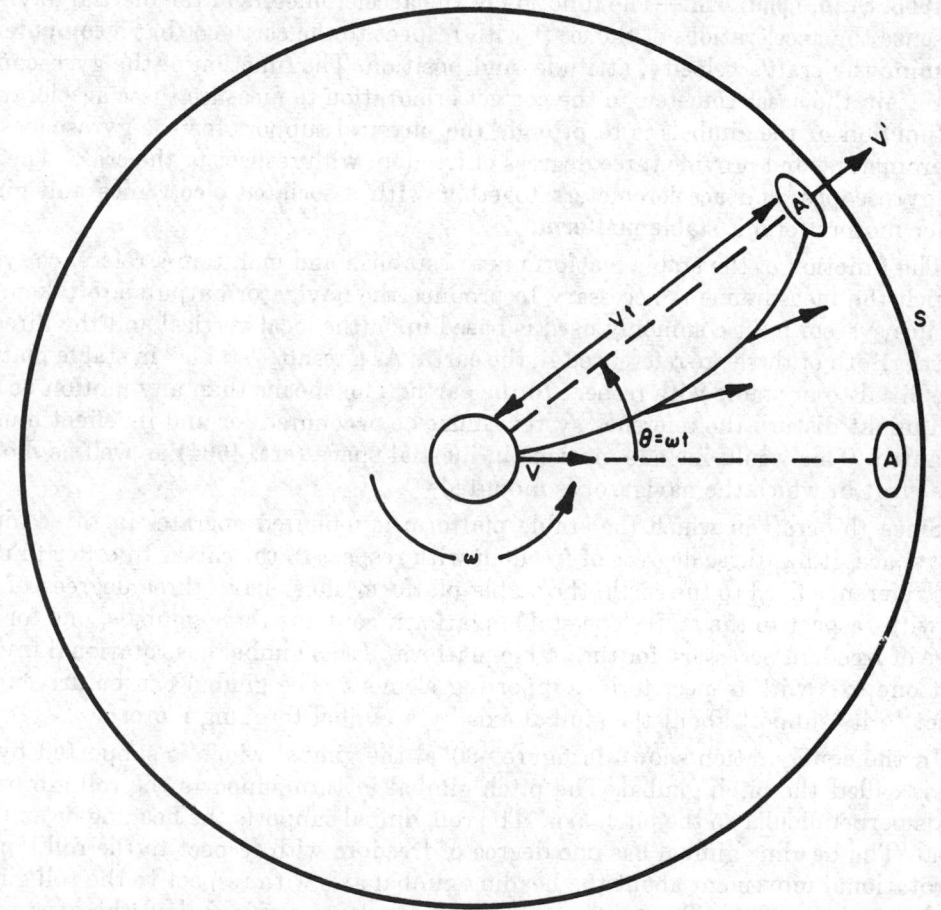

FIGURE 4604b.—Motion on a merry-go-round.

the solid curve even though his velocity with respect to the merry-go-round is directed radially at all times as shown by the two representative vectors along the path.

The Coriolis acceleration which causes the path over the ground to curve is determined as follows:

While going from the center to the horse the man was moved (with respect to the ground) counterclockwise, a distance S. This distance, written in terms of the acceleration which produced it, is:

$$S = 1/2 \ at^2.$$

The distance may also be expressed in terms of the angle θ (which equals the angular rate, ω, of the merry-go-round multiplied by the time, t, involved) and the radius (which equals the velocity, v, of the man with respect to the merry-go-round multiplied by the time, t, involved). This expression is:

$$S = \theta vt = \omega tvt = \omega vt^2.$$

By equating these two expressions and solving for a,

$$1/2 \ at^2 = \omega vt^2,$$
$$a = 2v\omega.$$

4605. Stable platform.—The function of the accelerometers in the inertial navigator is to sense the accelerations of the craft with respect to the earth so that a **computer** can determine the craft's velocity, attitude, and position. The function of the gyroscopes is to maintain the accelerometers in the correct orientation to measure these accelerations. The function of the gimbals is to provide the physical support for the gyroscopes and accelerometers, and provide three degrees of freedom with respect to the craft. The gimbals, gyroscopes, and accelerometers together with associated electronics and gimbal torquer motors form a **stable platform.**

The function of the stable platform is to establish and maintain a reference system in which the measurements necessary to produce the navigator outputs are taken. The reference system most commonly used is based upon the local vertical and the direction of north. Both of these are referenced to the earth. As a result, "stable" in stable platform means fixed to or stable with respect to the earth. This means than any motion or force which might disturb the reference system must be accounted for and its effect must be eliminated. This would include motions in inertial space (art. 4604) as well as motions of the craft in which the navigator is mounted.

Since the craft in which the stable platform is mounted operates in three dimensional space, it has three degrees of freedom with respect to the earth. In order to maintain a reference fixed to the earth, the stable platform must have three degrees of freedom with respect to the craft. The stable platform contains three gimbals, one for each degree of freedom necessary for the stable platform. Each gimbal has rotational freedom about one axis with respect to its supporting element. The gimbal can be driven with respect to its support about the gimbal axis by a gimbal torquing motor.

In the configuration shown in figure 4605a, the gimbal which is supported by the craft is called the pitch gimbal. The pitch gimbal in turn supports the roll gimbal on an axis perpendicular to the pitch axis. The roll gimbal supports the heading or azimuth gimbal. The heading gimbal has one degree of freedom with respect to the roll gimbal, and rotational movement about the heading gimbal axis with respect to the roll gimbal is a change in heading. The heading gimbal through its own axis and the axes of the roll and pitch gimbals has three-degree or complete rotational freedom with respect to the craft in which the platform is mounted. The heading gimbal is able to assume any orientation with respect to the craft within the limits of the gimbal physical restraints.

The heading gimbal, then, is the reference system which the stable platform maintains in some desired orientation with respect to the earth. Mounted on the heading gimbal are the accelerometers whose sensitive axes must be maintained within the desired reference system.

The following discussion of a single-degree-of-freedom stable platform (useful for training purposes only) is presented as an aid to understanding how the stable platform functions to maintain the reference system.

As shown in figure 4605b, the single-degree-of-freedom stable platform consists of a single-degree-of-freedom gyroscope, an accelerometer with integrator (velocity meter), a gimbal with rotational freedom about one axis with respect to the supporting craft, and a torquer motor which drives the gimbal with respect to the craft about the gimbal axis. The gyroscope input axis is aligned to the gimbal axis, and the input axis of the accelerometer is aligned perpendicular to the gimbal axis.

As discussed in article 4604, there are several motions which can disturb the orientation of the heading gimbal. These are divided into rotations and linear accelerations. Some of these motions do not change the craft's position or orientation on the earth. The single-degree-of-freedom platform can be used to examine each motion.

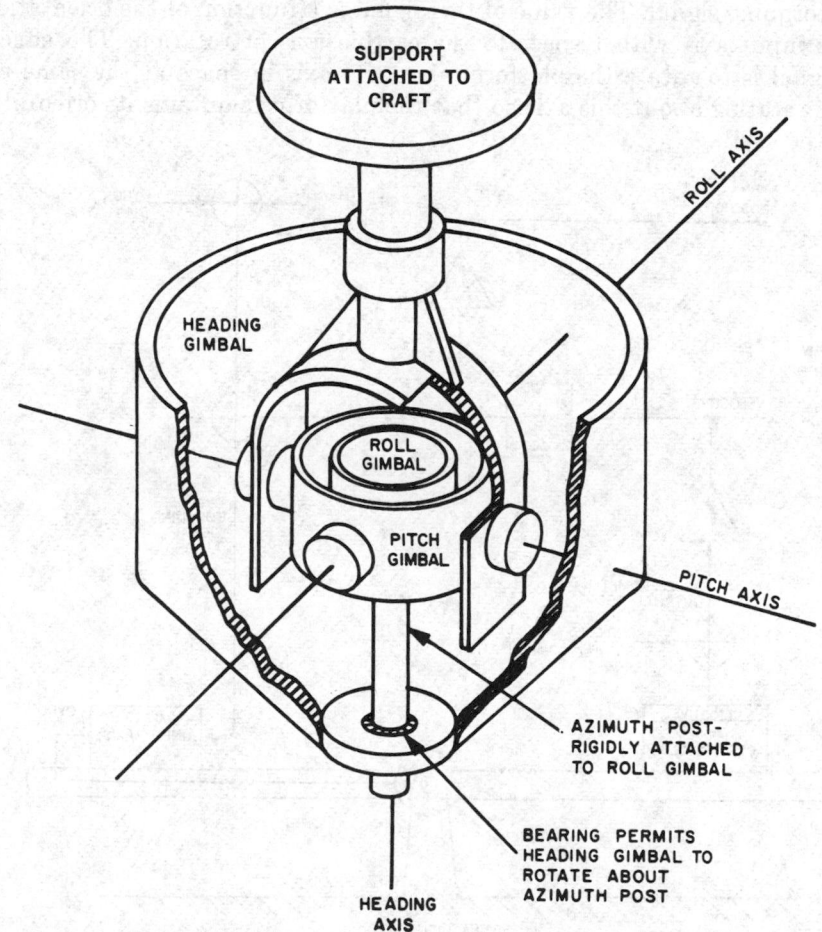

FIGURE 4605a.—Stable platform.

If the supporting craft should undergo any base motion (roll, pitch, or yaw) about the gimbal axis, the platform through friction in the gimbal axis would also start to rotate about the axis with respect to the earth. The rotation rate of the gimbal with respect to the earth would not be nearly so great as the rotation rate of the craft about this axis because the axis is made as frictionless as possible. There could, however, be some displacement of the gimbal. The gyroscope would sense this instantaneously since its input axis is aligned with the axis of the platform. This disturbance about the gyroscope's input axis would cause an output from the gyroscope. This output would go to and excite the gimbal torquing motor which in turn would drive the gimbal with respect to the craft about the gimbal axis.

The gimbal, gyroscope, and torquer motor form a **closed system** or **closed loop.** The gyroscope senses any rotation of the platform with respect to the earth, and the gyroscope output drives the gimbal through the torquer motor at the exact rate necessary to maintain its orientation with respect to the earth. If the rate of platform disturbance increases or decreases, the gyroscope output signal increases or decreases to keep the gimbal in the same position relative to the earth. This keeps the accelerometer in the original position because the reaction of the gimbal, gyroscope, and torquer motor loop is instantaneous and linear.

The rotation of the earth (earth rate) is another motion that tends to disturb the heading gimbal. Figure 4605b shows the earth rate torquing signal as a part of the total gyroscope torquing signal. The value of this signal is a function of the orientation of the gyroscope's input axis with respect to the earth's axis of rotation. The effect of the torquing signal is to rotate the platform about its axis in space at the same rate that the earth is rotating about this axis so that the platform maintains its orientation with respect to the earth.

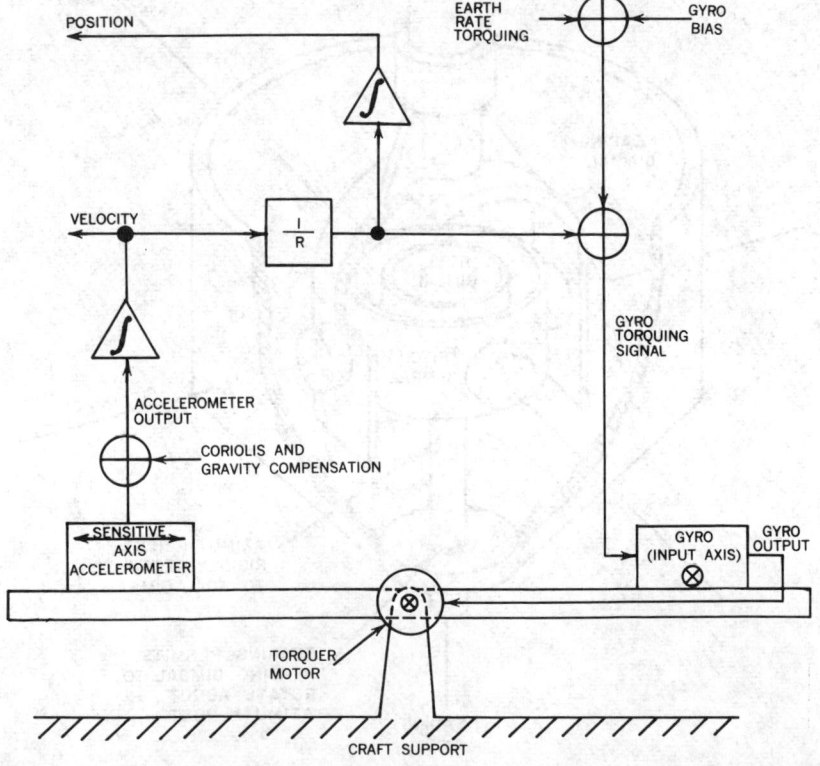

FIGURE 4605b.—Single-degree-of-freedom stable platform used for training purposes only.

The single-degree-of-freedom stable platform is also compensated for any disturbing effects of Coriolis acceleration and gravity acceleration. As shown in figure 4605b, the usual procedure is to make a correction to the output of the velocity meter in the computer of the inertial navigator. (If these errors are not compensated, they become part of the Schuler tuning gyroscope torquing signal and cause this signal to be in error.)

As indicated in article 4604, the purpose of **Schuler tuning** is to insure that the vertical indication of the inertial navigator remains correct as the craft moves over the curved surface of the earth. Two Schuler tuned loops are needed to maintain the desired orientation of the local vertical. One, called the X Schuler loop, consists of the X gyroscope and Y velocity meter, and controls the vertical indication about the input axis of the X gyroscope which is positioned in the horizontal plane normally in a north-south alignment. The other, the Y Schuler loop, consists of the Y gyroscope and X velocity meter, and controls the vertical indication about the input axis of the Y gyroscope which is in the horizontal plane perpendicular to the X gyroscope input axis. Since these Schuler loops are identical in operation, only the X Schuler loop will be examined.

Figure 4605c is a block diagram of the X Schuler loop. This figure shows only those signals primarily concerned with that characteristic of the inertial navigator called Schuler tuning. Other signals such as earth rate, gimbal movements due to vehicle base motions, gyro bias and drift, and Coriolis acceleration are not represented. The inputs to the accelerometer are the acceleration of the vehicle in the Y direction (AY) and the gravity acceleration $(g \cdot MX)$ caused by a tilt about the X axis (MX). The actual value of gravity acceleration is $g \sin MX$ but MX is small enough to write this as $g \cdot MX$. The inputs to the gyroscope are the accelerometer output scaled to be

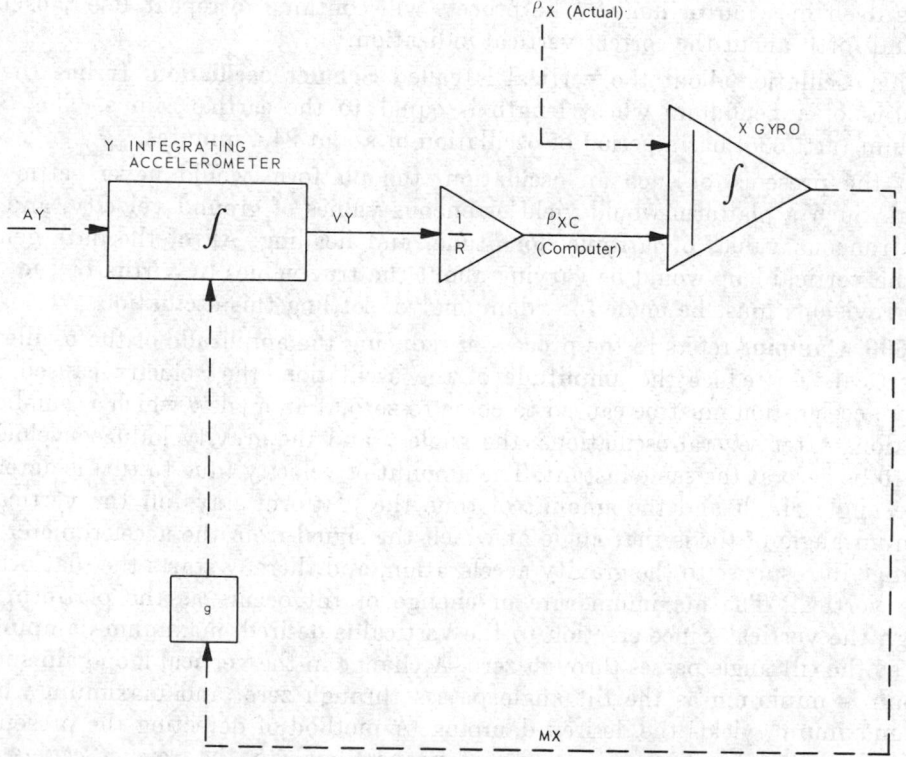

Figure 4605c.—Block diagram of Schuler tuned single-degree-of-freedom stable platform.

the Schuler gyro torquing signal and the rotation in space about the gyroscope's input axis due to the craft's movement over the surface of the earth.

Without tilt, no gravity acceleration is sensed by the accelerometer. The only input is an acceleration of the craft (AY) which produces the integrated output, velocity in the Y direction (VY). This is Schuler tuned by using the effective earth's radius as the scaling factor, and the signal that results (ρ_{xc}) is the computed value of angular rate of change of the vertical indication about the X axis. This should match the actual rate represented by ρ_x. When this happens there is no gyroscope output and therefore no tilt. Hence the system maintains its correct vertical indication and is properly Schuler tuned.

With the system Schuler tuned, if a tilt arises, the accelerometer has an output due to gravity $(g \cdot MX)$ which when integrated with time is represented as VY. This value is also scaled in the Schuler loop and becomes part of the gyro torquing signal. In fact, *the accelerometer is incapable of distinguishing between craft accelerations and gravity accelerations due to tilt*. This error in the gyro torquing signal causes the platform to turn at a rate different from its space angular rate due to change in position. Fortunately, this error always drives the platform toward the proper vertical indication, decreasing MX.

However, as the tilt is decreasing, the gyroscope torquing signal causing the tilt to disappear is increasing because it is the integral of the tilt. As a result when $MX = 0$, ρ_{xc} is a maximum and the platform continues to drive about the X axis causing a tilt to build up in the opposite sense. This $g \cdot (-MX)$ is integrated with time and causes the gyroscope torquing signal to decrease as the tilt builds up. The gyroscope torquing signal will be zero when the tilt has reached the original value with opposite sense. This tilt in turn causes the platform to drive back toward the vertical, and the process repeats itself in a mirror image. The process will continue to repeat itself, oscillating back and forth about the correct vertical indication.

This oscillation about the vertical is called **Schuler oscillation.** It has the characteristics of a pendulum whose length is equal to the earth's radius. This Schuler pendulum (art. 635) has a period of oscillation of about 84.4 minutes.

In the presence of such an oscillation, the platform would never settle to the vertical. Such a platform would yield erroneous values of ground velocity, and therefore, erroneous values of latitude, longitude, and heading. All of the data generated from the vertical loop would be varying about the true values by virtue of the oscillation. Provisions must be made for "damping" or settling this oscillation.

4606. Damping refers to the process of reducing the amplitude of the oscillation in the vertical. To reduce the amplitude of the oscillation, the velocity caused by the gravity acceleration must be caused to come to zero at an angle θ which is smaller each oscillation. After several oscillations, the angle θ and the gravity induced velocity are made to be zero at the same instant. The amount of velocity (due to tilt) is determined by the angle of tilt and the amount of time the platform stays off the vertical. The maximum angle of tilt is that angle at which the signal from the accelerometer begins to change in response to the gravity acceleration, and thereby starts the platform back to the vertical. The maximum rate of change of tilt occurs as the platform passes through the vertical. Since erection to the vertical is desired, maximum damping must occur as the tilt angle passes through zero. A change in the vertical loop gain such that the gain is minimum as the tilt angle passes through zero, and maximum when the tilt is maximum, yields the desired damping. A method of detecting the presence and magnitude of tilt, and of using a signal proportional to the *rate of change* of tilt to vary the gain of the vertical loop is necessary, then, to damp the vertical.

To detect the presence of rate of change of tilt, the change in velocity output of the accelerometer due to actual change in velocity of the craft must be distinguished from an output change due to gravity. To accomplish this differentiation, a secondary source of craft velocity unrelated to the accelerometers, and unaffected by gravity, must be used. By subtracting this secondary reference velocity from the accelerometer output, the actual craft velocity is cancelled out (if the secondary reference is accurate). The difference is the rate of change of tilt. This signal is maximum as θ passes through zero.

Since maximum damping is desired as θ passes through zero, a portion of this signal can be used for damping the vertical loop. It has the desired characteristic of being maximum in respect to the velocity signal when the platform is being driven through the vertical and minimum when the platform is a maximum tilt. Figure 4606 shows the block diagram of a damped vertical loop. The secondary velocity signal (VRL) from the electromagnetic log is resolved into the north and east components and subtracted from the inertial velocity. The velocity difference, ΔV, is multiplied by the damping constant (K) and applied as an input to the first integrator. This signal (ΔV) should represent the integral of the acceleration due to platform tilt, i.e., platform tilt rate. It is greatest when the platform crosses the vertical. Fed back in such a way as to subtract from and thereby reduce the velocity signal, it will settle or damp the vertical by reducing the amplitude of the maxima of the velocity oscillations.

Any velocity difference (ΔV) (inertial velocity in respect to secondary velocity) appears as a damping signal. A premium is placed on the secondary velocity source

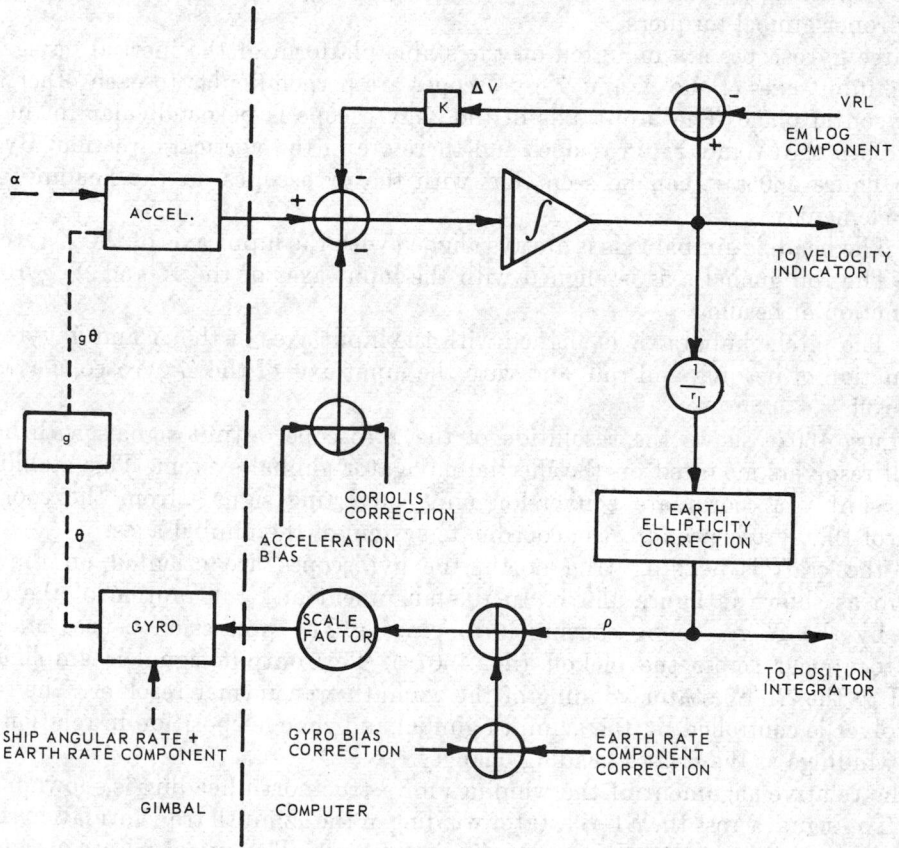

FIGURE 4606.—Block diagram of a damped vertical loop.

in this system because inaccurate response of the secondary velocity is interpreted by the damping circuitry as a tilt. When the reference velocity is noisy or inaccurate, a *forced error* is caused to appear in the vertical due to the damping circuitry. To prevent (or minimize) these errors, the value of K must be kept low (much less than unity), the secondary velocity source must be of good quality, *or* the damping circuit must be disabled during periods of error in the secondary source.

The electromagnetic log (art. 613) is subject to several errors. It does not measure the actual speed over the ground; in the presence of a current, there is a constant difference between the two velocities. The EM log lags the accelerometer in response to a change in velocity. The EM log is not usable in turbulent or shallow water, and its velocity components vary irregularly during ship maneuvers.

Figure 4606 shows a vertical loop which settles with a constant small tilt in the vertical when there is a constant ΔV. The constant tilt gives rise to an accelerometer output just equal and opposite to the product of ΔV and the damping constant. There is no error in the inertial velocity signal, however, and transient vertical disturbances are settled out. Constant electromagnetic log errors can be compensated by a technique known as "third-order damping."

4607. Stabilization loop.—When going from the single-degree-of-freedom to the three-degree-of-freedom stable platform of a practical inertial navigator, provision must be made for the fact that a gimbal is rotated about a gyroscope's input axis in response to an output from that gyroscope, and the output from a particular gyroscope is not always routed to the same gimbal torquer in the stable platform. The function of the *stabilization loop* is to provide the means for the gyroscope outputs to be routed to the proper gimbal torquers.

Three gyroscopes are mounted on the stable platform of the inertial navigator so that the input axes of the X and Y gyroscopes are perpendicular to each other and in the horizontal plane. The input axis of the Z gyroscope is perpendicular to the input axes of both the X and Y gyroscopes and therefore in the vertical direction. By reference to figure 4605a it can be seen that with the gyroscopes on the heading gimbal (stable element):

1. The heading gimbal axis is always aligned with the input axis of the Z gyroscope.
2. The roll gimbal axis is aligned with the input axes of the X and Y gyroscopes as a function of heading.
3. The pitch gimbal axis is aligned with the input axes of the X and Y gyroscopes as a function of heading and roll, and with the input axis of the Z gyroscope as a function of roll.

Figure 4607a shows the resolution of the gyroscope output signals with heading and roll resolvers mounted on the inertial navigator gimbal system. This stabilization loop is simply a coordinate conversion unit converting signals from the coordinate system of the gyroscopes into the coordinate system of the gimbal axes.

If the craft is heading true north, the gyroscopes are oriented on the stable platform as shown in figure 4607b. In this alignment any roll motion of the craft is sensed by the X gyroscope causing it to precess. The precession causes an output signal to appear across the pickoff (fig. 4607a). This output signal is amplified and applied to the $S1$–$S3$ stator winding of the azimuth transformer resolver. The rotor of the resolver is controlled by the azimuth gimbal and changes position in relation to the stator windings as the craft's heading changes.

The relative alignment of the windings for a true north heading is shown in figure 4607a. The signal across the $S1$–$S3$ stator winding of the azimuth transformation resolver produces a maximum output on rotor winding $R1$–$R3$. The signal passes through the slip ring assembly to the navigation console of this practical navigator. The signal is

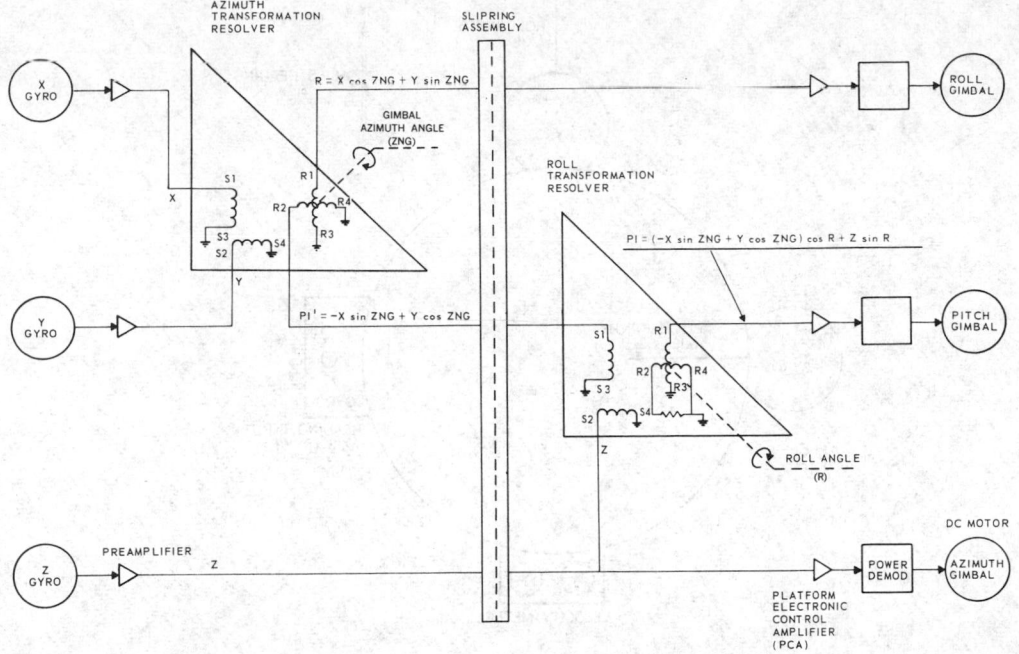

FIGURE 4607a.—Stabilization loop.

then amplified and modulated. The resulting DC signal to the roll DC gimbal torque motor drives the platform in the direction necessary to restore the gyroscope output to zero. Thus, the platform is stabilized about the craft's roll axis.

The Y gyroscope senses motion about the pitch axis and causes an amplified signal to be applied to the $S2$–$S4$ stator winding of the azimuth transformation resolver. With a heading of true north this causes a maximum signal at rotor winding $R2$–$R4$. The signal passes through the slip rings and is applied to the $S1$–$S3$ stator winding of the roll transformation resolver. This resolver is mounted between the roll and pitch gimbal and its rotor is positioned relative to the stator by the roll gimbal shaft. The output of the resolver is present at the $R1$–$R3$ winding of the rotor and is applied to the platform control amplifier and power demodulator. The pitch power demodulator DC output signal drives the pitch gimbal motor, which drives the gimbal in the correct direction to cancel the Y gyroscope output. Rotor winding $R2$–$R4$ of the roll transformation resolver is short circuited because its output is not used in the stabilization system.

Any change in heading introduces a torque about the input axis of the Z gyroscope and causes it to precess. The precession generates an output signal which is amplified by the azimuth gyroscope pickoff amplifier. The signal passes through the slip rings and branches off. One branch is applied to the $S2$–$S4$ stator winding of the roll transformation resolver. The other branch goes directly to the platform electronic control amplifier where the function is identical to that of the roll and pitch sections. The azimuth gimbal motor drives the azimuth gimbal in a direction to decrease the torque about the Z gyroscope. The orientation of the platform, therefore, remains unchanged in azimuth as the craft changes heading or experiences yaw.

If the craft changes heading to 090°, the motion sensed by the Z gyroscope drives the azimuth gimbal in the correct direction to cancel the torque. As a result the platform is oriented as shown in figure 4607c. The X gyroscope now senses pitch motions of the ship and the Y gyroscope senses roll motion. The operation of the stabilization loop, however, is not affected since the change in heading resulted in the azimuth gimbal

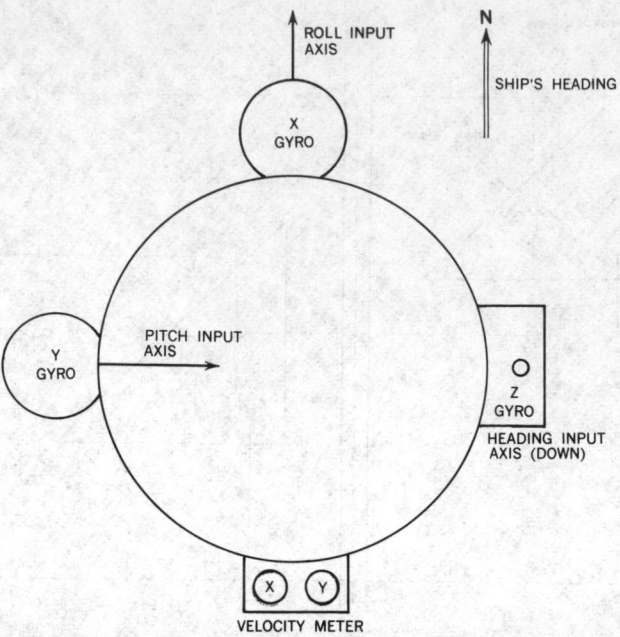

FIGURE 4607b.—Stable platform configuration and input axis for true north heading.

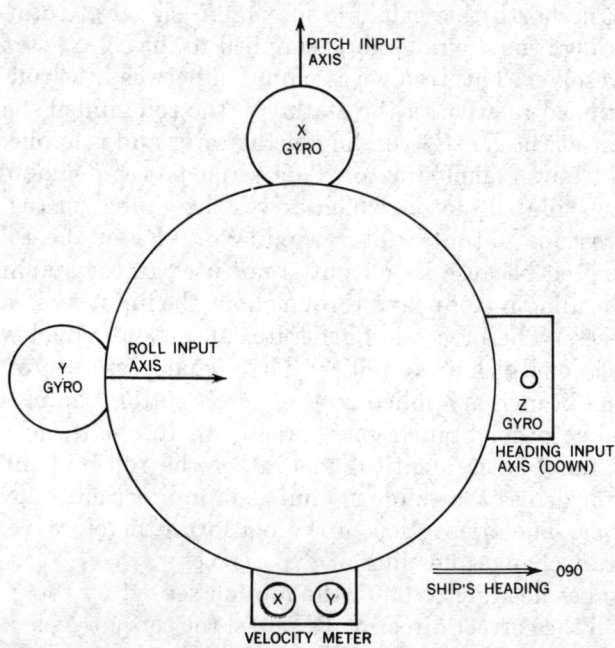

FIGURE 4607c.—Stable platform configuration and input axis for heading of 090°.

being driven 90° in the opposite direction. The rotor of the azimuth transformation resolver is controlled by the azimuth gimbal shaft, and therefore, has rotated 90° with the change in craft's heading. The signal from the X gyroscope, applied to stator winding $S1$–$S3$, is induced on winding $R2$–$R4$ of the rotor and is used to drive the pitch gimbal. The signal from the Y gyroscope, applied to stator $S2$–$S4$, induces a maximum signal on rotor winding $R1$–$R3$ and drives the roll gimbal.

At headings between 000° and 090°, outputs from the X or Y gyroscope result in a proportional mixture of the output signals applied to the pitch and roll gimbals. For example, at heading 045° an output signal from either gyroscope pickoffs will be applied equally to the roll and pitch gimbal drive motors. Thus, the azimuth transformation resolver causes the pickoff signal to drive the correct gimbal regardless of the heading. Similarly, if the craft should experience pitching motion while at some angle of roll, the pitch gimbal axis will not be in the level plane. The pitching motion will have a vertical component and the rotation of the stable platform about the pitch axis will be sensed not only by the X and Y gyroscopes, but also partly by the Z gyroscope. This results in a pickoff from the Z gyroscope being routed in the proper proportion through the roll transformation resolver to the pitch gimbal drive motor. The contributions from the level X and Y gyroscopes will be reduced appropriately by the same resolver.

4608. Coordinate systems.—Two orthogonal coordinate systems are used to relate the inherent errors (art. 4609) to the inertial navigator. One system consists of X, Y, and Z axes. The X and Y axes define the horizontal plane with the X axis directed northward and the Y axis directed eastward. The Z axis is directed downward along the local vertical. The relationship of this coordinate system to the second system, the equatorial coordinate system, is shown in figure 4608. The equatorial system consists of P (polar), Q (equatorial), and E (east) axes. The P axis is parallel to the earth's axis of rotation. The Q axis is parallel to the equatorial plane and is directed outward from the earth's axis of rotation. The E axis is coincident with the Y axis of the other coordinate system.

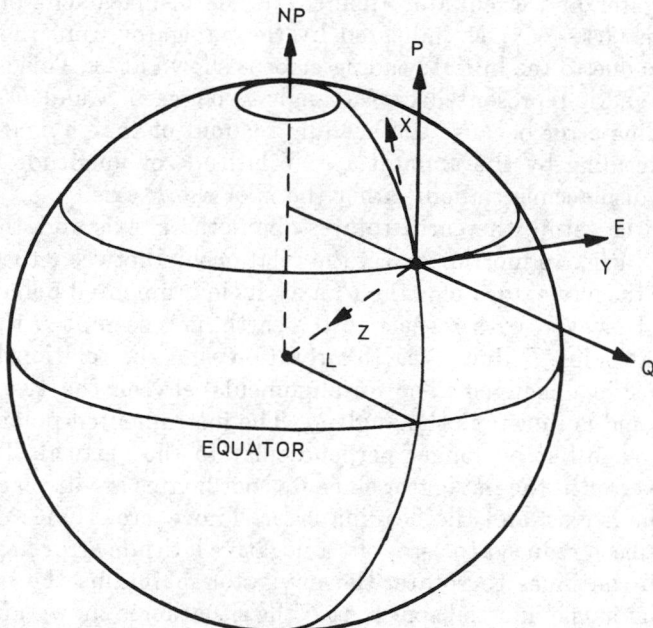

FIGURE 4608.—Orthogonal coordinate systems.

The first coordinate system is physically represented in the gyroscope arrangement on the stable platform of the inertial navigator. The computer of the inertial navigator maintains a mathematical representation of the equatorial coordinate system. The relationship of the two systems is expressed mathematically as:

$$X = P \cos L - Q \sin L$$

$$Y = E$$

$$Z = -P \sin L - Q \cos L.$$

4609. Inherent errors of an inertial navigator are the 84.4 minute Schuler oscillation and the 24-hour oscillations. The latter may have constant *standoffs* or *ramps* in the outputs associated with it.

As discussed in article 4607, the **84.4-minute Schuler oscillation** is an oscillation in the vertical loop resulting from initial tilts or velocity errors. It can also be caused by any transient disturbance in the system. The Schuler oscillations are continuously damped and limited in magnitude.

The **24-hour oscillation** is a property of a properly functioning practical inertial navigator which is caused by initial errors in position, heading, or gyro bias. An initial error in either latitude or heading causes both quantities to oscillate about their true values within a 24-hour period. A gyro bias error limits the ability of the inertial navigator to determine latitude and heading. A gyro bias error causes latitude or heading to oscillate about an offset value. A gyro bias error may also cause an ever increasing or *ramping* longitude error.

Although uncompensated gyro drift can cause a 24-hour oscillation, the following discussion is simplified by assuming properly biased gyros and therefore no uncompensated gyro drift. The discussion is also simplified by assuming that there is no Schuler oscillation.

Figure 4609a illustrates the 24-hour oscillation for an initial heading error. With the inertial navigator at the equator (point T_0), the displacement of the equatorial coordinate system (art. 4608) as indicated by the navigator from the true equatorial coordinate system due to the initial heading error is shown at A. This is a displacement about the Q axis and is represented by the angle δ_Q between E and E'. As shown, this is a positive heading error because the heading readout of the navigator will be larger than the actual heading by the amount δ_Q. No latitude or longitude error results because there is no displacement about either the E or the P axis.

After this initial setup, the earth rotates about the P axis and the navigator rotates about the P' axis. In inertial space, the relationship between these axes remains the same because the navigator holds the P' axis, its instrumented polar axis, stationary in inertial space. However, with respect to the earth, it is seen at B that after 6 hours the navigator is at point T_6 due to earth's rotation, and the relationship between the coordinate systems has changed. The misalignment between the two systems is now about the E axis and is shown as the angle δ_E. The instrumented polar axis, P', is now in the meridian plane but no longer perpendicular to the vertical. This represents a negative latitude error in the navigator since its coordinates are displaced in a negative rotation about the E axis, and the heading error is now zero. Hence after 6 hours the heading error has been reduced to zero, but a negative latitude error has been produced.

As the earth continues to rotate, the navigator maintains the orientation of its instrumented polar axis in inertial space. At C the situation is shown after 6 more hours or 12 hours after the initial situation at A. Once again the misalignment of the navigator's reference system with respect to the earth is about Q axis, meaning an error in

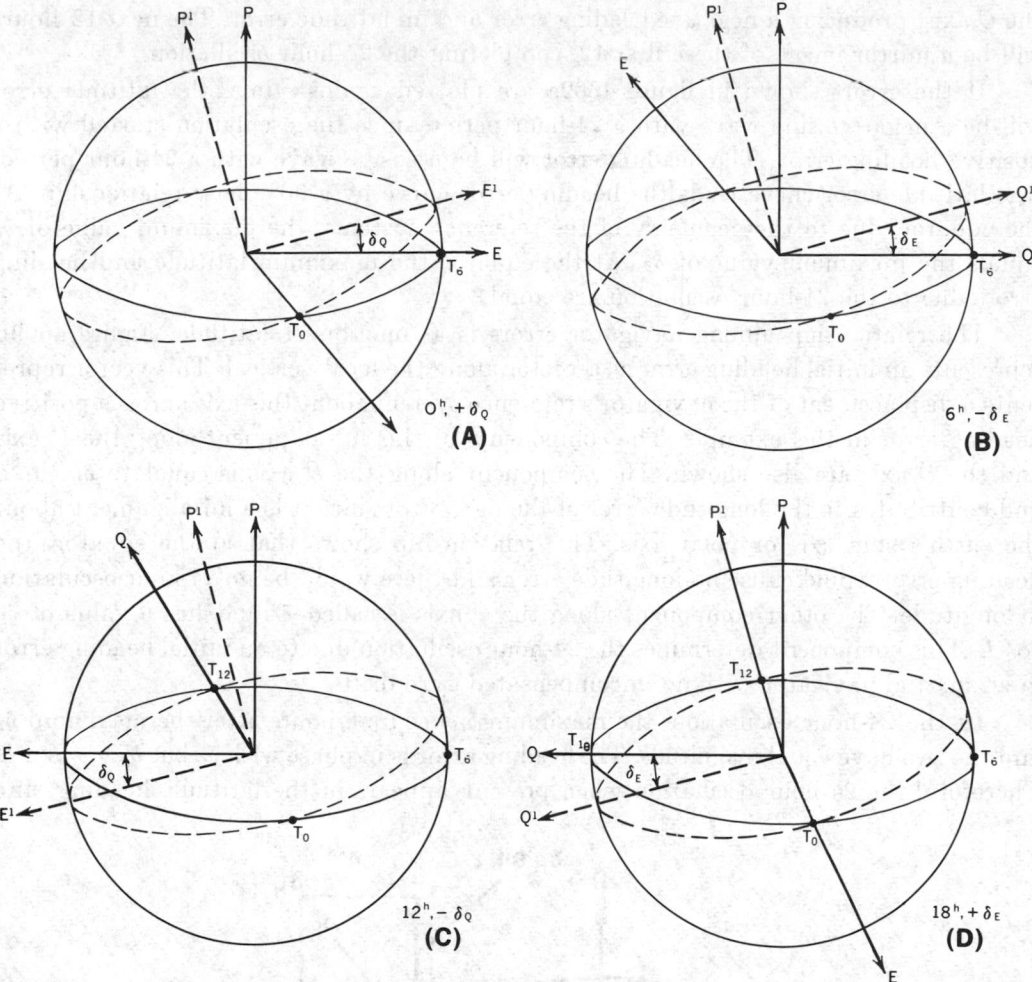

FIGURE 4609a.—The 24-hour oscillation for an initial heading error.

heading and no error in latitude. This time the heading error is negative but of the same magnitude as at T_0.

During the next 6 hours this negative heading error diminishes until it has decreased to zero as shown at D. At the same time the latitude error is building up in a positive direction to the value shown. At T_{18} the misalignment of the navigator is about the E axis again, which results in a positive latitude error and no heading error as stated. This positive latitude error has a magnitude equal to the negative latitude error at T_6.

View D of figure 4609a can be used to summarize the preceding action as follows: With the navigator on the equator at position T_0 set up with a positive heading error and no position error, the misalignments of its reference system with respect to the earth is about the Q axis. (It should be kept in mind that the Q axis goes through the position on the equator.) As position T_0 moves to position T_6 in space due to the rotation of the earth, the misalignment of the navigator with respect to the earth changes to be about the E axis. This means that the error in the navigator is latitude (negative at T_6) and there is no heading error. As the earth continues to rotate, the navigator reaches position T_{12} in space; and, because the instrumented polar axis has maintained its orientation in space, the navigator is now misaligned with respect to the earth about the Q axis, producing a negative heading error and no latitude error. The next 12 hours will be a mirror image of these first 12, completing the 24-hour oscillation.

If the errors shown in figure 4609a are plotted against time, the latitude error will be a negative sine wave with a 24-hour period since the oscillation started with a positive heading error. The heading error will be a cosine wave with a 24-hour period. The latitude error curve leads the heading error curve by a 90° phase relationship. At the equator, due to the geometry of the reference systems, the maximum value of δ_Q equals the maximum value of δ_E. At the equator the maximum latitude and heading errors due to the 24-hour oscillation are equal.

The relationship among navigator errors is a function of latitude. Figure 4609b represents an initial heading error as a vector along the local vertical. This vector represents a displacement of the navigator's reference system about this axis and is a positive heading error in this example. The components of this misalignment along the P axis and the Q axis are also shown. The component along the P axis is equal to $\delta_H \sin L$ and contributes to the longitude error of the navigator since it is a misalignment about the earth's spin axis or polar axis. This relationship shows that at the equator, the heading error would cause no longitude error and there would be no 24-hour oscillation in longitude. The other component along the Q axis is called δ_Q and has a value of δ_H $\cos L$. This component determines the 24-hour oscillation due to an initial heading error in an inertial navigator with no uncompensated gyro drifts.

In the 24-hour oscillation, the maximum δ_Q occurs 6 hours after the maximum δ_E and the two have equal magnitude. The heading error is in phase with δ_Q but $\delta_H = \delta_Q \sec L$. Therefore, the 24-hour oscillation when present appears in the latitude, heading, and

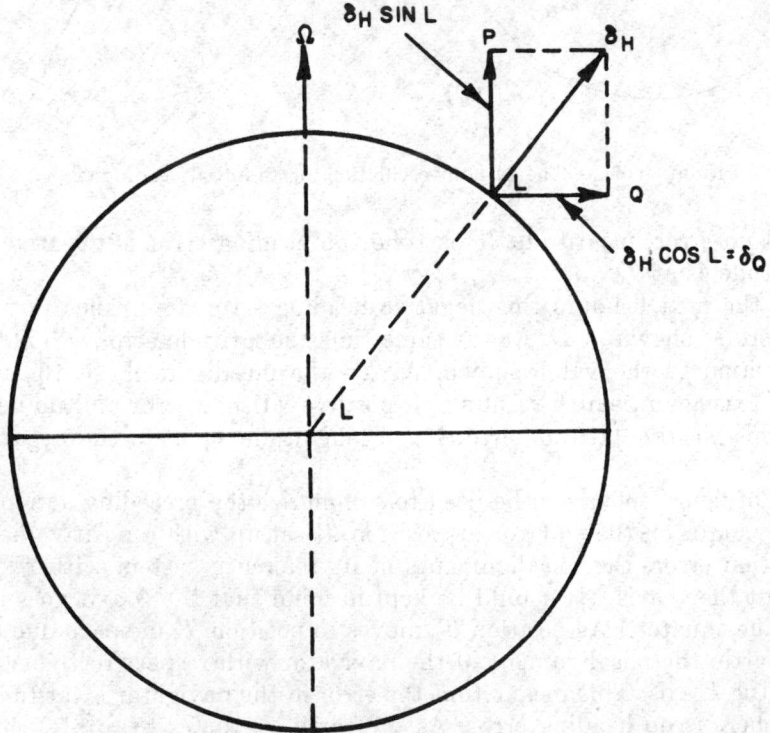

FIGURE 4609b.—Relationship among misalignment errors of inertial navigator.

longitude outputs of the inertial navigator with the following relationships as shown in figure 4609c.

1. The latitude error equals δ_E.

2. The heading error equals $\delta_Q \sec L$.

3. The longitude error equals $\delta_H \sin L$.

4. Latitude, heading, and longitude errors oscillate as a sine wave with a 24-hour period.

5. The latitude error leads the heading error by 6 hours or 90°.

6. The heading error and longitude error oscillations are in phase.

7. The maximum heading error equals the maximum latitude error multiplied by the secant of the latitude position.

8. The longitude error equals the heading error times the sine of the latitude position.

Since heading error is a function of latitude, the usual practice is to use a normalized heading value for the plotting of this error. This is accomplished by multiplying the heading error by the cosine of the latitude position. This results in a plot of δ_Q. The δ_Q curve is equal in amplitude to the δ_L curve.

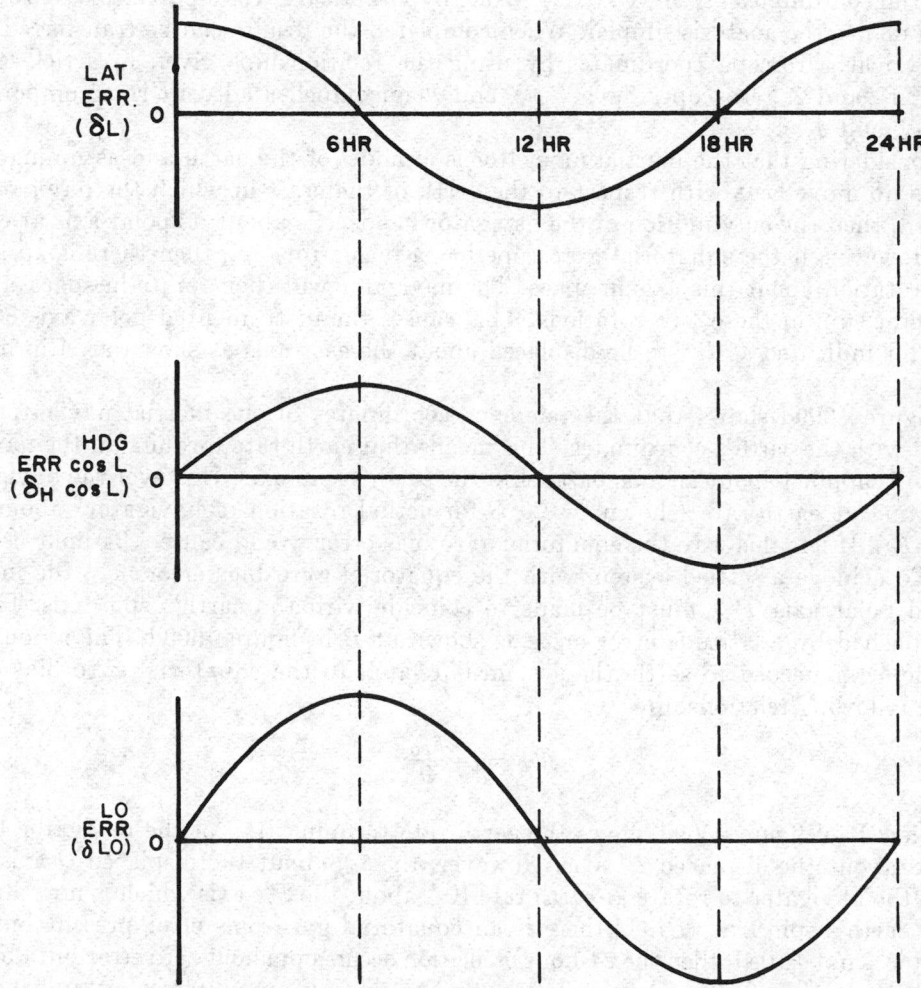

FIGURE 4609c.—Inertial navigator 24-hour oscillation error plots.

Gyro bias error. A gyro drift is an internal disturbance which causes an output signal from the gyroscope. The stabilization loop interprets it as a disturbance of the stable element's orientation and drives the gimbals accordingly. This causes a misorientation of the stable element and results in inertial navigator errors. Although the drift cannot be completely removed, it is possible to compensate for it by applying a gyro torquing signal called a **bias**. If the bias is proper, there is no gyroscope output due to drift. If the gyro bias is not correct or whenever the drift of a gyroscope changes and a new bias is needed, then there is a gyro bias error or a gyroscope with uncompensated drift.

To analyze the effect of gyro bias errors on the navigator it is advantageous to examine a settled system. This is a special case in which there is no 24-hour oscillation in the inertial navigator. When the system is settled with gyro bias errors, there will be errors in navigator outputs. These errors will be a function of the gyro bias errors since they compensate for the gyro bias errors. In fact it is only when these errors in the navigator outputs exactly compensate for the gyro bias errors that the navigator will be settled.

Although the gyroscopes are placed physically in the inertial navigator's coordinate system (X, Y, Z), the effect of gyro bias errors is better described in terms of the equatorial coordinate system (P, Q, E). Using hypothetical gyroscopes in this coordinate system makes the analysis simpler. When completed the results can be transferred into the physical gyroscope coordinates by using the relationships given in article 4608. The X, Y, and Z gyroscopes have P, Q, and E uncompensated drift rate components $(\delta_{BP}, \delta_{BQ}, \text{and } \delta_{BE})$.

Considering that the inertial navigator is a model of the earth and assuming that there is no movement with respect to the earth of the craft in which the navigator is installed, then the only motion of the navigator in space is about its polar axis at earth rate. However, if the equatorial gyroscope has a bias error, δ_{BQ}, then there is an additional rotation about this axis in space. The navigator will then rotate in space about the vector sum of these two rotations. This causes the instrumented polar axis of the navigator indicated as P'' to be displaced about the east axis as shown at A in figure 4609d.

Figure 4609d shows that the reference coordinates of the inertial navigator are aligned with the earth's coordinates. This means that earth rate torquing in the navigator (Ω_T) is applied about an axis parallel to the earth's spin axis. However the navigator is rotating at earth rate (shown by Ω_S, S for actual rotation of navigator) about P'' due to δ_{BQ}. If left this way the equatorial gyro bias error would cause a 24-hour oscillation. To achieve a settled system with the equatorial gyro bias error, δ_{BQ}, the instrumented polar axis, P'', must be made to coincide with the earth's spin axis. This is accomplished by a latitude error or δ_L as shown at B in figure 4609d. The amount of latitude error needed to settle the system is related to the equatorial gyro bias error by the following relationship:

$$\delta_E = \delta_L = \frac{\delta_{BQ}}{\Omega}.$$

View B of figure 4609d shows the earth rate torquing (Ω_T) of the navigator being applied about the displaced P' axis. However, the δ_{BQ} about the displaced Q axis (Q') causes the navigator to rotate at earth rate (Ω_S) about the P'' axis which is now aligned to the earth's spin axis (P). If there is an equatorial gyro bias error present but the navigator is not settled, then the 24-hour oscillation occurs not about zero error but about a latitude error given in the above relationship. As a result an equatorial gyro bias error results in a **stand-off** or constant error in latitude which may or may not have a 24-hour

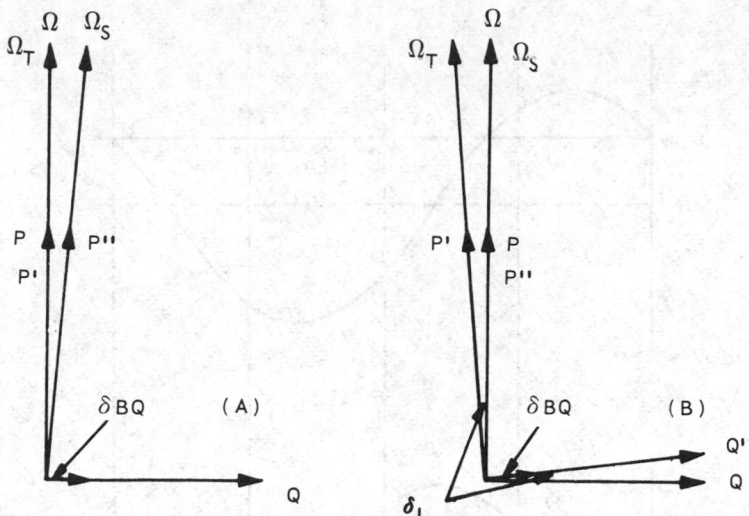

FIGURE 4609d.—Effect of equatorial gyro bias error.

oscillation superimposed upon it. The equatorial gyro bias error defines the settling point for latitude.

In the case of an east gyro bias error, δ_{BE}, the instrumented polar axis would be displaced about the equatorial axis. Again, to settle the navigator with an east gyro bias error, the instrumented polar axis must be made coincident with the earth's spin axis. To do this the navigator coordinates must be misaligned about the equatorial axis an amount given by:

$$\delta_Q = \delta_H \cos L = \frac{\delta_{BE}}{\Omega}.$$

If the displacement about the equatorial axis is the above amount, the navigator would be settled. The δ_Q results in a heading error which varies as a function of latitude as discussed with respect to the 24-hour oscillation. If the navigator is not settled and has an east gyro bias error, the 24-hour oscillation in heading will be about a stand-off error defined by the above equation. If heading error times the cosine of latitude is plotted for a given east gyro bias error, this stand-off is constant and is a function of the magnitude of the gyro bias error.

If there is both an equatorial and east gyro bias error, there is a settling point for the navigator involving both a latitude error and a heading error. Figure 4609e illustrates the error propagation in an inertial navigator which had no errors previous to time 0 and then at time zero a bias error occurs in each of the gyros. View A shows that the latitude error oscillates about a value determined by the equatorial gyro bias error (the stand-off error in latitude due to an equatorial gyro bias error). The heading error as seen at view B oscillates about the stand-off error due to the east gyro bias error. The phase relationship is as discussed earlier and the magnitude of the 24-hour oscillation errors is a function of the initial conditions of the navigator. These are more easily studied in the circle plot.

The remaining gyro bias error is the polar gyro bias error. Since this bias error occurs about the earth's spin axis, it doesn't change the orientation of the inertial navigator's instrumented polar axis. Instead the polar gyro bias error causes the navigator to rotate about the polar axis at a rate different from the earth's rotation.

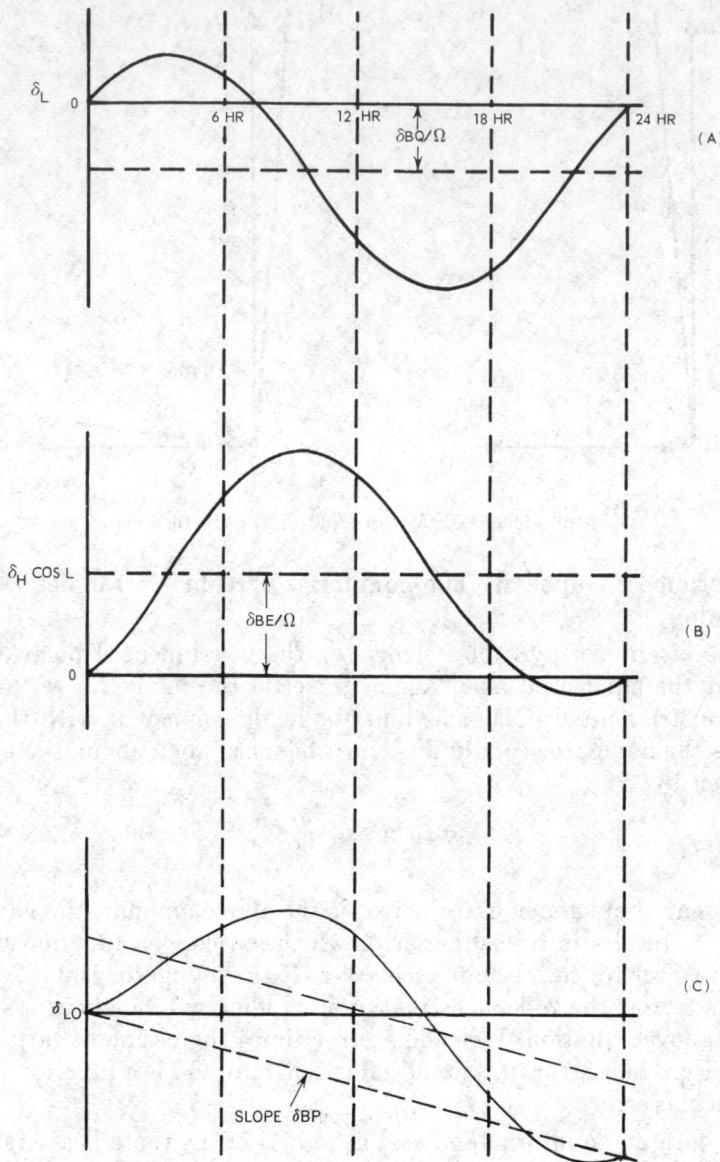

FIGURE 4609e.—Inertial navigator error plots.

The navigator interprets this as change of position on the earth about the polar axis which is longitude change or longitude rate. The bias error has a constant value and this results in a constant longitude rate error. The longitude rate is integrated with time in the navigator to produce an increasing longitude value. As a result the polar gyro bias error contributes a straight line function to the longitude error. The slope of this line equals the polar gyro bias error or longitude ramp.

View C of figure 4609e shows the longitude error at latitude 45°N. The longitude error starts at zero in this case because of the initial conditions previously set up. The longitude error oscillates relative to the polar gyro bias error in the same phase as the heading error oscillates about the latitude gyro bias error.

4610. The circle plot is a convenient method of representing the 24-hour oscillation. It combines both latitude and heading in one plot and shows all phase and amplitude relationships.

Latitude and heading errors oscillate with a 24-hour period. These oscillations are 90° out of phase. Also, the amplitude of the latitude oscillation equals the heading oscillation multiplied by cosine latitude. If latitude error is plotted against heading error times cosine latitude the result is a circle plot as shown in figure 4610a. Also shown are the latitude and heading cosine latitude curves which the circle represents. Note that the circle completely defines each of the component oscillations. A point on the circle is known as the operating point. Its coordinates represent the latitude and heading errors at a particular time. As the operating point moves around the circle its projection on the vertical axis is the latitude oscillation. Its projection on the horizontal axis is the heading error times the cosine latitude oscillation. As the point goes through one rotation, it projects one cycle of a sine curve. Thus 360° on the circle represents 24 hours of time or 15° equals 1 hour. Because of the phase relationships involved, the circle always propagates in a clockwise direction.

The location of the center of the circle is a function of gyro bias errors as they represent the standoff values in latitude and heading cosine latitude. The center of the circle is known as the bias center. The circle diagram can be used to determine how the system will behave starting with given initial conditions. For example, suppose the inertial navigator has zero initial latitude and heading error, but at time zero a bias error develops in the east gyro only. The circle plot will be used to determine the resulting oscillation.

The initial conditions are shown in figure 4610b at A. The operating point is at the origin and the bias center is along the heading cosine latitude axis. The circle propagates about the bias center in a clockwise direction as shown at B. To find the oscillations in latitude and heading, the operating point is projected on the vertical and horizontal axes as shown at C. Latitude error peaks at 6 hours, goes through zero at 12 hours, and reaches a negative peak at 18 hours. It is thus a sine curve oscillating about zero.

Heading error cosine latitude starts at zero, reaches a point of inflection at 6 hours, and a positive peak after 12 hours. It varies as a cosine function about an offset. The offset is due to the east gyro drift. The phase and amplitude relations may thus be determined from the circle plot directly. This can be done for any initial conditions or to see the effect of a reset or gyro drift change on the inertial navigator.

A longitude plot must be used in conjunction with the circle plot in order to describe the error propagation of the inertial navigator completely.

4611. Reset.—The characteristics of propagation of the 24-hour oscillation errors and the gyro bias error in the inertial navigator are well known. This knowledge is used with fix data to determine corrections which are entered into the navigator to eliminate the errors and to prevent the errors from occurring in the future. The process of entering these corrections into the navigator for this purpose is called *reset.*

To determine the error of the navigator, propagation plots such as those in 4609e could be made. Since the latitude error and heading error times the cosine of latitude are sine waves of known period, three points would be necessary to determine each curve. However, it is not always possible to determine points on the heading error plot due to lack of accurate heading information. If this happens it is still possible to determine the heading error oscillation from the latitude error plot because of their 90°

relationship. In fact, it is just this relationship which allows these two plots to be combined into one plot for a more useful display of the errors.

It has been found advantageous in the construction of the circle plot to use bias "corrections" rather than bias "errors." For example, an equatorial bias error (δ_{BE}) would be plotted as an equatorial bias correction (BEC).

4612. Geodetic and geophysical errors.—Even if it were possible to make perfect inertial sensors, inertial navigators would still experience errors. These errors are due to uncertainties in knowledge of the physical environment.

A particularly serious error in precision marine inertial navigation systems is due to lack of knowledge of the gravitational environment (art. X4). Since an accelerometer cannot distinguish between a kinematic acceleration and a gravitational acceleration, any uncertainty in the gravitational environment manifests itself as a system error. In the case of marine inertial navigation in locally level coordinates, it is the horizontal components of gravity that cause significant errors. These are directly due to deflections of the vertical (art. X4), which are tilts of the actual (plumb bob) vertical vector relative to the presumed reference vertical.

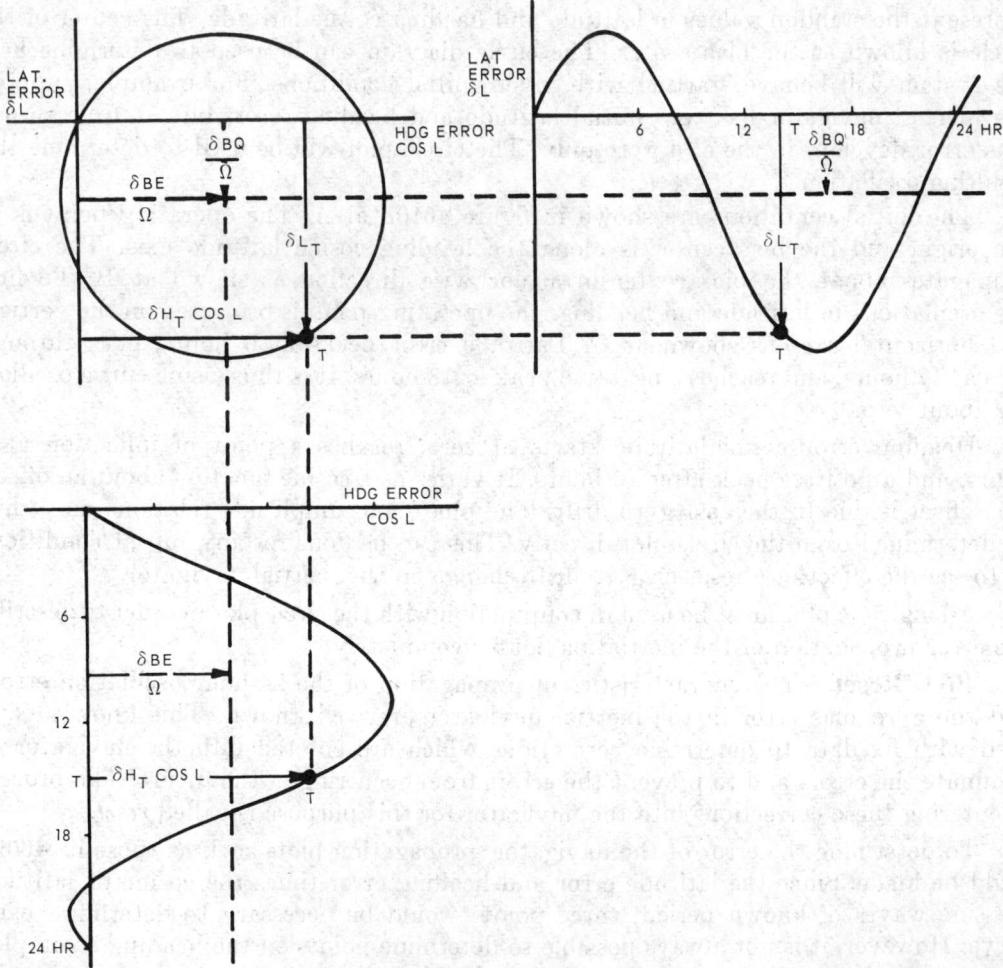

FIGURE 4610a.—Circle plot.

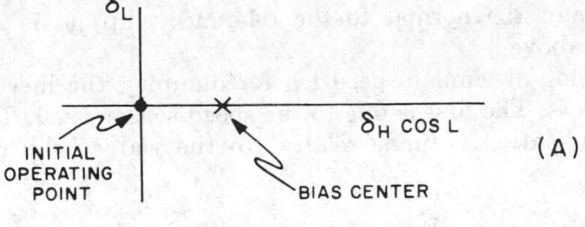

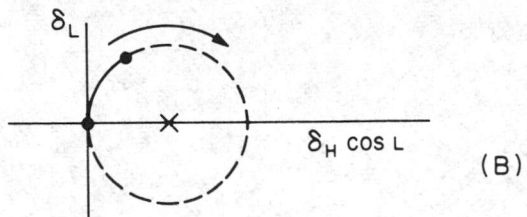

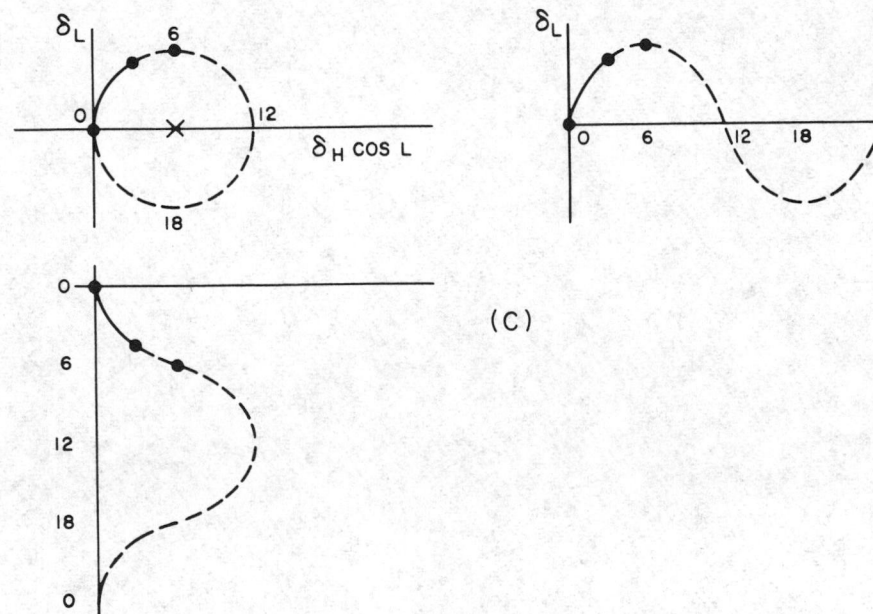

FIGURE 4610b.—Effect of east gyro bias error.

Departures of the magnitude of the gravity vector from the presumed model value are called **gravity anomalies.**

Inertial navigation systems are mechanized in terms of a reference ellipsoid (art. X7). The reference ellipsoid is chosen as a good approximation to a surface called the geoid (art. X2), which is that surface to which the oceans would conform over the entire earth if free to adjust to the combined effect of the earth's mass attraction and the centrifugal force of the earth's rotation. It has the special property that, at every point, the direction to the geoid is given by the direction of a plumb line. The angle between the normal to the geoid and the normal to the reference ellipsoid is the deflection of the vertical referred to above.

The use of an electromagnetic log or similar speed log for damping the inertial navigator results in two types of errors. The first is due to the speed sensor itself. The second occurs because the speed indication is made relative to the water, which is itself moving relative to the earth.

APPENDICES

APPENDICES

ABBREVIATIONS

Abbreviations used on nautical charts are given in appendix Z.

A, amplitude; augmentation; away (altitude intercept).

a, altitude intercept (Ho~Hc); altitude factor (change of altitude in 1 minute of time from meridian transit); assumed.

a_0, first Polaris correction.

a_1, second Polaris correction.

a_2, third Polaris correction.

AC, alternating current.

add'l, additional.

ADF, automatic radio direction finder.

AF, audio frequency.

aL, assumed latitude.

AM, amplitude modulation.

AM, ante meridian (before noon).

AMVER, Automated Mutual-assistance Vessel Rescue System.

antilog, antilogarithm.

AP, assumed position.

approx., approximate, approximately.

ASF, Additional Secondary Phase Factor.

AT, Atomic Time.

AU, astronomical unit.

AUSREP, Australian Ships Reporting System.

$a\lambda$, assumed longitude.

B, atmospheric pressure correction (altitude); bearing, bearing angle.

B_A, difference between heading and apparent wind direction.

BIH, Bureau Internationale de l'Heure.

Brg., bearing (as distinguished from bearing angle).

B_{pgc}, bearing per gyrocompass.

B_T, difference between heading and true wind direction.

C, Celsius (centigrade); chronometer time; compass (direction); correction; course, course angle.

CB, compass bearing.

CC, compass course; chronometer correction.

CCIR, International Radio Consultative Committee.

CCZ, Coastal Confluence Zone.

CE, chronometer error; compass error.

cec, centicycle.

cel, centilane.

CEP, circular probable error.

CFR, Code of Federal Regulations.

CH, compass heading.

cm, centimeter, centimeters.

CMG, course made good.

Cn, course (as distinguished from course angle).

co-, the complement of (90° minus).

COA, course of advance.

COG, course over ground.

coL, colatitude.

colog, cologarithm.

corr., correction.

cos, cosine.

cot, cotangent.

cov, coversine.

CPE, circular probable error.

cps, cycles per second.

C_{pgc}, course per gyrocompass.

C_{psc}, course per standard compass.

$C_{p\ stg\ c}$, course per steering compass.

CRT, cathode-ray tube.

csc, cosecant.

CW, continuous wave.

CZn, compass azimuth.

D, deviation; dip (of horizon); distance.

d, declination (astronomical); altitude difference.

d, declination change in 1 hour.

DC, direct current.

D. Lat., difference of latitude.

Dec., declination.

Dec. Inc., declination increment.

Dep., departure.

Dev., deviation.

DG, degaussing.

diff., difference.

Dist., distance.

DLo, difference of longitude (arc units).

DMAHC, Defense Mapping Agency Hydrographic Center.

DR, dead reckoning, dead reckoning position.

DRE, dead reckoning equipment.

DRT, dead reckoning tracer.

D_s, dip short of horizon.

DSD, double second difference.

dur., duration.

$d\lambda$, difference of longitude (time units).

E, east.

e, base of Naperian logarithms.

e, eccentricity.

EDD, estimated date of departure.

EHF, extremely high frequency.

EM, electromagnetic (underwater log).

EP, estimated position.

Eq.T, equation of time.

ET, Ephemeris Time.

ETA, estimated time of arrival.

ETD, estimated time of departure.

F, Fahrenheit; fast; longitude factor; phase correction (altitude).

f, latitude factor.

f, flattening or ellipticity.

FM, frequency modulation.

ft., foot, feet.

G, Greenwich, Greenwich meridian (upper branch); grid (direction).

g, acceleration due to gravity; Greenwich meridian (lower branch).

GAT, Greenwich apparent time.

GB, grid bearing.

GC, grid course.

GE, gyro error.

GH, grid heading.

GHA, Greenwich hour angle.

GMT, Greenwich mean time.

GP, geographical position.

Gr., Greenwich.

GRI, group repetition interval.

GST, Greenwich sidereal time.

GV, grid variation.

GZn, grid azimuth.

h, altitude (astronomical); height above sea level.

ha, apparent altitude.

hav, haversine.

Hc, computed altitude.

Hdg., heading.

HE, heeling error; height of eye.

HF, high frequency.

h_t, height above sea level in feet.

HHW, higher high water.

HLW, higher low water.

hm, height above sea level in meters.

Ho, observed altitude.

HP, horizontal parallax.

Hp, precomputed altitude.

H_{pgc}, heading per gyrocompass.

H_{psc}, heading per standard compass.

$H_{p\ stg\ c}$, heading per steering compass.

hr, rectified (apparent) altitude.

hr., hour.

hrs., hours.

hs, sextant altitude.

ht, tabulated altitude.

HW, high water.

HWF & C, high water full and change.

I, instrument correction.

IALA, International Association of Lighthouse Authorities.

IAU, International Astronomical Union.

IC, index correction.

ICW, Intracoastal Waterway.

IHB, International Hydrographic Bureau.

IHO, International Hydrographic Organization.

IMCO, Inter-Governmental Maritime Consultative Organization.

in., inch, inches.

INM, International Nautical Mile.

INS, inertial navigation system.

int., interval.

ISLW, Indian spring low water.

ITU, International Telecommunications Union.

IUGG, International Union of Geodesy and Geophysics.

J, irradiation correction (altitude).

K, Kelvin (temperature).

kHz, kilohertz.

km, kilometer, kilometers.

kn, knot, knots.

L, latitude; lower limb correction for moon (from *Nautical Almanac*).

l, difference of latitude; logarithm, logarithmic.

LAN, local apparent noon.

LAT, local apparent time.
lat., latitude.
LF, low frequency.
LHA, local hour angle.
LHW, lower high water.
LL, lower limb.
LLW, lower low water.
Lm, middle latitude; mean latitude.
LMT, local mean time.
log, logarithm, logarithmic.
log$_e$, natural logarithm (to the base e).
log$_{10}$, common logarithm (to the base 10).
long., longitude.
LOP, line of position.
LST, local sidereal time.
LW, low water.
M, celestial body; meridian (upper branch); magnetic (direction); meridional parts; nautical mile, miles.
m, meridian (lower branch); meridional difference $(M_1 \sim M_2)$; meter, meters; statute mile, miles.
mag., magnetic; magnitude.
MB, magnetic bearing.
mb, millibar, millibars.
MC, magnetic course.
mc, megacycle, megacycles; megacycles per second.
Mer. Pass., meridian passage.
MF, medium frequency.
MH, magnetic heading.
MHHW, mean higher high water.
MHW, mean high water.
MHWN, mean high water neaps.
MHWS, mean high water springs.
MHz, megahertz.
mi., mile, miles.
mid, middle.
min., minute, minutes.
MLLW, mean lower low water.
MLW, mean low water.
MLWN, mean low water neaps.
MLWS, mean low water springs.
mm, millimeter.
mo., month.
mos., months.
mph, miles (statute) per hour.
MPP, most probable position.
ms, millisecond, milliseconds.
MSL, mean sea level.
MZn, magnetic azimuth.

N, north.
n, natural (trigonometric function).
Na, nadir.
NASA, National Aeronautics and Space Administration.
NAVSAT, Navy Navigation Satellite System.
NBS, National Bureau of Standards.
NLT, not less than (used with danger bearing).
NM, nautical mile, miles.
n. mi., nautical mile, miles.
NMT, not more than (used with danger bearing).
NNSS, Navy Navigation Satellite System.
NOAA, National Oceanic and Atmospheric Administration.
NOS, National Ocean Survey.
OTSR, Optimum Track Ship Routing.
P, atmospheric pressure; parallax; planet; pole.
p, departure, polar distance.
PC, personal correction.
PCA, polar cap absorption.
PCD, polar cap disturbance.
pgc, per gyrocompass.
P in A, parallax in altitude.
PM, pulse modulation.
PM, post meridian (after noon).
Pn, north pole; north celestial pole.
PPC, predicted propagation correction.
PPI, plan position indicator.
PRR, pulse repetition rate.
Ps, south pole; south celestial pole.
psc, per standard compass.
p stg c, per steering compass.
Pub., publication.
PV, prime vertical.
Q, Polaris correction (*Air Almanac*).
QQ', celestial equator.
R, Rankine (temperature); refraction.
RA, right ascension.
rad, radian, radians.
RB, relative bearing.
R Bn, radiobeacon.
RDF, radio direction finder.
rev., reversed.
RF, radio frequency.
R Fix, running fix.
RMS, root mean square.
RSS, root sum square.

RZn, relative azimuth.

S, sea-air temperature difference correction (altitude); slow; south; set; speed.

S$_A$, speed of apparent wind in units of ship's speed.

SAM, system area monitor.

SAR, Search and Rescue.

SD, semidiameter.

sec, secant.

sec., second, seconds.

semidur., semiduration.

SF, Secondary Phase Factor.

SH, ship's head (heading).

SHA, sidereal hour angle.

SHF, super high frequency.

SI, International System of Units.

SID, sudden ionospheric disturbance.

sin, sine.

SINS, Ships Inertial Navigation System.

SMG, speed made good.

SOA, speed of advance.

SOG, speed over ground.

SPA, sudden phase anomoly.

S$_T$, speed of true wind in units of ship's speed.

St M, statute mile, miles.

T, air temperature correction (altitude); table; temperature; time; toward (altitude intercept); true (direction).

t, dry-bulb temperature; elapsed time; meridian angle.

t', wet-bulb temperature.

tab., table.

TAI, International Atomic Time scale.

tan, tangent.

TB, true bearing; turning bearing; air temperature-atmos pheric pressure correction (altitude).

TC, true course.

TcHHW, tropic higher high water.

TcHLW, tropic higher low water.

TcLHW, tropic lower high water.

TcLLW, tropic lower low water.

TD, time difference (Loran-C).

T$_G$, time difference of groundwaves from master and secondary (slave) stations (Loran).

T$_{GS}$, time difference of groundwave from master and skywave from secondary (slave) station (Loran).

TH, true heading.

TMG, track made good.

TOD, time of day (clock).

TR, track.

Tr., transit.

T$_S$, time difference of skywaves from master and secondary (slave) stations (Loran).

T$_{SG}$, time difference of skywave from master and groundwave from secondary (slave) station (Loran).

TZn, true azimuth.

U, upper limb correction for moon (from *Nautical Almanac*).

UHF, ultra high frequency.

UL, upper limb.

UPS, Universal Polar Stereographic.

USWMS, Uniform State Waterway Marking System.

UT, Universal Time.

UTC, Coordinated Universal Time.

UT0, Universal Time 0.

UT1, Universal Time 1.

UT2, Universal Time 2.

UTM, Universal Transverse Mercator.

V, variation; vertex.

v, excess of GHA change from adopted value for 1 hour.

Var., variation.

ver, versine.

VHF, very high frequency.

VLF, very low frequency.

W, west.

WARC, World Administrative Radio Council.

WE, watch error.

WGS, World Geodetic System.

WMO, World Meteorological Organization.

WT, watch time.

X, parallactic angle.

yd., yard.

yds., yards.

yr., year.

yrs., years.

Z, azimuth angle; zenith.

z, zenith distance.

ZD, zone description.

Z Diff., azimuth angle difference.

Zn, azimuth (as distinguished fom azimuth angle).

Zn$_{pgc}$, azimuth per gyrocompass.

ZT, zone time.

Δ, a small increment, or the change in one quantity corresponding to unit change in another.

λ, longitude; wavelength (radiant energy).

σ, standard deviation.

μ, index of refraction.

μS, microsecond.

π, ratio of circumference of circle to diameter $= 3.14159+$.

APPENDIX B

GREEK ALPHABET

A α a	Alpha	N ν — Nu
B β δ	Beta	Ξ ξ — Xi
Γ γ	Gamma	O o — Omicron
Δ δ	Delta	Π π ϖ — Pi
E ϵ	Epsilon	P ρ — Rho
Z ζ	Zeta	Σ σ s — Sigma
H η	Eta	T τ — Tau
Θ θ ϑ	Theta	Υ υ — Upsilon
I ι	Iota	Φ ϕ φ — Phi
K κ	Kappa	X χ — Chi
Λ λ	Lambda	Ψ ψ — Psi
M μ	Mu	Ω ω — Omega

APPENDIX C

SYMBOLS

Positions

◠ Dead reckoning position.
⊙ Fix.
⊡ Estimated position.
   See Note.

△ Symbol used for one set of fixes when simultaneously fixing by two means, e.g. visual and radar; sometimes used for radionavigation fixes.

Mathematical Symbols

+ Plus (addition)
− Minus (subtraction)
± Plus or minus
∼ Difference
∥ Absolute value
· Multiplied by
: Is to; ratio
× Times (multiplication)
÷ Divided by (division)
√ Square root
∠ Angle
∴ Therefore
∵ Because
ⁿ√ nth root
= Equals
≠ Not equal to

≅ Congruent to approximately equal
≡ Identical with
≢ Not identical with
≈ Nearly equal to
> Is greater than
< Is less than
≤ Equal to or less than
≥ Equal to or greater than
≪ Is dominated by
∂ or δ Differential; variation
f Function
∫ Integral sign
Σ Summation of; sum; sigma
→ Approaches limit of
∞ Infinity
⋯ Repeating decimal

Celestial Bodies

⊙ Sun
☾ Moon
☿ Mercury
♀ Venus
⊕ Earth
♂ Mars
♃ Jupiter
♄ Saturn
♅ Uranus
♆ Neptune
♇ Pluto
☆ Star

☆-P Star-planet altitude correction (altitude)
☉☾ Lower limb
⊖☾ Center
☉☾ Upper limb
● New moon
◗ Crescent moon
◑ First quarter
○ Gibbous moon
○ Full moon
○ Gibbous moon
◐ Last quarter
● Crescent moon

Signs of the Zodiac

♈ Aries (vernal equinox)
♉ Taurus
♊ Gemini
♋ Cancer (summer solstice)
♌ Leo
♍ Virgo

♎ Libra (autumnal equinox)
♏ Scorpius
♐ Sagittarius
♑ Capricornus (winter solstice)
♒ Aquarius
♓ Pisces

Miscellaneous Symbols

y	Years	✳	Interpolation impractical
m	Months	°	Degrees
d	Days	′	Minutes of arc
h	Hours	″	Seconds of arc
m	Minutes of time	☌	Conjunction
s	Seconds of time	☍	Opposition
▬	Remains below horizon	☐	Quadrature
☐	Remains above horizon	☊	Ascending node
////	Twilight all night	☋	Descending node

NOTE.—The digits indicating the times of fixes and estimated positions are printed horizontally on the chart or plotting sheet; the digits indicating the times of dead reckoning positions are not printed horizontally. The running fix is the only position indicated on the chart or plotting sheet by both symbol and label (R Fix).

MISCELLANEOUS DATA

Exact relationships shown by asterisk (*). See footnote on page 1125.

Area

1 square inch	=6.4516 square centimeters*
1 square foot	=144 square inches*
	=0.09290304 square meter*
	=0.000022957 acre
1 square yard	=9 square feet*
	=0.83612736 square meter
1 square (statute) mile	=27,878,400 square feet*
	=640 acres*
	=2.589988110336 square kilometers*
1 square centimeter	=0.1550003 square inch
	=0.00107639 square foot
1 square meter	=10.76391 square feet
	=1.19599005 square yards
1 square kilometer	=247.1053815 acres
	=0.38610216 square statute mile
	=0.29155335 square nautical mile

Astronomy

1 mean solar unit	=1.00273791 sidereal units
1 sidereal unit	=0.99726957 mean solar unit
1 microsecond	=0.000001 second*
1 second	=1,000,000 microseconds*
	=0.01666667 minute
	=0.00027778 hour
	=0.00001157 day
1 minute	=60 seconds*
	=0.01666667 hour
	=0.00069444 day
1 hour	=3,600 seconds*
	=60 minutes*
	=0.04166667 day

1 mean solar day $= 24^{h}03^{m}56^{s}.55536$ of mean sidereal time
= 1 rotation of earth with respect to sun (mean)*
= 1.00273791 rotations of earth with respect to vernal equinox (mean)
= 1.0027378118868 rotations of earth with respect to stars (mean)

1 mean sidereal day $= 23^{h}56^{m}04^{s}.09054$ of mean solar time

1 sidereal month $= 27.321661$ days
$= 27^{d}07^{h}43^{m}11^{s}.5$

1 synodical month $= 29.530588$ days
$= 29^{d}12^{h}44^{m}02^{s}.8$

1 tropical (ordinary) year $= 31,556,925.975$ seconds
= 525,948.766 minutes
= 8,765.8128 hours
$= 365^{d}.24219879 - 0^{d}.0000000614(t-1900)$, where t = the year (date)
$= 365^{d}05^{h}48^{m}46^{s} (-) 0^{s}.0053t$

Astronomy—Continued

1 sidereal year $\underline{\hspace{3cm}}$ $= 365\overset{d}{.}25636042 + 0.0000000011(t - 1900)$, where t
$= $ the year (date)
$= 365^d 06^h 09^m 09\overset{s}{.}5 \ (+) \ 0\overset{s}{.}0001t$

1 calendar year (common) $\underline{\hspace{2cm}}$ $= 31,536,000$ seconds*
$= 525\ 600$ minutes*
$= 8,760$ hours*
$= 365$ days*

1 calendar year (leap) $\underline{\hspace{2cm}}$ $= 31,622,400$ seconds*
$= 527,040$ minutes*
$= 8,784$ hours*
$= 366$ days*

1 light-year $\underline{\hspace{3cm}}$ $= 9,460,000,000,000$ kilometers
$= 5,880,000,000,000$ statute miles
$= 5,110,000,000,000$ nautical miles
$= 63,240$ astronomical units
$= 0.3066$ parsecs

1 parsec $\underline{\hspace{3cm}}$ $= 30,860,000,000,000$ kilometers
$= 19,170,000,000,000$ statute miles
$= 16,660,000,000,000$ nautical miles
$= 206,300$ astronomical units
$= 3.262$ light years

1 astronomical unit $\underline{\hspace{2cm}}$ $= 149,600,000$ kilometers
$= 92,960,000$ statute miles
$= 80,780,000$ nautical miles
$= 499\overset{s}{.}012$ light-time
$=$ mean distance, earth to sun

Mean distance, earth to moon $\underline{\hspace{1cm}}$ $= 384,400$ kilometers
$= 238,855$ statute miles
$= 207,559$ nautical miles

Mean distance, earth to sun $\underline{\hspace{1cm}}$ $= 149,600,000$ kilometers
$= 92,957,000$ statute miles
$= 80,780,000$ nautical miles
$= 1$ astronomical unit

Sun's diameter $\underline{\hspace{3cm}}$ $= 1,392,000$ kilometers
$= 865,000$ statute miles
$= 752,000$ nautical miles

Sun's mass $\underline{\hspace{3cm}}$ $= 1,987,000,000,000,000,000,000,000,000,000,000$
grams
$= 2,200,000,000,000,000,000,000,000,000,000$ short tons
$= 2,000,000,000,000,000,000,000,000,000,000$ long tons

Speed of sun relative to neighboring stars $\underline{\hspace{0.5cm}}$ $= 19.4$ kilometers per second
$= 12.1$ statute miles per second
$= 10.5$ nautical miles per second

Orbital speed of earth $\underline{\hspace{2cm}}$ $= 29.8$ kilometers per second
$= 18.5$ statute miles per second
$= 16.1$ nautical miles per second

Obliquity of the ecliptic $\underline{\hspace{2cm}}$ $= 23°27'08\overset{''}{.}26 - 0\overset{''}{.}4684(t - 1900)$, where $t =$ the year (date)

General precession of the equinoxes $\underline{\hspace{1cm}}$ $= 50\overset{''}{.}2564 + 0\overset{''}{.}000222(t - 1900)$ per year, where $t =$ the year (date)

Precession of the equinoxes in right ascension $\underline{\hspace{0.5cm}}$ $= 46\overset{''}{.}0850 + 0\overset{''}{.}000279(t - 1900)$ per year, where $t =$ the year (date)

Precession of the equinoxes in declination $\underline{\hspace{0.5cm}}$ $= 20\overset{''}{.}0468 - 0\overset{''}{.}000085(t - 1900)$ per year, where $t =$ the year (date)

Magnitude ratio $\underline{\hspace{3cm}}$ $= 2.512$
$= \sqrt[5]{100}$*

Charts

Nautical miles per inch   =reciprocal of natural scale÷72,913.39
Statute miles per inch _____ =reciprocal of natural scale÷63,360*
Inches per nautical mile _____ =72,913.39×natural scale
Inches per statute mile _____ =63,360×natural scale*
Natural scale _____ =1:72,913.39×nautical miles per inch
                            =1:63,360×statute miles per inch*

Earth

Acceleration due to gravity (standard) _____ =980.665 centimeters per second per second
                            =32.1740 feet per second per second
Mass-ratio—Sun/Earth _____ =332,958
Mass-ratio—Sun/(Earth & Moon) _____ =**328,912**
Mass-ratio—Earth/Moon _____ =81.30
Mean density _____ =5.517 **grams** per cubic centimeter
Velocity of escape _____ =6.94 statute miles per second
Curvature of surface _____ =0.8 foot per nautical mile

Airy ellipsoid

Equatorial radius (a) _____ =6,377,563.396 meters
                            =3,443.609 nautical miles
Polar radius (b) _____ =6,356,256.91 meters
                            =3,432.104 nautical miles
Mean radius $(2a+b)/3$ _____ =6,370,461.234 meters
                            =3,439.774 nautical miles
Flattening or ellipticity $(f=1-b/a)$ _____ =1/299.325
                            =0.00334085
Eccentricity $(e=(2f-f^2)^{1/2})$ _____ =0.081673374
Eccentricity squared (e^2) _____ =0.00667054

Australian National-South American ellipsoid of 1969

Equatorial radius (a) _____ =6,378,160 meters
                            =3,443.931 nautical miles
Polar radius (b) _____ =6,356,774.719 meters
                            =3,432.384 nautical miles
Mean radius $(2a+b)/3$ _____ =6,371,031.573 meters
                            =3,440.082 nautical miles
Flattening or ellipticity $(f=1-b/a)$ _____ =1/298.25
                            =0.00335289
Eccentricity $(e=(2f-f^2)^{1/2})$ _____ =0.0818202
Eccentricity squared (e^2) _____ =0.00669454

Bessel ellipsoid

Equatorial radius (a) _____ =6,377,397.155 meters
                            =3,443.52 nautical miles
Polar radius (b) _____ =6,356,078.963 meters
                            =**3,432.01 nautical miles**
Mean radius $(2a+b)/3$ _____ =6,370,291.091 meters
                            =3,439.682 nautical miles
Flattening or ellipticity $(f=1-b/a)$ _____ =1/299.1528
                            =0.00334277
Eccentricity $(e=(2f-f^2)^{1/2})$ _____ =0.08169683
Eccentricity squared (e^2) _____ =0.00667437

Clarke ellipsoid of 1866

Equatorial radius (a) _____ =6,378,206.4 meters
                            =3,443.957 nautical miles
Polar radius (b) _____ =6,356,583.8 meters
                            =3,432.281 nautical miles

Earth—Continued

Mean radius $(2a+b)/3$ _ _ _ _ _ _ _ _ _ _ _ _ _ _ _ _ _ = 6,370,998.9 meters
= 3,440.064 nautical miles

Flattening or ellipticity $(f=1-b/a)$ _ _ _ _ _ _ _ = 1/294.98
= 0.00339008

Eccentricity $(e=(2f-f^2)^{1/2})$ _ _ _ _ _ _ _ _ _ _ _ _ = 0.08227185
Eccentricity squared (e^2) _ _ _ _ _ _ _ _ _ _ _ _ _ _ = 0.00676866

Clarke ellipsoid of 1880

Equatorial radius (a) _ _ _ _ _ _ _ _ _ _ _ _ _ _ _ _ _ = 6,378,249.145 meters
= 3,443.98 nautical miles

Polar radius (b) _ = 6,356,514.87 meters
= 3,432.245 nautical miles

Mean radius $(2a+b)/3$ _ _ _ _ _ _ _ _ _ _ _ _ _ _ _ _ = 6,371,004.387 meters
= 3,440.067 nautical miles

Flattening or ellipticity $(f=1-b/a)$ _ _ _ _ _ _ _ _ = 1/293.465
= 0.00340756

Eccentricity $(e=(2f-f^2)^{1/2})$ _ _ _ _ _ _ _ _ _ _ _ = 0.0824834
Eccentricity squared (e^2) _ _ _ _ _ _ _ _ _ _ _ _ _ _ = 0.00680351

Everest ellipsoid

Equatorial radius (a) _ _ _ _ _ _ _ _ _ _ _ _ _ _ _ _ _ = 6,377,276.345 meters
= 3,443.454 nautical miles

Polar radius (b) _ = 6,356,075.413 meters
= 3,432,006 nautical miles

Mean radius $(2a+b)/3$ _ _ _ _ _ _ _ _ _ _ _ _ _ _ _ _ = 6,370,209.37 meters
= 3,439.638 nautical miles

Flattening or ellipticity $(f=1-b/a)$ _ _ _ _ _ _ _ _ = 1/300.8017
= 0.00332445

Eccentricity $(e=(2f-f^2)^{1/2})$ _ _ _ _ _ _ _ _ _ _ _ = 0.08147298
Eccentricity squared (e^2) _ _ _ _ _ _ _ _ _ _ _ _ _ _ = 0.00663785

Fischer ellipsoid of 1960 (Mercury Datum)

Equatorial radius (a) _ _ _ _ _ _ _ _ _ _ _ _ _ _ _ _ _ = 6,378,166 meters
= 3,443.934 nautical miles

Polar radius (b) _ = 6,356,784.284 meters
= 3,432.389 nautical miles

Mean radius $(2a+b)/3$ _ _ _ _ _ _ _ _ _ _ _ _ _ _ _ _ = 6,371,038.761 meters
= 3,440.086 nautical miles

Flattening or ellipticity $(f=1-b/a)$ _ _ _ _ _ _ _ _ = 1/298.3
= 0.00335233

Eccentricity $(e=(2f-f^2)^{1/2})$ _ _ _ _ _ _ _ _ _ _ _ = 0.081813334
Eccentricity squared (e^2) _ _ _ _ _ _ _ _ _ _ _ _ _ _ = 0.00669342

Fischer South Asia ellipsoid of 1960

Equatorial radius (a) _ _ _ _ _ _ _ _ _ _ _ _ _ _ _ _ _ = 6,378,155 meters
= 3,443.928 nautical miles

Polar radius (b) _ = 6,356,773.32 meters
= 3,432.383 nautical miles

Mean radius $(2a+b)/3$ _ _ _ _ _ _ _ _ _ _ _ _ _ _ _ _ = 6,371,027.773 meters
= 3,440.08 nautical miles

Flattening or ellipticity $(f=1-b/a)$ _ _ _ _ _ _ _ _ = 1/298.3
= 0.00335233

Eccentricity $(e=(2f-f^2)^{1/2})$ _ _ _ _ _ _ _ _ _ _ _ = 0.081813334
Eccentricity squared (e^2) _ _ _ _ _ _ _ _ _ _ _ _ _ _ = 0.00669342

Fischer ellipsoid of 1968

Equatorial radius (a) _ _ _ _ _ _ _ _ _ _ _ _ _ _ _ _ _ = 6,378,150 meters
= **3,443.925 nautical miles**

Polar radius (b) _ = 6,356,768.955 meters
= 3,432.381 nautical miles

Earth—Continued

Mean radius $(2a+b)/3$ _____ = 6,371,022.985 meters
                                              = 3,440.077 nautical miles
Flattening or ellipticity $(f=1-b/a)$ _____ = 1/298.3
                                              = 0.00335233
Eccentricity $(e=(2f-f^2)^{1/2})$ _____ = 0.08181333
Eccentricity squared (e^2) _____ = 0.00669342

Hough ellipsoid

Equatorial radius (a) _____ = 6,378,270 meters
                                              = 3,443.99 nautical miles
Polar radius (b) _____ = 6,356,794.343 meters
                                              = 3,432.394 nautical miles
Mean radius $(2a+b)/3$ _____ = 6,371,111.448 meters
                                              = 3,440.125 nautical miles
Flattening or ellipticity $(f=1-b/a)$ _____ = 1/297
                                              = 0.003367003
Eccentricity $(e=(2f-f^2)^{1/2})$ _____ = **0.08199189**
Eccentricity squared (e^2) _____ = 0.00672267

International ellipsoid

Equatorial radius (a) _____ = 6,378,388 meters
                                              = 3,444.054 nautical miles
Polar radius (b) _____ = 6,356,911.946 meters
                                              = 3,432.459 nautical miles
Mean radius $(2a+b)/3$ _____ = 6,371,229.315 meters
                                              = 3,440.19 nautical miles
Flattening or ellipticity $(f=1-b/a)$ _____ = 1/297
                                              = 0.003367003
Eccentricity $(e=(2f-f^2)^{1/2})$ _____ = 0.08199189
Eccentricity squared (e^2) _____ = 0.00672267

International Astronomical Union figure of earth (1968)

Equatorial radius (a) _____ = 6,378,160 meters
                                              = 3,443.931 nautical miles
Polar radius (b) _____ = **6,356,774.719 meters**
                                              = 3,432.384 nautical miles
Mean radius $(2a+b)/3$ _____ = 6,371,031.573 meters
                                              = 3,440.082 nautical miles
Flattening or ellipticity $(f=1-b/a)$ _____ = 1/298.25
                                              = 0.00335289
Eccentricity $(e=(2f-f^2)^{1/2})$ _____ = 0.0818202
Eccentricity squared (e^2) _____ = 0.00669454

Krassovskiy ellipsoid

Equatorial radius (a) _____ = 6,378,245 meters
                                              = **3,443.977 nautical miles**
Polar radius (b) _____ = 6,356,863.019 meters
                                              = 3,432.43 nautical miles
Mean radius $(2a+b)/3$ _____ = 6,371,117.673 meters
                                              = 3,440.128 nautical miles
Flattening or ellipticity $(f=1-b/a)$ _____ = 1/298.3
                                              = 0.00335233
Eccentricity $(e=(2f-f^2)^{1/2})$ _____ = 0.08181333
Eccentricity squared (e^2) _____ = 0.00669342

World Geodetic System (WGS) ellipsoid of 1972

Equatorial radius (a) _____ = 6,378,135 meters
                                              = 3,443.917 nautical miles

Earth—Continued

Polar radius (b) _____ = 6,356,750.52 meters
         = 3,432.371 nautical miles
Mean radius $(2a+b)/3$ _____ = 6,371,006.84 meters
         = 3,440.068 nautical miles
Flattening or ellipticity ($f = 1 - b/a$) _____ = 1/298.26
         = 0.00335278
Eccentricity ($e = (2f - f^2)^{1/2}$) _____ = 0.0818188
Eccentricity squared (e^2) _____ = 0.00669432

Length

1 inch _____ = 25.4 millimeters*
         = 2.54 centimeters*
1 foot (U.S.) _____ = 12 inches*
         = 1 British foot
         = ⅓ yard*
         = 0.3048 meter*
         = ⅙ fathom*
1 foot (U.S. Survey) _____ = 0.30480061 meter
1 yard _____ = 36 inches*
         = 3 feet*
         = 0.9144 meter*
1 fathom _____ = 6 feet*
         = 2 yards*
         = 1.8288 meters*
1 cable _____ = 720 feet*
         = 240 yards*
         = 219.4560 meters*
1 cable (British) _____ = 0.1 nautical mile
1 statute mile _____ = 5,280 feet*
         = 1,760 yards*
         = 1,609.344 meters*
         = 1.609344 kilometers*
         = 0.86897624 nautical mile
1 nautical mile _____ = 6,076.11548556 feet
         = 2,025.37182852 yards
         = 1,852 meters*
         = 1.852 kilometers*
         = 1.150779448 statute miles
1 meter _____ = 100 centimeters*
         = 39.370079 inches
         = 3.28083990 feet
         = 1.09361330 yards
         = 0.54680665 fathom
         = 0.00062137 statute mile
         = 0.00053996 nautical mile
1 kilometer _____ = 3,280.83990 feet
         = 1,093.61330 yards
         = 1,000 meters*
         = 0.62137119 statute mile
         = 0.53995680 nautical mile

Mass

1 ounce _____ = 437.5 grains*
         = 28.349523125 grams*
         = 0.0625 pound*
         = 0.028349523125 kilogram*

Mass — Continued

1 pound	=7,000 grains*
	=16 ounces*
	=0.45359237 kilogram*
1 short ton	=2,000 pounds*
	=907.18474 kilograms*
	=0.90718474 metric ton*
	=0.8928571 long ton
1 long ton	=2,240 pounds*
	=1,016.0469088 kilograms*
	=1.12 short tons*
	=1.0160469088 metric tons*
1 kilogram	=2.204623 pounds
	=0.00110231 short ton
	=0.0009842065 long ton
1 metric ton	=2,204.623 pounds
	=1,000 kilograms*
	=1.102311 short tons
	=0.9842065 long ton

Mathematics

π	=3.14159265358979323846264338327950288841971
π^2	=9.8696044011
$\sqrt{\pi}$	=1.7724538509
Base of Naperian logarithms (e)	=2.718281828459
Modulus of common logarithms ($\log_{10}e$)	=0.4342944819032518
1 radian	=206,264.″80625
	=3,437.′7467707849
	=57.°2957795131
	=57°17′44.″80625
1 circle	=1,296,000″*
	=21,600′*
	=360°*
	=2π radians*
180°	=π radians*
1°	=3600″*
	=60′*
	=0.017453292519943295766 radian
1′	=60″*
	=0.0002908882086657721596 radian
1″	=0.00000484813681109535993 radian
Sine of 1′	=0.00029088820456342460
Sine of 1″	=0.0000048481368110763763

Meteorology

Atmosphere (dry air)

Nitrogen	=78.08%
Oxygen	=20.95%
Argon	= 0.93%
Carbon dioxide	= 0.03%
	99.99%
Neon	= 0.0018%
Helium	= 0.000524%
Krypton	= 0.0001%
Hydrogen	= 0.00005%
Xenon	= 0.0000087%
Ozone	= 0 to 0.000007% (increasing with altitude)
Radon	= 0.000000000000000006% (decreasing with altitude)

Meteorology—Continued

Standard atmospheric pressure at sea level ___ = 1,013.250 dynes per square centimeter*
= 1,033.227 grams per square centimeter
= 1,033.227 centimeters of water
= 1,013.250 millibars*
= 760 millimeters of mercury
= 76 centimeters of mercury
= 33.8985 feet of water
= 29.92126 inches of mercury
= 14.6960 pounds per square inch
= **1.033227 kilograms per square centimeter**
= 1.013250 bars*

Absolute zero_____ = (−) 273°.16 C
= (−) 459°.69 F

Pressure

1 dyne per square centimeter_____ = 0.001 millibar*
= 0.000001 bar*

1 gram per square centimeter_____ = 1 centimeter of water
= 0.980665 millibar*
= 0.07355592 centimeter of mercury
= 0.0289590 inch of mercury
= 0.0142233 pound per square inch
= 0.001 kilogram per square centimeter*
= 0.000967841 atmosphere

1 millibar _____ = 1,000 dynes per square centimeter*
= 1.01971621 grams per square centimeter
= 0.7500617 millimeter of mercury
= **0.03345526 foot of water**
= **0.02952998 inch of mercury**
= 0.01450377 pound per square inch
= 0.001 bar*
= 0.00098692 atmosphere

1 millimeter of mercury_____ = 1.35951 grams per square centimeter
= 1.3332237 millibars
= 0.1 centimeter of mercury*
= 0.04460334 foot of water
= 0.039370079 inch of mercury
= 0.01933677 pound per square inch
= 0.001315790 atmosphere

1 centimeter of mercury_____ = 10 millimeters of mercury*

1 inch of mercury_____ = 34.53155 grams per square centimeter
= 33.86389 millibars
= 25.4 millimeters of mercury*
= 1.132925 feet of water
= 0.4911541 pound per square inch
= 0.03342106 atmosphere

1 centimeter of water_____ = 1 gram per square centimeter
= 0.001 kilogram per square centimeter

1 foot of water_____ = 30.48000 grams per square centimeter
= 29.89067 millibars
= 2.241985 centimeters of mercury
= 0.882671 inch of mercury
= 0.4335275 pound per square inch
= 0.02949980 atmosphere

1 pound per square inch _____ = 68,947.57 dynes per square centimeter
= 70.30696 grams per square centimeter
= 70.30696 centimeters of water

Pressure—Continued

1 pound per square inch_____ = **68.94757 millibars**
$\qquad$ = 51.71493 millimeters of mercury
$\qquad$ = 5.171493 centimeters of mercury
$\qquad$ = 2.306659 feet of water
$\qquad$ = 2.036021 inches of mercury
$\qquad$ = 0.07030696 kilogram per square centimeter
$\qquad$ = 0.06894757 bar
$\qquad$ = 0.06804596 atmosphere

1 kilogram per square centimeter_____ = 1,000 grams per square centimeter*
$\qquad$ = 1,000 centimeters of water

1 bar_____ = 1,000,000 dynes per square centimeter*
$\qquad$ = 1,000 millibars*

Speed

1 foot per minute _____ = 0.01666667 foot per second
$\qquad$ = 0.00508 meter per second*

1 yard per minute_____ = 3 feet per minute*
$\qquad$ = 0.05 foot per second*
$\qquad$ = 0.03409091 statute mile per hour
$\qquad$ = 0.02962419 knot
$\qquad$ = 0.01524 meter per second*

1 foot per second_____ = **60 feet per minute***
$\qquad$ = 20 yards per minute*
$\qquad$ = 1.09728 kilometers per hour*
$\qquad$ = 0.68181818 statute mile per hour
$\qquad$ = 0.59248380 knot
$\qquad$ = 0.3048 meter per second*

1 statute mile per hour_____ = 88 feet per minute*
$\qquad$ = 29.33333333 yards per minute
$\qquad$ = 1.609344 kilometers per hour*
$\qquad$ = **1.46666667 feet per second**
$\qquad$ = 0.86897624 knot
$\qquad$ = 0.44704 meter per second*

1 knot_____ = 101.26859143 feet per minute
$\qquad$ = 33.75619714 yards per minute
$\qquad$ = 1.852 kilometers per hour*
$\qquad$ = 1.68780986 feet per second
$\qquad$ = 1.15077945 statute miles per hour
$\qquad$ = 0.51444444 meter per second

1 kilometer per hour_____ = **0.62137119 statute mile per hour**
$\qquad$ = 0.53995680 knot

1 meter per second_____ = **196.85039340 feet per minute**
$\qquad$ = 65.6167978 yards per minute
$\qquad$ = 3.6 kilometers per hour*
$\qquad$ = 3.28083990 feet per second
$\qquad$ = 2.23693632 statute miles per hour
$\qquad$ = 1.94384449 knots

Light in vacuo_____ = 299,792.5 kilometers per second
$\qquad$ = 186,282 statute miles per second
$\qquad$ = 161,875 nautical miles per second
$\qquad$ = 983.570 feet per microsecond

Light in air_____ = 299,708 kilometers per second
$\qquad$ = 186,230 statute miles per second
$\qquad$ = 161,829 nautical miles per second
$\qquad$ = **983.294 feet per microsecond**

Speed—Continued

Sound in dry air at 59°F or 15°C and standard = 1,116.45 feet per second
sea level pressure

= 761.22 statute miles per hour
= 661.48 knots
= 340.29 meters per second

Sound in 3.485 percent saltwater at 60°F_____ = **4,945.37 feet per second**
= **3,371.85 statute miles per hour**
= 2,930.05 knots
= 1,507.35 meters per second

Volume

1 cubic inch_____ = 16.387064 cubic centimeters*
= 0.016387064 liter*
= 0.004329004 gallon

1 cubic foot_____ = 1,728 cubic inches*
= 28.316846592 liters*
= 7.480519 U.S. gallons
= 6.228822 imperial (British) gallons
= 0.028316846592 cubic meter*

1 cubic yard_____ = 46,656 cubic inches*
= 764.554857984 liters*
= 201.974026 U.S. gallons
= 168.1782 imperial (British) gallons
= 27 cubic feet*
= 0.764554857984 cubic meter*

1 milliliter_____ = 0.06102374 cubic inch
= 0.0002641721 U.S. gallon
= 0.00021997 imperial (British) gallon

1 cubic meter_____ = 264.172035 U.S. gallons
= 219.96878 imperial (British) gallons
= 35.31467 cubic feet
= 1.307951 cubic yards

1 quart (U.S.)_____ = 57.75 cubic inches*
= 32 fluid ounces*
= 2 pints*
= 0.9463529 liter
= 0.25 gallon*

1 gallon (U.S.)_____ = 3,785.412 milliliters
= 231 cubic inches*
= 0.1336806 cubic foot
= 4 quarts*
= 3.785412 liters
= 0.8326725 imperial (British) gallon

1 liter_____ = 1,000 milliliters
= 61.02374 cubic inches
= **1.056688 quarts**
= 0.2641721 gallon

1 register ton_____ = 100 cubic feet*
= 2.8316846592 cubic meters*

1 measurement ton_____ = 40 cubic feet*
= 1 freight ton*

1 freight ton_____ = 40 cubic feet*
= 1 measurement ton*

Volume-mass

1 cubic foot of seawater _____ = 64 pounds

Volume-Mass – Continued

1 cubic foot of freshwater_____ = 62.428 pounds at temperature of maximum density (4°C = 39°2F)

1 cubic foot of ice_____ = 56 pounds

1 displacement ton_____ = 35 cubic feet of seawater*

= 1 long ton

Vessel Tonnage

The several kinds of *vessel tonnage* are as follows:

Gross tonnage, or *gross register tonnage*, is the total cubical capacity of a ship expressed in *register* tons of 100 cubic feet, or 2.83 cubic meters, less such space as hatchways, bakeries, galleys, etc., as are exempted from measurement by different governments. There is some lack of uniformity in the gross tonnages as given by different nations on account of lack of agreement on the spaces that are to be exempted.

Official merchant marine statistics of most countries are published in terms of the *gross register tonnage*. Press references to *ship tonnage* are usually to the *gross tonnage*.

The *net tonnage*, or *net register tonnage*, is the *gross tonnage* less the different spaces specified by maritime nations in their measurement rules and laws. The spaces that are deducted are those totally unavailable for carrying cargo, such as the engine room, coal bunkers, crews quarters, chart and instrument room, etc.

The *net tonnage* is used in computing the amount of cargo that can be loaded on a ship. It is used as the basis for wharfage and other similar charges.

The *register under-deck tonnage* is the cubical capacity of a ship under her tonnage deck expressed in register tons. In a vessel having more than one deck the tonnage deck is the second from the keel.

There are several variations of *displacement tonnage*.

The *dead weight tonnage* is the difference between the "loaded" and "light" *displacement tonnages* of a vessel. It is espressed in terms of the long ton of 2,240 pounds, or the metric ton of 2,204.6 pounds, and is the weight of fuel, passengers, and cargo that a vessel can carry when loaded to her maximum draft.

The second variety of tonnage, *cargo tonnage*, refers to the weight of the particular items making up the cargo. In overseas traffic it is usually expressed in long tons of 2,240 pounds or metric tons of 2,204.6 pounds. The short ton is only occassionally used. The *cargo tonnage* is therefore very distinct from *vessel tonnage*.

NOTE:—All values in this appendix are based on the following relationships:

1 inch = 2.54 centimeters*

1 yard = 0.9144 meter*

1 pound (avoirdupois) = 0.45359237 kilogram*

1 nautical mile = 1852 meters*

Absolute zero = (−)273°16C = (−)459°69F.

Decibel Scale

The **decibel** (**dB**) is 10 times the logarithm to the base 10 of the ratio of two amounts of power. The decibel scale is used to express conveniently the ratio between widely different powers.

The ratio between one power P_1 and a second power P_2 is expressed in dB's as:

$$10 \log_{10} \left(\frac{P_1}{P_2} \right).$$

Thus if P_1 is 1,000 times P_2, their ratio is expressed as

$$10 \log_{10} (10) = 10 \times 3 = 30 \text{ dB}.$$

If P_2 is 1,000 times P_1, their ratio is expressed as

$$10 \log (10) = 10 \times (-3) = -30 \text{ dB}.$$

Power ratio	dB
1	0
2	3
4	6
10	10
100	20
1, 000	30
10, 000	40
100, 000	50
1, 000, 000	60

Prefixes to Form Decimal Multiples and Sub-Multiples of International System of Units (SI)

Multiplying factor		Prefix	Symbol
1 000 000 000 000	$=10^{12}$	tera	T
1 000 000 000	$=10^{9}$	giga	G
1 000 000	$=10^{6}$	mega	M
1 000	$=10^{3}$	kilo	k
100	$=10^{2}$	hecto	h
10	$=10^{1}$	deka	da
0. 1	$=10^{-1}$	deci	d
0. 01	$=10^{-2}$	centi	c
0. 001	$=10^{-3}$	milli	m
0. 000 001	$=10^{-6}$	micro	μ
0. 000 000 001	$=10^{-9}$	nano	n
0. 000 000 000 001	$=10^{-12}$	pico	p
0. 000 000 000 000 001	$=10^{-15}$	femto	f
0. 000 000 000 000 000 001	$=10^{-18}$	atto	a

APPENDIX E

NAVIGATIONAL COORDINATES

Coordinate	Symbol	Measured from	Measured along	Direction	Measured to	Units	Precision	Maximum value	Labels
latitude	L, lat.	equator	meridian	N, S	parallel	°,′	0′.1	90°	N, S
colatitude	colat.	poles	meridian	S, N	parallel	°,′	0′.1	90°	—
longitude	λ, long.	prime meridian	parallel	E, W	local meridian	°,′	0′.1	180°	E, W
declination	d, dec.	celestial equator	hour circle	N, S	parallel of declination	°,′	0′.1	90°	N, S
polar distance	p	elevated pole	hour circle	S, N	parallel of declination	°,′	0′.1	180°	—
altitude	h	horizon	vertical circle	up	parallel of altitude	°,′	0′.1	90°*	—
zenith distance	z	zenith	vertical circle	down	parallel of altitude	°,′	0′.1	180°	—
azimuth	Zn	north	horizon	E	vertical circle	°	0°.1	360°	—
azimuth angle	Z	north, south	horizon	E, W	vertical circle	°	0°.1	180° or 90°	N, S ... E, W
amplitude	A	east, west	horizon	N, S	body	°	0°.1	90°	E, W ... N, S
Greenwich hour angle	GHA	Greenwich celestial meridian	parallel of declination	W	hour circle	°,′	0′.1	360°	—
local hour angle	LHA	local celestial meridian	parallel of declination	W	hour circle	°,′	0′.1	360°	—
meridian angle	t	local celestial meridian	parallel of declination	E, W	hour circle	°,′	0′.1	180°	E, W
sidereal hour angle	SHA	hour circle of vernal equinox	parallel of declination	W	hour circle	°,′	0′.1	360°	—
right ascension	RA	hour circle of vernal equinox	parallel of declination	E	hour circle	h, m, s	1s	24h	—
Greenwich mean time	GMT	lower branch Greenwich celestial meridian	parallel of declination	W	hour circle mean sun	h, m, s	1s	24h	—
local mean time	LMT	lower branch local celestial meridian	parallel of declination	W	hour circle mean sun	h, m, s	1s	24h	—
zone time	ZT	lower branch zone celestial meridian	parallel of declination	W	hour circle mean sun	h, m, s	1s	24h	—
Greenwich apparent time	GAT	lower branch Greenwich celestial meridian	parallel of declination	W	hour circle apparent sun	h, m, s	1s	24h	—
local apparent time	LAT	lower branch local celestial meridian	parallel of declination	W	hour circle apparent sun	h, m, s	1s	24h	—
Greenwich sidereal time	GST	Greenwich celestial meridian	parallel of declination	W	hour circle vernal equinox	h, m, s	1s	24h	—
local sidereal time	LST	local celestial meridian	parallel of declination	W	hour circle vernal equinox	h, m, s	1s	24h	—

*When measured from celestial horizon.

APPENDIX F

EXTRACTS FROM *NAUTICAL ALMANAC*

ALTITUDE CORRECTION TABLES 10°-90°—SUN, STARS, PLANETS

SUN — OCT.–MAR. / APR.–SEPT.

App. Alt.	Lower Limb	Upper Limb	App. Alt.	Lower Limb	Upper Limb
9 34	+10·8	−21·5	9 39	+10·6	−21·2
9 45	+10·9	−21·4	9 51	+10·7	−21·1
9 56	+11·0	−21·3	10 03	+10·8	−21·0
10 08	+11·1	−21·2	10 15	+10·9	−20·9
10 21	+11·2	−21·1	10 27	+11·0	−20·8
10 34	+11·3	−21·0	10 40	+11·1	−20·7
10 47	+11·4	−20·9	10 54	+11·2	−20·6
11 01	+11·5	−20·8	11 08	+11·3	−20·5
11 15	+11·6	−20·7	11 23	+11·4	−20·4
11 30	+11·7	−20·6	11 38	+11·5	−20·3
11 46	+11·8	−20·5	11 54	+11·6	−20·2
12 02	+11·9	−20·4	12 10	+11·7	−20·1
12 19	+12·0	−20·3	12 28	+11·8	−20·0
12 37	+12·1	−20·2	12 46	+11·9	−19·9
12 55	+12·2	−20·1	13 05	+12·0	−19·8
13 14	+12·3	−20·0	13 24	+12·1	−19·7
13 35	+12·4	−19·9	13 45	+12·2	−19·6
13 56	+12·5	−19·8	14 07	+12·3	−19·5
14 18	+12·6	−19·7	14 30	+12·4	−19·4
14 42	+12·7	−19·6	14 54	+12·5	−19·3
15 06	+12·8	−19·5	15 19	+12·6	−19·2
15 32	+12·9	−19·4	15 46	+12·7	−19·1
15 59	+13·0	−19·3	16 14	+12·8	−19·0
16 28	+13·1	−19·2	16 44	+12·9	−18·9
16 59	+13·2	−19·1	17 15	+13·0	−18·8
17 32	+13·3	−19·0	17 48	+13·1	−18·7
18 06	+13·4	−18·9	18 24	+13·2	−18·6
18 42	+13·5	−18·8	19 01	+13·3	−18·5
19 21	+13·6	−18·7	19 42	+13·4	−18·4
20 03	+13·7	−18·6	20 25	+13·5	−18·3
20 48	+13·8	−18·5	21 11	+13·6	−18·2
21 35	+13·9	−18·4	22 00	+13·7	−18·1
22 26	+14·0	−18·3	22 54	+13·8	−18·0
23 22	+14·1	−18·2	23 51	+13·9	−17·9
24 21	+14·2	−18·1	24 53	+14·0	−17·8
25 26	+14·3	−18·0	26 00	+14·1	−17·7
26 36	+14·4	−17·9	27 13	+14·2	−17·6
27 52	+14·5	−17·8	28 33	+14·3	−17·5
29 15	+14·6	−17·7	30 00	+14·4	−17·4
30 46	+14·7	−17·6	31 35	+14·5	−17·3
32 26	+14·8	−17·5	33 20	+14·6	−17·2
34 17	+14·9	−17·4	35 17	+14·7	−17·1
36 20	+15·0	−17·3	37 26	+14·8	−17·0
38 36	+15·1	−17·2	39 50	+14·9	−16·9
41 08	+15·2	−17·1	42 31	+15·0	−16·8
43 59	+15·3	−17·0	45 31	+15·1	−16·7
47 10	+15·4	−16·9	48 55	+15·2	−16·6
50 46	+15·5	−16·8	52 44	+15·3	−16·5
54 49	+15·6	−16·7	57 02	+15·4	−16·4
59 23	+15·7	−16·6	61 51	+15·5	−16·3
64 30	+15·8	−16·5	67 17	+15·6	−16·2
70 12	+15·9	−16·4	73 16	+15·7	−16·1
76 26	+16·0	−16·3	79 43	+15·8	−16·0
83 05	+16·1	−16·2	86 32	+15·9	−15·9
90 00			90 00		

STARS AND PLANETS

App. Alt.	Corrn
9 56	−5·3
10 08	−5·2
10 20	−5·1
10 33	−5·0
10 46	−4·9
11 00	−4·8
11 14	−4·7
11 29	−4·6
11 45	−4·5
12 01	−4·4
12 18	−4·3
12 35	−4·2
12 54	−4·1
13 13	−4·0
13 33	−3·9
13 54	−3·8
14 16	−3·7
14 40	−3·6
15 04	−3·5
15 30	−3·4
15 57	−3·3
16 26	−3·2
16 56	−3·1
17 28	−3·0
18 02	−2·9
18 38	−2·8
19 17	−2·7
19 58	−2·6
20 42	−2·5
21 28	−2·4
22 19	−2·3
23 13	−2·2
24 11	−2·1
25 14	−2·0
26 22	−1·9
27 36	−1·8
28 56	−1·7
30 24	−1·6
32 00	−1·5
33 45	−1·4
35 40	−1·3
37 48	−1·3
40 08	−1·1
42 44	−1·0
45 36	−0·9
48 47	−0·8
52 18	−0·7
56 11	−0·6
60 28	−0·5
65 08	−0·4
70 11	−0·3
75 34	−0·2
81 13	−0·1
87 03	0·0
90 00	

Additional Corrn — 1975

VENUS

Jan. 1—June 7
App. Alt.	Corrn
0 42	+0·1

June 8—July 21
| 0 46 | +0·3 |

July 22—Aug. 6
| 0 11 | +0·4 |
| 41 | +0·5 |

Aug. 7—Aug. 15
0 6	+0·5
20	+0·6
31	+0·7

Aug. 16—Sept. 10
0 4	+0·6
12	+0·7
22	+0·8

Sept. 11—Sept. 19
0 6	+0·5
20	+0·6
31	+0·7

Sept. 20—Oct. 5
| 0 11 | +0·4 |
| 41 | +0·5 |

Oct. 6—Nov. 22
| 0 46 | +0·3 |

Nov. 23—Dec. 31
| 0 42 | +0·1 |

MARS

Jan. 1—Sept. 8
| 0 60 | +0·1 |

Sept. 9—Nov. 22
| 0 41 | +0·2 |
| 75 | +0·1 |

Nov. 23—Dec. 31
0 34	+0·3
60	+0·2
80	+0·1

DIP

Ht. of Eye (m)	Corrn	Ht. of Eye (ft)	Ht. of Eye (m)	Corrn
2·4	−2·8	8·0	1·0	− 1·8
2·6	−2·9	8·6	1·5	− 2·2
2·8	−3·0	9·2	2·0	− 2·5
3·0	−3·1	9·8	2·5	− 2·8
3·2	−3·2	10·5	3·0	− 3·0
3·4	−3·3	11·2	See table →	
3·6	−3·4	11·9		
3·8	−3·5	12·6	**m**	
4·0	−3·6	13·3	20	− 7·9
4·3	−3·7	14·1	22	− 8·3
4·5	−3·8	14·9	24	− 8·6
4·7	−3·9	15·7	26	− 9·0
5·0	−4·0	16·5	28	− 9·3
5·2	−4·1	17·4		
5·5	−4·2	18·3	30	− 9·6
5·8	−4·3	19·1	32	−10·0
6·1	−4·4	20·1	34	−10·3
6·3	−4·5	21·0	36	−10·6
6·6	−4·6	22·0	38	−10·8
6·9	−4·7	22·9		
7·2	−4·8	23·9	40	−11·1
7·5	−4·9	24·9	42	−11·4
7·9	−5·0	26·0	44	−11·7
8·2	−5·1	27·1	46	−11·9
8·5	−5·2	28·1	48	−12·2
8·8	−5·3	29·2	**ft.**	
9·2	−5·4	30·4	2	− 1·4
9·5	−5·5	31·5	4	− 1·9
9·9	−5·6	32·7	6	− 2·4
10·3	−5·7	33·9	8	− 2·7
10·6	−5·8	35·1	10	− 3·1
11·0	−5·9	36·3	See table →	
11·4	−6·0	37·6		
11·8	−6·1	38·9	**ft.**	
12·2	−6·2	40·1	70	− 8·1
12·6	−6·3	41·5	75	− 8·4
13·0	−6·4	42·8	80	− 8·7
13·4	−6·5	44·2	85	− 8·9
13·8	−6·6	45·5	90	− 9·2
14·2	−6·7	46·9	95	− 9·5
14·7	−6·8	48·4	100	− 9·7
15·1	−6·9	49·8	105	− 9·9
15·5	−7·0	51·3	110	−10·2
16·0	−7·1	52·8	115	−10·4
16·5	−7·2	54·3	120	−10·6
16·9	−7·3	55·8	125	−10·8
17·4	−7·4	57·4	130	−11·1
17·9	−7·5	58·9	135	−11·3
18·4	−7·6	60·5	140	−11·5
18·8	−7·7	62·1	145	−11·7
19·3	−7·8	63·8	150	−11·9
19·8	−7·9	65·4	155	−12·1
20·4	−8·0	67·1		
20·9	−8·1	68·8		
21·4		70·5		

App. Alt. = Apparent altitude = Sextant altitude corrected for index error and dip.
For daylight observations of Venus, see page 260.

ALTITUDE CORRECTION TABLES 0°–10°—SUN, STARS, PLANETS A3

App. Alt.	OCT.–MAR. SUN Lower Limb	Upper Limb	APR.–SEPT. Lower Limb	Upper Limb	STARS PLANETS
° ′	′	′	′	′	′
0 00	−18·2	−50·5	−18·4	−50·2	−34·5
03	17·5	49·8	17·8	49·6	33·8
06	16·9	49·2	17·1	48·9	33·2
09	16·3	48·6	16·5	48·3	32·6
12	15·7	48·0	15·9	47·7	32·0
15	15·1	47·4	15·3	47·1	31·4
0 18	−14·5	−46·8	−14·8	−46·6	−30·8
21	14·0	46·3	14·2	46·0	30·3
24	13·5	45·8	13·7	45·5	29·8
27	12·9	45·2	13·2	45·0	29·2
30	12·4	44·7	12·7	44·5	28·7
33	11·9	44·2	12·2	44·0	28·2
0 36	−11·5	−43·8	−11·7	−43·5	−27·8
39	11·0	43·3	11·2	43·0	27·3
42	10·5	42·8	10·8	42·6	26·8
45	10·1	42·4	10·3	42·1	26·4
48	9·6	41·9	9·9	41·7	25·9
51	9·2	41·5	9·5	41·3	25·5
0 54	−8·8	−41·1	−9·1	−40·9	−25·1
0 57	8·4	40·7	8·7	40·5	24·7
1 00	8·0	40·3	8·3	40·1	24·3
03	7·7	40·0	7·9	39·7	24·0
06	7·3	39·6	7·5	39·3	23·6
09	6·9	39·2	7·2	39·0	23·2
1 12	−6·6	−38·9	−6·8	−38·6	−22·9
15	6·2	38·5	6·5	38·3	22·5
18	5·9	38·2	6·2	38·0	22·2
21	5·6	37·9	5·8	37·6	21·9
24	5·3	37·6	5·5	37·3	21·6
27	4·9	37·2	5·2	37·0	21·2
1 30	−4·6	−36·9	−4·9	−36·7	−20·9
35	4·2	36·5	4·4	36·2	20·5
40	3·7	36·0	4·0	35·8	20·0
45	3·2	35·5	3·5	35·3	19·5
50	2·8	35·1	3·1	34·9	19·1
1 55	2·4	34·7	2·6	34·4	18·7
2 00	−2·0	−34·3	−2·2	−34·0	−18·3
05	1·6	33·9	1·8	33·6	17·9
10	1·2	33·5	1·5	33·3	17·5
15	0·9	33·2	1·1	32·9	17·2
20	0·5	32·8	0·8	32·6	16·8
25	−0·2	32·5	0·4	32·2	16·5
2 30	+0·2	−32·1	−0·1	−31·9	−16·1
35	0·5	31·8	+0·2	31·6	15·8
40	0·8	31·5	0·5	31·3	15·5
45	1·1	31·2	0·8	31·0	15·2
50	1·4	30·9	1·1	30·7	14·9
2 55	1·6	30·7	1·4	30·4	14·7
3 00	+1·9	−30·4	+1·7	−30·1	−14·4
05	2·2	30·1	1·9	29·9	14·1
10	2·4	29·9	2·1	29·7	13·9
15	2·6	29·7	2·4	29·4	13·7
20	2·9	29·4	2·6	29·2	13·4
25	3·1	29·2	2·9	28·9	13·2
3 30	+3·3	−29·0	+3·1	−28·7	−13·0

App. Alt.	OCT.–MAR. SUN Lower Limb	Upper Limb	APR.–SEPT. Lower Limb	Upper Limb	STARS PLANETS
° ′	′	′	′	′	′
3 30	+3·3	−29·0	+3·1	−28·7	−13·0
35	3·6	28·7	3·3	28·5	12·7
40	3·8	28·5	3·5	28·3	12·5
45	4·0	28·3	3·7	28·1	12·3
50	4·2	28·1	3·9	27·9	12·1
3 55	4·4	27·9	4·1	27·7	11·9
4 00	+4·5	−27·8	+4·3	−27·5	−11·8
05	4·7	27·6	4·5	27·3	11·6
10	4·9	27·4	4·6	27·2	11·4
15	5·1	27·2	4·8	27·0	11·2
20	5·2	27·1	5·0	26·8	11·1
25	5·4	26·9	5·1	26·7	10·9
4 30	+5·6	−26·7	+5·3	−26·5	−10·7
35	5·7	26·6	5·5	26·3	10·6
40	5·9	26·4	5·6	26·2	10·4
45	6·0	26·3	5·8	26·0	10·3
50	6·2	26·1	5·9	25·9	10·1
4 55	6·3	26·0	6·0	25·8	10·0
5 00	+6·4	−25·9	+6·2	−25·6	−9·9
05	6·6	25·7	6·3	25·5	9·7
10	6·7	25·6	6·4	25·4	9·6
15	6·8	25·5	6·6	25·2	9·5
20	6·9	25·4	6·7	25·1	9·4
25	7·1	25·2	6·8	25·0	9·2
5 30	+7·2	−25·1	+6·9	−24·9	−9·1
35	7·3	25·0	7·0	24·8	9·0
40	7·4	24·9	7·2	24·6	8·9
45	7·5	24·8	7·3	24·5	8·8
50	7·6	24·7	7·4	24·4	8·7
5 55	7·7	24·6	7·5	24·3	8·6
6 00	+7·8	−24·5	+7·6	−24·2	−8·5
10	8·0	24·3	7·8	24·0	8·3
20	8·2	24·1	8·0	23·8	8·1
30	8·4	23·9	8·1	23·7	7·9
40	8·6	23·7	8·3	23·5	7·7
6 50	8·7	23·6	8·5	23·3	7·6
7 00	+8·9	−23·4	+8·6	−23·2	−7·4
10	9·1	23·2	8·8	23·0	7·2
20	9·2	23·1	9·0	22·8	7·1
30	9·3	23·0	9·1	22·7	7·0
40	9·5	22·8	9·2	22·6	6·8
7 50	9·6	22·7	9·4	22·4	6·7
8 00	+9·7	−22·6	+9·5	−22·3	−6·6
10	9·9	22·4	9·6	22·2	6·4
20	10·0	22·3	9·7	22·1	6·3
30	10·1	22·2	9·8	22·0	6·2
40	10·2	22·1	10·0	21·8	6·1
8 50	10·3	22·0	10·1	21·7	6·0
9 00	+10·4	−21·9	+10·2	−21·6	−5·9
10	10·5	21·8	10·3	21·5	5·8
20	10·6	21·7	10·4	21·4	5·7
30	10·7	21·6	10·5	21·3	5·6
40	10·8	21·5	10·6	21·2	5·5
9 50	10·9	21·4	10·6	21·2	5·4
10 00	+11·0	−21·3	+10·7	−21·1	−5·3

Additional corrections for temperature and pressure are given on the following page.

For bubble sextant observations ignore dip and use the star corrections for Sun, planets, and stars.

ALTITUDE CORRECTION TABLES—ADDITIONAL CORRECTIONS

ADDITIONAL REFRACTION CORRECTIONS FOR NON-STANDARD CONDITIONS

App. Alt.	A	B	C	D	E	F	G	H	J	K	L	M	N	App. Alt.
0 00	−6·9	−5·7	−4·6	−3·4	−2·3	−1·1	0·0	+1·1	+2·3	+3·4	+4·6	+5·7	+6·9	0 00
0 30	5·2	4·4	3·5	2·6	1·7	0·9	0·0	0·9	1·7	2·6	3·5	4·4	5·2	0 30
1 00	4·3	3·5	2·8	2·1	1·4	0·7	0·0	0·7	1·4	2·1	2·8	3·5	4·3	1 00
1 30	3·5	2·9	2·4	1·8	1·2	0·6	0·0	0·6	1·2	1·8	2·4	2·9	3·5	1 30
2 00	3·0	2·5	2·0	1·5	1·0	0·5	0·0	0·5	1·0	1·5	2·0	2·5	3·0	2 00
2 30	−2·5	−2·1	−1·6	−1·2	−0·8	−0·4	0·0	+0·4	+0·8	+1·2	+1·6	+2·1	+2·5	2 30
3 00	2·2	1·8	1·5	1·1	0·7	0·4	0·0	0·4	0·7	1·1	1·5	1·8	2·2	3 00
3 30	2·0	1·6	1·3	1·0	0·7	0·3	0·0	0·3	0·7	1·0	1·3	1·6	2·0	3 30
4 00	1·8	1·5	1·2	0·9	0·6	0·3	0·0	0·3	0·6	0·9	1·2	1·5	1·8	4 00
4 30	1·6	1·4	1·1	0·8	0·5	0·3	0·0	0·3	0·5	0·8	1·1	1·4	1·6	4 30
5 00	−1·5	−1·3	−1·0	−0·8	−0·5	−0·2	0·0	+0·2	+0·5	+0·8	+1·0	+1·3	+1·5	5 00
6	1·3	1·1	0·9	0·6	0·4	0·2	0·0	0·2	0·4	0·6	0·9	1·1	1·3	6
7	1·1	0·9	0·7	0·6	0·4	0·2	0·0	0·2	0·4	0·6	0·7	0·9	1·1	7
8	1·0	0·8	0·7	0·5	0·3	0·2	0·0	0·2	0·3	0·5	0·7	0·8	1·0	8
9	0·9	0·7	0·6	0·4	0·3	0·1	0·0	0·1	0·3	0·4	0·6	0·7	0·9	9
10 00	−0·8	−0·7	−0·5	−0·4	−0·3	−0·1	0·0	+0·1	+0·3	+0·4	+0·5	+0·7	+0·8	10 00
12	0·7	0·6	0·5	0·3	0·2	0·1	0·0	0·1	0·2	0·3	0·5	0·6	0·7	12
14	0·6	0·5	0·4	0·3	0·2	0·1	0·0	0·1	0·2	0·3	0·4	0·5	0·6	14
16	0·5	0·4	0·3	0·3	0·2	0·1	0·0	0·1	0·2	0·3	0·3	0·4	0·5	16
18	0·4	0·4	0·3	0·2	0·2	0·1	0·0	0·1	0·2	0·2	0·3	0·4	0·4	18
20 00	−0·4	−0·3	−0·3	−0·2	−0·1	−0·1	0·0	+0·1	+0·1	+0·2	+0·3	+0·3	+0·4	20 00
25	0·3	0·3	0·2	0·2	0·1	−0·1	0·0	+0·1	0·1	0·2	0·2	0·3	0·3	25
30	0·3	0·2	0·2	0·1	0·1	0·0	0·0	0·0	0·1	0·1	0·2	0·2	0·3	30
35	0·2	0·2	0·1	0·1	0·1	0·0	0·0	0·0	0·1	0·1	0·1	0·2	0·2	35
40	0·2	0·1	0·1	0·1	−0·1	0·0	0·0	0·0	+0·1	0·1	0·1	0·1	0·2	40
50 00	−0·1	−0·1	−0·1	−0·1	0·0	0·0	0·0	0·0	0·0	+0·1	+0·1	+0·1	+0·1	50 00

The graph is entered with arguments temperature and pressure to find a zone letter; using as arguments this zone letter and apparent altitude (sextant altitude corrected for dip), a correction is taken from the table. This correction is to be applied to the sextant altitude in addition to the corrections for standard conditions (for the Sun, planets and stars from the inside front cover and for the Moon from the inside back cover).

INDEX TO SELECTED STARS, 1975

Name	No.	Mag.	S.H.A.	Dec.	No.	Name	Mag.	S.H.A.	Dec.
Acamar	7	3·1	316°	S. 40°	1	Alpheratz	2·2	358°	N. 29°
Achernar	5	0·6	336	S. 57	2	Ankaa	2·4	354	S. 42
Acrux	30	1·1	174	S. 63	3	Schedar	2·5	350	N. 56
Adhara	19	1·6	256	S. 29	4	Diphda	2·2	349	S. 18
Aldebaran	10	1·1	291	N. 16	5	Achernar	0·6	336	S. 57
Alioth	32	1·7	167	N. 56	6	Hamal	2·2	329	N. 23
Alkaid	34	1·9	153	N. 49	7	Acamar	3·1	316	S. 40
Al Na'ir	55	2·2	28	S. 47	8	Menkar	2·8	315	N. 4
Alnilam	15	1·8	276	S. 1	9	Mirfak	1·9	309	N. 50
Alphard	25	2·2	218	S. 9	10	Aldebaran	1·1	291	N. 16
Alphecca	41	2·3	127	N. 27	11	Rigel	0·3	282	S. 8
Alpheratz	1	2·2'	358	N. 29	12	Capella	0·2	281	N. 46
Altair	51	0·9	63	N. 9	13	Bellatrix	1·7	279	N. 6
Ankaa	2	2·4	354	S. 42	14	Elnath	1·8	279	N. 29
Antares	42	1·2	113	S. 26	15	Alnilam	1·8	276	S. 1
Arcturus	37	0·2	146	N. 19	16	Betelgeuse	Var.*	272	N. 7
Atria	43	1·9	108	S. 69	17	Canopus	−0·9	264	S. 53
Avior	22	1·7	234	S. 59	18	Sirius	−1·6	259	S. 17
Bellatrix	13	1·7	279	N. 6	19	Adhara	1·6	256	S. 29
Betelgeuse	16	Var.*	272	N. 7	20	Procyon	0·5	245	N. 5
Canopus	17	−0·9	264	S. 53	21	Pollux	1·2	244	N. 28
Capella	12	0·2	281	N. 46	22	Avior	1·7	234	S. 59
Deneb	53	1·3	50	N. 45	23	Suhail	2·2	223	S. 43
Denebola	28	2·2	183	N. 15	24	Miaplacidus	1·8	222	S. 70
Diphda	4	2·2	349	S. 18	25	Alphard	2·2	218	S. 9
Dubhe	27	2·0	194	N. 62	26	Regulus	1·3	208	N. 12
Elnath	14	1·8	279	N. 29	27	Dubhe	2·0	194	N. 62
Eltanin	47	2·4	91	N. 51	28	Denebola	2·2	183	N. 15
Enif	54	2·5	34	N. 10	29	Gienah	2·8	176	S. 17
Fomalhaut	56	1·3	16	S. 30	30	Acrux	1·1	174	S. 63
Gacrux	31	1·6	173	S. 57	31	Gacrux	1·6	173	S. 57
Gienah	29	2·8	176	S. 17	32	Alioth	1·7	167	N. 56
Hadar	35	0·9	149	S. 60	33	Spica	1·2	159	S. 11
Hamal	6	2·2	329	N. 23	34	Alkaid	1·9	153	N. 49
Kaus Australis	48	2·0	84	S. 34	35	Hadar	0·9	149	S. 60
Kochab	40	2·2	137	N. 74	36	Menkent	2·3	149	S. 36
Markab	57	2·6	14	N. 15	37	Arcturus	0·2	146	N. 19
Menkar	8	2·8	315	N. 4	38	Rigil Kentaurus	0·1	141	S. 61
Menkent	36	2·3	149	S. 36	39	Zubenelgenubi	2·9	138	S. 16
Miaplacidus	24	1·8	222	S. 70	40	Kochab	2·2	137	N. 74
Mirfak	9	1·9	309	N. 50	41	Alphecca	2·3	127	N. 27
Nunki	50	2·1	77	S. 26	42	Antares	1·2	113	S. 26
Peacock	52	2·1	54	S. 57	43	Atria	1·9	108	S. 69
Pollux	21	1·2	244	N. 28	44	Sabik	2·6	103	S. 16
Procyon	20	0·5	245	N. 5	45	Shaula	1·7	97	S. 37
Rasalhague	46	2·1	97	N. 13	46	Rasalhague	2·1	97	N. 13
Regulus	26	1·3	208	N. 12	47	Eltanin	2·4	91	N. 51
Rigel	11	0·3	282	S. 8	48	Kaus Australis	2·0	84	S. 34
Rigil Kentaurus	38	0·1	141	S. 61	49	Vega	0·1	81	N. 39
Sabik	44	2·6	103	S. 16	50	Nunki	2·1	77	S. 26
Schedar	3	2·5	350	N. 56	51	Altair	0·9	63	N. 9
Shaula	45	1·7	97	S. 37	52	Peacock	2·1	54	S. 57
Sirius	18	−1·6	259	S. 17	53	Deneb	1·3	50	N. 45
Spica	33	1·2	159	S. 11	54	Enif	2·5	34	N. 10
Suhail	23	2·2	223	S. 43	55	Al Na'ir	2·2	28	S. 47
Vega	49	0·1	81	N. 39	56	Fomalhaut	1·3	16	S. 30
Zubenelgenubi	39	2·9	138	S. 16	57	Markab	2·6	14	N. 15

* 0·1—1·2

1975 MAY 25, 26, 27 (SUN., MON., TUES.)

G.M.T.	ARIES G.H.A.	VENUS −3.8 G.H.A.	Dec.	MARS +1.0 G.H.A.	Dec.	JUPITER −1.7 G.H.A.	Dec.	SATURN +0.4 G.H.A.	Dec.	Name	S.H.A.	Dec.
25 00	241 57.5	133 22.6	N24 57.2	238 47.5	S 0 24.3	227 20.7	N 4 59.3	134 24.1	N22 20.6	Acamar	315 40.4	S40 24.1
01	257 00.0	148 22.1	56.9	253 48.2	23.5	242 22.7	59.5	149 26.2	20.5	Achernar	335 48.4	S57 21.5
02	272 02.4	163 21.6	56.5	268 49.0	22.8	257 24.7	59.7	164 28.4	20.5	Acrux	173 40.9	S62 58.1
03	287 04.9	178 21.1	.. 56.2	283 49.7	.. 22.1	272 26.7	4 59.9	179 30.6	.. 20.5	Adhara	255 35.3	S28 56.5
04	302 07.4	193 20.6	55.8	298 50.5	21.3	287 28.7	5 00.1	194 32.8	20.5	Aldebaran	291 22.5	N16 27.6
05	317 09.8	208 20.1	55.5	313 51.2	20.6	302 30.7	00.3	209 34.9	20.4			
06	332 12.3	223 19.6	N24 55.1	328 52.0	S 0 19.9	317 32.7	N 5 00.4	224 37.1	N22 20.4	Alioth	166 45.3	N56 05.7
07	347 14.7	238 19.1	54.8	343 52.7	19.1	332 34.7	00.6	239 39.3	20.4	Alkaid	153 20.9	N49 26.2
08	2 17.2	253 18.6	54.4	358 53.4	18.4	347 36.7	00.8	254 41.5	20.3	Al Na'ir	28 19.4	S47 04.5
S 09	17 19.7	268 18.1	.. 54.1	13 54.2	.. 17.6	2 38.7	.. 01.0	269 43.6	.. 20.3	Alnilam	276 15.7	S 1 13.1
U 10	32 22.1	283 17.6	53.7	28 54.9	16.9	17 40.7	01.2	284 45.8	20.3	Alphard	218 24.2	S 8 33.3
N 11	47 24.6	298 17.1	53.4	43 55.7	16.2	32 42.7	01.4	299 48.0	20.3			
D 12	62 27.1	313 16.6	N24 53.0	58 56.4	S 0 15.4	47 44.7	N 5 01.6	314 50.2	N22 20.2	Alphecca	126 34.8	N26 47.8
A 13	77 29.5	328 16.1	52.7	73 57.1	14.7	62 46.7	01.7	329 52.4	20.2	Alpheratz	358 13.2	N28 57.2
Y 14	92 32.0	343 15.7	52.3	88 57.9	14.0	77 48.7	01.9	344 54.5	20.2	Altair	62 35.8	N 8 48.2
15	107 34.5	358 15.2	.. 52.0	103 58.6	.. 13.2	92 50.7	.. 02.1	359 56.7	.. 20.2	Ankaa	353 44.0	S42 26.1
16	122 36.9	13 14.7	51.6	118 59.4	12.5	107 52.7	02.3	14 58.9	20.1	Antares	113 00.9	S26 22.7
17	137 39.4	28 14.2	51.3	134 00.1	11.8	122 54.7	02.5	30 01.1	20.1			
18	152 41.9	43 13.7	N24 50.9	149 00.9	S 0 11.0	137 56.7	N 5 02.7	45 03.2	N22 20.1	Arcturus	146 21.5	N19 18.6
19	167 44.3	58 13.2	50.5	164 01.6	10.3	152 58.7	02.9	60 05.4	20.0	Atria	108 27.9	S68 59.0
20	182 46.8	73 12.7	50.2	179 02.3	09.6	168 00.7	03.0	75 07.6	20.0	Avior	234 30.0	S59 26.2
21	197 49.2	88 12.3	.. 49.8	194 03.1	.. 08.8	183 02.7	.. 03.2	90 09.8	.. 20.0	Bellatrix	279 03.0	N 6 19.6
22	212 51.7	103 11.8	49.5	209 03.8	08.1	198 04.7	03.4	105 11.9	20.0	Betelgeuse	271 32.5	N 7 24.1
23	227 54.2	118 11.3	49.1	224 04.6	07.4	213 06.7	03.6	120 14.1	19.9			
26 00	242 56.6	133 10.8	N24 48.7	239 05.3	S 0 06.6	228 08.7	N 5 03.8	135 16.3	N22 19.9	Canopus	264 09.3	S52 41.2
01	257 59.1	148 10.3	48.4	254 06.1	05.9	243 10.7	04.0	150 18.5	19.9	Capella	281 17.1	N45 58.4
02	273 01.6	163 09.8	48.0	269 06.8	05.2	258 12.8	04.1	165 20.6	19.8	Deneb	49 50.7	N45 11.4
03	288 04.0	178 09.4	.. 47.6	284 07.5	.. 04.4	273 14.8	.. 04.3	180 22.8	.. 19.8	Denebola	183 02.6	N14 42.5
04	303 06.5	193 08.9	47.3	299 08.3	03.7	288 16.8	04.5	195 25.0	19.8	Diphda	349 24.7	S18 07.2
05	318 09.0	208 08.4	46.9	314 09.0	03.0	303 18.8	04.7	210 27.2	19.8			
06	333 11.4	223 07.9	N24 46.5	329 09.8	S 0 02.2	318 20.8	N 5 04.9	225 29.3	N22 19.7	Dubhe	194 26.4	N61 53.2
07	348 13.9	238 07.5	46.1	344 10.5	01.5	333 22.8	05.1	240 31.5	19.7	Elnath	278 49.1	N28 35.2
08	3 16.4	253 07.0	45.8	359 11.3	S 0 00.7	348 24.8	05.2	255 33.7	19.7	Eltanin	90 58.9	N51 29.4
M 09	18 18.8	268 06.5	.. 45.4	14 12.0	N 0 00.0	3 26.8	.. 05.4	270 35.9	.. 19.6	Enif	34 15.1	N 9 45.7
O 10	33 21.3	283 06.0	45.0	29 12.7	N 0 00.7	18 28.8	05.6	285 38.0	19.6	Fomalhaut	15 55.5	S29 45.0
N 11	48 23.7	298 05.6	44.6	44 13.5	01.5	33 30.8	05.8	300 40.2	19.6			
D 12	63 26.2	313 05.1	N24 44.3	59 14.2	N 0 02.2	48 32.8	N 5 06.0	315 42.4	N22 19.6	Gacrux	172 32.5	S56 58.9
A 13	78 28.7	328 04.6	43.9	74 15.0	02.9	63 34.8	06.2	330 44.6	19.5	Gienah	176 21.5	S17 24.6
Y 14	93 31.1	343 04.1	43.5	89 15.7	03.7	78 36.8	06.3	345 46.7	19.5	Hadar	149 27.9	S60 15.5
15	108 33.6	358 03.7	.. 43.1	104 16.5	.. 04.4	93 38.8	.. 06.5	0 48.9	.. 19.5	Hamal	328 33.3	N23 20.7
16	123 36.1	13 03.2	42.7	119 17.2	05.1	108 40.8	06.7	15 51.1	19.4	Kaus Aust.	84 21.3	S34 23.7
17	138 38.5	28 02.7	42.4	134 17.9	05.9	123 42.8	06.9	30 53.3	19.4			
18	153 41.0	43 02.3	N24 42.0	149 18.7	N 0 06.6	138 44.8	N 5 07.1	45 55.4	N22 19.4	Kochab	137 17.7	N74 15.5
19	168 43.5	58 01.8	41.6	164 19.4	07.3	153 46.8	07.3	60 57.6	19.4	Markab	14 06.8	N15 04.3
20	183 45.9	73 01.3	41.2	179 20.2	08.1	168 48.8	07.4	75 59.8	19.3	Menkar	314 45.2	N 3 59.6
21	198 48.4	88 00.9	.. 40.8	194 20.9	.. 08.8	183 50.8	.. 07.6	91 01.9	.. 19.3	Menkent	148 40.9	S36 15.2
22	213 50.9	103 00.4	40.4	209 21.7	09.5	198 52.9	07.8	106 04.1	19.3	Miaplacidus	221 46.0	S69 37.4
23	228 53.3	117 59.9	40.0	224 22.4	10.3	213 54.9	08.0	121 06.3	19.2			
27 00	243 55.8	132 59.5	N24 39.7	239 23.2	N 0 11.0	228 56.9	N 5 08.2	136 08.5	N22 19.2	Mirfak	309 21.8	N49 46.4
01	258 58.2	147 59.0	39.3	254 23.9	11.7	243 58.9	08.4	151 10.6	19.2	Nunki	76 33.4	S26 19.6
02	274 00.7	162 58.5	38.9	269 24.6	12.5	259 00.9	08.5	166 12.8	19.2	Peacock	54 03.8	S56 48.6
03	289 03.2	177 58.1	.. 38.5	284 25.4	.. 13.2	274 02.9	.. 08.7	181 15.0	.. 19.1	Pollux	244 02.8	N28 05.2
04	304 05.6	192 57.6	38.1	299 26.1	13.9	289 04.9	08.9	196 17.2	19.1	Procyon	245 29.8	N 5 17.2
05	319 08.1	207 57.2	37.7	314 26.9	14.7	304 06.9	09.1	211 19.3	19.1			
06	334 10.6	222 56.7	N24 37.3	329 27.6	N 0 15.4	319 08.9	N 5 09.3	226 21.5	N22 19.0	Rasalhague	96 32.6	N12 34.6
07	349 13.0	237 56.2	36.9	344 28.4	16.1	334 10.9	09.5	241 23.7	19.0	Regulus	208 13.9	N12 05.2
08	4 15.5	252 55.8	36.5	359 29.1	16.9	349 12.9	09.6	256 25.8	19.0	Rigel	281 39.8	S 8 13.9
T 09	19 18.0	267 55.3	.. 36.1	14 29.9	.. 17.6	4 14.9	.. 09.8	271 28.0	.. 18.9	Rigil Kent.	140 30.1	S60 44.2
U 10	34 20.4	282 54.9	35.7	29 30.6	18.3	19 16.9	10.0	286 30.2	18.9	Sabik	102 44.9	S15 41.7
E 11	49 22.9	297 54.4	35.3	44 31.3	19.1	34 19.0	10.2	301 32.4	18.9			
S 12	64 25.3	312 54.0	N24 34.9	59 32.1	N 0 19.8	49 21.0	N 5 10.4	316 34.5	N22 18.9	Schedar	350 13.5	N56 24.0
D 13	79 27.8	327 53.5	34.5	74 32.8	20.5	64 23.0	10.6	331 36.7	18.8	Shaula	97 00.3	S37 05.2
A 14	94 30.3	342 53.1	34.1	89 33.6	21.3	79 25.0	10.7	346 38.9	18.8	Sirius	258 59.2	S16 41.1
Y 15	109 32.7	357 52.6	.. 33.7	104 34.3	.. 22.0	94 27.0	.. 10.9	1 41.1	.. 18.8	Spica	159 01.1	S11 02.2
16	124 35.2	12 52.1	33.3	119 35.1	22.7	109 29.0	11.1	16 43.2	18.7	Suhail	223 13.6	S43 20.3
17	139 37.7	27 51.7	32.9	134 35.8	23.5	124 31.0	11.3	31 45.4	18.7			
18	154 40.1	42 51.2	N24 32.5	149 36.6	N 0 24.2	139 33.0	N 5 11.5	46 47.6	N22 18.7	Vega	80 57.9	N38 45.5
19	169 42.6	57 50.8	32.1	164 37.3	24.9	154 35.0	11.6	61 49.7	18.7	Zuben'ubi	137 36.7	S15 56.5
20	184 45.1	72 50.3	31.7	179 38.0	25.7	169 37.0	11.8	76 51.9	18.6		S.H.A.	Mer. Pass.
21	199 47.5	87 49.9	.. 31.2	194 38.8	.. 26.4	184 39.0	.. 12.0	91 54.1	.. 18.6	Venus	250 14.2	15 08
22	214 50.0	102 49.5	30.8	209 39.5	27.1	199 41.1	12.2	106 56.2	18.6	Mars	356 08.7	8 03
23	229 52.5	117 49.0	30.4	224 40.3	27.9	214 43.1	12.4	121 58.4	18.5	Jupiter	345 12.1	8 46
Mer. Pass.	7 46.9	v −0.5	d 0.4	v 0.7	d 0.7	v 2.0	d 0.2	v 2.2	d 0.0	Saturn	252 19.6	14 57

1975 MAY 25, 26, 27 (SUN., MON., TUES.)

G.M.T.	SUN G.H.A.	Dec.	MOON G.H.A.	v	Dec.	d	H.P.
25 00	180 48.4	N20 47.7	4 04.3	6.9	S20 14.7	4.1	58.3
01	195 48.4	48.2	18 30.2	7.0	20 18.8	4.0	58.3
02	210 48.3	48.7	32 56.2	6.9	20 22.8	3.8	58.3
03	225 48.2 ..	49.1	47 22.1	7.0	20 26.6	3.7	58.2
04	240 48.2	49.6	61 48.1	6.9	20 30.3	3.6	58.2
05	255 48.1	50.0	76 14.0	7.0	20 33.9	3.5	58.2
06	270 48.1	N20 50.5	90 40.0	6.9	S20 37.4	3.3	58.2
07	285 48.0	51.0	105 05.9	7.0	20 40.7	3.2	58.1
08	300 48.0	51.4	119 31.9	6.9	20 43.9	3.0	58.1
S 09	315 47.9 ..	51.9	133 57.8	7.0	20 46.9	3.0	58.1
U 10	330 47.8	52.3	148 23.8	7.0	20 49.9	2.7	58.1
N 11	345 47.8	52.8	162 49.8	7.0	20 52.6	2.7	58.0
D 12	0 47.7	N20 53.2	177 15.8	7.0	S20 55.3	2.5	58.0
A 13	15 47.7	53.7	191 41.8	7.0	20 57.8	2.4	58.0
Y 14	30 47.6	54.1	206 07.8	7.0	21 00.2	2.3	58.0
15	45 47.5 ..	54.6	220 33.8	7.1	21 02.5	2.1	57.9
16	60 47.5	55.0	234 59.9	7.0	21 04.6	2.0	57.9
17	75 47.4	55.5	249 25.9	7.1	21 06.6	1.9	57.9
18	90 47.4	N20 55.9	263 52.0	7.1	S21 08.5	1.8	57.8
19	105 47.3	56.4	278 18.1	7.2	21 10.3	1.6	57.8
20	120 47.2	56.8	292 44.3	7.1	21 11.9	1.5	57.8
21	135 47.2 ..	57.3	307 10.4	7.2	21 13.4	1.3	57.8
22	150 47.1	57.7	321 36.6	7.2	21 14.7	1.2	57.7
23	165 47.1	58.2	336 02.8	7.2	21 15.9	1.1	57.7
26 00	180 47.0	N20 58.6	350 29.0	7.2	S21 17.0	1.0	57.7
01	195 46.9	59.1	4 55.2	7.3	21 18.0	0.8	57.7
02	210 46.9	20 59.5	19 21.5	7.3	21 18.8	0.7	57.6
03	225 46.8	21 00.0	33 47.8	7.4	21 19.5	0.6	57.6
04	240 46.7	00.4	48 14.2	7.3	21 20.1	0.4	57.6
05	255 46.7	00.9	62 40.5	7.4	21 20.5	0.3	57.5
06	270 46.6	N21 01.3	77 06.9	7.5	S21 20.8	0.2	57.5
07	285 46.6	01.7	91 33.4	7.5	21 21.0	0.1	57.5
08	300 46.5	02.2	105 59.9	7.5	21 21.1	0.1	57.5
M 09	315 46.4 ..	02.6	120 26.4	7.5	21 21.0	0.2	57.4
O 10	330 46.4	03.1	134 52.9	7.6	21 20.8	0.3	57.4
N 11	345 46.3	03.5	149 19.5	7.6	21 20.5	0.5	57.4
D 12	0 46.2	N21 03.9	163 46.1	7.7	S21 20.0	0.6	57.3
A 13	15 46.2	04.4	178 12.8	7.7	21 19.4	0.7	57.3
Y 14	30 46.1	04.8	192 39.5	7.8	21 18.7	0.8	57.3
15	45 46.0 ..	05.3	207 06.3	7.8	21 17.9	1.0	57.3
16	60 46.0	05.7	221 33.1	7.8	21 16.9	1.0	57.2
17	75 45.9	06.1	235 59.9	7.9	21 15.9	1.2	57.2
18	90 45.8	N21 06.6	250 26.8	7.9	S21 14.7	1.4	57.2
19	105 45.8	07.0	264 53.7	8.0	21 13.3	1.4	57.1
20	120 45.7	07.4	279 20.7	8.1	21 11.9	1.6	57.1
21	135 45.7 ..	07.9	293 47.8	8.0	21 10.3	1.7	57.1
22	150 45.6	08.3	308 14.8	8.2	21 08.6	1.8	57.1
23	165 45.5	08.7	322 42.0	8.2	21 06.8	1.9	57.0
27 00	180 45.5	N21 09.2	337 09.2	8.2	S21 04.9	2.0	57.0
01	195 45.4	09.6	351 36.4	8.3	21 02.9	2.2	57.0
02	210 45.3	10.0	6 03.7	8.4	21 00.7	2.3	56.9
03	225 45.3 ..	10.4	20 31.1	8.4	20 58.4	2.4	56.9
04	240 45.2	10.9	34 58.5	8.5	20 56.0	2.5	56.9
05	255 45.1	11.3	49 26.0	8.5	20 53.5	2.6	56.9
06	270 45.0	N21 11.7	63 53.5	8.6	S20 50.9	2.8	56.8
07	285 45.0	12.2	78 21.1	8.6	20 48.1	2.8	56.8
08	300 44.9	12.6	92 48.7	8.7	20 45.3	3.0	56.8
T 09	315 44.8 ..	13.0	107 16.4	8.7	20 42.3	3.1	56.7
U 10	330 44.8	13.4	121 44.2	8.8	20 39.2	3.2	56.7
E 11	345 44.7	13.9	136 12.0	8.9	20 36.0	3.3	56.7
S 12	0 44.6	N21 14.3	150 39.9	9.0	S20 32.7	3.4	56.6
D 13	15 44.6	14.7	165 07.9	9.0	20 29.3	3.6	56.6
A 14	30 44.5	15.1	179 35.9	9.0	20 25.7	3.6	56.6
Y 15	45 44.4 ..	15.5	194 03.9	9.2	20 22.1	3.8	56.6
16	60 44.4	16.0	208 32.1	9.2	20 18.3	3.8	56.5
17	75 44.3	16.4	223 00.3	9.3	20 14.5	3.9	56.5
18	90 44.2	N21 16.8	237 28.6	9.3	S20 10.5	4.0	56.5
19	105 44.1	17.2	251 56.9	9.4	20 06.5	4.2	56.4
20	120 44.1	17.6	266 25.3	9.5	20 02.3	4.3	56.4
21	135 44.0 ..	18.1	280 53.8	9.5	19 58.0	4.4	56.4
22	150 43.9	18.5	295 22.3	9.7	19 53.6	4.4	56.4
23	165 43.9	18.9	309 51.0	9.6	19 49.2	4.6	56.3
	S.D. 15.8 d 0.4		S.D. 15.8		15.6		15.4

Lat.	Twilight Naut.	Civil	Sunrise	Moonrise 25	26	27	28
N 72	□	□	□	■	■	■	■
N 70	□	□	□				01 46
68	////	////	00 29	23 42	24 27	00 27	00 36
66	////	////	01 41	22 42	23 33	24 00	00 00
64	////	////	02 16	22 07	23 01	23 33	23 53
62	////	01 03	02 41	21 43	22 36	23 13	23 37
60	////	01 46	03 01	21 23	22 17	22 56	23 24
N 58	00 15	02 15	03 17	21 07	22 01	22 42	23 12
56	00 56	02 36	03 30	20 53	21 48	22 30	23 02
54	01 37	02 53	03 42	20 41	21 36	22 19	22 53
52	02 03	03 08	03 52	20 30	21 26	22 10	22 45
50	02 23	03 20	04 02	20 21	21 16	22 02	22 38
45	03 00	03 46	04 21	20 01	20 57	21 44	22 23
N 40	03 26	04 05	04 37	19 45	20 41	21 29	22 10
35	03 46	04 21	04 50	19 32	20 27	21 17	22 00
30	04 02	04 35	05 01	19 20	20 16	21 06	21 50
20	04 28	04 57	05 21	19 00	19 55	20 47	21 34
N 10	04 49	05 15	05 38	18 42	19 38	20 31	21 19
0	05 05	05 31	05 53	18 26	19 22	20 15	21 06
S 10	05 20	05 46	06 09	18 10	19 05	20 00	20 53
20	05 35	06 02	06 25	17 53	18 48	19 44	20 38
30	05 49	06 18	06 44	17 33	18 28	19 25	20 22
35	05 56	06 27	06 55	17 21	18 16	19 14	20 12
40	06 04	06 37	07 07	17 08	18 03	19 01	20 01
45	06 13	06 49	07 22	16 52	17 47	18 47	19 48
S 50	06 22	07 03	07 40	16 33	17 27	18 28	19 33
52	06 27	07 09	07 48	16 24	17 18	18 20	19 25
54	06 31	07 16	07 58	16 13	17 08	18 10	19 17
56	06 36	07 24	08 08	16 02	16 56	17 59	19 08
58	06 42	07 32	08 20	15 49	16 43	17 47	18 57
S 60	06 48	07 42	08 34	15 33	16 27	17 32	18 45

Lat.	Sunset	Twilight Civil	Naut.	Moonset 25	26	27	28
N 72	□	□	□	■	■	■	■
N 70	□	□	□				03 18
68	23 43	////	////	01 16	01 36	02 46	04 27
66	22 17	////	////	01 59	02 36	03 40	05 03
64	21 40	////	////	02 28	03 10	04 12	05 29
62	21 15	22 57	////	02 50	03 35	04 36	05 49
60	20 55	22 10	////	03 08	03 55	04 55	06 05
N 58	20 38	21 41	////	03 23	04 11	05 11	06 19
56	20 24	21 20	23 02	03 36	04 25	05 24	06 31
54	20 13	21 02	22 19	03 47	04 37	05 36	06 41
52	20 02	20 47	21 53	03 57	04 48	05 46	06 50
50	19 53	20 34	21 32	04 06	04 57	05 55	06 58
45	19 33	20 09	20 55	04 25	05 17	06 15	07 16
N 40	19 18	19 49	20 29	04 40	05 33	06 30	07 30
35	19 04	19 33	20 08	04 53	05 47	06 44	07 42
30	18 53	19 19	19 52	05 04	05 59	06 55	07 52
20	18 33	18 57	19 26	05 24	06 19	07 15	08 10
N 10	18 18	18 39	19 05	05 41	06 37	07 32	08 26
0	18 01	18 23	18 48	05 57	06 53	07 48	08 40
S 10	17 45	18 07	18 33	06 12	07 09	08 04	08 55
20	17 28	17 52	18 19	06 29	07 27	08 21	09 10
30	17 10	17 36	18 05	06 49	07 47	08 40	09 27
35	16 59	17 26	17 57	07 00	07 59	08 51	09 38
40	16 46	17 16	17 49	07 13	08 12	09 04	09 49
45	16 32	17 04	17 41	07 29	08 28	09 20	10 03
S 50	16 14	16 51	17 31	07 48	08 48	09 38	10 21
52	16 05	16 44	17 27	07 57	08 57	09 47	10 27
54	15 56	16 37	17 22	08 07	09 08	09 57	10 36
56	15 45	16 30	17 17	08 18	09 19	10 08	10 45
58	15 33	16 21	17 12	08 31	09 33	10 21	10 56
S 60	15 19	16 12	17 06	08 46	09 49	10 36	11 09

Day	SUN Eqn. of Time 00h	12h	Mer. Pass.	MOON Mer. Pass. Upper	Lower	Age	Phase
25	03 14	03 11	11 57	24 40	12 11	14	
26	03 08	03 05	11 57	00 40	13 07	15	○
27	03 02	02 59	11 57	01 35	14 02	16	

1975 MAY 31, JUNE 1, 2 (SAT., SUN., MON.)

G.M.T.	ARIES G.H.A.	VENUS −3.8 G.H.A.	Dec.	MARS +1.0 G.H.A.	Dec.	JUPITER −1.7 G.H.A.	Dec.	SATURN +0.4 G.H.A.	Dec.	STAR Name	S.H.A.	Dec.
31 00	247 52.3	132 18.6	N23 57.7	240 34.8	N 1 21.2	232 10.1	N 5 25.4	139 36.7	N22 16.3	Acamar	315 40.4	S40 24.1
01	262 54.8	147 18.2	57.2	255 35.6	22.0	247 12.2	25.6	154 38.8	16.3	Achernar	335 48.4	S57 21.4
02	277 57.3	162 17.8	56.7	270 36.3	22.7	262 14.2	25.8	169 41.0	16.3	Acrux	173 40.9	S62 58.2
03	292 59.7	177 17.5 ..	56.3	285 37.1 ..	23.4	277 16.2 ..	25.9	184 43.1 ..	16.2	Adhara	255 35.3	S28 56.5
04	308 02.2	192 17.1	55.8	300 37.8	24.2	292 18.2	26.1	199 45.3	16.2	Aldebaran	291 22.5	N16 27.6
05	323 04.7	207 16.7	55.3	315 38.6	24.9	307 20.2	26.3	214 47.5	16.2			
06	338 07.1	222 16.3	N23 54.8	330 39.3	N 1 25.6	322 22.3	N 5 26.5	229 49.6	N22 16.2	Alioth	166 45.3	N56 05.7
07	353 09.6	237 15.9	54.3	345 40.1	26.3	337 24.3	26.7	244 51.8	16.1	Alkaid	153 21.0	N49 26.2
S 08	8 12.1	252 15.6	53.8	0 40.8	27.1	352 26.3	26.8	259 54.0	16.1	Al Na'ir	28 19.4	S47 04.5
A 09	23 14.5	267 15.2 ..	53.3	15 41.6 ..	27.8	7 28.3 ..	27.0	274 56.1 ..	16.1	Alnilam	276 15.6	S 1 13.1
T 10	38 17.0	282 14.8	52.8	30 42.3	28.5	22 30.3	27.2	289 58.3	16.0	Alphard	218 24.2	S 8 33.3
U 11	53 19.4	297 14.4	52.3	45 43.1	29.3	37 32.4	27.4	305 00.5	16.0			
R 12	68 21.9	312 14.0	N23 51.8	60 43.8	N 1 30.0	52 34.4	N 5 27.5	320 02.6	N22 16.0	Alphecca	126 34.8	N26 47.8
D 13	83 24.4	327 13.7	51.3	75 44.6	30.7	67 36.4	27.7	335 04.8	15.9	Alpheratz	358 13.2	N28 57.2
A 14	98 26.8	342 13.3	50.8	90 45.3	31.4	82 38.4	27.9	350 06.9	15.9	Altair	62 35.8	N 8 48.2
Y 15	113 29.3	357 12.9 ..	50.4	105 46.1 ..	32.2	97 40.5 ..	28.1	5 09.1 ..	15.9	Ankaa	353 44.0	S42 26.1
16	128 31.8	12 12.5	49.9	120 46.8	32.9	112 42.5	28.2	20 11.3	15.8	Antares	113 00.9	S26 22.7
17	143 34.2	27 12.2	49.4	135 47.6	33.6	127 44.5	28.4	35 13.4	15.8			
18	158 36.7	42 11.8	N23 48.9	150 48.3	N 1 34.4	142 46.5	N 5 28.6	50 15.6	N22 15.8	Arcturus	146 21.5	N19 18.6
19	173 39.2	57 11.4	48.4	165 49.1	35.1	157 48.5	28.8	65 17.8	15.8	Atria	108 27.8	S68 59.1
20	188 41.6	72 11.1	47.9	180 49.8	35.8	172 50.6	28.9	80 19.9	15.7	Avior	234 30.1	S59 26.2
21	203 44.1	87 10.7 ..	47.4	195 50.6 ..	36.5	187 52.6 ..	29.1	95 22.1 ..	15.7	Bellatrix	279 02.9	N 6 19.6
22	218 46.5	102 10.3	46.8	210 51.3	37.3	202 54.6	29.3	110 24.2	15.7	Betelgeuse	271 32.5	N 7 24.1
23	233 49.0	117 10.0	46.3	225 52.1	38.0	217 56.6	29.5	125 26.4	15.6			
1 00	248 51.5	132 09.6	N23 45.8	240 52.8	N 1 38.7	232 58.7	N 5 29.6	140 28.6	N22 15.6	Canopus	264 09.3	S52 41.1
01	263 53.9	147 09.2	45.3	255 53.6	39.4	248 00.7	29.8	155 30.7	15.6	Capella	281 17.1	N45 58.4
02	278 56.4	162 08.9	44.8	270 54.3	40.2	263 02.7	30.0	170 32.9	15.5	Deneb	49 50.7	N45 11.4
03	293 58.9	177 08.5 ..	44.3	285 55.1 ..	40.9	278 04.7 ..	30.2	185 35.1 ..	15.5	Denebola	183 02.6	N14 42.5
04	309 01.3	192 08.1	43.8	300 55.8	41.6	293 06.7	30.3	200 37.2	15.5	Diphda	349 24.7	S18 07.2
05	324 03.8	207 07.8	43.3	315 56.6	42.4	308 08.8	30.5	215 39.4	15.4			
06	339 06.3	222 07.4	N23 42.8	330 57.3	N 1 43.1	323 10.8	N 5 30.7	230 41.5	N22 15.4	Dubhe	194 26.5	N61 53.2
07	354 08.7	237 07.1	42.3	345 58.1	43.8	338 12.8	30.9	245 43.7	15.4	Elnath	278 49.1	N28 35.2
08	9 11.2	252 06.7	41.8	0 58.8	44.5	353 14.8	31.0	260 45.9	15.3	Eltanin	90 58.9	N51 29.4
S 09	24 13.7	267 06.3 ..	41.3	15 59.6 ..	45.3	8 16.9 ..	31.2	275 48.0 ..	15.3	Enif	34 15.0	N 9 45.7
U 10	39 16.1	282 06.0	40.7	31 00.3	46.0	23 18.9	31.4	290 50.2	15.3	Fomalhaut	15 55.4	S29 44.9
N 11	54 18.6	297 05.6	40.2	46 01.1	46.7	38 20.9	31.5	305 52.3	15.2			
D 12	69 21.0	312 05.3	N23 39.7	61 01.8	N 1 47.4	53 22.9	N 5 31.7	320 54.5	N22 15.2	Gacrux	172 32.5	S56 58.9
A 13	84 23.5	327 04.9	39.2	76 02.6	48.2	68 25.0	31.9	335 56.7	15.2	Gienah	176 21.5	S17 24.6
Y 14	99 26.0	342 04.6	38.7	91 03.3	48.9	83 27.0	32.1	350 58.8	15.2	Hadar	149 27.9	S60 15.6
15	114 28.4	357 04.2 ..	38.2	106 04.1 ..	49.6	98 29.0 ..	32.2	6 01.0 ..	15.1	Hamal	328 33.3	N23 20.7
16	129 30.9	12 03.9	37.6	121 04.8	50.4	113 31.0	32.4	21 03.2	15.1	Kaus Aust.	84 21.2	S34 23.7
17	144 33.4	27 03.5	37.1	136 05.6	51.1	128 33.1	32.6	36 05.3	15.1			
18	159 35.8	42 03.2	N23 36.6	151 06.3	N 1 51.8	143 35.1	N 5 32.8	51 07.5	N22 15.0	Kochab	137 17.7	N74 15.5
19	174 38.3	57 02.8	36.1	166 07.1	52.5	158 37.1	32.9	66 09.6	15.0	Markab	14 06.8	N15 04.3
20	189 40.8	72 02.5	35.5	181 07.8	53.3	173 39.1	33.1	81 11.8	15.0	Menkar	314 45.2	N 3 59.6
21	204 43.2	87 02.1 ..	35.0	196 08.6 ..	54.0	188 41.2 ..	33.3	96 14.0 ..	14.9	Menkent	148 40.9	S36 15.2
22	219 45.7	102 01.8	34.5	211 09.3	54.7	203 43.2	33.5	111 16.1	14.9	Miaplacidus	221 46.1	S69 37.4
23	234 48.2	117 01.4	34.0	226 10.1	55.4	218 45.2	33.6	126 18.3	14.9			
2 00	249 50.6	132 01.1	N23 33.4	241 10.8	N 1 56.2	233 47.2	N 5 33.8	141 20.4	N22 14.8	Mirfak	309 21.7	N49 46.4
01	264 53.1	147 00.7	32.9	256 11.6	56.9	248 49.3	34.0	156 22.6	14.8	Nunki	76 33.3	S26 19.6
02	279 55.5	162 00.4	32.4	271 12.3	57.6	263 51.3	34.1	171 24.8	14.8	Peacock	54 03.7	S56 48.6
03	294 58.0	177 00.0 ..	31.9	286 13.1 ..	58.3	278 53.3 ..	34.3	186 26.9 ..	14.7	Pollux	244 02.8	N28 05.2
04	310 00.5	191 59.7	31.3	301 13.8	59.1	293 55.4	34.5	201 29.1	14.7	Procyon	245 29.8	N 5 17.2
05	325 02.9	206 59.4	30.8	316 14.6	1 59.8	308 57.4	34.7	216 31.2	14.7			
06	340 05.4	221 59.0	N23 30.3	331 15.3	N 2 00.5	323 59.4	N 5 34.8	231 33.4	N22 14.6	Rasalhague	96 32.6	N12 34.6
07	355 07.9	236 58.7	29.7	346 16.1	01.2	339 01.4	35.0	246 35.6	14.6	Regulus	208 13.9	N12 05.2
08	10 10.3	251 58.4	29.2	1 16.8	02.0	354 03.5	35.2	261 37.7	14.6	Rigel	281 39.8	S 8 13.9
M 09	25 12.8	266 58.0 ..	28.7	16 17.6 ..	02.7	9 05.5 ..	35.4	276 39.9 ..	14.6	Rigil Kent.	140 30.1	S60 44.2
O 10	40 15.3	281 57.7	28.1	31 18.3	03.4	24 07.5	35.5	291 42.0	14.5	Sabik	102 44.9	S15 41.7
N 11	55 17.7	296 57.3	27.6	46 19.1	04.1	39 09.5	35.7	306 44.2	14.5			
D 12	70 20.2	311 57.0	N23 27.1	61 19.8	N 2 04.9	54 11.6	N 5 35.9	321 46.4	N22 14.5	Schedar	350 13.4	N56 24.0
A 13	85 22.6	326 56.7	26.5	76 20.6	05.6	69 13.6	36.0	336 48.5	14.4	Shaula	97 00.2	S37 05.2
Y 14	100 25.1	341 56.3	26.0	91 21.3	06.3	84 15.6	36.2	351 50.7	14.4	Sirius	258 59.2	S16 41.1
15	115 27.6	356 56.0 ..	25.4	106 22.1 ..	07.0	99 17.7 ..	36.4	6 52.8 ..	14.4	Spica	159 01.1	S11 02.2
16	130 30.0	11 55.7	24.9	121 22.8	07.8	114 19.7	36.6	21 55.0	14.3	Suhail	223 13.6	S43 20.3
17	145 32.5	26 55.4	24.4	136 23.6	08.5	129 21.7	36.7	36 57.1	14.3			
18	160 35.0	41 55.0	N23 23.8	151 24.3	N 2 09.2	144 23.7	N 5 36.9	51 59.3	N22 14.3	Vega	80 57.9	N38 45.6
19	175 37.4	56 54.7	23.3	166 25.1	09.9	159 25.8	37.1	67 01.5	14.2	Zuben'ubi	137 36.7	S15 56.5
20	190 39.9	71 54.4	22.7	181 25.8	10.7	174 27.8	37.2	82 03.6	14.2			
21	205 42.4	86 54.0 ..	22.2	196 26.6 ..	11.4	189 29.8 ..	37.4	97 05.8 ..	14.2			
22	220 44.8	101 53.7	21.6	211 27.3	12.1	204 31.9	37.6	112 07.9	14.1			
23	235 47.3	116 53.4	21.1	226 28.1	12.8	219 33.9	37.8	127 10.1	14.1			
Mer. Pass.	h m 7 23.4	*v* −0.4 *d* 0.5		*v* 0.8 *d* 0.7		*v* 2.0 *d* 0.2		*v* 2.2 *d* 0.0				

	S.H.A.	Mer. Pass.
Venus	243 18.1	h m 15 12
Mars	352 01.3	7 56
Jupiter	344 07.2	8 27
Saturn	251 37.1	14 36

1975 MAY 31, JUNE 1, 2 (SAT., SUN., MON.)

G.M.T.	SUN G.H.A.	SUN Dec.	MOON G.H.A.	v	Dec.	d	H.P.	Lat.	Twilight Naut.	Twilight Civil	Sunrise	Moonrise 31	Moonrise 1	Moonrise 2	Moonrise 3
	o '	o '	o '		o '			o	h m	h m	h m	h m	h m	h m	h m
31 00	180 38.1	N21 47.6	289 46.4 14.5		S10 46.8	9.6	54.7	N 72	☐	☐	☐	01 05	00 49	00 36	00 23
01	195 38.0	47.9	304 19.9 14.5		10 37.2	9.6	54.6	N 70	☐	☐	☐	00 48	00 40	00 33	00 25
02	210 37.9	48.3	318 53.4 14.5		10 27.6	9.7	54.6	68	☐	☐	01 15	00 34	00 32	00 30	00 27
03	225 37.8 ··	48.7	333 26.9 14.6		10 17.9	9.7	54.6	66	////	////	02 00	00 23	00 26	00 27	00 29
04	240 37.7	49.0	348 00.5 14.7		10 08.2	9.7	54.6	64	////	////	02 28	00 14	00 20	00 25	00 30
05	255 37.6	49.4	2 34.2 14.6		9 58.5	9.8	54.6	62	////	00 15	02 28	00 06	00 15	00 24	00 31
06	270 37.6	N21 49.8	17 07.8 14.8		S 9 48.7	9.8	54.6	60	////	01 28	02 50	24 11	00 11	00 22	00 32
S 07	285 37.5	50.1	31 41.6 14.7		9 38.9	9.8	54.6	N 58	////	02 02	03 08	24 07	00 07	00 21	00 33
A 08	300 37.4	50.5	46 15.3 14.9		9 29.1	9.9	54.5	56	00 13	02 26	03 23	24 04	00 04	00 19	00 34
T 09	315 37.3 ··	50.9	60 49.2 14.8		9 19.2	9.9	54.5	54	01 20	02 45	03 35	24 01	00 01	00 18	00 35
U 10	330 37.2	51.2	75 23.0 14.9		9 09.3	9.9	54.5	52	01 51	03 00	03 46	23 58	24 17	00 17	00 36
R 11	345 37.1	51.6	89 56.9 15.0		8 59.4	10.0	54.5	50	02 14	03 14	03 56	23 56	24 16	00 16	00 36
D 12	0 37.0	N21 51.9	104 30.9 14.9		S 8 49.4	10.0	54.5	45	02 53	03 41	04 17	23 50	24 14	00 14	00 38
A 13	15 36.9	52.3	119 04.8 15.0		8 39.4	10.0	54.5	N 40	03 21	04 01	04 33	23 46	24 13	00 13	00 39
Y 14	30 36.9	52.7	133 38.8 15.1		8 29.4	10.1	54.5	35	03 43	04 18	04 47	23 42	24 11	00 11	00 40
15	45 36.8 ··	53.0	148 12.9 15.1		8 19.3	10.1	54.5	30	04 00	04 32	04 59	23 38	24 10	00 10	00 41
16	60 36.7	53.4	162 47.0 15.1		8 09.2	10.1	54.4	20	04 27	04 56	05 20	23 32	24 07	00 07	00 42
17	75 36.6	53.7	177 21.1 15.2		7 59.1	10.1	54.4	N 10	04 48	05 15	05 38	23 27	24 05	00 05	00 44
18	90 36.5	N21 54.1	191 55.3 15.2		S 7 49.0	10.2	54.4	0	05 06	05 32	05 54	23 22	24 04	00 04	00 45
19	105 36.4	54.5	206 29.5 15.2		7 38.8	10.2	54.4	S 10	05 22	05 48	06 10	23 17	24 02	00 02	00 46
20	120 36.3	54.8	221 03.7 15.3		7 28.6	10.2	54.4	20	05 37	06 04	06 27	23 11	24 00	00 00	00 48
21	135 36.2 ··	55.2	235 38.0 15.3		7 18.4	10.3	54.4	30	05 52	06 21	06 47	23 05	23 58	24 50	00 50
22	150 36.1	55.5	250 12.3 15.3		7 08.1	10.2	54.4	35	06 00	06 31	06 59	23 02	23 56	24 50	00 50
23	165 36.0	55.9	264 46.6 15.4		6 57.9	10.3	54.4	40	06 08	06 42	07 12	22 58	23 55	24 52	00 52
1 00	180 36.0	N21 56.2	279 21.0 15.4		S 6 47.6	10.4	54.4	45	06 17	06 54	07 27	22 53	23 53	24 53	00 53
01	195 35.9	56.6	293 55.4 15.4		6 37.2	10.3	54.4	S 50	06 28	07 09	07 46	22 47	23 51	24 54	00 54
02	210 35.8	56.9	308 29.8 15.4		6 26.9	10.4	54.4	52	06 33	07 16	07 55	22 45	23 50	24 55	00 55
03	225 35.7 ··	57.3	323 04.2 15.5		6 16.5	10.4	54.3	54	06 38	07 23	08 05	22 42	23 49	24 56	00 56
04	240 35.6	57.6	337 38.7 15.5		6 06.1	10.4	54.3	56	06 43	07 31	08 17	22 39	23 48	24 57	00 57
05	255 35.5	58.0	352 13.2 15.5		5 55.7	10.4	54.3	58	06 49	07 40	08 30	22 35	23 47	24 58	00 58
06	270 35.4	N21 58.3	6 47.7 15.6		S 5 45.3	10.4	54.3	S 60	06 55	07 51	08 45	22 31	23 45	24 59	00 59

G.M.T.	SUN G.H.A.	SUN Dec.	MOON G.H.A.	v	Dec.	d	H.P.	Lat.	Sunset	Twilight Civil	Twilight Naut.	Moonset 31	Moonset 1	Moonset 2	Moonset 3
07	285 35.3	58.7	21 22.3 15.5		5 34.9	10.5	54.3	o	h m	h m	h m	h m	h m	h m	h m
08	300 35.2	59.0	35 56.8 15.6		5 24.4	10.5	54.3	N 72	☐	☐	☐	08 53	10 38	12 18	13 58
S 09	315 35.1 ··	59.4	50 31.4 15.7		5 13.9	10.5	54.3	N 70	☐	☐	☐	09 09	10 45	12 19	13 52
U 10	330 35.0	21 59.7	65 06.1 15.6		5 03.4	10.5	54.3	68	☐	☐	☐	09 21	10 51	12 19	13 47
N 11	345 34.9	22 00.1	79 40.7 15.7		4 52.9	10.6	54.3	66	22 44	////	////	09 31	10 56	12 20	13 43
D 12	0 34.8	N22 00.4	94 15.4 15.6		S 4 42.3	10.5	54.3	64	21 58	////	////	09 39	11 00	12 20	13 40
A 13	15 34.8	00.8	108 50.0 15.7		4 31.8	10.6	54.3	62	21 28	////	////	09 46	11 04	12 20	13 37
Y 14	30 34.7	01.1	123 24.7 15.8		4 21.2	10.6	54.3	60	21 06	22 30	////	09 52	11 07	12 21	13 34
15	45 34.6 ··	01.5	137 59.5 15.7		4 10.6	10.6	54.3	N 58	20 48	21 55	////	09 58	11 10	12 21	13 32
16	60 34.5	01.8	152 34.2 15.7		4 00.0	10.6	54.3	56	20 33	21 31	////	10 03	11 12	12 21	13 30
17	75 34.4	02.1	167 08.9 15.8		3 49.4	10.6	54.3	54	20 21	21 12	22 37	10 07	11 14	12 21	13 28
18	90 34.3	N22 02.5	181 43.7 15.8		S 3 38.8	10.7	54.3	52	20 09	20 56	22 06	10 11	11 16	12 21	13 27
19	105 34.2	02.8	196 18.5 15.8		3 28.1	10.6	54.3	50	20 00	20 42	21 43	10 14	11 18	12 22	13 25
20	120 34.1	03.2	210 53.3 15.8		3 17.5	10.7	54.3	45	19 39	20 15	21 03	10 22	11 22	12 22	13 22
21	135 34.0 ··	03.5	225 28.1 15.8		3 06.8	10.7	54.3	N 40	19 22	19 54	20 35	10 28	11 25	12 22	13 19
22	150 33.9	03.8	240 02.9 15.8		2 56.1	10.7	54.3	35	19 08	19 37	20 13	10 33	11 28	12 22	13 17
23	165 33.8	04.2	254 37.7 15.9		2 45.4	10.6	54.3	30	18 56	19 23	19 56	10 38	11 31	12 23	13 15
2 00	180 33.7	N22 04.5	269 12.6 15.8		S 2 34.8	10.8	54.2	20	18 35	19 00	19 28	10 46	11 35	12 23	13 11
01	195 33.6	04.8	283 47.4 15.9		2 24.0	10.7	54.2	N 10	18 18	18 41	19 07	10 53	11 39	12 23	13 08
02	210 33.5	05.2	298 22.3 15.8		2 13.3	10.7	54.2	0	18 01	18 24	18 50	11 00	11 42	12 23	13 05
03	225 33.4 ··	05.5	312 57.1 15.9		2 02.6	10.7	54.2	S 10	17 45	18 08	18 34	11 06	11 46	12 24	13 02
04	240 33.3	05.9	327 32.0 15.9		1 51.9	10.8	54.2	20	17 28	17 51	18 19	11 13	11 49	12 24	12 59
05	255 33.2	06.2	342 06.9 15.8		1 41.1	10.7	54.2	30	17 08	17 34	18 04	11 21	11 53	12 24	12 55
06	270 33.1	N22 06.5	356 41.7 15.9		S 1 30.4	10.8	54.2	35	16 56	17 24	17 56	11 26	11 56	12 24	12 53
07	285 33.0	06.9	11 16.6 15.9		1 19.6	10.7	54.2	40	16 43	17 13	17 47	11 31	11 58	12 25	12 51
08	300 32.9	07.2	25 51.5 15.9		1 08.9	10.8	54.2	45	16 28	17 01	17 38	11 37	12 01	12 25	12 48
M 09	315 32.9 ··	07.5	40 26.4 15.9		0 58.1	10.7	54.2	S 50	16 09	16 46	17 27	11 44	12 05	12 25	12 45
O 10	330 32.8	07.9	55 01.3 15.9		0 47.4	10.8	54.3	52	16 00	16 40	17 22	11 47	12 07	12 25	12 44
N 11	345 32.7	08.2	69 36.2 15.9		0 36.6	10.8	54.3	54	15 50	16 32	17 17	11 51	12 08	12 25	12 42
D 12	0 32.6	N22 08.5	84 11.1 15.9		S 0 25.8	10.8	54.3	56	15 38	16 24	17 12	11 54	12 10	12 25	12 40
A 13	15 32.5	08.8	98 46.0 15.8		0 15.0	10.7	54.3	58	15 25	16 15	17 06	11 59	12 13	12 26	12 38
Y 14	30 32.4	09.2	113 20.8 15.9		S 0 04.3	10.8	54.3	S 60	15 10	16 04	16 59	12 04	12 15	12 26	12 36
15	45 32.3 ··	09.5	127 55.7 15.9		N 0 06.5	10.8	54.3								
16	60 32.2	09.8	142 30.6 15.9		0 17.3	10.8	54.3								
17	75 32.1	10.1	157 05.5 15.8		0 28.1	10.8	54.3								

								Day	SUN Eqn. of Time 00h	SUN Eqn. of Time 12h	SUN Mer. Pass.	MOON Mer. Pass. Upper	MOON Mer. Pass. Lower	Age	Phase
18	90 32.0	N22 10.5	171 40.3 15.9		N 0 38.9	10.8	54.3		m s	m s	h m	h m	h m	d	
19	105 31.9	10.8	186 15.2 15.8		0 49.6	10.8	54.3	31	02 32	02 28	11 58	04 49	17 11	20	
20	120 31.8	11.1	200 50.1 15.8		1 00.4	10.8	54.3	1	02 24	02 20	11 58	05 32	17 53	21	◑
21	135 31.7 ··	11.4	215 24.9 15.8		1 11.2	10.8	54.3	2	02 15	02 10	11 58	06 14	18 34	22	
22	150 31.6	11.8	229 59.7 15.9		1 22.0	10.8	54.3								
23	165 31.5	12.1	244 34.6 15.8		1 32.8	10.7	54.3								
	S.D. 15.8	d 0.3	S.D. 14.8		14.8		14.8									

1975 JUNE 12, 13, 14 (THURS., FRI., SAT.)

G.M.T.	ARIES G.H.A.	VENUS −3.9 G.H.A.	Dec.	MARS +0.8 G.H.A.	Dec.	JUPITER −1.9 G.H.A.	Dec.	SATURN +0.4 G.H.A.	Dec.
12 00	259 42.0	131 06.2	N21 02.9	244 12.2	N 4 47.9	241 58.0	N 6 13.1	149 56.7	N22 06.6
01	274 44.5	146 06.1	02.2	259 13.0	48.6	257 00.1	13.3	164 58.8	06.6
02	289 46.9	161 06.0	01.5	274 13.8	49.3	272 02.2	13.4	180 01.0	06.6
03	304 49.4	176 05.9 ··	00.8	289 14.5 ··	50.0	287 04.2 ··	13.6	195 03.1 ··	06.5
04	319 51.9	191 05.8	21 00.1	304 15.3	50.7	302 06.3	13.7	210 05.2	06.5
05	334 54.3	206 05.7	20 59.3	319 16.0	51.4	317 08.4	13.9	225 07.4	06.4
06	349 56.8	221 05.6	N20 58.6	334 16.8	N 4 52.1	332 10.4	N 6 14.0	240 09.5	N22 06.4
07	4 59.3	236 05.5	57.9	349 17.6	52.8	347 12.5	14.2	255 11.7	06.4
T 08	20 01.7	251 05.4	57.2	4 18.3	53.5	2 14.6	14.3	270 13.8	06.3
H 09	35 04.2	266 05.3 ··	56.5	19 19.1 ··	54.2	17 16.6 ··	14.5	285 16.0 ··	06.3
U 10	50 06.6	281 05.3	55.7	34 19.8	54.9	32 18.7	14.6	300 18.1	06.3
R 11	65 09.1	296 05.2	55.0	49 20.6	55.6	47 20.8	14.8	315 20.2	06.2
S 12	80 11.6	311 05.1	N20 54.3	64 21.4	N 4 56.3	62 22.8	N 6 15.0	330 22.4	N22 06.2
D 13	95 14.0	326 05.0	53.5	79 22.1	57.0	77 24.9	15.1	345 24.5	06.1
A 14	110 16.5	341 04.9	52.8	94 22.9	57.7	92 27.0	15.3	0 26.7	06.1
Y 15	125 19.0	356 04.8 ··	52.1	109 23.7 ··	58.4	107 29.0 ··	15.4	15 28.8 ··	06.1
16	140 21.4	11 04.7	51.3	124 24.4	59.1	122 31.1	15.6	30 30.9	06.0
17	155 23.9	26 04.6	50.6	139 25.2	4 59.8	137 33.2	15.7	45 33.1	06.0
18	170 26.4	41 04.5	N20 49.9	154 25.9	N 5 00.5	152 35.2	N 6 15.9	60 35.2	N22 06.0
19	185 28.8	56 04.5	49.2	169 26.7	01.2	167 37.3	16.0	75 37.4	05.9
20	200 31.3	71 04.4	48.4	184 27.5	01.9	182 39.4	16.2	90 39.5	05.9
21	215 33.8	86 04.3 ··	47.7	199 28.2 ··	02.6	197 41.4 ··	16.3	105 41.6 ··	05.9
22	230 36.2	101 04.2	47.0	214 29.0	03.3	212 43.5	16.5	120 43.8	05.8
23	245 38.7	116 04.1	46.2	229 29.7	04.0	227 45.6	16.6	135 45.9	05.8
13 00	260 41.1	131 04.1	N20 45.5	244 30.5	N 5 04.7	242 47.6	N 6 16.8	150 48.1	N22 05.7
01	275 43.6	146 04.0	44.8	259 31.3	05.4	257 49.7	16.9	165 50.2	05.7
02	290 46.1	161 03.9	44.0	274 32.0	06.1	272 51.8	17.1	180 52.4	05.7
03	305 48.5	176 03.8 ··	43.3	289 32.8 ··	06.8	287 53.8 ··	17.2	195 54.5 ··	05.6
04	320 51.0	191 03.8	42.6	304 33.6	07.5	302 55.9	17.4	210 56.6	05.6
05	335 53.5	206 03.7	41.8	319 34.3	08.2	317 58.0	17.5	225 58.8	05.6
06	350 55.9	221 03.6	N20 41.1	334 35.1	N 5 08.9	333 00.0	N 6 17.7	241 00.9	N22 05.5
07	5 58.4	236 03.5	40.3	349 35.8	09.6	348 02.1	17.9	256 03.1	05.5
08	21 00.9	251 03.5	39.6	4 36.6	10.3	3 04.2	18.0	271 05.2	05.4
F 09	36 03.3	266 03.4 ··	38.9	19 37.3 ··	11.0	18 06.3 ··	18.2	286 07.3 ··	05.4
R 10	51 05.8	281 03.3	38.1	34 38.1	11.7	33 08.3	18.3	301 09.5	05.4
I 11	66 08.3	296 03.3	37.4	49 38.9	12.4	48 10.4	18.5	316 11.6	05.3
D 12	81 10.7	311 03.2	N20 36.6	64 39.6	N 5 13.1	63 12.5	N 6 18.6	331 13.8	N22 05.3
A 13	96 13.2	326 03.1	35.9	79 40.4	13.8	78 14.5	18.8	346 15.9	05.3
Y 14	111 15.6	341 03.1	35.1	94 41.2	14.5	93 16.6	18.9	1 18.0	05.2
15	126 18.1	356 03.0 ··	34.4	109 41.9 ··	15.2	108 18.7 ··	19.1	16 20.2 ··	05.2
16	141 20.6	11 03.0	33.7	124 42.7	15.9	123 20.8	19.2	31 22.3	05.1
17	156 23.0	26 02.9	32.9	139 43.5	16.6	138 22.8	19.4	46 24.5	05.1
18	171 25.5	41 02.8	N20 32.2	154 44.2	N 5 17.3	153 24.9	N 6 19.5	61 26.6	N22 05.0
19	186 28.0	56 02.8	31.4	169 45.0	18.0	168 27.0	19.7	76 28.7	05.0
20	201 30.4	71 02.7	30.7	184 45.7	18.7	183 29.0	19.8	91 30.9	05.0
21	216 32.9	86 02.7 ··	29.9	199 46.5 ··	19.4	198 31.1 ··	20.0	106 33.0 ··	05.0
22	231 35.4	101 02.6	29.2	214 47.3	20.1	213 33.2	20.1	121 35.2	04.9
23	246 37.8	116 02.6	28.4	229 48.0	20.8	228 35.3	20.3	136 37.3	04.9
14 00	261 40.3	131 02.5	N20 27.7	244 48.8	N 5 21.5	243 37.3	N 6 20.4	151 39.4	N22 04.8
01	276 42.8	146 02.5	26.9	259 49.6	22.2	258 39.4	20.6	166 41.6	04.8
02	291 45.2	161 02.4	26.2	274 50.3	22.9	273 41.5	20.7	181 43.7	04.8
03	306 47.7	176 02.4 ··	25.4	289 51.1 ··	23.6	288 43.6 ··	20.9	196 45.9 ··	04.7
04	321 50.1	191 02.3	24.7	304 51.8	24.2	303 45.6	21.0	211 48.0	04.7
05	336 52.6	206 02.3	23.9	319 52.6	24.9	318 47.7	21.2	226 50.1	04.7
06	351 55.1	221 02.2	N20 22.2	334 53.4	N 5 25.6	333 49.8	N 6 21.3	241 52.3	N22 04.6
07	6 57.5	236 02.2	22.4	349 54.1	26.3	348 51.8	21.5	256 54.4	04.6
S 08	22 00.0	251 02.1	21.7	4 54.9	27.0	3 53.9	21.6	271 56.6	04.5
A 09	37 02.5	266 02.1 ··	20.9	19 55.7 ··	27.7	18 56.0 ··	21.8	286 58.7 ··	04.5
T 10	52 04.9	281 02.1	20.1	34 56.4	28.4	33 58.1	21.9	302 00.8	04.5
U 11	67 07.4	296 02.0	19.4	49 57.2	29.1	49 00.1	22.1	317 03.0	04.4
R 12	82 09.9	311 02.0	N20 18.6	64 58.0	N 5 29.8	64 02.2	N 6 22.2	332 05.1	N22 04.4
D 13	97 12.3	326 01.9	17.9	79 58.7	30.5	79 04.3	22.4	347 07.3	04.4
A 14	112 14.8	341 01.9	17.1	94 59.5	31.2	94 06.4	22.5	2 09.4	04.3
Y 15	127 17.2	356 01.9 ··	16.4	110 00.2 ··	31.9	109 08.4 ··	22.7	17 11.5 ··	04.3
16	142 19.7	11 01.8	15.6	125 01.0	32.6	124 10.5	22.8	32 13.7	04.2
17	157 22.2	26 01.8	14.8	140 01.8	33.3	139 12.6	23.0	47 15.8	04.2
18	172 24.6	41 01.8	N20 14.1	155 02.5	N 5 34.0	154 14.7	N 6 23.1	62 17.9	N22 04.2
19	187 27.1	56 01.8	13.3	170 03.3	34.7	169 16.7	23.3	77 20.1	04.1
20	202 29.6	71 01.7	12.6	185 04.1	35.4	184 18.8	23.4	92 22.2	04.1
21	217 32.0	86 01.7 ··	11.8	200 04.8 ··	36.1	199 20.9 ··	23.6	107 24.4 ··	04.1
22	232 34.5	101 01.7	11.0	215 05.6	36.8	214 23.0	23.7	122 26.5	04.0
23	247 37.0	116 01.6	10.3	230 06.3	37.5	229 25.1	23.9	137 28.6	04.0
Mer. Pass. 6 36.2		*v* −0.1	*d* 0.7	*v* 0.8	*d* 0.7	*v* 2.1	*d* 0.2	*v* 2.1	*d* 0.0

STARS

Name	S.H.A.	Dec.
Acamar	315 40.3	S40 24.0
Achernar	335 48.3	S57 21.4
Acrux	173 41.0	S62 58.2
Adhara	255 35.3	S28 56.5
Aldebaran	291 22.4	N16 27.6
Alioth	166 45.4	N56 05.7
Alkaid	153 21.0	N49 26.3
Al Na'ir	28 19.2	S47 04.5
Alnilam	276 15.6	S 1 13.1
Alphard	218 24.2	S 8 33.3
Alphecca	126 34.8	N26 47.9
Alpheratz	358 13.1	N28 57.2
Altair	62 35.7	N 8 48.2
Ankaa	353 43.9	S42 26.1
Antares	113 00.9	S26 22.7
Arcturus	146 21.5	N19 18.6
Atria	108 27.8	S68 59.1
Avior	234 30.1	S59 26.1
Bellatrix	279 02.9	N 6 19.6
Betelgeuse	271 32.5	N 7 24.1
Canopus	264 09.3	S52 41.1
Capella	281 17.1	N45 58.4
Deneb	49 50.6	N45 11.5
Denebola	183 02.7	N14 42.5
Diphda	349 24.6	S18 07.1
Dubhe	194 26.6	N61 53.2
Elnath	278 49.0	N28 35.2
Eltanin	90 58.8	N51 29.5
Enif	34 14.9	N 9 45.8
Fomalhaut	15 55.3	S29 44.9
Gacrux	172 32.6	S56 58.9
Gienah	176 21.6	S17 24.6
Hadar	149 28.0	S60 15.6
Hamal	328 33.2	N23 20.7
Kaus Aust.	84 21.2	S34 23.7
Kochab	137 17.9	N74 15.5
Markab	14 06.7	N15 04.4
Menkar	314 45.1	N 3 59.6
Menkent	148 41.0	S36 15.2
Miaplacidus	221 46.2	S69 37.4
Mirfak	309 21.7	N49 46.4
Nunki	76 33.2	S26 19.6
Peacock	54 03.6	S56 48.6
Pollux	244 02.8	N28 05.2
Procyon	245 29.8	N 5 17.2
Rasalhague	96 32.6	N12 34.7
Regulus	208 13.9	N12 05.2
Rigel	281 39.8	S 8 13.8
Rigil Kent.	140 30.1	S60 44.3
Sabik	102 44.9	S15 41.7
Schedar	350 13.3	N56 24.0
Shaula	97 00.2	S37 05.2
Sirius	258 59.2	S16 41.1
Spica	159 01.1	S11 02.2
Suhail	223 13.7	S43 20.3
Vega	80 57.8	N38 45.6
Zuben'ubi	137 36.7	S15 56.5

	S.H.A.	Mer. Pass.
Venus	230 22.9	15 16
Mars	343 49.4	7 42
Jupiter	342 06.5	7 48
Saturn	250 06.9	13 55

1975 JUNE 12, 13, 14 (THURS., FRI., SAT.)

SUN / MOON

G.M.T.	SUN G.H.A.	SUN Dec.	MOON G.H.A.	v	MOON Dec.	d	H.P.
12 00	180 06.5	N23 05.8	149 45.2	7.2	N18 13.9	7.0	58.9
01	195 06.3	05.9	164 11.4	7.2	18 06.9	7.1	58.9
02	210 06.2	06.1	178 37.6	7.2	17 59.8	7.2	58.9
03	225 06.1	06.3	193 03.8	7.3	17 52.6	7.3	59.0
04	240 06.0	06.4	207 30.1	7.3	17 45.3	7.4	59.0
05	255 05.8	06.6	221 56.4	7.3	17 37.9	7.5	59.0
06	270 05.7 N23	06.8	236 22.7	7.4	N17 30.4	7.7	59.0
07	285 05.6	06.9	250 49.1	7.4	17 22.7	7.7	59.0
T 08	300 05.4	07.1	265 15.5	7.4	17 15.0	7.9	59.0
H 09	315 05.3	07.3	279 41.9	7.5	17 07.1	8.0	59.0
U 10	330 05.2	07.4	294 08.4	7.5	16 59.1	8.1	59.0
R 11	345 05.1	07.6	308 34.9	7.6	16 51.0	8.2	59.1
S 12	0 04.9 N23	07.8	323 01.5	7.6	N16 42.8	8.3	59.1
D 13	15 04.8	07.9	337 28.1	7.6	16 34.5	8.4	59.1
A 14	30 04.7	08.1	351 54.7	7.7	16 26.1	8.5	59.1
Y 15	45 04.5	08.3	6 21.4	7.7	16 17.6	8.6	59.1
16	60 04.4	08.4	20 48.1	7.8	16 09.0	8.7	59.1
17	75 04.3	08.6	35 14.9	7.8	16 00.3	8.8	59.1
18	90 04.2 N23	08.7	49 41.7	7.8	N15 51.5	8.9	59.1
19	105 04.0	08.9	64 08.5	7.9	15 42.6	9.0	59.2
20	120 03.9	09.1	78 35.4	7.9	15 33.6	9.1	59.2
21	135 03.8	09.2	93 02.3	8.0	15 24.5	9.2	59.2
22	150 03.6	09.4	107 29.3	8.0	15 15.3	9.3	59.2
23	165 03.5	09.5	121 56.3	8.1	15 06.0	9.4	59.2
13 00	180 03.4 N23	09.7	136 23.4	8.0	N14 56.6	9.5	59.2
01	195 03.3	09.8	150 50.4	8.2	14 47.1	9.6	59.2
02	210 03.1	10.0	165 17.6	8.2	14 37.5	9.6	59.2
03	225 03.0	10.1	179 44.8	8.2	14 27.9	9.8	59.2
04	240 02.9	10.3	194 12.0	8.3	14 18.1	9.8	59.2
05	255 02.7	10.4	208 39.3	8.3	14 08.3	10.0	59.2
06	270 02.6 N23	10.6	223 06.6	8.3	N13 58.3	10.0	59.3
07	285 02.5	10.7	237 33.9	8.4	13 48.3	10.1	59.3
08	300 02.3	10.9	252 01.3	8.5	13 38.2	10.2	59.3
F 09	315 02.2	11.0	266 28.8	8.4	13 28.0	10.3	59.3
R 10	330 02.1	11.2	280 56.2	8.6	13 17.7	10.3	59.3
I 11	345 02.0	11.3	295 23.8	8.5	13 07.4	10.4	59.3
D 12	0 01.8 N23	11.5	309 51.3	8.7	N12 57.0	10.5	59.3
A 13	15 01.7	11.6	324 19.0	8.6	12 46.5	10.6	59.3
Y 14	30 01.6	11.8	338 46.6	8.7	12 35.9	10.7	59.3
15	45 01.4	11.9	353 14.3	8.7	12 25.2	10.7	59.3
16	60 01.3	12.1	7 42.0	8.8	12 14.5	10.8	59.3
17	75 01.2	12.2	22 09.8	8.9	12 03.7	10.9	59.3
18	90 01.0 N23	12.3	36 37.7	8.8	N11 52.8	11.0	59.3
19	105 00.9	12.5	51 05.5	8.9	11 41.8	11.0	59.3
20	120 00.8	12.6	65 33.4	9.0	11 30.8	11.1	59.4
21	135 00.6	12.8	80 01.4	9.0	11 19.7	11.2	59.4
22	150 00.5	12.9	94 29.4	9.0	11 08.5	11.2	59.4
23	165 00.4	13.1	108 57.4	9.1	10 57.3	11.3	59.4
14 00	180 00.3 N23	13.2	123 25.5	9.1	N10 46.0	11.4	59.4
01	195 00.1	13.3	137 53.6	9.2	10 34.6	11.4	59.4
02	210 00.0	13.5	152 21.8	9.2	10 23.2	11.5	59.4
03	224 59.9	13.6	166 50.0	9.2	10 11.7	11.5	59.4
04	239 59.7	13.7	181 18.2	9.3	10 00.2	11.6	59.4
05	254 59.6	13.9	195 46.5	9.3	9 48.6	11.7	59.4
06	269 59.5 N23	14.0	210 14.8	9.3	N9 36.9	11.7	59.4
07	284 59.3	14.1	224 43.1	9.4	9 25.2	11.8	59.4
S 08	299 59.2	14.3	239 11.5	9.4	9 13.4	11.8	59.4
A 09	314 59.1	14.4	253 39.9	9.5	9 01.6	11.9	59.4
T 10	329 58.9	14.5	268 08.4	9.5	8 49.7	11.9	59.4
U 11	344 58.8	14.7	282 36.9	9.5	8 37.8	12.0	59.4
R 12	359 58.7 N23	14.8	297 05.4	9.6	N8 25.8	12.0	59.4
D 13	14 58.5	14.9	311 34.0	9.6	8 13.8	12.1	59.4
A 14	29 58.4	15.0	326 02.6	9.6	8 01.7	12.1	59.4
Y 15	44 58.3	15.2	340 31.2	9.7	7 49.6	12.2	59.4
16	59 58.1	15.3	354 59.9	9.7	7 37.4	12.2	59.4
17	74 58.0	15.4	9 28.6	9.7	7 25.2	12.2	59.4
18	89 57.9 N23	15.6	23 57.3	9.8	N7 13.0	12.3	59.4
19	104 57.7	15.7	38 26.1	9.8	7 00.7	12.3	59.4
20	119 57.6	15.8	52 54.9	9.8	6 48.4	12.4	59.4
21	134 57.5	15.9	67 23.7	9.8	6 36.0	12.4	59.4
22	149 57.4	16.0	81 52.5	9.9	6 23.6	12.5	59.4
23	164 57.2	16.2	96 21.4	9.9	6 11.1	12.4	59.4
	S.D. 15.8	d 0.1	S.D. 16.1		16.2		16.2

Twilight / Sunrise / Moonrise

Lat.	Naut.	Civil	Sunrise	Moonrise 12	13	14	15
N 72	□	□	□	02 46	05 50	08 06	10 12
N 70	□	□	□	04 08	06 19	08 21	10 18
68	□	□	□	04 46	06 41	08 33	10 22
66	////	////	00 08	05 13	06 57	08 42	10 26
64	////	////	01 36	05 34	07 11	08 50	10 29
62	////	////	02 12	05 50	07 23	08 57	10 31
60	////	00 58	02 37	06 04	07 32	09 03	10 34
N 58	////	01 44	02 57	06 15	07 41	09 08	10 36
56	////	02 12	03 14	06 26	07 48	09 13	10 37
54	00 53	02 34	03 28	06 35	07 55	09 17	10 39
52	01 35	02 51	03 40	06 42	08 01	09 21	10 41
50	02 02	03 06	03 50	06 50	08 06	09 24	10 42
45	02 46	03 36	04 13	07 05	08 18	09 31	10 45
N 40	03 16	03 58	04 30	07 17	08 27	09 37	10 47
35	03 39	04 16	04 45	07 28	08 35	09 42	10 49
30	03 58	04 31	04 58	07 37	08 42	09 47	10 51
20	04 26	04 55	05 20	07 53	08 55	09 55	10 54
N 10	04 49	05 16	05 39	08 07	09 05	10 02	10 57
0	05 08	05 34	05 56	08 20	09 15	10 08	11 00
S 10	05 24	05 51	06 13	08 33	09 25	10 15	11 03
20	05 40	06 08	06 32	08 47	09 36	10 22	11 05
30	05 57	06 26	06 53	09 03	09 48	10 30	11 09
35	06 05	06 37	07 05	09 12	09 55	10 34	11 11
40	06 14	06 48	07 19	09 23	10 03	10 39	11 13
45	06 25	07 02	07 35	09 35	10 12	10 45	11 15
S 50	06 36	07 17	07 56	09 50	10 23	10 52	11 18
52	06 41	07 25	08 06	09 57	10 28	10 55	11 19
54	06 47	07 33	08 17	10 04	10 34	10 59	11 21
56	06 53	07 42	08 29	10 13	10 40	11 03	11 22
58	07 00	07 52	08 44	10 22	10 47	11 07	11 24
S 60	07 07	08 04	09 01	10 33	10 55	11 12	11 26

Sunset / Twilight / Moonset

Lat.	Sunset	Civil	Naut.	Moonset 12	13	14	15
N 72	□	□	□	01 39	00 31	{00 07 / 23 50}	23 35
N 70	□	□	□	00 16	{00 00 / 23 58}	23 42	23 34
68	□	□	□	23 38	23 37	23 35	23 33
66	□	□	□	23 20	23 26	23 29	23 32
64	22 25	////	////	23 05	23 16	23 25	23 32
62	21 48	////	////	22 53	23 08	23 20	23 31
60	21 23	23 04	////	22 42	23 01	23 17	23 30
N 58	21 03	22 17	////	22 33	22 55	23 13	23 30
56	20 46	21 48	////	22 25	22 50	23 11	23 30
54	20 32	21 26	23 09	22 17	22 45	23 08	23 29
52	20 20	21 09	22 25	22 11	22 40	23 06	23 29
50	20 09	20 54	21 58	22 05	22 36	23 03	23 29
45	19 47	20 24	21 14	21 52	22 27	22 59	23 28
N 40	19 29	20 02	20 44	21 42	22 20	22 55	23 27
35	19 14	19 44	20 21	21 33	22 13	22 51	23 27
30	19 01	19 29	20 02	21 24	22 08	22 48	23 26
20	18 40	19 04	19 33	21 11	21 58	22 42	23 26
N 10	18 21	18 44	19 11	20 58	21 49	22 38	23 25
0	18 03	18 26	18 52	20 47	21 41	22 33	23 24
S 10	17 46	18 09	18 35	20 35	21 32	22 28	23 23
20	17 28	17 52	18 19	20 23	21 23	22 23	23 23
30	17 07	17 33	18 03	20 08	21 13	22 18	23 22
35	16 55	17 23	17 54	20 00	21 07	22 14	23 21
40	16 41	17 11	17-45	19 50	21 00	22 11	23 20
45	16 24	16 58	17 35	19 39	20 52	22 06	23 20
S 50	16 04	16 42	17 23	19 25	20 43	22 01	23 19
52	15 54	16 35	17 18	19 19	20 38	21 58	23 18
54	15 43	16 26	17 13	19 12	20 33	21 56	23 18
56	15 30	16 17	17 06	19 04	20 28	21 53	23 17
58	15 16	16 07	17 00	18 55	20 22	21 49	23 17
S 60	14 59	15 56	16 52	18 44	20 15	21 46	23 16

SUN / MOON

Day	Eqn. of Time 00h	12h	Mer. Pass.	Mer. Pass. Upper	Lower	Age	Phase
	m s	m s	h m	h m	h m	d	
12	00 26	00 20	12 00	14 34	02 06	03	
13	00 14	00 08	12 00	15 28	03 01	04	◖
14	00 01	00 05	12 00	16 21	03 55	05	

STARS, 1975 JANUARY—JUNE

Mag.	Name and Number		S.H.A. JAN.	FEB.	MAR.	APR.	MAY	JUNE	Dec.	JAN.	FEB.	MAR.	APR.	MAY	JUNE
3·1	γ Ursæ Minoris †	129	49·3	48·8	48·3	47·9	47·8	48·0	N. 71	55·0	55·0	55·0	55·1	55·3	55·5
3·1	γ Trianguli Aust.	130	51·5	50·9	50·4	50·0	49·8	49·7	S. 68	35·1	35·1	35·2	35·3	35·5	35·6
2·7	β Libræ	131	05·0	04·7	04·5	04·4	04·3	04·2	S. 9	17·5	17·6	17·7	17·7	17·7	17·6
2·8	β Lupi	135	46·5	46·2	45·9	45·7	45·6	45·6	S. 43	01·9	02·0	02·1	02·2	02·3	02·3
2·2	β Ursæ Minoris 40	137	19·2	18·6	18·0	17·7	17·6	17·9	N. 74	15·1	15·0	15·1	15·2	15·4	15·5
2·9	α Libræ 39	137	37·4	37·2	37·0	36·8	36·7	36·7	S. 15	56·3	56·4	56·5	56·5	56·5	56·5
2·6	ε Bootis	139	01·5	01·2	01·0	00·9	00·8	00·9	N. 27	10·5	10·4	10·4	10·5	10·6	10·7
2·9	α Lupi	139	55·9	55·5	55·3	55·1	54·9	55·0	S. 47	16·8	16·8	16·9	17·0	17·1	17·2
0·1	α Centauri 38	140	31·2	30·8	30·5	30·2	30·1	30·2	S. 60	43·7	43·8	43·9	44·0	44·2	44·3
2·6	η Centauri	141	31·0	30·7	30·5	30·3	30·2	30·2	S. 42	02·8	02·9	03·0	03·1	03·2	03·3
3·0	γ Bootis	142	13·9	13·6	13·4	13·2	13·2	13·2	N. 38	24·7	24·7	24·7	24·8	24·9	25·0
0·2	α Bootis 37	146	22·0	21·8	21·6	21·5	21·5	21·5	N. 19	18·5	18·4	18·4	18·5	18·5	18·6
2·3	θ Centauri 36	148	41·6	41·3	41·1	41·0	40·9	41·0	S. 36	14·8	14·9	15·0	15·1	15·2	15·2
0·9	β Centauri 35	149	28·9	28·5	28·2	28·0	27·9	28·0	S. 60	15·0	15·1	15·2	15·4	15·5	15·6
3·1	ζ Centauri	151	30·1	29·8	29·5	29·4	29·3	29·4	S. 47	09·8	09·9	10·0	10·2	10·3	10·3
2·8	η Bootis	151	37·4	37·1	37·0	36·9	36·9	36·9	N. 18	31·1	31·0	31·0	31·1	31·2	31·2
1·9	η Ursæ Majoris 34	153	21·5	21·2	21·0	20·9	20·9	21·0	N. 49	25·9	25·9	25·9	26·0	26·2	26·3
2·6	ε Centauri†	155	25·2	24·8	24·6	24·4	24·4	24·5	S. 53	20·2	20·3	20·5	20·6	20·7	20·8
1·2	α Virginis 33	159	01·6	01·4	01·2	01·1	01·1	01·1	S. 11	02·0	02·1	02·1	02·2	02·2	02·2
2·2	ζ Ursæ Majoris	159	16·0	15·7	15·5	15·4	15·4	15·6	N. 55	02·9	02·9	03·0	03·1	03·3	03·4
2·9	ι Centauri	160	11·8	11·6	11·4	11·3	11·3	11·3	S. 36	34·8	34·9	35·0	35·1	35·2	35·3
3·0	ε Virginis	164	45·7	45·5	45·4	45·3	45·3	45·4	N. 11	05·4	05·3	05·3	05·4	05·4	05·4
2·9	α Canum Venat.	166	16·8	16·6	16·4	16·4	16·4	16·5	N. 38	26·8	26·8	26·9	27·0	27·1	27·1
1·7	ε Ursæ Majoris 32	166	45·8	45·4	45·2	45·2	45·3	45·4	N. 56	05·3	05·3	05·4	05·5	05·7	05·7
1·5	β Crucis	168	25·7	25·3	25·1	25·0	25·1	25·3	S. 59	33·0	33·1	33·3	33·4	33·6	33·7
2·9	γ Virginis	169	53·8	53·6	53·4	53·4	53·4	53·5	S. 1	18·9	19·0	19·0	19·1	19·0	19·0
2·4	γ Centauri	169	57·6	57·3	57·1	57·0	57·1	57·2	S. 48	49·3	49·4	49·5	49·7	49·8	49·8
2·9	α Muscæ	171	04·1	03·7	03·4	03·3	03·5	03·7	S. 68	59·7	59·8	60·0	60·2	60·3	60·4
2·8	β Corvi	171	43·5	43·3	43·2	43·1	43·2	43·2	S. 23	15·6	15·7	15·8	15·9	15·9	15·9
1·6	γ Crucis 31	172	32·9	32·6	32·4	32·3	32·4	32·6	S. 56	58·3	58·4	58·6	58·7	58·9	58·9
1·1	α Crucis 30	173	41·4	41·0	40·8	40·7	40·8	41·0	S. 62	57·5	57·6	57·8	58·0	58·1	58·2
2·8	γ Corvi 29	176	21·8	21·6	21·5	21·5	21·5	21·6	S. 17	24·3	24·4	24·5	24·5	24·6	24·6
2·9	δ Centauri	178	13·6	13·3	13·2	13·2	13·3	13·4	S. 50	34·9	35·1	35·2	35·4	35·5	35·5
2·5	γ Ursæ Majoris	181	51·7	51·4	51·3	51·3	51·5	51·7	N. 53	49·6	49·6	49·7	49·9	50·0	50·0
2·2	β Leonis 28	183	02·8	02·6	02·5	02·5	02·6	02·7	N. 14	42·4	42·4	42·4	42·4	42·5	42·5
2·6	δ Leonis	191	47·8	47·6	47·6	47·6	47·7	47·8	N. 20	39·4	39·3	39·4	39·4	39·5	39·5
3·2	ψ Ursæ Majoris	192	55·5	55·3	55·2	55·3	55·4	55·6	N. 44	37·7	37·7	37·8	37·9	38·0	38·0
2·0	α Ursæ Majoris 27	194	26·4	26·1	26·0	26·1	26·3	26·6	N. 61	52·8	52·8	53·0	53·1	53·2	53·2
2·4	β Ursæ Majoris	194	54·2	54·0	53·9	54·0	54·2	54·4	N. 56	30·6	30·7	30·8	30·9	31·0	31·0
2·8	μ Velorum	198	34·0	33·8	33·8	33·9	34·0	34·2	S. 49	17·2	17·4	17·6	17·7	17·8	17·8
3·0	θ Carinæ †	199	28·2	28·0	28·0	28·1	28·4	28·7	S. 64	15·7	15·9	16·1	16·2	16·3	16·4
2·3	γ Leonis	205	20·5	20·4	20·3	20·4	20·5	20·6	N. 19	57·8	57·8	57·8	57·9	57·9	57·9
1·3	α Leonis 26	208	13·8	13·7	13·7	13·7	13·8	13·9	N. 12	05·2	05·1	05·1	05·1	05·2	05·2
3·1	ε Leonis	213	52·9	52·8	52·8	52·8	53·0	53·1	N. 23	53·1	53·1	53·2	53·2	53·2	53·3
3·0	N Velorum	217	22·3	22·2	22·3	22·5	22·7	23·0	S. 56	55·4	55·6	55·8	55·9	56·0	55·9
2·2	α Hydræ 25	218	24·0	24·0	24·0	24·1	24·2	24·2	S. 8	33·1	33·2	33·3	33·3	33·3	33·3
2·6	κ Velorum	219	39·2	39·1	39·2	39·4	39·6	39·8	S. 54	54·2	54·4	54·6	54·7	54·7	54·7
2·2	ι Carinæ	220	52·9	52·8	52·9	53·1	53·4	53·7	S. 59	10·2	10·4	10·6	10·7	10·7	10·7
1·8	β Carinæ 24	221	44·9	44·9	45·1	45·4	45·9	46·3	S. 69	36·9	37·1	37·2	37·3	37·4	37·3
2·2	λ Velorum 23	223	13·2	13·1	13·2	13·4	13·5	13·7	S. 43	19·9	20·1	20·3	20·3	20·4	20·3
3·1	ι Ursæ Majoris	225	36·6	36·6	36·6	36·8	37·0	37·1	N. 48	08·2	08·3	08·3	08·4	08·4	08·4
2·0	δ Velorum	228	59·0	59·0	59·1	59·4	59·6	59·8	S. 54	37·0	37·2	37·4	37·5	37·5	37·4
1·7	ε Carinæ 22	234	29·1	29·2	29·3	29·6	29·9	30·2	S. 59	25·8	26·0	26·1	26·2	26·2	26·1
1·9	γ Velorum	237	47·9	47·9	48·0	48·2	48·4	48·6	S. 47	15·9	16·0	16·1	16·2	16·2	16·1
2·9	ρ Puppis	238	22·2	22·2	22·3	22·4	22·5	22·6	S. 24	14·0	14·2	14·2	14·3	14·3	14·2
2·3	ζ Puppis	239	18·8	18·8	18·9	19·1	19·2	19·4	S. 39	56·1	56·2	56·3	56·4	56·4	56·3
1·2	β Geminorum 21	244	02·5	02·4	02·5	02·7	02·8	02·8	N. 28	05·1	05·1	05·1	05·2	05·2	05·2
0·5	α Canis Minoris 20	245	29·5	29·4	29·5	29·7	29·8	29·8	N. 5	17·2	17·2	17·2	17·2	17·2	17·2

† Not suitable for use with H.O. 214 (H.D. 486)

POLARIS (POLE STAR) TABLES, 1975
FOR DETERMINING LATITUDE FROM SEXTANT ALTITUDE AND FOR AZIMUTH

L.H.A. ARIES	240°–249°	250°–259°	260°–269°	270°–279°	280°–289°	290°–299°	300°–309°	310°–319°	320°–329°	330°–339°	340°–349°	350°–359°
	a_0	a_0	a_0	a_0	a_0	a_0	a_0	a_0	a_0	a_0	a_0	a_0
0	1 43·8	1 39·1	1 33·1	1 26·1	1 18·3	1 09·9	1 01·1	0 52·3	0 43·6	0 35·4	0 27·9	0 21·3
1	43·4	38·5	32·5	25·4	17·5	09·0	1 00·2	51·4	42·8	34·6	27·2	20·7
2	43·0	38·0	31·8	24·6	16·7	08·2	0 59·4	50·5	41·9	33·8	26·5	20·1
3	42·5	37·4	31·1	23·9	15·8	07·3	58·5	49·6	41·1	33·1	25·8	19·6
4	42·1	36·8	30·4	23·1	15·0	06·4	57·6	48·8	40·3	32·3	25·1	19·0
5	1 41·6	1 36·2	1 29·7	1 22·3	1 14·2	1 05·5	0 56·7	0 47·9	0 39·4	0 31·5	0 24·5	0 18·5
6	41·1	35·6	29·0	21·5	13·3	04·7	55·8	47·0	38·6	30·8	23·8	17·9
7	40·6	35·0	28·3	20·7	12·5	03·8	54·9	46·2	37·8	30·0	23·2	17·4
8	40·1	34·4	27·6	19·9	11·6	02·9	54·0	45·3	37·0	29·3	22·5	16·9
9	39·6	33·8	26·9	19·1	10·8	02·0	53·2	44·5	36·2	28·6	21·9	16·4
10	1 39·1	1 33·1	1 26·1	1 18·3	1 09·9	1 01·1	0 52·3	0 43·6	0 35·4	0 27·9	0 21·3	0 15·9

Lat.	a_1	a_1	a_1	a_1	a_1	a_1	a_1	a_1	a_1	a_1	a_1	a_1
0	0·5	0·4	0·3	0·2	0·2	0·2	0·2	0·2	0·2	0·3	0·4	0·4
10	·5	·4	·4	·3	·3	·2	·2	·2	·3	·3	·4	·5
20	·5	·5	·4	·4	·3	·3	·3	·3	·3	·4	·4	·5
30	·5	·5	·5	·4	·4	·4	·4	·4	·4	·4	·5	·5
40	0·6	0·5	0·5	0·5	0·5	0·5	0·5	0·5	0·5	0·5	0·5	0·6
45	·6	·6	·6	·5	·5	·5	·5	·5	·5	·5	·6	·6
50	·6	·6	·6	·6	·6	·6	·6	·6	·6	·6	·6	·6
55	·6	·6	·7	·7	·7	·7	·7	·7	·7	·7	·6	·6
60	·7	·7	·7	·8	·8	·8	·8	·8	·8	·8	·7	·7
62	0·7	0·7	0·8	0·8	0·8	0·9	0·9	0·8	0·8	0·8	0·7	0·7
64	·7	·7	·8	·9	0·9	0·9	0·9	0·9	·9	·8	·8	·7
66	·7	·8	·9	0·9	1·0	1·0	1·0	1·0	0·9	·9	·8	·7
68	0·7	0·8	0·9	1·0	1·0	1·1	1·1	1·1	1·0	0·9	0·9	0·8

Month	a_2	a_2	a_2	a_2	a_2	a_2	a_2	a_2	a_2	a_2	a_2	a_2
Jan.	0·4	0·4	0·4	0·5	0·5	0·5	0·6	0·6	0·6	0·7	0·7	0·7
Feb.	·3	·3	·3	·3	·3	·4	·4	·4	·5	·5	·6	·6
Mar.	·3	·3	·3	·3	·3	·3	·3	·3	·3	·4	·4	·5
Apr.	0·4	0·4	0·3	0·3	0·3	0·2	0·2	0·2	0·2	0·3	0·3	0·3
May	·6	·5	·5	·4	·3	·3	·3	·2	·2	·2	·2	·2
June	·7	·7	·6	·5	·5	·4	·4	·3	·3	·3	·2	·2
July	0·8	0·8	0·8	0·7	0·6	0·6	0·5	0·5	0·4	0·4	0·3	0·3
Aug.	·9	·9	·9	·8	·8	·8	·7	·7	·6	·5	·5	·4
Sept.	·9	·9	·9	·9	·9	·9	·9	·8	·8	·7	·7	·6
Oct.	0·8	0·8	0·9	0·9	0·9	0·9	0·9	0·9	0·9	0·9	0·9	0·8
Nov.	·6	·7	·8	·8	·9	·9	1·0	1·0	1·0	1·0	1·0	1·0
Dec.	0·5	0·5	0·6	0·7	0·8	0·9	0·9	1·0	1·0	1·0	1·1	1·1

Lat.	AZIMUTH											
0	0·5	0·6	0·7	0·8	0·8	0·8	0·8	0·8	0·8	0·7	0·6	0·5
20	0·5	0·6	0·7	0·8	0·9	0·9	0·9	0·9	0·8	0·8	0·7	0·5
40	0·6	0·7	0·9	1·0	1·1	1·1	1·1	1·1	1·0	0·9	0·8	0·7
50	0·7	0·9	1·0	1·2	1·3	1·3	1·3	1·3	1·2	1·1	1·0	0·8
55	0·8	1·0	1·2	1·3	1·4	1·5	1·5	1·4	1·4	1·3	1·1	0·9
60	0·9	1·1	1·3	1·5	1·6	1·7	1·7	1·7	1·6	1·4	1·3	1·0
65	1·1	1·3	1·6	1·8	1·9	2·0	2·0	2·0	1·9	1·7	1·5	1·2

Latitude = Apparent altitude (corrected for refraction) $- 1° + a_0 + a_1 + a_2$

The table is entered with L.H.A. Aries to determine the column to be used; each column refers to a range of 10°. a_0 is taken, with mental interpolation, from the upper table with the units of L.H.A. Aries in degrees as argument; a_1, a_2 are taken, without interpolation, from the second and third tables with arguments latitude and month respectively. a_0, a_1, a_2 are always positive. The final table gives the azimuth of *Polaris*.

CONVERSION OF ARC TO TIME

0°–59°	h m	60°–119°	h m	120°–179°	h m	180°–239°	h m	240°–299°	h m	300°–359°	h m	′	0′.00 m s	0′.25 m s	0′.50 m s	0′.75 m s
0	0 00	60	4 00	120	8 00	180	12 00	240	16 00	300	20 00	0	0 00	0 01	0 02	0 03
1	0 04	61	4 04	121	8 04	181	12 04	241	16 04	301	20 04	1	0 04	0 05	0 06	0 07
2	0 08	62	4 08	122	8 08	182	12 08	242	16 08	302	20 08	2	0 08	0 09	0 10	0 11
3	0 12	63	4 12	123	8 12	183	12 12	243	16 12	303	20 12	3	0 12	0 13	0 14	0 15
4	0 16	64	4 16	124	8 16	184	12 16	244	16 16	304	20 16	4	0 16	0 17	0 18	0 19
5	0 20	65	4 20	125	8 20	185	12 20	245	16 20	305	20 20	5	0 20	0 21	0 22	0 23
6	0 24	66	4 24	126	8 24	186	12 24	246	16 24	306	20 24	6	0 24	0 25	0 26	0 27
7	0 28	67	4 28	127	8 28	187	12 28	247	16 28	307	20 28	7	0 28	0 29	0 30	0 31
8	0 32	68	4 32	128	8 32	188	12 32	248	16 32	308	20 32	8	0 32	0 33	0 34	0 35
9	0 36	69	4 36	129	8 36	189	12 36	249	16 36	309	20 36	9	0 36	0 37	0 38	0 39
10	0 40	70	4 40	130	8 40	190	12 40	250	16 40	310	20 40	10	0 40	0 41	0 42	0 43
11	0 44	71	4 44	131	8 44	191	12 44	251	16 44	311	20 44	11	0 44	0 45	0 46	0 47
12	0 48	72	4 48	132	8 48	192	12 48	252	16 48	312	20 48	12	0 48	0 49	0 50	0 51
13	0 52	73	4 52	133	8 52	193	12 52	253	16 52	313	20 52	13	0 52	0 53	0 54	0 55
14	0 56	74	4 56	134	8 56	194	12 56	254	16 56	314	20 56	14	0 56	0 57	0 58	0 59
15	1 00	75	5 00	135	9 00	195	13 00	255	17 00	315	21 00	15	1 00	1 01	1 02	1 03
16	1 04	76	5 04	136	9 04	196	13 04	256	17 04	316	21 04	16	1 04	1 05	1 06	1 07
17	1 08	77	5 08	137	9 08	197	13 08	257	17 08	317	21 08	17	1 08	1 09	1 10	1 11
18	1 12	78	5 12	138	9 12	198	13 12	258	17 12	318	21 12	18	1 12	1 13	1 14	1 15
19	1 16	79	5 16	139	9 16	199	13 16	259	17 16	319	21 16	19	1 16	1 17	1 18	1 19
20	1 20	80	5 20	140	9 20	200	13 20	260	17 20	320	21 20	20	1 20	1 21	1 22	1 23
21	1 24	81	5 24	141	9 24	201	13 24	261	17 24	321	21 24	21	1 24	1 25	1 26	1 27
22	1 28	82	5 28	142	9 28	202	13 28	262	17 28	322	21 28	22	1 28	1 29	1 30	1 31
23	1 32	83	5 32	143	9 32	203	13 32	263	17 32	323	21 32	23	1 32	1 33	1 34	1 35
24	1 36	84	5 36	144	9 36	204	13 36	264	17 36	324	21 36	24	1 36	1 37	1 38	1 39
25	1 40	85	5 40	145	9 40	205	13 40	265	17 40	325	21 40	25	1 40	1 41	1 42	1 43
26	1 44	86	5 44	146	9 44	206	13 44	266	17 44	326	21 44	26	1 44	1 45	1 46	1 47
27	1 48	87	5 48	147	9 48	207	13 48	267	17 48	327	21 48	27	1 48	1 49	1 50	1 51
28	1 52	88	5 52	148	9 52	208	13 52	268	17 52	328	21 52	28	1 52	1 53	1 54	1 55
29	1 56	89	5 56	149	9 56	209	13 56	269	17 56	329	21 56	29	1 56	1 57	1 58	1 59
30	2 00	90	6 00	150	10 00	210	14 00	270	18 00	330	22 00	30	2 00	2 01	2 02	2 03
31	2 04	91	6 04	151	10 04	211	14 04	271	18 04	331	22 04	31	2 04	2 05	2 06	2 07
32	2 08	92	6 08	152	10 08	212	14 08	272	18 08	332	22 08	32	2 08	2 09	2 10	2 11
33	2 12	93	6 12	153	10 12	213	14 12	273	18 12	333	22 12	33	2 12	2 13	2 14	2 15
34	2 16	94	6 16	154	10 16	214	14 16	274	18 16	334	22 16	34	2 16	2 17	2 18	2 19
35	2 20	95	6 20	155	10 20	215	14 20	275	18 20	335	22 20	35	2 20	2 21	2 22	2 23
36	2 24	96	6 24	156	10 24	216	14 24	276	18 24	336	22 24	36	2 24	2 25	2 26	2 27
37	2 28	97	6 28	157	10 28	217	14 28	277	18 28	337	22 28	37	2 28	2 29	2 30	2 31
38	2 32	98	6 32	158	10 32	218	14 32	278	18 32	338	22 32	38	2 32	2 33	2 34	2 35
39	2 36	99	6 36	159	10 36	219	14 36	279	18 36	339	22 36	39	2 36	2 37	2 38	2 39
40	2 40	100	6 40	160	10 40	220	14 40	280	18 40	340	22 40	40	2 40	2 41	2 42	2 43
41	2 44	101	6 44	161	10 44	221	14 44	281	18 44	341	22 44	41	2 44	2 45	2 46	2 47
42	2 48	102	6 48	162	10 48	222	14 48	282	18 48	342	22 48	42	2 48	2 49	2 50	2 51
43	2 52	103	6 52	163	10 52	223	14 52	283	18 52	343	22 52	43	2 52	2 53	2 54	2 55
44	2 56	104	6 56	164	10 56	224	14 56	284	18 56	344	22 56	44	2 56	2 57	2 58	2 59
45	3 00	105	7 00	165	11 00	225	15 00	285	19 00	345	23 00	45	3 00	3 01	3 02	3 03
46	3 04	106	7 04	166	11 04	226	15 04	286	19 04	346	23 04	46	3 04	3 05	3 06	3 07
47	3 08	107	7 08	167	11 08	227	15 08	287	19 08	347	23 08	47	3 08	3 09	3 10	3 11
48	3 12	108	7 12	168	11 12	228	15 12	288	19 12	348	23 12	48	3 12	3 13	3 14	3 15
49	3 16	109	7 16	169	11 16	229	15 16	289	19 16	349	23 16	49	3 16	3 17	3 18	3 19
50	3 20	110	7 20	170	11 20	230	15 20	290	19 20	350	23 20	50	3 20	3 21	3 22	3 23
51	3 24	111	7 24	171	11 24	231	15 24	291	19 24	351	23 24	51	3 24	3 25	3 26	3 27
52	3 28	112	7 28	172	11 28	232	15 28	292	19 28	352	23 28	52	3 28	3 29	3 30	3 31
53	3 32	113	7 32	173	11 32	233	15 32	293	19 32	353	23 32	53	3 32	3 33	3 34	3 35
54	3 36	114	7 36	174	11 36	234	15 36	294	19 36	354	23 36	54	3 36	3 37	3 38	3 39
55	3 40	115	7 40	175	11 40	235	15 40	295	19 40	355	23 40	55	3 40	3 41	3 42	3 43
56	3 44	116	7 44	176	11 44	236	15 44	296	19 44	356	23 44	56	3 44	3 45	3 46	3 47
57	3 48	117	7 48	177	11 48	237	15 48	297	19 48	357	23 48	57	3 48	3 49	3 50	3 51
58	3 52	118	7 52	178	11 52	238	15 52	298	19 52	358	23 52	58	3 52	3 53	3 54	3 55
59	3 56	119	7 56	179	11 56	239	15 56	299	19 56	359	23 56	59	3 56	3 57	3 58	3 59

The above table is for converting expressions in arc to their equivalent in time ; its main use in this Almanac is for the conversion of longitude for application to L.M.T. (*added* if *west*, *subtracted* if *east*) to give G.M.T. or vice versa, particularly in the case of sunrise, sunset, etc.

24ᵐ INCREMENTS AND CORRECTIONS **25ᵐ**

24ᵐ	SUN PLANETS	ARIES	MOON	v or d / Corrⁿ	v or d / Corrⁿ	v or d / Corrⁿ
00	6 00·0	6 01·0	5 43·6	0·0 0·0	6·0 2·5	12·0 4·9
01	6 00·3	6 01·2	5 43·8	0·1 0·0	6·1 2·5	12·1 4·9
02	6 00·5	6 01·5	5 44·1	0·2 0·1	6·2 2·5	12·2 5·0
03	6 00·8	6 01·7	5 44·3	0·3 0·1	6·3 2·6	12·3 5·0
04	6 01·0	6 02·0	5 44·6	0·4 0·2	6·4 2·6	12·4 5·1
05	6 01·3	6 02·2	5 44·8	0·5 0·2	6·5 2·7	12·5 5·1
06	6 01·5	6 02·5	5 45·0	0·6 0·2	6·6 2·7	12·6 5·1
07	6 01·8	6 02·7	5 45·3	0·7 0·3	6·7 2·7	12·7 5·2
08	6 02·0	6 03·0	5 45·5	0·8 0·3	6·8 2·8	12·8 5·2
09	6 02·3	6 03·2	5 45·7	0·9 0·4	6·9 2·8	12·9 5·3
10	6 02·5	6 03·5	5 46·0	1·0 0·4	7·0 2·9	13·0 5·3
11	6 02·8	6 03·7	5 46·2	1·1 0·4	7·1 2·9	13·1 5·3
12	6 03·0	6 04·0	5 46·5	1·2 0·5	7·2 2·9	13·2 5·4
13	6 03·3	6 04·2	5 46·7	1·3 0·5	7·3 3·0	13·3 5·4
14	6 03·5	6 04·5	5 46·9	1·4 0·6	7·4 3·0	13·4 5·5
15	6 03·8	6 04·7	5 47·2	1·5 0·6	7·5 3·1	13·5 5·5
16	6 04·0	6 05·0	5 47·4	1·6 0·7	7·6 3·1	13·6 5·6
17	6 04·3	6 05·2	5 47·7	1·7 0·7	7·7 3·1	13·7 5·6
18	6 04·5	6 05·5	5 47·9	1·8 0·7	7·8 3·2	13·8 5·6
19	6 04·8	6 05·7	5 48·1	1·9 0·8	7·9 3·2	13·9 5·7
20	6 05·0	6 06·0	5 48·4	2·0 0·8	8·0 3·3	14·0 5·7
21	6 05·3	6 06·3	5 48·6	2·1 0·9	8·1 3·3	14·1 5·8
22	6 05·5	6 06·5	5 48·8	2·2 0·9	8·2 3·3	14·2 5·8
23	6 05·8	6 06·8	5 49·1	2·3 0·9	8·3 3·4	14·3 5·8
24	6 06·0	6 07·0	5 49·3	2·4 1·0	8·4 3·4	14·4 5·9
25	6 06·3	6 07·3	5 49·6	2·5 1·0	8·5 3·5	14·5 5·9
26	6 06·5	6 07·5	5 49·8	2·6 1·1	8·6 3·5	14·6 6·0
27	6 06·8	6 07·8	5 50·0	2·7 1·1	8·7 3·6	14·7 6·0
28	6 07·0	6 08·0	5 50·3	2·8 1·1	8·8 3·6	14·8 6·0
29	6 07·3	6 08·3	5 50·5	2·9 1·2	8·9 3·6	14·9 6·1
30	6 07·5	6 08·5	5 50·8	3·0 1·2	9·0 3·7	15·0 6·1
31	6 07·8	6 08·8	5 51·0	3·1 1·3	9·1 3·7	15·1 6·2
32	6 08·0	6 09·0	5 51·2	3·2 1·3	9·2 3·8	15·2 6·2
33	6 08·3	6 09·3	5 51·5	3·3 1·3	9·3 3·8	15·3 6·2
34	6 08·5	6 09·5	5 51·7	3·4 1·4	9·4 3·8	15·4 6·3
35	6 08·8	6 09·8	5 52·0	3·5 1·4	9·5 3·9	15·5 6·3
36	6 09·0	6 10·0	5 52·2	3·6 1·5	9·6 3·9	15·6 6·4
37	6 09·3	6 10·3	5 52·4	3·7 1·5	9·7 4·0	15·7 6·4
38	6 09·5	6 10·5	5 52·7	3·8 1·6	9·8 4·0	15·8 6·5
39	6 09·8	6 10·8	5 52·9	3·9 1·6	9·9 4·0	15·9 6·5
40	6 10·0	6 11·0	5 53·1	4·0 1·6	10·0 4·1	16·0 6·5
41	6 10·3	6 11·3	5 53·4	4·1 1·7	10·1 4·1	16·1 6·6
42	6 10·5	6 11·5	5 53·6	4·2 1·7	10·2 4·2	16·2 6·6
43	6 10·8	6 11·8	5 53·9	4·3 1·8	10·3 4·2	16·3 6·7
44	6 11·0	6 12·0	5 54·1	4·4 1·8	10·4 4·2	16·4 6·7
45	6 11·3	6 12·3	5 54·3	4·5 1·8	10·5 4·3	16·5 6·7
46	6 11·5	6 12·5	5 54·6	4·6 1·9	10·6 4·3	16·6 6·8
47	6 11·8	6 12·8	5 54·8	4·7 1·9	10·7 4·4	16·7 6·8
48	6 12·0	6 13·0	5 55·1	4·8 2·0	10·8 4·4	16·8 6·9
49	6 12·3	6 13·3	5 55·3	4·9 2·0	10·9 4·5	16·9 6·9
50	6 12·5	6 13·5	5 55·5	5·0 2·0	11·0 4·5	17·0 6·9
51	6 12·8	6 13·8	5 55·8	5·1 2·1	11·1 4·5	17·1 7·0
52	6 13·0	6 14·0	5 56·0	5·2 2·1	11·2 4·6	17·2 7·0
53	6 13·3	6 14·3	5 56·2	5·3 2·2	11·3 4·6	17·3 7·1
54	6 13·5	6 14·5	5 56·5	5·4 2·2	11·4 4·7	17·4 7·1
55	6 13·8	6 14·8	5 56·7	5·5 2·2	11·5 4·7	17·5 7·1
56	6 14·0	6 15·0	5 57·0	5·6 2·3	11·6 4·7	17·6 7·2
57	6 14·3	6 15·3	5 57·2	5·7 2·3	11·7 4·8	17·7 7·2
58	6 14·5	6 15·5	5 57·4	5·8 2·4	11·8 4·8	17·8 7·3
59	6 14·8	6 15·8	5 57·7	5·9 2·4	11·9 4·9	17·9 7·3
60	6 15·0	6 16·0	5 57·9	6·0 2·5	12·0 4·9	18·0 7·4

25ᵐ	SUN PLANETS	ARIES	MOON	v or d / Corrⁿ	v or d / Corrⁿ	v or d / Corrⁿ
00	6 15·0	6 16·0	5 57·9	0·0 0·0	6·0 2·6	12·0 5·1
01	6 15·3	6 16·3	5 58·2	0·1 0·0	6·1 2·6	12·1 5·1
02	6 15·5	6 16·5	5 58·4	0·2 0·1	6·2 2·6	12·2 5·2
03	6 15·8	6 16·8	5 58·6	0·3 0·1	6·3 2·7	12·3 5·2
04	6 16·0	6 17·0	5 58·9	0·4 0·2	6·4 2·7	12·4 5·3
05	6 16·3	6 17·3	5 59·1	0·5 0·2	6·5 2·8	12·5 5·3
06	6 16·5	6 17·5	5 59·3	0·6 0·3	6·6 2·8	12·6 5·4
07	6 16·8	6 17·8	5 59·6	0·7 0·3	6·7 2·8	12·7 5·4
08	6 17·0	6 18·0	5 59·8	0·8 0·3	6·8 2·9	12·8 5·4
09	6 17·3	6 18·3	6 00·1	0·9 0·4	6·9 2·9	12·9 5·5
10	6 17·5	6 18·5	6 00·3	1·0 0·4	7·0 3·0	13·0 5·5
11	6 17·8	6 18·8	6 00·5	1·1 0·5	7·1 3·0	13·1 5·6
12	6 18·0	6 19·0	6 00·8	1·2 0·5	7·2 3·1	13·2 5·6
13	6 18·3	6 19·3	6 01·0	1·3 0·6	7·3 3·1	13·3 5·7
14	6 18·5	6 19·5	6 01·3	1·4 0·6	7·4 3·1	13·4 5·7
15	6 18·8	6 19·8	6 01·5	1·5 0·6	7·5 3·2	13·5 5·7
16	6 19·0	6 20·0	6 01·7	1·6 0·7	7·6 3·2	13·6 5·8
17	6 19·3	6 20·3	6 02·0	1·7 0·7	7·7 3·3	13·7 5·8
18	6 19·5	6 20·5	6 02·2	1·8 0·8	7·8 3·3	13·8 5·9
19	6 19·8	6 20·8	6 02·5	1·9 0·8	7·9 3·4	13·9 5·9
20	6 20·0	6 21·0	6 02·7	2·0 0·9	8·0 3·4	14·0 6·0
21	6 20·3	6 21·3	6 02·9	2·1 0·9	8·1 3·4	14·1 6·0
22	6 20·5	6 21·5	6 03·2	2·2 0·9	8·2 3·5	14·2 6·0
23	6 20·8	6 21·8	6 03·4	2·3 1·0	8·3 3·5	14·3 6·1
24	6 21·0	6 22·0	6 03·6	2·4 1·0	8·4 3·6	14·4 6·1
25	6 21·3	6 22·3	6 03·9	2·5 1·1	8·5 3·6	14·5 6·2
26	6 21·5	6 22·5	6 04·1	2·6 1·1	8·6 3·7	14·6 6·2
27	6 21·8	6 22·8	6 04·4	2·7 1·1	8·7 3·7	14·7 6·2
28	6 22·0	6 23·0	6 04·6	2·8 1·2	8·8 3·7	14·8 6·3
29	6 22·3	6 23·3	6 04·8	2·9 1·2	8·9 3·8	14·9 6·3
30	6 22·5	6 23·5	6 05·1	3·0 1·3	9·0 3·8	15·0 6·4
31	6 22·8	6 23·8	6 05·3	3·1 1·3	9·1 3·9	15·1 6·4
32	6 23·0	6 24·0	6 05·6	3·2 1·4	9·2 3·9	15·2 6·5
33	6 23·3	6 24·3	6 05·8	3·3 1·4	9·3 4·0	15·3 6·5
34	6 23·5	6 24·5	6 06·0	3·4 1·4	9·4 4·0	15·4 6·5
35	6 23·8	6 24·8	6 06·3	3·5 1·5	9·5 4·0	15·5 6·6
36	6 24·0	6 25·1	6 06·5	3·6 1·5	9·6 4·1	15·6 6·6
37	6 24·3	6 25·3	6 06·7	3·7 1·6	9·7 4·1	15·7 6·7
38	6 24·5	6 25·6	6 07·0	3·8 1·6	9·8 4·2	15·8 6·7
39	6 24·8	6 25·8	6 07·2	3·9 1·7	9·9 4·2	15·9 6·8
40	6 25·0	6 26·1	6 07·5	4·0 1·7	10·0 4·3	16·0 6·8
41	6 25·3	6 26·3	6 07·7	4·1 1·7	10·1 4·3	16·1 6·8
42	6 25·5	6 26·6	6 07·9	4·2 1·8	10·2 4·3	16·2 6·9
43	6 25·8	6 26·8	6 08·2	4·3 1·8	10·3 4·4	16·3 6·9
44	6 26·0	6 27·1	6 08·4	4·4 1·9	10·4 4·4	16·4 7·0
45	6 26·3	6 27·3	6 08·7	4·5 1·9	10·5 4·5	16·5 7·0
46	6 26·5	6 27·6	6 08·9	4·6 2·0	10·6 4·5	16·6 7·1
47	6 26·8	6 27·8	6 09·1	4·7 2·0	10·7 4·5	16·7 7·1
48	6 27·0	6 28·1	6 09·4	4·8 2·0	10·8 4·6	16·8 7·1
49	6 27·3	6 28·3	6 09·6	4·9 2·1	10·9 4·6	16·9 7·2
50	6 27·5	6 28·6	6 09·8	5·0 2·1	11·0 4·7	17·0 7·2
51	6 27·8	6 28·8	6 10·1	5·1 2·2	11·1 4·7	17·1 7·3
52	6 28·0	6 29·1	6 10·3	5·2 2·2	11·2 4·8	17·2 7·3
53	6 28·3	6 29·3	6 10·6	5·3 2·3	11·3 4·8	17·3 7·4
54	6 28·5	6 29·6	6 10·8	5·4 2·3	11·4 4·8	17·4 7·4
55	6 28·8	6 29·8	6 11·0	5·5 2·3	11·5 4·9	17·5 7·4
56	6 29·0	6 30·1	6 11·3	5·6 2·4	11·6 4·9	17·6 7·5
57	6 29·3	6 30·3	6 11·5	5·7 2·4	11·7 5·0	17·7 7·5
58	6 29·5	6 30·6	6 11·8	5·8 2·5	11·8 5·0	17·8 7·6
59	6 29·8	6 30·8	6 12·0	5·9 2·5	11·9 5·1	17·9 7·6
60	6 30·0	6 31·1	6 12·2	6·0 2·6	12·0 5·1	18·0 7·7

TABLES FOR INTERPOLATING SUNRISE, MOONRISE, ETC.

TABLE I—FOR LATITUDE

| Tabular Interval | | | Difference between the times for consecutive latitudes | | | | | | | | | | | | | | |
10°	5°	2°	5m	10m	15m	20m	25m	30m	35m	40m	45m	50m	55m	60m	1h 05m	1h 10m	1h 15m	1h 20m
° '	° '	° '	m	m	m	m	m	m	m	m	m	m	m	m	h m	h m	h m	h m
0 30	0 15	0 06	0	0	1	1	1	1	1	2	2	2	2	2	0 02	0 02	0 02	0 02
1 00	0 30	0 12	0	1	1	2	2	3	3	3	4	4	4	5	05	05	05	05
1 30	0 45	0 18	1	1	2	3	3	4	4	5	5	6	7	7	07	07	07	07
2 00	1 00	0 24	1	2	3	4	5	5	6	7	7	8	9	10	10	10	10	10
2 30	1 15	0 30	1	2	4	5	6	7	8	9	9	10	11	12	12	13	13	13
3 00	1 30	0 36	1	3	4	6	7	8	9	10	11	12	13	14	0 15	0 15	0 16	0 16
3 30	1 45	0 42	2	3	5	7	8	10	11	12	13	14	16	17	18	18	19	19
4 00	2 00	0 48	2	4	6	8	9	11	13	14	15	16	18	19	20	21	22	22
4 30	2 15	0 54	2	4	7	9	11	13	15	16	18	19	21	22	23	24	25	26
5 00	2 30	1 00	2	5	7	10	12	14	16	18	20	22	23	25	26	27	28	29
5 30	2 45	1 06	3	5	8	11	13	16	18	20	22	24	26	28	0 29	0 30	0 31	0 32
6 00	3 00	1 12	3	6	9	12	14	17	20	22	24	26	29	31	32	33	34	36
6 30	3 15	1 18	3	6	10	13	16	19	22	24	26	29	31	34	36	37	38	40
7 00	3 30	1 24	3	7	10	14	17	20	23	26	29	31	34	37	39	41	42	44
7 30	3 45	1 30	4	7	11	15	18	22	25	28	31	34	37	40	43	44	46	48
8 00	4 00	1 36	4	8	12	16	20	23	27	30	34	37	41	44	0 47	0 48	0 51	0 53
8 30	4 15	1 42	4	8	13	17	21	25	29	33	36	40	44	48	0 51	0 53	0 56	0 58
9 00	4 30	1 48	4	9	13	18	22	27	31	35	39	43	47	52	0 55	0 58	1 01	1 04
9 30	4 45	1 54	5	9	14	19	24	28	33	38	42	47	51	56	1 00	1 04	1 08	1 12
10 00	5 00	2 00	5	10	15	20	25	30	35	40	45	50	55	60	1 05	1 10	1 15	1 20

Table I is for interpolating the L.M.T. of sunrise, twilight, moonrise, etc. for latitude. It is to be noted that the interpolation is not linear, so that when using this table it is essential to take out the required phenomenon for the latitude *less* than the true latitude. The table is entered with the nearest value of the difference between the times for the tabular latitude and the next higher one, and, in the appropriate column, with the difference between true latitude and tabular latitude; the correction so obtained is applied to the time for the tabular latitude; the sign of the correction can be seen by inspection.

TABLE II—FOR LONGITUDE

| Long. East or West | Difference between the times for given date and preceding date (for east longitude) or for given date and following date (for west longitude) | | | | | | | | | | | | | | | | |
	10m	20m	30m	40m	50m	60m	1h+ 10m	20m	30m	1h+ 40m	50m	60m	2h 10m	2h 20m	2h 30m	2h 40m	2h 50m	3h 00m
°	m	m	m	m	m	m	m	m	m	m	m	m	h m	h m	h m	h m	h m	h m
0	0	0	0	0	0	0	0	0	0	0	0	0	0 00	0 00	0 00	0 00	0 00	0 00
10	0	1	1	1	1	2	2	2	2	3	3	3	04	04	04	04	05	05
20	1	1	2	2	3	3	4	4	5	6	6	7	07	08	08	09	09	10
30	1	2	2	3	4	5	6	7	7	8	9	10	11	12	12	13	14	15
40	1	2	3	4	6	7	8	9	10	11	12	13	14	16	17	18	19	20
50	1	3	4	6	7	8	10	11	12	14	15	17	0 18	0 19	0 21	0 22	0 24	0 25
60	2	3	5	7	8	10	12	13	15	17	18	20	22	23	25	27	28	30
70	2	4	6	8	10	12	14	16	17	19	21	23	25	27	29	31	33	35
80	2	4	7	9	11	13	16	18	20	22	24	27	29	31	33	36	38	40
90	2	5	7	10	12	15	17	20	22	25	27	30	32	35	37	40	42	45
100	3	6	8	11	14	17	19	22	25	28	31	33	0 36	0 39	0 42	0 44	0 47	0 50
110	3	6	9	12	15	18	21	24	27	31	34	37	40	43	46	49	0 52	0 55
120	3	7	10	13	17	20	23	27	30	33	37	40	43	47	50	53	0 57	1 00
130	4	7	11	14	18	22	25	29	32	36	40	43	47	51	54	0 58	1 01	1 05
140	4	8	12	16	19	23	27	31	35	39	43	47	51	54	0 58	1 02	1 06	1 10
150	4	8	13	17	21	25	29	33	38	42	46	50	0 54	0 58	1 03	1 07	1 11	1 15
160	4	9	13	18	22	27	31	36	40	44	49	53	0 58	1 02	1 07	1 11	1 16	1 20
170	5	9	14	19	24	28	33	38	42	47	52	57	1 01	1 06	1 11	1 16	1 20	1 25
180	5	10	15	20	25	30	35	40	45	50	55	60	1 05	1 10	1 15	1 20	1 25	1 30

Table II is for interpolating the L.M.T. of moonrise, moonset and the Moon's meridian passage for longitude. It is entered with longitude and with the difference between the times for the given date and for the preceding date (in east longitudes) or following date (in west longitudes). The correction is normally *added* for west longitudes and *subtracted* for east longitudes, but if, as occasionally happens, the times become earlier each day instead of later, the signs of the corrections must be reversed.

ALTITUDE CORRECTION TABLES 0°–35°—MOON

App. Alt.	0°–4° Corrⁿ	5°–9° Corrⁿ	10°–14° Corrⁿ	15°–19° Corrⁿ	20°–24° Corrⁿ	25°–29° Corrⁿ	30°–34° Corrⁿ	App. Alt.
00	0 33·8	5 58·2	10 62·1	15 62·8	20 62·2	25 60·8	30 58·9	00
10	35·9	58·5	62·2	62·8	62·1	60·8	58·8	10
20	37·8	58·7	62·2	62·8	62·1	60·7	58·8	20
30	39·6	58·9	62·3	62·8	62·1	60·7	58·7	30
40	41·2	59·1	62·3	62·8	62·0	60·6	58·6	40
50	42·6	59·3	62·4	62·7	62·0	60·6	58·5	50
00	1 44·0	6 59·5	11 62·4	16 62·7	21 62·0	26 60·5	31 58·5	00
10	45·2	59·7	62·4	62·7	61·9	60·4	58·4	10
20	46·3	59·9	62·5	62·7	61·9	60·4	58·3	20
30	47·3	60·0	62·5	62·7	61·9	60·3	58·2	30
40	48·3	60·2	62·5	62·7	61·8	60·3	58·2	40
50	49·2	60·3	62·6	62·7	61·8	60·2	58·1	50
00	2 50·0	7 60·5	12 62·6	17 62·7	22 61·7	27 60·1	32 58·0	00
10	50·8	60·6	62·6	62·6	61·7	60·1	57·9	10
20	51·4	60·7	62·6	62·6	61·6	60·0	57·8	20
30	52·1	60·9	62·7	62·6	61·6	59·9	57·8	30
40	52·7	61·0	62·7	62·6	61·5	59·9	57·7	40
50	53·3	61·1	62·7	62·6	61·5	59·8	57·6	50
00	3 53·8	8 61·2	13 62·7	18 62·5	23 61·5	28 59·7	33 57·5	00
10	54·3	61·3	62·7	62·5	61·4	59·7	57·4	10
20	54·8	61·4	62·7	62·5	61·4	59·6	57·4	20
30	55·2	61·5	62·8	62·5	61·3	59·6	57·3	30
40	55·6	61·6	62·8	62·4	61·3	59·5	57·2	40
50	56·0	61·6	62·8	62·4	61·2	59·4	57·1	50
00	4 56·4	9 61·7	14 62·8	19 62·4	24 61·2	29 59·3	34 57·0	00
10	56·7	61·8	62·8	62·3	61·1	59·3	56·9	10
20	57·1	61·9	62·8	62·3	61·1	59·2	56·9	20
30	57·4	61·9	62·8	62·3	61·0	59·1	56·8	30
40	57·7	62·0	62·8	62·2	60·9	59·1	56·7	40
50	57·9	62·1	62·8	62·2	60·9	59·0	56·6	50

H.P.	L U	L U	L U	L U	L U	L U	L U	H.P.
54·0	0·3 0·9	0·3 0·9	0·4 1·0	0·5 1·1	0·6 1·2	0·7 1·3	0·9 1·5	54·0
54·3	0·7 1·1	0·7 1·2	0·7 1·2	0·8 1·3	0·9 1·4	1·1 1·5	1·2 1·7	54·3
54·6	1·1 1·4	1·1 1·4	1·1 1·4	1·2 1·5	1·3 1·6	1·4 1·7	1·5 1·8	54·6
54·9	1·4 1·6	1·5 1·6	1·5 1·6	1·6 1·7	1·6 1·8	1·8 1·9	1·9 2·0	54·9
55·2	1·8 1·8	1·8 1·8	1·9 1·9	1·9 1·9	2·0 2·0	2·1 2·1	2·2 2·2	55·2
55·5	2·2 2·0	2·2 2·0	2·3 2·1	2·3 2·1	2·4 2·2	2·4 2·3	2·5 2·4	55·5
55·8	2·6 2·2	2·6 2·2	2·6 2·3	2·7 2·3	2·7 2·4	2·8 2·4	2·9 2·5	55·8
56·1	3·0 2·4	3·0 2·5	3·0 2·5	3·0 2·5	3·1 2·6	3·1 2·6	3·2 2·7	56·1
56·4	3·4 2·7	3·4 2·7	3·4 2·7	3·4 2·7	3·4 2·8	3·5 2·8	3·5 2·9	56·4
56·7	3·7 2·9	3·7 2·9	3·8 2·9	3·8 2·9	3·8 3·0	3·8 3·0	3·9 3·0	56·7
57·0	4·1 3·1	4·1 3·1	4·1 3·1	4·1 3·1	4·2 3·1	4·2 3·2	4·2 3·2	57·0
57·3	4·5 3·3	4·5 3·3	4·5 3·3	4·5 3·3	4·5 3·4	4·5 3·4	4·6 3·4	57·3
57·6	4·9 3·5	4·9 3·5	4·9 3·5	4·9 3·5	4·9 3·5	4·9 3·5	4·9 3·6	57·6
57·9	5·3 3·8	5·3 3·8	5·2 3·8	5·2 3·7	5·2 3·7	5·2 3·7	5·2 3·7	57·9
58·2	5·6 4·0	5·6 4·0	5·6 4·0	5·6 4·0	5·6 3·9	5·6 3·9	5·6 3·9	58·2
58·5	6·0 4·2	6·0 4·2	6·0 4·2	6·0 4·2	6·0 4·1	5·9 4·1	5·9 4·1	58·5
58·8	6·4 4·4	6·4 4·4	6·4 4·4	6·3 4·4	6·3 4·3	6·3 4·3	6·2 4·2	58·8
59·1	6·8 4·6	6·8 4·6	6·7 4·6	6·7 4·5	6·7 4·5	6·6 4·5	6·6 4·4	59·1
59·4	7·2 4·8	7·1 4·8	7·1 4·8	7·1 4·8	7·0 4·7	7·0 4·7	6·9 4·6	59·4
59·7	7·5 5·1	7·5 5·0	7·5 5·0	7·5 5·0	7·4 4·9	7·3 4·8	7·2 4·7	59·7
60·0	7·9 5·3	7·9 5·3	7·9 5·2	7·8 5·2	7·8 5·1	7·7 5·0	7·6 4·9	60·0
60·3	8·3 5·5	8·3 5·5	8·2 5·4	8·2 5·4	8·1 5·3	8·0 5·2	7·9 5·1	60·3
60·6	8·7 5·7	8·7 5·7	8·6 5·7	8·6 5·6	8·5 5·5	8·4 5·4	8·2 5·3	60·6
60·9	9·1 5·9	9·0 5·9	9·0 5·9	8·9 5·8	8·8 5·7	8·7 5·6	8·6 5·4	60·9
61·2	9·5 6·2	9·4 6·1	9·4 6·1	9·3 6·0	9·2 5·9	9·1 5·8	8·9 5·6	61·2
61·5	9·8 6·4	9·8 6·3	9·7 6·3	9·7 6·2	9·5 6·1	9·4 5·9	9·2 5·8	61·5

DIP

Ht. of Eye (m)	Corrⁿ	Ht. of Eye (ft.)	Ht. of Eye (m)	Corrⁿ	Ht. of Eye (ft.)
2·4	−2·8	8·0	9·5	−5·5	31·5
2·6	−2·9	8·6	9·9	−5·6	32·7
2·8	−3·0	9·2	10·3	−5·7	33·9
3·0	−3·1	9·8	10·6	−5·8	35·1
3·2	−3·2	10·5	11·0	−5·9	36·3
3·4	−3·3	11·2	11·4	−6·0	37·6
3·6	−3·4	11·9	11·8	−6·1	38·9
3·8	−3·5	12·6	12·2	−6·2	40·1
4·0	−3·6	13·3	12·6	−6·3	41·5
4·3	−3·7	14·1	13·0	−6·4	42·8
4·5	−3·8	14·9	13·4	−6·5	44·2
4·7	−3·9	15·7	13·8	−6·6	45·5
5·0	−4·0	16·5	14·2	−6·7	46·9
5·2	−4·1	17·4	14·7	−6·8	48·4
5·5	−4·2	18·3	15·1	−6·9	49·8
5·8	−4·3	19·1	15·5	−7·0	51·3
6·1	−4·4	20·1	16·0	−7·1	52·8
6·3	−4·5	21·0	16·5	−7·2	54·3
6·6	−4·6	22·0	16·9	−7·3	55·8
6·9	−4·7	22·9	17·4	−7·4	57·4
7·2	−4·8	23·9	17·9	−7·5	58·9
7·5	−4·9	24·9	18·4	−7·6	60·5
7·9	−5·0	26·0	18·8	−7·7	62·1
8·2	−5·1	27·1	19·3	−7·8	63·8
8·5	−5·2	28·1	19·8	−7·9	65·4
8·8	−5·3	29·2	20·4	−8·0	67·1
9·2	−5·4	30·4	20·9	−8·1	68·8
9·5		31·5	21·4		70·5

MOON CORRECTION TABLE

The correction is in two parts; the first correction is taken from the upper part of the table with argument apparent altitude, and the second from the lower part, with argument H.P., in the same column as that from which the first correction was taken. Separate corrections are given in the lower part for lower (L) and upper (U) limbs. All corrections are to be **added** to apparent altitude, *but 30′ is to be subtracted from the altitude of the upper limb.*

For corrections for pressure and temperature see page A4.

For bubble sextant observations ignore dip, take the **mean** of upper and lower limb corrections and subtract 15′ from the altitude.

App. Alt. = Apparent altitude = Sextant altitude corrected for index error and dip.

ALTITUDE CORRECTION TABLES 35°-90°—MOON

App. Alt.	35°–39° Corrⁿ	40°–44° Corrⁿ	45°–49° Corrⁿ	50°–54° Corrⁿ	55°–59° Corrⁿ	60°–64° Corrⁿ	65°–69° Corrⁿ	70°–74° Corrⁿ	75°–79° Corrⁿ	80°–84° Corrⁿ	85°–89° Corrⁿ	App. Alt.
00	35 56·5	40 53·7	45 50·5	50 46·9	55 43·1	60 38·9	65 34·6	70 30·1	75 25·3	80 20·5	85 15·6	00
10	56·4	53·6	50·4	46·8	42·9	38·8	34·4	29·9	25·2	20·4	15·5	10
20	56·3	53·5	50·2	46·7	42·8	38·7	34·3	29·7	25·0	20·2	15·3	20
30	56·2	53·4	50·1	46·5	42·7	38·5	34·1	29·6	24·9	20·0	15·1	30
40	56·2	53·3	50·0	46·4	42·5	38·4	34·0	29·4	24·7	19·9	15·0	40
50	56·1	53·2	49·9	46·3	42·4	38·2	33·8	29·3	24·5	19·7	14·8	50
00	36 56·0	41 53·1	46 49·8	51 46·2	56 42·3	61 38·1	66 33·7	71 29·1	76 24·4	81 19·6	86 14·6	00
10	55·9	53·0	49·7	46·0	42·1	37·9	33·5	29·0	24·2	19·4	14·5	10
20	55·8	52·8	49·5	45·9	42·0	37·8	33·4	28·8	24·1	19·2	14·3	20
30	55·7	52·7	49·4	45·8	41·8	37·7	33·2	28·7	23·9	19·1	14·1	30
40	55·6	52·6	49·3	45·7	41·7	37·5	33·1	28·5	23·8	18·9	14·0	40
50	55·5	52·5	49·2	45·5	41·6	37·4	32·9	28·3	23·6	18·7	13·8	50
00	37 55·4	42 52·4	47 49·1	52 45·4	57 41·4	62 37·2	67 32·8	72 28·2	77 23·4	82 18·6	87 13·7	00
10	55·3	52·3	49·0	45·3	41·3	37·1	32·6	28·0	23·3	18·4	13·5	10
20	55·2	52·2	48·8	45·2	41·2	36·9	32·5	27·9	23·1	18·2	13·3	20
30	55·1	52·1	48·7	45·0	41·0	36·8	32·3	27·7	22·9	18·1	13·2	30
40	55·0	52·0	48·6	44·9	40·9	36·6	32·2	27·6	22·8	17·9	13·0	40
50	55·0	51·9	48·5	44·8	40·8	36·5	32·0	27·4	22·6	17·8	12·8	50
00	38 54·9	43 51·8	48 48·4	53 44·6	58 40·6	63 36·4	68 31·9	73 27·2	78 22·5	83 17·6	88 12·7	00
10	54·8	51·7	48·2	44·5	40·5	36·2	31·7	27·1	22·3	17·4	12·5	10
20	54·7	51·6	48·1	44·4	40·3	36·1	31·6	26·9	22·1	17·3	12·3	20
30	54·6	51·5	48·0	44·2	40·2	35·9	31·4	26·8	22·0	17·1	12·2	30
40	54·5	51·4	47·9	44·1	40·1	35·8	31·3	26·6	21·8	16·9	12·0	40
50	54·4	51·2	47·8	44·0	39·9	35·6	31·1	26·5	21·7	16·8	11·8	50
00	39 54·3	44 51·1	49 47·6	54 43·9	59 39·8	64 35·5	69 31·0	74 26·3	79 21·5	84 16·6	89 11·7	00
10	54·2	51·0	47·5	43·7	39·6	35·3	30·8	26·1	21·3	16·5	11·5	10
20	54·1	50·9	47·4	43·6	39·5	35·2	30·7	26·0	21·2	16·3	11·4	20
30	54·0	50·8	47·3	43·5	39·4	35·0	30·5	25·8	21·0	16·1	11·2	30
40	53·9	50·7	47·2	43·3	39·2	34·9	30·4	25·7	20·9	16·0	11·0	40
50	53·8	50·6	47·0	43·2	39·1	34·7	30·2	25·5	20·7	15·8	10·9	50

H.P.	L U	L U	L U	L U	L U	L U	L U	L U	L U	L U	L U	H.P.
54·0	1·1 1·7	1·3 1·9	1·5 2·1	1·7 2·4	2·0 2·6	2·3 2·9	2·6 3·2	2·9 3·5	3·2 3·8	3·5 4·1	3·8 4·5	54·0
54·3	1·4 1·8	1·6 2·0	1·8 2·2	2·0 2·5	2·3 2·7	2·5 3·0	2·8 3·2	3·0 3·5	3·3 3·8	3·6 4·1	3·9 4·4	54·3
54·6	1·7 2·0	1·9 2·2	2·1 2·4	2·3 2·6	2·5 2·8	2·7 3·0	3·0 3·3	3·2 3·5	3·5 3·8	3·7 4·1	4·0 4·3	54·6
54·9	2·0 2·2	2·2 2·3	2·3 2·5	2·5 2·7	2·7 2·9	2·9 3·1	3·2 3·3	3·4 3·5	3·6 3·8	3·9 4·0	4·1 4·3	54·9
55·2	2·3 2·3	2·5 2·4	2·6 2·6	2·8 2·8	3·0 2·9	3·2 3·1	3·4 3·3	3·6 3·5	3·8 3·7	4·0 4·0	4·2 4·2	55·2
55·5	2·7 2·5	2·8 2·6	2·9 2·7	3·1 2·9	3·2 3·0	3·4 3·2	3·6 3·4	3·7 3·5	3·9 3·7	4·1 3·9	4·3 4·1	55·5
55·8	3·0 2·6	3·1 2·7	3·2 2·8	3·3 3·0	3·5 3·1	3·6 3·3	3·8 3·4	3·9 3·6	4·1 3·7	4·2 3·9	4·4 4·0	55·8
56·1	3·3 2·8	3·4 2·9	3·5 3·0	3·6 3·1	3·7 3·2	3·8 3·3	4·0 3·4	4·1 3·6	4·2 3·7	4·4 3·8	4·5 4·0	56·1
56·4	3·6 2·9	3·7 3·0	3·8 3·1	3·9 3·2	3·9 3·3	4·0 3·4	4·1 3·5	4·3 3·6	4·4 3·7	4·5 3·8	4·6 3·9	56·4
56·7	3·9 3·1	4·0 3·1	4·1 3·2	4·1 3·3	4·2 3·3	4·3 3·4	4·3 3·5	4·4 3·6	4·5 3·7	4·6 3·8	4·7 3·8	56·7
57·0	4·3 3·2	4·3 3·3	4·3 3·3	4·4 3·4	4·4 3·4	4·5 3·5	4·5 3·5	4·6 3·6	4·7 3·6	4·7 3·7	4·8 3·8	57·0
57·3	4·6 3·4	4·6 3·4	4·6 3·4	4·6 3·5	4·7 3·5	4·7 3·6	4·7 3·6	4·8 3·6	4·8 3·6	4·8 3·7	4·9 3·7	57·3
57·6	4·9 3·6	4·9 3·6	4·9 3·6	4·9 3·6	4·9 3·6	4·9 3·6	4·9 3·6	5·0 3·6	5·0 3·6	5·0 3·6	5·0 3·6	57·6
57·9	5·2 3·7	5·2 3·7	5·2 3·7	5·2 3·7	5·2 3·7	5·1 3·6	5·1 3·6	5·1 3·6	5·1 3·6	5·1 3·6	5·1 3·6	57·9
58·2	5·5 3·9	5·5 3·8	5·5 3·8	5·4 3·8	5·4 3·7	5·4 3·7	5·3 3·7	5·3 3·6	5·2 3·6	5·2 3·5	5·2 3·5	58·2
58·5	5·9 4·0	5·8 4·0	5·8 3·9	5·7 3·9	5·6 3·8	5·6 3·8	5·5 3·7	5·5 3·6	5·4 3·6	5·3 3·5	5·3 3·4	58·5
58·8	6·2 4·2	6·1 4·1	6·0 4·1	6·0 4·0	5·9 3·9	5·8 3·8	5·7 3·7	5·6 3·6	5·5 3·5	5·4 3·5	5·3 3·4	58·8
59·1	6·5 4·3	6·4 4·3	6·3 4·2	6·2 4·1	6·1 4·0	6·0 3·9	5·9 3·8	5·8 3·6	5·7 3·5	5·6 3·4	5·4 3·3	59·1
59·4	6·8 4·5	6·7 4·4	6·6 4·3	6·5 4·2	6·4 4·1	6·3 4·0	6·1 3·8	6·0 3·7	5·8 3·5	5·7 3·4	5·5 3·2	59·4
59·7	7·1 4·6	7·0 4·5	6·9 4·4	6·8 4·3	6·6 4·1	6·5 4·0	6·3 3·8	6·2 3·7	6·0 3·5	5·8 3·3	5·6 3·2	59·7
60·0	7·5 4·8	7·3 4·7	7·2 4·5	7·0 4·4	6·9 4·2	6·7 4·0	6·5 3·9	6·3 3·7	6·1 3·5	5·9 3·3	5·7 3·1	60·0
60·3	7·8 5·0	7·6 4·8	7·5 4·7	7·3 4·5	7·1 4·3	6·9 4·1	6·7 3·9	6·5 3·7	6·3 3·5	6·0 3·2	5·8 3·0	60·3
60·6	8·1 5·1	7·9 5·0	7·7 4·8	7·6 4·6	7·3 4·4	7·1 4·2	6·9 3·9	6·7 3·7	6·4 3·4	6·2 3·2	5·9 2·9	60·6
60·9	8·4 5·3	8·2 5·1	8·0 4·9	7·8 4·7	7·6 4·5	7·3 4·2	7·1 4·0	6·8 3·7	6·6 3·4	6·3 3·2	6·0 2·9	60·9
61·2	8·7 5·4	8·5 5·2	8·3 5·0	8·1 4·8	7·8 4·5	7·6 4·3	7·3 4·0	7·0 3·7	6·8 3·4	6·4 3·1	6·1 2·8	61·2
61·5	9·1 5·6	8·8 5·4	8·6 5·1	8·3 4·9	8·1 4·6	7·8 4·3	7·5 4·0	7·2 3·7	6·9 3·4	6·5 3·1	6·2 2·7	61·5

EXTRACTS FROM *AIR ALMANAC*

STARS, MAY—AUG., 1975

No.	Name		Mag.	S.H.A.	Dec.
				° ′	° ′
7*	Acamar		3·1	315 40	S. 40 24
5*	Achernar		0·6	335 48	S. 57 21
30*	Acrux		1·1	173 41	S. 62 58
19	Adhara	†	1·6	255 35	S. 28 56
10*	Aldebaran	†	1·1	291 22	N. 16 28
32*	Alioth		1·7	166 46	N. 56 06
34*	Alkaid		1·9	153 21	N. 49 26
55	Al Na'ir		2·2	28 19	S. 47 05
15	Alnilam	†	1·8	276 16	S. 1 13
25*	Alphard	†	2·2	218 24	S. 8 33
41*	Alphecca	†	2·3	126 35	N. 26 48
1*	Alpheratz	†	2·2	358 13	N. 28 57
51*	Altair	†	0·9	62 36	N. 8 48
2	Ankaa		2·4	353 44	S. 42 26
42*	Antares	†	1·2	113 01	S. 26 23
37*	Arcturus	†	0·2	146 22	N. 19 19
43	Atria		1·9	108 28	S. 68 59
22	Avior		1·7	234 30	S. 59 26
13	Bellatrix	†	1·7	279 03	N. 6 20
16*	Betelgeuse	†	0·1-1·2	271 32	N. 7 24
17*	Canopus		−0·9	264 09	S. 52 41
12*	Capella		0·2	281 17	N. 45 58
53*	Deneb		1·3	49 51	N. 45 12
28*	Denebola	†	2·2	183 03	N. 14 43
4*	Diphda	†	2·2	349 24	S. 18 07
27*	Dubhe		2·0	194 27	N. 61 53
14	Elnath	†	1·8	278 49	N. 28 35
47	Eltanin		2·4	90 59	N. 51 30
54*	Enif	†	2·5	34 15	N. 9 46
56*	Fomalhaut	†	1·3	15 55	S. 29 45
31	Gacrux		1·6	172 33	S. 56 59
29*	Gienah	†	2·8	176 22	S. 17 25
35	Hadar		0·9	149 28	S. 60 16
6*	Hamal	†	2·2	328 33	N. 23 21
48	Kaus Aust.		2·0	84 21	S. 34 24
40*	Kochab		2·2	137 18	N. 74 16
57	Markab	†	2·6	14 07	N. 15 04
8*	Menkar	†	2·8	314 45	N. 4 00
36	Menkent		2·3	148 41	S. 36 15
24*	Miaplacidus		1·8	221 46	S. 69 37
9*	Mirfak		1·9	309 21	N. 49 46
50*	Nunki	†	2·1	76 33	S. 26 20
52*	Peacock		2·1	54 03	S. 56 49
21*	Pollux	†	1·2	244 03	N. 28 05
20*	Procyon	†	0·5	245 30	N. 5 17
46*	Rasalhague	†	2·1	96 33	N. 12 35
26*	Regulus	†	1·3	208 14	N. 12 05
11*	Rigel	†	0·3	281 40	S. 8 14
38*	Rigil Kent.		0·1	140 30	S. 60 44
44	Sabik	†	2·6	102 45	S. 15 42
3*	Schedar		2·5	350 13	N. 56 24
45*	Shaula		1·7	97 00	S. 37 05
18*	Sirius	†	−1·6	258 59	S. 16 41
33*	Spica	†	1·2	159 01	S. 11 02
23*	Suhail		2·2	223 14	S. 43 20
49*	Vega		0·1	80 58	N. 38 46
39	Zuben'ubi	†	2·9	137 37	S. 15 57

*Stars used in H.O. 249 (A.P. 3270) Vol. 1.

†Stars that may be used with Vols. 2 and 3.

INTERPOLATION OF G.H.A.

Increment to be added for intervals of G.M.T. to G.H.A. of: Sun, Aries (♈) and planets; Moon

SUN, etc.		MOON	SUN, etc.		MOON	SUN, etc.		MOON
m s	° ′	m s	m s	° ′	m s	m s	° ′	m s
00 00	0 00	00 00	03 17	0 50	03 25	06 37	1 40	06 52
01	0 01	00 02	21	0 51	03 29	41	1 41	06 56
05	0 02	00 06	25	0 52	03 33	45	1 42	07 00
09	0 03	00 10	29	0 53	03 37	49	1 43	07 04
13	0 04	00 14	33	0 54	03 41	53	1 44	07 08
17	0 05	00 18	37	0 55	03 45	06 57	1 45	07 13
21	0 06	00 22	41	0 56	03 49	07 01	1 46	07 17
25	0 07	00 26	45	0 57	03 54	05	1 47	07 21
29	0 08	00 31	49	0 58	03 58	09	1 48	07 25
33	0 09	00 35	53	0 59	04 02	13	1 49	07 29
37	0 10	00 39	03 57	1 00	04 06	17	1 50	07 33
41	0 11	00 43	04 01	1 01	04 10	21	1 51	07 37
45	0 12	00 47	05	1 02	04 14	25	1 52	07 42
49	0 13	00 51	09	1 03	04 19	29	1 53	07 46
53	0 14	00 55	13	1 04	04 23	33	1 54	07 50
00 57	0 15	01 00	17	1 05	04 27	37	1 55	07 54
01 01	0 16	01 04	21	1 06	04 31	41	1 56	07 58
05	0 17	01 08	25	1 07	04 35	45	1 57	08 02
09	0 18	01 12	29	1 08	04 39	49	1 58	08 06
13	0 19	01 16	33	1 09	04 43	53	1 59	08 11
17	0 20	01 20	37	1 10	04 48	07 57	2 00	08 15
21	0 21	01 24	41	1 11	04 52	08 01	2 01	08 19
25	0 22	01 29	45	1 12	04 56	05	2 02	08 23
29	0 23	01 33	49	1 13	05 00	09	2 03	08 27
33	0 24	01 37	53	1 14	05 04	13	2 04	08 31
37	0 25	01 41	04 57	1 15	05 08	17	2 05	08 35
41	0 26	01 45	05 01	1 16	05 12	21	2 06	08 40
45	0 27	01 49	05	1 17	05 17	25	2 07	08 44
49	0 28	01 53	09	1 18	05 21	29	2 08	08 48
53	0 29	01 58	13	1 19	05 25	33	2 09	08 52
01 57	0 30	02 02	17	1 20	05 29	37	2 10	08 56
02 01	0 31	02 06	21	1 21	05 33	41	2 11	09 00
05	0 32	02 10	25	1 22	05 37	45	2 12	09 04
09	0 33	02 14	29	1 23	05 41	49	2 13	09 09
13	0 34	02 18	33	1 24	05 46	53	2 14	09 13
17	0 35	02 22	37	1 25	05 50	08 57	2 15	09 17
21	0 36	02 27	41	1 26	05 54	09 01	2 16	09 21
25	0 37	02 31	45	1 27	05 58	05	2 17	09 25
29	0 38	02 35	49	1 28	06 02	09	2 18	09 29
33	0 39	02 39	53	1 29	06 06	13	2 19	09 33
37	0 40	02 43	05 57	1 30	06 10	17	2 20	09 38
41	0 41	02 47	06 01	1 31	06 15	21	2 21	09 42
45	0 42	02 51	05	1 32	06 19	25	2 22	09 46
49	0 43	02 56	09	1 33	06 23	29	2 23	09 50
53	0 44	03 00	13	1 34	06 27	33	2 24	09 54
02 57	0 45	03 04	17	1 35	06 31	37	2 25	09 58
03 01	0 46	03 08	21	1 36	06 35	41	2 26	10 00
05	0 47	03 12	25	1 37	06 39	45	2 27	
09	0 48	03 16	29	1 38	06 44	49	2 28	
13	0 49	03 20	33	1 39	06 48	53	2 29	
17	0 50	03 25	37	1 40	06 52	09 57	2 30	
03 21		03 29	06 41		06 56	10 00		

(DAY 152) GREENWICH A. M. 1975 JUNE 1 (SUNDAY)

GMT	SUN GHA	SUN Dec.	ARIES GHA	VENUS–3.8 GHA	VENUS Dec.	JUPITER–1.7 GHA	JUPITER Dec.	SATURN 0.4 GHA	SATURN Dec.	MOON GHA	MOON Dec.
h m											
00 00	180 36.0	N21 56.2	248 51.5	132 10	N23 46	232 59	N 5 30	140 29	N22 16	279 21	S 6 47
10	183 06.0	56.3	251 21.9	134 40		235 29		142 59		281 47	45
20	185 36.0	56.3	253 52.3	137 09		237 59		145 29		284 13	43
30	188 06.0	56.4	256 22.7	139 39 ·		240 30 ·		148 00 ·		286 39 ·	42
40	190 35.9	56.5	258 53.1	142 09		243 00		150 30		289 04	40
50	193 05.9	56.5	261 23.5	144 39		245 30		153 00		291 30	38
01 00	195 35.9	N21 56.6	263 53.9	147 09	N23 45	248 01	N 5 30	155 31	N22 16	293 56	S 6 36
10	198 05.9	56.6	266 24.4	149 39		250 31		158 01		296 22	35
20	200 35.9	56.7	268 54.8	152 09		253 01		160 31		298 47	33
30	203 05.9 ·	56.8	271 25.2	154 39 ·		255 32 ·		163 02 ·		301 13 ·	31
40	205 35.8	56.8	273 55.6	157 09		258 02		165 32		303 39	29
50	208 05.8	56.9	276 26.0	159 39		260 32		168 03		306 05	28
02 00	210 35.8	N21 57.0	278 56.4	162 09	N23 45	263 03	N 5 30	170 33	N22 16	308 30	S 6 26
10	213 05.8	57.0	281 26.8	164 39		265 33		173 03		310 56	24
20	215 35.8	57.1	283 57.2	167 09		268 03		175 34		313 22	23
30	218 05.8 ·	57.1	286 27.6	169 39 ·		270 34 ·		178 04 ·		315 47 ·	21
40	220 35.8	57.2	288 58.0	172 09		273 04		180 34		318 13	19
50	223 05.7	57.2	291 28.5	174 39		275 34		183 05		320 39	17
03 00	225 35.7	N21 57.3	293 58.9	177 09	N23 44	278 05	N 5 30	185 35	N22 16	323 05	S 6 16
10	228 05.7	57.3	296 29.3	179 38		280 35		188 05		325 30	14
20	230 35.7	57.4	298 59.7	182 08		283 05		190 36		327 56	12
30	233 05.7 ·	57.5	301 30.1	184 38 ·		285 36 ·		193 06 ·		330 22 ·	10
40	235 35.7	57.5	304 00.5	187 08		288 06		195 37		332 48	09
50	238 05.6	57.6	306 30.9	189 38		290 36		198 07		335 13	07
04 00	240 35.6	N21 57.6	309 01.3	192 08	N23 44	293 07	N 5 30	200 37	N22 15	337 39	S 6 05
10	243 05.6	57.7	311 31.7	194 38		295 37		203 08		340 05	04
20	245 35.6	57.8	314 02.2	197 08		298 07		205 38		342 31	02
30	248 05.6 ·	57.8	316 32.6	199 38 ·		300 38 ·		208 08 ·		344 56	6 00
40	250 35.6	57.9	319 03.0	202 08		303 08		210 39		347 22	5 58
50	253 05.6	57.9	321 33.4	204 38		305 38		213 09		349 48	57
05 00	255 35.5	N21 58.0	324 03.8	207 08	N23 43	308 09	N 5 31	215 39	N22 15	352 14	S 5 55
10	258 05.5	58.0	326 34.2	209 38		310 39		218 10		354 39	53
20	260 35.5	58.1	329 04.6	212 08		313 09		220 40		357 05	51
30	263 05.5 ·	58.2	331 35.0	214 38 ·		315 40 ·		223 10 ·		359 31 ·	50
40	265 35.5	58.2	334 05.4	217 08		318 10		225 41		1 57	48
50	268 05.5	58.3	336 35.9	219 37		320 40		228 11		4 22	46
06 00	270 35.5	N21 58.3	339 06.3	222 07	N23 43	323 11	N 5 31	230 42	N22 15	6 48	S 5 44
10	273 05.4	58.4	341 36.7	224 37		325 41		233 12		9 14	43
20	275 05.4	58.5	344 07.1	227 07		328 11		235 42		11 40	41
30	278 05.4 ·	58.5	346 37.5	229 37 ·		330 42 ·		238 13 ·		14 05 ·	39
40	280 35.4	58.6	349 07.9	232 07		333 12		240 43		16 31	38
50	283 05.4	58.6	351 38.3	234 37		335 42		243 13		18 57	36
07 00	285 35.4	N21 58.7	354 08.7	237 07	N23 42	338 13	N 5 31	245 44	N22 15	21 23	S 5 34
10	288 05.3	58.7	356 39.1	239 37		340 43		248 14		23 49	32
20	290 35.3	58.8	359 09.5	242 07		343 13		250 44		26 14	31
30	293 05.3 ·	58.9	1 40.0	244 37 ·		345 44 ·		253 15 ·		28 40 ·	29
40	295 35.3	58.9	4 10.4	247 07		348 14		255 45		31 06	27
50	298 05.3	59.0	6 40.8	249 37		350 44		258 16		33 32	25
08 00	300 35.3	N21 59.0	9 11.2	252 07	N23 42	353 15	N 5 31	260 46	N22 15	35 57	S 5 24
10	303 05.3	59.1	11 41.6	254 37		355 45		263 16		38 23	22
20	305 35.2	59.1	14 12.0	257 07		358 16		265 47		40 49	20
30	308 05.2 ·	59.2	16 42.4	259 37 ·		0 46 ·		268 17 ·		43 15 ·	18
40	310 35.2	59.3	19 12.8	262 06		3 16		270 47		45 40	17
50	313 05.2	59.3	21 43.2	264 36		5 47		273 18		48 06	15
09 00	315 35.2	N21 59.4	24 13.7	267 06	N23 41	8 17	N 5 31	275 48	N22 15	50 32	S 5 13
10	318 05.2	59.4	26 44.1	269 36		10 47		278 18		52 58	11
20	320 35.1	59.5	29 14.5	272 06		13 18		280 49		55 23	10
30	323 05.1 ·	59.6	31 44.9	274 36 ·		15 48 ·		283 19 ·		57 49 ·	08
40	325 35.1	59.6	34 15.3	277 06		18 18		285 49		60 15	06
50	328 05.1	59.7	36 45.7	279 36		20 49		288 20		62 41	04
10 00	330 35.1	N21 59.7	39 16.1	282 06	N23 40	23 19	N 5 31	290 50	N22 15	65 07	S 5 03
10	333 05.1	59.8	41 46.5	284 36		25 49		293 21		67 32	5 01
20	335 35.1	59.8	44 16.9	287 06		28 20		295 51		69 58	4 59
30	338 05.0	21 59.9	46 47.4	289 36 ·		30 50 ·		298 21 ·		72 24 ·	57
40	340 35.0	22 00.0	49 17.8	292 06		33 20		300 52		74 50	56
50	343 05.0	00.0	51 48.2	294 36		35 51		303 22		77 15	54
11 00	345 35.0	N22 00.1	54 18.6	297 06	N23 40	38 21	N 5 32	305 52	N22 15	79 41	S 4 52
10	348 05.0	00.1	56 49.0	299 36		40 51		308 23		82 07	50
20	350 35.0	00.2	59 19.4	302 06		43 22		310 53		84 33	48
30	353 04.9 ·	00.2	61 49.8	304 35 ·		45 52 ·		313 23 ·		86 59 ·	47
40	355 34.9	00.3	64 20.2	307 05		48 22		315 54		89 24	45
50	358 04.9	00.4	66 50.6	309 35		50 53		318 24		91 50	43
Rate	14 59.9	NO 00.3		14 59.6	S0 00.5	15 02.0	N0 00.2	15 02.2	0 00.0	14 34.5	NO 10.4

Moonrise

Lat.	Moonrise	Diff.
N	h m	m
72	00 49	−07
70	00 40	−04
68	00 32	−01
66	00 26	+01
64	00 20	03
62	00 15	05
60	00 11	06
58	00 07	07
56	00 04	08
54	00 01	09
52	24 17	10
50	24 16	10
45	24 14	12
40	24 13	13
35	24 11	15
30	24 10	16
20	24 07	18
10	24 05	19
0	24 04	21
10	24 02	22
20	24 00	24
30	23 58	26
35	23 56	27
40	23 55	29
45	23 53	30
50	23 51	32
52	23 50	33
54	23 49	34
56	23 48	35
58	23 47	36
60	23 45	37
S		

Moon's P. in A.

Alt. °	Corr. + '	Alt. °	Corr. + '
0		57	29
10	54	58	28
15	53	59	27
18	52	60	26
21	51	62	25
24	50	63	24
26	49	64	23
29	48	65	22
31	47	66	21
33	46	67	20
35	45	68	19
36	44	70	18
38	43	71	17
40	42	72	16
41	41	73	15
43	40	74	14
44	39	75	13
46	38	76	12
47	37	77	11
49	36	78	10
50	35	79	
51	34		
53	33		
54	32		
55	31		
57	30		
58	29		

Sun SD 15.8
Moon SD 15'
Age 21d

(DAY 152) GREENWICH P. M. 1975 JUNE 1 (SUNDAY)

GMT	☉ SUN GHA	Dec.	ARIES GHA ♈	VENUS −3.8 GHA	Dec.	JUPITER −1.7 GHA	Dec.	SATURN 0.4 GHA	Dec.	☽ MOON GHA	Dec.
h m	° '	° '	° '	° '	° '	° '	° '	° '	° '	° '	° '
12 00	0 34.9	N22 00.4	69 21.0	312 05	N23 39	53 23	N 5 32	320 55	N22 15	94 16	S 4 41
10	3 04.9	00.5	71 51.5	314 35		55 53		323 25		96 42	40
20	5 34.9	00.5	74 21.9	317 05		58 24		325 55		99 07	38
30	8 04.8 ·	00.6	76 52.3	319 35 ·		60 54 ·		328 26 ·		101 33 ·	36
40	10 34.8	00.6	79 22.7	322 05		63 24		330 56		103 59	34
50	13 04.8	00.7	81 53.1	324 35		65 55		333 26		106 25	33
13 00	15 34.8	N22 00.8	84 23.5	327 05	N23 39	68 25	N 5 32	335 57	N22 15	108 51	S 4 31
10	18 04.8	00.8	86 53.9	329 35		70 55		338 27		111 16	29
20	20 34.8	00.9	89 24.3	332 05		73 26		340 57		113 42	27
30	23 04.8 ·	00.9	91 54.7	334 35 ·		75 56 ·		343 28 ·		116 08 ·	26
40	25 34.7	01.0	94 25.2	337 05		78 26		345 58		118 34	24
50	28 04.7	01.1	96 55.6	339 35		80 57		348 28		120 59	22
14 00	30 34.7	N22 01.1	99 26.0	342 05	N23 38	83 27	N 5 32	350 59	N22 15	123 25	S 4 20
10	33 04.7	01.2	101 56.4	344 35		85 57		353 29		125 51	19
20	35 34.7	01.2	104 26.8	347 04		88 28		356 00		128 17	17
30	38 04.7 ·	01.3	106 57.2	349 34 ·		90 58 ·		358 30 ·		130 43 ·	15
40	40 34.6	01.3	109 27.6	352 04		93 28		1 00		133 08	13
50	43 04.6	01.4	111 58.0	354 34		95 59		3 31		135 34	11
15 00	45 34.6	N22 01.5	114 28.4	357 04	N23 38	98 29	N 5 32	6 01	N22 15	138 00	S 4 10
10	48 04.6	01.5	116 58.8	359 34		100 59		8 31		140 26	08
20	50 34.6	01.6	119 29.3	2 04		103 30		11 02		142 52	06
30	53 04.6 ·	01.6	121 59.7	4 34 ·		106 00 ·		13 32 ·		145 17 ·	04
40	55 34.6	01.7	124 30.1	7 04		108 30		16 02		147 43	03
50	58 04.5	01.7	127 00.5	9 34		111 01		18 33		150 09	4 01
16 00	60 34.5	N22 01.8	129 30.9	12 04	N23 37	113 31	N 5 33	21 03	N22 15	152 35	S 3 59
10	63 04.5	01.9	132 01.3	14 34		116 01		23 34		155 00	57
20	65 34.5	01.9	134 31.7	17 04		118 32		26 04		157 26	56
30	68 04.5 ·	02.0	137 02.1	19 34 ·		121 02 ·		28 34 ·		159 52 ·	54
40	70 34.5	02.0	139 32.5	22 04		123 32		31 05		162 18	52
50	73 04.4	02.1	142 03.0	24 34		126 03		33 35		164 44	50
17 00	75 34.4	N22 02.1	144 33.4	27 04	N23 37	128 33	N 5 33	36 05	N22 15	167 09	S 3 49
10	78 04.4	02.2	147 03.8	29 33		131 03		38 36		169 35	47
20	80 34.4	02.3	149 34.2	32 03		133 34		41 06		172 01	45
30	83 04.4 ·	02.3	152 04.6	34 33 ·		136 04 ·		43 36 ·		174 27 ·	43
40	85 34.4	02.4	154 35.0	37 03		138 34		46 07		176 53	41
50	88 04.3	02.4	157 05.4	39 33		141 05		48 37		179 18	40
18 00	90 34.3	N22 02.5	159 35.8	42 03	N23 36	143 35	N 5 33	51 08	N22 15	181 44	S 3 38
10	93 04.3	02.5	162 06.2	44 33		146 05		53 38		184 10	36
20	95 34.3	02.6	164 36.7	47 03		148 36		56 08		186 36	34
30	98 04.3 ·	02.6	167 07.1	49 33 ·		151 06 ·		58 39 ·		189 02 ·	33
40	100 34.3	02.7	169 37.5	52 03		153 36		61 09		191 27	31
50	103 04.3	02.8	172 07.9	54 33		156 07		63 39		193 53	29
19 00	105 34.2	N22 02.8	174 38.3	57 03	N23 36	158 37	N 5 33	66 10	N22 15	196 19	S 3 27
10	108 04.2	02.9	177 08.7	59 33		161 07		68 40		198 45	25
20	110 34.2	02.9	179 39.1	62 03		163 38		71 10		201 11	24
30	113 04.2 ·	03.0	182 09.5	64 33 ·		166 08 ·		73 41 ·		203 36 ·	22
40	115 34.2	03.0	184 39.9	67 03		168 38		76 11		206 02	20
50	118 04.2	03.1	187 10.3	69 33		171 09		78 41		208 28	18
20 00	120 34.1	N22 03.2	189 40.8	72 03	N23 35	173 39	N 5 33	81 12	N22 15	210 54	S 3 17
10	123 04.1	03.2	192 11.2	74 32		176 09		83 42		213 20	15
20	125 34.1	03.3	194 41.6	77 02		178 40		86 13		215 45	13
30	128 04.1 ·	03.3	197 12.0	79 32 ·		181 10 ·		88 43 ·		218 11 ·	11
40	130 34.1	03.4	199 42.4	82 02		183 41		91 13		220 37	09
50	133 04.1	03.4	202 12.8	84 32		186 11		93 44		223 03	08
21 00	135 34.0	N22 03.5	204 43.2	87 02	N23 35	188 41	N 5 33	96 14	N22 15	225 29	S 3 06
10	138 04.0	03.6	207 13.6	89 32		191 12		98 44		227 54	04
20	140 34.0	03.6	209 44.0	92 02		193 42		101 15		230 20	02
30	143 04.0 ·	03.7	212 14.5	94 32 ·		196 12 ·		103 45 ·		232 46	3 01
40	145 34.0	03.7	214 44.9	97 02		198 43		106 15		235 12	2 59
50	148 04.0	03.8	217 15.3	99 32		201 13		108 46		237 38	57
22 00	150 34.0	N22 03.8	219 45.7	102 02	N23 34	203 43	N 5 34	111 16	N22 15	240 03	S 2 55
10	153 03.9	03.9	222 16.1	104 32		206 14		113 46		242 29	53
20	155 33.9	03.9	224 46.5	107 02		208 44		116 17		244 55	52
30	158 03.9 ·	04.0	227 16.9	109 32 ·		211 14 ·		118 47 ·		247 21 ·	50
40	160 33.9	04.1	229 47.3	112 02		213 45		121 18		249 47	48
50	163 03.9	04.1	232 17.7	114 31		216 15		123 48		252 12	46
23 00	165 33.9	N22 04.2	234 48.2	117 01	N23 34	218 45	N 5 34	126 18	N22 15	254 38	S 2 45
10	168 03.8	04.2	237 18.6	119 31		221 16		128 49		257 04	43
20	170 33.8	04.3	239 49.0	122 01		223 46		131 19		259 30	41
30	173 03.8 ·	04.3	242 19.4	124 31 ·		226 16 ·		133 49 ·		261 56 ·	39
40	175 33.8	04.4	244 49.8	127 01		228 47		136 20		264 21	37
50	178 03.8	04.5	247 20.2	129 31		231 17		138 50		266 47	36
Rate	14 59.9	N0 00.3		14 59.7	S0 00.5	15 02.0	N0 00.2	15 02.2	0 00.0	14 34.8	N0 10.6

Moonset

Lat.	Moon-set	Diff.
N	h m	m
72	10 38	51
70	10 45	48
68	10 51	45
66	10 56	42
64	11 00	40
62	11 04	39
60	11 07	37
58	11 10	36
56	11 12	35
54	11 14	34
52	11 16	33
50	11 18	32
45	11 22	30
40	11 25	29
35	11 28	27
30	11 31	26
20	11 35	24
10	11 39	23
0	11 42	21
10	11 46	20
20	11 49	18
30	11 53	16
35	11 56	15
40	11 58	14
45	12 01	12
50	12 05	10
52	12 07	10
54	12 08	09
56	12 10	08
58	12 13	07
60	12 15	06
S		

Moon's P. in A.

Alt °	Corr +	Alt °	Corr +
0	54	57	29
9	53	58	28
14	52	59	27
18	51	60	26
21	50	61	25
24	49	63	24
26	48	64	23
28	47	65	22
31	46	66	21
33	45	67	20
34	44	68	19
36	43	70	18
38	42	71	17
40	41	72	16
41	40	73	15
43	39	74	14
44	38	75	13
46	37	76	12
47	36	77	11
49	35	78	10
50	34	79	10
51	33		
53	32		
54	31		
55	30		
57	29		
58	29		

Sun SD 15.8
Moon SD 15'
Age 21d

APPENDIX G: EXTRACTS FROM *AIR ALMANAC*

(DAY 153) GREENWICH A. M. 1975 JUNE 2 (MONDAY)

GMT	☉ SUN GHA	Dec.	ARIES GHA ϒ	VENUS−3.8 GHA	Dec.	JUPITER−1.7 GHA	Dec.	SATURN 0.4 GHA	Dec.	☽ MOON GHA	Dec.
00 00	180 33.8	N22 04.5	249 50.6	132 01	N23 33	233 47	N 5 34	141 20	N22 15	269 13	S 2 34
10	183 03.7	04.6	252 21.0	134 31		236 18		143 51		271 39	32
20	185 33.7	04.6	254 51.4	137 01		238 48		146 21		274 05	30
30	188 03.7	· 04.7	257 21.8	139 31 ·		241 18 ·		148 52 ·		276 31 ·	29
40	190 33.7	04.7	259 52.3	142 01		243 49		151 22		278 56	27
50	193 03.7	04.8	262 22.7	144 31		246 19		153 52		281 22	25
01 00	195 33.7	N22 04.8	264 53.1	147 01	N23 33	248 49	N 5 34	156 23	N22 15	283 48	S 2 23
10	198 03.7	04.9	267 23.5	149 31		251 20		158 53		286 14	21
20	200 33.6	05.0	269 53.9	152 01		253 50		161 23		288 40	20
30	203 03.6	· 05.0	272 24.3	154 31 ·		256 20 ·		163 54 ·		291 05 ·	18
40	205 33.6	05.1	274 54.7	157 01		258 51		166 24		293 31	16
50	208 03.6	05.1	277 25.1	159 30		261 21		168 54		295 57	14
02 00	210 33.6	N22 05.2	279 55.5	162 00	N23 32	263 51	N 5 34	171 25	N22 15	298 23	S 2 12
10	213 03.6	05.2	282 26.0	164 30		266 22		173 55		300 49	11
20	215 33.5	05.3	284 56.4	167 00		268 52		176 26		303 14	09
30	218 03.5	· 05.4	287 26.8	169 30 ·		271 22 ·		178 56 ·		305 40 ·	07
40	220 33.5	05.4	289 57.2	172 00		273 53		181 26		308 06	05
50	223 03.5	05.5	292 27.6	174 30		276 23		183 57		310 32	03
03 00	225 33.5	N22 05.5	294 58.0	177 00	N23 32	278 53	N 5 34	186 27	N22 15	312 58	S 2 02
10	228 03.5	05.6	297 28.4	179 30		281 24		188 57		315 23	2 00
20	230 33.4	05.6	299 58.8	182 00		283 54		191 28		317 49	1 58
30	233 03.4	· 05.7	302 29.2	184 30 ·		286 24 ·		193 58 ·		320 15 ·	56
40	235 33.4	05.7	304 59.7	187 00		288 55		196 28		322 41	55
50	238 03.4	05.8	307 30.1	189 30		291 25		198 59		325 07	53
04 00	240 33.4	N22 05.9	310 00.5	192 00	N23 31	293 55	N 5 35	201 29	N22 15	327 33	S 1 51
10	243 03.4	05.9	312 30.9	194 30		296 26		203 59		329 58	49
20	245 33.4	06.0	315 01.3	197 00		298 56		206 30		332 24	47
30	248 03.3	· 06.0	317 31.7	199 30 ·		301 26 ·		209 00 ·		334 50 ·	46
40	250 33.3	06.1	320 02.1	202 00		303 57		211 31		337 16	44
50	253 03.3	06.1	322 32.5	204 29		306 27		214 01		339 42	42
05 00	255 33.3	N22 06.2	325 02.9	206 59	N23 31	308 57	N 5 35	216 31	N22 15	342 07	S 1 40
10	258 03.3	06.2	327 33.3	209 29		311 28		219 02		344 33	38
20	260 33.3	06.3	330 03.8	211 59		313 58		221 32		346 59	37
30	263 03.2	· 06.4	332 34.2	214 29 ·		316 28 ·		224 02 ·		349 25 ·	35
40	265 33.2	06.4	335 04.6	216 59		318 59		226 33		351 51	33
50	268 03.2	06.5	337 35.0	219 29		321 29		229 03		354 16	31
06 00	270 33.2	N22 06.5	340 05.4	221 59	N23 30	323 59	N 5 35	231 33	N22 15	356 42	S 1 30
10	273 03.2	06.6	342 35.8	224 29		326 30		234 04		359 08	28
20	275 33.2	06.6	345 06.2	226 59		329 00		236 34		1 34	26
30	278 03.1	· 06.7	347 36.6	229 29 ·		331 30 ·		239 05 ·		4 00 ·	24
40	280 33.1	06.7	350 07.0	231 59		334 01		241 35		6 25	22
50	283 03.1	06.8	352 37.5	234 29		336 31		244 05		8 51	21
07 00	285 33.1	N22 06.9	355 07.9	236 59	N23 29	339 01	N 5 35	246 36	N22 15	11 17	S 1 19
10	288 03.1	06.9	357 38.3	239 29		341 32		249 06		13 43	17
20	290 33.1	07.0	0 08.7	241 59		344 02		251 36		16 09	15
30	293 03.0	· 07.0	2 39.1	244 29 ·		346 32 ·		254 07 ·		18 35 ·	13
40	295 33.0	07.1	5 09.5	246 59		349 03		256 37		21 00	12
50	298 03.0	07.1	7 39.9	249 28		351 33		259 07		23 26	10
08 00	300 33.0	N22 07.2	10 10.3	251 58	N23 29	354 04	N 5 35	261 38	N22 15	25 52	S 1 08
10	303 03.0	07.2	12 40.7	254 28		356 34		264 08		28 18	06
20	305 33.0	07.3	15 11.1	256 58		359 04		266 38		30 44	04
30	308 02.9	· 07.4	17 41.6	259 28 ·		1 35 ·		269 09 ·		33 09 ·	03
40	310 32.9	07.4	20 12.0	261 58		4 05		271 39		35 35	1 01
50	313 02.9	07.5	22 42.4	264 28		6 35		274 10		38 01	0 59
09 00	315 32.9	N22 07.5	25 12.8	266 58	N23 28	9 06	N 5 35	276 40	N22 15	40 27	S 0 57
10	318 02.9	07.6	27 43.2	269 28		11 36		279 10		42 53	55
20	320 32.9	07.6	30 13.6	271 58		14 06		281 41		45 19	54
30	323 02.9	· 07.7	32 44.0	274 28 ·		16 37 ·		284 11 ·		47 44 ·	52
40	325 32.8	07.7	35 14.4	276 58		19 07		286 41		50 10	50
50	328 02.8	07.8	37 44.8	279 28		21 37		289 12		52 36	48
10 00	330 32.8	N22 07.9	40 15.3	281 58	N23 28	24 08	N 5 36	291 42	N22 15	55 02	S 0 47
10	333 02.8	07.9	42 45.7	284 28		26 38		294 12		57 28	45
20	335 32.8	08.0	45 16.1	286 58		29 08		296 43		59 53	43
30	338 02.8	· 08.0	47 46.5	289 28 ·		31 39 ·		299 13 ·		62 19 ·	41
40	340 32.7	08.1	50 16.9	291 57		34 09		301 43		64 45	39
50	343 02.7	08.1	52 47.3	294 27		36 39		304 14		67 11	38
11 00	345 32.7	N22 08.2	55 17.7	296 57	N23 27	39 10	N 5 36	306 44	N22 15	69 37	S 0 36
10	348 02.7	08.2	57 48.1	299 27		41 40		309 15		72 03	34
20	350 32.7	08.3	60 18.5	301 57		44 10		311 45		74 28	32
30	353 02.7	· 08.3	62 49.0	304 27 ·		46 41 ·		314 15 ·		76 54 ·	30
40	355 32.6	08.4	65 19.4	306 57		49 11		316 46		79 20	29
50	358 02.6	08.5	67 49.8	309 27		51 41		319 16		81 46	27
Rate	14 59.9	N0 00.3	14 59.7		S0 00.5	15 02.0	N0 00.2	15 02.2	0 00.0	14 34.9	N0 10.8

Lat. / Moon-rise / Diff.

Lat.	Moon-rise	Diff.
N °	h m	m
72	00 36	−07
70	00 33	−04
68	00 30	−01
66	00 27	+01
64	00 25	03
62	00 24	04
60	00 22	05
58	00 21	07
56	00 19	08
54	00 18	09
52	00 17	10
50	00 16	10
45	00 14	12
40	00 13	13
35	00 11	15
30	00 10	16
20	00 07	18
10	00 05	19
0	00 02	21
10	00 00	22
20	24 50	24
30	24 50	26
35	24 50	27
40	24 52	29
45	24 53	30
50	24 54	32
52	24 55	33
54	24 56	34
56	24 57	35
58	24 58	36
60	24 59	37
S		

Moon's P. in A.

Alt °	Corr +	Alt °	Corr +
0		57	29
9	54	58	28
14	53	59	28
18	52	60	27
21	51	61	26
24	50	63	25
26	49	64	24
28	48	65	23
31	47	66	22
33	46	67	21
34	45	68	20
36	44	70	19
38	43	71	18
40	42	72	17
41	41	73	16
43	40	74	15
44	39	75	14
46	38	76	13
47	37	77	12
49	36	78	11
50	35	79	10
51	34		
53	33		
54	32		
55	31		
57	30		
58	29		

Sun SD 15ʹ8
Moon SD 15ʹ
Age 22d

(DAY 153) GREENWICH P. M. 1975 JUNE 2 (MONDAY)

GMT	☉ SUN GHA	Dec.	ARIES GHA ♈	VENUS−3.8 GHA	Dec.	JUPITER−1.7 GHA	Dec.	SATURN 0.4 GHA	Dec.	☾ MOON GHA	Dec.	Lat.	Moon-set	Diff.
h m	° ′	° ′	° ′	° ′	° ′	° ′	° ′	° ′	° ′	° ′	° ′	°	h m	m
12 00	0 32.6	N22 08.5	70 20.2	311 57	N23 27	54 12	N 5 36	321 46	N22 14	84 12	S 0 25	N		
10	3 02.6	08.6	72 50.6	314 27		56 42		324 17		86 37	23		h m	m
20	5 32.6	08.6	75 21.0	316 57		59 12		326 47		89 03	21	72	12 18	50
30	8 02.6 ·	08.7	77 51.4	319 27 ·	·	61 43 ·	·	329 17 ·	·	91 29 ·	20	70	12 19	47
40	10 32.5	08.7	80 21.8	321 57		64 13		331 48		93 55	18	68	12 19	44
50	13 02.5	08.8	82 52.2	324 27		66 43		334 18		96 21	16	66	12 20	42
												64	12 20	40
13 00	15 32.5	N22 08.8	85 22.6	326 57	N23 26	69 14	N 5 36	336 49	N22 14	98 47	S 0 14	62	12 20	38
10	18 02.5	08.9	87 53.1	329 27		71 44		339 19		101 12	12			
20	20 32.5	08.9	90 23.5	331 57		74 14		341 49		103 38	11	60	12 21	37
30	23 02.5 ·	09.0	92 53.9	334 27 ·	·	76 45 ·	·	344 20 ·	·	106 04 ·	09	58	12 21	36
40	25 32.4	09.1	95 24.3	336 56		79 15		346 50		108 30	07	56	12 21	35
50	28 02.4	09.1	97 54.7	339 26		81 45		349 20		110 56	05	54	12 21	34
												52	12 21	33
14 00	30 32.4	N22 09.2	100 25.1	341 56	N23 26	84 16	N 5 36	351 51	N22 14	113 21	S 0 03			
10	33 02.4	09.2	102 55.5	344 26		86 46		354 21		115 47	S 0 02	50	12 22	32
20	35 32.4	09.3	105 25.9	346 56		89 16		356 51		118 13	0 00	45	12 22	30
30	38 02.4 ·	09.3	107 56.3	349 26 ·	·	91 47 ·	·	359 22 ·	·	120 39	N 0 02	40	12 22	29
40	40 32.3	09.4	110 26.8	351 56		94 17		1 52		123 05	04	35	12 22	27
50	43 02.3	09.4	112 57.2	354 26		96 47		4 22		125 30	06	30	12 23	26
15 00	45 32.3	N22 09.5	115 27.6	356 56	N23 25	99 18	N 5 37	6 53	N22 14	127 56	N 0 07	20	12 23	24
10	48 02.3	09.5	117 58.0	359 26		101 48		9 23		130 22	09	10	12 23	22
20	50 32.3	09.6	120 28.4	1 56		104 18		11 54		132 48	11	0	12 24	21
30	53 02.3 ·	09.7	122 58.8	4 26 ·	·	106 49 ·	·	14 24 ·	·	135 14 ·	13	10	12 24	19
40	55 32.3	09.7	125 29.2	6 56		109 19		16 54		137 39	15	20	12 24	18
50	58 02.2	09.8	127 59.6	9 26		111 49		19 25		140 05	16			
16 00	60 32.2	N22 09.8	130 30.0	11 56	N23 25	114 20	N 5 37	21 55	N22 14	142 31	N 0 18	30	12 24	16
10	63 02.2	09.9	133 00.5	14 26		116 50		24 25		144 57	20	35	12 24	14
20	65 32.2	09.9	135 30.9	16 56		119 20		26 56		147 23	22	40	12 25	13
30	68 02.2 ·	10.0	138 01.3	19 26 ·	·	121 51 ·	·	29 26 ·	·	149 49 ·	24	45	12 25	12
40	70 32.2	10.0	140 31.7	21 56		124 21		31 56		152 14	25	50	12 25	10
50	73 02.1	10.1	143 02.1	24 25		126 51		34 27		154 40	27	52	12 25	09
17 00	75 32.1	N22 10.1	145 32.5	26 55	N23 24	129 22	N 5 37	36 57	N22 14	157 06	N 0 29	54	12 25	09
10	78 02.1	10.2	148 02.9	29 25		131 52		39 27		159 32	31	56	12 25	08
20	80 32.1	10.3	150 33.3	31 55		134 22		41 58		161 58	33	58	12 26	06
30	83 02.1 ·	10.3	153 03.7	34 25 ·	·	136 53 ·	·	44 28 ·	·	164 23 ·	34	60	12 26	05
40	85 32.1	10.4	155 34.1	36 55		139 23		46 59		166 49	36			
50	88 02.0	10.4	158 04.6	39 25		141 53		49 29		169 15	38	S		
18 00	90 32.0	N22 10.5	160 35.0	41 55	N23 24	144 24	N 5 37	51 59	N22 14	171 41	N 0 40			
10	93 02.0	10.5	163 05.4	44 25		146 54		54 30		174 07	42		Moon's P. in A.	
20	95 32.0	10.6	165 35.8	46 55		149 24		57 00		176 32	43			
30	98 02.0 ·	10.6	168 06.2	49 25 ·	·	151 55 ·	·	59 30 ·	·	178 58 ·	45	Alt.	Corr.	Alt. Corr.
40	100 32.0	10.7	170 36.6	51 55		154 25		62 01		181 24	47	°	+ ′	° + ′
50	103 01.9	10.7	173 07.0	54 25		156 55		64 31		183 50	49	0	54	57
19 00	105 31.9	N22 10.8	175 37.4	56 55	N23 23	159 26	N 5 37	67 02	N22 14	186 16	N 0 51	9	54	57 29
10	108 01.9	10.9	178 07.8	59 25		161 56		69 32		188 42	52	14	53	58 28
20	110 31.9	10.9	180 38.3	61 55		164 26		72 02		191 07	54	18	52	59 27
30	113 01.9 ·	11.0	183 08.7	64 25 ·	·	166 57 ·	·	74 33 ·	·	193 33 ·	56	21	51	60 26
40	115 31.9	11.0	185 39.1	66 55		169 27		77 03		195 59	0 58	24	50	61 25
50	118 01.8	11.1	188 09.5	69 24		171 57		79 33		198 25	1 00	26	49	63 24
20 00	120 31.8	N22 11.1	190 39.9	71 54	N23 22	174 28	N 5 37	82 04	N22 14	200 51	N 1 01	29	48	64 23
10	123 01.8	11.2	193 10.3	74 24		176 58		84 34		203 16	03	31	47	65 22
20	125 31.8	11.2	195 40.7	76 54		179 28		87 04		205 42	05	33	46	66 21
30	128 01.8 ·	11.3	198 11.1	79 24 ·	·	181 59 ·	·	89 35 ·	·	208 08 ·	07	34	45	67 20
40	130 31.8	11.3	200 41.5	81 54		184 29		92 05		210 34	09	36	44	68 19
50	133 01.7	11.4	203 12.0	84 24		186 59		94 35		213 00	10	38	43	70 18
21 00	135 31.7	N22 11.4	205 42.4	86 54	N23 22	189 30	N 5 38	97 06	N22 14	215 25	N 1 12	40	42	71 17
10	138 01.7	11.5	208 12.8	89 24		192 00		99 36		217 51	14	41	41	72 16
20	140 31.7	11.6	210 43.2	91 54		194 31		102 07		220 17	16	43	40	73 15
30	143 01.7 ·	11.6	213 13.6	94 24 ·	·	197 01 ·	·	104 37 ·	·	222 43 ·	18	44	39	74 14
40	145 31.7	11.7	215 44.0	96 54		199 31		107 07		225 09	19	46	38	75 13
50	148 01.6	11.7	218 14.4	99 24		202 02		109 38		227 34	21	47	37	76 12
22 00	150 31.6	N22 11.8	220 44.8	101 54	N23 21	204 32	N 5 38	112 08	N22 14	230 00	N 1 23	49	36	77 11
10	153 01.6	11.8	223 15.2	104 24		207 02		114 38		232 26	25	49	35	78 11
20	155 31.6	11.9	225 45.6	106 54		209 33		117 09		234 52	27	50	34	79 10
30	158 01.6 ·	11.9	228 16.1	109 24 ·	·	212 03 ·	·	119 39 ·	·	237 18 ·	28	51	33	
40	160 31.6	12.0	230 46.5	111 54		214 33		122 09		239 43	30	53	33	
50	163 01.5	12.0	233 16.9	114 23		217 04		124 40		242 09	32	54	31	
23 00	165 31.5	N22 12.1	235 47.3	116 53	N23 21	219 34	N 5 38	127 10	N22 14	244 35	N 1 34	55	30	
10	168 01.5	12.1	238 17.7	119 23		222 04		129 40		247 01	35	57	30	
20	170 31.5	12.2	240 48.1	121 53		224 35		132 11		249 27	37	58	29	
30	173 01.5 ·	12.3	243 18.5	124 23 ·	·	227 05 ·	·	134 41 ·	·	251 53 ·	39			
40	175 31.5	12.3	245 48.9	126 53		229 35		137 12		254 18	41	Sun SD 15.8	
50	178 01.4	12.4	248 19.3	129 23		232 06		139 42		256 44	43	Moon SD 15′	
Rate	14 59.9	N0 00.3		14 59.7	S0 00.6	15 02.0	N0 00.2	15 02.2	0 00.0	14 34.9	N0 10.8	Age 22d	

F4   INTERPOLATION OF MOONRISE, MOONSET

FOR LONGITUDE

Add if longitude *west*
Subtract if longitude *east*

Longi-tude	Diff.*					
	05	10	15	20	25	30
°	m	m	m	m	m	m
0	00	00	00	00	00	00
20	01	01	02	02	03	03
40	01	02	03	04	06	07
60	02	03	05	07	08	10
80	02	04	07	09	11	13
100	03	06	08	11	14	17
120	03	07	10	13	17	20
140	04	08	12	16	19	23
160	04	09	13	18	22	27
180	05	10	15	20	25	30

Longi-tude	Diff.*					
	35	40	45	50	55	60
°	m	m	m	m	m	m
0	00	00	00	00	00	00
15	03	03	04	04	05	05
30	06	07	08	08	09	10
45	09	10	11	12	14	15
60	12	13	15	17	18	20
75	15	17	19	21	23	25
90	18	20	22	25	28	30
105	20	23	26	29	32	35
120	23	27	30	33	37	40
135	26	30	34	38	41	45
150	29	33	38	42	46	50
165	32	37	41	46	50	55
180	35	40	45	50	55	60

Longi-tude	Diff.*					
	65	70	75	80	85	90
°	m	m	m	m	m	m
0	00	00	00	00	00	00
10	04	04	04	04	05	05
20	07	08	08	09	09	10
30	11	12	12	13	14	15
40	14	16	17	18	19	20
50	18	19	21	22	24	25
60	22	23	25	27	28	30
70	25	27	29	31	33	35
80	29	31	33	36	38	40
90	32	35	38	40	42	45
100	36	39	42	44	47	50
110	40	43	46	49	52	55
120	43	47	50	53	57	60
130	47	51	54	58	61	65
140	51	54	58	62	66	70
150	54	58	62	67	71	75
160	58	62	67	71	76	80
170	61	66	71	76	80	85
180	65	70	75	80	85	90

*When negative *subtract* correction if longitude *west*, and *add* if *east*.

STAR INDEX, MAY—AUG., 1975

No.	Name		Mag.	S.H.A.	Dec.
				° '	° '
1*	Alpheratz	†	2.2	358 13	N. 28 57
2	Ankaa		2.4	353 44	S. 42 26
3*	Schedar		2.5	350 13	N. 56 24
4*	Diphda	†	2.2	349 24	S. 18 07
5*	Achernar		0.6	335 48	S. 57 21
6*	Hamal	†	2.2	328 33	N. 23 21
7*	Acamar		3.1	315 40	S. 40 24
8*	Menkar	†	2.8	314 45	N. 4 00
9*	Mirfak		1.9	309 21	N. 49 46
10*	Aldebaran	†	1.1	291 22	N. 16 28
11*	Rigel	†	0.3	281 40	S. 8 14
12*	Capella		0.2	281 17	N. 45 58
13	Bellatrix		1.7	279 03	N. 6 20
14	Elnath	†	1.8	278 49	N. 28 35
15	Alnilam	†	1.8	276 16	S. 1 13
16*	Betelgeuse	†	0.1–1.2	271 32	N. 7 24
17*	Canopus		−0.9	264 09	S. 52 41
18*	Sirius	†	−1.6	258 59	S. 16 41
19	Adhara	†	1.6	255 35	S. 28 56
20*	Procyon	†	0.5	245 30	N. 5 17
21*	Pollux	†	1.2	244 03	N. 28 05
22	Avior		1.7	234 30	S. 59 26
23*	Suhail		2.2	223 14	S. 43 20
24*	Miaplacidus		1.8	221 46	S. 69 37
25*	Alphard	†	2.2	218 24	S. 8 33
26*	Regulus	†	1.3	208 14	N. 12 05
27*	Dubhe		2.0	194 27	N. 61 53
28*	Denebola	†	2.2	183 03	N. 14 43
29*	Gienah	†	2.8	176 22	S. 17 25
30*	Acrux		1.1	173 41	S. 62 58
31	Gacrux		1.6	172 33	S. 56 59
32*	Alioth		1.7	166 46	N. 56 06
33*	Spica	†	1.2	159 01	S. 11 02
34*	Alkaid		1.9	153 21	N. 49 26
35	Hadar		0.9	149 28	S. 60 16
36	Menkent		2.3	148 41	S. 36 15
37*	Arcturus	†	0.2	146 22	N. 19 19
38*	Rigil Kentaurus		0.1	140 30	S. 60 44
39	Zubenelgenubi	†	2.9	137 37	S. 15 57
40*	Kochab		2.2	137 18	N. 74 16
41*	Alphecca	†	2.3	126 35	N. 26 48
42*	Antares	†	1.2	113 01	S. 26 23
43	Atria		1.9	108 28	S. 68 59
44	Sabik	†	2.6	102 45	S. 15 42
45*	Shaula		1.7	97 00	S. 37 05
46*	Rasalhague	†	2.1	96 33	N. 12 35
47	Eltanin		2.4	90 59	N. 51 30
48	Kaus Australis		2.0	84 21	S. 34 24
49*	Vega		0.1	80 58	N. 38 46
50*	Nunki	†	2.1	76 33	S. 26 20
51*	Altair	†	0.9	62 36	N. 8 48
52*	Peacock		2.1	54 03	S. 56 49
53*	Deneb		1.3	49 51	N. 45 12
54*	Enif	†	2.5	34 15	N. 9 46
55	Al Na'ir		2.2	28 19	S. 47 05
56*	Fomalhaut	†	1.3	15 55	S. 29 45
57	Markab	†	2.6	14 07	N. 15 04

*Stars used in H.O. 249 (A.P. 3270) Vol. 1.
†Stars that may be used with Vols. 2 and 3.

SUNRISE

(All times h m)

Lat.	Dec. 30	Jan 2	Jan 5	Jan 8	Jan 11	Jan 14	Jan 17	Jan 20	Jan 23	Jan 26	Jan 29	Feb 1	Feb 4	Feb 7	Feb 10	Lat.
N 72°	▬▬	▬▬	▬▬	▬▬	▬▬	▬▬	▬▬	▬▬	▬▬	12 04	11 03	10 33	10 09	09 48	09 28	N 72°
70	▬▬	▬▬	▬▬	▬▬	▬▬	▬▬	12 05	11 11	10 46	10 25	10 06	09 49	09 33	09 17	09 02	70
68	▬▬	▬▬	11 34	11 13	10 56	10 41	10 27	10 13	09 59	09 46	09 33	09 20	09 08	08 55	08 42	68
66	10 31	10 27	10 21	10 14	10 06	09 58	09 49	09 39	09 29	09 19	09 09	08 59	08 48	08 37	08 26	66
64	09 51	09 49	09 45	09 41	09 35	09 29	09 22	09 15	09 07	08 59	08 50	08 42	08 32	08 23	08 14	64
62	09 24	09 22	09 20	09 16	09 12	09 07	09 02	08 56	08 49	08 43	08 35	08 27	08 19	08 11	08 03	62
N 60	09 03	09 02	09 00	08 58	08 54	08 50	08 46	08 40	08 35	08 29	08 22	08 15	08 08	08 01	07 53	N 60
58	08 46	08 45	08 44	08 42	08 39	08 36	08 32	08 27	08 22	08 17	08 11	08 05	07 59	07 52	07 45	58
56	08 32	08 31	08 30	08 28	08 26	08 23	08 20	08 16	08 12	08 07	08 02	07 56	07 50	07 44	07 38	56
54	08 19	08 19	08 18	08 17	08 15	08 12	08 09	08 06	08 02	07 58	07 53	07 48	07 43	07 37	07 32	54
52	08 08	08 08	08 07	08 06	08 05	08 02	08 00	07 57	07 54	07 50	07 46	07 41	07 36	07 31	07 26	52
N 50	07 58	07 58	07 58	07 57	07 56	07 54	07 52	07 49	07 46	07 42	07 39	07 35	07 30	07 25	07 21	N 50
45	07 38	07 38	07 38	07 37	07 36	07 34	07 32	07 30	07 27	07 24	07 21	07 17	07 13	07 09	07 04	45
40	07 22	07 22	07 22	07 22	07 22	07 21	07 20	07 18	07 16	07 14	07 12	07 09	07 06	07 03	07 00	40
35	07 07	07 08	07 08	07 08	07 08	07 07	07 06	07 05	07 03	07 01	06 59	06 57	06 55	06 52	06 50	35
30	06 55	06 56	06 57	06 57	06 57	06 57	06 56	06 56	06 55	06 54	06 52	06 51	06 49	06 47	06 45	30
N 20	06 34	06 35	06 36	06 37	06 37	06 38	06 38	06 38	06 38	06 37	06 37	06 36	06 35	06 33	06 32	N 20
N 10	06 16	06 17	06 18	06 19	06 20	06 21	06 22	06 22	06 22	06 23	06 23	06 23	06 22	06 21	06 20	N 10
0	05 59	06 00	06 02	06 03	06 04	06 05	06 06	06 07	06 08	06 09	06 10	06 10	06 11	06 11	06 11	0
S 10	05 41	05 43	05 44	05 46	05 48	05 49	05 51	05 52	05 54	05 55	05 56	05 57	05 58	05 59	06 00	S 10
20	05 23	05 24	05 26	05 28	05 30	05 32	05 34	05 36	05 38	05 40	05 42	05 44	05 45	05 47	05 49	20
S 30	05 01	05 03	05 05	05 07	05 10	05 12	05 15	05 17	05 20	05 23	05 25	05 28	05 31	05 33	05 36	S 30
35	04 48	04 50	04 52	04 55	04 57	05 00	05 03	05 06	05 09	05 13	05 16	05 19	05 22	05 25	05 28	35
40	04 33	04 35	04 38	04 41	04 44	04 47	04 50	04 54	04 57	05 01	05 04	05 08	05 12	05 16	05 19	40
45	04 15	04 18	04 21	04 24	04 27	04 31	04 35	04 39	04 43	04 47	04 51	04 56	05 00	05 05	05 09	45
50	03 53	03 56	03 59	04 03	04 07	04 11	04 15	04 20	04 25	04 30	04 35	04 40	04 46	04 51	04 56	50
S 52	03 42	03 45	03 49	03 52	03 57	04 01	04 06	04 11	04 17	04 22	04 28	04 33	04 39	04 45	04 50	S 52
54	03 30	03 33	03 37	03 41	03 46	03 51	03 56	04 01	04 07	04 13	04 19	04 25	04 31	04 38	04 44	54
56	03 16	03 19	03 23	03 28	03 33	03 38	03 44	03 50	03 57	04 03	04 10	04 16	04 23	04 30	04 37	56
58	02 59	03 03	03 08	03 13	03 18	03 24	03 31	03 37	03 44	03 52	03 59	04 06	04 14	04 21	04 29	58
S 60	02 39	02 44	02 49	02 54	03 00	03 07	03 15	03 22	03 30	03 38	03 46	03 54	04 03	04 11	04 19	S 60

SUNSET

(All times h m)

Lat.	Dec. 30	Jan 2	Jan 5	Jan 8	Jan 11	Jan 14	Jan 17	Jan 20	Jan 23	Jan 26	Jan 29	Feb 1	Feb 4	Feb 7	Feb 10	Lat.
N 72°	▬▬	▬▬	▬▬	▬▬	▬▬	▬▬	▬▬	▬▬	▬▬	12 25	13 24	13 55	14 20	14 42	15 02	N 72°
70	▬▬	▬▬	▬▬	▬▬	▬▬	▬▬	12 21	13 11	13 39	14 01	14 21	14 39	14 56	15 12	15 28	70
68	▬▬	▬▬	12 36	13 00	13 20	13 37	13 54	14 09	14 25	14 39	14 54	15 08	15 21	15 35	15 48	68
66	13 33	13 41	13 49	13 59	14 09	14 20	14 32	14 43	14 55	15 06	15 18	15 29	15 41	15 52	16 03	66
64	14 13	14 19	14 25	14 32	14 40	14 49	14 58	15 07	15 17	15 27	15 36	15 46	15 56	16 06	16 16	64
62	14 40	14 45	14 50	14 57	15 03	15 10	15 18	15 26	15 35	15 43	15 52	16 00	16 09	16 18	16 27	62
N 60	15 02	15 06	15 10	15 16	15 22	15 28	15 35	15 42	15 49	15 57	16 05	16 12	16 20	16 28	16 36	N 60
58	15 19	15 22	15 27	15 32	15 37	15 43	15 49	15 55	16 02	16 09	16 15	16 23	16 30	16 37	16 44	58
56	15 33	15 37	15 41	15 45	15 50	15 55	16 01	16 06	16 12	16 19	16 25	16 32	16 38	16 45	16 51	56
54	15 46	15 49	15 53	15 57	16 01	16 06	16 11	16 16	16 22	16 28	16 34	16 40	16 46	16 52	16 58	54
52	15 57	16 00	16 03	16 07	16 11	16 16	16 20	16 25	16 30	16 36	16 41	16 47	16 52	16 58	17 03	52
N 50	16 06	16 09	16 13	16 16	16 20	16 24	16 29	16 33	16 38	16 43	16 48	16 53	16 58	17 03	17 09	N 50
45	16 27	16 29	16 32	16 35	16 39	16 42	16 46	16 50	16 54	16 58	17 03	17 07	17 11	17 16	17 20	45
40	16 44	16 46	16 48	16 51	16 54	16 57	17 01	17 04	17 08	17 11	17 15	17 18	17 22	17 25	17 29	40
35	16 57	17 00	17 02	17 04	17 07	17 10	17 13	17 16	17 19	17 22	17 25	17 28	17 31	17 34	17 37	35
30	17 10	17 12	17 14	17 16	17 19	17 21	17 24	17 27	17 29	17 32	17 34	17 37	17 39	17 42	17 44	30
N 20	17 31	17 32	17 34	17 36	17 38	17 40	17 42	17 44	17 46	17 48	17 50	17 52	17 53	17 55	17 57	N 20
N 10	17 49	17 50	17 52	17 54	17 55	17 57	17 58	18 00	18 01	18 02	18 04	18 05	18 06	18 07	18 07	N 10
0	18 06	18 07	18 09	18 10	18 11	18 12	18 14	18 14	18 15	18 16	18 17	18 17	18 17	18 18	18 18	0
S 10	18 24	18 25	18 26	18 27	18 28	18 29	18 29	18 29	18 30	18 30	18 30	18 30	18 29	18 29	18 28	S 10
20	18 42	18 43	18 44	18 45	18 45	18 46	18 46	18 46	18 45	18 45	18 44	18 43	18 42	18 41	18 39	20
S 30	19 04	19 05	19 05	19 06	19 06	19 05	19 05	19 04	19 03	19 02	19 00	18 59	18 57	18 55	18 52	S 30
35	19 17	19 17	19 18	19 18	19 18	19 17	19 16	19 15	19 14	19 12	19 10	19 08	19 05	19 03	19 00	35
40	19 32	19 32	19 32	19 32	19 31	19 30	19 29	19 28	19 26	19 24	19 22	19 18	19 15	19 12	19 09	40
45	19 49	19 50	19 49	19 49	19 48	19 46	19 45	19 42	19 40	19 37	19 34	19 31	19 27	19 23	19 18	45
50	20 12	20 12	20 11	20 10	20 08	20 06	20 04	20 01	19 58	19 54	19 50	19 46	19 41	19 36	19 31	50
S 52	20 22	20 22	20 21	20 20	20 18	20 16	20 13	20 09	20 06	20 02	19 57	19 53	19 48	19 42	19 37	S 52
54	20 34	20 34	20 33	20 31	20 29	20 26	20 23	20 19	20 15	20 11	20 06	20 01	19 55	19 49	19 43	54
56	20 48	20 48	20 46	20 44	20 41	20 38	20 35	20 30	20 26	20 21	20 15	20 09	20 03	19 57	19 50	56
58	21 05	21 04	21 02	20 59	20 56	20 52	20 48	20 43	20 38	20 32	20 26	20 19	20 13	20 06	19 58	58
S 60	21 25	21 23	21 21	21 18	21 14	21 09	21 04	20 58	20 52	20 45	20 38	20 31	20 23	20 15	20 07	S 60

MORNING CIVIL TWILIGHT

Lat.	Dec. 30	Jan 2	Jan 5	Jan 8	Jan 11	Jan 14	Jan 17	Jan 20	Jan 23	Jan 26	Jan 29	Feb 1	Feb 4	Feb 7	Feb 10	Lat.
N 72	10 49	10 41	10 32	10 21	10 10	09 58	09 46	09 33	09 21	09 08	08 55	08 41	08 28	08 14	08 01	N 72
70	09 52	09 49	09 44	09 38	09 30	09 22	09 14	09 04	08 54	08 44	08 33	08 22	08 11	08 00	07 48	70
68	09 19	09 16	09 13	09 08	09 03	08 57	08 50	08 42	08 34	08 26	08 17	08 07	07 58	07 48	07 37	68
66	08 54	08 53	08 50	08 47	08 42	08 37	08 32	08 25	08 18	08 11	08 03	07 55	07 46	07 38	07 28	66
64	08 35	08 34	08 32	08 29	08 26	08 21	08 17	08 11	08 05	07 59	07 52	07 45	07 37	07 29	07 21	64
62	08 19	08 18	08 17	08 15	08 12	08 08	08 04	07 59	07 54	07 48	07 42	07 36	07 29	07 22	07 14	62
N 60	08 06	08 05	08 04	08 02	08 00	07 57	07 53	07 49	07 44	07 39	07 34	07 28	07 22	07 15	07 08	N 60
58	07 54	07 54	07 53	07 51	07 49	07 47	07 44	07 40	07 36	07 31	07 26	07 21	07 15	07 09	07 03	58
56	07 44	07 44	07 44	07 42	07 41	07 38	07 35	07 32	07 29	07 24	07 20	07 15	07 10	07 04	06 58	56
54	07 36	07 35	07 35	07 34	07 32	07 30	07 28	07 25	07 22	07 18	07 14	07 09	07 05	07 00	06 54	54
52	07 27	07 28	07 27	07 26	07 25	07 23	07 21	07 18	07 15	07 12	07 08	07 04	07 00	06 55	06 50	52
N 50	07 20	07 20	07 20	07 19	07 18	07 17	07 15	07 13	07 10	07 07	07 03	07 00	06 56	06 51	06 47	N 50
45	07 04	07 05	07 05	07 04	07 04	07 03	07 01	07 00	06 58	06 55	06 52	06 49	06 46	06 43	06 39	45
40	06 51	06 52	06 52	06 52	06 51	06 50	06 49	06 47	06 45	06 43	06 41	06 38	06 35	06 32	06 28	40
35	06 39	06 40	06 40	06 41	06 41	06 40	06 39	06 38	06 36	06 35	06 33	06 31	06 28	06 26	06 24	35
30	06 29	06 30	06 30	06 31	06 31	06 31	06 31	06 30	06 29	06 28	06 27	06 26	06 24	06 22	06 20	30
N 20	06 10	06 11	06 12	06 13	06 14	06 14	06 14	06 14	06 14	06 14	06 13	06 13	06 12	06 11	06 10	N 20
N 10	05 53	05 54	05 55	05 55	05 57	05 58	05 59	06 00	06 00	06 01	06 01	06 01	06 00	06 00	06 00	N 10
0	05 36	05 38	05 39	05 40	05 42	05 43	05 44	05 45	05 46	05 47	05 48	05 48	05 49	05 49	05 49	0
S 10	05 18	05 20	05 22	05 23	05 25	05 27	05 28	05 30	05 31	05 33	05 34	05 35	05 36	05 38	05 38	S 10
20	04 58	05 00	05 02	05 04	05 06	05 08	05 10	05 12	05 14	05 16	05 18	05 20	05 22	05 24	05 26	20
S 30	04 33	04 35	04 38	04 40	04 43	04 45	04 48	04 51	04 54	04 56	04 59	05 02	05 05	05 08	05 10	S 30
35	04 18	04 20	04 23	04 26	04 28	04 31	04 35	04 38	04 41	04 44	04 47	04 51	04 54	04 58	05 01	35
40	04 00	04 03	04 05	04 08	04 12	04 15	04 19	04 22	04 26	04 30	04 34	04 38	04 42	04 46	04 50	40
45	03 38	03 41	03 44	03 47	03 51	03 55	03 59	04 04	04 08	04 13	04 18	04 22	04 27	04 32	04 37	45
50	03 09	03 12	03 15	03 19	03 24	03 29	03 34	03 39	03 45	03 51	03 56	04 02	04 08	04 14	04 20	50
S 52	02 54	02 57	03 01	03 05	03 10	03 16	03 21	03 27	03 34	03 40	03 46	03 53	03 59	04 06	04 12	S 52
54	02 36	02 40	02 44	02 49	02 55	03 01	03 07	03 14	03 20	03 27	03 34	03 42	03 49	03 56	04 03	54
56	02 14	02 19	02 24	02 29	02 36	02 43	02 50	02 57	03 05	03 13	03 21	03 29	03 37	03 45	03 53	56
58	01 45	01 50	01 57	02 04	02 12	02 20	02 28	02 37	02 46	02 56	03 05	03 14	03 23	03 32	03 41	58
S 60	00 58	01 07	01 16	01 27	01 38	01 49	02 00	02 12	02 23	02 34	02 45	02 56	03 06	03 17	03 27	S 60

EVENING CIVIL TWILIGHT

Lat.	Dec. 30	Jan 2	Jan 5	Jan 8	Jan 11	Jan 14	Jan 17	Jan 20	Jan 23	Jan 26	Jan 29	Feb 1	Feb 4	Feb 7	Feb 10	Lat.
N 72	13 16	13 26	13 39	13 52	14 06	14 20	14 35	14 49	15 04	15 18	15 33	15 47	16 01	16 15	16 29	N 72
70	14 12	14 19	14 27	14 36	14 45	14 56	15 07	15 18	15 30	15 42	15 54	16 06	16 18	16 30	16 42	70
68	14 46	14 51	14 57	15 05	15 13	15 21	15 30	15 41	15 49	15 57	16 06	16 15	16 24	16 42	16 53	68
66	15 10	15 15	15 20	15 27	15 33	15 41	15 49	15 57	16 06	16 15	16 24	16 33	16 42	16 52	17 01	66
64	15 30	15 34	15 38	15 44	15 50	15 57	16 04	16 11	16 19	16 27	16 35	16 43	16 52	17 00	17 09	64
62	15 45	15 49	15 54	15 58	16 04	16 10	16 16	16 23	16 30	16 37	16 45	16 52	17 00	17 08	17 16	62
N 60	15 59	16 02	16 06	16 11	16 16	16 21	16 27	16 33	16 40	16 46	16 53	17 00	17 07	17 14	17 21	N 60
58	16 10	16 13	16 17	16 21	16 26	16 31	16 36	16 42	16 48	16 54	17 00	17 07	17 13	17 20	17 26	58
56	16 20	16 23	16 27	16 31	16 35	16 40	16 45	16 50	16 56	17 01	17 07	17 13	17 19	17 25	17 31	56
54	16 29	16 32	16 36	16 39	16 43	16 48	16 52	16 57	17 02	17 08	17 13	17 18	17 24	17 30	17 35	54
52	16 38	16 40	16 43	16 47	16 51	16 55	16 59	17 04	17 09	17 13	17 18	17 23	17 29	17 34	17 39	52
N 50	16 45	16 47	16 50	16 54	16 57	17 01	17 05	17 10	17 14	17 19	17 23	17 28	17 33	17 38	17 42	N 50
45	17 01	17 03	17 06	17 09	17 12	17 15	17 19	17 23	17 26	17 30	17 34	17 38	17 42	17 46	17 50	45
40	17 14	17 16	17 19	17 21	17 24	17 27	17 30	17 33	17 37	17 40	17 43	17 47	17 50	17 54	17 57	40
35	17 26	17 28	17 30	17 32	17 35	17 38	17 40	17 43	17 46	17 49	17 52	17 55	17 58	18 00	18 03	35
30	17 36	17 38	17 40	17 42	17 45	17 47	17 49	17 52	17 54	17 57	17 59	18 02	18 04	18 07	18 09	30
N 20	17 55	17 56	17 58	18 00	18 02	18 04	18 06	18 08	18 09	18 11	18 13	18 15	18 16	18 18	18 19	N 20
N 10	18 12	18 13	18 15	18 16	18 18	18 19	18 21	18 22	18 23	18 25	18 26	18 27	18 28	18 28	18 29	N 10
0	18 29	18 30	18 32	18 33	18 34	18 35	18 36	18 37	18 37	18 38	18 38	18 39	18 39	18 39	18 39	0
S 10	18 47	18 48	18 49	18 51	18 52	18 52	18 52	18 52	18 52	18 52	18 52	18 51	18 51	18 51	18 50	S 10
20	19 07	19 08	19 08	19 09	19 09	19 10	19 10	19 09	19 09	19 08	19 07	19 06	19 05	19 04	19 02	20
S 30	19 31	19 32	19 32	19 33	19 33	19 32	19 31	19 31	19 29	19 28	19 26	19 24	19 22	19 20	19 18	S 30
35	19 46	19 47	19 47	19 47	19 47	19 46	19 45	19 43	19 42	19 40	19 38	19 35	19 33	19 30	19 27	35
40	20 05	20 05	20 05	20 04	20 03	20 02	20 01	19 59	19 57	19 54	19 51	19 48	19 45	19 42	19 38	40
45	20 27	20 27	20 26	20 25	20 24	20 22	20 20	20 17	20 14	20 11	20 08	20 04	20 00	19 55	19 51	45
50	20 56	20 56	20 54	20 53	20 51	20 48	20 45	20 41	20 37	20 33	20 28	20 24	20 18	20 13	20 07	50
S 52	21 11	21 10	21 09	21 07	21 04	21 01	20 57	20 53	20 49	20 44	20 39	20 33	20 27	20 21	20 15	S 52
54	21 28	21 27	21 25	21 23	21 19	21 16	21 11	21 07	21 02	20 56	20 50	20 44	20 38	20 31	20 24	54
56	21 50	21 48	21 46	21 42	21 38	21 34	21 28	21 23	21 17	21 10	21 03	20 56	20 49	20 42	20 34	56
58	22 19	22 16	22 12	22 07	22 02	21 56	21 49	21 42	21 35	21 27	21 19	21 11	21 03	20 54	20 46	58
S 60	23 04	22 58	22 51	22 44	22 35	22 26	22 17	22 07	21 58	21 48	21 38	21 29	21 19	21 09	20 59	S 60

SUNRISE

Lat.	Apr. 29	May 2	5	8	11	14	17	20	23	26	29	June 1	4	7	10	Lat.
	h m	h m	h m	h m	h m	h m	h m	h m	h m	h m	h m	h m	h m	h m	h m	
N 72°	02 14	01 50	01 22	00 41	□	□	□	□	□	□	□	□	□	□	□	N 72°
70	02 47	02 29	02 11	01 51	01 29	01 02	00 12	□	□	□	□	□	□	□	□	70
68	03 10	02 56	02 42	02 28	02 12	01 57	01 40	01 21	01 00	00 29	□	□	□	□	□	68
66	28	03 17	03 05	02 53	02 41	02 29	02 17	02 05	01 53	01 41	01 28	01 15	01 02	00 48	00 33	66
64	43	33	23	03 12	03 02	02 53	02 43	34	02 25	02 16	02 07	02 00	01 52	01 46	01 40	64
62	03 55	46	37	28	20	03 11	03 03	02 55	02 48	02 41	34	28	02 23	02 19	02 15	62
N 60	04 05	03 57	03 49	03 41	03 34	03 26	03 19	03 13	03 06	03 01	02 55	02 50	02 46	02 43	02 40	N 60
58	15	04 07	04 00	03 53	46	39	33	27	22	17	03 12	03 08	03 04	03 01	02 59	58
56	22	16	09	04 02	03 56	03 50	45	40	35	30	26	23	20	17	03 15	56
54	29	23	17	11	04 06	04 00	03 55	03 50	46	42	39	35	33	31	29	54
52	36	30	24	19	14	09	04 04	04 00	03 56	03 52	49	46	44	42	41	52
N 50	04 41	04 36	04 31	04 26	04 21	04 17	04 12	04 09	04 05	04 02	03 59	03 56	03 54	03 53	03 51	N 50
45	04 54	04 49	45	41	37	33	30	27	24	21	04 19	04 17	04 15	04 14	04 13	45
40	05 04	05 00	04 56	04 53	04 49	46	44	41	39	37	35	33	32	31	31	40
35	12	09	05 06	05 03	05 00	04 58	04 56	04 53	04 52	04 50	04 49	47	47	46	46	35
30	20	17	14	12	10	05 08	05 06	05 04	05 03	05 01	05 00	04 59	04 59	04 58	04 58	30
N 20	05 32	05 31	05 29	05 27	05 26	05 25	05 23	05 22	05 22	05 21	05 20	05 20	05 20	05 20	05 20	N 20
N 10	44	43	42	41	40	39	39	38	38	38	38	38	38	38	38	N 10
0	05 54	05 54	05 53	05 53	05 53	05 53	05 53	05 53	05 53	05 53	05 54	05 54	05 55	05 55	05 56	0
S 10	06 04	06 04	06 05	06 05	06 06	06 06	06 07	06 07	06 08	06 09	06 10	06 10	06 11	06 12	06 13	S 10
20	15	16	17	18	19	20	21	23	24	25	26	27	29	30	31	20
S 30	06 27	06 29	06 31	06 33	06 35	06 37	06 38	06 40	06 42	06 44	06 46	06 47	06 49	06 50	06 51	S 30
35	34	37	39	41	44	46	48	06 50	06 53	06 55	06 57	06 59	07 00	07 02	07 03	35
40	42	45	48	06 51	06 54	06 57	06 59	07 02	07 05	07 07	07 09	07 12	14	16	17	40
45	06 51	06 55	06 59	07 02	07 06	07 09	07 12	16	19	22	25	27	30	32	34	45
50	07 02	07 07	07 11	16	20	24	28	32	36	40	43	46	49	07 52	07 54	50
S 52	07 08	07 12	07 17	07 22	07 27	07 31	07 36	07 40	07 44	07 48	07 52	07 55	07 58	08 01	08 04	S 52
54	13	19	24	29	34	39	44	49	07 53	07 58	08 02	08 05	08 09	12	14	54
56	20	25	31	37	42	48	07 53	07 58	08 03	08 08	12	17	20	24	27	56
58	26	33	39	46	07 52	07 58	08 04	08 10	15	20	25	30	34	38	41	58
S 60	07 34	07 41	07 49	07 56	08 03	08 09	08 16	08 22	08 29	08 34	08 40	08 45	08 50	08 54	08 58	S 60

SUNSET

Lat.	Apr. 29	May 2	5	8	11	14	17	20	23	26	29	June 1	4	7	10	Lat.
	h m	h m	h m	h m	h m	h m	h m	h m	h m	h m	h m	h m	h m	h m	h m	
N 72°	21 47	22 11	22 41	23 35	□	□	□	□	□	□	□	□	□	□	□	N 72°
70	21 12	21 29	21 47	22 07	22 31	23 01	□	□	□	□	□	□	□	□	□	70
68	20 48	21 01	21 15	21 30	21 45	22 01	22 18	22 37	23 01	23 43	□	□	□	□	□	68
66	29	20 40	20 52	21 03	21 15	21 27	21 39	21 51	22 04	22 17	22 30	22 44	22 58	23 14	23 32	66
64	14	24	33	20 43	20 53	21 02	21 12	21 21	21 31	21 40	21 49	21 58	22 06	22 13	22 20	64
62	20 02	20 10	18	27	35	20 43	20 51	20 59	21 07	21 15	22	28	21 34	21 40	21 45	62
N 60	19 51	19 59	20 06	20 13	20 21	20 28	20 35	20 42	20 48	20 55	21 01	21 06	21 11	21 16	21 20	N 60
58	42	48	19 55	20 02	20 08	15	21	27	33	38	20 43	20 48	20 53	20 57	21 00	58
56	34	40	46	19 52	19 58	20 03	20 09	14	20	24	29	33	37	41	20 44	56
54	27	32	38	43	48	19 53	19 58	20 03	20 08	13	17	21	24	27	30	54
52	20	25	30	35	40	45	49	19 54	19 58	20 02	20 06	09	13	15	18	52
N 50	19 15	19 19	19 24	19 28	19 33	19 37	19 41	19 45	19 49	19 53	19 56	20 00	20 02	20 05	20 07	N 50
45	19 02	19 06	19 09	13	17	20	24	27	30	33	36	19 39	19 41	19 43	19 45	45
40	18 52	18 55	18 58	19 01	19 04	19 07	19 09	12	15	18	20	22	24	26	28	40
35	43	46	48	18 50	18 53	18 55	18 58	19 00	19 02	19 04	19 06	19 08	19 10	19 12	13	35
30	36	37	39	41	43	45	47	18 49	18 51	18 53	18 54	18 56	18 58	18 59	19 00	30
N 20	18 23	18 25	18 26	18 27	18 28	18 28	18 29	18 31	18 32	18 33	18 34	18 35	18 37	18 38	18 39	N 20
N 10	11	12	12	13	13	14	14	15	16	16	17	18	19	19	20	N 10
0	18 01	18 00	18 00	18 00	18 00	18 00	18 00	18 00	18 00	18 00	18 01	18 01	18 01	18 02	18 03	0
S 10	17 51	17 50	17 49	17 48	17 47	17 46	17 46	17 45	17 45	17 45	17 45	17 45	17 45	17 46	17 46	S 10
20	40	38	36	35	33	32	31	30	29	28	28	28	28	28	28	20
S 30	17 27	17 25	17 22	17 20	17 18	17 16	17 14	17 12	17 11	17 10	17 09	17 08	17 07	17 07	17 07	S 30
35	20	17	14	11	17 09	17 06	17 04	17 02	17 00	16 59	16 57	16 56	16 56	16 55	16 55	35
40	12	17 09	17 05	17 02	16 59	16 56	16 53	16 51	16 48	46	45	43	42	41	41	40
45	17 03	16 58	16 54	16 50	47	43	40	37	34	32	30	28	27	25	25	45
50	16 52	47	42	37	32	28	24	20	17	14	11	09	16 07	16 05	16 04	50
S 52	16 47	16 41	16 35	16 30	16 25	16 21	16 16	16 12	16 09	16 05	16 02	16 00	15 58	15 56	15 55	S 52
54	41	35	29	23	18	13	16 08	16 04	16 00	15 56	15 53	15 50	47	45	44	54
56	35	28	22	15	10	16 04	15 59	15 54	15 49	45	42	38	36	33	32	56
58	28	20	13	16 07	16 00	15 54	48	43	38	33	29	25	22	19	17	58
S 60	16 19	16 12	16 04	15 56	15 49	15 43	15 36	15 30	15 24	15 19	15 14	15 10	15 06	15 03	15 00	S 60

MORNING CIVIL TWILIGHT

Lat.	Apr. 29	May 2	5	8	11	14	17	20	23	26	29	June 1	4	7	10	Lat.
°	h m	h m	h m	h m	h m	h m	h m	h m	h m	h m	h m	h m	h m	h m	h m	°
N 72	////	////	////	////	□	□	□	□	□	□	□	□	□	□	□	N 72
70	////	////	////	////	////	////	////	////	□	□	□	□	□	□		70
68	01 33	01 04	00 02	////	////	////	////	////	////	////	////	////	////	////	////	68
66	02 12	01 54	01 34	01 10	00 37	////	////	////	////	////	////	////	////	////	////	66
64	38	02 24	02 10	01 54	01 38	01 20	00 59	00 27	////	////	////	////	////	////	////	64
62	02 58	02 46	35	02 23	02 11	01 59	01 46	01 32	01 18	01 03	00 44	00 15	////	////	////	62
N 60	03 14	03 04	02 54	02 44	02 35	02 25	02 15	02 05	01 56	01 46	01 37	01 28	01 20	01 11	01 04	N 60
58	27	19	03 10	03 02	02 53	02 45	37	29	02 22	02 15	02 08	02 02	01 56	01 51	01 47	58
56	39	31	23	16	03 09	03 01	02 55	02 48	42	36	31	26	02 21	02 18	02 14	56
54	49	42	35	28	22	15	03 09	03 04	02 58	02 53	02 49	02 45	41	38	36	54
52	03 58	51	45	39	33	27	22	17	03 12	03 08	03 04	03 00	02 57	02 55	02 53	52
N 50	04 05	03 59	03 54	03 48	03 43	03 38	03 33	03 28	03 24	03 20	03 17	03 14	03 11	03 09	03 07	N 50
45	22	04 17	04 12	04 07	04 03	03 59	03 55	03 52	03 49	03 46	03 43	03 41	03 39	37	36	45
40	35	31	27	23	19	04 16	04 13	04 10	04 07	04 05	04 03	04 01	04 00	03 59	03 58	40
35	45	42	39	36	33	30	27	25	23	21	20	18	17	04 16	04 16	35
30	04 55	04 52	04 49	04 46	04 44	04 42	04 40	38	36	35	33	32	32	31	31	30
N 20	05 10	05 08	05 06	05 04	05 03	05 01	05 00	04 59	04 58	04 57	04 56	04 56	04 55	04 55	04 55	N 20
N 10	22	21	20	19	18	17	16	05 16	05 15	05 15	05 15	05 15	05 15	05 15	05 15	N 10
0	33	32	32	31	31	31	31	31	31	31	31	32	32	33	33	0
S 10	43	43	43	43	44	44	44	45	05 46	05 46	05 47	05 48	05 48	05 49	05 50	S 10
20	05 52	05 53	05 54	05 55	05 56	05 57	05 58	05 59	06 00	06 02	06 03	06 04	06 05	06 06	06 07	20
S 30	06 03	06 04	06 06	06 08	06 11	06 13	06 15	06 16	06 18	06 20	06 21	06 23	06 24	06 25		S 30
35	08	10	12	15	17	19	21	23	25	27	29	31	32	34	36	35
40	14	17	20	22	25	27	30	33	35	37	40	42	44	45	06 47	40
45	21	24	28	31	34	37	40	43	46	06 49	06 52	06 54	06 56	06 58	07 00	45
50	28	33	37	41	45	49	52	06 56	06 59	07 03	07 06	07 09	07 11	07 14	16	50
S 52	06 32	06 37	06 41	06 45	06 50	06 54	06 58	07 02	07 06	07 09	07 12	07 16	07 18	07 21	07 23	S 52
54	36	41	46	50	06 55	06 59	07 04	08	12	16	20	23	26	29	31	54
56	40	45	51	06 56	07 01	07 06	10	15	19	24	27	31	34	37	40	56
58	44	50	06 56	07 02	07	13	18	23	28	32	36	40	44	47	07 50	58
S 60	06 49	06 56	07 02	07 08	07 14	07 20	07 26	07 31	07 37	07 42	07 46	07 51	07 55	07 58	08 01	S 60

EVENING CIVIL TWILIGHT

Lat.	Apr. 29	May 2	5	8	11	14	17	20	23	26	29	June 1	4	7	10	Lat.
°	h m	h m	h m	h m	h m	h m	h m	h m	h m	h m	h m	h m	h m	h m	h m	°
N 72	////	////	////	////	□	□	□	□	□	□	□	□	□	□	□	N 72
70	////	////	////	////	////	////	□	□	□	□	□	□	□	□		70
68	22 29	23 01	////	////	////	////	////	////	////	////	////	////	////	////	////	68
66	21 48	22 06	22 26	22 51	23 33	////	////	////	////	////	////	////	////	////	////	66
64	21	21 34	21 48	22 03	22 20	22 39	23 02	23 50	////	////	////	////	////	////	////	64
62	21 00	21 11	22	21 33	21 45	21 58	22 11	22 25	22 40	22 57	23 18	////	////	////	////	62
N 60	20 43	20 53	21 02	21 11	21 21	21 30	21 40	21 50	22 00	22 10	22 20	22 30	22 39	22 48	22 56	N 60
58	30	38	20 45	20 54	21 02	21 10	18	26	21 34	21 41	21 48	21 55	22 02	22 08	22 13	58
56	18	25	32	39	20 46	20 53	21 00	21 07	21 13	20	26	31	21 36	21 41	21 45	56
54	20 08	14	20	26	33	39	20 45	20 51	20 56	21 02	21 07	21 12	16	20	23	54
52	19 59	20 04	10	16	21	27	32	37	42	20 47	20 52	20 56	21 00	21 03	21 06	52
N 50	19 51	19 56	20 01	20 06	20 11	20 16	20 21	20 26	20 30	20 34	20 38	20 42	20 46	20 49	20 51	N 50
45	34	38	19 42	19 46	19 50	19 54	19 58	20 02	20 05	20 09	20 12	20 15	20 18	20 20	23	45
40	21	24	28	31	34	37	40	19 43	19 46	19 49	19 52	19 54	19 57	19 59	20 00	40
35	10	13	15	18	21	23	26	28	31	33	35	37	39	41	19 43	35
30	19 01	19 03	19 05	19 07	19 09	19 11	19 13	19 15	19 17	19 19	19 21	23	25	26	28	30
N 20	18 46	18 47	18 48	18 49	18 50	18 52	18 53	18 54	18 56	18 57	18 58	19 00	19 01	19 02	19 03	N 20
N 10	33	33	34	34	35	36	36	37	38	39	40	18 41	18 41	18 42	18 43	N 10
0	22	22	22	22	22	23	23	23	26	24	24	25	25	24	25	0
S 10	12	11	18 10	18 09	18 09	18 08	18 08	18 08	18 07	18 07	18 07	18 08	18 08	18 08	18 08	S 10
20	18 02	18 01	17 59	17 58	17 56	17 55	17 54	17 53	17 53	17 52	17 52	17 51	17 51	17 51	17 52	20
S 30	17 52	17 49	17 47	17 45	17 43	17 41	17 39	17 38	17 37	17 36	17 35	17 34	17 33	17 33	17 33	S 30
35	46	43	41	38	35	33	31	29	28	26	25	24	24	23	23	35
40	40	37	34	30	27	25	22	20	18	16	15	13	12	17 12	17 11	40
45	33	29	25	22	18	15	12	17 09	17 07	17 04	17 03	17 01	17 00	16 59	16 58	45
50	26	21	16	12	07	17 03	17 00	16 57	16 54	16 51	16 48	16 46	16 45	43	43	50
S 52	17 22	17 17	17 12	17 07	17 02	16 58	16 54	16 51	16 47	16 44	16 42	16 40	16 38	16 36	16 35	S 52
54	18	13	07	17 02	16 57	52	48	44	41	37	34	32	30	28	27	54
56	14	08	17 02	16 56	51	46	42	37	33	30	27	24	22	20	18	56
58	10	17 03	16 57	51	45	39	34	29	25	21	18	15	12	16 10	16 08	58
S 60	17 05	16 57	16 50	16 44	16 38	16 32	16 26	16 21	16 16	16 12	16 08	16 04	16 01	15 59	15 57	S 60

RISING, SETTING AND DEPRESSION GRAPHS

TABLE 1—MERIDIAN PASSAGE AND DECLINATION OF THE SUN AT 12ʰ G.M.T.

TABLES 2 and 3—DEPRESSION OF THE SUN AT VARIOUS HEIGHTS

Day	May Mer. Pass.	May Dec.	June Mer. Pass.	June Dec.	July Mer. Pass.	July Dec.	August Mer. Pass.	August Dec.	Height Feet	TABLE 2 AT SUNRISE AND SUNSET Depression	TABLE 2 AT SUNRISE AND SUNSET Diff. from 0°·8	TABLE 3 AT CIVIL TWILIGHT Depression	TABLE 3 AT CIVIL TWILIGHT Diff. from 0°·8
	h m	°	h m	°	h m	°	h m	°		°	°	°	°
1	11 57	N.15·0	11 58	N.22·0	12 04	N.23·1	12 06	N.18·1					
2	11 57	15·3	11 58	22·1	12 04	23·1	12 06	17·9					
3	11 57	15·6	11 58	22·3	12 04	23·0	12 06	17·6					
4	11 57	15·9	11 58	22·4	12 04	22·9	12 06	17·3	0	0·8	—	6·0	5·2
5	11 57	16·2	11 58	22·5	12 04	22·8	12 06	17·1	500	1·3	0·5	6·0	5·2
6	11 57	N.16·4	11 59	N.22·6	12 05	N.22·7	12 06	N.16·8	1 000	1·5	0·7	6·0	5·2
7	11 57	16·7	11 59	22·7	12 05	22·6	12 06	16·5	2 000	1·7	0·9	6·1	5·3
8	11 56	17·0	11 59	22·8	12 05	22·5	12 06	16·2	3 000	1·9	1·1	6·1	5·3
9	11 56	17·3	11 59	22·9	12 05	22·4	12 06	16·0	4 000	2·1	1·3	6·1	5·3
10	11 56	17·5	11 59	23·0	12 05	22·3	12 05	15·7	5 000	2·2	1·4	6·2	5·4
11	11 56	N.17·8	11 59	N.23·1	12 05	N.22·2	12 05	N.15·4	6 000	2·4	1·6	6·2	5·4
12	11 56	18·0	12 00	23·1	12 06	22·0	12 05	15·1	7 000	2·5	1·7	6·2	5·4
13	11 56	18·3	12 00	23·2	12 06	21·9	12 05	14·8	8 000	2·6	1·8	6·3	5·5
14	11 56	18·5	12 00	23·2	12 06	21·7	12 05	14·5	9 000	2·7	1·9	6·3	5·5
15	11 56	18·8	12 00	23·3	12 06	21·6	12 05	14·2	10 000	2·8	2·0	6·3	5·5
16	11 56	N.19·0	12 01	N.23·3	12 06	N.21·4	12 04	N.13·8	15 000	3·2	2·4	6·5	5·7
17	11 56	19·3	12 01	23·4	12 06	21·3	12 04	13·5	20 000	3·6	2·8	6·6	5·8
18	11 56	19·5	12 01	23·4	12 06	21·1	12 04	13·2	25 000	3·9	3·1	6·8	6·0
19	11 56	19·7	12 01	23·4	12 06	20·9	12 04	12·9	30 000	4·2	3·4	6·9	6·1
20	11 56	19·9	12 01	23·4	12 06	20·7	12 03	12·6	35 000	4·4	3·6	7·1	6·3
21	11 57	N.20·1	12 02	N.23·4	12 06	N.20·5	12 03	N.12·2	40 000	4·7	3·9	7·2	6·4
22	11 57	20·3	12 02	23·4	12 06	20·3	12 03	11·9	45 000	4·9	4·1	7·3	6·5
23	11 57	20·5	12 02	23·4	12 06	20·1	12 03	11·6	50 000	5·1	4·3	7·5	6·7
24	11 57	20·7	12 02	23·4	12 06	19·9	12 02	11·2	55 000	5·3	4·5	7·6	6·8
25	11 57	20·9	12 02	23·4	12 06	19·7	12 02	10·9	60 000	5·5	4·7	7·7	6·9
26	11 57	N.21·1	12 03	N.23·4	12 06	N.19·5	12 02	N.10·5					
27	11 57	21·2	12 03	23·3	12 06	19·3	12 02	10·2					
28	11 57	21·4	12 03	23·3	12 06	19·1	12 01	9·8					
29	11 57	21·6	12 03	23·2	12 06	18·8	12 01	9·5					
30	11 57	21·7	12 03	N.23·2	12 06	18·6	12 01	9·1					
31	11 58	N.21·9			12 06	N.18·4	12 00	N. 8·8					

An alternative method to those given on pages A12–A14 is to use the graphs to give the corrections to the tabulated times of sunrise and sunset at ground level; in this case it is adequate to use the graphs for the *nearest* tabular latitude and declination. The difference in hour angle is found between the hour angle for zero depression and the hour angle at the tabular depression minus 0°·8. The difference in hour angle so found is then applied to the time of sunrise or sunset. The result will be less than 5ᵐ in error if the declination curve cuts all the depression lines.

Example. To find the times of sunrise and sunset on 1975 August 23 in latitude N. 65° 17′, longitude W. 35° 15′, at a height of 37 000 feet. From Table **1**, Dec.= N. 11°·6; Table **2**, Depression diff. from 0°·8=3°·7.

	Sunrise h m	Sunset h m
Page A68, N. 65° 17′ (August 24)	04 10	19 53
Page A71, Lat. 66°, Dec. 11° (same); diff. in H.A. from depression 0° to 3°·7	45	45
L.M.T.	03 25	20 38
Longitude W. 35° 15′	2 21	2 21
G.M.T.	05 46	22 59

SEMIDURATION OF SUNLIGHT

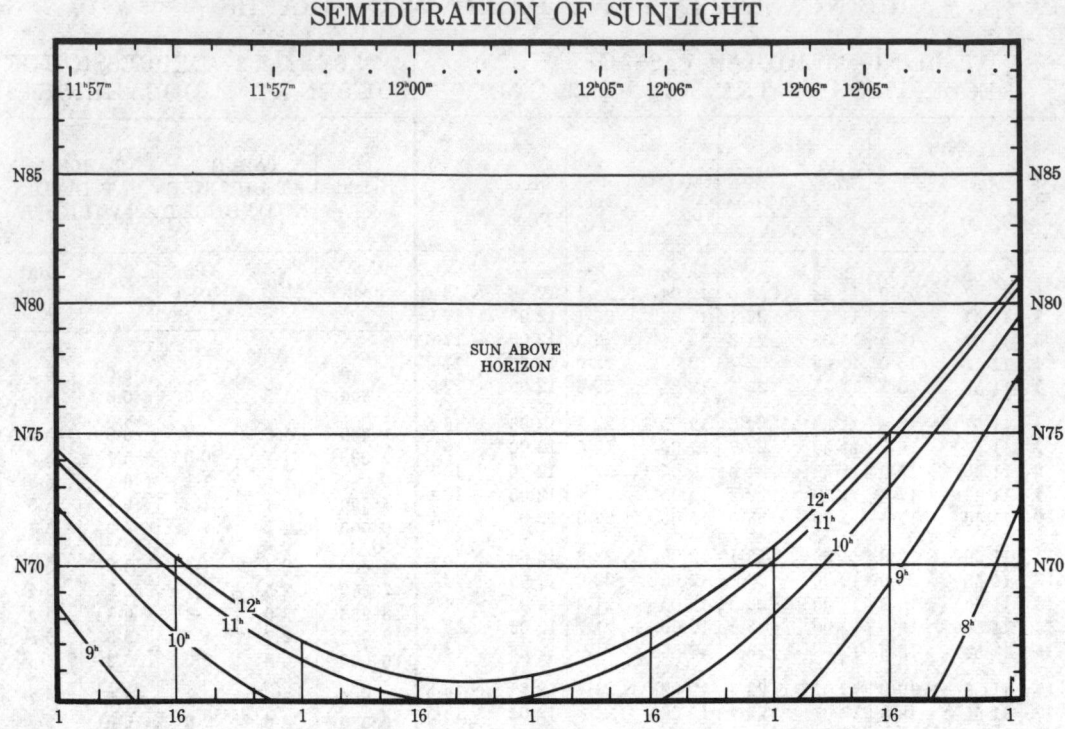

DURATION OF TWILIGHT

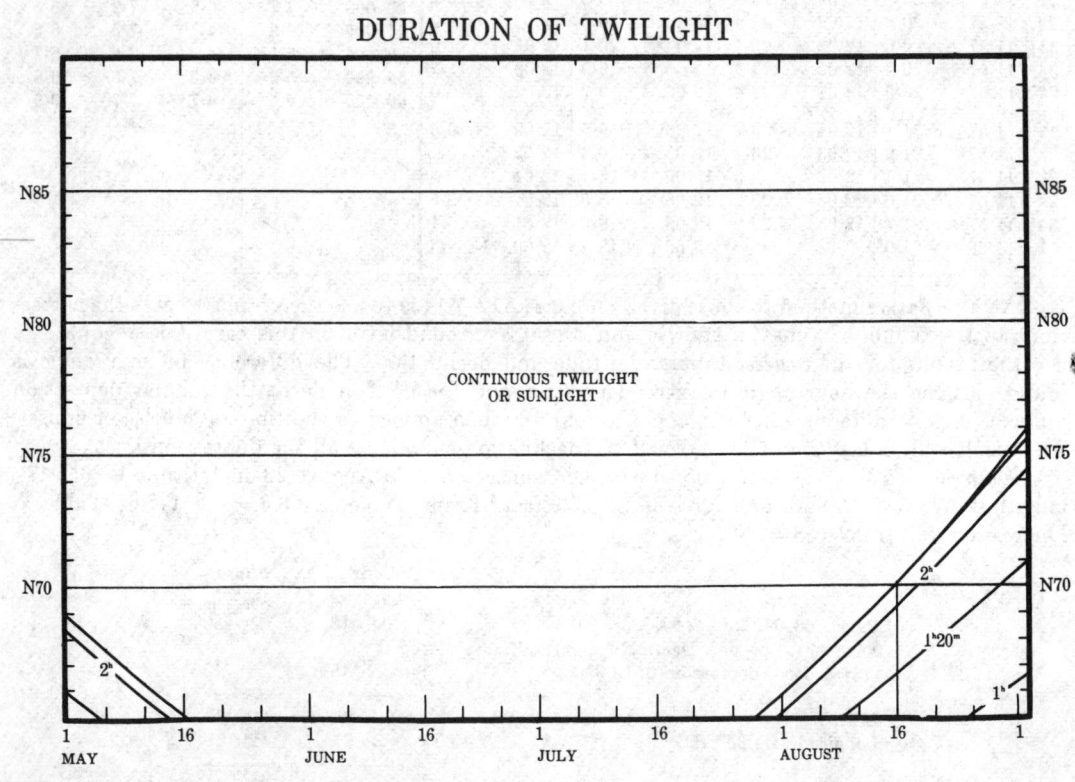

SEMIDURATION OF MOONLIGHT

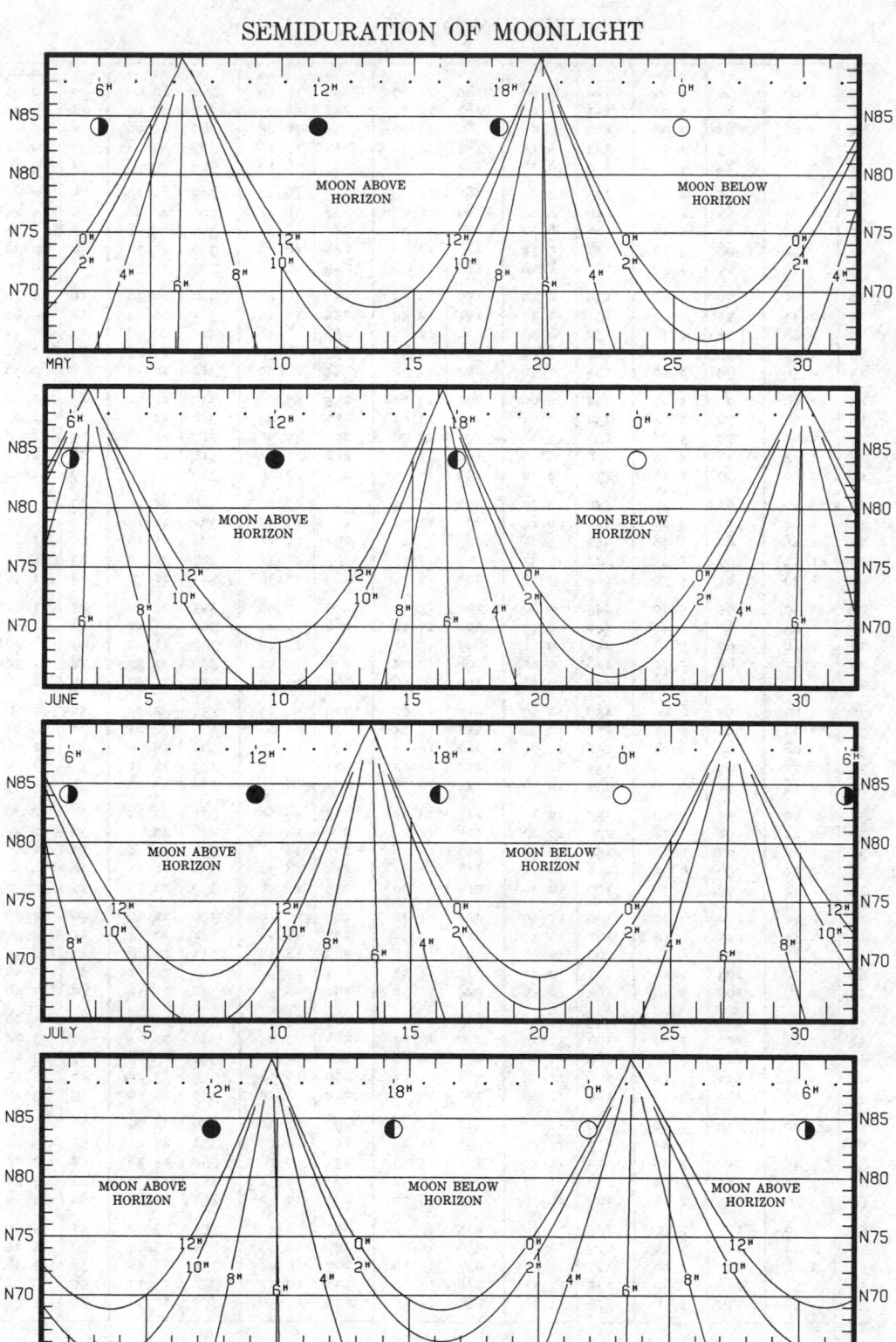

CONVERSION OF ARC TO TIME

°	h m	°	h m	°	h m	°	h m	°	h m	°	h m	′	m s
0	0 00	60	4 00	120	8 00	180	12 00	240	16 00	300	20 00	0	0 00
1	0 04	61	4 04	121	8 04	181	12 04	241	16 04	301	20 04	1	0 04
2	0 08	62	4 08	122	8 08	182	12 08	242	16 08	302	20 08	2	0 08
3	0 12	63	4 12	123	8 12	183	12 12	243	16 12	303	20 12	3	0 12
4	0 16	64	4 16	124	8 16	184	12 16	244	16 16	304	20 16	4	0 16
5	0 20	65	4 20	125	8 20	185	12 20	245	16 20	305	20 20	5	0 20
6	0 24	66	4 24	126	8 24	186	12 24	246	16 24	306	20 24	6	0 24
7	0 28	67	4 28	127	8 28	187	12 28	247	16 28	307	20 28	7	0 28
8	0 32	68	4 32	128	8 32	188	12 32	248	16 32	308	20 32	8	0 32
9	0 36	69	4 36	129	8 36	189	12 36	249	16 36	309	20 36	9	0 36
10	0 40	70	4 40	130	8 40	190	12 40	250	16 40	310	20 40	10	0 40
11	0 44	71	4 44	131	8 44	191	12 44	251	16 44	311	20 44	11	0 44
12	0 48	72	4 48	132	8 48	192	12 48	252	16 48	312	20 48	12	0 48
13	0 52	73	4 52	133	8 52	193	12 52	253	16 52	313	20 52	13	0 52
14	0 56	74	4 56	134	8 56	194	12 56	254	16 56	314	20 56	14	0 56
15	1 00	75	5 00	135	9 00	195	13 00	255	17 00	315	21 00	15	1 00
16	1 04	76	5 04	136	9 04	196	13 04	256	17 04	316	21 04	16	1 04
17	1 08	77	5 08	137	9 08	197	13 08	257	17 08	317	21 08	17	1 08
18	1 12	78	5 12	138	9 12	198	13 12	258	17 12	318	21 12	18	1 12
19	1 16	79	5 16	139	9 16	199	13 16	259	17 16	319	21 16	19	1 16
20	1 20	80	5 20	140	9 20	200	13 20	260	17 20	320	21 20	20	1 20
21	1 24	81	5 24	141	9 24	201	13 24	261	17 24	321	21 24	21	1 24
22	1 28	82	5 28	142	9 28	202	13 28	262	17 28	322	21 28	22	1 28
23	1 32	83	5 32	143	9 32	203	13 32	263	17 32	323	21 32	23	1 32
24	1 36	84	5 36	144	9 36	204	13 36	264	17 36	324	21 36	24	1 36
25	1 40	85	5 40	145	9 40	205	13 40	265	17 40	325	21 40	25	1 40
26	1 44	86	5 44	146	9 44	206	13 44	266	17 44	326	21 44	26	1 44
27	1 48	87	5 48	147	9 48	207	13 48	267	17 48	327	21 48	27	1 48
28	1 52	88	5 52	148	9 52	208	13 52	268	17 52	328	21 52	28	1 52
29	1 56	89	5 56	149	9 56	209	13 56	269	17 56	329	21 56	29	1 56
30	2 00	90	6 00	150	10 00	210	14 00	270	18 00	330	22 00	30	2 00
31	2 04	91	6 04	151	10 04	211	14 04	271	18 04	331	22 04	31	2 04
32	2 08	92	6 08	152	10 08	212	14 08	272	18 08	332	22 08	32	2 08
33	2 12	93	6 12	153	10 12	213	14 12	273	18 12	333	22 12	33	2 12
34	2 16	94	6 16	154	10 16	214	14 16	274	18 16	334	22 16	34	2 16
35	2 20	95	6 20	155	10 20	215	14 20	275	18 20	335	22 20	35	2 20
36	2 24	96	6 24	156	10 24	216	14 24	276	18 24	336	22 24	36	2 24
37	2 28	97	6 28	157	10 28	217	14 28	277	18 28	337	22 28	37	2 28
38	2 32	98	6 32	158	10 32	218	14 32	278	18 32	338	22 32	38	2 32
39	2 36	99	6 36	159	10 36	219	14 36	279	18 36	339	22 36	39	2 36
40	2 40	100	6 40	160	10 40	220	14 40	280	18 40	340	22 40	40	2 40
41	2 44	101	6 44	161	10 44	221	14 44	281	18 44	341	22 44	41	2 44
42	2 48	102	6 48	162	10 48	222	14 48	282	18 48	342	22 48	42	2 48
43	2 52	103	6 52	163	10 52	223	14 52	283	18 52	343	22 52	43	2 52
44	2 56	104	6 56	164	10 56	224	14 56	284	18 56	344	22 56	44	2 56
45	3 00	105	7 00	165	11 00	225	15 00	285	19 00	345	23 00	45	3 00
46	3 04	106	7 04	166	11 04	226	15 04	286	19 04	346	23 04	46	3 04
47	3 08	107	7 08	167	11 08	227	15 08	287	19 08	347	23 08	47	3 08
48	3 12	108	7 12	168	11 12	228	15 12	288	19 12	348	23 12	48	3 12
49	3 16	109	7 16	169	11 16	229	15 16	289	19 16	349	23 16	49	3 16
50	3 20	110	7 20	170	11 20	230	15 20	290	19 20	350	23 20	50	3 20
51	3 24	111	7 24	171	11 24	231	15 24	291	19 24	351	23 24	51	3 24
52	3 28	112	7 28	172	11 28	232	15 28	292	19 28	352	23 28	52	3 28
53	3 32	113	7 32	173	11 32	233	15 32	293	19 32	353	23 32	53	3 32
54	3 36	114	7 36	174	11 36	234	15 36	294	19 36	354	23 36	54	3 36
55	3 40	115	7 40	175	11 40	235	15 40	295	19 40	355	23 40	55	3 40
56	3 44	116	7 44	176	11 44	236	15 44	296	19 44	356	23 44	56	3 44
57	3 48	117	7 48	177	11 48	237	15 48	297	19 48	357	23 48	57	3 48
58	3 52	118	7 52	178	11 52	238	15 52	298	19 52	358	23 52	58	3 52
59	3 56	119	7 56	179	11 56	239	15 56	299	19 56	359	23 56	59	3 56

The above table is for converting expressions in arc to their equivalent in time; its main use in this Almanac is for the conversion of longitude for application to L.M.T. (*added if west, subtracted if east*) to give G.M.T., or vice versa, particularly in the case of sunrise, sunset, etc.

INTERPOLATION OF G.H.A. SUN

s	0ᵐ ° ′	1ᵐ ° ′	2ᵐ ° ′	3ᵐ ° ′	4ᵐ ° ′	5ᵐ ° ′	6ᵐ ° ′	7ᵐ ° ′	8ᵐ ° ′	9ᵐ ° ′	s
00	0 00.0	0 15.0	0 30.0	0 45.0	1 00.0	1 15.0	1 30.0	1 45.0	2 00.0	2 15.0	00
01	0 00.3	0 15.3	0 30.3	0 45.3	1 00.3	1 15.3	1 30.3	1 45.3	2 00.3	2 15.3	01
02	0 00.5	0 15.5	0 30.5	0 45.5	1 00.5	1 15.5	1 30.5	1 45.5	2 00.5	2 15.5	02
03	0 00.8	0 15.8	0 30.8	0 45.8	1 00.8	1 15.8	1 30.8	1 45.8	2 00.8	2 15.8	03
04	0 01.0	0 16.0	0 31.0	0 46.0	1 01.0	1 16.0	1 31.0	1 46.0	2 01.0	2 16.0	04
05	0 01.3	0 16.3	0 31.3	0 46.3	1 01.3	1 16.3	1 31.3	1 46.3	2 01.3	2 16.3	05
06	0 01.5	0 16.5	0 31.5	0 46.5	1 01.5	1 16.5	1 31.5	1 46.5	2 01.5	2 16.5	06
07	0 01.8	0 16.8	0 31.8	0 46.8	1 01.8	1 16.8	1 31.8	1 46.8	2 01.8	2 16.8	07
08	0 02.0	0 17.0	0 32.0	0 47.0	1 02.0	1 17.0	1 32.0	1 47.0	2 02.0	2 17.0	08
09	0 02.3	0 17.3	0 32.3	0 47.3	1 02.3	1 17.3	1 32.3	1 47.3	2 02.3	2 17.3	09
10	0 02.5	0 17.5	0 32.5	0 47.5	1 02.5	1 17.5	1 32.5	1 47.5	2 02.5	2 17.5	10
11	0 02.8	0 17.8	0 32.8	0 47.8	1 02.8	1 17.8	1 32.8	1 47.8	2 02.8	2 17.8	11
12	0 03.0	0 18.0	0 33.0	0 48.0	1 03.0	1 18.0	1 33.0	1 48.0	2 03.0	2 18.0	12
13	0 03.3	0 18.3	0 33.3	0 48.3	1 03.3	1 18.3	1 33.3	1 48.3	2 03.3	2 18.3	13
14	0 03.5	0 18.5	0 33.5	0 48.5	1 03.5	1 18.5	1 33.5	1 48.5	2 03.5	2 18.5	14
15	0 03.8	0 18.8	0 33.8	0 48.8	1 03.8	1 18.8	1 33.8	1 48.8	2 03.8	2 18.8	15
16	0 04.0	0 19.0	0 34.0	0 49.0	1 04.0	1 19.0	1 34.0	1 49.0	2 04.0	2 19.0	16
17	0 04.3	0 19.3	0 34.3	0 49.3	1 04.3	1 19.3	1 34.3	1 49.3	2 04.3	2 19.3	17
18	0 04.5	0 19.5	0 34.5	0 49.5	1 04.5	1 19.5	1 34.5	1 49.5	2 04.5	2 19.5	18
19	0 04.8	0 19.8	0 34.8	0 49.8	1 04.8	1 19.8	1 34.8	1 49.8	2 04.8	2 19.8	19
20	0 05.0	0 20.0	0 35.0	0 50.0	1 05.0	1 20.0	1 35.0	1 50.0	2 05.0	2 20.0	20
21	0 05.3	0 20.3	0 35.3	0 50.3	1 05.3	1 20.3	1 35.3	1 50.3	2 05.3	2 20.3	21
22	0 05.5	0 20.5	0 35.5	0 50.5	1 05.5	1 20.5	1 35.5	1 50.5	2 05.5	2 20.5	22
23	0 05.8	0 20.8	0 35.8	0 50.8	1 05.8	1 20.8	1 35.8	1 50.8	2 05.8	2 20.8	23
24	0 06.0	0 21.0	0 36.0	0 51.0	1 06.0	1 21.0	1 36.0	1 51.0	2 06.0	2 21.0	24
25	0 06.3	0 21.3	0 36.3	0 51.3	1 06.3	1 21.3	1 36.3	1 51.3	2 06.3	2 21.3	25
26	0 06.5	0 21.5	0 36.5	0 51.5	1 06.5	1 21.5	1 36.5	1 51.5	2 06.5	2 21.5	26
27	0 06.8	0 21.8	0 36.8	0 51.8	1 06.8	1 21.8	1 36.8	1 51.8	2 06.8	2 21.8	27
28	0 07.0	0 22.0	0 37.0	0 52.0	1 07.0	1 22.0	1 37.0	1 52.0	2 07.0	2 22.0	28
29	0 07.3	0 22.3	0 37.3	0 52.3	1 07.3	1 22.3	1 37.3	1 52.3	2 07.3	2 22.3	29
30	0 07.5	0 22.5	0 37.5	0 52.5	1 07.5	1 22.5	1 37.5	1 52.5	2 07.5	2 22.5	30
31	0 07.8	0 22.8	0 37.8	0 52.8	1 07.8	1 22.8	1 37.8	1 52.8	2 07.8	2 22.8	31
32	0 08.0	0 23.0	0 38.0	0 53.0	1 08.0	1 23.0	1 38.0	1 53.0	2 08.0	2 23.0	32
33	0 08.3	0 23.3	0 38.3	0 53.3	1 08.3	1 23.3	1 38.3	1 53.3	2 08.3	2 23.3	33
34	0 08.5	0 23.5	0 38.5	0 53.5	1 08.5	1 23.5	1 38.5	1 53.5	2 08.5	2 23.5	34
35	0 08.8	0 23.8	0 38.8	0 53.8	1 08.8	1 23.8	1 38.8	1 53.8	2 08.8	2 23.8	35
36	0 09.0	0 24.0	0 39.0	0 54.0	1 09.0	1 24.0	1 39.0	1 54.0	2 09.0	2 24.0	36
37	0 09.3	0 24.3	0 39.3	0 54.3	1 09.3	1 24.3	1 39.3	1 54.3	2 09.3	2 24.3	37
38	0 09.5	0 24.5	0 39.5	0 54.5	1 09.5	1 24.5	1 39.5	1 54.5	2 09.5	2 24.5	38
39	0 09.8	0 24.8	0 39.8	0 54.8	1 09.8	1 24.8	1 39.8	1 54.8	2 09.8	2 24.8	39
40	0 10.0	0 25.0	0 40.0	0 55.0	1 10.0	1 25.0	1 40.0	1 55.0	2 10.0	2 25.0	40
41	0 10.3	0 25.3	0 40.3	0 55.3	1 10.3	1 25.3	1 40.3	1 55.3	2 10.3	2 25.3	41
42	0 10.5	0 25.5	0 40.5	0 55.5	1 10.5	1 25.5	1 40.5	1 55.5	2 10.5	2 25.5	42
43	0 10.8	0 25.8	0 40.8	0 55.8	1 10.8	1 25.8	1 40.8	1 55.8	2 10.8	2 25.8	43
44	0 11.0	0 26.0	0 41.0	0 56.0	1 11.0	1 26.0	1 41.0	1 56.0	2 11.0	2 26.0	44
45	0 11.3	0 26.3	0 41.3	0 56.3	1 11.3	1 26.3	1 41.3	1 56.3	2 11.3	2 26.3	45
46	0 11.5	0 26.5	0 41.5	0 56.5	1 11.5	1 26.5	1 41.5	1 56.5	2 11.5	2 26.5	46
47	0 11.8	0 26.8	0 41.8	0 56.8	1 11.8	1 26.8	1 41.8	1 56.8	2 11.8	2 26.8	47
48	0 12.0	0 27.0	0 42.0	0 57.0	1 12.0	1 27.0	1 42.0	1 57.0	2 12.0	2 27.0	48
49	0 12.3	0 27.3	0 42.3	0 57.3	1 12.3	1 27.3	1 42.3	1 57.3	2 12.3	2 27.3	49
50	0 12.5	0 27.5	0 42.5	0 57.5	1 12.5	1 27.5	1 42.5	1 57.5	2 12.5	2 27.5	50
51	0 12.8	0 27.8	0 42.8	0 57.8	1 12.8	1 27.8	1 42.8	1 57.8	2 12.8	2 27.8	51
52	0 13.0	0 28.0	0 43.0	0 58.0	1 13.0	1 28.0	1 43.0	1 58.0	2 13.0	2 28.0	52
53	0 13.3	0 28.3	0 43.3	0 58.3	1 13.3	1 28.3	1 43.3	1 58.3	2 13.3	2 28.3	53
54	0 13.5	0 28.5	0 43.5	0 58.5	1 13.5	1 28.5	1 43.5	1 58.5	2 13.5	2 28.5	54
55	0 13.8	0 28.8	0 43.8	0 58.8	1 13.8	1 28.8	1 43.8	1 58.8	2 13.8	2 28.8	55
56	0 14.0	0 29.0	0 44.0	0 59.0	1 14.0	1 29.0	1 44.0	1 59.0	2 14.0	2 29.0	56
57	0 14.3	0 29.3	0 44.3	0 59.3	1 14.3	1 29.3	1 44.3	1 59.3	2 14.3	2 29.3	57
58	0 14.5	0 29.5	0 44.5	0 59.5	1 14.5	1 29.5	1 44.5	1 59.5	2 14.5	2 29.5	58
59	0 14.8	0 29.8	0 44.8	0 59.8	1 14.8	1 29.8	1 44.8	1 59.8	2 14.8	2 29.8	59
60	0 15.0	0 30.0	0 45.0	1 00.0	1 15.0	1 30.0	1 45.0	2 00.0	2 15.0	2 30.0	60

INTERPOLATION OF G.H.A. ARIES

s	0^m	1^m	2^m	3^m	4^m	5^m	6^m	7^m	8^m	9^m	s
	° ′	° ′	° ′	° ′	° ′	° ′	° ′	° ′	° ′	° ′	
00	0 00.0	0 15.0	0 30.1	0 45.1	1 00.2	1 15.2	1 30.2	1 45.3	2 00.3	2 15.4	00
01	0 00.3	0 15.3	0 30.3	0 45.4	1 00.4	1 15.5	1 30.5	1 45.5	2 00.6	2 15.6	01
02	0 00.5	0 15.5	0 30.6	0 45.6	1 00.7	1 15.7	1 30.7	1 45.8	2 00.8	2 15.9	02
03	0 00.8	0 15.8	0 30.8	0 45.9	1 00.9	1 16.0	1 31.0	1 46.0	2 01.1	2 16.1	03
04	0 01.0	0 16.0	0 31.1	0 46.1	1 01.2	1 16.2	1 31.2	1 46.3	2 01.3	2 16.4	04
05	0 01.3	0 16.3	0 31.3	0 46.4	1 01.4	1 16.5	1 31.5	1 46.5	2 01.6	2 16.6	05
06	0 01.5	0 16.5	0 31.6	0 46.6	1 01.7	1 16.7	1 31.8	1 46.8	2 01.8	2 16.9	06
07	0 01.8	0 16.8	0 31.8	0 46.9	1 01.9	1 17.0	1 32.0	1 47.0	2 02.1	2 17.1	07
08	0 02.0	0 17.0	0 32.1	0 47.1	1 02.2	1 17.2	1 32.3	1 47.3	2 02.3	2 17.4	08
09	0 02.3	0 17.3	0 32.3	0 47.4	1 02.4	1 17.5	1 32.5	1 47.5	2 02.6	2 17.6	09
10	0 02.5	0 17.5	0 32.6	0 47.6	1 02.7	1 17.7	1 32.8	1 47.8	2 02.8	2 17.9	10
11	0 02.8	0 17.8	0 32.8	0 47.9	1 02.9	1 18.0	1 33.0	1 48.0	2 03.1	2 18.1	11
12	0 03.0	0 18.0	0 33.1	0 48.1	1 03.2	1 18.2	1 33.3	1 48.3	2 03.3	2 18.4	12
13	0 03.3	0 18.3	0 33.3	0 48.4	1 03.4	1 18.5	1 33.5	1 48.5	2 03.6	2 18.6	13
14	0 03.5	0 18.6	0 33.6	0 48.6	1 03.7	1 18.7	1 33.8	1 48.8	2 03.8	2 18.9	14
15	0 03.8	0 18.8	0 33.8	0 48.9	1 03.9	1 19.0	1 34.0	1 49.0	2 04.1	2 19.1	15
16	0 04.0	0 19.1	0 34.1	0 49.1	1 04.2	1 19.2	1 34.3	1 49.3	2 04.3	2 19.4	16
17	0 04.3	0 19.3	0 34.3	0 49.4	1 04.4	1 19.5	1 34.5	1 49.5	2 04.6	2 19.6	17
18	0 04.5	0 19.6	0 34.6	0 49.6	1 04.7	1 19.7	1 34.8	1 49.8	2 04.8	2 19.9	18
19	0 04.8	0 19.8	0 34.8	0 49.9	1 04.9	1 20.0	1 35.0	1 50.1	2 05.1	2 20.1	19
20	0 05.0	0 20.1	0 35.1	0 50.1	1 05.2	1 20.2	1 35.3	1 50.3	2 05.3	2 20.4	20
21	0 05.3	0 20.3	0 35.3	0 50.4	1 05.4	1 20.5	1 35.5	1 50.6	2 05.6	2 20.6	21
22	0 05.5	0 20.6	0 35.6	0 50.6	1 05.7	1 20.7	1 35.8	1 50.8	2 05.8	2 20.9	22
23	0 05.8	0 20.8	0 35.8	0 50.9	1 05.9	1 21.0	1 36.0	1 51.1	2 06.1	2 21.1	23
24	0 06.0	0 21.1	0 36.1	0 51.1	1 06.2	1 21.2	1 36.3	1 51.3	2 06.3	2 21.4	24
25	0 06.3	0 21.3	0 36.3	0 51.4	1 06.4	1 21.5	1 36.5	1 51.6	2 06.6	2 21.6	25
26	0 06.5	0 21.6	0 36.6	0 51.6	1 06.7	1 21.7	1 36.8	1 51.8	2 06.8	2 21.9	26
27	0 06.8	0 21.8	0 36.9	0 51.9	1 06.9	1 22.0	1 37.0	1 52.1	2 07.1	2 22.1	27
28	0 07.0	0 22.1	0 37.1	0 52.1	1 07.2	1 22.2	1 37.3	1 52.3	2 07.3	2 22.4	28
29	0 07.3	0 22.3	0 37.4	0 52.4	1 07.4	1 22.5	1 37.5	1 52.6	2 07.6	2 22.6	29
30	0 07.5	0 22.6	0 37.6	0 52.6	1 07.7	1 22.7	1 37.8	1 52.8	2 07.8	2 22.9	30
31	0 07.8	0 22.8	0 37.9	0 52.9	1 07.9	1 23.0	1 38.0	1 53.1	2 08.1	2 23.1	31
32	0 08.0	0 23.1	0 38.1	0 53.1	1 08.2	1 23.2	1 38.3	1 53.3	2 08.4	2 23.4	32
33	0 08.3	0 23.3	0 38.4	0 53.4	1 08.4	1 23.5	1 38.5	1 53.6	2 08.6	2 23.6	33
34	0 08.5	0 23.6	0 38.6	0 53.6	1 08.7	1 23.7	1 38.8	1 53.8	2 08.9	2 23.9	34
35	0 08.8	0 23.8	0 38.9	0 53.9	1 08.9	1 24.0	1 39.0	1 54.1	2 09.1	2 24.1	35
36	0 09.0	0 24.1	0 39.1	0 54.1	1 09.2	1 24.2	1 39.3	1 54.3	2 09.4	2 24.4	36
37	0 09.3	0 24.3	0 39.4	0 54.4	1 09.4	1 24.5	1 39.5	1 54.6	2 09.6	2 24.6	37
38	0 09.5	0 24.6	0 39.6	0 54.6	1 09.7	1 24.7	1 39.8	1 54.8	2 09.9	2 24.9	38
39	0 09.8	0 24.8	0 39.9	0 54.9	1 09.9	1 25.0	1 40.0	1 55.1	2 10.1	2 25.1	39
40	0 10.0	0 25.1	0 40.1	0 55.2	1 10.2	1 25.2	1 40.3	1 55.3	2 10.4	2 25.4	40
41	0 10.3	0 25.3	0 40.4	0 55.4	1 10.4	1 25.5	1 40.5	1 55.6	2 10.6	2 25.6	41
42	0 10.5	0 25.6	0 40.6	0 55.7	1 10.7	1 25.7	1 40.8	1 55.8	2 10.9	2 25.9	42
43	0 10.8	0 25.8	0 40.9	0 55.9	1 10.9	1 26.0	1 41.0	1 56.1	2 11.1	2 26.1	43
44	0 11.0	0 26.1	0 41.1	0 56.2	1 11.2	1 26.2	1 41.3	1 56.3	2 11.4	2 26.4	44
45	0 11.3	0 26.3	0 41.4	0 56.4	1 11.4	1 26.5	1 41.5	1 56.6	2 11.6	2 26.7	45
46	0 11.5	0 26.6	0 41.6	0 56.7	1 11.7	1 26.7	1 41.8	1 56.8	2 11.9	2 26.9	46
47	0 11.8	0 26.8	0 41.9	0 56.9	1 11.9	1 27.0	1 42.0	1 57.1	2 12.1	2 27.2	47
48	0 12.0	0 27.1	0 42.1	0 57.2	1 12.2	1 27.2	1 42.3	1 57.3	2 12.4	2 27.4	48
49	0 12.3	0 27.3	0 42.4	0 57.4	1 12.4	1 27.5	1 42.5	1 57.6	2 12.6	2 27.7	49
50	0 12.5	0 27.6	0 42.6	0 57.7	1 12.7	1 27.7	1 42.8	1 57.8	2 12.9	2 27.9	50
51	0 12.8	0 27.8	0 42.9	0 57.9	1 12.9	1 28.0	1 43.0	1 58.1	2 13.1	2 28.2	51
52	0 13.0	0 28.1	0 43.1	0 58.2	1 13.2	1 28.2	1 43.3	1 58.3	2 13.4	2 28.4	52
53	0 13.3	0 28.3	0 43.4	0 58.4	1 13.5	1 28.5	1 43.5	1 58.6	2 13.6	2 28.7	53
54	0 13.5	0 28.6	0 43.6	0 58.7	1 13.7	1 28.7	1 43.8	1 58.8	2 13.9	2 28.9	54
55	0 13.8	0 28.8	0 43.9	0 58.9	1 14.0	1 29.0	1 44.0	1 59.1	2 14.1	2 29.2	55
56	0 14.0	0 29.1	0 44.1	0 59.2	1 14.2	1 29.2	1 44.3	1 59.3	2 14.4	2 29.4	56
57	0 14.3	0 29.3	0 44.4	0 59.4	1 14.5	1 29.5	1 44.5	1 59.6	2 14.6	2 29.7	57
58	0 14.5	0 29.6	0 44.6	0 59.7	1 14.7	1 29.7	1 44.8	1 59.8	2 14.9	2 29.9	58
59	0 14.8	0 29.8	0 44.9	0 59.9	1 15.0	1 30.0	1 45.0	2 00.1	2 15.1	2 30.2	59
60	0 15.0	0 30.1	0 45.1	1 00.2	1 15.2	1 30.2	1 45.3	2 00.3	2 15.4	2 30.4	60

POLARIS (POLE STAR) TABLE, 1975

FOR DETERMINING THE LATITUDE FROM A SEXTANT ALTITUDE

L.H.A.♈	Q	L.H.A.♈	Q	L.H.A.♈	Q	L.H.A.♈	Q	L.H.A.♈	Q	L.H.A.♈	Q	L.H.A.♈	Q	L.H.A.♈	Q
° ′	′	° ′	′	° ′	′	° ′	′	° ′	′	° ′	′	° ′	′	° ′	′
359 08	−43	80 32	−33	113 11	−7	143 05	+19	183 04	+45	264 07	+31	296 18	+5	326 18	−21
1 14	−44	82 00	−32	114 20	−7	144 18	+20	185 31	+46	265 33	+30	297 26	+5	327 32	−22
3 29	−45	83 27	−31	115 28	−6	145 32	+21	188 12	+47	266 57	+29	298 34	+4	328 47	−23
5 54	−46	84 52	−30	116 36	−5	146 46	+22	191 12	+48	268 20	+28	299 43	+3	330 03	−24
8 32	−47	86 15	−29	117 44	−4	148 01	+23	194 41	+49	269 41	+27	300 50	+2	331 19	−25
11 30	−48	87 38	−28	118 51	−3	149 18	+24	199 02	+50	271 01	+26	301 58	+1	332 37	−26
14 56	−49	88 58	−27	119 59	−2	150 35	+25	205 51	+51	272 20	+25	303 06	0	333 55	−27
19 13	−50	90 18	−26	121 07	−1	151 53	+26	218 22	+51	273 38	+24	304 14	−1	335 15	−28
25 56	−51	91 36	−25	122 15	0	153 12	+27	225 11	+50	274 55	+23	305 22	−2	336 35	−29
38 17	−50	92 54	−24	123 23	+1	154 32	+28	229 32	+49	276 12	+22	306 29	−3	337 58	−30
45 00	−49	94 10	−23	124 30	+2	155 53	+29	233 01	+48	277 27	+21	307 37	−4	339 21	−31
49 17	−48	95 26	−22	125 39	+3	157 16	+30	236 01	+47	278 41	+20	308 45	−5	340 46	−32
52 43	−47	96 41	−21	126 47	+4	158 40	+31	238 42	+46	279 55	+19	309 53	−6	342 13	−33
55 41	−46	97 55	−20	127 55	+5	160 06	+32	241 09	+45	281 08	+18	311 02	−7	343 41	−34
58 19	−45	99 08	−19	129 03	+6	161 34	+33	243 25	+44	282 21	+17	312 10	−8	345 12	−35
60 44	−44	100 21	−18	130 11	+7	163 03	+34	245 33	+43	283 33	+16	313 19	−9	346 45	−36
62 59	−43	101 33	−17	131 20	+8	164 35	+35	247 34	+42	284 44	+15	314 27	−10	348 20	−37
65 05	−42	102 45	−16	132 29	+9	166 09	+36	249 29	+41	285 55	+14	315 37	−11	349 59	−38
67 05	−41	103 56	−15	133 38	+10	167 45	+37	251 20	+40	287 06	+13	316 46	−12	351 40	−39
68 59	−40	105 07	−14	134 47	+11	169 24	+38	253 06	+39	288 16	+12	317 56	−13	353 25	−40
70 48	−39	106 17	−13	135 57	+12	171 07	+39	254 49	+38	289 26	+11	319 06	−14	355 14	−41
72 33	−38	107 27	−12	137 07	+13	172 53	+40	256 28	+37	290 35	+10	320 17	−15	357 08	−42
74 14	−37	108 36	−11	138 18	+14	174 44	+41	258 04	+36	291 44	+9	321 28	−16	359 08	−43
75 53	−36	109 46	−10	139 29	+15	176 39	+42	259 38	+35	292 53	+8	322 40	−17	1 14	−44
77 28	−35	110 54	−9	140 40	+16	178 40	+43	261 10	+34	294 02	+7	323 52	−18	3 29	−45
79 01	−34	112 03	−8	141 52	+17	180 48	+44	262 39	+33	295 10	+6	325 05	−19	5 54	−46
80 32		113 11		143 05	+18	183 04		264 07	+32	296 18		326 18	−20	8 32	

Q, which does *not* include refraction, is to be applied to the corrected sextant altitude of *Polaris*.
Polaris: Mag. 2·1, S.H.A. 327° 53′, Dec. N. 89° 09′·2

STANDARD DOME REFRACTION

To be *subtracted* from sextant altitude when using sextant suspension in a perspex dome

Alt.	Refn.	Alt.	Refn.
°	′	°	′
10	8	50	4
20	7	60	4
30	6	70	3
40	5	80	3

This table must not be used if a calibration table is fitted to the dome, or if a flat glass plate is provided, or for non-standard domes.

BUBBLE SEXTANT ERROR

Sextant Number	Alt.	Corr.
	°	′

L.H.A. ♈ 300°–120°	AZIMUTH OF *POLARIS* Latitude							L.H.A. ♈ 120°–300°
	0°	30°	50°	55°	60°	65°	70°	
°	°	°	°	°	°	°	°	°
300	0·8	1·0	1·3	1·5	1·7	2·0	2·5	300
310	0·8	1·0	1·3	1·4	1·7	2·0	2·4	290
320	0·8	0·9	1·2	1·4	1·6	1·9	2·3	280
330	0·7	0·8	1·1	1·2	1·4	1·7	2·1	270
340	0·6	0·7	1·0	1·1	1·3	1·5	1·8	260
350	0·5	0·6	0·8	0·9	1·0	1·2	1·5	250
0	0·4	0·5	0·6	0·7	0·8	0·9	1·2	240
10	0·3	0·3	0·4	0·5	0·5	0·6	0·8	230
20	0·1	0·1	0·2	0·2	0·2	0·3	0·3	220
30	0·0	0·0	0·0	0·1	0·1	0·1	0·1	210
40	359·9	359·9	359·8	359·8	359·8	359·7	359·7	200
50	359·7	359·7	359·6	359·5	359·5	359·4	359·2	190
60	359·6	359·5	359·4	359·3	359·2	359·1	358·8	180
70	359·5	359·4	359·2	359·1	359·0	358·8	358·5	170
80	359·4	359·3	359·0	358·9	358·7	358·5	358·2	160
90	359·3	359·2	358·9	358·8	358·6	358·3	357·9	150
100	359·2	359·1	358·8	358·6	358·4	358·1	357·7	140
110	359·2	359·0	358·7	358·6	358·3	358·0	357·6	130
120	359·2	359·0	358·7	358·5	358·3	358·0	357·5	120

When Cassiopeia is left (right), *Polaris* is west (east).

CORRECTIONS TO BE APPLIED TO SEXTANT ALTITUDE

REFRACTION

To be subtracted from sextant altitude (referred to as observed altitude in A.P. 3270).

R_o	Height above sea level in units of 1,000 ft.												R_o	$R = R_o \times f$			
	0	5	10	15	20	25	30	35	40	45	50	55		0·9	1·0	1·1	1·2
	Sextant Altitude																
	° ′	° ′	° ′	° ′	° ′	° ′	° ′	° ′	° ′	° ′	° ′	° ′		′	′	′	′
0	90	90	90	90	90	90	90	90	90	90	90	90	0	0	0	0	0
1	63	59	55	51	46	41	36	31	26	20	17	13	1	1	1	1	1
2	33	29	26	22	19	16	14	11	9	7	6	4	2	2	2	2	2
3	21	19	16	14	12	10	8	7	5	4	2 40	1 40	3	3	3	3	4
4	16	14	12	10	8	7	6	5	3 10	2 20	1 30	0 40	4	4	4	4	5
5	12	11	9	8	7	5	4 00	3 10	2 10	1 30	0 39	+0 05	5	5	5	5	6
6	10	9	7	5 50	4 50	3 50	3 10	2 20	1 30	0 49	+0 11	−0 19	6	5	6	7	7
7	8 10	6 50	5 50	4 50	4 00	3 00	2 20	1 50	1 10	0 24	−0 11	−0 38	7	6	7	8	8
8	6 50	5 50	5 00	4 00	3 10	2 30	1 50	1 20	0 38	+0 04	−0 28	−0 54	8	7	8	9	10
9	6 00	5 10	4 10	3 20	2 40	2 00	1 30	1 00	0 19	−0 13	−0 42	−1 08	9	8	9	10	11
10	5 20	4 30	3 40	2 50	2 10	1 40	1 10	0 35	+0 03	−0 27	−0 53	−1 18	10	9	10	11	12
12	4 30	3 40	2 50	2 20	1 40	1 10	0 37	+0 11	−0 16	−0 43	−1 08	−1 31	12	11	12	13	14
14	3 30	2 50	2 10	1 40	1 10	0 34	+0 09	−0 14	−0 37	−1 00	−1 23	−1 44	14	13	14	15	17
16	2 50	2 10	1 40	1 10	0 37	+0 10	−0 13	−0 34	−0 53	−1 14	−1 35	−1 56	16	14	16	18	19
18	2 20	1 40	1 20	0 43	+0 15	−0 08	−0 31	−0 52	−1 08	−1 27	−1 46	−2 05	18	16	18	20	22
20	1 50	1 20	0 49	+0 23	−0 02	−0 26	−0 46	−1 06	−1 22	−1 39	−1 57	−2 14	20	18	20	22	24
25	1 12	0 44	+0 19	−0 06	−0 28	−0 48	−1 09	−1 27	−1 42	−1 58	−2 14	−2 30	25	22	25	28	30
30	0 34	+0 10	−0 13	−0 36	−0 55	−1 14	−1 32	−1 51	−2 06	−2 21	−2 34	−2 49	30	27	30	33	36
35	+0 06	−0 16	−0 37	−0 59	−1 17	−1 33	−1 51	−2 07	−2 23	−2 37	−2 51	−3 04	35	31	35	38	42
40	−0 18	−0 37	−0 58	−1 16	−1 34	−1 49	−2 06	−2 22	−2 35	−2 49	−3 03	−3 16	40	36	40	44	48
45		−0 53	−1 14	−1 31	−1 47	−2 03	−2 18	−2 33	−2 47	−2 59	−3 13	−3 25	45	40	45	50	54
50		−1 10	−1 28	−1 44	−1 59	−2 15	−2 28	−2 43	−2 56	−3 08	−3 22	−3 33	50	45	50	55	60
55			−1 40	−1 53	−2 09	−2 24	−2 38	−2 52	−3 04	−3 17	−3 29	−3 41	55	49	55	60	66
60				−2 03	−2 18	−2 33	−2 46	−3 01	−3 12	−3 25	−3 37	−3 48	60	54	60	66	72
							−2 53	−3 07	−3 19	−3 31	−3 42	−3 53					

f	0	5	10	15	20	25	30	35	40	45	50	55	f	0·9	1·0	1·1	1·2
	Temperature in °C																
0·9	+47	+36	+27	+18	+10	+ 3	− 5	−13					0·9				
1·0	+26	+16	+ 6	− 4	−13	−22	−31	−40	For these heights no temperature correction is necessary: take $f=1·0$ and use $R=R_o$				1·0	When R_o is less than 10′ or the height is greater than 35,000 ft. take $f=1·0$ and use $R=R_o$			
1·1	+ 5	− 5	−15	−25	−36	−46	−57	−68					1·1				
1·2	−16	−25	−36	−46	−58	−71	−83	−95					1·2				
	−37	−45	−56	−67	−81	−95											

Choose the column appropriate to height, in units of 1,000 ft., and find the range of altitude in which the sextant altitude lies; the corresponding value of R_o is the refraction, to be subtracted from sextant altitude, unless conditions are extreme. In that case find f from the lower table, with critical argument temperature. Use the table on the right to form the refraction, $R = R_o \times f$.

CORIOLIS (Z) CORRECTION

To be applied by moving the position line a distance Z to starboard (right) of the track in northern latitudes and to port (left) in southern latitudes. The argument is given as T.A.S. (True Air Speed) in A.P. 3270.

G/S KNOTS	Latitude										G/S KNOTS	Latitude									
	0°	10°	20°	30°	40°	50°	60°	70°	80°	90°		0°	10°	20°	30°	40°	50°	60°	70°	80°	90°
150	0	1	1	2	3	3	3	4	4	4	450	0	2	4	6	8	9	10	11	12	12
200	0	1	2	3	3	4	5	5	5	5	500	0	2	4	7	8	10	11	12	13	13
250	0	1	2	3	4	5	6	6	6	7	550	0	3	5	7	9	11	12	14	14	14
300	0	1	3	4	5	6	7	7	8	8	600	0	3	5	8	10	12	14	15	16	16
350	0	2	3	5	6	7	8	9	9	9	650	0	3	6	9	11	13	15	16	17	17
400	0	2	4	5	7	8	9	10	10	10	700	0	3	6	9	12	14	16	17	18	18

CORRECTIONS TO BE APPLIED TO MARINE SEXTANT ALTITUDES

MARINE SEXTANT ERROR	CORRECTIONS	CORRECTION FOR DIP OF THE HORIZON To be subtracted from sextant altitude								
Sextant Number	In addition to sextant error and dip, corrections are to be applied for:	Ht.	Dip	Ht.	Dip	Ht.	Dip	Ht.	Dip	Ht.	Dip
		Ft.	′	Ft.	′	Ft.	′	Ft.	′	Ft.	′
Index Error	Refraction	0	1	114	11	437	21	968	31	1 707	41
	Semi-diameter (for the	2	2	137	12	481	22	1 033	32	1 792	42
	Sun and Moon)	6	3	162	13	527	23	1 099	33	1 880	43
	Parallax (for the Moon)	12	4	189	14	575	24	1 168	34	1 970	44
	Dome refraction (if	21	5	218	15	625	25	1 239	35	2 061	45
	applicable)	31	6	250	16	677	26	1 311	36	2 155	46
		43	7	283	17	731	27	1 386	37	2 251	47
		58	8	318	18	787	28	1 463	38	2 349	48
		75	9	356	19	845	29	1 543	39	2 449	49
		93	10	395	20	906	30	1 624	40	2 551	50
		114		437		968		1 707		2 655	

LIST OF CONTENTS

APPENDIX H

LONG-TERM ALMANAC

This appendix is intended for use when a more complete almanac is not available. It is based principally upon the fact that approximately correct values for the Greenwich hour angle and declination of the sun, and the Greenwich hour angle of Aries, can be obtained from an almanac that is exactly four years out of date. The differences in these values at intervals of exactly four years can be largely removed by applying an average correction to the values obtained from the tables of this appendix. The maximum error in an altitude computed by means of this appendix should not exceed 2'.0 for the sun or 1'.3 for stars.

This four-year, or quadrennial, correction varies throughout the year for the GHA of the sun (between about plus and minus one-half of a minute) and for the declination of the sun (between about plus and minus three-fourths of a minute). For the GHA of Aries the quadrennial correction is a constant, (+)1'.84. The appropriate quadrennial correction is applied once for each full four years which has passed since the base year of the tabulation (1972 in this appendix).

The tabulated values for GHA—175° and declination of the sun and GHA of Aries are given in four columns, labeled 0, 1, 2, and 3. The "0" column contains the data for the leap year in each four-year cycle and the 1, 2, and 3 columns contain data for, respectively, the first, second, and third years following each leap year.

The GHA—175° and declination of the sun are given at intervals of three days throughout the four-year cycle, except for the final days of each month, when the interval varies between one and four days. Linear interpolation is made between entries to obtain data for a given day. Additional corrections to the GHA of the sun of 15° per hour, 15' per minute, and 15" per second are made to obtain the GHA at a given time. Declination of the sun is obtained to sufficient accuracy by linear interpolation alone.

The GHA of Aries is given for each month of the four-year cycle. Additional corrections of 0°59'.14 per day, 15°02'.5 per hour, 15' per minute, and 15" per second are made to obtain the GHA at a given time.

The SHA and declination of 38 navigational stars are given for the base year, 1972.0. Annual (not quadrennial) corrections are made to these data to obtain the values for a given year and tenth of a year.

A multiplication table is included as an aid in applying corrections to tabulated values.

Sun tables. 1. Subtract 1972 from the year and divide the difference by four, obtaining (*a*) a whole number, and (*b*) a remainder. Enter column indicated by remainder (*b*) and take out values on either side of given time and date.

2. Multiply quadrennial correction for each value by whole number (*a*) obtained in step 1 and apply to tabulated values plus 175°.

3. Divide difference between corrected values by number of days (usually three) between them to determine daily change.

4. Multiply daily change by number of days and tenths since 0^h GMT of earlier tabulated date, and mark correction plus (+) or minus (−) as appropriate.

5. (GHA only.) Enter multiplication table with hours, minutes, and seconds of GMT, and take out corrections A, B, and C, respectively. These are all positive.

6. Apply corrections of steps 4 and 5 to corrected *earlier* values of step 2.

Example.—Find GHA and declination of sun at GMT $17^h13^m49^s$ on July 18, 2002.

Solution.—*Steps* 1 *and* 2: (2002−1972)÷4=7, remainder 2. Use column 2, and multiply quadrennial corrections by 7. Corrected values: GHA, July 16, 178°31ʹ1+ (7×0ʹ05)=178°31ʹ5; July 19, 178°27ʹ2+(7×0ʹ06)=178°27ʹ6. Dec., July 16, 21°27ʹ9N−(7×0ʹ41)=21°25ʹ0N; July 19, 20°57ʹ5N−(7×0ʹ44)=20°54ʹ4N.

	GHA				Declination		
July 16	178°31ʹ5			July 16	21°25ʹ0 N		
July 19	178°27ʹ6		Step 3	July 19	20°54ʹ4 N		Step 3
3-day change	(−)3ʹ9			3-day change	(−)30ʹ6		
daily change	(−)1ʹ3			daily change	(−)10ʹ2		
days and tenths	2.7		Step 4	days and tenths	2.7		Step 4
corr.	(−)3ʹ5			corr.	(−)27ʹ5		
A	255°00ʹ0			0^h July 16	21°25ʹ0 N		Step 6
B	3°15ʹ0		Step 5	Dec.	20°57ʹ5 N		
C	12ʹ1						
0^h July 16	178°31ʹ5		Step 6				
GHA	76°55ʹ2						

Aries table. 1. Subtract 1972 from the year and divide the difference by four, obtaining (*a*) a whole number, and (*b*) a remainder. Enter column indicated by remainder (*b*) and take out value for given month.

2. Enter multiplication table with whole number (*a*) of step 1, day of month, hours of GMT, minutes of GMT, and seconds of GMT, and take out corrections D, E, F, G, and C, respectively.

3. Add values of steps 1 and 2.

Example.—Find GHA♈ at GMT $11^h06^m33^s$ on November 28, 1995.

Solution.—*Step* 1: (1995−1972)÷4=5, remainder 3. Use column 3.

	GHA♈	
Nov.	38°40ʹ6	Step 1
D	9ʹ2	
E	27°35ʹ9	
F	165°27ʹ1	Step 2
G	1°30ʹ2	
C	8ʹ2	
GHA♈	233°31ʹ2	Step 3

Stars table. 1. Enter table with star name, and take out tabulated values.

2. Subtract 1972.0 from given year and tenth, and multiply annual correction by difference. Apply as correction (+or−, as appropriate) to value of step 1.

Example.—Find SHA and declination of Spica on September 11, 2011.

Solution.—From decimal table, September 11, 2011=2011.7. 2011.7—1972.0= 39.7.

SHA			Declination		
1972.0	159°04′.3	} *Step 1*	1972.0	11°01′.0 S	} *Step 1*
39.7×(−)0′.79	(−)31′.4	} *Step 2*	39.7×0.31	(+)12′.3	} *Step 2*
SHA	158°32′.9		Dec.	11°13′.3 S	

To determine GHA of star, add GHA ♈ and SHA ✮ for given time and date.

SUN

0 GHA −175°	0 Dec.	Quad. GHA Corr.	1 GHA −175°	1 Dec.	Date	2 GHA −175°	2 Dec.	Quad. Dec. Corr.	3 GHA −175°	3 Dec.
					JANUARY					
4 14.4	23 05.5 S	−0.11	4 09.0	23 02.0 S	1	4 10.8	23 03.1 S	−0.32	4 12.9	23 04.2 S
3 53.3	22 50.2 S	−0.13	3 48.0	22 45.6 S	4	3 49.8	22 47.0 S	−0.35	3 51.9	22 48.4 S
3 33.0	22 30.7 S	−0.12	3 27.8	22 25.1 S	7	3 29.8	22 26.8 S	−0.39	3 31.7	22 28.6 S
3 13.8	22 07.2 S	−0.09	3 08.8	22 00.6 S	10	3 10.8	22 02.7 S	−0.42	3 12.5	22 04.8 S
2 55.7	21 39.9 S	−0.04	2 51.1	21 32.2 S	13	2 53.0	21 34.7 S	−0.44	2 54.5	21 37.1 S
2 38.9	21 08.7 S	+0.03	2 34.8	21 00.2 S	16	2 36.6	21 02.9 S	−0.46	2 37.9	21 05.6 S
2 23.7	20 33.9 S	+0.09	2 20.1	20 24.5 S	19	2 21.7	20 27.5 S	−0.48	2 22.9	20 30.5 S
2 10.1	19 55.6 S	+0.13	2 07.0	19 45.4 S	22	2 08.4	19 48.7 S	−0.49	2 09.5	19 51.9 S
1 58.2	19 13.9 S	+0.15	1 55.7	19 02.9 S	25	1 56.8	19 06.4 S	−0.52	1 57.9	19 10.0 S
1 48.2	18 29.1 S	+0.15	1 46.1	18 17.3 S	28	1 47.0	18 21.1 S	−0.54	1 48.0	18 24.9 S
					FEBRUARY					
1 37.7	17 24.7 S	+0.13	1 36.1	17 11.9 S	1	1 36.8	17 16.0 S	−0.57	1 37.8	17 20.2 S
1 32.0	16 33.2 S	+0.14	1 30.7	16 19.6 S	4	1 31.3	16 24.0 S	−0.59	1 32.1	16 28.4 S
1 28.0	15 39.0 S	+0.15	1 27.1	15 24.8 S	7	1 27.8	15 29.5 S	−0.60	1 28.3	15 34.0 S
1 25.9	14 42.5 S	+0.19	1 25.4	14 27.7 S	10	1 26.0	14 32.5 S	−0.61	1 26.3	14 37.2 S
1 25.4	13 43.6 S	+0.24	1 25.4	13 28.4 S	13	1 25.9	13 33.4 S	−0.60	1 26.0	13 38.2 S
1 26.7	12 42.8 S	+0.29	1 27.2	12 27.1 S	16	1 27.5	12 32.3 S	−0.60	1 27.4	12 37.2 S
1 29.6	11 40.1 S	+0.34	1 30.6	11 24.0 S	19	1 30.7	11 29.3 S	−0.59	1 30.4	11 34.4 S
1 34.0	10 35.8 S	+0.36	1 35.6	10 19.3 S	22	1 35.4	10 24.7 S	−0.59	1 35.1	10 30.0 S
1 40.0	9 30.0 S	+0.36	1 41.9	9 13.2 S	25	1 41.5	9 18.6 S	−0.60	1 41.2	9 24.1 S
1 47.4	8 23.0 S	+0.34	1 49.5	8 05.8 S	28	1 49.0	8 11.3 S	−0.61	1 48.7	8 17.0 S
					MARCH					
1 52.9	7 37.6 S	+0.32	1 52.3	7 43.1 S	1	1 51.7	7 48.7 S	−0.62	1 51.4	7 54.3 S
2 03.3	6 28.8 S	+0.31	2 01.4	6 34.4 S	4	2 00.8	6 40.0 S	−0.62	2 00.4	6 45.7 S
2 12.6	5 19.2 S	+0.31	2 11.6	5 24.8 S	7	2 11.0	5 30.5 S	−0.62	2 10.5	5 36.3 S
2 23.8	4 08.9 S	+0.33	2 22.6	4 14.5 S	10	2 22.1	4 20.4 S	−0.61	2 21.4	4 26.1 S
2 35.7	2 58.2 S	+0.36	2 34.5	3 03.8 S	13	2 33.9	3 09.7 S	−0.59	2 33.1	3 15.5 S
2 48.2	1 47.1 S	+0.40	2 47.1	1 52.8 S	16	2 46.4	1 58.7 S	−0.56	2 45.4	7 04.5 S
3 01.1	0 35.9 S	+0.43	3 00.1	0 41.7 S	19	2 59.4	0 47.6 S	−0.54	2 58.3	0 53.3 S
3 14.5	0 35.2 N	+0.44	3 13.6	0 29.4 N	22	3 12.7	0 23.6 N	+0.53	3 11.6	0 17.8 N
3 28.1	1 46.1 N	+0.43	3 27.2	1 40.3 N	25	3 26.2	1 34.6 N	+0.52	3 25.2	1 28.8 N
3 41.9	2 56.6 N	+0.40	3 40.9	2 50.9 N	28	3 39.8	2 45.2 N	+0.52	3 38.9	2 39.4 N
					APRIL					
4 00.0	4 29.8 N	+0.35	3 59.0	4 24.3 N	1	3 57.9	4 18.6 N	+0.52	3 57.1	4 12.8 N
4 13.4	5 38.9 N	+0.33	4 12.3	5 33.4 N	4	4 11.2	5 27.8 N	+0.51	4 10.5	5 22.1 N
4 26.4	6 47.1 N	+0.32	4 25.2	6 41.7 N	7	4 24.3	6 36.2 N	+0.49	4 23.5	6 30.6 N
4 38.8	7 54.3 N	+0.33	4 37.7	7 49.0 N	10	4 36.9	7 43.5 N	+0.47	4 36.0	7 38.0 N
4 50.6	9 00.3 N	+0.35	4 49.6	8 55.1 N	13	4 48.9	8 49.7 N	+0.44	4 48.0	8 44.3 N
5 01.7	10 05.0 N	+0.37	5 00.9	9 59.8 N	16	5 00.2	9 54.5 N	+0.41	4 59.2	9 49.3 N
5 12.0	11 08.1 N	+0.39	5 11.3	11 03.0 N	19	5 10.6	10 57.9 N	+0.39	5 09.7	10 52.8 N
5 21.4	12 09.6 N	+0.37	5 20.9	12 04.6 N	22	5 20.0	11 59.7 N	+0.37	5 19.3	11 54.7 N
5 29.8	13 09.2 N	+0.33	5 29.4	13 04.4 N	25	5 28.5	12 59.7 N	+0.36	5 28.0	12 54.8 N
5 37.2	14 06.9 N	+0.28	5 36.8	14 02.3 N	28	5 36.0	13 57.7 N	+0.34	5 35.6	13 53.0 N
					MAY					
5 43.4	15 02.6 N	+0.24	5 43.0	14 58.1 N	1	5 42.3	14 53.7 N	+0.33	5 42.1	14 49.2 N
5 48.4	15 56.0 N	+0.20	5 48.0	15 51.7 N	4	5 47.5	15 47.5 N	+0.31	5 47.3	15 43.1 N
5 52.1	16 47.0 N	+0.19	5 51.7	16 43.0 N	7	5 51.4	16 38.9 N	+0.28	5 51.3	16 34.7 N
5 54.5	17 35.5 N	+0.19	5 54.2	17 31.7 N	10	5 54.1	17 27.8 N	+0.25	5 53.9	17 23.9 N
5 55.6	18 21.4 N	+0.21	5 55.5	18 17.7 N	13	5 55.5	18 14.1 N	+0.22	5 55.3	18 10.4 N
5 55.4	19 04.5 N	+0.23	5 55.5	19 01.0 N	16	5 55.5	18 57.6 N	+0.19	5 55.4	18 54.2 N
5 53.9	19 44.7 N	+0.23	5 54.3	19 41.4 N	19	5 54.3	19 38.3 N	+0.16	5 54.3	19 35.1 N
5 51.3	20 21.8 N	+0.20	5 51.8	20 18.8 N	22	5 51.7	20 15.9 N	+0.13	5 51.9	20 13.0 N
5 47.5	20 55.8 N	+0.16	5 48.1	20 53.1 N	25	5 48.0	20 50.5 N	+0.11	5 48.4	20 47.7 N
5 42.6	21 26.6 N	+0.11	5 43.2	21 24.2 N	28	5 43.2	21 21.8 N	+0.08	5 43.8	21 19.3 N
					JUNE					
5 34.5	22 02.4 N	+0.04	5 35.1	22 00.4 N	1	5 35.2	21 58.3 N	+0.04	5 36.0	21 56.2 N
5 27.4	22 25.3 N	+0.02	5 27.9	22 23.5 N	4	5 28.2	22 21.7 N	+0.01	5 28.9	22 19.9 N
5 19.4	22 44.6 N	+0.02	5 19.9	22 43.1 N	7	5 20.4	22 41.4 N	−0.02	5 21.1	22 40.1 N
5 10.7	23 00.3 N	+0.04	5 11.3	22 59.1 N	10	5 11.9	22 57.9 N	−0.05	5 12.5	22 56.7 N
5 01.5	23 12.4 N	+0.07	5 02.3	23 11.5 N	13	5 02.9	23 10.6 N	−0.08	5 03.4	23 09.7 N
4 51.9	23 20.8 N	+0.09	4 52.8	23 20.2 N	16	4 53.4	23 19.6 N	−0.12	4 53.9	23 19.0 N
4 42.1	23 25.5 N	+0.08	4 43.2	23 25.3 N	19	4 43.6	23 24.9 N	−0.15	4 44.2	23 24.6 N
4 32.4	23 26.5 N	+0.06	4 33.4	23 26.6 N	22	4 33.7	23 26.5 N	−0.18	4 34.5	23 26.5 N
4 22.8	23 23.8 N	+0.01	4 23.8	23 24.1 N	25	4 24.0	23 24.4 N	−0.22	4 24.8	23 24.6 N
4 13.4	23 17.4 N	−0.03	4 14.3	23 18.0 N	28	4 14.5	23 18.5 N	−0.25	4 15.4	23 19.1 N

SUN

0 GHA −175°	0 Dec.	Quad. GHA Corr.	1 GHA −175°	1 Dec.	Date	2 GHA −175°	2 Dec.	Quad. Dec. Corr.	3 GHA −175°	3 Dec.
					JULY					
4 04.5	23 07.3 N	− 0.06	4 05.2	23 08.2 N	1	4 05.4	23 09.0 N	− 0.28	4 06.3	23 09.9 N
3 56.1	22 53.5 N	− 0.07	3 56.6	22 54.7 N	4	3 57.0	22 55.8 N	− 0.31	3 57.7	22 57.0 N
3 48.4	22 36.2 N	− 0.05	3 48.8	22 37.6 N	7	3 49.2	22 39.1 N	− 0.34	3 49.8	22 40.5 N
3 41.5	22 15.3 N	− 0.01	3 41.9	22 17.1 N	10	3 42.3	22 18.8 N	− 0.37	3 42.7	22 20.5 N
3 35.5	21 51.0 N	+ 0.03	3 36.0	21 53.0 N	13	3 36.2	21 55.0 N	− 0.39	3 36.4	21 57.0 N
3 30.6	21 23.3 N	+ 0.05	3 31.1	21 25.7 N	16	3 31.1	21 27.9 N	− 0.41	3 31.3	21 30.1 N
3 26.9	20 52.4 N	+ 0.06	3 27.4	20 55.0 N	19	3 27.2	20 57.5 N	− 0.44	3 27.4	21 00.0 N
3 24.5	20 18.3 N	+ 0.04	3 24.9	20 21.2 N	22	3 24.5	20 23.8 N	− 0.47	3 24.7	20 26.6 N
3 23.4	19 41.1 N	+ 0.01	3 23.6	19 44.2 N	25	3 23.0	19 47.1 N	− 0.50	3 23.3	19 50.2 N
3 23.6	19 01.0 N	− 0.02	3 23.6	19 04.3 N	28	3 23.0	19 07.5 N	− 0.54	3 23.1	19 10.8 N
					AUGUST					
3 26.0	18 03.2 N	− 0.03	3 25.6	18 06.8 N	1	3 25.1	18 10.3 N	− 0.57	3 25.1	18 13.9 N
3 29.3	17 16.7 N	− 0.02	3 28.8	17 20.5 N	4	3 28.2	17 24.2 N	− 0.59	3 28.0	17 28.0 N
3 33.9	16 27.7 N	+ 0.02	3 33.4	16 31.6 N	7	3 32.8	16 35.6 N	− 0.60	3 32.3	16 39.6 N
3 39.9	15 36.3 N	+ 0.06	3 39.3	15 40.4 N	10	3 38.6	15 44.6 N	− 0.60	3 38.0	15 48.7 N
3 47.1	14 42.6 N	+ 0.09	3 46.5	14 47.0 N	13	3 45.7	14 51.3 N	− 0.61	3 44.9	14 55.6 N
3 55.7	13 46.8 N	+ 0.11	3 55.0	13 51.4 N	16	3 54.0	13 55.8 N	− 0.62	3 53.2	14 00.3 N
4 05.4	12 49.1 N	+ 0.11	4 04.7	12 53.9 N	19	4 03.4	12 58.4 N	− 0.64	4 02.7	13 03.1 N
4 16.2	11 49.6 N	+ 0.09	4 15.4	11 54.5 N	22	4 14.0	11 59.1 N	− 0.66	4 13.3	12 04.0 N
4 28.1	10 48.4 N	+ 0.06	4 27.2	10 53.3 N	25	4 25.7	10 58.1 N	− 0.68	4 24.9	11 03.2 N
4 40.9	9 45.6 N	+ 0.03	4 39.8	9 50.6 N	28	4 38.3	9 55.6 N	− 0.70	4 37.5	10 00.8 N
					SEPTEMBER					
4 59.2	8 19.8 N	+ 0.02	4 57.9	8 24.9 N	1	4 56.5	8 30.0 N	− 0.71	4 55.6	8 35.4 N
5 13.7	7 13.9 N	+ 0.04	5 12.3	7 19.2 N	4	5 10.9	7 24.4 N	− 0.70	5 09.9	7 29.8 N
5 28.7	6 07.0 N	+ 0.08	5 27.3	6 12.4 N	7	5 26.0	6 17.8 N	− 0.69	5 24.7	6 23.2 N
5 44.1	4 59.2 N	+ 0.11	5 42.8	5 04.7 N	10	5 41.4	5 10.1 N	− 0.68	5 40.1	5 15.6 N
5 59.9	3 50.7 N	+ 0.13	5 58.6	3 56.2 N	13	5 57.1	4 01.7 N	− 0.67	5 55.8	4 07.2 N
6 15.8	2 41.5 N	+ 0.13	6 14.7	2 47.1 N	16	6 13.0	2 52.6 N	− 0.67	6 11.7	2 58.2 N
6 31.9	1 31.9 N	+ 0.11	6 30.7	1 37.5 N	19	6 29.0	1 43.0 N	− 0.68	6 27.8	1 48.7 N
6 47.9	0 21.9 N	+ 0.08	6 46.6	0 27.6 N	22	6 44.9	0 33.1 N	− 0.68	6 43.8	0 38.8 N
7 03.6	0 48.1 S	+ 0.04	7 02.3	0 42.5 S	25	7 00.6	0 37.0 S	+ 0.69	6 59.6	0 31.2 S
7 19.0	1 58.3 S	+ 0.01	7 17.6	1 52.7 S	28	7 16.1	1 47.1 S	+ 0.68	7 15.1	1 41.3 S
					OCTOBER					
7 33.8	3 08.2 S	0.00	7 32.4	3 02.7 S	1	7 31.0	2 57.1 S	+ 0.67	7 30.0	2 51.4 S
7 48.0	4 17.9 S	+ 0.02	7 46.6	4 12.4 S	4	7 45.4	4 06.8 S	+ 0.65	7 44.3	4 01.2 S
8 01.3	5 27.2 S	+ 0.05	8 00.1	5 21.7 S	7	7 59.0	5 16.1 S	+ 0.62	7 57.9	5 10.5 S
8 13.7	6 35.8 S	+ 0.07	8 12.7	6 30.3 S	10	8 11.6	6 24.8 S	+ 0.60	8 10.5	6 19.3 S
8 25.1	7 43.6 S	+ 0.08	8 24.3	7 38.1 S	13	8 23.2	7 32.8 S	+ 0.57	8 22.2	7 27.3 S
8 35.4	8 50.5 S	+ 0.07	8 34.7	8 45.0 S	16	8 33.6	8 39.8 S	+ 0.56	8 32.8	8 34.4 S
8 44.4	9 56.2 S	+ 0.04	8 43.8	9 50.9 S	19	8 42.8	9 45.7 S	+ 0.54	8 42.2	9 40.3 S
8 52.0	11 00.6 S	− 0.01	8 51.5	10 55.4 S	22	8 50.5	10 50.3 S	+ 0.53	8 50.1	10 45.0 S
8 58.1	12 03.5 S	− 0.05	8 57.6	11 58.5 S	25	8 56.9	11 53.5 S	+ 0.52	8 56.6	11 48.3 S
9 02.6	13 04.7 S	− 0.08	9 02.1	12 59.9 S	28	9 01.6	12 55.0 S	+ 0.50	9 01.5	12 50.0 S
					NOVEMBER					
9 05.8	14 23.5 S	− 0.09	9 05.5	14 18.9 S	1	9 05.4	14 14.2 S	+ 0.46	9 05.3	14 09.4 S
9 06.1	15 20.3 S	− 0.07	9 06.0	15 15.8 S	4	9 06.1	15 11.2 S	+ 0.42	9 06.0	15 06.6 S
9 04.6	16 14.7 S	− 0.04	9 04.7	16 10.4 S	7	9 05.0	16 06.0 S	+ 0.38	9 04.9	16 01.6 S
9 01.1	17 06.7 S	− 0.03	9 01.6	17 02.5 S	10	9 01.9	16 58.4 S	+ 0.35	9 02.0	16 54.2 S
8 55.8	17 56.1 S	− 0.03	8 56.5	17 52.1 S	13	8 56.9	17 48.2 S	+ 0.31	8 57.2	17 44.2 S
8 48.6	18 42.6 S	− 0.05	8 49.5	18 38.8 S	16	8 49.9	18 35.2 S	+ 0.28	8 50.5	18 31.4 S
8 39.6	19 26.1 S	− 0.09	8 40.6	19 22.7 S	19	8 41.1	19 19.2 S	+ 0.25	8 41.9	19 15.7 S
8 28.7	20 06.5 S	− 0.14	8 29.8	20 03.3 S	22	8 30.5	20 00.1 S	+ 0.22	8 31.5	19 56.9 S
8 16.1	20 43.6 S	− 0.18	8 17.2	20 40.7 S	25	8 18.1	20 37.8 S	+ 0.19	8 19.3	20 34.8 S
8 01.7	21 17.2 S	− 0.20	8 02.8	21 14.6 S	28	8 04.1	21 11.9 S	+ 0.16	8 05.3	21 09.3 S
					DECEMBER					
7 45.6	21 47.3 S	− 0.18	7 46.9	21 44.9 S	1	7 48.4	21 42.5 S	+ 0.12	7 49.6	21 40.1 S
7 28.1	22 13.5 S	− 0.15	7 29.6	22 11.5 S	4	7 31.3	22 09.4 S	+ 0.08	7 32.5	22 07.3 S
7 09.3	22 35.9 S	− 0.11	7 11.0	22 34.2 S	7	7 12.8	22 32.4 S	+ 0.04	7 13.9	22 30.6 S
6 49.3	22 54.3 S	− 0.09	6 51.3	22 52.9 S	10	6 53.0	22 51.4 S	0.00	6 54.3	22 50.0 S
6 28.5	23 08.6 S	− 0.08	6 30.6	23 07.6 S	13	6 32.3	23 06.4 S	− 0.04	6 33.7	23 05.3 S
6 06.9	23 18.8 S	− 0.09	6 09.1	23 18.1 S	16	6 10.8	23 17.3 S	− 0.08	6 12.4	23 16.5 S
5 44.9	23 24.8 S	− 0.12	5 47.1	23 24.4 S	19	5 48.8	23 24.0 S	− 0.12	5 50.5	23 23.6 S
5 22.6	23 26.6 S	− 0.15	5 24.7	23 26.6 S	22	5 26.5	23 26.5 S	− 0.16	5 28.3	23 26.4 S
5 00.2	23 24.1 S	− 0.17	5 02.2	23 24.4 S	25	5 04.1	23 24.7 S	− 0.19	5 05.9	23 25.0 S
4 38.0	23 17.5 S	− 0.17	4 39.9	23 18.1 S	28	4 41.9	23 18.7 S	− 0.23	4 43.6	23 19.3 S

STARS

SHA (1972.0)	Annual Corr.	Star	Dec. (1972.0)	Annual Corr.
° '	'		° '	'
315 42.0	− 0.57	Acamar	40 25.0 S	− 0.24
335 49.9	− 0.56	Achernar	57 22.7 S	− 0.30
173 44.6	− 0.84	Acrux	62 56.6 S	+ 0.33
291 25.3	− 0.86	Aldebaran	16 27.2 N	+ 0.12
153 23.4	− 0.59	Alkaid	49 27.2 N	− 0.30
218 26.8	− 0.74	Alphard	8 32.2 S	+ 0.26
126 37.5	− 0.64	Alphecca	26 48.5 N	− 0.20
358 16.0	− 0.78	Alpheratz	28 56.2 N	+ 0.33
62 38.7	− 0.73	Altair	8 47.6 N	+ 0.16
113 04.7	− 0.92	Antares	26 22.3 S	+ 0.13
146 24.2	− 0.68	Arcturus	19 19.6 N	− 0.31
108 34.7	− 1.59	Atria	68 58.7 S	+ 0.11
271 35.2	− 0.81	Betelgeuse	7 24.2 N	+ 0.01
264 10.0	− 0.33	Canopus	52 40.8 S	+ 0.03
281 20.7	− 1.11	Capella	45 58.3 N	+ 0.06
49 52.9	− 0.51	Deneb	45 10.8 N	+ 0.22
183 05.5	− 0.76	Denebola	14 43.7 N	− 0.34
349 27.2	− 0.75	Diphda	18 08.4 S	− 0.33
194 29.8	− 0.92	Dubhe	61 54.2 N	− 0.32
34 17.8	− 0.74	Enif	9 44.8 N	+ 0.28
15 58.4	− 0.83	Fomalhaut	29 46.3 S	− 0.32
328 36.2	− 0.85	Hamal	23 19.8 N	+ 0.28
137 18.4	+ 0.04	Kochab	74 16.2 N	− 0.25
148 44.6	− 0.88	Menkent	36 14.0 S	+ 0.29
309 25.3	− 1.07	Mirfak	49 45.8 N	+ 0.21
76 37.1	− 0.93	Nunki	26 20.0 S	− 0.08
54 08.4	− 1.18	Peacock	56 49.6 S	− 0.19
244 05.9	− 0.92	Pollux	28 05.7 N	− 0.15
245 32.4	− 0.78	Procyon	5 17.9 N	− 0.16
96 35.5	− 0.70	Rasalhague	12 34.8 N	− 0.04
208 16.8	− 0.80	Regulus	12 06.3 N	− 0.29
281 42.1	− 0.72	Rigel	8 14.0 S	− 0.07
140 41.5	− 1.02	Rigil Kent.	60 43.2 S	+ 0.25
350 16.4	− 0.86	Schedar	56 23.0 N	+ 0.33
259 01.3	− 0.66	Sirius	16 40.6 S	+ 0.08
159 04.3	− 0.79	Spica	11 01.0 S	+ 0.31
223 15.5	− 0.55	Suhail	43 19.1 S	+ 0.24
81 00.2	− 0.51	Vega	38 45.4 N	+ 0.06

MULTIPLICATION TABLE

No.	A	B	C	D	E	F	G
	°	° '	'	'	° '	° '	° '
1	15	0 15	0.2	1.8	0 59.1	15 02.5	0 15.0
2	30	0 30	0.5	3.7	1 58.3	30 04.9	0 30.1
3	45	0 45	0.8	5.5	2 57.4	45 07.4	0 45.1
4	60	1 00	1.0	7.4	3 56.6	60 09.9	1 00.2
5	75	1 15	1.2	9.2	4 55.7	75 12.3	1 15.2
6	90	1 30	1.5	11.0	5 54.8	90 14.8	1 30.2
7	105	1 45	1.8	12.9	6 54.0	105 17.2	1 45.3
8	120	2 00	2.0	14.7	7 53.1	120 19.7	2 00.3
9	135	2 15	2.2	16.6	8 52.3	135 22.2	2 15.4
10	150	2 30	2.5	18.4	9 51.4	150 24.6	2 30.4
11	165	2 45	2.8	20.2	10 50.5	165 27.1	2 45.5
12	180	3 00	3.0	22.1	11 49.7	180 29.6	3 00.5
13	195	3 15	3.2	23.9	12 48.8	195 32.0	3 15.5
14	210	3 30	3.5	25.8	13 48.0	210 34.5	3 30.6
15	225	3 45	3.8	27.6	14 47.1	225 37.0	3 45.6
16	240	4 00	4.0	29.4	15 46.2	240 39.4	4 00.7
17	255	4 15	4.2	31.3	16 45.4	255 41.9	4 15.7
18	270	4 30	4.5	33.1	17 44.5	270 44.4	4 30.7
19	285	4 45	4.8	35.0	18 43.7	285 46.8	4 45.8
20	300	5 00	5.0	36.8	19 42.8	300 49.3	5 00.8
21	315	5 15	5.2	38.6	20 41.9	315 51.7	5 15.9
22	330	5 30	5.5	40.5	21 41.1	330 54.2	5 30.9
23	345	5 45	5.8	42.3	22 40.2	345 56.7	5 45.9
24	360	6 00	6.0	44.2	23 39.4	360 59.1	6 01.0
25	—	6 15	6.2	46.0	24 38.5		6 16.0
26	—	6 30	6.5	47.8	25 37.6	—	6 31.1
27	—	6 45	6.8	49.7	26 36.8	—	6 46.1
28	—	7 00	7.0	51.5	27 35.9	—	7 01.1
29	—	7 15	7.2	53.4	28 35.1	—	7 16.2
30	—	7 30	7.5	55.2	29 34.2	—	7 31.2
31	—	7 45	7.8	57.0	30 33.3	—	7 46.3
32	—	8 00	8.0	58.9	—	—	8 01.3
33	—	8 15	8.2	60.7	—	—	8 16.4
34	—	8 30	8.5	62.6	—	—	8 31.4
35	—	8 45	8.8	64.4	—	—	8 46.4
36	—	9 00	9.0	66.2	—	—	9 01.5
37	—	9 15	9.2	68.1	—	—	9 16.5
38	—	9 30	9.5	69.9	—	—	9 31.6
39	—	9 45	9.8	71.8	—	—	9 46.6
40	—	10 00	10.0	73.6	—	—	10 01.6
41	—	10 15	10.2	75.4	—	—	10 16.7
42	—	10 30	10.5	77.3	—	—	10 31.7
43	—	10 45	10.8	79.1	—	—	10 46.8
44	—	11 00	11.0	81.0	—	—	11 01.8
45	—	11 15	11.2	82.8	—	—	11 16.8
46	—	11 30	11.5	84.6	—	—	11 31.9
47	—	11 45	11.8	86.5	—	—	11 46.9
48	—	12 00	12.0	88.3	—	—	12 02.0
49	—	12 15	12.2	90.2	—	—	12 17.0
50	—	12 30	12.5	92.0	—	—	12 32.1
51	—	12 45	12.8	93.8	—	—	12 47.1
52	—	13 00	13.0	95.7	—	—	13 02.1
53	—	13 15	13.2	97.5	—	—	13 17.2
54	—	13 30	13.5	99.4	—	—	13 32.2
55	—	13 45	13.8	—	—	—	13 47.3
56	—	14 00	14.0	—	—	—	14 02.3
57	—	14 15	14.2	—	—	—	14 17.3
58	—	14 30	14.5	—	—	—	14 32.4
59	—	14 45	14.8	—	—	—	14 47.4
60	—	15 00	15.0	—	—	—	15 02.5

ARIES (♈)

0	1	Month	2	3
° '	° '		° '	° '
98 46.2	99 31.0	Jan.	99 16.7	99 02.4
129 19.5	130 04.4	Feb.	129 50.1	129 35.7
157 54.5	157 40.3	Mar.	157 25.9	157 11.6
188 27.8	188 13.5	Apr.	187 59.2	187 44.9
218 02.0	217 47.7	May	217 33.4	217 19.0
248 35.3	248 21.0	June	248 06.7	247 52.3
278 09.5	277 55.2	July	277 40.9	277 26.5
308 42.8	308 28.5	Aug.	308 14.2	307 59.8
339 16.1	339 01.8	Sept.	338 47.5	338 33.1
8 50.3	8 36.0	Oct.	8 21.6	8 07.3
39 23.6	39 09.2	Nov.	38 54.9	38 40.6
68 57.7	68 43.4	Dec.	68 29.1	68 14.7

DECIMAL PARTS OF DAY AND YEAR

Decimal	0.0	0.1	0.2	0.3	0.4	0.5	0.6	0.7	0.8	0.9	1.0
Hour of Day	0000 to 0112	0112 to 0336	0336 to 0600	0600 to 0824	0824 to 1048	1048 to 1312	1312 to 1536	1536 to 1800	1800 to 2024	2024 to 2248	2248 to 2400
Day of Year	Jan. 1 to Jan. 18	Jan. 19 to Feb. 23	Feb. 24 to Apr. 1	Apr 2 to May 7	May 8 to June 13	June 14 to July 19	July 20 to Aug. 25	Aug. 26 to Sept. 30	Oct. 1 to Nov. 6	Nov. 7 to Dec. 12	Dec. 13 to Dec. 31

APPENDIX I

IDENTIFICATION OF NAVIGATIONAL STARS

Introduction.—The following summary is not intended as a substitute for a star finder such as No. 2102–D, or of a knowledge of the heavens, but is given as a supplementary reference to assist in locating the 57 stars included in the main listing in the *Nautical Almanac*, plus Polaris. The observer is assumed to be at about the average latitude of the United States, unless another latitude is indicated. If a celestial body is said to be *east* of another, it is lower in the sky if both are rising and higher if both are setting. A body *north* of another is nearer the north celestial pole. Directions refer to great circles on the celestial sphere. Figures referred to are the star charts of chapter XXII, which should be of assistance in interpreting the descriptions given. It is assumed the reader is familiar with such well-known configurations as the Big Dipper and *Orion*. Constellation names are given in *italics*.

Acamar crosses the celestial meridian near the southern horizon during evening twilight in February, and during morning twilight in August. It is part of the constellation *Eridanus*, the river, which is not a striking configuration. It is the faintest star listed among the 57 in the almanac, but is the brightest in its immediate vicinity. The nearest bright star is Achernar, about 20° away in a generally southwesterly direction. Dec. 40°S, SHA 316°, mag. 3.1. Fig. 2205.

Achernar, at the southern end of the inconspicuous constellation *Eridanus*, the river, is one of the brightest stars of the Southern Hemisphere. It is not visible north of latitude 33°N. It crosses the celestial meridian during evening twilight in January, and during morning twilight in early August. Nearly a straight line is formed by Fomalhaut, about 40° WNW; Achernar; and Canopus, about the same distance in the opposite direction. However, since these stars are widely separated, the relationship is not striking. Achernar forms large triangles with Acamar and Ankaa, Ankaa and Al Na'ir, and with Al Na'ir and Peacock. Dec. 57°S, SHA 336°, mag. 0.6. Fig. 2205.

Acrux is the brightest and most southerly star in the famed Southern Cross. It is not visible north of latitude 27°N. It crosses the celestial meridian during evening twilight in early June and during morning twilight in January. It is about 15° WSW of first magnitude Hadar and Rigil Kentaurus. Dec. 63°S, SHA 174°, mag. 1.1. Fig. 2207.

Adhara. About 10° S and a little to the east of Sirius is a small, approximately equilateral triangle of three second magnitude stars. Adhara is the westernmost and brightest of the three. It crosses the celestial meridian to the south during evening twilight in March, and during morning twilight in October. Dec. 29°S, SHA 256°, mag. 1.6. Fig. 2206.

Aldebaran. If the line formed by the belt of *Orion*, the hunter, is extended about 20° to the northwestward, and curved somewhat toward the north, it leads to first magnitude Aldebaran in *Taurus*, the bull. This is a group of stars forming a V. A long, curving line starting at Sirius extends through Procyon, Pollux, Capella, and Aldebaran. Dec. 16°N, SHA 291°, mag. 1.1. Fig. 2206.

Alioth is the third star from the outer end of the handle of the Big Dipper, and the brightest star of the group. Dec. 56°N, SHA 167°, mag. 1.7. Fig. 2207.

1170

Alkaid is the star at the outer end of the handle of the Big Dipper, farthest from the bowl. It is the second brightest star of the group. Dec. 49°N, SHA 153°, mag. 1.9. Fig. 2207.

Al Na'ir is the westernmost of two second magnitude stars of nearly equal brightness about midway between first magnitude Fomalhaut, approximately 20° to the northeast, and second mangitude Peacock, about the same distance in the opposite direction. A curved line extending eastward from the Southern Cross passes through Hadar and Rigil Kentaurus and, if extended with less curvature, leads first to Peacock and then to Al Na'ir. This star forms triangles with Fomalhaut and Ankaa, Ankaa and Achernar, and with Achernar and Peacock. It is not visible north of latitude 43°N. It crosses the celestial meridan during evening twilight early in December, and during morning twilight in June. Dec. 47°S, SHA 28°, mag. 2.2. Figs. 2205, 2208.

Alnilam is the middle star of the belt of *Orion*, the hunter. Dec. 1°S, SHA 276°, mag. 1.8. Fig. 2206.

Alphard, a second magnitude star, is the brightest in the inconspicuous constellation *Hydra*, the water monster. The nearest bright star is first magnitude Regulus, about 20° NNE. It is about midway between the horizon and zenith when it crosses the celestial meridian to the southward during evening twilight in late April, and during morning twilight in November. Dec. 9°S, SHA 218°, mag. 2.2. Fig. 2207.

Alphecca is the brightest star of *Corona Borealis*, the Northern Crown, about 20° ENE of first magnitude Arcturus. It forms a triangle with Arcturus and Alkaid. It crosses the celestial meridian near the zenith during evening twilight in July, and during morning twilight in February. Dec. 27°N, SHA 127°, mag. 2.3. Figs. 2207, 2208.

Alpheratz, a second magnitude star, is at the northeast corner of the great square of *Pegasus*, the winged horse, and is the brightest of the four stars forming the square. It crosses the celestial meridian near the zenith during evening twilight early in January, and during morning twilight in July. Dec. 29°N, SHA 358°, mag. 2.2. Fig. 2205.

Altair is at the southern vertex of a large, nearly right triangle which is a conspicuous feature of the evening sky in late summer and in autumn. The right angle is at Vega and the northern vertex is at Deneb. All three are first magnitude stars. Two fainter stars close to Altair, one on each side in a line through Vega, form a characteristic pattern making Altair one of the easiest stars to identify. It crosses the celestial meridian during evening twilight in October, and during morning twilight in May. Dec. 9°N, SHA 63°, mag. 0.9. Fig. 2208.

Ankaa, a second magnitude star, is the brightest star in inconspicuous *Phoenix*. It is surrounded by and forms a series of triangles with Diphda, Fomalhaut, Al Na'ir, Achernar, and Acamar. It crosses the celestial meridian low in the southern sky in January, and during morning twilight in July. Dec. 42°S, SHA 354°, mag. 2.4. Fig. 2205.

Antares is the brightest star in the conspicuous constellation *Scorpio*, the scorpion, which is low in the southern sky during evening twilight in late July, and morning twilight in late February. No other first magnitude star is within 40° of Antares and none toward the north is within 60°. It has a noticeable reddish hue and in appearance somewhat resembles Mars, which is occasionally near it in the sky. Dec. 26°S, SHA 113°, mag. 1.2. Fig. 2208.

Arcturus. The curved line along the stars forming the handle of the Big Dipper, if continued in a direction away from the bowl, passes through brilliant, first magnitude Arcturus. The distance from Alkaid, at the end of the Big Dipper, to Arcturus is a little more than the length of the dipper. Arcturus forms a large triangle with Alkaid and Alphecca. Dec. 19°N, SHA 146°, mag. 0.2. Figs. 2207, 2208.

Atria is the brightest of three stars forming a small triangle called *Triangulum Australe*, the southern triangle, not far from the south celestial pole. It is not seen north of latitude 21°N. A line through the east-west arm of the Southern Cross, if continued toward the east and curved somewhat toward the south, leads first to Hadar, then to Rigil Kentaurus, then, by curving more sharply, to the northernmost star of the triangle, and finally to Atria, only about 21° from the south celestial pole. Dec. 69°S, SHA 108°, mag. 1.9. Fig. 2207.

Avior is the westernmost star of *Vela*, the sails, or false southern cross, about 30° WNW of the true Southern Cross, about 15° ESE of the brilliant Canopus, and nearly enclosed within a large triangle formed by Canopus, Suhail, and Miaplacidus. It is not visible north of latitude 31°N. Below this, it crosses the celestial meridian low in the southern sky during evening twilight in April, and morning twilight in early November. Dec. 59°S, SHA 234°, mag. 1.7. Figs. 2206, 2207.

Bellatrix is a second magnitude star north and a little west of the belt of *Orion*, the hunter. It is about equidistant from the belt and first magnitude, red Betelgeuse. Bellatrix is at the northwest corner of a box surrounding the belt of *Orion*. Dec. 6°N, SHA 279°, mag. 1.7. Fig. 2206.

Betelgeuse is a conspicuous, reddish star of variable brightness about 10° north and a little east of the belt of *Orion*, the hunter. A line through the center of the belt and perpendicular to it passes close to red Betelgeuse to the north and blue Rigel about the same distance south of the belt. Betelgeuse and Rigel are at opposite corners of a box surrounding the belt of *Orion*. Dec. 7°N, SHA 272°, mag. 0.1–1.2 (variable). Fig. 2206.

Canopus, second brightest star in the sky, is about 35° south of Sirius. A line extending eastward through the belt of *Orion* and curving toward the south passes first through Sirius, then through the small triangle of which Adhara is the brightest star, and finally to Canopus, which forms a large, almost equilateral triangle with Suhail and Miaplacidus. This triangle nearly encloses *Vela*, the sails or false southern cross, about 20° ESE of Canopus. Canopus is not visible north of latitude 37°N. It is on the edge of the Milky Way and while many relatively bright stars are nearby, none in the immediate vicinity of Canopus approaches it in brightness. Dec. 53°S, SHA 264°, mag. (−)0.9. Fig. 2206.

Capella is a brilliant star about 45° north of the belt of *Orion*, the hunter. A curved line starting at Sirius and extending through Procyon, Pollux, Capella, Aldebaran, the belt of *Orion*, and back to Sirius forms an inverted tear-drop figure with Capella at the top and the various parts being about equally spaced along the curve. Capella crosses the celestial meridian near the zenith during evening twilight in early March, and during morning twilight in late September. Dec. 46°N, SHA 281°, mag. 0.2. Fig. 2206.

Deneb is a bright star at the northeastern vertex of a large, nearly right triangle formed by Altair, Vega, and Deneb, the right angle being at Vega. These three stars are the brightest in the eastern sky during summer evenings. Deneb is not as bright as the other two, but is the brightest star in the constellation *Cygnus*, the swan. It crosses the celestial meridian near the zenith during evening twilight in November, and during morning twilight in late May. Dec. 45°N, SHA 50°, mag. 1.3. Fig. 2208.

Denebola, in *Leo*, the lion, is a second magnitude star at the opposite end of the constellation from Regulus. A straight line from Regulus, on the west, to Arcturus, on the east, passes close to Denebola, which is somewhat nearer Regulus. Denebola crosses the celestial meridian to the south during evening twilight in May, and during morning twilight in December. Dec. 15°N, SHA 183°, mag. 2.2. Fig 2207.

Diphda. A line extending southward through the eastern side of the great square of *Pegasus*, the winged horse, and curving slightly toward the east, leads to second magnitude Diphda. The distance from the southern star of *Pegasus* to Diphda is about twice the length of one side of the square. Diphda is part of the inconspicuous constellation *Cetus*, the whale. The only nearby first magnitude star is Fomalhaut, about 25° in a generally southwest direction. Diphda, Fomalhaut, and Ankaa form a nearly equilateral triangle. Dec. 18°S, SHA 349°, mag. 2.2. Fig. 2205.

Dubhe forms the outer rim of the bowl of the Big Dipper. It and Merak (not one of the 57 navigational stars) are the two "pointers" used to locate Polaris, Dubhe being the one nearer the Pole Star. Dec. 62°N, SHA 194°, mag. 2.0. Fig. 2207.

Elnath is a second magnitude star between Capella, about 15° to the north, and Betelgeuse, about 20° to the south. It is a little north of a line connecting Aldebaran and Pollux. It is at the end of the northern fork of V-shaped *Taurus*, the bull. Aldebaran is the principal star at the closed end of the V. This constellation is approximately 25° NNW of *Orion*, the hunter. Dec. 29°N, SHA 279°, mag. 1.8. Fig. 2206.

Eltanin is the southernmost and brightest star in the inconspicuous constellation *Draco*, the dragon, south and somewhat east of the Little Dipper. A straight line extending northwestward through Altair and its two fainter companions passes first through brilliant Vega, and, about 15° beyond, to second magnitude Eltanin. Eltanin crosses the celestial meridian high in the sky toward the north during evening twilight in early September, and during morning twilight in late March. Dec. 15°N, SHA 91°, mag. 2.4. Fig. 2208.

Enif is a third magnitude star approximately midway between Altair, about 25° west, and Markab, about 20° ENE. From Markab, at the southwestern corner of the great square of *Pegasus*, the winged horse, a line extending in a generally west-southwesterly direction passes through two almost equally spaced fourth magnitude stars. From the second of these, a line about 5° long extending in a northwesterly direction leads to Enif. Enif crosses the celestial meridian to the south during evening twilight in November, and during morning twilight in June. Dec. 10°N, SHA 34°, mag. 2.5. Figs. 2205, 2208.

Fomalhaut is a first magnitude star well separated from stars of comparable brightness and from conspicuous configurations. A line through the western side of the great square of *Pegasus*, the winged horse, and extended about 45° toward the south passes close to Fomalhaut, which forms two large, nearly equilateral triangles with Diphda and Ankaa and with Ankaa and Al Na'ir. Dec. 30°S, SHA 16°, mag. 1.3. Fig. 2205.

Gacrux is the northernmost star of the Southern Cross. It is bright for a second magnitude star, but its brilliance is overshadowed by the brighter β *Crucis* (not listed among the 57 navigational stars) and Acrux, the two brightest stars of the Southern Cross, and by Hadar and Rigil Kentaurus, about 15° ESE. Gacrux crosses the celestial meridian during evening twilight in early June, and during morning twilight in late December, but is not visible north of latitude 33°N. Dec. 57°S, SHA 173°, mag. 1.6. Fig. 2207.

Gienah is a third magnitude star, the brightest in the constellation *Corvus*, the crow. A long, sweeping arc starting with the handle of the Big Dipper and extending successively through Arcturus and Spica leads to this relatively small, four-sided figure made up of third magnitude stars. Gienah is at the northwest corner. It crosses the celestial meridian during evening twilight in late May, and during morning twilight in December. Dec. 17°S, SHA 176°, mag. 2.8. Fig. 2207.

Hadar is a first magnitude star about 10° east of the Southern Cross, and about 5° west of Rigil Kentaurus, the brightest of several bright stars in this part of the sky. Dec. 60°S, SHA 149°, mag. 0.9. Fig. 2207.

Hamal is the brightest star of the inconspicuous constellation *Aries*, the ram. A line through the center of the great square of *Pegasus*, the winged horse, extended about 25° east, and curved slightly toward the north, leads to Hamal. It is over the meridian to the south during evening twilight in January, and during morning twilight in August. Dec. 23°N, SHA 329°, mag. 2.2. Fig. 2205.

Kaus Australis is near the southern end of a group of second and third magnitude stars forming the constellation *Sagittarius*, the archer, about 25° ESE of Antares, in *Scorpio*, the scorpion. It is about 10° SW of Nunki, also in *Sagittarius*, and about the same distance ENE of Shaula, in *Scorpio*. With Antares, Sabik, and Nunki, it forms a large, poorly defined box. It is over the meridian to the south during evening twilight in September and during morning twilight in April. Dec. 34°S, SHA 84°, mag. 2.0. Fig. 2208.

Kochab forms the outer rim of the bowl of the Little Dipper, at the opposite end from Polaris, about 15° north. It is directly above the pole during evening twilight in early July and during morning twilight in January; and directly below the pole, low in the northern sky, during evening twilight of early February and morning twilight of late August. Dec. 74°N, SHA 137°, mag. 2.2. Fig. 2208.

Markab is the star at the southwest corner of the great square of *Pegasus*, the winged horse, at the opposite corner from Alpheratz. It is over the celestial meridian to the south during evening twilight in December, and during morning twilight late in June. Dec. 15°N, SHA 14°, mag. 2.6. Fig. 2205.

Menkar is a third magnitude star at the eastern end of the inconspicuous constellation *Cetus*, the whale. No bright stars are nearby. A straight line from Aldebaran extending about 25° in the direction indicated by the point of the V of *Taurus*, the bull, leads to Menkar. A long, straight line from Fomalhaut east-northeastward through Diphda, and extended about 40°, leads to Menkar. It crosses the celestial meridian during evening twilight in February, and during morning twilight in August. Dec. 4°N, SHA 315°, mag. 2.8. Figs. 2205, 2206.

Menkent is a second magnitude star about 25° north of Hadar and about 30° northeast of the Southern Cross. A line from Gienah across the opposite corner of the small, four-sided *Corvus*, the crow, and then curving a little toward the east, leads to Menkent. A number of third magnitude stars are nearby, but they do not form a conspicuous configuration. With Antares and Rigil Kentaurus, Menkent forms a large triangle. It crosses the celestial meridian low in the southern sky during evening twilight in late June and during morning twilight in early January. Dec. 36°S, SHA 149°, mag. 2.3. Figs. 2207, 2208.

Miaplacidus is a second magnitude star about 10° south of the false southern cross. It is the nearest of the 57 navigational stars to the south celestial pole, about 20° away, and is not visible north of latitude 20°N. With Suhail and brilliant Canopus it forms a large, nearly equilateral triangle almost enclosing the false southern cross. South of latitude 20°S, it does not set, but circles the south celestial pole in a clockwise direction, reaching its maximum altitude above the pole during evening twilight in early May and during morning twilight in November. Dec. 70°S, SHA 222°, mag. 1.8. Figs. 2206, 2207.

Mirfak is a second magnitude star at the northeastern end of a gently curving line extending in a northeasterly direction from Alpheratz at the northeastern corner of the great square of *Pegasus*, the winged horse, through two other second magnitude stars, Mirach and Almach, not included among the 57 navigational stars. Mirfak is about

25° east and a little south of *Cassiopeia*, and about 20° WNW of Capella. A line from Kochab through Polaris, and curved slightly toward the east, leads to Mirfak. Dec. 50°N, SHA 309°, mag. 1.9. Figs. 2205, 2206.

Nunki is the more northerly of the two brightest stars of a group of second and third magnitude stars forming the constellation *Sagittarius*, the archer, about 30° E of Antares. It is about 10° NE of Kaus Australis, also in *Sagittarius*. With Sabik, Antares, and Kaus Australis, it forms a large, poorly defined box. It is over the meridian to the south during evening twilight in early October and during morning twilight in April. Dec. 26°S, SHA 77°, mag. 2.1. Fig. 2208.

Peacock, the brightest star in the southern constellation of the same name, is not a part of a conspicuous configuration of stars. A curved line extending eastward from the Southern Cross passes through Hadar and Rigil Kentaurus and, if extended with less curvature, leads to Peacock, about 30° southeast of *Scorpio*, the scorpion, and about 20° southwest of Al Na'ir. With Al Na'ir and Achernar it forms a large, poorly defined triangle. It crosses the celestial meridian during evening twilight in early November, and during morning twilight in late May, but is not visible north of latitude 33°N. Dec. 57°S, SHA 54°, mag. 2.1. Figs. 2205, 2208.

Polaris is not listed among the 57 navigational stars, but is treated separately because it is less than 1° from the north celestial pole. It is about midway between the Big Dipper and *Cassiopeia*. A line through Dubhe and Merak (not one of the 57 navigational stars), the pointers forming the outer side of the bowl of the Big Dipper, if extended northward for about 30°, leads almost directly to Polaris. A line extending north from Alpheratz at the northwest corner of the great square of *Pegasus*, the winged horse, passes through Caph (not one of the 57 navigational stars) in *Cassiopeia* and then Polaris at about equal intervals. Dec. 89°N, SHA 328°, mag. 2.1. Figs. 2205–2208.

Pollux is the brighter of the "twins of *Gemini*," two relatively bright stars about 45° NE of *Orion*, the hunter, and about 45° ENE of Aldebaran. A curved line starting at Sirius extends through Procyon, Pollux, and Capella, all first magnitude stars. Dec. 28°N, SHA 244°, mag. 1.2. Fig. 2206.

Procyon is a bright star about 30° east of *Orion*, the hunter. A curved line starting at Sirius extends through Procyon, Pollux, and Capella, all first magnitude stars. Dec. 5°N, SHA 245°, mag. 0.5. Fig. 2206.

Rasalhague forms a large, nearly equilateral triangle with Altair and Vega, Rasalhague being at the western vertex. Both of the other stars are considerably brighter than Rasalhague. It crosses the celestial meridian to the south during evening twilight in early September, and during morning twilight in late March. Dec. 13°N, SHA 97°, mag. 2.1. Fig. 2208.

Regulus is at the opposite end of *Leo*, the lion, from Denebola, and is the brightest star of the constellation. A line through Dubhe and Merak (not one of the 57 navigational stars), the pointers by which Polaris is usually identified, extended about 45° *southward*, and curved slightly toward the west, leads to Regulus, which forms the southern end of the handle of the Sickle, part of *Leo*. Dec. 12°N, SHA 208°, mag. 1.3. Fig. 2207.

Rigel is a brilliant bluish star about 10°S and a little to the west of the belt of *Orion*, the hunter. A line through the center of the belt and perpendicular to it passes close to blue Rigel to the south and red Betelgeuse about the same distance north of the belt. Rigel and Betelgeuse are at opposite corners of a box surrounding the belt of *Orion*. Dec. 8°S, SHA 282°, mag. 0.3. Fig. 2206.

Rigil Kentaurus is the brighter and more easterly of two first magnitude stars about 15° east of the Southern Cross. It is over the meridian during evening twilight in early

July, and during morning twilight in late January, but is not visible north of latitude 29°N. Dec. 61°S, SHA 141°, mag. 0.1. Figs 2207, 2208.

Sabik is part of the inconspicuous constellation *Ophiuchus*, the serpent holder, about 20° north of *Scorpio*, the scorpion. With Antares, Kaus Australis, and Nunki, it forms a large, poorly defined box in the southern sky on summer evenings. Sabik crosses the celestial meridian during evening twilight in August, and during morning twilight in March. Dec. 16°S, SHA 103°, mag. 2.6. Fig. 2208.

Schedar is the southernmost star of the W (or M) of *Cassiopeia*, on the opposite side of Polaris from the Big Dipper. It is the second star from the leading edge of this configuration as it circles the north celestial pole. Dec. 56°N, SHA 350°, mag. 2.5. Figs. 2205, 2206, 2208.

Shaula is a second magnitude star marking the end of the tail of *Scorpio*, the scorpion, at the opposite end from Antares. This constellation is low in the southern sky on summer evenings. Shaula is about 15° southeast of Antares and about 10° WSW of Kaus Australis. It crosses the celestial meridian during evening twilight in early September, and during morning twilight in March. Dec. 37°S, SHA 97°, mag. 1.7. Fig. 2208.

Sirius, the brightest star in the heavens, is in the constellation *Canis Major*, the "large dog" of *Orion*, the hunter. The line formed by the belt of *Orion*, if extended about 20° to the eastward and curved toward the south, leads to Sirius. Dec. 17°S, SHA 259°, mag. (—)1.6. Fig. 2206.

Spica is the brightest star of *Virgo*, the virgin, an inconspicuous constellation on the celestial equator to the south during evening twilight in early summer. The curved line along the stars forming the handle of the Big Dipper, if continued in a direction away from the pointers, passes through Arcturus and then Spica. The distance between Alkaid, at the end of the Big Dipper, and Arcturus is about the same as that between Arcturus and Spica, and is a little more than the length of the Big Dipper. Spica crosses the celestial meridian during evening twilight in June, and during morning twilight late in December. Dec. 11°S, SHA 159°, mag. 1.2. Fig 2207.

Suhail is one of a number of second magnitude stars extending along the Milky Way between Sirius and the Southern Cross. It is about 10° north of the false southern cross, which is nearly enclosed by a large, nearly equilateral triangle formed by Suhail, Canopus, and Miaplacidus. Canopus and Suhail are on opposite edges of the Milky Way, with a number of second magnitude stars between them. A straight line extending eastward through the east-west arm of the Southern Cross leads to Suhail, about 35° away. In the southern United States, Suhail crosses the celestial meridian near the southern horizon during evening twilight in April, and during morning twilight in November. Dec. 43°S, SHA 223°, mag. 2.2. Figs. 2206, 2207.

Vega is the brightest star north of the celestial equator, and the third brightest in the entire sky. It is at the western vertex and the nearly right angle of a large triangle which is a conspicuous feature of the evening sky in late summer and in autumn. The other two stars of the triangle are Altair and Deneb, both of the first magnitude. Vega passes through the zenith approximately at latitude 38°45′N during evening twilight in September and during morning twilight in April. Dec. 39°N, SHA 81°, mag. 0.1. Fig. 2208.

Zubenelgenubi, a third magnitude star, is the southern (or western) basket of *Libra*, the balance. The boxlike *Libra* is about 25° WNW of Antares, in *Scorpio*, the scorpion. A long line extending eastward from Alphard, between Gienah and Spica, leads to Zubenelgenubi. Dec. 16°S, SHA 138°, mag. 2.9. Figs. 2207, 2208.

APPENDIX J

NAVIGATIONAL STARS AND THE PLANETS

Name	Pronunciation	Bayer name	Origin of name	Meaning of name	Distance*
Acamar	ā'ká·mär	θ Eridani	Arabic	another form of Achernar	120
Achernar	ā'kēr·när	α Eridani	Arabic	end of the river (Eridanus)	72
Acrux	ā'krŭks	α Crucis	Modern	coined from Bayer name	220
Adhara	á·dā'rá	ε Canis Majoris	Arabic	the virgin(s)	350
Aldebaran	ăl děb'á·răn	α Tauri	Arabic	follower (of the Pleiades)	64
Alioth	ăl'ĭ-ôth	ε Ursa Majoris	Arabic	another form of Capella	49
Alkaid	ăl·kād'	η Ursa Majoris	Arabic	leader of the daughters of the bier	190
Al Na'ir	ăl·när'	α Gruis	Arabic	bright one (of the fish's tail)	90
Alnilam	ăl'nĭ-lăm	ε Orionis	Arabic	string of pearls	410
Alphard	ăl'färd	α Hydrae	Arabic	solitary star of the serpent	200
Alphecca	ăl·fĕk'á	α Corona Borealis	Arabic	feeble one (in the crown)	76
Alpheratz	ăl·fē'răts	α Andromeda	Arabic	the horse's navel	120
Altair	ăl·tär'	α Aquilae	Arabic	flying eagle or vulture	16
Ankaa	ăn'kä	α Phoenicis	Arabic	coined name	93
Antares	ăn·tā'rēz	α Scorpii	Greek	rival of Mars (in color)	250
Arcturus	ärk·tū'rŭs	α Bootis	Greek	the bear's guard	37
Atria	ăt'rĭ·á	α Trianguli Australis	Modern	coined from Bayer name	130
Avior	ā'vĭ·ôr	ε Carinae	Modern	coined name	350
Bellatrix	bĕ·lă'trĭks.	γ Orionis	Latin	female warrior	250
Betelgeuse	bĕt'ĕl·jūz	α Orionis	Arabic	the arm pit (of Orion)	300
Canopus	ká·nō'pŭs	α Carinae	Greek	city of ancient Egypt	230
Capella	ká·pĕl'á	α Aurigae	Latin	little she-goat	46
Deneb	dĕn'ĕb	α Cygni	Arabic	tail of the hen	600
Denebola	dĕ·nĕb'ó·lá	β Leonis	Arabic	tail of the lion	42
Diphda	dĭf'dá	β Ceti	Arabic	the second frog (Fomalhaut was once the first)	57
Dubhe	dŭb'ē	α Ursa Majoris	Arabic	the bear's back	100
Elnath	ĕl'năth	β Tauri	Arabic	one butting with horns	130
Eltanin	ĕl·tā'nĭn	γ Draconis	Arabic	head of the dragon	150
Enif	ĕn'ĭf	ε Pegasi	Arabic	nose of the horse	250
Fomalhaut	fō'măl·ôt	α Piscis Austrini	Arabic	mouth of the southern fish	23
Gacrux	gă'krŭks	γ Crucis	Modern	coined from Bayer name	72
Gienah	jē'ná	γ Corvi	Arabic	right wing of the raven	136
Hadar	hă'där	β Centauri	Modern	leg of the centaur	200
Hamal	hăm'ál	α Arietis	Arabic	full-grown lamb	76
Kaus Australis	kôs ôs·trā'lĭs	ε Sagittarii	Ar., L.	southern part of the bow	163
Kochab	kō'kăb	β Ursa Minoris	Arabic	shortened form of "north star" (named when it was that, c. 1500 BC–AD 300)	100
Markab	măr'kăb	α Pegasi	Arabic	saddle (of Pegasus)	100
Menkar	mĕn'kär	α Ceti	Arabic	nose (of the whale)	1,100
Menkent	mĕn'kĕnt	θ Centauri	Modern	shoulder of the centaur	55
Miaplacidus	mī'á·plăs'ĭ·dŭs	β Carinae	Ar., L.	quiet or still waters	86
Mirfak	mĭr'făk	α Persei	Arabic	elbow of the Pleiades	130
Nunki	nŭn'kē	σ Sagittarii	Bab.	constellation of the holy city (Eridu)	150
Peacock	pē'kŏk	α Pavonis	Modern	coined from English name of constellation	250
Polaris	pō·lā'rĭs	α Ursa Minoris	Latin	the pole (star)	450
Pollux	pŏl'ŭks	β Geminorum	Latin	Zeus' other twin son (Castor, α Geminorum, is first twin)	33
Procyon	prō'sĭ·ŏn	α Canis Minoris	Greek	before the dog (rising before the dog star, Sirius)	11
Rasalhague	rás'ăl·hă'gwē	α Ophiuchi	Arabic	head of the serpent charmer	67
Regulus	rĕg'ū·lŭs	α Leonis	Latin	the prince	67
Rigel	rī'jĕl	β Orionis	Arabic	foot (left foot of Orion)	500
Rigil Kentaurus	rī'jĭl kĕn·tô'rŭs	α Centauri	Arabic	foot of the centaur	4.3
Sabik	să'bĭk	η Ophiuchi	Arabic	second winner or conqueror	69
Schedar	shĕd'ár	α Cassiopeiae	Arabic	the breast (of Cassiopeia)	360
Shaula	shō'lá	λ Scorpii	Arabic	cocked-up part of the scorpion's tail	200
Sirius	sĭr'ĭ·ŭs	α Canis Majoris	Greek	the scorching one (popularly, the dog star)	8.6
Spica	spī'ká	α Virginis	Latin	the ear of corn	155
Suhail	sōō·hăl'	λ Velorum	Arabic	shortened form of Al Suhail, one Arabic name for Canopus	200
Vega	vē'gá	α Lyrae	Arabic	the falling eagle or vulture	27
Zubenelgenubi	zōō·bĕn'ĕl·jē·nū'bē	α Librae	Arabic	southern claw (of the scorpion)	66

PLANETS

Name	Pronunciation	Origin of name	Meaning of name
Mercury	mûr'kū·rĭ	Latin	god of commerce and gain
Venus	vē'nŭs	Latin	goddess of love
Earth	ûrth	Mid. Eng.	—
Mars	märz	Latin	god of war
Jupiter	jōō'pĭ·tēr	Latin	god of the heavens, identified with the Greek Zeus, chief of the Olympian gods
Saturn	săt'ērn	Latin	god of seed-sowing
Uranus	ū'rá·nŭs	Greek	the personification of heaven
Neptune	nĕp'tūn	Latin	god of the sea
Pluto	plōō'tō	Greek	god of the lower world (Hades)

Guide to pronunciations:
    fāte, ădd, fĭnăl, lăst, ȧbound, ärm; bē, ĕnd, camĕl, reader; ĭce, bĭt, anĭmal; ōver, pôetic, hŏt, lôrd, mōōn; tūbe, ûnite, tŭb circŭs, ûrn

*Distances in light-years. One light-year equals approximately 63,300 AU, or 5,880,000,000,000 miles. Authorities differ on distances of the stars; the values given are representative.

APPENDIX K

CONSTELLATIONS

Name	Pronunciation	Genitive	Pronunciation	Meaning	Navigational stars or approximate position
Andromeda*	ăn·drŏm'·ĕ·dȧ	Andromedae	ăn·drŏm'ĕ·dē	Andromeda [the chained woman]†	Alpheratz
Antlia	ănt'lĭ·ȧ	Antliae	ănt'lĭ·ē	(air) pump††	d 35°S, SHA 210°
Apus	ā'pŭs	Apodis	ăp'ȯ·dĭs	bird of paradise	d 75°S, SHA 120°
Aquarius (≈)*	ȧ·kwâr'ĭ·ŭs	Aquarii	ȧ·kwâr'ĭ·ī	water carrier	d 5°S, SHA 25°
Aquila*	ăk'wĭ·lȧ	Aquilae	ăk'wĭ·lē	eagle	Altair
Ara*	ā'rȧ	Arae	ā'rē	altar	d 55°S, SHA 100°
Aries (♈)*	ā'rĭ·ēz	Arietis	ȧ·rī'ĕ·tĭs	ram	Hamal
Auriga*	ô·rī'gȧ	Aurigae	ô·rī'jē	charioteer	Capella
Bootes*	bō·ō'tēz	Bootis	bō·ō'tĭs	herdsman	Arcturus
Caelum	sē'lŭm	Caeli	sē'lī	graving tool	d 40°S, SHA 290°
Camelopardalis	kȧ·mĕl'ȯ·pär'dȧ·lĭs	Camelopardalis	kȧ·mĕl'ȯ·pär'dȧ·lĭs	giraffe	d 70°N, SHA 275°
Cancer (♋)*	kăn'sẽr	Cancri	kăng'krī	crab	d 20°N, SHA 230°
Canes Venatici	kā'nēz vē·năt'ĭ·sī	Canum Venaticorum	kā'nŭm vē·năt'ĭ·kō'rŭm	hunting dogs	d 40°N, SHA 165°
Canis Major*	kā'nĭs mā'jẽr	Canis Majoris	kā'nĭs mȧ·jō'rĭs	larger dog	Adhara, Sirius
Canis Minor*	kā'nĭs mī'nẽr	Canis Minoris	kā'nĭs mĭ·nō'rĭs	smaller dog	Procyon
Capricornus (♑)	kăp'rĭ·kôr'nŭs	Capricorni	kăp'rĭ·kôr'nī	horned goat	d 20°S, SHA 45°
Carina**	kȧ·rī'nȧ	Carinae	kȧ·rī'nē	keel	Avior, Canopus, Miaplacidus
Cassiopeia*	kăs'ĭ·ȯ·pē'yȧ	Cassiopeiae	kăs'ĭ·ȯ·pē'yē	Cassiopeia [the lady in the chair]†	Schedar
Centaurus*	sĕn·tô'rŭs	Centauri	sĕn·tô'rī	centaur	Hadar, Menkent, Rigil Kentaurus
Cepheus*	sē'fŭs	Cephei	sē'fĕ·ī	Cepheus [the shepherd]†	d 75°N, SHA 15°
Cetus*	sē'tŭs	Ceti	sē'tī	whale	Diphda, Menkar
Chamaeleon	kȧ·mē'lĕ·ŭn	Chamaeleontis	kȧ·mē'lĕ·ŏn'tĭs	chameleon	d 80°S, SHA 200°
Circinus	sûr'sĭ·nŭs	Circini	sûr'sĭ·nī	pair of compasses	d 65°S, SHA 140°
Columba	kȯ·lŭm'bȧ	Columbae	kȯ·lŭm'bē	dove	d 35°S, SHA 275°
Coma Berenices	kō'mȧ bĕr·ĕ·nī'sēz	Comae Berenices	kō'mē bĕr'ĕ·nī'sēz	Berenice's hair	d 25°N, SHA 170°
Corona Australis*	kȯ·rō'nȧ ôs·trā'lĭs	Coronae Australis	kȯ·rō'nē ôs·trā'lĭs	southern crown	d 40°S, SHA 80°
Corona Borealis*	kȯ·rō'nȧ bō'rĕ·ā'lĭs	Coronae Borealis	kȯ·rō'nē bō'rĕ·ā'lĭs	northern crown	Alphecca
Corvus*	kôr'vŭs	Corvi	kôr'vī	crow	Gienah
Crater*	krā'tẽr	Crateris	krȧ·tē'rĭs	cup	d 15°S, SHA 190°
Crux	krŭks	Crucis	krōō'sĭs	cross	Acrux, Gacrux
Cygnus*	sĭg'nŭs	Cygni	sĭg'nī	swan	Deneb
Delphinus*	dĕl·fī'nŭs	Delphini	dĕl·fī'nī	dolphin	d 15°N, SHA 50°
Dorado	dȯ·rä'dō	Doradus	dȯ·rä'dŭs	dorado [a fish]†	d 60°S, SHA 285°
Draco*	drā'kō	Draconis	drȧ·kō'nĭs	dragon	Eltanin
Equuleus*	ė·kwōō'lė·ŭs	Equulei	ė·kwōō'lė·ī	colt	d 10°N, SHA 40°
Eridanus*	ė·rĭd'ȧ·nŭs	Eridani	ė·rĭd'ȧ·nī	Eridanus [a river]†	Acamar, Achernar
Fornax	fôr'năks	Fornacis	fôr·nā'sĭs	furnace	d 30°S, SHA 320°
Gemini (II)*	jĕm'ĭ·nī	Geminorum	jĕm'ĭ·nō'rŭm	twins	Pollux
Grus	grŭs	Gruis	grōō'ĭs	crane [a bird]†	Al Na'ir
Hercules*	hûr'kŭ·lēz	Herculis	hûr'kŭ·lĭs	Hercules [mythological hero]†	d 30°N, SHA 100°
Horologium	hŏr'ȯ·lō'jĭ·ŭm	Horologii	hŏr'ȯ·lō'jĭ·ī	clock	d 50°S, SHA 310°

Zodiacal constellations are given in bold type, with their symbols.
*One of the original constellations of Ptolemy.
**Part of the single constellation Argo Navis of Ptolemy.
†Parts within brackets are amplifications of the meanings of constellation names.
††Parts within parentheses are the meanings of words deleted from former, more complete constellation names.

Guide to pronunciations:

fāte, cȧre, hăt, fīnȧl, ȧbound, sofȧ, ärm; bē, crĕate, ĕnd, readẽr; īce, bĭt; ōver, pȯetic, hŏt, cŏnnect, lôrd, mōōn; tūbe, ûnite, tŭb, circŭs, ûrn.

APPENDIX K

CONSTELLATIONS

Name	Pronunciation	Genitive	Pronunciation	Meaning	Navigational stars or approximate position
Hydra*	hī′drȧ	Hydrae	hī′drē	water monster	Alphard
Hydrus	hī′drŭs	Hydri	hī′drī	water snake	d 70°S, SHA 320°
Indus	ĭn′dŭs	Indi	ĭn′dī	Indian	d 60°S, SHA 35°
Lacerta	lȧ·sûr′tȧ	Lacertae	lȧ·sûr′tē	lizard	d 45°N, SHA 25°
Leo (♌)*	lē′ō	Leonis	lē·ō′nĭs	lion	Denebola, Regulus
Leo Minor	lē′ō mī′nẽr	Leonis Minoris	lē·ō′nĭs mĭ·nō′rĭs	smaller lion	d 35°N, SHA 205°
Lepus*	lē′pŭs	Leporis	lĕp′ō·rĭs	hare	d 20°S, SHA 275°
Libra (♎)*	lī′brȧ	Librae	lī′brē	balance [scales]†	Zubenelgenubi
Lupus*	lū′pŭs	Lupi	lū′pī	wolf	d 45°S, SHA 130°
Lynx	lĭngks	Lyncis	lĭn′sĭs	lynx	d 50°N, SHA 240°
Lyra*	lī′rȧ	Lyrae	lī′rē	lyre	Vega
Mensa	mĕn′sȧ	Mensae	mĕn′sē	table (mountain)††	d 75°S, SHA 275°
Microscopium	mī′krō·skō′pĭ·ŭm	Microscopii	mī′krō·skō′pĭ·ī	microscope	d 35°S, SHA 45°
Monoceros	mō·nŏs′ẽr·ŏs	Monocerotis	mō·nŏs′ẽr·ō′tĭs	unicorn	d 0°, SHA 255°
Musca	mŭs′kȧ	Muscae	mŭs′sē	fly	d 70°S, SHA 175°
Norma	nôr′mȧ	Normae	nôr′mē	square (and rule)††	d 50°S, SHA 120°
Octans	ŏk′tănz	Octantis	ŏk·tăn′tĭs	octant	d 85°S, SHA 40°
Ophiuchus*	ŏf′ĭ·ū′kŭs	Ophiuchi	ŏf′ĭ·ū′kī	serpent holder	Rasalhague, Sabik
Orion*	ō·rī′ŏn	Orionis	ō′rī·ō′nĭs	Orion [the hunter]†	Alnilam, Bellatrix, Betelgeuse, Rigel
Pavo	pā′vō	Pavonis	pȧ·vō′nĭs	peacock	Peacock
Pegasus*	pĕg′ȧ·sŭs	Pegasi	pĕg′ȧ·sī	Pegasus [winged horse]†	Enif, Markab
Perseus*	pûr′sūs	Persei	pûr′sĕ·ī	Perseus [mythological character]†	Mirfak
Phoenix	fē′nĭks	Phoenicis	fē·nī′sĭs	phoenix [the immortal bird]†	Ankaa
Pictor	pĭk′tẽr	Pictoris	pĭk·tō′rĭs	painter (easel of)††	d 55°S, SHA 275°
Pisces (♓)*	pĭs′ēz	Piscium	pĭsh′ĭ·ŭm	fishes	d 15°N, SHA 355°
Piscis Austrinus*	pĭs′ĭs ôs·trī′nŭs	Piscis Austrini	pĭs′ĭs ôs·trī′nī	southern fish	Fomalhaut
Puppis**	pŭp′ĭs	Puppis	pŭp′ĭs	stern [of ship]†	d 30°S, SHA 245°
Pyxis**	pĭk′sĭs	Pyxidis	pĭk′sĭ·dĭs	mariner's compass	d 25°S, SHA 230°
Reticulum	rē·tĭk′ů·lŭm	Reticuli	rē·tĭk′ů·lī	net	d 60°S, SHA 300°
Sagitta*	sȧ·jĭt′ȧ	Sagittae	sȧ·jĭt′ē	arrow	d 20°N, SHA 65°
Sagittarius (♐)*	săj′ĭ·tā′rĭ·ŭs	Sagittarii	săj′ĭ·tā′rĭ·ī	archer	Kaus Australis, Nunki
Scorpius (♏)*	skôr′pĭ·ŭs	Scorpii	skôr′pĭ·ī	scorpion	Antares, Shaula
Sculptor	skŭlp′tẽr	Sculptoris	skŭlp·tō′rĭs	sculptor (workshop of)††	d 30°S, SHA 355°
Scutum	skū′tŭm	Scuti	skū′tī	shield	d 10°S, SHA 80°
Serpens*	sûr′pĕnz	Serpentis	sẽr·pĕn′tĭs	serpent	d 10°N, SHA 125°
Sextans	sĕks′tănz	Sextantis	sĕks·tăn′tĭs	sextant	d 0°, SHA 205°
Taurus (♉)*	tô′rŭs	Tauri	tô′rī	bull	Aldebaran, Elnath
Telescopium	tĕl′ē·skō′pĭ·ŭm	Telescopii	tĕl′ē·skō′pĭ·ī	telescope	d 50°S, SHA 75°
Triangulum*	trī·ăng′gů·lŭm	Trianguli	trī·ăng′gů·lī	triangle	d 30°N, SHA 330°
Triangulum Australe	trī·ăng′gů·lŭm ôs·trā′lē	Trianguli Australis	trī·ăng′gů·lī ôs·trā′lĭs	southern triangle	Atria
Tucana	tů·kā′nȧ	Tucanae	tů·kā′nē	toucan [a bird]†	d 65°S, SHA 5°
Ursa Major*	ûr′sȧ mā′jẽr	Ursae Majoris	ûr′sē mā·jō′rĭs	larger bear	Alioth, Alkaid, Dubhe
Ursa Minor*	ûr′sȧ mī′nẽr	Ursae Minoris	ûr′sē mĭ·nō′rĭs	smaller bear	Kochab, Polaris
Vela**	vē′lȧ	Velorum	vē·lō′rŭm	sails	Suhail
Virgo (♍)*	vûr′gō	Virginis	vûr′jĭ·nĭs	virgin	Spica
Volans	vō′lănz	Volantis	vō·lăn′tĭs	flying (fish)††	d 70°S, SHA 240°
Vulpecula	vŭl·pĕk′ů·lȧ	Vulpeculae	vŭl·pĕk′ů·lē	little fox	d 25°N, SHA 60°

Zodiacal constellations are given in bold type, with their symbols.
*One of the original constellations of Ptolemy.
**Part of the single constellation Argo Navis of Ptolemy.
†Parts within brackets are amplifications of the meanings of constellation names.
††Parts within parentheses are the meanings of words deleted from former, more complete constellation names.
Guide to pronunciations:
    fāte, câre, hăt, finȧl, ȧbound, sofȧ, ärm; bē, crēate, ĕnd, readẽr; īce, bĭt; ōver, pōetic, hŏt, cŏnnect, lôrd, mōōn; tūbe, ůnite, tŭb, circŭs, ûrn.

APPENDIX L

EXTRACTS FROM TIDE TABLES

NEW YORK (THE BATTERY), N.Y., 1975

TIMES AND HEIGHTS OF HIGH AND LOW WATERS

JANUARY

DAY	TIME H.M.	HT. FT.	DAY	TIME H.M.	HT. FT.
1 W	0422	-0.8	16 TH	0431	0.0
	1043	5.1		1045	4.1
	1659	-1.1		1656	-0.2
	2321	4.6		2319	3.8
2 TH	0516	-0.6	17 F	0501	0.2
	1138	4.9		1120	3.9
	1749	-0.9		1722	0.0
				2357	3.7
3 F	0017	4.6	18 SA	0533	0.4
	0615	-0.4		1154	3.7
	1234	4.6		1746	0.2
	1847	-0.6			
4 SA	0111	4.6	19 SU	0029	3.7
	0724	-0.1		0613	0.6
	1329	4.3		1228	3.5
	1951	-0.4		1818	0.3
5 SU	0207	4.6	20 M	0108	3.8
	0835	0.0		0727	0.7
	1428	4.0		1311	3.4
	2053	-0.3		1917	0.4
6 M	0307	4.5	21 TU	0156	3.9
	0939	-0.1		0856	0.7
	1530	3.7		1404	3.3
	2153	-0.3		2050	0.4
7 TU	0407	4.5	22 W	0255	4.0
	1038	-0.2		1001	0.4
	1635	3.6		1515	3.2
	2247	-0.3		2157	0.2
8 W	0508	4.6	23 TH	0404	4.2
	1131	-0.3		1057	0.1
	1735	3.7		1637	3.4
	2339	-0.3		2256	0.0
9 TH	0603	4.7	24 F	0510	4.5
	1222	-0.4		1150	-0.2
	1828	3.8		1742	3.7
				2352	-0.3
10 F	0028	-0.4	25 SA	0609	4.9
	0649	4.8		1242	-0.6
	1310	-0.5		1838	4.0
	1915	3.9			
11 SA	0117	-0.4	26 SU	0048	-0.6
	0733	4.8		0701	5.2
	1354	-0.6		1330	-1.0
	1959	3.9		1929	4.4
12 SU	0202	-0.4	27 M	0140	-0.9
	0814	4.8		0749	5.4
	1436	-0.6		1419	-1.3
	2040	3.9		2019	4.7
13 M	0242	-0.4	28 TU	0231	-1.1
	0854	4.7		0840	5.5
	1516	-0.6		1505	-1.4
	2122	3.9		2110	4.9
14 TU	0321	-0.3	29 W	0321	-1.2
	0931	4.5		0931	5.4
	1552	-0.5		1550	-1.5
	2202	3.9		2203	5.0
15 W	0358	-0.1	30 TH	0410	-1.2
	1011	4.3		1024	5.2
	1625	-0.4		1635	-1.3
	2242	3.8		2258	5.0
			31 F	0459	-0.9
				1120	4.9
				1725	-1.0
				2354	4.9

FEBRUARY

DAY	TIME H.M.	HT. FT.	DAY	TIME H.M.	HT. FT.
1 SA	0554	-0.6	16 SU	0503	0.2
	1213	4.5		1111	3.8
	1818	-0.7		1704	0.1
				2338	4.0
2 SU	0047	4.8	17 M	0535	0.3
	0659	-0.2		1149	3.6
	1309	4.1		1733	0.2
	1919	-0.3			
3 M	0142	4.6	18 TU	0020	4.0
	0808	0.0		0621	0.5
	1405	3.8		1231	3.5
	2024	-0.1		1818	0.4
4 TU	0240	4.4	19 W	0108	4.1
	0915	0.1		0759	0.6
	1508	3.6		1329	3.4
	2129	0.0		1932	0.5
5 W	0341	4.3	20 TH	0211	4.1
	1015	0.0		0926	0.5
	1612	3.5		1439	3.3
	2225	0.0		2125	0.4
6 TH	0444	4.3	21 F	0327	4.2
	1110	-0.1		1026	0.2
	1715	3.5		1607	3.5
	2320	0.0		2233	0.1
7 F	0542	4.4	22 SA	0444	4.5
	1200	-0.2		1123	-0.2
	1811	3.7		1718	3.9
				2334	-0.3
8 SA	0009	-0.1	23 SU	0545	4.8
	0629	4.5		1214	-0.6
	1246	-0.3		1816	4.4
	1856	3.9			
9 SU	0057	-0.2	24 M	0030	-0.7
	0713	4.6		0640	5.2
	1329	-0.5		1306	-1.0
	1937	4.0		1909	4.8
10 M	0141	-0.3	25 TU	0123	-1.0
	0752	4.6		0731	5.4
	1410	-0.5		1354	-1.2
	2015	4.1		1959	5.2
11 TU	0222	-0.4	26 W	0215	-1.3
	0829	4.6		0820	5.4
	1449	-0.6		1441	-1.4
	2053	4.2		2048	5.4
12 W	0300	-0.4	27 TH	0305	-1.4
	0906	4.5		0912	5.3
	1523	-0.5		1526	-1.4
	2129	4.2		2139	5.4
13 TH	0335	-0.3	28 F	0352	-1.3
	0941	4.3		1003	5.1
	1555	-0.4		1612	-1.2
	2203	4.1		2232	5.3
14 F	0407	-0.2			
	1011	4.1			
	1622	-0.2			
	2235	4.1			
15 SA	0435	0.0			
	1043	3.9			
	1643	-0.1			
	2307	4.0			

MARCH

DAY	TIME H.M.	HT. FT.	DAY	TIME H.M.	HT. FT.
1 SA	0442	-1.0	16 SU	0416	-0.1
	1058	4.8		1013	4.0
	1658	-0.9		1613	0.0
	2325	5.1		2223	4.4
2 SU	0533	-0.6	17 M	0443	0.0
	1152	4.4		1043	3.8
	1749	-0.5		1637	0.2
				2259	4.4
3 M	0021	4.9	18 TU	0517	0.2
	0631	-0.2		1124	3.7
	1247	4.1		1708	0.3
	1847	0.0		2346	4.3
4 TU	0115	4.6	19 W	0602	0.4
	0739	0.1		1218	3.6
	1344	3.8		1752	0.5
	1956	0.3			
5 W	0212	4.3	20 TH	0042	4.3
	0848	0.3		0724	0.5
	1443	3.6		1318	3.6
	2103	0.4		1906	0.6
6 TH	0312	4.1	21 F	0146	4.3
	0949	0.3		0853	0.4
	1545	3.5		1429	3.6
	2204	0.4		2106	0.5
7 F	0415	4.1	22 SA	0300	4.3
	1041	0.2		0959	0.2
	1649	3.6		1548	3.9
	2258	0.3		2217	0.2
8 SA	0513	4.2	23 SU	0417	4.5
	1131	0.0		1056	-0.2
	1744	3.8		1658	4.3
	2347	0.1		2315	-0.2
9 SU	0603	4.3	24 M	0524	4.8
	1216	-0.1		1147	-0.5
	1830	4.1		1755	4.8
10 M	0033	0.0	25 TU	0011	-0.6
	0645	4.4		0620	5.0
	1259	-0.3		1238	-0.8
	1909	4.3		1848	5.2
11 TU	0117	-0.2	26 W	0107	-1.0
	0726	4.5		0712	5.2
	1341	-0.4		1328	-1.1
	1946	4.4		1938	5.6
12 W	0158	-0.3	27 TH	0157	-1.2
	0803	4.5		0802	5.3
	1418	-0.4		1416	-1.2
	2022	4.5		2025	5.7
13 TH	0237	-0.4	28 F	0247	-1.3
	0837	4.5		0852	5.2
	1453	-0.4		1502	-1.1
	2054	4.5		2114	5.7
14 F	0313	-0.4	29 SA	0334	-1.2
	0912	4.3		0942	4.9
	1525	-0.3		1547	-0.9
	2126	4.5		2206	5.5
15 SA	0346	-0.3	30 SU	0422	-0.9
	0941	4.2		1037	4.7
	1551	-0.1		1632	-0.6
	2152	4.5		2259	5.3
			31 M	0512	-0.6
				1132	4.3
				1721	-0.2
				2352	4.9

TIME MERIDIAN 75° W. 0000 IS MIDNIGHT. 1200 IS NOON.
HEIGHTS ARE RECKONED FROM THE DATUM OF SOUNDINGS ON CHARTS OF THE LOCALITY WHICH IS MEAN LOW WATER.

TABLE 2.—TIDAL DIFFERENCES AND OTHER CONSTANTS

No.	PLACE	POSITION		DIFFERENCES				RANGES		Mean Tide Level
		Lat.	Long.	Time		Height		Mean	Spring	
				High water	Low water	High water	Low water			
		° '	° '	h. m.	h. m.	feet	feet	feet	feet	feet
	NEW YORK and NEW JERSEY — Continued **Hudson River‡**	N.	W.		on NEW YORK, p.56						
	Time meridian, 75°W.									
1513	Jersey City, Pa. RR. Ferry, N. J	40 43	74 02	+0 07	+0 07	−0.1	0.0	4.4	5.3	2.2
1515	New York, Desbrosses Street	40 43	74 01	+0 10	+0 10	−0.1	0.0	4.4	5.3	2.2
1517	New York, Chelsea Docks	40 45	74 01	+0 17	+0 16	−0.2	0.0	4.3	5.2	2.1
1519	Hoboken, Castle Point, N. J	40 45	74 01	+0 17	+0 16	−0.2	0.0	4.3	5.2	2.1
1521	Weehawken, Days Point, N. J	40 46	74 01	+0 24	+0 23	−0.3	0.0	4.2	5.0	2.1
1523	New York, Union Stock Yards	40 47	74 00	+0 27	+0 26	−0.3	0.0	4.2	5.0	2.1
1525	New York, 130th Street	40 49	73 58	+0 37	+0 35	−0.5	0.0	4.0	4.8	2.0
1527	George Washington Bridge	40 51	73 57	+0 46	+0 43	−0.6	0.0	3.9	4.6	1.9
1529	Spuyten Duyvil, West of RR. bridge	40 53	73 56	+0 58	+0 53	−0.7	0.0	3.8	4.5	1.9
1531	Yonkers	40 56	73 54	+1 09	+1 10	−0.8	0.0	3.7	4.4	1.8
1533	Dobbs Ferry	41 01	73 53	+1 29	+1 40	−1.1	0.0	3.4	4.0	1.7
1535	Tarrytown	41 05	73 52	+1 45	+1 54	−1.3	0.0	3.2	3.7	1.6
1537	Ossining	41 10	73 52	+1 53	+2 14	−1.4	0.0	3.1	3.6	1.5
1539	Haverstraw	41 12	73 58	+1 59	+2 25	−1.6	0.0	2.9	3.4	1.4
1541	Peekskill	41 17	73 56	+2 24	+3 00	−1.3	+0.3	2.9	3.4	1.7
1543	West Point	41 24	73 57	+3 16	+3 37	−1.5	+0.3	2.7	3.1	1.6
1545	Newburgh	41 30	74 00	+3 42	+4 00	−1.5	+0.2	2.8	3.2	1.6
1547	New Hamburg	41 35	73 57	+4 00	+4 25	−1.5	+0.1	2.9	3.3	1.5
1549	Poughkeepsie	41 42	73 57	+4 30	+4 43	−1.3	+0.1	3.1	3.5	1.6
1551	Hyde Park	41 47	73 57	+4 56	+5 09	−1.3	0.0	3.2	3.6	1.6
1553	Kingston Point	41 56	73 58	+5 16	+5 31	−0.9	−0.1	3.7	4.2	1.7
1555	Tivoli	42 04	73 56	+5 46	+6 01	−0.8	−0.2	3.9	4.4	1.7
1557	Catskill	42 13	73 51	+6 37	+6 55	−0.7	−0.3	4.1	4.6	1.7
1559	Hudson	42 15	73 48	+6 54	+7 09	−0.9	−0.4	4.0	4.4	1.6
				on ALBANY, p.60						
1561	Coxsackie	42 21	73 48	−1 01	−1 38	−0.5	+0.2	3.9	4.3	2.1
1563	New Baltimore	42 27	73 47	−0 34	−0 56	−0.1	+0.4	4.1	4.5	2.4
1565	Castleton-on-Hudson	42 32	73 46	−0 17	−0 29	−0.2	+0.1	4.3	4.7	2.2
1567	ALBANY	42 39	73 45	Daily predictions				4.6	5.0	2.5
1569	Troy	42 44	73 42	+0 08	+0 10	+0.1	0.0	4.7	5.1	2.3
	The Kills and Newark Bay			on NEW YORK, p.56						
	Kill Van Kull									
1571	Constable Hook	40 39	74 05	−0 34	−0 21	0.0	0.0	4.5	5.4	2.2
1573	New Brighton	40 39	74 05	−0 12	−0 18	0.0	0.0	4.5	5.4	2.2
1575	Port Richmond	40 38	74 08	−0 03	+0 05	0.0	0.0	4.5	5.4	2.2
1577	Bergen Point	40 39	74 08	+0 03	+0 03	+0.1	0.0	4.6	5.5	2.3
1579	Shooters Island	40 39	74 10	+0 06	+0 18	+0.1	0.0	4.6	5.5	2.3
1581	Port Newark Terminal	40 41	74 08	−0 01	+0 18	+0.6	0.0	5.1	6.1	2.5
1583	Newark, Passaic River	40 44	74 10	+0 22	+0 52	+0.6	0.0	5.1	6.1	2.5
1585	Passaic, Gregory Ave. bridge	40 51	74 07	+0 49	+1 57	+0.6	0.0	5.1	6.1	2.5
	Hackensack River									
1586	Kearny Point	40 44	74 06	+0 09	+0 33	+0.5	0.0	5.0	6.0	2.5
1587	Secaucus	40 48	74 04	+1 13	+1 09	+0.6	0.0	5.1	6.1	2.6
1588	Little Ferry	40 51	74 02	+1 22	+1 14	+0.8	0.0	5.3	6.4	2.7
1589	Hackensack	40 53	74 02	+1 33	+1 58	+0.8	0.0	5.3	6.4	2.6
				on SANDY HOOK, p.64						
	Arthur Kill									
1591	Elizabethport	40 39	74 11	+0 25	+0 39	+0.3	0.0	4.9	5.9	2.4
1593	Chelsea	40 36	74 12	+0 24	+0 35	+0.4	0.0	5.0	6.0	2.5
1595	Carteret	40 35	74 13	+0 23	+0 31	+0.5	0.0	5.1	6.2	2.6
1597	Rossville	40 33	74 13	+0 17	+0 25	+0.7	0.0	5.3	6.4	2.6
1599	Tottenville	40 31	74 15	+0 03	+0 13	+0.7	0.0	5.3	6.4	2.6
1601	Perth Amboy	40 30	74 16	+0 13	+0 19	+0.6	0.0	5.2	6.3	2.6

‡Values for the Hudson River above the George Washington Bridge are based upon averages for the six months May to October, when the fresh-water discharge is a minimum.

APPENDIX L: EXTRACTS FROM TIDE TABLES

TABLE 3.—HEIGHT OF TIDE AT ANY TIME

Duration of rise or fall, see footnote	Time from the nearest high water or low water														
h. m.	h. m.	h. m.	h. m.	h. m.	h. m.	h. m.	h. m.	h. m.	h. m.	h. m.	h. m.	h. m.	h. m.	h. m.	h. m.
4 00	0 08	0 16	0 24	0 32	0 40	0 48	0 56	1 04	1 12	1 20	1 28	1 36	1 44	1 52	2 00
4 20	0 09	0 17	0 26	0 35	0 43	0 52	1 01	1 09	1 18	1 27	1 35	1 44	1 53	2 01	2 10
4 40	0 09	0 19	0 28	0 37	0 47	0 56	1 05	1 15	1 24	1 33	1 43	1 52	2 01	2 11	2 20
5 00	0 10	0 20	0 30	0 40	0 50	1 00	1 10	1 20	1 30	1 40	1 50	2 00	2 10	2 20	2 30
5 20	0 11	0 21	0 32	0 43	0 53	1 04	1 15	1 25	1 36	1 47	1 57	2 08	2 19	2 29	2 40
5 40	0 11	0 23	0 34	0 45	0 57	1 08	1 19	1 31	1 42	1 53	2 05	2 16	2 27	2 39	2 50
6 00	0 12	0 24	0 36	0 48	1 00	1 12	1 24	1 36	1 48	2 00	2 12	2 24	2 36	2 48	3 00
6 20	0 13	0 25	0 38	0 51	1 03	1 16	1 29	1 41	1 54	2 07	2 19	2 32	2 45	2 57	3 10
6 40	0 13	0 27	0 40	0 53	1 07	1 20	1 33	1 47	2 00	2 13	2 27	2 40	2 53	3 07	3 20
7 00	0 14	0 28	0 42	0 56	1 10	1 24	1 38	1 52	2 06	2 20	2 34	2 48	3 02	3 16	3 30
7 20	0 15	0 29	0 44	0 59	1 13	1 28	1 43	1 57	2 12	2 27	2 41	2 56	3 11	3 25	3 40
7 40	0 15	0 31	0 46	1 01	1 17	1 32	1 47	2 03	2 18	2 33	2 49	3 04	3 19	3 35	3 50
8 00	0 16	0 32	0 48	1 04	1 20	1 36	1 52	2 08	2 24	2 40	2 56	3 12	3 28	3 44	4 00
8 20	0 17	0 33	0 50	1 07	1 23	1 40	1 57	2 13	2 30	2 47	3 03	3 20	3 37	3 53	4 10
8 40	0 17	0 35	0 52	1 09	1 27	1 44	2 01	2 19	2 36	2 53	3 11	3 28	3 45	4 03	4 20
9 00	0 18	0 36	0 54	1 12	1 30	1 48	2 06	2 24	2 42	3 00	3 18	3 36	3 54	4 12	4 30
9 20	0 19	0 37	0 56	1 15	1 33	1 52	2 11	2 29	2 48	3 07	3 25	3 44	4 03	4 21	4 40
9 40	0 19	0 39	0 58	1 17	1 37	1 56	2 15	2 35	2 54	3 13	3 33	3 52	4 11	4 31	4 50
10 00	0 20	0 40	1 00	1 20	1 40	2 00	2 20	2 40	3 00	3 20	3 40	4 00	4 20	4 40	5 00
10 20	0 20	0 41	1 02	1 23	1 43	2 04	2 25	2 45	3 06	3 27	3 47	4 08	4 29	4 49	5 10
10 40	0 21	0 43	1 04	1 25	1 47	2 08	2 29	2 51	3 12	3 33	3 55	4 16	4 37	4 59	5 20

Range of tide, see footnote	Correction to height														
Ft.	Ft.	Ft.	Ft.	Ft.	Ft.	Ft.	Ft.	Ft.	Ft.	Ft.	Ft.	Ft.	Ft.	Ft.	Ft.
0.5	0.0	0.0	0.0	0.0	0.0	0.0	0.1	0.1	0.1	0.1	0.1	0.2	0.2	0.2	0.2
1.0	0.0	0.0	0.0	0.0	0.1	0.1	0.1	0.2	0.2	0.2	0.3	0.3	0.4	0.4	0.5
1.5	0.0	0.0	0.0	0.1	0.1	0.1	0.2	0.2	0.3	0.4	0.4	0.5	0.6	0.7	0.8
2.0	0.0	0.0	0.0	0.1	0.1	0.2	0.3	0.3	0.4	0.5	0.6	0.7	0.8	0.9	1.0
2.5	0.0	0.0	0.1	0.1	0.2	0.2	0.3	0.4	0.5	0.6	0.7	0.9	1.0	1.1	1.2
3.0	0.0	0.0	0.1	0.1	0.2	0.3	0.4	0.5	0.6	0.8	0.9	1.0	1.2	1.3	1.5
3.5	0.0	0.0	0.1	0.2	0.2	0.3	0.4	0.6	0.7	0.9	1.0	1.2	1.4	1.6	1.8
4.0	0.0	0.0	0.1	0.2	0.3	0.4	0.5	0.7	0.8	1.0	1.2	1.4	1.6	1.8	2.0
4.5	0.0	0.0	0.1	0.2	0.3	0.4	0.6	0.7	0.9	1.1	1.3	1.6	1.8	2.0	2.2
5.0	0.0	0.1	0.1	0.2	0.3	0.5	0.6	0.8	1.0	1.2	1.5	1.7	2.0	2.2	2.5
5.5	0.0	0.1	0.1	0.2	0.4	0.5	0.7	0.9	1.1	1.4	1.6	1.9	2.2	2.5	2.8
6.0	0.0	0.1	0.1	0.3	0.4	0.6	0.8	1.0	1.2	1.5	1.8	2.1	2.4	2.7	3.0
6.5	0.0	0.1	0.2	0.3	0.4	0.6	0.8	1.1	1.3	1.6	1.9	2.2	2.6	2.9	3.2
7.0	0.0	0.1	0.2	0.3	0.5	0.7	0.9	1.2	1.4	1.8	2.1	2.4	2.8	3.1	3.5
7.5	0.0	0.1	0.2	0.3	0.5	0.7	1.0	1.2	1.5	1.9	2.2	2.6	3.0	3.4	3.8
8.0	0.0	0.1	0.2	0.3	0.5	0.8	1.0	1.3	1.6	2.0	2.4	2.8	3.2	3.6	4.0
8.5	0.0	0.1	0.2	0.4	0.6	0.8	1.1	1.4	1.8	2.1	2.5	2.9	3.4	3.8	4.2
9.0	0.0	0.1	0.2	0.4	0.6	0.9	1.2	1.5	1.9	2.2	2.7	3.1	6.6	4.0	4.5
9.5	0.0	0.1	0.2	0.4	0.6	0.9	1.2	1.6	2.0	2.4	2.8	3.3	3.8	4.3	4.8
10.0	0.0	0.1	0.2	0.4	0.7	1.0	1.3	1.7	2.1	2.5	3.0	3.5	4.0	4.5	5.0
10.5	0.0	0.1	0.3	0.5	0.7	1.0	1.3	1.7	2.2	2.6	3.1	3.6	4.2	4.7	5.2
11.0	0.0	0.1	0.3	0.5	0.7	1.1	1.4	1.8	2.3	2.8	3.3	3.8	4.4	4.9	5.5
11.5	0.0	0.1	0.3	0.5	0.8	1.1	1.5	1.9	2.4	2.9	3.4	4.0	4.6	5.1	5.8
12.0	0.0	0.1	0.3	0.5	0.8	1.1	1.5	2.0	2.5	3.0	3.6	4.1	4.8	5.4	6.0
12.5	0.0	0.1	0.3	0.5	0.8	1.2	1.6	2.1	2.6	3.1	3.7	4.3	5.0	5.6	6.2
13.0	0.0	0.1	0.3	0.6	0.9	1.2	1.7	2.2	2.7	3.2	3.9	4.5	5.1	5.8	6.5
13.5	0.0	0.1	0.3	0.6	0.9	1.3	1.7	2.2	2.8	3.4	4.0	4.7	5.3	6.0	6.8
14.0	0.0	0.2	0.3	0.6	0.9	1.3	1.8	2.3	2.9	3.5	4.2	4.8	5.5	6.3	7.0
14.5	0.0	0.2	0.4	0.6	1.0	1.4	1.9	2.4	3.0	3.6	4.3	5.0	5.7	6.5	7.2
15.0	0.0	0.2	0.4	0.6	1.0	1.4	1.9	2.5	3.1	3.8	4.4	5.2	5.9	6.7	7.5
15.5	0.0	0.2	0.4	0.7	1.0	1.5	2.0	2.6	3.2	3.9	4.6	5.4	6.1	6.9	7.8
16.0	0.0	0.2	0.4	0.7	1.1	1.5	2.1	2.6	3.3	4.0	4.7	5.5	6.3	7.2	8.0
16.5	0.0	0.2	0.4	0.7	1.1	1.6	2.1	2.7	3.4	4.1	4.9	5.7	6.5	7.4	8.2
17.0	0.0	0.2	0.4	0.7	1.1	1.6	2.2	2.8	3.5	4.2	5.0	5.9	6.7	7.6	8.5
17.5	0.0	0.2	0.4	0.8	1.2	1.7	2.2	2.9	3.6	4.4	5.2	6.0	6.9	7.8	8.8
18.0	0.0	0.2	0.4	0.8	1.2	1.7	2.3	3.0	3.7	4.5	5.3	6.2	7.1	8.1	9.0
18.5	0.1	0.2	0.5	0.8	1.2	1.8	2.4	3.1	3.8	4.6	5.5	6.4	7.3	8.3	9.2
19.0	0.1	0.2	0.5	0.8	1.3	1.8	2.4	3.1	3.9	4.8	5.6	6.6	7.5	8.5	9.5
19.5	0.1	0.2	0.5	0.8	1.3	1.9	2.5	3.2	4.0	4.9	5.8	6.7	7.7	8.7	9.8
20.0	0.1	0.2	0.5	0.9	1.3	1.9	2.6	3.3	4.1	5.0	5.9	6.9	7.9	9.0	10.0

Obtain from the predictions the high water and low water, one of which is before and the other after the time for which the height is required. The difference between the times of occurrence of these tides is the duration of rise or fall, and the difference between their heights is the range of tide for the above table. Find the difference between the nearest high or low water and the time for which the height is required.

Enter the table with the duration of rise or fall, printed in heavy-faced type, which most nearly agrees with the actual value, and on that horizontal line find the time from the nearest high or low water which agrees most nearly with the corresponding actual difference. The correction sought is in the column directly below, on the line with the range of tide.

When the nearest tide is high water, subtract the correction.

When the nearest tide is low water, add the correction.

EXTRACTS FROM TIDAL CURRENT TABLES

THE NARROWS, NEW YORK HARBOR, N.Y., 1975

F-FLOOD, DIR. 340° TRUE   E-EBB, DIR. 160° TRUE

JANUARY

DAY	SLACK WATER TIME H.M.	MAX CURRENT TIME H.M.	VEL. KNOTS	DAY	SLACK WATER TIME H.M.	MAX CURRENT TIME H.M.	VEL. KNOTS
1 W		0254	2.4E	16 TH	0002	0310	1.8E
	0617	0857	2.2F		0641	0907	1.6F
	1211	1526	2.5E		1217	1532	2.0E
	1901	2132	2.0F		1917	2139	1.5F
2 TH	0037	0345	2.3E	17 F	0046	0351	1.7E
	0716	0952	2.1F		0730	0954	1.5F
	1301	1614	2.4E		1257	1611	1.9E
	1954	2227	2.0F		2000	2224	1.5F
3 F	0132	0440	2.2E	18 SA	0131	0437	1.6E
	0819	1049	1.9F		0823	1043	1.4F
	1352	1708	2.3E		1339	1654	1.8E
	2050	2321	2.0F		2045	2309	1.5F
4 SA	0230	0542	2.1E	19 SU	0218	0530	1.6E
	0924	1147	1.7F		0920	1130	1.3F
	1445	1807	2.1E		1424	1745	1.7E
	2146				2132	2358	1.5F
5 SU		0018	1.9F	20 M	0310	0631	1.5E
	0331	0648	2.0E		1017	1220	1.2F
	1027	1244	1.5F		1514	1842	1.6E
	1543	1909	2.0E		2220		
	2242						
6 M		0119	1.9F	21 TU		0047	1.6F
	0434	0751	2.0E		0407	0728	1.6E
	1129	1352	1.4F		1114	1313	1.1F
	1643	2007	2.0E		1610	1940	1.6E
	2337				2310		
7 TU		0232	1.9F	22 W		0140	1.6F
	0537	0850	2.0E		0505	0823	1.7E
	1230	1515	1.3F		1211	1410	1.1F
	1744	2102	2.0E		1710	2033	1.7E
8 W	0033	0343	1.9F	23 TH	0001	0237	1.7F
	0635	0946	2.0E		0602	0917	1.9E
	1328	1623	1.4F		1305	1509	1.2F
	1841	2154	1.9E		1808	2124	1.8E
9 TH	0127	0442	2.0F	24 F	0055	0337	1.9F
	0727	1037	2.1E		0655	1007	2.0E
	1423	1714	1.4F		1357	1612	1.4F
	1932	2242	1.9E		1903	2215	2.0E
10 F	0219	0527	2.0F	25 SA	0148	0434	2.1F
	0814	1126	2.1E		0745	1059	2.2E
	1511	1757	1.5F		1445	1703	1.6F
	2020	2336	1.9E		1955	2309	2.1E
11 SA	0307	0609	2.0F	26 SU	0240	0523	2.3F
	0857	1215	2.1E		0834	1150	2.4E
	1556	1836	1.5F		1531	1751	1.8F
	2106				2046		
12 SU		0023	1.9E	27 M		0003	2.3E
	0351	0638	2.0F		0330	0611	2.4E
	0938	1300	2.1E		0922	1241	2.5E
	1637	1906	1.5F		1615	1838	2.0F
	2150				2138		
13 M		0108	1.9E	28 TU		0057	2.4E
	0434	0709	1.9F		0420	0658	2.5F
	1018	1340	2.2E		1011	1329	2.6E
	1717	1937	1.5F		1659	1925	2.2F
	2235				2231		
14 TU		0151	1.9E	29 W		0148	2.5E
	0515	0743	1.8F		0510	0745	2.4F
	1058	1418	2.1E		1100	1416	2.7E
	1756	2010	1.5F		1745	2015	2.2F
	2318				2324		
15 W		0231	1.9E	30 TH		0237	2.6E
	0557	0822	1.7F		0602	0838	2.3F
	1137	1455	2.1E		1149	1503	2.6E
	1836	2051	1.5F		1833	2106	2.2F
				31 F	0017	0327	2.5E
					0659	0932	2.1F
					1238	1551	2.5E
					1925	2201	2.1F

FEBRUARY

DAY	SLACK WATER TIME H.M.	MAX CURRENT TIME H.M.	VEL. KNOTS	DAY	SLACK WATER TIME H.M.	MAX CURRENT TIME H.M.	VEL. KNOTS
1 SA	0111	0420	2.3E	16 SU	0058	0404	1.8E
	0759	1027	1.9F		0751	1011	1.4F
	1328	1643	2.3E		1307	1615	1.8E
	2021	2258	2.1F		1958	2236	1.6F
2 SU	0207	0517	2.1E	17 M	0144	0451	1.7E
	0902	1124	1.7F		0846	1100	1.3F
	1420	1738	2.1E		1350	1656	1.7E
	2118	2355	2.0F		2046	2325	1.6F
3 M	0305	0621	2.0E	18 TU	0233	0547	1.6E
	1005	1222	1.5F		0944	1151	1.2F
	1516	1839	1.9E		1439	1800	1.6E
	2216				2138		
4 TU		0056	1.8F	19 W		0015	1.6F
	0408	0727	1.9E		0329	0650	1.6E
	1107	1331	1.3F		1041	1242	1.1F
	1617	1943	1.8E		1535	1903	1.6E
	2314				2234		
5 W		0207	1.7F	20 TH		0108	1.6F
	0511	0830	1.9E		0429	0752	1.7E
	1208	1455	1.2F		1138	1337	1.1F
	1720	2039	1.8E		1638	2004	1.7E
					2331		
6 TH	0011	0322	1.7F	21 F		0205	1.7F
	0611	0925	1.9E		0529	0848	1.9E
	1306	1602	1.3F		1233	1439	1.2F
	1820	2133	1.8E		1741	2100	1.9E
7 F	0107	0422	1.8F	22 SA	0030	0308	1.8F
	0704	1016	1.9E		0627	0941	2.1E
	1359	1655	1.4F		1325	1544	1.5F
	1913	2226	1.8E		1840	2154	2.1E
8 SA	0200	0511	1.8F	23 SU	0127	0408	2.0F
	0751	1104	2.0E		0720	1032	2.2E
	1447	1741	1.5F		1415	1639	1.7F
	2001	2313	1.8E		1935	2248	2.2E
9 SU	0248	0552	1.9F	24 M	0222	0504	2.2F
	0833	1149	2.0E		0810	1123	2.4E
	1530	1818	1.5F		1502	1730	2.0F
	2045				2027	2343	2.4E
10 M		0000	1.9E	25 TU	0315	0552	2.4F
	0333	0625	1.9F		0859	1214	2.5E
	0912	1232	2.1E		1547	1818	2.2F
	1609	1845	1.6F		2119		
	2128						
11 TU		0044	1.9E	26 W		0037	2.6E
	0414	0650	1.8F		0405	0641	2.4F
	0951	1312	2.1E		0947	1304	2.6E
	1647	1911	1.6F		1632	1903	2.4F
	2209				2211		
12 W		0127	2.0E	27 TH		0129	2.7E
	0455	0718	1.8F		0455	0726	2.4F
	1029	1350	2.1E		1036	1353	2.7E
	1723	1942	1.7F		1718	1952	2.4F
	2251				2303		
13 TH		0207	2.0E	28 F		0218	2.7E
	0534	0757	1.7F		0547	0816	2.2F
	1108	1426	2.1E		1125	1439	2.6E
	1800	2019	1.7F		1805	2041	2.3F
	2332				2356		
14 F		0245	1.9E				
	0616	0838	1.6F				
	1147	1501	2.0E				
	1836	2102	1.7F				
15 SA	0015	0323	1.9E				
	0700	0923	1.5F				
	1226	1536	1.9E				
	1915	2149	1.6F				

TIME MERIDIAN 75° W.   0000 IS MIDNIGHT.   1200 IS NOON.

TABLE 2.—CURRENT DIFFERENCES AND OTHER CONSTANTS

No.	PLACE	POSITION		TIME DIFFERENCES		VELOCITY RATIOS		MAXIMUM CURRENTS			
								Flood		Ebb	
		Lat.	Long.	Slack water	Maximum current	Maximum flood	Maximum ebb	Direction (true)	Average velocity	Direction (true)	Average velocity
		° ′ N.	° ′ W.	h. m.	h. m.			deg.	knots	deg.	knots

LONG ISLAND, South Coast—Continued

on THE NARROWS, p.52
Time meridian, 75°W.

No.	PLACE	Lat.	Long.	Slack water	Maximum current	Maximum flood	Maximum ebb	Flood Dir.	Flood vel.	Ebb Dir.	Ebb vel.
2250	Shinnecock Inlet----------------	40 51	72 29	-0 20	-0 40	1.5	1.2	350	2.5	170	2.3
2255	Fire I. Inlet, 0.5 mi. S. of Oak Beach	40 38	73 18	+0 15	0 00	1.4	1.2	80	2.4	245	2.4
2260	Jones Inlet---------------------	40 35	73 34	-1 00	-0 55	1.8	1.3	35	3.1	215	2.6
2265	Long Beach, inside, between bridges---	40 36	73 40	-0 10	+0 10	0.3	0.3	75	0.5	275	0.6
2270	East Rockaway Inlet-------------	40 35	73 45	-1 25	-1 35	1.3	1.2	40	2.2	225	2.3
2275	Ambrose Light-------------------	40 27	73 49	See table 5.							
2280	Sandy Hook App. Lighted Horn Buoy 2A--	40 27	73 55	See table 5.							
	JAMAICA BAY										
2285	Rockaway Inlet------------------	40 34	73 56	-1 45	-2 15	1.1	1.3	85	1.8	245	2.7
2290	Barren Island, east of----------	40 35	73 53	-2 00	-2 25	0.7	0.9	5	1.2	190	1.7
2295	Canarsie (midchannel, off Pier)-------	40 38	73 53	-1 35	-1 50	0.3	0.3	45	0.5	220	0.7
2300	Beach Channel (bridge)----------	40 35	73 49	-1 20	-1 20	1.1	1.0	60	1.9	225	2.0
2305	Grass Hassock Channel-----------	40 37	73 47	-1 10	-1 00	0.6	0.5	50	1.0	230	1.0
	NEW YORK HARBOR ENTRANCE										
2310	Ambrose Channel entrance--------	40 30	73 58	-1 10	-1 05	1.0	1.2	310	1.7	110	2.3
2315	Ambrose Channel, SE. of West Bank Lt--	40 32	74 01	(1)	-0 25	0.8	0.9	310	1.3	170	1.8
2320	Coney Island Lt., 1.6 miles SSW. of--	40 33	74 01	-0 10	(2)	0.5	0.8	330	0.8	145	1.5
2325	Ambrose Channel, north end------	40 34	74 02	+0 05	+0 15	0.8	0.9	330	1.3	175	1.9
2330	Coney Island, 0.2 mile west of------	40 35	74 01	-0 55	-0 55	0.9	1.0	330	1.5	170	2.0
2335	Ft. Lafayette, channel east of------	40 36	74 02	(3)	(3)	0.6	0.5	345	1.1	195	0.9
2340	THE NARROWS, midchannel---------	40 37	74 03	Daily predictions				340	1.7	160	2.0
	NEW YORK HARBOR, Upper Bay										
2345	Tompkinsville-------------------	40 38	74 04	-0 10	+0 20	0.9	1.0	5	1.6	170	2.0
2350	Bay Ridge Channel---------------	40 39	74 02	-0 35	-0 45	0.6	0.6	40	1.0	220	1.1
2355	Red Hook Channel---------------	40 40	74 01	-0 35	-0 35	0.6	0.4	355	1.0	170	0.7
2360	Robbins Reef Light, east of------	40 39	74 03	+0 10	+0 20	0.8	0.8	15	1.3	205	1.6
2365	Red Hook, 1 mile west of--------	40 41	74 02	+0 45	+1 00	0.8	1.2	25	1.3	205	2.3
2370	Statue of Liberty, east of------	40 42	74 02	+0 55	+1 00	0.8	1.0	30	1.4	205	1.9
	HUDSON RIVER, Midchannel[4]										
2375	The Battery, northwest of-------	40 43	74 02	+1 30	+1 35	0.9	1.2	15	1.5	195	2.3
2380	Desbrosses Street---------------	40 43	74 01	+1 35	+1 40	0.9	1.2	10	1.5	-----	2.3
2385	Chelsea Docks-------------------	40 45	74 01	+1 30	+1 40	1.0	1.0	20	1.7	185	2.0
2390	Forty-second Street-------------	40 46	74 00	+1 35	+1 45	1.0	1.2	30	1.7	-----	2.3
2395	Ninety-sixth Street-------------	40 48	73 59	+1 40	+1 50	1.0	1.2	30	1.7	-----	2.3
2400	Grants Tomb, 123d Street--------	40 49	73 58	+1 45	+1 55	0.9	1.2	25	1.6	-----	2.3
2405	George Washington Bridge--------	40 51	73 57	+1 45	+2 00	0.9	1.1	20	1.6	200	2.2
2410	Spuyten Duyvil------------------	40 53	73 56	+2 00	+2 10	0.9	1.1	20	1.6	-----	2.1
2415	Riverdale-----------------------	40 54	73 55	+2 05	+2 20	0.8	1.0	15	1.4	200	2.0
2420	Dobbs Ferry---------------------	41 01	73 53	+2 25	+2 40	0.8	0.9	10	1.3	-----	1.7
2425	Tarrytown-----------------------	41 05	73 53	+2 40	+2 55	0.6	0.8	0	1.1	-----	1.5
2430	Ossining------------------------	41 10	73 54	+2 55	+3 10	0.5	0.7	320	0.9	-----	1.3
2435	Haverstraw----------------------	41 12	73 57	+3 05	+3 15	0.5	0.7	335	0.8	-----	1.3
2440	Peekskill-----------------------	41 17	73 57	+3 20	+3 35	0.5	0.6	0	0.8	-----	1.2
2445	Bear Mountain Bridge------------	41 19	73 59	+3 25	+3 35	0.5	0.6	0	0.8	-----	1.1
2450	Highland Falls------------------	41 22	73 58	+3 35	+3 50	0.6	0.6	5	1.0	185	1.2
2455	West Point, off Duck Island-----	41 24	73 57	+3 40	+3 55	0.5	0.6	10	1.0	-----	1.1

[1]Current is rotary, turning clockwise. Minimum current of 0.9 knot sets SW. about time of "Slack, flood begins" at The Narrows. Minimum current of 0.5 knot sets NE. about 1 hour before "Slack, ebb begins" at The Narrows.
[2]Maximum flood, -0h 50m; maximum ebb, +0h 55m.
[3]Flood begins, -2h 15m; maximum flood, -0h 05m; ebb begins, +0h 05m; maximum ebb, -1h 50m.
[4]The values for the Hudson River are for the summer months, when the fresh-water discharge is a minimum.

TABLE 3.—VELOCITY OF CURRENT AT ANY TIME

TABLE A

Interval between slack and maximum current

Interval between slack and desired time (h. m.)	1 20	1 40	2 00	2 20	2 40	3 00	3 20	3 40	4 00	4 20	4 40	5 00	5 20	5 40
0 20	0.4	0.3	0.3	0.2	0.2	0.2	0.2	0.1	0.1	0.1	0.1	0.1	0.1	0.1
0 40	0.7	0.6	0.5	0.4	0.4	0.3	0.3	0.3	0.3	0.2	0.2	0.2	0.2	0.2
1 00	0.9	0.8	0.7	0.6	0.6	0.5	0.5	0.4	0.4	0.4	0.3	0.3	0.3	0.3
1 20	1.0	1.0	0.9	0.8	0.7	0.6	0.6	0.5	0.5	0.5	0.4	0.4	0.4	0.4
1 40	-----	1.0	1.0	0.9	0.8	0.8	0.7	0.7	0.6	0.6	0.5	0.5	0.5	0.4
2 00	-----	-----	1.0	1.0	0.9	0.9	0.8	0.8	0.7	0.7	0.6	0.6	0.6	0.5
2 20	-----	-----	-----	1.0	1.0	0.9	0.9	0.8	0.8	0.7	0.7	0.7	0.6	0.6
2 40	-----	-----	-----	-----	1.0	1.0	1.0	0.9	0.9	0.8	0.8	0.7	0.7	0.7
3 00	-----	-----	-----	-----	-----	1.0	1.0	1.0	0.9	0.9	0.8	0.8	0.8	0.7
3 20	-----	-----	-----	-----	-----	-----	1.0	1.0	1.0	0.9	0.9	0.9	0.8	0.8
3 40	-----	-----	-----	-----	-----	-----	-----	1.0	1.0	1.0	0.9	0.9	0.9	0.9
4 00	-----	-----	-----	-----	-----	-----	-----	-----	1.0	1.0	1.0	1.0	0.9	0.9
4 20	-----	-----	-----	-----	-----	-----	-----	-----	-----	1.0	1.0	1.0	1.0	0.9
4 40	-----	-----	-----	-----	-----	-----	-----	-----	-----	-----	1.0	1.0	1.0	1.0
5 00	-----	-----	-----	-----	-----	-----	-----	-----	-----	-----	-----	1.0	1.0	1.0
5 20	-----	-----	-----	-----	-----	-----	-----	-----	-----	-----	-----	-----	1.0	1.0
5 40	-----	-----	-----	-----	-----	-----	-----	-----	-----	-----	-----	-----	-----	1.0

TABLE B

Interval between slack and maximum current

Interval between slack and desired time (h. m.)	1 20	1 40	2 00	2 20	2 40	3 00	3 20	3 40	4 00	4 20	4 40	5 00	5 20	5 40
0 20	0.5	0.4	0.4	0.3	0.3	0.3	0.3	0.3	0.2	0.2	0.2	0.2	0.2	0.2
0 40	0.8	0.7	0.6	0.5	0.5	0.5	0.4	0.4	0.4	0.4	0.3	0.3	0.3	0.3
1 00	0.9	0.8	0.8	0.7	0.7	0.6	0.6	0.5	0.5	0.5	0.4	0.4	0.4	0.4
1 20	1.0	1.0	0.9	0.8	0.8	0.7	0.7	0.6	0.6	0.6	0.5	0.5	0.5	0.5
1 40	-----	1.0	1.0	0.9	0.9	0.8	0.8	0.7	0.7	0.7	0.6	0.6	0.6	0.6
2 00	-----	-----	1.0	1.0	0.9	0.9	0.9	0.8	0.8	0.7	0.7	0.7	0.7	0.6
2 20	-----	-----	-----	1.0	1.0	1.0	0.9	0.9	0.8	0.8	0.8	0.7	0.7	0.7
2 40	-----	-----	-----	-----	1.0	1.0	1.0	0.9	0.9	0.9	0.8	0.8	0.8	0.7
3 00	-----	-----	-----	-----	-----	1.0	1.0	1.0	0.9	0.9	0.9	0.9	0.8	0.8
3 20	-----	-----	-----	-----	-----	-----	1.0	1.0	1.0	0.9	0.9	0.9	0.9	0.8
3 40	-----	-----	-----	-----	-----	-----	-----	1.0	1.0	1.0	1.0	0.9	0.9	0.9
4 00	-----	-----	-----	-----	-----	-----	-----	-----	1.0	1.0	1.0	1.0	0.9	0.9
4 20	-----	-----	-----	-----	-----	-----	-----	-----	-----	1.0	1.0	1.0	1.0	0.9
4 40	-----	-----	-----	-----	-----	-----	-----	-----	-----	-----	1.0	1.0	1.0	1.0
5 00	-----	-----	-----	-----	-----	-----	-----	-----	-----	-----	-----	1.0	1.0	1.0
5 20	-----	-----	-----	-----	-----	-----	-----	-----	-----	-----	-----	-----	1.0	1.0
5 40	-----	-----	-----	-----	-----	-----	-----	-----	-----	-----	-----	-----	-----	1.0

Use Table A for all places except those listed below for Table B.
Use Table B for Cape Cod Canal, Hell Gate, Chesapeake and Delaware Canal and all stations in Table 2 which are referred to them.

1. From predictions find the time of slack water and the time and velocity of maximum current (flood or ebb), one of which is immediately before and the other after the time for which the velocity is desired.
2. Find the interval of time between the above slack and maximum current, and enter the top of Table A or B with the interval which most nearly agrees with this value.
3. Find the interval of time between the above slack and the time desired, and enter the side of Table A or B with the interval which most nearly agrees with this value.
4. Find, in the table, the factor corresponding to the above two intervals and multiply the maximum velocity by this factor. The result will be the approximate velocity at the time desired.

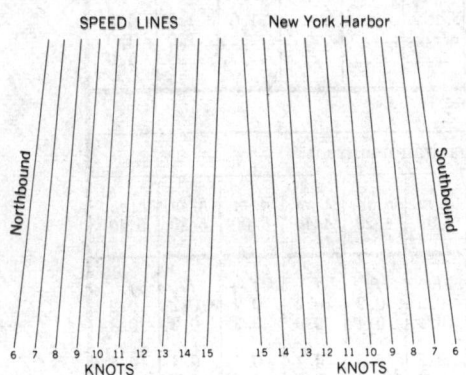

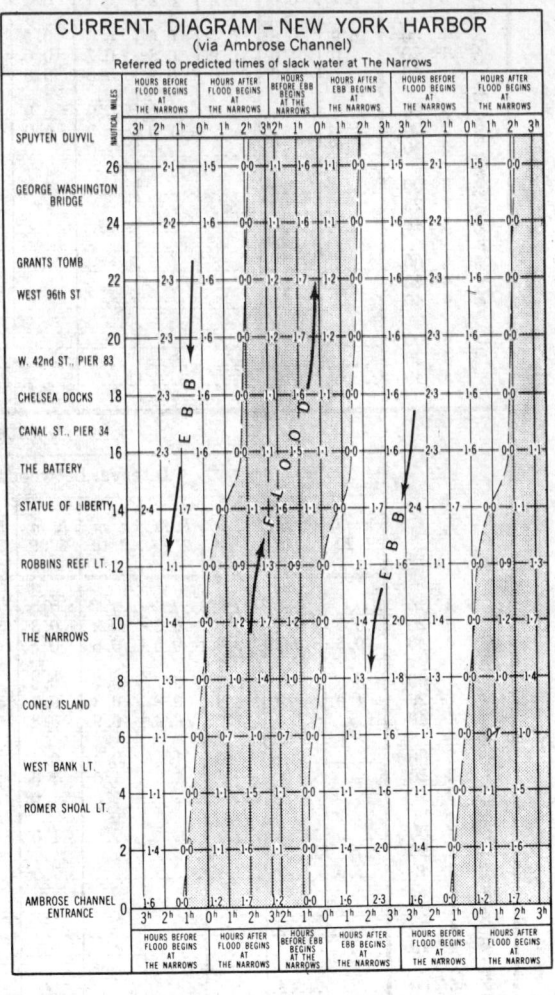

APPENDIX N

EXTRACTS FROM PUB. NO. 214

Lat. 41° — DECLINATION SAME NAME AS LATITUDE

H.A.	19°00' Alt.	Δd Δt	Az.	19°30' Alt.	Δd Δt	Az.	20°00' Alt.	Δd Δt	Az.	20°30' Alt.	Δd Δt	Az.	21°00' Alt.	Δd Δt	Az.	21°30' Alt.	Δd Δt	Az.	22°00' Alt.	Δd Δt	Az.	22°30' Alt.	Δd Δt	Az.	H.A.
00	68 00.0	1.0 02	180.0	68 30.0	1.0 02	180.0	69 00.0	1.0 02	180.0	69 30.0	1.0 02	180.0	70 00.0	1.0 02	180.0	70 30.0	1.0 02	180.0	71 00.0	1.0 02	180.0	71 30.0	1.0 02	180.0	00
1	67 59.0	1.0 05	177.5	68 29.0	1.0 05	177.4	68 59.0	1.0 05	177.7	69 28.9	1.0 05	177.3	69 58.9	1.0 05	177.3	70 28.9	1.0 06	177.2	70 58.9	1.0 06	177.2	71 28.8	1.0 06	177.1	1
2	67 56.0	1.0 08	175.0	68 25.9	1.0 08	174.9	68 55.9	1.0 09	174.8	69 25.8	1.0 09	174.7	69 55.7	1.0 09	174.6	70 25.6	1.0 09	174.4	70 55.5	1.0 09	174.3	71 25.4	1.0 10	174.2	2
3	67 51.1	99 12	172.5	68 20.9	99 12	172.3	68 50.7	99 12	172.3	69 20.5	99 12	172.0	69 50.3	99 12	171.9	70 20.1	99 13	171.7	70 49.9	99 13	171.5	71 19.7	99 13	171.3	3
4	67 44.1	99 15	170.0	68 13.8	99 15	169.8	68 43.5	99 15	169.6	69 13.2	99 16	169.4	69 42.9	99 16	169.2	70 12.5	99 16	168.9	70 42.1	99 17	168.7	71 11.7	99 17	168.5	4
05	67 35.3	99 18	167.5	68 04.8	98 18	167.3	68 34.4	98 18	167.0	69 03.9	98 19	166.8	69 33.3	98 19	166.5	70 02.8	98 20	166.3	70 32.2	98 20	166.0	71 01.6	98 20	165.7	05
6	67 24.6	98 21	165.1	67 53.9	98 21	164.8	68 23.2	98 22	164.5	68 52.5	98 22	164.2	69 21.8	97 22	163.9	69 51.0	97 23	163.6	70 20.2	97 23	163.3	70 49.3	97 24	162.9	6
7	67 12.0	97 24	162.7	67 41.1	97 24	162.4	68 10.2	97 25	162.0	68 39.3	97 25	161.7	69 08.3	97 26	161.4	69 37.2	96 27	161.0	70 06.1	96 27	160.6	70 35.0	96 27	160.2	7
8	66 57.7	96 27	160.4	67 26.5	96 27	160.0	67 55.4	96 28	159.6	68 24.2	96 28	159.3	68 52.9	96 29	158.9	69 21.5	95 30	158.4	69 50.2	95 30	158.0	70 18.7	95 30	157.6	8
9	66 41.6	95 30	158.0	67 10.2	95 30	157.7	67 38.7	95 31	157.3	68 07.2	95 31	156.8	68 35.6	95 32	156.4	69 04.0	94 33	156.0	69 32.3	94 33	155.5	70 00.5	94 33	155.0	9
10	66 23.8	94 32	155.8	66 52.1	94 33	155.4	67 20.4	94 33	154.9	67 48.6	94 34	154.5	68 16.7	94 34	154.0	68 44.7	93 35	153.5	69 12.6	93 36	153.0	69 40.4	93 36	152.5	10
1	66 04.5	93 35	153.6	66 32.5	93 35	153.1	67 00.4	93 36	152.6	67 28.2	93 36	152.2	67 56.0	93 37	151.7	68 23.3	92 38	151.2	68 51.2	92 38	150.6	69 18.1	91 39	150.1	1
2	65 43.6	92 37	151.4	66 11.2	92 38	151.0	66 38.8	92 38	150.5	67 06.3	92 39	150.0	67 33.7	93 40	149.4	68 01.0	91 40	148.9	68 28.2	90 41	148.3	68 55.3	90 42	147.7	2
3	65 21.2	91 40	149.3	65 48.5	91 40	148.8	66 15.8	91 41	148.3	66 42.9	90 41	147.8	67 10.0	90 42	147.2	67 36.9	90 43	146.7	68 03.7	89 43	146.1	68 30.3	89 44	145.4	3
4	64 57.4	90 42	147.3	65 24.4	90 42	146.8	65 51.3	89 43	146.2	66 18.1	89 44	145.7	66 44.8	89 44	145.1	67 11.3	88 45	144.5	67 37.7	88 46	143.9	68 03.9	87 46	143.2	4
30	56 15.7	73 65	121.7	56 37.6	73 65	121.0	56 59.3	72 65	120.4	57 20.9	71 66	119.8	57 42.2	71 66	119.1	58 03.4	70 67	118.2	58 24.3	69 67	117.8	58 45.0	69 68	117.1	30
1	55 36.9	73 65	120.4	55 58.6	72 66	119.8	56 20.0	71 66	119.2	56 41.3	71 67	118.5	57 02.4	70 67	117.9	57 23.3	69 67	117.1	57 44.0	68 68	116.6	58 04.4	68 68	115.9	1
2	54 57.6	72 66	119.2	55 19.0	71 67	118.6	55 40.3	71 67	118.0	56 01.3	70 67	117.4	56 22.2	69 68	116.7	56 42.8	68 68	116.1	57 03.3	68 68	115.4	57 23.5	67 69	114.7	2
3	54 17.9	71 67	118.1	54 39.1	70 67	117.5	55 00.1	70 68	116.8	55 20.9	69 68	116.2	55 41.5	68 68	115.6	56 02.0	68 69	114.9	56 22.2	67 69	114.2	56 42.2	66 69	113.6	3
4	53 37.7	70 68	116.9	53 58.7	70 68	116.3	54 19.5	69 68	115.7	54 40.1	69 69	115.1	55 00.5	68 69	114.4	55 20.7	67 69	113.8	55 40.7	66 70	113.1	56 00.5	66 70	112.5	4
35	52 57.1	70 68	115.8	53 17.9	69 69	115.2	53 38.5	68 69	114.6	53 58.9	68 69	114.0	54 19.1	66 70	113.4	54 39.1	66 70	112.7	54 58.9	66 71	112.1	55 18.5	65 71	111.4	35
6	52 16.2	69 69	114.7	52 36.8	68 69	114.1	52 57.1	68 69	113.5	53 17.4	67 70	112.9	53 37.4	66 70	112.3	53 57.2	66 70	111.7	54 16.8	65 71	111.0	54 36.2	64 71	110.4	6
7	51 34.9	68 69	113.7	51 55.3	68 70	113.1	52 15.5	67 70	112.5	52 35.5	66 70	111.9	52 55.3	65 71	111.3	53 14.9	65 71	110.6	53 34.4	64 71	110.0	53 53.6	64 71	109.3	7
8	50 53.3	68 70	112.7	51 13.5	67 70	112.1	51 33.5	67 70	111.5	51 53.3	66 71	110.9	52 13.0	65 71	110.3	52 32.4	65 71	109.6	52 51.7	64 72	109.0	53 10.7	63 72	108.4	8
9	50 11.3	67 70	111.7	50 31.4	67 71	111.1	50 51.2	66 71	110.5	51 10.9	65 71	109.9	51 30.4	64 71	109.3	51 49.7	64 72	108.7	52 08.8	63 72	108.0	52 27.6	63 72	107.4	9
60	34 46.6	61 75	94.5	35 04.7	60 75	94.0	35 22.7	60 75	93.5	35 40.6	59 75	93.0	35 58.4	59 75	92.5	36 16.0	59 75	92.0	36 33.5	58 75	91.5	36 50.9	58 75	91.0	60
1	34 01.5	60 75	93.8	34 19.6	60 75	93.3	34 37.5	60 75	92.8	34 55.4	59 75	92.3	35 13.1	59 75	91.9	35 30.7	59 75	91.4	35 48.2	58 75	90.9	36 05.6	58 75	90.4	1
2	33 16.3	60 75	93.1	33 34.3	60 75	92.6	33 52.3	60 75	92.2	34 10.1	59 75	91.7	34 27.9	59 75	91.3	34 45.5	58 75	90.7	35 02.9	58 75	90.2	35 20.3	58 75	89.7	2
3	32 31.0	60 75	92.4	32 49.1	60 75	92.0	33 07.0	60 75	91.5	33 24.9	59 75	91.0	33 42.6	59 75	90.7	34 00.2	58 75	90.0	34 17.7	58 75	89.5	34 35.0	58 75	89.1	3
4	31 45.8	60 75	91.8	32 03.8	60 75	91.3	32 21.8	60 75	90.8	32 39.6	59 75	90.3	32 57.3	59 75	89.9	33 14.9	58 75	89.4	33 32.4	58 75	88.9	33 49.8	58 75	88.4	4
80	19 43.5	61 75	81.6	20 01.9	61 75	81.1	20 20.2	61 74	80.7	20 38.5	61 74	80.3	20 56.7	60 74	79.9	21 14.8	60 74	79.5	21 32.9	60 74	79.0	21 50.9	60 74	78.6	80
1	18 58.7	61 74	80.5	19 17.2	61 74	80.1	19 35.5	61 74	80.1	19 53.9	61 74	79.7	20 12.1	60 74	79.3	20 30.3	60 74	78.9	20 48.5	60 74	78.4	21 06.5	60 74	78.0	1
2	18 14.1	62 74	80.3	18 32.5	62 74	79.9	18 51.0	62 74	79.5	19 09.4	61 74	79.1	19 27.6	61 74	78.7	19 45.5	61 74	78.2	20 04.1	60 74	77.8	20 22.3	60 74	77.4	2
3	17 29.5	62 74	79.7	17 48.0	62 74	79.3	18 06.5	62 74	78.9	18 24.9	62 74	78.5	18 43.1	61 74	78.1	19 01.7	61 74	77.6	19 19.9	61 73	77.2	19 38.1	61 73	76.8	3
4	16 45.0	62 74	79.1	17 03.6	62 74	78.7	17 22.1	62 74	78.3	17 40.6	62 74	77.9	17 58.4	61 74	77.5	18 17.5	61 74	77.0	18 35.8	61 73	76.6	18 54.1	61 73	76.2	4
85	16 00.5	62 74	78.5	16 19.2	62 74	78.1	16 37.8	62 74	77.7	16 56.4	62 73	77.3	17 14.0	61 73	76.9	17 33.4	61 73	76.4	17 51.8	61 73	76.0	18 10.2	61 73	75.6	85
6	15 16.2	63 74	77.9	15 34.9	63 74	77.5	15 53.6	62 73	77.1	16 12.3	62 73	76.7	16 30.0	62 73	76.3	16 49.4	61 73	75.8	17 07.9	61 73	75.4	17 26.4	61 73	75.0	6
7	14 32.0	63 74	77.3	14 50.8	63 73	76.9	15 09.6	63 73	76.5	15 28.3	62 73	76.1	15 45.9	62 73	75.7	16 05.6	62 73	75.2	16 24.2	62 73	74.8	16 42.7	62 73	74.4	7
8	13 47.9	63 73	76.7	14 06.7	63 73	76.3	14 25.6	63 73	75.9	14 44.4	63 73	75.5	15 02.0	62 73	75.1	15 21.8	62 73	74.6	15 40.5	62 72	74.2	15 59.1	62 72	73.8	8
9	13 03.9	63 73	76.0	13 22.8	63 73	75.6	13 41.7	63 73	75.3	14 00.6	63 73	74.8	14 18.2	63 73	74.4	14 38.2	63 72	74.0	14 57.0	62 72	73.6	15 15.7	62 72	73.2	9
90	12 20.0	63 73	75.4	12 39.0	63 73	75.0	12 58.0	63 73	74.6	13 17.0	63 73	74.2	13 36.0	63 73	73.8	13 54.8	63 72	73.4	14 13.6	63 72	73.0	14 32.4	63 72	72.6	90

Lat. 41°

DECLINATION CONTRARY NAME TO LATITUDE

H.A.	19° 00' Alt.	19° 00' Δd Δt	19° 00' Az.	19° 30' Alt.	19° 30' Δd Δt	19° 30' Az.	20° 00' Alt.	20° 00' Δd Δt	20° 00' Az.	20° 30' Alt.	20° 30' Δd Δt	20° 30' Az.	21° 00' Alt.	21° 00' Δd Δt	21° 00' Az.	21° 30' Alt.	21° 30' Δd Δt	21° 30' Az.	22° 00' Alt.	22° 00' Δd Δt	22° 00' Az.	22° 30' Alt.	22° 30' Δd Δt	22° 30' Az.	H.A.
00	30 00.0	1.00 1.01	180.0	29 30.0	1.00 1.01	180.0	29 00.0	1.00 1.01	180.0	28 30.0	1.00 1.01	180.0	28 00.0	1.00 1.01	180.0	27 30.0	1.00 1.01	180.0	27 00.0	1.00 1.01	180.0	26 30.0	1.01	180.0	00
1	29 59.6	1.00 1.02	178.9	29 29.6	1.00 1.02	178.9	28 59.6	1.00 1.02	178.9	28 29.6	1.00 1.02	178.9	27 59.6	1.00 1.02	178.9	27 29.6	1.00 1.02	179.0	26 59.6	1.00 1.02	179.0	26 29.6	1.00 1.02	179.0	1
2	29 58.3	1.04	177.8	29 28.3	1.04	177.8	28 58.3	1.04	177.9	28 28.3	1.03	177.9	27 58.3	1.04	177.9	27 28.3	1.03	177.9	26 58.4	1.03	177.9	26 28.4	1.03	177.9	2
3	29 56.1	1.05	176.7	29 26.2	1.05	176.8	28 56.2	1.05	176.8	28 26.2	1.05	176.8	27 56.2	1.05	176.8	27 26.3	1.05	176.9	26 56.3	1.05	176.9	26 26.3	1.05	176.9	3
4	29 53.1	1.06	175.6	29 23.2	1.06	175.7	28 53.2	1.06	175.7	28 23.3	1.06	175.7	27 53.3	1.06	175.8	27 23.4	1.06	175.8	26 53.4	1.06	175.8	26 23.5	1.06	175.9	4
05	29 49.2	1.08	174.5	29 19.3	1.08	174.6	28 49.4	1.08	174.6	28 19.5	1.08	174.7	27 49.6	1.08	174.7	27 19.7	1.08	174.8	26 49.7	1.08	174.8	26 19.8	1.07	174.8	05
6	29 44.5	1.09	173.5	29 14.6	1.09	173.5	28 44.7	1.09	173.6	28 14.9	1.09	173.6	27 45.0	1.09	173.7	27 15.1	1.09	173.7	26 45.2	1.09	173.7	26 15.3	1.09	173.8	6
7	29 38.9	99 11	172.4	29 09.1	99 11	172.4	28 39.3	99 11	172.5	28 09.4	99 10	172.6	27 39.6	99 10	172.6	27 09.7	99 10	172.7	26 39.9	99 10	172.7	26 10.1	99 10	172.8	7
8	29 32.5	99 12	171.3	29 02.7	99 12	171.3	28 32.9	99 12	171.4	28 03.1	99 12	171.5	27 33.4	99 12	171.6	27 03.6	99 12	171.6	26 33.8	99 12	171.7	26 04.0	99 11	171.8	8
9	29 25.2	99 14	170.2	28 55.5	99 13	170.3	28 25.8	99 13	170.3	27 56.0	99 13	170.5	27 26.3	99 13	170.5	26 56.6	99 13	170.6	26 26.8	99 13	170.7	25 57.1	99 13	170.8	9
10	29 17.1	99 16	169.1	28 47.5	99 15	169.2	28 17.8	99 15	169.2	27 48.1	99 15	169.4	27 18.5	99 14	169.5	26 48.8	99 14	169.6	26 19.1	99 14	169.7	25 49.4	99 14	169.7	10
1	29 08.2	99 16	168.1	28 38.6	99 16	168.2	28 09.0	99 16	168.2	27 39.4	99 16	168.4	27 09.8	99 16	168.5	26 40.2	99 16	168.6	26 10.6	99 16	168.6	25 41.0	99 15	168.7	1
2	28 58.4	98 18	167.0	28 28.9	98 18	167.1	27 59.4	98 17	167.2	27 29.9	98 17	167.3	27 00.3	98 17	167.4	26 30.8	98 17	167.6	26 01.3	98 17	167.6	25 31.7	98 17	167.7	2
3	28 47.8	98 19	166.1	28 18.4	98 19	166.1	27 49.0	98 18	166.2	27 19.5	98 19	166.3	26 50.1	98 18	166.4	26 20.6	98 18	166.5	25 51.2	98 18	166.6	25 21.7	98 18	166.7	3
4	28 36.4	98 20	164.9	28 07.1	98 20	165.0	27 37.7	98 20	165.1	27 08.4	98 20	165.2	26 39.0	98 20	165.4	26 09.6	98 20	165.5	25 40.3	98 19	165.6	25 10.9	98 19	165.7	4
15	28 24.2	98 22	163.8	27 55.0	98 22	164.0	27 25.7	98 21	164.1	26 56.5	98 21	164.2	26 27.2	98 21	164.3	25 57.9	98 21	164.5	25 28.6	98 21	164.6	24 59.3	98 21	164.7	15
6	28 11.2	97 23	162.8	27 42.1	97 23	162.9	27 12.9	97 23	163.1	26 43.8	97 22	163.2	26 14.6	97 22	163.3	25 45.4	97 22	163.5	25 16.2	97 22	163.6	24 47.0	97 22	163.7	6
7	27 57.5	97 24	161.8	27 28.4	97 24	161.9	26 59.3	97 24	161.9	26 30.3	97 24	162.1	26 01.2	97 24	162.3	25 32.1	97 23	162.5	25 03.0	97 23	162.6	24 33.9	97 24	162.7	7
8	27 42.9	98 26	160.7	27 14.0	98 25	160.9	26 45.0	97 25	161.0	26 16.0	97 25	161.2	25 47.1	97 25	161.3	25 18.1	97 25	161.5	24 49.1	97 24	161.6	24 20.1	97 24	161.7	8
9	27 27.6	97 27	159.7	26 58.7	96 27	159.9	26 29.9	96 26	160.0	26 01.0	96 26	160.2	25 32.2	96 26	160.3	25 03.3	96 26	160.5	24 34.4	96 26	160.6	24 05.5	96 25	160.8	9
20	27 11.5	96 28	158.7	26 42.8	96 28	158.8	26 14.0	96 28	159.0	25 45.3	96 27	159.2	25 16.6	96 27	159.3	24 47.8	96 27	159.5	24 19.0	96 27	159.6	23 50.3	96 27	159.8	20
1	26 54.7	96 29	157.7	26 26.1	95 29	157.8	25 57.5	95 29	158.0	25 28.8	95 29	158.2	25 00.2	95 28	158.3	24 31.6	95 28	158.7	24 02.9	96 28	158.7	23 34.3	96 28	158.8	1
2	26 37.1	95 31	156.7	26 08.6	96 30	156.8	25 40.1	96 30	157.0	25 11.6	96 30	157.2	24 43.1	96 30	157.2	24 14.6	96 30	157.7	23 46.1	96 29	157.7	23 17.6	96 29	157.9	2
3	26 18.8	94 32	155.7	25 50.4	94 31	155.8	25 22.1	95 31	156.0	24 53.7	95 31	156.2	24 25.3	95 31	156.4	23 57.0	95 31	156.7	23 28.6	95 30	156.7	23 00.1	95 30	156.9	3
4	25 59.8	94 33	154.7	25 31.6	94 33	154.7	25 03.3	94 32	155.0	24 35.1	94 32	155.2	24 06.9	94 32	155.4	23 38.6	94 32	155.6	23 10.3	94 32	155.8	22 42.0	94 31	156.0	4
25	25 40.0	94 34	153.7	25 12.0	94 34	153.7	24 43.9	94 34	154.1	24 15.8	94 33	154.3	23 47.7	94 33	154.5	23 19.5	94 33	154.6	22 51.4	94 33	154.8	22 23.3	94 32	155.0	25
6	25 19.6	93 35	152.7	24 51.7	93 35	152.9	24 23.7	93 35	153.1	23 55.7	93 34	153.3	23 27.8	93 34	153.4	22 59.8	93 34	153.9	22 31.8	93 34	154.1	22 03.8	93 33	154.1	6
7	24 58.5	93 36	151.7	24 30.7	93 36	151.9	24 02.9	93 36	152.1	23 35.1	93 36	152.4	23 07.3	93 35	152.6	22 39.4	93 35	153.0	22 11.6	93 35	153.0	21 43.7	93 35	153.2	7
8	24 36.7	92 37	150.8	24 09.1	92 37	151.0	23 41.4	92 37	151.2	23 13.8	92 37	151.4	22 46.1	92 36	151.6	22 18.4	92 36	152.2	21 50.6	92 36	152.0	21 22.9	92 36	152.2	8
9	24 14.3	92 38	149.8	23 46.8	92 38	150.0	23 19.3	92 38	150.2	22 51.8	92 38	150.3	22 24.2	92 38	150.7	21 56.7	92 37	151.3	21 29.1	92 37	151.1	21 01.5	92 37	151.2	9
55	11 17.2	78 60	127.8	10 53.9	78 60	128.2	10 30.5	78 59	128.8	10 07.2	78 59	128.8	9 43.9	78 59	129.1	9 20.5	78 59	129.4	8 57.1	78 59	129.7	8 33.7	78 59	130.1	55
6	10 41.2	77 60	127.1	10 18.1	77 60	127.4	9 54.9	77 60	128.1	9 31.7	77 60	128.1	9 08.5	77 59	128.4	8 45.3	77 59	128.7	8 22.1	77 59	129.0	7 58.8	78 59	129.3	6
7	10 04.9	77 61	126.3	9 41.9	77 61	126.7	9 18.9	77 61	127.3	8 55.9	77 60	127.3	8 32.9	77 60	127.7	8 09.8	77 60	128.0	7 46.7	77 60	128.3	7 23.6	77 59	128.6	7
8	9 28.3	76 62	125.6	9 05.4	76 61	125.9	8 42.6	76 61	126.6	8 19.7	76 61	126.6	7 56.8	76 61	127.0	7 33.9	76 60	127.3	7 11.0	76 60	127.6	6 48.1	77 60	127.9	8
9	8 51.3	76 62	124.9	8 28.6	76 62	125.2	8 05.9	76 62	125.8	7 43.2	76 61	125.9	7 20.5	76 61	126.2	6 57.7	76 61	126.5	6 35.0	76 61	126.9	6 12.2	76 60	127.2	9
60	8 14.0	75 63	124.2	7 51.5	75 62	124.5	7 28.9	75 62	125.2	7 06.3	75 62	125.2	6 43.8	75 62	125.5	6 21.2	75 61	125.8	5 58.6	75 61	126.2	5 35.9	75 61	126.5	60
1	7 36.4	75 63	123.5	7 14.0	75 63	123.8	6 51.6	75 63	124.5	6 29.2	75 62	124.5	6 06.7	75 62	124.8	5 44.3	75 62	125.1	5 21.8	75 62	125.5				1
2	6 58.4	74 64	122.7	6 36.2	74 63	123.1	6 13.9	74 63	123.8	5 51.7	74 63	123.8	5 29.4	74 63	124.1	5 07.1	74 62	124.4							2
3	6 20.2	74 64	122.0	5 58.1	74 64	122.4	5 36.0	74 64	123.1	5 13.9	74 63	123.1													3
4	5 41.7	73 65	121.3	5 19.7	73 64	121.7																			4

Lat. 42°

DECLINATION CONTRARY NAME TO LATITUDE

H.A.	19° 00' Alt.	Az.	19° 30' Alt.	Δd Δt	Az.	20° 00' Alt.	Δd Δt	Az.	20° 30' Alt.	Δd Δt	Az.	21° 00' Alt.	Δd Δt	Az.	21° 30' Alt.	Δd Δt	Az.	22° 00' Alt.	Δd Δt	Az.	22° 30' Alt.	Δd Δt	Az.	H.A.
00	29 00.0	180.0	28 30.0	1.01	180.0	28 00.0	1.01	180.0	27 30.0	1.01	180.0	27 00.0	1.01	180.0	26 30.0	1.01	180.0	26 00.0	1.01	180.0	25 30.0	1.01	180.0	00
1	28 59.6	178.9	28 29.6	1.02	178.9	27 59.6	1.02	178.9	27 29.6	1.02	179.0	26 59.6	1.02	179.0	26 29.6	1.02	179.0	25 59.6	1.02	179.0	25 29.6	1.02	179.0	1
2	28 58.3	177.9	28 28.3	1.03	177.9	27 58.3	1.03	177.9	27 28.4	1.03	177.9	26 58.4	1.03	177.9	26 28.4	1.03	177.9	25 58.4	1.03	177.9	25 28.4	1.03	178.0	2
3	28 56.2	176.8	28 26.2	1.05	176.8	27 56.3	1.05	176.8	27 26.3	1.05	176.8	26 56.3	1.05	176.9	26 26.3	1.05	176.9	25 56.4	1.05	176.9	25 26.4	1.05	176.9	3
4	28 53.3	175.7	28 23.3	1.06	175.7	27 53.4	1.06	175.7	27 23.4	1.06	175.8	26 53.5	1.06	175.8	26 23.5	1.06	175.8	25 53.6	1.06	175.8	25 23.6	1.06	175.9	4
05	28 49.5	174.6	28 19.6	1.08	174.6	27 49.7	1.08	174.7	27 19.7	1.08	174.7	26 49.8	1.07	174.8	26 19.9	1.07	174.8	25 50.0	1.07	174.8	25 20.1	1.07	174.9	05
6	28 44.9	173.5	28 15.0	1.09	173.6	27 45.1	1.09	173.6	27 15.2	1.09	173.7	26 45.4	1.09	173.7	26 15.5	1.09	173.8	25 45.6	1.09	173.8	25 15.7	1.09	173.9	6
7	28 39.4	172.5	28 09.6	99 10	172.5	27 39.8	99 10	172.6	27 09.9	99 10	172.6	26 40.1	99 10	172.7	26 10.2	99 10	172.7	25 40.4	99 10	172.8	25 10.5	99 10	172.9	7
8	28 33.2	171.4	28 03.4	99 12	171.5	27 33.6	99 11	171.5	27 03.8	99 12	171.6	26 34.0	99 11	171.6	26 04.2	99 11	171.7	25 34.4	99 11	171.8	25 04.6	99 11	171.8	8
9	28 26.1	170.3	27 56.4	99 13	170.4	27 26.6	99 13	170.5	26 56.9	99 13	170.5	26 27.1	99 13	170.6	25 57.4	99 13	170.6	25 27.6	99 13	170.8	24 57.9	99 12	170.8	9
10	28 18.2	169.4	27 48.5	99 14	169.3	27 18.8	99 14	169.4	26 49.1	99 14	169.5	26 19.5	99 14	169.6	25 49.8	99 14	169.7	25 20.1	99 14	169.7	24 50.4	99 14	169.7	10
1	28 09.5	168.3	27 39.9	99 16	168.3	27 10.2	99 16	168.4	26 40.6	99 16	168.4	26 11.0	99 15	168.6	25 41.4	99 15	168.6	25 11.7	99 15	168.7	24 42.1	99 15	168.8	1
2	27 59.9	167.1	27 30.4	98 17	167.2	27 00.9	98 17	167.3	26 31.3	98 17	167.4	26 01.8	99 17	167.5	25 32.2	99 17	167.6	25 02.6	99 16	167.7	24 33.1	99 16	167.8	2
3	27 49.6	166.1	27 20.1	98 19	166.2	26 50.7	98 18	166.3	26 21.2	98 18	166.4	25 51.7	98 18	166.6	25 22.3	98 18	166.6	24 52.8	98 18	166.7	24 24.3	98 18	166.8	3
4	27 38.5	165.0	27 09.1	98 20	165.2	26 39.7	98 20	165.3	26 10.3	98 19	165.3	25 40.9	98 19	165.5	25 11.5	98 19	165.5	24 42.1	98 19	165.7	24 12.7	98 19	165.8	4
15	27 26.6	164.0	26 57.3	98 21	164.1	26 28.0	98 21	164.2	25 58.7	98 21	164.2	25 29.4	98 20	164.5	25 00.1	98 20	164.5	24 30.8	98 20	164.7	24 01.4	98 20	164.8	15
6	27 13.9	163.0	26 44.7	97 22	163.1	26 15.5	97 23	163.2	25 46.3	97 22	163.2	25 17.1	97 22	163.6	24 47.9	97 22	163.6	24 18.6	97 21	163.7	23 49.4	97 21	163.8	6
7	27 00.4	161.9	26 31.4	97 24	162.1	26 02.2	97 24	162.2	25 33.1	97 23	162.3	25 04.0	97 23	162.5	24 34.9	97 23	162.6	24 05.7	97 23	162.7	23 36.6	97 23	162.9	7
8	26 46.2	160.9	26 17.2	97 25	161.0	25 48.2	97 25	161.2	25 19.2	97 24	161.3	24 50.2	97 24	161.5	24 21.2	97 24	161.6	23 52.1	97 24	161.7	23 23.1	97 24	161.9	8
9	26 31.3	159.9	26 02.4	96 26	160.0	25 33.5	96 26	160.2	25 04.6	96 26	160.2	24 35.7	96 25	160.5	24 06.7	96 25	160.6	23 37.8	96 25	160.7	23 08.9	96 25	160.9	9
20	26 15.6	158.9	25 46.8	96 27	159.0	25 18.0	96 27	159.2	24 49.2	96 27	159.2	24 20.4	96 27	159.5	23 51.6	96 26	159.6	23 22.8	96 26	159.8	22 53.9	96 26	159.9	20
1	25 59.1	157.9	25 30.5	96 28	158.0	25 01.8	96 28	158.2	24 33.1	96 28	158.2	24 04.4	96 28	158.5	23 35.7	96 28	158.7	23 07.0	96 27	158.8	22 38.3	96 27	159.0	1
2	25 41.9	156.9	25 13.4	95 30	157.0	24 44.9	95 29	157.2	24 16.3	95 29	157.3	23 47.7	95 29	157.5	23 19.1	95 29	157.7	22 50.5	95 29	157.9	22 21.9	95 28	158.0	2
3	25 24.1	155.9	24 55.7	95 31	156.0	24 27.2	95 31	156.2	23 58.8	95 30	156.3	23 30.3	95 30	156.4	23 01.9	95 30	156.7	22 33.2	95 30	156.8	22 04.9	95 30	157.1	3
4	25 05.5	154.9	24 37.2	94 32	155.1	24 08.9	94 32	155.2	23 40.6	94 32	155.2	23 12.3	94 31	155.6	22 43.9	94 31	155.8	22 15.6	94 31	155.9	21 47.2	94 31	156.1	4
25	24 46.2	153.9	24 18.0	94 33	154.1	23 49.9	94 33	154.3	23 21.7	94 33	154.3	22 53.5	94 32	154.6	22 25.3	94 32	154.8	21 57.1	94 32	155.2	21 28.8	94 32	155.2	25
6	24 26.2	152.9	23 58.2	93 34	153.1	23 30.2	93 34	153.3	23 02.1	94 34	153.3	22 34.1	94 34	153.7	22 06.0	94 33	153.9	21 37.9	94 33	154.3	21 09.8	94 33	154.3	6
7	24 05.6	152.0	23 37.7	93 35	152.2	23 09.8	93 35	152.3	22 41.9	93 35	152.4	22 14.0	93 35	152.8	21 46.0	93 34	153.1	21 18.1	93 34	153.1	20 50.1	93 34	153.3	7
8	23 44.3	151.0	23 16.6	93 36	151.2	22 48.8	93 36	151.4	22 21.0	93 36	151.4	21 53.2	93 36	151.6	21 25.4	93 35	152.0	20 57.6	93 35	152.2	20 29.8	93 35	152.2	8
9	23 22.4	150.0	22 54.8	92 37	150.3	22 27.1	92 37	150.5	21 59.5	92 37	150.7	21 31.9	92 37	150.9	21 04.2	92 36	151.1	20 36.5	92 36	151.3	20 08.8	92 36	151.5	9
55	10 40.3	128.0	10 16.7	79 59	128.3	9 53.2	79 58	128.6	9 29.6	79 58	128.9	9 06.0	79 58	129.2	8 42.3	79 57	129.6	8 18.7	79 57	129.9	7 55.0	79 57	130.2	55
6	10 05.0	127.2	9 41.6	78 59	127.6	9 18.1	78 59	127.9	8 54.7	78 59	128.2	8 31.2	78 58	128.5	8 07.8	78 58	128.8	7 44.3	78 58	129.1	7 20.8	78 58	129.4	6
7	9 29.3	126.5	9 06.0	78 60	126.8	8 42.8	78 60	127.1	8 19.5	78 59	127.4	7 56.2	78 59	127.8	7 32.8	78 58	128.1	7 09.5	78 58	128.4	6 46.2	78 58	128.7	7
8	8 53.3	125.7	8 30.2	77 60	126.1	8 07.0	77 60	126.4	7 43.9	77 60	126.7	7 20.7	77 60	127.0	6 57.6	77 59	127.4	6 34.4	77 59	127.7	6 11.2	77 59	128.0	8
9	8 16.9	125.0	7 54.0	77 61	125.3	7 31.0	77 61	125.7	7 08.0	77 60	126.0	6 45.0	77 60	126.3	6 22.0	77 60	126.6	5 58.9	77 59	127.0	5 35.9	77 59	127.3	9
60	7 40.2	124.3	7 17.4	76 61	124.6	6 54.6	76 61	124.9	6 31.7	76 61	125.2	6 08.9	76 61	125.6	5 46.0	76 60	125.9	5 23.1	76 60	126.2	5 00.2	76 60	126.6	60
1	7 03.2	123.6	6 40.6	76 62	123.9	6 17.9	76 62	124.2	5 55.2	76 61	124.6	5 32.5	76 61	124.9	5 09.7	76 61	125.2							1
2	6 25.9	122.8	6 03.4	75 62	123.2	5 40.9	75 62	123.5	5 18.3	75 62	123.8													2
3	5 48.3	122.1	5 26.1	75 63	122.5	5 03.5	75 63	122.8																3
4	5 10.4	121.4																						4

ALTITUDE CORRECTION FOR D. R. LATITUDE

LATITUDE DIFFERENCE (minutes of arc)

Az.	1'	2'	3'	4'	5'	6'	7'	8'	9'	10'	11'	12'	13'	14'	15'	Az.
0 / 180	1.0	2.0	3.0	4.0	5.0	6.0	7.0	8.0	9.0	10.0	11.0	12.0	13.0	14.0	15.0	0 / 180
1 / 179	1.0	2.0	3.0	4.0	5.0	6.0	7.0	8.0	9.0	10.0	11.0	12.0	13.0	14.0	15.0	1 / 179
2 / 178	1.0	2.0	3.0	4.0	5.0	6.0	7.0	8.0	9.0	10.0	11.0	12.0	13.0	14.0	15.0	2 / 178
3 / 177	1.0	2.0	3.0	4.0	5.0	6.0	7.0	8.0	9.0	10.0	11.0	12.0	13.0	14.0	15.0	3 / 177
4 / 176	1.0	2.0	3.0	4.0	5.0	6.0	7.0	8.0	9.0	10.0	11.0	12.0	13.0	14.0	15.0	4 / 176
5 / 175	1.0	2.0	3.0	4.0	5.0	6.0	7.0	8.0	9.0	10.0	11.0	12.0	13.0	13.9	14.9	5 / 175
6 / 174	1.0	2.0	3.0	4.0	5.0	6.0	7.0	8.0	8.9	9.9	10.9	11.9	12.9	13.9	14.9	6 / 174
7 / 173	1.0	2.0	3.0	4.0	5.0	6.0	6.9	7.9	8.9	9.9	10.9	11.9	12.9	13.9	14.9	7 / 173
8 / 172	1.0	2.0	3.0	4.0	5.0	5.9	6.9	7.9	8.9	9.9	10.9	11.9	12.9	13.8	14.8	8 / 172
9 / 171	1.0	2.0	3.0	4.0	4.9	5.9	6.9	7.9	8.9	9.9	10.9	11.9	12.8	13.8	14.8	9 / 171
10 / 170	1.0	2.0	3.0	3.9	4.9	5.9	6.9	7.9	8.9	9.8	10.8	11.8	12.8	13.8	14.8	10 / 170
11 / 169	1.0	2.0	3.0	3.9	4.9	5.9	6.9	7.9	8.8	9.8	10.8	11.8	12.7	13.7	14.7	11 / 169
12 / 168	1.0	2.0	2.9	3.9	4.9	5.9	6.8	7.8	8.8	9.8	10.7	11.7	12.7	13.6	14.7	12 / 168
13 / 167	1.0	1.9	2.9	3.9	4.9	5.8	6.8	7.8	8.7	9.7	10.7	11.6	12.6	13.6	14.6	13 / 167
14 / 166	1.0	1.9	2.9	3.9	4.9	5.8	6.8	7.8	8.7	9.7	10.7	11.6	12.6	13.6	14.6	14 / 166
15 / 165	1.0	1.9	2.9	3.9	4.8	5.8	6.8	7.7	8.7	9.7	10.6	11.6	12.6	13.6	14.5	15 / 165
16 / 164	1.0	1.9	2.9	3.8	4.8	5.7	6.7	7.7	8.6	9.6	10.6	11.5	12.5	13.5	14.4	16 / 164
17 / 163	1.0	1.9	2.9	3.8	4.8	5.7	6.7	7.6	8.6	9.6	10.5	11.5	12.4	13.4	14.3	17 / 163
18 / 162	1.0	1.9	2.8	3.8	4.7	5.7	6.7	7.6	8.5	9.5	10.4	11.4	12.3	13.3	14.2	18 / 162
19 / 161	0.9	1.8	2.8	3.7	4.7	5.7	6.6	7.6	8.5	9.5	10.4	11.3	12.3	13.2	14.2	19 / 161
20 / 160	0.9	1.9	2.8	3.8	4.7	5.6	6.6	7.5	8.5	9.4	10.3	11.3	12.2	13.2	14.1	20 / 160
21 / 159	0.9	1.8	2.8	3.7	4.7	5.6	6.5	7.5	8.4	9.3	10.3	11.2	12.1	13.1	14.0	21 / 159
22 / 158	0.9	1.8	2.8	3.7	4.6	5.5	6.5	7.4	8.3	9.3	10.2	11.1	12.0	13.0	13.9	22 / 158
23 / 157	0.9	1.8	2.7	3.7	4.6	5.5	6.4	7.3	8.3	9.2	10.1	11.0	12.0	12.9	13.8	23 / 157
24 / 156	0.9	1.8	2.7	3.6	4.6	5.5	6.4	7.3	8.2	9.1	10.0	11.0	11.9	12.8	13.7	24 / 156
25 / 155	0.9	1.8	2.7	3.6	4.5	5.4	6.3	7.3	8.2	9.1	10.0	10.9	11.8	12.7	13.6	25 / 155
26 / 154	0.9	1.8	2.7	3.6	4.5	5.4	6.3	7.2	8.1	9.0	9.9	10.8	11.7	12.6	13.5	26 / 154
27 / 153	0.9	1.8	2.7	3.6	4.5	5.3	6.2	7.1	8.0	8.9	9.8	10.7	11.5	12.5	13.4	27 / 153
28 / 152	0.9	1.8	2.6	3.5	4.4	5.3	6.2	7.0	8.0	8.8	9.7	10.6	11.5	12.4	13.2	28 / 152
29 / 151	0.9	1.7	2.6	3.5	4.4	5.2	6.1	7.0	7.9	8.7	9.6	10.5	11.4	13.1	13.1	29 / 151
60 / 120	0.5	1.0	1.5	2.0	2.5	3.0	3.5	4.0	4.5	5.0	5.5	6.0	6.5	7.0	7.5	60 / 120
61 / 119	0.5	1.0	1.5	2.0	2.4	2.9	3.4	3.9	4.4	4.8	5.3	5.8	6.3	6.8	7.3	61 / 119
62 / 118	0.5	0.9	1.4	1.9	2.3	2.8	3.3	3.8	4.2	4.7	5.2	5.6	6.1	6.6	7.0	62 / 118
63 / 117	0.5	0.9	1.4	1.8	2.3	2.7	3.2	3.6	4.1	4.5	5.0	5.4	5.9	6.4	6.8	63 / 117
64 / 116	0.4	0.9	1.3	1.8	2.2	2.6	3.1	3.5	3.9	4.4	4.8	5.3	5.7	6.1	6.6	64 / 116
75 / 105	0.3	0.5	0.8	1.0	1.3	1.6	1.8	2.1	2.3	2.6	2.8	3.1	3.4	3.6	3.9	75 / 105
76 / 104	0.2	0.5	0.7	1.0	1.2	1.5	1.7	1.9	2.2	2.4	2.7	2.9	3.1	3.4	3.6	76 / 104
77 / 103	0.2	0.4	0.6	0.9	1.1	1.3	1.5	1.7	2.0	2.2	2.5	2.7	2.9	3.1	3.4	77 / 103
78 / 102	0.2	0.4	0.6	0.8	1.0	1.2	1.5	1.7	1.9	2.1	2.3	2.5	2.7	2.9	3.1	78 / 102
79 / 101	0.2	0.4	0.6	0.8	1.0	1.1	1.3	1.5	1.7	1.9	2.1	2.3	2.5	2.7	2.9	79 / 101
80 / 100	0.2	0.3	0.5	0.7	0.9	1.0	1.2	1.4	1.6	1.7	1.9	2.1	2.3	2.4	2.6	80 / 100
81 / 99	0.2	0.3	0.5	0.6	0.8	0.9	1.1	1.3	1.4	1.6	1.8	1.9	2.1	2.2	2.3	81 / 99
82 / 98	0.1	0.3	0.4	0.5	0.7	0.8	1.0	1.1	1.2	1.4	1.5	1.6	1.7	1.9	2.1	82 / 98
83 / 97	0.1	0.2	0.3	0.4	0.6	0.7	0.9	1.0	1.1	1.2	1.3	1.5	1.6	1.7	1.8	83 / 97
84 / 96	0.1	0.2	0.3	0.4	0.5	0.6	0.7	0.8	0.9	1.0	1.1	1.3	1.4	1.5	1.6	84 / 96

LAT. DIFF. (tenths of minutes of arc)

Az.	0.1'	0.2'	0.3'	0.4'	0.5'	0.6'	0.7'	0.8'	0.9'	Az.
0–4 / 176–180	0.1	0.2	0.3	0.4	0.5	0.6	0.7	0.8	0.9	0–4 / 176–180
5–9 / 171–175	0.1	0.2	0.3	0.4	0.5	0.6	0.7	0.8	0.9	5–9 / 171–175
10–14 / 166–170	0.1	0.2	0.3	0.4	0.5	0.6	0.7	0.8	0.9	10–14 / 166–170
15–19 / 161–165	0.1	0.2	0.3	0.4	0.5	0.6 / 0.5	0.7 / 0.6	0.8 / 0.7	0.9	15–19 / 161–165
20–24 / 156–160	0.1	0.2	0.3	0.4	0.5 / 0.4	0.6 / 0.5	0.7 / 0.6	0.8 / 0.7	0.9 / 0.8	20–24 / 156–160
25–29 / 151–155	0.1	0.2	0.3	0.4 / 0.3	0.5 / 0.4	0.6 / 0.5	0.7 / 0.6	0.8 / 0.7	0.9 / 0.8	25–29 / 151–155
60–64 / 116–120	0.0	0.1	0.2	0.2	0.2	0.3	0.4 / 0.3	0.4	0.4	60–64 / 116–120
75–79 / 101–105	0.0	0.0	0.1	0.1	0.1	0.2	0.2 / 0.1	0.2	0.2	75–79 / 101–105
80–84 / 96–100	0.0	0.0	0.0	0.1	0.1	0.1	0.1	0.1	0.2 / 0.1	80–84 / 96–100

Azimuth angle greater than 90°:
If DR latitude is greater than selected tabulated latitude, ΔL correction is *minus*; but for DR latitude less than selected tabulated latitude, the correction is *plus*.
Azimuth angle less than 90°:
If DR latitude is greater than selected tabulated latitude, ΔL correction is *plus*; but for DR latitude less than selected tabulated latitude, the correction is *minus*.

ALTITUDE CORRECTION FOR D. R. LATITUDE

LATITUDE DIFFERENCE (minutes of arc)

Az.°	Az.°	16'	17'	18'	19'	20'	21'	22'	23'	24'	25'	26'	27'	28'	29'	30'
0	180	16.0	17.0	18.0	19.0	20.0	21.0	22.0	23.0	24.0	25.0	26.0	27.0	28.0	29.0	30.0
1	179	16.0	17.0	18.0	19.0	20.0	21.0	22.0	23.0	24.0	25.0	26.0	27.0	28.0	29.0	30.0
2	178	16.0	17.0	18.0	19.0	20.0	21.0	22.0	23.0	24.0	25.0	26.0	27.0	28.0	29.0	30.0
3	177	16.0	17.0	18.0	19.0	20.0	21.0	22.0	23.0	24.0	25.0	26.0	27.0	28.0	29.0	30.0
4	176	16.0	17.0	18.0	19.0	20.0	20.9	21.9	22.9	23.9	24.9	25.9	26.9	27.9	28.9	29.9
5	175	15.9	16.9	17.9	18.9	19.9	20.9	21.9	22.9	23.9	24.9	25.9	26.9	27.9	28.9	29.9
6	174	15.9	16.9	17.9	18.9	19.9	20.9	21.9	22.9	23.9	24.9	25.9	26.9	27.8	28.8	29.8
7	173	15.9	16.9	17.9	18.9	19.9	20.8	21.8	22.8	23.8	24.8	25.8	26.8	27.8	28.8	29.8
8	172	15.8	16.8	17.8	18.8	19.8	20.8	21.8	22.8	23.8	24.8	25.7	26.7	27.7	28.7	29.7
9	171	15.8	16.8	17.8	18.8	19.8	20.7	21.7	22.7	23.7	24.7	25.7	26.7	27.7	28.6	29.6
10	170	15.8	16.7	17.7	18.7	19.7	20.7	21.7	22.7	23.6	24.6	25.6	26.6	27.6	28.6	29.5
11	169	15.7	16.7	17.7	18.7	19.6	20.6	21.6	22.6	23.6	24.5	25.5	26.5	27.5	28.5	29.4
12	168	15.7	16.6	17.6	18.6	19.6	20.5	21.5	22.5	23.5	24.5	25.4	26.4	27.4	28.4	29.3
13	167	15.6	16.6	17.5	18.5	19.5	20.5	21.4	22.4	23.4	24.4	25.3	26.3	27.3	28.3	29.2
14	166	15.5	16.5	17.5	18.4	19.4	20.4	21.3	22.3	23.3	24.3	25.2	26.2	27.2	28.1	29.1
15	165	15.5	16.4	17.4	18.4	19.3	20.3	21.3	22.2	23.2	24.1	25.1	26.1	27.0	28.0	29.0
16	164	15.4	16.3	17.3	18.3	19.2	20.2	21.1	22.1	23.1	24.0	25.0	26.0	26.9	27.9	28.8
17	163	15.3	16.3	17.2	18.2	19.1	20.1	21.0	22.0	23.0	23.9	24.9	25.8	26.8	27.7	28.7
18	162	15.2	16.2	17.1	18.1	19.0	20.0	20.9	21.9	22.8	23.8	24.7	25.7	26.6	27.6	28.5
19	161	15.1	16.1	17.0	18.0	18.9	19.9	20.8	21.7	22.7	23.6	24.6	25.5	26.5	27.4	28.4
20	160	15.0	16.0	16.9	17.9	18.8	19.7	20.7	21.6	22.6	23.5	24.4	25.4	26.3	27.3	28.2
21	159	14.9	15.9	16.8	17.7	18.7	19.6	20.5	21.5	22.4	23.3	24.3	25.2	26.1	27.1	28.0
22	158	14.8	15.8	16.7	17.6	18.5	19.5	20.4	21.3	22.3	23.2	24.1	25.0	26.0	26.9	27.8
23	157	14.7	15.6	16.6	17.5	18.4	19.3	20.3	21.2	22.1	23.0	23.9	24.9	25.8	26.7	27.6
24	156	14.6	15.5	16.4	17.4	18.3	19.2	20.1	21.0	21.9	22.8	23.8	24.7	25.6	26.5	27.4
25	155	14.5	15.4	16.3	17.2	18.1	19.0	19.9	20.8	21.8	22.7	23.6	24.5	25.4	26.3	27.2
26	154	14.4	15.3	16.2	17.1	18.0	18.9	19.8	20.7	21.6	22.5	23.4	24.3	25.2	26.1	27.0
27	153	14.3	15.2	16.0	16.9	17.8	18.7	19.6	20.5	21.4	22.3	23.2	24.1	24.9	25.8	26.7
28	152	14.1	15.0	15.9	16.8	17.7	18.5	19.4	20.3	21.2	22.1	23.0	23.8	24.7	25.6	26.5
29	151	14.0	14.9	15.7	16.6	17.5	18.4	19.2	20.1	21.0	21.9	22.7	23.6	24.5	25.4	26.2
60	120	8.0	8.5	9.0	9.5	10.0	10.5	11.0	11.5	12.0	12.5	13.0	13.5	14.0	14.5	15.0
61	119	7.8	8.2	8.7	9.2	9.7	10.2	10.7	11.2	11.6	12.1	12.6	13.1	13.6	14.1	14.5
62	118	7.5	8.0	8.5	8.9	9.4	9.9	10.3	10.8	11.3	11.7	12.2	12.7	13.1	13.6	14.1
63	117	7.3	7.7	8.2	8.6	9.1	9.5	10.0	10.4	10.9	11.3	11.8	12.3	12.7	13.2	13.6
64	116	7.0	7.5	7.9	8.3	8.8	9.2	9.6	10.1	10.5	11.0	11.4	11.8	12.3	12.7	13.2
75	105	4.1	4.4	4.7	4.9	5.2	5.4	5.7	6.0	6.2	6.5	6.7	7.0	7.2	7.5	7.8
76	104	3.9	4.1	4.4	4.6	4.8	5.1	5.3	5.6	5.8	6.0	6.3	6.5	6.8	7.0	7.3
77	103	3.6	3.8	4.0	4.3	4.5	4.7	5.0	5.2	5.4	5.6	5.8	6.1	6.3	6.5	6.7
78	102	3.3	3.5	3.7	4.0	4.2	4.4	4.6	4.8	5.0	5.2	5.4	5.6	5.8	6.0	6.2
79	101	3.0	3.2	3.4	3.6	3.8	4.0	4.2	4.4	4.6	4.8	5.0	5.2	5.3	5.5	5.7
80	100	2.8	3.0	3.1	3.3	3.5	3.6	3.8	4.0	4.2	4.3	4.5	4.7	4.9	5.0	5.2
81	99	2.5	2.7	2.8	3.0	3.1	3.3	3.4	3.6	3.8	3.9	4.1	4.2	4.4	4.5	4.7
82	98	2.2	2.4	2.5	2.6	2.8	2.9	3.1	3.2	3.3	3.5	3.6	3.8	3.9	4.0	4.2
83	97	1.9	2.1	2.2	2.3	2.4	2.6	2.7	2.8	2.9	3.0	3.2	3.3	3.4	3.5	3.7
84	96	1.7	1.8	1.9	2.0	2.1	2.2	2.3	2.4	2.5	2.6	2.7	2.8	2.9	3.0	3.1

LAT. DIFF. (tenths of minutes of arc)

Az.°	Az.°	0.1'	0.2'	0.3'	0.4'	0.5'	0.6'	0.7'	0.8'	0.9'
0	180	0.1	0.2	0.3	0.4	0.5	0.6	0.7	0.8	0.9
5	175	0.1	0.2	0.3	0.4	0.5	0.6	0.7	0.8	0.9
10	170	0.1	0.2	0.3	0.4	0.5	0.6	0.7	0.8	0.9
15	165	0.1	0.2	0.3	0.4	0.5	0.6	0.7	0.8	0.9
16	164									0.9
17	163									0.8
20	160	0.1	0.2	0.3	0.4	0.5	0.6	0.7	0.8	
21	159						0.6	0.7		
22	158						0.5	0.6		
25	155	0.1	0.2	0.3	0.5	0.5	0.5	0.6	0.8	
27	153				0.4	0.4				
28	152				0.3					
60	120	0.0	0.1	0.2	0.2	0.2	0.3	0.4	0.4	0.4
61	119		0.0	0.1				0.3		
75	105	0.0	0.0				0.2	0.2	0.2	0.2
77	103						0.1	0.1		
80	100	0.0	0.0	0.1	0.1	0.1	0.1	0.1	0.1	0.2
81	99			0.0	0.0					0.1
84	96					0.1				

Azimuth angle greater than 90°:
If DR latitude is greater than selected tabulated latitude, ΔL correction is *minus*; but for DR latitude less than selected tabulated latitude, the correction is *plus*.
Azimuth angle less than 90°:
If DR latitude is greater than selected tabulated latitude, ΔL correction is *plus*; but for DR latitude less than selected tabulated latitude, the correction is *minus*.

MULTIPLICATION TABLE

Δd or Δt

DEC. DIFF. OR H. A. DIFF. (tenths of minutes)

Δ	0.1'	0.2'	0.3'	0.4'	0.5'	0.6'	0.7'	0.8'	0.9'	Δ
01	0.0	0.0	0.0	0.0	0.0	0.0	0.0	0.0	0.0	01
02	0.0	0.0	0.0	0.0	0.0	0.0	0.0	0.0	0.0	02
03	0.0	0.0	0.0	0.0	0.0	0.0	0.0	0.0	0.0	03
04	0.0	0.0	0.0	0.0	0.0	0.0	0.0	0.0	0.0	04
25	0.0	0.1	0.1	0.1	0.1	0.2	0.2	0.2	0.2	25
26										26
27					0.1			0.2	0.2	27
28								0.2	0.3	28
29										29
30	0.0	0.1	0.1	0.1	0.2	0.2	0.2	0.2	0.3	30
1								0.2		1
2								0.3		2
3										3
4							0.4			4
60	0.1	0.1	0.2	0.2	0.3	0.4	0.4	0.5	0.5	60
1				0.2					0.5	1
2				0.3					0.6	2
3										3
4							0.4			4
65	0.1	0.1	0.2	0.3	0.3	0.4	0.5	0.5	0.6	65
66										66
67					0.3					67
68								0.5		68
69						0.4		0.6		69
70	0.1	0.1	0.2	0.3	0.4	0.4	0.5	0.6	0.6	70
1									0.6	1
2									0.7	2
3		0.1					0.5			3
4		0.2					0.6			4
75	0.1	0.2	0.2	0.3	0.4	0.4	0.5	0.6	0.7	75
6						0.5				6
7										7
8										8
9										9
90	0.1	0.2	0.3	0.4	0.5	0.6	0.6	0.7	0.8	90
1										1
2							0.6	0.7		2
3								0.8	0.8	3
4										4
95	0.1	0.2	0.3	0.4	0.5	0.6	0.7	0.8	0.9	95
6										6
7										7
8										8
99										99
Δ	0.1'	0.2'	0.3'	0.4'	0.5'	0.6'	0.7'	0.8'	0.9'	Δ

DEC. DIFF. OR H. A. DIFF. (minutes of arc)

Δ	1'	2'	3'	4'	5'	6'	7'	8'	9'	10'	11'	12'	13'	14'	15'	Δ
01	0.0	0.0	0.0	0.0	0.0	0.1	0.1	0.1	0.1	0.1	0.1	0.2	0.1	0.1	0.3	01
02	0.0	0.0	0.1	0.1	0.1	0.1	0.1	0.2	0.2	0.2	0.2	0.2	0.3	0.3	0.3	02
03	0.0	0.1	0.1	0.1	0.2	0.2	0.2	0.2	0.3	0.3	0.3	0.4	0.4	0.4	0.5	03
04	0.0	0.1	0.1	0.2	0.2	0.2	0.3	0.3	0.4	0.4	0.4	0.5	0.5	0.6	0.6	04
25	0.3	0.5	0.8	1.0	1.3	1.5	1.8	2.0	2.3	2.5	2.8	3.0	3.3	3.5	3.8	25
6	.3	.6	.8	1.1	1.3	1.6	1.9	2.1	2.4	2.6	2.9	3.1	3.4	3.6	3.9	6
7	.3	.5	.8	1.1	1.4	1.6	1.9	2.2	2.4	2.7	3.0	3.2	3.5	3.8	4.0	7
8	.3	.6	.8	1.1	1.4	1.7	2.0	2.2	2.5	2.8	3.1	3.4	3.6	3.9	4.2	8
9	.3	.6	.9	1.2	1.5	1.7	2.0	2.3	2.6	2.9	3.2	3.5	3.8	4.1	4.4	9
30	0.3	0.6	0.9	1.2	1.5	1.8	2.1	2.4	2.7	3.0	3.3	3.6	3.9	4.2	4.5	30
1	.3	.6	.9	1.2	1.6	1.9	2.2	2.5	2.8	3.1	3.4	3.7	4.0	4.3	4.7	1
2	.3	.6	1.0	1.3	1.6	1.9	2.2	2.6	2.9	3.2	3.5	3.8	4.2	4.5	4.8	2
3	.3	.7	1.0	1.3	1.7	2.0	2.3	2.6	3.0	3.3	3.6	4.0	4.3	4.6	5.0	3
4	.3	.7	1.1	1.4	1.7	2.0	2.4	2.7	3.1	3.4	3.7	4.1	4.4	4.8	5.1	4
60	0.6	1.2	1.8	2.4	3.0	3.6	4.2	4.8	5.4	6.0	6.6	7.2	7.8	8.4	9.0	60
1	.6	1.2	1.8	2.4	3.1	3.7	4.3	4.9	5.5	6.1	6.7	7.3	7.9	8.5	9.2	1
2	.6	1.2	1.9	2.5	3.1	3.7	4.3	5.0	5.6	6.2	6.8	7.4	8.1	8.7	9.3	2
3	.6	1.3	1.9	2.5	3.2	3.8	4.4	5.0	5.7	6.3	6.9	7.6	8.2	8.8	9.5	3
4	.6	1.3	1.9	2.6	3.2	3.8	4.5	5.1	5.8	6.4	7.0	7.7	8.3	9.0	9.6	4
65	0.7	1.3	2.0	2.6	3.3	3.9	4.6	5.2	5.9	6.5	7.2	7.8	8.5	9.1	9.8	65
6	.7	1.3	2.0	2.6	3.3	4.0	4.6	5.3	5.9	6.6	7.3	7.9	8.6	9.2	9.9	6
7	.7	1.3	2.0	2.7	3.4	4.0	4.7	5.4	6.0	6.7	7.4	8.0	8.7	9.4	10.1	7
8	.7	1.4	2.0	2.7	3.4	4.1	4.8	5.4	6.1	6.8	7.5	8.2	8.8	9.5	10.2	8
9	.7	1.4	2.1	2.8	3.5	4.1	4.8	5.5	6.2	6.9	7.6	8.3	9.0	9.7	10.4	9
70	0.7	1.4	2.1	2.8	3.5	4.2	4.9	5.6	6.3	7.0	7.7	8.4	9.1	9.8	10.5	70
1	.7	1.4	2.1	2.8	3.6	4.3	5.0	5.7	6.4	7.1	7.8	8.5	9.2	9.9	10.7	1
2	.7	1.4	2.2	2.9	3.6	4.3	5.0	5.8	6.5	7.2	7.9	8.6	9.4	10.1	10.8	2
3	.7	1.5	2.2	2.9	3.7	4.4	5.1	5.8	6.6	7.3	8.0	8.8	9.5	10.2	11.0	3
4	.7	1.5	2.2	3.0	3.7	4.4	5.2	5.9	6.7	7.4	8.1	8.9	9.6	10.4	11.1	4
75	0.8	1.5	2.3	3.0	3.8	4.5	5.3	6.0	6.8	7.5	8.3	9.0	9.8	10.5	11.3	75
6	.8	1.5	2.3	3.0	3.8	4.6	5.3	6.1	6.8	7.6	8.4	9.1	9.9	10.6	11.4	6
7	.8	1.5	2.3	3.1	3.9	4.6	5.4	6.2	6.9	7.7	8.5	9.2	10.0	10.8	11.6	7
8	.8	1.6	2.3	3.1	3.9	4.7	5.5	6.2	7.0	7.8	8.6	9.4	10.1	10.9	11.7	8
9	.8	1.6	2.4	3.2	4.0	4.7	5.5	6.3	7.1	7.9	8.7	9.5	10.3	11.1	11.9	9
90	0.9	1.8	2.7	3.6	4.5	5.4	6.3	7.2	8.1	9.0	9.9	10.8	11.7	12.6	13.5	90
1	.9	1.8	2.7	3.6	4.6	5.5	6.4	7.3	8.2	9.1	10.0	10.9	11.8	12.7	13.7	1
2	.9	1.8	2.8	3.7	4.6	5.5	6.4	7.4	8.3	9.2	10.1	11.0	12.0	12.9	13.8	2
3	.9	1.9	2.8	3.7	4.7	5.6	6.5	7.4	8.4	9.3	10.2	11.2	12.1	13.0	14.0	3
4	.9	1.9	2.8	3.8	4.7	5.6	6.6	7.5	8.5	9.4	10.3	11.3	12.2	13.2	14.1	4
95	1.0	1.9	2.9	3.8	4.8	5.7	6.7	7.6	8.6	9.5	10.5	11.4	12.4	13.3	14.3	95
6	1.0	1.9	2.9	3.8	4.8	5.8	6.7	7.7	8.6	9.6	10.6	11.5	12.5	13.4	14.4	6
7	1.0	1.9	2.9	3.9	4.9	5.8	6.8	7.8	8.7	9.7	10.7	11.6	12.6	13.6	14.5	7
8	1.0	2.0	2.9	3.9	4.9	5.9	6.9	7.8	8.8	9.8	10.8	11.8	12.7	13.7	14.7	8
99	1.1	2.0	3.0	4.0	5.0	5.9	6.9	7.9	8.9	9.9	10.9	11.9	12.9	13.9	14.9	99
Δ	1'	2'	3'	4'	5'	6'	7'	8'	9'	10'	11'	12'	13'	14'	15'	Δ

Δd or Δt

STAR IDENTIFICATION TABLE

ALTITUDE

Lat. 41°

AZ.	44° H.A.	44° Dec.	40° Dec.	40° H.A.	36° Dec.	36° H.A.	32° Dec.	32° H.A.	28° Dec.	28° H.A.	24° Dec.	24° H.A.	20° Dec.	20° H.A.	16° Dec.	16° H.A.	12° Dec.	12° H.A.	8° Dec.	8° H.A.	4° Dec.	4° H.A.	AZ.
80	53	33	31	62	29	66	27	70	25	74	23	77	20	81	18	84	15	87	13	90	10	94	80
84	55	31	29	60	27	64	24	68	22	72	20	75	17	78	15	82	12	85	10	88	07	91	84
88	55	28	26	59	24	62	22	66	19	69	17	73	14	76	12	79	09	82	07	85	04	88	88
92	53	26	24	57	21	60	19	64	17	67	14	70	12	73	09	77	06	80	04	83	01	86	92
96	51	24	21	55	19	58	16	61	14	65	11	68	09	71	06	74	03	77	01	80	*02*	83	96
100	49	21	19	53	16	56	14	59	11	62	08	65	06	68	03	72	00	74	*02*	77	*05*	80	100
104	48	19	16	51	14	54	11	57	08	60	06	63	03	66	00	69	*02*	72	*05*	75	*08*	78	104
108	46	17	14	49	11	52	09	55	06	58	03	60	00	63	*02*	66	*05*	69	*08*	72	*11*	75	108
112	44	15	12	47	09	49	06	52	03	55	00	58	*02*	61	*05*	64	*08*	66	*11*	69	*14*	72	112
116	41	13	10	44	07	47	04	50	01	53	*02*	55	*05*	58	*08*	61	*11*	64	*14*	66	*17*	69	116
120	39	11	08	42	05	45	02	47	*01*	50	*04*	53	*07*	55	*10*	58	*13*	61	*16*	63	*19*	66	120
124	37	09	06	40	03	42	01	45	*04*	47	*07*	50	*10*	52	*13*	55	*16*	58	*19*	60	*22*	63	124
128	35	07	04	37	01	40	*03*	42	*06*	44	*09*	47	*12*	49	*15*	52	*19*	54	*22*	57	*25*	60	128
132	32	05	02	35	*01*	37	*05*	39	*08*	41	*11*	44	*14*	46	*18*	49	*21*	51	*24*	54	*27*	57	132
136	30	04	00	32	*03*	34	*06*	36	*10*	39	*13*	41	*17*	43	*20*	45	*23*	48	*27*	50	*30*	53	136
140	28	02	*01*	30	*05*	31	*08*	33	*12*	35	*15*	37	*19*	40	*22*	42	*25*	44	*29*	47	*32*	49	140
144	25	01	*03*	27	*06*	29	*10*	30	*13*	32	*17*	34	*20*	36	*24*	38	*27*	40	*31*	43	*34*	45	144
148	22	00	*04*	24	*08*	26	*11*	27	*15*	29	*19*	31	*22*	33	*26*	34	*29*	36	*33*	39	*36*	41	148
152	20	*01*	*05*	21	*09*	23	*13*	24	*16*	26	*20*	27	*24*	29	*27*	31	*31*	32	*35*	34	*38*	37	152
156	17	*02*	*06*	18	*10*	20	*14*	21	*18*	22	*21*	24	*25*	25	*29*	27	*33*	28	*36*	30	*40*	32	156
	44°			40°		36°		32°		28°		24°		20°		16°		12°		8°		4°	

FIGURES IN ITALICS INDICATE THAT DECLINATION IS OF CONTRARY NAME TO LATITUDE

APPENDIX O

EXTRACTS FROM PUB. NO. 229

INTERPOLATION TABLE

Dec. Inc.	Altitude Difference (d) Tens 10'	20'	30'	40'	50'	Decimals	Units 0'	1'	2'	3'	4'	5'	6'	7'	8'	9'	Double Second Diff. and Corr.
0.0	0.0	0.0	0.0	0.0	0.0	.0	0.0	0.0	0.0	0.0	0.0	0.0	0.0	0.1	0.1	0.1	0.0 0.0 48.2
0.1	0.0	0.0	0.0	0.0	0.1	.1	0.0	0.0	0.0	0.0	0.0	0.0	0.1	0.1	0.1	0.1	
0.2	0.0	0.0	0.1	0.1	0.1	.2	0.0	0.0	0.0	0.0	0.0	0.0	0.1	0.1	0.1	0.1	
0.3	0.0	0.1	0.1	0.2	0.2	.3	0.0	0.0	0.0	0.0	0.0	0.0	0.1	0.1	0.1	0.1	
0.4	0.1	0.1	0.2	0.3	0.3	.4	0.0	0.0	0.0	0.0	0.0	0.0	0.1	0.1	0.1	0.1	
0.5	0.1	0.2	0.3	0.3	0.4	.5	0.0	0.0	0.0	0.0	0.0	0.0	0.1	0.1	0.1	0.1	16.2 0.1 48.6
0.6	0.1	0.2	0.3	0.4	0.5	.6	0.0	0.0	0.0	0.0	0.0	0.0	0.1	0.1	0.1	0.1	
0.7	0.1	0.3	0.4	0.5	0.6	.7	0.0	0.0	0.0	0.0	0.0	0.0	0.1	0.1	0.1	0.1	
0.8	0.2	0.3	0.4	0.6	0.7	.8	0.0	0.0	0.0	0.0	0.0	0.0	0.1	0.1	0.1	0.1	
0.9	0.2	0.3	0.5	0.6	0.8	.9	0.0	0.0	0.0	0.0	0.0	0.0	0.1	0.1	0.1	0.1	
1.0	0.1	0.3	0.5	0.6	0.8	.0	0.0	0.0	0.0	0.1	0.1	0.1	0.1	0.2	0.2	0.2	8.2 0.1 24.6 0.2 41.0
1.1	0.2	0.3	0.5	0.7	0.9	.1	0.0	0.0	0.1	0.1	0.1	0.1	0.2	0.2	0.2	0.2	
1.2	0.2	0.4	0.6	0.8	1.0	.2	0.0	0.0	0.1	0.1	0.1	0.1	0.2	0.2	0.2	0.2	
1.3	0.2	0.4	0.6	0.9	1.1	.3	0.0	0.0	0.1	0.1	0.1	0.1	0.2	0.2	0.2	0.2	
1.4	0.2	0.5	0.7	0.9	1.2	.4	0.0	0.0	0.1	0.1	0.1	0.1	0.2	0.2	0.2	0.2	
1.5	0.3	0.5	0.8	1.0	1.3	.5	0.0	0.0	0.1	0.1	0.1	0.1	0.2	0.2	0.2	0.2	
1.6	0.3	0.5	0.8	1.1	1.3	.6	0.0	0.0	0.1	0.1	0.1	0.1	0.2	0.2	0.2	0.2	
1.7	0.3	0.6	0.9	1.2	1.4	.7	0.0	0.0	0.1	0.1	0.1	0.1	0.2	0.2	0.2	0.2	
1.8	0.3	0.6	0.9	1.2	1.5	.8	0.0	0.0	0.1	0.1	0.1	0.1	0.2	0.2	0.2	0.2	
1.9	0.4	0.7	1.0	1.3	1.6	.9	0.0	0.0	0.1	0.1	0.1	0.1	0.2	0.2	0.2	0.2	
2.0	0.3	0.6	1.0	1.3	1.6	.0	0.0	0.0	0.1	0.1	0.2	0.2	0.2	0.3	0.3	0.4	5.0 0.1 15.0 0.2 25.0 0.3 35.1
2.1	0.3	0.7	1.0	1.4	1.7	.1	0.0	0.0	0.1	0.1	0.2	0.2	0.3	0.3	0.3	0.4	
2.2	0.3	0.7	1.1	1.4	1.8	.2	0.0	0.0	0.1	0.1	0.2	0.2	0.3	0.3	0.3	0.4	
2.3	0.4	0.8	1.1	1.5	1.9	.3	0.0	0.1	0.1	0.1	0.2	0.2	0.3	0.3	0.3	0.4	
2.4	0.4	0.8	1.2	1.6	2.0	.4	0.0	0.1	0.1	0.1	0.2	0.2	0.3	0.3	0.3	0.4	
2.5	0.4	0.8	1.3	1.7	2.1	.5	0.0	0.1	0.1	0.1	0.2	0.2	0.3	0.3	0.4	0.4	
2.6	0.4	0.9	1.3	1.7	2.2	.6	0.0	0.1	0.1	0.1	0.2	0.2	0.3	0.3	0.4	0.4	
2.7	0.5	0.9	1.4	1.8	2.3	.7	0.0	0.1	0.1	0.2	0.2	0.2	0.3	0.3	0.4	0.4	
2.8	0.5	1.0	1.4	1.9	2.4	.8	0.0	0.1	0.1	0.2	0.2	0.2	0.3	0.3	0.4	0.4	
2.9	0.5	1.0	1.5	2.0	2.5	.9	0.0	0.1	0.1	0.2	0.2	0.2	0.3	0.3	0.4	0.4	
3.0	0.5	1.0	1.5	2.0	2.5	.0	0.0	0.1	0.1	0.2	0.2	0.3	0.3	0.4	0.5	0.5	3.6 0.1 10.9 0.2 18.2 0.3 25.5 0.4 32.8 0.5 40.1
3.1	0.5	1.0	1.5	2.0	2.6	.1	0.0	0.1	0.1	0.2	0.2	0.3	0.4	0.4	0.5	0.5	
3.2	0.5	1.0	1.6	2.1	2.6	.2	0.0	0.1	0.1	0.2	0.2	0.3	0.4	0.4	0.5	0.5	
3.3	0.5	1.1	1.6	2.2	2.7	.3	0.0	0.1	0.1	0.2	0.3	0.3	0.4	0.4	0.5	0.5	
3.4	0.6	1.1	1.7	2.3	2.8	.4	0.0	0.1	0.1	0.2	0.3	0.3	0.4	0.4	0.5	0.5	
3.5	0.6	1.2	1.8	2.3	2.9	.5	0.0	0.1	0.1	0.2	0.3	0.3	0.4	0.4	0.5	0.6	
3.6	0.6	1.2	1.8	2.4	3.0	.6	0.0	0.1	0.2	0.2	0.3	0.3	0.4	0.4	0.5	0.6	
3.7	0.6	1.3	1.9	2.5	3.1	.7	0.0	0.1	0.2	0.2	0.3	0.3	0.4	0.4	0.5	0.6	
3.8	0.7	1.3	1.9	2.6	3.2	.8	0.0	0.1	0.2	0.2	0.3	0.3	0.4	0.5	0.5	0.6	
3.9	0.7	1.3	2.0	2.6	3.3	.9	0.1	0.1	0.2	0.2	0.3	0.3	0.4	0.5	0.5	0.6	
4.0	0.6	1.3	2.0	2.6	3.3	.0	0.0	0.1	0.1	0.2	0.3	0.4	0.4	0.5	0.6	0.7	2.9 0.1 8.6 0.2 14.4 0.3 20.2 0.4 25.9 0.5 31.7 0.6 37.5
4.1	0.7	1.3	2.0	2.7	3.4	.1	0.0	0.1	0.2	0.2	0.3	0.4	0.5	0.5	0.6	0.7	
4.2	0.7	1.4	2.1	2.8	3.5	.2	0.0	0.1	0.2	0.2	0.3	0.4	0.5	0.5	0.6	0.7	
4.3	0.7	1.4	2.1	2.9	3.6	.3	0.0	0.1	0.2	0.2	0.3	0.4	0.5	0.5	0.6	0.7	
4.4	0.7	1.5	2.2	2.9	3.7	.4	0.0	0.1	0.2	0.3	0.3	0.4	0.5	0.6	0.6	0.7	
4.5	0.8	1.5	2.3	3.0	3.8	.5	0.0	0.1	0.2	0.3	0.3	0.4	0.5	0.6	0.6	0.7	
4.6	0.8	1.5	2.3	3.1	3.8	.6	0.0	0.1	0.2	0.3	0.3	0.4	0.5	0.6	0.6	0.7	
4.7	0.8	1.6	2.4	3.2	3.9	.7	0.1	0.1	0.2	0.3	0.4	0.4	0.5	0.6	0.7	0.7	
4.8	0.8	1.6	2.4	3.2	4.0	.8	0.1	0.1	0.2	0.3	0.4	0.4	0.5	0.6	0.7	0.7	
4.9	0.9	1.7	2.5	3.3	4.1	.9	0.1	0.1	0.2	0.3	0.4	0.4	0.5	0.6	0.7	0.7	
5.0	0.8	1.6	2.5	3.3	4.1	.0	0.0	0.1	0.2	0.3	0.4	0.5	0.5	0.6	0.7	0.8	2.4 0.1 7.2 0.2 12.0 0.3 16.8 0.4 21.6 0.5 26.4 0.6 31.2 0.7 36.0
5.1	0.8	1.7	2.5	3.4	4.2	.1	0.0	0.1	0.2	0.3	0.4	0.5	0.6	0.7	0.7	0.8	
5.2	0.8	1.7	2.6	3.4	4.3	.2	0.0	0.1	0.2	0.3	0.4	0.5	0.6	0.7	0.8	0.8	
5.3	0.9	1.8	2.6	3.5	4.4	.3	0.0	0.1	0.2	0.3	0.4	0.5	0.6	0.7	0.8	0.9	
5.4	0.9	1.8	2.7	3.6	4.5	.4	0.0	0.1	0.2	0.3	0.4	0.5	0.6	0.7	0.8	0.9	
5.5	0.9	1.8	2.8	3.7	4.6	.5	0.0	0.1	0.2	0.3	0.4	0.5	0.6	0.7	0.8	0.9	
5.6	0.9	1.9	2.8	3.7	4.7	.6	0.1	0.1	0.2	0.3	0.4	0.5	0.6	0.7	0.8	0.9	
5.7	1.0	1.9	2.9	3.8	4.8	.7	0.1	0.2	0.2	0.3	0.4	0.5	0.6	0.7	0.8	0.9	
5.8	1.0	2.0	2.9	3.9	4.9	.8	0.1	0.2	0.3	0.3	0.4	0.5	0.6	0.7	0.8	0.9	
5.9	1.0	2.0	3.0	4.0	5.0	.9	0.1	0.2	0.3	0.4	0.4	0.5	0.6	0.7	0.8	0.9	
6.0	1.0	2.0	3.0	4.0	5.0	.0	0.0	0.1	0.2	0.3	0.4	0.5	0.6	0.8	0.9	1.0	2.1 0.1 6.2 0.2 10.4 0.3 14.5 0.4 18.6 0.5 22.8 0.6 26.9 0.7 31.1 0.8 35.2
6.1	1.0	2.0	3.0	4.0	5.1	.1	0.0	0.1	0.2	0.3	0.4	0.6	0.7	0.8	0.9	1.0	
6.2	1.0	2.0	3.1	4.1	5.1	.2	0.0	0.1	0.2	0.3	0.5	0.6	0.7	0.8	0.9	1.0	
6.3	1.0	2.1	3.1	4.2	5.2	.3	0.0	0.1	0.2	0.4	0.5	0.6	0.7	0.8	0.9	1.0	
6.4	1.1	2.1	3.2	4.3	5.3	.4	0.0	0.2	0.3	0.4	0.5	0.6	0.7	0.8	0.9	1.0	
6.5	1.1	2.2	3.3	4.3	5.4	.5	0.1	0.2	0.3	0.4	0.5	0.6	0.7	0.8	0.9	1.0	
6.6	1.1	2.2	3.3	4.4	5.5	.6	0.1	0.2	0.3	0.4	0.5	0.6	0.7	0.8	0.9	1.0	
6.7	1.1	2.3	3.4	4.5	5.6	.7	0.1	0.2	0.3	0.4	0.5	0.6	0.7	0.8	0.9	1.1	
6.8	1.2	2.3	3.4	4.6	5.7	.8	0.1	0.2	0.3	0.4	0.5	0.6	0.7	0.8	1.0	1.1	
6.9	1.2	2.3	3.5	4.6	5.8	.9	0.1	0.2	0.3	0.4	0.5	0.6	0.7	0.9	1.0	1.1	
7.0	1.1	2.3	3.5	4.6	5.8	.0	0.0	0.1	0.2	0.4	0.5	0.6	0.7	0.9	1.0	1.1	1.8 0.1 5.5 0.2 9.1 0.3 12.8 0.4 16.5 0.5 20.1 0.6 23.8 0.7 27.4 0.8 31.1 0.9 34.7
7.1	1.2	2.3	3.5	4.7	5.9	.1	0.0	0.1	0.3	0.4	0.5	0.6	0.8	0.9	1.0	1.1	
7.2	1.2	2.4	3.6	4.8	6.0	.2	0.0	0.1	0.3	0.4	0.5	0.6	0.8	0.9	1.0	1.1	
7.3	1.2	2.4	3.6	4.9	6.1	.3	0.0	0.2	0.3	0.4	0.5	0.7	0.8	0.9	1.0	1.2	
7.4	1.2	2.5	3.7	4.9	6.2	.4	0.0	0.2	0.3	0.4	0.5	0.7	0.8	0.9	1.0	1.2	
7.5	1.3	2.5	3.8	5.0	6.3	.5	0.1	0.2	0.3	0.4	0.6	0.7	0.8	0.9	1.1	1.2	
7.6	1.3	2.5	3.8	5.1	6.3	.6	0.1	0.2	0.3	0.4	0.6	0.7	0.8	0.9	1.1	1.2	
7.7	1.3	2.6	3.9	5.2	6.4	.7	0.1	0.2	0.3	0.5	0.6	0.7	0.8	1.0	1.1	1.2	
7.8	1.3	2.6	3.9	5.2	6.5	.8	0.1	0.2	0.3	0.5	0.6	0.7	0.8	1.0	1.1	1.2	
7.9	1.4	2.7	4.0	5.3	6.6	.9	0.1	0.2	0.4	0.5	0.6	0.7	0.9	1.0	1.1	1.2	
	10'	20'	30'	40'	50'		0'	1'	2'	3'	4'	5'	6'	7'	8'	9'	

Dec. Inc.	Altitude Difference (d) Tens 10'	20'	30'	40'	50'	Decimals	Units 0'	1'	2'	3'	4'	5'	6'	7'	8'	9'	Double Second Diff. and Corr.
8.0	1.3	2.6	4.0	5.3	6.6	.0	0.0	0.1	0.3	0.4	0.6	0.7	0.8	1.0	1.1	1.3	1.6 0.1 4.8 0.2 8.0 0.3 11.2 0.4 14.5 0.5 17.7 0.6 20.9 0.7 24.1 0.8 27.3 0.9 30.5 1.0 33.7 1.1 36.9
8.1	1.3	2.7	4.0	5.4	6.7	.1	0.0	0.2	0.3	0.4	0.6	0.7	0.9	1.0	1.1	1.3	
8.2	1.3	2.7	4.1	5.4	6.8	.2	0.0	0.2	0.3	0.5	0.6	0.7	0.9	1.0	1.2	1.3	
8.3	1.4	2.8	4.1	5.5	6.9	.3	0.0	0.2	0.3	0.5	0.6	0.8	0.9	1.0	1.2	1.3	
8.4	1.4	2.8	4.2	5.6	7.0	.4	0.1	0.2	0.3	0.5	0.6	0.8	0.9	1.0	1.2	1.3	
8.5	1.4	2.8	4.3	5.7	7.1	.5	0.1	0.2	0.4	0.5	0.6	0.8	0.9	1.1	1.2	1.3	
8.6	1.4	2.9	4.3	5.7	7.2	.6	0.1	0.2	0.4	0.5	0.7	0.8	0.9	1.1	1.2	1.4	
8.7	1.5	2.9	4.4	5.8	7.3	.7	0.1	0.2	0.4	0.5	0.7	0.8	0.9	1.1	1.2	1.4	
8.8	1.5	3.0	4.4	5.9	7.4	.8	0.1	0.3	0.4	0.5	0.7	0.8	1.0	1.1	1.2	1.4	
8.9	1.5	3.0	4.5	6.0	7.5	.9	0.1	0.3	0.4	0.6	0.7	0.8	1.0	1.1	1.3	1.4	
9.0	1.5	3.0	4.5	6.0	7.5	.0	0.0	0.2	0.3	0.5	0.6	0.8	0.9	1.1	1.3	1.4	
9.1	1.5	3.0	4.5	6.0	7.6	.1	0.0	0.2	0.3	0.5	0.6	0.8	1.0	1.1	1.3	1.4	
9.2	1.5	3.0	4.6	6.1	7.6	.2	0.0	0.2	0.3	0.5	0.7	0.8	1.0	1.1	1.3	1.5	
9.3	1.5	3.1	4.6	6.2	7.7	.3	0.0	0.2	0.4	0.5	0.7	0.8	1.0	1.2	1.3	1.5	
9.4	1.6	3.1	4.7	6.3	7.8	.4	0.1	0.2	0.4	0.5	0.7	0.9	1.0	1.2	1.3	1.5	
9.5	1.6	3.2	4.8	6.3	7.9	.5	0.1	0.2	0.4	0.6	0.7	0.9	1.0	1.2	1.3	1.5	1.4 0.1 4.2 0.2 7.1 0.3 9.9 0.4 12.7 0.5 15.5 0.6 18.4 0.7 21.2 0.8 24.0 0.9 26.8 1.0 29.7 1.1 32.5 1.2 35.3
9.6	1.6	3.2	4.8	6.4	8.0	.6	0.1	0.3	0.4	0.6	0.7	0.9	1.0	1.2	1.4	1.5	
9.7	1.6	3.3	4.9	6.5	8.1	.7	0.1	0.3	0.4	0.6	0.7	0.9	1.1	1.2	1.4	1.5	
9.8	1.7	3.3	4.9	6.6	8.2	.8	0.1	0.3	0.4	0.6	0.8	0.9	1.1	1.2	1.4	1.6	
9.9	1.7	3.3	5.0	6.6	8.3	.9	0.1	0.3	0.5	0.6	0.8	0.9	1.1	1.3	1.4	1.6	
10.0	1.6	3.3	5.0	6.6	8.3	.0	0.0	0.2	0.3	0.5	0.7	0.9	1.0	1.2	1.4	1.6	
10.1	1.7	3.3	5.0	6.7	8.4	.1	0.0	0.2	0.4	0.5	0.7	0.9	1.1	1.2	1.4	1.6	
10.2	1.7	3.4	5.1	6.8	8.5	.2	0.0	0.2	0.4	0.6	0.7	0.9	1.1	1.3	1.4	1.6	
10.3	1.7	3.4	5.1	6.9	8.6	.3	0.1	0.2	0.4	0.6	0.8	0.9	1.1	1.3	1.5	1.6	
10.4	1.7	3.5	5.2	6.9	8.7	.4	0.1	0.2	0.4	0.6	0.8	0.9	1.1	1.3	1.5	1.6	
10.5	1.8	3.5	5.3	7.0	8.8	.5	0.1	0.3	0.4	0.6	0.8	1.0	1.1	1.3	1.5	1.7	
10.6	1.8	3.5	5.3	7.1	8.8	.6	0.1	0.3	0.5	0.6	0.8	1.0	1.2	1.3	1.5	1.7	
10.7	1.8	3.6	5.4	7.2	8.9	.7	0.1	0.3	0.5	0.6	0.8	1.0	1.2	1.3	1.5	1.7	
10.8	1.8	3.6	5.4	7.2	9.0	.8	0.1	0.3	0.5	0.7	0.8	1.0	1.2	1.4	1.5	1.7	
10.9	1.9	3.7	5.5	7.3	9.1	.9	0.2	0.3	0.5	0.7	0.9	1.0	1.2	1.4	1.6	1.7	
11.0	1.8	3.6	5.5	7.3	9.1	.0	0.0	0.2	0.4	0.6	0.8	1.0	1.1	1.3	1.5	1.7	1.3 0.1 3.8 0.2 6.3 0.3 8.9 0.4 11.4 0.5 14.0 0.6 16.5 0.7 19.0 0.8 21.6 0.9 24.1 1.0 26.7 1.1 29.2 1.2 31.7 1.3 34.3
11.1	1.8	3.7	5.5	7.4	9.2	.1	0.0	0.2	0.4	0.6	0.8	1.0	1.2	1.4	1.6	1.7	
11.2	1.8	3.7	5.6	7.4	9.3	.2	0.0	0.2	0.4	0.6	0.8	1.0	1.2	1.4	1.6	1.8	
11.3	1.9	3.8	5.6	7.5	9.4	.3	0.1	0.2	0.4	0.6	0.8	1.0	1.2	1.4	1.6	1.8	
11.4	1.9	3.8	5.7	7.6	9.5	.4	0.1	0.3	0.5	0.7	0.8	1.0	1.2	1.4	1.6	1.8	
11.5	1.9	3.8	5.8	7.7	9.6	.5	0.1	0.3	0.5	0.7	0.9	1.1	1.2	1.4	1.6	1.8	
11.6	1.9	3.9	5.8	7.7	9.7	.6	0.1	0.3	0.5	0.7	0.9	1.1	1.3	1.5	1.6	1.8	
11.7	2.0	3.9	5.9	7.8	9.8	.7	0.1	0.3	0.5	0.7	0.9	1.1	1.3	1.5	1.7	1.9	
11.8	2.0	4.0	5.9	7.9	9.9	.8	0.2	0.3	0.5	0.7	0.9	1.1	1.3	1.5	1.7	1.9	
11.9	2.0	4.0	6.0	8.0	10.0	.9	0.2	0.4	0.6	0.7	0.9	1.1	1.3	1.5	1.7	1.9	
12.0	2.0	4.0	6.0	8.0	10.0	.0	0.0	0.2	0.4	0.6	0.8	1.0	1.2	1.5	1.7	1.9	
12.1	2.0	4.0	6.0	8.0	10.1	.1	0.0	0.2	0.4	0.6	0.9	1.1	1.3	1.5	1.7	1.9	
12.2	2.0	4.0	6.1	8.1	10.1	.2	0.0	0.2	0.5	0.7	0.9	1.1	1.3	1.5	1.7	1.9	
12.3	2.0	4.1	6.1	8.2	10.2	.3	0.1	0.3	0.5	0.7	0.9	1.1	1.3	1.5	1.7	1.9	
12.4	2.1	4.1	6.2	8.3	10.3	.4	0.1	0.3	0.5	0.7	0.9	1.1	1.3	1.5	1.7	2.0	
12.5	2.1	4.2	6.3	8.3	10.4	.5	0.1	0.3	0.5	0.7	0.9	1.1	1.4	1.6	1.8	2.0	1.2 0.1 3.5 0.2 5.8 0.3 8.1 0.4 10.5 0.5 12.8 0.6 15.1 0.7 17.4 0.8 19.8 0.9 22.1 1.0 24.4 1.1 26.7 1.2 29.1 1.3 31.4 1.4 33.7 1.5 36.0
12.6	2.1	4.2	6.3	8.4	10.5	.6	0.1	0.3	0.5	0.7	1.0	1.2	1.4	1.6	1.8	2.0	
12.7	2.1	4.3	6.4	8.5	10.6	.7	0.1	0.4	0.6	0.8	1.0	1.2	1.4	1.6	1.8	2.0	
12.8	2.2	4.3	6.4	8.6	10.7	.8	0.2	0.4	0.6	0.8	1.0	1.2	1.4	1.6	1.8	2.0	
12.9	2.2	4.3	6.5	8.6	10.8	.9	0.2	0.4	0.6	0.8	1.0	1.2	1.4	1.6	1.9	2.1	
13.0	2.1	4.3	6.5	8.6	10.8	.0	0.0	0.2	0.4	0.7	0.9	1.1	1.3	1.6	1.8	2.0	
13.1	2.2	4.3	6.5	8.7	10.9	.1	0.0	0.2	0.5	0.7	0.9	1.1	1.4	1.6	1.8	2.0	
13.2	2.2	4.4	6.6	8.8	11.0	.2	0.0	0.3	0.5	0.7	0.9	1.2	1.4	1.6	1.8	2.1	
13.3	2.2	4.4	6.6	8.9	11.1	.3	0.1	0.3	0.5	0.7	1.0	1.2	1.4	1.6	1.9	2.1	
13.4	2.2	4.5	6.7	8.9	11.2	.4	0.1	0.3	0.5	0.8	1.0	1.2	1.4	1.7	1.9	2.1	
13.5	2.3	4.5	6.8	9.0	11.3	.5	0.1	0.3	0.6	0.8	1.0	1.2	1.5	1.7	1.9	2.1	
13.6	2.3	4.5	6.8	9.1	11.3	.6	0.1	0.4	0.6	0.8	1.0	1.3	1.5	1.7	1.9	2.2	
13.7	2.3	4.6	6.9	9.2	11.4	.7	0.2	0.4	0.6	0.8	1.1	1.3	1.5	1.7	2.0	2.2	
13.8	2.3	4.6	6.9	9.2	11.5	.8	0.2	0.4	0.6	0.9	1.1	1.3	1.5	1.8	2.0	2.2	
13.9	2.4	4.7	7.0	9.3	11.6	.9	0.2	0.4	0.7	0.9	1.1	1.3	1.6	1.8	2.0	2.2	
14.0	2.3	4.6	7.0	9.3	11.6	.0	0.0	0.2	0.5	0.7	1.0	1.2	1.4	1.7	1.9	2.2	1.1 0.1 3.2 0.2 5.3 0.3 7.5 0.4 9.6 0.5 11.7 0.6 13.9 0.7 16.0 0.8 18.1 0.9 20.3 1.0 22.4 1.1 24.5 1.2 26.7 1.3 28.8 1.4 30.9 1.5 33.1 1.6 35.2
14.1	2.3	4.7	7.0	9.4	11.7	.1	0.0	0.3	0.5	0.7	1.0	1.2	1.5	1.7	2.0	2.2	
14.2	2.3	4.7	7.1	9.4	11.8	.2	0.0	0.3	0.5	0.8	1.0	1.3	1.5	1.7	2.0	2.2	
14.3	2.4	4.8	7.1	9.5	11.9	.3	0.1	0.3	0.6	0.8	1.0	1.3	1.5	1.8	2.0	2.2	
14.4	2.4	4.8	7.2	9.6	12.0	.4	0.1	0.3	0.6	0.8	1.1	1.3	1.5	1.8	2.0	2.3	
14.5	2.4	4.8	7.3	9.7	12.1	.5	0.1	0.4	0.6	0.8	1.1	1.3	1.6	1.8	2.1	2.3	
14.6	2.4	4.9	7.3	9.7	12.2	.6	0.1	0.4	0.6	0.9	1.1	1.4	1.6	1.8	2.1	2.3	
14.7	2.5	4.9	7.4	9.8	12.3	.7	0.2	0.4	0.7	0.9	1.1	1.4	1.6	1.9	2.1	2.3	
14.8	2.5	5.0	7.4	9.9	12.4	.8	0.2	0.4	0.7	0.9	1.2	1.4	1.6	1.9	2.1	2.4	
14.9	2.5	5.0	7.5	10.0	12.5	.9	0.2	0.5	0.7	0.9	1.2	1.4	1.7	1.9	2.2	2.4	
15.0	2.5	5.0	7.5	10.0	12.5	.0	0.0	0.3	0.5	0.8	1.0	1.3	1.5	1.8	2.1	2.3	
15.1	2.5	5.0	7.5	10.0	12.6	.1	0.0	0.3	0.5	0.8	1.1	1.3	1.6	1.8	2.1	2.4	
15.2	2.5	5.0	7.6	10.1	12.6	.2	0.1	0.3	0.6	0.8	1.1	1.3	1.6	1.9	2.1	2.4	
15.3	2.5	5.1	7.6	10.2	12.7	.3	0.1	0.3	0.6	0.9	1.1	1.4	1.6	1.9	2.1	2.4	
15.4	2.6	5.1	7.7	10.3	12.8	.4	0.1	0.4	0.6	0.9	1.1	1.4	1.7	1.9	2.2	2.4	
15.5	2.6	5.2	7.8	10.3	12.9	.5	0.1	0.4	0.6	0.9	1.2	1.4	1.7	1.9	2.2	2.5	
15.6	2.6	5.2	7.8	10.4	13.0	.6	0.2	0.4	0.7	0.9	1.2	1.4	1.7	2.0	2.2	2.5	
15.7	2.6	5.3	7.9	10.5	13.1	.7	0.2	0.4	0.7	1.0	1.2	1.5	1.7	2.0	2.2	2.5	
15.8	2.7	5.3	7.9	10.6	13.2	.8	0.2	0.5	0.7	1.0	1.2	1.5	1.8	2.0	2.3	2.5	
15.9	2.7	5.3	8.0	10.6	13.3	.9	0.2	0.5	0.7	1.0	1.3	1.5	1.8	2.0	2.3	2.6	
	10'	20'	30'	40'	50'		0'	1'	2'	3'	4'	5'	6'	7'	8'	9'	

The Double-Second-Difference correction (Corr.) is always to be added to the tabulated altitude.

INTERPOLATION TABLE

Dec. Inc.	Tens 10'	20'	30'	40'	50'	Decimals	Units 0'	1'	2'	3'	4'	5'	6'	7'	8'	9'
16.0	2.6	5.3	8.0	10.6	13.3	.0	0.0	0.3	0.5	0.8	1.1	1.4	1.6	1.9	2.2	2.5
16.1	2.7	5.3	8.0	10.7	13.4	.1	0.0	0.3	0.6	0.9	1.1	1.4	1.7	2.0	2.2	2.5
16.2	2.7	5.4	8.1	10.8	13.5	.2	0.1	0.3	0.6	0.9	1.2	1.4	1.7	2.0	2.3	2.5
16.3	2.7	5.4	8.1	10.9	13.6	.3	0.1	0.4	0.6	0.9	1.2	1.5	1.7	2.0	2.3	2.6
16.4	2.7	5.5	8.2	10.9	13.7	.4	0.1	0.4	0.7	0.9	1.2	1.5	1.8	2.0	2.3	2.6
16.5	2.8	5.5	8.3	11.0	13.8	.5	0.1	0.4	0.7	1.0	1.2	1.5	1.8	2.1	2.3	2.6
16.6	2.8	5.5	8.3	11.1	13.8	.6	0.2	0.4	0.7	1.0	1.3	1.5	1.8	2.1	2.4	2.6
16.7	2.8	5.6	8.4	11.2	13.9	.7	0.2	0.5	0.7	1.0	1.3	1.6	1.8	2.1	2.4	2.7
16.8	2.8	5.6	8.4	11.2	14.0	.8	0.2	0.5	0.8	1.0	1.3	1.6	1.9	2.1	2.4	2.7
16.9	2.9	5.7	8.5	11.3	14.1	.9	0.2	0.5	0.8	1.1	1.3	1.6	1.9	2.2	2.4	2.7
17.0	2.8	5.6	8.5	11.3	14.1	.0	0.0	0.3	0.6	0.9	1.2	1.5	1.7	2.0	2.3	2.6
17.1	2.8	5.7	8.5	11.4	14.2	.1	0.0	0.3	0.6	0.9	1.2	1.5	1.8	2.1	2.4	2.7
17.2	2.8	5.7	8.6	11.4	14.3	.2	0.1	0.3	0.6	0.9	1.2	1.5	1.8	2.1	2.4	2.7
17.3	2.9	5.8	8.6	11.5	14.4	.3	0.1	0.4	0.7	1.0	1.3	1.5	1.8	2.1	2.4	2.7
17.4	2.9	5.8	8.7	11.6	14.5	.4	0.1	0.4	0.7	1.0	1.3	1.6	1.9	2.2	2.4	2.7
17.5	2.9	5.8	8.8	11.7	14.6	.5	0.1	0.4	0.7	1.0	1.3	1.6	1.9	2.2	2.5	2.8
17.6	2.9	5.9	8.8	11.7	14.7	.6	0.2	0.5	0.8	1.0	1.3	1.6	1.9	2.2	2.5	2.8
17.7	3.0	5.9	8.9	11.8	14.8	.7	0.2	0.5	0.8	1.1	1.4	1.7	2.0	2.2	2.5	2.8
17.8	3.0	6.0	8.9	11.9	14.9	.8	0.2	0.5	0.8	1.1	1.4	1.7	2.0	2.3	2.6	2.9
17.9	3.0	6.0	9.0	12.0	15.0	.9	0.3	0.6	0.8	1.1	1.4	1.7	2.0	2.3	2.6	2.9
18.0	3.0	6.0	9.0	12.0	15.0	.0	0.0	0.3	0.6	0.9	1.2	1.5	1.8	2.2	2.5	2.8
18.1	3.0	6.0	9.0	12.0	15.1	.1	0.0	0.3	0.6	1.0	1.3	1.6	1.9	2.2	2.5	2.8
18.2	3.0	6.0	9.1	12.1	15.1	.2	0.1	0.4	0.7	1.0	1.3	1.6	1.9	2.2	2.5	2.8
18.3	3.0	6.1	9.1	12.2	15.2	.3	0.1	0.4	0.7	1.0	1.3	1.6	1.9	2.3	2.6	2.9
18.4	3.1	6.1	9.2	12.3	15.3	.4	0.1	0.4	0.7	1.0	1.4	1.7	2.0	2.3	2.6	2.9
18.5	3.1	6.2	9.3	12.3	15.4	.5	0.2	0.5	0.8	1.1	1.4	1.7	2.0	2.3	2.6	2.9
18.6	3.1	6.2	9.3	12.4	15.5	.6	0.2	0.5	0.8	1.1	1.4	1.7	2.0	2.3	2.7	3.0
18.7	3.1	6.3	9.4	12.5	15.6	.7	0.2	0.5	0.8	1.1	1.4	1.8	2.1	2.4	2.7	3.0
18.8	3.2	6.3	9.4	12.6	15.7	.8	0.2	0.6	0.9	1.2	1.5	1.8	2.1	2.4	2.7	3.0
18.9	3.2	6.3	9.5	12.6	15.8	.9	0.3	0.6	0.9	1.2	1.5	1.8	2.1	2.4	2.7	3.1
19.0	3.1	6.3	9.5	12.6	15.8	.0	0.0	0.3	0.6	1.0	1.3	1.6	1.9	2.3	2.6	2.9
19.1	3.2	6.3	9.5	12.7	15.9	.1	0.0	0.4	0.7	1.0	1.3	1.7	2.0	2.3	2.6	3.0
19.2	3.2	6.4	9.6	12.8	16.0	.2	0.1	0.4	0.7	1.0	1.4	1.7	2.0	2.3	2.7	3.0
19.3	3.2	6.4	9.6	12.9	16.1	.3	0.1	0.4	0.7	1.1	1.4	1.7	2.0	2.4	2.7	3.0
19.4	3.2	6.5	9.7	12.9	16.2	.4	0.1	0.5	0.8	1.1	1.4	1.8	2.1	2.4	2.7	3.1
19.5	3.3	6.5	9.8	13.0	16.3	.5	0.2	0.5	0.8	1.1	1.5	1.8	2.1	2.4	2.8	3.1
19.6	3.3	6.5	9.8	13.1	16.3	.6	0.2	0.5	0.8	1.2	1.5	1.8	2.1	2.5	2.8	3.1
19.7	3.3	6.6	9.9	13.2	16.4	.7	0.2	0.6	0.9	1.2	1.5	1.9	2.2	2.5	2.8	3.2
19.8	3.3	6.6	9.9	13.2	16.5	.8	0.3	0.6	0.9	1.2	1.6	1.9	2.2	2.5	2.9	3.2
19.9	3.4	6.7	10.0	13.3	16.6	.9	0.3	0.6	0.9	1.3	1.6	1.9	2.2	2.6	2.9	3.2
20.0	3.3	6.6	10.0	13.3	16.6	.0	0.0	0.3	0.7	1.0	1.4	1.7	2.0	2.4	2.7	3.1
20.1	3.3	6.7	10.0	13.4	16.7	.1	0.0	0.4	0.7	1.1	1.4	1.7	2.1	2.4	2.8	3.1
20.2	3.3	6.7	10.1	13.4	16.8	.2	0.1	0.4	0.8	1.1	1.4	1.8	2.1	2.5	2.8	3.1
20.3	3.4	6.8	10.1	13.5	16.9	.3	0.1	0.4	0.8	1.1	1.5	1.8	2.2	2.5	2.8	3.2
20.4	3.4	6.8	10.2	13.6	17.0	.4	0.1	0.5	0.8	1.2	1.5	1.8	2.2	2.5	2.9	3.2
20.5	3.4	6.8	10.3	13.7	17.1	.5	0.2	0.5	0.9	1.2	1.5	1.9	2.2	2.6	2.9	3.2
20.6	3.4	6.9	10.3	13.7	17.2	.6	0.2	0.5	0.9	1.2	1.6	1.9	2.3	2.6	2.9	3.3
20.7	3.5	6.9	10.4	13.8	17.3	.7	0.2	0.6	0.9	1.3	1.6	1.9	2.3	2.6	3.0	3.3
20.8	3.5	7.0	10.4	13.9	17.4	.8	0.3	0.6	1.0	1.3	1.6	2.0	2.3	2.7	3.0	3.3
20.9	3.5	7.0	10.5	14.0	17.5	.9	0.3	0.6	1.0	1.3	1.7	2.0	2.4	2.7	3.0	3.4
21.0	3.5	7.0	10.5	14.0	17.5	.0	0.0	0.4	0.7	1.1	1.4	1.8	2.1	2.5	2.9	3.2
21.1	3.5	7.0	10.5	14.0	17.6	.1	0.0	0.4	0.8	1.1	1.5	1.8	2.2	2.5	2.9	3.3
21.2	3.5	7.0	10.6	14.1	17.6	.2	0.1	0.4	0.8	1.1	1.5	1.9	2.2	2.6	2.9	3.3
21.3	3.5	7.1	10.6	14.2	17.7	.3	0.1	0.5	0.8	1.2	1.5	1.9	2.3	2.6	3.0	3.3
21.4	3.6	7.1	10.7	14.3	17.8	.4	0.1	0.5	0.9	1.2	1.6	1.9	2.3	2.7	3.0	3.4
21.5	3.6	7.2	10.8	14.3	17.9	.5	0.2	0.5	0.9	1.3	1.6	2.0	2.3	2.7	3.0	3.4
21.6	3.6	7.2	10.8	14.4	18.0	.6	0.2	0.6	0.9	1.3	1.6	2.0	2.4	2.7	3.1	3.4
21.7	3.6	7.3	10.9	14.5	18.1	.7	0.3	0.6	1.0	1.3	1.7	2.0	2.4	2.8	3.1	3.5
21.8	3.7	7.3	10.9	14.6	18.2	.8	0.3	0.6	1.0	1.4	1.7	2.1	2.4	2.8	3.2	3.5
21.9	3.7	7.3	11.0	14.6	18.3	.9	0.3	0.7	1.0	1.4	1.8	2.1	2.5	2.8	3.2	3.5
22.0	3.6	7.3	11.0	14.6	18.3	.0	0.0	0.4	0.7	1.1	1.5	1.9	2.2	2.6	3.0	3.4
22.1	3.7	7.3	11.0	14.7	18.4	.1	0.0	0.4	0.8	1.2	1.5	1.9	2.3	2.7	3.0	3.4
22.2	3.7	7.4	11.1	14.8	18.5	.2	0.1	0.4	0.8	1.2	1.6	1.9	2.3	2.7	3.1	3.4
22.3	3.7	7.4	11.1	14.9	18.6	.3	0.1	0.5	0.9	1.2	1.6	2.0	2.4	2.7	3.1	3.5
22.4	3.7	7.5	11.2	14.9	18.7	.4	0.1	0.5	0.9	1.3	1.6	2.0	2.4	2.8	3.1	3.5
22.5	3.8	7.5	11.3	15.0	18.8	.5	0.2	0.6	0.9	1.3	1.7	2.1	2.4	2.8	3.2	3.6
22.6	3.8	7.5	11.3	15.1	18.8	.6	0.2	0.6	1.0	1.3	1.7	2.1	2.5	2.8	3.2	3.6
22.7	3.8	7.6	11.4	15.2	18.9	.7	0.3	0.6	1.0	1.4	1.8	2.1	2.5	2.9	3.3	3.6
22.8	3.8	7.6	11.4	15.2	19.0	.8	0.3	0.7	1.0	1.4	1.8	2.2	2.5	2.9	3.3	3.7
22.9	3.9	7.7	11.5	15.3	19.1	.9	0.3	0.7	1.1	1.5	1.8	2.2	2.6	3.0	3.3	3.7
23.0	3.8	7.6	11.5	15.3	19.1	.0	0.0	0.4	0.8	1.2	1.6	2.0	2.3	2.7	3.1	3.5
23.1	3.8	7.7	11.5	15.4	19.2	.1	0.0	0.4	0.8	1.2	1.6	2.0	2.4	2.8	3.2	3.6
23.2	3.8	7.7	11.6	15.4	19.3	.2	0.1	0.5	0.9	1.3	1.6	2.0	2.4	2.8	3.2	3.6
23.3	3.9	7.8	11.6	15.5	19.4	.3	0.1	0.5	0.9	1.3	1.7	2.1	2.5	2.9	3.3	3.6
23.4	3.9	7.8	11.7	15.6	19.5	.4	0.2	0.5	0.9	1.3	1.7	2.1	2.5	2.9	3.3	3.7
23.5	3.9	7.8	11.8	15.7	19.6	.5	0.2	0.6	1.0	1.4	1.8	2.2	2.5	2.9	3.3	3.7
23.6	3.9	7.9	11.8	15.7	19.7	.6	0.2	0.6	1.0	1.4	1.8	2.2	2.6	3.0	3.4	3.8
23.7	4.0	7.9	11.9	15.8	19.8	.7	0.3	0.7	1.1	1.4	1.8	2.2	2.6	3.0	3.4	3.8
23.8	4.0	8.0	11.9	15.9	19.9	.8	0.3	0.7	1.1	1.5	1.9	2.3	2.7	3.1	3.4	3.8
23.9	4.0	8.0	12.0	16.0	20.0	.9	0.4	0.7	1.1	1.5	1.9	2.3	2.7	3.1	3.5	3.9
	10'	20'	30'	40'	50'		0'	1'	2'	3'	4'	5'	6'	7'	8'	9'

Double Second Diff. and Corr. (Dec. Inc. 16.0–17.9)

Double Second Diff.	Corr.
1.0–3.0	0.1
3.0–4.9	0.2
4.9–6.9	0.3
6.9–8.9	0.4
8.9–10.8	0.5
10.8–12.8	0.6
12.8–14.8	0.7
14.8–16.7	0.8
16.7–18.7	0.9
18.7–20.7	1.0
20.7–22.7	1.1
22.7–24.6	1.2
24.6–26.6	1.3
26.6–28.6	1.4
28.6–30.5	1.5
30.5–32.5	1.6
32.5–34.5	1.7

Double Second Diff. and Corr. (Dec. Inc. 18.0–19.9)

Double Second Diff.	Corr.
0.9–2.8	0.1
2.8–4.6	0.2
4.6–6.5	0.3
6.5–8.3	0.4
8.3–10.2	0.5
10.2–12.0	0.6
12.0–13.9	0.7
13.9–15.7	0.8
15.7–17.6	0.9
17.6–19.4	1.0
19.4–21.3	1.1
21.3–23.1	1.2
23.1–25.0	1.3
25.0–26.8	1.4
26.8–28.7	1.5
28.7–30.5	1.6
30.5–32.3	1.7
32.3–34.2	1.8

Double Second Diff. and Corr. (Dec. Inc. 20.0–21.9)

Double Second Diff.	Corr.
0.9–2.6	0.1
2.6–4.4	0.2
4.4–6.2	0.3
6.2–7.9	0.4
7.9–9.7	0.5
9.7–11.4	0.6
11.4–13.2	0.7
13.2–14.9	0.8
14.9–16.7	0.9
16.7–18.5	1.0
18.5–20.2	1.1
20.2–22.0	1.2
22.0–23.7	1.3
23.7–25.5	1.4
25.5–27.3	1.5
27.3–29.0	1.6
29.0–30.8	1.7
30.8–32.5	1.8
32.5–34.3	1.9

Double Second Diff. and Corr. (Dec. Inc. 22.0–23.9)

Double Second Diff.	Corr.
0.8–2.5	0.1
2.5–4.2	0.2
4.2–5.9	0.3
5.9–7.6	0.4
7.6–9.3	0.5
9.3–11.0	0.6
11.0–12.7	0.7
12.7–14.4	0.8
14.4–16.1	0.9
16.1–17.8	1.0
17.8–19.5	1.1
19.5–21.2	1.2
21.2–22.8	1.3
22.8–24.5	1.4
24.5–26.2	1.5
26.2–27.9	1.6
27.9–29.6	1.7
29.6–31.3	1.8
31.3–33.0	1.9
33.0–34.7	2.0

Dec. Inc.	Tens 10'	20'	30'	40'	50'	Decimals	Units 0'	1'	2'	3'	4'	5'	6'	7'	8'	9'
24.0	4.0	8.0	12.0	16.0	20.0	.0	0.0	0.4	0.8	1.2	1.6	2.0	2.4	2.9	3.3	3.7
24.1	4.0	8.0	12.0	16.0	20.1	.1	0.0	0.4	0.9	1.3	1.7	2.1	2.5	2.9	3.3	3.7
24.2	4.0	8.0	12.1	16.1	20.1	.2	0.1	0.5	0.9	1.3	1.7	2.1	2.5	2.9	3.3	3.8
24.3	4.0	8.1	12.1	16.2	20.2	.3	0.1	0.5	0.9	1.3	1.8	2.2	2.6	3.0	3.4	3.8
24.4	4.1	8.1	12.2	16.3	20.3	.4	0.2	0.6	1.0	1.4	1.8	2.2	2.6	3.0	3.4	3.8
24.5	4.1	8.2	12.3	16.3	20.4	.5	0.2	0.6	1.0	1.4	1.8	2.2	2.7	3.1	3.5	3.9
24.6	4.1	8.2	12.3	16.4	20.5	.6	0.2	0.7	1.1	1.5	1.9	2.3	2.7	3.1	3.5	3.9
24.7	4.1	8.3	12.4	16.5	20.6	.7	0.3	0.7	1.1	1.5	1.9	2.3	2.7	3.1	3.6	4.0
24.8	4.2	8.3	12.4	16.6	20.7	.8	0.3	0.7	1.1	1.6	2.0	2.4	2.8	3.2	3.6	4.0
24.9	4.2	8.3	12.5	16.6	20.8	.9	0.4	0.8	1.2	1.6	2.0	2.4	2.8	3.2	3.6	4.0
25.0	4.1	8.3	12.5	16.6	20.8	.0	0.0	0.4	0.8	1.3	1.7	2.1	2.5	3.0	3.4	3.8
25.1	4.2	8.3	12.5	16.7	20.9	.1	0.0	0.5	0.9	1.3	1.7	2.2	2.6	3.0	3.4	3.9
25.2	4.2	8.4	12.6	16.8	21.0	.2	0.1	0.5	0.9	1.4	1.8	2.2	2.6	3.1	3.5	3.9
25.3	4.2	8.4	12.6	16.9	21.1	.3	0.1	0.6	1.0	1.4	1.8	2.3	2.7	3.1	3.5	4.0
25.4	4.2	8.5	12.7	16.9	21.2	.4	0.2	0.6	1.0	1.4	1.9	2.3	2.7	3.1	3.6	4.0
25.5	4.3	8.5	12.8	17.0	21.3	.5	0.2	0.6	1.1	1.5	1.9	2.3	2.8	3.2	3.6	4.0
25.6	4.3	8.5	12.8	17.1	21.3	.6	0.3	0.7	1.1	1.5	2.0	2.4	2.8	3.2	3.7	4.1
25.7	4.3	8.6	12.9	17.2	21.4	.7	0.3	0.7	1.1	1.6	2.0	2.4	2.8	3.3	3.7	4.1
25.8	4.3	8.6	12.9	17.2	21.5	.8	0.3	0.8	1.2	1.6	2.0	2.5	2.9	3.3	3.7	4.2
25.9	4.4	8.7	13.0	17.3	21.6	.9	0.4	0.8	1.2	1.7	2.1	2.5	2.9	3.4	3.8	4.2
26.0	4.3	8.6	13.0	17.3	21.6	.0	0.0	0.4	0.9	1.3	1.8	2.2	2.6	3.1	3.5	4.0
26.1	4.3	8.7	13.0	17.4	21.7	.1	0.0	0.5	0.9	1.4	1.8	2.3	2.7	3.1	3.6	4.0
26.2	4.3	8.7	13.1	17.4	21.8	.2	0.1	0.5	1.0	1.4	1.9	2.3	2.7	3.2	3.6	4.1
26.3	4.4	8.8	13.1	17.5	21.9	.3	0.1	0.6	1.0	1.5	1.9	2.3	2.8	3.2	3.7	4.1
26.4	4.4	8.8	13.2	17.6	22.0	.4	0.2	0.6	1.1	1.5	1.9	2.4	2.8	3.3	3.7	4.2
26.5	4.4	8.8	13.3	17.7	22.1	.5	0.2	0.7	1.1	1.5	2.0	2.4	2.9	3.3	3.8	4.2
26.6	4.4	8.9	13.3	17.7	22.2	.6	0.3	0.7	1.1	1.6	2.0	2.5	2.9	3.4	3.8	4.2
26.7	4.5	8.9	13.4	17.8	22.3	.7	0.3	0.8	1.2	1.6	2.1	2.5	3.0	3.4	3.8	4.3
26.8	4.5	9.0	13.4	17.9	22.4	.8	0.4	0.8	1.2	1.7	2.1	2.6	3.0	3.4	3.9	4.3
26.9	4.5	9.0	13.5	18.0	22.5	.9	0.4	0.8	1.3	1.7	2.2	2.6	3.0	3.5	3.9	4.4
27.0	4.5	9.0	13.5	18.0	22.5	.0	0.0	0.5	0.9	1.4	1.8	2.3	2.7	3.2	3.7	4.1
27.1	4.5	9.0	13.5	18.0	22.6	.1	0.0	0.5	1.0	1.4	1.9	2.3	2.8	3.3	3.7	4.2
27.2	4.5	9.0	13.6	18.1	22.6	.2	0.1	0.5	1.0	1.5	1.9	2.4	2.8	3.3	3.8	4.2
27.3	4.5	9.1	13.6	18.2	22.7	.3	0.1	0.6	1.1	1.5	2.0	2.4	2.9	3.3	3.8	4.3
27.4	4.6	9.1	13.7	18.3	22.8	.4	0.2	0.6	1.1	1.6	2.0	2.5	2.9	3.4	3.8	4.3
27.5	4.6	9.2	13.8	18.3	22.9	.5	0.2	0.7	1.1	1.6	2.1	2.5	3.0	3.4	3.9	4.4
27.6	4.6	9.2	13.8	18.4	23.0	.6	0.3	0.7	1.2	1.6	2.1	2.6	3.0	3.5	3.9	4.4
27.7	4.6	9.3	13.9	18.5	23.1	.7	0.3	0.8	1.2	1.7	2.2	2.6	3.1	3.5	4.0	4.4
27.8	4.7	9.3	13.9	18.6	23.2	.8	0.4	0.8	1.3	1.7	2.2	2.7	3.1	3.6	4.0	4.5
27.9	4.7	9.3	14.0	18.6	23.3	.9	0.4	0.9	1.3	1.8	2.2	2.7	3.2	3.6	4.1	4.5
28.0	4.6	9.3	14.0	18.6	23.3	.0	0.0	0.5	0.9	1.4	1.9	2.4	2.8	3.3	3.8	4.3
28.1	4.7	9.3	14.0	18.7	23.4	.1	0.0	0.5	1.0	1.5	1.9	2.4	2.9	3.4	3.8	4.3
28.2	4.7	9.4	14.1	18.8	23.5	.2	0.1	0.6	1.0	1.5	2.0	2.5	2.9	3.4	3.9	4.4
28.3	4.7	9.4	14.1	18.9	23.6	.3	0.1	0.6	1.1	1.6	2.0	2.5	3.0	3.5	3.9	4.4
28.4	4.7	9.5	14.2	18.9	23.7	.4	0.2	0.7	1.1	1.6	2.1	2.6	3.0	3.5	4.0	4.5
28.5	4.8	9.5	14.3	19.0	23.8	.5	0.2	0.7	1.2	1.7	2.1	2.6	3.1	3.6	4.0	4.5
28.6	4.8	9.5	14.3	19.1	23.8	.6	0.3	0.8	1.2	1.7	2.2	2.7	3.1	3.6	4.1	4.6
28.7	4.8	9.6	14.4	19.2	23.9	.7	0.3	0.8	1.3	1.8	2.2	2.7	3.2	3.7	4.1	4.6
28.8	4.8	9.6	14.4	19.2	24.0	.8	0.4	0.9	1.3	1.8	2.3	2.8	3.2	3.7	4.2	4.7
28.9	4.9	9.7	14.5	19.3	24.1	.9	0.4	0.9	1.4	1.9	2.3	2.8	3.3	3.8	4.2	4.7
29.0	4.8	9.6	14.5	19.3	24.1	.0	0.0	0.5	1.0	1.5	2.0	2.5	2.9	3.4	3.9	4.4
29.1	4.8	9.7	14.5	19.4	24.2	.1	0.0	0.5	1.0	1.5	2.0	2.5	3.0	3.5	4.0	4.5
29.2	4.8	9.7	14.6	19.4	24.3	.2	0.1	0.6	1.1	1.6	2.1	2.6	3.0	3.5	4.0	4.5
29.3	4.9	9.8	14.6	19.5	24.4	.3	0.1	0.6	1.1	1.6	2.1	2.6	3.1	3.6	4.1	4.6
29.4	4.9	9.8	14.7	19.6	24.5	.4	0.2	0.7	1.2	1.7	2.2	2.7	3.1	3.6	4.1	4.6
29.5	4.9	9.8	14.8	19.7	24.6	.5	0.2	0.7	1.2	1.7	2.2	2.7	3.2	3.7	4.2	4.7
29.6	4.9	9.9	14.8	19.7	24.7	.6	0.3	0.8	1.3	1.8	2.3	2.8	3.2	3.7	4.2	4.7
29.7	5.0	9.9	14.9	19.8	24.8	.7	0.3	0.8	1.3	1.8	2.3	2.8	3.3	3.8	4.3	4.8
29.8	5.0	10.0	14.9	19.9	24.9	.8	0.4	0.9	1.4	1.9	2.4	2.9	3.3	3.8	4.3	4.8
29.9	5.0	10.0	15.0	20.0	25.0	.9	0.4	0.9	1.4	1.9	2.4	2.9	3.4	3.9	4.4	4.9
30.0	5.0	10.0	15.0	20.0	25.0	.0	0.0	0.5	1.0	1.5	2.0	2.5	3.0	3.6	4.1	4.6
30.1	5.0	10.0	15.0	20.0	25.1	.1	0.1	0.6	1.1	1.6	2.1	2.6	3.1	3.6	4.1	4.6
30.2	5.0	10.0	15.1	20.1	25.1	.2	0.1	0.6	1.1	1.6	2.1	2.6	3.2	3.7	4.2	4.7
30.3	5.0	10.1	15.1	20.2	25.2	.3	0.2	0.7	1.2	1.7	2.2	2.7	3.2	3.7	4.2	4.7
30.4	5.1	10.1	15.2	20.3	25.3	.4	0.2	0.7	1.2	1.7	2.2	2.7	3.3	3.8	4.3	4.8
30.5	5.1	10.2	15.3	20.3	25.4	.5	0.3	0.8	1.3	1.8	2.3	2.8	3.3	3.8	4.3	4.8
30.6	5.1	10.2	15.3	20.4	25.5	.6	0.3	0.8	1.3	1.8	2.3	2.8	3.4	3.9	4.4	4.9
30.7	5.1	10.3	15.4	20.5	25.6	.7	0.4	0.9	1.4	1.9	2.4	2.9	3.4	3.9	4.4	4.9
30.8	5.2	10.3	15.4	20.6	25.7	.8	0.4	0.9	1.4	1.9	2.4	2.9	3.5	4.0	4.5	5.0
30.9	5.2	10.3	15.5	20.6	25.8	.9	0.5	1.0	1.5	2.0	2.5	3.0	3.5	4.0	4.5	5.0
31.0	5.1	10.3	15.5	20.6	25.8	.0	0.0	0.5	1.0	1.6	2.1	2.6	3.1	3.7	4.2	4.7
31.1	5.2	10.3	15.5	20.7	25.9	.1	0.1	0.6	1.1	1.6	2.2	2.7	3.2	3.7	4.3	4.8
31.2	5.2	10.4	15.6	20.8	26.0	.2	0.1	0.6	1.2	1.7	2.2	2.7	3.3	3.8	4.3	4.8
31.3	5.2	10.4	15.6	20.9	26.1	.3	0.2	0.7	1.2	1.7	2.3	2.8	3.3	3.8	4.4	4.9
31.4	5.2	10.5	15.7	20.9	26.2	.4	0.2	0.7	1.3	1.8	2.3	2.8	3.4	3.9	4.4	4.9
31.5	5.3	10.5	15.8	21.0	26.3	.5	0.3	0.8	1.3	1.8	2.4	2.9	3.4	3.9	4.5	5.0
31.6	5.3	10.5	15.8	21.1	26.3	.6	0.3	0.8	1.4	1.9	2.4	2.9	3.5	4.0	4.5	5.0
31.7	5.3	10.6	15.9	21.2	26.4	.7	0.4	0.9	1.4	1.9	2.5	3.0	3.5	4.0	4.6	5.1
31.8	5.3	10.6	15.9	21.2	26.5	.8	0.4	0.9	1.5	2.0	2.5	3.0	3.6	4.1	4.6	5.1
31.9	5.4	10.7	16.0	21.3	26.6	.9	0.5	1.0	1.5	2.0	2.6	3.1	3.6	4.1	4.7	5.2
	10'	20'	30'	40'	50'		0'	1'	2	3'	4'	5'	6'	7'	8'	9'

Double Second Diff. and Corr. (Dec. Inc. 24.0–25.9)

Double Second Diff.	Corr.
0.8–2.5	0.1
2.5–4.1	0.2
4.1–5.8	0.3
5.8–7.4	0.4
7.4–9.1	0.5
9.1–10.7	0.6
10.7–12.3	0.7
12.3–14.0	0.8
14.0–15.6	0.9
15.6–17.3	1.0
17.3–18.9	1.1
18.9–20.6	1.2
20.6–22.2	1.3
22.2–23.9	1.4
23.9–25.5	1.5
25.5–27.2	1.6
27.2–28.8	1.7
28.8–30.4	1.8
30.4–32.1	1.9
32.1–33.7	2.0
33.7–35.4	2.1

Double Second Diff. and Corr. (Dec. Inc. 26.0–27.9)

Double Second Diff.	Corr.
0.8–2.4	0.1
2.4–4.0	0.2
4.0–5.7	0.3
5.7–7.3	0.4
7.3–8.9	0.5
8.9–10.5	0.6
10.5–12.1	0.7
12.1–13.7	0.8
13.7–15.4	0.9
15.4–17.0	1.0
17.0–18.6	1.1
18.6–20.2	1.2
20.2–21.8	1.3
21.8–23.4	1.4
23.4–25.1	1.5
25.1–26.7	1.6
26.7–28.3	1.7
28.3–29.9	1.8
29.9–31.5	1.9
31.5–33.1	2.0
33.1–34.7	2.1

Double Second Diff. and Corr. (Dec. Inc. 28.0–29.9)

Double Second Diff.	Corr.
0.8–2.4	0.1
2.4–4.0	0.2
4.0–5.6	0.3
5.6–7.2	0.4
7.2–8.8	0.5
8.8–10.4	0.6
10.4–12.0	0.7
12.0–13.6	0.8
13.6–15.2	0.9
15.2–16.8	1.0
16.8–18.4	1.1
18.4–20.0	1.2
20.0–21.6	1.3
21.6–23.2	1.4
23.2–24.8	1.5
24.8–26.4	1.6
26.4–28.0	1.7
28.0–29.6	1.8
29.6–31.2	1.9
31.2–32.8	2.0
32.8–34.4	2.1

Double Second Diff. and Corr. (Dec. Inc. 30.0–31.9)

Double Second Diff.	Corr.
0.8–2.4	0.1
2.4–4.0	0.2
4.0–5.6	0.3
5.6–7.2	0.4
7.2–8.8	0.5
8.8–10.4	0.6
10.4–12.0	0.7
12.0–13.6	0.8
13.6–15.2	0.9
15.2–16.8	1.0
16.8–18.4	1.1
18.4–20.0	1.2
20.0–21.6	1.3
21.6–23.2	1.4
23.2–24.8	1.5
24.8–26.4	1.6
26.4–28.0	1.7
28.0–29.6	1.8
29.6–31.2	1.9
31.2–32.8	2.0
32.8–34.4	2.1

The Double-Second-Difference correction (Corr.) is always to be added to the tabulated altitude.

60°, 300° L.H.A. LATITUDE SAME NAME AS DECLINATION

N. Lat. {L.H.A. greater than 180°......Zn=Z; L.H.A. less than 180°............Zn=360°−Z}

Dec.	38° Hc	d	Z	39° Hc	d	Z	40° Hc	d	Z	41° Hc	d	Z	42° Hc	d	Z	43° Hc	d	Z	44° Hc	d	Z	45° Hc	d	Z	Dec.
°	° ′	′	°	° ′	′	°	° ′	′	°	° ′	′	°	° ′	′	°	° ′	′	°	° ′	′	°	° ′	′	°	°
0	23 12.2	+40.1	109.6	22 51.9	+40.9	110.0	22 31.3	+41.6	110.4	22 10.2	+42.4	110.7	21 48.8	+43.1	111.1	21 27.0	+43.8	111.5	21 04.8	+44.6	111.9	20 42.3	+45.3	112.2	0
1	23 52.3	39.8	108.8	23 32.8	40.6	109.2	23 12.9	41.4	109.6	22 52.6	42.2	110.0	22 31.9	42.9	110.4	22 10.8	43.7	110.8	21 49.4	44.4	111.1	21 27.6	45.0	111.5	1
2	24 32.1	39.5	107.9	24 13.4	40.4	108.4	23 54.3	41.2	108.8	23 34.8	41.9	109.2	23 14.8	42.7	109.6	22 54.5	43.4	110.0	22 33.8	44.2	110.4	22 12.6	45.0	110.8	2
3	25 11.6	39.3	107.1	24 53.8	40.1	107.6	24 35.5	40.9	108.0	24 16.7	41.7	108.4	23 57.5	42.5	108.8	23 37.9	43.3	109.3	23 18.0	43.9	109.7	22 57.6	44.7	110.1	3
4	25 50.9	39.0	106.3	25 33.9	39.8	106.7	25 16.4	40.6	107.2	24 58.4	41.5	107.6	24 40.0	42.3	108.1	24 21.2	43.0	108.5	24 01.9	43.8	108.9	23 42.3	44.5	109.3	4
5	26 29.9	+38.6	105.4	26 13.7	+39.5	105.9	25 57.0	+40.4	106.4	25 39.9	+41.1	106.8	25 22.3	+41.9	107.3	25 04.2	+42.8	107.7	24 45.7	+43.5	108.2	24 26.8	+44.3	108.6	5
6	27 08.5	38.4	104.6	26 53.2	39.2	105.1	26 37.4	40.0	105.5	26 21.0	40.9	106.0	26 04.2	41.8	106.5	25 47.0	42.5	107.0	25 29.2	43.3	107.4	25 11.1	44.0	107.9	6
7	27 46.9	38.0	103.7	27 32.4	38.9	104.2	27 17.4	39.8	104.7	27 01.9	40.7	105.2	26 46.0	41.4	105.7	26 29.5	42.3	106.2	26 12.5	43.1	106.7	25 55.1	43.8	107.1	7
8	28 24.9	37.7	102.8	28 11.3	38.6	103.3	27 57.2	39.5	103.9	27 42.6	40.3	104.4	27 27.4	41.2	104.9	27 11.8	41.9	105.4	26 55.6	42.8	105.9	26 38.9	43.6	106.4	8
9	29 02.6	37.3	101.9	28 49.9	38.2	102.5	28 36.7	39.1	103.0	28 22.9	40.0	103.5	28 08.6	40.8	104.1	27 53.7	41.7	104.6	27 38.4	42.5	105.1	27 22.5	43.3	105.6	9
10	29 39.9	+37.0	101.0	29 28.1	+37.9	101.6	29 15.8	+38.8	102.1	29 02.9	+39.7	102.7	28 49.4	+40.6	103.2	28 35.4	+41.4	103.8	28 20.9	+42.2	104.3	28 05.8	+43.1	104.8	10
11	30 16.9	36.5	100.1	30 06.0	37.5	100.7	29 54.6	38.4	101.3	29 42.6	39.3	101.8	29 30.0	40.2	102.4	29 16.8	41.1	102.9	29 03.1	42.0	103.5	28 48.9	42.8	104.0	11
12	30 53.4	36.2	99.2	30 43.5	37.2	99.8	30 33.0	38.1	100.4	30 21.9	39.0	101.0	30 10.2	39.9	101.5	29 57.9	40.8	102.1	29 45.1	41.6	102.7	29 31.7	42.4	103.2	12
13	31 29.6	35.8	98.3	31 20.7	36.7	98.9	31 11.1	37.7	99.5	31 00.9	38.6	100.1	30 50.1	39.6	100.7	30 38.7	40.5	101.2	30 26.7	41.3	101.8	30 14.1	42.2	102.4	13
14	32 05.4	35.3	97.3	31 57.4	36.3	97.9	31 48.8	37.3	98.6	31 39.5	38.3	99.2	31 29.7	39.1	99.8	31 19.2	40.0	100.4	31 08.0	41.0	101.0	30 56.3	41.9	101.6	14
15	32 40.7	+34.9	96.4	32 33.7	+35.9	97.0	32 26.1	+36.9	97.6	32 17.8	+37.8	98.3	32 08.8	+38.8	98.9	31 59.2	+39.8	99.5	31 49.0	+40.6	100.1	31 38.2	+41.5	100.7	15
16	33 15.6	34.5	95.4	33 09.6	35.5	96.1	33 03.0	36.4	96.7	32 55.6	37.5	97.3	32 47.6	38.4	98.0	32 39.0	39.3	98.6	32 29.6	40.3	99.3	32 19.7	41.1	99.9	16
17	33 50.1	33.9	94.4	33 45.1	35.0	95.1	33 39.4	36.0	95.7	33 33.1	37.0	96.4	33 26.0	38.0	97.1	33 18.3	38.9	97.7	33 09.9	39.9	98.4	33 00.8	40.8	99.0	17
18	34 24.0	33.5	93.4	34 20.1	34.5	94.1	34 15.4	35.6	94.8	34 10.1	36.5	95.5	34 04.0	37.6	96.1	33 57.2	38.6	96.8	33 49.8	39.5	97.5	33 41.6	40.5	98.1	18
19	34 57.5	33.0	92.4	34 54.6	34.0	93.1	34 51.0	35.1	93.8	34 46.6	36.1	94.5	34 41.6	37.1	95.2	34 35.8	38.1	95.9	34 29.3	39.1	96.6	34 22.1	40.0	97.2	19
20	35 30.5	+32.4	91.4	35 28.6	+33.6	92.1	35 26.1	+34.5	92.8	35 22.7	+35.7	93.5	35 18.7	+36.6	94.2	35 13.9	+37.7	94.9	35 08.4	+38.6	95.6	35 02.1	+39.6	96.3	20
21	36 02.9	31.9	90.4	36 02.2	32.9	91.1	36 00.6	34.1	91.8	35 58.4	35.1	92.5	35 55.3	36.2	93.3	35 51.6	37.2	94.0	35 47.0	38.2	94.7	35 41.7	39.2	95.4	21
22	36 34.8	31.3	89.3	36 35.1	32.5	90.0	36 34.7	33.6	90.8	36 33.5	34.6	91.5	36 31.5	35.7	92.3	36 28.8	36.7	93.0	36 25.2	37.8	93.7	36 20.9	38.8	94.5	22
23	37 06.1	30.8	88.2	37 07.6	31.9	89.0	37 08.3	32.9	89.8	37 08.1	34.1	90.5	37 07.2	35.2	91.3	37 05.5	36.2	92.0	37 03.0	37.2	92.8	36 59.7	38.2	93.5	23
24	37 36.9	30.2	87.2	37 39.5	31.3	87.9	37 41.2	32.5	88.7	37 42.2	33.5	89.5	37 42.4	34.6	90.2	37 41.7	35.7	91.0	37 40.2	36.8	91.8	37 37.9	37.8	92.6	24
25	38 07.1	+29.5	86.1	38 10.8	+30.7	86.8	38 13.7	+31.8	87.6	38 15.7	+33.0	88.4	38 17.0	+34.0	89.2	38 17.4	+35.2	90.0	38 17.0	+36.2	90.8	38 15.7	+37.3	91.6	25
26	38 36.6	28.9	85.0	38 41.5	30.0	85.7	38 45.5	31.2	86.5	38 48.7	32.4	87.4	38 51.0	33.5	88.2	38 52.6	34.6	89.0	38 53.2	35.7	89.8	38 53.0	36.8	90.6	26
27	39 05.5	28.3	83.8	39 11.5	29.5	84.6	39 16.7	30.6	85.4	39 21.1	31.7	86.3	39 24.5	32.9	87.1	39 27.2	34.0	87.9	39 28.9	35.2	88.7	39 29.8	36.3	89.6	27
28	39 33.8	27.5	82.7	39 41.0	28.7	83.5	39 47.3	30.0	84.3	39 52.8	31.1	85.2	39 57.4	32.3	86.0	40 01.2	33.4	86.8	40 04.1	34.5	87.7	40 06.1	35.6	88.5	28
29	40 01.3	26.9	81.5	40 09.7	28.1	82.4	40 17.3	29.2	83.2	40 23.9	30.5	84.0	40 29.7	31.7	84.9	40 34.6	32.8	85.7	40 38.6	34.0	86.6	40 41.7	35.1	87.5	29
30	40 28.2	+26.1	80.4	40 37.8	+27.4	81.2	40 46.5	+28.6	82.1	40 54.4	+29.8	82.9	41 01.4	+30.9	83.8	41 07.4	+32.2	84.6	41 12.6	+33.3	85.5	41 16.8	+34.5	86.4	30
31	40 54.3	25.5	79.2	41 05.2	26.6	80.0	41 15.1	27.9	80.9	41 24.2	29.1	81.8	41 32.3	30.3	82.6	41 39.6	31.4	83.5	41 45.9	32.6	84.4	41 51.3	33.8	85.3	31
32	41 19.8	24.6	78.0	41 31.8	25.9	78.8	41 43.0	27.1	79.7	41 53.3	28.3	80.6	42 02.6	29.6	81.5	42 11.0	30.8	82.4	42 18.5	32.0	83.3	42 25.1	33.2	84.2	32
33	41 44.4	23.9	76.8	41 57.7	25.1	77.6	42 10.1	26.4	78.5	42 21.6	27.6	79.4	42 32.2	28.8	80.3	42 41.8	30.1	81.2	42 50.5	31.3	82.1	42 58.3	32.5	83.0	33
34	42 08.3	23.0	75.5	42 22.8	24.4	76.4	42 36.5	25.6	77.3	42 49.2	26.9	78.2	43 01.0	28.1	79.1	43 11.9	29.3	80.0	43 21.8	30.6	81.0	43 30.8	31.8	81.9	34
35	42 31.3	+22.3	74.3	42 47.2	+23.5	75.2	43 02.1	+24.8	76.1	43 16.1	+26.0	77.0	43 29.1	+27.3	77.9	43 41.2	+28.6	78.8	43 52.4	+29.8	79.8	44 02.6	+31.0	80.7	35
36	42 53.6	21.4	73.0	43 10.7	22.7	73.9	43 26.9	23.9	74.8	43 42.1	25.3	75.7	43 56.4	26.5	76.7	44 09.8	27.8	77.6	44 22.2	29.0	78.6	44 33.6	30.3	79.5	36
37	43 15.0	20.5	71.7	43 33.4	21.8	72.6	43 50.8	23.1	73.5	44 07.4	24.3	74.5	44 22.9	25.7	75.4	44 37.6	26.9	76.4	44 51.2	28.3	77.3	45 03.9	29.5	78.3	37
38	43 35.5	19.7	70.4	43 55.2	20.9	71.3	44 13.9	22.2	72.3	44 31.7	23.6	73.2	44 48.6	24.8	74.1	45 04.5	26.1	75.1	45 19.5	27.4	76.1	45 33.4	28.7	77.1	38
39	43 55.2	18.7	69.1	44 16.1	20.0	70.0	44 36.1	21.4	71.0	44 55.3	22.6	71.9	45 13.4	24.0	72.9	45 30.6	25.3	73.8	45 46.9	26.5	74.8	46 02.1	27.8	75.8	39
40	44 13.9	+17.8	67.8	44 36.1	+19.2	68.7	44 57.5	+20.4	69.6	45 17.9	+21.7	70.6	45 37.4	+23.0	71.5	45 55.9	+24.3	72.5	46 13.4	+25.6	73.5	46 29.9	+27.0	74.5	40
41	44 31.7	16.9	66.5	44 55.3	18.1	67.4	45 17.9	19.5	68.3	45 39.6	20.8	69.3	46 00.4	22.1	70.2	46 20.2	23.4	71.2	46 39.0	24.8	72.2	46 56.9	26.0	73.2	41
42	44 48.6	15.9	65.1	45 13.4	17.2	66.0	45 37.4	18.5	67.0	46 00.4	19.8	67.9	46 22.5	21.1	68.9	46 43.6	22.5	69.9	47 03.8	23.8	70.9	47 22.9	25.2	71.9	42
43	45 04.5	15.0	63.8	45 30.6	16.3	64.7	45 55.9	17.5	65.6	46 20.2	18.8	66.5	46 43.6	20.2	67.5	47 06.1	21.5	68.5	47 27.6	22.8	69.5	47 48.1	24.1	70.5	43
44	45 19.5	13.9	62.4	45 46.9	15.2	63.3	46 13.4	16.5	64.2	46 39.0	17.9	65.2	47 03.8	19.1	66.1	47 27.6	20.5	67.1	47 50.4	21.8	68.1	48 12.2	23.2	69.2	44
45	45 33.4	+12.9	61.0	46 02.1	+14.2	61.9	46 29.9	+15.5	62.8	46 56.9	+16.8	63.8	47 22.9	+18.2	64.7	47 48.1	+19.4	65.7	48 12.2	+20.8	66.8	48 35.4	+22.2	67.8	45
46	45 46.3	11.9	59.6	46 16.3	13.1	60.5	46 45.4	14.5	61.4	47 13.7	15.7	62.4	47 41.1	17.0	63.3	48 07.5	18.4	64.3	48 33.0	19.8	65.3	48 57.6	21.1	66.4	46
47	45 58.2	10.9	58.2	46 29.4	12.1	59.1	46 59.9	13.3	60.0	47 29.4	14.7	60.9	47 58.1	16.0	61.9	48 25.9	17.4	62.9	48 52.8	18.7	63.9	49 18.7	20.0	65.0	47
48	46 09.1	9.7	56.8	46 41.5	11.1	57.7	47 13.2	12.4	58.6	47 44.1	13.6	59.5	48 14.1	15.0	60.5	48 43.3	16.2	61.4	49 11.5	17.6	62.5	49 38.7	19.0	63.5	48
49	46 18.8	8.8	55.3	46 52.6	9.9	56.2	47 25.6	11.2	57.1	47 57.7	12.5	58.0	48 29.1	13.7	59.0	48 59.5	15.1	60.0	49 29.1	16.4	61.0	49 57.7	17.8	62.0	49
50	46 27.6	+7.6	53.9	47 02.5	+8.9	54.8	47 36.8	+10.1	55.7	48 10.2	+11.4	56.6	48 42.8	+12.7	57.5	49 14.6	+14.0	58.5	49 45.5	+15.3	59.5	50 15.5	+16.7	60.5	50
51	46 35.2	6.5	52.5	47 11.4	7.7	53.3	47 46.9	8.9	54.2	48 21.6	10.2	55.1	48 55.5	11.5	56.0	49 28.6	12.8	57.0	50 00.8	14.2	58.0	50 32.2	15.4	59.0	51
52	46 41.7	5.5	51.0	47 19.1	6.7	51.9	47 55.8	7.9	52.7	48 31.8	9.1	53.6	49 07.0	10.3	54.5	49 41.4	11.6	55.5	50 15.0	12.9	56.5	50 47.6	14.3	57.5	52
53	46 47.2	4.3	49.6	47 25.8	5.5	50.4	48 03.7	6.7	51.2	48 40.9	7.9	52.1	49 17.3	9.2	53.0	49 53.0	10.4	54.0	50 27.9	11.7	55.0	51 01.9	13.0	56.0	53
54	46 51.5	3.3	48.1	47 31.3	4.3	48.9	48 10.4	5.5	49.8	48 48.8	6.7	50.6	49 26.5	7.9	51.5	50 03.4	9.2	52.5	50 39.6	10.5	53.4	51 14.9	11.8	54.4	54
55	46 54.8	+2.1	46.6	47 35.6	+3.3	47.4	48 15.9	+4.4	48.3	48 55.5	+5.6	49.1	49 34.4	+6.8	50.0	50 12.6	+8.0	50.9	50 50.1	+9.2	51.9	51 26.7	+10.6	52.8	55
56	46 56.9	+1.0	45.2	47 38.9	2.0	46.0	48 20.3	3.2	46.8	49 01.1	4.3	47.6	49 41.2	5.5	48.5	50 20.6	6.7	49.4	50 59.3	8.0	50.3	51 37.3	9.2	51.3	56
57	46 57.9	-0.2	43.7	47 40.9	+1.0	44.5	48 23.5	2.0	45.3	49 05.4	3.1	46.1	49 46.7	4.3	46.9	50 27.3	5.5	47.8	51 07.3	6.7	48.7	51 46.5	7.9	49.7	57
58	46 57.7	1.2	42.3	47 41.9	-0.2	43.0	48 25.5	+0.8	43.8	49 08.5	2.0	44.5	49 51.0	3.1	45.4	50 32.8	4.2	46.2	51 14.0	5.4	47.1	51 54.4	6.7	48.1	58
59	46 56.5	2.4	40.8	47 41.7	1.4	41.5	48 26.3	-0.3	42.2	49 10.5	+0.7	43.0	49 54.1	1.8	43.8	50 37.0	3.0	44.7	51 19.4	4.1	45.5	52 01.1	5.3	46.4	59
60	46 54.1	-3.5	39.3	47 40.3	-2.5	40.0	48 26.0	-1.5	40.7	49 11.2	-0.5	41.5	49 55.9	+0.5	42.3	50 40.0	+1.6	43.1	51 23.5	+2.8	43.9	52 06.4	+3.9	44.8	60
61	46 50.6	4.6	37.9	47 37.8	3.7	38.5	48 24.5	2.7	39.2	49 10.7	1.7	40.0	49 56.4	-0.6	40.7	50 41.6	+0.4	41.5	51 26.3	1.5	42.3	52 10.3	2.6	43.2	61
62	46 46.0	5.7	36.4	47 34.1	4.8	37.1	48 21.8	3.9	37.7	49 09.0	2.9	38.4	49 55.8	2.0	39.2	50 42.0	-0.9	39.9	51 27.8	+0.1	40.7	52 12.9	+1.3	41.6	62
63	46 40.3	6.8	35.0	47 29.3	6.0	35.6	48 17.9	5.1	36.2	49 06.1	4.1	36.9	49 53.8	3.1	37.6	50 41.1	2.1	38.4	51 27.9	-1.1	39.1	52 14.2	-0.1	39.9	63
64	46 33.5	7.9	33.5	47 23.3	7.0	34.1	48 12.8	6.2	34.7	49 02.0	5.4	35.4	49 50.7	4.4	36.1	50 39.0	3.5	36.8	51 26.8	2.5	37.5	52 14.1	1.4	38.3	64
65	46 25.6	-9.0	32.1	47 16.3	-8.2	32.6	48 06.6	-7.3	33.2	48 56.6	-6.5	33.9	49 46.3	-5.7	34.5	50 35.5	-4.7	35.2	51 24.3	-3.8	35.9	52 12.7	-2.8	36.7	65
66	46 16.6	10.0	30.6	47 08.1	9.3	31.2	47 59.3	8.5	31.8	48 50.1	7.7	32.4	49 40.6	6.8	33.0	50 30.8	6.0	33.6	51 20.5	5.0	34.3	52 09.9	4.1	35.0	66
67	46 06.6	11.1	29.2	46 58.8	10.4	29.7	47 50.8	9.6	30.3	48 42.4	8.8	30.8	49 33.8	8.1	31.4	50 24.8	7.2	32.1	51 15.5	6.4	32.7	52 05.8	5.5	33.4	67
68	45 55.5	12.1	27.8	46 48.4	11.4	28.3	47 41.2	10.8	28.8	48 33.6	10.0	29.4	49 25.7	9.2	29.9	50 17.6	8.5	30.5	51 09.1	7.6	31.1	52 00.3	6.8	31.8	68
69	45 43.4	13.2	26.4	46 37.0	12.5	26.9	47 30.4	11.8	27.4	48 23.6	11.2	27.9	49 16.5	10.5	28.4	50 09.1	9.7	29.0	51 01.5	9.0	29.6	51 53.5	8.1	30.2	69
70	45 30.2	-14.2	25.0	46 24.5	-13.6	25.4	47 18.6	-13.0	25.9	48 12.4	-12.3	26.4	49 06.0	-11.6	26.9	49 59.4	-10.9	27.4	50 52.5	-10.1	28.0	51 45.4	-9.4	28.6	70
71	45 16.0	15.1	23.6	46 10.9	14.6	24.0	47 05.6	14.0	24.5	48 00.1	13.4	24.9	48 54.4	12.7	25.4	49 48.5	12.1	25.9	50 42.4	11.4	26.4	51 36.0	10.7	27.0	71
72	45 00.9	16.2	22.2	45 56.3	15.6	22.6	46 51.6	15.0	23.0	47 46.7	14.4	23.5	48 41.7	13.9	23.9	49 36.4	13.2	24.4	50 31.0	12.7	24.9	51 25.3	12.0	25.4	72
73	44 44.7	17.1	20.9	45 40.7	16.6	21.2	46 36.6	16.1	21.6	47 32.3	15.6	22.0	48 27.8	15.0	22.4	49 23.2	14.5	22.9	50 18.3	13.8	23.4	51 13.3	13.2	23.8	73
74	44 27.6	18.0	19.5	45 24.1	17.6	19.9	46 20.5	17.1	20.2	47 16.7	16.6	20.6	48 12.8	16.1	21.0	49 08.7	15.5	21.4	50 04.5	15.0	21.8	51 00.1	14.4	22.3	74
75	44 09.6	-19.0	18.2	45 06.5	-18.5	18.5	46 03.4	-18.1	18.8	47 00.1	-17.7	19.2	47 56.7	-17.2	19.5	48 53.2	-16.7	19.9	49 49.5	-16.2	20.3	50 45.7	-15.6	20.8	75
76	43 50.6	19.8	16.9	44 48.0	19.5	17.2	45 45.3	19.1	17.5	46 42.4	18.6	17.8	47 39.5	18.2	18.1	48 36.5	17.8	18.5	49 33.3	17.3	18.8	50 30.1	16.9	19.2	76
77	43 30.8	20.8	15.6	44 28.5	20.4	15.8	45 26.2	20.0	16.1	46 23.8	19.6	16.4	47 21.3	19.2	16.7	48 18.7	18.8	17.0	49 16.0	18.4	17.4	50 13.2	17.9	17.7	77
78	43 10.0	21.6	14.3	44 08.1	21.3	14.5	45 06.2	21.0	14.8	46 04.2	20.6	15.0	47 02.1	20.3	15.3	47 59.9	19.9	15.6	48 57.6	19.5	15.9	49 55.3	19.1	16.2	78
79	42 48.4	22.4	13.0	43 46.8	22.1	13.2	44 45.2	21.8	13.5	45 43.6	21.6	13.7	46 41.8	21.2	13.9	47 40.0	20.9	14.2	48 38.1	20.5	14.5	49 36.2	20.2	14.8	79
80	42 26.0	-23.3	11.8	43 24.7	-23.0	11.9	44 23.4	-22.8	12.1	45 22.0	-22.5	12.4	46 20.6	-22.2	12.6	47 19.1	-21.9	12.8	48 17.6	-21.6	13.1	49 16.0	-21.2	13.3	80
81	42 02.7	24.0	10.5	43 01.7	23.8	10.7	44 00.6	23.6	10.9	44 59.5	23.3	11.0	45 58.4	23.1	11.2	46 57.2	22.8	11.4	47 56.0	22.6	11.7	48 54.8	22.3	11.9	81
82	41 38.7	24.9	9.3	42 37.9	24.7	9.4	43 37.0	24.4	9.6	44 36.2	24.2	9.7	45 35.3	24.0	9.9	46 34.4	23.8	10.1	47 33.4	23.5	10.3	48 32.5	23.3	10.5	82
83	41 13.8	25.6	8.1	42 13.2	25.4	8.2	43 12.6	25.2	8.3	44 12.0	25.1	8.5	45 11.3	24.9	8.6	46 10.6	24.7	8.8	47 09.9	24.5	8.9	48 09.2	24.3	9.1	83
84	40 48.2	26.3	6.9	41 47.8	26.2	7.0	42 47.4	26.1	7.1	43 46.9	25.9	7.2	44 46.4	25.7	7.3	45 45.9	25.6	7.5	46 45.4	25.4	7.6	47 44.9	25.3	7.7	84
85	40 21.9	-27.0	5.7	41 21.6	-26.9	5.8	42 21.3	-26.8	5.9	43 21.0	-26.7	6.0	44 20.7	-26.6	6.1	45 20.3	-26.4	6.2	46 20.0	-26.3	6.3	47 19.6	-26.2	6.4	85
86	39 54.9	27.7	4.5	40 54.7	27.7	4.6	41 54.5	27.6	4.7	42 54.3	27.5	4.7	43 54.1	27.4	4.8	44 53.9	27.3	4.9	45 53.7	27.2	5.0	46 53.4	27.1	5.1	86
87	39 27.2	28.5	3.4	40 27.0	28.3	3.4	41 26.9	28.2	3.5	42 26.8	28.2	3.5	43 26.7	28.1	3.6	44 26.6	28.1	3.6	45 26.5	28.1	3.7	46 26.3	27.9	3.8	87
88	38 58.7	29.0	2.2	39 58.7	29.0	2.3	40 58.7	29.0	2.3	41 58.6	28.9	2.3	42 58.6	29.0	2.4	43 58.5	28.9	2.4	44 58.4	28.8	2.4	45 58.4	28.8	2.5	88
89	38 29.7	29.7	1.1	39 29.7	29.7	1.1	40 29.7	29.7	1.1	41 29.7	29.7	1.2	42 29.6	29.6	1.2	43 29.6	29.6	1.2	44 29.6	29.6	1.2	45 29.6	29.6	1.2	89
90	38 00.0	-30.3	0.0	39 00.0	-30.3	0.0	40 00.0	-30.3	0.0	41 00.0	-30.3	0.0	42 00.0	-30.3	0.0	43 00.0	-30.4	0.0	44 00.0	-30.4	0.0	45 00.0	-30.4	0.0	90
	38°			39°			40°			41°			42°			43°			44°			45°			

60°, 300° L.H.A. LATITUDE SAME NAME AS DECLINATION

LATITUDE CONTRARY NAME TO DECLINATION L.H.A. 60°, 300°

Dec.	38°			39°			40°			41°		
	Hc	d	Z	Hc	d	Z	Hc	d	Z	Hc	d	Z
°	° ′	′	°	° ′	′	°	° ′	′	°	° ′	′	°
0	23 12.2	-40.3	109.6	22 51.9	-41.1	110.0	22 31.3	-41.9	110.4	22 10.2	-42.6	110.7
1	22 31.9	40.5	110.4	22 10.8	41.3	110.8	21 49.4	42.1	111.1	21 27.6	42.8	111.5
2	21 51.4	40.8	111.2	21 29.5	41.5	111.5	21 07.3	42.3	111.9	20 44.8	43.0	112.3
3	21 10.6	41.0	112.0	20 48.0	41.8	112.3	20 25.0	42.4	112.7	20 01.8	43.2	113.0
4	20 29.6	41.2	112.7	20 06.2	41.9	113.1	19 42.6	42.7	113.4	19 18.6	43.4	113.7
5	19 48.4	-41.4	113.5	19 24.3	-42.1	113.8	18 59.9	-42.8	114.2	18 35.2	-43.5	114.5
6	19 07.0	41.6	114.3	18 42.2	42.3	114.6	18 17.1	43.0	114.9	17 51.7	43.7	115.2
7	18 25.4	41.8	115.0	17 59.9	42.5	115.3	17 34.1	43.2	115.6	17 08.0	43.9	115.9
8	17 43.6	41.9	115.8	17 17.4	42.6	116.1	16 50.9	43.3	116.4	16 24.1	44.0	116.6
9	17 01.7	42.1	116.5	16 34.8	42.8	116.8	16 07.6	43.5	117.1	15 40.1	44.1	117.3
10	16 19.6	-42.3	117.3	15 52.0	-43.0	117.5	15 24.1	-43.6	117.8	14 56.0	-44.2	118.0
11	15 37.3	42.4	118.0	15 09.0	43.1	118.3	14 40.5	43.7	118.5	14 11.8	44.4	118.7
12	14 54.9	42.5	118.8	14 25.9	43.2	119.0	13 56.8	43.9	119.2	13 27.4	44.5	119.4
13	14 12.4	42.7	119.5	13 42.7	43.3	119.7	13 12.9	44.0	119.9	12 42.9	44.6	120.1
14	13 29.7	42.8	120.2	12 59.4	43.4	120.4	12 28.9	44.0	120.6	11 58.3	44.7	120.8
15	12 46.9	-42.9	120.9	12 16.0	-43.6	121.1	11 44.9	-44.2	121.3	11 13.6	-44.8	121.5
16	12 04.0	43.1	121.6	11 32.4	43.6	121.8	11 00.7	44.3	122.0	10 28.8	44.8	122.2
17	11 20.9	43.1	122.4	10 48.8	43.8	122.5	10 16.4	44.3	122.7	9 44.0	45.0	122.8
18	10 37.8	43.2	123.1	10 05.0	43.8	123.2	9 32.1	44.5	123.4	8 59.0	45.0	123.5
19	9 54.6	43.3	123.8	9 21.2	43.9	123.9	8 47.6	44.5	124.0	8 14.0	45.1	124.2
20	9 11.3	-43.4	124.5	8 37.3	-44.0	124.6	8 03.1	-44.5	124.7	7 28.9	-45.1	124.8
21	8 27.9	43.5	125.2	7 53.3	44.1	125.3	7 18.6	44.7	125.4	6 43.8	45.2	125.5
22	7 44.4	43.5	125.9	7 09.2	44.1	126.0	6 33.9	44.7	126.1	5 58.6	45.3	126.2
23	7 00.9	43.6	126.6	6 25.1	44.2	126.7	5 49.2	44.7	126.7	5 13.3	45.3	126.8
24	6 17.3	43.7	127.3	5 40.9	44.2	127.3	5 04.5	44.8	127.4	4 28.0	45.3	127.5
25	5 33.6	-43.7	127.9	4 56.7	-44.2	128.0	4 19.7	-44.8	128.1	3 42.7	-45.3	128.1
26	4 49.9	43.7	128.6	4 12.5	44.3	128.7	3 34.9	44.8	128.7	2 57.4	45.4	128.8
27	4 06.2	43.8	129.3	3 28.2	44.4	129.4	2 50.1	44.9	129.4	2 12.0	45.4	129.4
28	3 22.4	43.8	130.0	2 43.8	44.3	130.0	2 05.2	44.9	130.1	1 26.6	45.4	130.1
29	2 38.6	43.8	130.7	1 59.5	44.4	130.7	1 20.3	44.8	130.7	0 41.2	-45.4	130.8
30	1 54.8	-43.8	131.4	1 15.1	-44.3	131.4	0 35.5	-44.9	131.4	0 04.2	+45.4	48.6
31	1 11.0	43.9	132.1	0 30.8	-44.4	132.1	0 09.4	+44.9	47.9	0 49.6	45.4	47.9
32	0 27.1	-43.9	132.7	0 13.6	+44.4	47.3	0 54.3	44.9	47.3	1 35.0	45.4	47.3
33	0 16.8	+43.8	46.6	0 58.0	44.4	46.6	1 39.2	44.9	46.6	2 20.4	45.4	46.6
34	1 00.6	43.8	45.9	1 42.4	44.3	45.9	2 24.1	44.8	45.9	3 05.8	45.4	46.0
35	1 44.4	+43.9	45.2	2 26.7	+44.3	45.2	3 08.9	+44.9	45.3	3 51.2	+45.3	45.3
36	2 28.3	43.8	44.5	3 11.0	44.3	44.6	3 53.8	44.8	44.6	4 36.5	45.3	44.7
37	3 12.1	43.8	43.8	3 55.3	44.3	43.9	4 38.6	44.7	43.9	5 21.8	45.2	44.0
38	3 55.9	43.7	43.2	4 39.6	44.3	43.2	5 23.3	44.7	43.3	6 07.0	45.2	43.3
39	4 39.6	43.7	42.5	5 23.9	44.1	42.5	6 08.0	44.7	42.6	6 52.2	45.1	42.7
40	5 23.3	+43.7	41.8	6 08.0	+44.2	41.9	6 52.7	+44.6	41.9	7 37.3	+45.1	42.0
41	6 07.0	43.6	41.1	6 52.2	44.1	41.2	7 37.3	44.6	41.3	8 22.4	45.0	41.3
42	6 50.6	43.5	40.4	7 36.3	44.0	40.5	8 21.9	44.4	40.6	9 07.4	44.9	40.7
43	7 34.1	43.5	39.7	8 20.3	43.9	39.8	9 06.3	44.4	39.9	9 52.3	44.9	40.0
44	8 17.6	43.4	39.0	9 04.2	43.9	39.1	9 50.7	44.4	39.2	10 37.2	44.8	39.3
45	9 01.0	+43.4	38.3	9 48.1	+43.8	38.4	10 35.1	+44.2	38.5	11 22.0	+44.6	38.7
46	9 44.4	43.2	37.6	10 31.9	43.7	37.7	11 19.3	44.1	37.8	12 06.6	44.6	38.0
47	10 27.6	43.2	36.9	11 15.6	43.6	37.0	12 03.4	44.0	37.2	12 51.2	44.5	37.3
48	11 10.8	43.0	36.2	11 59.2	43.4	36.3	12 47.4	44.0	36.5	13 35.7	44.3	36.6
49	11 53.8	43.0	35.5	12 42.6	43.4	35.6	13 31.4	43.8	35.8	14 20.0	44.2	35.9
50	12 36.8	+42.8	34.8	13 26.0	+43.3	34.9	14 15.2	+43.7	35.1	15 04.2	+44.1	35.2
51	13 19.6	42.7	34.1	14 09.3	43.1	34.2	14 58.9	43.5	34.3	15 48.3	44.0	34.5
52	14 02.3	42.6	33.3	14 52.4	43.0	33.5	15 42.4	43.4	33.6	16 32.3	43.8	33.8
53	14 44.9	42.4	32.6	15 35.4	42.8	32.8	16 25.8	43.3	32.9	17 16.1	43.7	33.1
54	15 27.3	42.3	31.9	16 18.2	42.7	32.0	17 09.1	43.1	32.2	17 59.8	43.5	32.4
55	16 09.6	+42.2	31.1	17 00.9	+42.6	31.3	17 52.2	+42.9	31.5	18 43.3	+43.3	31.6
56	16 51.8	42.0	30.4	17 43.5	42.4	30.6	18 35.1	42.8	30.7	19 26.6	43.2	30.9
57	17 33.8	41.8	29.7	18 25.9	42.2	29.8	19 17.9	42.6	30.0	20 09.8	43.0	30.2
58	18 15.6	41.6	28.9	19 08.1	42.0	29.1	20 00.5	42.3	29.2	20 52.8	42.7	29.4
59	18 57.2	41.4	28.1	19 50.1	41.8	28.3	20 42.8	42.2	28.5	21 35.5	42.6	28.7
60	19 38.6	+41.3	27.4	20 31.9	+41.6	27.5	21 25.0	+42.0	27.7	22 18.1	+42.4	27.9
61	20 19.9	41.0	26.6	21 13.5	41.4	26.8	22 07.0	41.8	26.9	23 00.5	42.1	27.1
62	21 00.9	40.9	25.8	21 54.9	41.2	26.0	22 48.8	41.5	26.2	23 42.6	41.9	26.4
63	21 41.8	40.6	25.0	22 36.1	40.9	25.2	23 30.3	41.3	25.4	24 24.5	41.7	25.6
64	22 22.4	40.3	24.2	23 17.0	40.8	24.4	24 11.6	41.1	24.6	25 06.2	41.4	24.8
65	23 02.7	+40.2	23.4	23 57.8	+40.4	23.6	24 52.7	+40.8	23.8	25 47.6	+41.1	24.0
66	23 42.9	39.8	22.6	24 38.2	40.2	22.8	25 33.5	40.5	23.0	26 28.7	40.8	23.2
67	24 22.7	39.6	21.8	25 18.4	39.9	22.0	26 14.0	40.3	22.2	27 09.5	40.6	22.4
68	25 02.3	39.4	21.0	25 58.3	39.7	21.2	26 54.3	39.9	21.3	27 50.1	40.3	21.5
69	25 41.7	39.0	20.1	26 38.0	39.3	20.3	27 34.2	39.6	20.5	28 30.4	39.9	20.7
70	26 20.7	+38.7	19.3	27 17.3	+39.0	19.5	28 13.8	+39.4	19.6	29 10.3	+39.6	19.8
71	26 59.4	38.5	18.4	27 56.3	38.7	18.6	28 53.2	38.9	18.8	29 49.9	39.3	19.0
72	27 37.9	38.1	17.6	28 35.0	38.4	17.7	29 32.1	38.7	17.9	30 29.2	38.9	18.1
73	28 16.0	37.7	16.7	29 13.4	38.0	16.9	30 10.8	38.3	17.0	31 08.1	38.6	17.2
74	28 53.7	37.4	15.8	29 51.4	37.7	16.0	30 49.1	37.9	16.1	31 46.7	38.2	16.3
75	29 31.1	+37.1	14.9	30 29.1	+37.3	15.1	31 27.0	+37.5	15.2	32 24.9	+37.7	15.4
76	30 08.2	36.6	14.0	31 06.4	36.9	14.2	32 04.5	37.1	14.3	33 02.6	37.4	14.5
77	30 44.8	36.3	13.1	31 43.3	36.4	13.2	32 41.6	36.7	13.4	33 40.0	36.9	13.5
78	31 21.1	35.9	12.2	32 19.7	36.1	12.3	33 18.3	36.3	12.4	34 16.9	36.5	12.6
79	31 57.0	35.4	11.2	32 55.8	35.6	11.4	33 54.6	35.8	11.5	34 53.4	36.0	11.6
80	32 32.4	+35.0	10.3	33 31.4	+35.2	10.4	34 30.4	+35.4	10.5	35 29.4	+35.6	10.6
81	33 07.4	34.6	9.3	34 06.6	34.7	9.4	35 05.8	34.9	9.5	36 05.0	35.0	9.7
82	33 42.0	34.0	8.3	34 41.3	34.2	8.4	35 40.7	34.3	8.5	36 40.0	34.5	8.6
83	34 16.0	33.6	7.3	35 15.5	33.8	7.4	36 15.0	33.9	7.5	37 14.5	34.0	7.6
84	34 49.6	33.1	6.3	35 49.3	33.2	6.4	36 48.9	33.3	6.5	37 48.5	33.4	6.6
85	35 22.7	+32.6	5.3	36 22.5	+32.6	5.4	37 22.2	+32.8	5.4	38 21.9	+32.9	5.5
86	35 55.3	32.0	4.3	36 55.1	32.1	4.3	37 55.0	32.1	4.4	38 54.8	32.2	4.5
87	36 27.3	31.5	3.2	37 27.2	31.6	3.3	38 27.1	31.6	3.3	39 27.0	31.7	3.4
88	36 58.8	30.9	2.2	37 58.8	30.9	2.2	38 58.7	31.0	2.2	39 58.7	31.0	2.3
89	37 29.7	30.3	1.1	38 29.7	30.3	1.1	39 29.7	30.3	1.1	40 29.7	30.3	1.1
90	38 00.0	+29.7	0.0	39 00.0	+29.7	0.0	40 00.0	+29.7	0.0	41 00.0	+29.7	0.0
	38°			39°			40°			41°		

42°			43°			44°			45°			Dec.
Hc	d	Z	Hc	d	Z	Hc	d	Z	Hc	d	Z	
° ′	′	°	° ′	′	°	° ′	′	°	° ′	′	°	°
21 48.8	-43.4	111.1	21 27.0	-44.1	111.5	21 04.8	-44.8	111.9	20 42.3	-45.5	112.2	0
21 05.4	43.5	111.9	20 42.9	44.2	112.2	20 20.0	44.9	112.6	19 56.8	45.6	112.9	1
20 21.9	43.7	112.6	19 58.7	44.5	112.9	19 35.1	45.1	113.3	19 11.2	45.7	113.6	2
19 38.2	43.9	113.3	19 14.2	44.5	113.7	18 50.0	45.2	114.0	18 25.5	45.9	114.3	3
18 54.3	44.1	114.1	18 29.7	44.8	114.4	18 04.8	45.4	114.7	17 39.6	46.0	115.0	4
18 10.2	-44.2	114.8	17 44.9	-44.9	115.1	17 19.4	-45.6	115.3	16 53.6	-46.2	115.6	5
17 26.0	44.4	115.5	17 00.0	45.0	115.8	16 33.8	45.6	116.0	16 07.4	46.3	116.3	6
16 41.6	44.5	116.2	16 15.0	45.1	116.4	15 48.2	45.8	116.7	15 21.1	46.4	117.0	7
15 57.1	44.6	116.9	15 29.9	45.3	117.1	15 02.4	45.9	117.4	14 34.7	46.5	117.6	8
15 12.5	44.8	117.6	14 44.6	45.4	117.8	14 16.5	46.0	118.0	13 48.2	46.6	118.3	9
14 27.7	-44.9	118.3	13 59.2	-45.5	118.5	13 30.5	-46.1	118.7	13 01.6	-46.7	118.9	10
13 42.8	45.0	118.9	13 13.7	45.6	119.2	12 44.4	46.3	119.4	12 14.9	46.9	119.6	11
12 57.8	45.1	119.6	12 28.1	45.7	119.8	11 58.1	46.3	120.0	11 28.0	46.8	120.2	12
12 12.7	45.2	120.3	11 42.4	45.8	120.5	11 11.8	46.4	120.7	10 41.2	47.0	120.8	13
11 27.5	45.3	121.0	10 56.6	45.9	121.1	10 25.4	46.4	121.3	9 54.2	47.0	121.5	14
10 42.2	-45.4	121.6	10 10.7	-46.0	121.8	9 39.0	-46.6	121.9	9 07.2	-47.1	122.1	15
9 56.8	45.4	122.3	9 24.7	46.0	122.5	8 52.4	46.6	122.6	8 20.1	47.2	122.7	16
9 11.4	45.6	123.0	8 38.7	46.1	123.1	8 05.8	46.6	123.2	7 32.9	47.2	123.3	17
8 25.8	45.6	123.6	7 52.6	46.2	123.7	7 19.2	46.7	123.9	6 45.7	47.3	124.0	18
7 40.2	45.6	124.3	7 06.4	46.2	124.4	6 32.5	46.8	124.5	5 58.4	47.2	124.6	19
6 54.6	-45.7	124.9	6 20.2	-46.3	125.0	5 45.7	-46.8	125.1	5 11.2	-47.4	125.2	20
6 08.9	45.8	125.6	5 33.9	46.3	125.7	4 58.9	46.8	125.8	4 23.8	47.3	125.8	21
5 23.1	45.8	126.2	4 47.6	46.3	126.3	4 12.1	46.9	126.4	3 36.5	47.4	126.4	22
4 37.3	45.8	126.9	4 01.3	46.4	127.0	3 25.2	46.9	127.0	2 49.1	47.4	127.0	23
3 51.5	45.9	127.5	3 14.9	46.4	127.6	2 38.3	46.9	127.6	2 01.7	47.5	127.7	24
3 05.6	-45.9	128.2	2 28.5	-46.4	128.2	1 51.4	-46.9	128.3	1 14.2	-47.4	128.3	25
2 19.7	45.9	128.8	1 42.1	46.4	128.9	1 04.5	47.0	128.9	0 26.8	-47.4	128.9	26
1 33.8	45.9	129.5	0 55.7	46.4	129.5	0 17.5	-46.9	129.5	0 20.6	+47.5	50.5	27
0 47.9	45.9	130.1	0 09.3	-46.5	130.1	0 29.4	+46.9	49.9	1 08.1	47.4	49.9	28
0 02.0	-45.9	130.8	0 37.2	+46.4	49.2	1 16.3	47.0	49.3	1 55.5	47.4	49.3	29
0 43.9	+45.9	48.6	1 23.6	+46.4	48.6	2 03.3	+46.9	48.6	2 42.9	+47.4	48.7	30
1 29.8	45.9	48.0	2 10.0	46.4	48.0	2 50.2	46.9	48.0	3 30.3	47.4	48.0	31
2 15.7	45.9	47.3	2 56.4	46.4	47.3	3 37.1	46.8	47.4	4 17.7	47.3	47.4	32
3 01.6	45.9	46.7	3 42.8	46.3	46.7	4 23.9	46.8	46.8	5 05.0	47.3	46.8	33
3 47.5	45.8	46.0	4 29.1	46.4	46.1	5 10.7	46.8	46.1	5 52.3	47.3	46.2	34
4 33.3	+45.8	45.4	5 15.5	+46.2	45.4	5 57.5	+46.8	45.5	6 39.6	+47.2	45.6	35
5 19.1	45.8	44.7	6 01.7	46.3	44.8	6 44.3	46.7	44.9	7 26.8	47.1	45.0	36
6 04.9	45.7	44.1	6 48.0	46.1	44.1	7 31.0	46.6	44.2	8 13.9	47.1	44.3	37
6 50.6	45.7	43.4	7 34.1	46.2	43.5	8 17.6	46.6	43.6	9 01.0	47.1	43.7	38
7 36.3	45.6	42.8	8 20.3	46.0	42.9	9 04.2	46.5	43.0	9 48.1	47.0	43.1	39
8 21.9	+45.5	42.1	9 06.3	+46.0	42.2	9 50.7	+46.5	42.3	10 35.1	+46.9	42.4	40
9 07.4	45.5	41.5	9 52.3	46.0	41.6	10 37.2	46.4	41.7	11 22.0	46.8	41.8	41
9 52.9	45.4	40.8	10 38.3	45.8	40.9	11 23.6	46.2	41.0	12 08.8	46.7	41.2	42
10 38.3	45.3	40.1	11 24.1	45.7	40.2	12 09.8	46.2	40.4	12 55.5	46.6	40.5	43
11 23.6	45.2	39.5	12 09.8	45.7	39.6	12 56.0	46.1	39.7	13 42.1	46.6	39.9	44
12 08.8	+45.1	38.8	12 55.5	+45.5	38.9	13 42.1	+46.0	39.1	14 28.7	+46.4	39.2	45
12 53.9	45.0	38.1	13 41.0	45.5	38.3	14 28.1	45.9	38.4	15 15.1	46.3	38.6	46
13 38.9	44.9	37.4	14 26.5	45.3	37.6	15 14.0	45.7	37.7	16 01.4	46.2	37.9	47
14 23.8	44.8	36.7	15 11.8	45.2	36.9	15 59.7	45.7	37.1	16 47.6	46.0	37.3	48
15 08.6	44.6	36.1	15 57.0	45.1	36.2	16 45.4	45.5	36.4	17 33.6	45.9	36.6	49
15 53.2	+44.5	35.4	16 42.1	+44.9	35.5	17 30.9	+45.3	35.7	18 19.5	+45.8	35.9	50
16 37.7	44.4	34.7	17 27.0	44.8	34.8	18 16.2	45.2	35.0	19 05.3	45.6	35.2	51
17 22.1	44.3	34.0	18 11.8	44.7	34.1	19 01.4	45.1	34.3	19 50.9	45.5	34.5	52
18 06.4	44.0	33.3	18 56.5	44.5	33.4	19 46.5	44.9	33.6	20 36.4	45.3	33.8	53
18 50.4	43.9	32.5	19 41.0	44.3	32.7	20 31.4	44.7	32.9	21 21.7	45.1	33.1	54
19 34.3	+43.8	31.8	20 25.3	+44.1	32.0	21 16.1	+44.5	32.2	22 06.8	+44.9	32.4	55
20 18.1	43.5	31.1	21 09.4	43.9	31.3	22 00.6	44.4	31.5	22 51.7	44.8	31.7	56
21 01.6	43.4	30.4	21 53.3	43.8	30.6	22 45.0	44.1	30.8	23 36.5	44.5	31.0	57
21 45.0	43.1	29.6	22 37.1	43.5	29.8	23 29.1	43.9	30.0	24 21.0	44.3	30.2	58
22 28.1	43.0	28.9	23 20.6	43.4	29.1	24 13.0	43.7	29.3	25 05.3	44.1	29.5	59
23 11.1	+42.7	28.1	24 04.0	+43.1	28.3	24 56.7	+43.5	28.5	25 49.4	+43.8	28.8	60
23 53.8	42.5	27.3	24 47.1	42.8	27.5	25 40.2	43.3	27.8	26 33.2	43.7	28.0	61
24 36.3	42.3	26.6	25 29.9	42.7	26.8	26 23.5	42.9	27.0	27 16.9	43.3	27.2	62
25 18.6	42.0	25.8	26 12.6	42.3	26.0	27 06.4	42.8	26.2	28 00.2	43.1	26.4	63
26 00.6	41.7	25.0	26 54.9	42.1	25.2	27 49.2	42.4	25.4	28 43.3	42.8	25.7	64
26 42.3	+41.5	24.2	27 37.0	+41.8	24.4	28 31.6	+42.2	24.6	29 26.1	+42.5	24.9	65
27 23.8	41.2	23.4	28 18.8	41.6	23.6	29 13.8	41.8	23.8	30 08.6	42.2	24.0	66
28 05.0	40.9	22.6	29 00.4	41.2	22.8	29 55.6	41.6	23.0	30 50.8	41.9	23.2	67
28 45.9	40.6	21.7	29 41.6	40.9	21.9	30 37.2	41.2	22.1	31 32.7	41.6	22.4	68
29 26.5	40.2	20.9	30 22.5	40.6	21.1	31 18.4	40.9	21.3	32 14.3	41.2	21.5	69
30 06.7	+39.9	20.0	31 03.1	+40.2	20.2	31 59.3	+40.6	20.4	32 55.5	+40.9	20.7	70
30 46.6	39.6	19.2	31 43.3	39.9	19.4	32 39.9	40.1	19.6	33 36.4	40.4	19.8	71
31 26.2	39.2	18.3	32 23.2	39.4	18.5	33 20.0	39.8	18.7	34 16.8	40.1	18.9	72
32 05.4	38.8	17.4	33 02.6	39.2	17.6	33 59.8	39.4	17.8	34 56.9	39.7	18.0	73
32 44.2	38.5	16.5	33 41.8	38.7	16.7	34 39.2	39.0	16.9	35 36.6	39.2	17.1	74
33 22.7	+38.0	15.6	34 20.5	+38.2	15.8	35 18.2	+38.5	15.9	36 15.8	+38.8	16.1	75
34 00.7	37.6	14.6	34 58.7	37.9	14.8	35 56.7	38.1	15.0	36 54.6	38.4	15.2	76
34 38.3	37.2	13.7	35 36.6	37.4	13.9	36 34.8	37.6	14.0	37 33.0	37.9	14.2	77
35 15.5	36.7	12.7	36 14.0	36.9	12.9	37 12.4	37.2	13.1	38 10.9	37.3	13.2	78
35 52.2	36.2	11.8	36 50.9	36.4	11.9	37 49.6	36.6	12.1	38 48.2	36.9	12.2	79
36 28.4	+35.7	10.8	37 27.3	+35.9	10.9	38 26.2	+36.1	11.1	39 25.1	+36.3	11.2	80
37 04.1	35.2	9.8	38 03.2	35.4	9.9	39 02.3	35.6	10.0	40 01.4	35.7	10.2	81
37 39.3	34.7	8.8	38 38.6	34.8	8.9	39 37.9	35.0	9.0	40 37.1	35.2	9.1	82
38 14.0	34.1	7.7	39 13.4	34.3	7.8	40 12.9	34.4	7.9	41 12.3	34.5	8.1	83
38 48.1	33.5	6.7	39 47.7	33.6	6.8	40 47.3	33.7	6.9	41 46.8	33.9	7.0	84
39 21.6	+33.0	5.6	40 21.3	+33.1	5.7	41 21.0	+33.2	5.8	42 20.7	+33.3	5.9	85
39 54.6	32.3	4.5	40 54.4	32.4	4.6	41 54.2	32.5	4.7	42 54.0	32.6	4.7	86
40 26.9	31.7	3.4	41 26.8	31.8	3.5	42 26.7	31.8	3.5	43 26.6	31.9	3.6	87
40 58.6	31.1	2.3	41 58.6	31.0	2.3	42 58.5	31.1	2.4	43 58.5	31.1	2.4	88
41 29.7	30.3	1.2	42 29.6	30.4	1.2	43 29.6	30.4	1.2	44 29.6	30.4	1.2	89
42 00.0	+29.6	0.0	43 00.0	+29.6	0.0	44 00.0	+29.6	0.0	45 00.0	+29.6	0.0	90
42°			43°			44°			45°			

S. Lat. { L.H.A. greater than 180°......Zn=180°−Z; L.H.A. less than 180°............Zn=180°+Z }

LATITUDE SAME NAME AS DECLINATION L.H.A. 120°, 240°

INTERPOLATION TABLE

Left section (Dec. Inc. 28.0 – 35.9)

Dec. Inc.	Tens 10'	20'	30'	40'	50'	Dec.	Units 0'	1'	2'	3'	4'	5'	6'	7'	8'	9'
28.0	4.6	9.3	14.0	18.6	23.3	.0	0.0	0.5	0.9	1.4	1.9	2.4	2.8	3.3	3.8	4.3
28.1	4.7	9.3	14.0	18.7	23.4	.1	0.0	0.5	1.0	1.5	1.9	2.4	2.9	3.4	3.8	4.3
28.2	4.7	9.4	14.1	18.8	23.5	.2	0.1	0.6	1.0	1.5	2.0	2.5	2.9	3.4	3.9	4.4
28.3	4.7	9.4	14.1	18.9	23.6	.3	0.1	0.6	1.1	1.6	2.0	2.5	3.0	3.5	3.9	4.4
28.4	4.7	9.5	14.2	18.9	23.7	.4	0.2	0.7	1.1	1.6	2.1	2.6	3.0	3.5	4.0	4.5
28.5	4.8	9.5	14.3	19.0	23.8	.5	0.2	0.7	1.2	1.7	2.1	2.6	3.1	3.6	4.0	4.5
28.6	4.8	9.5	14.3	19.1	23.8	.6	0.3	0.8	1.2	1.7	2.2	2.7	3.1	3.6	4.1	4.6
28.7	4.8	9.6	14.4	19.2	23.9	.7	0.3	0.8	1.3	1.8	2.2	2.7	3.2	3.7	4.1	4.6
28.8	4.8	9.6	14.4	19.2	24.0	.8	0.4	0.9	1.3	1.8	2.3	2.8	3.2	3.7	4.2	4.7
28.9	4.9	9.7	14.5	19.3	24.1	.9	0.4	0.9	1.4	1.9	2.3	2.8	3.3	3.8	4.2	4.7
29.0	4.8	9.6	14.5	19.3	24.1	.0	0.0	0.5	1.0	1.5	2.0	2.5	2.9	3.4	3.9	4.4
29.1	4.9	9.7	14.5	19.4	24.2	.1	0.0	0.5	1.0	1.5	2.0	2.5	3.0	3.5	4.0	4.5
29.2	4.8	9.7	14.6	19.4	24.2	.2	0.1	0.6	1.1	1.6	2.1	2.6	3.0	3.5	4.0	4.5
29.3	4.9	9.8	14.6	19.5	24.4	.3	0.1	0.6	1.1	1.6	2.1	2.6	3.1	3.6	4.1	4.6
29.4	4.9	9.8	14.7	19.6	24.5	.4	0.2	0.7	1.2	1.7	2.2	2.7	3.1	3.6	4.1	4.6
29.5	4.9	9.8	14.8	19.7	24.6	.5	0.2	0.7	1.2	1.7	2.2	2.7	3.2	3.7	4.2	4.7
29.6	4.9	9.9	14.8	19.7	24.7	.6	0.3	0.8	1.3	1.8	2.3	2.8	3.2	3.7	4.2	4.7
29.7	5.0	9.9	14.9	19.8	24.8	.7	0.3	0.8	1.3	1.8	2.3	2.8	3.3	3.8	4.3	4.8
29.8	5.0	10.0	14.9	19.9	24.9	.8	0.4	0.9	1.4	1.9	2.4	2.9	3.3	3.8	4.3	4.8
29.9	5.0	10.0	15.0	20.0	25.0	.9	0.4	0.9	1.4	1.9	2.4	2.9	3.4	3.9	4.4	4.9
30.0	5.0	10.0	15.0	20.0	25.0	.0	0.0	0.5	1.0	1.5	2.0	2.5	3.0	3.6	4.1	4.6
30.1	5.0	10.0	15.0	20.1	25.1	.1	0.0	0.5	1.1	1.6	2.1	2.6	3.1	3.6	4.1	4.6
30.2	5.0	10.0	15.1	20.1	25.1	.2	0.1	0.6	1.1	1.6	2.1	2.6	3.2	3.7	4.2	4.7
30.3	5.0	10.1	15.1	20.2	25.2	.3	0.1	0.6	1.2	1.7	2.2	2.7	3.2	3.7	4.2	4.7
30.4	5.0	10.1	15.2	20.2	25.3	.4	0.2	0.7	1.2	1.7	2.2	2.7	3.3	3.8	4.3	4.8
30.5	5.1	10.2	15.3	20.3	25.4	.5	0.3	0.8	1.3	1.8	2.3	2.8	3.3	3.8	4.3	4.8
30.6	5.1	10.2	15.3	20.4	25.5	.6	0.3	0.8	1.3	1.8	2.3	2.8	3.4	3.9	4.4	4.9
30.7	5.1	10.3	15.4	20.5	25.6	.7	0.4	0.9	1.4	1.9	2.4	2.9	3.4	3.9	4.4	4.9
30.8	5.2	10.3	15.4	20.6	25.7	.8	0.4	0.9	1.4	1.9	2.4	2.9	3.5	4.0	4.5	5.0
30.9	5.2	10.3	15.5	20.6	25.8	.9	0.5	1.0	1.5	2.0	2.5	3.0	3.5	4.0	4.5	5.0
31.0	5.1	10.3	15.5	20.6	25.8	.0	0.0	0.5	1.0	1.6	2.1	2.6	3.1	3.7	4.2	4.7
31.1	5.2	10.3	15.5	20.7	25.9	.1	0.1	0.6	1.1	1.6	2.2	2.7	3.2	3.7	4.3	4.8
31.2	5.2	10.4	15.6	20.8	26.0	.2	0.1	0.6	1.2	1.7	2.2	2.7	3.3	3.8	4.3	4.8
31.3	5.2	10.4	15.6	20.9	26.1	.3	0.2	0.7	1.2	1.7	2.3	2.8	3.3	3.8	4.4	4.9
31.4	5.2	10.5	15.7	20.9	26.2	.4	0.2	0.7	1.2	1.8	2.3	2.8	3.4	3.9	4.4	4.9
31.5	5.3	10.5	15.8	21.0	26.3	.5	0.3	0.8	1.3	1.8	2.4	2.9	3.4	3.9	4.5	5.0
31.6	5.3	10.5	15.8	21.1	26.3	.6	0.3	0.8	1.4	1.9	2.4	2.9	3.5	4.0	4.5	5.0
31.7	5.3	10.6	15.9	21.2	26.4	.7	0.4	0.9	1.5	2.0	2.5	3.0	3.5	4.0	4.6	5.1
31.8	5.3	10.6	15.9	21.2	26.5	.8	0.4	0.9	1.5	2.0	2.5	3.0	3.6	4.1	4.6	5.1
31.9	5.4	10.7	16.0	21.3	26.6	.9	0.5	1.0	1.5	2.0	2.5	3.1	3.6	4.1	4.7	5.2
32.0	5.3	10.6	16.0	21.3	26.6	.0	0.0	0.5	1.1	1.6	2.2	2.7	3.2	3.8	4.3	4.9
32.1	5.3	10.7	16.0	21.4	26.7	.1	0.1	0.6	1.1	1.7	2.2	2.8	3.3	3.8	4.4	4.9
32.2	5.3	10.7	16.1	21.4	26.8	.2	0.1	0.6	1.2	1.8	2.3	2.8	3.4	3.9	4.5	5.0
32.3	5.4	10.8	16.1	21.5	26.9	.3	0.2	0.7	1.2	1.8	2.3	2.9	3.4	4.0	4.5	5.0
32.4	5.4	10.8	16.2	21.6	27.0	.4	0.2	0.8	1.3	1.8	2.4	2.9	3.5	4.0	4.6	5.1
32.5	5.4	10.8	16.3	21.7	27.1	.5	0.3	0.8	1.4	1.9	2.4	3.0	3.5	4.1	4.6	5.1
32.6	5.4	10.9	16.3	21.7	27.2	.6	0.3	0.9	1.4	1.9	2.5	3.0	3.6	4.1	4.7	5.2
32.7	5.5	10.9	16.4	21.8	27.3	.7	0.4	0.9	1.5	2.0	2.5	3.1	3.6	4.2	4.7	5.3
32.8	5.5	11.0	16.4	21.9	27.4	.8	0.4	1.0	1.5	2.1	2.6	3.1	3.7	4.2	4.8	5.3
32.9	5.5	11.0	16.5	22.0	27.5	.9	0.5	1.0	1.6	2.1	2.7	3.2	3.7	4.3	4.8	5.4
33.0	5.5	11.0	16.5	22.0	27.5	.0	0.0	0.6	1.1	1.7	2.2	2.8	3.3	3.9	4.5	5.0
33.1	5.5	11.0	16.5	22.1	27.6	.1	0.1	0.6	1.2	1.7	2.3	2.8	3.4	4.0	4.5	5.1
33.2	5.5	11.1	16.6	22.1	27.6	.2	0.1	0.7	1.2	1.8	2.3	2.9	3.5	4.0	4.6	5.1
33.3	5.5	11.1	16.6	22.2	27.7	.3	0.2	0.7	1.3	1.8	2.4	3.0	3.5	4.1	4.7	5.2
33.4	5.6	11.1	16.7	22.3	27.8	.4	0.2	0.8	1.3	1.9	2.5	3.0	3.6	4.1	4.7	5.2
33.5	5.6	11.2	16.8	22.3	27.9	.5	0.3	0.8	1.4	2.0	2.5	3.1	3.6	4.2	4.8	5.4
33.6	5.6	11.2	16.8	22.4	28.0	.6	0.3	0.9	1.5	2.0	2.6	3.1	3.7	4.2	4.8	5.4
33.7	5.6	11.3	16.9	22.5	28.1	.7	0.4	0.9	1.5	2.1	2.6	3.2	3.7	4.3	4.9	5.4
33.8	5.7	11.3	16.9	22.6	28.2	.8	0.4	1.0	1.6	2.1	2.7	3.2	3.8	4.4	4.9	5.5
33.9	5.7	11.3	17.0	22.6	28.3	.9	0.5	1.1	1.6	2.2	2.7	3.3	3.9	4.4	5.0	5.5
34.0	5.6	11.3	17.0	22.6	28.3	.0	0.0	0.6	1.1	1.7	2.3	2.9	3.4	4.0	4.6	5.2
34.1	5.7	11.3	17.0	22.7	28.4	.1	0.1	0.6	1.2	1.8	2.4	2.9	3.5	4.1	4.7	5.2
34.2	5.7	11.4	17.1	22.8	28.5	.2	0.1	0.7	1.3	1.8	2.4	3.0	3.6	4.1	4.7	5.3
34.3	5.7	11.4	17.1	22.9	28.6	.3	0.2	0.7	1.3	1.9	2.5	3.0	3.6	4.2	4.8	5.3
34.4	5.7	11.5	17.2	22.9	28.7	.4	0.2	0.8	1.4	2.0	2.5	3.1	3.7	4.3	4.8	5.4
34.5	5.8	11.5	17.3	23.0	28.8	.5	0.3	0.9	1.4	2.0	2.6	3.2	3.7	4.3	4.9	5.5
34.6	5.8	11.5	17.3	23.1	28.9	.6	0.3	0.9	1.5	2.1	2.6	3.2	3.8	4.4	5.0	5.6
34.7	5.8	11.6	17.4	23.2	29.0	.7	0.4	1.0	1.5	2.1	2.7	3.3	3.9	4.4	5.0	5.6
34.8	5.8	11.6	17.4	23.2	29.0	.8	0.5	1.0	1.6	2.2	2.8	3.3	3.9	4.5	5.1	5.7
34.9	5.9	11.7	17.5	23.3	29.1	.9	0.5	1.1	1.7	2.2	2.8	3.4	4.0	4.5	5.1	5.7
35.0	5.8	11.6	17.5	23.3	29.1	.0	0.0	0.6	1.2	1.8	2.3	2.9	3.5	4.1	4.7	5.3
35.1	5.8	11.7	17.5	23.4	29.2	.1	0.1	0.7	1.2	1.8	2.4	3.0	3.6	4.2	4.8	5.4
35.2	5.8	11.7	17.6	23.4	29.3	.2	0.1	0.7	1.3	1.9	2.5	3.1	3.7	4.3	4.9	5.5
35.3	5.9	11.8	17.6	23.5	29.4	.3	0.2	0.8	1.4	2.0	2.5	3.1	3.7	4.3	4.9	5.5
35.4	5.9	11.8	17.7	23.6	29.5	.4	0.2	0.8	1.4	2.0	2.6	3.2	3.8	4.4	5.0	5.6
35.5	5.9	11.8	17.8	23.7	29.6	.5	0.3	0.9	1.5	2.1	2.7	3.3	3.8	4.4	5.0	5.6
35.6	5.9	11.9	17.8	23.7	29.7	.6	0.4	0.9	1.5	2.1	2.7	3.3	3.9	4.5	5.1	5.7
35.7	6.0	11.9	17.9	23.8	29.8	.7	0.4	1.0	1.6	2.2	2.8	3.4	4.0	4.6	5.2	5.8
35.8	6.0	12.0	17.9	23.9	29.9	.8	0.5	1.1	1.7	2.2	2.8	3.4	4.0	4.6	5.2	5.8
35.9	6.0	12.0	18.0	24.0	30.0	.9	0.6	1.2	1.7	2.3	2.9	3.5	4.1	4.7	5.3	5.9

Double Second Difference and Correction (left section):

- 28.0–29.9: 0.8; 2.4 / 0.1; 4.0 / 0.2; 5.6 / 0.3; 7.2 / 0.4; 8.8 / 0.5; 10.4 / 0.6; 12.0 / 0.7; 13.6 / 0.8; 15.2 / 0.9; 16.8 / 1.0; 18.4 / 1.1; 20.0 / 1.2; 21.6 / 1.3; 23.2 / 1.4; 24.8 / 1.5; 26.4 / 1.6; 28.0 / 1.7; 29.6 / 1.8; 31.2 / 1.9; 32.8 / 2.0; 34.4 / 2.1
- 30.0–31.9: 0.8; 2.4 / 0.1; 4.0 / 0.2; 5.6 / 0.3; 7.2 / 0.4; 8.8 / 0.5; 10.4 / 0.6; 12.0 / 0.7; 13.6 / 0.8; 15.2 / 0.9; 16.8 / 1.0; 18.4 / 1.1; 20.0 / 1.2; 21.6 / 1.3; 23.2 / 1.4; 24.8 / 1.5; 26.4 / 1.6; 28.0 / 1.7; 29.6 / 1.8; 31.2 / 1.9; 32.8 / 2.0; 34.4 / 2.1
- 32.0–33.9: 0.8; 2.4; 4.0 / 0.2; 5.6 / 0.3; 7.3 / 0.4; 8.9 / 0.5; 10.5 / 0.6; 12.1 / 0.7; 13.7 / 0.8; 15.4 / 0.9; 17.0 / 1.0; 18.6 / 1.1; 20.2 / 1.2; 21.8 / 1.3; 23.4 / 1.4; 25.1 / 1.5; 26.7 / 1.6; 28.3 / 1.7; 29.9 / 1.8; 31.5 / 1.9; 33.1 / 2.0; 34.7 / 2.1
- 34.0–35.9: 0.8; 2.5 / 0.1; 4.1 / 0.2; 5.7 / 0.3; 7.4 / 0.4; 9.1 / 0.5; 10.7 / 0.6; 12.3 / 0.7; 14.0 / 0.8; 15.6 / 0.9; 17.3 / 1.0; 18.9 / 1.1; 20.6 / 1.2; 22.2 / 1.3; 23.9 / 1.4; 25.5 / 1.5; 27.2 / 1.6; 28.8 / 1.7; 30.4 / 1.8; 32.1 / 1.9; 33.7 / 2.0; 35.4 / 2.1

Right section (Dec. Inc. 36.0 – 43.9)

Dec. Inc.	Tens 10'	20'	30'	40'	50'	Dec.	Units 0'	1'	2'	3'	4'	5'	6'	7'	8'	9'
36.0	6.0	12.0	18.0	24.0	30.0	.0	0.0	0.6	1.2	1.8	2.4	3.0	3.6	4.3	4.9	5.5
36.1	6.0	12.0	18.0	24.0	30.1	.1	0.1	0.7	1.3	1.9	2.5	3.1	3.7	4.3	4.9	5.5
36.2	6.0	12.0	18.1	24.1	30.1	.2	0.1	0.7	1.3	1.9	2.6	3.2	3.8	4.4	5.0	5.6
36.3	6.0	12.1	18.1	24.2	30.2	.3	0.2	0.8	1.4	2.0	2.6	3.2	3.8	4.4	5.0	5.7
36.4	6.1	12.1	18.2	24.2	30.3	.4	0.2	0.9	1.5	2.1	2.7	3.3	3.9	4.5	5.1	5.7
36.5	6.1	12.2	18.3	24.3	30.4	.5	0.3	0.9	1.5	2.1	2.7	3.3	4.0	4.6	5.2	5.8
36.6	6.1	12.2	18.3	24.4	30.5	.6	0.4	1.0	1.6	2.2	2.8	3.4	4.0	4.6	5.2	5.8
36.7	6.1	12.3	18.4	24.5	30.6	.7	0.4	1.0	1.6	2.3	2.9	3.5	4.1	4.7	5.3	5.9
36.8	6.2	12.3	18.4	24.6	30.7	.8	0.5	1.1	1.7	2.3	2.9	3.5	4.1	4.7	5.4	6.0
36.9	6.2	12.3	18.5	24.6	30.8	.9	0.5	1.2	1.8	2.4	3.0	3.6	4.2	4.8	5.4	6.0
37.0	6.1	12.3	18.5	24.6	30.8	.0	0.0	0.6	1.2	1.9	2.5	3.1	3.7	4.4	5.0	5.6
37.1	6.2	12.3	18.5	24.7	30.9	.1	0.1	0.7	1.3	1.9	2.6	3.2	3.8	4.4	5.1	5.7
37.2	6.2	12.4	18.6	24.8	31.0	.2	0.1	0.7	1.4	2.0	2.6	3.3	3.9	4.5	5.1	5.7
37.3	6.2	12.4	18.6	24.9	31.1	.3	0.2	0.8	1.4	2.1	2.7	3.3	3.9	4.6	5.2	5.8
37.4	6.2	12.5	18.7	24.9	31.2	.4	0.2	0.9	1.5	2.1	2.7	3.4	4.0	4.6	5.2	5.9
37.5	6.3	12.5	18.8	25.0	31.3	.5	0.3	0.9	1.6	2.2	2.8	3.4	4.1	4.7	5.3	5.9
37.6	6.3	12.5	18.8	25.1	31.3	.6	0.4	1.0	1.6	2.2	2.9	3.5	4.1	4.7	5.4	6.0
37.7	6.3	12.6	18.9	25.2	31.4	.7	0.4	1.1	1.7	2.3	2.9	3.6	4.2	4.8	5.4	6.1
37.8	6.3	12.6	18.9	25.2	31.5	.8	0.5	1.1	1.7	2.4	3.0	3.6	4.2	4.9	5.5	6.1
37.9	6.4	12.6	19.0	25.3	31.6	.9	0.6	1.2	1.8	2.4	3.1	3.7	4.3	4.9	5.6	6.2
38.0	6.3	12.6	19.0	25.3	31.6	.0	0.0	0.6	1.3	1.9	2.6	3.2	3.8	4.5	5.1	5.8
38.1	6.3	12.7	19.0	25.4	31.7	.1	0.1	0.7	1.3	2.0	2.6	3.3	3.9	4.6	5.2	5.8
38.2	6.3	12.7	19.1	25.4	31.8	.2	0.1	0.8	1.4	2.1	2.7	3.3	4.0	4.6	5.3	5.9
38.3	6.4	12.8	19.1	25.5	31.9	.3	0.2	0.8	1.5	2.1	2.8	3.4	4.0	4.7	5.3	6.0
38.4	6.4	12.8	19.2	25.6	32.0	.4	0.3	0.9	1.5	2.2	2.8	3.5	4.1	4.7	5.4	6.0
38.5	6.4	12.8	19.3	25.7	32.1	.5	0.3	1.0	1.6	2.2	2.9	3.5	4.2	4.8	5.5	6.1
38.6	6.4	12.9	19.3	25.7	32.2	.6	0.4	1.0	1.7	2.3	3.0	3.6	4.2	4.9	5.5	6.2
38.7	6.5	12.9	19.4	25.8	32.3	.7	0.4	1.1	1.7	2.4	3.0	3.7	4.3	4.9	5.6	6.2
38.8	6.5	13.0	19.4	25.9	32.4	.8	0.5	1.2	1.8	2.4	3.1	3.7	4.4	5.0	5.6	6.3
38.9	6.5	13.0	19.5	26.0	32.5	.9	0.6	1.2	1.9	2.5	3.1	3.8	4.4	5.1	5.7	6.4
39.0	6.5	13.0	19.5	26.0	32.5	.0	0.0	0.7	1.3	2.0	2.6	3.3	3.9	4.6	5.3	5.9
39.1	6.5	13.0	19.5	26.0	32.6	.1	0.1	0.7	1.4	2.0	2.7	3.4	4.0	4.7	5.3	6.0
39.2	6.5	13.0	19.6	26.1	32.6	.2	0.1	0.8	1.4	2.1	2.8	3.4	4.1	4.7	5.4	6.1
39.3	6.5	13.1	19.6	26.2	32.7	.3	0.2	0.9	1.5	2.2	2.8	3.5	4.1	4.8	5.4	6.1
39.4	6.6	13.1	19.7	26.3	32.8	.4	0.3	0.9	1.6	2.2	2.9	3.6	4.2	4.9	5.5	6.2
39.5	6.6	13.2	19.8	26.3	32.9	.5	0.3	1.0	1.6	2.3	3.0	3.6	4.3	4.9	5.6	6.3
39.6	6.6	13.2	19.8	26.4	33.0	.6	0.4	1.1	1.7	2.4	3.0	3.7	4.3	5.0	5.7	6.3
39.7	6.6	13.3	19.9	26.5	33.1	.7	0.5	1.1	1.8	2.4	3.1	3.8	4.4	5.1	5.7	6.4
39.8	6.7	13.3	19.9	26.5	33.2	.8	0.5	1.2	1.8	2.5	3.2	3.8	4.5	5.1	5.8	6.5
39.9	6.7	13.3	20.0	26.6	33.3	.9	0.6	1.3	1.9	2.6	3.2	3.9	4.6	5.2	5.9	6.5
40.0	6.6	13.3	20.0	26.6	33.3	.0	0.0	0.7	1.3	2.0	2.7	3.4	4.0	4.7	5.4	6.1
40.1	6.7	13.3	20.0	26.7	33.4	.1	0.1	0.7	1.4	2.1	2.8	3.4	4.1	4.8	5.5	6.1
40.2	6.7	13.4	20.1	26.8	33.5	.2	0.1	0.8	1.5	2.2	2.8	3.5	4.2	4.9	5.5	6.2
40.3	6.7	13.4	20.1	26.9	33.6	.3	0.2	0.9	1.6	2.2	2.9	3.6	4.3	4.9	5.6	6.3
40.4	6.7	13.5	20.2	26.9	33.7	.4	0.3	0.9	1.6	2.3	3.0	3.6	4.3	5.0	5.7	6.3
40.5	6.8	13.5	20.3	27.0	33.8	.5	0.3	1.0	1.7	2.4	3.0	3.7	4.4	5.1	5.7	6.4
40.6	6.8	13.5	20.3	27.1	33.8	.6	0.4	1.1	1.8	2.4	3.1	3.8	4.5	5.1	5.8	6.5
40.7	6.8	13.6	20.4	27.2	33.9	.7	0.5	1.1	1.8	2.5	3.2	3.8	4.5	5.2	5.9	6.6
40.8	6.8	13.6	20.4	27.2	34.0	.8	0.5	1.2	1.9	2.6	3.2	3.9	4.6	5.3	5.9	6.6
40.9	6.9	13.7	20.5	27.3	34.1	.9	0.6	1.3	2.0	2.6	3.3	4.0	4.7	5.3	6.0	6.7
41.0	6.8	13.6	20.5	27.3	34.1	.0	0.0	0.7	1.4	2.1	2.8	3.5	4.1	4.8	5.5	6.2
41.1	6.8	13.7	20.5	27.4	34.2	.1	0.1	0.8	1.5	2.1	2.8	3.5	4.2	4.9	5.6	6.3
41.2	6.8	13.7	20.6	27.4	34.3	.2	0.1	0.8	1.5	2.2	2.9	3.6	4.3	5.0	5.7	6.4
41.3	6.9	13.8	20.6	27.5	34.4	.3	0.2	0.9	1.6	2.3	3.0	3.7	4.3	5.0	5.7	6.4
41.4	6.9	13.8	20.7	27.6	34.5	.4	0.3	1.0	1.7	2.4	3.0	3.7	4.4	5.1	5.8	6.5
41.5	6.9	13.8	20.8	27.7	34.6	.5	0.3	1.0	1.7	2.4	3.1	3.8	4.5	5.2	5.9	6.6
41.6	6.9	13.9	20.8	27.7	34.6	.6	0.4	1.1	1.8	2.5	3.2	3.9	4.5	5.2	5.9	6.6
41.7	7.0	13.9	20.9	27.8	34.8	.7	0.5	1.2	1.9	2.6	3.3	3.9	4.6	5.3	6.0	6.7
41.8	7.0	14.0	20.9	27.9	34.9	.8	0.6	1.2	1.9	2.6	3.3	4.0	4.7	5.4	6.1	6.8
41.9	7.0	14.0	21.0	28.0	35.0	.9	0.6	1.3	2.0	2.7	3.4	4.1	4.8	5.5	6.2	6.8
42.0	7.0	14.0	21.0	28.0	35.0	.0	0.0	0.7	1.4	2.1	2.8	3.5	4.2	5.0	5.7	6.4
42.1	7.0	14.0	21.0	28.0	35.1	.1	0.1	0.8	1.5	2.2	2.9	3.6	4.3	5.0	5.7	6.4
42.2	7.0	14.1	21.1	28.1	35.1	.2	0.1	0.8	1.6	2.3	3.0	3.7	4.4	5.1	5.8	6.5
42.3	7.0	14.1	21.1	28.2	35.2	.3	0.2	0.9	1.6	2.3	3.0	3.8	4.5	5.2	5.9	6.6
42.4	7.1	14.1	21.2	28.3	35.3	.4	0.3	1.0	1.7	2.4	3.1	3.8	4.5	5.2	5.9	6.7
42.5	7.1	14.2	21.3	28.3	35.4	.5	0.4	1.1	1.8	2.5	3.2	3.9	4.6	5.3	6.0	6.7
42.6	7.1	14.2	21.3	28.4	35.5	.6	0.4	1.1	1.8	2.5	3.3	4.0	4.7	5.4	6.1	6.8
42.7	7.1	14.3	21.4	28.5	35.6	.7	0.5	1.2	1.9	2.6	3.3	4.0	4.7	5.5	6.2	6.9
42.8	7.2	14.3	21.4	28.6	35.7	.8	0.6	1.3	2.0	2.7	3.4	4.1	4.8	5.5	6.2	6.9
42.9	7.2	14.3	21.5	28.6	35.8	.9	0.6	1.3	2.1	2.8	3.5	4.2	4.9	5.6	6.3	7.0
43.0	7.1	14.3	21.5	28.7	35.8	.0	0.0	0.7	1.4	2.2	2.9	3.6	4.3	5.1	5.8	6.5
43.1	7.2	14.3	21.5	28.7	35.9	.1	0.1	0.8	1.5	2.2	3.0	3.7	4.4	5.1	5.9	6.6
43.2	7.2	14.4	21.6	28.8	36.0	.2	0.1	0.9	1.6	2.3	3.0	3.8	4.5	5.2	5.9	6.7
43.3	7.2	14.4	21.6	28.9	36.1	.3	0.2	0.9	1.7	2.4	3.1	3.8	4.6	5.3	6.0	6.7
43.4	7.2	14.5	21.7	28.9	36.2	.4	0.3	1.0	1.7	2.5	3.2	3.9	4.6	5.4	6.1	6.8
43.5	7.3	14.5	21.8	29.0	36.3	.5	0.4	1.1	1.8	2.5	3.3	4.0	4.7	5.4	6.2	6.9
43.6	7.3	14.5	21.8	29.1	36.3	.6	0.4	1.2	1.9	2.6	3.4	4.1	4.8	5.5	6.2	7.0
43.7	7.3	14.6	21.9	29.2	36.4	.7	0.5	1.2	2.0	2.7	3.4	4.1	4.9	5.6	6.3	7.1
43.8	7.3	14.6	21.9	29.2	36.5	.8	0.6	1.3	2.0	2.8	3.5	4.2	4.9	5.7	6.4	7.1
43.9	7.4	14.7	22.0	29.3	36.6	.9	0.7	1.4	2.1	2.8	3.6	4.3	5.0	5.7	6.5	7.2

Double Second Difference and Correction (right section):

- 36.0–37.9: 0.8; 2.5 / 0.1; 4.2 / 0.2; 5.9 / 0.3; 7.6 / 0.4; 9.3 / 0.5; 11.0 / 0.6; 12.7 / 0.7; 14.4 / 0.8; 16.1 / 0.9; 17.8 / 1.0; 19.5 / 1.1; 21.2 / 1.2; 22.8 / 1.3; 24.5 / 1.4; 26.2 / 1.5; 27.9 / 1.6; 29.6 / 1.7; 31.3 / 1.8; 33.0 / 1.9; 34.7 / 2.0
- 38.0–39.9: 0.9; 2.6 / 0.1; 4.4 / 0.2; 6.2 / 0.3; 7.9 / 0.4; 9.7 / 0.5; 11.4 / 0.6; 13.2 / 0.7; 14.9 / 0.8; 16.7 / 0.9; 18.5 / 1.0; 20.2 / 1.1; 22.0 / 1.2; 23.7 / 1.3; 25.5 / 1.4; 27.3 / 1.5; 29.0 / 1.6; 30.8 / 1.7; 32.5 / 1.8; 34.3 / 1.9
- 40.0–41.9: 0.9; 2.8 / 0.1; 4.6 / 0.2; 6.4 / 0.3; 8.3 / 0.4; 10.2 / 0.5; 12.0 / 0.6; 13.9 / 0.7; 15.7 / 0.8; 17.6 / 0.9; 19.4 / 1.0; 21.3 / 1.1; 23.1 / 1.2; 25.0 / 1.3; 26.8 / 1.4; 28.7 / 1.5; 30.5 / 1.6; 32.3 / 1.7; 34.2 / 1.8
- 42.0–43.9: 1.0; 3.0 / 0.1; 4.9 / 0.2; 6.9 / 0.3; 8.9 / 0.4; 10.8 / 0.5; 12.8 / 0.6; 14.8 / 0.7; 16.7 / 0.8; 18.7 / 0.9; 20.7 / 1.0; 22.7 / 1.1; 24.6 / 1.2; 26.6 / 1.3; 28.6 / 1.4; 30.5 / 1.5; 32.5 / 1.6; 34.5 / 1.7

The Double-Second-Difference correction (Corr.) is always to be added to the tabulated altitude.

INTERPOLATION TABLE

Dec. Inc.	Tens 10'	20'	30'	40'	50'	Decimals	Units 0'	1'	2'	3'	4'	5'	6'	7'	8'	9'	Double Second Diff. and Corr.
44.0	7.3	14.6	22.0	29.3	36.6	.0	0.0	0.7	1.5	2.2	3.0	3.7	4.4	5.2	5.9	6.7	
44.1	7.3	14.7	22.0	29.4	36.7	.1	0.1	0.8	1.6	2.3	3.0	3.8	4.5	5.3	6.0	6.7	
44.2	7.3	14.7	22.1	29.4	36.8	.2	0.1	0.9	1.6	2.4	3.1	3.9	4.6	5.3	6.1	6.8	1.1
44.3	7.4	14.8	22.1	29.5	36.9	.3	0.2	1.0	1.7	2.4	3.2	3.9	4.7	5.4	6.2	6.9	3.2 0.1
44.4	7.4	14.8	22.2	29.6	37.0	.4	0.3	1.0	1.8	2.5	3.3	4.0	4.7	5.5	6.2	7.0	5.3 0.2
44.5	7.4	14.8	22.3	29.7	37.1	.5	0.4	1.1	1.9	2.6	3.3	4.1	4.8	5.6	6.3	7.0	7.5 0.3
44.6	7.4	14.9	22.3	29.7	37.2	.6	0.4	1.2	1.9	2.7	3.4	4.2	4.9	5.6	6.4	7.1	9.6 0.4
44.7	7.5	14.9	22.4	29.8	37.3	.7	0.5	1.3	2.0	2.7	3.5	4.2	5.0	5.7	6.5	7.2	11.7 0.5
44.8	7.5	15.0	22.4	29.9	37.4	.8	0.6	1.3	2.1	2.8	3.6	4.3	5.0	5.8	6.5	7.3	13.9 0.6
44.9	7.5	15.0	22.5	30.0	37.5	.9	0.7	1.4	2.2	2.9	3.6	4.4	5.1	5.9	6.6	7.3	16.0 0.7 18.1 0.8
45.0	7.5	15.0	22.5	30.0	37.5	.0	0.0	0.8	1.5	2.3	3.0	3.8	4.5	5.3	6.1	6.8	20.3 0.9
45.1	7.5	15.0	22.5	30.0	37.6	.1	0.1	0.8	1.6	2.4	3.1	3.9	4.6	5.4	6.1	6.9	22.4 1.0
45.2	7.5	15.0	22.6	30.1	37.6	.2	0.2	0.9	1.7	2.4	3.2	3.9	4.7	5.5	6.2	7.0	24.5 1.1
45.3	7.5	15.1	22.6	30.2	37.7	.3	0.2	1.0	1.7	2.5	3.3	4.0	4.8	5.5	6.3	7.1	26.7 1.2
45.4	7.6	15.1	22.7	30.3	37.8	.4	0.3	1.1	1.8	2.6	3.3	4.1	4.9	5.6	6.4	7.1	28.8 1.3
45.5	7.6	15.2	22.8	30.3	37.9	.5	0.4	1.1	1.9	2.7	3.4	4.2	4.9	5.7	6.4	7.2	30.9 1.4
45.6	7.6	15.2	22.8	30.4	38.0	.6	0.5	1.2	2.0	2.7	3.5	4.2	5.0	5.8	6.5	7.3	33.1 1.5
45.7	7.6	15.3	22.9	30.5	38.1	.7	0.5	1.3	2.0	2.8	3.6	4.3	5.1	5.8	6.6	7.4	35.2 1.6
45.8	7.7	15.3	22.9	30.6	38.2	.8	0.6	1.4	2.1	2.9	3.6	4.4	5.2	5.9	6.7	7.4	
45.9	7.7	15.3	23.0	30.6	38.3	.9	0.7	1.4	2.2	3.0	3.7	4.5	5.2	6.0	6.7	7.5	
46.0	7.6	15.3	23.0	30.6	38.3	.0	0.0	0.8	1.5	2.3	3.1	3.9	4.6	5.4	6.2	7.0	1.2
46.1	7.7	15.3	23.0	30.7	38.4	.1	0.1	0.9	1.6	2.4	3.2	4.0	4.7	5.5	6.3	7.1	3.5 0.1
46.2	7.7	15.4	23.1	30.8	38.5	.2	0.2	0.9	1.7	2.5	3.3	4.0	4.8	5.6	6.4	7.1	5.8 0.2
46.3	7.7	15.4	23.1	30.9	38.6	.3	0.2	1.0	1.8	2.6	3.3	4.1	4.9	5.7	6.4	7.2	8.1 0.3
46.4	7.7	15.5	23.2	30.9	38.7	.4	0.3	1.1	1.9	2.6	3.4	4.2	5.0	5.7	6.5	7.3	10.5 0.4
46.5	7.8	15.5	23.3	31.0	38.8	.5	0.4	1.2	1.9	2.7	3.5	4.3	5.0	5.8	6.6	7.4	12.8 0.5
46.6	7.8	15.5	23.3	31.1	38.8	.6	0.5	1.2	2.0	2.8	3.6	4.3	5.1	5.9	6.7	7.4	15.1 0.6
46.7	7.8	15.6	23.4	31.2	38.9	.7	0.5	1.3	2.1	2.9	3.6	4.4	5.2	6.0	6.7	7.5	17.4 0.7
46.8	7.8	15.6	23.4	31.2	39.0	.8	0.6	1.4	2.2	2.9	3.7	4.5	5.3	6.0	6.8	7.6	19.8 0.8
46.9	7.9	15.7	23.5	31.3	39.1	.9	0.7	1.5	2.2	3.0	3.8	4.6	5.3	6.1	6.9	7.7	22.1 0.9 24.4 1.0
47.0	7.8	15.6	23.5	31.3	39.1	.0	0.0	0.8	1.6	2.4	3.2	4.0	4.7	5.5	6.3	7.1	26.7 1.1
47.1	7.8	15.7	23.5	31.4	39.2	.1	0.1	0.9	1.7	2.5	3.2	4.0	4.8	5.6	6.4	7.2	29.1 1.2
47.2	7.8	15.7	23.6	31.4	39.3	.2	0.2	0.9	1.7	2.5	3.3	4.1	4.9	5.7	6.5	7.3	31.4 1.3
47.3	7.9	15.8	23.6	31.5	39.4	.3	0.2	1.0	1.8	2.6	3.4	4.2	5.0	5.8	6.6	7.4	33.7 1.4
47.4	7.9	15.8	23.7	31.6	39.5	.4	0.3	1.1	1.9	2.7	3.5	4.3	5.1	5.9	6.6	7.4	36.0 1.5
47.5	7.9	15.8	23.8	31.7	39.6	.5	0.4	1.2	2.0	2.8	3.6	4.4	5.1	5.9	6.7	7.5	
47.6	7.9	15.9	23.8	31.7	39.7	.6	0.5	1.3	2.1	2.8	3.6	4.4	5.2	6.0	6.8	7.6	1.3
47.7	8.0	15.9	23.9	31.8	39.8	.7	0.6	1.3	2.1	2.9	3.7	4.5	5.3	6.1	6.9	7.7	3.8 0.1
47.8	8.0	16.0	23.9	31.9	39.9	.8	0.6	1.4	2.2	3.0	3.8	4.6	5.4	6.2	7.0	7.8	6.3 0.2
47.9	8.0	16.0	24.0	32.0	40.0	.9	0.7	1.5	2.3	3.1	3.9	4.7	5.5	6.3	7.0	7.8	8.9 0.3 11.4 0.4
48.0	8.0	16.0	24.0	32.0	40.0	.0	0.0	0.8	1.6	2.4	3.2	4.0	4.8	5.7	6.5	7.3	14.0 0.5
48.1	8.0	16.0	24.0	32.0	40.1	.1	0.1	0.9	1.7	2.5	3.3	4.1	4.9	5.7	6.5	7.4	16.5 0.6
48.2	8.0	16.0	24.1	32.1	40.1	.2	0.2	1.0	1.8	2.6	3.4	4.2	5.0	5.8	6.6	7.4	19.0 0.7
48.3	8.0	16.1	24.1	32.2	40.2	.3	0.2	1.1	1.9	2.7	3.5	4.3	5.1	5.9	6.7	7.5	21.6 0.8
48.4	8.1	16.1	24.2	32.3	40.3	.4	0.3	1.1	1.9	2.7	3.6	4.4	5.2	6.0	6.8	7.6	24.1 0.9
48.5	8.1	16.2	24.3	32.3	40.4	.5	0.4	1.2	2.0	2.8	3.6	4.4	5.3	6.1	6.9	7.7	26.7 1.0
48.6	8.1	16.2	24.3	32.4	40.5	.6	0.5	1.3	2.1	2.9	3.7	4.5	5.3	6.1	7.0	7.8	29.2 1.1
48.7	8.1	16.3	24.4	32.5	40.6	.7	0.6	1.4	2.2	3.0	3.8	4.6	5.4	6.2	7.0	7.8	31.7 1.2
48.8	8.2	16.3	24.4	32.6	40.7	.8	0.6	1.5	2.3	3.1	3.9	4.7	5.5	6.3	7.1	7.9	34.3 1.3
48.9	8.2	16.3	24.5	32.6	40.8	.9	0.7	1.5	2.3	3.2	4.0	4.8	5.6	6.4	7.2	8.0	
49.0	8.1	16.3	24.5	32.6	40.8	.0	0.0	0.8	1.6	2.5	3.3	4.1	4.9	5.8	6.6	7.4	
49.1	8.2	16.3	24.5	32.7	40.9	.1	0.1	0.9	1.7	2.6	3.4	4.2	5.0	5.9	6.7	7.5	
49.2	8.2	16.4	24.6	32.8	41.0	.2	0.2	1.0	1.8	2.6	3.5	4.3	5.1	5.9	6.8	7.6	1.4
49.3	8.2	16.4	24.6	32.9	41.1	.3	0.2	1.1	1.9	2.7	3.5	4.4	5.2	6.0	6.8	7.7	4.2 0.1
49.4	8.2	16.5	24.7	32.9	41.2	.4	0.3	1.2	2.0	2.8	3.6	4.5	5.3	6.1	6.9	7.8	7.1 0.2 9.9 0.3
49.5	8.3	16.5	24.8	33.0	41.3	.5	0.4	1.2	2.1	2.9	3.7	4.5	5.4	6.2	7.0	7.8	12.7 0.4
49.6	8.3	16.5	24.8	33.1	41.3	.6	0.5	1.3	2.1	3.0	3.8	4.6	5.4	6.3	7.1	7.9	15.5 0.5
49.7	8.3	16.6	24.9	33.2	41.4	.7	0.6	1.4	2.2	3.1	3.9	4.7	5.5	6.4	7.2	8.0	18.4 0.6
49.8	8.3	16.6	24.9	33.2	41.5	.8	0.7	1.5	2.3	3.1	4.0	4.8	5.6	6.4	7.3	8.1	21.2 0.7
49.9	8.4	16.7	25.0	33.3	41.6	.9	0.7	1.6	2.4	3.2	4.0	4.9	5.7	6.5	7.3	8.2	24.0 0.8 26.8 0.9
50.0	8.3	16.6	25.0	33.3	41.6	.0	0.0	0.8	1.7	2.5	3.4	4.2	5.0	5.9	6.7	7.6	29.7 1.0
50.1	8.3	16.7	25.0	33.4	41.7	.1	0.1	0.9	1.8	2.6	3.5	4.3	5.1	6.0	6.8	7.7	32.5 1.1
50.2	8.3	16.7	25.1	33.4	41.8	.2	0.2	1.0	1.9	2.7	3.5	4.4	5.2	6.1	6.9	7.7	35.3 1.2
50.3	8.4	16.8	25.1	33.5	41.9	.3	0.3	1.1	1.9	2.8	3.6	4.5	5.3	6.1	7.0	7.8	
50.4	8.4	16.8	25.2	33.6	42.0	.4	0.3	1.2	2.0	2.9	3.7	4.5	5.4	6.2	7.1	7.9	
50.5	8.4	16.8	25.3	33.7	42.1	.5	0.4	1.3	2.1	2.9	3.8	4.6	5.5	6.3	7.2	8.0	
50.6	8.4	16.9	25.3	33.7	42.2	.6	0.5	1.3	2.2	3.0	3.9	4.7	5.6	6.4	7.2	8.1	
50.7	8.5	16.9	25.4	33.8	42.3	.7	0.6	1.4	2.3	3.1	4.0	4.8	5.6	6.5	7.3	8.2	
50.8	8.5	17.0	25.4	33.9	42.4	.8	0.7	1.5	2.4	3.2	4.0	4.9	5.7	6.6	7.4	8.2	1.6
50.9	8.5	17.0	25.5	34.0	42.5	.9	0.8	1.6	2.4	3.3	4.1	5.0	5.8	6.6	7.5	8.3	4.8 0.1 8.0 0.2
51.0	8.5	17.0	25.5	34.0	42.5	.0	0.0	0.9	1.7	2.6	3.4	4.3	5.1	6.0	6.9	7.7	11.2 0.3
51.1	8.5	17.0	25.5	34.0	42.6	.1	0.1	0.9	1.8	2.7	3.5	4.4	5.2	6.1	7.0	7.8	14.5 0.4
51.2	8.5	17.0	25.6	34.1	42.6	.2	0.2	1.0	1.9	2.7	3.6	4.5	5.3	6.2	7.0	7.9	17.7 0.5
51.3	8.5	17.1	25.6	34.2	42.7	.3	0.3	1.1	2.0	2.8	3.7	4.5	5.4	6.3	7.1	8.0	20.9 0.6
51.4	8.6	17.1	25.7	34.3	42.8	.4	0.3	1.2	2.1	2.9	3.8	4.6	5.5	6.4	7.2	8.1	24.1 0.7 27.3 0.8
51.5	8.6	17.2	25.8	34.3	42.9	.5	0.4	1.3	2.1	3.0	3.9	4.7	5.6	6.4	7.3	8.2	30.5 0.9
51.6	8.6	17.2	25.8	34.4	43.0	.6	0.5	1.4	2.2	3.1	3.9	4.8	5.7	6.5	7.4	8.2	33.7 1.0
51.7	8.6	17.3	25.9	34.5	43.1	.7	0.6	1.5	2.3	3.2	4.0	4.9	5.8	6.6	7.5	8.3	36.9 1.1
51.8	8.7	17.3	25.9	34.6	43.2	.8	0.7	1.5	2.4	3.3	4.1	5.0	5.8	6.7	7.6	8.4	
51.9	8.7	17.3	26.0	34.6	43.3	.9	0.8	1.6	2.5	3.3	4.2	5.1	5.9	6.8	7.6	8.5	
	10'	20'	30'	40'	50'		0'	1'	2'	3'	4'	5'	6'	7'	8'	9'	

Dec. Inc.	Tens 10'	20'	30'	40'	50'	Decimals	Units 0'	1'	2'	3'	4'	5'	6'	7'	8'	9'	Double Second Diff. and Corr.
52.0	8.6	17.3	26.0	34.6	43.3	.0	0.0	0.9	1.7	2.6	3.5	4.4	5.2	6.1	7.0	7.9	1.8
52.1	8.7	17.3	26.0	34.7	43.4	.1	0.1	1.0	1.8	2.7	3.6	4.5	5.3	6.2	7.1	8.0	5.5 0.1
52.2	8.7	17.4	26.1	34.8	43.5	.2	0.2	1.0	1.9	2.8	3.7	4.5	5.4	6.3	7.2	8.0	9.1 0.2
52.3	8.7	17.4	26.1	34.9	43.6	.3	0.3	1.1	2.0	2.9	3.8	4.6	5.5	6.4	7.3	8.1	12.8 0.3
52.4	8.7	17.5	26.2	34.9	43.7	.4	0.3	1.2	2.1	3.0	3.8	4.7	5.6	6.5	7.3	8.2	16.5 0.4
52.5	8.8	17.5	26.3	35.0	43.8	.5	0.4	1.3	2.2	3.1	3.9	4.8	5.7	6.6	7.4	8.3	20.1 0.5
52.6	8.8	17.5	26.3	35.1	43.8	.6	0.5	1.4	2.3	3.1	4.0	4.9	5.8	6.6	7.5	8.4	23.8 0.6
52.7	8.8	17.6	26.4	35.2	43.9	.7	0.6	1.5	2.4	3.2	4.1	5.0	5.9	6.7	7.6	8.5	27.4 0.7
52.8	8.8	17.6	26.4	35.2	44.0	.8	0.7	1.6	2.4	3.3	4.2	5.1	5.9	6.8	7.7	8.6	31.1 0.8
52.9	8.9	17.7	26.5	35.3	44.1	.9	0.8	1.7	2.5	3.4	4.3	5.2	6.0	6.9	7.8	8.7	34.7 0.9
53.0	8.8	17.6	26.5	35.3	44.1	.0	0.0	0.9	1.8	2.7	3.6	4.5	5.3	6.2	7.1	8.0	
53.1	8.8	17.7	26.5	35.4	44.2	.1	0.1	1.0	1.9	2.8	3.7	4.5	5.4	6.3	7.2	8.1	2.1
53.2	8.8	17.7	26.6	35.4	44.3	.2	0.2	1.1	2.0	2.9	3.7	4.6	5.5	6.4	7.3	8.2	6.2 0.1
53.3	8.9	17.8	26.6	35.5	44.4	.3	0.3	1.2	2.1	2.9	3.8	4.7	5.6	6.5	7.4	8.3	10.4 0.2
53.4	8.9	17.8	26.7	35.6	44.5	.4	0.4	1.2	2.1	3.0	3.9	4.8	5.7	6.6	7.5	8.4	14.5 0.3 18.6 0.4
53.5	8.9	17.8	26.8	35.7	44.6	.5	0.4	1.3	2.2	3.1	4.0	4.9	5.8	6.7	7.6	8.5	22.8 0.5
53.6	8.9	17.9	26.8	35.7	44.7	.6	0.5	1.4	2.3	3.2	4.1	5.0	5.9	6.8	7.7	8.6	26.9 0.6
53.7	9.0	17.9	26.9	35.8	44.8	.7	0.6	1.5	2.4	3.3	4.2	5.1	6.0	6.9	7.8	8.6	31.1 0.7
53.8	9.0	18.0	26.9	35.9	44.9	.8	0.7	1.6	2.5	3.4	4.3	5.2	6.1	7.0	7.8	8.7	35.2 0.8
53.9	9.0	18.0	27.0	36.0	45.0	.9	0.8	1.7	2.6	3.5	4.4	5.3	6.2	7.0	7.9	8.8	
54.0	9.0	18.0	27.0	36.0	45.0	.0	0.0	0.9	1.8	2.7	3.6	4.5	5.4	6.4	7.3	8.2	
54.1	9.0	18.0	27.0	36.0	45.1	.1	0.1	1.0	1.9	2.8	3.7	4.6	5.5	6.4	7.4	8.3	2.4
54.2	9.0	18.0	27.1	36.1	45.1	.2	0.2	1.1	2.0	2.9	3.8	4.7	5.6	6.5	7.4	8.4	7.2 0.1
54.3	9.0	18.1	27.1	36.2	45.2	.3	0.3	1.2	2.1	3.0	3.9	4.8	5.7	6.6	7.5	8.4	12.0 0.2
54.4	9.1	18.1	27.2	36.3	45.3	.4	0.4	1.3	2.2	3.1	4.0	4.9	5.8	6.7	7.6	8.5	16.8 0.3
54.5	9.1	18.2	27.3	36.3	45.4	.5	0.5	1.4	2.3	3.2	4.1	5.0	5.9	6.8	7.7	8.6	21.6 0.4
54.6	9.1	18.2	27.3	36.4	45.5	.6	0.5	1.5	2.4	3.3	4.2	5.1	6.0	6.9	7.8	8.7	26.4 0.5
54.7	9.1	18.3	27.4	36.5	45.6	.7	0.6	1.5	2.5	3.4	4.3	5.2	6.1	7.0	7.9	8.8	31.2 0.6
54.8	9.2	18.3	27.4	36.6	45.7	.8	0.7	1.6	2.5	3.5	4.4	5.3	6.2	7.1	8.0	8.9	36.0 0.7
54.9	9.2	18.3	27.5	36.6	45.8	.9	0.8	1.7	2.6	3.5	4.5	5.4	6.3	7.2	8.1	9.0	
55.0	9.1	18.3	27.5	36.6	45.8	.0	0.0	0.9	1.8	2.8	3.7	4.6	5.5	6.5	7.4	8.3	
55.1	9.2	18.3	27.5	36.7	45.9	.1	0.1	1.0	1.9	2.9	3.8	4.7	5.6	6.6	7.5	8.4	
55.2	9.2	18.4	27.6	36.8	46.0	.2	0.2	1.1	2.0	3.0	3.9	4.8	5.7	6.7	7.6	8.5	2.9
55.3	9.2	18.4	27.6	36.9	46.1	.3	0.3	1.2	2.1	3.1	4.0	4.9	5.8	6.8	7.7	8.6	8.6 0.1
55.4	9.2	18.5	27.7	36.9	46.2	.4	0.4	1.3	2.2	3.1	4.1	5.0	5.9	6.8	7.8	8.7	14.4 0.2 20.2 0.3
55.5	9.3	18.5	27.8	37.0	46.3	.5	0.5	1.4	2.3	3.2	4.2	5.1	6.0	6.9	7.9	8.8	25.9 0.4
55.6	9.3	18.5	27.8	37.1	46.3	.6	0.6	1.5	2.4	3.3	4.3	5.2	6.1	7.0	8.0	8.9	31.7 0.5
55.7	9.3	18.6	27.9	37.2	46.4	.7	0.6	1.6	2.5	3.4	4.3	5.3	6.2	7.1	8.0	9.0	37.5 0.6
55.8	9.3	18.6	27.9	37.2	46.5	.8	0.7	1.7	2.6	3.5	4.4	5.4	6.3	7.2	8.1	9.1	
55.9	9.4	18.7	28.0	37.3	46.6	.9	0.8	1.8	2.7	3.6	4.5	5.5	6.4	7.3	8.2	9.2	
56.0	9.3	18.6	28.0	37.3	46.6	.0	0.0	0.9	1.9	2.8	3.8	4.7	5.6	6.6	7.5	8.5	
56.1	9.3	18.7	28.0	37.4	46.7	.1	0.1	1.0	2.0	2.9	3.9	4.8	5.7	6.7	7.6	8.6	
56.2	9.3	18.7	28.1	37.4	46.8	.2	0.2	1.1	2.1	3.0	4.0	4.9	5.8	6.8	7.7	8.7	3.6
56.3	9.4	18.8	28.1	37.5	46.9	.3	0.3	1.2	2.2	3.1	4.0	5.0	5.9	6.9	7.8	8.8	10.9 0.1
56.4	9.4	18.8	28.2	37.6	47.0	.4	0.4	1.3	2.3	3.2	4.1	5.1	6.0	7.0	7.9	8.9	18.2 0.2
56.5	9.4	18.8	28.3	37.7	47.1	.5	0.5	1.4	2.4	3.3	4.2	5.2	6.1	7.1	8.0	8.9	25.5 0.3
56.6	9.4	18.9	28.3	37.7	47.2	.6	0.6	1.5	2.4	3.4	4.3	5.3	6.2	7.2	8.1	9.0	32.8 0.4
56.7	9.5	18.9	28.4	37.8	47.3	.7	0.7	1.6	2.5	3.5	4.4	5.4	6.3	7.3	8.2	9.1	40.1 0.5
56.8	9.5	19.0	28.4	37.9	47.4	.8	0.8	1.7	2.6	3.6	4.5	5.5	6.4	7.3	8.3	9.2	
56.9	9.5	19.0	28.5	38.0	47.5	.9	0.8	1.8	2.7	3.7	4.6	5.6	6.5	7.4	8.4	9.3	
57.0	9.5	19.0	28.5	38.0	47.5	.0	0.0	1.0	1.9	2.9	3.8	4.8	5.7	6.7	7.7	8.6	
57.1	9.5	19.0	28.5	38.0	47.6	.1	0.1	1.1	2.0	3.0	3.9	4.9	5.8	6.8	7.8	8.7	
57.2	9.5	19.0	28.6	38.1	47.6	.2	0.2	1.1	2.1	3.1	4.0	5.0	5.9	6.9	7.9	8.8	
57.3	9.5	19.1	28.6	38.2	47.7	.3	0.3	1.2	2.2	3.2	4.1	5.1	6.0	7.0	8.0	8.9	5.0
57.4	9.6	19.1	28.7	38.3	47.8	.4	0.4	1.3	2.3	3.3	4.2	5.2	6.1	7.1	8.0	9.0	15.0 0.1
57.5	9.6	19.2	28.8	38.3	47.9	.5	0.5	1.4	2.4	3.4	4.3	5.3	6.2	7.2	8.1	9.1	25.0 0.2
57.6	9.6	19.2	28.8	38.4	48.0	.6	0.6	1.5	2.5	3.4	4.4	5.4	6.3	7.3	8.2	9.2	35.1 0.3
57.7	9.6	19.3	28.9	38.5	48.1	.7	0.7	1.6	2.6	3.5	4.5	5.5	6.4	7.4	8.3	9.3	
57.8	9.7	19.3	28.9	38.6	48.2	.8	0.8	1.7	2.7	3.6	4.6	5.6	6.5	7.5	8.4	9.4	
57.9	9.7	19.3	29.0	38.6	48.3	.9	0.9	1.8	2.8	3.7	4.7	5.7	6.6	7.6	8.5	9.5	
58.0	9.6	19.3	29.0	38.6	48.3	.0	0.0	1.0	1.9	2.9	3.9	4.9	5.8	6.8	7.8	8.8	
58.1	9.7	19.3	29.0	38.7	48.4	.1	0.1	1.1	2.0	3.0	4.0	5.0	5.9	6.9	7.9	8.9	
58.2	9.7	19.4	29.1	38.8	48.5	.2	0.2	1.2	2.1	3.1	4.1	5.1	6.0	7.0	8.0	9.0	
58.3	9.7	19.4	29.1	38.9	48.6	.3	0.3	1.3	2.2	3.2	4.2	5.2	6.1	7.1	8.1	9.1	
58.4	9.7	19.5	29.2	38.9	48.7	.4	0.4	1.4	2.3	3.3	4.3	5.3	6.2	7.2	8.2	9.2	8.2 24.6 0.1
58.5	9.8	19.5	29.3	39.0	48.8	.5	0.5	1.5	2.4	3.4	4.4	5.4	6.3	7.3	8.3	9.3	41.0 0.2
58.6	9.8	19.5	29.3	39.1	48.8	.6	0.6	1.6	2.5	3.5	4.5	5.5	6.4	7.4	8.4	9.4	
58.7	9.8	19.6	29.4	39.2	48.9	.7	0.7	1.7	2.6	3.6	4.6	5.6	6.5	7.5	8.5	9.5	
58.8	9.8	19.6	29.4	39.2	49.0	.8	0.8	1.8	2.7	3.7	4.7	5.7	6.6	7.6	8.6	9.6	
58.9	9.9	19.7	29.5	39.3	49.1	.9	0.9	1.9	2.8	3.8	4.8	5.8	6.7	7.7	8.7	9.7	
59.0	9.8	19.6	29.5	39.3	49.1	.0	0.0	1.0	2.0	3.0	4.0	5.0	5.9	6.9	7.9	8.9	
59.1	9.8	19.7	29.5	39.4	49.2	.1	0.1	1.1	2.1	3.1	4.1	5.1	6.0	7.0	8.0	9.0	
59.2	9.8	19.7	29.6	39.4	49.3	.2	0.2	1.2	2.2	3.2	4.2	5.2	6.1	7.1	8.1	9.1	16.2
59.3	9.9	19.8	29.6	39.5	49.4	.3	0.3	1.3	2.3	3.3	4.3	5.3	6.2	7.2	8.2	9.2	48.6 0.1
59.4	9.9	19.8	29.7	39.6	49.5	.4	0.4	1.4	2.4	3.4	4.4	5.4	6.3	7.3	8.3	9.3	
59.5	9.9	19.8	29.8	39.7	49.6	.5	0.5	1.5	2.5	3.5	4.5	5.5	6.4	7.4	8.4	9.4	
59.6	9.9	19.9	29.8	39.7	49.7	.6	0.6	1.6	2.6	3.6	4.6	5.6	6.5	7.5	8.5	9.5	
59.7	10.0	19.9	29.9	39.8	49.8	.7	0.7	1.7	2.7	3.7	4.7	5.7	6.6	7.6	8.6	9.6	0.0
59.8	10.0	20.0	29.9	39.9	49.9	.8	0.8	1.8	2.8	3.8	4.8	5.8	6.7	7.7	8.7	9.7	48.2 0.0
59.9	10.0	20.0	30.0	40.0	50.0	.9	0.9	1.9	2.9	3.9	4.9	5.9	6.8	7.8	8.8	9.8	
	10'	20'	30'	40'	50'		0'	1'	2'	3'	4'	5'	6'	7'	8'	9'	

The Double-Second-Difference correction (Corr.) is always to be added to the tabulated altitude.

APPENDIX P

EXTRACTS FROM PUB. NO. 249

LAT 41°S

LHA ♈	Hc	Zn	Hc	Zn	Hc	Zn	Hc	Zn	Hc	Zn	Hc	Zn	Hc	Zn
	Alpheratz		Hamal		♦RIGEL		CANOPUS		♦RIGIL KENT.		Peacock		♦Enif	
0	20 02	002	19 21	031	14 11	089	28 22	137	16 43	199	52 19	226	30 14	320
1	20 03	001	19 43	030	14 56	088	28 53	136	16 28	198	51 46	226	29 45	319
2	20 03	000	20 05	029	15 41	087	29 25	136	16 14	198	51 13	226	29 15	318
3	20 02	359	20 27	028	16 26	087	29 56	136	16 00	198	50 40	226	28 44	317
4	20 01	358	20 48	027	17 12	086	30 28	135	15 46	197	50 08	226	28 13	316
5	19 59	357	21 08	026	17 57	085	31 00	135	15 33	197	49 35	226	27 41	315
6	19 56	356	21 27	025	18 42	085	31 32	135	15 20	196	49 02	226	27 09	314
7	19 53	355	21 46	024	19 27	084	32 04	134	15 08	196	48 29	226	26 37	313
8	19 49	354	22 04	023	20 12	083	32 37	134	14 56	195	47 57	226	26 03	312
9	19 44	353	22 22	022	20 57	083	33 09	134	14 44	195	47 24	226	25 30	312
10	19 38	352	22 39	021	21 42	082	33 42	133	14 33	194	46 51	226	24 56	311
11	19 32	351	22 55	020	22 27	081	34 15	133	14 21	194	46 19	226	24 21	310
12	19 25	351	23 10	019	23 11	080	34 48	133	14 11	193	45 46	226	23 46	309
13	19 17	350	23 25	018	23 56	080	35 22	132	14 00	193	45 14	226	23 11	308
14	19 08	349	23 39	017	24 40	079	35 55	132	13 50	193	44 41	226	22 35	307
	♦Hamal		RIGEL		♦CANOPUS		RIGIL KENT.		♦Peacock		FOMALHAUT		Alpheratz	
15	23 52	017	25 25	078	36 29	132	13 41	192	44 09	225	62 35	284	18 59	348
16	24 05	016	26 09	078	37 02	132	13 32	192	43 37	225	61 51	283	18 49	347
17	24 16	015	26 53	077	37 36	131	13 23	191	43 05	225	61 06	282	18 38	346
18	24 27	014	27 37	076	38 10	131	13 14	191	42 33	225	60 22	281	18 27	345
19	24 38	013	28 21	075	38 45	131	13 06	190	42 01	225	59 38	281	18 15	344
20	24 47	012	29 05	075	39 19	131	12 58	190	41 29	225	58 53	280	18 02	343
21	24 56	011	29 48	074	39 53	130	12 51	189	40 57	224	58 08	279	17 49	342
22	25 04	010	30 32	073	40 28	130	12 44	189	40 25	224	57 24	278	17 35	341
23	25 11	009	31 15	072	41 03	130	12 37	188	39 54	224	56 39	277	17 20	341
24	25 17	008	31 58	071	41 38	130	12 31	188	39 22	224	55 54	276	17 05	340
25	25 23	007	32 41	071	42 13	129	12 25	187	38 51	224	55 09	276	16 49	339
26	25 27	006	33 23	070	42 48	129	12 20	187	38 20	223	54 24	275	16 32	338
27	25 31	005	34 06	069	43 23	129	12 15	186	37 49	223	53 38	274	16 15	337
28	25 35	004	34 48	068	43 58	129	12 10	186	37 18	223	52 53	273	15 57	336
29	25 37	002	35 30	067	44 33	129	12 06	185	36 47	223	52 08	273	15 39	335
	♦Hamal		RIGEL		SIRIUS		♦CANOPUS		RIGIL KENT.		♦Peacock		FOMALHAUT	
30	25 38	001	36 11	066	25 04	091	45 09	128	12 02	185	36 17	222	51 23	272
31	25 39	000	36 53	065	25 49	090	45 45	128	11 58	184	35 46	222	50 38	271
32	25 39	359	37 34	065	26 34	089	46 20	128	11 55	184	35 16	222	49 52	271
33	25 38	358	38 15	064	27 19	089	46 56	128	11 52	183	34 45	222	49 07	270
34	25 37	357	38 55	063	28 05	088	47 32	128	11 50	183	34 15	221	48 22	269
35	25 34	356	39 35	062	28 50	087	48 08	128	11 48	182	33 46	221	47 36	269
36	25 31	355	40 15	061	29 35	087	48 44	127	11 46	182	33 16	221	46 51	268
37	25 27	354	40 54	060	30 20	086	49 20	127	11 45	181	32 46	221	46 06	267
38	25 22	353	41 33	059	31 05	085	49 56	127	11 44	181	32 17	220	45 21	267
39	25 16	352	42 12	058	31 51	085	50 32	127	11 44	180	31 48	220	44 35	266
40	25 10	351	42 50	057	32 36	084	51 08	127	11 44	180	31 19	220	43 50	266
41	25 03	350	43 27	056	33 21	083	51 44	127	11 44	179	30 50	219	43 05	265
42	24 55	349	44 05	055	34 06	083	52 20	127	11 45	179	30 21	219	42 20	264
43	24 46	348	44 41	054	34 50	082	52 57	127	11 46	178	29 53	219	41 35	264
44	24 36	347	45 18	053	35 35	081	53 33	127	11 48	178	29 24	218	40 50	263
	♦RIGEL		SIRIUS		CANOPUS		♦RIGIL KENT.		Peacock		♦FOMALHAUT		Hamal	
45	45 53	051	36 20	080	54 09	127	11 50	177	28 56	218	40 05	263	24 26	346
46	46 28	050	37 05	080	54 46	127	11 52	177	28 28	218	39 20	262	24 15	345
47	47 03	049	37 49	079	55 22	127	11 55	176	28 01	217	38 35	262	24 03	344
48	47 37	048	38 33	078	55 59	127	11 58	176	27 33	217	37 51	261	23 50	343
49	48 10	047	39 18	077	56 35	127	12 02	175	27 06	217	37 06	260	23 37	342
50	48 43	045	40 02	076	57 11	127	12 06	175	26 39	216	36 21	260	23 23	341
51	49 14	044	40 46	076	57 48	127	12 10	174	26 12	216	35 37	259	23 08	340
52	49 46	043	41 29	075	58 24	127	12 15	174	25 46	216	34 52	259	22 53	340
53	50 16	041	42 13	074	59 00	127	12 20	173	25 19	215	34 08	258	22 37	339
54	50 46	040	42 57	073	59 36	127	12 25	173	24 53	215	33 24	258	22 20	338
55	51 14	039	43 40	072	60 13	127	12 31	172	24 28	215	32 40	257	22 02	337
56	51 42	037	44 23	071	60 49	127	12 38	172	24 02	214	31 55	257	21 44	336
57	52 09	036	45 06	071	61 25	127	12 44	171	23 37	214	31 12	256	21 25	335
58	52 35	034	45 48	070	62 01	128	12 51	171	23 11	213	30 28	255	21 05	334
59	53 00	033	46 31	069	62 36	128	12 59	170	22 47	213	29 44	255	20 45	333
	ALDEBARAN		♦SIRIUS		Suhail		♦RIGIL KENT.		ACHERNAR		♦Diphda		Hamal	
60	31 59	010	47 13	068	35 10	120	13 06	170	61 57	222	42 07	283	20 24	332
61	32 06	009	47 54	067	35 49	120	13 15	169	61 27	223	41 23	283	20 03	331
62	32 13	008	48 36	066	36 28	119	13 23	169	60 56	223	40 39	282	19 41	330
63	32 18	006	49 17	065	37 08	119	13 32	168	60 25	223	39 54	281	19 18	329
64	32 23	005	49 58	064	37 48	118	13 41	168	59 54	224	39 10	280	18 54	329
65	32 26	004	50 38	063	38 27	118	13 51	167	59 23	224	38 25	279	18 31	328
66	32 29	003	51 18	062	39 08	118	14 01	167	58 51	224	37 41	279	18 06	327
67	32 31	002	51 58	060	39 48	117	14 11	167	58 20	224	36 56	278	17 41	326
68	32 32	001	52 37	059	40 28	117	14 22	166	57 48	224	36 11	277	17 15	325
69	32 32	000	53 15	058	41 08	117	14 33	166	57 16	225	35 26	276	16 49	324
70	32 32	358	53 54	057	41 49	116	14 45	165	56 45	225	34 41	276	16 22	323
71	32 30	357	54 31	056	42 30	116	14 56	165	56 13	225	33 56	275	15 55	323
72	32 27	356	55 08	054	43 10	116	15 09	164	55 41	225	33 11	274	15 27	322
73	32 24	355	55 45	053	43 51	115	15 21	164	55 08	225	32 26	274	14 59	321
74	32 19	354	56 21	052	44 32	115	15 34	163	54 36	225	31 40	273	14 30	320
	BETELGEUSE		♦SIRIUS		Suhail		♦RIGIL KENT.		ACHERNAR		♦Diphda		ALDEBARAN	
75	40 02	018	56 56	050	45 14	115	15 47	163	54 04	225	30 55	272	32 14	353
76	40 16	016	57 30	049	45 55	114	16 01	162	53 32	225	30 10	272	32 08	352
77	40 28	015	58 04	047	46 36	114	16 15	162	52 59	226	29 25	271	32 01	351
78	40 39	014	58 37	046	47 18	114	16 29	161	52 27	226	28 39	270	31 53	349
79	40 49	012	59 09	044	47 59	113	16 43	161	51 55	226	27 54	270	31 44	348
80	40 59	011	59 41	043	48 41	113	16 58	161	51 22	226	27 09	269	31 35	347
81	41 07	010	60 11	041	49 23	113	17 13	160	50 50	226	26 23	268	31 24	346
82	41 14	009	60 40	040	50 05	112	17 29	160	50 18	226	25 38	268	31 13	345
83	41 20	007	61 09	038	50 46	112	17 45	159	49 45	226	24 53	267	31 01	344
84	41 25	006	61 36	036	51 29	112	18 01	159	49 13	226	24 08	266	30 48	343
85	41 30	005	62 02	034	52 11	111	18 17	158	48 41	225	23 23	266	30 34	342
86	41 33	003	62 27	032	52 53	111	18 34	158	48 08	225	22 37	265	30 19	341
87	41 35	002	62 51	031	53 35	111	18 51	158	47 36	225	21 52	265	30 04	340
88	41 36	001	63 13	029	54 18	110	19 09	157	47 04	225	21 07	264	29 48	338
89	41 36	359	63 34	027	55 00	110	19 26	157	46 32	225	20 22	263	29 31	337

LAT 41°S

LHA ♈	Hc	Zn	Hc	Zn	Hc	Zn	Hc	Zn	Hc	Zn	Hc	Zn	Hc	Zn
	PROCYON		Alphard		♦Suhail		RIGIL KENT.		♦ACHERNAR		RIGEL		♦BETELGEUSE	
90	38 34	032	34 08	069	55 43	110	19 44	156	46 00	225	55 38	339	41 35	358
91	38 57	031	34 51	069	56 25	110	20 03	156	45 28	225	55 21	338	41 32	357
92	39 20	030	35 33	068	57 08	109	20 21	156	44 56	225	55 03	336	41 29	355
93	39 42	028	36 14	067	57 51	109	20 40	155	44 24	225	54 44	334	41 25	354
94	40 03	027	36 56	066	58 34	109	20 59	155	43 52	225	54 24	333	41 20	353
95	40 23	026	37 37	065	59 17	108	21 19	154	43 20	224	54 03	331	41 13	351
96	40 42	025	38 18	064	60 00	108	21 39	154	42 49	224	53 40	330	41 06	350
97	41 01	023	38 59	063	60 43	108	21 59	154	42 17	224	53 17	328	40 58	349
98	41 18	022	39 39	062	61 26	108	22 19	153	41 46	224	52 52	327	40 48	347
99	41 35	021	40 19	061	62 09	108	22 39	153	41 14	224	52 27	325	40 38	346
100	41 51	020	40 58	060	62 52	107	23 00	152	40 43	224	52 00	324	40 27	345
101	42 05	018	41 38	059	63 35	107	23 21	152	40 12	223	51 33	322	40 14	344
102	42 19	017	42 16	058	64 19	107	23 43	152	39 41	223	51 05	321	40 01	342
103	42 32	016	42 55	057	65 02	107	24 04	151	39 10	223	50 36	319	39 47	341
104	42 43	014	43 33	056	65 45	106	24 26	151	38 39	223	50 06	318	39 32	340
	PROCYON		REGULUS		♦Gienah		RIGIL KENT.		♦ACHERNAR		RIGEL		♦BETELGEUSE	
105	42 54	013	21 36	050	19 46	096	24 48	151	38 08	223	49 35	317	39 16	339
106	43 04	012	22 11	049	20 31	096	25 10	150	37 38	222	49 04	315	38 59	337
107	43 12	010	22 45	048	21 16	095	25 33	150	37 07	222	48 32	314	38 41	336
108	43 20	009	23 18	047	22 01	094	25 56	150	36 37	222	47 59	313	38 22	335
109	43 26	008	23 51	047	22 46	094	26 19	149	36 07	222	47 25	312	38 03	334
110	43 32	006	24 24	046	23 32	093	26 42	149	35 37	221	46 51	311	37 42	333
111	43 36	005	24 56	045	24 17	092	27 05	149	35 07	221	46 17	309	37 21	331
112	43 39	003	25 28	044	25 02	092	27 29	148	34 37	221	45 41	308	36 59	330
113	43 41	002	25 59	043	25 47	091	27 53	148	34 07	221	45 06	307	36 36	329
114	43 42	001	26 29	042	26 33	091	28 17	148	33 38	220	44 29	306	36 12	328
115	43 42	359	26 59	041	27 18	090	28 42	147	33 09	220	43 52	305	35 48	327
116	43 41	358	27 29	040	28 03	089	29 06	147	32 40	220	43 15	304	35 23	326
117	43 39	357	27 58	039	28 49	089	29 31	147	32 11	220	42 37	303	34 57	325
118	43 36	355	28 26	038	29 34	088	29 56	146	31 42	219	41 59	302	34 31	324
119	43 32	354	28 54	037	30 19	087	30 21	146	31 13	219	41 20	301	34 03	323
	REGULUS		♦SPICA		RIGIL KENT.		♦ACHERNAR		RIGEL		BETELGEUSE		♦PROCYON	
120	29 21	036	14 00	093	30 46	146	30 45	219	40 41	300	33 36	321	43 26	352
121	29 47	035	14 45	092	31 12	146	30 17	218	40 02	299	33 07	320	43 20	351
122	30 13	034	15 30	091	31 37	145	29 49	218	39 22	298	32 38	319	43 12	350
123	30 38	033	16 15	091	32 03	145	29 21	218	38 42	297	32 08	318	43 04	348
124	31 02	032	17 01	090	32 29	145	28 54	217	38 01	296	31 38	317	42 54	347
125	31 26	031	17 46	089	32 56	145	28 26	217	37 20	295	31 07	316	42 43	346
126	31 49	030	18 31	089	33 22	144	27 59	217	36 39	294	30 35	315	42 32	344
127	32 11	029	19 17	088	33 48	144	27 32	216	35 58	293	30 03	314	42 19	343
128	32 33	028	20 02	087	34 15	144	27 05	216	35 16	292	29 31	313	42 05	342
129	32 54	027	20 47	087	34 42	144	26 39	216	34 34	292	28 58	313	41 50	340
130	33 14	026	21 32	086	35 09	143	26 12	215	33 52	291	28 24	312	41 35	339
131	33 33	025	22 17	085	35 36	143	25 46	215	33 09	290	27 50	311	41 18	338
132	33 51	023	23 02	085	36 03	143	25 21	215	32 27	289	27 15	310	41 01	337
133	34 09	022	23 47	084	36 31	143	24 55	214	31 44	288	26 40	309	40 42	335
134	34 26	021	24 32	083	36 58	142	24 30	214	31 01	288	26 05	308	40 23	334
	REGULUS		♦SPICA		RIGIL KENT.		♦ACHERNAR		CANOPUS		SIRIUS		♦PROCYON	
135	34 42	020	25 17	083	37 26	142	24 04	214	61 14	233	51 59	300	40 03	333
136	34 57	019	26 02	082	37 54	142	23 40	213	60 38	233	51 19	299	39 42	332
137	35 11	018	26 47	081	38 22	142	23 15	213	60 02	233	50 39	297	39 20	330
138	35 24	017	27 32	080	38 50	142	22 51	212	59 25	233	49 59	296	38 57	329
139	35 37	015	28 16	080	39 18	141	22 26	212	58 49	233	49 18	295	38 34	328
140	35 48	014	29 01	079	39 46	141	22 03	212	58 13	233	48 37	294	38 09	327
141	35 59	013	29 45	078	40 15	141	21 39	211	57 37	233	47 55	293	37 44	326
142	36 09	012	30 29	077	40 43	141	21 16	211	57 00	233	47 14	292	37 18	325
143	36 18	011	31 14	077	41 12	141	20 53	210	56 24	233	46 31	291	36 52	324
144	36 26	009	31 58	076	41 40	141	20 30	210	55 48	233	45 49	290	36 25	322
145	36 33	008	32 41	075	42 09	141	20 07	210	55 11	233	45 07	289	35 57	321
146	36 39	007	33 25	074	42 38	140	19 45	209	54 35	233	44 24	289	35 28	320
147	36 44	006	34 09	074	43 07	140	19 23	209	53 58	233	43 41	288	34 59	319
148	36 48	005	34 52	073	43 36	140	19 02	208	53 22	233	42 58	287	34 29	318
149	36 51	003	35 35	072	44 05	140	18 40	208	52 46	233	42 14	286	33 58	317
	REGULUS		♦SPICA		RIGIL KENT.		♦ACHERNAR		CANOPUS		SIRIUS		♦PROCYON	
150	36 53	002	36 18	071	44 34	140	18 19	207	52 09	233	41 30	285	33 27	316
151	36 54	001	37 01	070	45 03	140	17 59	207	51 33	233	40 47	284	32 56	315
152	36 55	000	37 43	069	45 32	140	17 38	207	50 57	233	40 03	284	32 23	314
153	36 54	358	38 26	069	46 01	140	17 18	206	50 21	233	39 19	283	31 51	313
154	36 52	357	39 08	068	46 31	140	16 58	206	49 45	233	38 34	282	31 17	312
155	36 50	356	39 49	067	47 00	140	16 39	205	49 09	233	37 50	281	30 44	311
156	36 46	355	40 31	066	47 29	140	16 20	205	48 33	233	37 06	280	30 09	310
157	36 41	354	41 12	065	47 58	140	16 01	204	47 57	232	36 21	280	29 34	309
158	36 36	352	41 53	064	48 28	140	15 42	204	47 21	232	35 36	279	28 59	308
159	36 29	351	42 33	063	48 57	140	15 24	203	46 45	232	34 51	278	28 24	307
160	36 22	350	43 14	062	49 26	140	15 07	203	46 09	232	34 07	277	27 47	307
161	36 14	349	43 53	061	49 56	140	14 49	202	45 34	232	33 22	277	27 11	306
162	36 04	348	44 33	060	50 25	140	14 32	202	44 58	232	32 37	276	26 34	305
163	35 54	346	45 12	059	50 54	140	14 15	201	44 23	231	31 52	275	25 56	304
164	35 43	345	45 50	058	51 24	140	13 59	201	43 47	231	31 07	275	25 19	303
	SPICA		♦ANTARES		RIGIL KENT.		ACHERNAR		♦CANOPUS		SIRIUS		♦REGULUS	
165	46 28	057	22 42	106	51 53	140	13 43	201	43 12	231	30 21	274	35 31	344
166	47 06	056	23 26	105	52 22	140	13 27	200	42 37	231	29 36	273	35 18	343
167	47 43	055	24 10	105	52 51	140	13 12	200	42 02	231	28 51	273	35 04	342
168	48 20	053	24 53	104	53 20	140	12 57	199	41 27	230	28 06	272	34 50	341
169	48 56	052	25 37	104	53 49	140	12 42	199	40 52	230	27 20	271	34 34	339
170	49 32	051	26 21	103	54 18	140	12 28	198	40 18	230	26 35	271	34 18	338
171	50 07	050	27 06	103	54 47	141	12 14	198	39 43	230	25 50	270	34 01	337
172	50 41	049	27 50	102	55 15	141	12 00	197	39 09	229	25 05	269	33 43	336
173	51 14	047	28 34	101	55 44	141	11 47	197	38 34	229	24 19	269	33 24	335
174	51 47	046	29 19	101	56 12	141	11 35	196	38 00	229	23 34	268	33 04	334
175	52 20	045	30 03	100	56 41	141	11 22	196	37 26	229	22 49	267	32 44	333
176	52 51	043	30 48	100	57 09	142	11 10	195	36 52	228	22 04	267	32 23	332
177	53 22	042	31 32	099	57 37	142	10 59	195	36 19	228	21 18	266	32 01	331
178	53 52	040	32 17	098	58 05	142	10 48	194	35 45	228	20 33	265	31 38	329
179	54 21	039	33 02	098	58 32	143	10 37	194	35 12	227	19 48	265	31 15	328

TABLE 5.—Precession and Nutation Correction

Values are given as "mi. °" pairs (magnitude in miles, direction in degrees). "0 —" indicates no correction tabulated.

1976

L.H.A. ♈	N. 89°	N. 80°	N. 70°	N. 60°	N. 50°	N. 40°	N. 20°	0°	S. 20°	S. 40°	S. 50°	S. 60°	S. 70°	S. 80°	S. 89°	L.H.A. ♈
0	1 020	1 030	1 050	1 050	1 060	1 060	1 070	1 070	1 060	1 060	1 050	1 040	1 030	1 010	1 350	0
30	1 040	1 060	1 060	1 070	1 070	1 070	1 070	1 070	1 070	1 060	1 050	1 040	0 —	0 —	1 320	30
60	1 070	1 080	1 080	1 080	1 080	1 080	1 080	1 080	1 080	1 080	0 —	0 —	0 —	0 —	1 290	60
90	1 100	1 100	1 100	1 100	1 100	1 100	1 100	1 100	1 100	1 100	0 —	0 —	0 —	0 —	1 260	90
120	1 130	1 120	1 120	1 110	1 110	1 110	1 110	1 110	1 110	1 120	1 130	0 —	0 —	0 —	1 230	120
150	1 160	1 140	1 130	1 120	1 120	1 120	1 110	1 110	1 120	1 120	1 130	1 140	1 150	1 170	1 200	150
180	1 190	1 170	1 150	1 140	1 130	1 120	1 120	1 110	1 110	1 120	1 120	1 130	1 140	1 150	1 170	180
210	1 220	0 —	0 —	1 140	1 130	1 120	1 110	1 110	1 110	1 110	1 110	1 110	1 120	1 130	1 140	210
240	1 250	0 —	0 —	0 —	0 —	1 110	1 100	1 100	1 100	1 100	1 100	1 100	1 100	1 100	1 110	240
270	1 280	0 —	0 —	0 —	0 —	1 080	1 080	1 090	1 090	1 090	1 080	1 080	1 080	1 080	1 080	270
300	1 310	0 —	0 —	0 —	1 050	1 060	1 070	1 070	1 070	1 070	1 070	1 070	1 070	1 060	1 050	300
330	1 350	1 010	1 030	1 040	1 050	1 060	1 070	1 070	1 070	1 060	1 060	1 060	1 050	1 040	1 020	330
360	1 020	1 030	1 050	1 050	1 060	1 060	1 070	1 070	1 060	1 060	1 050	1 040	1 030	1 010	1 350	360

1977

L.H.A. ♈	N. 89°	N. 80°	N. 70°	N. 60°	N. 50°	N. 40°	N. 20°	0°	S. 20°	S. 40°	S. 50°	S. 60°	S. 70°	S. 80°	S. 89°	L.H.A. ♈
0	1 010	1 030	1 040	1 050	2 060	2 060	2 070	2 070	2 070	2 060	1 050	1 050	1 030	1 010	1 350	0
30	1 040	1 050	1 060	2 070	2 070	2 070	2 070	2 070	2 070	1 060	1 050	1 040	1 010	1 340	1 320	30
60	1 070	1 080	2 080	2 080	2 080	2 080	2 080	2 080	2 080	1 070	1 070	0 —	0 —	1 300	1 290	60
90	1 100	1 100	2 100	2 100	2 090	2 090	2 090	2 090	2 100	1 100	1 100	0 —	0 —	1 250	1 260	90
120	1 130	1 120	1 110	2 110	2 110	2 110	2 110	2 110	2 110	1 120	1 130	1 140	1 180	1 210	1 230	120
150	1 160	1 140	1 130	1 120	2 120	2 120	2 110	2 110	2 120	2 120	1 130	1 140	1 150	1 180	1 200	150
180	1 190	1 170	1 150	1 140	1 130	2 120	2 120	2 110	2 110	2 120	2 120	1 130	1 140	1 150	1 170	180
210	1 220	1 200	1 170	1 140	1 130	1 120	2 110	2 110	2 110	2 110	2 110	2 110	1 120	1 130	1 140	210
240	1 250	1 240	0 —	0 —	1 120	1 110	2 100	2 100	2 100	2 100	2 100	2 100	2 100	1 110	1 110	240
270	1 280	1 290	0 —	0 —	1 080	1 080	2 080	2 090	2 090	2 090	2 090	2 090	2 080	1 080	1 080	270
300	1 310	1 330	1 010	1 040	1 050	1 060	2 070	2 070	2 080	2 070	2 070	2 070	1 070	1 060	1 050	300
330	1 340	1 000	1 030	1 040	1 050	2 060	2 070	2 070	2 070	2 060	2 060	2 060	1 050	1 040	1 020	330
360	1 010	1 030	1 040	1 050	2 060	2 060	2 070	2 070	2 070	2 060	1 050	1 050	1 030	1 010	1 350	360

1978

L.H.A. ♈	N. 89°	N. 80°	N. 70°	N. 60°	N. 50°	N. 40°	N. 20°	0°	S. 20°	S. 40°	S. 50°	S. 60°	S. 70°	S. 80°	S. 89°	L.H.A. ♈
0	1 010	1 030	2 040	2 050	2 060	2 060	3 070	3 070	3 070	2 060	2 050	2 050	1 030	1 020	1 350	0
30	1 040	2 050	2 060	2 070	2 070	3 070	3 070	3 070	2 070	2 060	2 050	1 040	1 010	1 350	1 320	30
60	1 070	2 070	2 080	2 080	3 080	3 080	3 080	3 080	2 080	1 070	1 060	1 040	0 —	1 310	1 290	60
90	1 100	2 100	2 100	2 090	3 090	3 090	3 090	3 090	2 090	1 100	1 100	0 —	0 —	1 260	1 260	90
120	1 130	2 120	2 110	2 110	3 110	3 110	3 100	3 110	2 110	2 120	1 130	1 140	1 180	1 210	1 230	120
150	1 160	1 140	2 130	2 120	2 120	3 120	3 110	3 110	3 120	2 120	2 130	1 140	1 160	1 180	1 200	150
180	1 190	1 170	1 150	2 130	2 130	2 120	3 120	3 110	3 110	2 120	2 120	2 130	2 140	1 150	1 170	180
210	1 220	1 200	1 170	1 140	2 130	2 120	2 110	3 110	3 110	3 110	2 110	2 120	2 120	2 130	1 140	210
240	1 250	1 230	0 —	1 140	1 120	1 110	2 100	3 100	3 100	3 100	3 100	2 100	2 100	2 110	1 110	240
270	1 280	1 280	0 —	0 —	1 080	1 080	2 090	3 090	3 090	3 090	3 090	2 090	2 090	2 080	1 080	270
300	1 310	1 330	1 000	1 040	1 060	2 060	2 070	3 080	3 080	3 080	3 070	2 070	2 070	2 060	1 050	300
330	1 340	1 000	1 030	1 040	2 050	2 060	3 070	3 070	3 070	3 070	2 060	2 060	2 050	1 040	1 020	330
360	1 010	1 030	2 040	2 050	2 060	2 060	3 070	3 070	3 070	2 060	2 050	2 050	1 030	1 020	1 350	360

1979

L.H.A. ♈	N. 89°	N. 80°	N. 70°	N. 60°	N. 50°	N. 40°	N. 20°	0°	S. 20°	S. 40°	S. 50°	S. 60°	S. 70°	S. 80°	S. 89°	L.H.A. ♈
0	1 010	2 030	2 040	2 050	3 060	3 060	4 070	4 070	3 070	3 060	3 050	2 050	2 040	2 020	1 000	0
30	2 040	2 050	2 060	3 060	3 070	3 070	4 070	4 070	3 070	2 060	2 050	2 040	1 020	1 350	1 330	30
60	2 070	2 070	2 080	3 080	3 080	4 080	4 080	3 080	3 080	2 070	1 060	1 040	1 350	1 310	1 300	60
90	2 100	2 090	3 090	3 090	3 090	4 090	4 090	3 090	3 090	2 100	1 100	0 —	0 —	1 260	1 260	90
120	2 130	2 120	2 110	3 110	3 110	3 100	4 100	3 100	3 110	2 120	2 130	1 140	1 180	1 210	1 230	120
150	2 150	2 140	2 130	3 120	3 120	3 110	4 110	4 110	3 110	3 120	2 130	2 140	1 160	1 180	1 200	150
180	1 180	2 160	2 150	2 130	3 130	3 120	3 120	4 110	4 110	3 120	3 120	2 130	2 140	2 150	1 170	180
210	1 210	1 190	1 160	2 140	2 130	2 120	3 110	4 110	4 110	3 110	3 110	3 120	2 120	2 130	2 140	210
240	1 250	1 230	1 190	1 140	1 100	4 100	3 090	3 100	4 100	4 100	3 100	3 100	3 090	2 110	2 110	240
270	1 280	1 280	0 —	0 —	1 080	2 090	3 090	3 090	4 090	4 090	3 090	3 090	3 090	2 090	2 080	270
300	1 310	1 330	1 000	1 040	2 060	2 070	3 070	3 080	4 080	3 080	3 070	3 070	2 070	2 060	2 060	300
300	1 340	1 000	1 020	2 040	2 050	3 060	3 070	4 070	4 070	3 070	3 060	3 060	2 050	2 040	2 030	330
360	1 010	2 030	2 040	2 050	3 060	3 060	4 070	4 070	3 070	3 060	3 050	2 050	2 040	2 020	1 000	360

LAT 41°

DECLINATION (15°–29°) CONTRARY NAME TO LATITUDE

15°	16°	17°	18°	19°	20°	21°	22°	23°	24°	25°	26°	27°	28°	29°

N. Lat. {LHA greater than 180° ..... Zn=Z / LHA less than 180° ..... Zn=360–Z}

S. Lat. {LHA greater than 180° ..... Zn=180–Z / LHA less than 180° ..... Zn=180+Z}

LAT 41°

DECLINATION (15°–29°) CONTRARY NAME TO LATITUDE

TABLE 5.—Correction to Tabulated Altitude for Minutes of Declination

d / '	1 2 3	4 5	6	7	8	9 10 11	12	13 14 15	16 17 18	19 20 21	22	23 24 25	26 27 28	29 30	31 32 33	34 35 36	37 38 39	40 41 42	43 44 45	46 47 48	49 50 51	52 53 54	55 56 57	58 59 60	d / '
0																									0
1																									1

APPENDIX Q
NAVIGATIONAL ERRORS

Q1. Introduction.—As commonly practiced, navigation is not an exact science. A number of approximations which would be unacceptable in careful scientific work are used by the navigator, because greater accuracy may not be consistent with the requirements or time available, or because there is no alternative.

Thus, when the navigator uses his latitude graduations as a mile scale, or computes a great-circle course and distance, he neglects the flattening of the earth at the poles, a practice that is not acceptable to the geodetic surveyor. When the navigator plots a visual bearing, or an azimuth line for a celestial line of position, on a Mercator chart, he uses a rhumb line to represent a great circle. When he plots the celestial line of position, he substitutes a rhumb line for a small circle. When he interpolates in sight reduction or lattice tables, he assumes a linear (constant-rate) change between tabulated values. When he measures distance by radar, or depth by echo sounder, he assumes that the radio- or sound-wave has constant speed under all conditions. When he applies dip and refraction corrections to his sextant altitude, he generally assumes standard atmospheric conditions.

These are only a few of the approximations commonly applied by a navigator. There are so many that there is a natural tendency for some of them to cancel others. Thus, under favorable conditions, a position at sea, determined from celestial observation by an experienced observer, should seldom be in error by more than 2 miles. However, if the various small errors in a particular observation all have the same sign (all plus or all minus), the error might be several times this amount, without any mistake having been made by the navigator.

Greater accuracy could be attained, but at a price. The navigator is a practical individual. In the course of ordinary navigation, he would rather spend 10 minutes determining a position having a probable error of plus or minus 2 miles, than to spend several hours learning where he *was* to an accuracy of a few meters. But if he can determine a recent or present position to greater accuracy, the decrease in error is attractive to him. The various navigational aids have been designed with this in mind. Greater accuracy in plotting could be achieved by increasing the scale of the chart or plotting sheet. This has been done for confined waters where a higher degree of accuracy is needed, but a large-scale plotting sheet would be a nuisance at sea. The hand-held marine sextant is not sufficiently accurate for use in determining an astronomical position in a geodetic survey. But it is much more satisfactory at sea than the surveyor's astrolabe or theodolite, which require stable platforms if their potential accuracy is to be realized.

An understanding of the kinds of errors involved in navigation, and of the elementary principles of probability, should be of assistance to a navigator in interpreting his results.

Q2. Definitions.—The following definitions apply to the discussions of this chapter:

Error is the difference between a specific value and the correct or standard value. As used here, it does not include mistakes, but is related to lack of perfection. Thus, an altitude determined by marine sextant is corrected for a standard amount of refraction, but if the actual refraction at the time of observation varies from the standard, the value taken from the table is in error by the difference between standard and actual refraction. This error will be compounded with others in the observed altitude. Similarly, depth determined by echo sounder is in error, among other things, by the difference between the actual speed of sound waves in the water and the speed used for calibration of the instrument. The depth will also be in error if an echo is returned from a phantom bottom instead of from the actual bottom. This appendix is concerned primarily with the deviation from standards. Thus, while variation of the compass is an error when referred to true directions, the difference between the assumed variation and that actually existing is an error with reference to magnetic direction. Corrections can be applied for standard values of error. It is the deviation from standard, as well as mistakes, that produce inaccurate results in navigation. Various kinds of error are discussed in the following articles.

Mistake is a blunder, such as an incorrect reading of an instrument, the taking of a wrong value from a table, or the plotting of a reciprocal bearing. The mistake is discussed in more detail in article Q10.

Standard is something established by custom, agreement, or authority as a basis for comparison. It is customary to use nautical miles for measuring distances between ports. By international agreement the nautical mile is defined as exactly 1852 meters. By authority of various countries which are parties to the agreement, this length is translated to the linear units adopted by that country. It is the fact of establishment or general acceptance that determines whether a given quantity or condition has become a standard of measure or quality. Thus, in 1960, the standard unit of length agreed upon at the Eleventh General (International) Conference on Weights and Measures to redefine the meter was 1,650,763.73 wavelengths of the orange-red radiation in vacuum of krypton 86 corresponding to the unperturbed transition between the $2p_{10}$ and $5d_5$ levels. Where accepted, this established standard of length now serves as a basis for measurement of any physical magnitude, as the length of the meridian, rather than the reverse, which was originally proposed. Multiples and submultiples of a standard are exact. In 1959, the U. S. adopted the exact relationships of 1 yard as equal to 0.9144 meter and 1 inch as equal to 2.54 centimeters. Hence, 39.37 U. S. inches are approximately equal to 1 meter. Because 1 foot equals 12 inches by definition, and the international nautical mile has been defined as 1852 meters, the international nautical mile is equal to 6,076.11549 U. S. feet (approximately). The previous U. S. foot (6,076.10333 . . . feet equals 1 nautical mile) has been redesignated as the U. S. survey foot.

Frequently, a standard is so chosen that it serves as a model which approximates a mean or average condition. However, the distinction between the standard value and the actual value at any time should not be forgotten. Thus, a standard atmosphere has been established in which the temperature, pressure, density, etc., are *precisely* specified for each altitude. Actual conditions, however, are generally different from those defined by the standard atmosphere. Similarly, the values for dip given in the almanacs are considered standard by those who use them, but actual dip may be appreciably different from that tabulated.

Accuracy is the degree of conformance with the correct value, while **precision** is the degree of refinement of a value. Thus, an altitude determined by marine sextant might be stated to the nearest 0.1, and yet be accurate only to the nearest 1' if the horizon is indistinct. Accuracy and precision are further discussed in article 103 of volume II.

Q3. Systematic errors are those which follow some law by which they can be predicted. The accuracy with which a systematic error can be predicted depends upon the accuracy with which the governing law is understood. An error which can be predicted can be eliminated, or compensation can be made for it.

The simplest form of systematic error is one of unchanging magnitude and sign. This is called a **constant error.** Examples are the index error of a marine sextant, watch error, or the error resulting from a lubber's line not being accurately aligned with the longitudinal axis of the craft. In each of these cases, all readings are in error by a constant amount *as long as the adjustment remains unchanged,* and can be removed by applying a correction of equal magnitude and opposite sign. Index error and watch error can be removed by adjustment of the instrument. Lubber's line error can be removed by aligning the lubber's line with the longitudinal axis of the craft.

Another type of systematic error results from a nonstandard rate. If a watch is gaining 4 seconds per day, its readings will be in error by 1 second after an interval of 6 hours, 8 seconds at the end of 2 days, etc. This principle is used in establishing a chronometer rate (art. 1815) for determination of chronometer error between comparisons of the chronometer with time signals. It can be eliminated by adjusting the rate. If a current is running and no allowance for it is made in the dead reckoning, the DR position is in error by an amount proportional to elapsed time. The error introduced by maintaining heading by means of an inaccurate compass is proportional to distance, as is the lateral error in a line of position plotted from an inaccurate bearing.

One of the causes of equation of time (art. 1809) is the fact that the ecliptic, around which annual motion occurs, is not parallel to the celestial equator, around or parallel to which apparent daily motion takes place. The same type systematic error is involved in other measurements. Consider the measurement of bearing with a tilted compass card. Bearing is measured by a system of uniform graduations (degrees) of a circle (such as a compass card) in the horizontal plane. If the card is tilted, and its graduations are projected onto the horizontal plane, the circle becomes an ellipse with the graduations unequally spaced. Along the axis of tilt and a line perpendicular to it, directions are correct. But near the axis of tilt the graduations are too close together, and near the perpendicular they are too widely spaced. The error thus introduced is similar to that which would arise if a watch face were tilted but the motion of the hands remained horizontal. If it were tilted around the "3–9" line, it would appear to run slow near the hour and half hour, and fast near the quarter and three-quarter hours. If the direction to be observed is of an object above or below the horizontal, as the azimuth of a celestial body, measurement is made to the foot of the perpendicular through the object. The sight vanes of a compass move in a plane perpendicular to the compass card. Hence, if the card is tilted, measurement is made to the foot of a perpendicular to the card, rather than to the foot of a perpendicular to the horizontal, introducing an error which increases with the angle of tilt and also with the angle of elevation (or depression) of the object. This error is greatest along the axis of tilt, and zero along the perpendicular to it. Both of these tilt errors can be corrected by leveling the compass card.

A different type of tilt error occurs when a reflection takes place from a tilted surface, such as the ionosphere, the error being proportional to the angle of tilt. In some respects, this error is similar to coastal refraction of a radio wave.

Additional examples of systematic error are uncorrected deviation of the compass, error due to a position in a pattern of hyperbolas, error due to incorrect location of a Loran transmitter, uncorrected parallax, and uncorrected personal error.

Q4. Random errors are chance errors, unpredictable in magnitude or sign. They are governed by the laws of probability. If the altitude of a celestial body is observed, the reading may be (1) too great, (2) correct, or (3) too small. If a number of observations are made, and there is no systematic error, the probability of a positive error is

Error	No. of obs.	Percent of obs.
−10′	0	0. 0
− 9′	1	0. 2
− 8′	2	0. 4
− 7′	4	0. 8
− 6′	9	1. 8
− 5′	17	3. 4
− 4′	28	5. 6
− 3′	40	8. 0
− 2′	53	10. 6
− 1′	63	12. 6
0	66	13. 2
+ 1′	63	12. 6
+ 2′	53	10. 6
+ 3′	40	8. 0
+ 4′	28	5. 6
+ 5′	17	3. 4
+ 6′	9	1. 8
+ 7′	4	0. 8
+ 8′	2	0. 4
+ 9′	1	0. 2
+10′	0	0. 0
0	500	100. 0

TABLE Q4.—Normal distribution of random errors.

exactly equal to the probability of a negative error. This does not mean that every second observation having an error will be too great. However, the greater the number of observations, the greater is the probability that the percentage of positive errors will equal the percentage of negative ones, and that their magnitudes will correspond.

Suppose that 500 observations are made, with the results shown in table Q4. A close approximation of the plot of these errors is shown in figure Q4a. The plot has been modified slightly to constitute the **normal curve** of random errors, which is the same as the actual curve except that the normal curve *approaches* zero as the error increases, while the actual curve *reaches* zero at (+)10′ and (−)10′. The height of the curve at any point represents the percentage of observations that can be expected to have the error indicated at that point. The probability of any similar observation having any given error is the proportion of the number of observations having this error to the total number of observations, or the percentage expressed as a decimal. Thus, the probability of an observation having an error of (−)3′ is $\frac{40}{500} = \frac{1}{12.5} = 0.08$ (8%).

If the area under the curve represents 100 percent of the observations, half the area (the shaded portion of figure Q4a) represents 50 percent of the observations. The value of the error at the limits of this shaded portion is often called the "50 percent error," or **probable error,** meaning that 50 percent of the observations can be expected to have less error, and 50 percent greater error. Similarly, the limits which contain the central 95 percent of the area denote the 95 percent error. The percentage of error is found mathematically. For a normal curve, each error is squared, the sum of the squares is divided by one less than the number of observations, and the square root of the quotient is determined. This value is called the **standard deviation** or **standard error** (σ, the Greek letter sigma). In the illustration, the standard deviation is the square root of $0 \times (-)10^2 + 1 \times (-)9^2 + 2 \times (-)8^2 + 4 \times (-)7^2 + 9 \times (-)6^2$, etc., divided by 499 or $\sqrt{\frac{4474}{499}} = \sqrt{8.966} = 2.99$ (about 3). The standard deviation is the 68.27 percent error. The probability of the occurrence of an error of or less than a specific magnitude may be approximately determined by the following relationship (with the answers for the illustration given):

$$50\% \text{ error} = \tfrac{2}{3} \times \sigma = 2' \text{ (approx.)}$$
$$68\% \text{ error} = 1 \times \sigma = 3' \text{ (approx.)}$$
$$95\% \text{ error} = 2 \times \sigma = 6' \text{ (approx.)}$$
$$99\% \text{ error} = 2\tfrac{2}{3} \times \sigma = 8' \text{ (approx.)}$$
$$99.9\% \text{ error} = 3\tfrac{1}{3} \times \sigma = 10' \text{ (approx.)}$$

Many of the errors of navigation do not follow the normal distribution discussed above. Pub. No. 229 values of altitude can be taken only to the nearest 0.'1. The error in tabular altitude might have any value from (+) 0.'05 to (−) 0.'05, and any value within these limits is as likely to occur as any other of the same precision. The same is true of a sextant that cannot be read more precisely than 0.'1, and of a time-difference that cannot be measured more precisely than 1 μs. These values refer to the single errors indicated, and not to the total error that might be involved. This is a **rectangular error,** so called because of the shape of its plot, as shown in figure Q4b. The 100 percent error is half the difference between readings. The 50 percent error is half this amount, the 95 percent error is 0.95 times this amount, etc. In some cases it may be more meaningful to refer to the rectangular error as the **resolution error.**

Still another type random error is encountered in navigation. If a compass is fluctuating periodically due to yaw of a ship, its motion slows as the end of a swing is approached, when the error approaches maximum value. If readings were taken continuously or at equal intervals of time, the interval being a small percentage of the total period of oscillation, the curve of errors would have a characteristic U-shape, as shown in figure Q4c. The same type error is involved in measurement of altitude of a celestial body from a wing of the bridge of a heavily rolling vessel, when the roll causes large changes in the height of eye. This type of error is called a **periodic error.** The effect is accentuated by the tendency of the observer to make readings near one of the extreme values because the instrument appears steadiest at this time. If it is impractical to make a reading at the center of the period, the error can be eliminated or reduced by averaging readings taken continuously or at short intervals, as indicated above. This is the method used in averaging type artificial-horizon sextants. Generally, better results can be obtained by taking maximum positive and maximum negative readings, and averaging the results.

The curve of any type of random error is symmetrical about the line representing zero error. This means that in the ideal plot every point on one side of the curve is exactly matched by one on the other side, or for every positive error there is a negative error of the same magnitude. The average of all readings, considering signs, is zero. The larger the number of readings, the greater the probability of the errors fitting the ideal curve. Another way of stating this is that as the number of readings increases, the error of the average can be expected to decrease.

Q5. Combinations of errors.—Many of the results obtained in navigation are subject to more than one error. Chapter XVI lists 19 errors applicable to sextant altitudes. Some of these have several components. A number of possible errors are involved in the determination of computed altitude and azimuth. A rectangular error is possible in finding the altitude difference. Several additional errors may affect the accuracy of plotting. Thus, the line of position as finally plotted may include 30 errors or more. Corrections are applied for some of the larger ones, so that in each of these cases the applicable error is the difference between the applied correction and the actual error. Thus, a dip correction may be applied for a height of eye of 30 feet, while the actual height at the moment of observation may be 31 feet 6 inches. Even if the

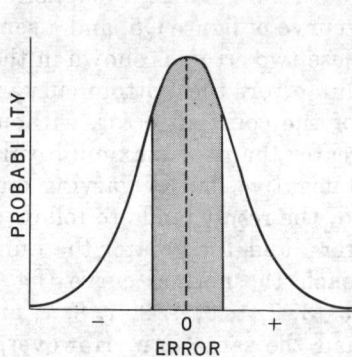

FIGURE Q4a.—Normal curve of random error with 50 percent of area shaded. Limits of shaded area indicate probable error.

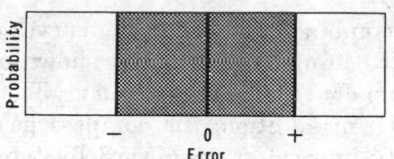

FIGURE Q4b.—Rectangular error, with 50 percent area shaded.

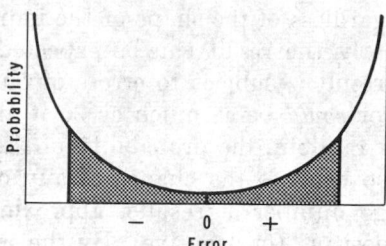

FIGURE Q4c.—Periodic error, with 50 percent area shaded.

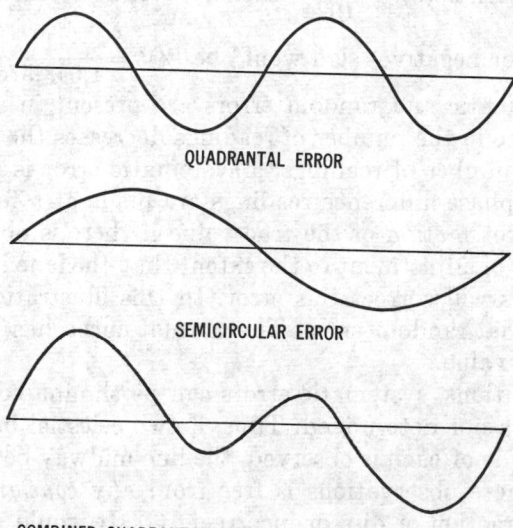

QUADRANTAL ERROR

SEMICIRCULAR ERROR

COMBINED QUADRANTAL ERROR AND SEMICIRCULAR ERROR

FIGURE Q5.—Combining systematic errors.

height of eye is exactly 30 feet, a rectangular error may be involved in taking the dip correction from the table.

Corrections which might be random as far as an individual observation is concerned may be systematic for a series of observations. Thus, if the average or standard conditions upon which a correction is based do not exist at the time of observation the value at any given time is as likely to be greater as it is to be less than the standard amount. But if a number of observations are taken in quick succession, the error will be about the same for each.

If two or more errors are applicable to a given result, the total error is equal to the algebraic sums of all errors. Thus, if a given number is subject to errors of (+) 4, (−) 2, (−) 1, (+) 3, (+) 2, 0, and (−) 2, the total error is (+) 4. Systematic errors can be combined by adding the curves of individual errors. Thus, a magnetic compass may have a quadrantal error as shown by the top curve of figure Q5, and a semicircular error as shown by the second curve. The sum of these two errors is shown in the bottom curve. If, in addition, the compass has a constant error, the bottom curve is moved vertically upward or downward by the amount of the constant error, without undergoing a change of form. If the constant error is greater than the maximum value of the combined curves, all errors are positive or all are negative, but of varying magnitude.

If a number of random errors are combined, the result tends to follow a normal curve regardless of the shape of the individual errors, and the greater the number, the more nearly the result can be expected to approach the normal curve (fig. Q4a). If a given result is subject to errors of plus or minus 3, 2, 1, 2, 4, 2, 1, 8, 1, and 2, the total error *could* be as much as 26 if all errors had the same sign. However, if these are truly random, the probability of them all having the same sign is only 1 in 1024. This is so because the chance of any one being positive (or negative) is ½. That is, of a large number of results, approximately half will have any one particular correction positive (or negative). By the same reasoning, approximately half of the positive (or negative) results will have any one particular additional correction positive (or negative). Thus, the probability of any two particular corrections having a positive (or negative) sign is $\frac{1}{2} \times \frac{1}{2} = (\frac{1}{2})^2 = \frac{1}{4}$. The probability of all 10 corrections having a positive (or negative) sign is $(\frac{1}{2})^{10} = \frac{1}{1024}$. If there were 20 corrections, the probability of all having a positive (or negative) sign would be $(\frac{1}{2})^{20} = \frac{1}{1,048,576}$.

When both systematic and random errors are present in a process, both effects are present. An increase in the number of readings decreases the residual random error, but regardless of the number of readings, a systematic error is present in its entirety. Thus, if a number of phase-difference readings are made at a fixed point, the average should be a good approximation of the true value if there is no systematic error. But if the equipment is out of adjustment to the extent that the lane is incorrectly identified, no number of readings will correct this error. In this illustration, a constant error is combined with a normal random error. The normal curve has the correct shape, but is offset from the zero value.

Under some conditions, systematic errors can be eliminated from the results even when the magnitude is not determined. Thus, if two celestial bodies differ in azimuth by 180°, and the altitude of each is observed, the line midway between the lines of position resulting from these observations is free from any *constant* error in the *altitude* (such as abnormal refraction or dip, or incorrect IC). It would *not* be free from such a constant error as one in time (unless the bodies were on the celestial meridian). Similarly, a fix obtained by observations of three stars differing in azimuth by 120°, or four stars differing by 90° is free from constant error in the altitude, if the center of the figure made by the lines of position is used. The center of the figure formed by circles of position from distances of objects equally spaced in azimuth is free from a constant error in range. A constant error in bearing lines does not introduce an error in the fix if the objects are equally spaced in azimuth. In all of these examples, the correct position is *outside* the figure formed by the lines of position if all objects observed are on the same side of the observer (that is, if they lie within an arc of less than 180°).

Q6. Navigation accuracy is normally expressed in terms of the probability of being within a specified distance of a desired point during the navigation process.

If the accuracy of only a single line of position is being considered, the specified distance may be stated as the standard deviation (art. Q4) or some multiple thereof, assuming that the errors of the line of position follow a **single-axis normal distribution**.

The distance as stated for the standard deviation of a line of position is measured from the arithmetic mean of the positions which could be established from a large number of observations at a given place and time. Therefore, this distance does not indicate the separation between the line of position and the observer's actual position, except by chance. If the error is stated as 1σ, 68.27 percent of the cases should result in line of position displacements from the arithmetic mean in any direction not exceeding the distance specified for 1σ. If the error is stated as 2σ, 95.45 percent of the lines of position should not be displaced from the arithmetic mean in any direction by more than the distance specified for 2σ. If the error is stated as the **probable error,** 50 percent of the lines of position should not be displaced from the arithmetic mean in any direction by more than the distance specified for 0.6745σ.

The standard deviation is also employed in developing expressions for the probability of a fix position being within a specified distance of the mean of the positions which could be established from a large number of observations at a given place and time by means of the system used to establish the fix.

In the following discussion, the fix is established by the intersection of two lines of position, each of which may be in error. The lines of position (fig. Q6a) are range measurements from two points at the extremities of a baseline of known length. Because of inaccuracies in measurement, the actual ranges differ from the measured values and may lie somewhere between the limits shown as additional arcs either side of the measured arc.

The intersection of the two lines of position together with the standard deviations associated with each are drawn to an expanded scale in figure Q6b. It can be shown that the *contours of equal probability density* about such an intersection are ellipses with their center at the intersection. Thus, the ellipse shown in figure Q6b might be the 75 percent probability ellipse, meaning that there are three chances in four that a fix will lie within such ellipse centered upon the mean of the positions which would be established from a

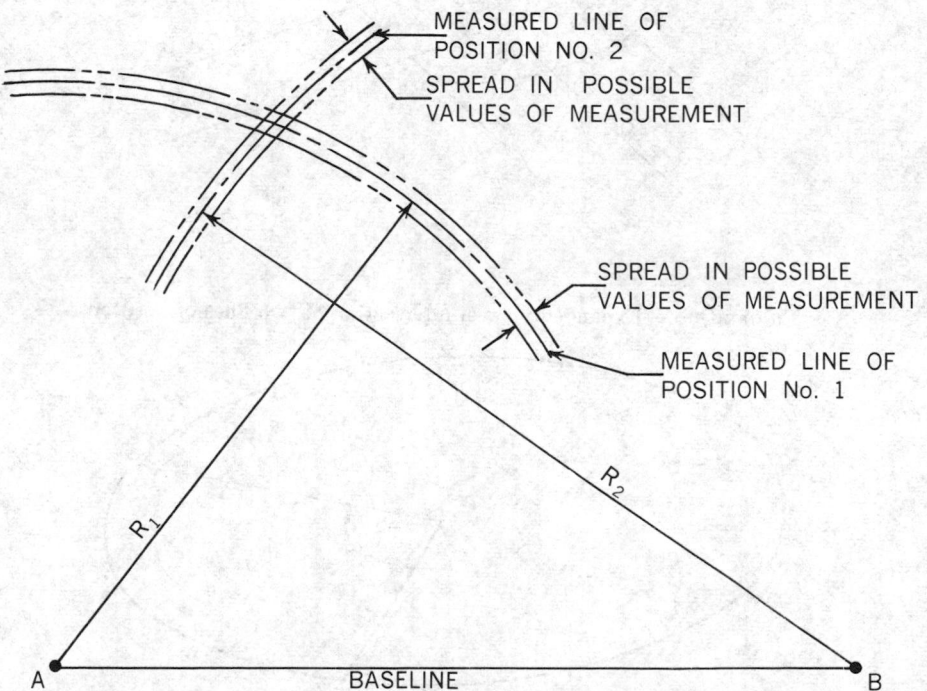

MEASURED LINE OF
POSITION NO. 2

SPREAD IN POSSIBLE
VALUES OF MEASUREMENT

SPREAD IN POSSIBLE
VALUES OF MEASUREMENT

MEASURED LINE OF
POSITION No. 1

R_1

R_2

A   BASELINE   B

FIGURE Q6a.—Fix established at intersection of two lines of position having different values of error.

large number of observations at a given place and time by means of the system used to establish the fix.

For simplicity in this discussion of navigation accuracy, the following assumptions are made:

1. All constant errors or **bias errors** have been removed, leaving only the random errors. Thus, the mean or average error is assumed to be zero.

2. These random errors are assumed to be normally distributed.

3. The errors associated with the two intersecting lines of position are assumed to be independent. This assumption implies that a change in the error of one line of position has no effect upon the other.

4. The lines of position are assumed to be straight lines in the small area in the immediate vicinity of their intersection. This assumption is valid so long as the standard deviation is small compared to the radius of curvature of the line of position.

5. Errors of position are limited to the two-dimensional case.

As shown in figure Q6b, the general case of the intersection of two lines of position at any angle of cut and with different values of error associated with each line of position results in an elliptical error figure. Figure Q6c shows the ellipse simplified to geometrical terms.

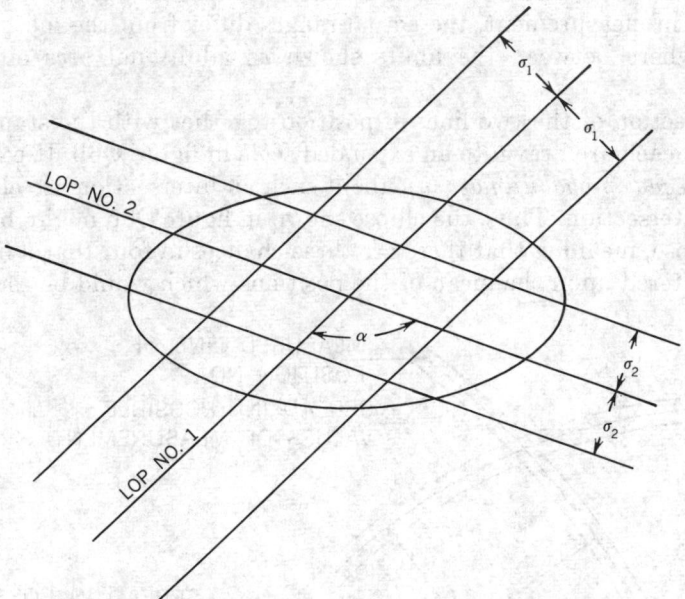

FIGURE Q6b.—Expanded view of intersection of two lines of position.

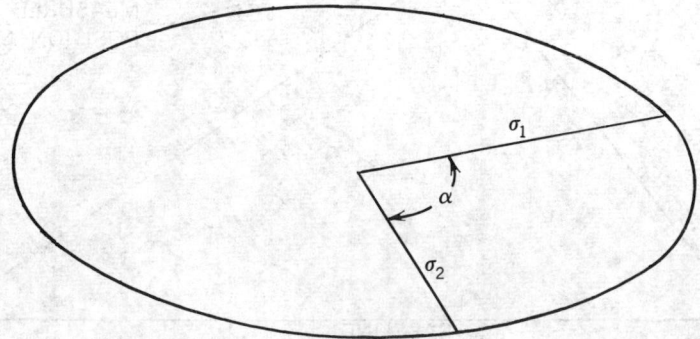

FIGURE Q6c.—Basic error ellipse.

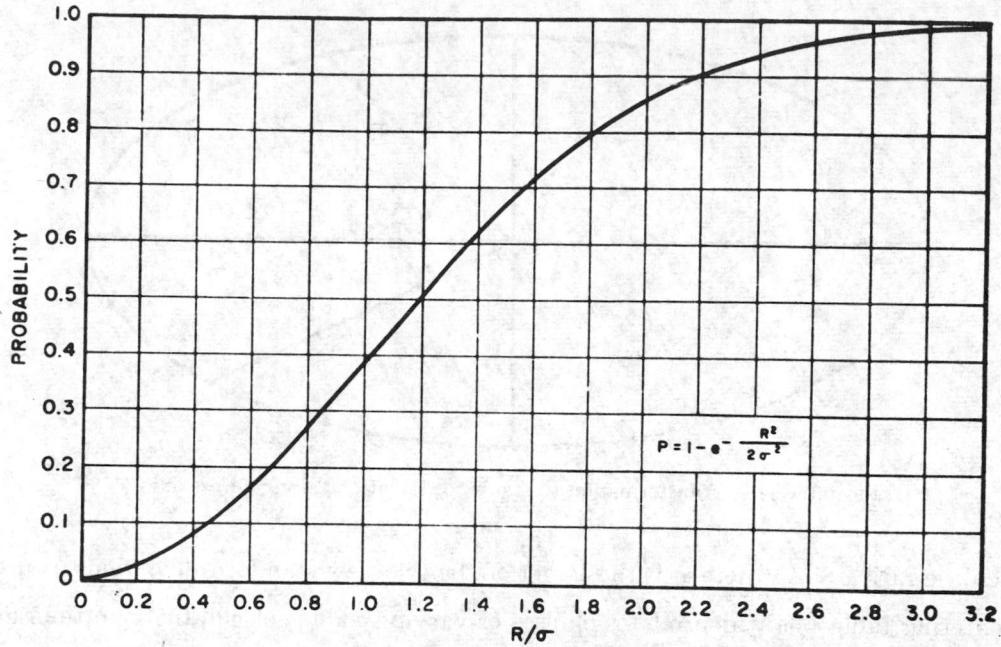

FIGURE Q6d.—Circular normal distribution.

One may readily surmise from figure Q6c that the exact shape of the error figure varies with the magnitudes of the two one-dimensional input errors, σ_1 and σ_2 as well as with the angle of cut, α. The angle α is also the angle between the two values of sigma because the standard deviations are mutually perpendicular to their corresponding lines of position. These variations can be calculated to provide the probability that a point is located within a circle of stated radius. *When this is done, the error is stated in terms more meaningful to the practicing navigator.* The basis of this concept may best be seen by first considering the special case when the two errors are equal, and the angle of intersection of the lines of position is a right angle. In this case, *and in this case alone,* the error figure becomes a circle and is described by the circular normal distribution. A plot of this special function is given in figure Q6d. In this plot, the horizontal axis is measured in terms of R/σ, R being the stated radius of the circle and σ being the measure of error. The error measure is given simply as σ, for in this circular case $\sigma_1 = \sigma_2$. To illustrate, a measurement system gives a circular error figure and has a value of $\sigma = 100$ meters; the probability of actually being located within a circle of 100 meters radius when $R/\sigma = 1.0$ may be read from the vertical axis to be 39.3 percent. To obtain the radius of a circle within which a 50 percent probability results, the corresponding value of R/σ is seen to be 1.18 from the graph. Thus, for this example, the **circular probable error** (**CPE** or **CEP**) would be 118 meters.

In one method of using error ellipses to obtain the radii of **circles of equivalent probability,** new values of σ are found along the major and minor axes of the ellipse (fig. Q6e) using the following equations:

$$\sigma_x^2 = \frac{1}{2 \sin^2 \alpha} \left[\sigma_1^2 + \sigma_2^2 + \sqrt{(\sigma_1^2 + \sigma_2^2)^2 - 4 \sin^2 \alpha \, \sigma_1^2 \sigma_2^2} \right]$$

$$\sigma_y^2 = \frac{1}{2 \sin^2 \alpha} \left[\sigma_1^2 + \sigma_2^2 - \sqrt{(\sigma_1^2 + \sigma_2^2)^2 - 4 \sin^2 \alpha \, \sigma_1^2 \sigma_2^2} \right].$$

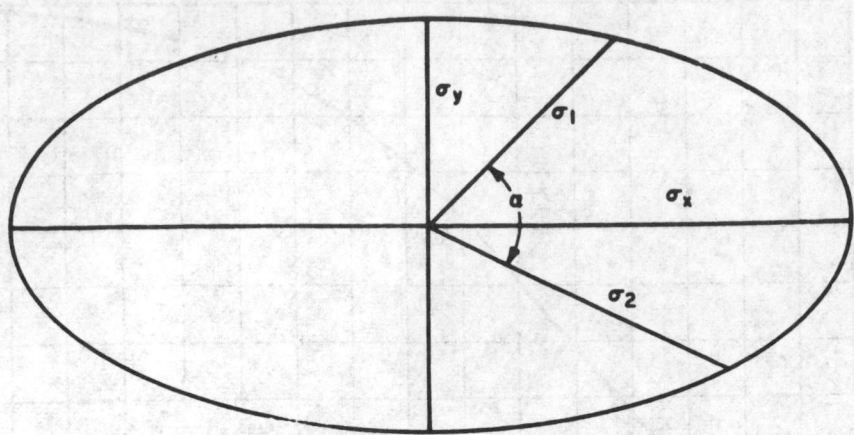

FIGURE Q6e.—Transformation to standard deviations along ellipse axes.

Then the ratio $c=\dfrac{\sigma_y}{\sigma_x}$, where σ_x is the larger of the two new standard deviations, is used in entering table Q6a which relates ellipses of varying values of ellipticity to the radii of circles of equivalent probability.

For a numerical example to illustrate the method of calculation, assume that the angle of cut α is 50°, σ_1 is 15 meters, and σ_2 is 20 meters to determine the probability of location within a circle of 30 meters radius.

For the computation the following numbers are needed:

$$\sigma_1{}^2 = 225$$

$$\sigma_2{}^2 = 400$$

$$\sin^2 \alpha = 0.5868.$$

Substituting in the equations for $\sigma_x{}^2$ and $\sigma_y{}^2$, σ_x and σ_y are calculated as 29.9 meters and 13.1 meters, respectively. Since the function K multiplied by the larger of the two standard deviations obtained by the transformation method gives the value of the radius of the circle of the corresponding value of probability shown in table Q6a, $K = 1.003$. On entering table Q6a with $K = 1.0$ and $c = 0.44$, the probability is found to be 62 percent.

Table Q6b and figure Q6f provide ready information about the sizes of circles of specific probability value associated with ellipses of varying eccentricities.

In another method, fictitious values of sigma of identical value, indicated by σ^*, are assumed to replace the two unequal values originally given (σ_1 and σ_2). A fictitious angle of cut α^* is also assumed to replace the angle of cut (α) originally given (fig. Q6g).

The method utilizes a set of probability curves, with a separate curve for each value of angle of cut (fig. Q6h). These curves can be used only when the two error measures are equal, hence the need for making the transformation to the fictitious σ^*.

The values of σ^* and α^* needed to utilize the probability curves may either be determined from figures Q6i and Q6j or by means of the following equations:

$$\sigma^* = \frac{\sin \beta \sqrt{\sigma_1{}^2 + \sigma_2{}^2}}{\sqrt{2}}$$

$$\alpha^* = \text{arc } \sin (\sin 2\beta \sin \alpha)$$

K \ c	0.0	0.1	0.2	0.3	0.4	0.5	0.6	0.7	0.8	0.9	1.0
0.1	.0796557	.0443987	.0242119	.0164176	.0123875	.0099377	.0082940	.0071157	.0062299	.0055400	.0049875
0.2	.1585194	.1339783	.0884533	.0628396	.0482413	.0390193	.0327123	.0281415	.0246824	.0219757	.0198013
0.3	.2358228	.2213804	.1739300	.1318281	.1039193	.0851535	.0719102	.0621386	.0546598	.0487639	.0440025
0.4	.3108435	.3010228	.2635181	.2139084	.1742045	.1451808	.1237982	.1076237	.0950495	.0850326	.0768837
0.5	.3829249	.3755884	.3481790	.3003001	.2532953	.2152886	.1857448	.1626829	.1443941	.1296286	.1175031
0.6	.4514938	.4457708	.4255605	.3846374	.3357384	.2914682	.2548177	.2251114	.2009797	.1811783	.1647298
0.7	.5160727	.5115048	.4960683	.4633258	.4170862	.3699305	.3280302	.2925654	.2629373	.2381583	.2172955
0.8	.5762892	.5725957	.5604457	.5349387	.4941882	.4474207	.4025628	.3627122	.3283453	.2989700	.2738510
0.9	.6318797	.6288721	.6191354	.5993140	.5651564	.5213998	.4759375	.4333628	.3953279	.3620135	.3330232
1.0	.6826895	.6802325	.6723586	.6568242	.6291249	.5900953	.5461319	.5025790	.4621421	.4257553	.3934693
1.1	.7286679	.7266597	.7202682	.7079681	.6859367	.6524489	.6116316	.5687467	.5272462	.4887873	.4539256
1.2	.7698607	.7682215	.7630305	.7532175	.7359558	.7079973	.6714269	.6306168	.5893494	.5498736	.5132477
1.3	.8063990	.8050648	.8008554	.7929968	.7793550	.7567265	.7249673	.6873122	.6474394	.6079822	.5704426
1.4	.8384867	.8374049	.8340018	.8277048	.8169851	.7989288	.7720889	.7383089	.7007900	.6623035	.6216889
1.5	.8663856	.8655127	.8627728	.8577362	.8493071	.8350816	.8129287	.7833962	.7489500	.7122546	.6753475
1.6	.8904014	.8897008	.8875060	.8834914	.8768644	.8657559	.8478393	.8226246	.7917194	.7574708	.7219627
1.7	.9108691	.9103102	.9085619	.9053766	.9001746	.8915536	.8773116	.8562471	.8291137	.7977882	.7462539
1.8	.9281394	.9276964	.9263125	.9237989	.9197275	.9130680	.9019110	.8846624	.8613238	.8332175	.8021013
1.9	.9425669	.9422182	.9411299	.9391586	.9359855	.9308615	.9222277	.9083609	.8886731	.8639149	.8355255
2.0	.9544997	.9542272	.9533775	.9518415	.9493815	.9454546	.9388448	.9278799	.9115762	.8901495	.8646647
2.1	.9642712	.9640598	.9634011	.9622127	.9603170	.9573205	.9522999	.9437668	.9305013	.9122714	.8897495
2.2	.9721931	.9720304	.9715237	.9706109	.9691597	.9668845	.9631017	.9565522	.9459386	.9306821	.9110784
2.3	.9785518	.9784275	.9780408	.9773450	.9762419	.9745239	.9716934	.9667306	.9583739	.9458085	.9289946
2.4	.9836049	.9835108	.9832180	.9826918	.9818594	.9805703	.9784661	.9747495	.9682698	.9580804	.9438652
2.5	.9875807	.9875100	.9872900	.9868953	.9862720	.9853112	.9837569	.9810035	.9760522	.9679136	.9560631
2.6	.9906776	.9906249	.9904612	.9901674	.9897045	.9889934	.9878527	.9858331	.9821023	.9756969	.9659525
2.7	.9930661	.9930271	.9929062	.9926894	.9923483	.9918260	.9909944	.9895268	.9867530	.9817837	.9738786
2.8	.9948897	.9948612	.9947727	.9946141	.9943649	.9939842	.9933821	.9923249	.9902888	.9864876	.9801589
2.9	.9962684	.9962477	.9961834	.9960684	.9958878	.9956126	.9951798	.9944246	.9929482	.9900803	.9850792
3.0	.9973002	.9972853	.9972391	.9971564	.9970266	.9968294	.9965205	.9959854	.9949274	.9927925	.9888910
3.1	.9980648	.9980542	.9980212	.9979622	.9978699	.9977296	.9975109	.9971348	.9963851	.9948168	.9918113
3.2	.9986257	.9986182	.9985949	.9985533	.9984880	.9983892	.9982356	.9979733	.9974478	.9963105	.9940240
3.3	.9990332	.9990279	.9990116	.9989824	.9989368	.9988677	.9987607	.9985792	.9982147	.9974004	.9956822
3.4	.9993261	.9993225	.9993112	.9992909	.9992593	.9992115	.9991376	.9990129	.9987626	.9981868	.9969113
3.5	.9995347	.9995323	.9995245	.9995105	.9994888	.9994559	.9994053	.9993204	.9991502	.9987480	.9978125
3.6	.9996818	.9996801	.9996748	.9996653	.9996505	.9996281	.9995938	.9995364	.9994218	.9991442	.9984662
3.7	.9997844	.9997832	.9997797	.9997733	.9997633	.9997482	.9997251	.9996867	.9996102	.9994208	.9989352
3.8	.9998553	.9998545	.9998522	.9998478	.9998412	.9998311	.9998157	.9997902	.9997396	.9996119	.9992682
3.9	.9999038	.9999033	.9999018	.9998989	.9998945	.9998878	.9998776	.9998608	.9998276	.9997426	.9995020
4.0	.9999367	.9999363	.9999353	.9999334	.9999305	.9999261	.9999195	.9999085	.9998870	.9998309	.9996645
4.1	.9999587	.9999585	.9999578	.9999566	.9999547	.9999519	.9999475	.9999404	.9999266	.9998900	.9997763
4.2	.9999733	.9999732	.9999727	.9999720	.9999707	.9999689	.9999661	.9999616	.9999527	.9999292	.9998523
4.3	.9999829	.9999828	.9999825	.9999821	.9999813	.9999801	.9999783	.9999754	.9999698	.9999548	.9999034
4.4	.9999892	.9999891	.9999889	.9999886	.9999881	.9999874	.9999863	.9999845	.9999809	.9999715	.9999375
4.5	.9999932	.9999932	.9999931	.9999929	.9999925	.9999921	.9999914	.9999902	.9999881	.9999822	.9999599
4.6	.9999958	.9999957	.9999957	.9999955	.9999954	.9999951	.9999947	.9999939	.9999926	.9999889	.9999746
4.7	.9999974	.9999974	.9999973	.9999973	.9999971	.9999970	.9999967	.9999963	.9999955	.9999932	.9999840
4.8	.9999984	.9999984	.9999984	.9999983	.9999983	.9999982	.9999980	.9999977	.9999972	.9999959	.9999901
4.9	.9999990	.9999990	.9999990	.9999990	.9999990	.9999989	.9999988	.9999986	.9999983	.9999975	.9999939
5.0	.9999994	.9999994	.9999994	.9999994	.9999994	.9999993	.9999993	.9999992	.9999990	.9999985	.9999963
5.1	.9999997	.9999997	.9999997	.9999996	.9999996	.9999996	.9999996	.9999995	.9999994	.9999991	.9999978
5.2	.9999998	.9999998	.9999998	.9999998	.9999998	.9999998	.9999998	.9999997	.9999997	.9999995	.9999987
5.3	.9999999	.9999999	.9999999	.9999999	.9999999	.9999999	.9999999	.9999999	.9999998	.9999997	.9999992
5.4	.9999999	.9999999	.9999999	.9999999	.9999999	.9999999	.9999999	.9999999	.9999999	.9999998	.9999995
5.5	1.0000000	1.0000000	1.0000000	1.0000000	1.0000000	1.0000000	1.0000000	.9999999	.9999999	.9999999	.9999997
5.6								1.0000000	1.0000000		.9999998
5.7										1.0000000	.9999999
5.8											1.0000000
5.9											
6.0											

TABLE Q6a.—Circular error probabilities. Argument c is the ratio of the smaller standard deviation to the larger standard deviation. For the arguments c and K, the table provides the probability that a point lies within a circle whose center is at the origin and whose radius is K times the larger standard deviation.

P \ c	0.0	0.1	0.2	0.3	0.4	0.5	0.6	0.7	0.8	0.9	1.0
.5000	0.67449	0.68199	0.70585	0.74993	0.80785	0.87042	0.93365	0.99621	1.05769	1.11807	1.17741
.7500	1.15035	1.15473	1.16825	1.19246	1.23100	1.28534	1.35143	1.42471	1.50231	1.58271	1.66511
.9000	1.64485	1.64791	1.65731	1.67383	1.69918	1.73708	1.79152	1.86253	1.94761	2.04236	2.14597
.9500	1.95996	1.96253	1.97041	1.98420	2.00514	2.03586	2.08130	2.14598	2.23029	2.33180	2.44775
.9750	2.24140	2.24365	2.25053	2.26255	2.28073	2.30707	2.34581	2.40356	2.48494	2.58999	2.71620
.9900	2.57583	2.57778	2.58377	2.59421	2.60995	2.63257	2.66533	2.71515	2.79069	2.89743	3.03485
.9950	2.80703	2.80883	2.81432	2.83289	2.83830	2.85894	2.88859	2.93347	3.00431	3.11073	3.25525
.9975	3.02334	2.02500	3.03010	3.03898	3.05234	3.07144	3.09871	3.13969	3.20586	3.31099	3.46164
.9990	3.29053	3.29206	3.29673	3.30489	3.31715	3.33464	3.35949	3.39647	3.45698	3.55939	3.71692

TABLE Q6b.—Factors for conversion of probability ellipse to circle of equivalent probability.

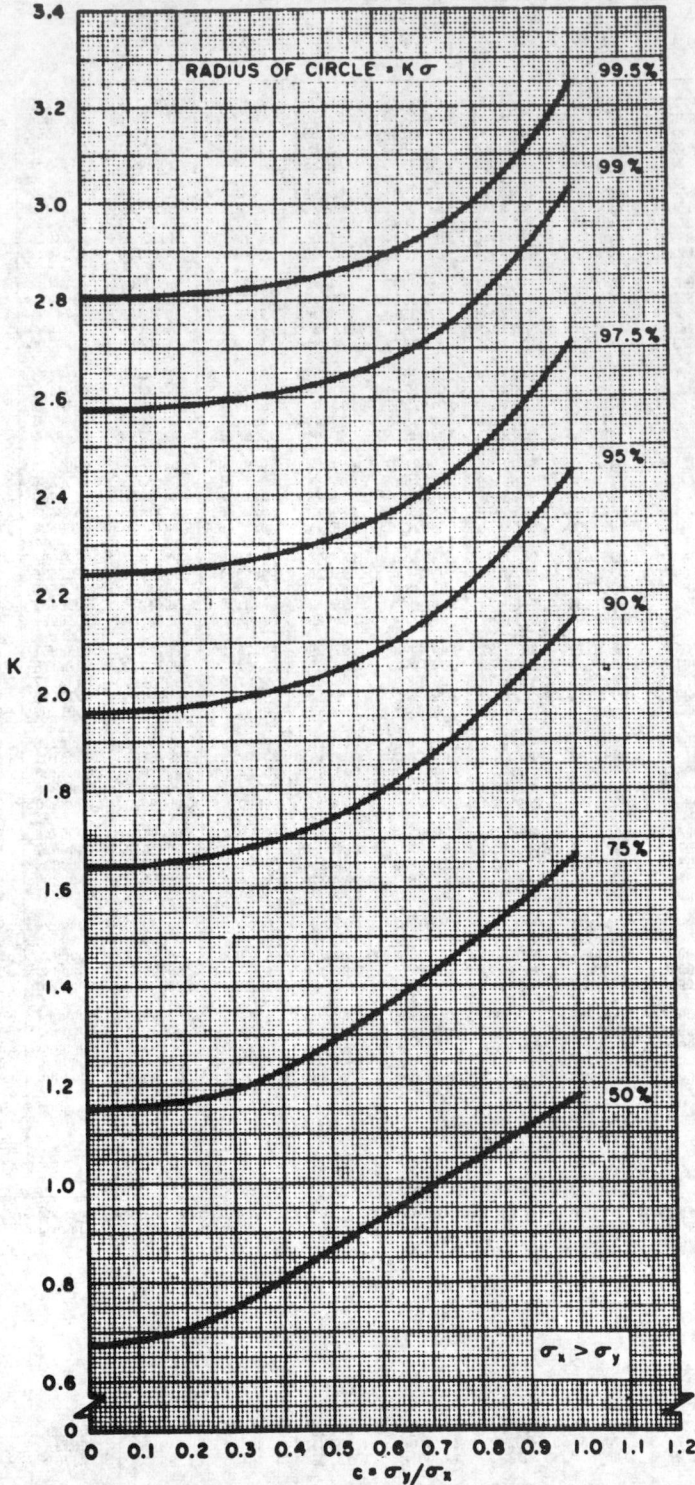

FIGURE Q6f.—Factors for conversion of probability ellipse to circle of equivalent probability.

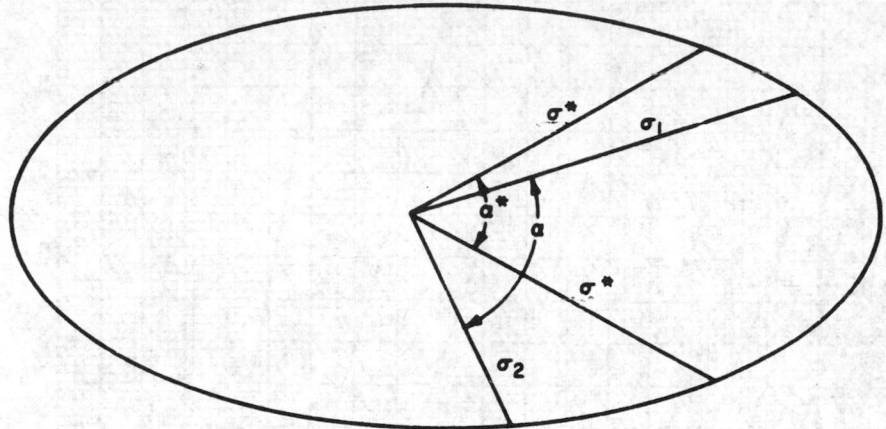

FIGURE Q6g.—Transformed parameters of error ellipse.

where

$$\beta = \text{arc tan } (\sigma_1/\sigma_2).$$

Thus,

$$\sin 2\beta = \frac{2\sigma_1\sigma_2}{\sigma_1{}^2 + \sigma_2{}^2}.$$

To use the curve and monogram for obtaining σ^* and α^*, one must first calculate the ratio σ_2/σ_1. The value σ_1, is always taken as the larger of the two in the ratio so that its value is always less than 1.0. With this ratio, enter the curve of figure Q6i and obtain the σ^* factor. Multiply σ_1 by this factor to obtain the fictitious function σ^*. The monogram of figure Q6j is entered with the same ratio to obtain the fictitious angle of cut α^*.

For a numerical example to illustrate the method of calculation, assume that the angle of cut of 50°, σ_1, is 20 meters, and σ_2 is 15 meters to determine the probability of location within a circle of 30 meters radius.

Calculate the ratio $\sigma_2/\sigma_1 = \dfrac{15}{20} = 0.75$.

Enter the curve of figure Q6i with this ratio and obtain the σ^* factor (0.845). Multiply this factor by σ_1 to obtain σ^* equals 16.9 meters. Calculate the ratio

$$R/\sigma^* = 30/16.9 = 1.78.$$

Enter the nomogram of figure Q6j with the ratio σ_2/σ_1, and with the given angle α to obtain the fictitious angle of cut $\alpha^* = 47°$.

The values $R/\sigma^* = 1.78$ and $\alpha^* = 47°$ are then used to enter the probability curves of figure Q6h to obtain P=0.62 or 62 percent, interpolating between the 40° and 50° curves for $\alpha^* = 47°$.

Table Q6c presents the same data as figure Q6h in numerical form.

Geometrical Error Considerations

From the information that can be derived using the two methods of transformation of elliptical error data, one can develop curves which show for constant values of initial error that the size of a circle of fixed value of probability varies as a function of the angle of cut of the lines of position.

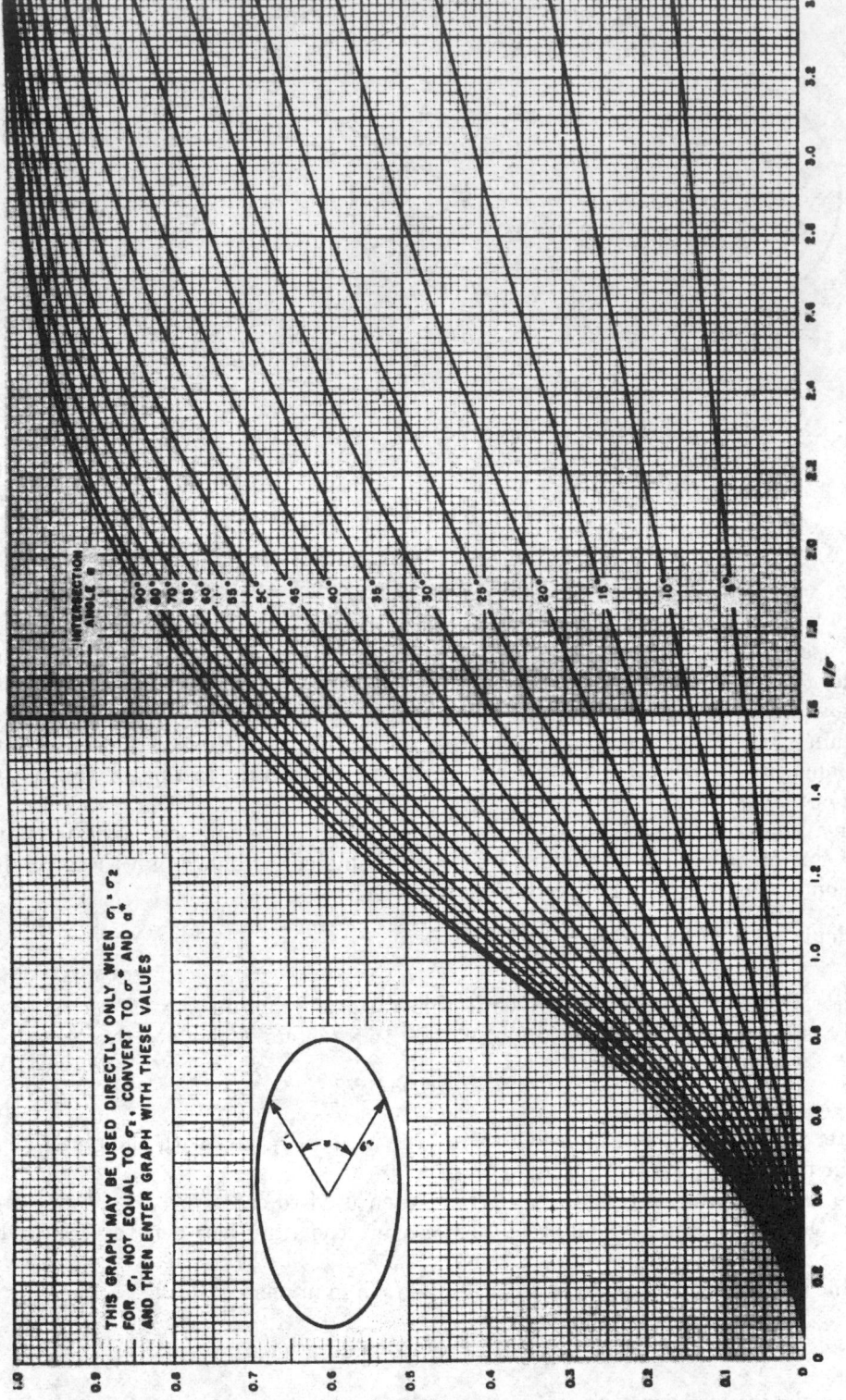

FIGURE Q6h.—Probability versus R/σ and α for elliptical bivariate distributions with two equal standard deviations.

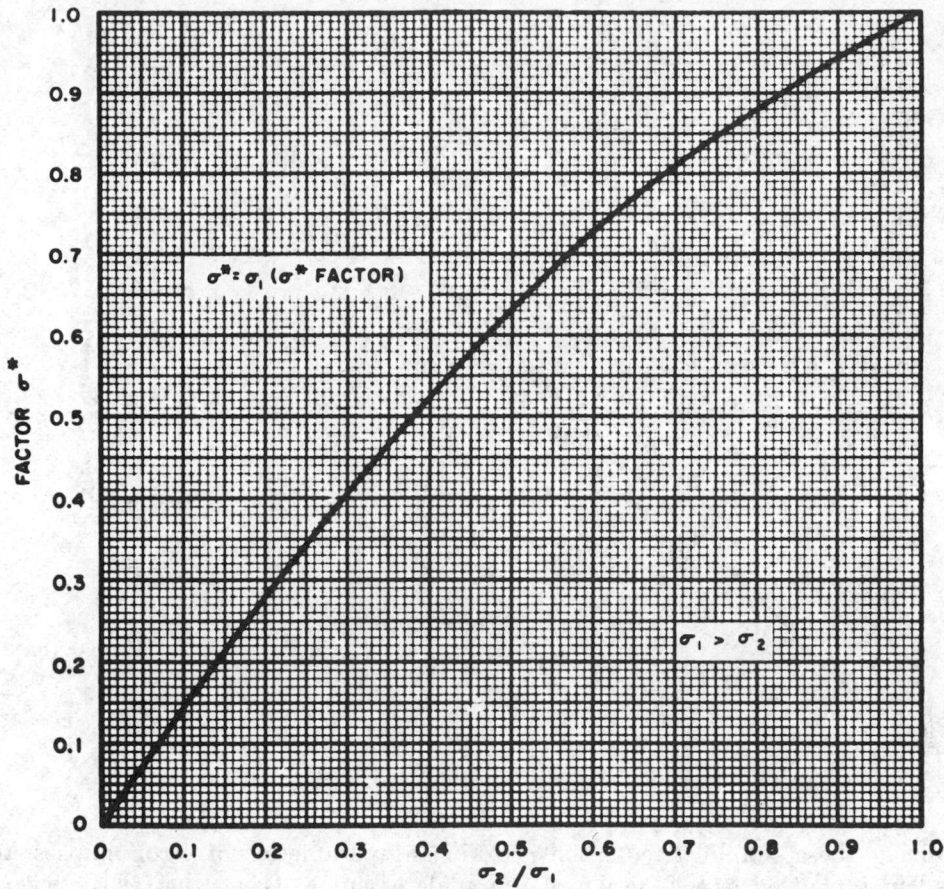

FIGURE Q6i.—σ^* factor versus σ_2/σ_1 ratio.

To simplify the investigation of geometrical factors, it is initially desirable to consider the special case of $\sigma_1 = \sigma_2 = \sigma$. Under this special condition, the long equations for σ_x and σ_y can be simplified to facilitate computation as follows:

$$\sigma_x = \frac{\sqrt{2}}{2 \sin \frac{1}{2}\alpha}\, \sigma \qquad (\sigma_1 = \sigma_2)$$

$$\sigma_y = \frac{\sqrt{2}}{2 \cos \frac{1}{2}\alpha}\, \sigma \qquad (\sigma_1 = \sigma_2).$$

Taking the ratio of these two values, a simple equation is found for the ratio c.

$$c = \frac{\sigma_y}{\sigma_x} = \tan \frac{1}{2}\alpha.$$

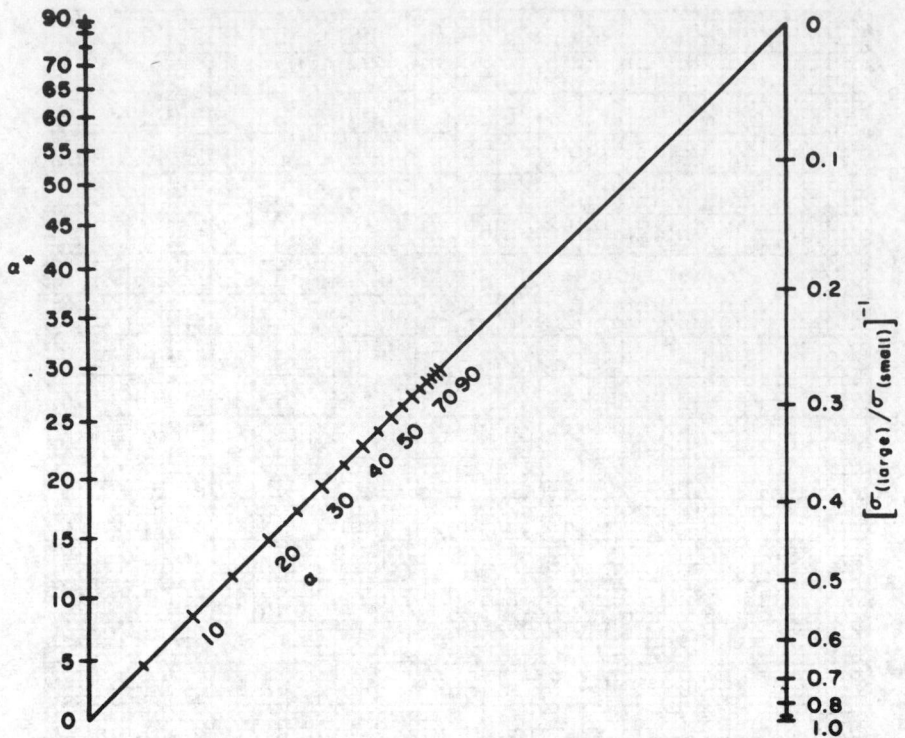

FIGURE Q6j.—Nomogram to obtain α^*.

Utilizing these simplified equations, significant parameters of error ellipses are tabulated in table Q6d as a function of the angle of cut α. Using the CEP curve of figure Q6f, values of the CEP are calculated for each angle, showing that the CEP increases as the angle of cut decreases. The last column in the table gives the factor by which the CEP for angles less than 90° is greater than the CEP for a right angle. This magnification of error curve is plotted in figure Q6k. The curve for the 90 percent probability circle has a slightly differing shape from the CEP curve as shown in figure Q6k. Values for the 90 percent probability circle are given in table Q6e. Figure Q6k indicates the magnitude of the growth of error as the angle of cut varies from 90°.

It is also of interest to consider what values of probability result if the radius of the circle is held constant at the minimum value corresponding to that obtained for the 90° angle of cut. These values may be obtained from the probability versus angle of cut curves in figure Q6h.

Along the ordinate $R/\sigma = 1.177$ which corresponds to the CEP for the circular case, one may read the lesser values of probability corresponding to the various angles of cut. Likewise, one may also obtain the probability values corresponding to holding a circle the size of the 90 percent probability circle for the circular case by using the ordinate $R/\sigma = 2.15$ (also equivalent to 1.82 times the CEP). These two curves are plotted in figure Q6l and the numerical values are given in table Q6f. It is to be noted that the probability values are not inversely related to the error factors plotted in the preceding curves. The geometric error factor is a simple trigonometric function; the probability curves are exponential functions.

R/σ \ α	5°	10°	15°	20°	25°	30°	35°	40°	45°	50°	55°	60°	65°	70°	75°	80°	85°	90°
0.0																		.000
0.1																		.005
0.2	.001	.004	.006	.007	.009	.011	.011	.012	.014	.015	.016	.017	.018	.018	.019	.019	.019	.020
0.3	.005	.009	.012	.015	.019	.022	.025	.028	.031	.034	.036	.038	.040	.041	.042	.043	.044	.044
0.4	.008	.014	.021	.027	.033	.039	.045	.050	.055	.059	.063	.067	.070	.072	.074	.076	.077	.077
0.5	.009	.019	.029	.039	.048	.057	.066	.074	.083	.090	.096	.102	.106	.110	.114	.116	.117	.118
0.6	.014	.029	.043	.057	.070	.082	.095	.106	.117	.127	.135	.143	.150	.156	.159	.162	.164	.165
0.7	.020	.039	.057	.075	.093	.110	.126	.141	.155	.168	.179	.189	.198	.205	.211	.215	.217	.217
0.8	.025	.048	.072	.095	.117	.138	.158	.177	.195	.211	.226	.238	.249	.258	.265	.270	.273	.274
0.9	.031	.060	.088	.116	.143	.169	.196	.217	.238	.257	.275	.290	.303	.314	.322	.328	.332	.333
1.0	.035	.070	.104	.137	.169	.199	.228	.256	.281	.305	.326	.343	.358	.371	.381	.388	.392	.393
1.1	.040	.080	.120	.158	.196	.231	.265	.296	.325	.352	.376	.396	.414	.428	.440	.448	.452	.454
1.2	.046	.092	.136	.181	.224	.264	.302	.337	.370	.400	.426	.449	.469	.485	.497	.506	.512	.513
1.3	.053	.104	.155	.204	.251	.296	.339	.378	.414	.446	.475	.501	.522	.540	.553	.563	.569	.570
1.4	.058	.115	.171	.226	.278	.327	.374	.417	.456	.491	.523	.550	.573	.582	.606	.617	.623	.625
1.5	.063	.126	.188	.247	.304	.358	.408	.455	.497	.535	.568	.597	.621	.641	.656	.667	.673	.675
1.6	.069	.138	.204	.269	.330	.388	.442	.491	.536	.576	.611	.640	.666	.686	.702	.713	.720	.722
1.7	.074	.148	.220	.289	.355	.417	.471	.526	.573	.615	.650	.682	.707	.728	.744	.756	.762	.764
1.8	.079	.159	.236	.310	.380	.445	.505	.559	.608	.651	.688	.719	.745	.766	.782	.793	.800	.802
1.9	.084	.169	.251	.329	.403	.471	.536	.591	.641	.685	.722	.754	.780	.800	.816	.827	.833	.836
2.0	.089	.179	.266	.349	.426	.498	.563	.621	.672	.716	.753	.785	.810	.832	.846	.856	.862	.865
2.1	.093	.189	.280	.367	.448	.523	.589	.649	.700	.744	.780	.812	.837	.857	.871	.881	.887	.890
2.2	.099	.199	.295	.386	.470	.546	.615	.675	.727	.771	.808	.838	.861	.880	.894	.903	.909	.911
2.3	.104	.209	.309	.404	.490	.570	.639	.700	.752	.795	.831	.860	.883	.900	.913	.922	.927	.929
2.4	.109	.219	.324	.422	.512	.592	.663	.724	.775	.818	.852	.880	.901	.918	.930	.938	.942	.944
2.5	.115	.229	.338	.440	.532	.614	.686	.746	.797	.838	.871	.897	.918	.933	.943	.951	.955	.956
2.6	.119	.239	.352	.457	.551	.634	.706	.766	.816	.856	.888	.912	.931	.945	.954	.961	.964	.966
2.7	.124	.248	.366	.474	.570	.654	.726	.786	.835	.873	.903	.926	.943	.955	.964	.969	.973	.974
2.8	.129	.258	.379	.490	.589	.674	.746	.805	.851	.888	.916	.937	.953	.963	.971	.976	.979	.980
2.9	.134	.268	.393	.507	.607	.692	.763	.821	.867	.902	.928	.947	.961	.971	.978	.982	.984	.985
3.0	.139	.277	.406	.522	.624	.710	.781	.837	.880	.914	.938	.956	.968	.976	.982	.986	.988	.989
3.1	.144	.287	.419	.538	.641	.727	.797	.852	.893	.924	.947	.963	.974	.982	.986	.989	.991	.992
3.2	.149	.296	.432	.553	.657	.743	.812	.865	.905	.934	.955	.969	.979	.985	.990	.992	.993	.994
3.3	.154	.306	.445	.568	.673	.759	.826	.878	.916	.943	.962	.975	.983	.989	.992	.994	.995	.996
3.4	.159	.315	.458	.583	.688	.773	.840	.889	.925	.951	.968	.979	.986	.991	.994	.996	.997	.997
3.5	.164	.324	.470	.597	.703	.788	.852	.900	.934	.957	.973	.983	.989	.993	.996	.997	.998	.998
3.6	.169	.333	.482	.611	.717	.801	.864	.910	.942	.963	.977	.986	.991	.995	.997	.998	.998	.999
3.7	.174	.343	.494	.625	.731	.814	.875	.919	.949	.968	.981	.988	.993	.996	.998	.998	.999	.999
3.8	.179	.352	.506	.638	.744	.826	.886	.927	.955	.973	.984	.990	.995	.997	.998	.999	.999	.999
3.9	.183	.360	.518	.651	.757	.838	.895	.935	.961	.977	.987	.993	.996	.998	.999	.999	.999	.999
4.0	.189	.370	.529	.664	.770	.848	.904	.942	.966	.980	.989	.994	.997	.998	.999	.999	1.000	1.000
4.1	.193	.378	.541	.676	.781	.859	.913	.948	.970	.983	.991	.995	.998	.999	.999	1.000	1.000	1.000
4.2	.198	.387	.552	.688	.793	.869	.920	.954	.974	.986	.993	.996	.998	.999	.999	1.000	1.000	1.000
4.3	.203	.396	.564	.700	.804	.878	.927	.958	.978	.988	.994	.997	.999	.999	1.000	1.000	1.000	1.000
4.4	.207	.404	.575	.711	.814	.886	.933	.962	.981	.990	.996	.998	.999	1.000	1.000	1.000	1.000	1.000

TABLE Q6c.—Probability versus R/σ and α for elliptical bivariate distributions with two equal standard deviations.

a	σ_x	σ_y	c	K	CEP	ERROR FACTOR
90	1.0	1.0	1.0	1.177	1.177	1.00
80	1.10	0.924	0.839	1.078	1.186	1.01
70	1.234	0.865	0.700	0.996	1.228	1.042
60	1.414	0.817	0.577	0.914	1.292	1.099
50	1.672	0.782	0.466	0.847	1.420	1.206
45	1.847	0.766	0.414	0.815	1.508	1.281
40	2.06	0.753	0.364	0.783	1.620	1.376
30	2.74	0.733	0.268	0.734	2.01	1.710
20	4.06	0.718	0.176	0.700	2.85	2.42
10	8.11	0.710	0.087	0.680	5.52	4.69

TABLE Q6d.—Significant parameters of error ellipses when $\sigma_1 = \sigma_2$.

a	c	K	90% R	ERROR FACTOR
90	1.0	2.145	2.145	1.00
80	0.839	1.98	2.18	1.015
70	0.700	1.86	2.30	1.07
60	0.577	1.775	2.51	1.17
50	0.466	1.72	2.88	1.34
45	0.414	1.702	3.15	1.47
40	0.364	1.687	3.47	1.615
30	0.268	1.665	4.53	2.11
20	0.176	1.652	6.72	3.13
10	0.087	1.645	13.35	6.22

TABLE Q6e.—90 percent error factor.

a	P	P
90	50	90
80	49.4	89.2
70	47.5	86.9
60	44.0	82.4
50	39.5	76
40	37	66
30	25	53
20	17	37
10	8	19

ABLE Q6f.—Probability decrease with decreasing angle of cut for a circle of constant radius ($\sigma_1 = \sigma_2$).

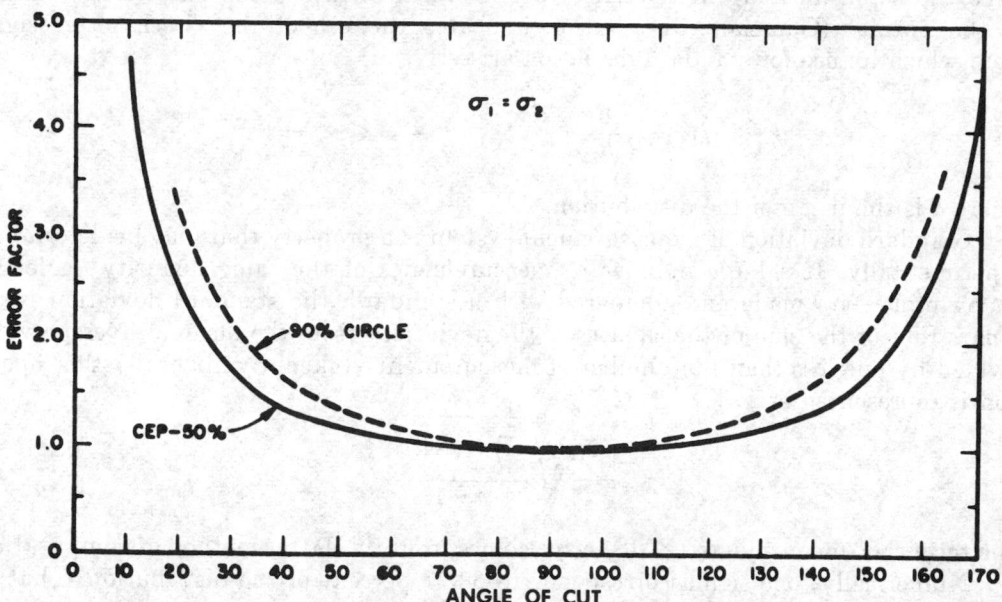

FIGURE Q6k.—CEP magnification versus angle of cut.

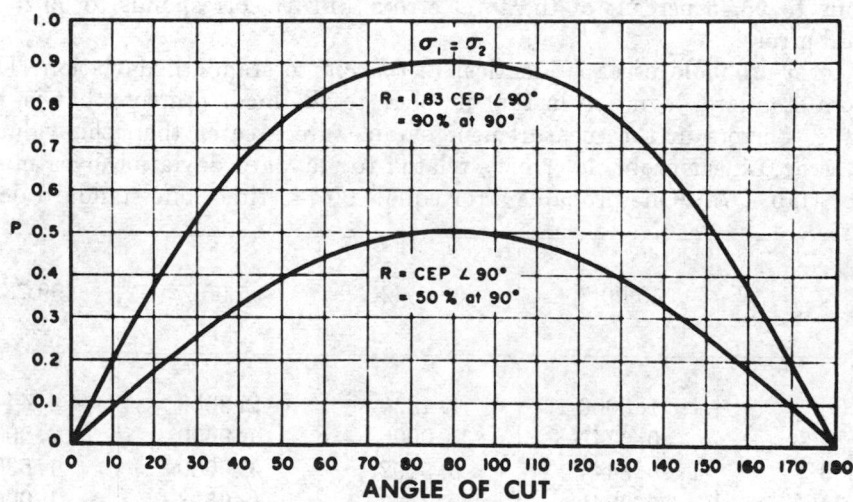

FIGURE Q6l.—Decrease in probability for a circle of constant radius versus angle of cut.

Q7. Clarification of terminology.—The following discussion is presented to insure that there is no misunderstanding with respect to the use of terms having one meaning when discussing one-dimensional errors and another when discussing two-dimensional errors.

Although the basic problem of position location is concerned with the two dimensions necessary to describe an area, one-dimensional error measures are commonly applied to each of the two dimensions involved. As demonstrated in article Q6, the use of the one-dimensional standard deviation of each line of position permitted a general approach to the consideration of the error ellipse.

One-Dimensional Errors

The terms **standard deviation, sigma** (σ), and **root mean square (RMS) error** have the same meaning in reference to one-dimensional errors. The basic equation of the normal (Gaussian) distribution indicates the use of the Greek letter sigma from which its use for standard deviation arises:

$$f(x) = \frac{1}{\sigma\sqrt{2\pi}} e^{-\frac{(x-a)^2}{2\sigma^2}} \qquad -\infty < x < \infty$$

where a is the mean of the distribution.

Standard deviation of a measurement system is a property that may be determined experimentally. If a large number of measurements of the same quantity—a length for example—are made and compared with a standard, the standard deviation is the square root of the sum of the squares of the deviations from the mean or average value divided by one less than the number of measurements taken. Symbolically this operation is represented as:

$$\sigma = \sqrt{\frac{\sum_{i=1}^{n} (x_i - a)^2}{n-1}}.$$

The term root-mean-square (RMS) error comes from this latter method of computation.

Numerically, one sigma corresponds to 68.27 percent of the distribution. That is, if a large number of measurements were made of a given quantity, 68.27 percent of the errors would be no greater than the value of one standard deviation. Likewise 2σ corresponds to 95.45 percent of the total errors and 3σ corresponds to 99.73 percent of the total errors.

The term **probable error** is identical *in concept* to standard deviation. The term differs from standard deviation in that it refers to the median error; that is, no more than half the errors in the measurement sample are greater than the value of the probable error. Linear probable error is related to standard deviation by a multiplication factor (tab. Q7a). One probable error equals 0.6745 times one standard deviation.

From \ To	50.00%	68.27%	95.00%	99.73%
50.00%	1.0000	1.4826	2.9059	4.4475
68.27%	0.6745	1.0000	1.9600	3.0000
95.00%	0.3441	0.5102	1.0000	1.5307
99.73%	0.2248	0.3333	0.6533	1.0000

TABLE Q7a.—Linear error conversion factors.

The term **variance** is met most frequently in detailed mathematical discussions. The term refers to a square of a standard deviation. It is useful in simplifying the algebra of some complex mathematical derivations.

Two-Dimensional Errors

Terms similar or identical in words to those used for one-dimensional error descriptions are also used with two-dimensional or **bivariate error** descriptions. However, in the two-dimensional case, not all of these terms have the same meaning as before; considerable care is needed to avoid confusion.

Standard deviation or sigma has a definable meaning only in the specific case of the circular normal distribution where $\sigma_x = \sigma_y$:

$$P_R = 1 - e^{-\frac{R^2}{2\sigma^2}}.$$

In the case of the circular normal distribution, the standard deviation σ is equivalent to the standard deviation along both orthogonal axes. Because of concern with a radial distribution, the total distribution of errors involves numbers different from those of the linear case (tabs. Q7a and Q7b). In the circular case, 1σ error indicates that 39.35 percent of the errors would not exceed the value of the 1σ error; 86.47 percent would not exceed the 2σ error; 98.89 percent would not exceed the 3σ error; and 99.78 percent would not exceed the 3.5σ error.

From \ To	39. 35%	50. 00%	63. 21%	95. 00%	99. 78%
39. 35%	1. 0000	1. 1774	1. 4142	2. 4477	3. 5000
50. 00%	0. 8493	1. 0000	1. 2011	2. 0789	2. 9726
63. 21%	0. 7071	0. 8325	1. 0000	1. 7308	2. 4749
95. 00%	0. 4085	0. 4810	0. 5778	1. 0000	1. 4299
99. 78%	0. 2857	0. 3364	0. 4040	0. 6993	1. 0000

TABLE Q7b.—Circular error conversion factors.

Because the usual case where there are two-dimensional distributions is that the standard deviations are different, resulting in an elliptical distribution, the circular standard deviation is less useful than the linear standard deviation. It is more common to describe two-dimensional distributions by the two separate one-dimensional standard deviations associated with each error axis. References, however, often do not make this distinction, referring to the position accuracy of a system as 600 feet (2σ), for example. Such a description should leave the reader wondering whether the measure is circular error, in which case the numbers describe the 86 percent probability circle, or whether the numbers are to be interpreted as one-dimensional sigmas along each axis, in which case the 95 percent probability circle is indicated (assuming the distribution to be circular, which actually it may not be).

The term **RMS (root mean square) error** when applied to two-dimensional errors does not have the same meaning as standard deviation. The term has the same meaning as radial error or d_{rms}, discussed later. Such use of the term is deprecated.

In a circular normal distribution, the term **circular probable error (CPE)** or **circular error probable (CEP)** refers to the radius of the circle inside of which there is a 50 percent probability of being located.

The term CEP is also used to indicate the radius of a circle inside of which there is a 50 percent probability of being located, even though the actual error figure (fig. Q7a) is an ellipse. Article Q6 describes one of the methods of obtaining such CEP equivalents when given ellipses of varying eccentricities. Curves and tables are available for perform-

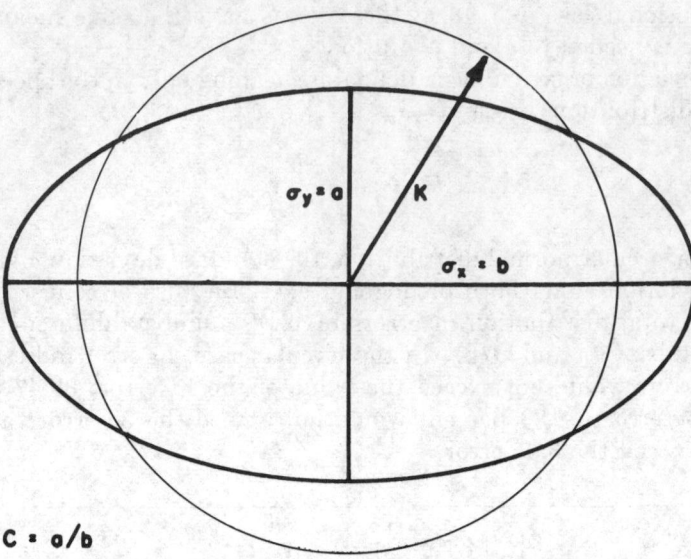

$C = a/b$

FIGURE Q7a.—Error ellipse and circle of equivalent probability.

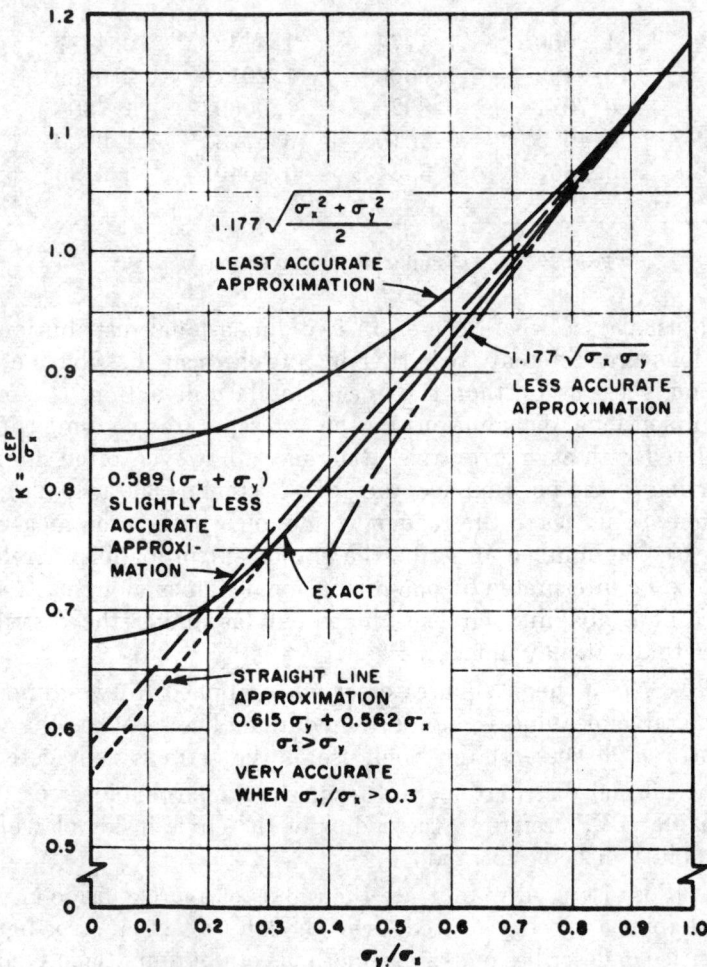

FIGURE Q7b.—CEP for elliptical error distribution approximations.

ing this calculation. Despite the availabilty of these curves and tables, approximations are often made for this calculation of a CEP when the actual error distribution is elliptical. Several of these approximations are indicated and plotted for comparison with the exact curve in figure Q7b. Of the various approximations shown, the top curve, the one which diverges the most rapidly, appears to be the most commonly used.

Another factor of interest concerning the relationship of the CEP to various ellipses is that the area of the CEP circle is always greater than the basic ellipse. Table Q7c indicates that the divergence between the actual area of the ellipse of interest and the circle of equivalent probability increases as the ellipse becomes thinner and more elongated.

$C = a/b$	Area of 50% ellipse	Area of equivalent circle
0.0	0	1. 43
0.1	0. 437	1. 46
0.2	0. 874	1. 56
0.3	1. 31	1. 76
0.4	1. 75	2. 06
0.5	2. 08	2. 37
0.6	2. 62	2. 74
0.7	3. 06	3. 12
0.8	3. 49	3. 52
0.9	3. 93	3. 94
1.0	4. 37	4. 37

TABLE Q7c.—Comparison of areas of 50 percent ellipses of varying eccentricities with areas of circles of equivalent probability.

The value of the CEP may be related to the radius of other values of probability circles analytically for the case of the circular normal distribution by solving the basic equation for various values of probability. For this special case of the circular normal distribution, these relationships are shown drawn to scale in figure Q7c with the associated values tabulated in table Q7d.

The derivation of these values is shown in the following analysis. First, the factor relating the CEP to the circular sigma is derived, then, as a second example, the relationship between the 75 percent probability circle and the circular sigma is derived. The ratio of these two values is then the value shown in table Q7d for the 75 percent value.

The circular normal distribution equation is:

$$P_R = 1 - e^{-\frac{R^2}{2\sigma^2}},$$

and

$$\text{CEP} \equiv P(R) = 0.5$$

$$1 - e^{-\frac{R^2}{2\sigma^2}} = 0.5$$

$$e^{-\frac{R^2}{2\sigma^2}} = 0.5.$$

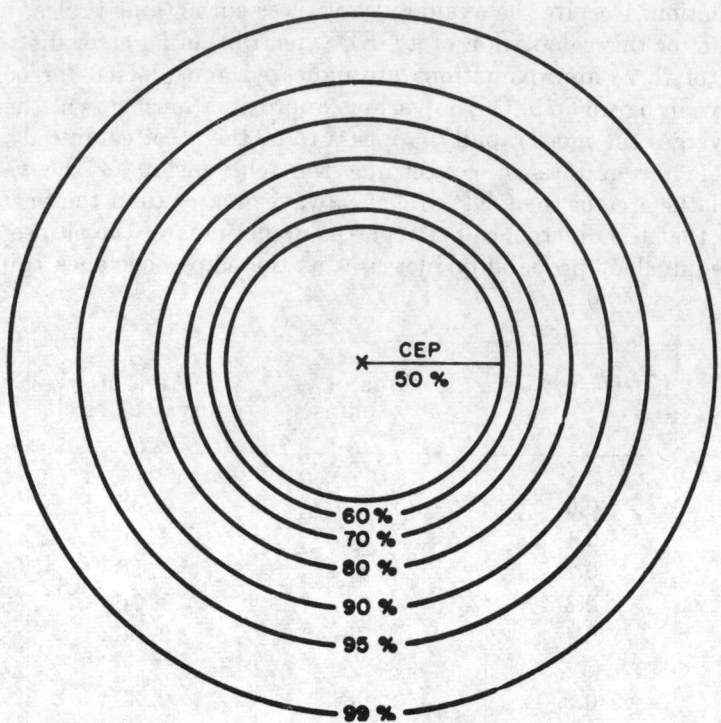

FIGURE Q7c.—Relationship between CEP and other probability circles.

Take natural logarithm of both sides

$$\ln\left(e^{-\frac{R^2}{2\sigma^2}}\right)=\ln 0.5$$

$$\frac{R^2}{2\sigma^2}=\ln 2 \qquad (\ln 0.5=-\ln 2)$$

$$R=1.1774\sigma.$$

For the 75 percent probability circle,

$$1-e^{-\frac{R^2}{2\sigma^2}}=0.75$$

$$e^{-\frac{R^2}{2\sigma^2}}=0.25$$

$$\ln\left(e^{-\frac{R^2}{2\sigma^2}}\right)=\ln 0.25$$

$$\frac{R^2}{2\sigma^2}=\ln 4$$

$$R=1.665\sigma$$

$$\frac{R\,(75\%)}{R\,(50\%)}=\frac{1.665\sigma}{1.177\sigma}=1.414\cdot$$

Multiply value of CEP by	To obtain radius of circle of probability
1. 150	60%
1. 318	70%
1. 414	75%
1. 524	80%
1. 655	85%
1. 823	90%
2. 079	95%
2. 578	99%

TABLE Q7d.—Relationship between CEP and radii of other probability circles of the circular normal distribution.

The factors tabulated in table Q7d are sometimes used to relate varying probability circles when the basic distribution is not circular, but elliptical. That such a procedure is inaccurate may be seen by the curves of figure Q7d. It can be seen that the errors involved are small when the eccentricities are small. But the errors increase significantly when both high values of probability are desired and when the ellipticity increases in the direction of long, narrow distributions.

The terms **radial error, root mean square error,** and d_{rms} are identical in meaning when applied to two-dimensional errors. Figure Q7e illustrates the definition of d_{rms}. It is seen to be the square root of the sum of the square of the 1 sigma error components along the major and minor axes of a probability ellipse. The figure details the definition of 1 d_{rms}. Similarly, other values of d_{rms} can be derived by using the corresponding values of sigma. The measure d_{rms} is not equal to the square root of the sum of the squares of σ_1 and σ_2 that are the basic errors associated with the lines of position of a particular measuring system. The procedures described in art. Q6 must first be utilized to obtain the values shown as σ_x and $_y\sigma$.

The three terms (radial error, root-sum-square error, and d_{rms}) used as a measure of error are somewhat confusing because they do not correspond to a fixed value of probability for a given value of the error measure. The terms can be conveniently related to other error measures only when $\sigma_x = \sigma_y$, and the probability figure is a circle. In the more common elliptical cases, the probability associated with a fixed value of d_{rms} varies as a function of the eccentricity of the ellipse. One d_{rms} is defined as the radius of the circle obtained when $\sigma_x = 1$, in figure Q7e, and σ_y varies from 0 to 1. Likewise, 2 d_{rms} is the radius of the circle obtained when $\sigma_x = 2$, and σ_y varies from 0 to 2. Values of the length of the radius d_{rms} can be calculated as shown in table Q7e. From these values the associated probabilities can be determined from the tables of article Q6. The variations of probability associated with the values of 1 d_{rms} and 2 d_{rms} are shown in the curves of figures Q7f and Q7g. Figure Q7h shows the lack of a constant relationship in a slightly different way. Here the ratio $d_{rms}/$CEP is plotted against the same measure of ellipticity. The three figures show graphically that there is not a constant value of probability associated with a single value of d_{rms}.

Figure Q7i shows the substitution of the circular form for elliptical error distributions. When σ_x and σ_y are equal, the probability represented by 1 d_{rms} is 63.21 percent. When σ_x and σ_y are unequal (σ_x being the greater value), the probability varies from 64 percent when $\sigma_y/\sigma_x = 0.8$ to 68 percent when $\sigma_y/\sigma_x = 0.3$.

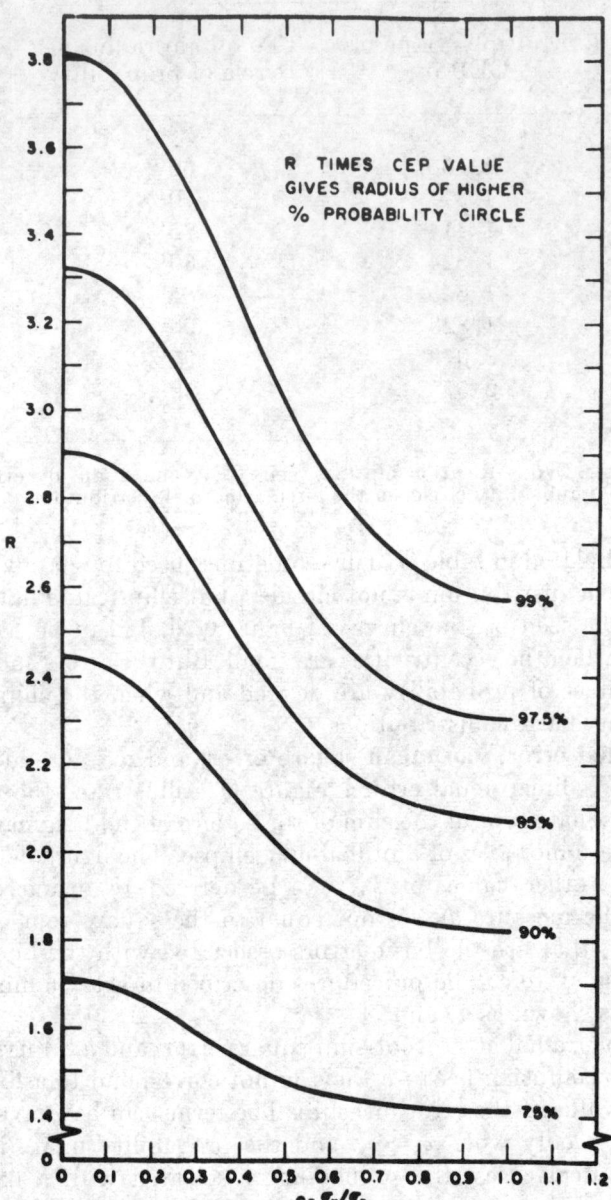

FIGURE Q7d.—Relation of probability circles to CEP versus ellipticity.

Q8. Navigation system accuracy.—In a navigation system, **predictability** is the measure of the accuracy with which the system can define the position in terms of geographical coordinates; **repeatability** is the measure of the accuracy with which the system permits the user to return to a position as defined only in terms of the coordinates peculiar to that system. **Predictable accuracy,** therefore, is the accuracy of positioning with respect to geographical coordinates; **repeatable accuracy** is the accuracy with which the user can return to a position whose coordinates have been measured previously with the same system. For example, the distance specified for the repeatable accuracy of a system such as Loran-C is the distance between two Loran-C positions established using the same stations and time-difference readings

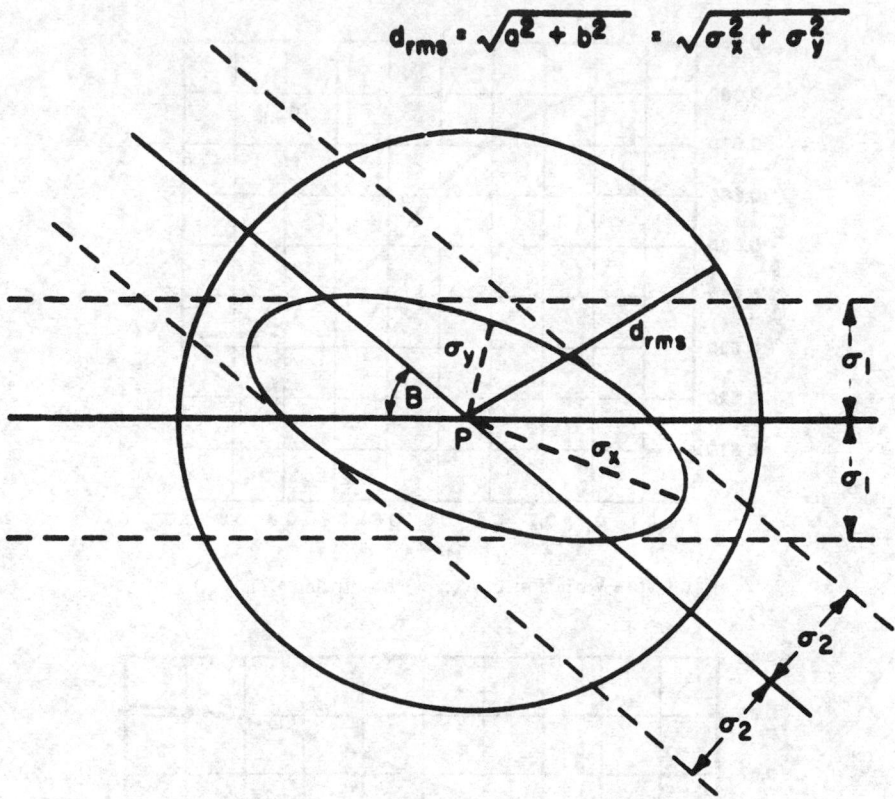

$$d_{rms} = \sqrt{a^2 + b^2} = \sqrt{\sigma_x^2 + \sigma_y^2}$$

FIGURE Q7e.—Illustration of radial error or d_{rms}.

σ_y	σ_x	LENGTH OF 1 d_{rms}	PROBABILITY	
			1 d_{rms}	2 d_{rms}
0.0	1.0	1.000	0.683	0.954
0.1	1.0	1.005	0.682	0.955
0.2	1.0	1.020	0.682	0.957
0.3	1.0	1.042	0.676	0.961
0.4	1.0	1.077	0.671	0.966
0.5	1.0	1.118	0.662	0.969
0.6	1.0	1.166	0.650	0.973
0.7	1.0	1.220	0.641	0.977
0.8	1.0	1.280	0.635	0.980
0.9	1.0	1.345	0.632	0.981
1.0	1.0	1.414	0.632	0.982

$d_{rms} = \sqrt{\sigma_x^2 + \sigma_y^2}$ when σ_x and σ_y are at right angles to each other.

TABLE Q7e.—Calculation of d_{rms}.

at different times. The correlation between the geographical coordinates and the system coordinates may or may not be known.

Relative accuracy is the accuracy with which a user can determine his position relative to that of another user of the same navigation system at the same time. Hence, a system with high relative accuracy provides good rendezvous capability for the users of the system. The correlation between the geographical coordinates and the system coordinates is not relevant.

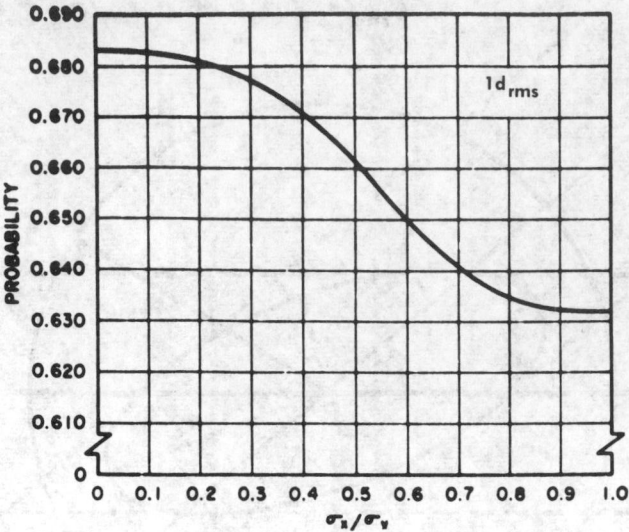

FIGURE Q7f.—Variation in d_{rms} with ellipticity (1 d_{rms}).

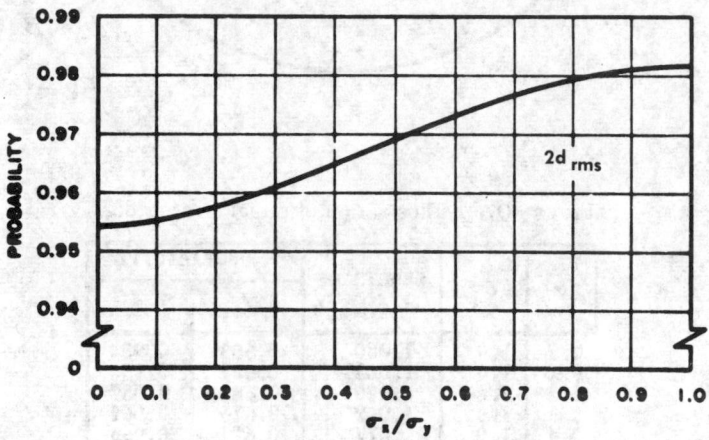

FIGURE Q7g.—Variation in d_{rms} with ellipticity (2 d_{rms}).

Q9. Most probable position.—Some navigators, particuarly those of little experience, have been led by the simplified definitions and explanations usually given in texts to conclude that the line of position is infallible, and that a fix is without error, overlooking the frequent incompatibility of these two notions. Too often the idea has prevailed that information is either all right or all wrong. An example is the practice of establishing an estimated position at the foot of the perpendicular from a dead reckoning position to a line of position. The assumption is that the vessel *must* be somewhere on the line of position. The limitations of this often valuable practice are not understood by these inexperienced navigators.

A more realistic concept is that of the **most probable position (MPP),** which recognizes the probability of error in *all* navigational information, and determines position by an evaluation of all available information, using the principles of errors.

Suppose a vessel were to start from a completely accurate position and proceed on dead reckoning. If course and speed over the bottom were of equal accuracy, the uncertainty of dead reckoning positions would increase equally in all directions with

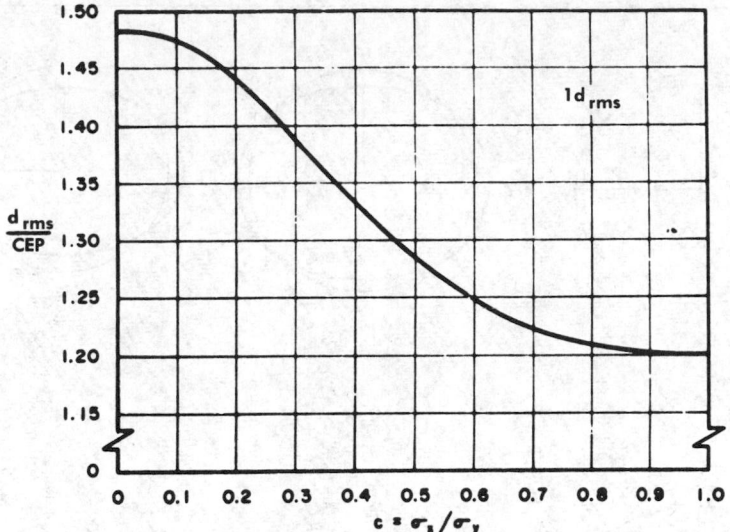

FIGURE Q7h.—Ellipticity versus d_{rms}/CEP (1 d_{rms}).

either distance or elapsed time (for any one speed these would be directly proportional and therefore either could be used). Therefore, a circle of uncertainty would grow around the dead reckoning position as the vessel proceeded. If the navigator had full knowledge of the distribution and nature of the errors of course and speed, and the necessary knowledge of statistical analysis, he could compute the radius of the circle of uncertainty, using the 50 percent, 95 percent, or other probabilities.

In ordinary navigation, this is not practicable, but based upon his experience and judgment, the navigator might estimate at any time the likely error of his dead reckoning or estimated position. With practice, he might acquire considerable skill in making this estimate. He would take into account, too, the fact that the area of uncertainty might better be represented by an ellipse than a circle, the major axis being along the course line if the estimated error of the speed were greater than that of the course, and the minor axis being along the course line if the estimated error of the course were greater. He would recognize, too, that the size of the area of uncertainty would not grow in direct proportion to the distance or elapsed time, because disturbing factors such as wind and current could not be expected to remain of constant magnitude and direction. Also, he would know that the starting point of the dead reckoning would not be completely free from error.

At some future time additional positional information would be obtained. This might be a line of position from a celestial observation or by Omega. This, too, would be accompanied by an estimated error which might be computed for a certain probability if the necessary information and knowledge were available. If the dead reckoning had started from a good position obtained by means of landmarks, the likely error of the initial position would be very small. At first the dead reckoning or estimated position would probably be more reliable than a line of position obtained by celestial observation or Omega. But at *some* distance the two would be equal, and beyond this the line of position might be more accurate.

However, the determination of most probable position does not depend upon determination of *which* information is most accurate. In figure Q9a a dead reckoning position is shown surrounded by a circle of uncertainty. A line of position is also shown, with its area of uncertainty. The most probable position is within the overlapping area, and if the uncertainty of the dead reckoning position and that of the line of position are

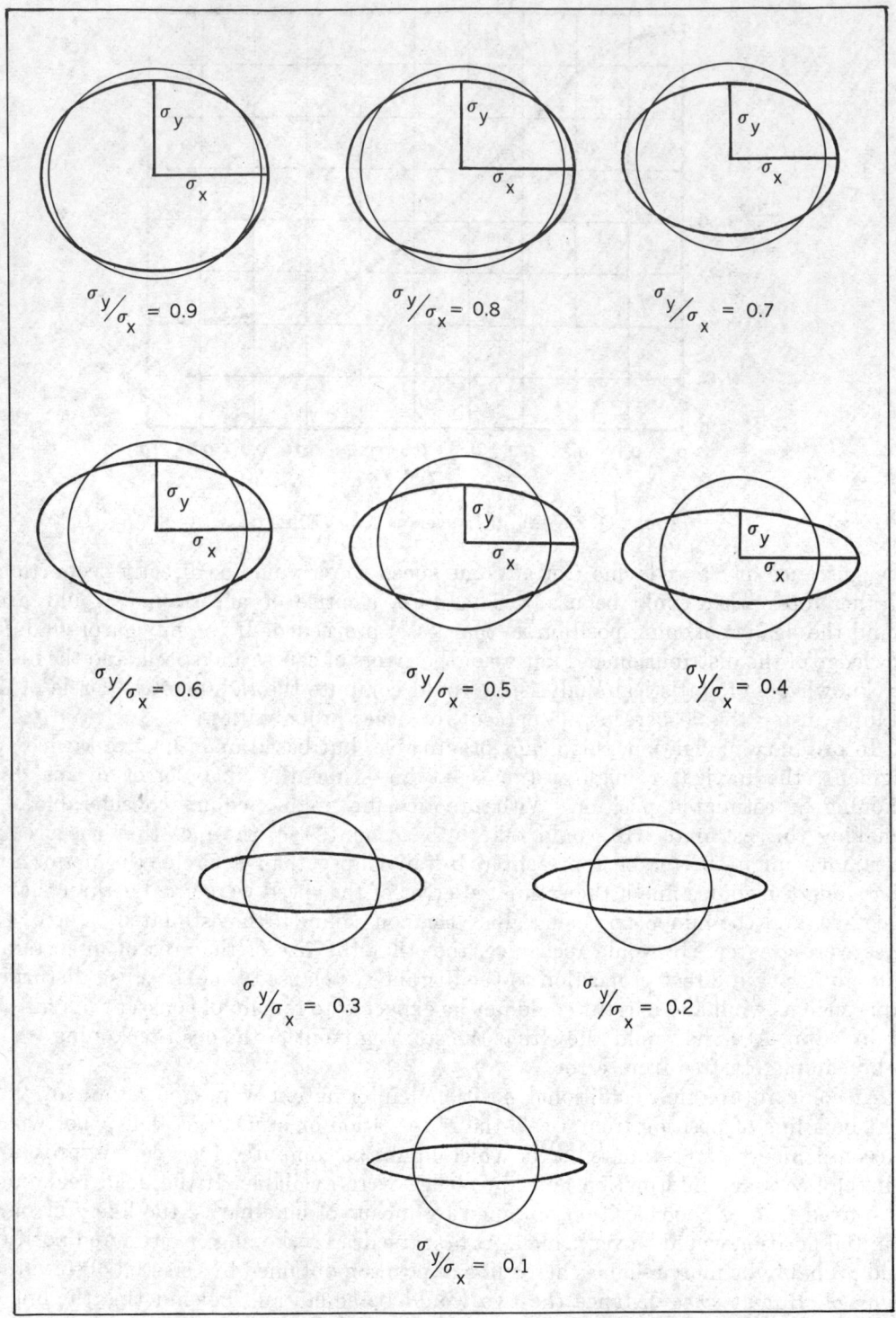

FIGURE Q7i.—Substitution of the circular form for elliptical error distributions.

about equal, it might be taken at the center of the area. If the overall errors are considered normal, and they are probably approximately so, *the effect of each error is proportional to its square.* Thus, if the likely error of a dead reckoning position is 3 miles, and that of a line of position is 2 miles, the most probable position is nearer the line of position, being at a distance equal to $\frac{2^2}{3^2} = \frac{4}{9}$ that from the dead reckoning position (or ⁴⁄₁₃ of the perpendicular distance from the dead reckoning position to the line of position).

If a fix is obtained from two lines of position, the area of uncertainty is a circle if the lines are perpendicular, have equal likely errors, and these errors can be considered normal. If one is considered more accurate than the other, the area is an ellipse, the two axes being proportional to the standard deviations of the two lines of position. As shown in figure Q9b, it is also an ellipse if the likely error of each is equal and the lines cross at an oblique angle. If the errors are unequal, the major axis of the ellipse is more nearly in line with the line of position having the smaller likely error.

If a fix is obtained from three or more lines of position spread in azimuth by more than 180°, and the error of each line is normal and equal to that of the others, the most probable position is the center of the figure. By "center" is meant that point within the figure which is equidistant from the sides. If the lines are of unequal likely error, the distance of the most probable position from each line of position is proportional to the *square* of the likely error of that line times the sine of the angle formed by the other two lines.

In the discussion of most probable position from lines of position, it has been assumed that no other positional information is available. Usually, this is an incorrect assumption, for there is nearly always a dead reckoning or estimated position. This can be considered in any of several ways. The square of its likely error can be used in the same manner as the square of the likely error of each line of position. A most probable position based upon the dead reckoning or estimated position and the most reliable line of position might be determined as explained above, and that line of position replaced with a new one parallel to it but passing through the most probable position just determined. This adjusted line of position can then be assigned a smaller likely error and used with the other lines of position to determine the overall most probable position. A third way is to establish a likely error for the fix, and consider the most probable position as that point along the straight line joining the fix and the dead reckoning or estimated position, the relative distances being equal to the square of the likely error of each position.

The value of the most probable position determined as suggested above depends upon the degree to which the various errors are in fact normal, and the accuracy with which the likely error of each is established. From a practical standpoint, the second factor is largely a matter of judgment based upon experience. It might seem that interpretation of results and establishment of most probable position is a matter of judgment anyway, and that the procedure outlined above is not needed. If a person will follow this procedure while gaining experience, and evaluate his results, the judgment he develops should be more reliable than if developed without benefit of a knowledge of the principles involved. The important point to remember is that the relative effects of normal random errors in any one direction are proportional to their *squares.*

Systematic errors are treated differently. Generally, an attempt is made to discover the errors and eliminate them or compensate for them. In the case of a position determined by three or more lines of position resulting from readings with constant error, the error might be eliminated by finding and applying that correction (including sign) which will bring all lines through a common point.

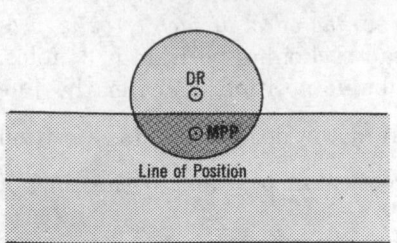

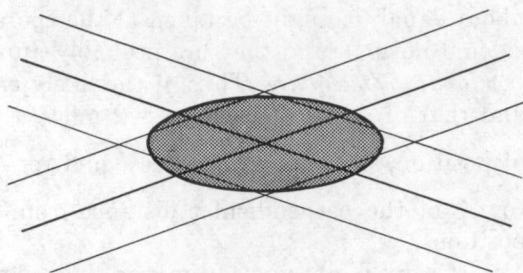

FIGURE Q9a.—A most probable position based upon a dead reckoning position and line of position having equal probable errors.

FIGURE Q9b.—Ellipse of uncertainty with lines of position of equal probable errors crossing at an oblique angle.

Q10. Mistakes.—The recognition of a mistake, as contrasted with an error (art. Q2), is not always easy, since a mistake may have any magnitude, and may be either positive or negative. A large mistake should be readily apparent if the navigator is alert and has an understanding of the size of error to be reasonably expected. A small mistake is usually not detected unless the work is checked.

If results by two methods are compared, as a dead reckoning position and a line of position, exact agreement is not to be expected. But if the discrepancy is unreasonably large, a mistake is logically suspected. The definition of "unreasonably large" is a matter of opinion. If the 99.9 percent areas of the two results just touch, it is *possible* that no mistake has been made. However, the *probability* of either one having so great an error is remote if the errors are normal. The probability of both having 99.9 percent error of opposite sign at the same instant is very small indeed. Perhaps a reasonable standard is that unless the most accurate result lies within the 95 percent area of the least accurate result, the possibility of a mistake should be investigated. Thus, if the areas of uncertainty shown in figure Q9a represent the 95 percent areas, it is probable that a mistake has been made.

As in other matters pertaining to navigation, judgment is important. The use to be made of the results is certainly a consideration. In the middle of an ocean passage a mistake is usually not serious, and will undoubtedly be corrected before it jeopardizes the safety of the vessel. But if landfill is soon to be made, or if search and rescue operations are to be based upon the position, almost any mistake is intolerable.

Q11. Conclusion.—The correct identification of the nature of an error is important if the error is to be handled intelligently. Thus, the statement is sometimes made that a radio bearing need not be corrected if the receiver is within 50 miles of the transmitter. The need for a correction arises from the fact that radio waves are assumed to follow great circles, and if radio bearings are to be plotted on a Mercator chart, the equivalent rhumb line is needed. The statement regarding 50 miles implies that the size of the correction is proportional to distance only. It overlooks the fact that latitude and direction of the bearing line are also important factors, and is therefore a dangerous statement unless its limitations are understood.

The recognition of the type of error is also important. A systematic error has quite a different effect than a random error, and cannot be reduced by additional readings unless some method or procedure is instituted which will cause the errors to cancel each other.

The errors for various percentage probabilities are usually of greater interest than the "average" value. The average of a large number of normal errors approaches zero, but the probable (50 percent) error might be quite large.

A person who understands the nature of errors avoids many pitfalls. Thus, the magnitude of the errors of individual lines of position is not a reliable indication of the size of the error of the fix obtained from them. The size of the triangle formed by three lines of position has often been used as a guide to the accuracy of the fix, although a large triangle might be the result of a large constant error if the objects observed are equally spaced in azimuth. On the other hand, two lines of position with small errors might produce a fix having a much larger error if the lines cross at a small angle.

References

Burt, W. A., D. J. Kaplan, and R. R. Keenly, et al. "Mathematical Considerations Pertaining to the Accuracy of Position Location and Navigation Systems." Naval Warfare Research Center Research Memorandum NWRC—RM 34, Stanford Research Institute, Menlo Park, California, November 1965.

Greenwalt, C. R. and M. E. Shultz. "Principles of Error Theory and Cartographic Applications." Aeronautical Chart and Information Center Technical Report No. 96, St. Louis, Missouri, February 1962.

APPENDIX R

LORAN-A

R1. Introduction.—During World War II a pioneering long range radio-navigation system, Loran-A, was developed at the Massachusetts Institute of Technology, and subsequently implemented under the auspices of the U. S. Coast Guard to fulfill wartime operational needs (art. 136). At the conclusion of the war, 70 transmitting stations were sending Loran-A pulses to some 75,000 receivers aboard military and commercial ships and planes. By 1971, there were 83 stations, with many of the Loran-A transmitters having been in constant service for almost 20 years. The equipment was showing signs of age and obsolescence.

Meanwhile, during the late 1950's and early 1960's, the Department of Defense instituted a program designed to develop a new generation of radionavigation aids. The result was Loran-C, a system less costly to the government to operate and more accurate than Loran-A. Unfortunately, the cost of Loran-C receivers, until very recently, made the superior system less appealing to potential users in the commercial and recreational boating communities. Now the Loran-C system expansion, additional research in receiver design, and a concurrent rise in demand for Loran-C receivers has enabled manufacturers to produce sets at a cost competitive with the Loran-A receivers.

Today there are 8 Loran-C transmitting chains, with a total of 12 expected to be in operation by 1980. In many areas Loran-C and Loran-A services will be overlapping, a situation that the Department of Transportation sees as unnecessary if continued over a long period of time. In May 1970, the Secretary of Transportation published the *National Plan for Navigation* which, among other things, identified the U. S. Coastal Confluence Zone (CCZ), and listed several candidate navigation systems for that zone. After extensive study, the Coast Guard recommended and the Secretary of Transportation approved selection of Loran-C as the government sponsored navigation system for the CCZ. A plan has been developed which provides for the improvement and expansion of Loran-C to cover the entire CCZ, and the eventual phase out of existing Loran-A stations. Such a phase out, once initiated, will be accomplished over a minimum of 2 years to provide a sufficient period of dual Loran-A/Loran-C operation to cover amortization of existing Loran-A receivers and the conversion of historical Loran-A position data to Loran-C coordinates.

While it might appear that Loran-C is merely a duplication of the Loran-A service, differences in the transmitted signals and in receiver operations make Loran-C a much more accurate system. While Loran-A can be used to identify a position that is accurate to from 1 to 5 nautical miles of a particular point in the groundwave coverage area, Loran-C can identify a position with 0.25-mile accuracy. This increased accuracy can be critical to the navigator operating in confined, crowded, or otherwise hazardous sealanes. The accuracy of Loran-C extends to "repeatability." That is, a mariner can employ Loran-C to return to within 300 feet of a particular point. However, depending upon chain geometry, receiving equipment, and system stability, the Loran-C user may be able to return to within 50 feet of a particular point. Similarly, one mariner can rely on Loran-C to govern his position in relation to another. Whereas it would take 30 Loran-A transmitting stations to cover the Coastal Confluence Zone, Loran-C will provide more accurate coverage with about half as many stations.

In anticipation of the phase out discussed above, the discussion of Loran-A was transferred to this appendix to facilitate the removal or revisions in the treatment of Loran-A in subsequent printings of this edition.

R2. Loran-A is a hyperbolic system of navigation by which difference in distance from two fixed points on shore is determined by measurement of the time interval between reception of pulse-modulated (art. 4016), synchronized signals from transmitters at the two points. The name **Loran** is derived from **lo**ng **ra**nge **n**avigation. Since it operates in the 1,850 to 1,950 kHz frequency range, both groundwaves and skywaves can be used to provide coverage over an extensive area with relatively few stations. The system is passive.

Usually, stations of a pair are located from 200 to 400 miles apart, although they may be as close as 100 miles or as far as 700 miles. Generally, a number of stations are located so as to form a **chain,** with all but the end stations in the group being "double pulsing." In most parts of the coverage area, signals can be received from at least two pairs of stations, thus making it possible to obtain a fix by Loran-A alone.

The range at which signals are received varies considerably with kind of signal (groundwave or skywave), route of the signal (over land or water), time of day, atmospheric noise level, geographic region, ionospheric conditions, and possible directional properties of the receiving antenna.

As a general rule, groundwave coverage during the day extends to about 700 miles in the Atlantic and 800 miles in the Pacific. At night the range is about two-thirds this amount. During daylight hours, relatively few skywave signals are received, but at night, signals arrive by so many different paths that a **train** of signals may be received from a single transmitted pulse. Figure R2a shows a typical scope appearance of such a train near the limit of groundwave coverage. All of the signals are from a single transmitted pulse. One-hop-E signals are received to a maximum distance of about 1,400 miles. Curvature of the earth prevents their reception at greater distances regardless of power of the transmitter. Beyond this, strong signals may be received by multihop-E waves or by one or more reflections from the F layer. Because of relatively large uncertainties in the lengths of the paths of such signals, and the increased uncertainty of identification, Loran-A tables and charts do not provide facilities for their use. The extending of lines to provide coverage for such signals is not recommended. Reception of reliable signals on some occasions is no assurance that those received at other times can be trusted. Typical variation in appearance of groundwave and skywave signals with time of day is shown in figure R2b.

The range at which a groundwave signal can be received is much less if the path is across land than if it is across water. For this reason Loran-A stations are located so that signal paths are as much as possible across water in the direction of greatest importance, and it is desirable that the baseline also be across water. The retarding effect varies greatly with the type of land, and is somewhat less when the land is not adjacent to the transmitter. The paths of skywaves are so high that signal strengths are not noticeably affected by land unless it is within about 20 or 30 miles of the transmitter or receiver.

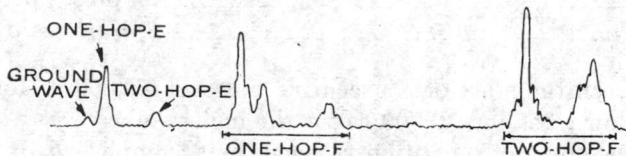

FIGURE R2a.—A typical train of Loran-A signals from a single transmitted pulse.

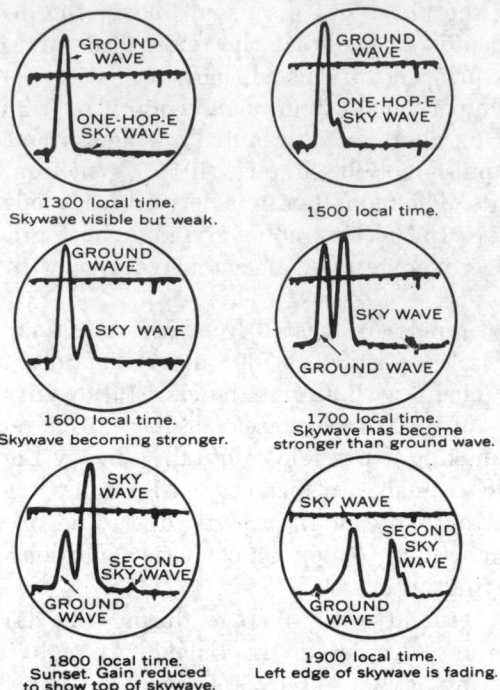

FIGURE R2b.—Typical variation in appearance of signals with local time.

When the atmospheric noise level is high, signals which may otherwise be usable are lost in the clutter.

The areas near the baseline extensions are excluded from Loran-A coverage diagrams because of the relatively large error of position for a small error in the time difference reading.

Transmitting antennas are vertical to avoid directional properties in the horizontal plane. Vertical receiving antennas are desirable for the same reason.

Pulse signals from each pair of stations are transmitted continually. Identification is by means of frequency and **pulse repetition rate** (**PRR**), sometimes called **pulse recurrence rate.** Frequency is identified by channel number, as follows:

Channel No.	Frequency (kHz)	Channel No.	Frequency (kHz)
1	1950	3	1900
2	1850		

The same frequency can be used for signals from a number of different station pairs by varying the rate at which the signals are transmitted. Three **basic pulse repetition rates** are available, as follows:

Special (S)	20 pulses per second,
Low (L)	25 pulses per second,
High (H)	33⅓ pulses per second.

The interval between the start of consecutive pulses is 50,000 μs for the special rate, 40,000 μs for the low rate, and 30,000 μs for the high rate.

A further breakdown of repetition rate can be accomplished by varying the basic rate slightly. In practice, the difference between consecutive **specific pulse repetition**

rates is 100 µs. The specific rates in use are identified by number, starting with 0 for the basic rate and increasing to 7 (eight rates), each higher number *increasing* slightly the rate at which signals are transmitted, and *decreasing* by 100 µs the interval between signals.

Thus, a total of 24 rates is available (if the special basic rate is used) for each of the 4 frequencies. The same rate may be used in areas so widely separated that interference is not likely to occur. Each rate is identified by three characters. The first is a number identifying the frequency channel, the second a letter identifying the basic pulse repetition rate, and the third a number identifying the specific pulse repetition rate. Thus, the designation 1L7 indicates frequency channel 1, low basic pulse repetition rate, and specific pulse repetition rate 7. Stated differently, pulses are transmitted at intervals of 39,300 µs, on a frequency of 1950 kHz. The term **rate,** implying the number of pulses per unit time, is now used for the full three-character designation, and even for the station pair, their signals, and the resulting hyperbolic lines of position and the tables and curves by which they are represented.

R3. The Loran-A receiver-indicator.—The receiver used for Loran-A signals is similar to that used in ordinary radio communication, except that it has no speaker. Signals are sent to an indicator consisting of a cathode ray tube (art. 4019) and the necessary timing circuits and controls. The major portion of the space needed for the equipment is occupied by the indicator.

On the face of the scope a visible line is produced by the spot of light formed at the point of impact of the moving beam of electrons. This line is divided into two parts, one above the other. The upper part is called the **A trace,** and the lower part the **B trace.** When the controls are set for a given rate, the length of the combined trace, in microseconds, is adjusted to the interval between beginning of pulses. Thus, if a reading is desired on rate 2H5, separate switches are set on 2, H, and 5 to control the frequency, basic pulse repetition rate, and specific pulse repetition rate, respectively. The combined length of the two traces is then 29,500 µs.

When the controls are thus set for a given rate, the signals of that rate appear as vertical deflections which remain stationary because a signal is received at the same part of each trace. Signals of the same basic pulse repetition rate, but of a different specific pulse repetition rate, appear to drift along the trace. Those of a *lower* rate drift to the right and those of a *higher* rate drift to the left. The greater the difference between the given rate and that of the signal, the faster the rate of drift.

The drift is due to the difference between the length of the combined trace and the time interval between the start of consecutive signals. Suppose the indicator is set for rate 2H3. The length of the combined A and B traces is 29,700 µs. A rate 2H2 signal is received at intervals of 29,800 µs. The spot of light forming the traces completes a cycle in 29,700 µs and moves an additional 100 µs before the next 2H2 signal is received. Each succeeding 2H2 signal appears 100 µs to the *right* (motion is left-to-right) of the previous one, and after 297 signals have been received (9 seconds), will have moved the entire length of both traces and returned to its original position. Signals of rate 2H5 will move to the *left* at twice the speed, completing the circuit in 4½ seconds. On some scopes a faint line called a **retrace** (fig. R4a) can be seen connecting the ends of the two traces. This indicates the path of the spot of light in moving from the end of one trace to the beginning of the next, during a period of about 70 µs. These two periods of 70 µs are part of the total length of the combined trace.

Signals of the same frequency but another basic pulse repetition rate can be seen, but they appear as flickering signals called **ghosts,** which may drift faster than other signals. Each succeeding signal appears at a point 10,000 µs from the preceding one. Thus, every third or fourth signal may appear at about the same place, but the rate at

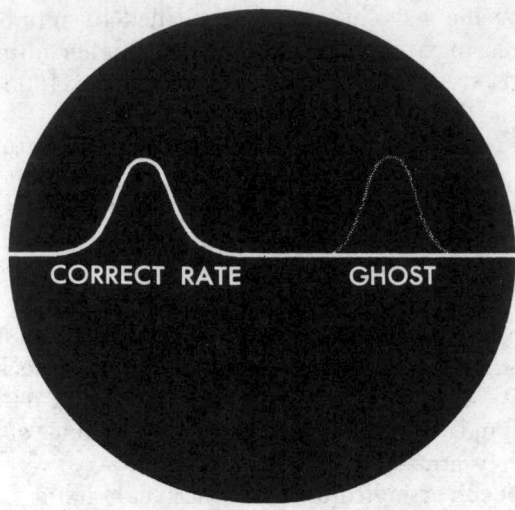

FIGURE R3.—A signal of the correct basic pulse repetition rate, and a ghost.

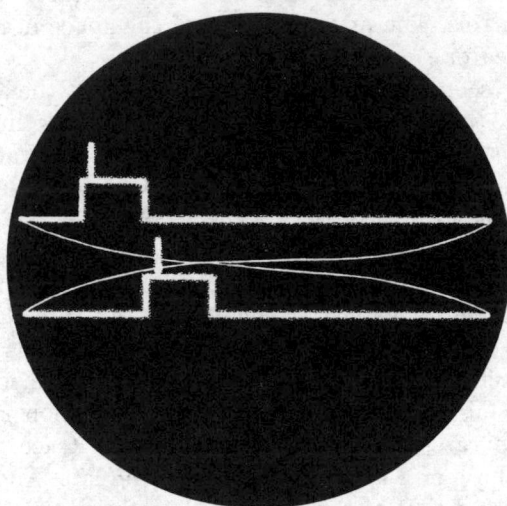

FIGURE R4a.—The Loran-A scope.

any given place is so slow (approximately six or eight per second) that the deflection does not appear continuous. Since the spot of light is not deflected in most of its passages, the line appears continuous with the deflection superimposed on it. The appearance of a signal of the correct rate and a ghost is shown in figure R3.

Strong signals from a frequency channel different from that to which the receiver is tuned may be received. This is called **spillover.** It can be detected by tuning to a different frequency. The frequency at which the signal appears strongest is the correct one.

R4. A Loran-A reading.—Details of Loran-A receiver-indicators differ, but the principles of all are the same. Near the start of each trace of a typical indicator, a portion of the visible line is raised to form a **pedestal,** as shown in figure R4a. The pedestal of the A trace is fixed, but that of the B trace can be moved to nearly any location along the line.

When the entire cycle is shown, as in figure R4a, a signal of 40 μs duration appears as a vertical line, as indicated. It can be moved right or left by means of a switch which temporarily shortens or lengthens the trace by a small amount, causing the signal to

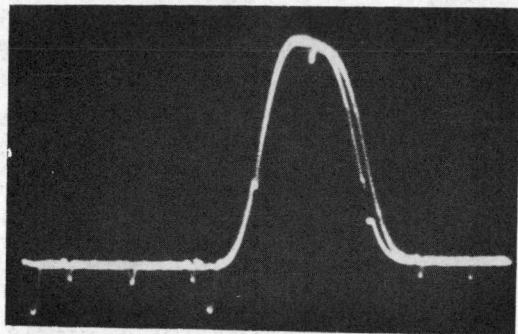

FIGURE R4b.—The Loran-A signals properly matched.

drift. After the correct signals have been identified, they are moved, if necessary, until the signal on the A trace is to the *left* of that on the B trace, and *mounted* near the left edge of the pedestal. The pedestal of the B trace is moved until the other signal is mounted near its left edge. By a series of successive magnifications, the left portions of the two pedestals are placed under each other and made to occupy the entire length of the original trace. The two traces are then brought to the same horizontal line, and one signal superimposed over the other, a process called **matching.** Figure R4b is a photograph of a Loran-A scope with signals properly matched, at greatest magnification. When the signals are matched, they occupy the same position with respect to the two pedestals. The reading is the distance (time separation) between the two pedestals, indicated by *downward* deflections of the traces, or by dial. At greatest amplification, the signals appear as in figure R3 or figure R4b.

A Loran-A reading is influenced by three delays introduced in the transmission of the slave signal, as follows:

Half pulse repetition rate delay. A delay equal to half the interval between start of consecutive pulses is introduced so that one signal can be placed on each trace at approximately the same relative position. If this were the only delay, and a receiver were at some point on the centerline, one signal would be directly under the other. Without the delay they would appear at the same place on the same trace. This delay is introduced for convenience in making a reading, and is not included in the reading.

Baseline delay. If the half pulse repetition rate delay were the only one, readings would increase from zero along the centerline to a maximum along each baseline extension. Since both master and slave signals look alike, there would be no way of identifying them if the position of the receiver was sufficiently in doubt that it might be on either side of the centerline. The baseline delay, equal to the length of time needed for a signal to travel the length of the baseline (6.18 μs times the length of the baseline in nautical miles), causes the readings to increase from zero along the baseline extension beyond the slave to a value of twice the baseline delay along the baseline extension beyond the master station. Because of this delay, the master signal can never appear to the *right* of the slave signal if one signal is placed on each trace.

Coding delay. With a reading near zero one might find difficulty at small scale in determining which signal was left and which was right. An additional delay of 500, 950, or 1,000 μs is provided to increase all readings by this amount. This increases the distance between the master signal and the slave signal when one is on each trace. This delay can be changed easily at the slave transmitter according to a prearranged schedule, to provide some measure of security in time of war.

The reading at any point is equal to 6.18 times the difference in distance (in nautical miles) of the receiver from the two stations (considered negative if nearer the slave), plus the baseline delay, plus the coding delay.

R5. Identification and use of various waves.—Travel times of groundwaves and various skywaves differ, resulting in reception of a wave train (fig. R2a) from a single transmitted signal. Since different readings are obtained with different combinations of signals, identification is important.

If a single wave is received, it is almost surely a groundwave. If a groundwave is received as part of a train of waves, it is the first or *left-hand* wave of the group. The position of the receiver relative to the transmitter is some guide. Within a few hundred miles of the station, the first signal is nearly always a groundwave, unless there is intervening land. Near the extreme limit of the coverage area, groundwaves are not received. Between these limits is a **critical range** in which the first signal may be either a groundwave or skywave. This critical range varies with time of day, location, and conditions, as discussed in article R2. In general, it can be considered to be between about 600 and 900 miles by day, and between about 500 and 700 miles by night.

The *appearance* of the waves can be helpful in their identification. A groundwave is characteristically steady in shape and amplitude. Skywaves may at times appear as steady as groundwaves, but such steadiness seldom lasts for more than a few minutes. Because of constant changes in the intensity (reflecting power) and height of the ionosphere (arts. 4007, 4008), and changing phase relationships, skywaves are subject to two characteristic fluctuations.

Changes in intensity, and changing phase relationships, cause changes in the strength of the reflected signal arriving at the receiver. This is called **fading.** It may be a relatively small change in the amplitude of the signal, or it may be so severe that the signal disappears altogether for a short time. The complete cycle of fading from full strength to minimum and back to full strength may be completed in a period of less than a minute, or it may extend over several minutes.

Changes in height of the ionosphere cause the signal to move right or left along the trace. This motion is not apparent by itself, and equal changes in those parts of the ionosphere reflecting signals from the two transmitters has little effect on the reading. However, a change in intensity may result in shifting the reflecting surface to a higher level. When there are two or more such surfaces a short distance apart, **splitting** of the signal occurs, resulting in more than one crest of the same signal, close together. As the various reflecting surfaces change in intensity and height, the different crests move up and down relative to each other, and change their spacing.

It is good practice to watch the signals for several minutes before making a reading, to be sure of their identification and also to be sure that the *leading* edge of each is visible, for it is this edge, however weak, that should be matched. In a Loran-A area the best practice is to make readings at regular intervals, at least once each hour. The changing appearance with time of day (fig. R2b) should be helpful in identifying signals. Also, an inconsistency of one Loran-A fix relative to such a series is an indication of possible error of identification.

In general, skywaves are steadier at greater distances from the transmitter, because reflection takes place over a larger area and local variations have less effect, and also because changes in height have less effect upon the length of the path. Therefore, the changes are less extreme. One-hop-E waves are usually steadier than multihop-E waves, or those reflected from the F layer (fig. R2a). Changes in these signals are so great that intolerably large errors in readings may be introduced. For this reason and the uncertainty in identification of these waves, it is generally considered advisable to limit readings to groundwaves and one-hop-E waves.

If a vessel is rolling heavily all signals of a train may fade somewhat in synchronism with the roll. A weak groundwave signal may flicker due to random noise signals which appear as continually-fluctuating **grass** on the trace. This momentary change is not easily confused with the slower fading.

For most rates, groundwaves should always be matched if available. If ground-waves are available from one station, but not from the other, the one-hop-E skywaves of both stations should be matched. In general, multihop-E waves and F waves should not be used. In some instances, where the baseline is long, a correction table is provided for matching a groundwave from one station with a skywave from the other.

R6. Accuracy.—The accuracy of a Loran-A fix depends upon the accuracy of the individual lines of position, and the angle at which the lines intersect. The accuracy of individual lines of position depends upon the following factors:

Synchronization of signals. Transmission of Loran-A signals is continuously moni-tored. Normally, the timing is correct to a fraction of 1 microsecond, but if the signals get out of synchronization by as much as 2 microseconds (5 microseconds for rate 1L4), either the master or slave signals, or both are made to **blink** to warn the user of the situation, so that readings on this rate can be avoided until the synchronization is restored, usually in a matter of minutes. Blinking is the shifting of signals right and left about 1,000 microseconds, at intervals of 2 seconds.

Position relative to transmitting stations. Accuracy is related to the spacing between consecutive lines of position separated by a constant difference of reading, as every microsecond. Lines are most closely spaced, giving highest accuracy, along the base-line between the stations, where an error of 1 microsecond in the reading produces an error of 0.081 mile, or 492 feet. From this the lines of position diverge. Near the base-line extensions, an error of 1 microsecond in the reading produces an error of several miles in position. Any groundwave reading within 25 μs of the baseline extensions, or any skywave reading within 200 μs of those along these lines, should be considered of doubtful value.

Uncertainty in travel time of signal. The time needed for a signal to travel from the transmitter to the receiver depends upon the speed and distance. The speed is so nearly constant that the slight variations involved do not introduce a significant error. The distance between two points, however, depends upon the path followed by the wave. Groundwaves follow the curvature of the earth with little variation, so that any error introduced by variations in the path is negligible. This is not true, however, of skywaves. Continual changes in the height and intensity of the ionosphere, as well as tilting of it from the horizontal, produce changes in the length of the path of the radio signal. The increased length of the skywave path over the groundwave path *decreases* with greater distance from the transmitter. Along the centerline, where the distance from the two transmitters is the same, the time *difference* is the same for sky-waves as for groundwaves. At other places, signals from one station are delayed more than those from the other. A **skywave correction** is provided in the Loran-A tables and on the Loran A charts to convert a skywave reading to the equivalent groundwave reading. At distances of 800 miles or more, carefully made skywave readings have an average error of about 2 microseconds. The error increases as the stations are ap-proached, reaching an average value of about 7 microseconds at a distance of 250 miles from one of the transmitters. This increased error is partly offset by closer spacing of the lines of position. However, since individual errors can be more than twice the average, the use of skywaves is not generally recommended within 250 miles of either station, and corrections for these areas are not usually tabulated.

Skill in making a reading. The principal source of error in making a reading is in identifying the signals. Patience and judgment are needed to avoid an error due to use of the wrong wave or failure to detect the true leading edge. With a reasonable signal-to-noise ratio, a careful operator should be able to match signals and read the indicator with an error not to exceed 1 microsecond. With patience, even very weak signals can be matched with an error of not more than a few microseconds.

Alignment of the indicator. Instructions for checking the "alignment" (adjustment) of the indicator are included in the instruction manual provided with each Loran-A receiver-indicator. If the alignment is incorrect, errors may be introduced in the readings.

Incorrect location of transmitters. Computations are made for carefully determined positions of transmitters. However, where isolated stations require independent position determinations, the *relative* positions of the two stations may not be correct, however carefully determined, because of deflection of the vertical (app. X). When errors are established through usage, correction chartlets are provided in the Loran-A tables and on Loran-A charts. If the position of one station is found to be in error, the corrections are applicable in radial sectors around that station. If the positions of both stations are incorrect, the pattern is more involved.

Errors in Loran-A tables and charts. Errors due to imperfections in tables and charts are negligible.

Plotting errors. Plotting of Loran-A lines of position requires the same care as plotting of other navigational information if accurate results are to be obtained. For maximum accuracy, a large scale should be used

R7. Loran-A lines of position.—Computation of the coordinates of points along various Loran-A lines of position is performed by digital computer, allowance being made for the spheroidal shape of the earth.

The Loran-A tables for each rate consist of a small-scale chartlet showing the pattern of the Loran-A lines of position, and any corrections due to incorrect locations of the stations, a skywave correction table for one-hop-E waves, and the principal table giving coordinates of points on the lines of position. This table is entered with the Loran-A reading in microseconds, and the latitude *or* longitude. For a line running in a generally north-south direction, the table is entered with the latitude, and the corresponding longitude is taken from the table. For an east-west line, the table is entered with longitude, and latitude is taken from the table. Two such points are thus determined and plotted, usually one on each side of the dead reckoning position. The straight line connecting them is an approximation of a small part of the line of position. Latitude and longitude are given at intervals of whole degrees, half degrees, or quarter degrees, depending upon the degree of curvature of the line. A separate column is given for each tabulated reading, at suitable intervals. An auxiliary tabulation labeled Δ (delta) gives the change in longitude or latitude (to 0.01) for a 1-microsecond change in the reading. The main table should be entered with the *nearest* reading. If interpolation is toward a *smaller* reading, the printed sign of Δ should be reversed. Extracts from a Loran-A table are given in figures R7a, R7b, and R7c.

Tabulated readings are for groundwaves. Skywave readings are corrected to the equivalent groundwave readings before entering the tables. A groundwave reading is designated T_G, and a skywave reading T_S. If a groundwave is matched with a skywave, the reading is labeled T_{GS} if the groundwave is from the master station, and T_{SG} if from the slave station. A line of position may appropriately be labeled with the time above the line and the identification below the line. It is good practice to give full identification, as 2H3 T_G 2154 or 1L0 T_S 1893 (T_G 1891).

SH

Lat. N	3H 4-6300 Lo	Δ	3H 4-6320 Lo	Δ	3H 4-6340 Lo	Δ	3H 4-6360 Lo	Δ	3H 4-6380 Lo	Δ
44	70 18.3W	-42	70 09.7W	-45	70 00.5W	-47	59 50.8W	-51	69 40.2W	-56
43 30	70 25.6	37	70 18.1	39	70 10.1	41	70 01.6	44	69 52.4	48
43	70 31.7	31	70 25.3	33	70 18.5	35	70 11.3	38	70 03.5	41
42 30	70 36.0	26	70 30.7	27	70 25.2	29	70 19.2	31	70 12.9	33
42	70 37.4	20	70 33.3	21	70 29.0	22	70 24.5	23	70 19.7	25

3H 4-6300 L	Δ	3H 4-6320 L	Δ	3H 4-6340 L	Δ	3H 4-6360 L	Δ	3H 4-6380 L	Δ	Long W
42 23.8N	+46	42 33.2N	+49	42 43.4N	+53	42 54.4N	+58	43 06.4N	+64	64
42 43.1	51	42 53.6	55	43 04.9	59	43 17.2	64	43 30.6	71	63
43 02.0	56	43 13.6	60	43 26.0	65	43 39.5	71	43 54.3	78	62
43 20.5	61	43 33.1	65	43 46.6	71	44 01.3	77	44 17.3	85	61
43 38.5	66	43 52.1	71	44 06.7	76	44 22.5	83	44 39.8	91	60
43 55.9N	+71	44 10.5N	+76	44 26.1N	+81	44 43.0N	+89	45 01.5N	+98	59
44 12.8	75	44 28.3	81	44 45.0	87	45 02.9	94	45 22.6	104	58
44 29.1	80	44 45.6	85	45 03.2	92	45 22.2	100	45 42.9	109	57
44 44.8	84	45 02.2	90	45 20.7	96	45 40.7	105	46 02.5	115	56
45 00.0N	+89	45 18.2N	+94	45 37.6N	+101	45 58.6N	+110	46 21.5N	+121	55

DB

Lat ° N	1H 2-2200 Lo	Δ	1H 2-2220 Lo	Δ	1H 2-2240 Lo	Δ	1H 2-2260 Lo	Δ	1H 2-2280 Lo	Δ	Long. °
51	70 55.2W	-82	70 39.2W	-79	70 23.7W	-76	70 08.6W	-74	69 53.9W	-73	
50	69 37.1	66	69 24.0	65	69 11.2	63	68 58.8	62	68 46.6	60	
49	68 23.5W	-54	68 12.9W	-52	68 02.6W	-51	67 52.6W	-50	67 42.7W	-49	
48	67 13.8	42	67 05.6	40	66 57.6	40	66 49.7	39	66 42.0	38	
47	66 07.9	31	66 01.8	30	65 55.9	30	65 50.0	29	65 44.3	28	
46 30	65 36.5	26	65 31.3	26	65 26.3	25	65 21.3	25	65 16.4	24	
46	65 06.1	22	65 01.8	21	64 57.6	21	64 53.4	21	64 49.3	20	
45 30N	64 36.9W	-18	64 33.3W	-18	64 29.8W	-17	64 26.4W	-17	64 23.0W	-17	
45	64 09.2	15	64 06.2	15	64 03.2	15	64 00.3	14	63 57.4	14	
44 30	63 43.3	13	63 40.7	13	63 38.0	13	63 35.4	13	63 32.8	13	
44	63 19.5	13	63 16.9	13	63 14.3	13	63 11.7	13	63 09.1	13	
43 30	62 57.6	14	62 54.8	14	62 51.9	14	62 49.1	14	62 46.2	14	
43	62 37.1W	-16	62 33.9W	-16	62 30.7W	-16	62 27.4W	-16	62 24.2W	-16	
42 30	62 17.6	18	62 13.9	18	62 10.2	18	62 06.5	19	62 02.7	19	
42	61 58.9	21	61 54.7	21	61 50.4	22	61 46.1	22	61 41.7	22	
41	61 23.0	27	61 17.7	27	61 12.2	28	61 06.7	28	61 01.1	28	
40	60 48.8	33	60 42.2	33	60 35.6	34	60 28.8	34	60 22.0	34	

FIGURE R7b.—Loran-A tables.

SH

	\multicolumn{15}{c	}{LONGITUDE WEST}	
Lat.	74	73	72	71	70	69	68	67	66	65	64	63	62	61	60
46	+36	41	+46	+50	+52	+52	+49	+45	41	35	+31	27	23	20	16
45	+46	+56							+53	+45	+38	32	27	22	19
44	+59									+56	+46	+37	+30	+25	+21
43											+52	41	33	26	22
42											+56	43	34	27	22
41											+55	42	33	26	21
40	+46										+49	38	30	24	20
39	+4	+35	+12	+38	+55	+24	+59	+52	+44	+51	+40	+32	+26	+21	+18
38	−50	−20				+1	29	30	27	37	31	26	21	18	15
37			−36	−7	+13	−12	+9	14	15	25	22	19	16	14	12
36			−51	−36	−13	−3	6			15	15	13	12	11	10
35					27					8	9	9	9	8	7
34	−57			−53	−33	−19	−10	−4	+1	+3	+4	+5	+6	+5	+5
33	−49		−53	−47	32	−21	−13	7	−3	−1	+1	+2	3	3	3
32	−41	36	41	40	29	−20	14	9	6	−3	−1	0	+1	2	2
31			32	32	25	−19	14	10	7	4	−2	−1	0	+1	+1
30			31	26	21	−16	13	9	7	4	−3	2	−1	0	0
29	−30	−28	−24	−21	−17	−14	−11	−9	−6	−5	−3	−2	−1	−1	0
28	−23	21	19	17	14	12	10	7	6	4	3	2	1	−1	0

Region labels appearing across the central band of the table:
ADD (upper region) — **SUBTRACT** (lower region) —
DO NOT USE SKY WAVES IN THIS REGION — **DO NOT USE HERE**

FIGURE R7c.—Skywave correction table for 3H4.

Example 1.—The 1900 DR position of a ship is lat. 42°48′.3N, long. 62°28′.3W. About this time Loran-A readings are obtained, as follows:

$$
\begin{array}{llll}
1859 & 3H4 & T_S & 6258 \\
1900 & 1H2 & T_G & 2229
\end{array}
$$

Required.—The 1900 fix.

Solution.—Enter the skywave correction table of 3H4 with the dead reckoning position, and find the correction, (+)37, by double interpolation. The equivalent groundwave reading is 6258+37=6295. Enter the 6300 column of the 3H4 table, with the following results:

Long.	Tab. lat	Δ	Corr.	Lat.
62°W	43°02′.0N	(+)56	(−)2′.8	42°59′.2N
63°W	42°43′.1N	(+)51	(−)2′.6	42°40′.5N

Next, enter the 2220 column of the 1H2 table, with the following results:

Lat.	Tab. long.	Δ	Corr.	Long.
42°30′N	62°13′.9W	(−)18	(−)1′.6	62°12′.3W
43°00′N	62°33′.9W	(−)16	(−)1′.4	62°32′.5W

Plot the two points of each line of position, and draw and label the lines. The common intersection of the two lines is the required fix, as shown in figure R7d.

Answer.—1900 fix: L 42°51′.0N, λ 62°26′.2W.

It is good practice to watch the scope for a few minutes before making a reading to be sure of correct identification of signals. If this is done for all rates before a reading is made, and skywave readings are made first, the intervals between readings can be kept to a minimum, and a skillful operator can often obtain two or three readings, over such a short period of time that the run between them can be ignored. However, where necessary, Loran lines of position should be advanced or retired in the same

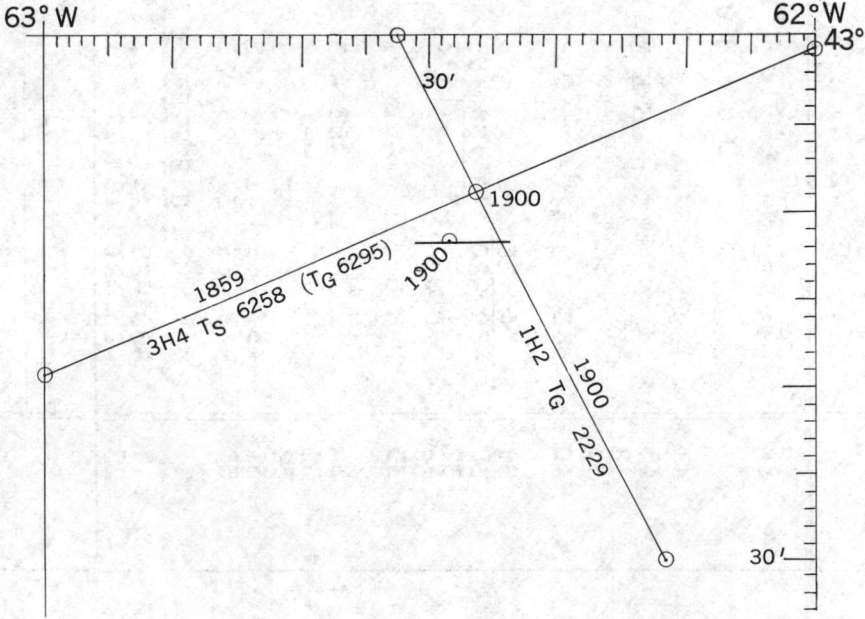

FIGURE R7d.—A Loran-A fix by table and plotting sheet.

manner as other lines of position. If all readings are made within an interval of a few minutes, as customary, the position is considered a fix, rather than a running fix, following the practice of celestial navigation (art. 1707) rather than that of piloting.

On Loran-A charts, the plotted lines are for groundwave readings. The small numbers near the intersections of printed meridians and parallels are one-hop-E skywave corrections at the intersections.

Eye interpolation can be used to locate lines between those printed. Graphs to facilitate such interpolation have been devised. When the correct position has been located, a short line is drawn parallel to the printed lines. The common intersection of the various lines of position, advanced or retired as necessary, is the fix.

APPENDIX S

CHARTS AND PUBLICATIONS OF OTHER AGENCIES

(Not for sale by the Defense Mapping Agency Hydrographic Center)

The following items are publications and charts about which the Defense Mapping Agency Hydrographic Center frequently receives inquiries. Application should be made to the authorities named.

Charts

United States waters and possessions.—Published by National Ocean Survey. Charts and related publications may be ordered from Distribution Division, C44, National Ocean Survey, Riverdale, Maryland 20840 (Counter Sales: 6501 Lafayette Avenue, Riverdale, Maryland—Lobby, Building 1, 6001 Executive Boulevard, Rockville, Maryland—439 West York Street, Norfolk, Virginia) or from authorized sales agents.

Orders mailed to Riverdale, Maryland should be accompanied by a check or money order payable to NOS, Department of Commerce. Remittance from outside of the United States should be made either by an International Money Order or by a check payable on a United States Bank.

Canadian coastal and Great Lakes waters.—Charts may be ordered from Hydrographic Chart Distribution Office, Department of the Environment, 1675 Russel Road, P.O. Box 8080, Ottawa, Ontario, KIG 3H6, Canada. Pacific Coast and Western Arctic charts may be ordered from Canadian Hydrographic Service, Department of the Environment, 512 Federal Building, Victoria, British Columbia. Payment in the form of a money order or bankable remittance payable in Canadian funds to the Receiver General of Canada must accompany an order. C.O.D. orders and postage stamps are not accepted.

Lower Mississippi River.—Charts and maps of the Mississippi River from the Gulf of Mexico to the Ohio River (also St. Francis, White, Big Sunflower, and other rivers) may be ordered from U. S. Army Corps of Engineers, Vicksburg District, P.O. Box 60, Vicksburg, Mississippi 39180.

Middle and Upper Mississippi River and Illinois Waterway to Lake Michigan.— Charts may be ordered from U. S. Army Corps of Engineers, Chicago District, 219 South Dearborn Street, Chicago, Illinois, 60604.

Missouri River.—Charts may be ordered from U. S. Army Corps of Engineers, Omaha District, U. S. Post Office and Courthouse, 215 North 17th Street, Omaha, Nebraska 68102.

Ohio River.—Charts may be ordered from U. S. Army Corps of Engineers, Ohio River Division, P.O. Box 1159, Cincinnati, Ohio 45201.

Tennessee River and tributaries.—Charts may be ordered from Tennessee Valley Authority, Map Sales, 400 Commerce Avenue (WP A3), Knoxville, Tennessee 37902.

Black Warrior River, Alabama River, Tombigbee River, Apalachicola River, Chattahooche River, Flint River, and Pearl River.—Charts may be ordered from U.S. Army Corps of Engineers, Mobile District, P.O. Box 2288, Mobile Alabama 36628 (Attention SAMEN–DI).

Gulf Intracoastal Waterway.—A *booklet* made from National Ocean Survey nautical charts and showing depths of water, channels, navigation markers, and types of bottom from New Orleans, Louisiana to St. Marks, Florida may be ordered from U.S. Army Engineer District, Mobile, P.O. Box 2288, Mobile, Alabama 36628 (Attention: SAMEN–DI). *Nautical charts* for the Gulf Intracoastal Waterway from Brownsville, Texas to New Orleans, Louisiana, and from St. Marks Florida to the Florida Keys may be obtained from Distribution Division, C44, National Ocean Survey, Riverdale, Maryland 20840.

National Ocean Survey Publications

Tide Tables, *Tidal Current Tables*, and *United States Coast Pilots* are sold by the Distribution Division, C44, National Ocean Survey, Riverdale, Maryland 20840, National Ocean Survey, and its agents.

U.S. Naval Observatory Publications

Air Almanac, *Nautical Almanac*, and *American Ephemeris* and *Nautical Almanac* are for sale by Superintendent of Documents, Government Printing Office, Washington, D.C. 20402.

U.S. Coast Guard Publications

Light Lists, United States coasts and possessions, are for sale by Coast Guard Sales Agents and by the Superintendent of Documents, Government Printing Office, Washington, D.C. 20402.

Navigation Rules, International—Inland, CG–169, *Rules of the Road, Western Rivers*, CG–184, and *Rules of the Road, Great Lakes*, CG–172, may be obtained upon request to U.S. Coast Guard Marine Inspection Offices or the Commandant (WLE–4/73), U.S. Coast Guard Headquarters, 400 Seventh Street, SW., Washington, D.C. 20590.

Local Notice to Mariners may be obtained free from the Commander of the local Coast Guard District.

National Weather Service Publications

Worldwide Marine Weather Broadcasts, published jointly by the Naval Weather Service Command and the National Weather Service of the National Oceanic and Atmospheric Administration, is for sale by the Distribution Division, C44, National Ocean Survey, Riverdale, Maryland 20840, Sales Agents of the National Ocean Survey, and by the Superintendent of Documents, Government Printing Office, Washington, D.C. 20402.

HAND-HELD DIGITAL CALCULATORS

T1. Introduction.—Many hand-held digital calculators are available for solving calculations in the practice of navigation. Any advantage obtained over manual or tabular methods through use of any one of these calculators is largely dependent upon the sophistication of the calculator, the user's familiarity with it, and the navigational problem involved. However, even the simplest calculator can be used to save time and increase reliability and accuracy in some common calculations. Since the sophistication of calculators is so diverse, they will be discussed in three general categories described here as **basic, intermediate,** and **advanced** or **programmable calculators.**

Basic Calculators

T2. Basic calculators can be used to add, subtract, multiply, and divide. Some calculators in this category can be used for obtaining square roots, reciprocals, and the logarithms of numbers, but they cannot be used for obtaining trigonometric functions or the inverse trigonometric functions. The basic calculators lack the addressable storage features of the more advanced calculators which can be used to facilitate arithmetic operations.

The navigational applications of the basic calculators include: (1) linear interpolation, (2) solution of basic formulas requiring only routine arithmetic operations, (3) use with tables of trigonometric functions for solutions of basic formulas involving trigonometric functions, and (4) other routine arithmetic operations.

T3. Linear interpolation.—The use of the basic calculator for linear interpolation is simple, accurate, reliable, and time saving. The calculator can be used to expedite the linear interpolations normally associated with the use of sight reduction tables. Note that the interpolation table of Pub. No. 229 does not always provide interpolations to the nearest tenth of a minute.

T4. Basic calculator with square root capability.—The basic calculators that provide the square roots of numbers can be used for the solution of several common navigation problems.

Distance to the visible horizon (art. 724, vol. II) in *nautical miles* can be calculated using the formula:

$$d = 1.15\sqrt{h_f}$$

or

$$d = 2.07\sqrt{h_m},$$

depending upon whether the height of eye of the observer above sea level is in *feet* (h_f) or in *meters* (h_m).

Dip of the visible horizon (art. 725, vol. II) in *minutes of arc* can be calculated using the formula:

$$D = 0\!'\!97\sqrt{h_f}$$

or

$$D = 1\!'\!76\sqrt{h_m},$$

depending upon whether the height of eye of the observer above sea level is in *feet* (h_f) or in *meters* (h_m).

Distance to the radar horizon (art. 1207, vol. II), in *nautical miles* can be calculated using the formula:

$$d = 1.22\sqrt{h_f}$$

or

$$d = 2.21\sqrt{h_m},$$

depending upon whether the height of the antenna above sea level is in *feet* (h_f) or in *meters* (h_m).

T5. Dip of the sea short of the horizon.—The basic calculator can be used instead of table 22 for the solution of the dip of the sea short of the horizon (art. 726, vol. II) by means of the formula:

$$D_s = 0.4156d + 0.5658\,\frac{h_f}{d}$$

or

$$D_s = 0.4156d + 0.1725\,\frac{h_m}{d},$$

in which D_s is the dip of the sea short of the horizon, in minutes of arc; d is the distance to the waterline of the obstruction, in nautical miles; and h_f and h_m are the heights of eye of the observer above sea level in feet and meters, respectively.

Values of dip of the sea short of the horizon in table 22 are for heights of eye in feet only.

T6. Use with tables of trigonometric functions.—The basic calculator can be used with tables of natural trigonometric functions (table 31) to avoid the use of logarithmic functions which might otherwise be necessary.

The solutions of the examples given in article 706 of volume II can be effected with the basic calculator if the natural trigonometric functions are extracted from table 31 or other table of trigonometric functions. The solutions by this method are generally more laborious and time consuming than the use of the intermediate calculator (art. T7) or modern sight reduction tables.

Intermediate Calculators

T7. Intermediate calculators provide the trigonometric functions and inverse trigonometric functions lacking in the basic calculator, but these calculators cannot be programmed. The intermediate calculators normally contain many of the special features which enhance the use of the calculator for solving navigational problems. In addition to the special features which the basic calculator may have, the intermediate calculator may have the capability for conversion of degrees and minutes to degrees and decimal degree, and for rectangular to polar coordinate conversion. These intermediate calculators usually have additional working storage registers and addressable storage registers for expeditious solution of the more complex arithmetic operations.

The intermediate calculators can be used for the solutions of most, if not all, of the problems normally encountered in marine navigation. Some of the applications of these intermediate calculators are discussed under the following categories: (1) sight reduction, (2) azimuth and amplitude solutions, and (3) the sailings.

T8. Sight reduction by basic formulas permits the use of the normally nonintegral values of latitude of the observer, and LHA and declination of the celestial body. The reductions are effected without need for the interpolation normally associated with the use of sight reduction tables of the inspection type. Solving the formulas by means of the intermediate calculator, the sights can be readily reduced from the observer's most probable position or any assumed position of his choice. Simultaneous, or nearly simultaneous, observations can be reduced using a single assumed position. The use of the most probable position for the assumed position instead of that position which would provide integral values of latitude and LHA to avoid interpolation for these quantities generally tends to provide a shorter straight line LOP, and thus a better representation of the circle of equal altitude (art. 1701).

The computed altitude is calculated using the basic formula for solution of the undivided navigational triangle (art. 706, vol. II):

$$\sin h = \sin L \sin d + \cos L \cos d \cos \text{LHA},$$

in which h is the altitude to be computed (Hc), L is the latitude of the assumed position for the reduction, d is the declination of the celestial body, and LHA is the local hour angle of the body. Meridian angle (t) can be substituted for LHA in the basic formula.

For use with the intermediate calculator, the basic formula is restated in terms of the inverse trigonometric function (art. 141, vol. II):

$$\text{Hc} = \sin^{-1} [(\sin L \sin d) + (\cos L \cos d \cos \text{LHA})].$$

When latitude and declination are of contrary name, declination is treated as a negative quantity. No special sign convention is required for the local hour angle as in the following azimuth angle calculations.

The azimuth angle (Z) can be calculated using the *altitude azimuth* formula (art. 709, vol. II) if the altitude is known. The formula stated in terms of the inverse trigonometric function is

$$Z = \cos^{-1} \left[\frac{\sin d - (\sin L \sin \text{Hc})}{(\cos L \cos \text{Hc})} \right].$$

If the altitude is unknown or a solution independent of altitude is required, the azimuth angle can be calculated using the *time azimuth* formula (art. 707, vol. II). The formula stated in terms of the inverse trigonometric function is

$$Z = \tan^{-1} \left[\frac{\sin \text{LHA}}{(\cos L \tan d) - (\sin L \cos \text{LHA})} \right].$$

The sign conventions used in the calculations of both azimuth formulas are as follows: (1) If latitude and declination are of contrary name, declination is treated as a negative quantity; (2) If the local hour angle is greater than 180°, it is treated as a negative quantity.

If the azimuth angle as calculated is negative, it is necessary to add 180° to obtain the desired value.

The calculation of altitude and azimuth angle by means of the intermediate calculator requires many individual key strokes. Error-free accomplishment of a large number of strokes is not easy. Skill can be obtained by practice using values differing by only a few minutes from the integral entering arguments of Pub. No. 229. The tabulated values in the tables provide a convenient means of checking the solution by calculator for gross error.

T9. Azimuths.—When checking the error of the compass by an azimuth observation of a celestial body, it is necessary to compute the azimuth for the time and place of observation for comparison with the observed azimuth. When tables are used for the purpose (art. 719, vol. II) tedious triple interpolation is usually required. When calculators are used, solution can be effected by one of several formulas, including the **time and altitude azimuth** formula:

$$\sin Z = \frac{\sin t \cos d}{\cos h}.$$

This formula is not generally recommended because of ambiguity with respect to quadrant as discussed in article 710 of volume II.

When the altitude is known and a solution independent of the altitude is not desired, solution can be effected by the **altitude azimuth** formula or by the **time azimuth** formula given in article T8.

Example.—In DR lat. 41°25'.9S, the azimuth of the sun is observed as 016°0 pgc. At the time of the observation, the declination of the sun is 22°19'.6N; the local hour angle of the sun is 342°37'.6.

Required.—The gyro error by calculation of

$$Z=\tan^{-1}\left[\frac{\sin \text{LHA}}{(\cos L \tan d)-(\sin L \cos \text{LHA})}\right],$$

using the intermediate calculator.

Preliminary.—(1) Convert each known quantity to degrees and decimal degree:

$$\begin{aligned}
&\text{Latitude } 41°25'.9S &&=41°.432 \\
&\text{Declination } 22°19'.6N &&=(-) 22°.327 \\
&\text{LHA } 342°37'.6 &&=(-) 342°.627
\end{aligned}$$

(2) Prepare form on which to record results obtained in the several procedural steps of the calculations.

Solution.—(1) Procedure varies according to calculator design and the degree to which the user employs the features of the design enabling more expeditious solutions.

(2) In this example, only the initial step of substituting the given quantities in the formula, in accordance with the sign conventions, is given before the azimuth angle as obtained by the calculator is stated.

$$Z=\tan^{-1}\left[\frac{\sin \text{LHA}}{(\cos L \tan d)-(\sin L \cos \text{LHA})}\right]$$

$$=\tan^{-1}\left[\frac{\sin (-) 342°.627}{(\cos 41°.432\times\tan (-) 22°.327)-(\sin 41°.432\times\cos (-) 342°.627)}\right]$$

$$Z=(-)17°.6.$$

(3) Since Z as calculated is a negative angle (−17°.6), 180° is added to obtain the desired azimuth angle, 162°.4.

$$\begin{aligned}
&Z &&S162°.4E \\
&Zn &&017°.6 \\
&Zn \text{ pgc } &&016°.0
\end{aligned}$$

Answer.—Gyro Error 1°.6E.

T10. Amplitudes (art. 720, vol. II) can be easily computed by means of the intermediate calculator. The basic formula is

$$A=\sin^{-1} (\sin d \sec L),$$

which can be stated as

$$A=\sin^{-1}\left(\frac{\sin d}{\cos L}\right).$$

Where A is the arc of the horizon between the prime vertical and the body, L is the latitude at the point of observation, and d is the declination of the celestial body, usually the sun.

Example.—The DR latitude of a ship is 51°24′.6N, at a time when the declination of the sun is 19°40′.4N.

Required.—The amplitude (A), when the center of the setting sun is on the celestial horizon, by calculation of $A = \sin^{-1}\left(\dfrac{\sin d}{\cos L}\right)$ using the intermediate calculator.

Preliminary.—(1) Convert each known quantity to degrees and decimal degree.

$$\text{Latitude } 51°24′.6\text{N} = 51°.410$$
$$\text{Declination } 19°40′.4\text{N} = 19°.673$$

(2) Prepare form on which to record results obtained in the several procedural steps of the calculations.

Rules.—(1) All terms are treated as positive quantities, whether or not latitude and declination are of contrary name.

(2) The amplitude is given the prefix E if the body is rising and W if it is setting; it is given the suffix N when the declination is north and the suffix S when the declination is south.

Solution.—(1) Procedure varies according to calculator design and the degree to which the user employs the features of the design enabling more expeditious solutions.

(2) In this example, only the initial step of substituting the given quantities in the formula, in accordance with the rules, is given before the amplitude as obtained by the calculator is stated.

$$A = \sin^{-1}\left(\frac{\sin d}{\cos L}\right)$$

$$= \sin^{-1}(\sin 19°.673 \div \cos 51°.410)$$

$$A = 32°.7$$

Answer.—A W32°.7N.

Interconversion of amplitude and azimuth is similar to that of azimuth angle and azimuth. Thus, if the amplitude is E15°S, the body is 15° south of east or 90°+15°=Zn 105°.

T11. Great-circle solutions for distance and initial course angle can be calculated from the formulas:

$$D = \cos^{-1}[(\sin L_1 \sin L_2) + (\cos L_1 \cos L_2 \cos \text{DLo})]$$

$$C = \tan^{-1}\left[\frac{\sin \text{DLo}}{(\cos L_1 \tan L_2) - (\sin L_1 \cos \text{DLo})}\right]$$

where D is the great-circle distance, C is the initial great-circle course angle, L_1 is the latitude of the point of departure, L_2 is the latitude of the destination, and DLo is the difference of longitude of the points of departure and destination. If the name of the latitude of the destination is contrary to that of the point of departure, it is treated as a negative quantity.

Example 1.—A ship is proceeding from Manila to Los Angeles. The captain desires to use great-circle sailing from lat. 12°45′.2N, long. 124°20′.1E, off the entrance to San Bernardino Strait, to lat. 33°48′.8N, long. 120°07′.1W, 5 miles south of Santa Rosa Island.

Required.—(1) The great-circle distance and

(2) initial great-circle course.

Preliminary.—(1) Convert each known quantity to degrees and decimal degree:

$$L_1 \; 12°45'.2N = 12°.753N$$

$$L_2 \; 33°48'.8N = 33°.813N$$

$$DLo \; 115°32'.8E = 115°.547E$$

(2) Prepare form on which to record results obtained in the several procedural steps of the calculations.

Rule.—When the latitudes of departure and destination are of contrary name, the latitude of the destination is treated as a negative quantity.

Solution.—(1) Procedure varies according to calculator design and the degree to which the user employs the features of the design enabling more expeditious solutions.

(2) In this example, only the initial step of substituting the given quantities in the formula, in accordance with the sign convention or rule, is given before the distance and course angle as obtained by the calculator are stated.

$$D = \cos^{-1}[(\sin L_1 \sin L_2) + (\cos L_1 \cos L_2 \cos DLo)]$$

$$= \cos^{-1}[(\sin 12°.753 \times \sin 33°.813) + (\cos 12°.753 \times \cos 33°.813 \times \cos 115°.547)]$$

$$D = 103°.099$$

$$C = \tan^{-1}\left[\frac{\sin DLo}{(\cos L_1 \tan L_2) - (\sin L_1 \cos DLo)}\right]$$

$$= \tan^{-1}\left[\frac{\sin 115°.547}{(\cos 12°.753 \times \tan 33°.813) - (\sin 12°.753 \times \cos 115°.547)}\right]$$

$$C = 50°.322$$

Answers.—(1) D 6,186 nautical miles.

(2) C N50°.3E, Cn 050°.3.

The Vertex

The latitude of the vertex, L_v, is always numerically equal to or greater than L_1 or L_2. If initial course angle, C, is less than 90°, the nearer vertex is toward L_2; but if C is greater than 90°, the nearer vertex is in the opposite direction. The vertex nearer L_1 has the same name as L_1.

The latitude of the vertex can be calculated from the formula:

$$L_v = \cos^{-1}(\cos L_1 \sin C).$$

The difference of longitude of the vertex and the point of departure (DLo_v) can be calculated from the formula:

$$DLo_v = \sin^{-1}\left(\frac{\cos C}{\sin L_v}\right).$$

The distance from the point of departure to the vertex (D_v) can be calculated from the formula:

$$D_v = \sin^{-1}(\cos L_1 \sin DLo_v).$$

Example 2.—The situation is the same as in example 1.

Required.—(1) The latitude of the vertex.

     (2) The longitude of the vertex.

     (3) The distance from the point of departure to the vertex.

Solution.—(1) Procedure varies according to calculator design and the degree to which the user employs the design features enabling more expeditious solutions.

(2) In this example, only the initial steps of substituting the given quantities in the formulas are given before the latitude of the vertex, difference of longitude of the vertex, and the distance from the point of departure to the vertex are stated.

$$L_v = \cos^{-1}\,[\cos L_1 \sin C]$$

$$= \cos^{-1}\,[\cos 12°753 \times \sin 50°322]$$

Answers.—(1) $L_v = 41°21'1\text{N}.$

$$\text{DLo}_v = \sin^{-1}\left[\frac{\cos C}{\sin L_v}\right]$$

$$= \sin^{-1}\,[\cos 50°322 \div \sin 41°353]$$

$$\text{DLo}_v = 75°05'8.$$

(2) $\lambda_v = 160°34'1\,\text{W}.$

$$D_v = \sin^{-1}\,[\cos L_1 \sin \text{DLo}_v]$$

$$= \sin^{-1}\,[\cos 12°753 \times \sin 75°097]$$

$$D_v = 70°480.$$

(3) 4,229 nautical miles.

Points on the Great-Circle Track

DLo_v and D_v of the nearer vertex are never greater than 90°. However, when L_1 and L_2 are of contrary name, the other vertex, 180° away, may be the better one to use in the solution for points on the great-circle track if it is nearer the mid point of the track.

The latitudes of points on the great-circle track can be determined for equal DLo intervals each side of the vertex (DLo_{vx}) using the formula:

$$L_x = \tan^{-1}\,(\cos \text{DLo}_{vx} \tan L_v).$$

Example 3.—Same situation as example 1.

Required.—Points on the great-circle track for equal DLo intervals each side of the vertex (DLo_{vx}).

Preliminary.—Select DLo interval appropriate for latitude and speed of advance, 12°.

Solution.—(1) Procedure varies according to calculator design and the degree to which the user employs the design features enabling more expeditious solutions.

(2) In this example, only the initial steps of substituting the given quantities in the formulas are given before the latitudes of points on the great-circle track are stated.

$$L_x = \tan^{-1}\,[\cos \text{DLo}_{vx} \tan L_v]$$

$$= \tan^{-1}\,[\cos 12° \times \tan 41°353]$$

$$L_x = 40°726.$$

Answers.—(1) $\qquad L_x = 40°43'.6.$

$$\lambda_x = 172°34'.1\,W\,(12°W \text{ of } \lambda_v).$$

$$\lambda_x = 148°34'.1\,W\,(12°E \text{ of } \lambda_v).$$

$$L_x = \tan^{-1}\,[\cos 24° \times \tan 41°.353]$$

$$L_x = 38°.802$$

(2) $\qquad L_x = 38°48'.1.$

$$\lambda_x = 175°25'.6\,E\,(24°W \text{ of } \lambda_v).$$

$$\lambda_x = 136°34'.1\,W\,(24°E \text{ of } \lambda_v).$$

Other points are similarly found.

Alternative Solution for Points on Track

The method of selecting the longitude (or DLo_{vx}) and determining the latitude at which the great-circle crosses the selected meridian provides shorter legs in higher latitudes and longer legs in lower latitudes. Points at desired distances or desired equal intervals of distance on the great-circle from the vertex can be calculated using the formulas:

$$L_x = \sin^{-1}\,[\sin L_v \cos D_{vx}]$$

$$\mathrm{DLo}_{vx} = \sin^{-1}\left[\frac{\sin D_{vx}}{\cos L_x}\right].$$

Example 4.—Same situation as example 1.

Required.—Points on the great-circle track at equal intervals of distance from the vertex.

Preliminary.—Select distance intervals appropriate for speed of advance, 300 nautical miles (5°).

Solution.—(1) Procedure varies according to calculator design and the degree to which the user employs the design features enabling more expeditious solutions.

(2) In this example, only the initial steps of substituting the given quantities in the formulas are given before the latitude and the difference of longitude of the point at the desired distance from the vertex are stated.

$$L_x = \sin^{-1}\,[\sin L_v \cos D_{vx}]$$

$$= \sin^{-1}\,[\sin 41°.353 \times \cos 5°]$$

$$L_x = 41°.161$$

$$L_x = 41°09'.7\,N.$$

$$\mathrm{DLo}_{vx} = \sin^{-1}\left[\frac{\sin D_{vx}}{\cos L_x}\right]$$

$$= \sin^{-1}\,[\sin 5° \div \cos 41°.353]$$

$$\mathrm{DLo}_{vx} = 6°.667$$

$$\mathrm{DLo}_{vx} = 6°40'.0.$$

Answer.—(1) $L_x 41°09'.7N.$

$\lambda_x 153°54'.1W.$

$\lambda_x 167°14'.1W.$

$L_x = \sin^{-1}[\sin L_v \cos D_{vx}]$

$= \sin^{-1}[\sin 41°.353 \times \cos 10°]$

$L_x = 40°.591$

$L_x = 40°35'.5N.$

$DLo_{vx} = \sin^{-1}\left[\dfrac{\sin D_{vx}}{\cos L_x}\right]$

$= \sin^{-1}[\sin 10° \div \cos 41°.353]$

$DLo_{vx} = 13°.375$

$DLo_{vx} = 13°22'.5.$

(2) $L_x = 40°35'.55N.$

$\lambda_x = 147°11'.6W(300 \text{ miles W of } \lambda_v).$

$\lambda_x = 173°56'.6W(300 \text{ miles E of } \lambda_v).$

Other points are similarly found.

T12. Plane sailings.—A calculator having the rectangular to polar coordinate conversion feature affords expeditious solutions of plane sailings. However, the user must keep in mind whether the *difference of latitude corresponds to the calculator's X-coordinate or to its Y-coordinate.*

Example 1.—A vessel steams 188 miles on course 005°.

Required.—(1) Difference of latitude, (2) departure.

Solution.—(1) This problem involves converting polar coordinates (188 miles, 005°) to rectangular coordinates.

(2) Procedure varies according to calculator design.

X-coordinate 187.285
Y-coordinate 16.385

Answer.—(1) l 187'.3 N.
          (2) p 16.4 mi. E.

Advanced Calculators

T13. Advanced or programmable calculators have the potential for significantly reducing the quantity and complexity of the navigator's computational workload. Properly programmed calculators now available have the capability for "memorizing" and executing specific keystroke sequences required in the solution of a problem. This feature eliminates the requirement for calculating each step of a formula when using the basic or intermediate calculator. The need for format conversion (i.e., degrees and minutes to degrees and decimal degree) and calculating the formula in a specific order is no longer necessary. Thus, computation time is greatly reduced along with chances for human error.

Sight reduction speed is further enhanced when the "memory" of the calculator is stored with almanac data.

Other advantages to be derived from an advanced calculator include:

1. Relatively error-free reductions of a large number of celestial observations to improve position information.

2. Enables navigators to concentrate more on analysis and evaluation by freeing them from time-consuming and error prone repetitious tasks.

APPENDIX U

UNDERWATER LOG CALIBRATION GUIDELINES

U1. Introduction.—During the calibration of the underwater log on the measured mile course, the applicable requirements and procedures specified for the ship's standardization trial should be followed as closely as possible. The calibration should not be conducted when the effects of wind and sea can materially affect the accuracy of the results. Preferably, the measured mile should be run in a calm sea. The following guidelines do not include the computational procedures and equipment adjustments which may be found in the manufacturer's manual for the log being calibrated.

Guidelines

U2. Limiting sea and wind conditions.—The recommended maximum sea and wind conditions are sea state 3 and wind force 5 on the Beaufort scale (app. V). No more than 3° of rudder movement should be required to steer a steady course while on the measured mile. Excessive use of the rudder will reduce the accuracy of the calibration.

U3. Minimum depths.—The runs should be made on measured miles where the water is of such depth that shallow-water effects will not be experienced. A reasonable estimate of the required minimum depth in feet in the approach, measured mile, and turn around area is three times the square root of the product of the ship's beam and draft in feet, or 0.3 times the square of the ship's speed in knots, whichever is greater.

U4. Tidal current.—Each series of runs of the measured mile at the same speed must be made while the tidal current is running in the same direction. The method of averaging which compensates for water current will produce correct ship's speed only if the speed of the tidal current is increasing or decreasing uniformly with time. The time interval between runs of a series should be kept reasonably constant. If the first run of a series starts, for example, at 0900 and the second at 0920, then the third run should start at about 0940.

U5. Draft and trim.—Unless the log is to be calibrated for different loadings or different displacements, the runs should be made at normal trim and at approximately average draft.

U6. Propeller RPM.—During the run of the measured mile at a specific speed, RPM must be maintained constant within a tolerance of plus or minus two RPM's. If this tolerance is exceeded during any run, the data for the run should be discarded; the run should be repeated. To insure that the ship has reached its terminal speed for the RPM during a run, the ship must be steady on course at the required RPM when at least 1 mile from the range of the first set of markers. The speed at the various RPM's is obtained in addition to the log calibration data.

U7. Runs required.—A series of three consecutive runs, alternating in direction, should be made for each speed for which the log is to be calibrated. If any run must be discarded, additional runs must be made to obtain three consecutive runs alternating in direction. The effects of current and sea conditions being additive in one direction and subtractive in the other direction, the data for the second run of a series is used as a hypothetical fourth run in calculating the average speed through the water. The mathematical derivation is referred to as a mean of means. The correct mean value for speed and the RPM is the sum of the data for the first and third runs plus two times the data for the second run, and this sum total divided by four. This can be stated in the following formula:

$$v_m = \frac{v_1 + 2v_2 + v_3}{4}.$$

After a run has been completed in one direction, the ship should be taken well beyond the measured mile course and turned without excessive use of rudder so that the same track will be repeated on the following run. The limit on the rudder angle is to limit the loss of speed during the turn. The ship should be taken well away from the measured mile course to insure sufficient time to reach terminal speed for the RPM prior to passing the range of the first set of markers on the following run. The ship should be steady on course at the required RPM when at least 1 mile from the first set of markers.

In calibrating an electromagnetic log, each series of runs must be made at a speed as specified in the manufacturer's instruction manual. Thus, the number of runs and speeds during each series of runs are governed by equipment design. As specified in the manufacturer's instruction manual, a series of runs may have to be discarded if the speeds ascertained are not within certain limits.

Advance Preparations

U8. Advance preparations.—Complete calibration of the underwater log may require a full working day in an area distant from the area of the ship's normal operations. Advance preparations should include equipment tests in accordance with the manufacturer's instruction manual, and practice runs on a simulated measured mile to insure that the log is functioning properly (except for calibration) and that personnel are familiar with the procedures to be followed.

U9. Verification.—Since the markers for measured-mile courses are not U. S. Coast Guard maintained aids to navigation, advance preparation should include verification that the markers are in place.

Duties of Observers

U10. Duties of observers.—Two observers on the navigation bridge must make independent observations of the time required to run the measured mile. One bridge observer acts as coordinator; the other insures that the course is held steady during the run and that excessive rudder is not used. Approximately 3 minutes before the first set of markers are "in range" (or "in transit") the coordinator calls out "Get ready." A few seconds before the first set of markers are in range, the coordinator calls out "Stand by." At the instant the first set of markers are in range by his observation, the coordinator calls out "Mark" and simultaneously starts his stopwatch. The other bridge observer starts his stopwatch at the instant of his independent observation that the first set of markers are in range.

The engine room observer records the shaft RPM at the coordinator's "Mark" and at each 15-second interval thereafter during the run. The engine room observer insures that the tolerance of + or − two RPM's is not exceeded during the run.

The log observer determines the time required for the distance counter to increase 1 mile. He does not necessarily record the mileage on the counter and start his stopwatch at the instant of the coordinator's "Mark." Because of the difficulty of reading intermediate values on the counter, the normal procedure is to delay the log distance timing until such time after the coordinator's "Mark" that the bottom of the hundredths digit just appears in the window of the counter.

An assistant log observer may be employed for independent timing of the distance counter and for recording of data.

The coordinator must insure that speed and course are held steady until such time that the log counter has registered an increase of 1 mile. An initial high negative error in the log may extend the run several seconds beyond the time the second set of markers are in range. By comparing the time required to run the measured mile with the time required for the log counter to increase exactly 1 mile the percentage error of the log can be determined.

While running the measured mile for calibration of an electromagnetic log, the instantaneous readings of the speed dial can be ignored.

APPENDIX V
BEAUFORT WIND SCALE
WITH CORRESPONDING SEA STATE CODES

Beaufort number or force	Wind speed				World Meteorological Organization (1964)	Effects observed far from land	Effects observed near coast	Effects observed on land	Sea State	
	knots	mph	meters per second	km per hour					Term and height of waves, in meters	Code
0	under 1	under 1	0.0–0.2	under 1	Calm	Sea like mirror.	Calm.	Calm; smoke rises vertically.	Calm, glassy, 0	0
1	1–3	1–3	0.3–1.5	1–5	Light air	Ripples with appearance of scales; no foam crests.	Fishing smack just has steerage way.	Smoke drift indicates wind direction; vanes do not move.	Calm, rippled, 0–0.1	1
2	4–6	4–7	1.6–3.3	6–11	Light breeze	Small wavelets; crests of glassy appearance, not breaking.	Wind fills the sails of smacks which then travel at about 1–2 miles per hour.	Wind felt on face; leaves rustle; vanes begin to move.	Smooth, wavelets, 0.1–0.5	2
3	7–10	8–12	3.4–5.4	12–19	Gentle breeze	Large wavelets; crests begin to break; scattered whitecaps.	Smacks begin to career and travel about 3–4 miles per hour.	Leaves, small twigs in constant motion; light flags extended.	Slight, 0.5–1.25	3
4	11–16	13–18	5.5–7.9	20–28	Moderate breeze	Small waves, becoming longer; numerous whitecaps.	Good working breeze, smacks carry all canvas with good list.	Dust, leaves, and loose paper raised up; small branches move.	Moderate, 1.25–2.5	4
5	17–21	19–24	8.0–10.7	29–38	Fresh breeze	Moderate waves, taking longer form; many whitecaps; some spray.	Smacks shorten sail.	Small trees in leaf begin to sway.	Rough, 2.5–4	5
6	22–27	25–31	10.8–13.8	39–49	Strong breeze	Larger waves forming; whitecaps everywhere; more spray.	Smacks have doubled reef in mainsail; care required when fishing.	Larger branches of trees in motion; whistling heard in wires.	Very rough, 4–6	6
7	28–33	32–38	13.9–17.1	50–61	Near gale	Sea heaps up; white foam from breaking waves begins to be blown in streaks.	Smacks remain in harbor and those at sea lie-to.	Whole trees in motion; resistance felt in walking against wind.		
8	34–40	39–46	17.2–20.7	62–74	Gale	Moderately high waves of greater length; edges of crests begin to break into spindrift; foam is blown in well-marked streaks.	All smacks make for harbor, if near.	Twigs and small branches broken off trees; progress generally impeded.	High, 6–9	7
9	41–47	47–54	20.8–24.4	75–88	Strong gale	High waves; sea begins to roll; dense streaks of foam; spray may reduce visibility.		Slight structural damage occurs; slate blown from roofs.		
10	48–55	55–63	24.5–28.4	89–102	Storm	Very high waves with overhanging crests; sea takes white appearance as foam is blown in very dense streaks; rolling is heavy and visibility reduced.		Seldom experienced on land; trees broken or uprooted; considerable structural damage occurs.		
11	56–63	64–72	28.5–32.6	103–117	Violent storm	Exceptionally high waves; sea covered with white foam patches; visibility still more reduced.		Very rarely experienced on land; usually accompanied by widespread damage.	Very high, 9–14	8
12	64 and over	73 and over	32.7 and over	118 and over	Hurricane	Air filled with foam; sea completely white with driving spray; visibility greatly reduced.			Phenomenal, over 14	9

Note: Since January 1, 1955, weather map symbols have been based upon wind speed in knots, at five-knot intervals, rather than upon Beaufort number.

APPENDIX W

SEA STATE

This appendix provides, by means of representative photographs illustrating the effects of the wind on the sea surface, a pictorial guide to mariners for estimating the wind speed at sea.

The photographs and associated text are taken from *State of Sea Photographs for the Beaufort Wind Scale*, Crown Copyright, Ottawa, 1975. The material is reprinted with minor changes through permission of the Atmospheric Environment Service, Department of the Environment, Canada.

State of Sea Photographs for the Beaufort Wind Scale

W1. Introduction.—This appendix presents the results of a project carried out on board the Canadian Ocean Weather Ships C.C.G.S. *St. Catharines* and C.C.G.S. *Stonetown*. The aim of the project was to collect photographs of the sea surface as it appears under the influence of the various ranges of wind speed defined by The Beaufort Scale of Wind Force (app. V). Word descriptions of the appearance of the sea for each Beaufort Force have been available for many years, but it was felt that photographs illustrating the conditions associated with each force would be of some assistance to ships' officers in estimating wind speed. Sea photographs taken by low-flying aircraft of the United States Navy were published by the Meteorological Branch under a circular memorandum dated December 20, 1957. However, these aerial photographs, while good, do not depict the aspect of the sea as viewed from the bridge of a ship. The apparent lack of good photographs of this nature prompted this project on the Ocean Weather Ships. A selection of the best photographs resulting from the project are presented.

W2. Estimating the wind at sea.—Observers on board ships at sea usually determine the speed of the wind by estimating its Beaufort Force, as merchant ships are not normally equipped with wind measuring instruments. Through experience, ships' officers have developed various methods of estimating this force. The effect of the wind on the observer himself, the ship's rigging, flags, etc., is used as a criterion; but, estimates based on these indications give the relative wind which must be corrected for the motion of the ship before an estimate of the true wind speed can be obtained.

The most common method involves the appearance of the sea surface. The state of the sea disturbance, i.e. the dimensions of the waves, the presence of white caps, foam or spray, depends principally on three factors:

1. *The wind speed.* The higher the speed of the wind, the greater is the sea disturbance.

2. *The duration of the wind.* At any point on the sea, the disturbance will increase the longer the wind blows at a given speed, until a maximum state of disturbance is reached.

3. *The fetch.* This is the length of the stretch of water over which the wind acts on the sea surface from the same direction. For a given wind speed and duration, the longer the fetch, the greater is the sea disturbance. If the fetch is short, say a few miles, the disturbance will be relatively small no matter how great the wind speed is or how long it has been blowing.

There are other factors which can modify the appearance of the sea surface caused by wind alone. These are strong currents, shallow water, swell, precipitation, ice, and wind shifts. Their affects will be described later.

A wind of a given Beaufort Force will, therefore, produce a characteristic appearance of the sea surface provided that it has been blowing for a sufficient length of time, and over a sufficiently long fetch. The effects of currents, shallow water, swell, precipitation, etc., should also be absent. The "Sea Criteria" associated with each Beaufort Force from force 0 to force 12 were agreed upon and drawn up by the International Meteorological Committee in 1939. These word descriptions of the state of the sea are known as the Sea Criterion of the Beaufort Scale of Wind Force.

The use of the sea criterion has the advantage that the speed of the ship need not be considered. In practice, the mariner observes the sea surface, noting the size of the waves, the white caps, spindrift, etc., and then finds the criterion (app. V) which best describes the sea surface as he saw it. This criterion is associated with a Beaufort number, for which a corresponding mean wind speed and range in knots are given. Since meteorological reports require that wind speeds be reported in knots, the mean speed for the Beaufort number may be reported, or an experienced observer may judge that the sea disturbance is such that a higher or lower speed within the range for the force is more accurate.

This method, while it appears simple, should be used with caution however. It should be borne in mind that the sea conditions described for each Beaufort Force (app. V) are "steady-state" conditions; i.e. the conditions which result when the wind has been blowing for a relatively long time, and over a great stretch of water. At any particular time at sea, though, the duration of the wind or the fetch, or both, may not have been great enough to produce these "steady-state" conditions. When a high wind springs up suddenly after previously calm or near calm conditions, it will require some hours, depending on the strength of the wind, to generate waves of maximum height. The height of the waves increases rapidly in the first few hours after the commencement of the blow, but increases at a much slower rate later on. Considering the effect of fetch, if the observer could start at the beginning of the fetch (say at a coastline when the wind is offshore) after the wind has been blowing for a long time, and proceed downwind, he would notice that the waves were quite small at the beginning, and increased in height rapidly over the first 50 miles or so of the fetch. Farther along he would notice that the rate of increase in height with distance would slow down, and after 500 miles or so from the beginning of the fetch there would be little or no increase in height.

To illustrate the duration of winds and the length of fetches required for various wind forces to build seas to 50 percent, 75 percent, and 90 percent of their theoretical maximum heights, table W2 is of interest.

The theoretical maximum wave heights represent the average heights of the highest third of the waves, as these waves are of the most practical significance.

It will be seen that winds of force 5 or less can build seas to 90 percent of their maximum height in less than 12 hours, provided the fetch is long enough. Higher winds require a much greater time—force 11 winds requiring 32 hours to build waves to 90 percent of their maximum height. The times given in table W2 represent those required to build waves starting from initially calm sea conditions. If waves are already present at the onset of the blow, the times would be somewhat less depending on the initial wave heights and their direction relative to the direction of the wind which has sprung up.

The first consideration when using the sea criterion to estimate wind speed, therefore, is to decide whether the wind has been blowing long enough from the same direction to produce a steady state sea condition. If not, then it is possible that the wind speed may be underestimated. For example, if a wind with an actual speed of force 9 has been blowing for only 7 hours, it may have generated a sea condition which would perhaps correspond to a steady state for force 6. If, in this case, the sea criterion was used blindly without considering the short duration, and force 6 was reported, then the wind would be underestimated by three Beaufort forces, or approximately 20 knots. This is an extreme example however, as it is very unlikely that even an inexperienced seaman could not distinguish a force 6 from a force 9 wind.

Beaufort force of wind.	Theoretical maximum wave height (ft) unlimited duration and fetch.	Duration jof winds, (hours), with unlimited fetch, to produce percent of maximum wave height indicated.			Fetch (nautical miles), with unlimited duration of blow, to produce percent of maximum wave height indicated.		
		50%	75%	90%	50%	75%	90%
3	2	1. 5	5	8	3	13	25
5	8	3. 5	8	12	10	30	60
7	20	5. 5	12	21	22	75	150
9	40	7	16	25	55	150	280
11	70	9	19	32	85	200	450

TABLE—W2.

Experience has shown that the appearance of white caps, foam, spindrift, etc., reaches a steady state condition before the height of the waves attain their maximum value. It is a safe assumption that the appearance of the sea (as regards white caps, etc.) will reach a steady state in the time required to build the waves to 50—75 percent of their maximum height. Thus, from table W2, it is seen that a force 5 wind could require 8 hours at most to produce a characteristic appearance of the sea surface.

A second consideration when using the sea criterion is the length of the fetch over which the wind has been blowing to produce the present state of the sea. On the open sea, unless the mariner has a copy of the latest synoptic weather map available, he will not know the length of the fetch. It will be seen from table W2, though, that only relatively short fetches are required for the lower wind forces to generate their characteristic seas. On the open sea, the fetches associated with most storms and other weather systems are usually long enough so that even winds up to force 9 can build seas up to 90 percent or more of their maximum height, providing the wind blows from the same direction long enough.

When navigating close to a coast or in restricted waters, however, it may be necessary to make allowances for the shorter stretches of water over which the wind blows. For example, referring to table W2, if the ship is 22 miles from a coast and an offshore wind with an actual speed of force 7 is blowing, the waves at the ship will never attain more than 50 percent of their maximum height for this speed no matter how long the wind blows. Hence, if the sea criterion were used under these conditions without consideration of the short fetch, the wind speed would be underestimated. With an offshore wind, the sea criterion may be used with confidence if the distance to the coast is greater than the values given in the extreme right-hand column of table W2; again, provided that the wind has been blowing offshore for a sufficient length of time.

Other factors aside from the duration of the blow and the fetch affect the appearance of the sea surface, and should be considered if they are present.

W3. Tides and Currents.—A wind blowing against a tide or strong current causes a greater sea disturbance than normal, which may result in an overestimate of the wind speed. On the other hand, a wind blowing in the same direction as a tide or strong current causes less sea disturbance than normal, and may result in an underestimate of the wind speed.

W4. Shallow Water.—Waves running into shallow water increase in steepness, and hence, their tendency to break. With an onshore wind there will, therefore, be more white caps over the shallow waters than over the deeper water farther offshore. It is only over relatively deep water that the sea criterion can be used with confidence.

W5. Swell.—Swell is the name given to waves, generally of considerable length, which were raised in some distant area by winds blowing there, and which have moved into the vicinity of the ship; or to waves raised nearby and which continue to advance after the wind at the ship has abated or changed direction. The direction of swell waves is usually different from the direction of the wind and the sea waves. *Swell waves are not to be considered when estimating wind speed and direction. Only those waves raised by the wind blowing at the time are of any significance.* The wind-driven waves show a greater tendency to break when superimposed on the crests of swell, and hence more white caps may be formed than if the swell were absent. Under these conditions the use of the sea criterion may result in a slight overestimate of the wind speed.

W6. Precipitation.—Heavy rain has a damping or smoothing effect on the sea surface which must be mechanical in character. Since the sea surface will therefore appear less disturbed than would be the case without the rain, the wind speed may be underestimated unless the smoothing effect is taken into account.

W7. Ice.—Even small concentrations of ice floating on the sea surface will dampen waves considerably, and concentrations greater than about seven tenths average will eliminate waves altogether. Young sea ice, which in the early stages of formation has a thick soupy consistency, and later takes on a rubbery appearance, is very effective in dampening waves. Consequently, the sea criterion cannot be used with any degree of confidence when sea ice is present. In higher latitudes, the presence of an ice field some distance to windward of the ship may be suspected if, when the ship is not close to any coast, the wind is relatively strong but the seas abnormally underdeveloped. The edge of the ice field acts like a coastline, and the short fetch between the ice and the ship is not sufficient for the wind to develop the seas fully.

W8. Wind shifts.—Following a rapid change in the direction of the wind, as occurs at the passage of a cold front, the new wind will flatten out to a great extent the waves which were present before the wind shift. This is so because the direction of the wind after the shift may differ by 90° or more from the direction of the waves, which does not change. Hence, the wind may oppose the progress of the waves and dampen them out quickly. At the same time the new wind begins to generate its own waves on top of this dissipating swell, and it is not long before the cross pattern of waves gives the sea a "choppy" or confused appearance. It is during the first few hours following the wind shift that the appearance of the sea surface may not provide a reliable indication of the wind speed. The wind is normally stronger than the sea would indicate, as old waves are being flattened out, and new waves are just beginning to be developed.

W9. Night Observations.—On a dark night, when it is impossible to see the sea clearly, the observer may estimate the apparent wind from its effect on the ship's rigging, flags, etc., or simply the "feel" of the wind. A guide to estimating the apparent wind is given in the Meteorological Branch publication *Manual of Marine Weather Observing* (MANMAR), to which the observer is referred. Tables for converting the apparent wind to true wind may also be found in MANMAR.

The State of Sea Photographs

The photographs were taken by the Meteorological Branch personnel of the Canadian Ocean Weather Ships C.C.G.S. *St. Catharines* and C.C.G.S. *Stonetown* which occupy Ocean Weather Station "P" in the North Pacific Ocean at 50°N, 145°W, or approximately 1,000 miles west of Vancouver. The ships man the station for alternate periods of 6 weeks.

The photographs were taken between March, 1960 and May, 1961. In this period a total of 247 photographs were obtained. Zeiss Ikon (2¼×3¼) cameras and Kodak Verichrome Pan film were used.

Of the 247 pictures available, 2 pictures were chosen to illustrate conditions associated with each Beaufort force from force 1 to force 10. Only one picture was considered acceptable to illustrate force 0. No representative photographs were available to illustrate force 11 conditions, and no photographs were made of force 12 conditions.

In selecting the pictures for presentation here, it was considered that they should meet two requirements. Firstly, a picture illustrating the effects of a given wind force should conform as closely as possible to the Sea Criterion for that force. Secondly, the wind prior to the time of the picture should be relatively steady both in direction and at the given force over many hours to ensure that near steady-state sea conditions for that force at the time of the picture existed. A large percentage of the photographs available were rejected because the wind at the time of the picture had not been blowing long enough to produce a disturbance of near steady-state proportion.

The pictures which follow were judged to fulfill best the requirements stated above. Opposite each picture is the accompanying technical and other data appropriate to each. In addition to the wind at the time of the photograph, the wind at 3-hourly intervals over the previous 24 hours is also included. The height of the ships' anemometers above the sea surface was approximately 60 feet. The synoptic weather situation at the time of the picture is described briefly, and other comments are given when warranted.

BEAUFORT FORCE 0

Wind speed less than 1 knot

Sea Criterion: Sea like a mirror.

Date/Time of photograph: June 5, 1960, 2340 GMT.

Height of Camera above sea: 35 Feet.

Time (GMT)	Direction (°T)	Wind speed (kn)
2340	—	calm
2100	190	01
1800	080	03
1500	040	07
1200	040	09
0900	030	10
0600	030	11
0300	030	11
0000	040	10

Waves at time of picture

	Direction (°T)	Period (sec.)	Height (ft.)
Sea Waves	—	—	—
Swell	100°	5	2

Synoptic Situation

High pressure area centered at 49°N, 144°W, or approximately 50 nautical miles southeast of ship at time of picture. Center of high moving southeastward.

Remarks

Calm winds, and hence calm sea conditions, are rare at Station "P," occurring only about 1.5 percent of the time during the course of a year. Although the wind was essentially calm during the 3 hours prior to this photograph, it averaged 4 knots (force 2) over the previous 12 hours, and 7 knots (force 3) in the previous 24 hours. Air temperature 52.2F, sea temperature 45.7F.

Crown Copyright, Ottawa, 1975. Reprinted through permission of the Atmospheric Environment Service, Department of the Environment, Canada.

Crown Copyright, Ottawa, 1975. Reprinted through permission of the Atmospheric Environment Service, Department of the Environment, Canada.

BEAUFORT FORCE 0   SEA STATE 0

BEAUFORT FORCE 1

Wind Speed 1 to 3 knots, mean 2 knots

Sea Criterion: Ripples with the appearance of scales are formed, but without foam crests.

Date/Time of Photograph: May 22, 1960, 2000 GMT.

Height of camera above sea: 35 feet.

Time (GMT)	Direction (°T)	Wind speed (kn)
2000	290	02
1800	—	calm
1500	220	04
1200	260	08
0900	280	02
0600	—	calm
0300	290	10
0000	290	12
2100	290	13

Waves at time of picture

	Direction (°T)	Period (sec.)	Height (ft.)
Sea Waves	—	—	—
Swell	290	10	3

Synoptic situation

The station was near the center of a narrow ridge of high pressure which extended northward into the Gulf of Alaska from a high centered near 30°N, 147°W. A low pressure area, elongated in a north-south direction, lay just off the coast of Canada and the United States. Another low was centered in the eastern Bering Sea.

Remarks

Winds averaged less than 3 knots (force 1) over the previous 14 hours, and less than 6 knots (force 2) over the previous 24 hours. Air temperature 44°F, sea temperature 44°F.

Crown Copyright, Ottawa, 1975. Reprinted through permission of the Atmospheric Environment Service, Department of the Environment, Canada.

BEAUFORT FORCE 1   **SEA STATE 0**

BEAUFORT FORCE 2

Wind speed 4 to 6 knots, mean 5 knots

Sea criterion: Small wavelets, still short but more pronounced—crests have a glassy appearance and do not break.

Date/Time of photograph: May 26, 1961, 1700 GMT.

Height of camera above sea: 45 ft.

Time (GMT)	Direction (°T)	Wind speed (kn)
1700	120	05
1500	100	03
1200	—	calm
0900	340	06
0600	010	07
0300	340	03
0000	320	04
2100	310	04
1800	310	03

Waves at time of picture

	Direction (°T)	Period (sec.)	Height (ft.)
Sea waves	120	—	—
Swell	050	6	1

Synoptic situation

A weak trough of low pressure, lying in a general northwest-southeast direction, was immediately west of the ship and passed by during the next hour. The centerline of the following ridge of high pressure was approximately 400 nautical miles west of the ship.

Remarks

This picture, taken from the C.C.G.S. *ST. CATHARINES*, shows her sister ship the C.C.G.S. *STONETOWN*, and was taken at 49°8N, 142°5W, or approximately 100 nautical miles east of the Station "P" position. The wind speed averaged close to 4 knots (force 2) during the previous 24 hours. Air temperature 46°5F; sea temperature 45°0F.

Crown Copyright, Ottawa, 1975. Reprinted through permission of the Atmospheric Environment Service, Department of the Environment, Canada.

BEAUFORT FORCE 2 **SEA STATE 1**

BEAUFORT FORCE 3

Wind speed 7 to 10 knots, mean 9 knots

Sea criterion: Large wavelets. Crests begin to break. Foam of a glassy appearance. Perhaps scattered white caps.

Date/Time of photograph: Feb. 19, 1961, 2000 GMT.

Height of camera above sea: 45 ft.

Time (GMT)	Direction (°T)	Wind speed (kn)
2000	190	03
1800	160	09
1500	180	10
1200	190	11
0900	260	08
0600	300	10
0300	320	10
0000	010	16
2100	090	10

Waves at time of picture

	Direction (°T)	Period (sec.)	Height (ft.)
Sea waves	—	—	—
Swell	180	7	8

Synoptic situation

Small low pressure area centered approximately 170 nautical miles west of station. The ship was approximately 40 nautical miles north of a warm front that extended eastward from the low center.

Remarks

Although the wind speed at the time of this picture was only 3 knots (force 1), it had decreased from 9 knots 2 hours previously, and had averaged almost 10 knots over the previous 24 hours. The direction had been constant from the south for 8 hours. Air temperature 44.2F; sea temperature 40.8F.

Crown Copyright, Ottawa, 1975. Reprinted through permission of the Atmospheric Environment Service, Department of the Environment, Canada.

Crown Copyright, Ottawa, 1975. Reprinted through permission of the Atmospheric Environment Service, Department of the Environment, Canada.

BEAUFORT FORCE 3   SEA STATE 2

BEAUFORT FORCE 4

Wind speed 11 to 16 knots, mean 13 knots

Sea criterion: Small waves, becoming longer, fairly frequent white caps.

Date/Time of photograph: July 3, 1960, 2240 GMT.

Height of camera above sea: 35 ft.

Time (GMT)	Direction (°T)	Wind speed (kn)
2240	320	16
2100	320	16
1800	340	11
1500	270	05
1200	270	08
0900	140	08
0600	230	09
0300	260	09
0000	250	13

NOTE:—Between 0000 and 2240 GMT, the ship had traveled eastward from 49.3N, 133.7W to 48.8N, 128.2W, a distance of approximately 220 nautical miles.

Waves at time of picture

	Direction (°T)	Period (sec.)	Height (ft.)
Sea waves	310	5	3
Swell	—	—	—

Synoptic situation

High pressure area centered at 40°N, 137°W, with ridge line extending northeastward to 100 nautical miles west of the ship, then northward to the northern section of the British Columbia coast. Low pressure area centered at 55°N, 150°W, in the Gulf of Alaska.

Remarks

This picture was made at 48°8N, 128°2W, or approximately 200 nautical miles west of Vancouver while the ship was returning from Station "P." The ship was moving into the area of northwesterly circulation east of the ridge of high pressure, and had passed the ridge line approximately 11 hours before the time of this picture. It is likely that force 4 winds had been acting on the area longer than would appear from the wind data, as the ship was moving eastward into the area. Air temperature 55.6F; sea temperature 52.7F.

Crown Copyright, Ottawa, 1975. Reprinted through permission of the Atmospheric Environment Service, Department of the Environment, Canada.

Crown Copyright, Ottawa, 1975. Reprinted through permission of the Atmospheric Environment Service, Department of the Environment, Canada.

BEAUFORT FORCE 4   SEA STATE 3

BEAUFORT FORCE 5

Wind speed 17 to 21 knots, mean 19 knots

Sea criterion: Moderate waves taking a more pronounced long form; many white caps are formed. (Chance of some spray.)

Date/Time of photograph: Apr. 7, 1961, 2315 GMT.

Height of camera above sea: 35 ft.

Time (GMT)	Direction (°T)	Wind speed (kn)
2315	280	23
2100	270	19
1800	240	20
1500	220	21
1200	220	24
0900	200	26
0600	190	25
0300	180	27
0000	180	30

Waves at time of picture

	Direction (°T)	Period (sec.)	Height (ft.)
Sea waves	280	6	7
Swell	240	8	6

Synoptic situation

High pressure area centered 550 nautical miles southeast of the station, which was in a northwesterly circulation 200 nautical miles northeast of the ridge line extending northwestward from the high. Low pressure area centered near 56°N, 136°W, in the Gulf of Alaska.

Remarks

The wind speed at the time of the picture was 23 knots (force 6), but had averaged less than 21 knots (force 5) over the previous 8 hours. In this period, the wind veered from southwest to west. Air temperature 41.0F; sea temperature 41.2F.

Crown Copyright, Ottawa, 1975. Reprinted through permission of the Atmospheric Environment Service, Department of the Environment, Canada.

BEAUFORT FORCE 5   SEA STATE 4

BEAUFORT FORCE 6

Wind speed 22 to 27 knots, mean 24 knots

Sea criterion: Large waves begin to form; the white foam crests are more extensive everywhere. (Probably some spray.)

Date/Time of photograph: Feb. 10, 1961, 2115 GMT.

Waves at time of picture

	Direction (°T)	Period (sec.)	Height (ft.)
Sea waves	280	6	11
Swell	—	—	—

Synoptic situation

Station in a northwesterly flow south of a low pressure area centered at 56°N, 144°W, or 380 nautical miles north of the ship. Trough of low pressure extending southeastward from low to second low lying off west coast of the United States. Ridge of pressure 300 nautical miles west of the ship.

Remarks

Except for a period between 3 and 9 hours ago, the wind was fairly constant, in both speed and duration, over the previous 24 hours. The fetch of the wind at the time of the picture was at least 300 nautical miles. Air temperature 37.4°F; sea temperature 41.0F.

Height of camera above sea: 20 ft.

Time (GMT)	Direction (°T)	Wind speed (kn)
2115	280	25
1800	300	26
1500	300	14
1200	280	23
0900	280	26
0600	280	23
0300	310	26
0000	300	27
	280	

Crown Copyright, Ottawa, 1975. Reprinted through permission of the Atmospheric Environment Service, Department of the Environment, Canada.

BEAUFORT FORCE 6   SEA STATE 5

BEAUFORT FORCE 7

Wind speed 28 to 33 knots, mean 30 knots

Sea criterion: Sea heaps up and white foam from breaking waves begins to be blown in streaks along the direction of the wind.

Date/Time of photograph: Feb 28, 1961, 1900 GMT.

Height of camera above sea: 45 ft.

Time (GMT)	Direction (°T)	Wind speed (kn)
1900	300	30
1800	300	30
1500	260	35
1200	260	35
0900	270	30
0600	250	38
0300	220	39
0000	210	39
2100	180	30

Waves at time of picture

	Direction (°T)	Period (sec.)	Height (ft.)
Sea waves	300	6	13
Swell	250	9	10

Synoptic situation

A deep low pressure area centered at 60°N, 144°W dominated the northeastern Pacific east of 160°W and north of 45°N. Station in northwesterly circulation approximately 575 nautical miles south of the low center.

Remarks

Although the wind speed was force 7 at the time of the picture, it had decreased from low force 8 between 1 and 4 hours previously. The wind veered from south to northwest during the previous 24 hours as the low center passed west of the ship while moving northward into the Gulf of Alaska. The fetch of the wind at the time of the picture was approximately 350 nautical miles. Air temperature 38.°4F; sea temperature 40.°7F.

Crown Copyright, Ottawa, 1975. Reprinted through permission of the Atmospheric Environment Service, Department of the Environment, Canada.

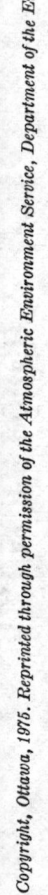

Crown Copyright, Ottawa, 1975. Reprinted through permission of the Atmospheric Environment Service, Department of the Environment, Canada.

BEAUFORT FORCE 7   SEA STATE 6

BEAUFORT FORCE 8

Wind speed 34 to 40 knots, mean 37 knots

Sea criterion: Moderately high waves of greater length; edges of crests begin to break into spindrift. The foam is blown in well-marked streaks along the direction of the wind.

Date/Time of photograph: Jan. 15, 1961, 1955 GMT.

Height of camera above sea: 35 ft.

Time (GMT)	Direction (°T)	Wind speed (kn)
1955	250	45
1800	240	38
1500	240	38
1200	250	37
0900	250	35
0600	250	35
0300	250	43
0000	250	40
2100	240	30

Waves at time of picture

	Direction (°T)	Period (sec.)	Height (ft.)
Sea waves	260	7	18
Swell	—	—	—

Synoptic situation

Low pressure area centered at 58°N, 142°W, in the Gulf of Alaska. Station in southwesterly circulation 500 nautical miles south-southwest of the low center.

Remarks

Although the wind speed at the time of the picture was 45 knots (force 9), it had been force 8 for 12 hours previously, and had increased in speed less than 2 hours prior to the picture. The wind direction was remarkably constant at 240° to 250° over the previous 24 hours. Air temperature 39.0F.; sea temperature 41.2F.

Crown Copyright, Ottawa, 1975. Reprinted through permission of the Atmospheric Environment Service, Department of the Environment, Canada.

BEAUFORT FORCE 8   **SEA STATE 6**

BEAUFORT FORCE 9

Wind speed 41 to 47 knots, mean 44 knots

Sea criterion: High waves. Dense streaks of foam along the direction of the wind. Crests of waves begin to topple, tumble, and roll over. Spray may affect visibility.

Date/Time of photograph: Jan. 17, 1961, 2130 GMT.

Height of camera above sea: 35 ft.

Time (GMT)	Direction (°T)	Wind speed (kn)
2130	120	50
2100	120	48
1800	120	46
1500	110	44
1200	110	30
0900	120	17
0600	140	08
0300	—	calm
0000	250	10

Waves at time of picture

	Direction (°T)	Period (sec.)	Height (ft.)
Sea waves	120	7	20
Swell	—	—	—

Synoptic situation

Station in strong southeasterly circulation, approximately 600 nautical miles east-northeast of a deep low, centered about 48°N, 160°W.

Remarks

Although the wind speed was 50 knots (force 10) at the time of the picture, the average speed over the previous 9½ hours was force 9. The wind had increased from calm conditions 18 hours ago. The appearance of the sea surface conforms well to the force 9 specification, but the reported wave heights are only 50 percent of the maximum theoretical height for force 9. It would be necessary for the wind to blow another 15 to 20 hours at force 9 before the waves approached their maximum height. Air temperature 42°.1F; sea temperature 41°.6F.

Crown Copyright, Ottawa, 1975. Reprinted through permission of the Atmospheric Environment Service, Department of the Environment, Canada.

Crown Copyright, Ottawa, 1975. Reprinted through permission of the Atmospheric Environment Service, Department of the Environment, Canada.

BEAUFORT FORCE 9   SEA STATE 6

BEAUFORT FORCE 10

Wind speed 48 to 55 knots, mean 52 knots

Sea criterion: Very high waves with long overhanging crests. The resulting foam, in great patches, is blown in dense white streaks along the direction of the wind. On the whole, the surface of the sea takes on a white appearance. The tumbling of the sea becomes heavy and shock-like. Visibility affected.

Date/Time of photograph: Mar. 14, 1961, 2330 GMT.

Height of camera above sea: 15 ft.

Time (GMT)	Direction (°T)	Wind speed (kn)
2330	340	55
2100	350	52
1800	000	55
1500	010	52
1200	010	44
0900	030	43
0600	030	29
0300	040	17
0000	050	12

Waves at time of picture

	Direction (°T)	Period (sec.)	Height (ft.)
Sea waves	340	9	22
Swell	—	—	—

Synoptic situation

Deep low pressure area centered at 49°N, 138°W, moving northeastward. Station in strong northerly circulation 250 nautical miles west-northwest of the low center.

Remarks

The wind had been blowing at force 10 for the past 8½ hours, the direction backing from 010° to 340°. Because of the relatively short duration of the force 10 winds, the wave heights have only attained roughly 50 percent of their maximum height for this force. The fetch of the wind at the time of the picture was estimated to lie between 150 and 200 nautical miles. Air temperature 37.6°F; sea temperature 40.0°F.

Crown Copyright, Ottawa, 1975. Reprinted through permission of the Atmospheric Environment Service, Department of the Environment, Canada.

Crown Copyright, Ottawa, 1975. Reprinted through permission of the Atmospheric Environment Service, Department of the Environment, Canada.

BEAUFORT FORCE 10   SEA STATE 7

APPENDIX X

GEODESY FOR THE NAVIGATOR

X1. Geodesy may be defined as that science concerned with the exact positioning of points on the surface of the earth, and the determination of the exact size and shape of the earth. It also involves the study of the variations of the earth's gravity (art. X4), and the application of these variations to exact measurements on the earth.

X2. Shape of the earth.—Although the irregular topographic surface (fig. X2a) is most apparent and is, in fact, the surface on which actual measurements are made, references to the earth's shape are not made with respect to the topography but to a mean sea-level surface. This surface, the **geoid,** is that surface to which the oceans would conform over the entire earth if free to adjust to the combined effect of the earth's mass attraction and the centrifugal force of the earth's rotation. As a result of the uneven distribution of the earth's mass, the geoidal surface is irregular (fig. X2a).

The geoid is a surface along which the gravity potential is everywhere equal and to which the direction of gravity is always perpendicular. The latter is particularly significant because optical instruments containing level devices are commonly used to make geodetic measurements. When properly adjusted, the vertical axis of the instrument coincides with the direction of gravity and is, therefore, perpendicular to the geoid.

The **equipotential surface** or the geoid is what is meant when referring to the size and shape of the earth, but such "potato-shaped" surface has serious limitations as an earth model: (1) It has no complete mathematical expression; (2) If it could be defined by an infinite series of measurements, there would still be a problem because of small variations in surface shape with time; and (3) The irregularity of the surface would necessitate a prohibitive amount of computations and complicate the problem of representation on the flat surface of a map. For geodetic and mapping purposes, it is therefore necessary to use a regular or geometric shape which provides a close approximation to the shape of the geoid.

Since the earth is in fact flattened slightly at the poles and bulges somewhat at the equator, the geometrical figure used in geodesy to most nearly approximate the shape of the earth is the oblate spheroid or **ellipsoid of revolution.** This is the figure obtained by rotating an ellipse about its minor axis (fig. X2b). The ellipsoidal earth model has its minor axis parallel to the earth's polar axis.

An ellipsoid of revolution is uniquely defined by specifying two dimensions. Goedesists, by convention, use the semimajor axis and flattening. The size is represented by the radius at the equator, the semimajor axis. The shape of the ellipsoid is given by the flattening, which indicates how closely an ellipsoid approaches a spherical shape. The **flattening** is the ratio of the difference between the semimajor and semiminor axes of the ellipsoid and the semimajor axis. If a and b represent the semimajor and semiminor axes, respectively, of the ellipsoid, and f is the flattening,

$$f = \frac{a-b}{a}.$$

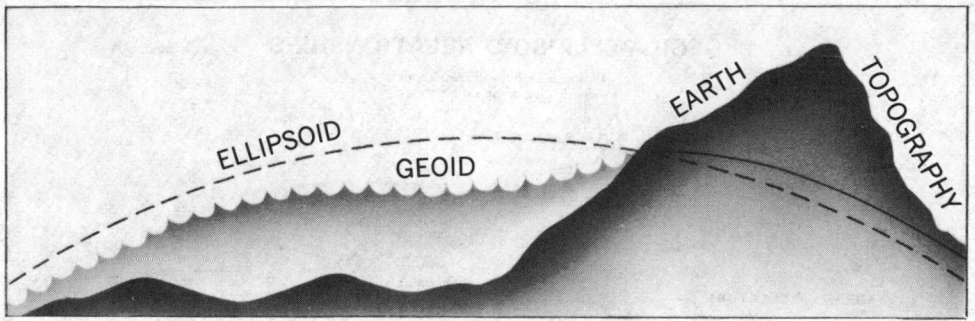

FIGURE X2a.—Surfaces of the earth, geoid, and ellipsoid.

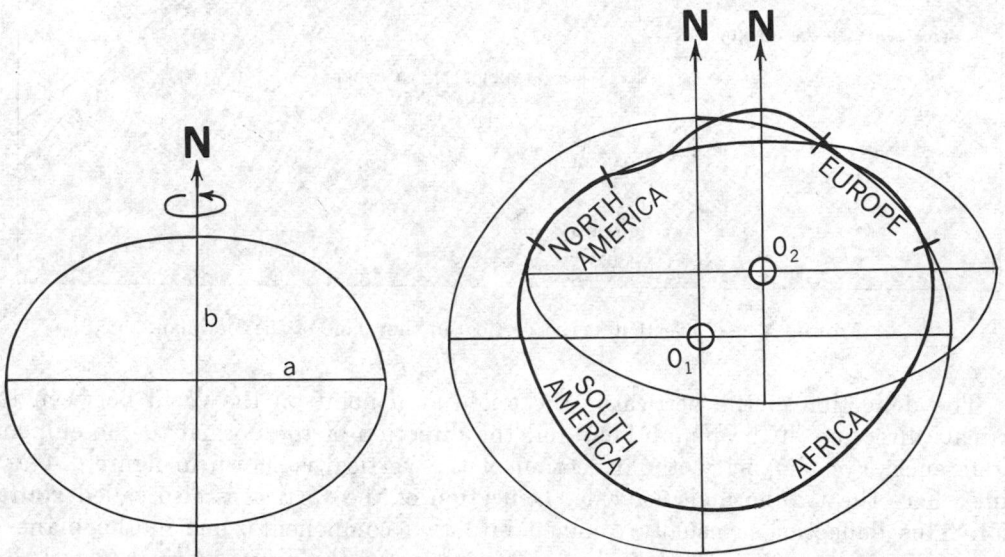

FIGURE X2b.—The ellipsoid of revolution.   FIGURE X3.—The geoid and two ellipsoids.

As shown in figure X2a, the surface of the geoid tends to rise under mountains and to dip above ocean basins. The separations of the geoid and ellipsoid are called **geoidal heights, geoidal undulations,** or **geoidal separations.**

X3. Ellipsoids and the geoid.—Since the surface of the geoid is irregular and the surface of the ellipsoid is regular, no one ellipsoid can provide other than an approximation of part of the geoidal surface. As shown in figure X3, the ellipsoid that fits well in North America does not fit well in Europe.

X4. Deflection of the vertical.—Gravitation (art. 1407) is the mutual attraction between masses of matter. In geodesy, **gravitation** is the mutual attraction between the earth and bodies on or near its surface. **Gravity** is that force which tends to pull bodies toward the earth. It is the resultant of two opposing forces: gravitation and the centrifugal force due to the rotation of the earth.

The irregularities in density and heights of the material making up the surface crust of the earth result in slight alterations of the direction of gravity. These alterations are reflected in the irregular shape of the geoid, the surface of which is perpendicular to the plumb line.

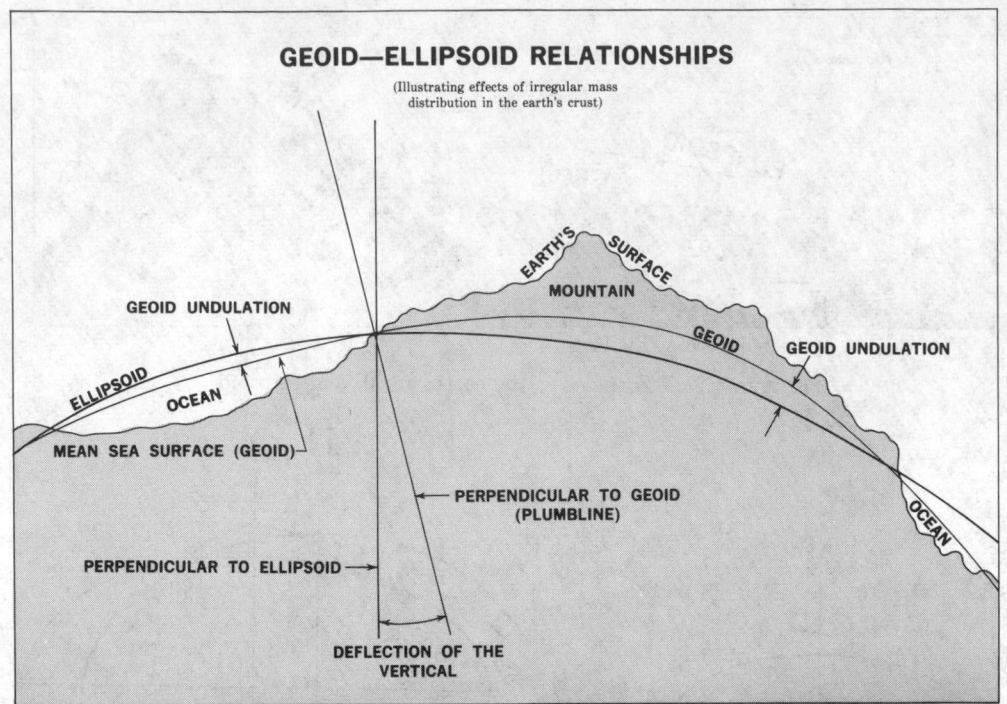

FIGURE X4.—Deflection of the vertical in the plane of the meridian.

The deflection of the vertical is the angle at a point on the geoid between the vertical (direction of the plumb line) and the direction of the normal to the ellipsoid of reference. For simplicity, the deflection of the vertical is shown in figure X4 at a point where the two normals coincide. Deflection of the vertical is also called **station error.** This deflection is usually resolved into two components, one in the plane of the meridian (art. 203) and the other in the plane of the prime vertical (art. 1430).

X5. Coordinates.—The **astronomic latitude** is the angle between the plumb line at a station and the plane of the celestial equator (fig. X5a). It is the latitude which results directly from observations of celestial bodies, uncorrected for deflection of the vertical which, in the United States, may amount to as much as 25″. Astronomic latitude applies only to positions on the earth, and is reckoned from the astronomic equator (0°), north and south through 90°.

The **astronomic longitude** is the angle between the plane of the celestial meridian at a station and the plane of the celestial meridian at Greenwich. It is the longitude which results directly from observations of celestial bodies, uncorrected for deflection of the vertical, the prime vertical component of which, in the United States, may amount to more than 18″.

Astronomic observations are made by optical instruments—theodolite, zenith camera, prismatic astrolabe—which all contain leveling devices. When properly adjusted, the vertical axis of the instrument coincides with the direction of gravity and is, therefore, perpendicular to the geoid. Thus, astronomic positions are referenced to the geoid. Since the geoid is an irregular, nonmathematical surface, astronomic positions are wholly independent of each other.

The **geodetic latitude** is the angle which the normal to the ellipsoid at a station makes with the plane of the geodetic equator (fig. X5b). In recording a geodetic position, it is essential that the *geodetic datum* (art. X8) on which it is based be also stated. A geodetic latitude differs from the corresponding astronomic latitude by the amount of the meridional component of the local deflection of the vertical.

Geodetic longitude is the angle between the plane of the geodetic meridian at a station and the plane of the geodetic meridian at Greenwich. A geodetic longitude differs from the corresponding astronomic longitude by the amount of the prime-vertical component of the local deflection of the vertical divided by the cosine of the latitude.

The geodetic coordinates are the ones used for mapping.

Geographic latitude is a general term applying alike to astronomic latitudes and geodetic latitudes. **Geographic longitude** is a general term applying alike to astronomic longitudes and geodetic longitudes.

Geocentric latitude is the angle at the center of the ellipsoid (used to represent the earth) between the plane of its equator and a straight line (or radius vector) to a point on the surface of the ellipsoid. This differs from geodetic latitude because the earth is a spheroid rather than a sphere, and the meridians are ellipses. Since the parallels of latitude are considered to be circles, geodetic longitude is geocentric, and a separate expression is not used. The difference between geocentric and geodetic latitudes has a maximum of about 11'.6 at latitude 45°.

Because of the oblate shape of the ellipsoid, the length of a degree of geodetic latitude is not everywhere the same, increasing from about 59.7 nautical miles at the equator to about 60.3 nautical miles at the poles, as shown by table 6.

X6. Geodetic surveys.—The most common type of geodetic survey is known as **triangulation** (fig. X6a). Basically, triangulation consists of the measurement of the angles of a series of triangles. The principle of triangulation is based on simple trigonometric procedures. If the distance along one side of the triangle and the angles at each end are accurately measured, the other two sides and the remaining angle can be computed. In practice all of the angles of every triangle are measured to provide exact data for use in computing the precision of the measurements. Also, the latitude and longitude of one end of the measured side along with the length and direction (azimuth)

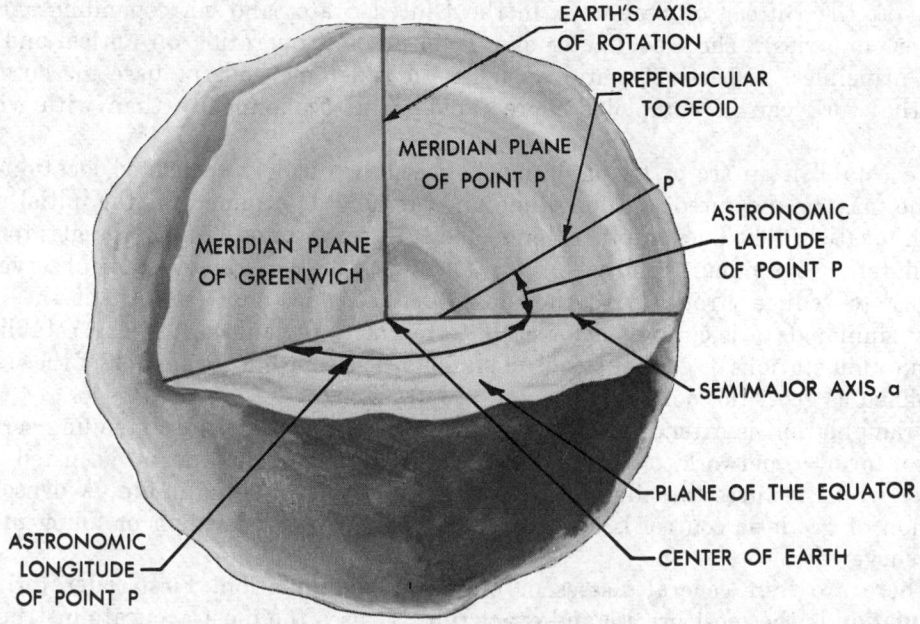

FIGURE X5a.—Astronomic coordinates.

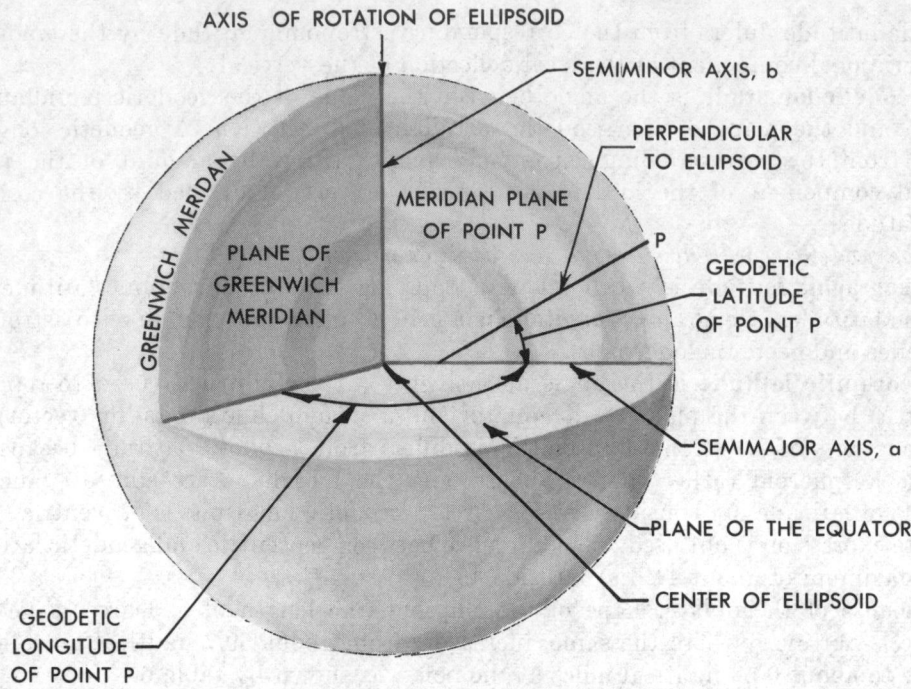

FIGURE X5b.—Geodetic coordinates.

of the side provide sufficient data to compute the latitude and longitude of the other end of the side.

The measured side of the base triangle is called a **baseline.** Measurements are made as carefully and accurately as possible with specially calibrated tapes or wires of Invar, an alloy, highly resistant to changes in length resulting from changes in temperature. The tape or wires are checked periodically against standard measures of length (at the Bureau of Standards in the United States and corresponding agencies in other countries). The Geodimeter and Tellurometer, operating on optical and electronic principles, respectively, are replacing the older methods of base measurement since the work can be completed more rapidly and economically than with wire or tape.

To establish an arc of triangulation between two widely separated locations, the baseline may be measured and longitude and latitude determined for the initial points at each location. The lines are then connected by a series of adjoining triangles forming quadrilaterals extending from each end. All angles of the triangles are observed repeatedly to reduce errors. With the longitude, latitude, and azimuth of the initial points, similar data is computed for each vertex of the triangles, thereby establishing triangulation stations or **geodetic control stations.** The coordinates of each of the stations are defined as geodetic coordinates.

Triangulation is extended over large areas by connecting and extending series of arcs to form a network or triangulation system. The network is adjusted in a manner which reduces the effect of observational errors to a minimum. A denser distribution of geodetic control is achieved in a system by subdividing or filling in with other surveys.

There are four general classes or orders of triangulation. **First-order (primary) triangulation** is the most precise and exact type. It uses the most accurate instruments and rigorous computation methods. It is costly and time-consuming and is usually

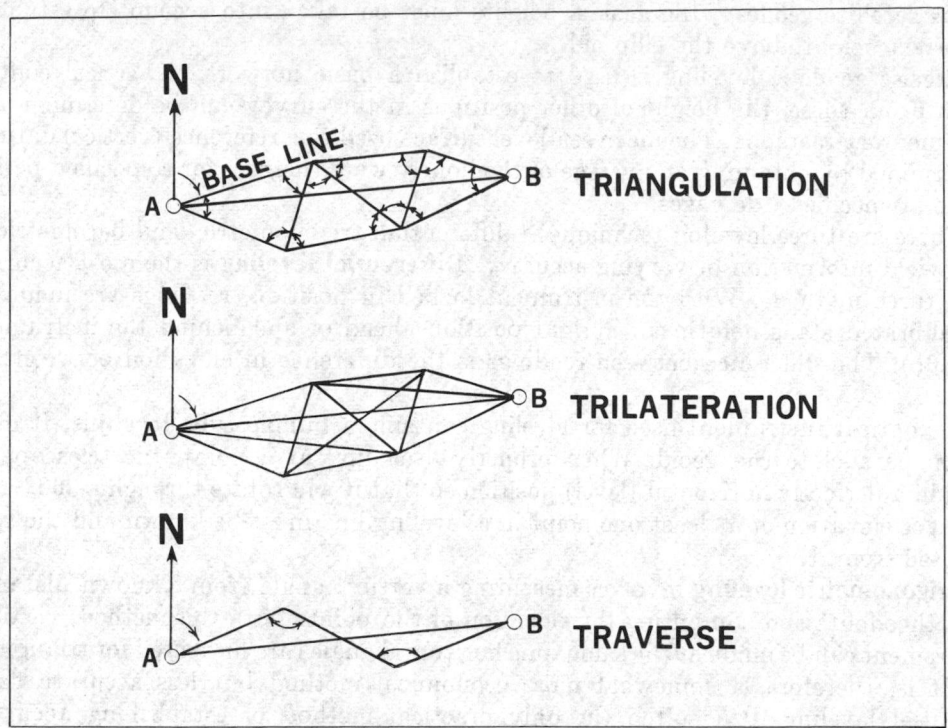

FIGURE X6a.—Triangulation, trilateration, and traverse.

used to provide the basic framework of control data for an area and the determination of the figure of the earth. No precaution is ignored in making the linear and angular measurements, or in the computations. The most accurate first-order surveys furnish control points which can be interrelated with an accuracy ranging from 1 part in 25,000 over short distances to approximately 1 part in 100,000 for long distances.

Second-order triangulation furnishes points closer together than in the primary network. While second-order surveys may cover quite extensive areas, they are usually tied to a primary system where possible. The procedures are less exacting and the proportional error is 1 part in 10,000.

Third-order triangulation is run between points in a secondary survey. It is used to densify local control nets and thereby position the topographic and hydrographic detail of the area. Triangle error can amount to 1 part in 5,000 in third-order triangulation.

The sole accuracy requirement for **fourth-order triangulation** is that the positions be located without any appreciable error on maps compiled on the basis of the control. Fourth-order control is executed primarily as mapping control.

Trilateration involves the measuring of the sides of a chain of triangles or other polygons. From them, the distance and direction from A to B (fig. X6a) can be computed.

Traverse involves measuring distances, and the angles between them, without triangles for the purpose of computing the distance and direction from A to B (fig. X6a).

Vertical surveying is the process of determining elevations above the mean sea-level surface. In geodetic surveys executed primarily for mapping purposes, there is no problem in the fact that geodetic positions are referred to an ellipsoid, and the elevations of the positions are referred to the geoid. However, for certain other purposes such as satellite geodesy, the geoidal heights must be taken into account to establish the correct height above the ellipsoid.

Precise geodetic leveling is used to establish a basic network of vertical control points. From these, the height of other positions in the survey can be determined by supplementary methods. The mean sea-level surface used as a reference (vertical datum) is determined by obtaining an average of the hourly water heights for a specified period of time at specified tide gages.

There are three leveling techniques—differential, trigonometric, and barometric—which yield information of varying accuracy. **Differential leveling** is the most accurate of the three methods. With the instrument locked in position, readings are made on two calibrated staffs held in an upright position ahead of and behind the instrument (fig. X6b). The difference between readings is the difference in elevation between the points.

The optical instrument used for leveling contains a bubble tube to adjust it in a position parallel to the geoid. When properly "set up" at a point, the telescope is locked in a perfectly horizontal (level) position so that it will rotate through a 360° arc. The exact elevation of at least one point in a leveling line must be known and the rest computed from it.

Trigonometric leveling involves measuring a vertical angle from a known distance with a theodolite and computing the elevation of the point. With this method, vertical measurement can be made at the same time horizontal angles are measured for triangulation. It is, therefore, a somewhat more economical method but less accurate than differential leveling. It is often the only practical method of establishing accurate elevation control in mountainous areas.

In **barometric leveling,** differences in height are determined by measuring the differences in atmospheric pressure at various elevations. Air pressure is measured by mercurial or aneroid barometer, or a boiling point thermometer. Although the degree of accuracy possible with this method is not as great as either of the other two, it is a method which obtains relative heights very rapidly at points which are fairly far apart. It is widely used in reconnaissance and exploratory surveys where more exacting measurements will be made later or are not required.

X7. Reference ellipsoids.—A number of reference ellipsoids are used in geodesy and mapping because an ellipsoid is mathematically simpler than the geoid. Some of these ellipsoids and areas where used are as follows:

Clarke 1866 (North and Central America, Greenland)
International 1924 (Hayford 1909) (Europe, various countries in South America)
Modified Clarke 1880 (Africa)
Everest 1830 (India, Southeast Asia, Indonesia)
Bessell 1841 (China, Korea, Japan)
Krasovskiy 1942 (U.S.S.R. and adjacent countries)
Australian National 1965 (Australia)
South American 1969 (South America).

Reference ellipsoid constants are given in appendix D.

In the late 1950's, an earth model fitting the world as a whole was needed for manned space flights. The National Aeronautics and Space Administration, and the Department of Defense selected the Fischer Ellipsoid 1960 (Mercury Datum) for this program. A modification of the Mercury Datum in 1968 produced the Fischer Ellipsoid 1968, having a semimajor axis of 6,378,150 meters and a flattening of 1/298.3. The geoidal heights are shown in figure X7. These heights range from about 80 meters below the ellipsoid to about 60 meters above.

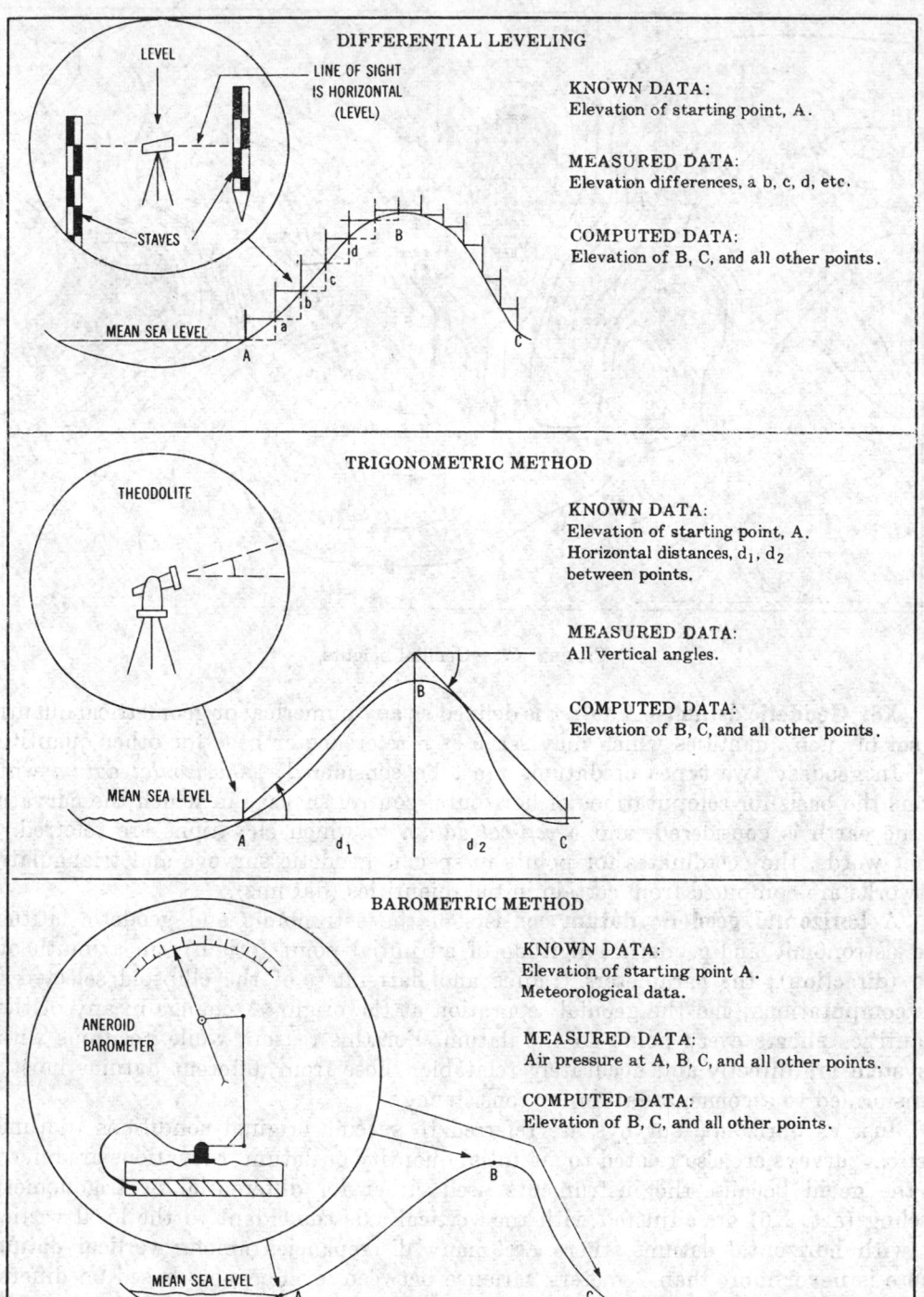

FIGURE X6b.—Methods of elevation determination.

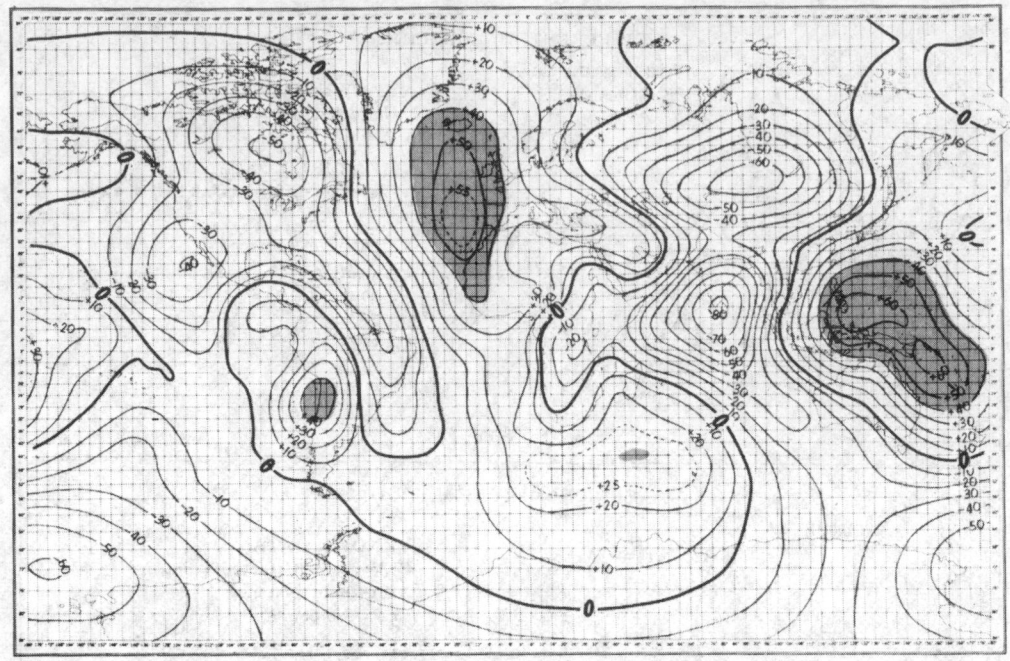

FIGURE X7.—Geoidal heights.

X8. Geodetic datum.—A *datum* is defined as any numerical or geometrical quantity or set of such quantities which may serve as a reference or base for other quantities.

In geodesy two types of datums must be considered: a *horizontal datum* which forms the basis for computations of horizontal control surveys in which the curvature of the earth is considered, and a *vertical datum* to which elevations are referred. In other words, the coordinates for points in specific geodetic surveys and triangulation networks are computed from certain initial quantities (datums).

A **horizontal geodetic datum** consists of the astronomic and geodetic latitude, and astronomic and geodetic longitude of an initial point (origin); an azimuth of a line (direction); the parameters (radius and flattening) of the ellipsoid selected for the computations; and the geoidal separation at the origin. A change in any of these quantities affects every point on the datum. For this reason, while positions within a system are directly and accurately relatable, those from different datums must be transformed to a common datum for consistency.

Just as horizontal surveys are referred to specific original conditions (datums), vertical surveys are also related to an initial quantity or datum. Elevations are referred to the geoid because the instruments used either for differential or trigonometric leveling (art. X6) are adjusted with the vertical axis coincident to the local vertical. As with horizontal datums, there are many discrepancies among **vertical datums.** There is never more than 2 meters variance between leveling nets based on different mean sea-level datums; however, elevations in some areas are related to surfaces other than the geoid; and barometrically determined heights are usually relative.

X9. Orientation of ellipsoid to geoid.—The selection of the reference ellipsoid provides two quantities of the geodetic datum: semimajor axis and flattening of the ellipsoid. The simplest means of obtaining the remaining quantities to establish the geodetic datum is to select a first-order triangulation station, preferably one located near the center of a triangulation network, to serve as the datum origin. Then the astronomical coordinates of the station and the astronomical azimuth of a line from the station to another control station are observed. The observed astronomical coordinates and azimuth are adopted without any correction as the geodetic coordinates and azimuth of the datum origin on the reference ellipsoid. Further, the geoid and ellipsoid are assumed to coincide at that point. This means that the deflection of the vertical and separation between the ellipsoid and geoid are defined as zero at the origin. By using this **single astronomical station datum orientation,** the normal to the ellipsoid is arbitrarily made to coincide with the plumb line at the datum origin (fig. X9).

Although the computed positions will be correct with respect to each other in this type of orientation, the entire net will be shifted with respect to the axis of the earth. This is not significant for local use of the positions but may introduce large systematic errors as the survey is expanded.

It should be noted that although the deflection of the vertical and the geoidal height are defined as zero at the origin, deflections will occur at other positions within the network. Therefore, when comparing the geodetic latitude and longitude of any other point in the net with the corresponding astronomic latitude and longitude of that point, systematic discrepancies will appear between the two sets of values.

A datum oriented by a single astronomical point may produce large systematic geoidal separations. The ellipsoid is not earth-centered and its rotational axis is not coincident with the axis of the earth. The inconvenience of such an orientation is that the positions derived from different astronomically oriented datums are not directly comparable to each other in any geodetic computation.

In the **astrogeodetic datum orientation,** the geoid and ellipsoid are oriented so that the sum of the squares of geoidal separations and several deflections of the vertical selected throughout the geodetic network is made as small as possible. Astrogeodetic datums are better suited over larger areas than those oriented by a single astronomic position because the separation between ellipsoid and geoid is minimized for a best fit.

X10. Datum connection.—In areas of overlapping geodetic triangulation networks, each computed on a different datum, the coordinates of the points given with respect to one datum will differ from those given with respect to the other. The differences can be used to derive transformation formulas.

Datums are connected by developing transformation formulas at common points, either between overlapping control networks or by satellite connections.

X11. Preferred datums.—Different countries developed their own geodetic datums which usually differed from those of their neighbors. Accordingly, national maps did not agree along the borders with those of the neighboring countries.

As military distance requirements increased, positioning information of local or even national scope became unsatisfactory. The capabilities of the various weapon systems increased until datums of at least continental limits were required. The best solution was the establishment of a preferred datum for an area and adjusting all local systems to it. The North American, Ordnance Survey of Great Britain, European, Tokyo, and Indian Datums are some of those selected for this purpose.

The **North American Datum, 1927,** is used in the United States. The origin is at Meades Ranch, Kansas. The datum is computed on the Clarke Ellipsoid 1866 which was oriented by a modified astrogeodetic method. The system incorporates Canada, Mexico, the West Indies, Greenland, and Central America.

The origin of the **European Datum** is at Potsdam, Germany. Numerous national systems have been joined into a large datum based upon the International Ellipsoid 1924 which was oriented by a modified astrogeodetic method. European, African, and Asian triangulation chains were connected. African arc measurements from Cairo to Cape Town were completed. Thus all of Europe, Africa, and Asia are molded into one great system. Through common survey stations, it was also possible to convert data

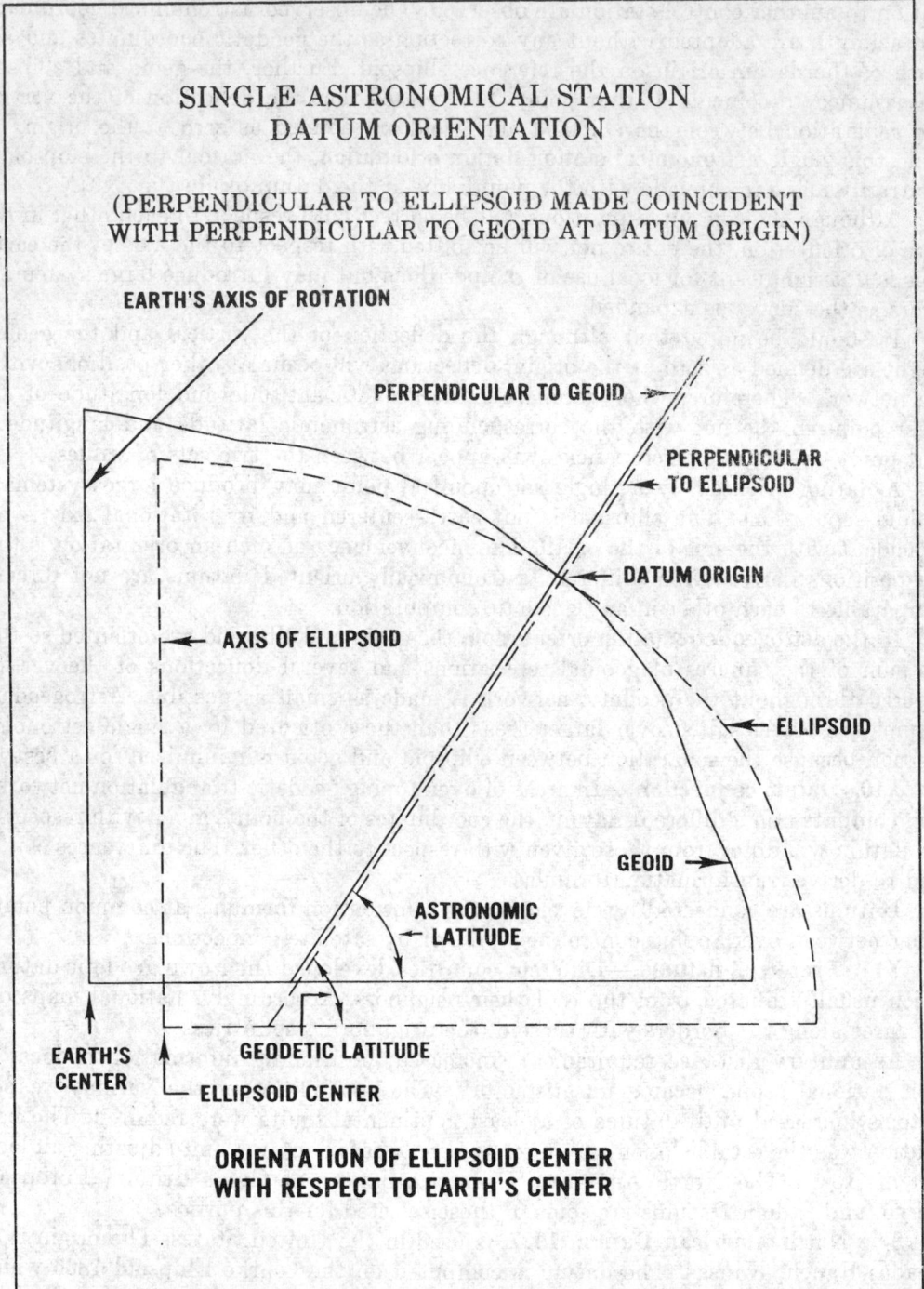

SINGLE ASTRONOMICAL STATION
DATUM ORIENTATION

(PERPENDICULAR TO ELLIPSOID MADE COINCIDENT
WITH PERPENDICULAR TO GEOID AT DATUM ORIGIN)

EARTH'S AXIS OF ROTATION

PERPENDICULAR TO GEOID

PERPENDICULAR
TO ELLIPSOID

DATUM ORIGIN

AXIS OF ELLIPSOID

ELLIPSOID

GEOID

ASTRONOMIC
LATITUDE

EARTH'S
CENTER

GEODETIC LATITUDE

ELLIPSOID CENTER

ORIENTATION OF ELLIPSOID CENTER
WITH RESPECT TO EARTH'S CENTER

FIGURE X9.—Single astronomical station datum orientation.

from the Russian Pulkova 1932 system to the European Datum, and as a result the European Datum includes triangulation as far east as the 84th meridian. Additional ties across the Middle East have permitted connection of the Indian and European Datums.

The **Ordnance Survey of Great Britain 1936 Datum** has no point of origin. The datum was derived as a best fit between retriangulation and original values of 11 points of the earlier Principal Triangulation of Great Britain (1783–1853).

The **Tokyo Datum** has its origin in Tokyo. It is defined in terms of the Bessel Ellipsoid and oriented by means of a single astronomic station. By means of triangulation ties through Korea, the Japanese datum is connected with the Manchurian datum. Unfortunately, Tokyo is situated on a steep slope on the geoid, and the single-station orientation has resulted in large systematic geoidal separations as the system is extended from its initial point.

The **Indian Datum** is accepted as the preferred datum for India and several adjacent countries in Southeast Asia. It is computed on the Everest Ellipsoid with its origin at Kalianpur in Central India.

Derived in 1830, the Everest Ellipsoid is one of the oldest of the ellipsoids in common use and is much too small. As a result, the datum cannot be extended too far from the origin or very large geoidal separations will occur. For this reason and the fact that the ties between local triangulation in Southeast Asia are typically weak, the Indian Datum is probably the least satisfactory of the preferred datums.

X12. World Geodetic System.—The Department of Defense (DoD) in the late 1950's generated a *geocentric* reference system to which different geodetic networks could be referred, and compatibility established between the coordinates of sites of interest. Efforts of the Army, Navy, and Air Force were combined leading to the development of the DoD World Geodetic System 1960 (WGS 60). In accomplishing WGS 60, a combination of available surface gravity data, astrogeodetic data, and results from Hiran and Canadian Shoran surveys were used to obtain a best-fitting ellipsoid for the major datum areas. The sole contribution of satellite data to the development of WGS 60 was the value for the ellipsoid flattening ($1/298.3 \pm 0.1$), which was obtained from the nodal motion of Satellite 1958β. The semimajor axis of the WGS 60 Ellipsoid was determined as $6,378,165 \pm 50$ meters.

In January 1966, a World Geodetic System Committee was charged with the responsibility for developing an improved WGS needed to satisfy mapping, charting, and geodetic requirements. Additional surface gravity observations, results from the extension of triangulation and trilateration networks, and large amounts of doppler and optical satellite data had become available since the development of WGS 60. Using the additional data and improved techniques, the Committee produced WGS 66 which served DoD needs following its implementation in 1967. The defining parameters of the WGS 66 Ellipsoid were the flattening ($1/298.25 \pm 0.02$), determined from satellite data, and the semimajor axis ($6,378,145 \pm 20$ meters), determined from a combination of doppler satellite and astrogeodetic data involving a geoid-match technique. A 24th degree and order geopotential coefficient set derived from a harmonic analysis of a worldwide $5° \times 5°$ mean free air gravity anomaly field was selected as the WGS 66 Gravitational Model. This geopotential coefficient set was also used in a spherical harmonic expansion to obtain the Worldwide WGS 66 Geoid. Also, a geoid referenced to the WGS 66 Ellipsoid, providing a detailed representation for limited land areas, was derived from available astrogeodetic data. Datum shift constants for the North American Datum 1927, European Datum, and Tokyo Datum were obtained for each datum.

The same World Geodetic System Committee began work in 1970 to develop a replacement for WGS 66. Since the development of WGS 66, large quantities of additional data had become available from both doppler and optical satellites, surface gravity surveys, triangulation and trilateration surveys, high precision traverses, and astronomic surveys. In addition, greater capabilities had been developed in both computers and computer software. Further, continued research in improved computational procedures and error analyses had produced better methods and a greater facility for handling and combining data.

After an extensive effort extending over a period of approximately 3 years, the Committee completed the development of the Department of Defense World Geodetic System 1972 (WGS 72). Selected satellite, surface gravity, and astrogeodetic data available through 1972 from both DoD and non-DoD sources was used in a Unified WGS Solution (a large scale least squares adjustment). The results of the adjustment consists of corrections to initial station coordinates and geopotential coefficients.

In determining the WGS 72 Ellipsoid and associated parameters, the Committee decided quite early to closely adhere to the approach used by the **International Union of Geodesy and Geophysics** (**IUGG**) in establishing the Geodetic Reference System 1967 (GRS 67). Accordingly, an equipotential ellipsoid of revolution was taken as the form for the WGS 72 Ellipsoid. An **equipotential ellipsoid** is simply an ellipsoid defined to be an equipotential surface; i.e., a surface on which all values of the potential are equal. Given an ellipsoid of revolution, it can be made an equipotential surface of a certain potential function, the normal gravity potential, U. This normal gravity potential can be uniquely determined, independent of the density distribution within the ellipsoid, by using any system of four independent parameters as the defining constants of the ellipsoid. To determine the normal gravity potential without resorting to the use of a mass distribution model for the ellipsoid, U can be expanded into a series of zonal ellipsoidal harmonics of linear eccentricity in $(a^2 - b^2)^{1/2}$. The coefficients in the series are determined by using the condition that the ellipsoid is an equipotential surface (U=constant). Since all the zonal coefficients vanish, except the two of degree zero and two, a closed finite expression is obtained for U. Normal gravity (γ), the gradient of U, is given at the surface of the ellipsoid by the closed formula:

$$\gamma = \frac{a\gamma_e \cos^2 \phi + b\gamma_p \sin^2 \phi}{(a^2 \cos^2 \phi + b^2 \sin^2 \phi)^{1/2}}$$

where a is the semimajor axis, b is the semiminor axis, γ_e is the normal gravity at the equator, γ_p is the normal gravity at the poles, and ϕ is the geodetic latitude.

Thus the equipotential ellipsoid serves not only as the reference surface or geometric figure of the earth but leads to a closed formula for normal gravity at the ellipsoidal surface, a formula easily modified for spatial applications.

Consistent with the IUGG definition of GRS 67, the Committee took the four defining parameters of the WGS 72 Ellipsoid to be the semimajor axis (a), the earth's gravitational constant (GM) and angular velocity (ω), and the second degree zonal harmonic coefficient of the geopotential ($\overline{C}_{2,0}$). Other parameters associated with the ellipsoid, such as the semiminor axis (b) and the flattening (f), including the normal gravity formula, are calculated using the defining parameters. These and other parameters associated with the ellipsoid are given in table X12.

Parameters	Notation	Magnitude	Standard error (68.27%)
Gravitational constant	GM	398600.5 km³/sec²	±0.4
Second degree zonal	$\overline{C}_{2,0}$	-484.1605×10^{-6}	—
Angular velocity	ω	$0.7292115147 \times 10^{-4}$ rad/sec	$\pm 0.1 \times 10^{-13}$
Semimajor axis	a	6378135 meters	±5
Flattening	f	1/298.26	$\pm 0.6 \times 10^{-7}$
Equatorial gravity (Absolute system).	γ_e	978033.26 mgal	±1.8
Gravitational constant (Mass of earth's atmosphere included).	GM'	398600.8 km³/sec²	±0.4

TABLE X 12.—Geodetic and geophysical parameters of World Geodetic System 1972 ellipsoid.

APPENDIX Y

BUOYAGE SYSTEMS

With modifications, two systems of buoyage have been in general use throughout the world from 1936 to 1977. These are the **lateral system** and the **cardinal system.**

The lateral system is best suited for well-defined channels. The location of each buoy indicates the direction of the danger it marks relative to the course which should normally be followed. Thus, a buoy which should be kept on the port hand lies between the vessel and the danger when the buoy is abeam to port, approximately.

In principle, the positions of marks in the lateral system are determined by the general direction taken by the mariner when approaching a harbor, river, estuary, or other waterway from seaward, and may also be determined with reference to the main stream of flood current. The application of this principle is defined, as required, by nautical documents such as sailing directions.

The cardinal system is best suited for coasts with numerous rocks, shoals, and islands, and for dangers in the open sea. The location of each buoy indicates the approximate true bearing of the danger it marks. Thus, an eastern quadrant buoy marks a danger, such as a shoal, which lies to the west of the buoy, approximately.

Although almost all of the major maritime nations have used either the lateral or the cardinal system for many years, details such as the shapes and colors of the buoys, and the characteristics and colors of lighted aids generally have varied from country to country. With the passage of time and the increase in maritime communication between countries, the desirability of a uniform system of buoyage has become increasingly apparent. Consequently, over the past century a number of attempts have been made to standardize the various systems of buoyage. International conferences have been held on the subject and recommendations have been made. These recommendations have often been conflicting, however, and although the differences in the various methods as applied to the cardinal system are comparatively slight, two distinct methods of applying the lateral system have evolved. The major discrepancy has been in the colors of the buoys and of their lights.

In 1889, the *International Marine Conference* held in Washington, D.C., recommended that in the lateral system starboard hand buoys be painted red and port hand buoys black. With the introduction of lighted aids to navigation, these recommendations logically led to the use, by nations which had accepted the recommendation, of red or white lights on the starboard side and green or white lights on the port side.

In 1936, a League of Nations subcommittee recommended a coloring system diametrically opposed to the 1889 proposal. This is part of the **Uniform System,** and it provides for black buoys with green or white lights on the starboard side and red buoys with red or white lights on the port side.

Most maritime countries using the lateral system have adopted one of these two systems, usually with small variations. Until 1977 it could be said that, *very generally,* European countries followed the Uniform System of 1936 and most other countries followed the system proposed in 1889.

In 1973, new terms of reference were given to the Technical Committee of the International Association of Lighthouse Authorities (IALA), which had been studying various projects, including buoyage, for the previous 8 years. IALA, a nongovernmental body which brings together representatives from the aids to navigation services in order to exchange information and recommend improvements to aids to navigation based on the latest technology, has decided that a single worldwide system of buoyage cannot be achieved at present but considers that the use of only two alternative systems is practicable. The two systems are termed: IALA Maritime Buoyage System 'A'—Combined Cardinal and Lateral System (Red to Port); IALA Maritime Buoyage System 'B'—Lateral System only (Red to Starboard).

While System 'B' is still being studied, the rules of System 'A' have been completed and have the support of the Inter-governmental Maritime Consultative Organization (IMCO). Implementation of System 'A' will begin in the waters of northwest Europe in 1977.

It is expected that the following countries will adopt System 'A':

Belgium	Norway
Denmark	Poland
Federal Republic of Germany	Republic of Ireland
France	Sweden
German Democratic Republic	United Kingdom
Netherlands	U.S.S.R.

United States System

The waters of the United States are marked by the lateral system of buoyage recommended by the International Marine Conference of 1889. As all channels do not lead from seaward, arbitrary assumptions are at times made in order that the system may be consistently applied. Along the sea coasts of the United States, the characteristics are based upon the assumption that proceeding "from seaward" constitutes a *clockwise* direction: a southerly direction along the Atlantic coast, a northerly and westerly direction along the gulf coast, and a northerly direction along the Pacific coast. On the Great Lakes, a westerly and northerly direction is taken as being "from seaward" (except on Lake Michigan, where a southerly direction is used). On the Mississippi and Ohio Rivers and their tributaries, the characteristics of aids to navigation are determined as proceeding from sea toward the head of navigation. On the Intracoastal Waterway, proceeding in a generally southerly direction along the Atlantic coast and in a generally westerly direction along the gulf coast is considered as proceeding "from seaward."

The continuation of the lateral system along the coasts in the order indicated refers only to the side of the vessel on which buoys are to be kept, as indicated by color, shape, and light, if any; there is no numerical continuity between coast buoys. In fairways and channels, however, buoys are numbered consecutively from seaward.

In the United States System, lighted buoys, bell buoys, whistle buoys, and combination buoys differ in shape (fig. 409a) from the unlighted buoys shown in this appendix, but not in color or marking.

In the Mississippi River, the numbering and lighting of buoys differ from that shown under "Fairways and Channels."

The United States System is discussed in more detail in chapter IV

Uniform System

As recommended by the League of Nations in 1936, a country uses the *Uniform Lateral System* or the *Uniform Cardinal System*, or both, according to its requirements or preference. When both are used, the transition from one to the other must be clearly indicated in appropriate publications, such as sailing directions, or by suitable buoyage marks.

Both the Uniform Lateral System and the Uniform Cardinal System employ **topmarks** as an additional means of identification. Unless otherwise stated in this appendix, a topmark is painted the darker of the colors used on the buoy. They are optional in every case except on wreck buoys in the Uniform Cardinal System. Topmarks are not used in the United States System.

In both the Uniform Lateral System and the Uniform Cardinal System, lighted buoys have the same shape as the unlighted buoys shown.

In both the Uniform Lateral System and the Uniform Cardinal System, a quick flashing light is regarded as a single flashing light.

The numbering or lettering of fairway and channel buoys is an optional feature of the Uniform Lateral System. In the United States System these buoys are always numbered, commencing from seaward.

IALA MARITIME BUOYAGE SYSTEM 'A'

Combined Cardinal and Lateral System
(Red to Port)

General

System 'A' applies to all fixed and floating marks, other than lighthouses, sector lights, leading lights and marks, lightships and large navigational buoys (lighthouse buoys), and serves to indicate:

1. the sides and centerlines of navigable channels;
2. natural dangers and other obstructions, such as wrecks;
3. areas in which navigation may be subject to regulation;
4. other features of importance to the mariner.

It should be understood that most lighted and unlighted beacons, other than leading marks, are included in the system. In general, beacon topmarks will have the same shape and colors as those used on buoys. (Because of the variety of beacon structures, the accompanying diagrams show mainly buoy shapes.)

The system provides *five types of marks* which may be used in any combination:

1. **lateral** marks indicate the port and starboard hand sides of channels;
2. **cardinal** marks, used in conjunction with the compass, indicate that the navigable water lies to the named side of the mark;
3. **isolated danger** marks erected on, or moored directly on or over, dangers of limited extent;
4. **safe water** marks, such as mid-channel buoys; and
5. **special** marks, the purpose of which is apparent from reference to the chart or other nautical documents.

Marks currently used which will be superseded include those which indicate wrecks, middle grounds, secondary channels, bifurcations, and junctions; there are no special "landfall" or "transition" marks in System 'A'. There is no differentiation between the marks for such special features as spoil grounds, anchorages, cable areas, and military exercise areas, all of which will be marked by yellow buoys which may, in addition, carry lettering to indicate the purpose of the buoy.

The significance of a mark depends on one or more features:

1. *by day*—color, shape, and topmark;
2. *by night*—light color and phase characteristics.

Red and green (without stripes or bands) are reserved, respectively, for port and starboard lateral marks, and yellow for special marks. The other types of marks have horizontal bands or vertical stripes, as described later.

There are *five basic buoy shapes*, namely, can, conical, spherical, pillar, and spar. In the case of can, conical, and spherical, the shape indicates the correct side to pass. With pillar and spar buoys, the shape has no such special significance.

The term "pillar" is used to describe any buoy which is smaller than a "lighthouse buoy" and which has a tall, central structure on a broad base; it includes beacon buoys, high focal plane buoys, and others (except spar buoys) whose body shape does not indicate the correct side to pass.

It must be understood that much existing equipment will be used in the new system including, for example, light-floats. Variations on the basic shapes will therefore be fairly common but, by day, the colors and topmarks should prevent ambiguity.

System 'A' makes use of can, conical, spherical, and X-shaped topmarks only. Topmarks on pillar and spar buoys are particularly important and will be used wherever practicable, but ice or other severe conditions may occasionally prevent their use.

Where marks are lighted, red and green lights are reserved, respectively, for port and starboard lateral marks, and yellow for special marks. The other types of mark have a white light, distinguished one from another by phase characteristic.

Red and green lights may have any phase characteristic, as the color alone is sufficient to show on which side they should be passed. Special marks, when lighted, have a yellow light with any phase characteristic not reserved for white lights of the system. The other types of mark have clearly specified phase characteristics of white light: various quick flashing phase characteristics for cardinal marks, group flashing (2) for isolated danger marks, and relatively long periods of light for safe water marks.

Single fixed lights (often found on shore marks at present) are being discontinued in the United Kingdom because of the possibility of confusion with ships' lights.

Lateral Marks

Lateral marks are generally used for well-defined channels; they indicate the port and starboard hand sides of the route to be followed, and are used in conjunction with a *conventional direction of buoyage*.

This direction is defined in one of two ways:

1. **local direction of buoyage**—the direction taken by the mariner when approaching a harbor, river estuary, or other waterway from seaward;

2. **general direction of buoyage**—in other areas, a direction determined by the buoyage authorities, following a clockwise direction around continental landmasses, given in sailing directions, and, if necessary, indicated on charts by a symbol.

Around the British Isles the general direction of buoyage will run northward along the west coasts and through the Irish Sea, eastward through the English Channel, and northward through the North Sea. This will reverse the former direction of buoyage in certain areas, including the east coasts of England and Scotland from Orfordness to the Shetland Islands.

A **port hand mark** is colored red and its basic shape is can, for either buoy body or topmark, or both.

A **starboard hand mark** is normally colored green, and its basic shape is conical, for either buoy body or topmark (point up), or both.

By night a port hand buoy is identifiable by its red light, and a starboard hand buoy by its green light; and phase characteristic (flashing, occulting, etc.) may be used.

The lateral colors of red or green will frequently be used for minor shore lights, such as those marking pierheads and the extremities of jetties. In British waters, to avoid confusion with the navigation lights of ships, minor lights, if fixed, will be shown in pairs, disposed vertically. Alternatively, single red or green lights will be flashing or occulting.

Variations on the simple system will occur in particular instances: Starboard hand marks may exceptionally be colored black instead of green, but not in the United Kingdom.

In some places, particularly straits (being open at both ends), the local direction of buoyage may be over-ridden by the general direction.

Special marks, with can and conical shapes but painted yellow, may be used in conjunction with the standard lateral marks for special types of channel marking.

Cardinal Marks

A **cardinal mark** is used in conjunction with the compass to indicate where the mariner may find the best navigable water. It is placed in one of the four quadrants (north, east, south, and west), bounded by the true bearings NW–NE, NE–SE, SE–SW, and SW–NW, taken from the point of interest. A cardinal mark takes its name from the quadrant in which it is placed.

The mariner is safe if he passes north of a north mark, east of an east mark, south of a south mark, and west of a west mark.

A cardinal mark may be used to:

1. indicate that the deepest water in an area is on the named side of the mark;
2. indicate the safe side on which to pass a danger; and
3. draw attention to a feature in a channel such as a bend, junction, bifurcation, or end of a shoal.

Black double-cone topmarks are the most important feature, by day, of cardinal marks; *the arrangement of the cones must be memorized.* Note that for north the point of each cone is up, and for south the point of each cone is down. The resemblance of the double-cone topmarks for west to a wineglass may serve as a useful memory aid.

Cardinal marks carry topmarks whenever practicable, with the cones as large as possible and clearly separated.

Black and yellow horizontal bands are used to color a cardinal mark. The position of the black band, or bands, is related to the points of the black topmarks, thus:

North—Points up—Black band above yellow band.
South—Points down—Black band below yellow band.
West—Points inward—Black band with yellow bands above and below.
East—Points outward—Black bands above and below yellow band.

The shape of a cardinal mark is not significant, but in the case of a buoy will be pillar or spar.

When lighted, a cardinal mark exhibits a white light; its characteristics are based on a group of quick or very quick flashes which distinguish it as a cardinal mark and indicate its quadrant.

The distinguishing quick or very quick flashes are:

North—Uninterrupted.
East—three flashes in a group.
South—six flashes in a group followed by a long flash.
West—nine flashes in a group.

As a memory aid, the number of flashes in each group can be associated with a clock face (3 o'clock—E, 6 o'clock—S, and 9 o'clock—W).

The long flash (of not less than 2 seconds duration), immediately following the group of flashes of a south cardinal mark, is to ensure that its six flashes cannot be mistaken for three or nine.

The periods of the east, south, and west lights are, respectively, 10, 15, and 15 seconds if quick flashing; and 5, 10, and 10 seconds if very quick flashing.

Quick flashing lights at the rate of either 60 or 50 flashes per minute: very quick flashing lights at the rate of either 120 or 100 flashes per minute.

It is necessary to have a choice of quick flashing or very quick flashing lights in order to avoid confusion if, for example, two north buoys are placed near enough to each other for one to be mistaken for the other.

Isolated Danger Marks

An **isolated danger mark** is erected on, or moored on or above, an isolated danger of limited extent which has navigable water all around it. The extent of the surrounding navigable water is immaterial: such a mark can, for example, indicate either a shoal which is well offshore or an islet separated by a narrow channel from the coast.

On a chart, the position of a danger is the center of the symbol or sounding indicating it; an isolated danger buoy will inevitably therefore be slightly displaced on the chart.

A **black double-sphere topmark** is, by day, the most important feature of an isolated danger mark and, whenever practicable, this topmark will be carried, with the spheres as large as possible, disposed vertically, and clearly separated.

Black with one or more red horizontal bands are the colors used for isolated danger marks.

The shape of an isolated danger mark is not significant, but in the case of a buoy will be pillar or spar.

When lighted, a white flashing light showing a group of two flashes is used to denote an isolated danger mark. The association of two flashes and two spheres in the topmark may be a help in remembering these characteristics.

Safe Water Marks

A **safe water mark** is used to indicate that there is navigable water all around the mark. Such a mark may be used as a centerline, mid-channel, or landfall buoy.

Red and white vertical stripes are used for safe water marks, and distinguish them from the black-banded, danger-marking marks.

Spherical, pillar, or spar buoys may be used as safe water marks.

A **single red sphere topmark** will be carried, whenever practicable, by a pillar or spar buoy used as a safe water mark.

When lighted, safe water marks exhibit a white light, occulting, or equal interval (isophase), or showing a single long flash. If a long flash (i.e. a flash of not less than 2 seconds) is used, the period of the light will be 10 seconds.

The association of a single flash and a single sphere in the topmark may be a help in remembering these characteristics.

Special Marks

A **special mark** may be used to indicate to the mariner a special area or feature, the nature of which is apparent from reference to a chart, sailing directions, or notices to mariners. Uses include:

1. Ocean Data Acquisition System (ODAS), i.e. buoys carrying oceanographic or meteorological sensors;
2. traffic separation marks;
3. spoil ground marks;

4. military exercise zone marks;

5. cable or pipeline marks, including outfall pipes; and

6. recreation zone marks.

Another function of a special mark is to define a channel within a channel. For example, a channel for deep draft vessels in a wide estuary, where the limits of the channel for normal navigation are marked by red and green lateral buoys, may have the boundaries of the deep channel indicated by yellow buoys of the appropriate lateral shapes, or its centerline marked by yellow spherical buoys.

Yellow is the color used for special marks.

The shape of a special mark is optional, but must not conflict with that used for a lateral or a safe water mark. For example, an outfall buoy on the port hand side of a channel could be can-shaped but not conical.

When a topmark is carried it takes the form of a single yellow X.

When a light is exhibited it is yellow; the phase characteristic may be any, other than those used for the white lights of cardinal, isolated danger, and safe water marks, i.e.:

North mark—Quick (or very quick) flashing.

East mark—Quick (or very quick) flashing (3) 10 seconds (or 5 seconds).

South mark—Quick (or very quick) flashing (6) + long flash 15 seconds (or 10 seconds).

West mark—Quick (or very quick) flashing (9) 15 seconds (or 10 seconds).

Isolated danger mark—Group flashing (2).

Safe water mark
- Occulting
- Equal interval (isophase)
- Long flash 10 seconds.

New Dangers

A newly discovered hazard to navigation not yet shown on charts, or included in sailing directions, or sufficiently promulgated by notices to mariners, is termed a **new danger.** The term covers naturally occurring obstructions such as sandbanks, rocks, or man-made dangers such as wrecks.

A new danger is marked by one or more cardinal or lateral marks in accordance with the System 'A' rules. If the danger is especially grave, at least one of the marks will be duplicated as soon as practicable by an identical mark until the danger has been sufficiently promulgated.

If a lighted mark is used for a new danger, it must exhibit a quick flashing or very quick flashing light: If is it a cardinal mark, it must exhibit a white light; if a lateral mark, a red or green light.

The duplicate mark may carry a Racon, coded W ($\cdot$$-$$-$), showing a signal length of 1 nautical mile on a radar display.

The above discussion of System 'A' is adapted from NP 735, *IALA Maritime Buoyage System 'A'*, Edition 1, 1976, published by the Hydrographer of the Navy, Taunton, England.

UNITED STATES SYSTEM

Fairways and Channels

PORT HAND	STARBOARD HAND

BUOY:

MARKING: Odd numbers, commencing from seaward.

Even numbers, commencing from seaward.

LIGHTED BUOY: *White* or *green*, flashing or occulting; or, when marking important turns, quick flashing.

White or *red*, flashing or occulting; or, when marking important turns, quick flashing.

Middle Grounds

MAIN CHANNEL TO RIGHT   MAIN CHANNEL TO LEFT

BUOY:

MARKING: May be lettered.   May be lettered.

LIGHTED BUOY: *White* or *green*, interrupted quick flashing.   *White* or *red*, interrupted quick flashing.

Where channels are of equal importance, either of the above buoys is used, without regard to the uppermost band.

Mid Channel

BUOY:

MARKING: May be lettered.

LIGHTED BUOY: *White*, short-long flashing.

Wrecks or Other Obstructions

TO BE PASSED ON PORT HAND   TO BE PASSED ON STARBOARD HAND

BUOY:

MARKING: Usually lettered "WR."   Usually lettered "WR."

LIGHTED BUOY: *White* or *green*, quick flashing.   *White* or *red*, quick flashing.

Where wrecks or other obstructions may be passed on either hand, either Middle Ground *buoy is used, without regard to the uppermost band.*

UNITED STATES SYSTEM

Miscellaneous

SHAPE: Optional.

COLOR: **Quarantine**—*Yellow*.
Anchorage—*White*.
Fish Nets—*Black-and-white* horizontal bands.
Dredging—*White* with *green* top.
Seadromes—*Yellow-and-black* vertical stripes.
Special Purpose—*White-and-international orange* horizontal or vertical bands.

MARKING: May be lettered.

LIGHTED BUOY: Any color except *red* or *green*; fixed, occulting, or slow flashing.

UNIFORM LATERAL SYSTEM

Fairways and Channels

	PORT HAND	STARBOARD HAND
TOPMARK:		
	"T"-shaped topmark not used at channel entrance.	*Diamond-shaped topmark not used at channel entrance.*
BUOY:		

In secondary channels only, yellow may be substituted for white in checkered buoys.

MARKING:	Even numbers, commencing from seaward.	Odd numbers, commencing from seaward.
LIGHT:	*Red*, single flashing or occulting or group flashing or occulting, with a number of flashes or occultations up to four; or *white*, group flashing or occulting (2 or 4); both *red and white* with above characteristics.	*White*, single flashing or occulting, or group flashing or occulting (3); or *green*, of a different character from wreck markings; or both *white and green* with the above characteristics.

UNIFORM LATERAL SYSTEM

Middle Grounds

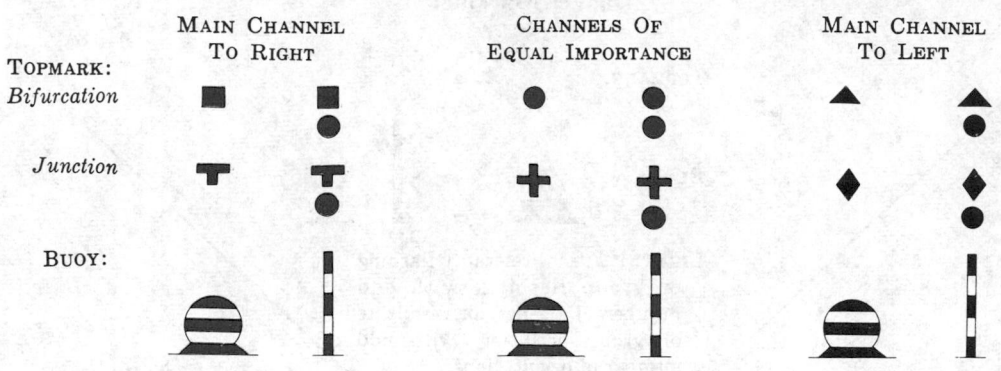

	MAIN CHANNEL TO RIGHT	CHANNELS OF EQUAL IMPORTANCE	MAIN CHANNEL TO LEFT
TOPMARK: *Bifurcation*			
Junction			
BUOY:			
LIGHT:	Distinctive where possible.	Distinctive where possible.	Distinctive where possible.

Mid Channel

TOPMARK: Shape optional, but not conical, cylindrical, or spherical.

BUOY: Shape optional, but not conical, cylindrical, or spherical.

COLOR: *Red-and-white* or *black-and-white* vertical stripes; topmark *red* or *black* to conform with buoy.

LIGHT: Different from neighboring lights.

Marking of Wrecks

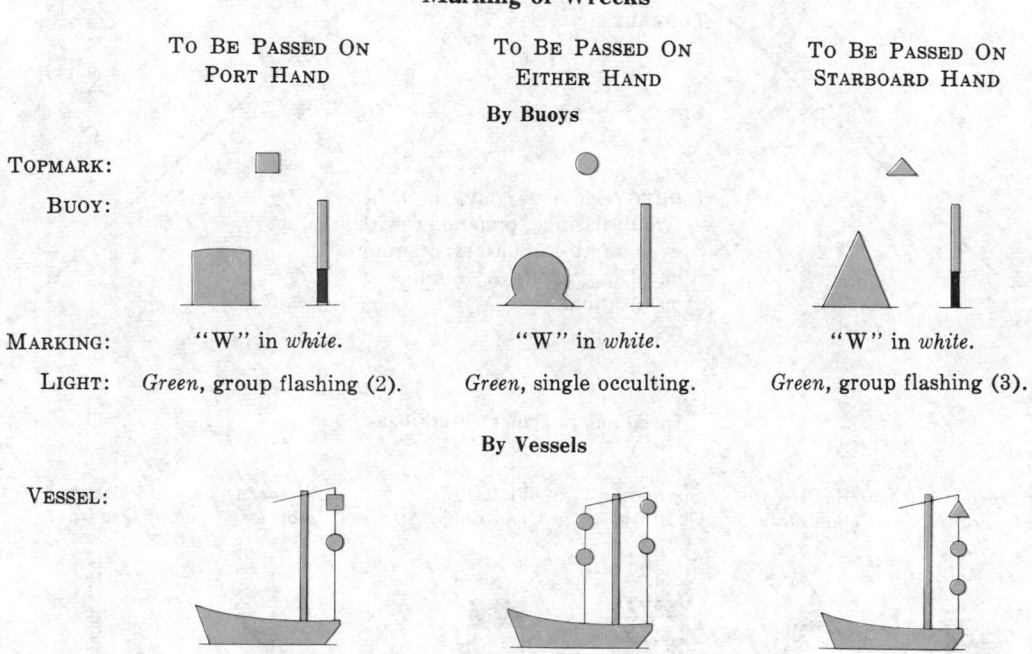

	TO BE PASSED ON PORT HAND	TO BE PASSED ON EITHER HAND	TO BE PASSED ON STARBOARD HAND
		By Buoys	
TOPMARK:			
BUOY:			
MARKING:	"W" in *white*.	"W" in *white*.	"W" in *white*.
LIGHT:	*Green*, group flashing (2).	*Green*, single occulting.	*Green*, group flashing (3).
		By Vessels	
VESSEL:			
MARKING:	"W" or "WRECK" in *white*.	"W" or "WRECK" in *white*.	"W" or "WRECK" in *white*.
LIGHT:	Fixed *green*, corresponding in number and arrangement to shapes displayed by day.		
BELL:	Two strokes at intervals of not more than 30 seconds.	Four strokes at intervals of not more than 30 seconds.	Three strokes at intervals of not more than 30 seconds.

UNIFORM CARDINAL SYSTEM

Danger Markings

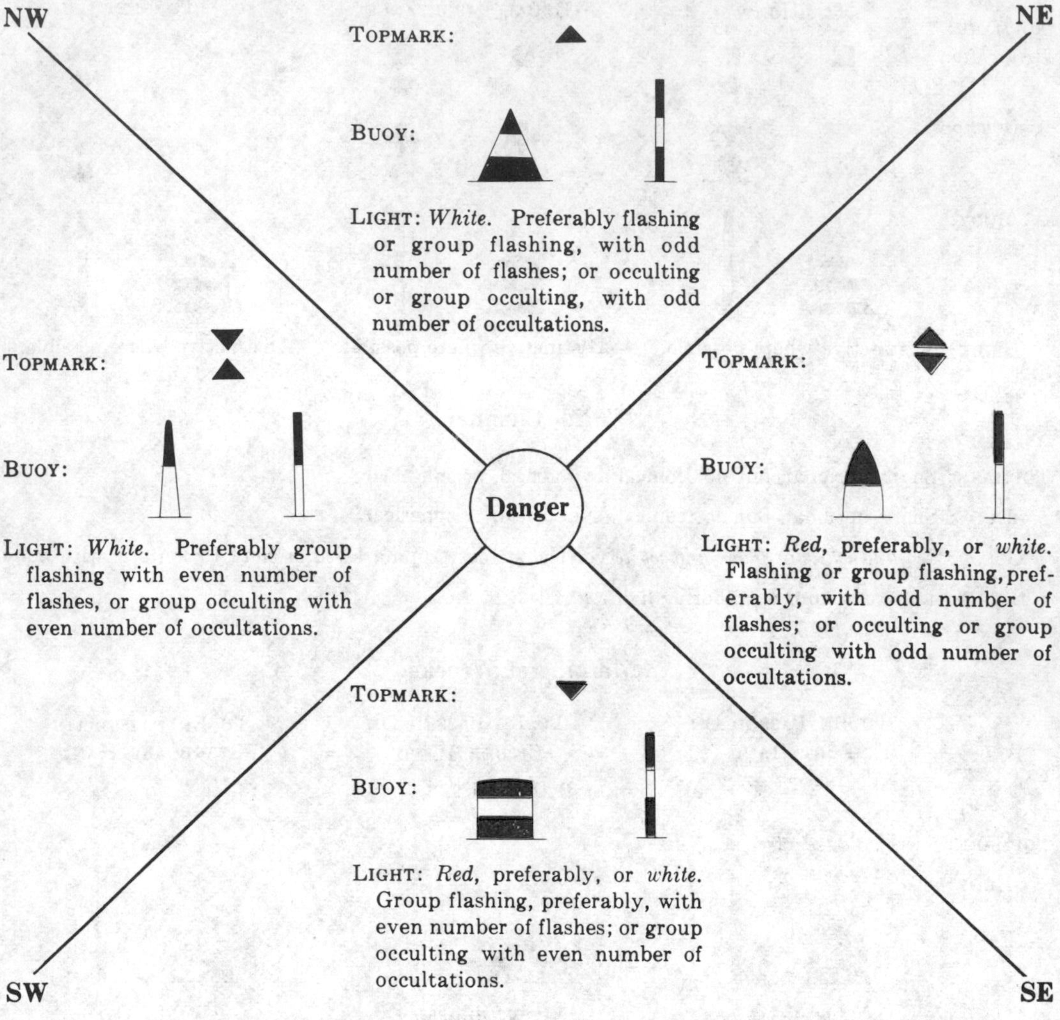

NW

NE

TOPMARK:

BUOY:

LIGHT: *White*. Preferably flashing or group flashing, with odd number of flashes; or occulting or group occulting, with odd number of occultations.

TOPMARK:

BUOY:

LIGHT: *White*. Preferably group flashing with even number of flashes, or group occulting with even number of occultations.

Danger

TOPMARK:

BUOY:

LIGHT: *Red*, preferably, or *white*. Flashing or group flashing, preferably, with odd number of flashes; or occulting or group occulting with odd number of occultations.

TOPMARK:

BUOY:

LIGHT: *Red*, preferably, or *white*. Group flashing, preferably, with even number of flashes; or group occulting with even number of occultations.

SW

SE

Variations in Danger Markings

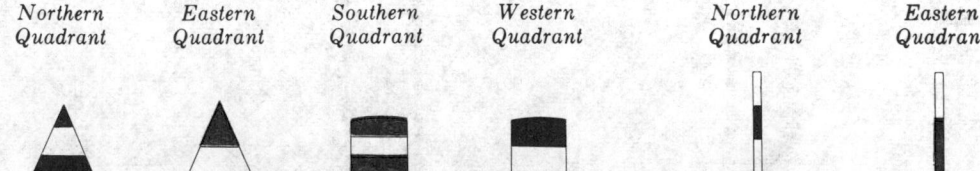

| *Northern Quadrant* | *Eastern Quadrant* | *Southern Quadrant* | *Western Quadrant* | *Northern Quadrant* | *Eastern Quadrant* |

Note: The number of characteristic shapes employed for the buoy itself may be limited to two, the conical shape being employed in the northern and eastern quadrants and the cylindrical shape in the southern and western quadrants, as shown above.

Note: When spars only are used, it may be advantageous in the northern and eastern quadrants to reverse the positions of the dark colors, as shown above.

UNIFORM CARDINAL SYSTEM

Marking of Wrecks

WESTERN QUADRANT   EASTERN QUADRANT

TOPMARK:

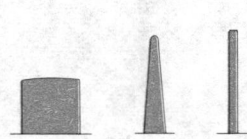

BUOY:

MARKING: "W" in *white*, if possible.   "W" in *white*, if possible.

LIGHT: *Green*, quick flashing.   *Green*, interrupted quick flashing.

In the Uniform Cardinal System, wreck buoys are not used in the northern or southern quadrants.

UNIFORM SYSTEM—LATERAL AND CARDINAL
(Common To Both)

Isolated Dangers

TOPMARK:
BUOY:

LIGHT: *White* or *red*, rhythmic.

Miscellaneous

TOPMARK: **Landfall**—Shape optional, but not misleading.
            Transition—Shape optional, but not misleading.
            Others—None.

BUOY: Shape optional, but not misleading.

COLOR: **Landfall**—*Black-and-white* or *red-and-white* vertical stripes.
          Transition—*Red-and-white* or *black-and-white* spiral bands.
          Quarantine—*Yellow.*
          Outfall—*Yellow* above and *black* below.
          Military Practice Area—*White*, with two *blue* stripes rising from the waterline and
              intersecting at right angles on top of the buoy, and, optionally, lettering in the
              national language indicating a danger area (*e.g.*, in English, "D.A.").

LIGHT: **Landfall**—Rhythmic.
          Outfall—Optional, with due regard to other lights in the area.
          Others—None.

IALA MARITIME BUOYAGE SYSTEM 'A'
CARDINAL MARKS

Topmarks are always fitted (when practicable)

Buoy shapes are pillar or spar

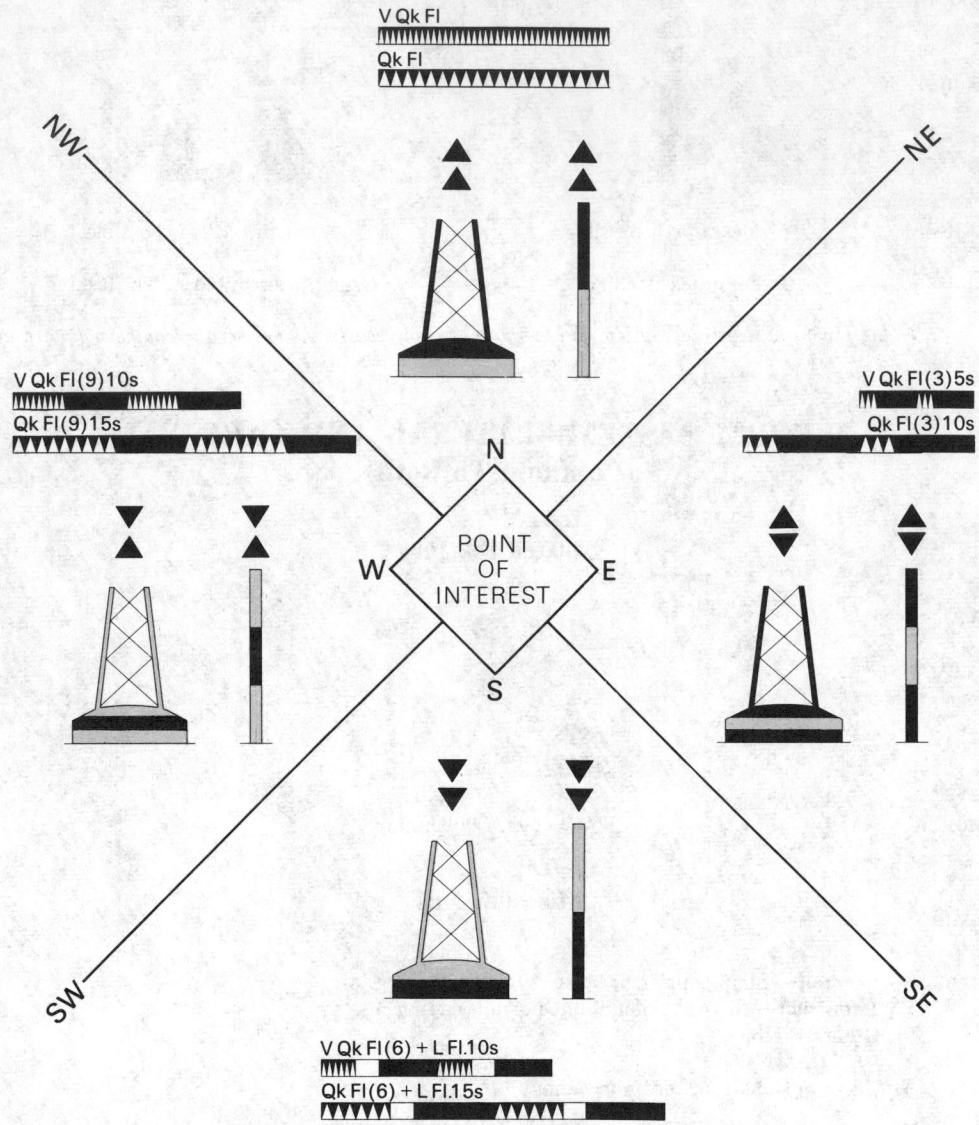

Lights, when fitted, are **white**, Very Quick Flashing
or Quick Flashing; a South mark also has a Long
Flash immediately following the quick flashes.

IALA MARITIME BUOYAGE SYSTEM 'A'

LATERAL MARKS

PORT HAND

STARBOARD HAND

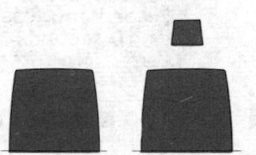

can

conical

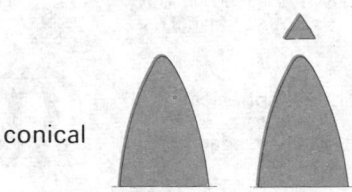

Topmark
(always fitted*
if buoy is not
can or conical)

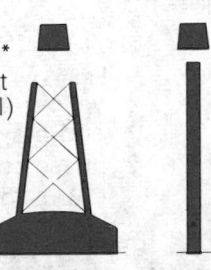

pillar or spar

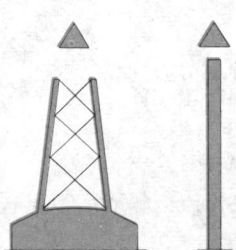

Exceptionally, black may
be used instead of green

Lights, when fitted, may have any phase characteristic

<u>Examples</u>

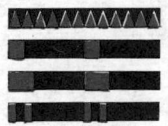

Quick Flashing
Flashing
Long Flashing
Group Flashing

ISOLATED DANGER MARKS

Topmark
(always fitted)*

Light, when fitted, is
white
Group Flashing (2)

GpFl(2)

Shape: pillar or spar

*when practicable

IALA MARITIME BUOYAGE SYSTEM 'A'

SAFE WATER MARKS

Topmark
(always fitted* if buoy
 is not spherical)

Shape: spherical
  or
 pillar or spar

Light, when fitted, is
white
Isophase or Occulting,
or Long Flashing every
10 seconds

Iso
Occ
L Fl.10s

SPECIAL MARKS

Topmark
(if fitted)

Shape: optional

**Light, when fitted, is
yellow**
and may have any
phase characteristic
not used for white lights

Examples

Fl Y
Gp Fl (4) Y

Topmark
(if fitted)

If these shapes are
used they will indicate
the side on which the
buoys should be passed.

*when practicable

APPENDIX Z

EXTRACTS FROM CHART NO. 1

Chart No. 1

United States of America

Nautical Chart Symbols and Abbreviations

SIXTH EDITION

JULY 1975

Prepared jointly by

DEPARTMENT OF COMMERCE

National Oceanic and Atmospheric Administration

National Ocean Survey *(Formerly Coast and Geodetic Survey, and U.S. Lake Survey)*

DEPARTMENT OF DEFENSE

Defense Mapping Agency

Hydrographic Center

Published at Washington, D.C.

U.S. DEPARTMENT OF COMMERCE

National Oceanic and Atmospheric Administration

National Ocean Survey

GENERAL REMARKS

This publication (CHART NO. 1) contains symbols and abbreviations that have been approved for use on nautical charts published by the United States of America. The buoyage systems used by other countries often vary from that used by the United States. Charts produced by the Defense Mapping Agency Hydrographic Center (DMAHC) will show the colors, lights, and other characteristics in use for the area of the individual chart. Certain modified reproduction charts distributed by DMAHC will also show the shapes and other distinctive features that may vary from those illustrated in this chart. Terms, symbols, and abbreviations are numbered in accordance with a standard form approved by a 1952 resolution of the International Hydrographic Organization (IHO). Although the use of IHO-approved symbols and abbreviations is not mandatory, the United States has cooperated to adopt many IHO-approved symbols for standard use on U.S. nautical charts. Alphanumeric style differences in the first column of the following pages indicate symbol and abbreviation status as follows:

VERTICAL FIGURES indicate those items for which the symbol and abbreviation are in accordance with resolutions of the IHO.

SLANTING FIGURES indicate those symbols for which no IHO resolution has been adopted.

SLANTING FIGURES UNDERSCORED indicate IHO and U.S. symbols do not agree.

SLANTING FIGURES ASTERISKED indicate that no symbol has been adopted by the United States.

SLANTING FIGURES IN PARENTHESES indicate that the items are in addition to those appearing in the "Glossary of Cartographic Terms", SP No. 22, 3rd Edition, 1951, IHO, and subsequent revisions.

† All changes since the July 1972 edition of this publication are indicated by the dagger symbol in the margin immediately adjacent to the item identification of the symbol or abbreviation affected.

BUILDINGS. A conspicuous feature on a building may be shown by a landmark symbol with a descriptive label. (See I 8b, 36, 44, 72.) Prominent buildings that are of assistance to the mariner may be shown by actual shape as viewed from above (see I 3a, 19, 47, 66), and may be marked "CONSPICUOUS".

BUOYS and BEACONS. On entering a channel from seaward, buoys on starboard side are red with even numbers, on port side black with odd numbers. Lights on buoys on starboard side of channel are red or white, on port side white or green. Mid-channel buoys have black-and-white vertical stripes. Junction or obstruction buoys, which may be passed on either side, have red-and-black horizontal bands. This system does not always apply to foreign waters.

The position of a fixed beacon is represented by the center of the beacon symbol or the circle at the base of the symbol. The approximate position of a buoy is represented by the dot or circle associated with the buoy symbol. The approximate position is used because of practical limitations in positioning and maintaining buoys and their sinkers in precise geographical locations. These limitations include, but are not limited to, inherent imprecisions in position fixing methods, prevailing atmospheric and sea conditions, the slope of and the material making up the seabed, the fact that buoys are moored to sinkers by varying lengths of chain, and the fact that buoy body and/or sinker positions are not under continuous surveillance, but are normally checked only during periodic maintenance visits which often occur more than a year apart. The position of the buoy body can be expected to shift inside and outside the charting symbol due to the forces of nature. The mariner is also cautioned that buoys are liable to be carried away, shifted, capsized, sunk, etc. Lighted buoys may be extinguished or sound signals may not function as a result of ice, running ice or other natural causes, collisions, or other accidents. For the foregoing reasons, a prudent mariner must not rely completely upon the charted position or operation of floating aids to navigation, but will also utilize bearings from fixed objects and aids to navigation on shore. Further, a vessel attempting to pass close aboard always risks collision with a yawing buoy or with the obstruction the buoy marks.

COLORS are optional for characterizing various features and areas in the charts.

DEPTH contours and soundings are shown in meters on an increasing number of new charts and new editions; the depth unit is stated on all charts.

HEIGHTS of land and conspicuous objects are given in feet above Mean High Water, unless otherwise stated in the title of the chart.

IMPROVED CHANNELS are shown by limiting dashed lines with the depth and date of the latest examination placed adjacent to the channel except when the channel data is tabulated.

LETTERING styles and capitalization as indicated in Chart No. 1 are not always rigidly adhered to on the charts.

LONGITUDES are referred to the Meridian of Greenwich.

OBSOLESCENT SYMBOLIZATION on charts will be revised to agree with the current preferred usage as soon as opportunity affords.

SHORELINE shown on charts represents the line of contact between the land and a selected water elevation. In areas affected by tidal fluctuation, this line of contact is usually the mean high-water line. In confined coastal waters of diminished tidal influence, a mean water level line may be used. The shoreline of interior waters (rivers, lakes) is usually a line representing a specified elevation above a selected datum. Shoreline is symbolized by a heavy line (A 9).

APPARENT SHORELINE is used on charts to show the outer edge of marine vegetation where that limit would reasonably appear as the shoreline to the mariner or where it prevents the shoreline from being clearly defined. Apparent shoreline is symbolized by a light line (A 7, C 17).

U.S. COAST PILOTS, SAILING DIRECTIONS, LIGHT LISTS, RADIO AIDS, and related publications furnish information required by the navigator that cannot be shown conveniently on the nautical chart.

U.S. NAUTICAL CHART CATALOGS and INDEXES list nautical charts, auxiliary maps and related publications, and include general information relative to the charts.

Some differences may be observed between Chart No. 1 and symbols shown on certain reproductions of foreign charts and special charts. Foreign symbols may be interpreted by reference to the Symbol Sheet or Chart No. 1 of the originating country. A glossary of foreign terms and abbreviations is generally given on charts on which they are used, as well as in the Sailing Directions.

A. The Coastline (Nature of the Coast) (see General Remarks)

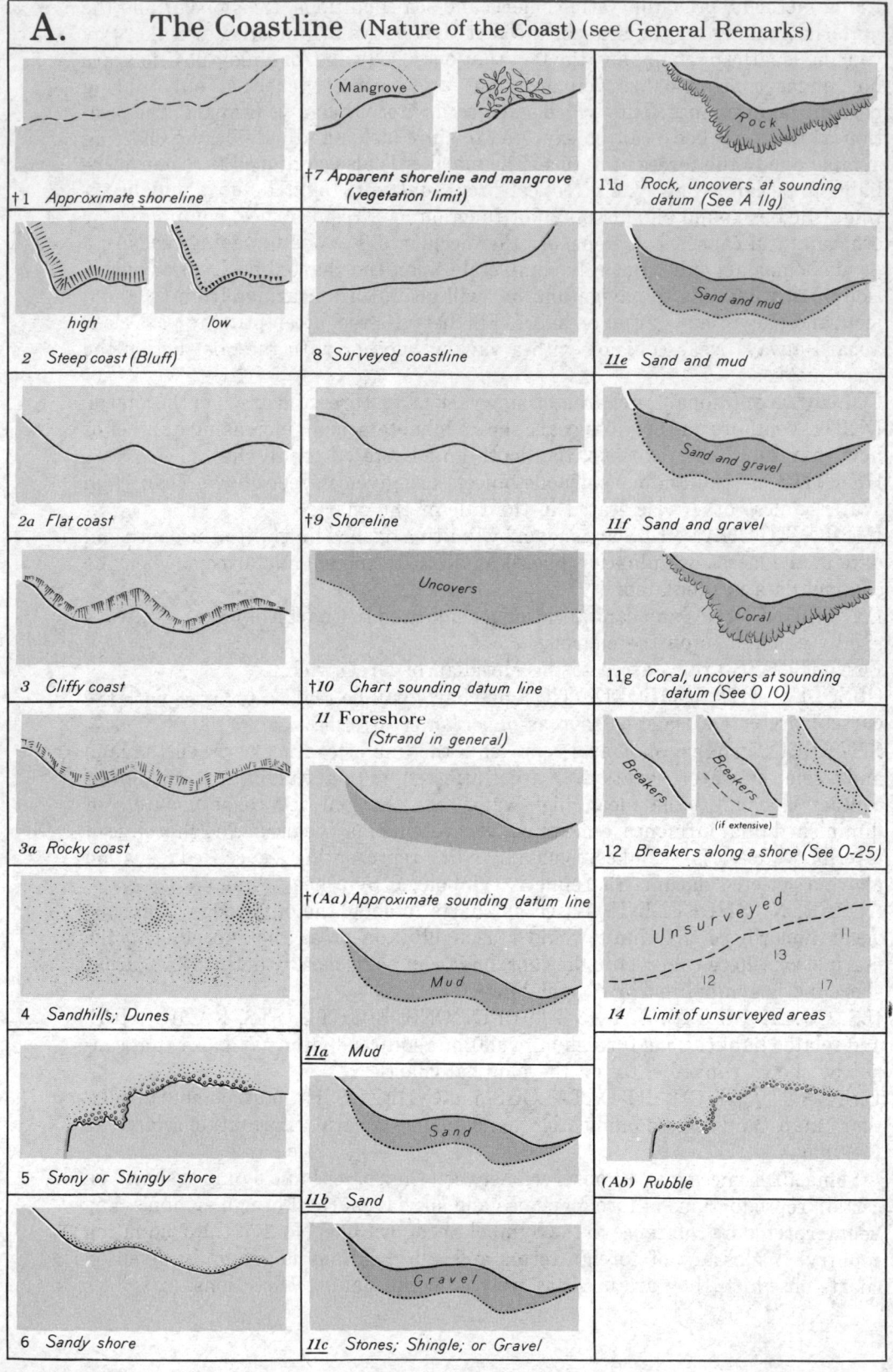

†1 *Approximate shoreline*

†7 *Apparent shoreline and mangrove (vegetation limit)*

11d *Rock, uncovers at sounding datum (See A 11g)*

2 *Steep coast (Bluff)* — high, low

8 *Surveyed coastline*

11e *Sand and mud*

2a *Flat coast*

†9 *Shoreline*

11f *Sand and gravel*

3 *Cliffy coast*

†10 *Chart sounding datum line* — Uncovers

11g *Coral, uncovers at sounding datum (See O 10)*

3a *Rocky coast*

11 Foreshore (Strand in general)

†(Aa) *Approximate sounding datum line*

12 *Breakers along a shore (See O-25)* — Breakers, Breakers (if extensive)

4 *Sandhills; Dunes*

11a *Mud*

14 *Limit of unsurveyed areas* — Unsurveyed

5 *Stony or Shingly shore*

11b *Sand*

6 *Sandy shore*

11c *Stones; Shingle; or Gravel*

(Ab) *Rubble*

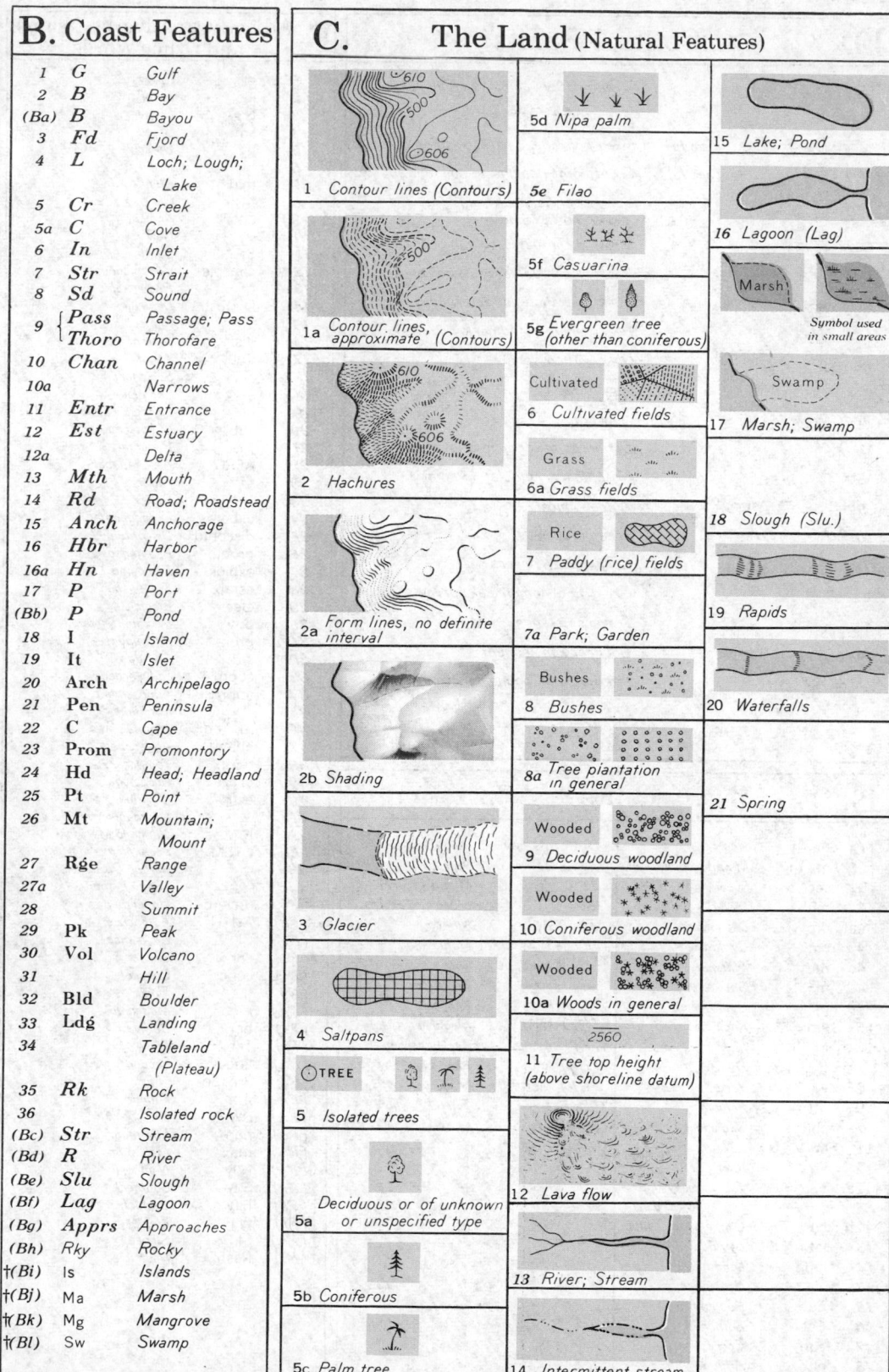

B. Coast Features

1	G	Gulf
2	B	Bay
(Ba)	B	Bayou
3	Fd	Fjord
4	L	Loch; Lough; Lake
5	Cr	Creek
5a	C	Cove
6	In	Inlet
7	Str	Strait
8	Sd	Sound
9	Pass	Passage; Pass
	Thoro	Thorofare
10	Chan	Channel
10a		Narrows
11	Entr	Entrance
12	Est	Estuary
12a		Delta
13	Mth	Mouth
14	Rd	Road; Roadstead
15	Anch	Anchorage
16	Hbr	Harbor
16a	Hn	Haven
17	P	Port
(Bb)	P	Pond
18	I	Island
19	It	Islet
20	Arch	Archipelago
21	Pen	Peninsula
22	C	Cape
23	Prom	Promontory
24	Hd	Head; Headland
25	Pt	Point
26	Mt	Mountain; Mount
27	Rge	Range
27a		Valley
28		Summit
29	Pk	Peak
30	Vol	Volcano
31		Hill
32	Bld	Boulder
33	Ldg	Landing
34		Tableland (Plateau)
35	Rk	Rock
36		Isolated rock
(Bc)	Str	Stream
(Bd)	R	River
(Be)	Slu	Slough
(Bf)	Lag	Lagoon
(Bg)	Apprs	Approaches
(Bh)	Rky	Rocky
†(Bi)	Is	Islands
†(Bj)	Ma	Marsh
†(Bk)	Mg	Mangrove
†(Bl)	Sw	Swamp

C. The Land (Natural Features)

1 Contour lines (Contours)

1a Contour lines, approximate (Contours)

2 Hachures

2a Form lines, no definite interval

2b Shading

3 Glacier

4 Saltpans

5 Isolated trees

5a Deciduous or of unknown or unspecified type

5b Coniferous

5c Palm tree

5d Nipa palm

5e Filao

5f Casuarina

5g Evergreen tree (other than coniferous)

6 Cultivated fields

6a Grass fields

7 Paddy (rice) fields

7a Park; Garden

8 Bushes

8a Tree plantation in general

9 Deciduous woodland

10 Coniferous woodland

10a Woods in general

11 Tree top height (above shoreline datum)

12 Lava flow

13 River; Stream

14 Intermittent stream

15 Lake; Pond

16 Lagoon (Lag)

17 Marsh; Swamp

Symbol used in small areas

18 Slough (Slu.)

19 Rapids

20 Waterfalls

21 Spring

D. Control Points

1	△		Triangulation point (station)
1a			Astronomic station
2	⊙	(See In)	Fixed point (landmark, position accurate)
(Da)	○	(See Io)	Fixed point (landmark, position approx.)
3	· 256		Summit of height (Peak) (when not a landmark)
(Db)	◎ 256		Peak, accentuated by contours
(Dc)	☀ 256		Peak, accentuated by hachures
(Dd)	☀		Peak, elevation not determined
(De)	⊙ 256		Peak, when a landmark
4	⊕	Obs Spot	Observation spot
*5		BM	Bench mark
6	View X		View point
7			Datum point for grid of a plan
8			Graphical triangulation point
9		Astro	Astronomical
10		Tri	Triangulation
(Df)		C of E	Corps of Engineers
12			Great trigonometrical survey station
13			Traverse station
14		Bdy Mon	Boundary monument
(Dg)	◇		International boundary monument

E. Units

†1	hr, h	Hour	19	ht; elev	Height; Elevation
†2	m, min	Minute (of time)	20	°	Degree
†3	sec, s	Second (of time)	21	'	Minute (of arc)
4	m	Meter	22	"	Second (of arc)
4a	dm	Decimeter	23	No	Number
4b	cm	Centimeter	†(Ea)	St M, St Mi	Statute mile
4c	mm	Millimeter	†(Eb)	μsec, μs	Microsecond
4d	m²	Square meter	(Ec)	Hz	Hertz (cps)
4e	m³	Cubic meter	(Ed)	kHz	Kilohertz (kc)
5	km	Kilometer	(Ee)	MHz	Megahertz (Mc)
6	in	Inch	†(Ef)	cps, c/s	Cycles/second (Hz)
7	ft	Foot	(Eg)	kc	Kilocycle (kHz)
8	yd	Yard	(Eh)	Mc	Megacycle (MHz)
9	fm	Fathom	†(Ei)	T	Ton (U.S. short ton=2,000 lbs.)
10	cbl	Cable length			
†11	M, Mi, N Mi	Nautical mile			
12	kn	Knot			
†12a	t	Tonne (metric ton= 2,204.6 lbs.)			
12b	cd	Candela (new candle)			
13	lat	Latitude			
14	long	Longitude			
14a		Greenwich			
15	pub	Publication			
16	Ed	Edition			
17	corr	Correction			
18	alt	Altitude			

F. Adjectives, Adverbs, Nouns, and Other Words

1	gt	Great
2	lit	Little
3	Lrg	Large
4	sml	Small
5		Outer
6		Inner
7	mid	Middle
8		Old
9	anc	Ancient
10		New
11	St	Saint
12	conspic	Conspicuous
13		Remarkable
14	D, Destr	Destroyed
15		Projected
16	dist	Distant
17	abt	About
18		See chart
18a		See plan
19		Lighted; Luminous
20	sub	Submarine
21		Eventual
22	AERO	Aeronautical
23		Higher
23a		Lower
24	exper	Experimental
25	discontd	Discontinued
26	prohib	Prohibited
27	explos	Explosive
28	estab	Established
29	elec	Electric
30	priv	Private, Privately
31	prom	Prominent
32	std	Standard
33	subm	Submerged
34	approx	Approximate
35		Maritime
36	maintd	Maintained
37	aband	Abandoned
38	temp	Temporary
39	occas	Occasional
40	extr	Extreme
41		Navigable
42	N M	Notice to Mariners
(Fa)	L N M	Local Notice to Mariners
43		Sailing Directions
44		List of Lights
(Fb)	unverd	Unverified
(Fc)	AUTH	Authorized
(Fd)	CL	Clearance
(Fe)	cor	Corner
(Ff)	concr	Concrete
(Fg)	fl	Flood
(Fh)	mod	Moderate
(Fi)	bet	Between
(Fj)	1st	First
†(Fk)	2nd, 2d	Second
†(Fl)	3rd, 3d	Third
(Fm)	4th	Fourth
(Fn)	DW	Deep Water
(Fo)	min	Minimum
(Fp)	max	Maximum
†(Fq)	N'ly	Northerly
†(Fr)	S'ly	Southerly
†(Fs)	E'ly	Easterly
†(Ft)	W'ly	Westerly
†(Fu)	Sk	Stroke
†(Fv)	Restr	Restricted

G.   Ports and Harbors

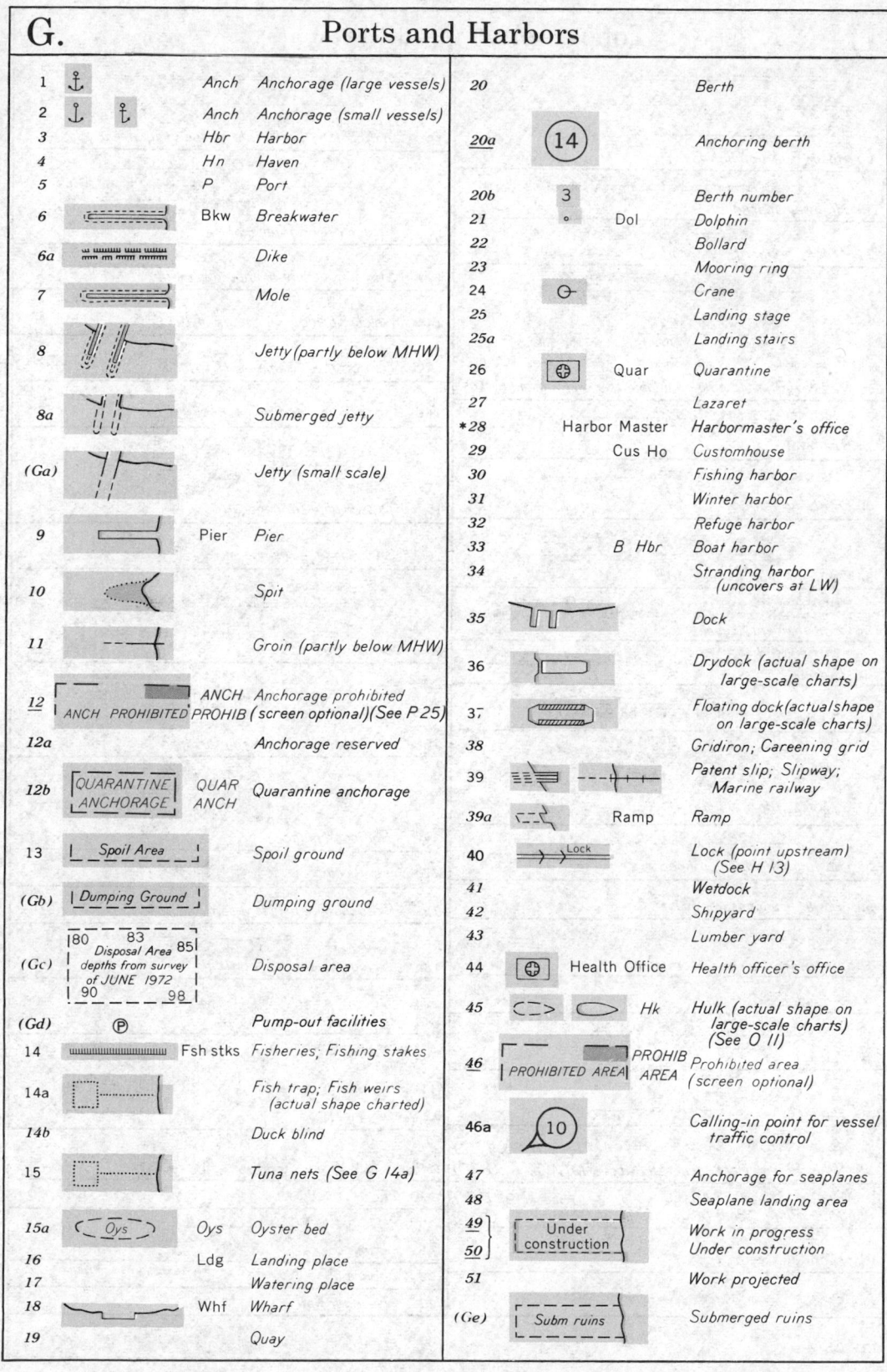

№			
1		Anch	Anchorage (large vessels)
2		Anch	Anchorage (small vessels)
3		Hbr	Harbor
4		Hn	Haven
5		P	Port
6		Bkw	Breakwater
6a			Dike
7			Mole
8			Jetty (partly below MHW)
8a			Submerged jetty
(Ga)			Jetty (small scale)
9		Pier	Pier
10			Spit
11			Groin (partly below MHW)
12		ANCH PROHIB	Anchorage prohibited (screen optional)(See P 25)
12a			Anchorage reserved
12b		QUAR ANCH	Quarantine anchorage
13			Spoil ground
(Gb)			Dumping ground
(Gc)			Disposal area
(Gd)			Pump-out facilities
14		Fsh stks	Fisheries; Fishing stakes
14a			Fish trap; Fish weirs (actual shape charted)
14b			Duck blind
15			Tuna nets (See G 14a)
15a		Oys	Oyster bed
16		Ldg	Landing place
17			Watering place
18		Whf	Wharf
19			Quay

№			
20			Berth
20a			Anchoring berth
20b			Berth number
21		Dol	Dolphin
22			Bollard
23			Mooring ring
24			Crane
25			Landing stage
25a			Landing stairs
26		Quar	Quarantine
27			Lazaret
*28		Harbor Master	Harbormaster's office
29		Cus Ho	Customhouse
30			Fishing harbor
31			Winter harbor
32			Refuge harbor
33		B Hbr	Boat harbor
34			Stranding harbor (uncovers at LW)
35			Dock
36			Drydock (actual shape on large-scale charts)
37			Floating dock (actual shape on large-scale charts)
38			Gridiron; Careening grid
39			Patent slip; Slipway; Marine railway
39a		Ramp	Ramp
40			Lock (point upstream) (See H 13)
41			Wetdock
42			Shipyard
43			Lumber yard
44		Health Office	Health officer's office
45		Hk	Hulk (actual shape on large-scale charts) (See O 11)
46		PROHIB AREA	Prohibited area (screen optional)
46a			Calling-in point for vessel traffic control
47			Anchorage for seaplanes
48			Seaplane landing area
49		Under construction	Work in progress
50			Under construction
51			Work projected
(Ge)		Subm ruins	Submerged ruins

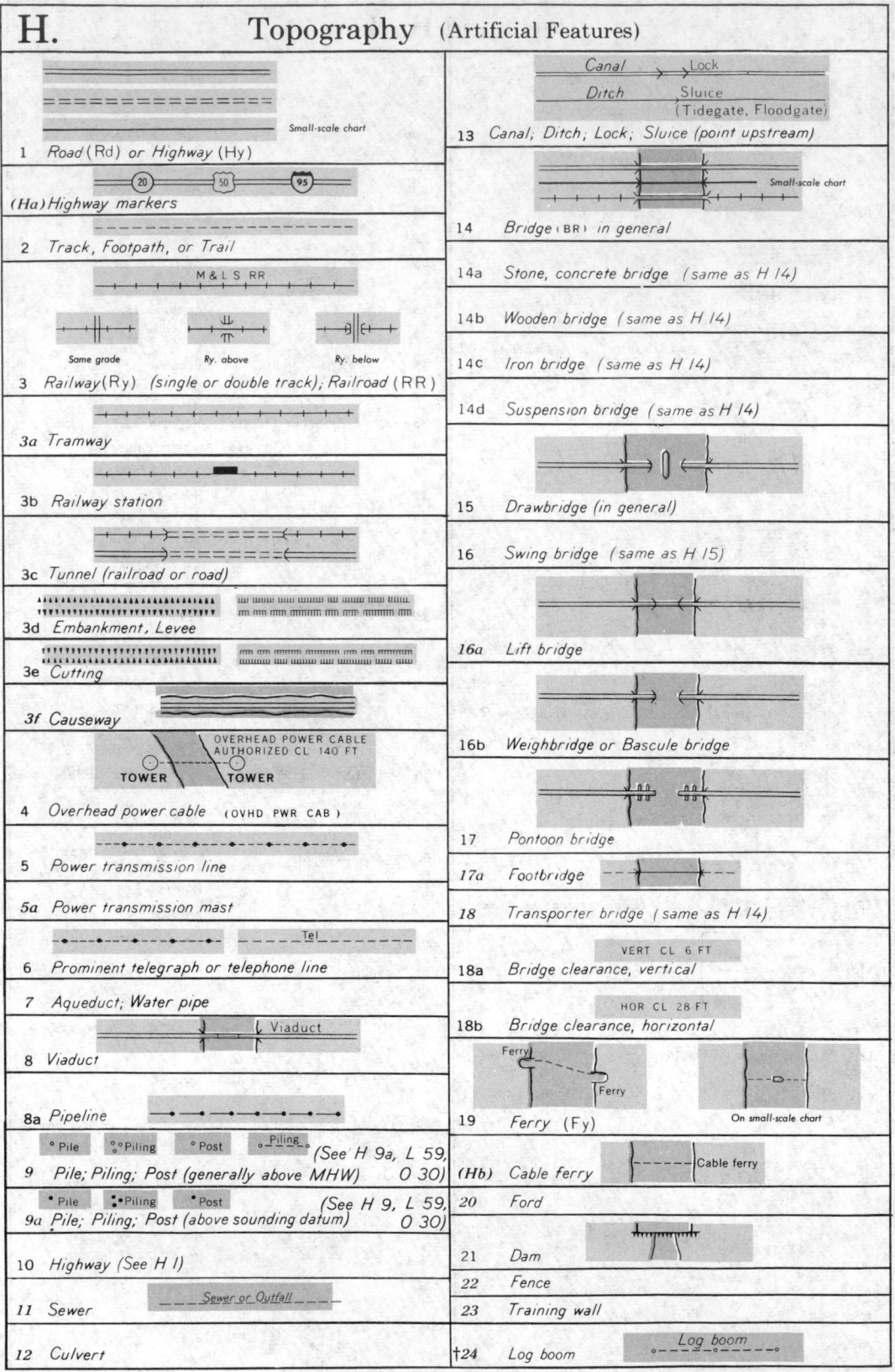

H.   Topography (Artificial Features)

1   Road (Rd) or Highway (Hy)   *Small-scale chart*

(Ha) Highway markers

2   Track, Footpath, or Trail

3   Railway (Ry) (single or double track); Railroad (RR)

Same grade   Ry. above   Ry. below

3a   Tramway

3b   Railway station

3c   Tunnel (railroad or road)

3d   Embankment, Levee

3e   Cutting

3f   Causeway

4   Overhead power cable (OVHD PWR CAB)   OVERHEAD POWER CABLE AUTHORIZED CL 140 FT   TOWER   TOWER

5   Power transmission line

5a   Power transmission mast

6   Prominent telegraph or telephone line   Tel

7   Aqueduct; Water pipe

8   Viaduct

8a   Pipeline

9   Pile; Piling; Post (generally above MHW)   Pile Piling Post Piling   (See H 9a, L 59, O 30)

9a   Pile; Piling; Post (above sounding datum)   Pile Piling Post   (See H 9, L 59, O 30)

10   Highway (See H 1)

11   Sewer   Sewer or Outfall

12   Culvert

13   Canal; Ditch; Lock; Sluice (point upstream)   Canal Lock Ditch Sluice (Tidegate, Floodgate)

14   Bridge (BR) in general   *Small-scale chart*

14a   Stone, concrete bridge (same as H 14)

14b   Wooden bridge (same as H 14)

14c   Iron bridge (same as H 14)

14d   Suspension bridge (same as H 14)

15   Drawbridge (in general)

16   Swing bridge (same as H 15)

16a   Lift bridge

16b   Weighbridge or Bascule bridge

17   Pontoon bridge

17a   Footbridge

18   Transporter bridge (same as H 14)

18a   Bridge clearance, vertical   VERT CL 6 FT

18b   Bridge clearance, horizontal   HOR CL 28 FT

19   Ferry (Fy)   Ferry Ferry   On small-scale chart

(Hb)   Cable ferry   Cable ferry

20   Ford

21   Dam

22   Fence

23   Training wall

†24   Log boom   Log boom

I. Buildings and Structures (see General Remarks)

No.	Symbol	Description		No.	Symbol	Description
1		City or Town (large scale)		26a	Locust Ave — Ave	Avenue
(Ia)		City or Town (small scale)		26b	Grand Blvd — Blvd	Boulevard
2		Suburb		27	Tel	Telegraph
3	Vil	Village		28	Tel Off	Telegraph office
3a		Buildings in general		29	PO	Post office
4	Cas	Castle		30	Govt Ho	Government house
5		House		31		Town hall
6		Villa		32	Hosp	Hospital
7		Farm		33		Slaughterhouse
8		Church		34	Magz	Magazine
8a	Cath	Cathedral		34a		Warehouse; Storehouse
8b	SPIRE — Spire	Spire; Steeple		35	MON — Mon	Monument
9		Roman Catholic Church		36	CUP — Cup	Cupola
10		Temple		37	ELEV — Elev	Elevator; Lift
11		Chapel		(Ie)	Elev	Elevation; Elevated
12		Mosque		38		Shed
12a		Minaret		39		Zinc roof
(Ib)		Moslem Shrine		40	Ruins — Ru	Ruins
13		Marabout		41	TR — Tr	Tower
14	Pag	Pagoda		(If)	ABAND LT HO	Abandoned lighthouse
15		Buddhist Temple; Joss-House		42	WINDMILL	Windmill
15a		Shinto Shrine		43		Watermill
16		Monastery; Convent		43a	WINDMOTOR	Windmotor
17		Calvary; Cross		44	CHY — Chy	Chimney; Stack
17a		Cemetery, Non-Christian		45	S·PIPE — S'pipe	Water tower; Standpipe
18	Cem	Cemetery, Christian		46		Oil tank
18a		Tomb		47	Facty	Factory
19		Fort (actual shape charted)		48		Saw mill
20		Battery		49		Brick kiln
21		Barracks		50		Mine; Quarry
22		Powder magazine		51	Well	Well
23	Airport	Airplane landing field		52		Cistern
24		Airport, large scale (See P-13)		53	TANK — Tk	Tank
(Ic)		Airport, military (small scale)		54		Noria
(Id)		Airport, civil (small scale)		55		Fountain
25		Mooring mast				
26	King St — St	Street				

I. Buildings and Structures (continued)

61		Inst	*Institute*
62			*Establishment*
63			*Bathing establishment*
64		Ct Ho	*Courthouse*
65		Sch	*School*
(Ig)		HS	*High school*
(Ih)		Univ	*University*
66		Bldg	*Building*
67		Pav	*Pavilion*
68			*Hut*
69			*Stadium*
70		T	*Telephone*
71			*Gas tank; Gasometer*

72	⊙GAB °Gab		*Gable*
73			*Wall*
74			*Pyramid*
75			*Pillar*
76			*Oil derrick*
(Ii)		Ltd	*Limited*
(Ij)		Apt	*Apartment*
(Ik)		Cap	*Capitol*
(Il)		Co	*Company*
(Im)		Corp	*Corporation*
(In)	⊙		*Landmark (position accurate)(See D 2)*
(Io)	○		*Landmark (position approximate)(See Da)*

J. Miscellaneous Stations

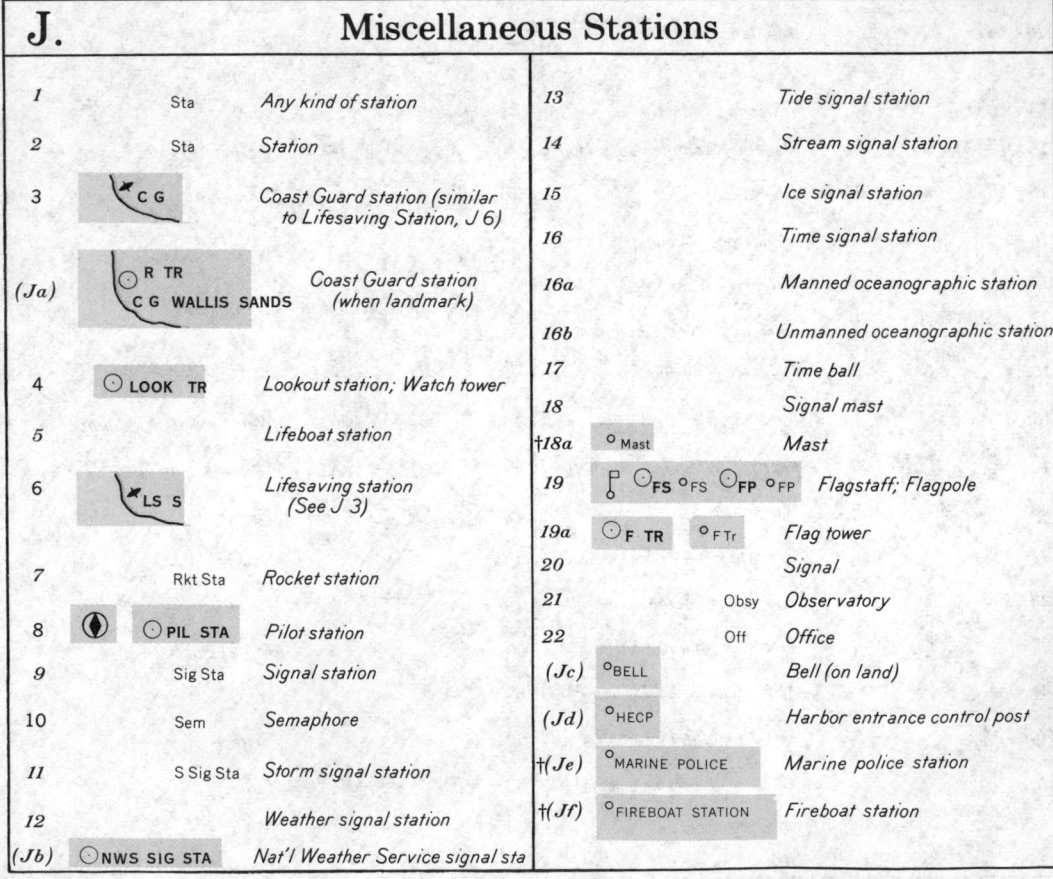

1		Sta	*Any kind of station*
2		Sta	*Station*
3	C G		*Coast Guard station (similar to Lifesaving Station, J 6)*
(Ja)	R TR C G WALLIS SANDS		*Coast Guard station (when landmark)*
4	⊙ LOOK TR		*Lookout station; Watch tower*
5			*Lifeboat station*
6	LS S		*Lifesaving station (See J 3)*
7		Rkt Sta	*Rocket station*
8	⊙ PIL STA		*Pilot station*
9		Sig Sta	*Signal station*
10		Sem	*Semaphore*
11		S Sig Sta	*Storm signal station*
12			*Weather signal station*
(Jb)	⊙NWS SIG STA		*Nat'l Weather Service signal sta*

13			*Tide signal station*
14			*Stream signal station*
15			*Ice signal station*
16			*Time signal station*
16a			*Manned oceanographic station*
16b			*Unmanned oceanographic station*
17			*Time ball*
18			*Signal mast*
†18a	○ Mast		*Mast*
19	⊙FS °FS ●FP °FP		*Flagstaff; Flagpole*
19a	⊙ F TR °F Tr		*Flag tower*
20			*Signal*
21		Obsy	*Observatory*
22		Off	*Office*
(Jc)	°BELL		*Bell (on land)*
(Jd)	°HECP		*Harbor entrance control post*
†(Je)	°MARINE POLICE		*Marine police station*
†(Jf)	°FIREBOAT STATION		*Fireboat station*

K.   Lights

1		Position of light	29	F Fl	Fixed and flashing light	
2	Lt	Light	30	F Gp Fl	Fixed and group flashing light	
(Ka)		Riprap surrounding light	30a	Mo	Morse code light	
3	Lt Ho	Lighthouse	31	Rot	Revolving or Rotating light	
4	AERO	Aeronautical light (See F-22)	41		Period	
4a		Marine and air navigation light	42		Every	
5	Bn	Light beacon	43		With	
6		Light vessel; Lightship	44		Visible (range)	
8		Lantern	†(Kb)	M; Mi; N Mi	Nautical mile (See E-11)	
9		Street lamp	(Kc)	m. min	Minutes (See E-2)	
10	REF	Reflector	†(Kd)	s; sec	Seconds (See E-3)	
11	Ldg Lt	Leading light	45	Fl	Flash	
12	RED	Sector light	46	Occ	Occultation	
13	GREEN RED	Directional light	46a		Eclipse	
14		Harbor light	47	Gp	Group	
15		Fishing light	48	Occ	Intermittent light	
16		Tidal light	49	SEC	Sector	
17	Priv maintd	Private light (maintained by private interests; to be used with caution)	50		Color of sector	
21	F	Fixed light	51	Aux	Auxiliary light	
22	Occ	Occulting light	52		Varied	
23	Fl	Flashing light	61	Vi	Violet	
23a	Iso E Int	Isophase light (equal interval)	62		Purple	
24	Qk Fl	Quick flashing (scintillating) light	63	Bu	Blue	
25	Int Qk Fl I Qk Fl	Interrupted quick flashing light	64	G	Green	
			65	Or	Orange	
25a	S Fl	Short flashing light	66	R	Red	
26	Alt	Alternating light	67	W	White	
27	Gp Occ	Group occulting light	67a	Am	Amber	
28	Gp Fl	Group flashing light	67b	Y	Yellow	
28a	S-L Fl	Short-long flashing light	68	OBSC	Obscured light	
28b		Group short flashing light	68a	Fog Det Lt	Fog detector light (See Nb)	

K. Lights (continued)

69		Unwatched light	79		Front light
70	Occas	Occasional light	80	Vert	Vertical lights
71	Irreg	Irregular light	81	Hor	Horizontal lights
72	Prov	Provisional light	(Kf)	VB	Vertical beam
73	Temp	Temporary light	(Kg)	RGE	Range
(Ke)	D: Destr	Destroyed	(Kh)	Exper	Experimental light
74	Exting	Extinguished light	(Ki)	TRLB	Temporarily replaced by lighted buoy showing the same characteristics
75		Faint light	(Kj)	TRUB	Temporarily replaced by unlighted buoy
76		Upper light	(Kk)	TLB	Temporary lighted buoy
77		Lower light	(Kl)	TUB	Temporary unlighted buoy
78		Rear light			

L. Buoys and Beacons
(see General Remarks)

† (new standard symbols)

1	Approximate position of buoy	†17	RB RB RB	Bifurcation buoy (RBHB)
†2	Light buoy	†18	RB RB RB	Junction buoy (RBHB)
†3	BELL BELL BELL Bell buoy	†19	RB RB RB	Isolated danger buoy (RBHB)
†3a	GONG GONG GONG Gong buoy	†20	RB RB / G G G G G	Wreck buoy (RBHB or G)
†4	WHIS WHIS Whistle buoy	†20a	RB RB / G G	Obstruction buoy (RBHB or G)
†5	C C Can or Cylindrical buoy	†21	Tel Tel	Telegraph-cable buoy
†6	N N Nun or Conical buoy	22		Mooring buoy (colors of mooring buoys never carried)
†7	SP SP Spherical buoy	22a		Mooring
†8	S S Spar buoy	22b	Tel Tel	Mooring buoy with telegraphic communications
†8a	P P Pillar or Spindle buoy	22c	T T	Mooring buoy with telephonic communications
†9	Buoy with topmark (ball) (see L-70)	†23		Warping buoy
†10	Barrel or Ton buoy	†24	Y Y	Quarantine buoy
†(La)	Color unknown	24a		Practice area buoy
†(Lb)	FLOAT FLOAT Float	†25	Explos Anch Explos Anch	Explosive anchorage buoy
†12	FLOAT FLOAT FLOAT Lightfloat	†25a	AERO AERO	Aeronautical anchorage buoy
13	Outer or Landfall buoy	†26	Deviation Deviation	Compass adjustment buoy
†14	BW BW Fairway buoy (BWVS)	†27	BW BW	Fish trap (area) buoy (BWHB)
†14a	BW BW Midchannel buoy (BWVS)	†27a		Spoil ground buoy
†15	R"2" R"2" R"2" Starboard-hand buoy (entering from seaward)	†28	W W	Anchorage buoy (marks limits)
†16	"1" "1" Port-hand buoy (entering from seaward)	†29	Priv maintd Priv maintd	Private aid to navigation (buoy) (maintained by private interests, use with caution)

L. Buoys and Beacons (continued)

29 (cont.)	R	Starboard-hand buoy (entering from seaward)
	B	Port-hand buoy
30		Temporary buoy (See Ki, j, k, l)
30a		Winter buoy
†31	HB	Horozontal stripes or bands HB
†32	VS	Vertical stripes VS
†33	Chec	Checkered Chec
†33a	Diag	Diagonal bands
41	W	White
42	B	Black
43	R	Red
44	Y	Yellow
45	G	Green
46	Br	Brown
47	Gy	Gray
48	Bu	Blue
48a	Am	Amber
48b	Or	Orange
†51		Floating beacon
52	△RW Bn △W Bn ▲R Bn	Fixed beacon (unlighted or daybeacon)
	▲ Bn	Black beacon
	△ Bn	Color unknown
(Lc)	⊙MARKER ° Marker	Private aid to navigation
53	Bn	Beacon, in general (See L 52)
54		Tower beacon

55		Cardinal marking system
56	△ Deviation Bn	Compass adjustment beacon
57		Topmarks (See L 9, 70)
58		Telegraph-cable (landing) beacon
59	°° Piles •° Piles	Piles (See O 30; H 9, 9a)
	⊥ ⊥	Stakes
	°° Stumps	Stumps (See O 30)
	⊥ ⊥	Perches
61	⊙CAIRN °Cairn	Cairn
62		Painted patches
63	⊙TR	Landmark (position accurate) (See D 2)
(Ld)	° Tr	Landmark (position approximate)
64	REF	Reflector
65	⊙MARKER	Range targets, markers
†(Le)	W Or W Or W Or W Or	Special-purpose buoys
66		Oil installation buoy
67		Drilling platform (See Of, Og)
70	Note:	TOPMARKS on buoys and beacons may be shown on charts of foreign waters. The abbreviation for black is not shown adjacent to buoys or beacons.
(Lf)	Ra Ref	Radar reflector (See M 13)

L.   **Buoys and Beacons** (continued)

Symbols and abbreviations for buoyage to be introduced into European waters from April 1977.

IALA Buoyage System 'A'

The combined Cardinal and Lateral System (Red to Port)

Fathoms and Metric Charts

Where in force, System 'A' applies to all fixed and floating marks other than lighthouses, sector lights and leading-marks, lightships and 'lighthouse buoys.' There are no special characteristics reserved for marking wrecks.

UNLIT MARKS

LIGHTED MARKS

Lateral, generally marking the limits of well-defined channels.

Port Hand

All red
Topmark (if any): can

Fl.R   Occ.R   etc   Red light *(any phase characteristic)*

Symbol used to indicate buoyage direction where not obvious; size and orientation varied to suit its situation.

Starboard Hand

All green or black
Topmark (if any): cone

Fl.G   Occ.G   etc   Green light *(any phase characteristic)*

Cardinal, indicating navigable water to the named side of the mark.

Topmarks: 2 black cones

White light

Time (seconds)
0   5   10   15

North Mark
Black above yellow

NW   NE

West Mark   East Mark

Point of interest

Yellow with black band   Black with yellow band

SW   SE
South Mark
Yellow above black

North Mark	V Qk Fl or Qk Fl	BY
East Mark	V Qk Fl(3)5s or Qk Fl(3)10s	BYB
South Mark	V Qk Fl(6)+L Fl.10s or Qk Fl(6)+L Fl.15s	YB
West Mark	V Qk Fl(9)10s or Qk Fl(9)15s	YBY

The same abbreviations are used for lights on spar buoys.
The periods, 5s, 10s and 15s, may not always be charted.

Isolated danger, stationed over a danger with navigable water around it.

Body: black with red horizontal band(s)
Topmarks: 2 black spheres

Gp Fl(2)   Gp Fl(2)   White light

Safe water, such as mid-channel and landfall marks.

Body: red and white vertical stripes
Topmark (if any): red sphere

Iso,Occ or L Fl   Iso,Occ or L Fl   Iso,Occ or L Fl   White light

Special, not primarily to assist navigation but to indicate special features.

Body (shape optional): yellow
Topmark (if any): yellow X

Fl.Y   Fl.Y   Fl.Y   etc   Yellow light

NOTES

STANDARD BUOY SHAPES are can ⊏, conical ▲, spherical ◯, pillar (including high focal plane) ⊿, and spar ∤, but variations may occur.

COLOR ABBREVIATIONS under buoy symbols, especially spar buoys, may sometimes be omitted.

PERIODS of lights, where charted, are shown thus: 10s (for 10 seconds).

RADAR REFLECTORS are not charted.

Chart 1 page 10a

M.   Radio and Radar Stations

1	° R Sta	Radio telegraph station
2	°RT	Radio telephone station
3	⊙ R Bn	Radiobeacon
4	⊙ R Bn	Circular radiobeacon
5	⊙ RD	Directional radiobeacon; Radio range
6		Rotating loop radiobeacon
7	⊙ RDF	Radio direction finding station
†(Ma)	⊙ ANTENNA (TELEM) / TELEM ANT	Telemetry antenna
(Mb)	⊙ R RELAY MAST	Radio relay mast
(Mc)	⊙ MICRO TR	Microwave tower
9	⊙ R MAST / ⊙ R TR	Radio mast / Radio tower
9a	⊙ TV TR	Television mast; Television tower
10	⊙ R TR (WBAL) 1090 KHZ	Radio broadcasting station (commercial)
10a	° R Sta	QTG radio station
11	⊙ Ra	Radar station

12	⊙ Racon	Radar responder beacon
13	Ra Ref	Radar reflector (See L-Lf)
14	Ra (conspic)	Radar conspicuous object
14a		Ramark
15	D F S	Distance finding station (synchronized signals)
16	⊙ AERO R Bn 302 ▬▬·▬··	Aeronautical radiobeacon
17	° Decca Sta	Decca station
18	° Loran Sta Venice	Loran station (name)
19	⊙ CONSOL Bn 190 kHz MMF ▬▬·	Consol (Consolan) station
(Md)	⊙ AERO R Rge 342 ▬▬·▬··	Aeronautical radio range
(Me)	⊙ Ra Ref Calibration Bn	Radar calibration beacon
(Mf)	⊙ LORAN TR SPRING ISLAND	Loran tower (name)
(Mg)	⊙ R TR F R Lt	Obstruction light
†(Mh)	⊙ RA DOME ⊙ DOME (RADAR) o Ra Dome o Dome (Radar)	Radar dome
†(Mi)	uhf	Ultrahigh frequency
†(Mj)	vhf	Very high frequency

N.   Fog Signals

1	Fog Sig	Fog-signal station
2		Radio fog-signal station
3	GUN	Explosive fog signal
4		Submarine fog signal
5	SUB-BELL	Submarine fog bell (action of waves)
6	SUB-BELL	Submarine fog bell (mechanical)
7	SUB-OSC	Submarine oscillator
8	NAUTO	Nautophone
9	DIA	Diaphone
10	GUN	Fog gun
11	SIREN	Fog siren
12	HORN	Fog trumpet

13	HORN	Foghorn
13a	HORN	Electric foghorn
14	BELL	Fog bell
15	WHIS	Fog whistle
16	HORN	Reed horn
17	GONG	Fog gong
18	◎	Submarine sound signal not connected to the shore (See N 5,6,7)
18a	⊙〰	Submarine sound signal connected to the shore (See N 5,6,7)
(Na)	HORN	Typhon
(Nb)	Fog Det Lt	Fog detector light (See K 68a)

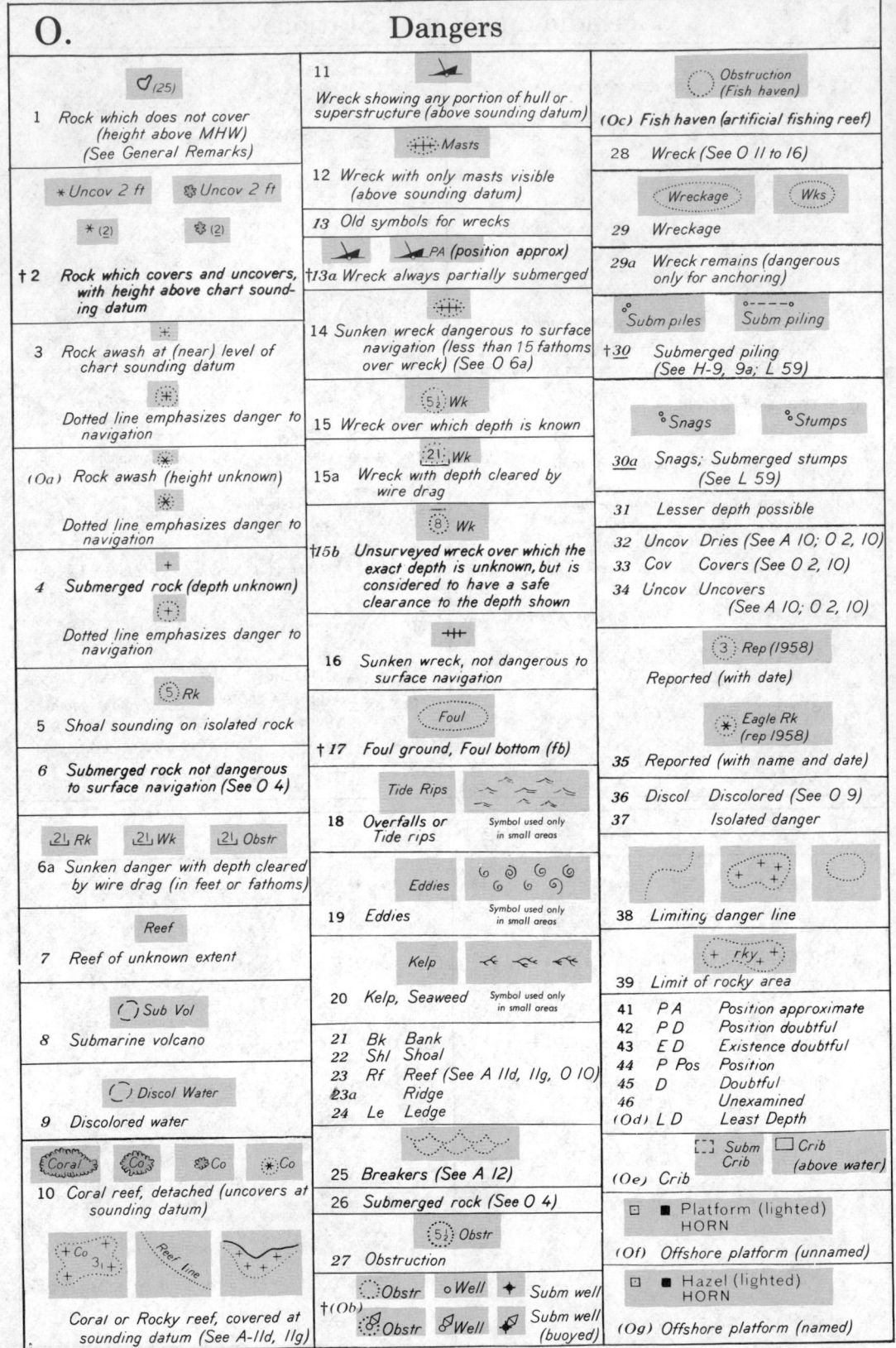

O. Dangers

1. Rock which does not cover (height above MHW) (See General Remarks)

   Uncov 2 ft ✻(2) ✿(2)

†2. Rock which covers and uncovers, with height above chart sounding datum

3. Rock awash at (near) level of chart sounding datum

   Dotted line emphasizes danger to navigation

(Oa) Rock awash (height unknown)

   Dotted line emphasizes danger to navigation

4. Submerged rock (depth unknown)

   Dotted line emphasizes danger to navigation

   5) Rk

5. Shoal sounding on isolated rock

6. Submerged rock not dangerous to surface navigation (See O 4)

   2) Rk   2) Wk   2) Obstr

6a. Sunken danger with depth cleared by wire drag (in feet or fathoms)

   Reef

7. Reef of unknown extent

   ⬭Sub Vol

8. Submarine volcano

   ⬭Discol Water

9. Discolored water

   Coral   Co   ✿Co   ✻Co

10. Coral reef, detached (uncovers at sounding datum)

   +Co+ Reef line

   Coral or Rocky reef, covered at sounding datum (See A-11d, 11g)

11. Wreck showing any portion of hull or superstructure (above sounding datum)

   ╬Masts

12. Wreck with only masts visible (above sounding datum)

13. Old symbols for wrecks

   PA (position approx)

†13a Wreck always partially submerged

   ╬╬╬

14. Sunken wreck dangerous to surface navigation (less than 15 fathoms over wreck) (See O 6a)

   5) Wk

15. Wreck over which depth is known

   21) Wk

15a. Wreck with depth cleared by wire drag

   8) Wk

†15b Unsurveyed wreck over which the exact depth is unknown, but is considered to have a safe clearance to the depth shown

   ╫╫╫

16. Sunken wreck, not dangerous to surface navigation

   Foul

†17 Foul ground, Foul bottom (fb)

   Tide Rips

18. Overfalls or Tide rips   Symbol used only in small areas

   Eddies

19. Eddies   Symbol used only in small areas

   Kelp

20. Kelp, Seaweed   Symbol used only in small areas

21. Bk   Bank
22. Shl   Shoal
23. Rf   Reef (See A 11d, 11g, O 10)
23a   Ridge
24. Le   Ledge

25. Breakers (See A 12)

26. Submerged rock (See O 4)

   5) Obstr

27. Obstruction

   ⬭Obstr ○Well ✦Subm well
†(Ob)
   ⬭Obstr Ǫ Well ✦Subm well (buoyed)

   ⬭Obstruction (Fish haven)

(Oc) Fish haven (artificial fishing reef)

28. Wreck (See O 11 to 16)

   Wreckage   Wks

29. Wreckage

29a. Wreck remains (dangerous only for anchoring)

   Subm piles   Subm piling

†30. Submerged piling (See H-9, 9a; L 59)

   °Snags   °Stumps

30a. Snags; Submerged stumps (See L 59)

31. Lesser depth possible

32. Uncov Dries (See A 10; O 2, 10)
33. Cov   Covers (See O 2, 10)
34. Uncov Uncovers (See A 10; O 2, 10)

   3) Rep (1958)

   Reported (with date)

   ✳Eagle Rk (rep 1958)

35. Reported (with name and date)

36. Discol Discolored (See O 9)
37.   Isolated danger

38. Limiting danger line

   +rky+

39. Limit of rocky area

41. P A   Position approximate
42. P D   Position doubtful
43. E D   Existence doubtful
44. P Pos Position
45. D   Doubtful
46.   Unexamined
(Od) L D   Least Depth

   Subm Crib   Crib (above water)

(Oe) Crib

   ⊡ ■ Platform (lighted) HORN

(Of) Offshore platform (unnamed)

   ⊡ ■ Hazel (lighted) HORN

(Og) Offshore platform (named)

P.   Various Limits, etc.

1	Leading line; Range Line
2	Transit
3	In line with
4	Limit of sector
5	Channel, Course, Track recommended (marked by buoys or beacons) (See P 21)
(Pa)	Alternate course
6	— Ra ——— Ra — Radar-guided track
7	Submarine cable (power, telegraph, telephone, etc.)
7a	Cable Area Submarine cable area
7b	Abandoned submarine cable (includes disused cable)
8	Submarine pipeline
8a	Pipeline Area Submarine pipeline area
†8b	Abandoned submarine pipeline
9	Maritime limit in general
(Pb)	RESTRICTED AREA Limit of restricted area
10	Limit of fishing zone (fish trap areas)
(Pc)	U.S. Harbor Line
11	Limit of dumping ground, spoil ground (See P 9; G 13)
12	Anchorage limit
13	Limit of airport (See I 23, 24)
13a	Limit of military practice areas
14	Limit of sovereignty (Territorial waters)
15	Customs boundary
16	International boundary (also State boundary)
17	Stream limit
18	Ice limit
19	Limit of tide
20	Limit of navigation
21	Course of recommended (not marked by buoys or beacons) (See P 5)
	District or province limit
23	Reservation line
	(Options)
24	COURSE 053°00' TRUE MARKERS MARKERS Measured distance
25	PROHIBITED AREA Prohibited area (See G 12, 46) (Screen optional)
(Pd)	SAFETY FAIRWAY Shipping safety fairway
(Pe)	Directed traffic lanes

Q.   Soundings

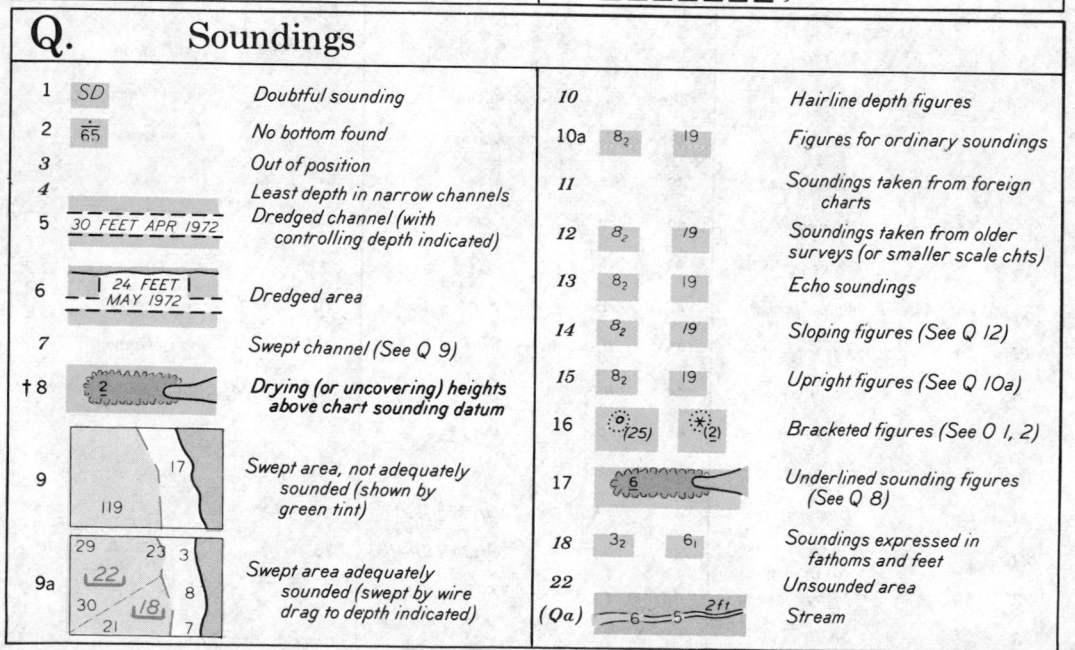

1	SD Doubtful sounding
2	65 No bottom found
3	Out of position
4	Least depth in narrow channels
5	30 FEET APR 1972 Dredged channel (with controlling depth indicated)
6	24 FEET MAY 1972 Dredged area
7	Swept channel (See Q 9)
†8	Drying (or uncovering) heights above chart sounding datum
9	Swept area, not adequately sounded (shown by green tint)
9a	Swept area adequately sounded (swept by wire drag to depth indicated)
10	Hairline depth figures
10a	8₂ 19 Figures for ordinary soundings
11	Soundings taken from foreign charts
12	8₂ 19 Soundings taken from older surveys (or smaller scale chts)
13	8₂ 19 Echo soundings
14	8₂ 19 Sloping figures (See Q 12)
15	8₂ 19 Upright figures (See Q 10a)
16	(25) (2) Bracketed figures (See O 1, 2)
17	6 Underlined sounding figures (See Q 8)
18	3₂ 6₁ Soundings expressed in fathoms and feet
22	Unsounded area
(Qa)	6—5 2ft Stream

R. Depth Contours and Tints (see General Remarks)

Feet	Fm / Meters		Feet	Fm / Meters
0	0		300	50
6	1		600	100
12	2		1,200	200
18	3		1,800	300
24	4		2,400	400
30	5		3,000	500
36	6		6,000	1,000
60	10		12,000	2,000
120	20		18,000	3,000
180	30		Or continuous lines, with values	
240	40			

(blue or black) ———5——— ———100———

S. Quality of the Bottom

1	Grd	Ground	24	Oys	Oysters	50	spk	Speckled
2	S	Sand	25	Ms	Mussels	51	gty	Gritty
3	M	Mud; Muddy	26	Spg	Sponge	52	dec	Decayed
4	Oz	Ooze	27	K	Kelp	53	fly	Flinty
5	Ml	Marl	28	Wd	Seaweed	54	glac	Glacial
6	Cl	Clay	28	Grs	Grass	55	ten	Tenacious
7	G	Gravel	29	Stg	Sea-tangle	56	wh	White
8	Sn	Shingle	31	Spi	Spicules	57	bk	Black
9	P	Pebbles	32	Fr	Foraminifera	58	vi	Violet
10	St	Stones	33	Gl	Globigerina	59	bu	Blue
11	Rk; rky	Rock; Rocky	34	Di	Diatoms	60	gn	Green
11a	Blds	Boulders	35	Rd	Radiolaria	61	yl	Yellow
12	Ck	Chalk	36	Pt	Pteropods	62	or	Orange
12a	Ca	Calcareous	37	Po	Polyzoa	63	rd	Red
13	Qz	Quartz	38	Cir	Cirripedia	64	br	Brown
13a	Sch	Schist	38a	Fu	Fucus	65	ch	Chocolate
14	Co	Coral	38b	Ma	Mattes	66	gy	Gray
(Sa)	Co Hd	Coral head	39	fne	Fine	67	lt	Light
15	Mds	Madrepores	40	crs	Coarse	68	dk	Dark
16	Vol	Volcanic	41	sft	Soft			
(Sb)	Vol Ash	Volcanic ash	42	hrd	Hard	70	vard	Varied
17	La	Lava	43	stf	Stiff	71	unev	Uneven
18	Pm	Pumice	44	sml	Small	(Sc)	S/M	Surface layer and Under layer
19	T	Tufa	45	lrg	Large			
20	Sc	Scoriae	46	stk	Sticky			
21	Cn	Cinders	47	brk	Broken			
21a		Ash	47a	grd	Ground (Shells)	76		Freshwater springs in seabed
22	Mn	Manganese	48	rt	Rotten			
23	Sh	Shells	49	str	Streaky			

#		
T.		**Tides and Currents**

1	HW	High water
1a	HHW	Higher high water
2	LW	Low water
(Ta)	LWD	Low-water datum
2a	LLW	Lower low water
3	MTL	Mean tide level
4	MSL	Mean sea level
4a		Elevation of mean sea level above chart (sounding) datum
5		Chart datum (datum for sounding reduction)
6	Sp	Spring tide
7	Np	Neap tide
7a	MHW	Mean high water
8	MHWS	Mean high-water springs
8a	MHWN	Mean high-water neaps
8b	MHHW	Mean higher high water
8c	MLW	Mean low water
9	MLWS	Mean low-water springs
9a	MLWN	Mean low-water neaps
9b	MLLW	Mean lower low water
10	ISLW	Indian spring low water
11		High-water full and change (vulgar establishment of the port)
12		Low-water full and change
13		Mean establishment of the port
13a		Establishment of the port
14		Unit of height
15		Equinoctial
16		Quarter; Quadrature
17	Str	Stream
18		Current, general, with rate
19		Flood stream (current) with rate
20		Ebb stream (current) with rate
21		Tide gauge; Tidepole; Automatic tide gauge
23	vel	Velocity; Rate
24	kn	Knots
25	ht	Height
26		Tide
27		New moon
28		Full moon
29		Ordinary
30		Syzygy
31	fl	Flood
32		Ebb
33		Tidal stream diagram
34		Place for which tabulated tidal stream data are given
35		Range (of tide)
36		Phase lag
(Tb)		Current diagram, with explanatory note

#		
U.		**Compass**

Compass Rose

The outer circle is in degrees with zero at true north. The inner circles are in points and degrees with the arrow indicating magnetic north.

1	N	North
2	E	East
3	S	South
4	W	West
5	NE	Northeast
6	SE	Southeast
7	SW	Southwest
8	NW	Northwest
9	N	Northern
10	E	Eastern
11	S	Southern
12	W	Western
21	brg	Bearing
22	T	True
23	mag	Magnetic
24	var	Variation
25		Annual change
25a		Annual change nil
26		Abnormal variation; Magnetic attraction
27	deg	Degrees (See E-20)
28	dev	Deviation

Index of Abbreviations

A

aband	Abandoned	F 37
ABAND LT HO	Abandoned lighthouse	If
abt	About	F 17
AERO	Aeronautical	F 22; K 4
AERO R Bn	Aeronautical radiobeacon	M 16
AERO R Rge	Aeronautical radio range	Md
alt	Altitude	E 18
Alt	Alternating (light)	K 26
Am	Amber	K 67a; L 48a
anc	Ancient	F 9
Anch	Anchorage	B 15; G 1, 2
Anch prohib	Anchorage prohibited	G 12
Ant	Antenna	Ma
approx	Approximate	F 34
Apprs	Approaches	Bg
Apt	Apartment	Ij
Arch	Archipelago	B 20
Astro	Astronomical	D 9
AUTH	Authorized	Fc
Aux	Auxiliary (light)	K 51
Ave	Avenue	I 26a

B

B	Bay	B 2
B	Bayou	Ba
B, b, bk	Black	L 42; S 57
Bdy Mon	Boundary monument	D 14
BELL	Fog Bell	N 14
bet	Between	Fi
B Hbr	Boat harbor	G 33
Bk	Bank	O 21
Bkw	Breakwater	G 6
Bl	Blast	
Bld, Blds	Boulder, Boulders	B 32; S 11a
Bldg	Building	I 66
Blvd	Boulevard	I 26b
BM	Bench mark	D 5
Bn	Beacon (in general)	L 52, 53
BR	Bridge	H 14
Br, br	Brown	L 46; S 64
brg	Bearing	U 21
brk	Broken	S 47
Bu, bu	Blue	K 63; L 48; S 69
BWHB	Black and white horizontal bands	L 27
BWVS	Black and white vertical stripes	L 14, 14a

C

C	Can, Cylindrical (buoy)	L 5
C	Cape	B 22
C	Cove	B 5a
Ca	Calcareous	S 12a
Cap	Capitol	Ik
Cas	Castle	I 4
Cath	Cathedral	I 8a
cbl	Cable length	E 10
cd	Candela	E 12b
C G	Coast Guard	J 3, Ja
ch	Chocolate	S 65
Ch	Church	I 8

Chan	Channel	B 10
Chec	Checkered (buoy)	L 33
CHY	Chimney	I 44
Cir	Cirripedia	S 38
Ck	Chalk	S 12
Cl	Clay	S 6
CL	Clearance	Fd
cm	Centimeter	E 4b
Cn	Cinders	S 21
Co	Company	II
Co	Coral	S 14
Co Hd	Coral head	Sa
concr	Concrete	Ff
conspic	Conspicuous	F 12
C of E	Corps of Engineers	Df
cor	Corner	Fe
Corp	Corporation	Im
Cov	Covers	O 33
corr	Correction	E 17
cps, c/s	Cycles per second	Ef
Cr	Creek	B 5
crs	Coarse	S 40
Cswy	Causeway	H 3f
Ct Ho	Courthouse	I 64
CUP	Cupola	I 36
Cus Ho	Customhouse	G 29

D

D	Doubtful	O 45
DD	Deep Draft	F n
D, Destr	Destroyed	F 14; Ke
dec	Decayed	S 52
deg	Degrees	U 27
dev	Deviation	U 28
Diag	Diagonal bands	L 33a
D F S	Distance finding station	M 15
Di	Diatoms	S 34
DIA	Diaphone	N 9
Discol	Discolored	O 36
discontd	Discontinued	F 25
dist	Distant	F 16
dk	Dark	S 68
dm	Decimeter	E 4a
Dol	Dolphin	G 21
DRDG RGE	Dredging Range	

E

E	East, Eastern	U 2, 10
Ed	Edition	E 16
ED	Existence doubtful	O 43
elec	Electric	F 29
elev	Elevation	E 19
ELEV	Elevator, Lift	I 37
Elev	Elevation, Elevated	Ie
E'ly	Easterly	Fq
Entr	Entrance	B 11
E Int	Isophase light (equal interval)	K 23a
Est	Estuary	B 12
estab	Established	F 28
Exper	Experimental (light)	Kh
exper	Experimental	F 24
explos	Explosive	F 27

Abbreviations

Explos Anch	Explosive Anchorage (buoy)	L 25	H S	High School	lg
Exting	Extinguished (light)	K 74	ht	Height	E 19; T 25
extr	Extreme	F 40	HW	High water	T 1
			Hy	Highway	H 1
F			Hz	Hertz	Ec
F	Fixed (light)	K 21			
Facty	Factory	I 47	**I**		
Fd	Fjord	B 3	I	Island	B 18
F Fl	Fixed and flashing (light)	K 29	I Qk, Int Qk	Interrupted quick	K 25
F Gp Fl	Fixed and group		in	Inch	E 6
	flashing (light)	K 30	In	Inlet	B 6
Fl	Flash, Flashing (light)	K 23, 45	Inst	Institute	I 61
fl	Flood	Fg; T 31	Irreg	Irregular	K 71
fly	Flinty	S 53	ISLW	Indian spring low water	T 10
fm	Fathom	E 9	Is	Islands	Bi
fne	Fine	S 39	Iso	Isophase	K 23a
Fog Det Lt	Fog detector light	K 68a; Nb	It	Islet	B 19
Fog Sig	Fog signal station	N 1			
FP	Flagpole	J 19	**K**		
Fr	Foraminifera	S 32	K	Kelp	S 27
FS	Flagstaff	J 19	kc	Kilocycle	Eg
Fsh stks	Fishing stakes	G 14	kHz	Kilohertz	Ed
ft	Foot	E 7	km	Kilometer	E 5
Ft	Fort	I 19	kn	Knots	E 12; T 24
F TR	Flag tower	J 19a			
Fu	Fucus	S 38a	**L**		
Fy	Ferry	H 19	L	Loch, Lough, Lake	B 4
			La	Lava	S 17
G			Lag	Lagoon	Bf; C 16
G	Gulf	B 1	lat	Latitude	E 13
G	Gravel	S 7	LD	Least Depth	Od
G, Gn, gn	Green	K 64; L 20, 20a, 45; S 60	Ldg	Landing, Landing place	B 33; G 16
GAB	Gable	I 72	Ldg Lt	Leading light	K 11
Gl	Globigerina	S 33	Le	Ledge	O 24
glac	Glacial	S 54	Lit	Little	F 2
GONG	Fog gong	N 17	LLW	Lower low water	T 2a
Govt Ho	Government House	I 30	LNM	Local Notice to Mariners	Fa
Gp	Group	K 47	long	Longitude	E 14
Gp Fl	Group flashing	K 28	LOOK TR	Lookout station, Watch tower	J 4
Gp Occ	Group occulting	K 27	lrg	Large	F 3; S 45
Grd, grd	Ground	S 1, 47a	LS S	Lifesaving station	J 6
Grs	Grass	S 28	Lt	Light	K 2
gt	Great	F 1	lt	Light	S 67
gty	Gritty	S 51	Ltd	Limited	li
GUN	Explosive fog signal	N 3	Lt Ho	Lighthouse	K 3
GUN	Fog gun	N 10	LW	Low water	T 2
Gy, gy	Gray	L 47; S 66	LWD	Low water datum	Ta
H			**M**		
HB	Horizontal bands or stripes	L 31	M, Mi	Nautical mile	E11; Kb
Hbr	Harbor	B 16; G 3	M	Mud, Muddy	S 3
Hd	Head, Headland	B 24	m	Meter	E 4, d, e
HECP	Harbor entrance control post	Jd	m²	Square meter	E4d
Hk	Hulk	G 45	m³	Cubic meter	E4c
HHW	Higher high water	T la	m, min	Minute (of time)	E2; Kc
Hn	Haven	B 16a; G 4	Ma	Marsh	Bj
Hor	Horizontal lights	K 81	Ma	Mattes	S 38b
HOR CL	Horizontal clearance	H 18b	mag	Magnetic	U 23
HORN	Fog trumpet, Foghorn, Reed horn,		Magz	Magazine	I 34
	Typhon	N 12, 13, 13a, 16, Na	maintd	Maintained	F 36
Hosp	Hospital	I 32	max	Maximum	Fp
hr, h	Hour	E 1	Mc	Megacycle	Eh
hrd	Hard	S 42	Mds	Madrepores	S 15

Abbreviations

Mg	Mangrove	Bk	Pag	Pagoda	I 14
MHHW	Mean higher high water	T 8b	Pass	Passage, Pass	B 9
MHW	Mean high water	T 7a	Pav	Pavilion	I 67
MHWN	Mean high-water neaps	T 8a	PD	Position doubtful	O 42
MHWS	Mean high-water springs	T 8	Pen	Peninsula	B 21
MHz	Megahertz	Ee	PIL STA	Pilot station	J 8
MICRO TR	Microwave tower	Mc	Pk	Peak	B 29
mid	Middle	F 7	Pm	Pumice	S 18
min	Minimum	Fo	Po	Polyzoa	S 37
Mkr	Marker	Lc	P O	Post Office	I 29
Ml	Marl	S 5	P, Pos	Position	O 44
MLLW	Mean lower low water	T 9b	priv	Private, Privately	F 30
MLW	Mean low water	T 8c	Priv maintd	Privately maintained	K 17; L 29
MLWN	Mean low-water neaps	T 9a	Prohib	Prohibited	F 26
MLWS	Mean low-water springs	T 9	prom	Prominent	F 31
mm	Millimeter	E 4c	Prom	Promontory	B 23
Mn	Manganese	S 22	Prov	Provisional (light)	K 72
Mo	Morse code light	K 30a	Pt	Point	B 25
mod	Moderate	Fh	Pt	Pteropods	S 36
MON	Monument	I 35	pub	Publication	E 15
Ms	Mussels	S 25	P F	Pump-out facilities	Gd
μsec, μs	Microsecond (one millionth)	Eb	PWI	Potable water intake	
MSL	Mean sea level	T 4			
Mt	Mountain, Mount	B 26	**Q**		
Mth	Mouth	B 13	Quar	Quarantine	G 26
MTL	Mean tide level	T 3	Qk Fl	Quick flashing (light)	K 24
			Qz	Quartz	S 13
N					
N	North; Northern	U 1, 9	**R**		
N	Nun; Conical (buoy)	L 6	R	Red	K 66; L 15, 43
N M, N Mi	Nautical mile	E 11	R	River	Bd
NAUTO	Nautophone	N 8	Ra	Radar station	M 11
NE	Northeast	U 5	Racon	Radar responder beacon	M 12
N'Ly	Northerly	Fq	Ra (conspic)	Radar conspicuous object	M 14
NM	Notice to Mariners	F 42	RA DOME	Radar dome	Mh
No	Number	E 23	Ra Ref	Radar reflector	Lf; M 13
Np	Neap tide	T 7	RBHB	Red and black horizontal	
NW	Northwest	U 8		bands	L 17, 18, 19, 20, 20a
NWS	National Weather Service		R Bn	Red beacon	L 52
	Signal Station	Jb	R Bn	Radiobeacon	M 3, 4, 16
			Rd	Radiolaria	S 35
O			rd	Red	S 63
OBSC	Obscured (light)	K 68	Rd	Road, Roadstead	B 14; H 1
Obs Spot	Observation spot	D 4	RD	Directional Radiobeacon,	
Obstr	Obstruction	O 27		Radio range	M 5
Obsy	Observatory	J 21	RDF	Radio direction finding station	M 7
Occ	Occulting (light),		REF	Reflector	K 10; L 64
	Occultation	K 22, 46	Rep	Reported	O 35
Occ	Intermittent (light)	K 48	Restr	Restricted	Fv
Occas	Occasional (light)	F 39; K 70	Rf	Reef	O 23
Off	Office	J 22	Rge	Range	B 27
Or, or	Orange	K 65; L48b; S 62	RGE	Range	Kg
OVHD			Rk	Rock	B 35
PWR CAB	Overhead power cable	H 4	Rk, rky	Rock, Rocky	S 11
Oys	Oysters, Oyster bed	S 24; G 15a	Rky	Rocky	Bh
Oz	Ooze	S 4	R MAST	Radio mast	M 9
			Rot	Rotating (light), Revolving	K 31
P			RR	Railroad	H 3
P	Pebbles	S 9	R RELAY MAST	Radio relay mast	Mb
P	Pillar (buoy)	L 8a	R Sta	Radio telegraph station,	
P	Pond	Bb		QTG Radio station	M1, 10a
P	Port	B 17; G 5	RT	Radio telephone station	M 2
PA	Position approximate	O 41			

Abbreviations

rt	Rotten	S 48	T	Telephone	I 70; L 22c
R TR	Radio tower	M 9	T	True	U 22
Ru	Ruins	I 40	T	Tufa	S 19
RW Bn	Red and white beacon	L 52	TB	Temporary buoy	L 30
Rv	Railway	H 3	Tel	Telegraph	I 27; L 22b
			Telem Ant	Telemetry antenna	Ma
S			Tel Off	Telegraph office	I 28
S	Sand	S 2	Temp	Temporary (light)	F 38; K 73
S	South; Southern	U 3, 11	ten	Tenacious	S 55
S	Spar (buoy)	L 8	Thoro	Thorofare	B 9
Sc	Scoriae	S 20	Tk	Tank	I 53
Sch	Schist	S 13a	TR	Tower	I 41
Sch	School	I 65	TRLB, TRUB,	TLB, TUB	Ki, j, k, l
Sd	Sound	B 8	Tri	Triangulation	D 10
SD	Sounding doubtful	Q 1	TV TR	Television tower (mast)	M 9a
SE	Southeast	U 6			
sec, s	Second (time; geo. pos.)	E 3; Kd	**U**		
SEC	Sector	K 49	uhf	Ultra high frequency	Mi
Sem	Semaphore	J 10	Uncov	Uncovers; Dries	O 2, 32, 34
S Fl	Short flashing (light)	K 25a	Univ	University	Ih
sft	Soft	S 41	unverd	Unverified	Fb
Sh	Shells	S 23	unev	Uneven	S 71
Shl	Shoal	O 22	μsec, μs	Microsecond (one millionth)	Eb
Sig Sta	Signal station	J 9			
SIREN	Fog siren	N 11	**V**		
Sk	Stroke	Fu	var	Variation	U 24
S-L Fl	Short-long flashing (light)	K 28a	vard	Varied	S 70
Slu	Slough	Be; C 18	VB	Vertical beam	Kf
S'ly	Southerly	Fr	vel	Velocity	T 23
sml	Small	F4; S 44	Vert	Vertical (lights)	K 80
Sn	Shingle	S 8	VERT CL	Vertical clearance	H 18a
Sp	Spring tide	T 6	vhf	Very high frequency	Mi
SP	Spherical (bouy)	L 7	Vi, vi	Violet	K 61; S 68
Spg	Sponge	S 26	View X	View point	D 6
Spi	Spicules	S 31	Vil	Village	I 3
S'PIPE	Standpipe	I 45	Vol	Volcanic	S 16
spk	Speckled	S 50	Vol Ash	Volcanic ash	Sb
S Sig Sta	Storm signal station	J 11	VS	Vertical stripes	L 32
St	Saint	F 11			
St	Street	I 26	**W**		
St	Stones	S 10	W	West, Western	U 4, 12
Sta	Station	J 1, 2	W, wh	White	K 67; L 41; S 56
std	Standard	F 32	W Bn	White beacon	L 52
stf	Stiff	S 43	Wd	Seaweed	S 28
Stg	Sea-tangle	S 29	Whf	Wharf	G 18
stk	Sticky	S 46	WHIS	Fog whistle	N 15
St M, St Mi	Statute mile	Ea	Wk	Wreck	O 15, 28
Str	Strait	B 7	Wks	Wrecks, Wreckage	O 29
Str	Stream	Bc; T 17	W Or	White and orange	Le
str	Streaky	S 49	W'ly	Westerly	Ft
sub	Submarine	F 20			
SUB-BELL	Submarine fog bell	N 5, 6	**Y**		
Subm, subm	Submerged	F 33; Oa, 30	Y, yl	Yellow	L 24, 44; S 61
Subm Ruins	Submerged ruins	Gd	yd	Yard	E 8
SUB-OSC	Submarine oscillator	N 7			
Sub Vol	Submarine volcano	O 8	1st	First	Fj
Subm W	Submerged Well	Ob	2nd, 2d	Second	Fk
SW	Southwest	U 7	3rd, 3d	Third	Fl
sw	Swamp	B 1	4th	Fourth	Fm
T			°	Degree	E 20
t	Tonne	E12a	'	Minute (of arc)	E 21
T	Ton	Ei	"	Second (of arc)	E 22

NAVIGATIONAL AIDS

IN

UNITED STATES WATERS

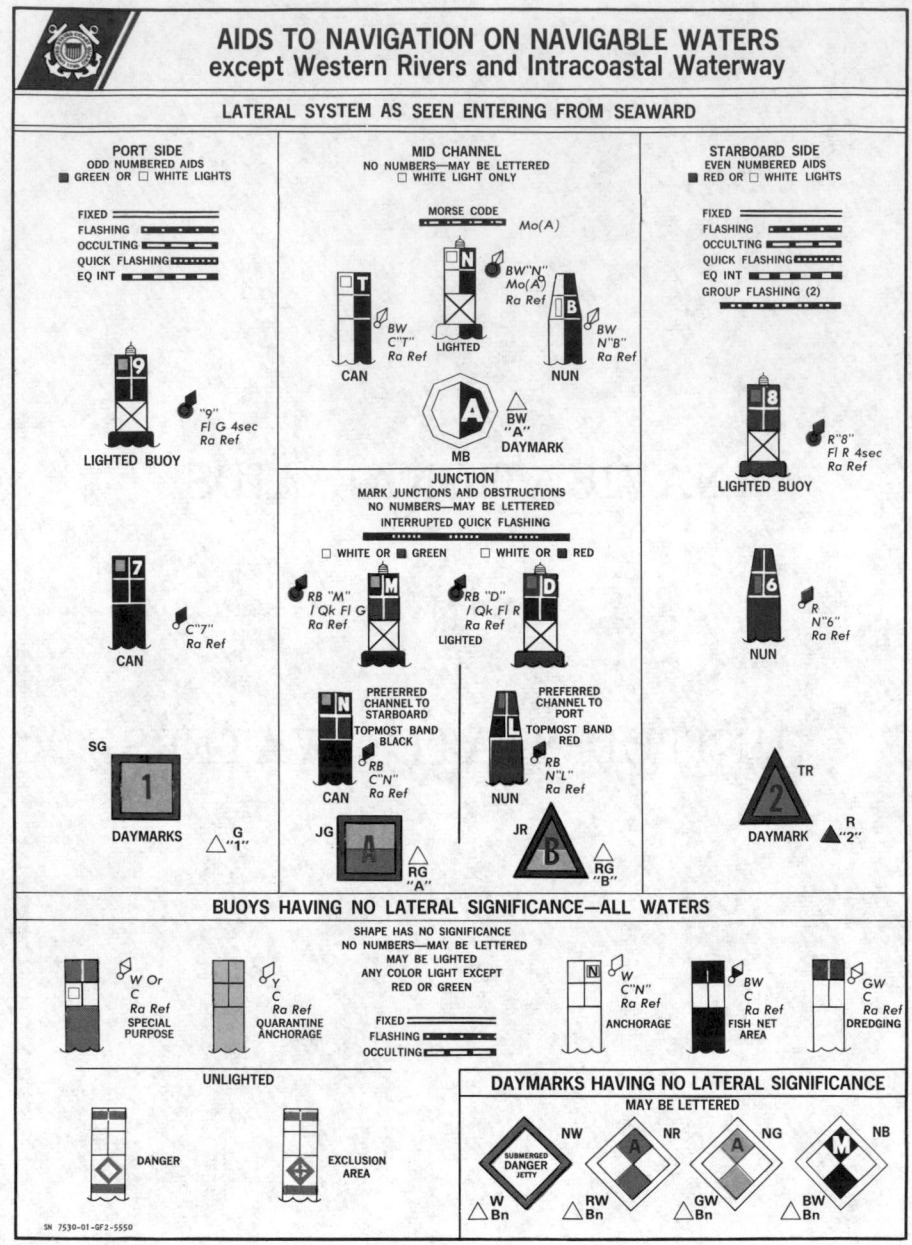

AIDS TO NAVIGATION ON NAVIGABLE WATERS
except Western Rivers and Intracoastal Waterway

LATERAL SYSTEM AS SEEN ENTERING FROM SEAWARD

AIDS TO NAVIGATION ON THE INTRACOASTAL WATERWAY

AS SEEN ENTERING FROM NORTH AND EAST—PROCEEDING TO SOUTH AND WEST

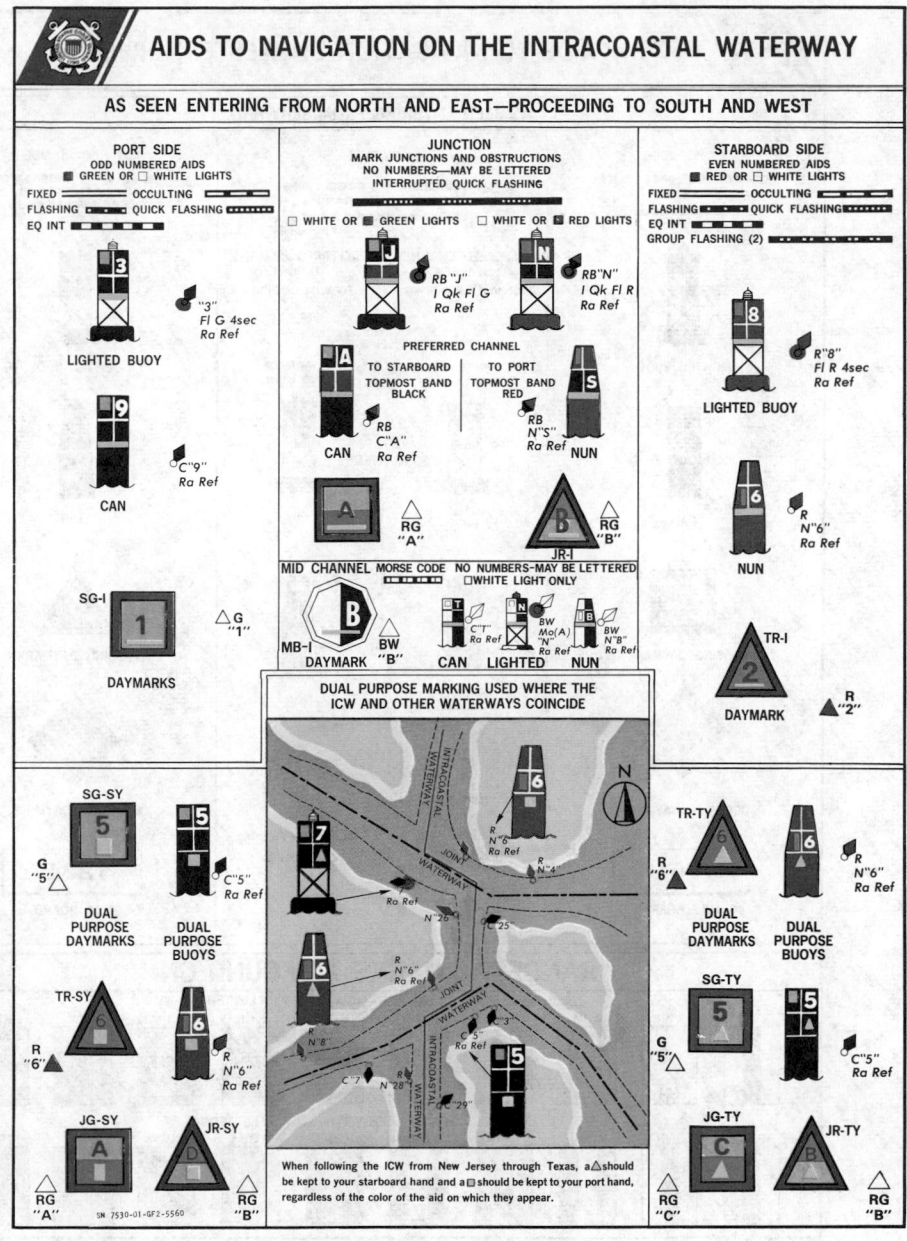

PORT SIDE
ODD NUMBERED AIDS
■ GREEN OR □ WHITE LIGHTS

FIXED ══════ OCCULTING ══ ══ ══
FLASHING ══ ══ ══ QUICK FLASHING ▪▪▪▪▪▪▪
EQ INT ══ ▪ ══ ▪ ══

"3"
Fl G 4sec
Ra Ref
LIGHTED BUOY

C"9"
Ra Ref
CAN

SG-I

△ G "1"

DAYMARKS

JUNCTION
MARK JUNCTIONS AND OBSTRUCTIONS
NO NUMBERS—MAY BE LETTERED
INTERRUPTED QUICK FLASHING
▪▪▪▪▪▪▪

□ WHITE OR ■ GREEN LIGHTS   □ WHITE OR ■ RED LIGHTS

RB "J"
I Qk Fl G
Ra Ref

RB"N"
I Qk Fl R
Ra Ref

PREFERRED CHANNEL
TO STARBOARD   TO PORT
TOPMOST BAND   TOPMOST BAND
BLACK   RED

RB
C"A"
Ra Ref
CAN

RB
N"S"
Ra Ref **NUN**

△ RG "A"

JR-I △ RG "B"

MID CHANNEL MORSE CODE NO NUMBERS—MAY BE LETTERED
□ WHITE LIGHT ONLY
▪▪▪▪▪▪▪

MB-I
DAYMARK "B"   BW **"B"**   C"T" Ra Ref **CAN**   BW Mo(A) "N" Ra Ref **LIGHTED**   BW N"B" Ra Ref **NUN**

STARBOARD SIDE
EVEN NUMBERED AIDS
■ RED OR □ WHITE LIGHTS

FIXED ══════ OCCULTING ══ ══ ══
FLASHING ══ ══ ══ QUICK FLASHING ▪▪▪▪▪▪▪
EQ INT ══ ▪ ══ ▪ ══
GROUP FLASHING (2) ══ ▪ ▪ ══ ▪ ▪ ══

R"8"
Fl R 4sec
Ra Ref
LIGHTED BUOY

R
N"6"
Ra Ref
NUN

TR-I
DAYMARK

R "2"

DUAL PURPOSE MARKING USED WHERE THE ICW AND OTHER WATERWAYS COINCIDE

SG-SY
G "5"
DUAL PURPOSE DAYMARKS

C"5" Ra Ref
DUAL PURPOSE BUOYS

TR-SY
R "6"
R N"6" Ra Ref

JG-SY
△ RG "A"

JR-SY
△ RG "B"

SN 7530-01-GF2-5560

TR-TY
R "6"
R N"6" Ra Ref
DUAL PURPOSE DAYMARKS   **DUAL PURPOSE BUOYS**

SG-TY
G "5"
C"5" Ra Ref

JG-TY
△ RG "C"

JR-TY
△ RG "B"

When following the ICW from New Jersey through Texas, a △ should be kept to your starboard hand and a ■ should be kept to your port hand, regardless of the color of the aid on which they appear.

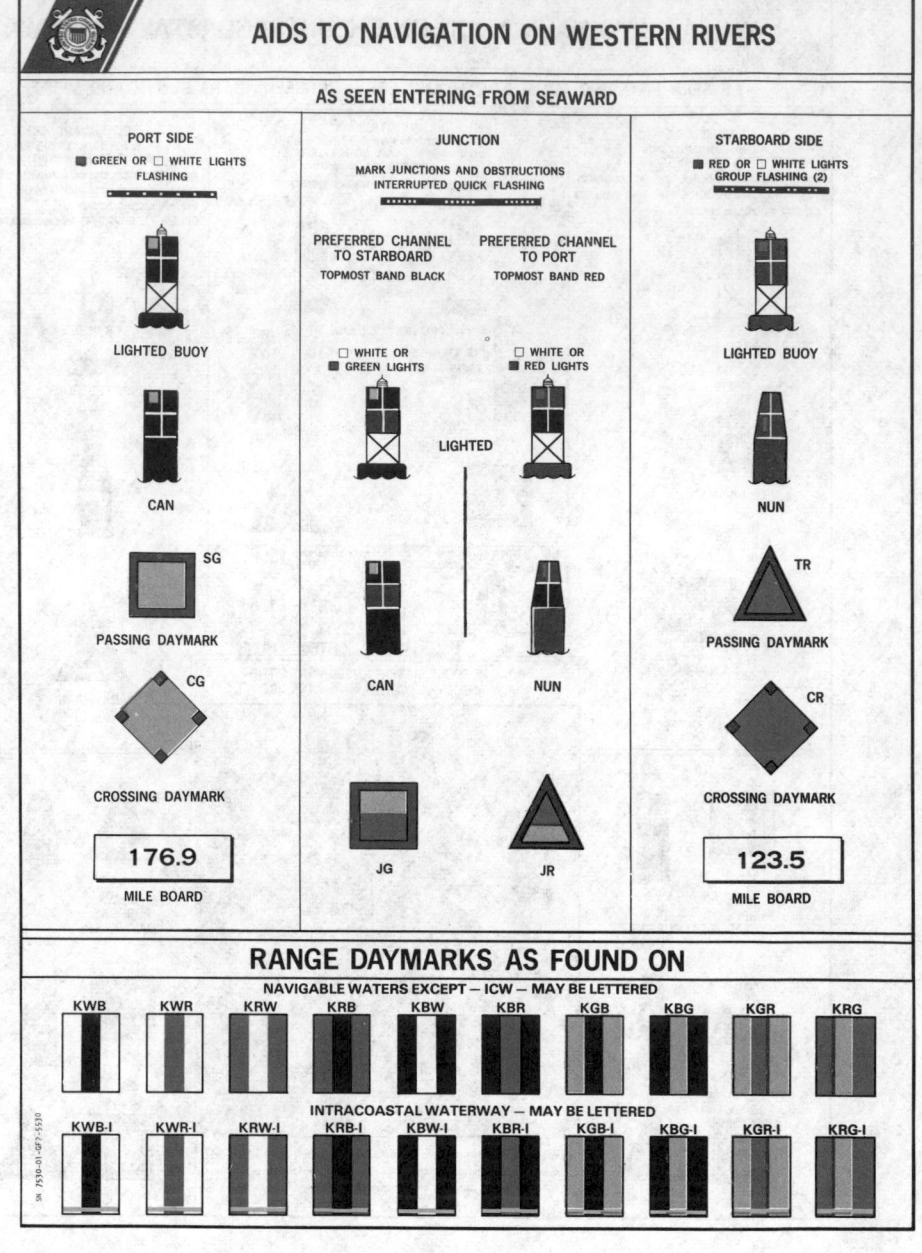

AIDS TO NAVIGATION ON WESTERN RIVERS

AS SEEN ENTERING FROM SEAWARD

PORT SIDE
■ GREEN OR □ WHITE LIGHTS
FLASHING

LIGHTED BUOY

CAN

PASSING DAYMARK   SG

CROSSING DAYMARK   CG

176.9
MILE BOARD

JUNCTION
MARK JUNCTIONS AND OBSTRUCTIONS
INTERRUPTED QUICK FLASHING

PREFERRED CHANNEL
TO STARBOARD
TOPMOST BAND BLACK

PREFERRED CHANNEL
TO PORT
TOPMOST BAND RED

□ WHITE OR
■ GREEN LIGHTS

□ WHITE OR
■ RED LIGHTS

LIGHTED

CAN

NUN

JG

JR

STARBOARD SIDE
■ RED OR □ WHITE LIGHTS
GROUP FLASHING (2)

LIGHTED BUOY

NUN

PASSING DAYMARK   TR

CROSSING DAYMARK   CR

123.5
MILE BOARD

RANGE DAYMARKS AS FOUND ON

NAVIGABLE WATERS EXCEPT — ICW — MAY BE LETTERED

KWB   KWR   KRW   KRB   KBW   KBR   KGB   KBG   KGR   KRG

INTRACOASTAL WATERWAY — MAY BE LETTERED

KWB-I   KWR-I   KRW-I   KRB-I   KBW-I   KBR-I   KGB-I   KBG-I   KGR-I   KRG-I

SN 7530-01-GF7-5530

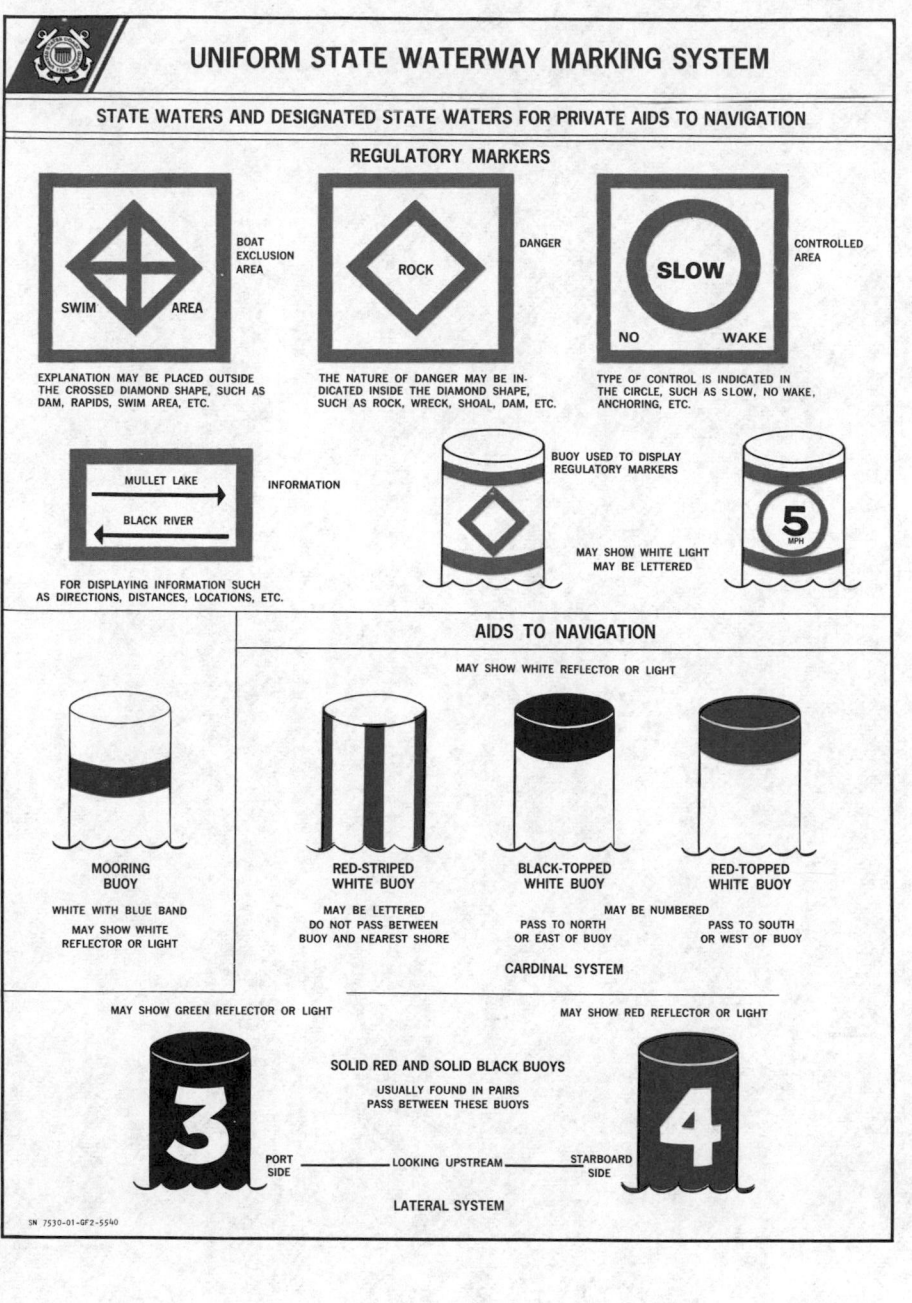

UNIFORM STATE WATERWAY MARKING SYSTEM

STATE WATERS AND DESIGNATED STATE WATERS FOR PRIVATE AIDS TO NAVIGATION

REGULATORY MARKERS

BOAT EXCLUSION AREA

SWIM AREA

EXPLANATION MAY BE PLACED OUTSIDE THE CROSSED DIAMOND SHAPE, SUCH AS DAM, RAPIDS, SWIM AREA, ETC.

DANGER

ROCK

THE NATURE OF DANGER MAY BE IN-DICATED INSIDE THE DIAMOND SHAPE, SUCH AS ROCK, WRECK, SHOAL, DAM, ETC.

CONTROLLED AREA

SLOW

NO   WAKE

TYPE OF CONTROL IS INDICATED IN THE CIRCLE, SUCH AS SLOW, NO WAKE, ANCHORING, ETC.

MULLET LAKE

BLACK RIVER

INFORMATION

FOR DISPLAYING INFORMATION SUCH AS DIRECTIONS, DISTANCES, LOCATIONS, ETC.

BUOY USED TO DISPLAY REGULATORY MARKERS

MAY SHOW WHITE LIGHT
MAY BE LETTERED

5 MPH

AIDS TO NAVIGATION

MAY SHOW WHITE REFLECTOR OR LIGHT

MOORING BUOY

WHITE WITH BLUE BAND
MAY SHOW WHITE REFLECTOR OR LIGHT

RED-STRIPED WHITE BUOY

MAY BE LETTERED
DO NOT PASS BETWEEN BUOY AND NEAREST SHORE

BLACK-TOPPED WHITE BUOY

MAY BE NUMBERED
PASS TO NORTH OR EAST OF BUOY

RED-TOPPED WHITE BUOY

PASS TO SOUTH OR WEST OF BUOY

CARDINAL SYSTEM

MAY SHOW GREEN REFLECTOR OR LIGHT

MAY SHOW RED REFLECTOR OR LIGHT

SOLID RED AND SOLID BLACK BUOYS

USUALLY FOUND IN PAIRS
PASS BETWEEN THESE BUOYS

3

PORT SIDE

LOOKING UPSTREAM

STARBOARD SIDE

4

LATERAL SYSTEM

SN 7530-01-GF2-5540

INDEX